Hoover's Handbook of

Emerging Companies

2014

HOOVERS™

A D&B COMPANY

Austin, Texas

Hoover's Handbook of Emerging Companies 2014 is intended to provide readers with accurate and authoritative information about the enterprises covered in it. Hoover's researched all companies and organizations profiled, and in many cases contacted them directly so that companies represented could provide information. The information contained herein is as accurate as we could reasonably make it. In many cases we have relied on third-party material that we believe to be trustworthy, but were unable to independently verify. We do not warrant that the book is absolutely accurate or without error. Readers should not rely on any information contained herein in instances where such reliance might cause financial loss. The publisher, the editors, and their data suppliers specifically disclaim all warranties, including the implied warranties of merchantability and fitness for a specific purpose. This book is sold with the understanding that neither the publisher, the editors, nor any content contributors are engaged in providing investment, financial, accounting, legal, or other professional advice.

The financial data (Historical Financials sections) in this book are from a variety of sources. Mergent Inc., provided selected data for the Historical Financials sections of publicly traded companies. For private companies and for historical information on public companies prior to their becoming public, we obtained information directly from the companies or from trade sources deemed to be reliable. Hoover's, Inc., is solely responsible for the presentation of all data.

Many of the names of products and services mentioned in this book are the trademarks or service marks of the companies manufacturing or selling them and are subject to protection under US law. Space has not permitted us to indicate which names are subject to such protection, and readers are advised to consult with the owners of such marks regarding their use. Hoover's is a trademark of Hoover's, Inc.

10 9 8 7 6 5 4 3 2 1

Publishers Cataloging-in-Publication Data
Hoover's Handbook of Emerging Companies 2014
    Includes indexes.
    ISBN: 978-1-63053-003-7
    ISSN 1073-6433
    1. Business enterprises — Directories. 2. Corporations — Directories.
HF3010 338.7

U.S. AND WORLD BOOK SALES

Mergent Inc.
580 Kingsley Park Drive
Fort Mill, SC
29715
Phone: 800-342-5647
e-mail: orders@mergent.com
Web: www.mergents.com

ii

Mergent Inc.

Publisher: Jonathan Worrall

Executive Managing Director: John Pedernales

Executive Vice President of Sales: Fred Jenkins

Managing Director of Relationship Management: Chris Henry

Senior Product Manager: Neel Gandhi

Managing Director of Print Products: Thomas Wecera

Director Print Products: Charlot Volny

Quality Assurance Editor: Wayne Arnold

Production Research Assistant: Erin Keane

Mergent Customer Service

Support and Fulfillment Manager: Melanie Horvat

ABOUT MERGENT INC.

Mergent, Inc. is a leading provider of business and financial data on global publicly listed companies. Based in the U.S, the company maintains a strong global presence, with offices in New York, Charlotte, San Diego, London, Tokyo and Melbourne.

Founded in 1900, Mergent operates one of the longest continuously collected databases of: descriptive and fundamental information on domestic and international companies; pricing and terms and conditions data on fixed income and equity securities; and corporate action data. In addition, Mergent's Indxis subsidiary develops and licenses equity and fixed income investment products based on its proprietary investment methodologies. Our licensed products have over $9 billion in assets under management and are offered by major investment management firms. The Indxis calculation platform is the chosen technology for some of the world's largest index companies. Its index calculation and pricing distribution protocols are used to administer index rules and distribute real-time pricing data.

Abbreviations

AFL-CIO – American Federation of Labor and Congress of Industrial Organizations

AMA – American Medical Association

AMEX – American Stock Exchange

ARM – adjustable-rate mortgage

ASP – application services provider

ATM – asynchronous transfer mode

ATM – automated teller machine

CAD/CAM – computer-aided design/computer-aided manufacturing

CD-ROM – compact disc – read-only memory

CD-R – CD-recordable

CEO – chief executive officer

CFO – chief financial officer

CMOS – complementary metal oxide silicon

COO – chief operating officer

DAT – digital audiotape

DOD – Department of Defense

DOE – Department of Energy

DOS – disk operating system

DOT – Department of Transportation

DRAM – dynamic random-access memory

DSL – digital subscriber line

DVD – digital versatile disc/digital video disc

DVD-R – DVD-recordable

EPA – Environmental Protection Agency

EPS – earnings per share

ESOP – employee stock ownership plan

EU – European Union

EVP – executive vice president

FCC – Federal Communications Commission

FDA – Food and Drug Administration

FDIC – Federal Deposit Insurance Corporation

FTC – Federal Trade Commission

GATT – General Agreement on Tariffs and Trade

GDP – gross domestic product

HMO – health maintenance organization

HR – human resources

HTML – hypertext markup language

ICC – Interstate Commerce Commission

IPO – initial public offering

IRS – Internal Revenue Service

ISP – Internet service provider

kWh – kilowatt-hour

LAN – local-area network

LBO – leveraged buyout

LCD – liquid crystal display

LNG – liquefied natural gas

LP – limited partnership

Ltd. – limited

mips – millions of instructions per second

MW – megawatt

NAFTA – North American Free Trade Agreement

NASA – National Aeronautics and Space Administration

NASDAQ – National Association of Securities Dealers Automated Quotations

NATO – North Atlantic Treaty Organization

NYSE – New York Stock Exchange

OCR – optical character recognition

OECD – Organization for Economic Cooperation and Development

OEM – original equipment manufacturer

OPEC – Organization of Petroleum Exporting Countries

OS – operating system

OSHA – Occupational Safety and Health Administration

OTC – over-the-counter

PBX – private branch exchange

PCMCIA – Personal Computer Memory Card International Association

P/E – price to earnings ratio

RAID – redundant array of independent disks

RAM – random-access memory

R&D – research and development

RBOC – regional Bell operating company

RISC – reduced instruction set computer

REIT – real estate investment trust

ROA – return on assets

ROE – return on equity

ROI – return on investment

ROM – read-only memory

S&L – savings and loan

SEC – Securities and Exchange Commission

SEVP – senior executive vice president

SIC – Standard Industrial Classification

SOC – system on a chip

SVP – senior vice president

USB – universal serial bus

VAR – value-added reseller

VAT – value-added tax

VC – venture capitalist

VoIP – Voice over Internet Protocol

VP – vice president

WAN – wide-area network

Contents

Companies Profiled

Companies Profiled (continued)

Companies Profiled (continued)

About Hoover's Handbook of Emerging Companies 2014

Hoover's Handbook of Emerging Companies enters its 20th year as one of America's premier sources of business information on younger, growth-oriented enterprises. Given our current economic realities, finding value in the marketplace becomes ever more difficult, and so we are particularly pleased to present this edition of Hoover's Handbook of Emerging Companies 2014 — the result of a search of our extensive database of business information for companies with demonstrated growth and the potential for future gains.

The 600 companies in this book were chosen from the universe of public US companies with sales between $10 million and $2.5 billion. Their selection was based primarily on sales growth and profitability, although in a few cases we made some rather subjective decisions about which companies we chose to include. They all have reported at least three years of sales and have sustained annualized sales growth of at least 7% during that time. Also, they are profitable (through year-end September 2013).

In addition to the companies featured in our handbooks, comprehensive coverage of more than 40,000 business enterprises is available in electronic format on our website, Hoover's Online (www.hoovers.com). Our goal is to provide one site that offers authoritative, updated intelligence on US and global companies, industries, and the people who shape them. Hoover's has partnered with other prestigious business information and service providers to bring you all the right business information, services, and links in one place.

Hoover's Handbook of Emerging Companies is one of our four-title series of handbooks that covers, literally, the world of business. The series is available as an indexed set, and also includes Hoover's Handbook of American Business, Hoover's Handbook of World Business, and Hoover's Handbook of Private Companies. This series brings you information on the biggest, fastest-growing, and most influential enterprises in the world.

We believe that anyone who buys from, sells to, invests in, lends to, competes with, interviews with, or works for a company should know as much as possible about that enterprise. Taken together, Hoover's Handbook of Emerging Companies 2014 and the other Hoover's products represent the most complete source of basic corporate information readily available to the general public.

How to use this book

This book has four sections:

1. "Using Hoover's Handbooks" describes the contents of our profiles.

2. "A List-Lover's Compendium" contains lists of the fastest-growing and most profitable companies. The lists are based on the information in our profiles, or compiled from well-known sources.

3. The company profiles section makes up the largest and most important part of the book — 600 profiles arranged alphabetically. Each profile features an overview of the company; some larger and more visible companies have an additional History section. All companies have up to five years of financial information, product information where available, and a list of company executives and key competitors.

4. At the end of this volume are the combined indexes from our 2014 editions of all Hoover's Handbooks. The information is organized into three separate sections. The first sorts companies by industry groups, the second by headquarters location. The third index is a list of all the executives found in the Executives section of each company profile. For a more thorough description of our indexing style, see page xii.

Using Hoover's Handbooks

ORGANIZATION

The profiles in this volume are presented in alphabetical order. This alphabetization is generally word by word, which means that Bridge Bancorp precedes Bridgepoint Education. You will find the commonly used name of the enterprise at the beginning of the profile; the full, legal name is found in the Locations section. If a company name starts with initials, such as BJ's Restaurants or U.S. Physical Therapy, look for it under the combined initials (in the above example, BJ or US, respectively).

Basic financial data is listed under the heading Historical Financials; also included is the exchange on which the company's stock is traded, the ticker symbol used by the stock exchange, and the company's fiscal year-end. The annual financial information contained in the profiles is current through fiscal year-ends occurring as late as September 2013. We have included certain non-financial developments, such as officer changes, through January 2013.

OVERVIEW

In the first section of the profile, we have tried to give a thumbnail description of the company and what it does. The description will usually include information on the company's strategy, reputation, and ownership. We recommend that you read this section first.

HISTORY

This extended section, which is available for some of the larger and more well-known companies, reflects our belief that every enterprise is the sum of its history and that you have to know where you came from in order to know where you are going. While some companies have limited historical awareness, we think the vast majority of the enterprises in this book have colorful backgrounds. We have tried to focus on the people who made the enterprises what they are today. We have found these histories to be full of twists and ironies; they make fascinating reading.

EXECUTIVES

Here we list the names of the people who run the company, insofar as space allows. In the case of public companies, we have shown the ages and pay of key officers. The published data is for the previous fiscal year, although the company may have announced promotions or retirements since year-end. The pay represents cash compensation, including bonuses, but excludes stock option programs.

Although companies are free to structure their management titles any way they please, most modern corpora-

tions follow standard practices. The ultimate power in any corporation lies with the shareholders, who elect a board of directors, usually including officers or "insiders," as well as individuals from outside the company. The chief officer, the person on whose desk the buck stops, is usually called the chief executive officer (CEO). Often, he or she is also the chairman of the board.

As corporate management has become more complex, it is common for the CEO to have a "right-hand person" who oversees the day-to-day operations of the company, allowing the CEO plenty of time to focus on strategy and long-term issues. This right-hand person is usually designated the chief operating officer (COO) and is often the president of the company. In other cases one person is both chairman and president.

A multitude of other titles exists, including chief financial officer (CFO), chief administrative officer, and vice chairman. We have always tried to include the CFO, the chief legal officer, and the chief human resources or personnel officer. Our best advice is that officers' pay levels are clear indicators of who the board of directors thinks are the most important members of the management team.

The people named in the Executives section are indexed at the back of the book.

The Executives section also includes the name of the company's auditing (accounting) firm, where available.

LOCATIONS

Here we include the company's full legal name and its headquarters, street address, telephone and fax numbers, and website, as available. The back of the book includes an index of companies by headquarters locations.

In some cases we have also included information on the geographic distribution of the company's business, including sales and profit data. Note that these profit numbers, like those in the Products/Operations section below, are usually operating or pretax profits rather than net profits. Operating profits are generally those before financing costs (interest income and payments) and before taxes, which are considered costs attributable to the whole company rather than to one division or part of the world. For this reason the net income figures (in the Historical Financials section) are usually much lower, since they are after interest and taxes. Pretax profits are after interest but before taxes.

PRODUCTS/OPERATIONS

This section lists as many of the company's products, services, brand names, divisions, subsidiaries, and joint ventures as we could fit. We have tried to include all its major lines and all familiar brand names. The nature of this section varies by company and the amount of information available. If the company publishes sales and profit information by type of business, we have included it.

COMPETITORS

In this section we have listed companies that compete with the profiled company. This feature is included as a quick way to locate similar companies and compare them. The universe of competitors includes all public companies and all private companies with sales in excess of $500 million. In a few instances we have identified smaller private companies as key competitors.

HISTORICAL FINANCIALS

Here we have tried to present as much data about each enterprise's financial performance as we could compile in the allocated space. Although the information varies somewhat from industry to industry, the following is generally present.

A five-year table, with relevant annualized compound growth rates, covers:

- Sales — fiscal year sales (year-end assets for most financial companies)
- Net income — fiscal year net income (before accounting changes)
- Net profit margin — fiscal year net income as a percent of sales (as a percent of assets for most financial firms)
- Employees — fiscal year-end or average number of employees
- Stock price — the fiscal year closing price
- P/E — high and low price/earnings ratio
- Earnings per share — fiscal year earnings per share (EPS)
- Dividends per share — fiscal year dividends per share
- Book value per share — fiscal year-end book value (common shareholders' equity per share)

The information on the number of employees is intended to aid the reader interested in knowing whether a company has a long-term trend of increasing or decreasing employment. As far as we know, we are the only company that publishes this information in print format.

The numbers on the left in each row of the Historical Financials section give the month and the year in which the company's fiscal year actually ends. Thus, a company with a September 30, 2010, year-end is shown as 9/10.

In addition, we have provided in graph form a stock price history for each company. The graphs, covering up to five years, show the range of trading between the high and the low price, as well as the closing price for each fiscal year.

Key year-end statistics in this section generally show the financial strength of the enterprise, including:

- Debt ratio (long-term debt as a percent of shareholders' equity)
- Return on equity (net income divided by the average of beginning and ending common shareholders' equity)
- Cash and cash equivalents
- Current ratio (ratio of current assets to current liabilities)
- Total long-term debt (including capital lease obligations)
- Number of shares of common stock outstanding
- Dividend yield (fiscal year dividends per share divided by the fiscal year-end closing stock price)
- Dividend payout (fiscal year dividends divided by fiscal year EPS)
- Market value at fiscal year-end (fiscal year-end closing stock price multiplied by fiscal year-end number of shares outstanding)

Per-share data has been adjusted for stock splits. The data for public companies has been provided to us by Morningstar, Inc. Other public company information was compiled by Hoover's, which takes full responsibility for the content of this section.

Hoover's Handbook of

Emerging Companies

A List-Lover's Compendium

The 200 Largest Companies by Sales in Hoover's Handbook of Emerging Companies 2014

Rank	Company	Sales ($ mil.)	Rank	Company	Sales ($mil.)	Rank	Company	Sales ($ mil.)
1	Qualitas Comp De Seguros	$758,786	61	Assicurazioni Generali S.p.A	$97,046	121	Barclays PLC	$66,387
2	Exxon Mobil Corp.	$486,429	62	Honda Motor Co., Ltd.	$96,892	122	Deutsche Bank AG	$65,528
3	Royal Dutch Shell Plc	$484,489	63	SK Holdings Co Ltd	$95,985	123	Tokyo Electric Power Co. Inc	$65,213
4	Wal-Mart Stores, Inc.	$446,950	64	Panasonic Corp	$95,650	124	Johnson & Johnson	$65,030
5	China Petr & Chem Co	$398,081	65	BASF SE	$95,065	125	Aeon Co. Ltd. (Japan)	$64,737
6	BP plc	$382,333	66	ArcelorMittal SA	$93,973	126	Lloyds Banking Group Plc	$64,655
7	PetroChina Co Ltd	$318,353	67	China Construction Bnk Corp	$92,082	127	American Intl Group	$64,237
8	Cementos Bio-Bio S.A.Chile	$317,739	68	Rosneft Oil Co OJSC Moscow	$91,975	128	Mitsui & Co., Ltd.	$64,020
9	Hansol Chemical Co Ltd	$256,350	69	Societe Generale	$91,732	129	RWE AG	$63,984
10	Chevron Corporation	$253,706	70	Kroger Co.	$90,374	130	EADS N.V.	$63,545
11	ConocoPhillips	$251,226	71	Nestle S.A.	$89,042	131	Dell Inc	$62,071
12	Toyota Motor Corp	$226,546	72	Archer Daniels Midland Co.	$89,038	132	Landesbank Baden-W.	$62,055
13	Total S.A.	$215,424	73	Bayerische Motoren Werke	$89,017	133	Reliance Industries Ltd	$61,189
14	Volkswagen A.G. Germany	$206,095	74	Freddie Mac	$88,262	134	WellPoint Inc	$60,711
15	Phillips 66	$200,614	75	Federal Reserve System	$88,027	135	Rio Tinto Plc (United Kingdo	$60,537
16	Glencore International PLC,	$186,152	76	Wells Fargo & Co.	$87,597	136	Rio Tinto Ltd	$60,537
17	Apple Inc	$156,508	77	Nippon Life Insurance Co.	$87,550	137	Royal Bank of Scotland Grp	$60,447
18	General Motors Co.	$150,276	78	Agricultural Bank of China	$87,102	138	Caterpillar Inc.	$60,138
19	General Electric Co	$147,300	79	Metro AG	$86,276	139	Unilever Plc (UK)	$60,103
20	E.ON SE	$146,751	80	Electricite de France	$84,471	140	Unilever N.V.	$60,103
21	Petroleo Brasileiro S.A.	$145,915	81	China Mobile Limited	$83,884	141	Dow Chemical Co.	$59,985
22	Gazprom OAO	$143,741	82	Procter & Gamble Co.	$83,680	142	Seven & i Holdings Co. Ltd.	$59,517
23	Berkshire Hathaway Inc.	$143,688	83	Bank of China Ltd., Beijing	$82,487	143	POSCO (South Korea)	$59,497
24	ENI S.p.A.	$142,955	84	Telefonica, S.A.	$81,277	144	Novartis AG Basel	$59,375
25	Samsung Electronics Co Ltd	$142,403	85	Repsol S.A.	$80,849	145	China Life Insurance Co Ltd	$59,277
26	ING Groep N.V.	$138,041	86	Noble Group Ltd	$80,732	146	Wesfarmers Ltd.	$59,149
27	Daimler AG	$137,804	87	AmerisourceBergen Corp.	$79,490	147	SK Innovation Co Ltd	$59,007
28	Fannie Mae	$137,451	88	Sony Corp	$79,156	148	Vale S. A.	$58,990
29	Ford Motor Co. (DE)	$136,264	89	Itau Unibanco Holding S.A.	$79,115	149	Bunge Ltd.	$58,743
30	Oil Co Lukoil	$133,650	90	Munich Re Group	$78,782	150	ThyssenKrupp AG	$58,490
31	AXA S.A.	$131,698	91	Marathon Petroleum Corp.	$78,759	151	France Telecom S.A.	$58,438
32	JX Holdings, Inc.	$130,731	92	Peugeot S.A. (France)	$77,493	152	United Technologies Corp.	$58,190
33	Nippon Telegraph & Teleph	$128,091	93	PTT Public Co Ltd.	$77,158	153	AUDI AG	$57,036
34	AT&T Inc	$126,723	94	Fiat S.P.A Torino	$77,037	154	Prudential Plc	$56,396
35	Valero Energy Corp.	$125,987	95	Philip Morris International	$76,346	155	A.P. Moller - Maersk A/S	$56,114
36	Allianz SE	$123,706	96	Deutsche Telekom AG	$75,865	156	Meiji Yasuda Life Insurance	$55,968
37	McKesson Corp.	$122,734	97	Toshiba Corp	$75,640	157	Comcast Corp	$55,842
38	Hewlett-Packard Co	$120,357	98	Vodafone Group Plc	$74,380	158	Dai-Ichi Life Insurance Co.,	$55,775
39	BNP Paribas (France)	$118,801	99	Microsoft Corporation	$73,723	159	Aviva Plc (United Kingdom)	$55,619
40	Hitachi, Ltd.	$117,833	100	China Railway Construction	$72,662	160	Woolworths Ltd.	$55,515
41	GDF SUEZ	$117,281	101	Banco do Brasil S.A.	$72,400	161	Renault S.A. (France)	$55,137
42	Bank of America Corp.	$115,074	102	BHP Billiton Ltd.	$72,226	162	TNK-BP Holding, Moscow	$54,890
43	Nissan Motor Co., Ltd.	$114,702	103	BHP Billiton Plc	$72,226	163	Sojitz Corp	$54,788
44	Hon Hai Precision Indus Co	$113,912	104	Toyota Tsusho Corp	$72,129	164	Compagnie de Saint-Gobain	$54,475
45	HSBC Holdings Plc	$113,405	105	Walgreen Co.	$71,633	165	Fujitsu Ltd.	$54,463
46	Indust and Commercial Ba	$112,384	106	Indian Oil Corp., Ltd. (India	$71,603	166	Mondelez International Inc	$54,365
47	Statoil ASA	$111,468	107	Home Depot Inc	$70,395	167	Intel Corp	$53,999
48	Verizon Communications In	$110,875	108	MetLife Inc	$70,262	168	Unicredito S.p.A. Roma	$53,994
49	JPMorgan Chase & Co.	$110,838	109	China Railway Group Ltd	$70,255	169	Marubeni Corp.	$53,521
50	Banco Santander SA	$108,856	110	Target Corp	$69,865	170	United Parcel Service Inc	$53,105
51	Cardinal Health, Inc.	$107,552	111	INTL FCStone Inc.	$69,249	171	Zurich Insurance Group Ltd	$52,983
52	CVS Caremark Corporation	$107,100	112	SAIC Motor Corp Ltd	$69,078	172	Idemitsu Kosan Co Ltd	$52,546
53	Carrefour S.A.	$107,051	113	Boeing Co.	$68,735	173	ITOCHU Corp. (Japan)	$52,067
54	Intl Business Machi	$106,916	114	Deutsche Post AG	$68,332	174	Banco Bradesco S.A.	$51,877
55	Citigroup Inc	$102,587	115	Mitsubishi Corp	$67,851	175	NTT DOCOMO, Inc.	$51,688
56	Tesco PLC	$101,974	116	Pfizer Inc	$67,425	176	LyondellBasell Industries NV	$51,035
57	UnitedHealth Group Inc	$101,862	117	Hyundai Motor Co., Ltd.	$67,143	177	SSE PLC	$50,835
58	Siemens AG (Germany)	$101,237	118	Bosch (Robert) GmbH Germ	$66,605	178	Best Buy Inc	$50,705
59	Costco Wholesale Corp	$99,137	119	Barclays Bank Plc	$66,534	179	Saudi Basic Industries Corp -	$50,640
60	Credit Agricole SA	$98,123	120	Pepsico Inc.	$66,504	180	Lowe's Companies Inc	$50,208

SOURCE: HOOVER'S, INC., DATABASE, DECEMBER 2013

The 200 Largest Companies by Sales in
Hoover's Handbook of Emerging Companies 2014 (continued)

Rank	Company	Sales ($ mil.)	Rank	Company	Sales ($mil.)	Rank	Company	Sales ($ mil.)
181	Nokia Corp.	$50,004						
182	Nippon Steel-Sumitomo Met	$49,871						
183	Prudential Financial, Inc.	$49,045						
184	Vinci SA	$49,024						
185	Sumitomo Mitsui Financ Grp	$48,434						
186	Amazon.com Inc.	$48,077						
187	Commonwealth Bnk of Aust	$48,061						
188	Merck & Co., Inc	$48,047						
189	CNP Assurances S.A.	$47,927						
190	America Movil, S.A.B. de C.V	$47,627						
191	Royal Bank of Scotland plc	$47,373						
192	Bayer AG	$47,247						
193	Banco Bilbao Vizcaya Argent	$47,172						
194	Roche Holding Ltd.	$46,889						
195	LG Electronics Inc	$46,826						
196	China Communications Const	$46,753						
197	Coca-Cola Co (The)	$46,542						
198	Lockheed Martin Corp.	$46,499						
199	Hyundai Hvy Industries Co.	$46,355						
200	Mitsubishi UFJ Financial Gro	$46,316						

The 200 Largest Employers in
Hoover's Handbook of Emerging Companies 2014

Rank	Company	Employees	Rank	Company	Employees	Rank	Company	Employees
1	Wal-Mart Stores, Inc.	2200000	61	Lowe's Companies Inc	248000	121	Nissan Motor Co., Ltd.	157365
2	A.P. Moller - Maersk A/S	1107080	62	Onex Corp.	246000	122	Starwood Hotels & Resorts	154000
3	Hon Hai Precision Indust Co	961000	63	China Railway Construction C	241621	123	Publix Super Markets, Inc.	152000
4	Tesco PLC	925759	64	GDF SUEZ	240303	124	Electricite de France	151804
5	G4S Plc	657200	65	Walgreen Co.	240000	125	Infosys Ltd.	150000
6	Randstad Holding N.V.	605500	66	Wal-Mart de Mexico S.A.B.	238128	126	Barclays Bank Plc	149700
7	Kelly Services, Inc.	558200	67	Deutsche Telekom AG	235132	127	Fresenius SE & Co KGaA	149351
8	PetroChina Co Ltd	552810	68	Rallye S.A.	227995	128	FedEx Corp	149000
9	Metro AG	533233	69	Koninklijke Ahold NV (Nether	218000	129	Coca-Cola Co (The)	146200
10	Volkswagen A.G. (Germany)	501956	70	China United Ntwrk Communi	215954	130	Accor SA	144893
11	Agricultural Bank of China	490121	71	Toshiba Corp	209784	131	Bridgestone Corp. (Japan)	143124
12	Pou Chen Corp	484035	72	Casino Guichard Perrachon S.	207498	132	Royal Bank of Scotland Grp	142600
13	Compass Group PLC (UK)	471108	73	General Motors Co.	207000	133	Weston (George) Limited	142000
14	Deutsche Post AG	467188	74	China Resources Enterprise	200000	134	Kohl's Corp.	142000
15	Yum! Brands, Inc.	466000	75	United Technologies Corp.	199900	135	Allianz SE	141938
16	Yue Yuen Industrial (Holding	460000	76	Robert Half International In	199300	136	Barclays PLC	141100
17	International Business Machi	433362	77	HCA Holdings Inc	199000	137	Jabil Circuit, Inc.	141000
18	Sodexo	421391	78	Tata Consultancy Services Lt	198614	138	PICC Property and Casualty C	140942
19	McDonald's Corp	420000	79	BNP Paribas (France)	198423	139	Schneider Electric S.A.	140491
20	Carrefour S.A.	412443	80	Canon, Inc.	198307	140	Eurazeo Paris	140000
21	Industrial and Commercial Ba	408859	81	Fiat S.P.A Torino	197021	141	Xerox Corp	139650
22	Gazprom OAO	401000	82	Sumitomo Electric Industries,	194734	142	Cognizant Technology Solutio	137700
23	United Parcel Service Inc	398000	83	Compagnie de Saint-Gobain	194658	143	Loblaw Cos. Ltd.	135000
24	China Petroleum & Chem Co	377235	84	Verizon Communications Inc	193900	144	Emerson Electric Co.	134900
25	Siemens AG (Germany)	370000	85	Banco Santander SA	187233	145	ABB Ltd	133600
26	Hitachi, Ltd.	369722	86	Honda Motor Co., Ltd.	187094	146	EADS N.V.	133115
27	Target Corp	365000	87	Vinci SA	183320	147	The Gap, Inc.	132000
28	Kroger Co.	339000	88	ThyssenKrupp AG	180050	148	Honeywell International, Inc	132000
29	Hewlett-Packard Co	331800	89	Darden Restaurants, Inc. (Un	180000	149	Morrison (Wm.) Supermrkets	131207
30	Veolia Environnement	331266	90	Freescale Semiconductor Ltd	180000	150	Bouygues S.A.	130827
31	Home Depot Inc	331000	91	Safeway Inc.	178000	151	Nokia Corp.	130050
32	Panasonic Corp	330767	92	Fomento Economico Mexican	177470	152	SUPERVALU INC	130000
33	China Construction Bnk Corp	329438	93	Yamato Holdings Co., Ltd.	177301	153	Wipro Ltd	130000
34	Nestle S.A.	328000	94	Royal Mail Holdings Plc	176242	154	Renault S.A. (France)	128322
35	Toyota Motor Corp	325905	95	China Mobile Limited	175336	155	Cencosud SA	128029
36	Nippon Telegraph & Teleph	313586	96	Ping An Insurance (Group)	175136	156	Weyerhaeuser Co.	128000
37	China Telecom Corp Ltd	309799	97	Costco Wholesale Corp	174000	157	Metallurgical Corp China Ltd	127746
38	Bosch (Robert) GmbH (Ger)	302519	98	Fujitsu Ltd.	173155	158	China Communications Svc	127000
39	General Electric Co	301000	99	France Telecom S.A.	171949	159	Denso Corp. (Japan)	126036
40	HSBC Holdings Plc	298000	100	Boeing Co.	171700	160	Procter & Gamble Co.	126000
41	China Unicom (HK) Ltd	297210	101	Macys Inc	171000	161	Mondelez International Inc	126000
42	Pepsico Inc.	297000	102	Johnson Controls Inc	170000	162	Comcast Corp.	126000
43	China Railway Group Ltd	294761	103	BYD Co Ltd	170000	163	Koninklijke Philips Electron	125241
44	Sears Holdings Corp	293000	104	Unilever Plc (UK)	169000	164	Caterpillar Inc.	125099
45	Telefonica, S.A.	291027	105	Unilever N.V.	169000	165	FirstGroup Plc	124705
46	Bank of China Ltd., Beijing	289951	106	TJX Companies, Inc.	168000	166	Novartis AG Basel	123686
47	Bank of America Corp.	282000	107	Unicredito S.p.A. Roma	167014	167	Magnit Ojsc	123506
48	CVS Caremark Corporation	280000	108	Best Buy Inc	167000	168	Lockheed Martin Corp.	123000
49	Securitas AB	272425	109	Disney (Walt) Co. (The)	166000	169	Lufthansa AG (Germany, Fed.	120055
50	Daimler AG	271370	110	ACS Actividades de Construc	164923	170	Marriott International, Inc.	120000
51	Berkshire Hathaway Inc.	271000	111	Ford Motor Co. (DE)	164000	171	Capgemini	119707
52	Sberbank Russia	266187	112	Continental AG (Germany)	163788	172	BRF- Brasil Foods S.A.	119167
53	Citigroup Inc	266000	113	Sony Corp	162700	173	Prosegur Cia De Seguridad	118285
54	Wells Fargo & Co.	264200	114	Rosneft Oil Co OJSC Moscow	160837	174	Johnson & Johnson	117900
55	ArcelorMittal SA	260523	115	Etablissements Delhaize Frer	160000	175	Mitsubishi Electric Corp.	117314
56	JPMorgan Chase & Co.	260157	116	Starbucks Corp.	160000	176	Teleperformance SA	116764
57	Accenture plc	257000	117	Societe Generale	159616	177	Anheuser-Busch Inbev SA	116278
58	AT&T Inc	256420	118	Penney (J.C.) Co.,Inc. (Hold	159000	178	Innolux Corp	116056
59	Hutchison Whampoa Ltd.	250000	119	Flextronics International Lt	159000	179	Tyson Foods, Inc.	115000
60	ARAMARK Corp.	250000	120	America Movil, S.A.B. de C.V	158694	180	Oracle Corp.	115000

SOURCE: HOOVER'S, INC., DATABASE, DECEMBER 2013

The 200 Largest Employers in
Hoover's Handbook of Emerging Companies 2014 (continued)

Rank	Company	Employees
181	Banco do Brasil S.A.	113810
182	Sanofi	113719
183	Royal Bank of Scotland plc	113700
184	WPP Plc (New)	113615
185	Schlumberger Ltd.	113000
186	Pegatron Corp	112318
187	Bayer AG	111800
188	BASF SE	111141
189	Steel Authority of India Ltd	110794
190	Mitsubishi UFJ Financial Gro	110500
191	Banco Bilbao Vizcaya Argent	109694
192	Dell Inc	109400
193	Ricoh Co., Ltd. (Japan)	109241
194	NEC Corp	109102
195	Evraz PLC	109061
196	Quanta Computer Inc	108872
197	Compagnie Generale des Eta	108300
198	Magna International Inc.	108275
199	Nidec Corp	107489
200	Associated British Foods Plc	106243

The Top 200 Companies by Net Income in Hoover's Handbook of Emerging Companies 2014

Rank	Company	Net Income ($ mil.)
1	Federal Reserve System	$78538
2	Qualitas Comp De Seguros	$59743
3	Apple Inc	$41733
4	Exxon Mobil Corp.	$41060
5	Gazprom OAO	$40491
6	Federal Reserve Bank Of NY	$35026
7	Industrial and Commercial Ba	$33087
8	Royal Dutch Shell Plc	$30918
9	Chevron Corporation	$26895
10	China Construction Bank Corp	$26890
11	BP plc	$25700
12	Vale S. A.	$22885
13	PetroChina Co Ltd	$21124
14	Ford Motor Co. (DE)	$20213
15	Petroleo Brasileiro S.A.	$20121
16	China Mobile Limited	$19997
17	Volkswagen A.G. (Germany)	$19931
18	Bank of China Ltd., Beijing	$19729
19	Agricultural Bank of China	$19371
20	JPMorgan Chase & Co.	$18976
21	American International Group	$17798
22	Microsoft Corporation	$16978
23	HSBC Holdings Plc	$16797
24	Hansol Chemical Co Ltd	$16103
25	Total S.A.	$15878
26	Wells Fargo & Co.	$15869
27	International Business Machi	$15855
28	Wal-Mart Stores, Inc.	$15699
29	BHP Billiton Ltd.	$15417
30	BHP Billiton Plc	$15417
31	General Electric Co	$14151
32	Statoil ASA	$13104
33	Intel Corp	$12942
34	Rosneft Oil Co OJSC (Moscow)	$12452
35	ConocoPhillips	$12436
36	China Petroleum & Chemical C	$11633
37	Samsung Electronics Co., Ltd	$11530
38	Cnooc Ltd.	$11162
39	Vodafone Group Plc	$11148
40	Citigroup Inc	$11067
41	Procter & Gamble Co.	$10756
42	Oil Co Lukoil	$10357
43	Berkshire Hathaway Inc.	$10254
44	Nestle S.A.	$10084
45	Pfizer Inc	$10009
46	AstraZeneca Plc	$9983
47	Oracle Corp.	$9981
48	Roche Holding Ltd.	$9931
49	Sberbank Russia	$9796
50	Google Inc	$9737
51	Johnson & Johnson	$9672
52	Federal Reserve Bank of Richm	$9222
53	TNK-BP Holding, Moscow	$9208
54	General Motors Co.	$9190
55	Novartis AG Basel	$9113
56	ENI S.p.A.	$8873
57	Philip Morris International	$8591
58	Coca-Cola Co (The)	$8572
59	GlaxoSmithKline Plc	$8127
60	Federal Reserve Bank of San F	$8071

Rank	Company	Net Income ($ mil.)
61	Bank of Communications Co.,	$8060
62	Cisco Systems, Inc.	$8041
63	BASF SE	$8004
64	Ecopetrol SA	$7973
65	BNP Paribas (France)	$7825
66	Saudi Basic Industries Corp -	$7798
67	Royal Bank of Canada	$7462
68	Itau Unibanco Holding S.A.	$7419
69	Sanofi	$7364
70	Daimler AG	$7330
71	China Shenhua Energy Co., Lt	$7257
72	Surgutneftegas OAO	$7223
73	Commonwealth Bank of Austral	$7220
74	Hutchison Whampoa Ltd.	$7212
75	Telefonica, S.A.	$6989
76	MetLife Inc	$6981
77	Banco Santander SA	$6921
78	Banco do Brasil S.A.	$6800
79	Occidental Petroleum Corp	$6771
80	Hyundai Motor Co., Ltd.	$6607
81	Federal Reserve Bank Of Atlan	$6498
82	Pepsico Inc.	$6443
83	Sumitomo Mitsui Financial Gr	$6321
84	Bayerische Motoren Werke AG	$6313
85	Merck & Co., Inc	$6272
86	Westpac Banking Corp	$6230
87	Toronto Dominion Bank	$6188
88	Anglo American Plc (United K	$6169
89	ING Groep N.V.	$6131
90	Qualcomm, Inc.	$6109
91	Bank of Nova Scotia Halifax	$6039
92	America Movil, S.A.B. de C.V	$5931
93	Cheung Kong (Holdings) Ltd.	$5929
94	Banco Bradesco S.A.	$5876
95	Anheuser-Busch Inbev SA	$5855
96	Rio Tinto Ltd	$5826
97	Siemens AG (Germany)	$5764
98	Freeport-McMoRan Copper & Go	$5747
99	China Merchants Bank Co Ltd	$5740
100	$Xstrata Plc	$5713
101	$Nippon Telegraph & Telephone	$5702
102	$Disney (Walt) Co. (The)	$5682
103	$AUDI AG	$5677
104	$NTT DOCOMO, Inc.	$5655
105	$AXA S.A.	$5593
106	$Barclays Bank Plc	$5586
107	$Sun Hung Kai Properties Ltd.	$5554
108	$Mitsubishi Corp	$5533
109	$McDonald's Corp	$5503
110	$Unilever Plc (United Kingdom)	$5500
111	Unilever N.V.	$5500
112	$Gazprom Neft	$5352
113	$Deutsche Bank AG	$5345
114	$Hongkong Land Holdings Ltd.	$5306
115	$Mitsui & Co., Ltd.	$5297
116	$Australia and New Zealand Ba	$5202
117	$GDF SUEZ	$5178
118	$UnitedHealth Group Inc	$5142
119	$Oil and Natural Gas Corp. Lt	$5119
120	$Mitsubishi UFJ Financial Gro	$5074

Rank	Company	Sales ($mil.)
121	$National Australia Bank Ltd.	$5070
122	$France Telecom S.A.	$5038
123	$Federal Reserve Bank Of Chica	$5026
124	$Schlumberger Ltd.	$4997
125	$Eksportfinans ASA	$4996
126	$United Technologies Corp.	$4979
127	$American Express Co.	$4935
128	$Caterpillar Inc.	$4928
129	$China Citic Bank Corp Ltd	$4896
130	$U.S. Bancorp (DE)	$4872
131	$Standard Chartered Plc	$4849
132	$British Amer Tobacco Plc (UK)	$4781
133	$Phillips 66	$4775
134	$Abbott Laboratories	$4728
135	$Devon Energy Corp.	$4704
136	$Barclays PLC	$4645
137	$Companhia de Bebidas das Ame	$4633
138	$Apache Corp.	$4584
139	$Barrick Gold Corp.	$4484
140	$SAP AG	$4447
141	$Goldman Sachs Group, Inc.	$4442
142	$China Minsheng Banking Corp	$4436
143	$Tesco PLC	$4434
144	$Taiwan Semiconductor Manufac	$4428
145	$UBS AG (Switzerland)	$4421
146	$Lilly (Eli) & Co.	$4348
147	$Reliance Industries Ltd	$4327
148	$3M Co	$4283
149	$BG Group Plc	$4234
150	$Hitachi, Ltd.	$4232
151	$SABMiller Plc (United Kingdo	$4221
152	$Suncor Energy Inc.	$4219
153	$Nissan Motor Co., Ltd.	$4162
154	$Comcast Corp	$4160
155	$Banco Santander Brasil SA	$4154
156	$Swire Pacific Ltd. (Hong Kon	$4146
157	$Bank of Montreal	$4126
158	$Morgan Stanley	$4110
159	$Industrial Bank Co., Ltd.	$4052
160	$Glencore International PLC,	$4048
161	$Boeing Co.	$4018
162	$LVMH Moet Hennessy Louis Vui	$3964
163	$AT&T Inc	$3944
164	$Jardine Strategic Holdings L	$3943
165	$Wharf (Holdings) Ltd. (The)	$3935
166	$Japan Tobacco Inc.	$3912
167	$Electricite de France	$3893
168	$Banco Bilbao Vizcaya Argent SA	$3886
169	$Home Depot Inc	$3883
170	$Softbank Corp. (Japan)	$3825
171	$United Parcel Service Inc	$3804
172	$Zurich Insurance Group Ltd	$3766
173	$Bristol-Myers Squibb Co.	$3709
174	$Novatek Joint Stock Co	$3707
175	$Amgen Inc	$3683
176	$Prudential Financial, Inc.	$3666
177	$ITOCHU Corp. (Japan)	$3663
178	$Transport For London	$3647
179	$Iberdrola SA	$3628
180	$Medtronic, Inc.	$3617

*Average annual sales growth measured over a three-year period.

SOURCE: INC., SEPTEMBER 2013

The Top 200 Companies by Net Income in
Hoover's Handbook of Emerging Companies 2014 (continued)

Rank	Company	Net Income ($ mil.)	Rank	Company	Net Income ($ mil.)	Rank	Company	Sales ($mil.)
181	JSC MMC Norilsk Nickel	$3604						
182	HSBC Bank Plc (UK)	$3598						
183	Mondelez International Inc	$3527						
184	Dell Inc	$3492						
185	Du Pont (E.I.) de Nemours &	$3474						
186	Vivendi	$3468						
187	Telstra Corp., Ltd.	$3468						
188	CVS Caremark Corporation	$3461						
189	Toyota Motor Corp	$3457						
190	Jardine Matheson Holdings Ltd	$3449						
191	AbbVie Inc.	$3433						
192	Nordea Bank AB	$3398						
193	Nordea Bank Denmark A/S	$3398						
194	Altria Group Inc	$3390						
195	PTT Public Co Ltd.	$3346						
196	Canadian Imperial Bank of Co	$3340						
197	Imperial Oil Ltd.	$3305						
198	Union Pacific Corp	$3292						
199	Allianz SE	$3292						
200	KGHM Polska Miedz S.A.	$3289						

Hoover's Handbook of

Emerging Companies

2014

3D Systems Corp. (DE)

3D Systems helps product designers and engineers bring their concepts to life. The company's stereolithography apparatuses (SLAs) and other machines create 3-D prototypes of everything from toys to airplane parts. Its SLAs rapidly produce 3-D objects designed in CAD/CAM software in a process called solid imaging which uses a laser to sculpt plastic resin materials into physical models. Its ThermoJet solid object printer also fabricates plastic models using a modified ink jet printing system. Additionally 3D Systems sells the raw plastic and metal consumable material used in its machinery. Customers have included General Electric Hasbro and Texas Instruments. The company does business in Europe the US and Asia.

Thanks in part to more sales of professional and production printers and income from a business operation created in 2009 3Dproparts 3D Systems' revenue rose more than 41% in 2010 over 2009 and net income was up more than 75%. Sales in all the company's operating territories were up as the global economy began recovering from a tough economic climate.

3D Systems uses a steady stream of acquisitions to supplement the development of its products and services and expand its customer base. In early 2013 it acquired Geomagic which provides complementary 3-D design sculpt and scan software. It also brought COWEB that year a Paris start-up that makes custom 3-D printed products and Rapid Product Development Group a quick-turn manufacturer that expands 3D Systems' on-demand parts manufacturing capabilities. In 2012 the company bought VIDAR Systems and Z Corporation from Danish large format scanner maker Contex for more than $135 million. 3D Systems saw the companies as a natural fit with its own technologies with potential to accelerate its growth in the 3-D content-to-print market. The acquisitions also added complementary products to the company's portfolio and expand its distribution and market reach.

3D Systems also acquired direct manufacturing and product development services provider Paramount Industries that year to boost its ability to serve the aerospace and medical device industries. 3D Systems integrated Paramount's manufacturing facilities and advanced tooling and assembly operations with its on-demand direct manufacturing facilities.

Also in 2012 3D Systems expanded its reach in the consumer market with the purchase of Amsterdam-based FreshFiber a leading 3-D printed consumer electronics accessories brand sold online and in retail stores such as Apple Fnac and Gravis. 3D Systems plans to extend the company's customized products portfolio (including its flagship personalized iPhone cases) through its extensive manufacturing infrastructure and its Cubify.com platform. Cubify's Cube 3-D printer is a low-cost (under $1500) wireless printer geared toward the home market. 3D Systems boosted that acquisition with another buying Viztu Technologies which offers customers a way to make interactive and printable 3-D models from pictures and video. Also that year the company bought San Francisco-based startup Bespoke —adding scan design and print technology used to deliver custom fit prosthetics orthotics and orthopedic devices —and South Korea's Rapidform which offers complementary products and gives 3D Systems a foothold in South Korea and Japan.

In 2011 3D Systems bought National RP Support an Iowa-based company that already provided customer support and parts for 3D Systems' equipment. Shortly afterward it paid $15.9 million in cash for Quickparts an Atlanta-based company that offers an e-commerce platform for custom manufactured parts. 3D Systems integrated its own parts fulfillment operations with Quickparts. It also acquired SYCODE adding computer-aided design software used by designers for building digital prototypes Alibre a provider of affordable 3-D software and Formero a Melbourne-based custom parts and 3-D printer manufacturer that will help 3D Systems expand in Asia/Pacific.

Additionally 3D Systems bought two Dutch companies that year expanding its presence in the Benelux region. It acquired Kemo Modelmakerij a provider of custom parts 3-D parts services which was renamed 3D Systems Benelux and it purchased Freedom of Creation.

3D Systems primarily sells via a direct sales force but it also uses distributors and resellers for select products and regions. The company targets manufacturers of automotive aerospace consumer dental electronics defense education and medical products; independent prototyping service providers; and universities and government agencies performing research activities. International clients account for more than half of its business.

HISTORY

3D Systems was founded in 1986 by Charles Hull a veteran of Bell & Howell and DuPont who pioneered the stereolithography modeling method. 3D Systems shipped its first product in 1988. It went public that year; Ciba-Geigy (now Ciba Specialty Chemicals) took a stake. The technology attracted attention but market reception was lukewarm. In 1991 3D Systems hired automation software executive Arthur Sims as CEO. Sims added system maintenance and outsourcing services but sales and earnings remained low.

In 1997 3D Systems bought the Stereos business of EOS a German maker of rapid prototyping systems. That year Hull became vice chairman and chief technology officer EVP Richard Balanson replaced him as president and COO. (Balanson resigned in 1999.)

3D Systems inked a pact with Sony in 1998 to make a version of 3D Systems' machines available in Asia. Hull retired in 1999; Walter Loewenbaum was elected chairman and Brian Service became CEO. Also in 1999 the company introduced its ThermoJet ink jet solid imaging device. Late that year Hull returned as CTO.

The company received its largest order ever in 2000 when a Hong Kong-based business group bought 100 ThermoJet systems. In 2001 3D Systems acquired Texas-based rapid prototyping systems builder DTM for about $45 million in cash. Also in 2001 3D Systems acquired OptoForm (metal and ceramic tooling technology) and RPC (stereolithography material).

Service resigned as CEO and director in 2003; Hull succeeded him as CEO on an interim basis. Later that year 3D Systems named former Sealed Air Corp. executive Abe Reichental president and CEO.

In 2004 3D Systems decided to outsource assembly of its products to manufacturing contractors. Also that year the company introduced a manufacturing-capable selective laser sintering system the Sinterstation HiQ SLS system. In 2005 the company moved its headquarters to Rock Hill South Carolina consolidating several US facilities.

In 2009 it acquired the assets of Acu-Cast Technologies a provider of rapid prototyping and manufacturing services for precision parts employing a variety of casting finishing and molding methods. Using the acquisition as a springboard the company launched 3Dproparts. The scope of that service soon expanded into the military/aerospace market with a subsequent purchase of assets from AdvaTech Manufacturing.

3Dproparts continued to grow in 2010 when 3D Systems made seven acquisitions for the division beginning with the assets of Moeller Design & Development adding aerospace medical device and mechanical CAD prototyping applications. It bought online rapid prototyping specialist Design Prototyping Technologies soon after to improve the ability of 3Dproparts to provide service via the Internet then acquired French prototyping and manufacturing service providers CEP (laser sintering manufacturing services) and Protometal (die cast metal parts) expanding its 3Dproparts' services in Europe.

Also that year it bought the assets of Express Pattern a rapid prototyper that served defense transportation and health care clients; UK-based Bits From Bytes Limited a maker of 3-D printers and accessories primarily for education and hobbyist applications; and Italy-based Provel a provider of rapid prototyping tooling and manufacturing services.

EXECUTIVES

President; Chief Executive Officer; Director, Abraham N. (Abe) Reichental, age 56, $577,500 total compensation
Chairman, G. Walter Loewenbaum II, age 68
EVP CTO and Director, Charles W. (Chuck) Hull, age 74, $290,000 total compensation
Senior Vice President - Production Printer Solutions, Kevin P. McAlea, age 55, $275,000 total compensation
Senior Vice President Chief Financial Officer, Damon J. Gregoire, age 44, $250,000 total compensation
Director Corporate Marketing, Katharina Hayes
VP Healthcare Business Development, Lee Dockstader
VP Global Engineering, Rajeev Kulkarni
VP Sales 3D Printer, Michele Marchesan
Chief Marketing Officer, Cathy Lewis
Global Director Sales and Marketing Rapid Manufacturing Materials, Steve Hanna
Vice President; General Counsel; Secretary, Andrew Johnson
President CEO and Director, Abraham N. (Abe) Reichental, age 56
Director, Daniel S. (Dan) Van Riper, age 72
EVP CTO and Director, Charles W. (Chuck) Hull, age 74
Director, William E. (Bill) Curran, age 65
Director, Jim D. Kever, age 60
Director, Karen E. Welke, age 68
Director, Kevin S. Moore, age 59
Independent Director, Daniel Riper
Auditors: BDOUSALLP

LOCATIONS

HQ: 3D Systems Corporation
333 Three D Systems Circle, Rock Hill SC 29730
Phone: 803-326-3900   **Fax:** 803-324-8810
Web: www.3dsystems.com

2012 Sales

	$ mil.	% of total
US	196	56
Europe		

	$ mil.	% of total
Germany	39	11
Other	60	17
Asia/Pacific	56	16
Total	**353**	**100**

PRODUCTS/OPERATIONS

2012 Sales

	$ mil.	% of total
Printers and other products	126	36
Services	123	35
Materials	103	29
Total	**353**	**100**

COMPETITORS

DSM	Soligen 2006
Dassault	Stratasys
Delcam	Stratasys
DuPont	Vero Software
ExOne	voxeljet
SOGECLAIR	

HISTORICAL FINANCIALS

Company Type: Public

Income Statement

FYE: December 31

	REVENUE ($ mil.)	NET INCOME ($ mil.)	NET PROFIT MARGIN	EMPLOYEES
12/12	353.6	38.9	11.0%	1,010
12/11	230.4	35.4	15.4%	714
12/10	159.8	19.5	12.2%	484
12/09	112.8	1.0	0.9%	387
12/08	138.9	(6.1)	—	331
Annual Growth	**26.3%**	**—**	**—**	**32.2%**

2012 Year-End Financials

Debt ratio: 13.0%
Return on equity: 10.5%
Cash ($ mil.): 155
Current ratio: 3.82
Long-term debt ($ mil.): 87

No. of shares (mil.): 89
Dividends
  Yield: —
  Payout: —
Market value ($ mil.): 4,761

	STOCK PRICE ($) FY Close	P/E High/Low		PER SHARE ($) Earnings	Dividends	Book Value
12/12	53.35	108	32	0.47	0.00	5.38
12/11	14.40	122	29	0.47	0.00	3.35
12/10	31.49	120	37	0.28	0.00	1.90
12/09	11.30	701	233	0.02	0.00	1.54
12/08	7.94	—	—	(0.09)	0.00	1.52
Annual Growth	**61.0%**	**—**	**—**	**—**	**—**	**37.1%**

8x8 Inc.

8x8 is counting on Internet telephony usage to multiply. The company provides services powered by its software that enable voice and video communication over Internet Protocol (IP) networks. Its services are used primarily by business subscribers in the US to make phone calls over broadband connections and access other functions including voice mail caller ID call waiting call forwarding and conferencing. 8x8 sells directly and through resellers and retailers to businesses government agencies and educational institutions as well as a dwindling number of residential subscribers. 8x8's MobileTalk service targets mobile phone users who want to lower their rates by making international calls over the Web.

The company pushed its sales up by more than 10% in 2011 after a dip in 2010; profits rose again for the year despite a slight uptick in costs due to an increase in payroll expenses caused by staff expansion. The company attributed the improved results to an increased number of business clients; meanwhile its residential subscriber base continued to decline. Overall 8x8 has kept the trajectory of its sales going in an upward direction since 2005; 2010 and 2011 have been its only consecutive profitable years.

8x8's main competitors are incumbent phone and cable companies such as Cablevision Verizon Comcast AT&T and Time Warner Cable as well as other VoIP alternative providers such as Skype and Vonage. Faced with these larger rivals who operate at a scale that enables them to better capitalize on the consumer market the company has shifted its strategy away from residential customers toward businesses in pursuit of growth higher margins and better customer retention rates. The focus on the enterprise market has made it necessary for 8x8 to respond to demand from businesses in many industries for more hosted telecom services as they look to cut costs by outsourcing more of their communications and IT activities.

As part of that push the company acquired bought two cloud computing specialists in 2011. It bought Colorado-based virtual server software developer Zerigo in a deal that enabled 8x8 to improve its hosting services by providing faster provisioning of network resources to clients. The company also bought California-based call center Software-as-a-Service (SaaS) provider Contactual in a stock transaction that year which expanded its enterprise client base domestically and overseas. Contactual served small and large businesses in North America Europe Japan and Australia. In 2010 8x8 acquired Web hosting and cloud computing services provider Central Host for $1 million in cash plus stock to expand its managed business communications services.

Customers typically use 8x8's services by setting up broadband Internet access on their own and then using an 8x8 supplied IP phone or terminal adapter that enables the voice and video communications services. Sales of phones account for about 5% of the company's revenue.

EXECUTIVES

Chairman and CEO, Bryan R. Martin, age 45, $245,000 total compensation
VP Business and Channel Development, Huw Rees, age 52, $235,000 total compensation
President, Kim Niederman, age 60
Director Corporate Communications, Joan Citelli
VP Engineering and CTO, Ramprakash Narayanaswamy, $210,000 total compensation
CFO, Daniel (Dan) Weirich, age 39, $245,000 total compensation
VP Research and Development, Garth Judge
VP Network Operations, Mehdi Salour, $193,333 total compensation
Manager New York Sales Office, Vincent Mussumeci
VP Marketing and Chief Marketing Officer, Debbie Jo Severin, age 53, $232,063 total compensation
Federal Government Sales Executive, Brian Ianniello
VP Channel Sales, Don Trimble
VP Product Management and Adoptio, Ramana Gottipati
VP of SMB Sales, Ben Taft
VP of Mid-Market Distributed Enterprise Sales, Chris Bartolo
Director, Guy L. Hecker Jr., age 80
Director, Donn R. Wilson, age 77
Director, Christopher (Chris) McNiffe, age 52
Independent Director, Vikram Verma
Independent Director, Eric Salzman
Independent Director, Mansour Salame
Auditors: MossAdamsLLP

LOCATIONS

HQ: 8x8 Inc.
  810 W. Maude Ave., Sunnyvale CA 94085
Phone: 408-727-1885   **Fax:** 514-822-6363
Web: www.matrox.com

PRODUCTS/OPERATIONS

2011 Sales

	$ mil.	% of total
Services	65	93
IP telephones	5	7
Total	**70**	**100**

COMPETITORS

AT&T	NewMarket Technology
Avaya	Primus
Cablevision Systems	Telecommunications
Cbeyond	ShoreTel
CenturyLink	Skype
Cisco Systems	Sprint Communications
Comcast	Time Warner Cable
Cox Communications	Toshiba
Deltathree	Verizon
Fusion	Vonage
Telecommunications	Windstream
Mitel Networks	XO Holdings
Net2Phone	iBasis

HISTORICAL FINANCIALS

Company Type: Public

Income Statement

FYE: March 31

	REVENUE ($ mil.)	NET INCOME ($ mil.)	NET PROFIT MARGIN	EMPLOYEES
03/13	107.6	13.9	13.0%	357
03/12	85.8	69.2	80.7%	301
03/11	70.1	6.4	9.3%	254
03/10	63.4	3.8	6.1%	242
03/09	64.6	(2.5)	—	244
Annual Growth	**13.6%**	**—**	**—**	**10.0%**

2013 Year-End Financials

Debt ratio: —
Return on equity: 10.9%
Cash ($ mil.): 50
Current ratio: 4.64
Long-term debt ($ mil.): —

No. of shares (mil.): 72
Dividends
  Yield: —
  Payout: —
Market value ($ mil.): 494

	STOCK PRICE ($) FY Close	P/E High/Low		PER SHARE ($) Earnings	Dividends	Book Value
03/13	6.85	40	19	0.19	0.00	1.90
03/12	4.20	5	3	0.99	0.00	1.68
03/11	2.81	33	11	0.10	0.00	0.25
03/10	1.45	27	10	0.06	0.00	0.21
03/09	0.57	—	—	(0.04)	0.00	0.14
Annual Growth	**86.2%**	**—**	**—**	**—**	**—**	**90.6%**

AAR Corp

On much more than a wing and a prayer AAR provides a wide variety of products and services primarily for the aerospace and defense industries. The company supplies commercial customers and the US government and its contractors with aircraft components such as transportation pallets containers shelters mobility systems and control systems used in support of the deployment of military and humanitarian activities. AAR also provides inventory management and parts distribution; aircraft maintenance repair and overhaul; and expeditionary airlift services. The company traces its historical roots to 1955 when it was founded as Allen Aircraft Radio.

Geographic Reach

AAR operates through more than 60 locations in 17 countries. It has a presence in the Americas EMEA (Germany France Sweden Norway the United Arab Emirates and the UK) the Asia/Pacific and Australia. Maintenance facilities reside in Indianapolis; Oklahoma City; Duluth Minnesota; and Miami.

Operations

In 2013 AAR streamlined its organizations from four segments into two. Aviation Services (its main segment representing 75% of total sales) provides inventory management and parts distribution; aircraft maintenance repair and overhaul; and expeditionary airlift services. It sells and leases new overhauled and repaired engine and airframe parts to commercial and defense customers. The segment also acts as a distributor for 80 aviation product manufacturers.

AAR's Technology Products segment makes and repairs transportation pallets containers shelters mobility systems and control systems used in support of the deployment of military and humanitarian activities. The segment also makes transportation pallets and containers used by commercial airlines.

Sales and Marketing

Customers include airlines business aircraft operators cargo carriers aviation OEMs and militaries; the US government accounts for about 35% of sales.

Financial Performance

AAR has enjoyed unprecedented growth over the last three years. Revenues jumped nearly 4% from $2.06 billion in 2012 to reach $2.14 in 2013 a new historical milestone.

The growth for 2013 was attributed to an uptick in sales to commercial customers coupled with strong organic growth (5%) in Aviation Services. Previous acquisitions also accounted for the rise in revenue. Technology Products saw revenues decrease slightly due to lower sales of shelters and containers as a result of the drawdown of the war effort in Afghanistan and lower spending from the Department of Defense.

Profits decreased 18% from $68 million in 2012 to $55 million in 2013 as a result of a $174 million increase in cost of services and a $30 million pre-tax charge on a support contract.

Strategy

As sales to government and defense customers decrease but business with commercial customers rises AAR has been making acquisitions that boosts its operations in the civilian sector. In 2011 the company acquired Telair which makes cargo loading systems for wide-body and narrow-body Airbus and Boeing aircraft; Nordisk a maker of heavy-duty pallets and lightweight cargo containers for commercial airlines; and Airinmar which provides aircraft component repair management services.

Ownership

Franklin Resources an investment firm owns around 10% of AAR.

HISTORY

Ira Allen Eichner began selling aircraft radios and instruments out of his car in 1951; in 1955 he incorporated his business as Allen Aircraft Radio. He opened a maintenance facility in Oklahoma City in 1959 and moved into aircraft overhaul. The firm entered Europe in 1965 became AAR in 1966 and went public the next year. AAR began selling commercial aircraft in 1973 and expanded into manufacturing with the 1981 acquisition of Brooks & Perkins. AAR flew high and fast during the late 1980s but lost altitude in the recession of the early 1990s as the airline industry hit a major air pocket.

The company restructured in 1993 and AAR rose again along with a resurgent airline industry. In 1997 AAR bought Cooper Aviation Industries Avsco Aviation Service and ATR International (composite structures and parts). It bought 14 used 747s from British Airways and inked maintenance deals with the US Air Force Hughes and GE. A loading systems contract with FedEx provided more lift. In 1998 AAR won a $67 million deal to maintain aircraft for the US Marshals Service and the Immigration and Naturalization Service. It also sold its floor maintenance equipment business (AAR PowerBoss) to Minuteman International.

AAR gained investment and technology potential in 1999 when it formed Aviation Inventory Management Co. with GE Capital Aviation and GE Engine Services. The following year AAR announced a deal with Societe Internationale de Telecommunication Aeronautiques (SITA) an air-transport information technology cooperative to sell airline and aerospace products and services online but later in 2000 it decreased its stake in the venture (Aerospan.com).

Late in 2001 AAR formed a joint venture Spairwise L.L.C. with Air France Industries (AFI) to provide component management support to operators of Airbus A320 family of aircraft in North and Central America. In 2002 the company inked a three-year deal to supply American Airlines with parts. As sales slumped in 2003 AAR made several refinancing moves to improve liquidity.

AAR bolstered its MRO operations in early 2007 with the purchase of Reebair Aircraft. Based in Arkansas the business operates under the name AAR Aircraft Services —Hot Springs.

In 2008 the company acquired Avborne Heavy Maintenance which provides maintenance services for Airbus and Boeing aircraft; it is part of AAR's MRO operations. The prior year AAR bought Brown International a provider of engineering design manufacturing and systems integration services to the aerospace industry. Brown International is being integrated into AAR's Structures and Systems division. It also purchased Summa Technology a provider of machining fabrication welding engineering and test services. Some of Summa's projects have included the Space Shuttle Tomahawk cruise missiles air defense systems and even lawn tractors. Summa operates as part of AAR's Structures and Systems division. AAR exited its non-core industrial turbine business.

On the military front AAR became the exclusive provider of composite interiors for the Sikorsky S-92 and H-60 helicopter programs in 2010; the two-year contract deal is valued at $6 million. Multiply that amount by 100 and you'll know the value of AAR's largest deal in company history –in 2009 it was awarded a $600 million contract (over nine years) to provide supply chain and logistics services as well as maintenance operations for Northrop Grumman's KC-10 air-to-air tanker aircraft program. Northrop Grumman is the prime contractor for the US Air Force's project.

In April 2010 AAR purchased Aviation Worldwide Services (renamed AAR Airlift Group) a provider of expeditionary airlift services and aircraft modifications to the US Department of Defense. AAR Airlift brought a fleet of 58 aircraft which has been deployed in Afghanistan. The $200 million acquisition included two operating subsidiaries —Presidential Airways and STI Aviation. The acquisition expanded AAR's offerings to government customers engaged in national defense nation building efforts and humanitarian relief projects.

EXECUTIVES

CFO and Treasurer, Michael J. Sharp, age 50, $171,300 total compensation

VP Tax and Assistant Treasurer, Michael K. Carr

VP and Co-Chief Commercial Officer, Peter K. Chapman

President COO and Director, Timothy J. Romenesko, age 57, $454,500 total compensation

Chairman and CEO, David P. Storch, age 60, $799,208 total compensation

VP Defense Programs, David E. Prusiecki

Executive Vice President, Terry D. Stinson, age 72, $341,230 total compensation

Aviation Services Group Vice President ? Airlift, Randy J. Martinez, age 58

VP and Co-Chief Commercial Officer, Jack M. Arehart, age 57

VP CFO and Treasurer, Richard J. (Rick) Poulton, age 47, $360,000 total compensation

Vice President and Chief Information Officer, Kevin M. Larson

VP and Chief Human Resources Officer, Timothy O. Skelly

SVP Government and Defense Business Development, Donald J. (Don) Wetekam

VP General Counsel and Secretary, Robert J. (Bob) Regan, age 55

Group Vice President - Maintenance; Repair and Overhaul, Dany Kleiman, age 52

VP Government Affairs and Corporate Development, Cheryle Robinson Jackson

VP Sales and Marketing Maintenance Repair and Overhaul, Matt Eaton

Aviation Services Group Vice President ? Inventory Management and Distribution, John M. Holmes

Vice President Chief Financial Officer & Treasurer, John C. Fortson, age 46

Vice President ? Cargo Systems, Axel P. Hauner

President COO and Director, Timothy J. Romenesko, age 56

Director, James E. Goodwin, age 68

Director, Gen. Ronald R. (Ron) Fogelman, age 70

Director, Norman R. (Norm) Bobins, age 69

Director, James G. Brocksmith Jr., age 71

Director, Gen. Peter Pace, age 67

Director, Marc J. Walfish, age 60

Director, Ronald B. Woodard, age 69

Director, Michael R. Boyce, age 64

Director, Patrick J. Kelly, age 57

Auditors: KPMGLLP

LOCATIONS

HQ: AAR CORP.
1 AAR Pl. 1100 N. Wood Dale Rd., Wood Dale IL 60191
Phone: 630-227-2000   **Fax:** 630-227-2039
Web: www.aarcorp.com

PRODUCTS/OPERATIONS

2013 Sales

Aviation Services	1,614	75
Total	2,137	100

2013 Sales

Products	1,228	57
Total	2,137	100

Selected Products

Aircraft Sales and Leasing
Airframe Parts Supply
Aviation Worldwide Services
Cargo Handling Systems
Component Repair
Containers Shelters and Pallets
Engine Parts Supply
Engineering Services
Enterprise Applications Integration
Inventory Management Programs
Landing Gear Services
Maintenance Repair and Overhaul
Mobility Systems
Precision Machined Parts
Wheel and Brake Services

Selected Services

Aircraft maintenance and modification
Component repair
Logistics support
Parts distribution
Supply chain management

COMPETITORS

Airbus Americas	Kaman
Alabama Aircraft	Kennametal
Applied Industrial	L-3 Vertex
Technologies	LMI Aerospace
Aviall	Lufthansa Technik
Banner Aerospace	MSC Industrial Direct
Boeing	Midcoast Aviation
Crane Co.	Moog
Cubic Corp.	Rockwell Collins
Curtiss-Wright	Sequa
Esterline	Spirit AeroSystems
GECAS Asset Management	TIMCO Aviation
Services	Teledyne Technologies
Goodrich Corp.	TransDigm Group
HEICO	Triumph Group
Hawker Beechcraft	United Technologies
Services	VAS Aero
Hawker Pacific	Willis Lease
Hexcel	Wyman-Gordon

HISTORICAL FINANCIALS

Company Type: Public

Income Statement

FYE: May 31

	REVENUE ($ mil.)	NET INCOME ($ mil.)	NET PROFIT MARGIN	EMPLOYEES
05/13	2,137.3	55.0	2.6%	7,200
05/12	2,065.0	67.7	3.3%	7,600
05/11	1,775.7	69.8	3.9%	6,870
05/10	1,352.1	44.6	3.3%	6,340
05/09	1,423.9	78.6	5.5%	5,930
Annual Growth	10.7%	(8.6%)	—	5.0%

Aaron's, Inc.

For customers who desire a desk seek a sofa or lust for an LCD TV Aaron's rents —and sells –all of these and more. One of the nation's top furniture rental and rent-to-own companies (behind industry leader Rent-A-Center) Aaron's purveys home furnishings electronics computers and appliances through nearly 2100 eponymous stores and 70 HomeSmart locations in the US and Canada. Its Woodhaven Furniture Industries unit makes most of the firm's furniture and bedding at more than a dozen plants in the US. Also Aaron's leases tires rims and wheels through its RIMCO chain of about 15 stores. Founded in 1955 Aaron's exited the office furniture rental business to focus on household goods.

Geographic Reach

Aaron's operates both company-owned and franchised stores in 48 states and in Canada.

Sales and Marketing

The rental company has logged advertising expenses of $36.5 million $38.9 million and $31.7 million in 2012 2011 and 2010 respectively. The amount of cooperative advertising consideration netted against advertising expenses was $31.1 million $25.4 million and $27.2 million in 2012 2011 and 2010 respectively. The prepaid advertising asset was $3.2 million in 2012 and $1.6 million in 2011.

Aaron's uses brand/image messaging and product/price promotions to reach its target demographic via national broadcast and cable television and radio networks. It typically taps networks such as ABC FOX TBS TELEMUNDO and UNIVISION among others to reach its customers. In 2012 Aaron's boosted its use of digital marketing and social media the likes of Facebook and Twitter.

To ensure that each new store is given the opportunity to quickly ramp up its customer counts Aaron's leverages a grand opening "Jump Start" marketing initiative. The company also distributes millions of email and direct mail promotions. Aaron's sponsors motorsports teams and event broadcasts at various levels along with select professional and collegiate sports such as NFL and NBA teams SEC and ACC college athletic programs and an IMG collegiate sports national sponsorship package of more than schools. Additionally Aaron's sponsors Michael Waltrip Racing in the NASCAR Sprint Cup Series with drivers Mark Martin and Michael Waltrip both driving the Aaron's #55 "Dream Machine." (The company's

premier title sponsorship continues to be the Aaron's Dream Weekend at Talladega Superspeedway which is broadcast live on national television and is among the most watched events on the NASCAR circuit.) All of its sports partnerships are supported with proven advertising promotional marketing and brand activation initiatives.

Operations

As part of its business Aaron's boasts five operating segments: Sales and Lease Ownership RIMCO HomeSmart Franchise and Manufacturing. RIMCO stores lease automobile wheels tires and rims to customers under sales and lease ownership agreements. The Aaron's Sales & Lease Ownership division which generates about 94% of its revenue offers electronics residential furniture appliances and computers to consumers mostly on a monthly payment basis with no credit requirements. The HomeSmart division offers electronics residential furniture appliances and computers to consumers on a weekly payment basis with no credit requirements. Aaron's franchise operation sells and supports franchisees of its sales and lease ownership concept. Lastly the Manufacturing segment is focused on making upholstered furniture and bedding for use by company-operated and franchised stores. (To this end the Manufacturing segment revenues and earnings before income taxes are primarily the result of intercompany transactions.)

The company's network of 2073 stores comprises 1324 company-operated locations in 29 states and 749 independently-owned franchised stores in 48 states and Canada. Since 2008 Aaron's has added 294 company-operated and 265 franchised stores. The company's store count also includes 1246 Aaron's Sales & Lease Ownership stores and 78 company-operated HomeSmart stores. Aaron's Sales & Lease Ownership division includes 19 company-operated RIMCO stores as well as its wheels tires and accessories sales and lease ownership concept.

Strategy

In recent years Aaron's has expanded into Delaware Ohio Michigan Kentucky Mississippi Maryland. Fast-growing Aaron's is opening sales and lease ownership stores in existing and select new geographic markets. Indeed additional stores help Aaron's to realize economies of scale in purchasing marketing and distribution. In 2012 the company added a net of 93 company-operated sales and lease ownership stores. It's also working to expand its HomeSmart network which took root in 2010. In 2012 the company had opened 78 stores and in 2012 Aaron's counted its first HomeSmart franchised store.

Aaron's is also expanding globally as well by purchasing 12% of newly issued shares of common stock of a UK rent-to-own company. The company also received notes and an option to acquire the remaining interest in the at any time through 2013.

Mergers and Acquisitions

In 2012 Aaron's acquired the lease agreements merchandise and assets of 48 sales and lease ownership stores. Twenty-six of the stores were subsequently merged with existing locations resulting in 22 new stores from acquisitions. It works to convert the stores of existing independent lease operators to Aaron's Sales & Lease Ownership franchised stores.

Financial Performance

Aaron's has seen positive growth in both revenue and profits since fiscal 2008.

The company's revenue rose 10% in fiscal 2012 to $2.2 billion from $2 billion in 2011. Aaron's attributes the growth to a sales boost from its Sales and Lease Ownership; Franchise; and Manufacturing segments offset in part by sales slips from HomeSmart. The Sales and Lease Ownership segment posted gains thanks to an 11% increase in lease revenues and fees and a 10% increase in non-retail sales. The segment was helped by the net addition of 100 company-operated stores since the beginning of 2011 and a 5% increase in same store revenues. Non-retail sales increased primarily due to net additions of 84 franchised stores since the beginning of 2011. Sales and Lease Ownership segment revenues include a $660000 gain from the sale of three Sales and Lease Ownership stores in 2012 and a $3 million gain on the sale of 25 Sales and Lease Ownership stores in 2011. Its Franchise segment revenues saw a 9% increase in royalty income from franchisees. Franchise royalty income increased due to the growth in the number of franchised stores and a 5% increase in same store revenues of existing franchised stores. The total number of franchised sales and lease ownership stores in 2012 was 749 reflecting a net addition of 85 stores since the beginning of 2011.Aaron's logged a 52% increase in profits in fiscal 2012 vs. 2011. As a percentage of total revenues profits from continuing operations were 8%. Contributing to a more than 5% increase in same store revenues and another more than 5% increase in franchise royalties and fees were Aaron's increased profitability of new company-operated sales and lease ownership stores added during the past several years.

Company Ownership

Company founder and chairman R. Charles Loudermilk Sr. has reduced his holding in the company from more than 60% of the shares in 2009 to less than 7% in 2012.

HISTORY

Aaron of Aaron Rents is the Betty Crocker of the furniture rental world (i.e. there is no Aaron). The firm was named to appear first in the Yellow Pages. Charles Loudermilk and his mother Addie founded Aaron Rents in 1955 with 300 folding chairs. Loudermilk opened the second store in Atlanta in the early 1960s and then a third in 1964.

The company ventured outside Atlanta for the first time by opening a Baltimore store in 1967. After acquiring MacTavish Furniture Industries in 1971 it became the only rental company with manufacturing facilities. The firm went public in 1982. Aaron Rents launched its rent-to-own business in 1987 and began franchising the stores in 1992.

In 1998 the company joined the NYSE. Aaron Rents also opened several furniture warehouses in Florida Georgia Ohio and Texas to speed delivery time to rental stores. It opened its first Aaron's Plus retail and rent-to-own store in Sandersville Georgia. It also bought California-based Lamps Forever to add designer accessories to its offerings.

Aaron Rents continued to expand through 1999. In 2000 the company made its first move outside the US with its purchase of 10 stores in Puerto Rico. Aaron Rents purchased 52 locations from bankrupt furniture chain Heilig-Meyers in 2001. In 2002 Aaron Rents bought Sight 'n Sound Appliance Centers a specialty retailer of furniture appliances and consumer electronics.

In November 2003 Aaron Rents entered into an agreement with Rosey Rentals to convert 31 of its stores to franchised Aaron Rents stores. In June 2004 Aaron Rents acquired 26 rental stores from privately held Easy Way. Several months later (September 2004) the company acquired 25 stores from Home Express. Overall the company opened

68 company-operated stores and 79 new franchised outlets in 2004.

Aaron Rents acquired the rental contracts and merchandise of 19 stores from rival Rent-A-Center for about $4.4 million in 2005 and acquired 33 stores on the East Coast from Prime Time Rentals in 2007 (with about half of those stores changed to the Aaron format and the rest merged into existing Aaron stores).

In June 2008 Robert Loudermilk Jr. the son of chairman and ex-CEO Charles Loudermilk was promoted to chief executive of the company. In November Aaron's sold its corporate furnishings unit (Aaron Corporate Furnishings) to Berkshire Hathaway's CORT Business Services for about $72 million. As a result Aaron Rents exited the rent-to-rent market. In December the firm acquired its largest franchisee 35-store Rosey Rentals in a cash transaction. It changed its name and ticker symbol in April 2009. The name change served to call attention to the company's sales and lease owership business model.

In 2009 Aaron's added 45 company-operated stores and more than 90 franchised locations. The previous year's purchase of Rosey Rentals added to its company-owned store network and its franchise count was boosted when Kelly's Sales & Leasing agreed to convert its roughly 20-store chain in North Carolina and Virginia to the Aaron's banner.

EXECUTIVES

VP and Corporate Controller, Robert P. Sinclair Jr., age 51

President Rent-to-Rent Division, Eduardo Qui?ones, age 51

COO and Director, William K. (Ken) Butler Jr., age 60, $600,000 total compensation

Executive Vice President Chief Financial Officer; Director, Gilbert L. Danielson, age 66, $525,000 total compensation

Chairman, R. Charles (Charlie) Loudermilk Sr., age 84, $500,000 total compensation

Chairman President & Chief Executive Officer, Ronald W. (Ron) Allen, age 72

SVP; SVP Merchandising and Logistics Aaron's Sales & Lease Ownership Division, Mitchell S. (Mitch) Paull, age 54

Senior Group VP and Secretary, James L. Cates, age 62

VP Franchising, K. Todd Evans, age 49, $220,000 total compensation

VP Northern Operations Aaron's Sales and Lease Ownership Division, Michael P. Ryan

VP Mississippi Valley Operations Aaron's Sales and Lease Ownership Division, David A. (Dave) Boggan Sr.

VP Western Operations Aaron's Sales and Lease Ownership Division, Kevin J. Hrvatin

Chief Operating Officer, David L. Buck

VP Marketing HomeSmart, Mark A. Rudnick

VP Mid-Atlantic Operations Aaron's Sales and Lease Ownership Division, Gregory G. (Greg) Bellof

Vice President Manufacturing, Michael W. Jarnagin

VP Eastern Operations Aaron's Sales and Lease Ownership Division, Joseph N. Fedorchak

VP Management Development Aaron's Sales & Lease Ownership Division, Michael B. Hickey

VP Internal Audit, James C. Johnson

VP Central Operations Aaron's Sales and Lease Ownership Division, Tristan J. Montanero

VP Internal Security, Danny Walker Sr.

VP Real Estate Aaron's Sales and Lease Ownership Division, Paul A. Doize

VP Finance Aaron's Sales and Lease Ownership Division, Steven A. (Steve) Michaels

VP Employee Relations, D. Chad Strickland

VP and General Counsel, Elizabeth L. Gibbs, age 51

Investor Relations Contact, Lee Wilder

Vice President Chief Information Officer, John T. Trainor, age 40

VP Midwest Operations Aaron's Sales and Lease Ownership Division, Todd G. Coppedge

VP Northeast Operations Aaron?s Sales and Lease Ownership Division, Michael H. Pokorny

VP Management Development Aaron's Sales and Lease Ownership Division, Scott L. Harvey

VP Mid-American Operations Aaron's Sales and Lease Ownership Division, Jason M. McFarland

VP Operations Aaron?s Office Furniture Division, Ronald M. Benedit

Financial Reporting, Aleksandra (Aleks) Nearing

Divisional Analyst RIMCO Operations Aaron's Sales and Lease Ownership Division, Michael Ramirez

VP Great Lakes Operations Aaron's Sales & Lease Ownership Division, Michael C. Bennett

VP Northeastern Operations Aaron's Sales & Lease Ownership Division, Brock M. Roberts

VP Customer Account Management Aaron's Sales & Lease Ownership Division, Marco A. Scalise

VP Marketing, Tom Peterson

Vice President Marketing, Andrea P. Freeman

COO and Director, William K. (Ken) Butler Jr., age 60

EVP CFO and Director, Gilbert L. Danielson, age 66

Director, David L. Kolb, age 74

Director, John B. Schuerholz, age 72

Director, Leo Benatar, age 83

President and CEO; Director, Ronald W. (Ron) Allen, age 70

Director, Ray M. Robinson, age 65

Director, John C. Portman Jr., age 87

Independent Director, Cynthia Day

Auditors: Ernst&YoungLLP

LOCATIONS

HQ: Aaron' s, Inc.
309 E. Paces Ferry Road, N.E., Atlanta, GA 30305-2377
Phone: 404 231-0011
Web: www.aarons.com

2012 Stores

Company-owned	1,324
Franchised	750
RIMCO	19

PRODUCTS/OPERATIONS

2012 Sales

	$ mil.	% of total
Leasing & fees	1,676	75
Nonretail sales	425	19
Franchising royalties & fees	66	3
Retail sales	38	2
Other	15	1
Total	**2,222**	**100**

2012 Sales

	% of total
Electronics	32
Furniture	35
Appliances	20
Computers	10
Total	**100**

Selected Rental Equipment

Automotive
  Tires
  Wheel rims
Office
  Accessories
  Business equipment
  Chairs
  Conference tables

Credenzas
Desks
Sofas
Residential
Appliances
Dining room living room and bedroom furniture
Electronics

COMPETITORS

Best Buy	Rooms To Go
Bestway	Sears
Brook Furniture Rental	W.S. Badcock
Rent-A-Center	

HISTORICAL FINANCIALS
Company Type: Public

Income Statement
FYE: December 31

	REVENUE ($ mil.)	NET INCOME ($ mil.)	NET PROFIT MARGIN	EMPLOYEES
12/12	2,222.5	173.0	7.8%	11,900
12/11	2,024.0	113.7	5.6%	11,200
12/10	1,876.8	118.3	6.3%	10,400
12/09	1,752.7	112.6	6.4%	10,000
12/08	1,592.6	90.1	5.7%	9,600
Annual Growth	8.7%	17.7%		5.5%

2012 Year-End Financials

Debt ratio: 7.8%	No. of shares (mil.): 75
Return on equity: 16.3%	Dividends
Cash ($ mil.): 129	Yield: 0.0%
Current ratio: 4.94	Payout: 27.5%
Long-term debt ($ mil.): 141	Market value ($ mil.): 2,141

	STOCK PRICE ($) FY Close	P/E High/Low		Earnings	PER SHARE ($) Dividends	Book Value
12/12	28.28	14	11	2.25	0.62	15.00
12/11	26.68	20	13	1.43	0.05	12.91
12/10	20.39	20	9	1.44	0.05	12.23
12/09	22.50	22	12	1.37	0.05	10.91
12/08	21.95	22	13	1.11	0.04	9.46
Annual Growth	6.5%	—	—	19.4%	94.5%	12.2%

Abaxis, Inc.

Abaxis makes a praxis of analyzing blood. Its two types of point-of-care blood analyzers (one for animals and one for humans) can each perform more than a dozen tests on their respective veterinary and human health patients. The analyzers are portable require little training provide on-the-spot results and offer built-in quality control and calibration. Abaxis also sells compatible chemical reagent supplies. In the veterinary market its systems bear the VetScan name; in the human medical market Piccolo Xpress. Abaxis sells to veterinarians hospitals managed care organizations and the military.

Operations

The company's veterinary segment accounts for about three-fourths of revenues. Abaxis sells its chemistry blood analysis systems to vets and doctors and then generates additional income from the same customers by supplying consumable supplies for the systems. These supplies which account for about 70% of annual revenues primarily consist of single-use reagent disks that allow for automated testing of several conditions at once.

The company's vet division also sells a handheld testing instrument as well as hematology instru-

ments for blood clot detection. In addition in 2011 Abaxis formed its Abaxis Veterinary Reference Laboratories (AVRL) unit; AVRL operates a reference lab facility in Olathe Kansas that provides routine and specialty testing services to vets across the US.

Marketing and Sales

A direct sales force markets the company's products to health professionals in North America where the company conducts more than 80% of its business. Products are then delivered to end-users by third-party distributors including Animal Health International which accounts for 15% of Abaxis' annual revenues. Other distributors include McKesson Medical-Surgical Henry Schein and PSS World Medical. Outside the US Abaxis' products are sold in 30 countries through direct sales units (including Abaxis Europe) and through independent representatives and distributors for sales.

Financial Analysis

Revenues for Abaxis climbed 9% in 2012 to some $157 million due to increased sales of consumables in the medical and veterinary markets. The company has generally experienced a growth pattern in both sales and income levels in recent years; however profits declined 10% to some $13 million in 2012. The decline was due to increased sales marketing administrative and general operating expenses including startup costs for the AVRL division and legal costs related to a patent infringement case.

Strategy

The company regularly introduces new and next-generation versions of its veterinary blood analyzers instruments and testing reagents to keep pace with customer demand for innovative and easy-to-use products. For instance in 2011 Abaxis introduced new VetScan rapid canine tests for heartworm Lyme disease and parvovirus and in 2012 it launched a feline rapid heartworm test and a kidney disease test for multiple species of animals. The company is also working to expand its foothold in the human diagnostics market.

EXECUTIVES

VP Government Affairs and VP Marketing Pacific Rim, Vladimir E. Ostoich, age 67, $210,000 total compensation
Chairman President and CEO, Clinton H. (Clint) Severson, age 64, $360,000 total compensation
CTO, Kenneth P. Aron, age 59, $210,000 total compensation
VP Finance and CFO, Alberto R. (Al) Santa Ines, age 65, $200,000 total compensation
Chief Commercial Officer, Martin V. (Marty) Mulroy, age 51, $183,077 total compensation
Director Government Affairs, Randy Knick
Managing Director Abaxis Europe, Achim Henkel, age 54
COO, Donald P. (Don) Wood, age 60, $196,923 total compensation
Director Marketing Veterinary Diagnostics, Valerie Goodwin-Adams
Area Sales Director West US Medical Sales, Matthew Rapp
Area Sales Manager Northeast US Veterinary Sales, Gerard Cabrera
Area Sales Manager North Central US Veterinary Sales, John Therrien
Director Marketing Medical Diagnostics US Medical Marketing, Rick Betts
Area Sales Manager Central US Veterinary Sales and US Distribution Manager, Jeff Sumpter
Director Business Development Veterinary Diagnostics, Michael Solomon

Area Sales Director East US Medical Sales, Mike Petrunich
VP North American Medical Sales and Marketing, Brenton G. A. Hanlon, age 66
Area Sales Director Central US Medical Sales, Bob Deans
Area Sales Manager US Veterinary Sales, Candice Cayson
Area Sales Manager Great Lakes US Veterinary Sales, Tom Beaver
Area Sales Manager Southeast US Veterinary Sales, Nick Malz
Area Sales Manager South Central US Veterinary Sales, Rick Heimendinger
Area Sales Manager West US Veterinary Sales, Kimjera Whittington
Chief Financial Officer; Vice President - Finance, Alberto Ines
Sales Manager Mid-Atlantic, Casey Rineh
Director Sales, Troy Gaylor
Executive Vice President General Counsel Secretary, Christopher L. Howard
Director, Henk J. Evenhuis, age 69
Director, Michael D. (Mike) Casey, age 66
Director, Richard J. Bastiani, age 69
Director, Prithipal Singh, age 73
Director, Ernest S. Tucker III, age 79
Independent Director, Vernon Altman
Auditors: BurrPilger&MayerLLP

LOCATIONS

HQ: Abaxis Inc.
3240 Whipple Rd., Union City CA 94587
Phone: 510-675-6500   **Fax:** 510-441-6150
Web: www.abaxis.com

2012 Sales

	$ mil.	% of total
North America	129	82
Asia/Pacific & other regions	5	4

PRODUCTS/OPERATIONS

2012 Sales

	$ mil.	% of total
Veterinary market	121	78
Medical market	30	19
Other	4	3
Total	**156**	**100**

Selected Products

Piccolo Xpress (human blood chemistry analyzer and panels)
VetScan HM5 and HM2 (blood cell counters and reagents)
VetScan i-STAT (handheld analyzer for veterinarians amd cartridges)
VetScan Rapid Test Kits
  VetScan Avian Influenza Rapid Test Kit
  VetScan Giardia Rapid Test Kit
  VetScan Canine Heartworm Rapid Test Kit
  VetScan Canine Parvovirus Rapid Test Kit
  VetScan Canine Lyme Rapid Test
  VetScan Kidney Profile Plus Rotor
VetScan VS2 (veterinary blood chemistry analyzer and profiles)
VetScan VSpro (point-of-care coagulation analyzer and cartridges)

COMPETITORS

Abbott Labs	IDEXX Labs
Alere	Immucor
Beckman Coulter	Johnson & Johnson
Becton Dickinson	Quidel
Hemagen Diagnostics	Roche Diagnostics
Heska	VCA Antech

HISTORICAL FINANCIALS

Company Type: Public

Income Statement

FYE: March 31

	REVENUE ($ mil.)	NET INCOME ($ mil.)	NET PROFIT MARGIN	EMPLOYEES
03/13	186.0	27.4	14.8%	535
03/12	156.6	13.0	8.4%	491
03/11	143.6	14.5	10.1%	388
03/10	124.5	13.0	10.5%	354
03/09	105.5	12.0	11.4%	339
Annual Growth	15.2%	23.0%	—	12.1%

2013 Year-End Financials

Debt ratio: 0.3%	No. of shares (mil.): 22
Return on equity: 16.3%	Dividends
Cash ($ mil.): 54	Yield: 0.0%
Current ratio: 7.64	Payout: 81.3%
Long-term debt ($ mil.): 0	Market value ($ mil.): 1,047

	STOCK PRICE ($) FY Close	P/E High/Low	PER SHARE ($) Earnings	PER SHARE ($) Dividends	PER SHARE ($) Book Value
03/13	47.32	38 21	1.23	1.00	7.97
03/12	29.13	53 34	0.58	0.00	7.36
03/11	28.84	47 27	0.64	0.00	7.47
03/10	27.19	50 24	0.58	0.00	6.65
03/09	17.24	55 19	0.54	0.00	5.79
Annual Growth	28.7%	— —	22.9%	—	8.3%

ABIOMED, Inc.

ABIOMED gives weary hearts a rest. The medical device maker has developed a range of cardiac assist devices and is developing a self-contained artificial heart. Its Impella micro heart pumps can temporarily take over blood circulation during surgery or catheterization. Its BVS5000 and AB5000 ventricular assist devices products temporarily take over the heart's pumping function and improve circulatory flow in patients with acute heart failure thus allowing their hearts to rest and recover. ABIOMED markets its products through both a direct sales force and distributors.

ABIOMED has also developed a battery-powered implantable replacement heart system called AbioCor which can be used to extend life for dying patients who aren't eligible for a heart transplant. ABIOMED developed the AbioCor system based on technology developed at Pennsylvania State University. However due to the limited number of patients that qualify for use of the AbioCor the company places little emphasis on marketing efforts for this product line.

While many of ABIOMED's products are approved for use in in other countries international sales make up less than 10% of the company's revenues. The company intends to improve its international sales with more sales and support teams in Europe. It manufactures its Impella products at a facility in Germany while the rest of its products are made in Massachusetts.

After years of steady sales growth ABIOMED made its first profit in 2012. Previously its research and development expenditures had outpaced its sales income. That year's profit came from strong reorders of its Impella systems which now account for more than 80% of company revenues. In addition to expanding its product portfolio and approvals the company is working to raise awareness of its products in the medical community. ABIO-

MED is also evaluating opportunities for strategic acquisitions.

The company's research efforts are focused on developing new products for acute heart failure patients as well as next-generation versions and support systems for its existing products. Following the 2008 FDA approval of the first Impella system the company shifted more of its development and sales efforts onto that product line.

HISTORY

Chairman David Lederman founded ABIOMED in 1981 to make products he had designed (such as artificial heart pumps and valves) as well as dental diagnostic products. ABIOMED went public in 1987. In 1988 it got about $1 million from the National Institutes of Health for heart replacement device (HRD) research and development. In 1990 it began working with Canada's World Heart on HRD technology. In 1992 ABIOMED launched BVS-5000.

In 1990 the company formed ABIODENT to consolidate its dental operations. It received FDA clearance to market the PerioTemp device in 1994. In 1996 it voluntarily recalled some of its BVS-5000 blood pumps citing component irregularities (it said no patients were affected).

To fund product development ABIOMED accepted government funding to finish testing its battery-powered HRD (1996) and to develop a laser-based tissue-welding system (1998). Biotech firm Genzyme invested about $15 million in ABIOMED that year acquiring 14% of the firm.

In 1998 ABIOMED again recalled some lots of BVS-5000 this time for electrical problems. The company attributed 1998's losses to an increase in self-funding on the HRD project as well as to red ink in its now-discontinued dental business.

ABIOMED received funding from the National Heart Lung and Blood Institutes in 2000 to support the testing of its AbioCor product an implantable heart replacement device. The following year AbioCor became the first artificial heart implanted in a patient.

The FDA approved the use of the artificial hearts in five patients in 2001 all of whom were considered too sick to receive heart transplants. The first patient died the same year but the cause of death was not attributed to AbioCor.

The fifth patient to receive the device died early in 2002. By late 2002 seven patients had been fitted with the device but only one was living. A moratorium on recruiting new patients was imposed. ABIOMED wanted patients that were healthy enough to live long past the time of implantation but only patients that were extremely ill would be considered candidates for the device.

By January of 2003 the moratorium had been lifted and three more patients had received implants by March. Because of the troubles with finding qualified recipients for its AbioCor product the company began focusing on other products to sustain revenues. It got good news on that front that same year when the FDA approved ABIOMED's AB5000 Circulatory Support System Console a device that temporarily pumps the patient's blood when the heart has failed.

David Lederman stepped down as CEO in 2004 but remained chairman. He was replaced by then-37-year-old Michael Minogue.

The following year the company made good on its pledge to focus on other products when it purchased German firm Impella CardioSystems whose mini-heart pumps had already been approved in Europe.

In 2006 ABIOMED received FDA approval for its intra-aortic balloons (IABs) which are used in cardiac catheterization labs to assist heart functioning.

EXECUTIVES

Senior Vice President - Global Product Operations, William J. Bolt, age 62, $237,800 total compensation

Chief Financial Officer; Vice President; Treasurer, Robert L. (Bob) Bowen, age 63, $290,000 total compensation

Chairman of the Board; President; Chief Executive Officer, Michael R. Minogue, age 46, $371,700 total compensation

VP Healthcare Solutions, Andrew J. Greenfield, age 41, $211,592 total compensation

CTO, Thorsten Siess

Chief Operating Officer, David M. Weber, age 52, $272,917 total compensation

VP and General Manager Global Sales and Marketing, Michael Howley, age 49

Vice President General Counsel, Stephen C. McEvoy

Director, Desmond H. O'Connell Jr., age 76

Director, Martin P. Sutter, age 58

Director, Paul G. Thomas, age 58

Director, Henri A. Termeer, age 67

Director, Louis E. Lataif, age 74

Director, Eric A. Rose, age 61

Director, W. Gerald Austen, age 83

Auditors: Deloitte&ToucheLLP

LOCATIONS

HQ: ABIOMED Inc.
22 Cherry Hill Dr., Danvers MA 01923
Phone: 978-777-5410   **Fax:** 978-777-8411
Web: www.abiomed.com

PRODUCTS/OPERATIONS

2012 Revenues

	$ mil.	% of total
Impella products	106	84
Service & other revenue	7	6
Total	**126**	**100**

Selected Products

AB5000 Circulatory Support System (ventricular assist device)
AbioCor (artificial heart)
BVS 5000 (ventricular assist device)
Impella 2.5 5.0 and LD (minimally invasive cardiac assist device)
Symphony (implantable cardiac assist device)

COMPETITORS

Boston Scientific	St. Jude Medical
CardiacAssist	Teleflex
Edwards Lifesciences	Terumo
Getinge	Thoratec Corp
HeartWare	World Heart
Medtronic	ZOLL

HISTORICAL FINANCIALS

Company Type: Public

Income Statement

FYE: March 31

	REVENUE ($ mil.)	NET INCOME ($ mil.)	NET PROFIT MARGIN	EMPLOYEES
03/13	158.1	15.0	9.5%	467
03/12	126.3	1.5	1.2%	397
03/11	101.1	(11.7)	—	374
03/10	85.7	(19.0)	—	365
03/09	73.2	(31.6)	—	386
Annual Growth	21.2%	—	—	4.9%

2013 Year-End Financials

Debt ratio: —
Return on equity: 11.4%
Cash ($ mil.): 9
Current ratio: 4.31
Long-term debt ($ mil.): —

No. of shares (mil.): 38
Dividends
  Yield: —
  Payout: —
Market value ($ mil.): 721

	STOCK PRICE ($) FY Close	P/E High/Low	PER SHARE ($) Earnings	Dividends	Book Value
03/13	18.67	65 32	0.37	0.00	3.55
03/12	22.19	605252	0.04	0.00	3.22
03/11	14.53	— —	(0.32)	0.00	2.78
03/10	10.32	— —	(0.52)	0.00	2.88
03/09	4.90	— —	(0.91)	0.00	3.16
Annual Growth	**39.7%**	— —	—	—	2.9%

Acacia Research Corp

Acacia Research provides protection under its canopy for intellectual property. The company acquires develops licenses and protects patented technologies for individual inventors and small companies that have limited resources to protect against infringement. The company owns or controls the rights to more than 250 patent portfolios in the US and abroad. It typically buys portfolios and pays its clients an upfront fee or becomes the exclusive licensing agent and doles out royalties. It has out-licensed to such companies as 3M Dell IBM Texas Instruments and Walt Disney Company. Acacia Research primarily operates through its Acacia Research Group (formerly Acacia Technologies) and Acacia Global Acquisition subsidiaries.

Geographic Reach

Acacia Research and its subsidiaries have locations in Atlanta Georgia; Alexandria Virginia; and Plano Texas.

Operations

The company has completed more than 1200 licensing agreements covering more than 154 different technologies. Among the patented technologies that have rights owned or controlled by Acacia Research are anti-theft car systems credit card fraud protection medical imaging pop-up Internet advertising and TV signal scrambling.

Financial Performance

Acacia Research's revenues increased by 36% in 2012 as the result of higher average revenues per executed agreement and an increase in the total number of agreements.

Net income was higher in 2012 thanks to an increase in revenues partially offset by an increase in income taxes. The increase in provision for income taxes in 2012 reflects the impact of foreign withholding taxes on revenue agreements executed with third party licensees domiciled outside of the US.

Strategy

The company continues to seek acquisition opportunities through new and existing relationships with inventors universities and research institutions. The success of its strategy is partially dependent on its ability to monitor and assess where demand lies in high-technology-based industries that are constantly evolving such as communications and high-speed computing.

Mergers and Acquisitions

In 2013 Acacia Research acquired rights to a portion of the location-based services patent portfolio of TeleCommunication Systems. The prior year it bought ADAPTIX which holds some 230 4G technology patents in more than 10 countries. In 2011 Acacia acquired 86 microprocessor and digital signal processing patents and 30 mobile communications patents for such technologies as call and message routing and roaming and picked up a hearing aid technology a few months later. Also in 2011 the company acquired more than 30 circuit patents for advanced memory and processor technology.

Company Background

Acacia Research formerly operated as two business groups Acacia Technologies (formed in 1993) and CombiMatrix but it split CombiMatrix off into a separate public company in 2007.

EXECUTIVES

Chief Executive Officer; Director, Paul R. Ryan, age 67, $362,172 total compensation
Executive Chairman, Robert L. (Chip) Harris II, age 54, $355,659 total compensation
Chief Financial Officer, Clayton J. Haynes, age 43, $271,165 total compensation
Senior Vice President; General Counsel; Secretary, Edward J. Treska, age 47, $257,644 total compensation
SVP Corporate Finance, Robert B. (Rob) Stewart
SVP, Marvin E. Key
Senior Vice President Corporate Finance, Robert Stew
Chairman of the Board; President; Chief Executive Officer; Chief Financial Officer, Asaf Porat
President and CEO, Matthew Vella
Director, G. Louis Graziadio III, age 63
President and Director, Robert L. (Chip) Harris II, age 53
Director, Edward W. Frykman, age 76
Director, Fred A. deBoom, age 77
Director, William S. Anderson, age 53
Auditors: PricewaterhouseCoopersLLP

LOCATIONS

HQ: Acacia Research Corporation
500 Newport Center Dr. 7th Fl., Newport Beach CA 92660
Phone: 949-480-8300   **Fax:** 949-480-8301
Web: www.acaciaresearch.com

PRODUCTS/OPERATIONS

Selected Licensing Program Technologies
Audio/video enhancement
Computer memory cache coherency
Computer simulation
Credit card fraud protection
Data encryption and product activation
Digital media transmission
Digital video production
Dynamic manufacturing modeling
Enhanced Internet navigation
High capacity compact disks
Image resolution
Interactive television
Laptop connectivity
Multi-dimensional bar codes
Network data storage
Resource scheduling
User-activated Internet advertising
Web conferencing and software collaboration

COMPETITORS

Accel Partners

ICG Group

BTG plc
Benchmark Capital
Competitive
  Technologies
Draper Fisher
  Jurvetson
Hummer Winblad

Innovaro
Kleiner Perkins
ModusLink Global
  Solutions
RPX
Safeguard Scientifics
Vulcan

HISTORICAL FINANCIALS

Company Type: Public

Income Statement

FYE: December 31

	REVENUE ($ mil.)	NET INCOME ($ mil.)	NET PROFIT MARGIN	EMPLOYEES
12/12	250.7	59.4	23.7%	55
12/11	172.2	21.1	12.3%	55
12/10	131.8	34.0	25.8%	48
12/09	67.3	(11.2)	—	44
12/08	48.2	(13.7)	—	41
Annual Growth	**51.0%**	—	—	7.6%

2012 Year-End Financials

Debt ratio: —
Return on equity: 12.7%
Cash ($ mil.): 221
Current ratio: 14.76
Long-term debt ($ mil.): —

No. of shares (mil.): 49
Dividends
  Yield: —
  Payout: —
Market value ($ mil.): 1,261

	STOCK PRICE ($) FY Close	P/E High/Low	PER SHARE ($) Earnings	Dividends	Book Value
12/12	25.66	34 16	1.24	0.00	12.44
12/11	36.51	88 43	0.51	0.00	7.45
12/10	25.94	28 8	0.97	0.00	3.08
12/09	9.11	— —	(0.38)	0.00	1.68
12/08	3.04	— —	(0.47)	0.00	1.90
Annual Growth	**70.4%**	— —	—	—	60.0%

Acadia Healthcare Company Inc.

Acadia Healthcare help people to be mentally healthy. Acadia operates more than 45 behavioral health facilities with 3700 licensed beds in 21 US states and Puerto Rico. Its mental health and addiction treatment services include adult geriatric and adolescent inpatient residential and partial hospitalization programs. The company also offers treatment options for children with autism eating disorders fetal alcohol syndrome substance abuse and traumatic brain injury as well as for sexually abused children. Acadia offers services nationwide.

Sales and Marketing

Patients are referred to Acadia's behavioral healthcare facilities through healthcare workers public programs other treatment facilities managed care organizations unions emergency departments judicial officials social workers and police departments. It also gets patient referrals via word of mouth from previously treated patients and their families and other sources.

Financial Performance

The company's revenues spiked by 88% in 2012 thanks to new revenues from 2011 and 2012 acquisitions (including Youth & Family Centered Services PHC Haven Facilities Timberline Knolls and Park Royal). Same-facility revenues increased by $20.5 million or 9.3% primarily due to a higher patient enrollment. Medicaid accounted for more than 60% of Acadia's 2012 revenues.Acadia reported net income of $20.4 million in 2012 (compared to loss of $34.9 million in 2011) due to higher revenues in and a drop in transaction-related expenses (stemming from the absence of fees paid for the termination of professional services agreement investment banking advisory and bridge commitment fees and advisory fees) partially offset by a rise in salaries wages and benefits professional fees supplies interest expense and other operating expenses.

The increase in interest expense was primarily a result of borrowings under its senior credit facility and interest on the $150 million of senior notes issued in late 2011. Higher operating expenses were primarily due to a slight increase in other operating expenses.

Strategy

The company primarily grows through acquisitions.

Mergers and Acquisitions

In 2013 the company acquired nashiville-based Behavioral Centers of America for $145 million. The firm operates three inpatient psychiatric facilities and one psychiatric hospital in Michigan Ohio and Texas.

In 2012 Acadia acquired three acute care inpatient psychiatric hospitals from Haven Behavioral Healthcare for $91 million in cash. The purchase added about 165 beds at facilities in Tucson; Wichita Falls Texas; and Ada Oklahoma and marked the company's entrance into the Oklahoma market. The company also entered Illinois in 2012 by acquiring a 122-bed inpatient behavioral health care facility in Lemont Illinois for about $90 million. It also picked up Park Royal Hospital a 76-bed acute inpatient psychiatric hospital in Ft. Myers Florida for $33.4 million.

In a major move the company merged with mental health services provider PHC in late 2011. Through all-stock transaction Acadia added more than a dozen mental health and substance abuse centers in six states. When the companies combined Acadia's existing shareholders including majority owner Waud Capital Partners wound up with nearly 80% of the combined firm. The acquisition also let formerly private Acadia take a place on the NASDAQ stock exchange while PHC's NYSE Amex stock was delisted. While PHC's dba Pioneer Behavioral Health continues to be used following the transaction the legal PHC entity was absorbed into a subsidiary of Acadia. The merger created a company with a strong foundation in services for special populations including armed forces police transportation and gaming employees.

Acadia already operated about 20 behavioral health centers in more than a dozen states prior to its acquisition of PHC. Many of these facilities were gained through an earlier 2011 acquisition the purchase of Youth & Family Centered Services (YFCS) for some $178 million. YFCS operated about a dozen centers in eight states primarily focused on providing adolescent services.

PHC had also been expanding its operations prior to its merger into Acadia. The firm purchased the MeadowWood Behavioral Health center in mid-2011 for about $21 million. With about 60 beds on an 11-acre campus MeadowWood moved the company into Delaware and geriatric care. Before the Acadia deal PHC planned to expand the facility. PHC also grew in 2011 through the opening of a newly constructed inpatient treatment center in Michigan. In addition to its inpatient facilities PHC operated outpatient centers through its Har-mony Healthcare and North Point Pioneer subsidiaries.

Ownership

Waud Capital Partners owns 29% of Acadia.

Company Background

Acadia was founded in 2005 by Waud Capital Partners to acquire and operate behavioral health facilities. Its first centers were purchased in 2008 and 2009 in Georgia Louisiana and Tennessee.

EXECUTIVES

Executive Vice Chairman and Director, Bruce A. Shear, age 59
Chairman and CEO, Joey A. Jacobs, age 60
CFO, Jack E. Polson, age 47
Co-President, Brent Turner, age 48
Co-President, Trey Carter, age 47
EVP and General Counsel, Christopher L. (Chris) Howard, age 47
COO, Ron Fincher, age 60
Chief Development Officer, Steve T. Davidson
Executive Vice Chairman and Director, Bruce A. Shear, age 58
Auditors: Ernst&YoungLLP

LOCATIONS

HQ: Acadia Healthcare Company Inc.
830 Crescent Centre Drive, Suite 610, Franklin, TN 37067
Phone: 615 861-6000
Web: www.acadiahealthcare.com/

PRODUCTS/OPERATIONS

2012 Sales

	% of total
Medicaid	64
Commercial	20
Medicare	12
Self-pay	2
Other	2
Total	**100**

Selected Facilities

Arizona
Parc-Place (residential adolescents ages 11-17)
Arkansas
Ascent Children's Health Services (day treatment all ages)
Millcreek of Arkansas (long-term residential ages 6-21 years with mental retardation and/or related developmental disabilities)
Delaware
MeadowWood Hospital (in-patient and out-patient adults and seniors)
Florida
Park Royal Hospital
The Refuge
Georgia
Blue Ridge Mountain Recovery
Greenleaf Centers
Lakeview Behavioral Health
RiverWoods Behavioral Health System (outpatient and partial hospitalization adults and seniors)
Illinois
Timberline Knolls (residential treatment)
Indiana
Resolute Treatment Center (residential males ages 11-18)
Resource Treatment Center (residential ages 8-20)
Options Behavioral Health System (residential ages 8-18)
Louisiana
Acadia Vermilion Hospital (inpatient and outpatient all ages)
Acadiana Addiction Center (inpatient and outpatient adults)
Michigan
Detroit Capstone Academy (residential adjudicated adolescents)

Harbor Oaks Hospital (inpatient all ages)
Harbor Oaks Outpatient Clinic (outpatient all ages)
Pioneer Counseling Centers (outpatient all ages)
Renaissance Recovery (residential ages 12-17)
Wellplace Michigan (local call center clinical screening and access center)
Mississippi
Millcreek of Magee (residential 21 years and younger)
Millcreek of Pontotoc (residential ages 6-18)
Missouri
Lakeland Regional Hospital (residential and long term ages 4-17)
Montana
Acadia Montana (residential ages 5-18)
Nevada
Harmony Healthcare (outpatient all ages)
Seven Hills Behavioral Institute (outpatient ages 12 and up)
New Mexico
Desert Hills of New Mexico (residential ages 5-18)
Ohio
Ohio Hospital for Psychiatry (adults and seniors)
Shaker Clinic (adults and seniors)
Ten Lakes Center (adults ages 55 and up)
Oklahoma
Rolling Hills Hospital (acute inpatient psychiatric care for adults geriatrics intellectually disabled patients as well as addiction treatment)
Pennsylvania
Southwood Hospital (various programs ages 4-18)
Wellplace (outpatient all ages)
Tennessee
Dealt Medical Center
The Village (residential ages 13-17)
Texas
Acadia Abilene (residential all ages)
Utah
Highland Ridge Hospital (inpatient all ages)
Wellplace (employee assistance programs and 24 hour call center)
Virginia
Mount Regis Center (inpatient and outpatient adults)
Puerto Rico
Hospital San Juan Capestrano Rio Piedras Puerto (treatment services for mental health conditions and addiction problems of Puerto Rico)

COMPETITORS

Betty Ford	Horizon Health
CIGNA Behavioral	Magellan Health
Health	Mental Health Network
CRC Health	Northwestern Human
Comprehensive Care	Services
Devereux Foundation	Universal Health
HCA	Services
Hazelden	

HISTORICAL FINANCIALS

Company Type: Public

Income Statement

	REVENUE ($ mil.)	NET INCOME ($ mil.)	NET PROFIT MARGIN	EMPLOYEES
12/12	407.4	20.4	5.0%	7,200
12/11	221.3	(34.8)	—	5,820
12/10	64.3	6.2	9.7%	4,857
12/09	51.8	2.8	5.6%	0
Annual Growth	98.9%	92.1%	—	—

FYE: December 31

2012 Year-End Financials

Debt ratio: 48.1%	No. of shares (mil.): 49
Return on equity: 7.6%	Dividends
Cash ($ mil.): 49	Yield: —
Current ratio: 1.96	Payout: —
Long-term debt ($ mil.): 465	Market value ($ mil.): 1,165

	STOCK PRICE ($)	P/E	PER SHARE ($)		
	FY Close	High/Low	Earnings	Dividends	Book Value
12/12	23.35	46 18	0.53	0.00	8.67
12/11	9.97	— —	(1.86)	0.00	3.00
12/10	0.00	— —	0.62	0.00	55.48
Annual Growth (60.5%)	—	— —	(7.5%)	—	

Access National Corp

Enabling easy access to your money is Access National's aim. The holding company owns Access National Bank a thrift founded in 1999 that serves the suburbs of Washington DC in Northern Virginia through about five branches. The bank offers deposit lending and investment services to consumers professionals and small to midsized businesses. Subsidiary Access National Mortgage originates residential real estate loans in the bank's market and in selected cities nationwide. Commercial mortgages make up more than 40% of the company's portfolio; residential real estate accounts for another 30%. Real estate construction business and consumer loans round out the bank's lending activities.

Access National Corporation gleans a significant portion of its revenue by selling loans that it originates into the secondary market.

As a group executive officers and board members of the company own about a quarter of Access National Corporation. Former chairman Jacques Rebibo and his son Michael Rebibo a former president of Access National Mortgage own about an additional 10%.

EXECUTIVES

President Chief Executive Officer, Michael W. (Mike) Clarke, age 51, $285,000 total compensation
Executive Vice President Chief Lending Officer, Robert C. Shoemaker, age 52, $230,000 total compensation
President Access National Mortgage, Dean F. Hackemer, age 48, $280,000 total compensation
VP and Corporate Secretary, Sheila M. Linton
Sales Manager Access National Mortgage, Mark Kuchik
Chief Financial Officer; Senior Vice President; Chief Accounting Officer; Principal Financial Officer and Principal Accounting Officer, Meg Taylor
EVP and Director; Senior Loan Officer Access National Bank, Robert C. Shoemaker, age 52
Director, John W. (Skip) Edgemond IV, age 51
Director, James L. (Ted) Jadlos, age 47
Director, Thomas M. Kody, age 51
Director, Martin S. Friedman, age 44
Auditors: BDOSeidmanLLP

LOCATIONS

HQ: Access National Corporation
 1800 Robert Fulton Dr. Ste. 300, Reston VA 20191
Phone: 703-871-2100   **Fax:** 703-766-3386
Web: www.accessnationalbank.com

PRODUCTS/OPERATIONS

2009 Sales

	$ mil.	% of total
Noninterest		
Gain on sale of loans	49	52
Other	7	8
Interest & dividends		
Loans	34	37
Securities	3	3
Other	0	-
Total	**94**	**100**

COMPETITORS

BB&T	PNC Financial
Capital One	SunTrust
Cardinal Financial	United Bankshares
Millennium Bankshares	

HISTORICAL FINANCIALS

Company Type: Public

Income Statement

FYE: December 31

	ASSETS ($ mil.)	NET INCOME ($ mil.)	INCOME AS % OF ASSETS	EMPLOYEES
12/12	863.9	17.7	2.1%	305
12/11	809.7	11.3	1.4%	286
12/10	831.8	7.5	0.9%	277
12/09	666.8	9.6	1.4%	328
12/08	702.3	4.7	0.7%	285
Annual Growth	**5.3%**	**39.0%**	**—**	**1.7%**

2012 Year-End Financials

Return on assets: 2.1%
Return on equity: 20.3%
Long-term debt ($ mil.): —
No. of shares (mil.): 10
Sales ($ mil): 91
Dividends
 Yield: 7.3%
 Payout: 55.5%
Market value ($ mil.): 134

	STOCK PRICE ($)	P/E	PER SHARE ($)		
	FY Close	High/Low	Earnings	Dividends	Book Value
12/12	13.00	8 5	1.71	0.95	8.85
12/11	8.80	8 6	1.10	0.13	8.12
12/10	6.46	9 8	0.72	0.04	6.96
12/09	5.90	7 4	0.92	0.04	6.43
12/08	4.79	18 10	0.46	0.04	5.66
Annual Growth	**28.4%**	**— —**	**38.9%**	**120.8%**	**11.8%**

Aceto Corp.

Distributor Aceto (pronounced "a-seat-o") is getting bigger through chemicals –primarily specialty chemicals and pharmaceuticals. It sources and distributes more than 1100 chemical products through three segments. Its largest segment is Performance Chemicals which sources and distributes specialty chemicals and agricultural protection products. Aceto's other business segments include Pharmaceutical Ingredients (active pharmaceutical ingredients or APIs and pharmaceutical intermediates) and Human Health (finished dosage form generic drugs and nutraceutical products). Aceto sources about two-thirds of its products from Asia mostly China and India and turns around to sell more than half of them in the US.

Geographic Reach

Aceto has operations in China France Germany Hong Kong India the Netherlands Singapore the UK and the US.

Financial Analysis

Aceto saw an increase in revenues of 8% in 2011 thanks to a 51% increase in Human Health segment revenues due to a $27703 increase in sales of Rising Pharmaceuticals products and a jump in sales of domestic nutritional supplements of $4869 due to new business development from existing customers and new projects from Aceto's pipeline. In addition the company recorded a 9% increase in Pharmaceutical Ingredients as a result of a growth in sales of APIs thanks to the reorders of existing products. In addition the Pharmaceutical Ingredients segment saw international sales rise $5963 over the prior year thanks to an increase in sales of APIs and pharmaceutical intermediates. However the Performance Chemicals segment revenues declined by 9% due to a drop of $5768 in sales of specialty chemicals sold outside the US as well as a decline in agricultural protection products sales of $20482 primarily due to lower glyphosate sales caused by poor market conditions.

Aceto's 2011 net income increased by 89% thanks to strong revenue growth an increase in gross profit and lower operating assets and liability costs.

Strategy

Leveraging its access local professionals in areas with lower pricing Aceto sources more than two-thirds of its products from Asia buying from about 500 companies in China and 200 in India.

In 2012 it reorganized from six segments to three to provide a simpler more efficient operational structure for customers suppliers employees and shareholders.

Customers include major and generic pharmaceutical makers as well as chemical companies. It works with makers of generics well in advance of the drugs coming off patent to ensure those customers are ready to go with their products as soon as legally allowed to do so. In 2011 through a subsidiary Aceto acquired New Jersey-based Rising Pharmaceuticals in a transaction valued at $80 million. Buying Rising which manufactures and distributes generic prescription and over-the-counter drugs expands Aceto's reach into the pharmaceutical market.

In 2010 Aceto broke into new markets with the acquisition of Andrews Paper & Chemical which serves the paper films and electronics industries. Some of its products include diazos and couplers that are used in the manufacture of microfilm and printed circuit boards.

HISTORY

Chemical engineers Frankel and Seymour Mann set up Aceto Chemical Co. (the name relates to acetic acid an ingredient used in synthesizing plastics) in 1947. The two built the business around the reviving chemical industry in Europe during the 1950s by acting as the US agent for British chemical firms (including BP Chemical). Aceto began to import from Asia in the 1960s and it went public in 1962. In 1969 the company set up a manufacturing plant in Carlstadt New Jersey. Up until the late 1970s the company principally operated as a US sales agent for non-US companies.

The company changed its name to Aceto Corporation in 1985. President and CEO Seymour Mann died of a heart attack in 1989 and Frankel (then chairman and CFO) assumed the CEO position the next year.

During the 1990s Aceto purchased raw materials from Chinese and Indian suppliers at half the price of those produced by some European and Japanese makers. To ensure quality control from its suppliers Aceto hired field technicians including a team based in Shanghai. To lower capital costs and concentrate on distribution the company closed its two manufacturing plants.

Aceto sold its Pfaltz & Bauer subsidiary in 1996. Frankel stepped down as CEO in 1997 and company veteran and president Leonard Schwartz filled the position. Lower sales of agricultural chemicals and bulk pharmaceuticals led to a drop in revenues that year.

In 2001 Aceto acquired the Schweizerhall Pharma division of Schweizerhall Holding AG for about $25 million. The acquisition included facilities in Germany the Netherlands France Singapore India and Hong Kong. The acquisition strengthened its international operations and its pharmaceutical and nutraceutical businesses.

The company bolstered its biopharmaceutical distribution operations in 2004 with the acquisition of Pharma Waldhof from Roche. Aceto announced plans to exit the sanitary supplies segment late that year and it sold most of the assets of its CDC Products and Magnum Research subsidiaries the following year.

Albert Eilender was named CEO of Aceto in 2010. He replaced Vincent Miata who continued as president and COO of the company.

EXECUTIVES

SVP Specialty Chemicals, Roger Weaving Jr.
Group VP, Leonard Lawton
President COO and Director, Vincent G. Miata, age 58, $269,854 total compensation
Group VP, Roy Goodman
President Aceto Agricultural Chemicals, Michael Feinman, age 65, $216,000 total compensation
Senior Vice President - Corporate Business Development, Frank DeBenedittis, age 59, $270,030 total compensation
Head Pharmaceuticals Intermediates Business, Brian Shapiro
President and CEO, Salvatore J. Guccione, age 50
Senior Vice President - Nutritionals, Raymond Bartone
VP, Albert Miseje
Managing Director Aceto Shanghai, Gary Mo
Assistant VP and Director Transportation, Amy Tam Rogers
VP Global Business Development Specialty Chemicals Business, Keith Wilkinson
SVP and CFO, Douglas Roth, age 56, $277,807 total compensation
Chairman, Albert L. Eilender, age 70
Assistant VP and Controller, Edward Kelly
VP-Speciality Chemicals, Peter Tomasino
Managing Director Aceto France, Philippe Potelle
General Manager Aceto Pharma India, Pradeep Thakur
Managing Director Aceto Singapore, Jason Yu
Director Corporate Communications and Investor Relations, Theodore Ayvas
Managing Director Pharma Waldhof, Ulf Bender
Assistant VP, David Bercher
Assistant VP IT, Marlene Felix
Corporate Director Environmental and Regulatory Affairs, Simone Miller
Assistant VP, Sean Isacsson
Assistant VP Aceto Agricultural Chemicals, Terry Kippley
Assistant VP, James Sammer
Director Financial Reporting and Compliance, Frances Scally

VP-Intl Ops & Intl Pharmaceutical Strategy, Jan Van Eis
VP Human Resources, Charles Alaimo
Senior Manager Business Development, Birgit Wonka
Sales Manager - API Divisio, Cyrille Arlandis
Vice President - International Operations, Jan Eis
SVP Active Pharmaceutical Ingredients, Nicholas Shackley
Sales Manager - Intermediate Division, Valerie Noireaut
IR Officer, Amy Glynn
Senior Vice President - Business Development, David Rosen
Vice President - Pharmaceutical Intermediates Business, Guillaume Saint-Clair
Managing Director; Pharma Waldhof GmbH, Lukas Hippel
President and Chief Operating Officer Rising Pharmaceuticals, Ronald Gold
Senior Vice President; General Counsel; Corporate Secretary, Steven Rogers
President COO and Director, Vincent G. Miata, age 58
Director, Salvatore J. Guccione, age 49
Director, Robert A. Wiesen, age 62
Director, Stanley H. Fischer, age 69
Director, Richard P. (Dick) Randall, age 75
Director, Hans C. Noetzli, age 72
Director, William N. Britton, age 68
Auditors: BDOUSALLP

LOCATIONS

HQ: Aceto Corporation
4 Tri Harbor Ct., Port Washington NY 11050
Phone: 516-627-6000   **Fax:** 516-627-6093
Web: www.aceto.com

2011 Sales

	$ mil.	% of total
US	289	65
Germany	82	19
Netherlands	13	3
Total	**444**	**100**

PRODUCTS/OPERATIONS

2011 Sales

Performance Chemicals	176	40
Human Health	105	23

Selected Products

Performance Chemicals (specialty chemicals agricultural protection products and active ingredients for pharmaceuticals)
Pharmaceutical Ingredients (pharmaceutical intermediates and active pharmaceutical ingredients)
Human Health (finished dosage form generics and nutritionals)

COMPETITORS

Air Products	Sigma-Aldrich
American Vanguard	Synthomer
Brenntag	Univar USA
Farma International	Young Chemical Co.
K.A. Steel Chemicals	

HISTORICAL FINANCIALS

Company Type: Public

Income Statement

FYE: June 30

	REVENUE ($ mil.)	NET INCOME ($ mil.)	NET PROFIT MARGIN	EMPLOYEES
06/13	499.6	22.3	4.5%	234
06/12	444.3	16.9	3.8%	233
06/11	412.4	8.9	2.2%	238
06/10	346.6	6.5	1.9%	216
06/09	322.6	8.6	2.7%	221
Annual Growth	**11.6%**	**26.8%**	**—**	**1.4%**

2013 Year-End Financials

Debt ratio: 9.9%	No. of shares (mil.): 27
Return on equity: 12.3%	Dividends
Cash ($ mil.): 33	Yield: 0.0%
Current ratio: 2.43	Payout: 27.1%
Long-term debt ($ mil.): 20	Market value ($ mil.): 388

	STOCK PRICE ($) FY Close	P/E High/Low	Earnings	PER SHARE ($) Dividends	Book Value
06/13	13.93	17 10	0.81	0.22	6.99
06/12	9.03	16 8	0.63	0.20	6.24
06/11	6.71	27 15	0.34	0.20	6.04
06/10	5.73	28 19	0.26	0.20	5.49
06/09	6.67	32 14	0.35	0.20	5.72
Annual Growth	**20.2%**	**— —**	**23.3%**	**2.4%**	**5.2%**

ACI Worldwide Inc

ACI Worldwide helps money go mobile. The company develops e-payment and electronic funds transfer (EFT) software for companies around the world. Customers use its software to process transactions involving ATMs credit and debit cards online banking and payment processing point-of-sale terminals smart cards and wire transfers. ACI also makes network integration software and it offers services such as design implementation and facilities management. The company serves the financial services and retail industries with more than 750 customers in some 80 countries.

Sales and Marketing The company distributes products primarily through its own sales force but also utilizes third-party distributors in certain regions (primarily Asia and Latin America). Among those distributors are DataOne (Thailand) Optimisa (Chile) and Syscom Computer (China).

Geographic Reach ACI generates more than half its sales from the Americas with the EMEA and Asia-Pacific regions contributing 35% and more than 10% respectively. The company saw revenues rise across all regions in 2011 with the Asia-Pacific region showing the strongest growth at nearly 20%.

Financial Analysis ACI has reported strong revenue growth since 2009 when sales fell amid the worst of the economic recession. The company's 2011 revenue hit $465 million which is up 11% from 2010 as it saw double-digit increases in software license and maintenance fees and smaller growth in service and software hosting fees. Net income was also up in 2011 jumping nearly 70% to $46 million on the increase in revenue as well as lower growth in maintenance fees general and administrative costs and other expenses. ACI also saw lower income tax expenses in 2011.

Mergers and Acquisitions ACI Worldwide has worked to strengthen its international presence and add new technology to its repertoire in part through acquisitions. In 2012 it bought rival S1 Corporation for about $540 million in cash and stock. The two companies had very similar product lines and customers and ACI Worldwide believed the merger would create significant cost savings and cross-selling opportunities as well as boost its profile among community financial and branch banking institutions. S1 was integrated into ACI's other operations. The deal added a consumer online banking division and a significant retail presence outside North America. Additionally that year ACI acquired payments software developer Distra to extend the feature set of its products to address mobile usage social channels and payment services hubs. In 2011 the company bought Dallas-based ISD Corporation to add functionality to its products for retailers. ISD's applications were designed to consolidate manage and route electronic transactions for authorization and settlement processing. ACI Worldwide integrated the acquired technology into its On-Demand hosted service and its Retail Commerce Server product to add flexibility for its customers.

HISTORY

oApplied Communications Inc. (ACI) was formed by computer programmer James Cody and two other men in 1975. ACI's electronic funds software for banks seemed to be so ahead of its time that Cody made one successful sales call in mismatched shoes. The company went public in 1983. Combining its software with Tandem computers also aided ACI's fortunes. ACI was acquired by Baby Bell U S WEST in 1986; it then formed ACIL a joint venture with Sema Group. In 1991 Tandem Computers (later acquired by Compaq which was itself bought by Hewlett-Packard) bought ACI and ACIL. Management led by president and CEO William Fisher bought the units in 1993. The company changed its name to Transaction Systems Architects (TSA) in 1994 and went public again the next year.

In the mid-1990s the company went on a buying spree. It acquired Open Systems Solutions a maker of Windows NT-based payment management software in 1996. The next year TSA expanded its presence in Europe by buying the software and service division of Italian firm Banksiel. With the acquisitions of Smart Card Integrators and Media Integration which were among TSA's half-dozen 1998 purchases the company further expanded its smart card product expertise.

In 1999 TSA bought SDM International a provider of electronic payment and electronic data interchange software. That year the company acquired and restructured Insession a maker of ICE network connectivity software. In 2000 TSA filed to spin off the subsidiary renamed Insession Technologies in a public stock offering (plans which were shelved in 2001 amid a weakening economy).

In 2001 TSA acquired MessagingDirect a provider of software for the delivery and processing of electronic statements and bills. The following year the company sold its Regency Systems subsidiary a provider of software for community banks to S1 Corporation.

The company bought S2 Systems a provider of electronic payments software with operations in Europe the Middle East and the Asia/Pacific region in 2005. Later that year the company implemented a reorganization which combined three of its subsidiaries (ACI Worldwide Intranet World-

wide and Insession Technologies) into one organization operating under the ACI Worldwide name; in 2007 the company officially changed its name to ACI Worldwide.

In 2006 the company acquired P&H Solutions for $150 million. Later that year the company completed the divestiture of its e-Courier and Work-Point product lines.

Its 2007 purchase of Visual Web Solutions expanded its presence in the Asia/Pacific region (and bolstered its product offerings by adding international trade finance and Web-based cash management capabilities) while its acquisition that year of Stratasoft Sdn. Bhd. added electronic payment offerings in Malaysia.

In 2009 the company purchased UK-based Euronet Essentis Limited a division of Euronet Worldwide that provided payment products and services for card issuing and merchant acquisition. ACI also began selling its products directly in some international markets instead of relying on distributors for sales as it had in the past.

EXECUTIVES

President CEO and Director, Philip G. (Phil) Heasley, age 63, $575,000 total compensation
Vice President Global Markets and Product ManagementACI Worldwide, Daniel J. (Dan) Frate, age 52
Chairman, Harlan F. Seymour, age 63
EVP Chief Administrative Officer General Counsel and Secretary, Dennis P. Byrnes, age 49, $275,000 total compensation
EVP Global Development, Tony Scotto
Chief Technology Officer, Charles H. Linberg, age 55
Executive Vice President Global Customer Operations, David N. Morem, age 55, $260,000 total compensation
SVP ACI On Demand, Jan Kruger, age 50
President Asia Pacific Region, Jeremy Wilmot
SVP Chief Corporate Development Officer and Treasurer, Craig A. Maki, age 46, $250,008 total compensation
Executive Vice President Chief Financial Officer, Scott W. Behrens, age 41, $250,000 total compensation
VP Investor Relations, Tamar Gerber
VP, Victoria H. Sitz
Chief Technical Officer, Charles LinbergChief
Vice President Customer Management Operations & PricingACI Worldwide, Carolyn Homberger
President CEO and Director, Philip G. (Phil) Heasley, age 63
Director, Alfred R. (Al) Berkeley III, age 68
Director, John E. Stokely, age 59
Director, Jan H. Suwinski, age 71
Director, James C. McGroddy, age 76
Director, John D. Curtis, age 72
Director, John M. Shay Jr., age 65
Auditors: Deloitte&ToucheLLP

LOCATIONS

HQ: ACI Worldwide Inc.
3520 Kraft Rd. Ste. 300, Naples FL 34105
Phone: 402-390-7600   **Fax:** 919-573-3551
Web: www.generalparts.com

2011 Sales

	$ mil.	% of total
Americas	245	53
EMEA	164	35
Asia/Pacific	54	12
Total	**465**	**100**

PRODUCTS/OPERATIONS

2011 Sales

	$ mil.	% of total
Software license fees	189	41
Maintenance fees	148	32
Services	79	17
Software hosting fees	47	10
Total	**465**	**100**

Selected Service Areas

Online banking and cash management
Payment fraud detection
Retail
Retail banking payments
Tools and infrastructure
Wholesale banking payments

COMPETITORS

Fair Isaac	Ingenico Corp.
Fidelity National	Intuit Financial
Information Services	Services
First Data	Total System Services
Fiserv	VeriFone
Fundtech	

HISTORICAL FINANCIALS

Company Type: Public

Income Statement

FYE: December 31

	REVENUE ($ mil.)	NET INCOME ($ mil.)	NET PROFIT MARGIN	EMPLOYEES
12/12	666.5	48.8	7.3%	3,530
12/11	465.1	45.8	9.9%	2,131
12/10	418.4	27.2	6.5%	2,134
12/09	405.7	19.6	4.8%	2,114
12/08	417.6	10.5	2.5%	2,154
Annual Growth	**12.4%**	**46.6%**	**—**	**13.1%**

2012 Year-End Financials

Debt ratio: 29.9%   No. of shares (mil.): 39
Return on equity: 11.4%   Dividends
Cash ($ mil.): 76   Yield: —
Current ratio: 1.34   Payout: —
Long-term debt ($ mil.): 356 Market value ($ mil.): 1,723

	STOCK PRICE ($) FY Close	P/E High/Low	PER SHARE ($) Earnings	Dividends	Book Value
12/12	43.69	37 22	1.22	0.00	13.55
12/11	28.64	28 18	1.34	0.00	9.43
12/10	26.87	35 19	0.80	0.00	7.68
12/09	17.15	36 23	0.57	0.00	6.94
12/08	15.90	73 29	0.30	0.00	6.13
Annual Growth	**28.7%**	**—**	**42.0%**	**—**	**21.9%**

Acorda Therapeutics Inc

Acorda Therapeutics hopes its products really get on your nerves. The company is developing prescription drugs that aim to restore neurological function for patients with central nervous system disorders. The company's marketed drugs include Ampyra which enhances conduction in nerves damaged from multiple sclerosis (MS) and Zanaflex a muscle spasm controller. Acorda is working with Biogen Idec to market Ampyra outside the US. Acorda's other drug candidates include potential new therapies for MS and other central nervous system disorders as well as cardiac conditions.

Operations

Sales of its two commercial products have helped the company increase its product revenues in recent years with Ampyra as the company's main breadwinner that the firm hopes will drive growth in future years. The drug is the first to improve the functionality of damaged nerve fibers; other MS treatments generally treat symptoms or slow its progression. Biogen Idec holds rights to market Ampyra outside of the US and pays royalties to Acorda on the drug's sales. Biogen Idec has gained approval for Ampyra (known internationally as Fampyra) in areas including Australia Canada Israel and the European Union.

Zanaflex on the other hand is facing dwindling sales after Zanaflex capsules began facing generic competition in 2012 when its patent expired. (The Zanaflex tablets are still under patent protection.) Acorda launched an authorized generic capsule version with Actavis (formerly Watson Pharmaceuticals) that year to help offset losses. In addition Acorda is stepping up efforts to broaden its product offerings.

The company doesn't have its own manufacturing operations; it instead uses Patheon and Alkermes as its third-party manufacturers.

Sales and Marketing

The company markets its products in the US through a direct sales force that targets neurologists and other specialists as well as primary care physicians specialty pharmacies hospitals managed care companies and drug distribution companies.

Financial Performance

Though the company has products on the market it still invests heavily in R&D efforts for new candidates as well as to build up a marketing and sales support network for existing products. However Acorda experienced its first profitable year in 2011 when it reported a net income of $30 million. Its transition from a development-stage firm to a profitable drugmaker came primarily from increased revenues on sales of Ampyra in both 2010 and 2011 (the company more than doubled revenues both years).

Sales grew another 5% in 2012 to $306 million due to higher Ampyra sales and increased royalty revenues on both Ampyra and generic Zanaflex offset by lower sales of its branded Zanaflex offerings. Profits also increased by more than 400% in 2012 due to income tax over-provision benefits.

Strategy

The company is focused on increasing sales of Ampyra. It is also looking to add new uses for Ampyra which was first approved by the FDA in 2010 as a therapy to improve the ability to walk in people who suffer from MS. The firm is developing the drug for additional MS-related functional impairment indications as well as for potential use in cerebral palsy and chronic stroke treatment.

In its internal R&D programs Acorda is exploring applications for its nerve and tissue repair technologies in cardiology and neurology fields. For instance in addition to the Ampyra development programs the company has candidates for treatment of spinal cord injury stroke epilepsy and heart failure as well as a new potential treatment for MS.

Mergers and Acquisitions

In 2012 the company expanded its pipeline by acquiring development firm Neuronex in a deal worth some $9.3 million (plus potential future milestone payments) to gain access to Neuronex's

nasal spray epilepsy candidate. It first paid $2.5 million to gain a minority stake in Neuronex and then exercised its option to purchase the rest for $6.8 million later in the year.

Ownership

Investment firm Blackrock owns an 11% stake in Acorda.

Company Background

The company was founded by CEO Ron Cohen in 1995 to develop therapies for multiple sclerosis and other neurological conditions.

EXECUTIVES

CFO, Michael W. Rogers

President and CEO, Ron Cohen, $460,800 total compensation

Chief Scientific Officer, Andrew R. Blight, $295,000 total compensation

Chief of Business Operations, David Lawrence, $252,400 total compensation

Senior Director Corporate Communications, Jeff Macdonald

President International and General Counsel, Jane Wasman, $325,000 total compensation

Senior Vice President of Corporate Communications at Acorda, Tierney Saccavino

Senior Vice President of Human Resources at Acorda, Denise J. Duca

EVP Commercial Development, Lauren M. Sabella

Vice President of Research & Development at Acorda, Anthony O. (Tony) Caggiano

Vice President of Business Development at Acorda, Ruhi Khan

Senior Vice President Clinical Development and Medical Affairs at Acorda, Adrian L. Rabinowicz

Chief Medical Officer, Enrique J Carrazana

Vice President Quality at Acorda, Bonnie M. Pappacena

Vice President of Sales at Acorda, Kerry Clem

Vice President of Regulatory Affairs at Acorda, Brian Walter

Vice President of Marketing at Acorda, Elizabeth Keating

Vice President of Finance of Acorda, Jennifer Burstein

Vice President of Drug Safety and Risk Management at Acorda, Thomas C. Aquilina

Director, Steven M. Rauscher, age 59

Director, Lorin J. (Jeff) Randall, age 69

Director, Barry E. Greene, age 50

Director, Sandra Panem, age 66

Director, Ian F. Smith, age 47

President CEO and Director, Ron Cohen, age 57

Director, John P. Kelley, age 59

Independent Director, Peder Jensen

Auditors: KPMGLLP

LOCATIONS

HQ: Acorda Therapeutics Inc.
15 Skyline Dr., Hawthorne NY 10532
Phone: 914-347-4300   **Fax:** 914-347-4560
Web: www.acorda.com

PRODUCTS/OPERATIONS

2012 Sales

	$ mil.	% of total
Product sales	282	92
Royalty	14	5
License	9	3
Total	**305**	**100**

COMPETITORS

Actavis Inc.	Cephalon
Alseres	Cytokinetics
Pharmaceuticals	Elan
Apotex	InVivo Therapeutics
Bayer HealthCare	Meda Pharmaceuticals
Pharmaceuticals	Merck Serono
Bayhill	Mylan
BioMarin	Novartis
Pharmaceutical	Sanofi
Biogen Idec	Shire
Catalyst	Teva
Pharmaceutical	Upsher-Smith

HISTORICAL FINANCIALS
Company Type: Public

Income Statement
FYE: December 31

	REVENUE ($ mil.)	NET INCOME ($ mil.)	NET PROFIT MARGIN	EMPLOYEES
12/12	305.8	154.9	50.7%	378
12/11	292.2	30.6	10.5%	328
12/10	191.0	(11.7)	—	305
12/09	54.6	(83.9)	—	249
12/08	47.8	(74.3)	—	174
Annual Growth	**59.0%**	**—**		**21.4%**

2012 Year-End Financials

Debt ratio: 0.9%	No. of shares (mil.): 39
Return on equity: 52.2%	Dividends
Cash ($ mil.): 41	Yield: —
Current ratio: 3.37	Payout: —
Long-term debt ($ mil.): 4	Market value ($ mil.): 989

	STOCK PRICE ($) FY Close	P/E High/Low		Earnings	PER SHARE ($) Dividends	Book Value
12/12	24.86	7	6	3.84	0.00	9.70
12/11	23.84	42	24	0.76	0.00	5.22
12/10	27.26	—	—	(0.31)	0.00	3.90
12/09	25.20	—	—	(2.22)	0.00	3.62
12/08	20.51	—	—	(2.19)	0.00	5.51
Annual Growth	**4.9%**	—	—		—	**15.2%**

Adelphia Recovery Trust

LOCATIONS

HQ: Adelphia Recovery Trust
919 North Market Street, 17th Floor, P.O. Box 8705,
Wilmington, DE 19899
Phone: 302 652-4100

HISTORICAL FINANCIALS
Company Type: Public

Income Statement
FYE: December 31

	REVENUE ($ mil.)	NET INCOME ($ mil.)	NET PROFIT MARGIN	EMPLOYEES
12/12	34.4	25.4	74.0%	0
12/11	0.4	(10.9)	—	0
12/10	175.6	138.6	79.0%	0
12/09	40.8	1.1	2.8%	0
12/08	5.8	(21.7)	—	0
Annual Growth	**55.6%**	**—**	**—**	**—**

2012 Year-End Financials

Debt ratio: —	No. of shares (mil.): —
Return on equity: —	Dividends
Cash ($ mil.): 38	Yield: 0.5%
Current ratio: 143.45	Payout: —
Long-term debt ($ mil.): —	Market value ($ mil.): —

Advanced Energy Industries Inc.

Advanced Energy Industries advances ordinary electrical power to the head of the high-tech class. The company's power conversion products transform raw electricity making it uniform enough to ensure consistent production in high-precision manufacturing. Semiconductor and solar manufacturing equipment maker Applied Materials (14% of sales) is its top customer. Advanced Energy's gear also is used in the production of solar panels and other thin-film products such as cell phones computers cars and glass panels for windows and electronic devices. The company gets around 70% of sales from the US.

Operations

Advanced Energy Industries operates in two divisions - Thin Films and Solar Energy. Each division accounts for about half of sales. Sales for the Solar Energy division rose 15% in 2012 as more large utility-scale projects use its high-efficiency inverters while sales of Thin Film products fell almost 30% as demand from semiconductor equipment makers and other OEMs decreased.

Geographic Reach

Advanced Energy Industries has manufacturing plants in Canada China South Korea and the US (in Washington state). Design facilities are located in the US and Switzerland while the company has sales and services offices in China Germany India Japan Singapore South Korea and Taiwan.

Sales and Marketing

Products are sold to more than 450 OEMs and integrators and directly to almost 1500 end users. It uses a direct sales force as well as independent sales representatives and distributors such as wholesaler Scientech in Taiwan. The company's 10 largest customers account for about half of sales.

Financial Performance

Overall sales fell 12% in 2012 to $451 million as semiconductor equipment makers and other OEMs didn't need to make as many products and didn't need Advanced Energy Industries' products to do so. The semiconductor market experienced excess manufacturing capacity which reduced demand while the company did see growth for its solar energy division. In 2012 profits also fell to $20 million down 43% from $36 million in 2011 even though the company was able to keep operating expenses down after 2011's restructuring.

Strategy

The company reorganized late in 2011 to reduce costs by aligning its R&D and manufacturing operations with the location of its customers. It cut its workforce by 12% closed facilities and transferred the production of solar inverter components to China.

Mergers and Acquisitions

Advanced Energy Industries has made two recent acquisitions for both its Thin Films and Solar Energy divisions. In 2013 it paid ?59 million ($79 million) for REFUsol Holding GmbH a Germany-based provider of three-phase string solar PV inverters for commercial applications. The year before it bought Solvix SA a Swiss company that makes power supplies for the surface treatment and thin films industry. Solvix's Switzerland office also became a new engineering and development center for its thin-film industrial products business.

HISTORY

Douglas Schatz (chairman) a veteran of Applied Materials and Brent Backman who had worked for Hughes Aircraft (sold to General Motors in 1986) founded Advanced Energy Industries in 1981. The company's first product replaced a refrigerator-sized power source with one the size of a bread box. Also during the 1980s the company introduced its first direct-current system for use in semiconductor deposition processes.

The company went public in 1995. The following year sales growth slowed as the chip industry went through one of its periodic slumps. To cushion its dependence on the volatile semiconductor market in 1997 and 1998 Advanced Energy acquired power supply firms Tower Electronics (products used in the telecommunications medical and non-impact printing industries) and MIK Physics (power supplies used in industrial vacuum coating) among others. Advanced Energy also bought one of its main rivals RF Power Products. In 2000 Advanced Energy bought Noah Holding a privately held maker of temperature control systems.

In 2001 the company acquired Engineering Measurements Company (EMCO) a maker of flow meters and other precision measurement equipment. During 2001 the company twice cut its workforce —by a total of one-fourth —in response to a sharp decline in the worldwide electronics industry.

In 2002 Advanced Energy acquired Aera Japan (mass flow controllers) for about $80 million in cash and debt assumption. Later that year it acquired Germany-based Dressler HF Technik (power systems for plasma-based production equipment) and the e-diagnostics applications of privately held Symphony Systems (Web-based software used to control wafer manufacturing processes).

In 2005 Doug Schatz said he would retire as president and CEO once a successor could be found. Hans-Georg Betz CEO of West STEAG Partners (a German venture capital firm) and a director of Advanced Energy since 2004 was named president and CEO later that year. Schatz remained as nonexecutive chairman of the company.

Later that year Advanced Energy raised around $92 million in a secondary stock offering. The company marked its 25th anniversary in business during 2006.

The company closed its plant in Stolberg Germany in 2007. Manufacturing was shifted to Advanced Energy's high-volume plant in Shenzhen China and to its advanced manufacturing facility in Fort Collins Colorado. The company said the decision came down to deciding whether to expand the plants in Stolberg and Shenzhen with the Chinese facility getting the nod. Advanced Energy acquired the Stolberg location through the acquisition of Dressler HF Technik in 2002. The German plant employed about 65 people.

Bolstering its power conversion products for the solar market in 2010 Advanced Energy acquired PV Powered a maker solar inverters for the commercial residential and utility-scale markets. Later the same year the company sold its Aera mass flow control and related product lines to Hitachi Metals for about $44 million in order to focus on its core power product lines.

EXECUTIVES

Chairman, Douglas S. (Doug) Schatz, age 67, $237,000 total compensation
Executive Vice President - Corporate Development; General Counsel, Thomas O. (Tom) McGimpsey, age 51
Chief Financial Officer; Executive Vice President, Danny C. Herron, age 58
President - Thin Films Business Unit, Yuval Wasserman, age 59, $255,057 total compensation
Principal Financial Officer; VP and Corporate Controller, John McMahon
Chief Executive Officer; Director, Garry Rogerson
President - Solar Energy, Gordon Tredger
Executive Vice President Human Resources, Randall S. Hester
Director, Terry F. Hudgens
Director, Edward C. (Ed) Grady, age 66
Director, Trung T. Doan, age 55
Director, Frederick A. (Fred) Ball
Director, Richard P. (Dick) Beck, age 80
CEO and Director, Hans-Georg Betz, age 65
Director, Thomas M. (Tom) Rohrs, age 62
Auditors: GrantThorntonLLP

LOCATIONS

HQ: Advanced Energy Industries Inc.
1625 Sharp Point Drive, Fort Collins, CO 80525
Phone: 970 221-4670
Web: www.advanced-energy.com

2012 Sales

	$ mil.	% of total
North America		
US	322	71
Canada	30	7
Asia/Pacific		
China	20	5
Other countries	54	12
Europe		
Germany	18	4
Other countries	5	1
Total	**451**	**100**

PRODUCTS/OPERATIONS

2012 Sales

	$ mil.	% of total
Solar energy	216	48
Thin films		
Semiconductor capital equipment	134	30
Non-semiconductor capital equipment	51	11
Global support	50	11
Total	**451**	**100**

Selected Products

Inductively coupled plasma sources
Ion sources
Optical fiber thermometers
Photovoltaic (PV) power inverters
  Bipolar transformerless inverters (Solaron)
  Grid-tie PV inverters (PV Powered)
Power control and conversion systems (used with wafer etching and vapor deposition equipment)
  AC power supply
  Direct-current (DC) products
  High-power products

Low-frequency products
Mid-frequency power supplies
Radio-frequency generators
Radio-frequency power systems (cables generators
instrumentation power supplies power delivery
systems and variable frequency generators)

Selected Acquisitions

2013
REFUsol Holding GmbH (Germany; solar inverters)
2012
Solvix (Switzerland; arc detection and suppression)
2010
PV Powered (Bend OR; solar inverters)

COMPETITORS

Acme Electric	SMA Solar Technology
BASF SE	Satcon Technology
MKS Instruments	Schneider Electric
Power-One	Siemens AG

HISTORICAL FINANCIALS

Company Type: Public

Income Statement

FYE: December 31

	REVENUE ($ mil.)	NET INCOME ($ mil.)	NET PROFIT MARGIN	EMPLOYEES
12/12	451.9	20.5	4.6%	1,354
12/11	516.8	36.3	7.0%	1,471
12/10	459.4	71.1	15.5%	1,788
12/09	186.4	(102.7)	—	1,316
12/08	328.9	(1.7)	—	1,679
Annual Growth	8.3%	—	—	(5.2%)

2012 Year-End Financials

Debt ratio: —
Return on equity: 5.1%
Cash ($ mil.): 146
Current ratio: 4.18
Long-term debt ($ mil.): —

No. of shares (mil.): 37
Dividends
  Yield: —
  Payout: —
Market value ($ mil.): 525

	STOCK PRICE ($) FY Close	P/E High/Low	PER SHARE ($) Earnings	Dividends	Book Value
12/12	13.81	27 20	0.52	0.00	10.20
12/11	10.73	20 10	0.83	0.00	9.71
12/10	13.64	11 7	1.64	0.00	8.63
12/09	15.08	— —	(2.45)	0.00	6.62
12/08	9.95	— —	(0.04)	0.00	9.00
Annual Growth	8.5%	— —	—	—	3.2%

Advent Software, Inc.

Advent Software manages investments from beginning to end. A provider of investment management software for advisers brokers funds and other financial firms Advent offers applications for managing everything from client relationships to trade order executions. The company's products (marketed under the APX Geneva Black Diamond and Tamale brands among others) are used to manage portfolio accounting trading and order execution hedge and venture fund allocation reconciliation and other functions. Advent also offers services such as consulting hosting support and maintenance. More than 80% of sales come from customers in the US including TIAA CREF Merrill Lynch and Wells Capital Management.

Geographic Reach

The company has operations in China Denmark Norway Singapore Sweden the UK the United Arab Emirates and the US. The US generates 83% of total revenues.

Sales and Marketing Advent sells its products directly to customers via one of five sales groups centered around product and/or geography. It primarily targets investment firms and institutions that include asset managers wealth managers registered investment advisers brokers fund managers pension funds and endowments.

Financial Performance The company has seen solid revenue growth over the last three years. Revenues jumped 10% from $326 million in 2011 to $359 million in 2012. Its profits hovered at the $30 million mark for both 2011 and 2012.

The growth for 2012 was the result of increased revenues of APX and Geneva products as well as contributions from Syncova and Black Diamond which were acquired in 2011. Its revenues from the US surged by 12% from 2011 to 2012 while international revenues spiked by 2%.

Mergers and Acquisitions The company has used acquisitions to expand its product lines and customer base as well as to grow its international operations. In 2011 Advent bought UK-based Syncova Solutions a developer of margin management and financing software for hedge fund operators and prime brokers. Advent cited its desire to diversify its product line with Syncova's margin calculation application Optima and its debit finance reconciliation and tool Abacus as the reason for the deal. The company bought Black Diamond Performance Reporting later that year for about $73 million. The deal extended Advent's ability to offer Web-based portfolio management and reporting tools to financial advisers. Ownership Chairman John Scully through hedge fund SPO Advisory owns about 30% of Advent Software.

HISTORY

Stephanie DiMarco was a financial analyst at a small investment bank when she sought to computerize the firm's back-office operations. The IBM PC soon came out and DiMarco foresaw a promising market; she started Advent in 1985 with programmer Steve Strand. The following year the company sold its first product Professional Portfolio designed to help smaller investment firms with accounting and record keeping.

Sales grew to more than $4 million by 1990. The company introduced Axys the first Windows-based portfolio management system software in 1993. That year DiMarco bought out Strand. Advent went public in 1995. The next year the company bought Data Exchange a maker of portfolio and trade order software designed for large regional broker/dealers and money managers.

In 1997 Advent released Geneva software for managing investments with international accounting requirements. The company bought the grants management operations of Blackbund and MicroEdge a provider of software for charitable trusts and other grant-giving organizations in 1998. New product releases that year included Advent Office a suite of applications for automating investment management.

DiMarco handed over the CEO post in 1999 to president Peter Caswell; DiMarco remained chairman. The company expanded into the UK in 2000 when it opened a London office.

In 2001 the company continued to expand its offerings branching out into not-for-profit software products through its purchase of privately held NPO Solutions. The next year Advent added wealth management software to its product line

through its purchase of privately held Kinexus for about $68 million and it acquired portfolio management software provider Techfi for about $23 million.

As part of a larger restructuring designed to reduce costs and refocus on core markets Caswell resigned as president and CEO in 2003. DiMarco resumed the CEO position and handed over the chairman title to director John Scully.

In late 2008 the company acquired Tamale Software for about $28 million; the purchase expanded Advent's front office software applications and helps it establish a presence in the research management solutions niche market.

Advent sold its MicroEdge subsidiary in 2009 to Vista Equity Partners for about $30 million in cash. The deal enabled the company to focus on its core market of serving investment management industry clients. In early 2010 the company purchased Goya AS a Norway-based provider of software for fund managers and fund distributors in Europe and the Middle East. Goya's Tradex software was combined with Advent's Portfolio Exchange product which gave Advent an integrated product for managing front- and back-office tasks related to fund and asset management.

EXECUTIVES

CEO and Director, Stephanie G. DiMarco, age 55, $452,400 total compensation
President and CEO, Peter F. (Pete) Hess, age 43, $320,000 total compensation
EVP Global Client Experience, Anthony Sperling
Chairman, John H. Scully, age 68
VP Marketing, Katherine Calvert
SVP Human Resources Facilities and Community Involvement, John P. Brennan, age 56, $227,400 total compensation
EVP and CTO, Todd Gottula
VP Finance and Investor Relations, Heidi Flaherty
EVP Sales and Solutions Management, Chris Momsen
SVP; President Europe Middle East and Africa, H?kan Valberg, age 51
Vice President of Product Marketing at Advent, Chris Flynn
EVP and CFO, James S. (Jim) Cox, age 41, $228,950 total compensation
Director Product Marketing, Michele Holton
Senior Vice President General Manager of Tamale at Advent, Mark Rice
SVP and CIO, Doug Yokoyama
Media Contact, Smita Topolski
Director Business Development Asia Pacific, Guillermo Orselli
VP Global Accounts Solutions Consulting and Business Development, Thomas (Tom) Zdon
SVP and General Manager Black Diamond, Reed Colley
Managing Director for technology, Jeff Huse
Chief Operating Officer, Maureen Maguire
Director of Finance and Operations, Richard Sellner
Senior Vice President General Counsel Corporate Secretary, Randall Cook
SVP; General Manager Black Diamond, Dave Welling
Vice President Solutions Consulting 1, Robert Roley
Director, James D. (Jim) Kirsner, age 70
Director, Wendell G. (Van) Van Auken, age 68
CEO and Director, Stephanie G. DiMarco, age 55
Director, Christine S. Manfredi, age 62
Independent Director, Asiff Hirji
Independent Director, Wendell Auken
Auditors: PricewaterhouseCoopersLLP

Advisory Board Company (The)

Here's where a hospital might go for a second opinion. The Advisory Board Company specializes in providing best practices consulting to member-clients in the health care and education industries. Members include more than 3700 hospitals pharmaceutical and insurance companies universities and related organizations. The Advisory Board offers more than 50 programs across three key areas: best practices research software tools and management and advisory services. Members buy subscriptions to its programs and participate in research efforts. Programs typically include research studies seminars customized reports and decision-support tools. The firm was founded in 1979 as the Research Council of Washington.

Operations

The company has counted among its members such industry leaders as The Cleveland Clinic Johns Hopkins Hospital Massachusetts General Hospital and Johnson & Johnson.

Advisory Board spinoff The Corporate Executive Board operates on a similar membership business model serving companies in a variety of industries. The Corporate Executive Board and The Advisory Board collaborate on projects and have agreed to refrain from competing in core business areas.

Geographic Reach

The Advisory Board Company has six regional offices in the US as well as offices in Europe and Asia serving international members.

Strategy

The Advisory Board hopes to grow not only by adding members particularly from outside the US but also by selling additional services to existing members. It also plans to continue to add to its list of programs. Since 2001 it has added almost 40 programs to its list of offerings and it plans to launch about three to four new programs each year.

The program-membership business model distinguishes The Advisory Board from many of its competitors —consulting firms that are hired on a job-by-job basis. Benefits for The Advisory Board include the ability to spread program costs over a growing membership base and the opportunity to involve members in identifying issues and conducting research.

Sales and Marketing

The company's sales force consists of more than 150 new business development teams that are responsible for selling new memberships. Each new business development team generally consists of two employees: one marketer who travels to prospective members to meet in person and one marketing associate who provides support from the office. The two-person new business development teams sell programs to new members as well as cross-sell additional programs to existing members of other programs. Separate member services teams are responsible for servicing and renewing existing memberships.

Financial Analysis

Revenue increased more than 30% and net income increased by more than 36% in 2012 compared to 2011. The increase in revenue was due to growth in the healthcare and education markets that year. Net income increased due to the growth in revenue as well as a gain on the sale of its OptiLink business.

The company's cash flow increased by $61.1 million in 2012 over 2011 thanks to financing activities including the exercise of stock options the issuance of common stock under its employee stock purchase plan and tax benefits resulting from the exercise of employee options.

Mergers and Acquisitions

In addition to rolling out new programs the company sees acquisitions as a means for achieving growth. In 2012 it purchased PivotHealth a physician practice management firm for nearly $20 million. It made the acquisition to to supplement its existing physician practice management capabilities while leveraging PivotHealth's expertise in long-term physician practice management.

The Advisory Board in 2011 acquired Cielo MedSolutions a provider of population management analytics and patient registry software in the ambulatory environment for nearly $12 million. It bought Cielo to enhance its existing suite of physician performance management solutions. The purchase added analytics and workflow tools that give providers visibility to patients and enable appropriate clinical decisions.

In 2010 it acquired Concuity the health care division of Trintech Group PLC. Concuity makes billing and recovery software catering to health care providers. The deal strengthened its revenue cycle management capabilities by allowing it to offer a more scalable Web-based software used for improving its customers' financial performance. The Advisory Board in 2009 obtained Southwind a consulting firm with expertise in physician employment clinical integration and information technology deployment practices.

EXECUTIVES

President, David L. Felsenthal, age 42, $425,000 total compensation
Executive Chairman, Frank J. Williams, age 46, $400,000 total compensation
Executive Vice President, Richard A. Schwartz, age 47, $482,040 total compensation
Lead Director, Kelt Kindick, age 58
Chief Financial Officer, Michael T. Kirshbaum, age 36, $225,000 total compensation
IR Contact Officer, Gail Jacobs
Chief Talent Officer, Mary D. Van Hoose, age 47
General Counsel; Corporate Secretary, Evan R. Farber, age 40
EVP, Cormac F. Miller
Chief Executive Officer, David Kapaska
Chief Medical Officer Vice President Southwind, Dennis Weaver
Chief Medical Officer, Matt Miller
Executive Vice President, Martin Coulter
Chief Talent Officer, Mary VanHoose
Director, Peter J. Grua, age 58
Director, LeAnne M. Zumwalt, age 54
Lead Director, Kelt Kindick, age 58
Director, Leon D. Shapiro, age 54
CEO and Director, Robert W. Musslewhite, age 42
Independent Director, Mark Neaman
Auditors: Ernst&YoungLLP

LOCATIONS

HQ: The Advisory Board Company
2445 M St. NW, Washington DC 20037
Phone: 202-266-5600   **Fax:** 202-266-5700
Web: www.advisory.com

2012 Sales

		% of total
US	357	97
Other countries	12	3
Total		**100**

PRODUCTS/OPERATIONS

2012 Sales

	% of total
Healthcare	95
Education	5
Total	**100**

Selected Products and Services

Best practices installation and support
Business intelligence and analytics
Clinical research
Daily briefings and news
Executive education
Executive watches
Leadership development
Online advisory resources
Strategy and operations research
Workforce performance

COMPETITORS

Accenture	IMS Health
Accretive Health	Ingenix Consulting
Booz Allen	McKesson
Boston Consulting	McKinsey & Company
Conference Board	MedAssets
Deloitte Consulting	Navigant Consulting
Emdeon	Premier Inc.
Huron Consulting	

HISTORICAL FINANCIALS

Company Type: Public

Income Statement

FYE: March 31

	REVENUE ($ mil.)	NET INCOME ($ mil.)	NET PROFIT MARGIN	EMPLOYEES
03/13	450.8	22.1	4.9%	2,400
03/12	370.3	25.2	6.8%	1,850
03/11	290.2	18.5	6.4%	1,600
03/10	239.3	11.4	4.8%	1,100
03/09	230.3	21.4	9.3%	1,021
Annual Growth	**18.3%**	**0.8%**		**23.8%**

2013 Year-End Financials

Debt ratio: —	No. of shares (mil.): 35
Return on equity: 8.8%	Dividends
Cash ($ mil.): 57	Yield: —
Current ratio: 0.93	Payout: —
Long-term debt ($ mil.): —	Market value ($ mil.): 1,845

	STOCK PRICE ($) FY Close	P/E High/Low		PER SHARE ($) Earnings	Dividends	Book Value
03/13	52.52	153	64	0.61	0.00	8.01
03/12	88.62	116	60	0.73	0.00	6.43
03/11	51.50	89	53	0.57	0.00	4.64
03/10	31.50	90	44	0.37	0.00	3.61
03/09	16.58	84	21	0.65	0.00	3.18
Annual Growth	**33.4%**			**— — (1.6%)**	**—**	**26.0%**

Aegion Corp

Aegion owns a legion of companies that aim to prop up aging highways bridges and pipes. Its energy- and mining-focused companies –Bayou Corrpro CCSI CRTS and United Pipeline –rehab pipelines and provide corrosion protection for pipes storage tanks and water treatment facilities. Insituform the water and wastewater unit refur-bishes water distribution stormwater and wastewater pipes in situ that is without digging them up. Its commercial and structural reinforcement firm Fyfe makes the Tyfo and Fibrwrap brands of support and strengthening systems for masonry steel concrete and wooden structures. Aegion which has more than 20 global offices was formed in 2011 as a holding company.

Geographic Reach

The US is Aegion's largest market accounting of nearly 60% of its revenue. Canada accounts for more than 15% followed by Europe with less than 10%. The company's Energy and Mining segment is active in the US Canada Mexico South America the Middle East and Europe.

Operations

Aegion's largest business is Energy & Mining representing about 50% of total revenue. The global operation conducts business in the US through subsidiaries in Colorado Louisiana Texas and Oklahoma. Overseas Aegion's Hockway unit is located in the United Arab Emirates and the firm has other subsidiaries in the UK Portugal Argentina Brazil and Chile.

The company's North American Water and Wastewater unit (about 30% of revenue) has counterparts in Europe and Asia which combined contribute about 10% of sales. The firm's Commercial and Structural operations rehabilitate and strengthen pipelines buildings bridges tunnels and waterfront structures in the US and Canada. Aegion's Fyfe subsidiary provides product and engineering services in Latin America and the Asia-Pacific Region.

Financial Performance

Aegion's revenue topped $1 billion in 2012 a 10% increase compared with 2011. Net income rose 105% to $56.8 billion over the same period. 2012 marked the fourth consecutive year of increasing revenue for the firm. Growth of its Energy and Mining business drove Aegion's results in 2012 as did additional revenue from the acquisitions of CRTS Hockway and Fyfe. Partially offsetting the gains from Energy and Mining were losses across all of the company's Water and Wastewater operations.

Strategy

While about three-quarters of the company's revenue comes from North America it has been actively expanding into other regions since it feels the growth opportunities are low in the region due to its market penetration and the slow US economy. Australia India and Singapore are on Aegion's radar as potential growth markets for its water and wastewater group while energy and mining looks to Saudi Arabia Morocco and offshore in the Gulf of Mexico. Since its commercial and structural group is the smallest and newest the company sees great growth potential as the unit makes its fiber-reinforced polymer system known to engineers.

Mergers and Acquisitions

Aegion in June 2013 acquired oil-and-gas services provider Brinderson LP for $150 million. Brinderson provides maintenance construction engineering and turnaround activities for the upstream and downstream oil and gas markets primarily in California. The purchase bolstered Aegion's Energy and Mining business.

The 2011 purchase of the North American operations of Fyfe Group LLC contributed to the launch of Aegion's fast-growing Commercial and Structural business segment. The acquisition brought Fyfe's highway bridge and pipeline reinforcement systems into the Aegion fold. In 2012 the firm acquired Fyfe's operations in Asia Europe and Latin America.

In 2011 Aegion had added UK pipe coating maker Hockway and its Hockway Middle East unit to Corrpro.

EXECUTIVES

SVP General Counsel and Chief Administrative Officer, David F. Morris, age 51
Senior Vice President Water & Wastewater, Thomas E. (Tom) Vossman, age 51
VP & Treasurer, Kenneth L. (Ken) Young, age 60
President and CEO, J. Joseph (Joe) Burgess
SVP and CFO, David A. Martin
SVP Business Integration, Brian J. Clarke
Senior Vice President Energy & Mining, Dorwin E. Hawn
Vice President Corporate Development, Daniel E. Cowan
Auditors: PricewaterhouseCoopersLLP

LOCATIONS

HQ: Aegion Corporation
17988 Edison Ave., St. Louis MO 63005
Phone: 636-530-8000 **Fax:** 635-519-8010
Web: www.aegion.com

2012 Sales

	$ mil.	% of total
US	600	58
Canada	180	18
Europe	86	8
Other countries	160	16
Total	**1,028**	**100**

PRODUCTS/OPERATIONS

2012 Sales

	$ mil.	% of total
Energy & mining	525	51
North American water &wastewater	317	31
Commercial & structural	74	7
European water &wastewater	72	7
Asia-Pacific water &wastewater	38	4
Total	**1,028**	**100**

COMPETITORS

Aquarius Coatings	Northern Technologies
Bodycote	Praxair
Cohesant	RPM International
Daubert Industries	Severn Trent Services
Holloman	Sterling Construction
Jones Bros.	Willbros
MPW	

HISTORICAL FINANCIALS

Company Type: Public

Income Statement

FYE: December 31

	REVENUE ($ mil.)	NET INCOME ($ mil.)	NET PROFIT MARGIN	EMPLOYEES
12/12	1,027.9	56.8	5.5%	3,400
12/11	938.5	27.6	2.9%	3,000
12/10	914.9	61.8	6.8%	3,200
12/09	726.8	26.1	3.6%	3,000
12/08	536.6	21.6	4.0%	1,550
Annual Growth	**17.6%**	**27.3%**	**—**	**21.7%**

2012 Year-End Financials

Debt ratio: 20.9%	No. of shares (mil.): 38
Return on equity: 8.4%	Dividends
Cash ($ mil.): 133	Yield: —
Current ratio: 2.50	Payout: —
Long-term debt ($ mil.): 221	Market value ($ mil.): 864

STOCK PRICE ($)		P/E	PER SHARE ($)		
	FY Close	High/Low	Earnings	Dividends	Book Value
12/12	22.19	17 11	1.33	0.00	17.95
12/11	15.34	45 16	0.67	0.00	16.28
12/10	26.51	18 12	1.53	0.00	15.44
12/09	22.72	34 17	0.70	0.00	13.82
12/08	19.69	25 13	0.77	0.00	13.15
Annual Growth	3.0%	— —	14.6%	—	8.1%

AEP Industries Inc.

Making plastic cling is this company's thing! AEP Industries manufactures plastic packaging films —more than 35000 types —including stretch wrap for industrial pallets packaging for foods and beverages and films for agricultural uses such as wrap for hay bales. AEP also makes dispenser-boxed plastic wraps which are sold to consumers as well as institutions ranging from schools to hospitals. Other industries courted by AEP are packaging transportation food autos chemicals textiles and electronics. The company operates in the US and in Canada.

Geographic Reach

AEP conducts more than 90% of its business in the US market. Remaining sales take place in Canada.

Sales and Marketing

About two-thirds of AEP's sales are made to distributors and the remainder directly to end-users of its products. It serves about 3000 customers. The company works to maintain customer relationships and it provides technical training to its sales personal so that they are able to provide customer support and communicate customer needs to the company's product development team. Distribution functions are mostly contracted to third parties.

Financial Performance

AEP has steadily increased revenues over the last three years after conducting a series of restructuring moves in 2008 and 2009. The company reported an 18% sales increase in 2012 to some $1.15 billion due to a jump in food contact and canliner products (primarily from the Webster acquisition) as well as higher sales volumes across the rest of its product segments (especially the printed and converted films and stretch wrap markets).

After suffering a slight loss in 2010 AEP returned to profitability in 2011 and increased net income by 87% in 2012 to some $23.1 million. Some of the company's irregular bottom line performance over the last decade is due to the price of raw materials particularly petroleum and natural gas used to make its products. Raw material costs are to a degree passed on in the selling prices of its products driving up sales revenue but reducing profitability (due to the higher costs of sales).

Strategy

With little product differentiation among plastic film producers AEP positions itself as the low-cost source with technological expertise to customize value-added flexible films to satisfy myriad manufacturing and processing applications. The company aims to provide long-term value to shareholders by becoming the preferred provider of flexible packaging products in the North American market.

To strengthen its finances and increase manufacturing output and productivity AEP is investing heavily in capital improvements. During the last decade it has purchased or leased new equipment and made equipment upgrades intended to optimize its manufacturing footprint in high-growth product categories.

The company looks for success in its sales and distribution model by establishing long-term relationships with its customers. To mitigate the volatility of raw material prices the company pursues volume raw material rebates by making most of its purchases from three primary suppliers.

The company has enacted occasional divestitures to focus on core operations.

Mergers and Acquisitions

AEP also looks to bolster its business through strategic acquisitions. In October 2011 it bought private-label plastic bag maker Webster Industries for $25.9 million. The purchase added food and trash bag offerings —a new line of business that provided cross-selling opportunities. Following the purchase AEP revamped the Webster manufacturing equipment to increase efficiencies. Also in 2012 the company expanded its capacity for plastic packaging products (including performance and industrial films and specialty bags) through a $5 million purchase of machinery and equipment from Transco Plastics.

Ownership

AEP's direction is further influenced by its co-founder and chairman president and CEO Brendan Barba and members of his family. Collectively they hold about 25% of the company. Investment firm KSA Capital Management owns a 17% stake.

HISTORY

Brendan Barba a former salesman for polyethylene film maker PPD formed Flexible Plastics in 1967 in Lodi New Jersey. In 1970 his partner bought him out. That year Barba founded AEP Industries briefly called Automatically Extruded Products. In 1982 the company moved into the specialty and premium films market. It established a plant in Waxahachie Texas in 1985 and went public a year later. AEP Industries acquired Design Poly Bag in 1989.

In 1990 the company purchased the Super-Stretch brand of industrial stretch film from Princeton Packaging. AEP Industries established its Midwest operations in Alsip Illinois in 1994 and a year later it built a plant to make stretch film in Wright Township Pennsylvania.

AEP Industries bought Borden's worldwide packaging business in 1996 for $280 million in cash and about $80 million in AEP Industries stock a deal that nearly tripled AEP Industries' sales. The company expanded further in 1997 with the acquisition of ICI Australia's Visqueen polyethylene plastic film unit.

AEP Industries' sales and earnings suffered in 1998 after it sold off its South African operations and its five rigids businesses (wet-food containers food trays). That year it acquired Italy's Termofilm and the product line of now-defunct bag maker Citibag. In 1999 AEP Industries sold its Proponite oriented polypropylene films business to market leader Applied Extrusion. A string of discontinued operations and rising resin prices resulted in a fiscal 1999 loss.

AEP Industries announced in 2000 that it would close one of its PVC film plants in North Baddesley England due to inefficiencies there. It completed the closure in 2001. The same year it divested three non-core businesses and closed its plant in Melbourne Australia.

International operations continued to rack up losses and AEP Industries' Italian company FIAP SPA was liquidated in 2003.

The company announced in 2007 that it would explore strategic options for its subsidiary in the Netherlands including its possible sale. The following year AEP sold AEP Industries Nederland for about $28 million in cash to Euro-M Flexible Packaging S.A. and Ghlin S.r.L. The buyers also assumed the unit's debt and pension obligations.

The company sold off its last international subsidiary shifting AEP to an all-North American market in 2008.

In 2009 AEP closed plants in California and Georgia. The decision was concurrent with its on-the-cheap purchase of the Plastic Films unit of Atlantis Plastics in late 2008. AEP's $99.2 million deal check-mated a former rival and capitalized on Atlantis Plastics' Chapter 11 bankruptcy status. Management also saw the Atlantis assets as an opportunity for product consolidation and resin cost efficiencies as well as manufacturing synergies and logistical savings for its existing plants in California Minnesota and North Carolina.

EXECUTIVES

VP Manufacturing Polyvinyl Chloride Products, Richard Boyette
EVP Operations, Paul C. Vegliante, age 48, $281,946 total compensation
VP Treasurer and Secretary, James B. Rafferty, age 61
EVP Sales and Marketing, John J. Powers, age 49, $310,302 total compensation
VP Tax and Administration and Director, Lawrence R. Noll, age 65
EVP Finance CFO and Director, Paul M. Feeney, age 71, $412,109 total compensation
EVP Manufacturing, David J. Cron, age 59, $299,162 total compensation
Chairman President and CEO, J. Brendan Barba, age 73, $851,851 total compensation
Executive Vice President National Accounts, Robert Cron
VP Custom Films, Robert Covella
VP Supply Chain, Michael O'Neill
Division Manager Resinite Products, Steve Firmery
VP and Controller, Linda N. Guerrera, age 46
VP Stretch Film Products, Brian Ochsner
Vice President PROformance Films Group, Gary Bobko
VP and Secretary, Sandra Major, age 62
Vice President Supply Chain, Michael ONeill
Vice President IPD Division, Philip A. Hernberg
VP Tax and Administration and Director, Lawrence R. Noll, age 65
EVP Finance CFO and Director, Paul M. Feeney, age 71
Director, Frank P. Gallagher, age 70
Director, Lee C. Stewart, age 65
Director, Richard E. (Dick) Davis, age 71
Director, Robert T. Bell, age 70
Director, Ira Belsky, age 61
Auditors: KPMGLLP

LOCATIONS

HQ: AEP Industries Inc.
125 Phillips Ave., South Hackensack NJ 07606-1546
Phone: 201-641-6600　　**Fax:** 201-807-6801
Web: www.aepinc.com

2012 Sales

	$ mil.	% of total
US	1,075	93
Canada	76	7
Total	**1,152**	**100**

PRODUCTS/OPERATIONS

2012 Sales

	$ mil.	% of total
Custom films	347	30
Stretch (pallet) wrap	337	29
Food contact	197	17
Canliners	123	11
PROformance films	76	7
Printed & converted films specialty films & other	71	6
Total	**1,152**	**100**

Selected Products

Custom films (polyethylene co-extruded and monolayer custom designed film)
  Drum box carton pail liners
  Films to cover high value products
  Furniture and mattress bags
  Magazine overwrap
PROformance films (co-extruded and monolayer polyolefin films)
  Cereal box liners
  Fresh cut produce packaging
  Frozen foods
  Medical
  Polyvinyl chloride wrap
  Food and freezer wrap
Printed and converted films (polyethylene)
  Printed laminated converted films for flexible packaging to consumer markets
  Printed shrink films
Stretch (pallet) wrap (polyethylene)
  Pallet wrap
Other products and specialty films (unplasticized polyvinyl chloride polyethylene)
  Agricultural films
  Battery labels
  Canliners
  Credit card laminate
  Retail and institutional films and products
  Table covers aprons bibs and gloves
  Twist wrap

COMPETITORS

Acme Packaging	Intertape Polymer
Ampac	Pactiv
Bemis	Plastic Suppliers
Berry Plastics	Pliant Corporation
Curwood	Primex Plastics
Dow Chemical	Printpack
DuPont	S.C. Johnson
FlexSol Packaging	Sealed Air Corp.
Griffon	Sigma Plastics
Inteplast	Tredegar

HISTORICAL FINANCIALS

Company Type: Public

Income Statement
FYE: October 31

	REVENUE ($ mil.)	NET INCOME ($ mil.)	NET PROFIT MARGIN	EMPLOYEES
10/13	1,143.8	10.7	0.9%	2,600
10/12	1,152.5	23.1	2.0%	2,600
10/11	974.7	12.3	1.3%	2,600
10/10	800.5	(0.5)	—	2,000
10/09	744.8	31.5	4.2%	2,000
Annual Growth	**11.3%**	**(23.6%)**	**—**	**6.8%**

2013 Year-End Financials

Debt ratio: 51.3%
Return on equity: 13.5%
Cash ($ mil.): 13
Current ratio: 2.02
Long-term debt ($ mil.): 238
No. of shares (mil.): 5
Dividends
  Yield: —
  Payout: —
Market value ($ mil.): 333

	STOCK PRICE ($) FY Close	P/E High/Low	PER SHARE ($) Earnings	Dividends	Book Value
10/13	59.42	46 27	1.92	0.00	15.25
10/12	63.93	15 5	4.16	0.00	13.33
10/11	27.03	15 10	2.09	0.00	9.10
10/10	24.37	— —	(0.08)	0.00	9.22
10/09	34.88	9 2	4.61	0.00	11.06
Annual Growth	**14.2%**	**— —**	**(19.7%)**	**—**	**8.4%**

Affiliated Managers Group Inc.

AMG knows a good asset when it sees one. Affiliated Managers Group (AMG) is an asset management company that owns interests in more than 30 boutique investment management firms in the US Canada and the UK. Together the company's affiliates manage approximately $327 billion in assets and offer more than 350 investment products more than 100 mutual funds. AMG typically acquires majority stakes in its affiliates which cater to institutional investors and wealthy individuals. The structure allows affiliates to retain partial ownership of their firms and operate with relative autonomy. AMG usually allocates a percentage of revenues to affiliates for operating expenses like compensation.

AMG's Managers Investment Group provides an avenue through which affiliates can distribute mutual funds and other products through intermediaries such as banks or brokerage firms.

AMG's largest mutual fund families include Tweedy Browne's Global Value and American Value funds Brandywine funds Third Avenue Value funds and The Managers Funds. Institutional investors account for nearly two-thirds of AMG's aggregate assets under management.

The company is eyeing international expansion and in 2009 made its first acquisition in Asia a modest 5% stake in Value Partners Group a Hong-Kong based boutique asset manager. The following year the company jumped headlong into the overseas market when it acquired a majority of UK-based Artemis Investment Management from BNP Paribas (Artemis' management retained the remaining share). Also in 2010 AMG bought Pantheon Ventures a UK-based private equity fund-of-funds from Russell Investments.

The company expanded further in 2011 when it opened a sales and marketing office in Hong Kong and hired a director of business development for Europe's Nordic region. The following year AMG opened a sales and marketing office in Dubai to focus on the Middle East. AMG also has offices in London Sydney. Clients outside the US now account for more than half of AMG's assets under management and approximately 40% its revenue.

Growth in the US also is a key strategy. In 2010 AMG purchased a majority interest in Chicago-based Aston Asset Management by acquiring Aston's parent company Highbury Financial. Aston is the principal advisor to the Aston Funds a family of about 25 mutual funds with some $6 billion of assets. AMG later purchased a controlling stake in investment manager Trilogy Global

Advisors which specializes in global and emerging markets strategies.

In 2012 AMG announced plans to acquire a majority stake in Austin Texas-based Yacktman Asset Management which has approximately $17 billion of assets under management.

Acquisitions have helped boost AMG's total assets under management and in turn its revenue from asset-based fees and transaction fees. Revenues and net income have steadily increased since 2010. Sales were up by 25% in 2011 and net income increased by more than 18%.The acquisition deals also not only help to diversify the company geographically but also in the types of products it offers (e.g. alternative investments like hedge funds which typically bring in higher fees).

In 2011 AMG further diversified its service offerings by establishing a wealth management arm. AMG Wealth Partners handles the needs of high-net-worth clients. The subsidiary intends to expand AMG's partnership strategy by acquiring boutique wealth management firms. In 2012 AMG made its first wealth management investment by taking an equity stake in Veritable L.P. which has $10 billion under management.

EXECUTIVES

President; Chief Operating Officer, Nathaniel Dalton, age 46, $500,000 total compensation
Chairman of the Board; Chief Executive Officer, Sean M. Healey, age 51, $750,000 total compensation
Vice Chairman and General Counsel, John Kingston III, age 47, $350,000 total compensation
Chief Financial Officer; Treasurer, Jay C. Horgen, age 43, $500,000 total compensation
Senior Vice President, Riz Jamal
VP-Affiliate Dev, Benjamin M. Scott
President, John W. Copeland III
Executive Vice President and Head of Global Distribution, Andrew Dyson
Senior Vice President, Dean A. Maines
Director, William J. (Bill) Nutt, age 68
Vice Chairman and General Counsel, John Kingston III, age 47
Director, Harold J. Meyerman, age 74
Director, Rita M. Rodriquez, age 70
Director, Dwight D. Churchill
Director, Patrick T. Ryan, age 55
Director, Jide J. Zeitlin, age 50
Director, Samuel T. (Sam) Byrne
Independent Director, Rita Rodriguez
Independent Director, Tracy Palandjian
Auditors: PricewaterhouseCoopersLLP

LOCATIONS

HQ: Affiliated Managers Group Inc.
600 Hale St., Prides Crossing MA 01965
Phone: 617-747-3300   **Fax:** 617-747-3380
Web: www.amg.com

PRODUCTS/OPERATIONS

2011 Sales by segment

	$ mil.	% of total
Institutional clients	841	49
Mutual funds	723	43
High-net-worth clients	139	8
Total	**1,704**	**100**

Selected Affiliates

AQR Capital Management Holdings LLC
Artemis Investment Management LLP (UK)
Aston Asset Management LLC
Beutel Goodman & Company Ltd.
BlueMountain Capital Management LLC
Chicago Equity Partners LLC

Deans Knight Capital Management Ltd. (Canada)
Essex Investment Management Company LLC
First Quadrant L.P.
Foyston Gordon & Payne Inc. (Canada)
Friess Associates LLC
Frontier Capital Management Company LLC
Gannett Welsh & Kotler LLC
Genesis Asset Managers LLP (UK)
Harding Loevner LP
J.M. Hartwell L.P.
Managers Investment Group LLC
Montrusco Bolton Investments Inc. (Canada)
Pantheon (UK)
The Renaissance Group LLC
Systematic Financial Management L.P.
Third Avenue Management LLC
TimesSquare Capital Management LLC
Trilogy Global Advisors
Tweedy Browne Company LLC
ValueAct Capital Management L.P.
Welch & Forbes LLC

COMPETITORS

AllianceBernstein	Neuberger Berman
Asset Alliance	Nuveen
Bank of America	Old Mutual (US)
Conning	T. Rowe Price
FMR	The Vanguard Group
Federated Investors	U.S. Trust
GAMCO Investors	Virtus Investment
National Financial	Partners
Partners	

HISTORICAL FINANCIALS

Company Type: Public

Income Statement

FYE: December 31

	REVENUE ($ mil.)	NET INCOME ($ mil.)	NET PROFIT MARGIN	EMPLOYEES
12/12	1,805.5	411.4	22.8%	2,230
12/11	1,704.8	359.6	21.1%	2,020
12/10	1,358.2	291.7	21.5%	1,910
12/09	841.8	186.2	22.1%	1,580
12/08	1,158.2	23.1	2.0%	1,680
Annual Growth	11.7%	105.3%	—	7.3%

2012 Year-End Financials

Debt ratio: 26.3%
Return on equity: 20.7%
Cash ($ mil.): 430
Current ratio: 2.43
Long-term debt ($ mil.): 1,630

No. of shares (mil.): 53
Dividends
 Yield: —
 Payout: —
Market value ($ mil.): 7,015

	STOCK PRICE ($) FY Close	P/E High/Low	PER SHARE ($) Earnings	Dividends	Book Value
12/12	130.15	39 29	3.28	0.00	38.67
12/11	95.95	35 23	3.11	0.00	34.62
12/10	99.22	35 20	2.81	0.00	33.37
12/09	67.35	51 20	1.38	0.00	24.23
12/08	41.92	193 31	0.57	0.00	23.86
Annual Growth	32.7%	— —	54.9%	—	12.8%

Air Methods Corp.

It's a bird it's a plane ... it's an ambulance! With a fleet of more than 400 medically equipped aircraft mainly helicopters Air Methods is the largest provider of emergency medical air-transportation services in the US. The company operates through three divisions. A community-based operating segment which represents roughly 60% of revenues offers transportation and in-flight medical care from hubs in some two dozen states. A hospital-based segment contracts with hospitals in 30 states to transport critically ill patients; the hospitals themselves provide in-flight medical personnel. The smallest division United Rotorcraft designs manufactures and installs aircraft medical-transport products.

Financial Analysis

Despite a slow economy Air Methods is maintaining a near three-decade-long positive trajectory. In 2010 the company posted more than a 50% year-over-year rise in earnings. The next year the company posted historic totals in both revenue (which increased by almost 18% to $660.5 million) and profits (spiking 9% to $46.7 million).

Its 2011 growth was driven by a 26% increase in flight revenues attributable to the company's mainstay business community-based services (CBS). CBS revenues which benefited from price increases the addition of bases and new service agreements helped to offset a 20% increase in flight center costs related to higher workers compensation and expenses made from acquisitions.

Strategy

Business acquisitions are part of the company's strategy to gain market share. It acquired Las Vegas helicopter tour operator Sundance Helicopters for $44 million in late 2012. Sundance offers helicopter services to support efforts in fire fighting natural resource agency operations vertical lifts and news gathering and it generated $52 million in revenue for its fiscal year ended March 2012.

Air Methods spent approximately $200 million in mid-2011 to take over OF Air Holdings Corporation owned by Wind Point Partners. The move secured all of its subsidiaries including rival Omniflight Helicopters a Texas-based air medical transport service (comprising both community-based and hospital-based business) spanning 18 states and 75-base locations. On the heels of acquiring Omniflight Air Methods bought out Texas-based United Rotorcraft Solutions a full-service helicopter and fixed-wing completions and maintenance repair operation.

EXECUTIVES

CEO and Director, Aaron D. Todd, age 51, $392,200 total compensation
Chief Operating Officer, Paul H. Tate, age 62, $314,734 total compensation
Chief Accounting Officer and Controller, Sharon J. Keck, age 46, $189,500 total compensation
CFO Secretary and Treasurer, Trent J. Carman, age 52, $246,900 total compensation
Chairman, C. David Kikumoto, age 63
Senior Vice President - Hospital-Based Services, Michael D. Allen
Director Operations, William (Bill) Salus
President United Rotorcraft Division, Tom Curtis
SVP Business Development, Howard Ragsdale
SVP Western Operations, Jonathan Collier
General Counsel; Secretary, Crystal Gordon
SVP Aviation Services, Archie Gray
Director of Operations, Chris Bassett
SVP Eastern Operations, Edward Rupert
VP Information Technology, Doni Perry
Director Operations, Dennis McCall
CEO and Director, Aaron D. Todd, age 51
Director, David A. (Dave) Roehr, age 56
Director, Ralph J. Berstein, age 55
Director, Samuel H. Gray, age 74
Director, Lowell D. Miller, age 79
Director, Morad Tahbaz, age 57
Director, Maj. Gen. Carl H. McNair Jr., age 78
Director, C. David Kikumoto, age 62
Director, Ralph J. Bernstein, age 55
Director, Mark D. Carleton, age 51
Auditors: KPMGLLLP

LOCATIONS

HQ: Air Methods Corporation
7301 S. Peoria St., Englewood CO 80112
Phone: 303-792-7400   **Fax:** 303-790-0499
Web: www.airmethods.com

PRODUCTS/OPERATIONS

2011 Sales

Hospital-based services (HBS)	198	29
United Rotorcraft	57	8
Total	**660**	**100**

COMPETITORS

Acadian Ambulance Service Inc.	CHC Helicopter
	Evergreen Holdings
Bristow Group Inc	PHI Inc.

HISTORICAL FINANCIALS

Company Type: Public

Income Statement

FYE: December 31

	REVENUE ($ mil.)	NET INCOME ($ mil.)	NET PROFIT MARGIN	EMPLOYEES
12/12	850.8	93.1	10.9%	3,961
12/11	660.5	46.5	7.1%	3,935
12/10	562.0	44.1	7.8%	2,960
12/09	510.6	28.9	5.7%	2,942
12/08	498.8	19.2	3.9%	2,976
Annual Growth	14.3%	48.3%	—	7.4%

2012 Year-End Financials

Debt ratio: 57.5%
Return on equity: 31.6%
Cash ($ mil.): 3
Current ratio: 2.14
Long-term debt ($ mil.): 581

No. of shares (mil.): 38
Dividends
 Yield: 18.9%
 Payout: 324.5%
Market value ($ mil.): 1,431

	STOCK PRICE ($) FY Close	P/E High/Low	PER SHARE ($) Earnings	Dividends	Book Value
12/12	36.91	50 33	2.39	7.00	7.73
12/11	84.45	72 41	1.21	0.00	7.53
12/10	56.27	48 22	1.17	0.00	6.50
12/09	33.62	45 17	0.78	0.00	5.26
12/08	15.99	96 28	0.51	0.00	4.44
Annual Growth	23.3%	— —	46.9%	—	14.9%

Akamai Technologies Inc

Akamai offers an accelerated course on digital delivery. The company's technology enables corporations and government agencies to deliver digital content and applications such as ads business transaction tools streaming video and websites over the Internet. It also offers applications that supply network data feeds and website analytics to customers. With a network of more than 137000 servers in 87 countries around the world Akamai analyzes and manages Web traffic transmitting content from servers that are geographically closest to end users. In addition to its 11 US offices the company has more than 25 international locations. Customers include Apple Hitachi and SAP.

Operations

The company has five different core products - AQUA Web Solutions AURA Network Solutions KONA Security Solutions SOLA Media Solutions and TERRA Enterprise Solutions - that provide application and cloud performance services digital media and software distribution and storage website optimization and security tools.

For example AQUA WEB Solutions speeds up applications using compression connection optimization dynamic caching and routing technologies. It is tailored for such online applications as airline reservation systems course planning tools customer order processing and human resources.

KONA is a suite of services and software used to guard against data theft and other Web attacks while SOLA enables streaming live or on-demand HD video to online viewers across several technologies including Adobe Flash Microsoft Silverlight and Apple iOS.

Geographic Reach

Akamai operates from about 40 offices in 25 countries across the Americas Asia and Europe. The US however is its largest market accounting for about 70% of sales. The company has about a dozen US locations.

Sales and Marketing

The comp any sells its products through a direct sales force as well as more than 100 channel partners such as AT&T IBM Verizon and Spain's top telco Telefonica. It does business with a large number of private and public sector customers; no one accounts for more than 10% of sales.

Financial Performance

Overall sales grew almost 20% in 2012 reaching a record $1.3 billion. That year the company cited robust growth in traffic from clients in the media and entertainment industries as they consume more bandwidth to feed increasing amounts of digital content to wireless devices. Akamai also saw sales to companies in a variety of other industries rise as more enterprises turn to hosted applications outsourced IT systems management and other cloud-based services.

Profits only increased slightly (2%) to $203 million as the company spent an additional $77 million on sales and marketing expenses - primarily from paying commissions to salespeople.

Mergers and Acquisitions

Akamai uses acquisitions to supplement its internal product development efforts particularly in the area of optimizing Web page and data delivery to the growing number of mobile devices tapping the Internet.

In 2012 it made four acquisitions. The largest was Cotendo a provider of Web and mobile acceleration services for about $268 million. It also bought Blaze Software a developer of Web optimization applications to complement its website acceleration products with technology designed to maximize the speed at which a Web page is rendered. Later in the year it bought network optimization software provider FastSoft and Verivue which offers licensed content delivery network (CDN) infrastructure services for network operators.

Also that year it sold its Advertising Decision Solutions (ADS) data cooperative to media-buying platform MediaMath. As part of the deal MediaMath has exclusive rights to its pixel-free technology for use within digital advertising and marketing applications.

In 2013 Akamai bought Velocius Networks a provider of quality of service (QoS) technology that optimizes traffic to keep networks from running slowing for remote end-users. The acquisition is expected to complement Akamai's hybrid cloud optimization strategy for optimizing IP application traffic.

EXECUTIVES

SVP Human Resources, Debra Canner, age 54, $286,906 total compensation
EVP General Counsel and Secretary, Melanie Haratunian, age 53, $336,566 total compensation
President Products and Development, Rick M. McConnell, age 47
CEO, F. Thomson (Tom) Leighton, age 56
CEO and Director, Paul L. Sagan, age 54, $536,113 total compensation
Chairman, George H. Conrades, age 74, $20,000 total compensation
SVP and General Manager Security Division, Ronni Zehavi, age 44
Executive Vice President of Technology and Networks, Chris Schoettle, age 49, $302,155 total compensation
VP Engineering Cloud Platforms, Chuck Neerdaels
Senior Director Corporate Communications, Jeff Young
Chief Security Officer, Andy Ellis
President Worldwide Operations, Robert W. (Bob) Hughes, age 46, $428,453 total compensation
Director Digital Media Europe, Alex Gibbons
SVP and General Manager Web Experience Division, Michael M. (Mike) Afergan
Director Southern Europe, Henri d'Oriola
Investor Relations Manager, Noelle Faris
VP and General Manager Carrier Products Division, Mick Scully
SVP and Chief Development Officer, Robert Wood
SVP and CIO, Kumud Kalia
SVP Engineering, Harald Prokop
EVP Platform Division, Robert Blumofe
Manager Media Relations, Helen Yang
VP International Marketing, Martin Haering
VP and General Manager APAC EMEA and South America, Greg Lazar
Country Manager Singapore and Malaysia, Philip Chua
Regional Public Relations Director Asia Pacific, Mylinh Cheung
EVP and CFO, James (Jim) Benson
SVP and Chief Marketing Officer, Brad Rinklin
Vice President Global Human Resources, Linda Pettingell
Chief Human Resource Officer, James Gemmell
Chief Executive Officer, Tom Dr
SVP and General Manager Americas, Jim Ebzery
SVP and General Manager APJ, Sanjay Singh
SVP and General Manager Emerging Products Division, Willie Tejada
SVP and General Manager EMEA, Mark Vargo
SVP and General Manager Media Products Division, Bill Wheaton
Vice President Global Services & Support, Adam Karon
Vice President Global Carrier Strategy and Sales, Ed McGowan
Director, Peter J. (Pete) Kight, age 57
Director, C. Kim Goodwin, age 53
Chief Scientist and Director, F. Thomson (Tom) Leighton, age 56
CEO and Director, Paul L. Sagan, age 54
Chairman, George H. Conrades, age 74
Director, Frederic V. (Fred) Salerno, age 69
Director, Martin M. Coyne II, age 64
Director, Naomi O. Seligman, age 73
Director, Pamela J. (Pam) Craig, age 55
Director, Jill A. Greenthal, age 56
Director, Geoffrey A. Moore, age 66
Auditors: PricewaterhouseCoopersLLP

LOCATIONS

HQ: Akamai Technologies Inc
8 Cambridge Center, Cambridge, MA 02142
Phone: 617 444-3000　　**Fax:** 617 444-3001
Web: www.akamai.com

2012 Sales

	% of total
US	72
Europe	17
Other	11
Total	**100**

PRODUCTS/OPERATIONS

Selected Products

Terra
　Alta
Aqua
　Aqua Ion
　Aqua Ion Mobile
　Dynamic Site Accelerator
Sola
　Sola Media Experience
　Sola Software Distribution
Kona
　Site Defender
　Web Application Firewall
Aura
　Aura Accelerated Network Partner Program
　Managed CDN
　Licensed CDN

Selected Acquisitions

2013
Velocius Networks (Quality of Service (QoS) technology)
2012
　Blaze Software ($19.3 million; frontend (FEO) technology)
　Cotendo ($278 million; Web & mobile acceleration software)
　FastSoft ($14.4 million; content acceleration software)
　Verivue ($30.9 million; high-performance IP platforms)

COMPETITORS

Brilliant Digital Entertainment	Level 3 Communications
CDNeworks Co.	Limelight
Digital Generation	MediaMind
Digital River	Mirror Image Internet
EyeWonder	NaviSite
Internap Network Services	NeuStar
	Onstream Media

HISTORICAL FINANCIALS

Company Type: Public

Income Statement

FYE: December 31

	REVENUE ($ mil.)	NET INCOME ($ mil.)	NET PROFIT MARGIN	EMPLOYEES
12/12	1,373.9	203.9	14.8%	3,074
12/11	1,158.5	200.9	17.3%	2,380
12/10	1,023.5	171.2	16.7%	2,200
12/09	859.7	145.9	17.0%	1,750
12/08	790.9	145.1	18.4%	1,500
Annual Growth	14.8%	8.9%	—	19.6%

2012 Year-End Financials

Debt ratio: —		No. of shares (mil.): 177		
Return on equity: 9.0%		Dividends		
Cash ($ mil.): 201		Yield: —		
Current ratio: 3.59		Payout: —		
Long-term debt ($ mil.): —		Market value ($ mil.): 7,273		

	STOCK PRICE ($) FY Close	P/E High/Low	PER SHARE ($) Earnings	Dividends	Book Value
12/12	40.91	36 24	1.12	0.00	13.19
12/11	32.28	48 17	1.07	0.00	12.15
12/10	47.05	56 25	0.90	0.00	11.67
12/09	25.34	30 15	0.78	0.00	10.15
12/08	15.09	46 11	0.79	0.00	9.26
Annual Growth	28.3%	— —	9.1%	—	9.2%

Akorn Inc

Akorn has its roots firmly planted in the pharmaceutical industry. The company makes and sells branded and generic drugs in therapeutic and diagnostic categories including ophthalmology injectables and specialty therapeutics. Akorn's ophthalmic segment includes antibiotics steroids glaucoma treatments and diagnostic stains and dyes as well as prescription and OTC eye care products. The firm's injectable and hospital-administered therapeutics segment includes anti-infectives antidotes anesthesia agents pain management drugs and other specialty substances. Akorn also provides contract drug manufacturing services.

Geographic Reach

Akorn has manufacturing plants in the US (one in Illinois and one in New Jersey) and India and nearly all of its revenues come from sales in the US market.

Operations

The company's largest operating segment is ophthalmics which brings in about half of annual revenues followed by hospital drugs and injectables which together account for 40% of sales. Many of Akorn's products are generic drugs licensed from external sources though it is working to increase the number of internally developed products in both the branded and generic categories.

Sales and Marketing

Akorn's products are sold nationally to hospitals physicians pharmacies and wholesalers via direct sales representatives and independent distributors. The company's three biggest customers accounting for about two-thirds of its annual sales are wholesalers Cardinal Health McKesson and AmerisourceBergen.

Financial Performance

Akorn reported a 58% increase in revenues (to some $137 million) in 2011 primarily due to growth from acquisitions in the ophthalmic and hospital/injectables segments. The firm also benefited from increased sales of existing drugs (partly due to market shortages of some medications) and newly launched products. Profits also doubled (to $43 million) in 2011 due to Akorn's focus on high-profit margin products and from streamlining efforts in its manufacturing organizations. The contract manufacturing segment declined in 2011 as some capacity was shifted to branded products; Akorn exited its former vaccines segment in 2010.

Strategy

In addition to regular growth through acquisitions Akorn is working to increase its internal product development efforts to speed up the time it takes to bring a new product to market (as well as to reduce its dependence on licensing deals and acquisitions). The company centralized its R&D operations in early 2010 by opening a focused R&D center in Skokie Illinois; previously the company's internal research was performed at its two manufacturing plants. Akorn continues to conduct limited R&D efforts at its plants as well as through external strategic partners.

Mergers and Acquisitions

In 2013 Akorn agreed to acquire Hi-Tech Pharmacal for some $640 million. The purchase will expand Akorn's development pipeline as well as its offerings of generic and branded OTC and prescription products. Hi-Tech Pharmacal makes a number of dosage forms including liquid semi-solid oral topical nasal spray and sterile ointments and gels.

To increase its production of injectables Akorn acquired a compound of contract manufacturing facilities for sterile injectables from India-based Kilitch Drugs in a deal worth some $60 million in 2012. The purchase expands Akorn's capabilities in emerging international markets and the firm plans to apply for FDA certification of the facility to boost its US offerings as well. As portions of the India facility are still under construction the purchase will also provide future capacity for additional products including new ophthalmics and expansion into cancer drugs in both the US and international markets.

Ownership

Chairman John Kapoor is the company's largest shareholder owning a one-third stake in Akorn.

HISTORY

Joseph Yazbeck founded Akorn in Metairie Louisiana in 1971; the name was chosen so the firm would appear near the front of alphabetical listings. Akorn initially distributed eye care products from various suppliers. In 1988 the firm went public. In 1989 Yazbeck retired (replaced by John Kapoor) and Akorn bought its first manufacturing facility from Irish drug company Norbrook Holdings; two years later after product recalls and a push from the FDA to modernize Akorn closed the facility. The company resumed manufacturing operations in 1992 with the purchase of Taylor Pharmaceuticals.

Akorn diversified in 1995 starting a surgical instrument repair unit and boosted its line of injectable drugs the next year. Akorn moved its headquarters from Louisiana to Illinois in 1997 and introduced a generic version of Merck's antiglaucoma drug Timoptic.

In 1998 Akorn increased earnings by acquiring eight new products including worldwide rights to Allergan's Fluress stain. The purchase of a manufacturing facility in New Jersey decreased dependency on outside suppliers. In 1999 Akorn partnered with CIBA Vision to market a generic form of that company's Ocupress glaucoma treatment. In 2000 the company sought permission to begin testing a treatment for age-related macular degeneration a leading cause of blindness in elderly people.

That same year the FDA issued a warning about problems at the company's manufacturing facility in Decatur Illinois. Additional inspections in 2002 2003 and 2004 revealed other "deviations" at the facility which the company has since responded to and corrected. These difficulties prevented Akorn from developing new products at Decatur for several years which had a significant impact on its business.

Arthur Przybyl resigned as CEO in 2009. The board then appointed newcomer Raj Rai as CEO in mid-2009.

Akorn decided in 2009 to exit the market for flu vaccine distribution. Biologics and vaccines previously accounted for about 40% of Akorn's sales in 2009. The company discontinued the rest of the division's operations (tetanus-diphtheria vaccines) in early 2010. The exit didn't impact Akorn's revenues as it increased sales within its other segments during 2009 and 2010.

A major boost in the ophthalmics segment came when Akorn entered the OTC eye care market through the 2011 purchase of Advanced Vision Research for some $26 million in cash. The purchase added such brands as TheraTears and MacuTrition. Akorn is already familiar with the products having been their primary contract manufacturer for several years. To round out its offerings it plans to manufacture private label eye care products and license new products.

The company's generic injectables division experienced increased demand in 2011 (due to shortages of certain products in the US market) and in response Akorn decided to ride that wave by growing the segment's operations. To expand its portfolio of proprietary branded products Akorn acquired manufacturing and marketing rights for three injectable drugs from Danish firm Lundbeck for some $50 million that year (plus potential future milestone payments). The drugs include Nembutal a controversial drug used in lethal injection executions; Cogentin for Parkinson's disease symptoms; and Diuril a diuretic and antihypertensive medicine. To focus on its most profitable growth offerings the firm sold its stake in a portfolio of injectable products marketed with Strides Arcolab to Pfizer in 2011.

EXECUTIVES

Chairman, John N. Kapoor, age 68, $2,083 total compensation

SVP General Counsel and Secretary, Joseph P. Bonaccorsi, age 48, $161,588 total compensation

EVP Operations Global Quality Assurance and Technical Services, Mark M. Silverberg, age 60, $256,370 total compensation

SVP Global Sales and Marketing and National Accounts, John R. Sabat, age 63, $255,458 total compensation

VP Human Resources, Neill Shanahan

SVP Operations, Michael P. Stehn

SVP Regulatory Affairs, Sam Boddapati

CEO, Raj Rai, age 46

CFO, Timothy A. (Tim) Dick, age 43, $126,538 total compensation

VP New Business Development and Research and Development, Sean Brynjelsen

Controller, Wilson Troutman

First Deputy Managing Director-Chief Engineer; Director, Viktor Kochubey

Chairman of the Board; Deputy Chairman of the Management Board; First Vice President, Aleksandr Popov

Member of the Management Board; Finance Director, Aleksey Milenkov

Vice President Overseas; Member of the Management Board, Dmitry Golubkov

Vice President for Production and Development; Member of the Management Board, Ivan Antonov

Head of the Finance and Economics Department; Director, Valery Shvalyuk

Director, Kenneth S. (Ken) Abramowitz, age 62

Director, Ronald M. Johnson, age 67

Director, Alan Weinstein, age 70

Director, Steven J. Meyer, age 57

LOCATIONS

HQ: Akorn Inc
1925 W. Field Court, Suite 300, Lake Forest, IL 60045
Phone: 847 279-6100
Web: www.akorn.com

PRODUCTS/OPERATIONS

2011 Sales

	$ mil.	% of total
Ophthalmic	68	50
Hospital drugs & injectables	55	40
Total	**136**	**100**

COMPETITORS

APP Pharmaceuticals	Hikma
Aerie Pharmaceuticals	Hospira
Alcon	InSite Vision
Allergan	Novartis
Apotex	Patheon
Bausch & Lomb	Pfizer
Baxter International	Sagent Pharmaceuticals
Ben Venue	Sanofi
CBL	Sun Pharmaceutical
Fresenius Kabi	Teva
GlaxoSmithKline	

HISTORICAL FINANCIALS

Company Type: Public

Income Statement

FYE: December 31

	REVENUE ($ mil.)	NET INCOME ($ mil.)	NET PROFIT MARGIN	EMPLOYEES
12/12	256.1	35.3	13.8%	767
12/11	136.9	43.0	31.4%	564
12/10	86.4	21.8	25.3%	410
12/09	75.8	(25.3)	—	329
12/08	93.6	(7.9)	—	351
Annual Growth	**28.6%**	—	—	**21.6%**

2012 Year-End Financials

Debt ratio: 28.3%
Return on equity: 19.6%
Cash ($ mil.): 40
Current ratio: 3.67
Long-term debt ($ mil.): 104

No. of shares (mil.): 95
Dividends
Yield: —
Payout: —
Market value ($ mil.): 1,280

	STOCK PRICE ($) FY Close	P/E High/Low		PER SHARE ($) Earnings	Dividends	Book Value
12/12	13.36	45	29	0.32	0.00	2.10
12/11	11.12	26	11	0.41	0.00	1.67
12/10	6.07	27	6	0.22	0.00	0.92
12/09	1.79	—	—	(0.28)	0.00	0.43
12/08	2.30	—	—	(0.09)	0.00	0.68
Annual Growth	**55.2%**	—	—	—	—	**32.4%**

Alexion Pharmaceuticals Inc.

Alexion Pharmaceuticals can't suppress its enthusiasm for treating immune functions gone awry. The firm develops drugs that inhibit certain immune system functions that cause rare hematology nephrology oncology neurology inflammatory and metabolic disorders. The company's first marketed antibody product Soliris has won approval in the US Canada and some European and Asian countries for the treatment of two rare genetic blood disorders known as paroxysmal nocturnal hemoglobinuria (PNH) and atypical hemolytic uremic syndrome (aHUS). Alexion is also developing Soliris as a potential treatment for other kidney and neurology conditions and it has development programs for other disease-fighting antibodies.

Geographic Reach

Alexion has a manufacturing facility in Rhode Island where it makes a portion of its supply of biopharmaceuticals; it also relies on contract manufacturers (primarily Lonza) to make some of its Soliris supply. It also has service administration and research facilities in the US (Massachusetts) Switzerland and France as well as sales offices in Canada Australia Europe and Asia.

Alexion has expanded sales of Soliris into markets including the EU the US Australia Canada South Korea Japan and Switzerland; the drug has gained approval for treatment of PNH in more than 40 countries and is approved to treat aHUS in the US and European Union. In 2012 Europe surpassed the US for the largest geographic segment accounting for 37% of annual revenues.

Operations

Soliris is the first and only drug approved for the treatment of PNH a rare disorder in which the death of red blood cells can bring on conditions including blood clotting and organ damage. In 2011 the drug gained an additional indication when it was approved for the treatment of aHUS a rare genetic disease that causes blood clots leading to kidney failure in both the US and European markets. The drug is taken by relatively few and at a hefty cost: more than $400000 per patient per year (making it one of the world's most expensive drugs).

Sales and Marketing

Alexion markets the drug through a specialized direct sales force as well as through distribution partners in select geographic markets. In the US the company serves customers including specialty distributors and specialty pharmacies which in turn supply Solaris to physicians and clinics. Internationally its customers include hospitals pharmacies distributors and buying groups.

Financial Analysis

Revenues for Alexion have grown since its first commercial product Soliris gained regulatory approval in the EU and the US in 2007 increasing each year as the company has moved the drug into new territories. Profits have also steadily risen excluding a drop in 2010 caused by a sharp rise the previous year from a one-time tax benefit. In 2012 revenues increased by 45% to some $1.1 billion and net income rose 45% to $255 million primarily attributed to increased use of Soliris in new and existing markets.

Strategy

The company is pursuing regulatory approval to launch Soliris in new markets; for instance it introduced the drug in Japan in 2010 and in Australia in 2011. Alexion is also researching Soliris as a treatment for additional conditions including other rare blood disorders organ transplant rejection and eye and nerve conditions.

With the success of Soliris underway the company has laid out a strategy for research partnership and acquisition activities that capitalizes on its ability to develop and commercialize drugs for rare conditions. In addition to Soliris Alexion has candidates in its pipeline for the treatment of rare metabolic and inflammatory disorders.

Following increased sales of Soliris in 2012 the company announced plans to build a new global headquarters building in New Haven Connecticut. The facility is scheduled for completion in 2015.

Mergers and Acquisitions

The company expanded into metabolic disease treatment in 2011 by buying up the rights to an investigational drug for the treatment of Type A molybdenum cofactor deficiency (MoCD) a rare disorder that can cause severe brain damage in newborns from Orphatec Pharmaceuticals. In early 2012 it also paid $610 million to acquire Montreal-based Enobia Pharma; the purchase added a development candidate to treat an ultra-rare metabolic disease known as hypophosphatasia (HPP) which currently has no treatment options.

In 2011 Alexion acquired Taligen Therapeutics which had a drug in development stages that would have competed with Soliris for about $111 million. Taligen Therapeutic's pipeline also included a potential treatment for ophthalmic diseases.

Ownership

Investors in Alexion include Capital Research Global Investors with an 11% ownership stake and T. Rowe Price (10%).

EXECUTIVES

SVP and Chief Legal Officer, Thomas Dubin, age 50, $299,507 total compensation
Chairman, Max E. Link, age 74
EVP and Head Research and Development, Stephen P. Squinto, age 56, $335,240 total compensation
CEO Treasurer and Director, Leonard Bell, age 55, $622,752 total compensation
VP Site Operations and Engineering, Daniel N. (Dan) Caron, age 49
SVP Technical Operations, M. Stacy Hooks, age 45
SVP Global Commercial Operations, David L. Hallal, age 47
Chief Human Resources Officer; Senior Vice President, Clare M. Carmichael, age 53
SVP and CFO, Vikas Sinha, age 49, $349,370 total compensation
SVP and President Alexion Pharma International Sarl, Patrice Coissac, age 64
SVP and Chief Medical Officer, Camille L. Bedrosian, age 59
SVP Strategic Product Development and Global Regulatory Affairs, Claude Nicaise
Senior Vice President Global Government Affairs, Heidi L. Wagner
VP and CIO, James P. Bilotta
VP Corporate Strategy and Business Development, Jeremy P. Springhorn
VP Global Hematology Franchise, Margaret M. Olinger
SVP Global Medical Affairs, Thomas Bock
Vice President of HR, Jeroen Beek
Senior Vice President Corporate Quality and Compliance, Claus Weisemann
Vice President Chief Information Officer, James M.B.A
Vice President Global Government Affairs, Heidi Esq
Senior Vice President Alexion Pharmaceuticals, Frank Wright
Senior Vice President General Counsel, John Moriarty
Executive Vice President, Martin Mackay
Senior Vice President Chief Strategy and Portfolio Officer, Saqib Islam
CEO Treasurer and Director, Leonard Bell, age 55
Director, R. Douglas (Doug) Norby, age 78
Director, Joseph A. Madri, age 66

Director, Alvin S. Parven, age 72
Director, Ann M. Veneman, age 64
Director, Larry L. Mathis, age 69
Director, Andreas Rummelt, age 57
Director, William R. Keller, age 65
Auditors: PricewaterhouseCoopersLLP

LOCATIONS

HQ: Alexion Pharmaceuticals Inc.
352 Knotter Dr., Cheshire CT 06410
Phone: 203-272-2596   **Fax:** 203-271-8198
Web: www.alxn.com

2012 Sales

	$ mil.	% of total
Europe	418	37
US	400	35
Asia Pacific (mostly Japan)	161	14
Other regions & countries	153	14
Total	**1,134**	**100**

PRODUCTS/OPERATIONS

Selected Products

Approved
Soliris (eculizumab paroxysmal nocturnal
  hemoglobinuria - PNH - and atypical hemolytic
  uremic syndrome - aHUS)
In development
ALXN 1007 (inflammatory disorders)
ALXN 1102/1103 (inflammatory disorders)
Asfotase alfa (hypophosphatasia)
cPMP (molybdenum cofactor deficiency - MoCD - type
  A)
Soliris (STEC-HUS myasthenia gravis neuromyelitis
  optica transplant rejection neuromyelitis optica
  other disorders)
TT30 (paroxysmal nocturnal hemoglobinuria)

COMPETITORS

Abbott Labs	Genzyme
Allergan	Gilead Sciences
Amgen	GlaxoSmithKline
Archemix	Human Genome Sciences
AstraZeneca	Medicis Pharmaceutical
Baxter International	Millennium: The Takeda
BioMarin	Oncology Company
Pharmaceutical	MorphoSys
Biogen Idec	Novo Nordisk
CSL Behring	Pfizer
Celgene	Pharming
Celldex Therapeutics	Regeneron
ChemoCentryx	Pharmaceuticals
Cubist Pharmaceuticals	Vertex Pharmaceuticals
Dyax	ViroPharma
Forest Labs	XOMA
Genentech	

HISTORICAL FINANCIALS

Company Type: Public

Income Statement

FYE: December 31

	REVENUE ($ mil.)	NET INCOME ($ mil.)	NET PROFIT MARGIN	EMPLOYEES
12/13	1,551.3	252.9	16.3%	1,774
12/12	1,134.1	254.8	22.5%	1,373
12/11	783.4	175.3	22.4%	1,008
12/10	540.9	97.0	17.9%	792
12/09	386.8	295.1	76.3%	673
Annual Growth	**41.5%**	**(3.8%)**	**—**	**27.4%**

2013 Year-End Financials

Debt ratio: 4.3%	No. of shares (mil.): 196
Return on equity: 11.6%	Dividends
Cash ($ mil.): 529	Yield: —
Current ratio: 3.75	Payout: —
Long-term debt ($ mil.): 97	Market value ($ mil.): 26,172

	STOCK PRICE ($) FY Close	P/E High/Low	PER SHARE ($) Earnings	Dividends	Book Value
12/13	132.88	103 65	1.27	0.00	12.09
12/12	93.74	88 52	1.28	0.00	10.12
12/11	71.50	109 46	0.91	0.00	6.12
12/10	80.55	151 83	0.52	0.00	4.70
12/09	48.82	28 18	1.63	0.00	3.87
Annual Growth	**28.4%**	**— —**	**(6.0%)**	**—**	**33.0%**

Align Technology Inc

Brace-face begone! Align Technology produces and sells the Invisalign system which corrects malocclusion or crooked teeth. Instead of using metal or ceramic mounts that are cemented on the teeth and connected by wires (traditional braces) the system involves using an array of clear and removable dental Aligners to move a patient's teeth into a desired tooth alignment. The company markets its products to orthodontists and dentists worldwide. Align also provides training for practitioners to model treatment schemes using its online ClinCheck application which simulates tooth movement and suggests the appropriate Aligner. It also makes and sells orthodontic scanning and CAD (computer-assisted design) devices.

Geographic Reach

Align Technology has administrative and manufacturing locations in Costa Rica Mexico Israel the Netherlands and the US. Its products are primarily marketed in North America (accounting for three-fourths of sales) and Europe. It also operates in areas of Latin America and the Asia/Pacific and is working to expand sales into Middle Eastern African and smaller European countries.

Sales and Marketing

Align Technology sells its products through a direct sales force in North America and select international markets as well as through distribution partners in other regions. The company primarily markets its products to orthodontist and dental practices who then commit to sell the products to consumers. It is targeting general practice dentists as a primary sales growth channel since general dentists have larger patient populations than orthodontists who traditionally treat malocclusion.

Financial Analysis

Sales growth within the newer Invisalign Teen Invisalign Assist and Vivera product lines as well as revenues from the new scanner and CAD/CAM services business (added through the 2011 acquisition of imaging systems manufacturer Cadent) led to a 24% increase in revenues (to some $480 million) for Align Technology in 2011. Profits however decreased by 10% to $67 million that year due to increased sales marketing and compensation expenses (mostly related to the Cadent acquisition).

Strategy

To stay ahead of potential competitors looking to enter the clear alignment market Align Technology is working to expand sales of its Invisalign system by increasing the number of dentists and orthodontists that are committed to selling the products. It also increases brand awareness through consumer marketing programs. Geographically the firm is looking to expand into new markets. For instance it launched the Invisalign

product in China in 2011 and in 2012 it moved into the Russian market and select Middle Eastern markets through an existing distribution partner.

To widen use of its products Align Technology is also developing new versions and variations of the Invisalign system as well as tools that make it easier for dentists to adopt use of the Invisalign offerings. In 2011 it launched the Invisalign G4 system which helps doctors manage treatment of patients with open bite conditions and in 2012 it introduced the Express 5 system for minor treatment of orthodontic relapse crowding or spacing conditions. Some of the company's product development efforts are conducted through partnerships with other medical device firms such as Danaher.

Despite its growth Align Technology has been conducting restructuring measures to lower its expenses in recent years. To streamline its scanning and CAD/CAM operations following the 2011 purchase of Cadent the company is consolidating some manufacturing and service facilities.

Mergers and Acquisitions

Align Technology diversified its product line in 2011 by acquiring Cadent Holdings for $190 million. Cadent provides three-dimensional digital scanning services for dentists and orthodontists. The two companies already were working together to develop Invisalign software designed to run on Cadent's equipment.

Ownership

Danaher owns a 10% stake in Align Technology down from a 70% interest that Danaher gained in 2009 through a litigation settlement with Ormco unit over a patent infringement disagreement.

EXECUTIVES

VP Finance and CFO, Kenneth B. (Ken) Arola, age 57, $275,000 total compensation
CFO, David L. White, age 57
VP North American Sales, Dan S. Ellis, age 61
Director President and Chief Executive Officer, Thomas M. Prescott, age 57, $519,840 total compensation
Interim Chief Financial Officer; Vice President - Legal and Corporate Affairs; General Counsel; Corporate Secretary, Roger E. George, age 47, $292,496 total compensation
SVP Business Operations, Len M. Hedge, age 55, $315,000 total compensation
Chairman, C. Raymond Larkin Jr., age 64
VP Research and Development and Information Technology, Dana C. Cambra, age 55
Investor Relations, Shirley Stacy
Vice President - Operations, Emory M. Wright, age 43, $255,000 total compensation
VP International, Richard Twomey
Vice President - Global Human Resources, Jennifer M Erfurth
Senior Vice President - Marketing and Business Development, Timothy A. Mack
VP Marketing & Chief Marketing Officer, John P Graham
Vice President - North American Sales, Christopher C. Puco
Director, David C. (Dave) Nagel, age 67
Director, Joseph S. (Joe) Lacob, age 57
Director, David E. Collins, age 78
President CEO and Director, Thomas M. Prescott, age 57
Director, George J. Morrow, age 61
Director, Gregory J. (Greg) Santora, age 61
Director, Warren S. Thaler, age 50
Auditors: PricewaterhouseCoopersLLP

LOCATIONS

HQ: Align Technology Inc.
2560 Orchard Pkwy., San Jose CA 95131
Phone: 408-470-1000   **Fax:** 408-470-1010
Web: www.aligntech.com

2011 Sales

	$ mil.	% of total
US	359	75
Netherlands	109	23
Other countries	10	2
Total	**479**	**100**

PRODUCTS/OPERATIONS

2011 Sales

	$ mil.	% of total
Clear Aligner	451	94
Scanners & CAD/CAM services	28	6
Total	**479**	**100**

Selected Products and Services

CAD/CAM services
Invisalign Assist
Invisalign Express 5
Invisalign Express 10
Invisalign Full
Invisalign G3
Invisalign G4
Invisalign Lite
Invisalign Teen
iTero scanners
OrthoCad iOC intra-oral scanners
Vivera Retainers

COMPETITORS

3M	Patterson Companies
Ceradyne	Sirona
DENTSPLY	Straumann
Henry Schein	Sybron Dental
National Dentex	Young Innovations
Nobel Biocare	

HISTORICAL FINANCIALS

Company Type: Public

Income Statement
FYE: December 31

	REVENUE ($ mil.)	NET INCOME ($ mil.)	NET PROFIT MARGIN	EMPLOYEES
12/12	560.0	58.6	10.5%	3,176
12/11	479.7	66.7	13.9%	2,593
12/10	387.1	74.2	19.2%	2,097
12/09	312.3	(31.2)	—	1,895
12/08	303.9	79.9	26.3%	1,394
Annual Growth	**16.5%**	**(7.4%)**	**—**	**22.9%**

2012 Year-End Financials

Debt ratio: —   No. of shares (mil.): 80
Return on equity: 10.9%   Dividends
Cash ($ mil.): 306   Yield: —
Current ratio: 3.12   Payout: —
Long-term debt ($ mil.): —   Market value ($ mil.): 2,237

	STOCK PRICE ($) FY Close	P/E High/Low		Earnings	PER SHARE ($) Dividends	Book Value
12/12	27.75	54	31	0.71	0.00	7.21
12/11	23.73	30	17	0.83	0.00	6.23
12/10	19.54	22	14	0.95	0.00	4.94
12/09	17.82	—	—	(0.45)	0.00	3.66
12/08	8.75	14	4	1.18	0.00	3.33
Annual Growth	**33.4%**	—	—(11.9%)		—	**21.3%**

ALJ Regional Holdings Inc

ALJ Regional Holdings owns a steel mini-mill in Kentucky which it acquired in 2005. The mill is operated by Kentucky Electric Steel which produces bar flat products that it sells to service centers as well as makers of truck trailers steel springs and cold drawn bars. Kentucky Electric Steel produces steel in both Merchant Bar Quality and Special Bar Quality. The company also recycles steel from scrap to produce steel. Kentucky Electric Steel operates mainly in the US Canada and Mexico.

EXECUTIVES

President and CEO, John Scheel, age 58
CFO and Secretary, Rob Christ
Auditors: MountjoyChiltonMedleyLLP

LOCATIONS

HQ: ALJ Regional Holdings Inc
244 Madison Avenue, PMB #358, New York, NY 10016
Phone: 212 883-0083   **Fax:** 606 929-1261

COMPETITORS

Nucor	United States Steel
Steel Dynamics	

HISTORICAL FINANCIALS

Company Type: Public

Income Statement
FYE: September 30

	REVENUE ($ mil.)	NET INCOME ($ mil.)	NET PROFIT MARGIN	EMPLOYEES
09/12	158.7	13.2	8.4%	152
09/11	162.0	11.4	7.0%	0
09/10	112.8	5.6	5.0%	0
09/06	139.7	2.4	1.7%	146
09/05	69.1	(3.4)	—	143
Annual Growth	**23.1%**	**—**	**—**	**1.5%**

2012 Year-End Financials

Debt ratio: 61.7%   No. of shares (mil.): 57
Return on equity: ***,***.*%   Dividends
Cash ($ mil.): 2   Yield: —
Current ratio: 2.79   Payout: —
Long-term debt ($ mil.): 26   Market value ($ mil.): 23

	STOCK PRICE ($) FY Close	P/E High/Low		Earnings	PER SHARE ($) Dividends	Book Value
09/12	0.41	2	2	0.22	0.00	(0.23)
09/11	0.44	3	1	0.21	0.00	(0.47)
09/10	0.26	3	1	0.11	0.00	(0.84)
09/06	0.17	4	2	0.06	0.00	(1.97)
09/05	0.10	—	—	(0.09)	0.00	(2.03)
Annual Growth	**41.9%**	—	—	—	—	—

Allegiant Travel Company

Allegiant Travel pledges to serve the vacation needs of residents of more than 60 small US cities in 35 states. Through Allegiant Air the company provides nonstop service to tourist destinations such as Las Vegas Los Angeles and Orlando Florida from places such as Cedar Rapids Iowa; Fargo North Dakota; and Toledo Ohio. It maintains a fleet of about 50 MD-80 series aircraft. Besides scheduled service Allegiant Air offers charter flights for casino operators Caesars Entertainment (formerly Harrah's Entertainment) and MGM MIRAGE in addition to other customers. Sister company Allegiant Vacations works with partners to allow customers to book hotel rooms and rental cars along with their airline tickets.

The company hopes to thrive by sticking to what it believes to be an underserved niche: Allegiant Air is the only provider of nonstop service to its chosen destinations from most of the markets where it operates. Allegiant Travel has identified about 100 more small cities in the US and Canada as candidates for its services; it also plans to expand its list of leisure destinations. In addition to Las Vegas Los Angeles and Orlando Allegiant Travel offers service to Phoenix; and to two other Florida markets (Fort Lauderdale and Tampa/St. Petersburg).

Allegiant Travel believes the diversity of its revenue mix will help ensure the company's success. The long-term fixed-fee contract with Harrah's is a predictable and useful supplement to its scheduled airline service. Other sources of revenue include the fees it collects when customers arrange lodging and ground transportation via the Allegiant Air website and the charges for ancillary services such as advance seat assignments and in-flight food and beverages. The fees added up allowing the company to realize a whopping 50% increase in ancillary revenue in 2010; these additional fees played a great part in the company's overall revenue increase of 11%.

Even with these increases the company is still interested in controlling aircraft-related costs. Allegiant Travel has chosen to fly planes from the venerable MD-80 series which are readily available second-hand. (The average age of the company's MD-80s is just over 21 years.) The aircraft formerly an industry mainstay cost less than new planes and using a single type of plane makes maintenance simpler and thus less expensive. On the downside MD-80s are less fuel-efficient than newer aircraft.

In early 2010 the company shifted its business strategy slightly to include longer-haul transportation. It agreed to purchase six Boeing 757-200 aircraft in order to extend its services to Hawaii. Seeing Hawaii as an untapped leisure market ripe with growth Allegiant Travel plans to have all the new aircraft delivered by 2012. It will cost the company between $75 million and $90 million to acquire and prepare the fleet for service. Until it recieves regulatory approval for extended over water operations the company has leased two of the Boeing aircraft to a third party.

Just as the company's aircraft have been tested so has Allegiant Travel's management team. This isn't the first go-round in the airline industry for CEO Maurice Gallagher who helped found low-fare carrier ValuJet (now AirTran). Gallagher controls about 20% of Allegiant Travel.

EXECUTIVES

Chairman and CEO, Maurice J. (Maury) Gallagher Jr., age 63
SVP Marketing, Michael Reichartz
Senior Vice President OperationsKris, Kris B. Bauer, age 49
Director Corporate Communications, Tyri Squyres
President, Andrew C. Levy, age 43, $185,000 total compensation
SVP and CIO, Scott Allard, age 45
Chief Financial Officer, Scott Sheldon, age 35, $120,000 total compensation
Senior Vice President - Planning, Jude Bricker
Director, John T. Redmond, age 55
Director, Montie R. Brewer, age 55
Director, Timothy P. Flynn, age 62
Director, Gary E. Ellmer, age 59
Director, Charles W. Pollard, age 55
Auditors: Ernst&YoungLLP

LOCATIONS

HQ: Allegiant Travel Company
8360 S. Durango Dr., Las Vegas NV 89113
Phone: 702-851-7300   **Fax:** 702-589-7213
Web: www.allegiantair.com

2010 Selected Routes

Destination	No. of routes
Las Vegas	45
Orlando	29
Phoenix	27
Tampa Bay/St. Petersburg	20
Los Angeles/Lon Beach	17
Ft. Lauderdale	7
Other cities	15
Total	**160**

PRODUCTS/OPERATIONS

2010 Sales

	$ mil.	% of total
Scheduled service	427	64
Ancillary revenues		
Third party products	24	4
Fixed fee contract revenues	40	6
Total	**663**	**100**

COMPETITORS

AirTran Airways
Alaska Air
American Airlines Group
Delta Air Lines
Frontier Airlines
Horizon Air
JetBlue
Southwest Airlines
US Airways
United Continental

HISTORICAL FINANCIALS

Company Type: Public

Income Statement

FYE: December 31

	REVENUE ($ mil.)	NET INCOME ($ mil.)	NET PROFIT MARGIN	EMPLOYEES
12/12	908.7	78.6	8.6%	1,938
12/11	779.1	49.4	6.3%	1,719
12/10	663.6	65.7	9.9%	1,826
12/09	557.9	76.3	13.7%	1,734
12/08	504.0	35.4	7.0%	1,567
Annual Growth	**15.9%**	**22.1%**	**—**	**5.5%**

2012 Year-End Financials

Debt ratio: 18.9%
Return on equity: 20.8%
Cash ($ mil.): 99
Current ratio: 1.97
Long-term debt ($ mil.): 139
No. of shares (mil.): 19
Dividends
Yield: 2.7%
Payout: 49.2%
Market value ($ mil.): 1,419

	STOCK PRICE ($) FY Close	P/E High/Low	PER SHARE ($) Earnings	Dividends	Book Value
12/12	73.41	19 12	4.06	2.00	20.71
12/11	53.34	21 15	2.57	0.00	18.42
12/10	49.24	17 11	3.32	0.75	15.67
12/09	47.17	15 9	3.76	0.00	14.71
12/08	48.57	28 10	1.73	0.00	11.50
Annual Growth	**10.9%**	**— —**	**23.8%**	**—**	**15.8%**

Alliance Holdings Group LP

When it comes to coal mining it takes more than one company to make this Alliance work. Alliance Holdings GP owns Alliance Resource Management GP which is the managing general partner of major coal mining company Alliance Resource Partners L.P. That operational company has seven coal mining complexes in Illinois Indiana Kentucky and Maryland plus other coal interests in West Virginia. Alliance Holdings GP generates all of its revenues from its general partnership interest and its ownership stake in Alliance Resource Partners L.P.

Geographic Reach

The company's Alliance Resource Partners unit has coal mining operations in Illinois Basin Central Appalachia and Northern Appalachian.

Sales and Marketing

Alliance Resource Partners' two largest customers in 2012 were Louisville Gas and Electric Company and Tennessee Valley Authority which together accounted for 28.5% of that unit's total revenues.

Financial Performance

The company's revenues grew by 10% in 2012 thanks to record sales and production volumes (35.2 million tons sold and 34.8 million tons produced). Higher coal sales prices in 2012 (which increased to $56.3 per ton sold due to improved contract pricing for Illinois Basin coal sales) were partially offset by lower coal volumes from Mettiki mine sales into metallurgical export markets. Increased production at the Tunnel Ridge mine expansion of production at the River View and Warrior mines and the acquisition of the Onton mine lifted overall production in 2012.

Net income declined by 8% in 2012 due to higher operating expenses an asset impairment charge associated with the long-lived assets at the Pontiki mining complex and equity losses from affiliates.

Strategy

The primary business objective of Alliance Holdings is to increase its cash distributions to unit holders by actively supporting its main operating unit (Alliance Resource Partners) in implementing its business activities.

Mergers and Acquisitions

Growing its coal assets in 2012 Alliance Resource Partners acquired Green River Collieries (coal mining business and operations in Webster and Hopkins Counties Kentucky).

Ownership

Chairman president CEO Joseph Craft owns 43% Alliance Holdings GP.

Company Background

The Alliance companies were assembled by Joseph Craft.

EXECUTIVES

Executive Vice President - Marketing, Robert G. Sachse, age 64, $261,971 total compensation
Chairman of the Board President and Chief Executive Officer, Joseph W. Craft III, age 62, $334,828 total compensation
Senior Vice President and Chief Financial Officer, Brian L. Cantrell, age 53, $218,619 total compensation
SVP General Counsel and Secretary, R. Eberley Davis, age 56, $236,369 total compensation
Senior Vice President and Chief Operating Officer, Thomas M. Wynne, age 56, $176,854 total compensation
Director, Michael J. Hall, age 69
Director, Robert J. Druten, age 65
Director, Thomas M. Davidson Sr., age 76
Auditors: Deloitte&ToucheLLP

LOCATIONS

HQ: Alliance Holdings GP L.P.
1717 S. Boulder Ave. Ste. 400, Tulsa OK 74119
Phone: 918-295-1415   **Fax:** 918-295-7361
Web: www.ahgp.com

2012 Sales

Illinois Basin	1,499	73
Central Appalachia	157	8
Adjustments	(16.5)	-

PRODUCTS/OPERATIONS

2012 Sales

Coal	1,979	97
Other	32	2

COMPETITORS

Alpha Natural Resources
Arch Coal
CONSOL Energy
Drummond Company
James River Coal
Peabody Energy

HISTORICAL FINANCIALS

Company Type: Public

Income Statement

FYE: December 31

	REVENUE ($ mil.)	NET INCOME ($ mil.)	NET PROFIT MARGIN	EMPLOYEES
12/12	2,033.9	196.0	9.6%	4,345
12/11	1,843.2	214.1	11.6%	3,832
12/10	1,609.7	174.3	10.8%	3,558
12/09	1,230.6	114.2	9.3%	3,090
12/08	1,156.1	81.2	7.0%	2,955
Annual Growth	**15.2%**	**24.7%**	**—**	**10.1%**

2012 Year-End Financials

Debt ratio: 41.3%
Return on equity: —
Cash ($ mil.): 31
Current ratio: 1.36
Long-term debt ($ mil.): 791
No. of shares (mil.): 59
Dividends
Yield: 5.7%
Payout: 83.0%
Market value ($ mil.): 2,848

	STOCK PRICE ($) FY Close	P/E High/Low		PER SHARE ($) Earnings	Dividends	Book Value
12/12	47.58	16	12	3.28	2.72	7.19
12/11	51.98	16	12	3.58	2.28	6.63
12/10	48.13	17	9	2.91	1.90	5.38
12/09	27.41	15	7	1.91	1.69	4.38
12/08	14.80	22	8	1.36	1.32	3.95
Annual Growth	33.9%		—	24.6%	19.9%	16.2%

Alliance Resource Partners LP

Coal is the main resource of Alliance Resource Partners which operates in the Illinois Basin Central Appalachia and Northern Appalachia. The company has 11 underground coal mining complexes in Illinois Indiana Kentucky Maryland Pennsylvania and West Virginia. Alliance controls about 650 million tons of reserves. Approximately 205 million tons of these reserves located in Hamilton County Illinois are leased to independent coal company White Oak Resources. Alliance produces about 32 million tons of coal annually nearly all of which is sold to electric utilities.

Geographic Reach

The company operates 11 underground mining complexes in five states (Illinois Indiana Kentucky Maryland and West Virginia) and also operates a coal-loading terminal on the Ohio River at Mt. Vernon Indiana.

Operations

Alliance's coal is transported from its mines to customers by rail truck and barge. In 2011 61% of its coal was shipped by rail 25% by barge and 14% by truck.

Sales and Marketing

The company's two largest customers in 2011 were Louisville Gas and Electric Company and the Tennessee Valley Authority.

Financial Perfomance

Alliance's revenues increased by 15% in 2011 due to higher average coal sales prices (contributing $151.2 million in coal sales) and increased tons sold (contributing $83.4 million in additional coal sales). Average coal sales price also increased primarily as a result of improved contract pricing across all regions.

The company's net income increased by 21% in 2011 due to higher revenues a decrease in interest expense (attributable to a nonrecurring adjustment to capitalized interest) and reduced interest expense resulting from annual principal repayments made during August 2011 and 2010 of $18.0 million on our original senior notes issued in 1999. Other factors included a decrease in transportation revenues and expenses primarily attributable to reduced tonnage in 2011.

Alliance saw an upward trend in revenue from 2007 to 2011. The year-over year upward trend was mainly attributable to the increased coal prices primarily as a result of improved contract pricing.

Strategy

In 2012 Alliance Coal expanded its holdings in the Illinois Basin coal basin by acquiring Kentucky-based Green River Collieries. The deal includes the Onton No. 9 mining complex which produces about 1.5 million tons of coal per year as well as the addition of an estimated 40 million tons of coal reserves in the West Kentucky No. 9 coal seam.

Ownership

President and CEO Joseph Craft III controls 42% of Alliance Resource Partners. Craft a coal industry veteran owns his stake in Alliance Resource Partners through Alliance Holdings GP a company he controls that went public in 2006.

EXECUTIVES

Executive Vice President - Marketing of General Partner, Robert G. Sachse, age 64, $261,971 total compensation

Executive Vice President; Director of General Partner, Charles R. Wesley, age 58, $236,280 total compensation

Chairman, John P. Neafsey, age 72

Chief Financial Officer; Senior Vice President of General Partner, Brian L. Cantrell, age 53, $218,619 total compensation

SVP General Counsel and Secretary, R. Eberley Davis, age 56, $236,369 total compensation

Chief Operating Officer; Senior Vice President of General Partner, Thomas M. Wynne, age 56, $169,100 total compensation

Chief Medical Officer of Allscripts, Doug Gentile

Chief Executive Officer of Allscripts, Glen Tullman

President CEO of Holston Medical Group, Scott Fowler

Senior Vice President; General Counsel; Secretary of General Partner, Eberley Davis

Director, Michael J. Hall, age 68

EVP and Director, Charles R. Wesley, age 58

President CEO and Director, Joseph W. Craft III, age 61

Director, John H. Robinson, age 62

Director, Wilson M. (Mack) Torrence, age 71

Auditors: Deloitte&ToucheLLP

LOCATIONS

HQ: Alliance Resource Partners L.P.
1717 S. Boulder Ave. Ste. 400, Tulsa OK 74119
Phone: 918-295-7600 **Fax:** 918-295-7358
Web: www.arlp.com

PRODUCTS/OPERATIONS

2011 Sales

	$ mil.	% of total
Coal sales	1786.1	97
Transportation	32	2
Other	25	1
Total	**1,843**	**100**

COMPETITORS

Alpha Natural Resources
Arch Coal
CONSOL Energy

Drummond Company
James River Coal
Peabody Energy

HISTORICAL FINANCIALS

Company Type: Public

Income Statement

FYE: December 31

	REVENUE ($ mil.)	NET INCOME ($ mil.)	NET PROFIT MARGIN	EMPLOYEES
12/12	2,034.3	335.5	16.5%	4,345
12/11	1,843.5	389.3	21.1%	3,832
12/10	1,610.0	321.0	19.9%	3,558
12/09	1,231.0	192.1	15.6%	3,090
12/08	1,156.5	134.1	11.6%	2,955
Annual Growth	15.2%	25.8%	—	10.1%

2012 Year-End Financials

Debt ratio: 41.4%
Return on equity: —
Cash ($ mil.): 28
Current ratio: 1.35
Long-term debt ($ mil.): 791

No. of shares (mil.): 36
Dividends
Yield: 7.1%
Payout: 67.1%
Market value ($ mil.): 2,141

	STOCK PRICE ($) FY Close	P/E High/Low		PER SHARE ($) Earnings	Dividends	Book Value
12/12	58.06	13	8	6.12	4.16	19.13
12/11	75.58	10	7	8.13	3.63	16.96
12/10	65.76	10	6	6.68	3.21	12.41
12/09	43.37	13	7	2.95	2.95	8.72
12/08	26.88	23	8	2.41	2.53	7.90
Annual Growth	21.2%		—	26.2%	13.3%	24.7%

Almost Family Inc

Almost Family steps in when you're more than an arm's reach from family members with health needs. With its home health nursing services Almost Family offers senior citizens in nearly a dozen states (including Florida) an alternative to institutional care. Its Visiting Nurse unit provides skilled nursing care at home under a variety of names including Apex Caretenders Community Home Health and Mederi-Caretenders. Its Personal Care Services segment operating under the Almost Family banner offers custodial care such as housekeeping meal preparation and medication management. Almost Family operates about 105 Visiting Nurse agencies and more than 60 Personal Care Services locations.

Geographic Reach

As part of its business Almost Family extends its reach to several US states including Florida Ohio Kentucky Connecticut New Jersey Massachusetts Missouri Alabama Illinois Pennsylvania and Indiana.

Operations

The company's services are carried out by nurses speech and occupational therapists medical social workers and home health aides. The services provided to a patient are determined by physician's prescribed plan of care —generally issued upon the patient's discharge from a hospital. Payments from Medicare account for 92% of revenue in the Visiting Nurse segment making Almost Family sensitive to any changes in Medicare reimbursement policies. The Personal Care segment receives 81% of its revenues from Medicare payments with the balance coming from private insurance private pay and Medicaid. This diversification of reimbursement risk is intentional but the company is also confident that its home-based services will always be lower in cost than institutional care.

Mergers and Acquisitions

While the Visiting Nurse segment brings in the largest portion of revenue Almost Family's strategy has been to grow that part of the business through a steady stream of acquisitions. During 2008 the company acquired nearly a dozen visiting nurse branch locations adding to its market presence in Florida Connecticut and Ohio as well as marking its entry into the New Jersey and Pennsylvania skilled nursing markets. Acquisitions in 2009 and 2010 brought in the home health agencies affiliated with Florida-based Central Florida Health Alliance and a small home health agency in Ohio. In 2011 it paid some $32.5 million to acquire Cambridge Home Health Care greatly deepening its coverage in Ohio and Pennsylvania. To continue with its strategy of growing by buying (which it maintains it does) Almost Family intends to seek additional capital investments.

Financial Analysis

Albeit a modest increase Almost Family logged a 1% rise in revenue in 2011 as compared to 2010. The company points to Medicare reimbursement rate cuts which reduced both consolidated and Visiting Nurse segment revenue and pre-tax operating income by $15.7 million. Net income during the same reporting period dipped by 32% due to the decline in operating income before corporate expenses. It cites Medicare rate cuts and performance issues within its Florida Visiting Nurse operations for the results despite offsets from operating income before corporate expenses from its purchase of Cambridge.

HISTORY

Almost Family was founded in 1976 as National Health Industries a Louisville Kentucky-based home health care company. After William Yarmuth became president in 1981 he expanded the company into such service areas as home infusion and home medical equipment.

The company became Caretenders Health in 1985 and in 1991 the company merged with Senior Service Corporation a small public adult day care services company. The company further expanded the range of services it offered to the elderly through its home health care operations. It established beachheads in new geographic markets by opening home health offices (or buying them) and then adding day care centers. It also bought some existing care centers.

The company grew energetically following its decision to specialize in elder care. It made three acquisitions in 1997 and surpassed that feat by closing on four acquisitions in little over a month in early 1998. The company lost one of its revenue streams that year: Two home health agencies in the Louisville area that had been managed by Caretenders were sold by their owner Columbia/HCA (now HCA) for breach of contract and in 1999 won a $1.5 million settlement.

That year the company also sharpened its focus by selling its product operations (including infusion therapy respiratory and medical equipment) to Lincare Holdings but decided not to discontinue its visiting nurses services.

In 2000 the company changed its name to Almost Family to underscore its focus on adult day care. The following year it bought back the 23% stake that rehabilitation titan HEALTHSOUTH had maintained in the company.

Almost Family acquired one adult day care center per year during 1999 2000 and 2001. In July 2002 the company announced it had completed the acquisition of Medlink of Ohio a provider of home health care services that operated in Cleveland and Akron Ohio.

To expand its visiting nurse segment Almost Family acquired two home health agencies in 2005: Florida Palliative Home Care and Bradenton Florida Home Health. Also in 2005 the company sold its adult day care division to Active Services for $15 million.

In 2006 it acquired several home health agencies in Florida including 21 locations owned by Mederi in Florida Missouri and Illinois for some $20 million.

EXECUTIVES

Senior Vice President, Anne Liechty, age 60
Senior Vice President - Administration, Patrick (Todd) Lyles, age 51, $216,580 total compensation
President and Principal Financial Officer, C. Steven (Steve) Guenthner, age 52, $240,772 total compensation
Chairman and CEO, William B. Yarmuth, age 60, $421,418 total compensation
Vice President - Human Resources, Mark Sutton
SVP Sales and Clinical Programs, Cathy S. Newhouse, $182,116 total compensation
VP and Chief Accounting Officer, John Walker, age 54
SVP Operations, Phillis D. Montville, age 64, $168,077 total compensation
VP and General Counsel, Jerry Perchik
Vice President - Reimbursement, Cathy Pedigo
VP Marketing and Development, James Spriggs
Vice President - Personal Care Operations, Carla J. Hengst, age 56
VP and CIO, Michael Spurlock
VP and Chief Accounting Officer, Jeff Reibel
SVP Operations, Daniel Schwartz
Senior Vice President & Chief Clinical Officer, Raj Kaushal
Vice President - Government Relations, Denis B. Fleming
Senior Vice President - Administration, Todd Lyles
Director, Donald G. McClinton, age 79
Director, Steven B. Bing, age 66
Director, Tyree G. Wilburn, age 60
Director, Jonathan Goldberg, age 61
Director, W. Earl Reed III, age 61
Director, Henry M. (Sonny) Altman Jr., age 75
Auditors: Ernst&YoungLLP

LOCATIONS

HQ: Almost Family Inc.
9510 Ormsby Station Rd. Ste. 300, Louisville KY 40223
Phone: 502-891-1000   **Fax:** 502-891-8067
Web: www.almostfamily.com

2011 Branch Locations

Florida	43	7
Ohio	16	39
Illinois	4	—
New Jersey	4	—
Alabama	3	—
Pennsylvania	3	3

PRODUCTS/OPERATIONS

2011 Revenue

Visiting Nurses	284	84
Total	**339**	**100**

Selected Agencies

Almost Family Medlink
Apex Home Healthcare Services
Better@Home

Cambridge Home Health Care
Caretenders
Community Home Health
Florida Home Health
Mederi Caretenders
Patient Care
Quality of Life

COMPETITORS

Amedisys	HCR ManorCare
Apria Healthcare	Home Instead
Capital Senior Living	Hooper Holmes
Chemed	LHC Group
Continucare	NHC
Diversicare Healthcare Services	National Home Health
Gentiva	Odyssey HealthCare
Girling Health Care	Providence Service
	U.S. Physical Therapy

HISTORICAL FINANCIALS

Company Type: Public

Income Statement

FYE: December 31

	REVENUE ($ mil.)	NET INCOME ($ mil.)	NET PROFIT MARGIN	EMPLOYEES
12/12	348.5	17.2	5.0%	8,000
12/11	339.8	20.8	6.1%	9,000
12/10	336.9	30.7	9.1%	6,400
12/09	297.8	24.5	8.2%	6,123
12/08	212.6	16.2	7.7%	5,700
Annual Growth	**13.2%**	**1.5%**	**—**	**8.8%**

2012 Year-End Financials

Debt ratio: 0.4%	No. of shares (mil.): 9
Return on equity: 8.4%	Dividends
Cash ($ mil.): 26	Yield: 9.8%
Current ratio: 3.31	Payout: 99.0%
Long-term debt ($ mil.): 0	Market value ($ mil.): 189

	STOCK PRICE ($) FY Close	P/E High/Low		PER SHARE ($) Earnings	Dividends	Book Value
12/12	20.26	14	9	1.85	2.00	21.90
12/11	16.58	18	6	2.22	0.00	22.02
12/10	38.42	13	7	3.28	0.00	19.72
12/09	39.53	16	5	2.86	0.00	16.28
12/08	44.98	23	8	2.16	0.00	11.65
Annual Growth	**(18.1%)**	**—**	**—**	**(3.8%)**	**—**	**17.1%**

Altera Corp.

Altera is a fabless semiconductor company that specializes in high-density programmable logic devices (PLDs) —integrated circuits (ICs) that OEMs can program to perform logic functions in electronic systems. PLDs are an alternative to custom-designed ICs and offer a quick reduced-cost chip. The company's products are used by its more than 13000 customers worldwide in communications network gear consumer electronics medical systems and industrial equipment. Altera outsources fabrication of the devices to top silicon foundry Taiwan Semiconductor Manufacturing Company. Customers outside the US represent most of the company's sales.

Operations Altera classifies its products by life-cycle stage into new mainstream and mature and other products. New products are the company's most advanced products generally used in next-generation electronic systems. Mainstream products are a bit older and not dependent on design wins. Mature products are for the oldest systems that continue to be used. Altera's mature and other products category also includes software licensing of intellectual property (IP) cores and configuration and other devices. Geographic Reach Altera has facilities in Canada China Finland France Hong Kong Ireland Italy Germany India Japan Malaysia Singapore South Korea Sweden Taiwan the UK and the US. China is the company's largest marketing accounting for about a third of sales; the US and Japan generate 17% and 14% of sales respectively.

Sales and Marketing The company markets its products directly as well as through a network of independent sales representatives and distributors. Distributors make up nearly three-quarters of the company's sales with Arrow and Macnica accounting for 40% and 21% respectively. Huawei Technologies (16% of sales) is its largest OEM customer.

Financial Performance Altera saw its revenue fall by 14% in 2012 to $1.8 billion as demand weakened across all vertical and geographic markets. Growth in sales of new products was not enough to offset substantial declines in mainstream and mature products. Net income also fell that year tumbling 28% to $557 million.

Strategy Among the PLD types made by Altera field-programmable gate arrays (FPGAs) are the most popular device of choice representing about 85% of sales in the PLD category. Altera's share of the FPGA market is estimated at around 39% and the company considers market share important to long-term growth prospects. Its offerings frequently compete with chief rival Xilinx (the two companies dominate the market for PLDs) and makers of application-specific integrated circuits (ASICs) a type of customized chip used for many of the same functions as PLDs. Altera PLDs' competitive position claims greater functionality and reduced power consumption at a lower price.

Mergers and Acquisitions Though it tends to rely on product development for growth Altera made its first acquisition in more than a decade when it bought Avalon Microelectronics in late 2010. Avalon based in Canada provides wireline equipment manufacturers with optical transport network (OTN) intellectual property (IP); it is the sole supplier of Altera's 100G OTN in its FPGAs. With the acquisition Altera expanded its portfolio of custom IP products for OTN applications.

HISTORY

Altera (short for "alterable") was formed in 1983 by a group of former Fairchild Semiconductor managers. The company introduced the world's first erasable programmable logic device (PLD) in 1984 and the first high-density PLD the following year. In 1988 Altera went public and bought a stake in Cypress Semiconductor. Altera trotted out new generations of chips in 1988 1991 and 1992 (the company's first electrically erasable read-only memory). In 1994 it acquired Intel's PLD business increasing its market share to 20% and adding 15 devices to its product line.

The company joined Taiwan Semiconductor Manufacturing (TSMC) Integrated Silicon Solution and Analog Devices in 1996 to form a wafer fabrication joint venture called WaferTech. New chips in Altera's FLEX family unveiled in 1997 expanded the company's product range into the higher-end PLD market (dominated by rival Xilinx).

In 1999 the company acquired software maker Boulder Creek Engineering as well as Hammer-

cores a Canadian developer of programmable chip cores. That year the company sold its stake in Cypress. Late in 1999 longtime chairman and CEO Rodney Smith announced the search for his successor.

The next year Altera bought DesignPRO (chip cores and other technologies for optical networking) and Right Track CAD (PLD design software). Later that year the company tapped LSI Logic (now LSI Corp.) executive John Daane as CEO; Smith remained chairman. Also in 2000 the company sold its interest in WaferTech to joint-venture partner TSMC.

Smith retired as chairman in 2003; Daane succeeded him in that role as well. In 2004 Altera opened an office at the Cork Airport Business Park in Ireland to support its European customer base. The company also consolidated its product marketing and applications business groups that year.

In 2005 the Securities and Exchange Commission asked Altera to voluntarily provide information on the company's communications with stock analysts and investment firms. The request came after an equity analyst for Wells Fargo Securities reported he would stop covering the company after Altera cut off all communications to him and wouldn't let him ask questions on quarterly conference calls. Altera's CFO publicly apologized for the gaffe.

The following year the company's board set up a special committee to review Altera's practices in granting stock options from 1996 through 2000. Soon after the company received a subpoena from federal prosecutors in Northern California regarding information on stock options and the SEC opened an informal inquiry into the same topic.

Like many other high-tech firms Altera's special committee found there were discrepancies between the recorded dates of stock-option grants and the actual dates those options were granted. As a result the company restated financial results from 1996 to 2005. The SEC investigation into stock-option practices ended in 2007 with the commission not taking any enforcement actions.

Rodney Smith the company's CEO for its first 17 years of existence and its chairman for 20 years was killed in 2007 while he was riding a bicycle on Sand Hill Road in Menlo Park California and was struck by an automobile. He was 67 years old.

Altera made its first acquisition in more than a decade when it bought Avalon Microelectronics in late 2010. Avalon based in Canada provides wireline equipment manufacturers with optical transport network (OTN) intellectual property (IP). With the acquisition Altera expanded its portfolio of custom IP products for OTN applications.

Altera managed to increase its market share in PLDs field-programmable gate arrays and complex PLDs between 2004 and 2011.

EXECUTIVES

SVP Business Development, Lance M. Lissner, age 63
SVP Worldwide Sales, George A. Papa, age 64, $350,013 total compensation
Vice President Investor Relations, Scott Wylie
Chairman President and CEO, John P. Daane, age 50, $700,027 total compensation
SVP and General Manager Altera Penang, Jordan S. Plofsky, age 52, $350,013 total compensation
CTO, Misha R. Burich, age 66, $375,014 total compensation
VP Finance and Corporate Controller, James W. Callas, $240,009 total compensation
SVP Worldwide Operations and Engineering, William Y. Hata, age 54

SVP General Counsel and Secretary, Katherine E. Schuelke, age 50
SVP Human Resources, Kevin H. Lyman, age 58
Senior Director Component Product Marketing, Luanne M. Schirrmeister
SVP Research and Development, Bradley Howe
SVP Corporate Strategy and Marketing, Danny K. Biran, age 56
Senior Vice President Worldwide Sales, Mark J. Nelson
SVP and General Manager Communications Division, Scott A. Bibaud, age 50
SVP and CFO, Ronald J. (Ron) Pasek, age 53, $13,846 total compensation
Senior Manager Public Relations, Mark Plungy
SVP and General Manager Military Industrial and Computing Division, Jeffrey W. Waters, age 48
Director, John C. Shoemaker, age 69
Director, Krish A. Prabhu, age 57
Director, Kevin J. McGarity, age 66
Director, T. Michael (Mike) Nevens, age 63
Auditors: PricewaterhouseCoopersLLP

LOCATIONS

HQ: Altera Corporation
  101 Innovation Dr., San Jose CA 95134-2020
Phone: 408-544-7000   **Fax:** 408-544-6408
Web: www.altera.com

2012 Sales

	$ mil.	% of total
China	582	33
US	302	17
Japan	256	14
Other countries	641	36
Total	**1,783**	**100**

PRODUCTS/OPERATIONS

2012 Sales by Product Category

	% of total
New	32
Mainstream	30
Mature &	38
Total	**100**

2012 Sales

	% of total
Field-programmable gate arrays	84
Complex programmable logic devices	9
HardCopy ASICs configuration devices IP cores development tools &	7
Total	**100**

2012 Sales by Vertical Market

	% of total
Telecom &	44
Industrial automation military &	21
Networking computer &	17
Other	18
Total	**100**

Selected Products

Development Tools
  Software used to design for and program programmable logic devices (PLDs)
Intellectual Property (IP)
  Proprietary chip core designs (IP cores)
Semiconductors
  Complex programmable logic devices (CPLDs)
  Field-programmable gate arrays (FPGAs)
    Embedded intellectual property-based productsEmbedded processors (Excalibur line)Programmable application-specific standard products (ASSPs)
    General-purpose FPGAs (ACEX APEX Cyclone FLEX and Stratix lines)
  Masked devices (HardCopy; converts PLD designs into application-specific integrated circuit —or ASIC — format to reduce development time and manufacturing complexity)

COMPETITORS

Altium
Analog Devices
Applied Micro Circuits
Atmel
Broadcom
Cypress Semiconductor
Freescale Semiconductor
Intel
LSI Corp.
Lattice Semiconductor
Marvell Technology
Microchip Technology
Microsemi SoC
NEC
NVIDIA
PMC-Sierra
STMicroelectronics
Texas Instruments
Toshiba Semiconductor & Storage Products
Vitesse Semiconductor
Xilinx

HISTORICAL FINANCIALS

Company Type: Public

Income Statement

FYE: December 30

	REVENUE ($ mil.)	NET INCOME ($ mil.)	NET PROFIT MARGIN	EMPLOYEES
12/13	1,732.5	440.0	25.4%	3,094
12/12	1,783.0	556.8	31.2%	3,129
12/11	2,064.4	770.7	37.3%	2,884
12/10	1,954.4	782.8	40.1%	2,666
12/09	1,195.4	251.0	21.0%	2,551
Annual Growth	9.7%	15.1%	—	4.9%

2013 Year-End Financials

Debt ratio: 24.8%
Return on equity: 12.8%
Cash ($ mil.): 3,010
Current ratio: 5.45
Long-term debt ($ mil.): 1,491

No. of shares (mil.): 317
Dividends
　Yield: 1.5%
　Payout: 34.9%
Market value ($ mil.): 10,308

	STOCK PRICE ($) FY Close	P/E High/Low	PER SHARE ($) Earnings	Dividends	Book Value
12/13	32.44	28　23	1.36	0.50	11.05
12/12	34.39	24　17	1.72	0.36	10.43
12/11	37.10	21　13	2.35	0.28	9.30
12/10	35.58	15　8	2.49	0.22	7.27
12/09	22.63	27　16	0.84	0.20	3.66
Annual Growth	9.4%	—　—	12.8%	25.7%	31.9%

AMC Networks Inc

AMC Networks is now somewhere over the rainbow. Formerly Rainbow Media Holdings the company is a leading cable television broadcaster with a portfolio of popular TV networks anchored by American Movie Classics (AMC) the cable network airing such critical hits as Mad Men and Breaking Bad that reaches more than 95 million households. It also owns The Independent Film Channel (IFC) the Sundance Channel and WE: Women's Entertainment (WE tv) one of the top networks aimed at women viewers. The company was a former subsidiary of Cablevision Systems until mid-2011 when Cablevision spun off Rainbow Media Hold-

ings into a publicly traded company and changed its name to AMC Networks.

Change in Company Type

Believing that both companies would operate more effectively if they were two distinct companies Cablevision Systems spun-off of Rainbow Media in order to focus on its core cable television service business.

Geographic Reach

Headquartered in New York City the company has a broadcasting and technology center in Bethpage New York. In addition the company has properties in California Illinois Georgia and Michigan. Its channels are distributed throughout the US Europe and Asia. amctv.com delivers more than 4 million unique browsers each month.

Operations

The company is comprised of two reportable segments: National Networks and International and other. The National Networks segment includes four nationally distributed programming networks: AMC WE tv IFC and Sundance Channel.

International and Other includes AMC/Sundance Channel Global (international programming business) IFC Films (independent film distribution business) and AMC Networks Broadcasting & Technology (network technical services business). It also includes VOOM HD Holdings LLC which the company is winding down and which continues to sell certain limited amounts of programming through program license agreements.

AMC Networks brought in about 92% of its revenue from its National Networks segment during fiscal 2012 while the remaining 8% of revenue came from the International and other segment.

AMC Networks also make its IFC Films library content available on third-party digital platforms such as Netflix and iTunes.

Financial Performance

The company's annual revenue increased by 14% while its profits increased by 8% in fiscal 2012 compared to fiscal 2011. The growth was powered by increased revenue from the National Networks segment while revenue from International and other segment decreased in fiscal 2012 compared to the previous year.

The company gets the majority of its revenue from distribution includes affiliation fees paid by distributors to carry its programming networks as well as the licensing of programming for digital foreign and home video distribution.

In fiscal 2012 distribution and other revenue accounted for 61% of the company's revenues while the remaining 39% of revenue came from its advertising sales.

Strategy

Like other cable network operators AMC Networks is constantly focused on developing or acquiring new programming to attract viewers to its television properties. It also targets the networks to specific demographic groups or niche interests such as women and film fans. By targeting the programming the company can deliver specific audiences that advertisers want to reach.

AMC Newtorks has used partnerships and licensing to grow its business. In 2013 Rogers Communications Canada's leading diversified communications company signed a multi-year agreement with AMC to continue to offer Rogers digital cable customers new seasons of hit original series including Breaking Bad Mad Men and The Walking Dead.

EXECUTIVES

President Chief Executive Officer, Joshua W. Sapan
Executive Vice President Operations Rainbow Media, Michael (Mike) DiPasquale
SVP Broadcasting Information Systems and Technology, Steven J. Pontillo
Chief Operating Officer, Ed Carroll
President IFC Entertainment, Jonathan Sehring
President General Manager AMC, Charles (Charlie) Collier
President IFC tv and Sundance Channel, Evan Shapiro
President General Manager WE tv, Kim Martin, age 52
Senior Vice President Creative Services, Rob Battles
Executive Vice President General Counsel, James G. (Jamie) Gallagher
Executive Vice President General Manager Sundance Channel, Sarah Barnett
Executive Vice President Programming and Operations, Harold Gronenthal
SVP Communications, Ellen Kroner
President National Advertising Sales, Arlene Manos
Executive Vice President General Manager IFC, Jennifer Caserta
President AMC Network Distribution, Robert (Bob) Broussard
EVP Finance, John Huffman
SVP Marketing Sundance Channel, Shari Weisenberg
VP Corporate Marketing and Communications, Christine Bragan
Senior Vice President Broadband, David Evans
SVP and General Manager Rainbow Network Communications, John Barbieri
Senior Vice President General Manager, Michael Lahey
SVP Research, Thomas (Tom) Ziangas
VP Communications, Georgia Juvelis
VP Public Relations IFC, Marie Stenberg
SVP Public Relations Sundance Channel, Sarah Eaton
VP Public Relations WE tv, Alice Rao
Director Programs and Promotions IFC Center, Harris Dew
VP Ad Sales Western Region, Danielle Pantages-Baker
Senior Vice President Original Production & Development, Lauren Gellert
EVP Distribution Operations and Business Development, Lisa Schwartz
Vice President Business Affairs, Mary Scotti
Senior Vice President Business Development, Paul Rehrig
Executive Vice President Human Resources, Rob Doodian
President AMC Sundance Channel Global Networks, Bruce Tuchman
Executive Vice President Global Distribution, Ed Palluth
President General Manager IFC, Jennifer Priore
Chief Accounting Officer, John P. Giraldo
Auditors: KPMGLLP

LOCATIONS

HQ: AMC Networks Inc
11 Penn Plaza, New York, NY 10001
Phone: 212 324-8500
Web: www.amcnetworks.com

PRODUCTS/OPERATIONS

2012 Sales

	% of total
National	92
International and Inter-segment	8
Total	**100**

Selected Television Networks

American Movie Classics (classic films)
The Independent Film Channel
IFC Films
Sundance Channel (independent films)
WE tv (entertainment and information for women)

COMPETITORS

A&E Networks	NBCUniversal
ABC Cable Networks	Scripps Networks
Discovery	Showtime Networks
Communications	Starz
HBO	Turner Broadcasting
MTV Networks	

HISTORICAL FINANCIALS

Company Type: Public

Income Statement
FYE: December 31

	REVENUE ($ mil.)	NET INCOME ($ mil.)	NET PROFIT MARGIN	EMPLOYEES
12/12	1,352.5	136.5	10.1%	1,010
12/11	1,187.7	126.4	10.6%	956
12/10	1,078.3	80.1	7.4%	876
12/09	973.6	53.7	5.5%	0
12/08	893.5	(47.4)	—	0
Annual Growth	**10.9%**	**—**	**—**	**—**

2012 Year-End Financials

Debt ratio: 82.8%
Return on equity: ***.***.*%
Cash ($ mil.): 610
Current ratio: 1.64
Long-term debt ($ mil.): 2,167

No. of shares (mil.): 72
Dividends
  Yield: —
  Payout: —
Market value ($ mil.): 3,583

	STOCK PRICE ($) FY Close	P/E High/Low	PER SHARE ($) Earnings	Dividends	Book Value
12/12	49.50	27 18	1.89	0.00	(12.19)
12/11	37.58	22 17	1.79	0.00	(14.41)
Annual Growth	**31.7%**	**— —**	**5.6%**	**—**	**—**

AMCON Distributing Company

AMCON Distributing enjoys a healthy meal but the company is not without its vices. A leading consumer products wholesaler AMCON distributes more than 16000 different consumer products including cigarettes and other tobacco products as well as candy beverages groceries paper products and health and beauty aids. AMCON serves about 4500 convenience stores supermarkets drugstores tobacco shops and institutional customers in the Great Plains and Rocky Mountain regions. Throughout the Midwest and Florida the company also operates a growing chain of health food stores

under the Chamberlin's Natural Foods and Akin's Natural Foods Market banners.

Geographic Reach

The Omaha-based wholesaler supplies stores in the Central Rocky Mountain and southern regions of the US from six distribution centers located in Illinois Missouri Nebraska the Dakotas and Tennessee. AMCON's smaller retail arm operates 16 health food stores in Florida Arkansas Kansas Missouri Nebraska and Oklahoma.

Operations

AMCON's wholesaling business accounts for 97% of its sales while its chain of retail health food stores brings in the rest. Cigarettes have consistently been AMCON's best-selling product generating nearly 75% of total sales. The company's principal suppliers include Altria RJ Reynolds Commonwealth Brands Lorillard Kellogg Kraft Foods and candy giants Hershey and Mars.

Sales and Marketing

Convenience stores represent AMCON's largest customer category. Indeed in fall 2013 the trade publication Convenience Store News ranked the company as the seventh largest convenience store distributor in the US based on annual sales.

Financial Performance

Despite highly competitive conditions in both wholesaling and retailing AMCON's fiscal 2013 (ended September) sales increased 3% versus the prior year to $1.2 billion. Indeed fiscal 2013 marked the seventh consecutive year of increasing sales for the company. Profits however have been harder to come by. Net income declined for the fourth consecutive year: down 20% compared with fiscal 2012 to about $5.8 million. In general profits have been trending upward in the wholesaling business and are being squeezed on the retail side due to increased operating expenses associated with the opening of two new health food stores in fiscal 2013. Driving the 3% sales gain was increased revenue from the wholesale segment –primarily due to higher cigarette prices –offset by flat sales at AMCON's retail operation.

Strategy

AMCON is hooked on cigarettes which accounted for nearly three-quarters of its sales in fiscal 2013. However sales of cigarettes peaked in 2007 and have fallen since then. While AMCON believes demand for cigarettes and tobacco products will continue to fall –in light of such trends as rising taxes smoking bans and a shrinking population of smokers –it continues to expand its distribution business both organically and through acquisitions in regions where it already operates. Indeed the company is expanding its food service facilities at its Rapid City South Dakota branch.

On the retail side of the business AMCON is continuing to seek out new locations for its health food stores. It added two new stores in fiscal 2013 including its first in Arkansas.

Mergers and Acquisitions

AMCON acquired Tennessee-based L.P. Shanks Co. a distributor to convenience stores in half a dozen states in the Southeast for about $13.4 million in cash in May 2011.

EXECUTIVES

President; Director, Kathleen M. Evans, age 66, $375,000 total compensation
VP Sales, Clem O'Donnell
Division Manager Omaha Distribution Center, Dan Johnson
President Chamberlin Natural Foods and Health Food Associates, Eric J. Hinkefent, age 53, $150,000 total compensation

Chairman and CEO, Christopher H. Atayan, age 54, $425,000 total compensation
Chief Financial Officer; Vice President; Secretary, Andrew C. Plummer, age 40, $149,000 total compensation
VP Marketing, Rick Vance
Division Manager Bismarck Distribution Center, John Job
Division Sales Manager Omaha Distribution Center, Wally Smolinski
Division Manager Quincy Distribution Center, Chuck Fosnaugh
Regional VP Springfield Distribution Center, Dave Clem
Division Sales Manager Rapid City Distribution Center, Tim Nold
General Manager Rapid City Distribution Center, Bill Bailey
Division Sales Manager Quincy Distribution Center, Doug Sperry
SVP Planning and Compliance, Philip E. Campbell, age 53, $110,000 total compensation
President and Director, Kathleen M. Evans, age 66
Director, Raymond F. Bentele, age 76
Director, Timothy R. Pestotnik, age 53
Director, Stanley (Stan) Mayer, age 68
Director, John R. Loyack, age 50
Director, Jeremy W. Hobbs, age 53
Auditors: McGladreyLLP

LOCATIONS

HQ: AMCON Distributing Company
7405 Irvington Rd., Omaha NE 68122
Phone: 402-331-3727   **Fax:** 402-331-4834
Web: www.amcon.com

2013 Stores

	No.
Florida	6
Oklahoma	5
Nebraska	2
Arkansas	1
Kansas	1
Missouri	1
Total	**16**

PRODUCTS/OPERATIONS

2013 Sales

	$ mil.	% of total
Cigarettes	878	73
Confectionery	75	6
Health food	37	3
Tobacco food service & other	219	18
Total	**1,211**	**100**

2013 Sales

	$ mil.	% of total
Wholesale	1,174	97
Retail	37	3
Total	**1,211**	**100**

COMPETITORS

Associated Food	H. T. Hackney
Associated Wholesale Grocers	McLane
	Natural Grocers by
Coca-Cola	Vitamin Cottage
Core-Mark	Performance Food
Costco Wholesale	Sprouts
Eby-Brown	Trader Joe's
Farner-Bocken	Vitamin World
GNC	Whole Foods
GSC Enterprises	

HISTORICAL FINANCIALS

Company Type: Public

Income Statement

FYE: September 30

	REVENUE ($ mil.)	NET INCOME ($ mil.)	NET PROFIT MARGIN	EMPLOYEES
09/13	1,211.0	5.8	0.5%	874
09/12	1,174.1	7.3	0.6%	875
09/11	1,041.6	8.0	0.8%	895
09/10	1,010.5	8.9	0.9%	785
09/09	907.9	12.9	1.4%	801
Annual Growth	7.5%	(18.0%)	—	2.2%

2013 Year-End Financials

Debt ratio: 18.7%
Return on equity: 10.8%
Cash ($ mil.): 0
Current ratio: 2.89
Long-term debt ($ mil.): 18

No. of shares (mil.): 0
Dividends
Yield: 0.8%
Payout: 7.9%
Market value ($ mil.): 51

	STOCK PRICE ($) FY Close	P/E High/Low		PER SHARE ($) Earnings	Dividends	Book Value
09/13	81.89	9	7	7.79	0.72	89.29
09/12	65.00	6	5	9.40	0.72	85.59
09/11	57.00	6	4	10.44	0.72	75.10
09/10	61.72	5	3	11.99	0.72	64.55
09/09	61.00	3	1	16.61	0.40	49.31
Annual Growth	7.6%	—	—	(17.2%)	15.8%	16.0%

Ameresco Inc.

Ameresco gives its customers alternative ways to cut their energy bills. Primarily serving commercial and industrial customers along with municipal and federal government agencies Ameresco provides development engineering and installation services to clients seeking to upgrade and improve the efficiency of their heating and air conditioning ventilation lighting and other building systems. Other services include developing and constructing small-scale on-site (or near-site) renewable energy plants for customers as well as installing solar panels wind turbines and other alternative energy sources. Founded in 2000 by CEO George Sakellaris Ameresco operates through 65 locations in the US and Canada.

IPO

Ameresco went public via an initial public offering (IPO) in July 2010. The offering raised $87 million —somewhat less than the $125 million it hoped to. (The company wasn't alone in experiencing lukewarm response to its IPO as the broader markets struggled with lackluster pricings in the wake of the financial crisis.) It used the proceeds to repay debt and to fund general corporate activities including opening new offices expanding sales and marketing efforts and increasing renewable energy plant activities.

Geographic Reach

Massachusetts-based Ameresco operates throughout North America with 65 offices in 34 US states and five Canadian provinces. The US is the company's largest market representing more than two-thirds of sales. Canada accounts for about 10%. The firm also does business in Europe.

Operations

The specialty contractor has constructed more than 100 renewable energy projects and owns and operates 38 small-scale renewable energy plants and solar photovoltaic installations. Energy efficiency services account for about 70% of the company's sales while its renewable energy activities bring in the rest.

Although system design and development services account for most of Ameresco's sales the company also earns recurring contract-based revenue by selling electricity and other energy it produces. Its plants often built near landfills convert biomass (fermented plant and other matter) or methane gas released by landfill waste into energy. The company has been growing its renewable energy plants business and plans to continue to do so in the future.

Financial Performance

Ameresco's 2012 sales fell 13% versus the prior year due primarily to a 23% decline in energy efficiency revenue partially offset by an increase in renewable energy sales (up 3%). Also longer conversion times from awarded projects to signed contracts depressed revenue while sales from companies acquired in 2011 gave it a boost. Revenue from the firm's government sector declined nearly 50% in 2012 compared with 2011 because of a decline in revenue from the Savannah River project and business in Canada. The firm blamed the drop off in government-derived revenue on uncertainty related to election results in 2012.

Net income fell 45% over the same period due to increased operating expenses.

Strategy

Since the company's founding in 2000 rising and volatile energy prices advances in energy efficiency and renewable energy technologies and aging facility infrastructure have driven demand for Ameresco's services. The firm has responded through a combination of organic growth and strategic acquisitions designed to expand its offerings and geographic reach.

Mergers and Acquisitions

In 2013 the firm purchased Ennovate Corp. an energy services company active in Colorado Montana Nebraska and Wyoming thereby expanding its presence in the Rocky Mountain area. In July 2012 Ameresco Canada bought FAME a privately-held company offering infrastructure asset management services to public and private sector clients in Western Canada for about $4.5 million. In 2011 it bought utility specialist Applied Energy Group and APS Energy Services (now Ameresco Southwest) as well as the xChangePoint and energy projects business of Energy and Power Solutions.

Ownership

Founder and CEO George P. Sakellaris owns about 13% of the firm's Class A and all of its Class B common stock which gives him nearly 80% of the voting power.

EXECUTIVES

Chairman President and CEO, George P. Sakellaris, age 66
EVP Business Development and Director, David J. Anderson, age 52
SVP Renewable Energy, Michael T. Bakas, age 44
Executive Vice President General Counsel Corporate Secretary, David J. Corrsin, age 54
SVP Corporate Government Relations, William J. (Bill) Cunningham, age 53
EVP Engineering and Operations, Joseph P. DeManche, age 56
Executive Vice President General Manager Federal Operations, Keith A. Derrington, age 52
President Ameresco Canada, Mario P. Iusi

Executive Vice President General Manager Central Region, Louis P. Maltezos, age 46
VP and CFO, Andrew B. Spence, age 56
VP Planning, Michael R. Castonguay
Vice President Strategic Development, Peter W. Wallis
VP Citizens Conservation Services, Janice S. DeBarros
Vice President, Anthony A. DaSilva
VP Utility Information Management and Analytics, Mark Feichtner
VP, John L. Bosch
Vice President of Energy Supply and Risk Management, Bruce McLeish
Vice President Human Resources and Administration, Kathleen A. Devlin
Vice President Strategic Marketing, CarolAnn M. Hibbard
Vice President Eastern Region, David J. Seymour
Vice President Western Region, Douglas J. Wall
Vice President Northwest Region, Michael J. OConnor
Senior Vice President of Asset Management, Tim Dettlaff
Vice President Ameresco Solar, Bryan J. Martin
IR Contact Officer, Suzanne Messere
Vice President Sales and Marketing, Colin Gates
Vice President General Counsel, Paul Iacono
Vice President Northwest Region, Michael J. O'Connor
Vice President Central Region, Enzo Colangelo
Vice President of Marketing and Business Development Services, Craig Piercey
Vice President Controller Chief Accounting Officer, John R. Granara
Director, Joseph W. Sutton, age 65
Director, William M. Bulger, age 79
EVP Business Development and Director, David J. Anderson, age 52
EVP General Counsel and Director, David J. Corrsin, age 54
Independent Director, Douglas Foy
Independent Director, Frank Wisneski
Independent Director, Michael Jesanis
Auditors: McGladreyLLP

LOCATIONS

HQ: Ameresco Inc.
111 Speen St. Ste. 410, Framingham MA 01701
Phone: 508-661-2200   **Fax:** 484-321-5301
Web: www.vishaypg.com

2012 Sales

	$ mil.	% of total
US		
Federal	73	12
Central region	87	14
Other regions	262	41
Canada	60	10
Other	147	23
Total	**631**	**100**

PRODUCTS/OPERATIONS

2012 Sales

	$ mil.	% of total
Energy efficiency services	449	71
Renewable energy	182	29
Total	**631**	**100**

Selected Subsidiaries

Ameresco Canada Inc.
Ameresco CEPEO Solar Inc.
Ameresco Duffering Solar Inc.
Ameresco Enertech Inc.
Ameresco Federal Solutions Inc.
Ameresco Geothermal Inc.
Ameresco Langstaff Solar Inc.

Ameresco Myles Solar Inc.
Ameresco Planergy Housing Inc.
Ameresco Quantum Inc.
Ameresco Select Inc.
Ameresco Solar - Solutions Inc.
Ameresco Vasco Road LLC
AmerescoSolutions Inc.
EI Fund One Inc.

COMPETITORS

Building Technologies	Lime Energy
Constellation Energy	NORESCO
Group	Onsite Energy
EPS	Siemens Corp.
Honeywell ACS	SolarCity Corp
Johnson Controls	

HISTORICAL FINANCIALS

Company Type: Public

Income Statement

FYE: December 31

	REVENUE ($ mil.)	NET INCOME ($ mil.)	NET PROFIT MARGIN	EMPLOYEES
12/12	631.1	18.3	2.9%	922
12/11	728.2	34.7	4.8%	947
12/10	618.2	28.7	4.6%	735
12/09	428.5	19.9	4.6%	649
12/08	395.8	18.2	4.6%	0
Annual Growth	12.4%	0.1%	—	—

2012 Year-End Financials

Debt ratio: 31.7%
Return on equity: 7.3%
Cash ($ mil.): 63
Current ratio: 2.00
Long-term debt ($ mil.): 201

No. of shares (mil.): 45
Dividends
　Yield: —
　Payout: —
Market value ($ mil.): 443

	STOCK PRICE ($) FY Close	P/E High/Low	PER SHARE ($) Earnings	Dividends	Book Value
12/12	9.81	35　22	0.40	0.00	5.79
12/11	13.72	20　11	0.78	0.00	5.39
12/10	14.36	13　9	0.69	0.00	4.75
Annual Growth	(17.3%)	—　—	(23.9%)	—	10.5%

America's Car-Mart Inc

No Credit? Bad Credit? No problem. America's Car-Mart targets car buyers with poor or limited credit histories. The company's subsidiaries operate more than 115 used car dealerships in eight states primarily in smaller urban and rural markets throughout the US South Central region. Dealerships focus on selling basic and affordable transportation with an average selling price of about $9600 in 2012. It has been expanding primarily in Alabama Tennessee and Mississippi. While the company's business plan has focused on cities with up to 50000 in population (73% of sales) it sees better collection results among the smaller communities it serves. America's Car-Mart was founded in 1981 as the Crown Group.

Operations

America's Car-Mart operates its business through two subsidiaries: one that sells cars (America's Car Mart Inc. also known as Car-Mart of Arkansas) and one that finances them (Colonial Auto Finance Inc.). Substantially all of its cus-

tomers take advantage of financing offered by Colonial Auto Finance. The company's dealerships operate within a decentralized model. For instance dealers conduct their own collections with support from corporate management.

Financial Analysis

Business has been good for America's Car-Mart. As more consumers put off purchasing higher-priced new cars they opt instead to buy older used cars. And with the car retailer's in-house financing option car buyers don't have to jump through as many financial hoops to purchase a vehicle compared to stricter financial terms for new autos with big lenders. To this end America's Car-Mart has logged an average growth rate of 13% during the past decade (taking into account revenue growth of between 3% and 21% per year). Store openings increased retail unit volumes higher average selling prices and a whopping 16% rise in interest and other income have all contributed positively to the retailer's bottom line. America's Car-Mart sold more than 37700 cars in 2012 vs. about 32200 in 2010 thanks to an average of 15 more dealerships in operation during that period and a rise in the average number of units sold per location. The company's steady 42% gross margin doesn't hurt either. The new dealerships helped to offset declines in same-store revenue growth among its existing dealer network —from 11% in 2010 to 7% in 2012.

Strategy

As a result of banking on those with less stellar credit histories America's Car-Mart as part of its business strategy focuses keenly on collections a function conducted at the dealer level with supervisory oversight at the corporate level. During the past five years credit losses as a percentage of sales have ranged between 20% and 22%. What the company has found is that credit losses are higher at its new and developing dealerships due to less experienced management making calls on a potential customer's creditworthiness. To offset these slips America's Car-Mart's mature dealerships log more traffic from repeat customers and have a seasoned staff that has a history of determining credit risk. The car retailer typically sells cars that are six to 12 years old having bought them for $3000 to $6000 at auction or wholesale. It sells them year-round but experiences sales dips during its third fiscal quarter in November through January. Also the company typically sets up shop in cities with up to 50000 in population but historically it has logged better collection results among smaller communities.

Traditionally America's Car-Mart expands its business in existing and contiguous markets. While the company put the brakes on growth in recent years as it rode out the recession America's Car-Mart is back in expansion mode as part of its focus on controlled organic new dealership openings. Since 2010 its retail operation has added 17 new dealerships across Alabama Tennessee Mississippi Kentucky Missouri and Oklahoma. The company tends to add one dealership for every 10 existing dealerships. Besides smaller cities it has found successes in larger cities such as Tulsa (Oklahoma) Lexington (Kentucky) Springfield (Missouri) and Little Rock (Arkansas) and plans to expand its dealer network for the next several years.

EXECUTIVES

Chairman and General Counsel, Tilman J. (Skip) Falgout III, age 63, $330,000 total compensation
Vice Chairman of the Board; President; Chief Executive Officer, William H. (Hank) Henderson, age 50, $300,000 total compensation
Chief Operating Officer, Eddie L. Hight, age 50, $187,455 total compensation
Chief Financial Officer; Vice President - Finance; Secretary; Director, Jeffrey A. Williams, age 51, $182,389 total compensation
Director, John David Simmons, age 77
Vice Chairman President and CEO, William H. (Hank) Henderson, age 49
Director, William M. (Bill) Sams, age 75
Director, Daniel (Dan) Englander, age 43
Director, William A. Swanston, age 58
Director, Robert C. Smith, age 61
Auditors: GrantThorntonLLP

LOCATIONS

HQ: America's Car-Mart Inc.
　802 SE Plaza Ave. Ste. 200, Bentonville AR 72712
Phone: 479-464-9944　　**Fax:** 479-273-7556
Web: www.car-mart.com

2012 Stores

Arkansas	37
Missouri	14
Texas	14
Alabama	10
Kentucky	10
Tennessee	4
Mississippi	3
Total	**114**

PRODUCTS/OPERATIONS

2012 Sales

	$ mil.	% of total
Sales	387	90
Total	**430**	**100**

Selected Subsidiaries

Auto Finance Investors Inc.
Colonial Auto Finance Inc.
Colonial Underwriting Inc.
Crown Delaware Investments Corp.
Crown Group of Nevada Inc.
Texas Car-Mart Inc.

COMPETITORS

Ancira	Carbiz
Asbury Automotive	DriveTime Automotive
AutoNation	Group 1 Automotive
CarMax	Sonic Automotive

HISTORICAL FINANCIALS

Company Type: Public

Income Statement

FYE: April 30

	REVENUE ($ mil.)	NET INCOME ($ mil.)	NET PROFIT MARGIN	EMPLOYEES
04/13	464.6	32.1	6.9%	1,200
04/12	430.1	32.9	7.7%	1,100
04/11	379.2	28.2	7.4%	1,025
04/10	338.9	26.8	7.9%	959
04/09	298.9	17.9	6.0%	915
Annual Growth	11.7%	15.8%	—	7.0%

2013 Year-End Financials

Debt ratio: 27.7%
Return on equity: 16.6%
Cash ($ mil.): 0
Current ratio: 8.59
Long-term debt ($ mil.): 99

No. of shares (mil.): 9
Dividends
　Yield: —
　Payout: —
Market value ($ mil.): 418

	STOCK PRICE ($) FY Close	P/E High/Low		PER SHARE ($) Earnings	Dividends	Book Value
04/13	46.27	14	10	3.36	0.00	22.45
04/12	45.94	14	7	3.24	0.00	19.70
04/11	24.48	12	8	2.54	0.00	17.84
04/10	25.33	12	6	2.27	0.00	14.39
04/09	16.22	15	5	1.52	0.00	13.38
Annual Growth	30.0%	—	—	21.9%	—	13.8%

American Campus Communities Inc

American Campus Communities (ACC) actually does most of its business off campus. The self-managed real estate investment trust (REIT) owns and operates student housing properties located at or near colleges and universities in more than 25 states. The company leases the ground for on-campus properties from the schools which in turn receive half of the net cash flow from these properties. ACC also works with schools to develop new properties and renovate existing housing and provides third-party leasing and management services for other student housing owners. In all the REIT manages about 170 properties (with some 108000 beds) at more than 85 schools in the US and Canada.

ACC has expanded its portfolio by both buying existing properties and developing new ones. It regularly buys properties in bulk adding thousands of beds at a time. In 2012 acquired 15 properties with nearly 6600 beds in several states for some $627 million. The previous year the REIT acquired four properties as well as shopping center it plans to redevelop into a mixed-use community. It also completed and opened four new communities.

Thanks to its expanding portfolio as well as improved occupancy rates and some rent hikes the company's profits more than doubled to $56.6 million in 2011 while revenues grew 13% to $390.3 million. Although third-party development and management services earnings slipped as the REIT wrapped up projects and exited certain contracts the wholly-owned property portfolio saw a gain of 22% that year. On-campus participating properties (it operates four with more than 4500 beds) earnings also grew in 2011 also due to increases in occupancy and rental rates.

Many of ACC's properties feature resort-style amenities making them more desirable than your typical dorm facility. The company has been successful in establishing strong relationships with school systems which pays off in earning repeat business as various campuses seek to add new housing options. Among the REIT's most recent developments are new sites in Texas and New Mexico which opened for business in 2011.

In addition to buying and developing new housing communities the REIT also sells properties when they are no longer considered core to its long-term investment strategy.

EXECUTIVES

EVP CFO and Treasurer, Jonathan A. Graf, age 48, $203,438 total compensation

Jr. President CEO, William C. Bayless Jr., age 49, $352,000 total compensation
senior executive Vice President Chief Operating Officer, Greg A. Dowell, age 50, $248,375 total compensation
SVP Transactions, Brian N. Winger, age 46
SVP On-Campus Development, Jason R. Wills, age 42
EVP Project Management and Construction, James C. Hopke Jr., age 52, $198,525 total compensation
SVP Management Services, Steve Crawford, age 44
SVP Management Services, James R. (Jim) Sholders, age 44
EVP Chief Investment Officer, William Talbot, age 39
EVP Public and Private Partnerships, Jamie E. Wilhelm III, age 50
Executive Vice President - Capital Markets, Daniel Perry, age 40
SVP and Controller, Kim K. Voss, age 39
SVP Project Management and Construction, Victor Young, age 41
SVP Leasing Administration, Jennifer Beese, age 40
SVP Construction Management, Clint Braun, age 41
Investor Relations, Gina Cowart
SVP Development and Finance, Jennifer Jones
Vice President Public-Private Partnerships, Michael Cipriano
SVP Human Resources, Ronald A. Weaver
Vice President Public-Private Partnerships, Noel Brinkman
SVP Chief Technology Officer, Jorge Cardenas
Director, Edward Lowenthal, age 69
Director, Winston W. Walker, age 69
President CEO and Director, William C. Bayless Jr., age 48
Director, Cydney C. Donnell, age 54
Director, G. Steven (Steve) Dawson, age 55
Auditors: Ernst&YoungLLP

LOCATIONS

HQ: American Campus Communities Inc.
12700 Hill Country Blvd. Ste. T-200, Austin TX 78738
Phone: 512-732-1000   **Fax:** 512-732-2450
Web: www.americancampus.com

Selected Property Locations

Alabama
Shelton State College
Stillman College
University of Alabama - Birmingham
University of Alabama - Tuscaloosa
Alberta
Southern Alberta Institute of Technology
Arizona
Arizona State University
Pima Community College
University of Arizona
California
American River Community College
California State University - Fresno
Fresno Pacific University
San Diego State University
Sierra College
Colorado
Community College of Denver
Front Range Community College
Regis University
University of Denver
Florida
Santa Fe Community College
Seminole State College of Florida
University of Florida - Gainesville
Valencia Comunity College
Georgia
Athens Technical College
East Georgia College
Georgia Gwinnett College
Piedmont College - Athens Campus
Wiregrass Georgia Technical College
Hawaii

University of Hawaii - Manoa
Illinois
Parkland College University of Illinois
Indiana
Indiana/Purdue University
Indiana University
Iowa
Des Moines University
Drake University
Kaplin University
Kentucky
Blue Grass Technical College
Bowling Green Community College
Western Kentucky University
Louisiana
Baton Rouge Community College
Louisiana State University
Southern University
University of New Orleans
Maryland
Morgan State University
University of Maryland
Michigan
Central Michigan University
Eastern Michigan University
Kalamazoo Valley Community College
Michigan State University
University of Michigan
Western Michigan University
Minnesota
Art Institute International
Minnesota State University
University of Minnesota
Mississippi
East Mississippi Community College
Mississippi State University
Nebraska
Nebraska Wesleyan University
Southeast Community College
University of Nebraska
Nevada
University of Nevada at Reno
New Jersey
Bloomfield College
Essex County College
Seton Hall University
New Mexico
University of New Mexico
New York
Buffalo State College
Canisius College
Medaille College
State University of New York at Buffalo
North Carolina
Central Piedmont Community College
Durham Tech
Johnson & Wales
UNC Chapel Hill
Ohio
Cleveland State University
Owens Community College
University of Toledo
Oklahoma
Oklahoma City Community College
Rose State College
University of Oklahoma
Ontario
Fanshawe College
London College
University of Western Ontario
Pennsylvania
Drexel
Penn State University
Temple University
South Carolina
Columbia College
Midlands Tech
Tennessee
Daymar Institute
East Tennessee State University
Milligan College
Pellissippi State Community College
University of Tennessee
Texas
Blinn College
Lubbock Christian University
Sam Houston State University

Texas A&M University
University of Houston - Victoria
Virginia
 Blue Ridge Community College
 Eastern Mennonite University
 New River Community College
 University of Virginia
 Virginia Tech
West Virginia
 Fairmont State College
 Marshall University
 Potomac State
 West Virginia University

PRODUCTS/OPERATIONS

2011 Sales

	$ mil.	% of total
Wholly owned properties	349	89
On-campus participating properties	25	7
Third-party development services	7	2
Third-party management services	7	2
Resident services	1	-
Total	**390**	**100**

COMPETITORS

AMLI Residential	Campus Apartments
Allen & O' Hara	Campus Crest
Alliance Residential	Education Realty
Apartment Investment	Fairfield Residential
and Management	JPI
Camden Property	Place Properties

HISTORICAL FINANCIALS
Company Type: Public

Income Statement
FYE: December 31

	REVENUE ($ mil.)	NET INCOME ($ mil.)	NET PROFIT MARGIN	EMPLOYEES
12/12	491.2	56.6	11.5%	2,913
12/11	390.3	56.6	14.5%	2,387
12/10	344.9	16.2	4.7%	2,334
12/09	309.5	(12.8)	—	2,183
12/08	235.4	(13.0)	—	2,301
Annual Growth	**20.2%**	**—**	**—**	**6.1%**

2012 Year-End Financials

Debt ratio: 43.3%
Return on equity: 2.8%
Cash ($ mil.): 21
Current ratio: 1.29
Long-term debt ($ mil.): 2,221
No. of shares (mil.): 104
Dividends
 Yield: 2.9%
 Payout: 204.5%
Market value ($ mil.): 4,828

	STOCK PRICE ($) FY Close	P/E High/Low		PER SHARE ($) Earnings	Dividends	Book Value
12/12	46.13	72	61	0.65	1.35	25.30
12/11	41.96	52	38	0.80	1.35	18.90
12/10	31.76	124	91	0.26	1.35	18.15
12/09	28.10	—	—	(0.28)	1.35	17.22
12/08	20.48	—	—	(0.34)	1.35	18.60
Annual Growth	**22.5%**	**—**	**—**	**—**	**(0.0%)**	**8.0%**

American Capital Agency Corp

American Capital Agency is taking on the rocky real estate market. The real estate investment trust (REIT) was created in 2008 to invest in securities backed by single-family residential mortgages and collateralized mortgage obligations guaranteed by government agencies Fannie Mae Freddie Mac and Ginnie Mae. The company is externally managed and advised by American Capital Agency Management a subsidiary of US publicly traded alternative asset manager American Capital which spun off American Capital Agency in 2008 but retained about a 33% stake in the REIT.

American Capital Agency raised some $300 million from its 2008 IPO. The REIT used the proceeds from the offering to build and develop its investment portfolio.

EXECUTIVES

EVP and CFO; VP and Treasurer American Capital Agency Management, John R. Erickson, age 53
Chairman President and CEO; President American Capital Agency Management, Malon Wilkus, age 61
VP American Capital Agency Management, Thomas A. (Tom) McHale
EVP and Secretary; VP and Secretary American Capital Agency Management, Samuel A. Flax, age 56
SVP and Chief Investment Officer; SVP and Managing Director American Capital, Gary D. Kain, age 48
Senior Vice President Treasurer, Jeffrey S. Beyersdorfer
Senior Vice President General Counsel Secretary, Lowry Barfield
Senior Vice President - Agency Portfolio Investments, Christopher Kuehl
Senior Vice President; Chief Risk Officer, Peter Federico
Director, Larry K. Harvey, age 48
Director, Alvin N. Puryear, age 76
Director, Randy E. Dobbs, age 62
Director, Morris A. Davis, age 40
Independent Director, Robert Couch
Auditors: Ernst&YoungLLP

LOCATIONS

HQ: American Capital Agency Corp.
 2 Bethesda Metro Center 14th Fl., Bethesda MD 20814
Phone: 301-968-9300   **Fax:** -14236
Web: www.mexichem.com

PRODUCTS/OPERATIONS

2009 Sales
$ mil % of total

Interest income	127	72
Gain on sale of agency securities	49	28
Adjustments	(4.2)	-
Total	**173**	**100**

COMPETITORS

ARMOUR Residential	CIFC
REIT	Capstead Mortgage
Annaly Capital	Chimera
Management	Hatteras Financial
Anworth Mortgage Asset	JAVELIN Mortgage

Bimini Capital	MFA Financial
Management	Redwood Trust

HISTORICAL FINANCIALS
Company Type: Public

Income Statement
FYE: December 31

	REVENUE ($ mil.)	NET INCOME ($ mil.)	NET PROFIT MARGIN	EMPLOYEES
12/12	1,440.0	1,277.0	88.7%	0
12/11	850.6	770.4	90.6%	0
12/10	307.3	288.1	93.7%	0
12/09	130.0	118.6	91.2%	0
12/08	41.1	35.3	86.0%	0
Annual Growth	**143.3%**	**145.2%**	**—**	**—**

2012 Year-End Financials

Debt ratio: 0.9%
Return on equity: 14.8%
Cash ($ mil.): 2,430
Current ratio: 0.17
Long-term debt ($ mil.): —
No. of shares (mil.): 338
Dividends
 Yield: 17.3%
 Payout: 174.8%
Market value ($ mil.): 9,794

	STOCK PRICE ($) FY Close	P/E High/Low		PER SHARE ($) Earnings	Dividends	Book Value
12/12	28.90	9	7	4.17	5.00	32.15
12/11	28.08	6	5	5.02	5.60	27.71
12/10	28.74	4	3	7.89	5.60	24.24
12/09	26.54	5	2	6.78	5.15	22.48
12/08	21.36	9	6	2.36	2.51	17.20
Annual Growth	**7.9%**	**—**	**—**	**15.3%**	**18.8%**	**16.9%**

American Equity Investment Life Holding Co

Eagles' nests aren't particularly downy but American Equity Investment Life Holding Company helps middle income investors plan for a softer retirement. The company issues and administers fixed-rate and indexed annuities through subsidiaries American Equity Investment Life Insurance and American Equity Investment Life Insurance Company of New York. Licensed in 50 states and the District of Columbia the company sells its products through more than 35000 independent agents and 60 national marketing associations. American Equity Investment Life targets individuals between the ages of 45 to 75. The company also offers a variety of whole term and universal life insurance products.

Five big states bring in the bulk of American Equity Investment Life's business. California Florida Illinois Pennsylvania and Texas together account for some 35% of premiums.

As consumers have sought stable predictable returns American Equity Investment Life has seen sales of its annuity products increase. In 2011 it boasted annuity deposits of some $5.1 billion up 11% from $4.7 billion in 2010. As a result of increased sales general improvements in investment income and higher fees for products the company's net income see-sawed upwards to $86.2

million in 2011 up 101% from $42.9 million in 2010. However its total revenue slid to $1.14 billion in 2011 from $1.28 billion in 2010 as it experienced losses in the value of derivatives and other investments. Lower interest rates are also likely to dampen investors' affection for fixed index annuities.

The company is working to increase sales in core service territories by enhancing its relationships with regional independent agents and a key component in the company's rebound could be its Gold Eagle program. Launched in 2007 the number of Gold Eagle agents working for the company has more than doubled from 566 in 2008 to more than 1200 in 2011. Gold Eagle agents are those capable of $1 million or more in annuity premium sales per year and altogether they account for more than 55% of the company's total production.

EXECUTIVES

Chairman American Equity Investment and American Equity Life, David J. (D.J.) Noble, age 81, $500,000 total compensation
Director, Wendy C. Waugaman, age 52, $450,000 total compensation
Executive Vice President; Director, James M. Gerlach, age 70, $250,000 total compensation
CEO and President, John M. Matovina, age 58, $350,000 total compensation
Executive Vice President, Terry A. Reimer, age 67, $160,000 total compensation
EVP Chief Administrative Officer Secretary and Director, Debra J. Richardson, age 56, $400,000 total compensation
President American Equity Life Insurance Co., Ronald J. (Ron) Grensteiner
SVP Annuity Administration, Jamie D. Moher
SVP and Chief Investment Officer, Jeffrey D. (Jeff) Lorenzen, age 47
CFO and Treasurer, Ted M. Johnson, age 43
Director Investor Relations, Julie L. LaFollette
Vice President; Controller, Scott Samuelson
Executive Vice President - Legal; General Counsel, William Kunkel
Director, Alexander M. (Alex) Clark, age 80
Director, Joyce A. Chapman, age 68
EVP and Director, James M. Gerlach, age 70
EVP Chief Administrative Officer Secretary and Director, Debra J. Richardson, age 56
Director, Robert L. Hilton, age 84
Independent Director, David S. Mulcahy, age 60
Director, A. J. Strickland III, age 71
Director, Harley A. Whitfield Sr., age 82
Director, Robert L. Howe, age 70
Director, Gerard D. Neugent
Auditors: KPMGLLP

LOCATIONS

HQ: American Equity Investment Life Holding Company
5000 Westown Pkwy. Ste. 440, West Des Moines IA 50266
Phone: 515-221-0002   **Fax:** 515-221-9947
Web: www.american-equity.com

COMPETITORS

AEGON USA	Lincoln Financial
AIG	Group
Allianz Life	MetLife
Aviva	Midland National Life
FBL Financial	National Western
Fidelity &	Nationwide
Guaranty Life	Northwestern Mutual
Great American Life	Presidential Life
ING	Prudential
ING Americas	Sammons Financial
Integrity Life	Security Benefit Group
Kansas City Life	The Hartford

HISTORICAL FINANCIALS
Company Type: Public

Income Statement
FYE: December 31

	REVENUE ($ mil.)	NET INCOME ($ mil.)	NET PROFIT MARGIN	EMPLOYEES
12/12	1,588.5	57.8	3.6%	388
12/11	1,139.7	86.2	7.6%	386
12/10	1,285.5	42.9	3.3%	360
12/09	1,188.9	68.5	5.8%	360
12/08	341.8	20.7	6.1%	330
Annual Growth	46.8%	29.1%	—	4.1%

2012 Year-End Financials

Debt ratio: 1.5%
Return on equity: 3.6%
Cash ($ mil.): 1,268
Current ratio: 28.31
Long-term debt ($ mil.): 555

No. of shares (mil.): 61
Dividends
Yield: 1.2%
Payout: 13.5%
Market value ($ mil.): 754

	STOCK PRICE ($) FY Close	P/E High/Low		Earnings	PER SHARE ($) Dividends	Book Value
12/12	12.21	14	11	0.89	0.15	27.86
12/11	10.40	10	6	1.37	0.12	24.36
12/10	12.55	18	9	0.68	0.10	16.47
12/09	7.44	7	3	1.18	0.08	13.43
12/08	7.00	30	10	0.39	0.07	9.70
Annual Growth	14.9%	—	—	22.9%	21.0%	30.2%

American National Bankshares, Inc. (Danville, VA)

American National Bankshares is the holding company for American National Bank and Trust. Founded in 1909 the bank operates about 30 locations serving southern and central Virginia and north central North Carolina. It offers checking and savings accounts CDs IRAs and insurance. Its lending activities primarily consist of real estate loans: Commercial mortgages account for about one-third of the company's loan portfolio; residential mortgages are about another quarter. The bank's trust and investment services division manages some $475 million in assets. American National Bankshares acquired bank holding company MidCarolina Financial in 2011. The deal expanded its presence in North Carolina.

EXECUTIVES

Chief Financial Officer; Senior Vice President; Treasurer; Secretary, William W. Traynham, age 56
EVP; President and Director American National Bank, Jeffrey V. Haley, age 52, $156,318 total compensation
President CEO and Director; President and CEO American National Bank and Trust, Charles H. (Charlie) Majors, age 67, $361,846 total compensation
Senior Vice President American National Bankshares Inc, Dabney T. P. Gilliam Jr., age 57, $124,544 total compensation
Vice President &Trust Officer, John B. Hall Jr.
SVP; EVP and Chief Credit Officer American National Bank and Trust, R. Helm Dobbins, age 61, $139,570 total compensation
Senior Vice President American National Bankshares Inc, Charles T. Canaday Jr., age 52
Senior Vice President American National Bankshares Inc, Cabell Dudley
Vice President & Senior Investment Officer, William W. Clingempeel
Vice President & Trust Officer, Debra C. Carlson
Director; Senior Advisor American National Bank and Trust, E. Budge Kent Jr., age 72
President CEO and Director; President and CEO American National Bank and Trust, Charles H. (Charlie) Majors, age 67
Director, Lester A. Hudson Jr., age 73
Director, Ben J. Davenport Jr., age 70
Director, Fred A. Blair, age 66
Director, Claude B. Owen Jr., age 67
Director, H. Dan Davis, age 74
Director, Michael P. Haley, age 62
Director, Franklin W. Maddux, age 55
Director; President North Carolina Banking, Charles T. Canaday Jr., age 50
Director, Frank C. Crist Jr., age 67
Director, Charles H. Harris, age 62
Director, Martha W. Medley, age 56
Independent Director, Robert Ward
Independent Director, John Love
Independent Director, Dan Pleasant
Independent Director, F Hornaday
Auditors: YountHyde&BarbourP.C.

LOCATIONS

HQ: American National Bankshares Inc.
628 Main St., Danville VA 24541
Phone: 434-792-5111   **Fax:** 434-792-1582
Web: www.amnb.com

COMPETITORS

BB&T	First Citizens
Bank of America	BancShares
First Century	NewBridge Bancorp
Bankshares	

HISTORICAL FINANCIALS
Company Type: Public

Income Statement
FYE: December 31

	ASSETS ($ mil.)	NET INCOME ($ mil.)	INCOME AS % OF ASSETS	EMPLOYEES
12/12	1,283.6	16.0	1.2%	307
12/11	1,304.7	11.5	0.9%	315
12/10	833.6	8.2	1.0%	242
12/09	808.9	6.8	0.8%	238
12/08	789.1	8.0	1.0%	258
Annual Growth	12.9%	18.9%	—	4.4%

2012 Year-End Financials

Return on assets: 1.2%
Return on equity: 10.1%
Long-term debt ($ mil.): —
No. of shares (mil.): 7
Sales ($ mil): 69

Dividends
Yield: 4.5%
Payout: 45.1%
Market value ($ mil.): 158

	STOCK PRICE ($) FY Close	P/E High/Low		PER SHARE ($) Earnings	Dividends	Book Value
12/12	20.19	12	9	2.04	0.92	20.80
12/11	19.49	15	11	1.64	0.92	19.58
12/10	23.55	18	13	1.35	0.92	17.64
12/09	21.90	21	13	1.12	0.92	17.41
12/08	17.00	17	11	1.31	0.92	16.81
Annual Growth	4.4%	—	—	11.7%	(0.0%)	5.5%

American Public Education Inc

American Public Education (APE) promotes military intelligence. The company offers online post-secondary education to those in the military and other public servants such as police and firefighters. Its American Military University and American Public University make up the American Public University System which offers roughly 90 degree programs and 70 certificate programs in such disciplines as business administration criminal justice intelligence technology liberal arts and homeland security. Enrollment in the online university consists of more than 100000 students from all 50 states and about 100 foreign countries. More than 60% of APE's students serve in the US military on active duty.

APE's nationally and regionally accredited online education system offers associate's bachelor's and master's degrees. It is specifically geared toward adult students who are on call for rapid-response missions or extended deployment. APE has an open enrollment system accepting all applicants with a high school diploma or equivalent and it has some 1800 full- and part-time faculty members to support its students. For those with limited financial resources tuition assistance programs offered by the US Department of Defense constitute about half of the company's annual revenues.

APE is ramping up its outreach efforts focusing on retention of students in its core military market (which represents more than 2 million potential students) while marketing the availability of federal student aid grants and low-cost loans to the public service and civilian markets. It is also expanding the number and type of degrees offered based on demographic trends. In 2011 for instance APE received approval from the Higher Learning Commission to offer degree programs in eight new areas including retail management and accounting.

Its efforts have paid off with the company experiencing rapidly climbing revenues since 2007 including a 31% increase in 2011 to some $260 million. Profits have followed suit with APE reporting a 36% increase in net income in 2011 (to some $41 million). Its annual course registration rate increased more than 30% in both 2010 and 2011. APE attributes the increases to the cost and variety of its programs student referral and satisfaction rates new course accreditations and increasing acceptance of online learning as a viable alternative to bricks and mortar schooling.

APE was founded in 1991 as American Military University by a retired Marine Corps major. It went public in 2007 and used the proceeds to pay stockholders more than $93 million.

EXECUTIVES

EVP Chief Development Officer; CEO Hondros College of Nursing, Harry T. Wilkins, $250,000 total compensation
President and CEO, Wallace E. (Wally) Boston Jr., $357,692 total compensation
EVP and CFO, Richard W. Sunderland Jr.
Chairman, Timothy T. (Tim) Weglicki
Senior Vice President; Chief Administrative Officer, Peter W. (Pete) Gibbons, age 60
EVP Programs and Marketing, Carol S. Gilbert, $187,200 total compensation
Vice Chairman, J. Christopher Everett, age 66
Chief Information Officer, Michael P. Miotto
EVP and Provost, Karan H. Powell
Vice President Registrar, Lyn M. Geer
EVP and COO, Sharon van Wyk
Vice President Student Retention, Ronald Kovach
Vice President Internal Audit, Amy Weber
Vice President Technology Operations and Services, Tracy Woods
Vice President Tax & Budgeting, Mike White
Vice President Student Services, Caroline Simpson
Vice President Strategic Markets and Relationships, Mike Harbert
Vice President Regulatory and Governmental Relations, Russell Kitchner
Vice President Controller, Claudine Stubblefield
Vice President Marketing, Beth Cooper
Vice President Legal Affairs, Tom Beckett
Vice President and Dean, Wynn Berry
Vice President Human Resources, Amy Panzarella
Vice President Financial Aid Services Operations, Gary Spoales
Vice President Enrollment Management, Terry Grant
Vice President Dean of Libraries & Course Materials, Fred Stielow
Vice President Community College Relations and Outreach, John Hough
SVP Academic Operations Officer, Gwendolyn M. (Gwen) Hall
Vice President Military Programs, Jim Sweizer
Vice President Institutional Accreditation, Lynn Wright
Vice President Investor Relations, Chris Symanoskie
Director, F. David Fowler, age 79
President Chief Executive Officer, Wallace E. (Wally) Boston Jr., age 59
Director, Maj. Gen. Barbara G. Fast
Auditors: McGladreyLLP

LOCATIONS

HQ: American Public Education Inc.
111 W. Congress St., Charles Town WV 25414
Phone: 304-334-3880   **Fax:** 304-724-3780
Web: www.americanpubliceducation.com

PRODUCTS/OPERATIONS

2011 Selected Programs

Programs	Number
Undergraduate certificates	35
Graduate certificates	34
Bachelor of Arts	24
Master of Arts	17
Associate of Arts	13
Bachelor of Science	12
Associate of Science	8
Master of Science	6
Master of Education	3
Master of Public Administration	1
Master of Public Health	1
Master of Business Administration	1
Bachelor of Business Administration	1
Total	**156**

Selected Degree Programs

Accounting
Business Administration
Communication
Computer Applications
Counter Terrorism
Criminal Justice
Database Application
Early Childhood Development
Emergency and Disaster Management
English
Environmental Services
Explosive Ordnance Disposal
Fire Science
General Studies
History
Homeland Security
Hospitality
Information Technology
Intelligence Studies
Legal Studies
Management
Marketing
Middle Eastern Studies
Military History
Paralegal Studies
Personnel Administration
Philosophy
Psychology
Public Health
Real Estate Studies
Religion
Space Studies
Transportation and Logistics Management
Weapons of Mass Destruction Preparedness
Web Publishing

COMPETITORS

Apollo Education
Bridgepoint Education
Capella Education
Career Education
Corinthian Colleges
DeVry Education Group
Embry-Riddle Aeronautical University
Grand Canyon Education
Heald College
ITT Educational
Kaplan
Strayer Education
Touro College
University of Maryland

HISTORICAL FINANCIALS

Company Type: Public

Income Statement

FYE: December 31

	REVENUE ($ mil.)	NET INCOME ($ mil.)	NET PROFIT MARGIN	EMPLOYEES
12/12	313.5	42.3	13.5%	2,950
12/11	260.3	40.7	15.7%	1,790
12/10	198.1	29.8	15.1%	1,500
12/09	149.0	23.9	16.1%	1,480
12/08	107.1	16.1	15.1%	1,140
Annual Growth	**30.8%**	**27.2%**	**—**	**26.8%**

2012 Year-End Financials

Debt ratio: —	No. of shares (mil.): 17
Return on equity: 27.6%	Dividends
Cash ($ mil.): 114	Yield: —
Current ratio: 2.56	Payout: —
Long-term debt ($ mil.): —	Market value ($ mil.): 641

	STOCK PRICE ($) FY Close	P/E High/Low	Earnings	PER SHARE ($) Dividends	Book Value
12/12	36.12	19 11	2.35	0.00	9.64
12/11	43.28	21 14	2.23	0.00	7.50
12/10	37.24	29 15	1.59	0.00	5.43
12/09	34.36	35 23	1.27	0.00	4.49
12/08	37.19	55 31	0.86	0.00	2.97
Annual Growth	(0.7%)	— —	28.6%	—	34.3%

American States Water Co.

American States Water holds the essence of life for Californians. Its main subsidiary regulated public utility Golden State Water Company (GSWC) which was formerly known as Southern California Water Company supplies water to more than 255650 customers in 75 communities primarily in Los Angeles San Bernardino and Orange counties. GSWC's Bear Valley Electric subsidiary distributes electricity to almost 23380 Californians in the Big Bear area. American States Water operates in non-regulated water markets through American States Utility Services (ASUS) which offers billing and meter reading services and contracts to operate water and wastewater systems.

Operations

American States Water has two primary business units: Water and Electric Service Utility operations conducted through GSWC; and Contracted Services conducted through ASUS and its subsidiaries (Fort Bliss Water Services Old Dominion Utility Services Old North Utility Services Palmetto State Utility Services and Terrapin Utility Services).

Geographic Reach

GSWC serves customers in 10 counties in California. ASUS and its subsidiaries provide services to customers in California Georgia Maryland New Mexico North Carolina South Carolina Texas and Virginia.

Financial Performance

American States Water's revenues increased by 11% in 2012 due higher ASUS sales thanks to a growth in construction activities at all military bases served particularly at Fort Bragg in North Carolina Fort Jackson in South Carolina Fort Bliss in Texas and military bases in Virginia. Net income grew by 18% in 2012 as a result of higher revenues and increased interest income stemming from changes in a settlement of refund claims approved by the Internal Revenue Service.

The company has seen steady revenue growth since 2008 with the exception of a global recession-induced revenue slump in 2009.

Strategy

Expanding its regulated water customer base in 2011 GSWC signed a deal with a group of developers in Sutter County (California) and a group of water customers in that county to allow GSWC to provide retail water service in a proposed new development (Sutter Pointe).

American States Water's Chaparral City Water unit served more than 13000 customers in Fountain Hills and Scottsdale Arizona. In 2011 in order to pay down debt the company sold this Arizona unit to EPCOR Utilities for about $35 million. It also sold EPCOR Water (USA) unit for $29.6 million.

EXECUTIVES

President and CEO; President and CEO Golden State Water Chaparral City Water and American States Utility Services, Robert J. Sprowls, age 55, $449,212 total compensation

SVP Regulated Utilities Golden State Water and Chaparral City Water, Denise L. Kruger, age 49, $322,827 total compensation

Chair, Lloyd E. Ross, age 72

SVP and Assistant Secretary American States Utility Services, McClellan (Bud) Harris III, age 61, $313,867 total compensation

SVP Finance CFO Treasurer and Corporate Secretary, Eva G. Tang, age 57, $277,792 total compensation

VP Management Services American States Utility Services, James B. Gallagher, age 58, $247,388 total compensation

VP Water Operations Golden State Water and Chaparral City Water, Patrick R. Scanlon, age 55

VP Customer Support Services Golden State Water, Roland S. Tanner, age 56

VP Finance Treasurer and Assistant Secretary Golden State Water; Treasurer and Assistant Secretary American States Water, Gladys M. Farrow, age 48

VP Human Capital Management Golden State Water, Diane D. Rentfrow, age 64

VP Regulatory Affairs Golden State Water, Bryan K. (Keith) Switzer, age 56

VP Environmental Quality Golden State Water, Shengder D. (David) Chang, age 56

VP Asset Management Golden State Water, William C. (Bill) Gedney, age 58

VP Operations American States Utility Services, Granville R. (Rusty) Hodges, age 53

Vice President of Contracts of American States Utility Services; Inc., James Cotton

Director, John R. Fielder, age 67

President CEO and Director; President and CEO Golden State Water Chaparral City Water and American States Utility Services, Robert J. Sprowls, age 55

Director, James F. (Jim) McNulty, age 70

Director, James L. Anderson, age 69

Director, Anne M. Holloway, age 60

Director, N. P. Dodge Jr., age 76

Director, Robert F. Kathol, age 72

Director, Diana M. Bonta, age 61

Director, Gary F. King, age 66

Independent Director, Janice Wilkins

Independent Director, Diana Bonta

Auditors: PricewaterhouseCoopersLLP

LOCATIONS

HQ: American States Water Co.
630 East Foothill Boulevard, San Dimas, CA 91773-1212
Phone: 909 394-3600 **Fax:** 909 394-1382
Web: www.aswater.com

PRODUCTS/OPERATIONS

2012 Sales

	$ mil.	% of total
Water	305	65
Contracted services	124	27
Electricity	37	8
Total	**466**	**100**

Selected Subsidiaries

American States Utility Services Inc. (contracted water and wastewater systems management and utility billing and other services)
 Fort Bliss Water Services
 Old Dominion Utility Services
 Old North Utility Services
 Palmetto State Utility Services
 Terrapin Utility Services
Golden State Water Company (water utility)
 Bear Valley Electric (electric utility)

COMPETITORS

American Water
California Water
 Service
Los Angeles Water and
 Power
Pacific Gas and
 Electric

SJW
SouthWest Water
Southern California
 Edison
Utilities Inc.
Veolia Water North
 America

HISTORICAL FINANCIALS

Company Type: Public

Income Statement

FYE: December 31

	REVENUE ($ mil.)	NET INCOME ($ mil.)	NET PROFIT MARGIN	EMPLOYEES
12/12	466.9	54.1	11.6%	728
12/11	419.2	45.8	10.9%	732
12/10	398.9	33.2	8.3%	127
12/09	360.9	29.5	8.2%	121
12/08	318.7	22.0	6.9%	106
Annual Growth	10.0%	25.2%	—	61.9%

2012 Year-End Financials

Debt ratio: 26.2%
Return on equity: 12.5%
Cash ($ mil.): 23
Current ratio: 1.96
Long-term debt ($ mil.): 332

No. of shares (mil.): 38
Dividends
 Yield: 5.2%
 Payout: 90.0%
Market value ($ mil.): 1,846

	STOCK PRICE ($) FY Close	P/E High/Low	Earnings	PER SHARE ($) Dividends	Book Value
12/12	47.98	34 24	1.41	1.27	11.82
12/11	34.90	30 26	1.22	0.55	10.88
12/10	34.47	44 36	0.89	1.04	10.13
12/09	35.41	47 37	0.81	1.01	9.70
12/08	32.98	66 44	0.63	1.00	8.97
Annual Growth	9.8%	— —	22.3%	6.2%	7.1%

American Vanguard Corp.

American Vanguard Corporation (AMVAC) bugs bugs roots out roots weeds out weeds and helps people take care of their health and personal appearance. The company makes specialty chemicals designed to protect the health of animals crops and people. Products made by its AMVAC Chemical subsidiary include pesticides plant-growth regulators herbicides and soil fumigants. Its GemChem subsidiary distributes the company's chemicals nationally to the cosmetic nutritional and pharmaceutical industries. AMVAC also has marketing subsidiaries in the UK and Mexico.

Operations

The company's SmartBox delivery system allows for controlled and regular dissemination of crop protection products. AMVAC pairs the SmartBox system with its own insecticides as well as with products of Bayer CropScience and Syngenta Crop Protection (through licensing agreements). This allows AMVAC to offer farmers multiple crop protection options thereby not allowing insects to develop resistance to any one pesticide.

Sales and Marketing

Tenkoz; Crop Production Services (formerly United Agri Products Western Farm Services and Crop Production Services); and Winfield accounted for 26% 18% and 11% respectively of AMVAC's revenues in 2011. The US accounted for 79% of 2011 revenues. The largest non-US customer Mexico accounted for 5% of total revenues that year.

Financial Analysis

AMVAC's revenues increased by 34% in 2011 due to a growth in sales of insecticides as a result of sales of granular soil insecticides which were up approximately 125% driven by a strong performance from primary corn soil insecticides - Aztec Smartchoice Counter and Force. This product group also benefitted from the newly acquired Mocap and Nemacur granular insecticides/nematicides which were purchased in December 2010 and net sales of herbicides were up by 5% over prior year whereas non-crop segment net sales were up by about 24%.

Net income increased by 101% in 2011 thanks to higher revenues offset in part by a 28% increase in operating expenses.

Strategy

The company has pursued a growth strategy of acquiring established product lines and companies that complement its core businesses. It also develops and commercializes new compounds through licensing arrangements.

AMVAC acquired the domestic segment of the cotton defoliant product Tribufos (sold under the trade name Def) and the global insecticide Ethoprophos (marketed as Mocap) from Bayer CropScience in 2010. The international segment was acquired in late 2011. The acquisition of Def complements AMVAC's existing cotton defoliant product Folex which it has marketed since 2002. Mocap is used globally to eradicate nematode species in a variety of crops.

In 2010 the company also acquired the Nemacur insecticide from Bayer CropScience which is used in more than 30 countries to fight above-ground sucking insects.

Ownership

Heartland Advisors Herbert A. Kraft (Co-Chairman) and T. Rowe Price Associates own 17% 10% and 10% of the company respectively.

EXECUTIVES

President GemChem, Robert F. (Bob) Gilbane, age 61, $230,022 total compensation

SVP and Director Business Development and Marketing AMVAC Chemical, Glen D. Johnson, age 58, $258,011 total compensation

Chairman and CEO; CEO AMVAC Chemical, Eric G. Wintemute, age 57, $497,870 total compensation

President GemChem, Robert V. (Bob) Gilbane

Human Resources Manager, Teresa Chavez

Co-Chairman, Glenn A. Wintemute, age 88

Co-Chairman, Herbert A. Kraft, age 89

Chief Scientist, William A. (Bill) Feiler

VP and Director Regulatory Affairs AMVAC Chemical, Ian S. Chart

Director Registrations AMVAC Chemical, Jon Wood

Director Toxicology AMVAC Chemical, Ann Manley

VP and Director Manufacturing AMVAC Chemical, Douglas (Doug) Ashmore, age 65, $219,085 total compensation

Customer Service Manager, Glen Anderson

General Manager Quimica Amvac de Mexico, Charles van der Mersch

Director International Business AMVAC Chemical, Alfredo Pelaez

International Product Development Manager AMVAC Chemical, John A. Immaraju

VP Chief Administrative Officer General Counsel and Secretary, Timothy J. (Tim) Donnelly, age 52

Director Marketing AMVAC Chemical, Ted Ramirez

Director Investor Relations and Corporate Communications, William A. Kuser

Senior Regulatory Affairs Manager, Ann Taylor

Product Development Manager Midwest Region AMVAC Chemical, Richard M. Porter

Product Development Manager Northern Region AMVAC Chemical, John E. Orr

Technical Product Manager Impact and Product Development Manager Northeast Region AMVAC Chemical, Bill O'Neal

CFO, David T. Johnson, age 56, $500,000 total compensation

Product Development Manager Southern Region AMVAC Chemical, H. Gary Hancock

Sales and Marketing Manager Central America and The Caribbean AMVAC Chemical, Gerardo Suarez

Sales and Marketing Manager Europe Middle East and Africa AMVAC Chemical, Nicolas Vincent

Sales Manager Central and Southern Illinois AMVAC Chemical, John Jennings

Sales Manager Northern Illinois and Southern Wisconsin AMVAC Chemical, Mark Chastain

Sales Manager Central and Eastern Iowa AMVAC Chemical, Paul Van Zee

Sales Manager Nebraska AMVAC Chemical, Ted Grau

Sales Manager Indiana and Ohio AMVAC Chemical, Toni Whiteside

Sales Manager Central and Western Iowa AMVAC Chemical, Doug DeGraff

Sales Manager Minnesota and South Dakota AMVAC Chemical, Jed Gulbranson

Sales Manager Kansas and Western Missouri AMVAC Chemical, David (Dave) Kriegshauser

Sales Manager Southern Iowa and Eastern Missouri AMVAC Chemical, Rex Rysdam

Sales Manager Kentucky and Southern Indiana AMVAC Chemical, Matthew Mattingly

Sales Manager Michigan Minnesota North Dakota and Northern Wisconsin AMVAC Chemical, Ralph Frederick

Sales Manager Colorado Eastern North Dakota and Northwest Minnesota AMVAC Chemical, Elton Hendrickson

VP Sales AMVAC Chemical Corporation, James (Jim) Lehman

South-East Regional Sales Manager AMVAC Chemical, Scott Hendrix

Sales Manager Texas AMVAC Chemical, Tommy Barton

Sales Manager North East inc. PA NY NC AMVAC Chemical, John Harper

Sales Manager GA SC So. AL FL panhandle AMVAC Chemical, Gerald Harrison

Sales Manager Florida AMVAC Chemical, Michael (Mike) Herrington

Sales Manager AR North ALabama AMVAC Chemical, Tyrus Teague

Western Regional Sales Manager AMVAC Chemical, Kem Cunningham

Sales Manager Indiana AMVAC Chemical, Michael Bell

Sales Manager Washington AMVAC Chemical, Kyle Coleman

Sales Manager California AMVAC Chemical, Steve Hardgrave

Sales Manager Washington AMVAC Chemical, Rennie Kubik

Sales Manager Arizona Southern California and New Mexico AMVAC Chemical, Bryan McCleery

Sales Manager California AMVAC Chemical, Joseph (Joe) Mier

Sales Manager Central Coast California AMVAC Chemical, Michael (Mike) Rover

Manager Purchasing, Maria Rutti

VP and Director Technology AMVAC Chemical Corporation, Johann Venter

Manufacturing Director AMVAC Chemical, John Rizzi

Managing Director AMVAC Netherlands BV, Ad de Jong

Chairman and CEO, Eric G. Wintemute, age 56

Director, Alfred F. Ingulli, age 70

Co-Chairman, Glenn A. Wintemute, age 88

Director, John B. Miles, age 69

Director, Carl R. Soderlind, age 79

Director, Irving J. Thau, age 73

Director, Lawrence S. (Larry) Clark, age 54

Director, John L. Killmer, age 62

Director, Esmail Zirakparvar

Auditors: BDO USA LLP

LOCATIONS

HQ: American Vanguard Corporation
4695 MacArthur Ct., Newport Beach CA 92660
Phone: 949-260-1200   **Fax:** 949-260-1214
Web: www.american-vanguard.com

2011 Sales

US	241	79
Total	**304**	**100**

PRODUCTS/OPERATIONS

2011 Sales

	$ mil.	% of total
Crops		
Insecticides	137	45
Herbicides	90	30
Other	47	15
Non-crop	29	10
Total	**304**	**100**

COMPETITORS

Aceto	DuPont Agriculture
Bayer CropScience	FMC
Dow AgroSciences	KMG Chemicals

HISTORICAL FINANCIALS

Company Type: Public

Income Statement   FYE: December 31

	REVENUE ($ mil.)	NET INCOME ($ mil.)	NET PROFIT MARGIN	EMPLOYEES
12/12	366.1	36.8	10.1%	504
12/11	304.4	22.0	7.2%	390
12/10	229.6	10.9	4.8%	350
12/09	209.3	(5.7)	—	330
12/08	237.5	20.0	8.4%	320
Annual Growth	**11.4%**	**16.5%**	**—**	**12.0%**

2012 Year-End Financials

Debt ratio: 13.1%
Return on equity: 17.8%
Cash ($ mil.): 38
Current ratio: 1.96
Long-term debt ($ mil.): 36

No. of shares (mil.): 28
Dividends
  Yield: 0.7%
  Payout: 19.6%
Market value ($ mil.): 884

STOCK PRICE ($)	P/E		PER SHARE ($)		
FY Close	High/Low	Earnings	Dividends	Book Value
12/12	31.07	28 10	1.28	0.22	7.91
12/11	13.34	18 10	0.79	0.08	6.78
12/10	8.54	24 15	0.40	0.03	6.06
12/09	8.30	— —	(0.21)	0.06	5.60
12/08	11.70	24 10	0.73	0.08	5.79
Annual Growth 27.7%	— —	15.1%	28.8%	8.1%

Amsurg Corp.

It's not quite an assembly line but AmSurg aims to make outpatient surgeries more efficient cost effective and up to date. The company operates ambulatory surgery centers that specialize in a few high-volume low-risk procedures with no overnight stays. Its specialties include gastroenterology (colonoscopy and endoscopy) orthopedics (knee scopes and carpal tunnel repair) ophthalmology (cataracts and laser eye surgery) otolaryngology (earn nose and throat) and urology. Each of its centers are affiliated with physicians practice group and offer either a single or multiple specialty.

Geographic Reach

AmSurg owns a majority interest in more than 240 outpatient centers in 35 US states and Washington DC.

Operations

In 2012 about 1.5 million surgical procedures were performed in its ambulatory surgery centers which have a total of 2000 physician partners.

Typically the local physician practice groups own 49% of each center while AmSurg holds 51%. Gastroenterology and ophthalmology procedures account for the bulk the company's revenues. Because colonoscopies and cataract surgeries are more common among older patients AmSurg is optimistic that the aging population will provide a lucrative revenue stream.

Outpatient surgery is generally less expensive than any hospital stay and managed care plans like to steer their customers to such facilities when possible. AmSurg negotiates to secure managed care contracts with health plan providers and also markets its centers to referring physicians.

Sales and Marketing

The company markets its surgery centers directly to patients referring physicians and third-party payors including health maintenance organizations (HMOs) preferred provider organizations (PPOs) and other managed care organizations.

Financial Performance

AmSurg's revenues grew by 18% in 2012 thanks to an increase in procedures performed in its ASCs as the result of the acquisition of additional centers. The company's net income increased by 25% in 2012 thanks to higher revenues partially offset by an increase in operating expenses.

AmSurg derived 27% of its 2012 revenues from Medicare and other government programs. Changes in reimbursement rates affect the company's revenues directly —up or down. Reforms in the health care law will also affect the company: for instance Medicare and other health plans are now required to completely cover certain preventive screening procedures including colonoscopies.

Strategy

AmSurg acquires develops and operates ambulatory surgery centers in partnership with physician practice groups throughout the US.

The US market is reaching a saturation point with ambulatory surgical centers and procedure volume at its existing centers is limited by facility capacity so AmSurg's primary revenue growth strategy involves acquiring new centers. Historically it has made small acquisitions of centers that already have minority physician ownership.

Mergers and Acquisitions

However in 2011 it bought National Surgical Care which included 17 centers for $135 million.

EXECUTIVES

Chairman, Thomas G. (Tom) Cigarran, age 71
Executive Vice President; Chief Development Officer, David L. Manning, age 65, $384,038 total compensation
Chief Financial Officer; Executive Vice President; Secretary; Director, Claire M. Gulmi, age 60, $387,038 total compensation
President; Chief Executive Officer; Director, Christopher A. Holden, age 49, $537,500 total compensation
Senior Vice President - Operations, Billie A. Payne, $293,123 total compensation
Senior Vice President - Finance; Chief Accounting Officer, Kevin D. Eastridge, age 48, $235,198 total compensation
Executive Vice President - Operations, Phillip A. Clendenin, age 49
Senior Vice President - Corporate Services, Shawn Strash
Director, Henry D. Herr, age 66
EVP CFO Secretary and Director, Claire M. Gulmi, age 59
Director, Ken P. McDonald, age 72
President; Chief Executive Officer; Director, Christopher A. Holden, age 49
Director, James A. Deal, age 63
Director, Steven I. Geringer, age 67
Director, Kevin P. Lavender, age 51
Director, John W. Popp Jr., age 65
Independent Director, Cynthia Miller
Auditors: Deloitte&ToucheLLP

LOCATIONS

HQ: AmSurg Corp.
20 Burton Hills Blvd. Ste. 500, Nashville TN 37215
Phone: 615-665-1283 **Fax:** 615-665-0755
Web: www.amsurg.com

PRODUCTS/OPERATIONS

Strategic Services
Advocacy
Anesthesia Management Services
Development
Information Technology
Marketing and Media Relations
Physician Recruitmen
Quality
Operational Services
Business Operations
Clinical
Compliance
Contracting
Facilities Management and Constructi
Finance
Human Resources
Materials Management

COMPETITORS

Community Health Systems	Symbion
	TLC Vision
Dynacq Healthcare	Tenet Healthcare
HCA	United Surgical Partners
LCA	
Surgical Care Affiliates Inc.	Universal Health Services

HISTORICAL FINANCIALS
Company Type: Public

Income Statement
FYE: December 31

	REVENUE ($ mil.)	NET INCOME ($ mil.)	NET PROFIT MARGIN	EMPLOYEES
12/12	928.5	62.5	6.7%	6,100
12/11	786.8	50.0	6.4%	5,500
12/10	710.4	49.8	7.0%	3,100
12/09	668.7	52.1	7.8%	2,780
12/08	600.6	47.0	7.8%	2,460
Annual Growth	11.5%	7.4%		25.5%

2012 Year-End Financials

Debt ratio: 31.2%	No. of shares (mil.): 31
Return on equity: 9.5%	Dividends
Cash ($ mil.): 46	Yield: —
Current ratio: 2.28	Payout: —
Long-term debt ($ mil.): 620	Market value ($ mil.): 959

STOCK PRICE ($)	P/E		PER SHARE ($)		
FY Close	High/Low	Earnings	Dividends	Book Value
12/12	30.01	16 12	1.98	0.00	21.59
12/11	26.04	17 12	1.60	0.00	19.70
12/10	20.95	14 10	1.62	0.00	18.17
12/09	22.02	14 8	1.69	0.00	16.47
12/08	23.34	19 12	1.47	0.00	14.69
Annual Growth 6.5%	— —	7.7%	—	10.1%

AmTrust Financial Services Inc

Insurance holding company AmTrust Financial Services likes a mix of businesses on its plate. Its subsidiaries offer a range of commercial property/casualty insurance products for small and midsized customers including workers' compensation products auto and general liability workplace and agricultural coverage and extended service and warranty coverage of consumer and commercial goods. It also provides a small amount of personal auto reinsurance. It operates in Bermuda Ireland the UK and the US and distributes its products through brokers agents and claims administrators. The company's customers include restaurants retailers physicians' offices auto and electronics manufacturers and trucking operations.

OperationsAmTrust's revenue comes primarily from premium income from its largest three segments: Specialty Risk and Extended Warranty (about 35% of revenue) Small Commercial Business (30%) and Specialty Program operations (20%). The remainder of revenue comes primarily from the smaller Personal Lines Reinsurance segment and from investment income.

Financial PerformanceAs a result of an aggressive acquisition strategy AmTrust has seen steadily increasing revenue and profits over the last five years. Revenue increased 37% to nearly $1.9 billion in 2012 due to increased workers' compensation policy sales and acquisitions in the Small Commercial Business segment as well as increased underwriting activities in the specialty program segment and higher investment income. Net income rose 4% to $178 million that year on strong revenue growth.StrategyKey to AmTrust's overall business strategy is keeping its portfolio diversified by both business line and geography. Acquisitions are a key aspect of growth; the company also expands by forming new distribution partnerships hiring new specialty lines underwriters and developing new client relationships.

For example in 2012 the company expanded its six-year strategic partnership with CNH Capital by establishing a long-term licensing and service agreement with the company and acquiring its affiliate agencies CNH Capital Insurance Agency and CNH Capital Canada Insurance Agency. The companies will collaborate to expand CNH Capital's offering of equipment extended service contracts and other insurance products to equipment dealers in the US and Canada including CNH-affiliated companies Case New Holland and Kobelco.Mergers and AcquisitionsThe company has been able to expand its product offerings and geographic reach through acquisitions of smaller competitors though it approaches its purchases with a conservative eye avoiding huge financial investments.

In 2013 AmTrust acquired Sequoia Insurance (a provider of commercial property/casualty products in the Western US) for some $60 million as well as Mutual Insurers Holding parent of First Nonprofit Insurance (property and liability coverage for not-for-profit entities) for an undisclosed price.AmTrust also expanded in the warranty market through the purchase of UK-based Car Car Plan from Ally Financial for $70 million in 2013.

In other instances the company simply acquires the renewal rights to blocks of policies issued by other companies. It acquired the renewal rights to a block of workers' compensation policies from Majestic Insurance Company in 2011 and in early 2012 AmTrust added coverage for community banks when it acquired renewal rights to the in-force policies of Oklahoma-based BancInsure.

OwnershipChairman Michael Karfunkel and his family members together own about 50% of AmTrust.

EXECUTIVES

President CEO and Director, Barry D. Zyskind, age 42, $637,019 total compensation
COO, Michael J. Saxon, age 55, $509,615 total compensation
CFO, Ronald E. Pipoly Jr., age 47, $407,962 total compensation
CIO, Christopher M. Longo, age 40, $306,250 total compensation
General Counsel; Secretary, Stephen B. Ungar
CEO AmTrust Europe; President AmTrust International Insurance, Max G. Caviet, age 60, $365,475 total compensation
Chairman, Michael Karfunkel, age 71
Senior Vice President of Finance and Treasurer, Harry Schlachter, age 57
Chief Legal Officer, David H. Saks
President CEO and Director, Barry D. Zyskind, age 42
Director, Donald T. DeCarlo, age 75
Director, George Karfunkel, age 66
Director, Abraham Gulkowitz, age 66
Director, Jay J. Miller, age 82
Independent Director, Susan Fisch
Auditors: BDOSeidmanLLP

LOCATIONS

HQ: AmTrust Financial Services Inc.
59 Maiden Ln. 6th Fl., New York NY 10038
Phone: 212-220-7120 **Fax:** 212-220-7130
Web: www.amtrustgroup.com

2012 Sales

	$ mil.	% of total
Bermuda	1,175	63
US	468	25
Other countries	221	12
Total	**1,865**	**100**

PRODUCTS/OPERATIONS

2012 Sales

	$ mil.	% of total
Specialty risk & extended warranty	693	37
Small commercial business	540	29
Specialty program	411	22
Personal lines reinsurance	112	6
Net investment income	68	4
Net gain on investments	9	-
Corporate & other	30	2
Total	**1,865**	**100**

Selected Acquisitions

2013
Car Care Plan ($70 million warranties)
CPPNA Holdings ($40 million Saint Louis Park Minnesota; administrative services)
Mutual Insurers Holding Company (including subsidiary First Nonprofit Insurance Company property and liability for charitable nonprofits)
Sequoia Insurance ($60 million property/casualty in Western US)
2012
Block of community bank coverage policies (from BancInsure)
Builders & Tradesmen's Insurance Services
2011
Block of workers' compensation policies (from Majestic Insurance Company)
2010
GMAC Insurance Personal Lines (auto policy reinsurance)
Risk Services (80% captive management provider)
Tiger Capital (60% life settlement contract acquisition)
Warrantech (73% it didn't already own for $35 million; third-party warranty administration)

Selected Subsidiaries

AmTrust Europe Ltd. (specialty risk and extended warranty coverage EU)
AmTrust International Insurance Ltd. (reinsurance Bermuda)
AmTrust International Underwriters Limited (specialty risk and extended warranty coverage EU)
Associated Industries Insurance Company Inc. (workers' compensation)
Milwaukee Casualty Insurance Company (small commercial business)
Rochdale Insurance Company (specialty property/casualty specialty risk and extended warranty workers' compensation)
Security National Insurance Company (small commercial business)
Technology Insurance Company Inc. (specialty property/casualty specialty risk and extended warranty workers' compensation)
Wesco Insurance Company (specialty property/casualty specialty risk and extended warranty workers' compensation)

COMPETITORS

AIG	Liberty Mutual
Allianz Insurance	National Indemnity
Amica Mutual	Company
Bankers Financial	The Hartford
Berkshire Hathaway	Travelers Companies
FCCI	

HISTORICAL FINANCIALS

Company Type: Public

Income Statement

FYE: December 31

	ASSETS ($ mil.)	NET INCOME ($ mil.)	INCOME AS % OF ASSETS	EMPLOYEES
12/12	7,417.2	177.9	2.4%	2,100
12/11	5,682.5	170.4	3.0%	1,900
12/10	4,182.4	142.4	3.4%	1,400
12/09	3,400.3	103.2	3.0%	1,000
12/08	3,143.8	82.9	2.6%	900
Annual Growth	23.9%	21.0%	—	23.6%

2012 Year-End Financials

Return on assets: 2.7%
Return on equity: 17.4%
Long-term debt ($ mil.): —
No. of shares (mil.): 73
Sales ($ mil): 1,865
Dividends
Yield: 1.4%
Payout: 15.9%
Market value ($ mil.): 2,121

	STOCK PRICE ($) FY Close	P/E High/Low		PER SHARE ($) Earnings	Dividends	Book Value
12/12	28.69	13	9	2.34	0.37	15.48
12/11	23.75	12	7	2.29	0.28	12.25
12/10	17.50	9	6	1.95	0.26	9.94
12/09	11.82	9	5	1.42	0.21	7.93
12/08	11.60	15	6	1.13	0.16	5.40
Annual Growth	25.4%	—	—	19.9%	22.9%	30.1%

Analogic Corp

Analogic envisions a logical use for data. The company's data acquisition conversion and signal processing gear converts analog signals such as pressure temperature and X-rays into digital computer data. Its medical image processing systems and security imaging products are used in equipment such as CT and MRI scanners and other diagnostic screeners as well as luggage inspection systems. The company also makes ultrasound systems (primarily under the B-K Medical brand) for the surgery anesthesia and general imaging markets among others. Analogic has facilities in Asia Europe and North America and generates more than 60% of its sales outside the US.

Geographic ReachThe US is Analogic's largest single market representing nearly 40% of sales. Japan contributes more than 15% of sales with Germany and The Netherlands adding more than 10% each.

Sales & MarketingThe company's medical imaging and security products are sold to OEMs such as Royal Philips Electronics (14% of sales) L-3 Communications (12%) and Toshiba (10%). Its ultrasound systems are sold to end-users through a direct sales force as well as by independent sales representatives and distributors. Analogic's top 10 customers together account for nearly 70% of sales.

Financial AnalysisAnalogic has experienced consistent revenue and net income growth since fiscal 2009. In fiscal 2012 (ended July 31) the company reported a 9% rise in revenue to about $516 million. Net income more than doubled to $43 million. Although its largest segment medical imaging was flat year-over-year Analogic saw growth in its ultrasound and security segments of 24% and 17% respectively. The ultrasound segment was powered by increased US sales of the Flex Focus product while the security segment rose on demand for Analogic's new high-speed and small-footprint luggage screener systems. The company was able to keep operating expense growth to less than 1% which helped improve net income.

StrategyRecent business activity at Analogic has included the fiscal 2011 sale of a Boston-area hotel and an agreement with London-based Smiths Detection for the creation of a next-generation explosives detection system. The company also underwent some restructuring that year including cutting more than 150 employees from its global workforce.As the health-care market accounts for nearly 90% of Analogic's business the recently passed federal Affordable Care Act may have a significant impact with its provision to impose taxes on medical equipment makers that could add up to $20 billion over ten years. Other provisions of the act such as changes in payment processes could also affect the company.

In mid-2013 Analogic initiated a strategic restructuring to streamline operations following its acquisition of Utrasonix Medical. The restructuring scheduled for completion by the end of fiscal 2014 includes the shuttering of ultrasound transducer operations in Colorado and the loss of about 140 jobs.

Mergers and Acquisitions

In early 2013 the company purchased Vancouver-based Ultrasonix Medical for $83 million as part of it strategy to expand its ultrasound business.

HISTORY

Analogic was founded as Gordon Engineering in 1964 changing its name in 1969.

In 2008 Analogic agreed to give L-3 Communications exclusive worldwide rights to market and service its KING COBRA and XLB1100 checked-baggage screening systems. L-3 was previously marketing Analogic's EXACT/eXaminer 3DX 6000 system for detecting explosives in checked baggage.

That same year Analogic acquired Copley Controls Corp. for nearly $77 million in cash. Copley makes gradient amplifiers for magnetic resonance imaging (MRI) equipment and precision motion control systems. Matthew Lorber the founder president and CEO of Copley Controls was also a founder of Analog Devices an archrival to Analogic.

In 2009 due to worsening global economic conditions the company restructured its operations including a 15% reduction of its workforce and consolidation of office facilities.

Founder and chairman emeritus Bernard Gordon whose engineering work won him a US National Medal of Technology in 1986 left the Analogic board in mid-2009. He has served as chairman of Neurologica Corp. a developer of imaging equipment for neurological scanning applications since 2004.

EXECUTIVES

VP and General Manager Security Systems Business, Eric F. Zanin, age 49
Chairman, Edward F. Voboril, age 71
SVP; General Manager Medical Imaging, Mervat Faltas
President BK Medical, Michael Brock
VP and Corporate Controller, Donald B. (Don) Melson, age 61, $225,522 total compensation
Director Investor Relations and Corporate Marketing, Mark J. Namaroff, age 48

President and CEO; Director, James W. (Jim) Green, age 55, $490,522 total compensation
Vice President Global Human Resources and Administration, Douglas B. (Doug) Rosenfeld
Senior Vice President General Counsel and Secretary, John J. Fry, age 52, $295,022 total compensation
VP Engineering and CTO, John P. O'Connor
SVP Global Operations, James (Jim) Ryan
VP CFO and Treasurer, Michael L. Levitz, age 40, $265,000 total compensation
SVP and General Manager Global Ultrasound Business, Farley Peechatka
VP Global Sales and Service, Matthew (Matt) Theiler
VP and General Manager Asia, Shalabh Chandra
VP Global Marketing, Lars Shaw
VP Global Quality Assurance Regulatory Affairs and Compliance, Joyce Kilroy
Vice President Chief Technology Officer, John O?
Vice President Corporate Strategy and Development, Yash Singh
Vice President Chief Technology Officer, John P. P.
Director, James J. (Jim) Judge, age 57
Director, Fred B. Parks, age 66
Director, Kevin C. Melia, age 65
Director, Michael T. Modic, age 63
Director, Jeffrey P. Black, age 53
Director, Sophie V. Vandebroek, age 51
Director, Bernard C. Bailey, age 60
President and CEO; Director, James W. (Jim) Green, age 55
Auditors: PricewaterhouseCoopersLLP

LOCATIONS

HQ: Analogic Corporation
8 Centennial Dr., Peabody MA 01960
Phone: 978-326-4000   **Fax:** 978-977-6809
Web: www.analogic.com

2012 Sales

	$ mil.	% of total
US	199	39
Japan	81	16
Germany	63	12
Netherlands	61	12
Other	110	21
Total	**516**	**100**

PRODUCTS/OPERATIONS

2012 Sales

	$ mil.	% of total
		% of total
Medical Technology		
Medical		59
Ultrasound		29
Security		12
Total		**100**

Selected Products and Applications

Computed tomography (CT) systems and subsystems
Data acquisition and conversion products
Digital radiography
Explosives detection systems
Magnetic resonance imaging (MRI) subsystems
Motion controls (for auto assembly food and beverage packaging life sciences medical imaging renewable energy semiconductor manufacturing)
Patient monitoring
Radiation therapy
Security imaging
Ultrasound systems and subsystems
Ultrasound transducers and probes

COMPETITORS

American Science and Engineering	Linear Technology
Analog Devices	Maxim Integrated Products
Cirrus Logic	Mercury Systems
Elecsys	Noninvasive Medical Technologies
FUJIFILM Medical Systems	OSI Systems
Fairchild Semiconductor	Overwatch Systems
Freescale Semiconductor	Philips Electronics
GE	STMicroelectronics
Hitachi Medical Systems America	Sensata
Hologic	Smiths Detection
Leidos	Thermo Fisher Scientific
	VASAMED

HISTORICAL FINANCIALS

Company Type: Public

Income Statement

FYE: July 31

	REVENUE ($ mil.)	NET INCOME ($ mil.)	NET PROFIT MARGIN	EMPLOYEES
07/13	550.3	31.1	5.7%	1,700
07/12	516.5	43.0	8.3%	1,600
07/11	473.6	17.8	3.8%	1,500
07/10	423.6	15.5	3.7%	1,400
07/09	396.1	3.7	0.9%	1,450
Annual Growth	**8.6%**	**70.2%**	**—**	**4.1%**

2013 Year-End Financials

Debt ratio: —	No. of shares (mil.): 12
Return on equity: 6.6%	Dividends
Cash ($ mil.): 113	Yield: 0.5%
Current ratio: 3.97	Payout: 15.9%
Long-term debt ($ mil.): —	Market value ($ mil.): 873

	STOCK PRICE ($) FY Close	P/E High/Low		PER SHARE ($) Earnings	Dividends	Book Value
07/13	71.39	33	25	2.48	0.40	39.75
07/12	64.02	20	12	3.42	0.40	36.70
07/11	53.79	40	28	1.42	0.40	33.78
07/10	45.47	39	28	1.23	0.40	31.75
07/09	37.91	258	86	0.29	0.40	31.04
Annual Growth	**17.1%**	**—**	**—**	**71.0%**	**(0.0%)**	**6.4%**

Anika Therapeutics Inc.

Anika Therapeutics uses hyaluronic acid (HA) a natural polymer extracted from rooster combs and other sources to make products that treat bone cartilage and soft tissue. Anika's Orthovisc treats osteoarthritis of the knee and other joints and is available in the US and overseas. (DePuy Mitek sells the product in the US.) The company also makes and sells products that maintain eye shape and protect tissue during eye surgery some of which are marketed by Bausch & Lomb. Other items include surgical anti-adhesive products veterinary osteoarthritis therapies and dermatology products. The US accounts for about three-fourths of sales.

Operations Orthopedic products make up more than 60% of the company's annual revenues. In addition to Orthovisc Anika markets two newer osteoarthritis drugs in international markets: Orthovisc mini (for treatment in small joints) and Monovisc a next-generation single-injection therapy. Anika is looking to move these products into new markets. For instance it received Canadian approval for Monovisc in 2009 and it hopes to gain FDA approval to market Monovisc in the US. It has additional osteoarthritis and joint health treatments under development.

Sales and Marketing As the exclusive marketer of eye surgery viscoelastic agent Amvisc Bausch & Lomb (B&L) has historically accounted for the bulk of Anika's ophthalmic revenues. However an agreement restricting Anika from marketing its own viscoelastic products expired at the end of 2010 after which the firm moved to commercialize its own product AnikaVisc. While Anika markets some products on its own a number are sold through additional partnering firms and distribution representatives. DePuy Mitek and B&L are Anika's largest customers accounting for 47% and 16% of product sales respectively.

Financial Analysis Anika has seen strong revenue growth over the past several years including a 17% jump to $65 million in 2011. Growth that year was led by a 30% year-over-year increase in joint health (orthobiologics) products including Orthovisc in the US and Monovisc internationally. On the back of its strong sales growth the company's net income nearly doubled to more than $8 million in 2011.

Mergers and Acquisitions The company expanded its orthobiologic offerings in 2009 when it acquired Fidia Farmaceutici Biopolymers (FAB) an Italian producer of HA-based products in a number of therapeutic areas including the regeneration of connective and structural tissues damaged by injuries aging or degenerative diseases. FAB's products which are primarily marketed in Europe include Hyalograft C for cartilage regeneration and Hyalofast for bone marrow support. The purchase of FAB also added commercialized products in a range of wound care and surgical areas which were added to Anika's existing dermatology and surgical product lines. Ownership Italian drugmaker Fidia Farmaceutici former parent of Fidia Farmaceutici Biopolymers (which Anika acquired in 2009) owns about 14% of the company.

EXECUTIVES

President and CEO, Charles H. Sherwood, $445,619 total compensation
Vice President - Human Resources, William J. Mrachek, age 69, $219,712 total compensation
CFO Treasurer and Secretary, Kevin W. Quinlan, age 63, $272,364 total compensation
Chief Operating Officer, Frank J. Luppino, age 44, $168,807 total compensation
Chief Scientific Officer, John W. Sheets Jr.
Chief Scientific Officer, Jing-Wen Kuo
Chief Commercial Officer, Carol Barnett
CFO, Sylvia Cheung
President CEO and Director, Charles H. Sherwood, age 66
Director, Raymond J. (Ray) Land, age 68
Director, Joseph L. Bower, age 74
Director, Eugene A. Davidson, age 81
Director, Steven E. Wheeler, age 66
Director, John C. Moran, age 60
Director, Jeffery S. Thompson, age 46
Auditors: PricewaterhouseCoopersLLP

LOCATIONS

HQ: Anika Therapeutics Inc.
32 Wiggins Ave., Bedford MA 01730
Phone: 781-457-9000   **Fax:** 781-305-9720
Web: www.anikatherapeutics.com

2011 Sales

	$ mil.	% of total
US	48	75
Europe	11	17
Other	5	8
Total	**64**	**100**

PRODUCTS/OPERATIONS

2011 Sales

	$ mil.	% of total
Product sales		
Orthobiologics	39	61
Opthalmic surgery	11	17
Surgical	5	8
Dermal	3	6
Veterinary	2	4
Licensing milestone & contract revenue	2	4
Total	**64**	**100**

Selected Products

Orthobiologics
  Hyalofast (bone marrow support)
  Hyaloglide (tenolysis)
  Hyalograft C (autograft for cartilage regeneration)
  Hyalonect (graft gauze wrap)
  Hyaloss (bone regeneration)
  Monovisc (osteoarthritis)
  OrthoVisc (osteoarthritis marketed by DePuy Mitek)
  OrthoVisc mini (osteoarthritis in small joints)
Dermal
  Elevess/Hydrelle (aesthetic dermatology products)
  Hyalograft 3D (skin regeneration)
  Hyalomatrix (burn and ulcer treatment)
Ophthalmic
  Amvisc (eye surgery product sold by Bausch & Lomb)
  Amvisc Plus (eye surgery product sold by Bausch & Lomb)
  AnikaVisc (eye surgery product)
  Optivisc (formerly ShellGel ophthalmic product)
  STAARVISC II (ophthalmic product sold by STAAR Surgical)
Surgical
  Hyalobarrier (post-operative adhesion barrier)
  Incert (post-surgical adhesion prevention product)
Veterinary
  Hyvisc (equine osteoarthritis treatment distributed by Boehringer Ingelheim)

COMPETITORS

Allergan	Pathfinder Cell Therapy
Exactech	
Fibrocell Science	Pfizer
Genzyme Biosurgery	Quidel
Harvard Bioscience	RTI Biologics
ImmunoGen	Smith & Nephew
Integra LifeSciences	Solta Medical
Kensey Nash	Stellar Pharmaceuticals
Lifecore Biomedical	
Medicis Pharmaceutical	Stryker
Merz Aesthetics	XOMA
Obagi Medical	Zimmer Holdings
OrthoLogic	

HISTORICAL FINANCIALS

Company Type: Public

Income Statement

FYE: December 31

	REVENUE ($ mil.)	NET INCOME ($ mil.)	NET PROFIT MARGIN	EMPLOYEES
12/12	71.3	11.7	16.5%	106
12/11	64.7	8.4	13.1%	129
12/10	55.5	4.3	7.8%	114
12/09	40.1	3.6	9.2%	133
12/08	35.7	3.6	10.1%	84
Annual Growth	**18.8%**	**34.2%**	**—**	**6.0%**

2012 Year-End Financials

Debt ratio: 6.7%
Return on equity: 11.5%
Cash ($ mil.): 44
Current ratio: 5.35
Long-term debt ($ mil.): 8
No. of shares (mil.): 13
Dividends
  Yield: —
  Payout: —
Market value ($ mil.): 138

	STOCK PRICE ($) FY Close	P/E High/Low		PER SHARE ($) Earnings	Dividends	Book Value
12/12	9.94	20	10	0.82	0.00	7.86
12/11	9.80	17	8	0.62	0.00	6.95
12/10	6.67	23	15	0.32	0.00	6.32
12/09	7.63	28	10	0.32	0.00	6.12
12/08	3.04	47	9	0.32	0.00	5.34
Annual Growth	**34.5%**	**—**	**—**	**26.5%**	**—**	**10.1%**

Annie's Inc

While doing what it loves Annie's also wouldn't mind taking a bite out of Kraft's business. An organic and natural food producer Annie's makes about 125 products consisting of pastas cereals dressings condiments and snacks through its Annie's Homegrown and Annie's Naturals units. Annie's Homegrown banner includes boxed organic macaroni and cheese breakfast cereals (Cinna Bunnies) fruit snacks (Bunny Fruit) organic granola bars and organic ready meals. Under the Annie's Naturals name the company offers organic and natural salad dressings condiments (marinades sauces mustard ketchup) and olive oil. Annie's which began trading in 2012 is 63%-owned by private equity firm Solera Capital.

Solera which took an equity stake in Annie's in 2002 typically invests in companies that have the potential to become leaders in rapidly growing markets. After completion of the initial public offering (which raised $95 million) Solera retained a controlling interest in Annie's. The natural foods maker plans to use proceeds from going public for working capital and general corporate purposes that likely will include product innovation and development among other initiatives.

Annie's chases after the world's largest organic food market –the US –where the company generates 97% of its revenue. Sales of natural and organic foods in the US exceeded $40 billion in 2010. The company's strategy of targeting this niche of the vast food market has been paying off. Since 2007 Annie's has logged growth in both sales and profit. Sales rose from about $65 million in 2007 to more than $117 million in 2011 resulting in a compound annual growth rate of 15.7%.

The natural food company sells its products through US and Canadian grocery retailers specialty food shops and club stores. Its primary customer wants food made without the use of artificial flavors synthetic colors and preservatives. Among the natural and organic market Annie's holds the #1 spot in four product lines: macaroni and cheese snack crackers fruit snacks and graham crackers. To this end Annie's meals and snacks comprise 80% of its segment sales. The remaining segment –dressings condiments and other –makes up the rest.

For more elbow room and to accommodate the company's larger products portfolio Annie's moved into new corporate digs in 2011. The company entered a lease agreement to rent 34000 sq. ft. of office space in hip hotbead Berkeley California. The move was necessitated by Annie's increased product selection and expanded distribution. Since opening its former office in Napa the natural foods maker had reached $100 million in sales annually. Annie's new office where it also conducts research and development boasts a 4000-sq.-ft. organic garden and green space.

Annie's plans to enter new product categories while it expands its fast-growing snack and pasta products. Such recent introductions include Organic Granola Bars Organic Pretzel Bunnies and Gingersnap and SnickerDoodle Gluten-Free Bunny Cookies. Other initiatives include reducing sodium in its products by another 15% during the next five years sourcing all milk ingredients from cows not treated with synthetic growth hormones to be rBST-free reformulating its products that have cocoa so that the taste is milder and offering its customers more organic products. Annie's Organic Bunny Fruit Snacks (the company's version of gummie bears) have proven to be the company's most successful new product launch ever.

EXECUTIVES

Chairman, Molly F. Ashby, age 54
Chief Executive Officer; Director, John M. Foraker, age 50
SVP Marketing, Sarah Bird, age 53
SVP Sales and Chief Customer Officer, Mark Mortimer, age 53
SVP and Chief Innovation Officer, Robert M. (Bob) Kaake, age 53
Director Human Resources, Amy Barberi
Chief Financial Officer; Treasurer, Kelly J. Kennedy, age 45
VP Finance, Chris Folena
Director of Sustainability, Shauna Sadowski
Director, Bettina M. Whyte, age 64
CEO and Director, John M. Foraker, age 49
Director, Brian T. Murphy, age 59
Director, David A. Behnke, age 62
Auditors: PricewaterhouseCoopersLLP

LOCATIONS

HQ: Annie' s Inc.
1610 Fifth St., Berkeley CA 94710
Phone: 510-558-7500 **Fax:** 907-586-2304
Web: www.sealaska.com

2011 Sales

	$ mil.	% of total
US	114	97
Canada	3	3
Total	**117**	**100**

PRODUCTS/OPERATIONS

2011 Sales

	$ mil.	% of total
Meals	49	42
Snacks	44	38
Dressings condiments & other	23	20
Total	**117**	**100**

COMPETITORS

American Italian Pasta	Kellogg
Amy' s Kitchen	Ken' s Foods
Barbara' s Bakery	Litehouse Inc.
Barilla	Mondelez International
Campbell Soup	Naturally Fresh Inc.
Clif Bar	Nature' s Path
Clorox	Nestle
Frito-Lay	New World Pasta
General Mills	Newman' s Own
HARIBO	Pepperidge Farm
Hain Celestial	PepsiCo
Heinz	Unilever

HISTORICAL FINANCIALS

Company Type: Public

Income Statement

FYE: March 31

	REVENUE ($ mil.)	NET INCOME ($ mil.)	NET PROFIT MARGIN	EMPLOYEES
03/13	169.9	11.5	6.8%	114
03/12	141.3	9.5	6.8%	93
03/11	117.6	20.1	17.1%	86
03/10	96.0	6.0	6.3%	0
03/09	93.6	(0.9)	—	0
Annual Growth	**16.1%**	**—**	**—**	**—**

2013 Year-End Financials

Debt ratio: 7.7%
Return on equity: 20.4%
Cash ($ mil.): 4
Current ratio: 2.95
Long-term debt ($ mil.): 7

No. of shares (mil.): 16
Dividends
  Yield: —
  Payout: —
Market value ($ mil.): 645

	STOCK PRICE ($) FY Close	P/E High/Low	PER SHARE ($) Earnings	Dividends	Book Value
03/13	38.26	72 49	0.65	0.00	3.91
03/12	34.84	61 56	0.26	0.86	97.13
Annual Growth (96.0%)	**9.8%**	**—**	**—150.0%**		

Ansys Inc.

ANSYS helps designers and engineers around the world visualize their ideas. With the company's software product developers can see a simulation of their design concept on their desktop computer before a prototype is built. The computerized models are analyzed for their response to combinations of such physical variables as stress pressure impact temperature and velocity. Ranging from small consulting firms to multinational enterprises its customers come from a broad range of industries and have included Delphi EADS Invensys and Plexus. ANSYS generates two-thirds of its revenues from outside the US with Japan and Germany among its leading international markets.

Geographic Reach
ANSYS has more than 75 sales offices around the world. The US only accounts for about one-third of revenue.

Sales and Marketing
The company sells its products directly and through channel partners worldwide. It uses distribution partners in more than 40 countries. Indirect sales accounted for about one-fourth of ANSYS' total revenues in 2012.

ANSYS also partners with hardware suppliers — including AMD Dell Cray Intel Microsoft and HP among others —to ensure that its products are compatible with technology upgrades. In addition it collaborates with CAD and electronic design automation (EDA) system providers such as Autodesk and Cadence to provide links between products and support data transfer between design packages and ANSYS' simulation portfolio. These strategic alliances provide additional marketing opportunities for the company.

Financial Performance
Sales for 2012 were up 15% to $798 million on increases in both software license and maintenance revenues. New sales also contributed to the year's revenue growth. Net income for 2012 rose to an all-time high of $203 million.

Mergers and Acquisitions
The company periodically makes acquisitions to bolster its product offerings. In 2014 it bought Reaction Design a California company whose CHEMKIN-PRO chemistry simulation software is used by more than 400 customers around the world. Chemistry simulation software is used by transportation and energy companies to develop products without having to rely solely on experiments which could be dangerous. The prior year it bought Evolutionary Engineering AG a Swiss provider of composite analysis to help automotive aerospace energy and marine companies find the best composite materials to build products.

In 2012 it bought French software developer Esterel Technologies for about $58 million. The deal will add Esterel's SCADE application a tool used by software and systems engineers to design simulate and produce embedded software for electronics in aircraft rail automotive and energy systems.

EXECUTIVES

VP Finance and Administration and CFO, Maria T. Shields, age 48, $225,000 total compensation
President CEO and Director, James E. (Jim) Cashman III, age 59, $510,000 total compensation
Chairman, Peter J. Smith, age 68, $130,770 total compensation
Vice President Physics Business Unit, Joseph S. (Joe) Solecki, $119,283 total compensation
VP Worldwide Sales and Support, Joseph C. (Joe) Fairbanks Jr., age 58, $240,000 total compensation
VP General Counsel and Secretary, Sheila S. DiNardo, age 52, $165,000 total compensation
Global Insurance Officer and Investor Relations, Annette N. Arribas, age 46
VP and General Manager; President Apache Designs, Andrew T. Yang, age 52
VP and General Manager Electronics Business Unit, Shane R. Emswiler
VP and General Manager Central Development, Brian C. Drew, age 55, $180,000 total compensation
VP Turbomachinery Industry Marketing, Brad Hutchinson
Lead Academic Product Manager, Paul Lethbridge
VP Marketing, Joshua (Josh) Fredberg, age 43, $38,333 total compensation
Manager Aerospace and Defense Vertical Marketing Strategy, Greg Stuckert
Manager Automotive Vertical Marketing Strategy, Sandeep Sovani
Vice President Human Resources, Debra Burk
Vice President General Manager President Apache, Andrew Ph
Chief Product Officer, Walid Abu-Hadba
Director, William R. (Bill) McDermott, age 51
President CEO and Director, James E. (Jim) Cashman III, age 59
Director, Michael C. Thurk, age 60
Director, Jacqueline C. (Jackie) Morby, age 76
Director, Patrick J. (Pat) Zilvitis, age 70
Director, Bradford C. (Brad) Morley, age 66
Director, John F. Smith, age 78
Directors, Ajei S. Gopal, age 51
Independent Director, Ronald Hovsepian
Auditors: Deloitte&ToucheLLP

LOCATIONS

HQ: ANSYS Inc.
275 Technology Dr., Canonsburg PA 15317
Phone: 724-746-3304 **Fax:** 724-514-9494
Web: www.ansys.com

2012 Sales

	$ mil.	% of total
Europe		
Germany	82	10
Other countries	177	22
North America		
US	265	33
Canada	12	2
Japan	123	15
Other regions	139	18
Total	**798**	**100**

PRODUCTS/OPERATIONS

2012 Sales

	$ mil.	% of total
Software licenses	502	63
Maintenance & service	296	37
Total	**798**	**100**

Selected Acquisitions

FY 2014
Reaction Design (California chemistry simulation
   software)
FY 2013
Evolutionary Engineering AG (Switzerland composite
   analysis)
FY 2012
Esterel Technologies (France critical systems simulation
   software)
FY 2011
Apache Design Solutions (semiconductor simulation
   software)
FY 2008
Ansoft (electronic design automation software)
FY 2006
Aavid Thermal Technologies
FY 2005
Century Dynamics

COMPETITORS

Altair Engineering	Kubotek USA
Autodesk	MSC Software
Bentley Systems	MathWorks
Cadence Design	Mentor Graphics
Dassault	PTC
Delcam	Siemens PLM Software

HISTORICAL FINANCIALS

Company Type: Public

Income Statement
FYE: December 31

	REVENUE ($ mil.)	NET INCOME ($ mil.)	NET PROFIT MARGIN	EMPLOYEES
12/12	798.0	203.4	25.5%	2,400
12/11	691.4	180.6	26.1%	2,100
12/10	580.2	153.1	26.4%	1,660
12/09	516.8	116.3	22.5%	1,600
12/08	478.3	111.6	23.3%	1,750
Annual Growth	**13.6%**	**16.2%**	**—**	**8.2%**

2012 Year-End Financials

Debt ratio: 2.0%
Return on equity: 10.9%
Cash ($ mil.): 576
Current ratio: 1.91
Long-term debt ($ mil.): —
No. of shares (mil.): 92
Dividends
   Yield: —
   Payout: —
Market value ($ mil.): 6,240

	STOCK PRICE ($) FY Close	P/E High/Low		PER SHARE ($) Earnings	Dividends	Book Value
12/12	67.34	34	26	2.14	0.00	20.94
12/11	57.28	32	23	1.91	0.00	18.94
12/10	52.07	32	23	1.64	0.00	16.69
12/09	43.46	33	14	1.27	0.00	14.64
12/08	27.89	36	18	1.29	0.00	13.23
Annual Growth	**24.7%**	**—**	**—**	**13.5%**	**—**	**12.2%**

Apollo Commercial Real Estate Finance Inc.

Apollo Commercial Real Estate Finance invests in buys and manages commercial real estate mortgage loans and other real estate-related debt investments. The company was formed in 2009 by Apollo Global Management to be a mortgage real estate investment trust (REIT). Externally managed by ACREFI Management (an indirect subsidiary of Apollo Global Management) the firm is using proceeds from its 2009 IPO to invest in performing non-distressed US commercial real estate loans; commercial mortgage-backed securities (CMBS); and other commercial real estate debt investments. Apollo Commercial Real Estate Finance expects its average investment to range between $25 million and $75 million.

The REIT raised $200 million from its initial public offering. While Apollo's priority is to invest in senior performing commercial mortgage loans CMBS and commercial real estate debt and loans it may choose to invest in short-term interest-bearing investments such as money market accounts.

EXECUTIVES

CFO Secretary and Treasurer, Stuart A. Rothstein, age 47
Chairman of the Board COO of Apollo Global Management, Henry R. Silverman, age 73
President CEO and Director, Joseph F. Azrack, age 66
Chief Investment Officer, Scott Weiner
President CEO and Director, Joseph F. Azrack, age 66
Independent Director, Alice Connell
Independent Director, Douglas Abbey
Independent Director, Mark Biderman
Independent Director, Michael Salvati
Auditors: Deloitte&ToucheLLP

LOCATIONS

HQ: Apollo Commercial Real Estate Finance Inc.
c/o Apollo Global Management, LLC, 9 West 57th Street, 43rd Floor, New York, NY 10019
Phone: 212 515-3200
Web: www.apolloreit.com

COMPETITORS

Capital Trust	Resource Capital
Petra Real Estate	iStar Financial Inc

HISTORICAL FINANCIALS

Company Type: Public

Income Statement
FYE: December 31

	REVENUE ($ mil.)	NET INCOME ($ mil.)	NET PROFIT MARGIN	EMPLOYEES
12/12	57.0	40.1	70.4%	0
12/11	52.9	25.8	48.9%	0
12/10	32.4	11.0	33.9%	0
12/09	0.6	(2.1)	—	0
Annual Growth	**357.8%**	**—**	**—**	**—**

2012 Year-End Financials

Debt ratio: 28.5%
Return on equity: 9.0%
Cash ($ mil.): 108
Current ratio: 6.97
Long-term debt ($ mil.): 225
No. of shares (mil.): 28
Dividends
   Yield: 9.8%
   Payout: 86.9%
Market value ($ mil.): 455

	STOCK PRICE ($) FY Close	P/E High/Low		PER SHARE ($) Earnings	Dividends	Book Value
12/12	16.23	11	8	1.64	1.60	19.50
12/11	13.13	13	9	1.35	1.60	16.39
12/10	16.35	21	18	0.87	1.50	16.97
12/09	17.99	—	—	(0.21)	0.00	18.15
/0.00	—	—	(0.00)	0.00	(0.00)	
Annual Growth	**—**	**—**	**—**	**—**	**—**	**—**

Approach Resources Inc

Approach Resources takes a different approach to natural gas and oil exploration development and production. Specializing in finding and exploiting unconventional reservoirs the company operates primarily in West Texas' Permian Basin. It also has operations in East Texas. The company's unconventional designation results from a focus on developing natural gas reserves in tight gas sands and shale areas necessitating a reliance on advanced completion fracturing and drilling techniques. In 2012 Approach Resources reported proved reserves of 95.5 million barrels of oil equivalent.

Geographic Reach

The company's operations are focused on the Wolfcamp oil shale resource play in the Permian Basin in West Texas; all of its proved reserves are located in Crockett and Schleicher Counties. It also has minor operations in the East Texas Basin in East Texas.

Operations

In 2012 Approach Resources owned and operated 594 producing oil and gas wells in the Permian Basin and had an estimated 2983 identified drilling and recompletion locations of which 359 were proved. Some 39% of the company's 2012 production was oil; 31% natural gas; and 30% NGLs.

Sales and Marketing

In 2012 Shell Trading (US) and BML each accounted for 22% of company's revenues. Belvan Partners DCP Midstream and Plains Marketing accounted for 20% 17% and 6% respectively.

Financial Performance

Approach Resources revenues increased by 19% in 2012 due to a growth in production volumes (the result of the development of its Pangea project in the Permian Basin) offset by a decrease in oil and gas prices. The average price received for production before the effect of commodity derivatives declined by 4%. The company reported a 12% drop in net income in 2012 as higher revenues were outpaced by higher expenses. Depletion depreciation and amortization expenses increased as the result of higher production and oil and gas property carrying costs.

Strategy

The markets for oil NGLs and gas are volatile and modest drops in prices can affect financial results. Prices for oil NGLs and gas fluctuate widely in response to relatively minor changes in the supply and demand for these commodities market uncertainty and other factors. As "growth-through-the-drillbit" company with limited capital all of the company's proved reserves and production have so far been limited to its core West Texas operations.

In 2013 Approach Resources reported that its production was temporarily negatively affected due to a power outage at the Phillips 66 Sweeny Texas refinery. In 2011 it acquired the remaining 38% working interest (for $76 million) in its Cinco Terry operating area in the Permian Basin Crockett County Texas from two non-operating partners boosting total working and net revenue interests in Cinco Terry to 100% and 76% respectively. That year it acquired additional acreage in Crockett County Texas (10900 contiguous net acres) from private parties. The new acreage (Pangea West) nine miles west of the company's existing acreage boosted Approach Resources' total Permian Basin holdings to 109000 net acres (148000 net acres by the end of 2012).

Ownership
First Manhattan Co. owns 11% of Approach Resources.

EXECUTIVES

EVP and General Counsel, J. Curtis Henderson, age 51, $250,000 total compensation
Chairman, Bryan H. Lawrence, age 71
President CEO and Director, J. Ross Craft, age 57, $297,100 total compensation
EVP and CFO, Steven P. Smart, age 59, $256,000 total compensation
EVP Land, Ralph P. Manoushagian, age 62, $170,000 total compensation
COO, Qingming Yang
Executive VP CFO, Steven P. Sm
Director, James H. Brandi, age 64
Director, James C. (Jim) Crain, age 64
Director, Alan D. Bell, age 67
President CEO and Director, J. Ross Craft, age 56

LOCATIONS

HQ: Approach Resources Inc.
1 Ridgmar Centre 6500 West Fwy. Ste. 800, Fort Worth TX 76116
Phone: 817-989-9000   **Fax:** 817-989-9001
Web: www.approachresources.com
Areas of Operation
West Texas
Ozona Northeast field (Wolfcamp Canyon Sands Strawn and Ellenburge
Cinco Terry project (Wolfcamp Canyon Sands and Ellenburge
East Texas
(Cotton Valley Sands Bossier and Cotton Valley Lime)

PRODUCTS/OPERATIONS

2012 Sales

Oil	82	64
Gas	16	12

COMPETITORS

Abraxas Petroleum	Halcon Resources
Anadarko Petroleum	Legacy Reserves
Chesapeake Energy	Occidental Permian
Clayton Williams Energy	Parallel Petroleum
	Permian Basin
Concho	Quicksilver Resources
Crimson Exploration	Whiting Petroleum
Freeport-McMoRan Oil & Gas LLC	

HISTORICAL FINANCIALS

Company Type: Public

Income Statement

FYE: December 31

	REVENUE ($ mil.)	NET INCOME ($ mil.)	NET PROFIT MARGIN	EMPLOYEES
12/12	128.8	6.3	5.0%	95
12/11	108.3	7.2	6.7%	81
12/10	57.5	7.4	13.0%	55
12/09	40.6	(5.2)	—	45
12/08	79.8	23.3	29.3%	36
Annual Growth	12.7%	(27.7%)	—	27.5%

2012 Year-End Financials

Debt ratio: 12.3%	No. of shares (mil.): 38
Return on equity: 1.1%	Dividends
Cash ($ mil.): 0	Yield: —
Current ratio: 0.26	Payout: —
Long-term debt ($ mil.): 106	Market value ($ mil.): 971

	STOCK PRICE ($) FY Close	P/E High/Low	PER SHARE ($) Earnings	Dividends	Book Value
12/12	25.01	214 125	0.18	0.00	16.31
12/11	29.41	134 61	0.25	0.00	14.13
12/10	23.10	69 18	0.34	0.00	11.80
12/09	7.72	— —	(0.25)	0.00	10.52
12/08	7.31	25 5	1.12	0.00	10.82
Annual Growth	36.0%	— —	(36.7%)	—	10.8%

Arabian American Development Co.

Arabian American Development may dream of making a fortune exploring for precious minerals in Saudi Arabia but it generates its bread-and-butter income as an independent refiner in Texas. Through US subsidiary Texas Oil and Chemical Co. II which owns South Hampton Resources it operates a specialty petrochemical product refinery that primarily produces high-purity solvents used in the plastics and foam industries. South Hampton subsidiary Gulf State Pipe Line owns and operates seven pipelines. It owns a minority stake in the Al Masane mineral ore project in Saudi Arabia and 55% of inactive Nevada-based mining company Pioche-Ely Valley Mines.

Geographic Reach
Arabian American Development's primary operational asset is a specialty petrochemical facility near Silsbee Texas about 30 miles north of Beaumont and 90 miles east of Houston.

Operations
The company's petrochemical product refinery operates seven interconnected operating units which make distinct products: a Penhex unit; a Reformer; a Cyclo-pentane unit; an Aromax? unit; an Aromatics Hydrogenation unit; a White Oil Fractionation unit; and a Hydrocarbon Processing Demonstration unit.

South Hampton owns 16 trucks and 23 trailers. Gulf State owns and operates three 8-inch diameter pipelines and five 4-inch diameter pipelines which connect South Hampton's facility to a natural gas line a truck and rail loading terminal and

a major third party-owned petroleum products pipeline system.

Financial Performance
Arabian American Development's revenues grew by 11% in 2012 primarily due to an increase in sales volume offset by a decrease in selling prices and processing revenues. Sales of petrochemical products increased to 12% due to higher sales volumes. Processing revenue dropped by 11% due to a tolling customer's inability to obtain raw material which impacted their run rates.

Net income declined by 17% in 2012 thanks to increased General and administrative expenses and depreciation due to expenses recorded for administrative payroll costs officers' compensation directors' fees insurance premiums travel costs and other expenses (property taxes accounting fees investor relations' expenses and expenses in Saudi Arabia). A cost of living adjustment and an increase in management and officer compensation increased payroll costs.

Ownership
Fahad Mohammed Saleh Al Athel owns almost 18% of Arabian American Development.

Company Background
Arabian American Development was founded following former CEO Hatem El-Khalidi's 1967 discovery by air of the Al Masane project which El-Khalidi later mapped on camelback. The project contains extensive ancient minerals originally mined from 1000 BC to 700 AD. These undeveloped mineral interests will require a major capital investment to make them commercially viable. Hatem El-Khalidi stepped down as CEO in 2009.

To generate cash for its long term mineral ore project in Saudi Arabia in 2009 Arabian American transferred its mining lease (for copper gold silver and zinc) in the Al Masane area to Saudi Arabia-based Al Masane Al Kobra Mining in return for a 41% stake (37% in 2012).

EXECUTIVES

President Chief Executive Officer, Nicholas N. Carter, age 66, $209,918 total compensation
Chief Accounting Officer Secretary and Treasurer; Secretary and Treasurer TOCCO, Connie J. Cook, age 50, $133,009 total compensation
VP Marketing Petrochemical Company, Mark D. Williamson, $240,705 total compensation
Vice President - Manufacturing of TOCCO, Ronald Franklin
Executive Vice President of South Hampton Resources; Inc, Simon Upfill-Brown
President Chief Executive Officer, Nicholas N. August
President Chief Executive Officer, Nicholas N. Carter, age 66
Director, Mohammed O. Al Omair, age 69
Director, Ghazi Sultan, age 75
Director, Robert E. Kennedy, age 67
Director, Charles W. Goehringer Jr., age 54
Director, Allen P. McKee
Director, John R. Townsend
Independent Director, Joseph Palm
Auditors: MooreStephensTravisWolffLLP

LOCATIONS

HQ: Arabian American Development Co.
1650 Hwy 6 South, Suite 190, Sugar Land, TX 77478
Phone: 409 385-8300
Web: www.arabianamericandev.com

PRODUCTS/OPERATIONS

2012 Sales

	$ mil.	% of total
Petrochemical product sales	218	98
Processing	4	2
Total	**222**	**100**
Subsidiaries and Affiliates		
Al Masane Al Kobra Mining Company (37%)		
Gulf State Pipe Line Company		
Pioche-Ely Valley Mines Inc. (55%)		
South Hampton Resources Inc.		
Texas Oil and Chemical Co. II Inc.		

COMPETITORS

ConocoPhillips	Equistar Chemicals
Dow Chemical	Formosa Plastics USA

HISTORICAL FINANCIALS

Company Type: Public

Income Statement

FYE: December 31

	REVENUE ($ mil.)	NET INCOME ($ mil.)	NET PROFIT MARGIN	EMPLOYEES
12/12	222.8	11.4	5.1%	168
12/11	199.5	8.4	4.2%	160
12/10	139.1	2.6	1.9%	145
12/09	117.5	6.6	5.6%	140
12/08	154.6	(8.8)	—	145
Annual Growth	**9.6%**	**—**	**—**	**3.7%**

2012 Year-End Financials

Debt ratio: 12.9%	No. of shares (mil.): 23
Return on equity: 15.2%	Dividends
Cash ($ mil.): 9	Yield: —
Current ratio: 3.39	Payout: —
Long-term debt ($ mil.): 14	Market value ($ mil.): 198

	STOCK PRICE ($) FY Close	P/E High/Low		PER SHARE ($) Earnings	Dividends	Book Value
12/12	8.31	23	15	0.46	0.00	3.49
12/11	8.48	29	9	0.35	0.00	2.78
12/10	4.42	39	16	0.11	0.00	2.39
12/09	2.40	14	3	0.28	0.00	2.23
12/08	1.60	—	—	(0.38)	0.00	2.00
Annual Growth	**51.0%**			**—**	**—**	**14.9%**

Asia Carbon Industries Inc.

LOCATIONS

HQ: Asia Carbon Industries Inc.
Xi Gu Nan Street, Qing Xu County, Taiyuan City, Shanxi Province 030407
Phone: (86) 351 5966868   **Fax:** (86) 351 5966308
Web: www.asiacarbonindustries.com

HISTORICAL FINANCIALS

Company Type: Public

Income Statement

FYE: December 31

	REVENUE ($ mil.)	NET INCOME ($ mil.)	NET PROFIT MARGIN	EMPLOYEES
12/12	45.9	6.4	14.0%	202
12/11	49.1	7.3	14.9%	221
12/10	29.6	3.2	11.0%	222
12/09	20.6	2.9	14.5%	0
Annual Growth	**30.5%**	**29.3%**	**—**	**—**

2012 Year-End Financials

Debt ratio: 3.4%	No. of shares (mil.): 52
Return on equity: 20.2%	Dividends
Cash ($ mil.): 6	Yield: —
Current ratio: 2.99	Payout: —
Long-term debt ($ mil.): —	Market value ($ mil.): 10

	STOCK PRICE ($) FY Close	P/E High/Low		PER SHARE ($) Earnings	Dividends	Book Value
12/12	0.19	4	1	0.12	0.00	0.67
12/11	0.64	8	4	0.14	0.00	0.55
12/10	1.15	17	16	0.07	0.00	0.38
12/09	0.00	—	—	0.07	0.00	0.36
Annual Growth	**—**		**—**	**19.7%**	**—**	**23.4%**

Astronics Corp.

In the glare of its own lights but without histrionics Astronics Corporation displays its talents daily to a specialized audience. Astronics makes external and internal lighting systems as well as power generation and distribution technology for commercial general aviation and military defense aircraft. Products include cabin emergency lighting systems (escape path markers and exit locators) cockpit lighting systems (avionics keyboards ambient light sensors annunciator panels and electronic dimmers) external lights and military test equipment. Astronics operates subsidiaries include Astronics Advanced Electronic Systems Corp. Ballard Luminescent Systems and DME Corporation.

Operations

The company operates in two segments: Aerospace and Test Systems. The Aerospace segment designs and makes a range of products for the global aerospace industry. Its products include aircraft lighting airframe power avionics airfield lighting and cabin electronics. The Test Systems segment designs develops and manufactures communications and weapons test systems and training and simulation devices for military clients.

Sales and Marketing

Astronics' customers include the Department of Defense (DOD) Federal Aviation Administration and airport operators US military forces foreign military agencies and makers of military communication systems.

Financial Performance

The company's revenues grew by 17% in 2012 thanks to a 19% increase in Aerospace sales partially offset by lower sales volume in Test Systems segment. Sales growth was primarily driven by higher sales of cabin electronics to commercial airlines as well as the impact of the Ballard acquisition.

Astronics' net income bumped up by 1% in 2012 as the result of higher revenues partially offset by the increase in SG&A expenses (including higher legal expenses and cost related to the Ballard and Max-Viz acquisitions). It also benefited from the absence of an impairment loss (it carried one in 2011).

Strategy

The company continues to invest in new technologies and aircraft programs for each of its markets even while the aerospace industry as a whole is experiencing a slowdown along with the economy in general. In particular Astronics is developing an electrical power distribution system for the Learjet 85 that shows promise of becoming a standard component of business jets. Its products and technologies are also used in the F-35 Joint Strike Fighter the Airbus A380 XWB and the Boeing 787 to name a few.

Mergers and Acquisitions

Growing its Aerospace portfolio in 2012 Astronics acquired Max-Viz a designer and manufacturer of enhanced vision systems for defense and commercial aerospace applications. In 2011 Astronics bought Ballard Technology which designs and manufactures avionics databus solutions for aerospace applications.

Ownership

Astronics' Chairman Kevin Keane owns about 28% of the company.

Company Background

Astronics has become more dependent on the DoD since its 2009 acquisition of DME Corporation a provider of military test training and simulation equipment. The company is expected to make a substantial increase in product offerings sales and headcount due to the acquisition. The addition of DME gives Astronics a stronger foothold in the defense industry and is intended to provide balance to its core lighting systems business. In mid-2010 DME won a five-year $7.4 million contract with the US Air Force to install airfield lighting at bases across the country.

HISTORY

Founded in 1968 Astronics was originally involved in electroluminescent products until it began to diversify into the packaging and printing industries. The company acquired MOD-PAC a maker of paperboard packaging in 1972 and Krepe-Kraft a specialized printing company in 1987.

In 1995 Astronics bought Loctite Luminescent Systems and integrated it with E-L FlexKey Technologies which specialized in components used in the aerospace and military electronics industries. Later renamed Luminescent Systems the division was awarded two high-dollar Canadian contracts the following year. One contract was for cockpit lighting systems for Bombardier's long-range business jets; the other was for ruggedized keyboards for the control room of a Canadian nuclear power plant.

The US Air Force awarded Astronics a contract to manufacture night-vision lighting for the F-16 aircraft in 1998. The next year the company was awarded an additional contract that almost doubled the number of units it would provide for F-16s. Astronics' aerospace and electronics segment doubled its manufacturing capabilities with the addition of two new facilities.

The company further enhanced its ability to fulfill its F-16 contract with the acquisition of Canada-based CRL Technologies (lighted keyboards) in 2000. Also that year Astronics acquired illuminated indicators for use in aircraft cockpits from

Aerospace Avionics. In late 2001 the company was awarded a contract from the US government to provide lighted control panels for the Bradley M2A3 infantry fighting vehicle. The following year it received a contract from the US Air Force valued at up to $30 million to develop spare parts for the F-16.

Astronics discontinued its electroluminescent lamp business in 2002 and spun off MOD-PAC in 2003. It entered the market for electrical power generation control and distribution systems for aircraft in 2005 by buying the assets of Airborne Electronics Systems from a unit of General Dynamics. Astronics paid $13 million for Airborne Electronics Systems which had revenues of about $25 million in 2004.

EXECUTIVES

Executive Vice President Luminescent Systems, James S. (Jim) Kramer
President and Chief Executive Officer; Director, Peter J. Gundermann, age 51, $295,000 total compensation
Chairman of the Board, Kevin T. Keane, age 80, $150,000 total compensation
VP Luminescent Systems, Frank G. Johns III
VP Luminescent Systems, Richard C. (Rick) Miller
Vice President and Chief Financial Officer; Secretary, David C. Burney, age 51, $200,000 total compensation
Executive Vice President Astronics Advanced Electronic Systems, Mark Peabody
Manager Human Resources, Jill Draper
Director, John B. Drenning, age 76
Director, Robert J. McKenna, age 64
Director, Robert T. (Bob) Brady, age 73
President and Chief Executive Officer; Director, Peter J. Gundermann, age 51
Director, Raymond W. (Ray) Boushie, age 73
Auditors: Ernst&YoungLLP

LOCATIONS

HQ: Astronics Corporation
130 Commerce Way, East Aurora NY 14052
Phone: 716-805-1599   **Fax:** 716-805-1286
Web: www.astronics.com

2010 Sales

	$ mil.	% of total
North America	168	86
Asia	13	7
Europe	11	6
South America	2	1
Other regions	0	-
Total	**195**	**100**

PRODUCTS/OPERATIONS

2012 Sales

Aerospace	254	96
Total	**266**	**100**

2012 Sales by Product Line

Aerospace		
Aircraft lighting	69	26
Avionics	15	6
Airfield lighting	9	4
Total	**266**	**100**

Selected Products:

Aircraft lighting
  Cabin Lighting
  Cockpit Lighting Systems
  Escape Slide Lighting
  Exterior Lighting
  Flashlights
  Lighting Control Products
  Night Vision

Aircraft Power
  System Design Analysis & Integration
  CorePower Systems
  Power Management
  Control Systems
Aircraft Safety
  Child Restraint Systems
  Emergency Beacons
  Escape Path Marking
  Escape Slide Lighting
  First Aid Kits
  Flashlights
  Interior Signs and Lighting
  Survival Kits
Airfield Lighting
  Approach & NavAids Systems
  Design-Build NavAids Lighting Solutions
  Elevated Lights
  Guidance Signs
  Heliport Lights
  In-Pavement Lights
  Markers
  Obstruction Lights
  Power & Control Equipment
  Solar Lights
  Tools & Accessories
  Tower Equipment
Cabin Power
  In-Seat Power Systems
  Integrated Seat Power
  Other Products
Test solutions
  ArcSafe
  Automated Test Equipment
  Factory Test Systems
  Radio Test Solutions
  Software Development
  Test EZ
  Test Program Sets

Selected Subsidiaries

Astronics Advanced Electronic Systems Corp
Ballard Technology Inc
DME Corporation
Luminescent Systems Canada Inc
Luminescent Systems Inc
Max-Viz Inc

COMPETITORS

AIM Aviation	L-3/IS
B/E Aerospace	Premium Aircraft
C&D Zodiac	Interiors Group
Ducommun	TransDigm Group
Goodrich Corp.	Ultra Electronics
Honeywell Aerospace	Zodiac Aerospace
Indel	

HISTORICAL FINANCIALS

Company Type: Public

Income Statement

FYE: December 31

	REVENUE ($ mil.)	NET INCOME ($ mil.)	NET PROFIT MARGIN	EMPLOYEES
12/12	266.4	21.8	8.2%	1,156
12/11	228.1	21.5	9.5%	1,081
12/10	195.7	14.9	7.6%	1,010
12/09	191.2	(3.8)	—	1,035
12/08	173.7	8.3	4.8%	989
Annual Growth	**11.3%**	**27.2%**	**—**	**4.0%**

2012 Year-End Financials

Debt ratio: 14.1%
Return on equity: 19.1%
Cash ($ mil.): 7
Current ratio: 2.25
Long-term debt ($ mil.): 20
No. of shares (mil.): 17
Dividends
  Yield: —
  Payout: —
Market value ($ mil.): 397

	STOCK PRICE ($) FY Close	P/E High/Low	PER SHARE ($) Earnings	Dividends	Book Value
12/12	22.88	29 16	1.21	0.00	7.21
12/11	35.81	26 13	1.39	0.00	6.94
12/10	21.00	20 6	1.10	0.00	5.88
12/09	8.55		(0.29)	0.00	4.65
12/08	8.90	62 11	0.66	0.00	4.73
Annual Growth	**26.6%**	**— —**	**16.4%**	**—**	**11.1%**

Athenahealth Inc

athenahealth knows that managing physician practices can result in a splitting headache especially when patients are late paying bills or missing appointments. The company provides health care organizations with online software for cloud-based electronic health record (EHR) practice management and patient communication services. Offerings include revenue cycle management (athenaCollector) medical record automation (athenaClinicals) and patient relations and referral systems (athenaCommunicator and athenaCoordinator). Its services help health care providers streamline workflow data and billing and collection tasks. athenahealth's programs are managed through its cloud-based athenaNet network.

Geographic Reach
athenahealth serves clients in more than 45 states. It has a half dozen offices in the US and one in India.

Operations
Almost 40000 medical providers (including more than 28000 physicians) use the company's athenaCollector services. In 2011 athenahealth's offerings were used by its clients to post more than $7 billion in physicians' collections and to process about 60 million medical claims.

Sales and Marketing
athenahealth primarily uses a direct sales force to promote its products though it also has third-party distribution channels in certain regions. Its sales force is divided into enterprise group and small group teams while the channel partners are typically compensated for passing on sale leads. Channel partners (such as Humana and PSS World Medical) account for about 40% of new business.

The company serves hospitals clinics and medical professionals including family practice offices and practitioners in more than 75 medical specialty fields. athenahealth employs a variety of marketing techniques to recruit new customers and increase its brand awareness including online and print advertising campaigns; trade shows; email and phone programs; and information sessions and seminars for potential clients.

Financial Performance
athenahealth reported a 30% increase in revenues in 2012 to $422 million which was attributed to its larger customer base and a broader array of implementation and business services provided to those customers. Profits dipped slightly (1%) to $18 million as operating expenses grew from the company's expanded headcount - athenahealth boosted its workforce by 30% in 2012 (going from 1800 employees to 2300).

Still the company has been in the black for the past five years. It's experienced rapid growth over those years as demand for health care information technology services has increased.

Strategy

There is a huge opportunity for health care information technology services in the US as the Patient Protection and Affordable Care Act (PPACA) is driving more people to have health insurance.

athenahealth's strategy includes meeting the needs of specific clients (and thus garnering loyalty) integrating multiple programs into clients' comprehensive workflows and forming new client relationships through focused marketing efforts. It also seeks to provide products that are easy to adopt into daily practice routines while helping customers to reduce administrative costs. athenahealth is especially focused on increasing use of its newer athenaRules offering which helps health care clients comply with the reimbursement rules of government and commercial health plans.

Mergers and Acquisitions

In 2013 the company bought Epocrates which provides doctors with clinical information software in a mobile format. Some 330000 physicians use Epocrates and athenahealth believes its mobile technology can be leveraged for other applications.

The prior year athenahealth acquired Healthcare Data Services a provider of online population-based cost and quality data analysis and reporting tools that give health care organizations a way to manage the new risk-based payment models being enacted under health care reform initiatives. The purchase also extended athenahealth's cloud-based physician practice services adding population health management capabilities to its existing EHR platform. In 2011 athenahealth expanded its cloud services through the $28 million purchase of Proxsys.

EXECUTIVES

SVP and Chief Marketing Officer, Robert L. (Rob) Cosinuke, age 52, $250,000 total compensation
President Enterprise Services, Stephen N. Kahane, age 55
SVP CFO and Treasurer, Timothy M. (Tim) Adams, age 54
SVP General Counsel and Secretary, Daniel H. Orenstein
VP and Chief Medical Officer, Todd Rothenhaus
EVP and COO, Ed Park
VP Business Development, Derek Hedges
Senior Vice President Chief Technology Officer, Jeremy Delinsky
CEO, Timothy W. McGill
Director - Investor Relations, Dana Quattrochi
Director, David E. (Dave) Robinson, age 69
Director, James L. (Jim) Mann, age 79
Director, John A. (Jack) Kane, age 60
Director, William Winkenwerder Jr.
Director, Dev Ittycheria, age 47
Director, Brandon H. Hull, age 52
Auditors: Deloitte&ToucheLLP

LOCATIONS

HQ: athenahealth Inc.
311 Arsenal St., Watertown MA 02472
Phone: 617-402-1000   **Fax:** 617-402-1099
Web: www.athenahealth.com

PRODUCTS/OPERATIONS

2012 Sales

	$ mil.	% of total
Business services	408	97
Implementation & other	13	3
Total	**422**	**100**

Selected Software

athenaClinicals (medical record management)
athenaCollector (claims management)
athenaCommunicator (patient communication management)
athenaCoordinator (referrals management)
athenaNet (cloud system)
athenaRules (compliance system)

COMPETITORS

Allscripts	Quality Systems
CBIZ	Sage Group
Epic Systems	Sage Software
GE Healthcare	Siemens Healthcare
Greenway Medical	UnitedHealth Group
Technologies	eClinicalWorks
McKesson	

HISTORICAL FINANCIALS

Company Type: Public

Income Statement

FYE: December 31

	REVENUE ($ mil.)	NET INCOME ($ mil.)	NET PROFIT MARGIN	EMPLOYEES
12/12	422.2	18.7	4.4%	2,339
12/11	324.0	19.0	5.9%	1,795
12/10	245.5	12.7	5.2%	1,242
12/09	188.5	9.2	4.9%	1,035
12/08	139.5	28.8	20.7%	824
Annual Growth	**31.9%**	**(10.3%)**	**—**	**29.8%**

2012 Year-End Financials

Debt ratio: —	No. of shares (mil.): 36
Return on equity: 6.8%	Dividends
Cash ($ mil.): 156	Yield: —
Current ratio: 4.10	Payout: —
Long-term debt ($ mil.): —	Market value ($ mil.): 2,660

	STOCK PRICE ($) FY Close	P/E High/Low	PER SHARE ($) Earnings	Dividends	Book Value
12/12	73.29	186 96	0.50	0.00	8.59
12/11	49.12	128 73	0.53	0.00	6.68
12/10	40.98	128 60	0.36	0.00	4.95
12/09	45.24	167 84	0.27	0.00	3.76
12/08	37.62	42 24	0.83	0.00	3.48
Annual Growth	**18.1%**	**— —**	**(11.9%)**	**—**	**25.4%**

Atlantic Tele-Network, Inc.

Atlantic Tele-Network (ATN) makes connections from the maple groves of Vermont to the rain forests of Guyana. In the US where it does more than 90% of its business the company provides wholesale wireless voice and data roaming services to local and national communications carriers through subsidiary Commnet Wireless. ATN provides retail mobile service under the Alltel brand in rural markets of the Southwest and Midwest and it provides voice and broadband Internet services in New England particularly Vermont through its SoVerNet subsidiary. SoVerNet subsidiary ION offers fiber-optic transport services in New York State on a wholesale basis.

ATN also provides communications services in the Caribbean through its subsidiaries including Choice Communications which offers Internet access in the US Virgin Islands under the ClearChoice brand. The company owns 80% of phone service carrier Guyana Telephone & Telegraph (GT&T) the government of Guyana owns the rest which serves both fixed-access telephone lines and cellular subscribers under the Cellink brand. Top customers for long-distance calls into and out of Guyana have historically been US carriers like AT&T and IDT.

The company serves mobile customers in Bermuda through Bermuda Digital Communications (BDC) which trades as CellularOne and in the Turks and Caicos islands through Islandcom Telecommunications. CellularOne merged with another Bermuda carrier M3 Wireless in 2011 to expand its market share on the island; the business retained the CellularOne brand.

On the mainland that year ATN through Commnet formed a joint venture with the non-profit Navajo Tribal Utility Authority (NTUA) to provide the first 3G and 4G wireless services to residents of the Navajo Nation. Known as NTUA Wireless the venture is upgrading telecommunications systems in areas of Arizona New Mexico and Utah partly using about $32 million in grant funding from the American Investment and Recovery Act. Cell phone and wireless Internet service will be rolled out in 2012 and 2013.

ATN acquired wireless assets in six states (Georgia Idaho Illinois North Carolina Ohio and South Carolina) from Verizon Wireless in 2010. The deal was part of a broader disposal by Verizon of certain overlapping operations acquired in its 2009 purchase of Alltel; the sale was required to satisfy anti-trust conditions laid out by federal regulators. The $200 million purchase which expanded ATN's subscriber base by about 800000 in mostly rural areas was part of the company's ongoing plan to build its service area through acquisitions and partnerships with other carriers. In 2013 however it agreed to sell those retail wireless assets to AT&T for some $780 million. ATN plans to use the proceeds to strengthen its core business possibly through acquisition.

ATN's sales jumped by about 150% in 2010 due to more than $290 million in US wireless revenue added by the assets gained in the Verizon/Alltel deal. The company had no retail wireless business in the US prior to that year. The deal also boosted its wholesale business in 2010. Meanwhile in keeping with the broader industry trend ATN's wireline sales decreased for the year.

The company turned in another profitable year in 2010 but its profit margin dropped by more than half due to significantly higher expenses (more than 230%) caused by massive increases in the costs of equipment sales and marketing related to ATN's expanded business. Termination and access fees also rose notably and engineering and administrative costs were higher as well.

Chairman Cornelius Prior owns about 36% of the company.

EXECUTIVES

CEO Guyana Telephone and Telegraph, Sonita Jagan, age 46
Chairman; Chairman Guyana Telephone and Telegraph, Cornelius B. Prior Jr., age 79, $306,000 total compensation
CEO Atlantic Wireless Communications, Frank A. O'Mara, age 45
Chief Financial Officer; Treasurer, Justin D. Benincasa, age 51, $230,000 total compensation

President; Chief Executive Officer; Director, Michael T. Prior, age 48, $430,000 total compensation

VP General Counsel and Secretary, Douglas J. Minster, age 52, $149,000 total compensation

Chief Accounting Officer, Andrew S. Fienberg, age 45, $140,000 total compensation

VP Financial Analysis and Planning, John P. Audet, age 55, $145,000 total compensation

Senior Vice President Corporate Development, William F. (Bill) Kreisher, age 50, $210,000 total compensation

Senior Vice President Controller, Karl D. Noone, age 44

President of International Operations, Paul R. Bowersock

Corporate Secretary, Cynthia Solano

Senior Vice President General Counsel, Leonard Slap

Director, Charles J. Roesslein, age 64

Director, Henry U. Wheatly, age 81

President; Chief Executive Officer; Director, Michael T. Prior, age 48

Director, Martin L. (Marty) Budd, age 72

Director, Thomas V. (Tom) Cunningham, age 45

Director, Brian A. Schuchman, age 45

Independent Director, Gen He

Independent Director, Michael Flynn

Auditors: PricewaterhouseCoopersLLP

LOCATIONS

HQ: Atlantic Tele-Network Inc.
10 Derby Sq., Salem MA 01970
Phone: 978-619-1300   **Fax:** 978-744-3951
Web: www.atni.com

2010 Sales

	$ mil.	% of total
US	567	92
Caribbean	51	8
Total	**619**	**100**

PRODUCTS/OPERATIONS

2010 Sales

	$ mil.	% of total
Wireless	504	82
Wireline	84	14
Equipment & other	30	4
Total	**619**	**100**

COMPETITORS

AT&T Mobility	Sprint Communications
America Movil	Telephone & Data
Digicel Jamaica	Systems
FairPoint	Verizon
Communications Inc.	

HISTORICAL FINANCIALS

Company Type: Public

Income Statement

FYE: December 31

	REVENUE ($ mil.)	NET INCOME ($ mil.)	NET PROFIT MARGIN	EMPLOYEES
12/12	741.3	48.9	6.6%	1,800
12/11	759.2	21.7	2.9%	1,884
12/10	619.1	38.4	6.2%	1,765
12/09	241.7	35.5	14.7%	889
12/08	207.3	34.8	16.8%	864
Annual Growth	**37.5%**	**8.9%**	**—**	**20.1%**

2012 Year-End Financials

Debt ratio: 29.2%	No. of shares (mil.): 15
Return on equity: 15.5%	Dividends
Cash ($ mil.): 136	Yield: 2.6%
Current ratio: 1.61	Payout: 37.5%
Long-term debt ($ mil.): 250	Market value ($ mil.): 572

	STOCK PRICE ($) FY Close	P/E High/Low		PER SHARE ($) Earnings	Dividends	Book Value
12/12	36.71	14	10	3.13	0.96	21.45
12/11	39.05	30	21	1.41	0.90	19.04
12/10	38.37	23	13	2.48	0.84	18.45
12/09	54.95	25	6	2.32	0.76	16.79
12/08	26.55	15	8	2.28	0.68	15.03
Annual Growth	**8.4%**	**—**	**—**	**8.2%**	**9.0%**	**9.3%**

Atwood Oceanics, Inc.

Atwood Oceanics is at work in oceans all over the world. An offshore oil and gas drilling contractor the firm owns about a dozen drilling rigs including six semisubmersible rigs five jack-ups and one semisubmersible tender assist vessel (which places drilling equipment on permanent platforms). Its rigs operate in the Gulf of Mexico offshore Southeast Asia offshore West Africa offshore Australia and in the Mediterranean. Atwood Oceanics serves a limited number of customers at one time and generates nearly all of its sales internationally.

Geographic Reach Australia represents the company's largest market contributing about 45% of sales in fiscal 2012; Africa accounts for about a third. Australian revenue increased more than 80% year-over-year as 2012 marked the first full year of operation for the Atwood Osprey semisubmersible which is working for Chevron Australia.

Atwood Oceanics has offices in the US as well as Australia Malaysia Singapore and the UK.

Sales and Marketing The company provided services for 16 customers in fiscal 2012 including Chevron Australia (34% of sales) Noble Energy (17%) and Kosmos Energy Ghana (11%). Other clients included Hess Apache Energy and CEC International.

Financial Performance With commodity prices bouncing back after the global recession in 2010 Atwood Oceanics posted a jump in revenues and net income. Revenue dropped slightly in 2011 but returned to growth in fiscal 2012 (ended September) rising 22% to $787 million.

Revenue from new rigs including the Condor in the Gulf of Mexico and the Osprey in Australia contributed positively to the results and offset flat or reduced sales in other areas as projects remained steady or ended. Net income in 2012 remained flat at $272 million as the rise in revenue was accompanied by an increase in contract drilling costs and depreciation expenses. Strategy The company is committed to upgrading its fleet to keep pace with the increasing demand for global offshore exploration. Its newest semisubmersible drilling rig began operating in fiscal 2012 in the Gulf of Mexico; Atwood Oceanics anticipates this rig (Condor) will increase its US revenue in coming years. In addition the company has three ultra-deepwater drillships and two jack up rigs scheduled to come online between 2013 and 2015. Ownership Fellow drilling contractor Helmerich & Payne owns 12% of Atwood Oceanics. Its CEO Hans Helmerich serves as a director of Atwood Oceanics. Wellington Management owns about 10%.

EXECUTIVES

Chairman, George S. Dotson, age 73

SVP Marketing and Business Development, Glen P. Kelley, age 64, $283,200 total compensation

Senior Vice President and SecretaryJames, James M. (Jim) Holland, age 68

Senior Vice President Chief Financial Officer, Mark L. Mey, age 48

Vice President Technical Services, Barry M. Smith, age 54

President and Chief Executive Officer; Director, Robert J. (Rob) Saltiel, age 50

Vice President Operations, Arthur M. (Mac) Polhamus, age 59

Vice President Controller, Michael A. (Mike) Campbell, age 44

Vice President - Human Resources, Luis A. Jimenez, age 62

Vice President - Technical Ser, Smith Michael

Accounting Manager after seven years with the public accounting firm, Arthur Andersen

Vice President OperationsRonnie, Ronnie L. Hall

Vice President Operations, Polhamus McGinnis

Senior Vice President Marketin, Kelley Glen

Vice President - Operations, Hall Lee

Vice President Operations., Atwood Oceanics

Vice President - Marketing and Business Development, Geoff Wagner

Vice President General Counsel and Corporate Secretary, Walter (Drew) Baker, age 51

Vice President General Counsel Corporate Secretary, Drew Baker

Vice President Marketing and Business Development, Geoffrey Wagner, age 34

Vice President Corporate Services, Mark W. Smith, age 42

Vice President Controller, Mike Campbell

Director, Hans Helmerich, age 55

Director, Deborah A. Beck, age 66

Director, Robert W. Burgess, age 70

Director, James R. Montague, age 66

President and Chief Executive Officer; Director, Robert J. (Rob) Saltiel, age 50

Director, Jack E. Golden, age 65

Independent Director, Phil Wedemeyer

Auditors: PricewaterhouseCoopersLLP

LOCATIONS

HQ: Atwood Oceanics Inc.
15835 Park Ten Place Dr., Houston TX 77084
Phone: 281-749-7800   **Fax:** 281-492-7871
Web: www.atwd.com

2012 Sales

	$ mil.	% of total
Australia	363	46
Africa	252	32
Asia	84	10
South America	45	6
US	36	5
Middle East	6	1
Total	**787**	**100**

PRODUCTS/OPERATIONS

2012 Sales

	% of total
Chevron	34
Noble	17
Kosmos Energy	11
Other	38
Total	**100**

COMPETITORS

Diamond Offshore	Pride International
Ensco	Rowan Companies

Nabors Industries
Noble
Oceaneering
International
Parker Drilling

Saipem
Schlumberger
Seadrill
Transocean
Vantage Drilling

HISTORICAL FINANCIALS

Company Type: Public

Income Statement
FYE: September 30

	REVENUE ($ mil.)	NET INCOME ($ mil.)	NET PROFIT MARGIN	EMPLOYEES
09/13	1,063.6	350.2	32.9%	1,830
09/12	787.4	272.1	34.6%	1,460
09/11	645.0	271.6	42.1%	1,300
09/10	650.5	257.0	39.5%	1,200
09/09	586.5	250.7	42.8%	1,000
Annual Growth	16.0%	8.7%	—	16.3%

2013 Year-End Financials

Debt ratio: 34.7%
Return on equity: 16.8%
Cash ($ mil.): 88
Current ratio: 2.89
Long-term debt ($ mil.): 1,263

No. of shares (mil.): 64
Dividends
Yield: —
Payout: —
Market value ($ mil.): 3,526

	STOCK PRICE ($) FY Close	P/E High/Low		PER SHARE ($) Earnings	Dividends	Book Value
09/13	55.04	11	8	5.32	0.00	34.46
09/12	45.45	12	8	4.14	0.00	29.63
09/11	34.36	12	7	4.15	0.00	25.44
09/10	30.45	10	6	3.95	0.00	21.26
09/09	35.27	9	3	3.89	0.00	17.16
Annual Growth	11.8%	—	—	8.1%	—	19.0%

Auxilium Pharmaceuticals Inc

Auxilium Pharmaceuticals wants to be the wingman for patients suffering from ailments including hormonal imbalances or tissue conditions. The biopharmaceutical developer markets products that include Testim a topical testosterone gel used to treat hypogonadism (low testosterone production) and XIAFLEX an injectable enzyme approved to treat Dupuytren's contracture (a progressive disease which causes a person's fingers to permanently contract). Auxilium added several testosterone replacement and erectile dysfunction drugs through the 2013 acquisition of Actient. The company's pipeline of candidates includes potential treatments for unusual soft tissue conditions and pain.

Operations

Sales of its first commercial product Testim account for about 80% of Auxilium's annual revenues. To increase Testim's market penetration Auxilium has entered into partnerships to disseminate its product abroad: Paladin Labs sells Testim in Canada while Ferring markets it in Europe where it is approved for sale in some 15 countries. While third parties manufacture its finished products Auxilium manufactures the active ingredient for XIAFLEX at its own facility.

XIAFLEX received FDA approval to treat Dupuytren's contracture in 2010 where it was launched by Auxilium's own sales force after the company invested in readying its manufacturing facility and building up its sales and marketing resources. In 2011 XIAFLEX was also approved for sale in Europe where partner Pfizer handles sales; Pfizer also has marketing rights in some Asian countries (except Japan where Asahi Kasei is working to gain approval). Additionally in 2012 Actelion Pharmaceuticals signed on to commercialize XIAFLEX for treating Dupuytren's and Peyronie's disease in Australia Brazil Canada and Mexico pending regulatory approvals; the partnership yielded its first success later that year when XIAFLEX was approved for sale in Canada.

The company's 2013 purchase of Actient Holdings brought additional medicines to Auxilium's lineup including TESTOPEL and Striant for testosterone conditions and Osbon ErecAid and Edex for erectile dysfunction. It also added legacy medications for respiratory conditions.

Sales and Marketing

Auxilium's products are marketed both directly and through partners and distributors. While Testim holds a quarter of the US market of testosterone gels it faces stiff competition from other testosterone and erectile dysfunction treatments. The company uses aggressive sales tactics to retain its market share targeting physicians that prescribe large volumes of testosterone replacement drugs.

Financial Performance

Auxilium's sales have seen a sharp increase since XIAFLEX hit the market helping the company to achieve a 25% revenue increase to some $264 million in 2011. Most of its revenues come from sales within the US though the firm expects revenues from development and marketing partnerships to increase as it broadens its product distribution network. However as the company is largely still in development-stage mode spending more on R&D and sales ramp-up costs than it makes Auxilium has yet to turn a profit. The company aims to report positive net income in the coming years as it increases market penetration for existing products and gains market approval for new indications and products.

Strategy

Auxilium aims to increase sales of XIAFLEX through additional market approvals for Dupuytren's contracture as well as by developing and gaining approval for the drug as a treatment other conditions. The firm is exploring XIAFLEX as a potential treatment for Peyronie's disease (which leads to penile scar tissue that can interfere with sexual intercourse) adhesive capsulitis (frozen shoulder syndrome) and edematous fibrosclerotic panniculopathy (cellulite). The company has also conducted R&D programs in other areas of medicine and it is looking for opportunities to acquire or license additional candidates.

Mergers and Acquisitions

Auxilium extended its commercial offerings through the purchase of Actient Holdings for some $585 million in 2013. The purchase added specialty therapeutics for urological conditions. In addition to widening the company's product offerings the purchase expanded Auxilium's sales and marketing resources.

EXECUTIVES

Chairman, Rolf A. Classon, age 67
Executive Vice President - Regulatory Affairs and Project Management, Benjamin J. Del Tito Jr., age 57

EVP Sales and Marketing, Roger D. Graham Jr., age 50, $336,766 total compensation
EVP Secretary General Counsel and Human Resources, Jennifer Evans-Stacey, age 48, $316,646 total compensation
SVP Sales, Edward F. (Ed) Kessig, age 52, $239,742 total compensation
Chief Financial Officer, James E. (Jim) Fickenscher, age 49, $332,131 total compensation
VP Investor Relations and Corporate Communications, William Q. (Will) Sargent Jr.
Executive Vice President - Corporate Development, Alan J. Wills, age 49
Senior Vice President - Marketing, Richard Dudek
President; Chief Executive Officer; Director, Adrian Adams
Chief Administrative Officer; General Counsel, Andrew Koven
Chief Compliance Officer, Elizabeth Jobes
Chief Medical Officer, James Tursi
Senior Vice President - Human Resources, Jennifer L. Armstrong
EVP Sales and Marketing, Mark Glickman
Executive Vice President - Regulatory Affairs and Project Management, Benjamin Tito
Director, William T. (Bill) McKee, age 51
Director, Paul A. Friedman, age 70
Director, Peter C. Brandt
Director, Oliver S. Fetzer, age 48
Independent Director, Nancy Lurker
Auditors: PricewaterhouseCoopersLLP

LOCATIONS

HQ: Auxilium Pharmaceuticals Inc.
40 Valley Stream Pkwy., Malvern PA 19355
Phone: 484-321-5900   Fax: 484-321-5999
Web: www.auxilium.com

PRODUCTS/OPERATIONS

2011 Sales

	$ mil.	% of total
Testim	207	79
XIAFLEX	56	20
Total	264	100

COMPETITORS

Abbott Labs
Actavis Inc.
BioSante
Clarus Therapeutics
Eli Lilly
Endo
Halozyme

Par Pharmaceutical Companies
Perrigo
ProStrakan
Repros Therapeutics
Teva

HISTORICAL FINANCIALS

Company Type: Public

Income Statement
FYE: December 31

	REVENUE ($ mil.)	NET INCOME ($ mil.)	NET PROFIT MARGIN	EMPLOYEES
12/12	395.2	85.9	21.7%	526
12/11	264.3	(32.9)	—	530
12/10	211.4	(51.2)	—	565
12/09	164.0	(53.4)	—	540
12/08	125.3	(46.2)	—	340
Annual Growth	33.3%	—	—	11.5%

2012 Year-End Financials

Debt ratio: —
Return on equity: 60.3%
Cash ($ mil.): 35
Current ratio: 2.48
Long-term debt ($ mil.): —

No. of shares (mil.): 49
Dividends
Yield: —
Payout: —
Market value ($ mil.): 914

	STOCK PRICE ($) FY Close	P/E High/Low	PER SHARE ($) Earnings	Dividends	Book Value
12/12	18.54	16 10	1.74	0.00	4.06
12/11	19.93	— —	(0.69)	0.00	1.75
12/10	21.10	— —	(1.08)	0.00	1.98
12/09	29.98	— —	(1.22)	0.00	2.55
12/08	28.44	— —	(1.12)	0.00	0.83
Annual Growth	(10.1%)	— —	—	—	48.6%

AZZ Inc

When companies need to power up or get "in zink" they give AZZ incorporated a buzz. The company has two business segments: galvanizing services and electrical and industrial products. To protect steel from environmental corrosion galvanizing services dip steel products into baths of molten zinc. The process is vital for steel fabricators who serve highway construction electrical utility transportation and water-treatment firms. Through subsidiaries AZZ makes electrical power distribution systems industrial lighting switchgear motor control centers bus duct systems and tubular goods. Industrial petrochemical and power generation and transmission companies use the company's products.

Although sales in 2011 saw an increase of more than 6% net income was down more than 7%. While operating income for its galvanizing services jumped $12.1 million the electrical and industrial products unit decreased nearly $14 million as orders from electrical transmission and petrochemical markets slowed.

Electrical and industrial products once the AZZ's largest unit in terms of sales is not expected to see any vast improvements in the near future. Increased competition and a rise in costs for raw materials (aluminum copper and steel) has pushed operating margins down from 20% to 17%. Adding to electrical and industrial products' woes international sales tumbled more than 35%.

Galvanizing services became the powerhouse for AZZ for fiscal 2011. Volume of steel processed was up about 40% compared to the previous year and selling prices increased about 2%. The lion's share of the galvanizing segment's success can be attributed to the $126 million acquisition of North American Galvanizing & Coatings (renamed AZZ Galvanizing Services) in 2010. Excluding revenues from AZZ Galvanizing Services steel volumes and selling prices increased 6% and 3% respectively. Operating margins for the unit dropped slightly due in part to an increase in the price of zinc.

Going forward AZZ plans to enhance its position in the power generation market. In mid-2012 it acquired Nuclear Logistics a Texas-based provider of electrical and mechanical equipment and services used in promoting safety for nuclear facilities. The deal added a new portfolio of brands to AZZ's Electrical and Industrial Products segment.

In 2013 AZZ acquired Aquilex Holdings' Specialty Repair and Overhaul (SRO) business. The SRO unit added global maintenance revitalization and repair services to customers in the fossil fuel and nuclear power generation market as well as other energy and industrial customers.

EXECUTIVES

President; Chief Executive Officer; Director, David H. Dingus, age 66, $436,250 total compensation
SVP Finance CFO Secretary and Director, Dana L. Perry, age 64, $244,250 total compensation
VP-Sls & Mktg-Electrical Products, Clement H. Watson, age 66, $197,000 total compensation
Chairman, H. Kirk Downey, age 69
SVP Operations Electrical Products, John V. Petro, age 66, $221,500 total compensation
VP Galvanizing Northern Operations, John S. Lincoln, age 51
VP Business and Manufacturing Systems, James C. (Jim) Stricklen, age 63, $160,000 total compensation
VP and Corporate Controller, Richard W. Butler, age 47
VP Operations Galvanizing Services Segment, Tim E. Pendley, age 52, $200,000 total compensation
VP Business Development, Ashok E. Kolady, age 39
VP Galvanizing Southern Operations, Bryan Stovall, age 49
VP Electrical and Industrial Products, Bill Estes, age 47
VP Electrical and Industrial Products, John Petitto
VP Human Resources, Francis D. Quinn, age 47
Vice President - Manufacturing Strategies, Jim Stricklen
Independent Chairman of the Board, Kirk Downey
Vice President - Bus Duct Systems, William Estes
Director, Daniel R. Feehan, age 62
President CEO and Director, David H. Dingus, age 65
SVP Finance CFO Secretary and Director, Dana L. Perry, age 64
Director, Daniel E. (Dan) Berce, age 60
Director, Sam Rosen, age 77
Director, Martin C. Bowen, age 69
Director, Kevern R. Joyce, age 66
Director, Peter A. Hegedus, age 72
Auditors: BDOSeidmanLLP

LOCATIONS

HQ: AZZ Inc
One Museum Place, Suite 500, 3100 West Seventh Street, Fort Worth, TX 76107
Phone: 817 810-0095 **Fax:** 817 336-5354
Web: www.azz.com

PRODUCTS/OPERATIONS

2011 Sales

	$ mil.	% of total
Galvanizing services	218	57
Electrical & industrial products	162	43
Total	**380**	**100**

Selected Products and Services

Galvanizing Services
  Coordinated multi-plant operations
  Custom hot-dip galvanizing
  Duplex finishes
  Finished material warehousing
Electrical and Industrial Products
  Air and gas insulated bus duct
  Electrical power distribution centers
  Industrial hazardous-duty lighting
  Metal-clad outdoor switchgear
  Protective relay panels
  Tubular goods

COMPETITORS

ABB
AZZ Galvanizing Services
Chamberlin
Earle M. Jorgensen
Eaton
Energy Focus
Friedman Industries
GE
Gewiss
JJI Lighting
Jarden
LSI Industries
Legrand
Powell Industries
Professional Luminaires North America
SPX

HISTORICAL FINANCIALS
Company Type: Public

Income Statement
FYE: February 28

	REVENUE ($ mil.)	NET INCOME ($ mil.)	NET PROFIT MARGIN	EMPLOYEES
02/13	570.5	60.4	10.6%	2,632
02/12	469.1	40.7	8.7%	2,154
02/11	380.6	34.9	9.2%	1,956
02/10	357.0	37.7	10.6%	1,530
02/09	412.3	42.2	10.2%	1,722
Annual Growth	8.5%	9.4%	—	11.2%

2013 Year-End Financials

Debt ratio: 30.3%
Return on equity: 19.4%
Cash ($ mil.): 55
Current ratio: 2.21
Long-term debt ($ mil.): 196

No. of shares (mil.): 25
Dividends
  Yield: 1.1%
  Payout: 22.8%
Market value ($ mil.): 1,133

	STOCK PRICE ($) FY Close	P/E High/Low	PER SHARE ($) Earnings	Dividends	Book Value
02/13	44.66	28 13	2.37	0.53	13.16
02/12	50.20	33 23	1.61	0.50	11.43
02/11	42.66	32 23	1.39	0.50	10.24
02/10	31.41	28 11	1.51	0.13	9.22
02/09	20.24	27 9	1.72	0.00	7.70
Annual Growth	21.9%	— —	8.4%	—	14.3%

Balchem Corp.

Believe Balchem when they say they have it covered. The company has developed a technology that covers or encapsulates ingredients used in food and animal health products; the encapsulation improves nutritional value and shelf life and allows for controlled time release. Balchem also provides specialty gases such as ethylene oxide (used to sterilize medical instruments) propylene oxide (used to reduce bacteria in spice treating and chemical processing) and methyl chloride (a refrigerant). The company's unencapsulated feed ingredients unit (BCP Ingredients) supplies the nutrient choline chloride to poultry and swine farmers. Reashure an encapsulated choline product increases milk production in dairy cows.

Balchem's operations are divided into three main business segments. Its ARC Specialty Products segment offers re-packaging and distribution of select chemicals (including ethylene oxide and propylene oxide) to healthcare and other markets. Its Animal Nutrition and Health segment manufactures and supplies products (including choline chloride) to several animal health markets and also certain derivative chemical products for industrial use. Balchem's Food Pharma and Nutrition segment provides human-grade choline and microencapsulation products for a range of applications in human food pharmaceutical and nutrition markets.

Balchem operates two subsidiaries in the US: BCP Ingredients and Aberco. It also has three subsidiaries in Europe: Balchem BV and Balchem Trading in the Netherlands and Balchem Italia which has a manufacturing facility in Italy that makes and distributes methylamines (a building block for choline products) and choline.

The company's revenues rose more than 14% in 2011 to $291.9 million due mainly to increased sales volumes and higher prices. Net income was up about 17% for the year. All three of its business segments saw sales increases over the previous year. However its Food Pharma and Nutrition segment was up only slightly at a little more than 1%. Although its sales of human choline products were up slightly in 2011 the segment realized lower sales in certain flavor and confection markets that year in the US. The segment also lost a source of income because its calcium products had been sold the previous year.

The Animal Nutrition and Health segment was up 18% driven by sales volume increases in its specialty ingredients for animal markets.

The Specialty Products segment was up 13% from sales of its ethylene oxide products for medical device sterilization and from higher sales of propylene oxide due to the company's acquisition in 2010 of Aberco a marketer and distributor of the specialty gas.

HISTORY

Herbert Weiss Leslie Balassa three ex officers of the Alcolac company and a group of Baltimore-based investors founded Balchem in 1967 in New York City. The company focused on the development of encapsulated specialty ingredients (the coating of individual particles that allow precise control of nutrient delivery). Initially Balchem developed food ingredients used in meat processing flavor enhancement and dough leavening as well as in nutritional supplements. In 1971 the company won its first big order: encapsulating the ingredients in pudding mix for General Foods. Balchem later applied the same technology to foaming agents for plastics aquaculture supplements and animal feeds. It also developed a line of specialty gases.

In 1994 Balchem boosted its gas business with the purchase of AlliedSignal's sterilant gas business (used to sterilize medical devices). Weiss retired as CEO in 1996 and was succeeded by EVP Raymond Reber. Reber left the company a few months later and chemical industry veteran Dino Rossi replaced him. The next year Balchem developed a rumen-protected choline chloride for the animal nutrition market.

Balchem restructured its operations in 1998 away from aquaculture and towards animal nutrition and other growth markets. After successful university and field trials the company introduced Reashure its encapsulated choline product for dairy cows.

In 2000 Balchem was granted a patent for its technology that increases milk production in dairy cows. In 2001 the company acquired the choline and encapsulated product lines of DCV Inc. and its DuCoa L.P. affiliate which contributed to the company's increase in net sales by about 30% in 2002. In 2002 sales continued to build as the encapsulated/nutritional products segment introduced several new products and product applications for the enhancement of shelf-life and fortification of products in certain markets of the food industry.

Balchem's unencapsulated feed ingredients segment also referred to as BCP Ingredients got larger in 2007 when the company acquired two choline-related businesses. The first was in Italy from Akzo Nobel and the other deal was for a company called Chinook Global Limited whose operations were integrated into Balchem's business. Those deals nearly tripled the size of BCP Ingredients making it Balchem's largest unit.

In 2010 the company's growth increased again with the acquisition of Maryland-based Aberco a marketer and distributor of propylene oxide.

EXECUTIVES

Chief Financial Officer; Treasurer; Assistant Secretary, Francis J. (Frank) Fitzpatrick, age 52, $215,400 total compensation
Chairman of the Board; President; Chief Executive Officer, Dino A. Rossi, age 58, $467,500 total compensation
Executive Vice President Arsenal Capital Partners, John Y. Televantos, age 60
Vice President General Manager, David R. Ludwig, age 55, $220,000 total compensation
President of Nestles Research & Development Center, Elaine R. Wedral, age 69
VP Research and Development, Paul H. Richardson, age 42, $191,000 total compensation
General Counsel; Secretary, Matthew D. Houston, age 49, $177,000 total compensation
Vice President General Manager Animal Nutrition, Dana Putnam
Vice President Human Resources, Bob Miniger
Vice President of Operations, John E. Kuehner
Chief Accounting Officer Treasurer, William A. Backus
IR Contact, Karin McCaffery
Chief Operating Officer, Richard Bendure
Member of the Executive Board; Chief Risk Officer, Hassan Basri
Chairman of the Board and Chief Executive Officer, Mohamed Benchaaboun
Director, Paul D. Coombs, age 57
Director, Perry W. Premdas, age 60
Director, Edward L. McMillan, age 67
Director, Elaine R. Wedral, age 69
Director, John Y. Televantos
Auditors: McGladreyLLP

LOCATIONS

HQ: Balchem Corporation
52 Sunrise Park Rd., New Hampton NY 10958
Phone: 845-326-5600   **Fax:** 845-326-5742
Web: www.balchem.com

2010 Sales

	$ mil.	% of total
US	171	67
Other countries	84	33
Total	**255**	**100**

PRODUCTS/OPERATIONS

2011 Sales

	$ mil.	% of total
Animal Nutrition & Health	201	69
Specialty Products	47	16
Food Pharma & Nutrition	42	15
Total	**291**	**100**

2010 Sales

	$ mil.	% of total
Animal nutrition & health	170	67
Specialty products	42	17
Food pharma & nutrition	42	16
Total	**255**	**100**

Selected Products

BCP Ingredients
Choline chloride (essential nutrient for animal health)
Choline chloride derivatives
Encapsulated/Nutritional Products
Food Pharma & Human Nutrition Products
Bakeshure (leavening agents dough conditioners fortifiers acidifiers and antimicrobials)
Confecshure (acidulants for flavor)
Flavorshure (taste and flavor masking)
Meatshure (acidifiers antioxidants and flavors)
Vitashure (vitamins nutraceuticals and botanicals)
Animal Nutrition & Health Products
NiashureNiacine (prevents niacin degradation)Urea (regulates nitrogen/carbohydrates ratio in proteins)
Reashure (rumen-stable choline for dairy cows)
Specialty Products
Ethylene oxide (sterilant gas for the health care industry)
Methyl chloride (specialty herbicides)
Propylene oxide (bacteria reduction in spices)

COMPETITORS

ABCO Laboratories	Coating Place
Air Products	Dow Chemical
Airgas	IGENE
BASF Corporation	Mitsubishi Chemical
BioDelivery Sciences	Praxair
International	Sigma-Aldrich
Clariant	

HISTORICAL FINANCIALS

Company Type: Public

Income Statement

FYE: December 31

	REVENUE ($ mil.)	NET INCOME ($ mil.)	NET PROFIT MARGIN	EMPLOYEES
12/12	310.3	40.0	12.9%	376
12/11	291.8	38.7	13.3%	365
12/10	255.0	33.2	13.0%	351
12/09	219.4	26.7	12.2%	337
12/08	232.0	19.0	8.2%	332
Annual Growth	**7.5%**	**20.4%**	**—**	**3.2%**

2012 Year-End Financials

Debt ratio: —
Return on equity: 15.8%
Cash ($ mil.): 144
Current ratio: 7.01
Long-term debt ($ mil.): —

No. of shares (mil.): 29
Dividends
  Yield: 0.6%
  Payout: 16.7%
Market value ($ mil.): 1,074

	STOCK PRICE ($) FY Close	P/E High/Low	Earnings	PER SHARE ($) Dividends	Book Value
12/12	36.45	30 19	1.32	0.22	9.27
12/11	40.54	34 24	1.28	0.18	7.95
12/10	33.81	29 15	1.12	0.15	6.52
12/09	33.51	35 19	0.93	0.11	5.24
12/08	24.91	42 27	0.67	0.07	4.18
Annual Growth	**10.0%**	**— —**	**18.6%**	**31.6%**	**22.0%**

Baldwin & Lyons, Inc.

Baldwin & Lyons (B&L) insures truckers and the bad motorists who terrorize them. The company's Protective Insurance subsidiary licensed in the US and Canada writes property/casualty insurance for large to midsized trucking fleets and public transportation fleets. It also covers independent contractors in the trucking industry. B&L's Sagamore Insurance subsidiary provides insurance to high-risk private auto drivers throughout most of the US through a network of independent agents. It also markets physical-damage insurance and liability insurance for small trucking fleets and for large and midsized bus fleets. Founded in 1930 B&L also provides property/casualty reinsurance and brokerage services.

Operations

The company's largest operating segment property/casualty insurance accounts for about 70% of revenues and includes fleet contractor personal auto business owners professional liability and commercial property coverage. The reinsurance unit brings in around 20% and includes casualty and catastrophe coverage.

Other services provided by B&L's divisions include risk analysis safety design compliance assistance cost studies loss control claims management third-party administration and product development (such as the development of custom automated claims tracking systems).

Sales and Marketing

B&L markets its policies through its brokerage services division which offers insurance placement claims handling loss prevention and Department of Transportation compliance services. The brokerage unit caters directly to transportation fleet clients. B&L sells other types of insurance coverage through a network of independent agents and managing general agents. Customers include FedEx Ground and other public and private transportation companies ranging from small contractors to large motor carriers.

Financial Performance

B&L increased revenues by 8% in 2012 due to higher direct premiums written for fleet transportation products (from both existing and new clients) as well as higher gains on investments (primarily from improved limited partnership results). The company also experienced growth in its newer professional liabilities line. However it reported decreased premiums from multi-peril commercial policies as it exited the business line as well as lower sales of auto policies (prompted by rate increases which served to return the division to profitability). The revenue increase in 2012 followed a decline in 2011.

Overall B&L reported a profit of $32 million — compared to a net loss in 2011 —primarily due to a decrease in major catastrophe losses.

Strategy

Besides its services products and experienced management the company counts among its competitive advantages its willingness to custom build policies for its customers and its extensive use of technology with regard to its insureds and independent agents. The company grows its operations by adding new products and services; for instance it started offering professional liability policies in 2010 and expanded its professional offerings in 2012. In 2011 and 2012 B&L focused on expanding its distribution network by utilizing managing general agents (in addition to retail agents). In 2013 the firm moved to expand its workforce in response to increased sales.

The company decided to exit the commercial multi-peril line of business in 2012 as it worked to reduce property catastrophe loss exposures.

Financial Performance

In fiscal 2011 B&L's premiums earned increased almost 14% from 2010 mainly due to product expansion and continued marketing efforts in its property and casualty insurance segment along with continued growth of professional liability reinsurance within its reinsurance segment. Despite the growth in premiums catastrophic losses in unprecedented amounts together with significant net investment losses contributed to a net loss of $28 million for 2011 compared to net income of $25 million for 2010.

Ownership

The Shapiro family owns approximately 49% of Baldwin & Lyons.

EXECUTIVES

President CEO COO and Director; President and Director Protective Insurance and Sagamore Insurance, Joseph J. DeVito, age 61, $808,683 total compensation

Director Human Resources, Hugh Cameron

Chief Financial Officer; Executive Vice President, G. Patrick (Pat) Corydon, age 64, $465,722 total compensation

Chairman; Chairman and CEO Protective Sagamore and B & L Insurance, Gary W. Miller, age 72, $898,867 total compensation

VP-Admin, James D. Isham

EVP Sales Marketing and Underwriting, Mark L. Bonini, age 54, $385,972 total compensation

Treasurer; VP Protective, Walter D. (Daryl) Osborne

VP-Underwriting, Jennie L. LaReau

VP Reinsurance and Actuarial Services, John E. Mitchell

Executive Vice President; Secretary, Craig C. Morfas, age 54

Director, Thomas H. (Tom) Patrick, age 68

Director, John D. Weil, age 72

President CEO COO and Director; President and Director Protective Insurance and Sagamore Insurance, Joseph J. DeVito, age 61

Director, Stuart D. Bilton, age 66

Director, John M. O'Mara, age 85

Director, John A. Pigott, age 81

Director, Nathan Shapiro, age 76

Director, Norton Shapiro, age 80

Director, Robert Shapiro, age 74

Director, Steven A. Shapiro, age 49

Director, Kenneth D. Sacks, age 48

Director, Otto N. Frenzel IV, age 53

Independent Director, John Mara

Independent Director, John OMara

Auditors: Ernst&YoungLLP

LOCATIONS

HQ: Baldwin & Lyons Inc.
1099 N. Meridian St. Ste. 700, Indianapolis IN 46204
Phone: 317-636-9800   **Fax:** 317-632-9444
Web: www.baldwinandlyons.com

PRODUCTS/OPERATIONS

2012 Revenues

	$ mil.	% of total
Net premiums earned		
Property & casualty insurance	186	71
Reinsurance	50	19
Net investment income	9	4
Net realized investment gains	9	4
Commissions & other	5	2
Total	**262**	**100**

Selected Subsidiaries

B&L Brokerage Services Inc. - insurance broker licensed in the US

B&L Insurance Ltd. - domiciled and licensed in Bermuda

Protective Insurance Company

Protective Specialty Insurance - approved for excess and surplus lines business in 40 states

Sagamore Insurance Company - licensed in 47 states and approved for excess and surplus lines business in Florida

COMPETITORS

AMERISAFE	McM Corporation
Allstate	Nationwide
Canal Insurance	Philadelphia Insurance
Carolina Casualty	Companies
EMC Insurance	Progressive
Essex Insurance	Corporation
Fairfax Financial	State Farm
Holdings	Transport Insurance
GAINSCO	Agency
GEICO	United Fire
Great West Casualty	Zenith National
Kingsway America	

HISTORICAL FINANCIALS

Company Type: Public

Income Statement

FYE: December 31

	ASSETS ($ mil.)	NET INCOME ($ mil.)	INCOME AS % OF ASSETS	EMPLOYEES
12/12	983.0	31.9	3.2%	360
12/11	905.2	(28.1)	—	330
12/10	837.9	25.0	3.0%	299
12/09	851.3	44.8	5.3%	293
12/08	777.7	(7.7)	—	312
Annual Growth	**6.0%**	**—**		**3.6%**

2012 Year-End Financials

Return on assets: 3.3%	Dividends
Return on equity: 9.5%	Yield: 4.1%
Long-term debt ($ mil.): —	Payout: 46.5%
No. of shares (mil.): 14	Market value ($ mil.): 356
Sales ($ mil): 262	

	STOCK PRICE ($) FY Close	P/E High/Low		Earnings	PER SHARE ($) Dividends	Book Value
12/12	23.86	11	10	2.15	1.00	23.25
12/11	21.80	—	—	(1.90)	1.00	21.49
12/10	23.53	16	12	1.69	2.25	24.90
12/09	24.62	8	5	3.04	1.00	25.31
12/08	18.19	—	—	(0.51)	1.00	22.32
Annual Growth	**7.0%**	—	—	**—**	**(0.0%)**	**1.0%**

Banc of California, Inc.

First PacTrust Bancorp is the holding company for Pacific Trust Bank (aka PacTrust Bank) which offers deposit and loan services from about 20 branches in Southern California's Los Angeles Riverside and San Diego counties. Mortgages secured by one- to four-family residences account more than half of the company's loan portfolio. Expanding in Southern California First PacTrust bought Beach Business Bank and Gateway Business Bank in separate transactions in 2012. Beach Business Bank which has three branches maintained its identity after it was acquired while Gateway was merged into PacTrust Bank. The company now plans to buy The Private Bank of California which serves businesses and wealthy individuals.

PacTrust Bank was founded in 1941 as Rohr Employees Federal Credit Union;.

EXECUTIVES

Chairman, Timothy R. Chrisman, age 66

EVP and Chief Credit Officer Pactrust Bank, Matthew J. Bonaccorso

EVP and Chief Financial Officer, Ronald J. Nicolas Jr., age 54

EVP and Corporate Secretary, Richard A. Herrin, age 44
EVP and Chief Lending Officer Pactrust Bank, Chang Ming Liu
CEO, Steven A. Sugarman, age 38
President; CEO PacTrust Bank and Beach Business Bank, Robert M. Franko, age 65
EVP Treasurer and Chief Investment Officer, Craig S. Naselow, age 49
Managing Director Residential Lending, Jeffrey T. Seabold
Auditors: CroweHorwathLLP

LOCATIONS

HQ: Banc of California Inc.
18500 Von Karman Ave. Ste. 1100, Irvine CA 92612
Phone: 949-236-5211 **Fax:** 619-691-1350
Web: www.firstpactrustbancorp.com

COMPETITORS

Bank of America	JPMorgan Chase
Bank of the West	U.S. Bancorp
City National	UnionBanCal
Comerica	Zions Bancorporation

HISTORICAL FINANCIALS

Company Type: Public

Income Statement

FYE: December 31

	ASSETS ($ mil.)	NET INCOME ($ mil.)	INCOME AS % OF ASSETS	EMPLOYEES
12/12	1,682.7	6.0	0.4%	614
12/11	999.0	(2.7)	—	147
12/10	861.6	2.8	0.3%	107
12/09	893.9	(1.0)	—	98
12/08	876.5	(0.5)	—	107
Annual Growth	17.7%			54.8%

2012 Year-End Financials

Return on assets: 0.4%
Return on equity: 3.2%
Long-term debt ($ mil.): —
No. of shares (mil.): 11
Sales ($ mil): 91

Dividends
Yield: 0.0%
Payout: 120.0%
Market value ($ mil.): 146

	STOCK PRICE ($) FY Close	P/E High/Low	PER SHARE ($) Earnings	Dividends	Book Value
12/12	12.27	33 26	0.40	0.48	15.87
12/11	10.25	— —	(0.31)	0.45	15.85
12/10	13.27	35 14	0.37	0.25	13.98
12/09	5.35	— —	(0.48)	0.25	22.97
12/08	9.65	— —	(0.15)	0.74	23.22
Annual Growth	6.2%	— —	—(10.3%)	(9.1%)	

Bankrate Inc (DE)

Bankrate knows there's life after budget-cutting. The firm's online network including flagship Bankrate.com provides information (including rate data and reviews) on more than 300 personal finance products including mortgages credit cards money market accounts and car and home equity loans. Bankrate culls information from about 4800 institutions covers nearly 600 local markets across the US and distributes content to about 175 media partners. Other Bankrate sites include InsureMe.com and NetQuote which sell leads to insurance agents and carriers and CreditCardGuide.com a credit card comparison website. Bankrate in 2011 filed to go public.

IPO
In 2011 the company raised a total of about $170 million through its IPO. It used some $123 million of the proceeds to pay down debt for other general corporate purposes and financing its growth strategy.

Geographic Reach
The company generates nearly all of its revenues (some 98%) in the US. However it is expanding internationally. It has a Chinese-language Bankrate website as well as websites in the UK and Canada.

Operations
Once a print publisher today most of Bankrate's revenues (some 98%) are generated from online products and services.

Sales and Marketing
The company spent almost $120 million on advertising and marketing expenses during fiscal 2012. Bankrate has 75 co-branded partners including some of the most popular personal finance sites on the Internet including Yahoo! CNN Money CNBC and Comcast. In addition the company has partnered with some 450 newspapers including The Wall Street Journal USA Today and The New York Times.

Bankrate relies heavily on its largest customer Capital One which accounted for 12% of its total revenue during fiscal 2012. Ten of Bankrate's largest customers accounted for almost 50% of total revenue in fiscal 2012.

Financial Performance
The company's revenue has been growing year-over-year. Its revenue increased by 8% in fiscal 2012 compared to fiscal 2011. The increase in revenue was the result of growth in hyperlink revenue but also due to a slight growth in its display advertising. The hyperlink and advertising revenue growth was offset by a decrease in lead generation revenue during fiscal 2012.

Hyperlink revenue increased by $43.4 million in fiscal 2012 compared to 2011 due to an increase in the number of clicks and calls and an increase in the overall rate. The increase in the overall rate was driven primarily by increased rates in mortgage and deposit products. Display advertising revenue increased by $6.8 million during fiscal 2012 compared to the previous year driven by the increase in sold impressions and an increase in cost per impressions yield per page. Lead generation revenue decreased by $17.1 million in fiscal 2012 compared to fiscal 2011 due to a decrease in marketing activities and spend on the part of the credit card issuers.

Strategy
Bankrate is benefitting from consumer habits in the digital information era as people increasingly turn to the Internet to research and shop for personal finance products. The company filed its IPO in the wake of a recovering economy and improving macroeconomic trends.

Company Background
Bankrate was founded as a print-based business in 1976 when it began publishing the Bank Rate Monitor newsletter. The company expanded to the Internet in 1996. Thomas Evans was appointed CEO of Bankrate in 2004.

EXECUTIVES

Senior Vice President - Chief Financial Officer, Edward J. (Ed) DiMaria, age 47, $350,000 total compensation
Senior Vice President - Chief Marketing/Communications Officer, Bruce J. Zanca, age 52, $231,000 total compensation
Chairman, Peter C. Morse, age 66
Senior Vice President and Chief Operating Officer, Kenneth S. (Ken) Esterow, age 48
Senior Vice President - Chief Technology Officer, Daniel P. Hoogterp, age 53, $230,000 total compensation
Senior Vice President - Chief Revenue Officer, Donaldson M. Ross, age 49, $300,000 total compensation
Senior Vice President - Business Development and Consumer Marketing, Michael J. Ricciardelli, age 41
CEO InsureME, Lou Geremia
President Chief Executive Officer; Director, Thomas R. Evans, age 59, $450,000 total compensation
Manager Public Relations, Chris Spagnuolo
Senior Vice President Corporate Finance and M&A, Hanno M. Damm
Vice President of technical training, Trevor Welby-Solomon
Independent Director, Richard J. (Rich) Pinola, age 67
Director, Jeffery H. (Jeff) Boyd, age 55
Director, Christian Stahl, age 42
Director, Seth Brody, age 37
President CEO and Director, Thomas R. Evans, age 58
Director, Mitch Truwit, age 44
Independent Director, Michael Kelly
Auditors: GrantThorntonLLP

LOCATIONS

HQ: Bankrate Inc (DE)
11760 U.S. Highway One, Suite 200, North Palm Beach, FL 33408
Phone: 561 630-2400
Web: www.bankrate.com

2012 Sales

US	449	98
Total	**457**	**100**

PRODUCTS/OPERATIONS

2012 Sales

Online	449	98
Total	**457**	**100**

Selected Topics Covered

Credit Cards
Insurance
  Auto
  Business
  Home
  Life
  Health
  Long-term care
Mortgages
Money market accounts
Retirement
Taxes

Selected Websites

Bankrate.com
Bankaholic.com
CreditCards.com
CreditCardGuide.com
InsureMe.com
Interest.com
Mortgage-calc.com
NetQuote.com

Selected Licensing Partners

The Wall Street Journal
USA Today
The New York Times

The Los Angeles Times
The Boston Globe

COMPETITORS

Bloomberg L.P.	Morningstar
E-LOAN	Motley Fool
Forbes	PCQuote.com
InsWeb	PNC Financial
Intuit	Reuters
Kiplinger	SmartMoney
Life Quotes	TheStreet
MarketWatch	Tree.com
McGraw Hill Financial	Value Line

HISTORICAL FINANCIALS

Company Type: Public

Income Statement

FYE: December 31

	REVENUE ($ mil.)	NET INCOME ($ mil.)	NET PROFIT MARGIN	EMPLOYEES
12/12	457.1	29.3	6.4%	452
12/11	424.2	(13.4)	—	438
12/10	220.6	(21.5)	—	378
12/09	43.8	(8.4)	—	0
Annual Growth	118.5%	—	—	—

2012 Year-End Financials

Debt ratio: 16.7%	No. of shares (mil.): 100
Return on equity: 3.6%	Dividends
Cash ($ mil.): 83	Yield: —
Current ratio: 3.01	Payout: —
Long-term debt ($ mil.): 193	Market value ($ mil.): 1,246

	STOCK PRICE ($) FY Close	P/E High/Low		PER SHARE ($) Earnings	Dividends	Book Value
12/12	12.45	87	35	0.29	0.00	8.28
12/11	21.50	—	—	(0.14)	0.00	7.89
12/10	0.00	—	—	(0.70)	0.00	7.14
Annual Growth	—	—	—	—	—	7.6%

BankUnited Inc.

BankUnited is uniting the north and south again. The company owns Florida's BankUnited which provides standard banking offerings through about 100 branches. In early 2012 BankUnited acquired the three-branch New York private bank Herald National. BankUnited was formed in 2009 following the demise of the former BankUnited FSB which collapsed under the weight of bad mortgages. A team of private investors didn't miss a beat. They bought BankUnited from the FDIC injected $900 million in fresh capital and assumed its $12.8 billion in assets and $8.3 billion in deposits. The company took itself public via an initial public offering (IPO) in 2011; it was the first IPO of a rescued bank during the economic crisis.

BankUnited raised some $783 million in its IPO nearly 20% more than it sought in its pricing. The funds are helping the bank expand both in Florida (where it operates in about a dozen counties) and into select new markets (such as New York). CEO Kanasthe former head of North Fork Bank led a similar expansion for North Fork in the first half of the decade and will likely use his experience to repeat the strategy with BankUnited.

The $71.4 million acquisition of Herald National marked the company's first post-IPO acquisition. At the time of the purchase BankUnited converted to a bank holding company. It also converted the charter of subsidiary BankUnited from a thrift to a national commercial bank. Herald National will be made into a subsidiary of the bank in mid-2012.

The company hopes to use its capital strength and expertise to take advantage of the weakened markets in Florida which have seen considerably slowed-down lending. It has been growing its loan portfolio both through originations and acquisitions with a primary focus on commercial and commercial real estate lending. (It also invests in residential real estate but does not acquire or write subprime residential loans.)

The growth of BankUnited's loan portfolio has helped increase the company's interest revenues but profits were impacted in 2011 by an equity-based compensation charge. The company has also earned an atypical amount of noninterest revenues —some $186 million —related to its acquisition of the failed bank and its assets.

In 2010 BankUnited expanded its offerings and diversified its loan portfolio when it acquired a small business lending platform from Butler Capital Corporation. It also bought a municipal leasing business from Koch Financial Corporation. The company now offers national equipment financing services through United Capital Business Lending and municipal leasing via Pinnacle Public Finance. BankUnited also provides wealth management through insurance agency BankUnited Investment Services.

Financier Wilbur Ross who serves on BankUnited's board of directors owns 15% of the company through WL Ross & Co.

EXECUTIVES

Vice Chairman and Chief Lending Officer, John Bohlsen, age 71
Chairman President and CEO, John A. Kanas, age 66
Chief Financial Officer of BankUnited, Douglas J. (Doug) Pauls, age 55
COO, Rajinder P. (Raj) Singh, age 42
SVP and Director Marketing, Melissa Gracey
SEVP and Chief Risk Officer at BankUnited, Randy R. Melby
SEVP Corporate and Commercial Banking BankUnited, Abel Iglesias
EVP Banking Services BankUnited, Douglas Sawyer
CIO, Joseph Kissel
CFO, Leslie Lunak
Vice Chairman and Chief Lending Officer, John Bohlsen, age 70
Director, Richard S. LeFrak, age 65
Director, Chinh E. Chu, age 46
Director, Sue M. Cobb, age 75
Director, Wilbur L. Ross Jr., age 75
Director, Pierre Olivier Sarkozy, age 43
Director, Lance N. West, age 51
Director, Eugene F. DeMark, age 65
Independent Director, Thomas OBrien
Auditors: PricewaterhouseCoopersLLP

LOCATIONS

HQ: BankUnited Inc.
14817 Oak Lane, Miami Lakes FL 33016
Phone: 786-313-1010   **Fax:** 786-313-1011
Web: www.bankunited.com

PRODUCTS/OPERATIONS

2011 Sales

	$ mil.	% of total
Interest		
Loans including fees	512	59
Interest & dividends on investments available for sale	122	14
Other	2	-
Noninterest		
Net gain on indemnification asset	79	9
Accretion of discount on FDIC indemnification asset	55	7
FDIC reimbursement of costs of resolution of covered assets	31	4
Net income from resolution of covered assets	18	2
Mortgage insurance	16	2
Service charges & fees	11	1
Investment services	7	1
Other	11	1
Adjustments	(69.7)	
Total	**801**	**100**

COMPETITORS

1st United Bank	JPMorgan Chase
BB&T	Ocean Bankshares
BBX Capital	Regions Financial
Bank of America	SunTrust
Citibank	TD Bank USA
Great Florida Bank	Wells Fargo
Interamerican Bank	

HISTORICAL FINANCIALS

Company Type: Public

Income Statement

FYE: December 31

	REVENUE ($ mil.)	NET INCOME ($ mil.)	NET PROFIT MARGIN	EMPLOYEES
12/12	810.1	211.2	26.1%	1,429
12/11	801.3	63.1	7.9%	1,365
12/10	855.4	184.7	21.6%	1,263
12/09	588.3	119.0	20.2%	1,169
Annual Growth	11.3%	21.1%	—	6.9%

2012 Year-End Financials

Debt ratio: 15.4%	No. of shares (mil.): 95
Return on equity: 12.6%	Dividends
Cash ($ mil.): 495	Yield: 2.9%
Current ratio: 0.55	Payout: 38.5%
Long-term debt ($ mil.): 1,916	Market value ($ mil.): 2,322

	STOCK PRICE ($) FY Close	P/E High/Low		PER SHARE ($) Earnings	Dividends	Book Value
12/12	24.44	13	11	2.05	0.72	19.02
12/11	21.99	47	31	0.62	0.56	15.71
12/10	0.00	—	—	1.99	0.00	13.48
Annual Growth	—	—	—	1.5%	—	18.8%

Barrett Business Services, Inc.

Barrett Business Services likes to put people to work. The company offers both temporary and long-term staffing to some 1750 small and mid-sized businesses. Its staffing services focus on light industrial clerical and technical businesses. Barrett also does business as a professional employment organization (PEO) providing outsourced human resource services such as payroll management benefits administration risk management recruiting and placement for more than 1500 clients. Established in 1965 Barrett operates through about 45 branch offices across 10 US states. Each year about 90% of its PEO revenue comes from customers residing in the states of California and Oregon.

Barrett depends mostly on the light-industrial sector for the majority of its staffing services revenue (the sector represented 86% of its total revenue in 20010). Its light-industrial workers operate machinery and perform manufacturing loading and unloading and construction-site cleanup tasks.

After experiencing declines in revenue and a net loss for 2009 Barrett bounced back by generating a 15.5% increase in revenue and a positive net income of $7.4 million at the end of 2010. The increase in PEO service fee revenue was mostly attributed to the signing of new customers while its staffing revenue levels rose because of increased demand for existing customers in its northwest and intermountain markets. Barrett's growth strategy involves diversifying its revenue mix by expanding (through acquisitions) outside of California and Oregon.

EXECUTIVES

VP Finance Treasurer and Secretary, James D. Miller, age 47, $175,000 total compensation
VP, Gregory R. (Greg) Vaughn, age 55, $190,000 total compensation
Chairman, Anthony Meeker, age 71
Interim President Interim CEO and Director, Michael L. (Mike) Elich, age 45, $200,000 total compensation
Owner, Ron Dumas
Owner, Steve Mumm
Owner, Jeff Bucholz
Controller, Ken Cunningham
Owner, Karen Ashcraft
Director, Thomas J. Carley, age 52
Director, James B. Hicks, age 64
Director, Jon L. Justesen, age 59
Interim President Interim CEO and Director, Michael L. (Mike) Elich, age 45
Director, Roger L. Johnson, age 67
Auditors: MossAdamsLLP

LOCATIONS

HQ: Barrett Business Services Inc.
8100 NE Parkway Dr. Ste. 200, Vancouver WA 98662
Phone: 360-828-0700 **Fax:** 360-828-0701
Web: www.barrettbusiness.com

PRODUCTS/OPERATIONS

2010 Sales

	$ mil.	% of total
PEO service fees	147	54
Total	**273**	**100**

Selected Services

PEO services
  Employee benefits
  Health insurance
  Human resource administrationDrug testingHiringInterviewingPlacementRecruitingRegulatory compliance
  Payroll
  Workers' compensation coverage
  Workplace safety programs
Staffing services
  Contract
  Long-term
  Short-term

COMPETITORS

ADP TotalSource	Paychex
Adecco	SFN Group
Insperity	TeamStaff
Kelly Services	TriNet Group
ManpowerGroup	

HISTORICAL FINANCIALS
Company Type: Public

Income Statement
FYE: December 31

	REVENUE ($ mil.)	NET INCOME ($ mil.)	NET PROFIT MARGIN	EMPLOYEES
12/12	402.6	13.1	3.3%	64,315
12/11	314.8	14.3	4.5%	49,355
12/10	273.1	7.3	2.7%	40,935
12/09	236.4	(4.7)	—	34,725
12/08	280.4	6.2	2.2%	33,555
Annual Growth	**9.5%**	**20.3%**	**—**	**17.7%**

2012 Year-End Financials

Debt ratio: 4.3%
Return on equity: 16.8%
Cash ($ mil.): 45
Current ratio: 1.25
Long-term debt ($ mil.): 5

No. of shares (mil.): 7
Dividends
  Yield: 1.2%
  Payout: 27.5%
Market value ($ mil.): 267

	STOCK PRICE ($) FY Close	P/E High/Low		PER SHARE ($) Earnings	Dividends	Book Value
12/12	38.09	23	9	1.67	0.46	7.68
12/11	19.96	14	9	1.41	0.38	10.30
12/10	15.55	24	17	0.71	0.33	9.35
12/09	12.29	—	—	(0.46)	0.32	9.57
12/08	10.90	32	16	0.56	0.32	10.45
Annual Growth	**36.7%**	**—**	**—**	**31.4%**	**9.5%**	**(7.4%)**

Basic Energy Services Inc

Oil and gas producers turn to Basic Energy Services for the fundamentals. The company provides well site services with its fleet of well-servicing rigs (425 the third-largest in the US behind Key Energy Services and Nabors Industries) 955 fluid service trucks and related equipment. These services include acidizing cementing fluid handling fracturing well construction well maintenance and workover. Basic Energy Services serves more than 2000 producers primarily in Texas Louisiana and Oklahoma as well as in Arkansas Kansas New Mexico and the Rocky Mountain and Appalachian regions (where there are more than 600000 active wells). The company also provides contract drilling operations.

Geographic Reach

Basic Energy Services assets are concentrated in major onshore oil and natural gas producing regions located in Arkansas Colorado Kansas Louisiana Montana New Mexico North Dakota Oklahoma Pennsylvania Texas Utah West Virginia and Wyoming.

Operations

The company's operating segments are Completion and Remedial Services Fluid Services Well Servicing and Contract Drilling.

The completion and remedial services segment operates a fleet of pressure pumping units an array of specialized rental equipment and fishing tools coiled tubing units snubbing units and related equipment.

The fluid services segment operates a fleet of 955 fluid service trucks and related assets including specialized tank trucks storage tanks water wells disposal facilities and construction and other related equipment.

The well servicing segment operates a fleet of 425 well servicing rigs. Its services include the installation and removal of downhole equipment and elimination of obstructions in the well bore to facilitate the flow of oil and natural gas.

The contract drilling segment operates 12 land drilling rigs.

Sales and Marketing

Basic Energy Services' customers are primarily major and independent oil and gas companies. In 2012 its top five customers accounted for 25% of the company's total revenues.

Financial Performance

Basic Energy Services' revenues grew by 11% in 2012 thanks to a strong oil market notwithstanding lower natural gas commodity prices. Acquisitions in 2011 and 2012 (including Maverick Companies) also increased revenues. Contract drilling segment revenues jumped by 47% thanks to the deployment of two additional drilling rigs during 2012; and well servicing sales increased by 13% reflecting the continued high demand levels for oil drilling in the US market.Despite higher revenues the company's net income dropped by 56% in 2012 due to a rise in general and administrative expenses and depreciation and amortization as the result of a growth in personnel and incentive compensation costs the relocation of Basic Energy Services' headquarters and the full-year impact of expenses related to the acquisition of Maverick Companies in July 2011.

Following a revenue slump in 2009 Basic Energy Services has seen an upward trend in revenues from 2010 to 2012 thanks to the recovery of the oil and gas industry. The slump in 2009 was primarily due to lower expenditures by company's customers for its services and increased price competition from competitors due to the decline in oil and natural gas prices during the global economic downturn.

Strategy

Basic Energy Services grows both organically and by making complementary acquisitions.

Mergers and Acquisitions

In 2012 the company acquired Saltwater Disposal of North Dakota for a $43 million. The purchase boosted Basic Energy Services' salt water disposal facilities to a total of 72 (in Texas Oklahoma North Dakota New Mexico and Louisiana). The company plans to develop its existing fluid services operations in North Dakota to support the expansion of its integrated fluid services capabilities in a large and growing portion of the Bakken Shale market.

Growing its completion and remedial servicing segment in 2012 Basic Energy Services acquired Surface Stac Inc. for $23.2 million.

Expanding its well services portfolio in 2011 Basic Energy Services bought stimulation coil tubing and through-tubing services company Maverick Companies (60000 horsepower in its stimulation segment and seven coil tubing spreads) for $180 million.

Ownership

Investment firm Credit Suisse including DLJ Merchant Banking Partners III L.P. and affiliated funds owns 29% of the company; BlackRock 13%.

EXECUTIVES

VP Information Systems and Technology, Barbara S. Wood

Chairman, Steven A. Webster, age 61

President CEO and Director, Kenneth V. (Ken) Huseman, age 61, $510,008 total compensation

VP Gulf Coast Region, Charles W. (Charlie) Swift, age 65, $250,000 total compensation

SVP CFO Treasurer and Secretary, Alan Krenek, age 58, $282,661 total compensation

SVP and COO, Thomas M. (Roe) Patterson, age 39, $259,123 total compensation

Group VP Permian Basin Unit, James F. (Jim) Newman, age 48, $197,923 total compensation

VP Marketing, Douglas B. (Doug) Rogers, age 49

VP Permian Business Unit, Lynn Wigington

VP Rocky Mountain Region, Jerry Tufly

VP Pumping Services Division, Tim Dame

Vice President Controller Chief Accounting Officer, Cody Bissett

VP Mid Continent Region, Lance Green

Vice President Ark-La-Tex Region, Roger Massey

Vice President Safety and Operations Support, Trampas Poldrack

VP Drilling, Ron Scandolari

Vice President Manufacturing and Equipment, Brett Taylor

Vice President Financial Services and Assistant Treasurer, Mike Dye

President CEO and Director, Kenneth V. (Ken) Huseman, age 60

Director, William E. (Bill) Chiles, age 63

Director, Thomas P. Moore Jr., age 73

Director, James S. D'Agostino Jr., age 65

Director, Antonio O. Garza Jr., age 52

Director, Robert F. Fulton, age 60

Director, Sylvester P. Johnson IV, age 56

Auditors: KPMGLLP

LOCATIONS

HQ: Basic Energy Services Inc.
801 Cherry St. Ste. 2100, Fort Worth TX 76102
Phone: 817-334-4100   **Fax:** 434-817-1010
Web: www.crutchfield.com

PRODUCTS/OPERATIONS

2012 Sales

Completion & remedial services	586	43
Fluid services	352	26
Total	**1,374**	**100**

Selected Services

Coil Tubing
Contract Drilling
Fluid Services
Pumping Services
Rental/Fishing Tools
Snubbing Services
Water Recycling Services
Well Servicing
Well Site Construction
Wireline

Selected Mergers and Acquisitions

2012
Saltwater Disposal ($43 million; North Dakota; salt water disposal facilities)
Surface Stac Inc. ($23.2 million; completion and remedial services)
2011
Maverick Companies ($180 million; stimulation coil tubing and through-tubing services)

COMPETITORS

Chesapeake Oilfield Services Inc.

Pioneer Energy Services

Ensign Energy Services
Halliburton
Helmerich & Payne
Key Energy
Nabors Industries
Oil States International
Patterson-UTI Energy

Precision Drilling
Pride International
RPC
Schlumberger
Superior Energy
Weatherford International

HISTORICAL FINANCIALS

Company Type: Public

Income Statement

FYE: December 31

	REVENUE ($ mil.)	NET INCOME ($ mil.)	NET PROFIT MARGIN	EMPLOYEES
12/12	1,374.8	20.8	1.5%	5,600
12/11	1,243.2	47.1	3.8%	5,600
12/10	728.2	(43.5)	—	4,500
12/09	526.6	(253.5)	—	3,800
12/08	1,004.9	68.2	6.8%	5,000
Annual Growth	**8.2%**	**(25.6%)**	**—**	**2.9%**

2012 Year-End Financials

Debt ratio: 55.3%
Return on equity: 5.6%
Cash ($ mil.): 134
Current ratio: 2.46
Long-term debt ($ mil.): 844
No. of shares (mil.): 41
Dividends
  Yield: —
  Payout: —
Market value ($ mil.): 476

	STOCK PRICE ($) FY Close	P/E High/Low		PER SHARE ($) Earnings	Dividends	Book Value
12/12	11.41	43	17	0.51	0.00	8.97
12/11	19.70	32	11	1.14	0.00	8.47
12/10	16.48	—	—	(1.10)	0.00	7.31
12/09	8.90	—	—	(6.39)	0.00	8.36
12/08	13.04	20	5	1.64	0.00	14.56
Annual Growth (11.4%)	**(3.3%)**	**—**	**—**	**(25.3%)**	**—**	

Berkshire Hills Bancorp, Inc.

Berkshire Hills Bancorp is the holding company for Berkshire Bank which serves individuals and small businesses through some 60 branches in Massachusetts New York Connecticut and Vermont. Established in 1846 the bank provides standard deposit products such as savings checking and money market accounts CDs and IRAs in addition to credit cards investments private banking wealth management and lending services. Real estate mortgages make up nearly three-quarters of Berkshire Hills Bancorp's loan portfolio which also includes business and consumer loans. In addition to its banking activities Berkshire Hills also owns insurance agency Berkshire Insurance Group.

Berkshire Bank is transition into a regional bank and is growing its geographic footprint by acquiring other banks. On the heels of its 2011 acquisitions of Rome Bancorp and Legacy Bancorp Berkshire Hills Bancorp bought The Connecticut Bank and Trust which gave the company its first eight branches in Connecticut. The previous acquisitions expanded Berkshire's presence in Massachusetts and New York two target markets in which it has also opened new branches. (However the company sold four branches from the Legacy deal to NBT Bancorp in order to satisfy antitrust concerns.) Berkshire Hills also is eyeing further expansion into Connecticut and other parts of New England and New York by opening new branches and through acquisitions.

The company which was established in 1846 believes one of its competitive advantages is the regional niche it serves which has been relatively unscathed by the recession compared to other parts of the country. The bank's performance has been boosted by an increase in business development in the company's market area in addition to growth in its asset-based lending and private banking businesses. The bank also has grown its loans and deposits and has plans to grow its insurance and wealth management operations as well.

Berkshire reported a more than 20% increase in revenues in 2011 and a 28% jump in net income. The company's 2011 acquisitions for Rome Bancorp and Legacy Bancorp as well as organic growth helped boost revenues. Berkshire now plans to buy Beacon Federal Bancorp in a $132 million deal that will add seven branches serving primarily the Syracuse market.

HISTORY

.

EXECUTIVES

President Chief Executive Officer, Michael P. Daly, age 51, $450,000 total compensation

Chairman, Lawrence A. (Larry) Bossidy, age 78

Executive Vice President of Human Resources, Linda A. Johnston

SVP Commercial Lending, Michael J. Ferry

EVP, Michael J. (Mike) Oleksak, age 54, $225,000 total compensation

Executive Vice President of Retail Banking, Sean A. Gray

Executive Vice President Chief Financial Officer Treasurer, Kevin P. Riley, age 53, $250,000 total compensation

Executive Vice President Chief Risk Officer, Richard M. Marotta

Chief Compliance Officer and Anti Money Laundering Officer, Brian Kindelan

Chief Investment Officer, Charles N. Leach

Executive Vice President of Commercial Banking and Wealth Management, Patrick Sullivan

Vice President Manager, Paul Lesukoski

Vice President Personal Lines, James Herrick

Director, Rodney C. Dimock, age 66

Director, Cornelius D. Mahoney, age 67

President CEO and Director Berkshire Hills Bancorp and Berkshire Bank, Michael P. Daly, age 51

Director, Catherine B. Miller, age 70

Director, Corydon L. Thurston, age 59

Director, D. Jeffrey Templeton, age 71

Director, David E. Phelps, age 60

Director, Robert M. Curley

Director, John B. Davis, age 63

Director, Wallace W. Altes, age 70

Director, Susan M. Hill, age 63

Independent Director, John Davies

Independent Director, Williar Dunlaevy

Auditors: PricewaterhouseCoopersLLP

LOCATIONS

HQ: Berkshire Hills Bancorp Inc.
24 North St., Pittsfield MA 01201
Phone: 413-443-5601   **Fax:** 413-443-3587
Web: www.berkshirebank.com

PRODUCTS/OPERATIONS

2011 Sales

	$ mil.	% of total
Interest		
Loans	124	71
Securities & other	13	8
Noninterest		
Deposit related fees	13	8
Insurance commissions & fees	11	7
Wealth management fees	5	3
Loan related fees	3	2
Other	2	1
Total	**174**	**100**

COMPETITORS

Bank of America	RBS Citizens Financial
Hudson City Bancorp	Group
KeyCorp	Sovereign Bank
Pathfinder Bancorp	TD Bank USA

HISTORICAL FINANCIALS

Company Type: Public

Income Statement

FYE: December 31

	ASSETS ($ mil.)	NET INCOME ($ mil.)	INCOME AS % OF ASSETS	EMPLOYEES
12/12	5,296.8	33.1	0.6%	1,012
12/11	3,991.2	17.5	0.4%	760
12/10	2,880.7	13.7	0.5%	599
12/09	2,700.4	(16.0)	—	622
12/08	2,666.7	22.2	0.8%	610
Annual Growth	**18.7%**	**10.5%**	**—**	**13.5%**

2012 Year-End Financials

Return on assets: 0.7%	Dividends
Return on equity: 5.4%	Yield: 2.8%
Long-term debt ($ mil.): —	Payout: 44.5%
No. of shares (mil.): 25	Market value ($ mil.): 600
Sales ($ mil): 230	

	STOCK PRICE ($) FY Close	P/E High/Low	PER SHARE ($) Earnings	Dividends	Book Value
12/12	23.86	16 14	1.49	0.69	26.53
12/11	22.19	24 18	0.98	0.65	26.17
12/10	22.11	23 17	0.99	0.64	27.56
12/09	20.68	— —	(1.52)	0.64	27.64
12/08	30.86	15 10	2.06	0.63	33.33
Annual Growth	**(6.2%)**	**— —**	**(7.8%)**	**2.3%**	**(5.5%)**

BGC Partners, Inc.

BGC Partners provides inter-dealer brokerage services for banks investment firms and other institutional traders around the world through about 115 offices. Through its eSpeed and BGC Trader-branded platform it offers voice electronic and hybrid trade brokerage for a broad range of financial products including government and corporate bonds interest rate swaps foreign exchange derivatives and futures. The company also provides processing clearing and settlement services as well as market data and analytics products. BGC Partners was established by Cantor Fitzgerald which controls nearly half of the company. (BGC is named after Cantor Fitzgerald founder B. Gerald Cantor.)

Operations

The company has been entering new lines of business. In 2011 it launched BGC Environmental Brokerage Services following the acquisition of CantorCO2e from Cantor Fitzgerald. The subsequent acquisition of Newmark the US arm of global brokerage partnership Knight Frank added commercial real estate brokerage services. On the heels of its acquisition of Newmark BGC acquired the assets of bankrupt commercial real estate services firm Grubb & Ellis. The deal underscored BGC's commitment to build a strong position in the property services market. Upon the completion of that acquisition BGC launched Newmark Grubb Knight Frank a full-service commercial real estate platform. The move included BGC realigning its business under real estate services and financial services banners.

The Financial Services segment specializes offers fixed income securities interest rate swaps foreign exchange equities equity derivatives credit derivatives commodities futures and structured products. Real Estate Services serves commercial tenants owners investors and developers with a full range of services including consulting project and development management leasing and other consulting services along with investment sales debt placement appraisal and valuation services.

Geographic Reach

The company has been expanding worldwide including in the US. It has also established or added to existing operations in Brazil China Russia Turkey and other markets in recent years. BGC Partners plans to continue its global growth with Asia as a key target market.

Sales and Marketing

BGC markets its financial services through its salespeople and its real estate services through traditional advertising event sponsorship and sales collateral.

Financial Performance

The Grubb & Ellis acquisition pushed the company into a 21% revenue gain for 2012. An 11% decline in financial services offset the big real estate gains. Net income and cash flow also improved.

Strategy

BGC continues to expand through acquisitions technology investments and hiring new brokers.

Mergers and Acquisitions

In 2012 BGC Partners purchased real estate services firm Grubb & Ellis for about $47 million. Other purchases that year included Wolfe & Hurst Bond Brokers a municipal bonds interdealer broker in North America and totaled about $24 million.

Ownership

Cantor Fitzgerald L.P. and CF Group Management each own about 50% of the company.

Company Background

BGC lost nearly all of its US employees in the September 11 2001 terrorist attacks. Subsequently it set up funds for survivors and families of victims and paid healthcare for affected employees for 10 years.

EXECUTIVES

Executive Vice President General Counsel Secretary, Stephen M. Merkel, age 55, $1,000,000 total compensation
Chairman and CEO, Howard W. Lutnick, age 52, $1,000,000 total compensation
Vice Chairman, Lee M. Amaitis, age 63, $1,339,410 total compensation
Executive Managing Director North America; Global Head FX Products, Daniel M. LaVecchia, age 53

Executive Managing Director and Director BGCantor Market Data, Bernard A. (Bernie) Weinstein
Executive Managing Director e-Commerce, Philip (Phil) Norton
Executive Managing Director and General Manager North America, Louis (Lou) Scotto, age 60
Executive Managing Director Asia, Mark E. Spring, age 55
President, Shaun D. Lynn, age 50, $1,000,000 total compensation
Executive Managing Director Global Head Listed Products and General Manager Continental Europe, Jean-Pierre Aubin
Chief Administrative Officer North America, Roger C. Campbell
CIO, Yevette Tierney
COO, Sean A. Windeatt, age 40, $310,040 total compensation
Executive Managing Director and General Manager Asia/Pacific, Leonard (Len) Harvey
CFO, A. Graham Sadler, age 57, $232,530 total compensation
Executive Managing Director and General Manager London, Mark Webster
Head of Credit and Repo, Rob Kitchin
Media Relations US, Florencia Panizza
Global Head of Real Estate, Michael Lehrman
Executive Managing Director and Director of BCG Market Data, Mark Benfield
Director, John H. Dalton, age 70
Director, Barry R. Sloane, age 57
Vice Chairman, Lee M. Amaitis, age 63
Director, Albert M. Weis, age 85
Director, Stephen T. Curwood, age 64
Auditors: Ernst&YoungLLP

LOCATIONS

HQ: BGC Partners Inc.
499 Park Ave., New York NY 10022
Phone: 212-610-2200 **Fax:** 646-346-6919
Web: www.bgcpartners.com

PRODUCTS/OPERATIONS

2012 Sales

	$ mil.	% of total
Financial Services		
Non-interest income	1,220	69
Interest income	1	-
Real Estate Services		
Non-interest income	454	26
Interest income .4 -		
Other	91	5
Total	**1,767**	**100**

Selected Subsidiaries

Ameefi Services Inc.
Aqua Securities Holdings LLC
Aqua Securities L.P.
Aurel BGC
BGC Brokers Gp Limited
BGC Brokers Holdings L.P.
BGC Brokers Holdings LLC
BGC Brokers Investment L.P.
BGC Brokers L.P.
BGC Brokers Limited
BGC Brokers US Holdings LLC
BGC Brokers US L.P.
BGC Canada Securities Company
BGC Canada Securities Company Holdings L.P.
BGC Canada Securities Company Holdings LLC
BGC Capital Markets (Hong Kong) Limited
BGC Capital Markets (Japan) LLC
BGC Capital Markets (Switzerland) LLC
BGC Capital Markets And Foreign Exchange Broker (Korea) Limited
BGC Capital Markets L.P.
BGC China Holdings LLC

BGC China L.P.
BGC European GP Limited
BGC European Holdings L.P.
BGC Financial Group Inc.
BGC Financial L.P.
BGC France Holdings
BGC Global Holdings GP Limited
BGC Global Holdings L.P.
BGC Global Limited
BGC GP Limited
BGC GP LLC
BGC Holdings (Turkey) LLC
BGC Holdings II LLC
BGC Holdings U.S. Inc.
BGC Holdings L.P.
BGC Holdings LLC
BGC Information Holdings LLC
BGC Information L.P.
BGC International
BGC International GP Limited
BGC International Holdings L.P.
BGC International L.P.
BGC Mexico R.E. Holdings LLC
BGC Mexico R.E. Holdings S. de R.L. de C.V.
BGC Notes LLC
BGC Partners (Australia) Pty Limited
BGC Partners (Singapore) Limited
BGC Partners Menkul Degerler A.S.
BGC Partners L.P.
BGC Radix Energy L.P.
BGC Real Estate LLC
BGC Rie Holdings LLC
BGC SA Financial Brokers (Pty) Limited
BGC Securities (Hong Kong) LLC
BGC Securities (South Africa) Pty Limited
BGC Shoken Kaisha Limited
BGC Trading Holdings LLC
BGC USA Holdings LLC
BGC USA L.P.
BGCantor Market Data Holdings LLC
BGCantor Market Data L.P.
BGCCMHK Holdings LLC
ECCO LLC
ELX Futures Holdings LLC
eSpeed (Hong Kong) Limited
eSpeed Markets L.P.
eSpeed LLC
ESX Clearing Holdings LLC
Euro Brokers Holdings Ltd.
FHLP LLC
Freedom International Brokerage Company
G&E Management Services LLC
G&E Real Estate Inc.
Ginalfi Finance
Itsecco Holdings Limited
Jadestone Consultants Limited
Kleos Managed Services L.P.
MIS Holdings LLC
Newmark & Company Real Estate Inc.
Seminole Financial
Tower Bridge GP Limtied
Tradesoft Technologies Inc.
Treasuryconnect LLC

COMPETITORS

Bloomberg L.P.	Interactive Brokers
CBRE Group	
Colliers International	Jones Lang LaSalle
Collins Stewart	London Stock Exchange
Hawkpoint	MarketAxess
Cushman &	NASDAQ OMX
Wakefield	Penson.Worldwide
Eastdil Secured	Thomson Reuters
GFI Group	Tradeweb
HFF	Tullett Prebon
ICAP	VIEL

HISTORICAL FINANCIALS

Company Type: Public

Income Statement

FYE: December 31

	REVENUE ($ mil.)	NET INCOME ($ mil.)	NET PROFIT MARGIN	EMPLOYEES
12/12	1,766.9	23.8	1.4%	6,547
12/11	1,464.6	20.1	1.4%	4,129
12/10	1,331.1	21.1	1.6%	2,743
12/09	1,162.3	20.0	1.7%	2,524
12/08	1,228.9	(29.7)	—	2,277
Annual Growth	9.5%	—	—	30.2%

2012 Year-End Financials

Debt ratio: 27.5%
Return on equity: 5.8%
Cash ($ mil.): 391
Current ratio: 1.85
Long-term debt ($ mil.): 451

No. of shares (mil.): 158
Dividends
  Yield: 18.2%
  Payout: 700.0%
Market value ($ mil.): 549

	STOCK PRICE ($) FY Close	P/E High/Low		PER SHARE ($) Earnings	Dividends	Book Value
12/12	3.46	50	20	0.16	0.63	2.60
12/11	5.94	58	32	0.17	0.65	3.05
12/10	8.31	36	16	0.24	0.48	3.43
12/09	4.62	23	6	0.24	0.30	3.70
12/08	2.76	—	—	(0.28)	0.23	3.57
Annual Growth	5.8%	—	—	—	28.6%	(7.6%)

Bio-Reference Laboratories, Inc.

Bio-Reference Laboratories tests positive as the lab of choice for many in the Northeast. Primarily serving the greater New York Metropolitan Area the company offers routine clinical tests including Pap smears pregnancy tests cholesterol checks and blood cell counts. Through its GenPath business unit it also performs more sophisticated esoteric testing such as cancer pathology and molecular diagnostics. It gets most of its orders (close to 5 million per year) from doctors' offices collecting specimens at draw stations scattered throughout its primary service area in the New York area. Bio-Reference Laboratories also provides services in Connecticut Delaware Maryland New Jersey and Pennsylvania.

Geographic Reach

The company's laboratory service in the New York Metro area is its core business but it is growing steadily and now offers some of its testing services nationwide.

Operations

The company offers focused expertise in specialty areas through its various subsidiaries. It operates as a national oncology laboratory through its GenPath subsidiary. GenPath also houses Bio-Reference's women's health testing unit. GeneDX another wholly owned subsidiary performs testing of rare and ultra-rare genetic diseases nationally. Bio-Reference intends to build a marketing team to cross-sell its genetic testing and women's health testing capabilities to doctors who specialize in prenatal care.

Bio-Reference's specialty testing operations (both esoteric and for emerging markets) have been growing at a faster clip than its core routine testing business and now routine lab tests account for less than half of the company's sales.

Another Bio-Reference unit PSIMedica makes health informatics software that combines information from health care claims lab results and other sources and markets it to managed care organizations. The CareEvolve subsidiary markets the company's online connectivity software to other laboratories. Revenues from PSIMedica and CareEvolve contribute a negligible percentage of the company's overall sales.

Sales and Marketing

Bio-Reference's primary client base is composed of doctors employers clinics and governmental units.

Bio-Reference grows its services by tapping into emerging laboratory markets. The company is focused on developing its cardiology histology and women's health diagnostic testing capabilities to complement its existing hemostasis (process by which blood changes from fluid to a solid state) hematopathology (tests for congenital disorders) and correctional health care initiatives.

Still demand for the both its routine and esoteric lab testing is expected to increase thanks to a growing US trend of shorter inpatient stays at hospitals. With patients being discharged earlier some of the business that would typically go straight to the hospital-based lab is instead being sent to labs like Bio-Reference by the patients' after-care physicians.

Financial Analysis

The company has enjoyed an upward trend in revenue the past five fiscal years. Net revenues were $.4 million in fiscal 2010 $.5 million in fiscal 2011 and $.66 million in fiscal 2012. Bio-Reference's increase in revenue per patient was due to increases in esoteric testing.

Strategy

Part of Bio-Reference's strategy for expanding its testing areas is to partner with medical providers whose expertise can help expedite the development process. In 2010 Bio-Reference entered into one such agreement with Massachusetts General Hospital to develop a line of clinical diagnostic tests designed to identify and help treat solid tumors. The test will make use of the emerging field of personalized medicine in which a patient's unique genetic make-up is used to help tailor testing and treatment to best address that patient's individual needs.

Doctors can place orders for lab tests and get test results using the company's proprietary CareEvolve online portal. Outside of its customer relationships with doctors' offices Bio-Reference serves government agencies large employers (for substance abuse testing for instance) and prison systems in the northeastern US.

Mergers and Acquisitions

The company occasionally purchases other testing businesses to expand its reach. It acquired clinical laboratory business The Genetics Center in 2011. In 2010 Bio-Reference acquired clinical testing laboratory Lenetix Medical Screening Laboratory.

Ownership

Founder chairman and CEO Marc Grodman owns 10% of the company.

HISTORY

Marc Grodman founded Med-Mobile in 1981 offering mobile medical examination services. In 1987 it opened a clinical laboratory in New Jersey.

The purchase of Cytology and Pathology Associates a small specialized lab followed in 1988. Demand for tests rose leading the company to relocate all operations to a modern lab near New York City. It renamed itself Bio-Reference Laboratories in 1989 and went public in 1993.

The company moved into specialty testing to compensate for the industrywide drop in reimbursement rates that hit its general labs acquiring GenCare Biomedical Research (cancer testing 1995) Oncodec Labs (gene mutations 1995) and SmithKline Beecham's renal dialysis testing business (1996). Late in 1996 the firm sued SmithKline Beecham accusing it of fraud regarding the purchase.

In 1997 the company sold part of its GenCare oncology laboratory services division to IMPATH. To build its regional presence the company acquired Medilabs from Long Term Care in 1998. The next year it ventured into new frontiers opening and acquiring websites for online ventures and buying the Right Body Foods health foods business.

In 2000 Bio-Reference Laboratories expanded its Internet presence (including a business-to-business Web portal for health care professionals CareEvolve.com) and re-entered the oncology market resuming full-service testing to physicians and institutions.

In the following years the company was intent on expanding its geographic reach and adding services to its roster to make push itself into a leading position in the testing industry. Some of its key acquisitions include the 2006 purchases of Diagnostic Pathology Services a Maryland-based anatomic pathology lab serving the mid-Atlantic states and GeneDx which specializes in diagnosing rare genetic disorders using DNA sequencing technology. That buy fit with GeneDx' strategy to develop and its expand its genetic diagnostic testing capabilities.

EXECUTIVES

Senior Vice President, Azmy Awad
SVP and CFO, Sam Singer Sr., age 70, $381,425 total compensation
EVP COO and Director, Howard Dubinett, age 62, $381,425 total compensation
Chairman President and CEO, Marc D. Grodman, age 62, $965,180 total compensation
SVP Sales and Marketing, Charles T. Todd Jr., age 61, $540,000 total compensation
CIO; President PsiMedica, Richard L. Faherty, age 67, $516,091 total compensation
SVP and Director Operations, Warren Erdmann
VP Technical Operations and Laboratory Director, Nick Cetani
SVP Chief Medical Officer and Laboratory Director, James Weisberger, age 58
President CareEvolve, Cory Fishkin
Vice President of Marketing, Amar Kamath
Director Technical Sales and Marketing, Edward Clayton
Manager Operations, Ada Gazzillo
VP and Director Logistics, Ron Rayot
VP and Director Phlebotomy, Chris Smith
VP Genpath, Maryanne Amato
IR Contact Officer, Tara Mackay
CEO and Scientific Director GeneDx, John Compton, age 64
Manager Laboratory and Operations, Patricia Neybold
Director Quality Systems, Kathleen (Kathy) Phillips
Manager Client Service, Marisol Aviles
Manager Technical Services, Estrella Moran

SVP CFO Chief Accounting Officer and Director, Sam Singer Sr., age 69
EVP COO and Director, Howard Dubinett, age 62
Director, John Roglieri, age 74
Director, Gary Lederman, age 78
Director, Joseph Benincasa, age 64
Director, Harry Elias, age 83
Auditors: MooreStephensP.C.

LOCATIONS

HQ: Bio-Reference Laboratories Inc.
481 Edward H. Ross Dr., Elmwood Park NJ 07407
Phone: 201-791-2600   **Fax:** 201-791-1941
Web: www.bioreference.com

PRODUCTS/OPERATIONS

Selected Products and Services

Routine testing (Performed in Elmwood Park New Jersey)
  Blood cell counts
  Cholesterol levels
  HIV tests
  Pap smears
  Pregnancy tests
  Substance abuse tests
  Urinalysis
Esoteric testing (Performed in Elmwood Park Milford Massachusetts and Gaithersburg Maryland)
  Endocrinology
  Genetics
  Immunology
  Microbiology
  Oncology
  Serology
  Toxicology
Other
  CareEvolve (physician-based connectivity portal for clinical laboratories)
  PSIMedica Clinical Knowledge Management System (health informatics software)

Selected Mergers and Acquisitions

FY2011
The Genetics Center Inc. (undisclosed price; Smithtown NY; clinical laboratory business)
FY2010
Lenetix Medical Screening Laboratory Inc. (undisclosed price; Mineola NY; clinical testing laboratory)

COMPETITORS

American Bio Medica	LabCorp
Athena Diagnostics	MEDTOX Laboratories
IDENTIGENE	Orchid Cellmark
Integrated Genetics	Quest Diagnostics
Kroll Background America	Solstas
	eScreen

HISTORICAL FINANCIALS

Company Type: Public

Income Statement

FYE: October 31

	REVENUE ($ mil.)	NET INCOME ($ mil.)	NET PROFIT MARGIN	EMPLOYEES
10/13	715.3	45.8	6.4%	4,427
10/12	661.6	42.1	6.4%	3,564
10/11	558.6	36.3	6.5%	3,155
10/10	458.0	26.3	5.8%	2,424
10/09	362.6	21.8	6.0%	2,174
Annual Growth	18.5%	20.3%	—	19.5%

2013 Year-End Financials

Debt ratio: 10.9%	No. of shares (mil.): 27
Return on equity: 18.3%	Dividends
Cash ($ mil.): 17	Yield: —
Current ratio: 2.20	Payout: —
Long-term debt ($ mil.): 14	Market value ($ mil.): 897

	STOCK PRICE ($) FY Close	P/E High/Low	PER SHARE ($) Earnings	Dividends	Book Value
10/13	32.41	20 14	1.65	0.00	9.81
10/12	27.76	21 8	1.51	0.00	8.20
10/11	20.04	19 13	1.29	0.00	6.79
10/10	21.56	51 19	0.94	0.00	5.47
10/09	32.33	45 25	0.79	0.00	4.50
Annual Growth	0.1%	— —	20.4%	—	21.5%

Biomed Realty Trust Inc

BioMed Realty knows its niche. A self-administered real estate investment trust (REIT) the firm acquires develops leases and manages laboratory and office space for biotechnology and pharmaceutical companies scientific research institutions government agencies and other life science tenants. BioMed owns more than 80 properties with around 150 buildings and more than 16 million sq. ft. of rentable space. The REIT's properties which span about a dozen states are often located near universities; its preferred markets include research and development hubs such as Boston New York San Diego San Francisco and Seattle. In 2013 BioMed acquired Wexford Science & Technology.

Geographic Reach

San Diego-based BioMed Realty's preferred markets include research and development hubs such as Boston San Francisco Maryland San Diego New York/New Jersey Pennsylvania Seattle and Cambridge in the UK. With nearly three million leased square feet of space Boston is the REIT's largest market and accounts for a third of its annualized base rent.

Sales and Marketing

Pharmaceutical giant GlaxoSmithKline plc is the REIT's #1 tenant contributing 10% of its annual base rent. Vertex Pharmaceuticals accounts for about 8%.

Financial Performance

BioMed Realty's revenue increased 18% in 2012 compared with 2011 to $518 million. The double-digit gain was driven by the purchase of more than 1 million rentable square feet of lab and office space during the course of the year and rising income from previously owned properties due to higher leasing activity. Net income declined 72% over the same period to $11.8 million on rising expenses including costs related to the acquisition of Granta Park in the UK in 2012. Cash flow increased by $9 million in 2012 versus 2011. BioMed Realty has logged a decade of steady revenue growth (from $13.7 million in 2003 to $518 million in 2012). However profit growth has been less dependable.

At the end of 2012 the REIT had 209 tenants and its portfolio of properties was 92.1% leased.

Strategy

BioMed Realty Trust's growth strategy includes converting properties to higher-yielding laboratory space and developing new office and lab space. When considering acquisitions the REIT sometimes looks for properties with vacancies and utilizes its business contacts in the life science industry to fill them. Acquisitions and new development have boosted the REIT's revenue in recent years though its net income and same-property rents were down. BioMed Realty Trust is banking on the continued growth of the life sciences industry because of an aging populace and rising health care costs.

The firm's leasing strategy for 2013 is focused on leasing vacant space negotiating renewals for leases scheduled to expire during the year and identifying new tenants or existing tenants seeking additional space.

Mergers and Acquisitions

In June 2013 BioMed acquired Wexford Science & Technology (WS&T) for about $672 million. The purchase of WS&T a private real estate and development company with about 2.5 million in square feet of rentable space furthers BioMed's position as a leading provider of real estate to the life science industry. As a wholly-owned subsidiary of BioMed WS&T will develop life science real estate for academic and medical research organizations with a specialization in urban development and redevelopment of life science properties. Also in the 2013 the firm acquired 99500 square feet of lab and office space in Cambridge Massachusetts for $52 million.

BioMed Realty entered the UK market with the 2012 acquisition of Granta Park a complex with 11 laboratory and office buildings in Cambridge. Other recent transactions include the 2011 acquisition of life science campus Ardsley Park in New York which included some 160500 sq. ft. of rentable space and another 500000 sq. ft. of developable space. In 2012 the REIT bought the three-building 80%-leased Cambridge Place boosting its presence in the Boston market. By acquiring leased properties the company is able to secure relatively stable revenue lines although the health of its tenants' businesses always has the ability to impact BioMed's bottom line.

Ownership

The Vanguard Group owns 11% of BioMed Realty's shares.

EXECUTIVES

Chairman Chief Executive Officer, Alan D. Gold, age 52, $472,500 total compensation
Executive Vice President Director, Gary A. Kreitzer, age 58, $157,500 total compensation
Executive Vice President Real Estate, Matthew G. McDevitt, age 47, $313,500 total compensation
Chief Financial Officer, Greg N. Lubushkin, age 61
Executive Vice President Asset Management, Karen A. Sztraicher, age 49
Jr. President Chief Operating Officer, R. Kent Griffin Jr., age 43, $313,500 total compensation
VP Development, John P. Bonanno
Senior Vice President; General Counsel, Jonathan P. Klassen
VP Real Estate Counsel, Kevin M. Simonsen
Director Corporate Communications, Rick Howe
Director Acquisitions and Leasing, Bill Kane
Senior Director Acquisitions and Leasing, Chris Elmendorf
Vice President Acquisitions, Denis Sullivan
Vice President Finance, Robert M. Sistek
Vice President Human Resources, Janice Kameir
Vice President Chief Accounting Officer, Stephen A. Willey
Senior Vice President Leasing & Development, Anne L. Hoffman
Senior Vice President Development Wexford Science & Technology, Daniel C. Cramer
President Wexford Science & Technology, James R. Berens

Vice President Leasing & Development, William F. Kane
Director, Theodore D. Roth, age 62
Director, M. Faye Wilson, age 75
Director, Richard I. (Rick) Gilchrist, age 68
EVP General Counsel and Director, Gary A. Kreitzer, age 58
Director, Barbara R. Cambon, age 59
Director, Edward A. Dennis, age 71
Auditors: KPMGLLP

LOCATIONS

HQ: BioMed Realty Trust Inc.
17140 Bernardo Center Dr. Ste. 222, San Diego CA 92128
Phone: 858-485-9840   **Fax:** 858-485-9843
Web: www.biomedrealty.com

Selected Markets
California
Colorado
Delaware
Maryland
Massachusetts
New Hampshire
New Jersey
New York
North Carolina
Pennsylvania
Washington

PRODUCTS/OPERATIONS

2012 Sales

	$ mil.	% of total
Rental income	392	76
Tenant recoveries	120	23
Other	4	1
Total	**518**	**100**

COMPETITORS

Alexandria Real Estate Equities	Health Care REIT
Boston Properties	Liberty Property Trust
CommonWealth REIT	Mission West Properties
HCP	PS Business Parks

HISTORICAL FINANCIALS

Company Type: Public

Income Statement   FYE: December 31

	REVENUE ($ mil.)	NET INCOME ($ mil.)	NET PROFIT MARGIN	EMPLOYEES
12/12	518.1	11.8	2.3%	175
12/11	439.7	42.1	9.6%	166
12/10	386.4	38.8	10.0%	159
12/09	361.1	58.7	16.3%	132
12/08	301.9	64.9	21.5%	126
Annual Growth	**14.5%**	**(34.7%)**	**—**	**8.6%**

2012 Year-End Financials

Debt ratio: 44.8%	No. of shares (mil.): 154
Return on equity: 0.4%	Dividends
Cash ($ mil.): 19	Yield: 4.5%
Current ratio: 0.14	Payout: —
Long-term debt ($ mil.): 2,169	Market value ($ mil.): 2,983

	STOCK PRICE ($) FY Close	P/E High/Low	PER SHARE ($) Earnings	Dividends	Book Value
12/12	19.33	— —	(0.03)	0.88	16.05
12/11	18.08	109 81	0.19	0.80	16.89
12/10	18.65	102 71	0.19	0.63	17.58
12/09	15.78	36 13	0.45	0.70	18.33
12/08	11.72	42 11	0.67	1.34	20.02
Annual Growth	**13.3%**	**— —**	**—**	**(10.0%)**	**(5.4%)**

BJ's Restaurants Inc

The Windy City inspires the food and drink at BJ's. BJ's Restaurants owns and operates 130 restaurants in California and 14 other mostly western states under the names BJ's Restaurant & Brewhouse BJ's Restaurant & Brewery and BJ's Pizza & Grill. The casual-dining eateries offer Chicago-style pizza salads sandwiches pasta and the company's own hand-crafted beers. Its Restaurant & Brewery locations which feature an onsite microbrewery help supply beer to the rest of the chain. The Brewhouse locations sell beer from company breweries and from third-parties using the company's recipes. The smaller Pizza & Grill shops have limited menus. The first BJ's opened in California in 1978.

Geographic Reach

The company has 130 restaurants in 15 states mostly concentrated in California Texas and Florida.

Financial Performance

BJ's has enjoyed unprecedented growth over the years. In 2012 its revenues increased 14% from $621 million in 2011 to peak at $708 million in 2012 a historic milestone for the company. Profits remained flat from 2011 to 2012 hovering around the $31 million mark.

Such growth has been the result of increases in both guest traffic and the average amount spent per guest. This was in part due to higher menu prices which were raised by about 3%. In addition BJ's opened 16 new restaurants in 2012 which added to the revenue spike.

Strategy

More than 80% of its locations operate under the Brewhouse brand which is similar to its Brewery restaurants except they do not manufacture beer. However the company will continue to build additional Brewery locations in certain areas where it is more appropriate to brew its own beer. It also opens smaller-format BJ's Pizza and Grill locations (the company's legacy format) in densely-populated urban areas or in smaller cities where a larger location is not feasible or appropriate.

EXECUTIVES

Chairman President and CEO, Gerald W. (Jerry) Deitchle, age 61, $450,000 total compensation
President and CEO, Gregory A. (Greg) Trojan, age 54
SVP Brewing Operations, Alexander M. (Alex) Puchner, age 51, $111,780 total compensation
EVP CFO and Secretary, Gregory S. (Greg) Levin, age 46, $315,000 total compensation
Chief Marketing Officer, Matthew W. (Matt) Hood, age 43
EVP and Chief Development Officer, Gregory S. (Greg) Lynds, age 52, $287,500 total compensation
EVP and Chief Restaurant Operations Officer, Wayne L. Jones, age 54, $259,135 total compensation

Chief Supply Chain Officer, John D. Allegretto, age 50, $218,500 total compensation
Senior Regional VP Operations, Christopher (Chris) Pinsak
SVP Operations Talent Development, Lon F. Ledwith, age 55, $175,000 total compensation
Chief Information Officer, John A. Johnson
Senior Vice President; General Counsel, Kendra P. Miller
Director, John F. (Jack) Grundhofer, age 74
Director, William L. (Bill) Hyde Jr., age 65
Director, Peter A. (Pete) Bassi, age 63
Director, J. Roger King, age 72
Director, Larry D. Bouts, age 64
Director, Lea Anne S. Ottinger, age 54
Independent Director, Henry Gomez
Auditors: Ernst&YoungLLP

LOCATIONS

HQ: BJ' s Restaurants Inc.
7755 Center Ave. Ste. 300, Huntington Beach CA 92647
Phone: 714-500-2400   **Fax:** 770-729-5999
Web: www.wafflehouse.com

2012 Locations

California	61
Florida	11
Nevada	5
Ohio	3
Indiana	1
Louisiana	1
New Mexico	1

PRODUCTS/OPERATIONS

Restaurant Brands
BJ's Restaurant & Brewery
BJ's Restaurant & Brewhouse
BJ's Pizza & Grill
BJ's Grill

Selected Menu Items
Appetizers
Desserts
Entrees
Microbrews
Pastas
Salads
Sandwiches
Soups

COMPETITORS

Applebee' s	Johnny Rockets
International	OSI Restaurant
Brinker	Partners
California Pizza	Pat & Oscars
Kitchen	Rock Bottom
Carlson Restaurants	Restaurants
Darden	Round Table Pizza
Elephant Bar	Ruby Tuesday
Gordon Biersch	Uno Restaurants
Jerry' s Famous Deli	

HISTORICAL FINANCIALS

Company Type: Public

Income Statement

FYE: January 1

	REVENUE ($ mil.)	NET INCOME ($ mil.)	NET PROFIT MARGIN	EMPLOYEES
01/13	708.3	31.4	4.4%	16,250
01/12*	620.9	31.5	5.1%	14,360
12/10	513.8	23.1	4.5%	12,230
12/09	426.7	13.0	3.1%	11,000
12/08	374.0	10.3	2.8%	9,330
Annual Growth	17.3%	32.1%	—	14.9%

*Fiscal year change

2013 Year-End Financials

Debt ratio: —
Return on equity: 8.9%
Cash ($ mil.): 15
Current ratio: 1.00
Long-term debt ($ mil.): —
No. of shares (mil.): 28
Dividends
Yield: —
Payout: —
Market value ($ mil.): 924

	STOCK PRICE ($) FY Close	P/E High/Low		PER SHARE ($) Earnings	Dividends	Book Value
01/13	32.90	48	29	1.09	0.00	13.25
01/12*	44.03	49	29	1.08	0.00	11.98
12/10	36.18	45	22	0.82	0.00	10.53
12/09	18.78	39	19	0.48	0.00	9.45
12/08	10.35	44	17	0.39	0.00	8.69
Annual Growth	33.5%	—	—	29.3%	—	11.1%

*Fiscal year change

Blackbaud, Inc.

Blackbaud provides financial fundraising and administrative software for not-for-profit organizations and educational institutions. Software offerings include The Raiser's Edge for fundraising management Blackbaud Enterprise CRM for customer relationship management The Financial Edge for accounting and The Education Edge for managing school admissions registration and billing. Blackbaud has about 28000 customers in 60 countries including colleges environmental groups health and human services providers churches and animal welfare groups. The company generates most of its sales in the US.

Operations
Blackbaud generates revenue for its software through product licenses subscriptions maintenance and services. Most of its software is sold on a subscription basis; product licensing revenue only accounts for about 5% of overall sales. Subscription revenue has experienced the most growth over the years; however it has substantially lower gross margins than product licensing. Services revenue accounts for nearly 30% of sales much of that from training. In addition the company makes about a quarter of sales from ongoing support and maintenance for existing customers.

Geographic Reach The US is its largest market accounting for 86% of sales. Although the Asia-Pacific region accounts for only 4% of total sales it's the fastest-growing market with sales rising more than 40% year-over-year. Canada and Europe each account for 5% of sales.

Financial Analysis Blackbaud has experienced strong revenue growth over the past decade for its niche products with 2012 sales up 20% to $447 million. But that growth is primarily attributed to the 2012 acquisition on Convio. (Excluding the Convio addition sales would have been up 6%.) The increase in sales is due primarily to demand for its hosted online fundraising and data management products as the company transitions from a license-based to subscription-based business. It has also enjoyed an increase in transaction fees for payment processing services. While the company has been consistently profitable net income (profits) fell 80% to $6.5 million in 2012 due to increased financing expenses for the Convio acquisition. Nominal increases in sales and marketing R&D and other expenses were offset by overall revenue growth.

Strategy Blackbaud is looking to expand its product offerings for the Internet. Online donations account for a growing percentage of charitable donations and marketing membership newsletters event management and volunteer recruitment can often be done over the Internet at a lower cost and a higher success rate. Its Sphere eMarketing Suite which facilitates online giving can be integrated into its most popular product The Raiser's Edge. The company's strategy also includes expanding geographically. In early 2010 it established a separate business unit to focus on expanding its international customer base. Blackbaud opened a Hong Kong office in 2010 and a Mexico City office in 2011 which join other international offices in Canada the UK and Australia.

Mergers and Acquisitions Blackbaud has expanded its product line and its customer roster in part through acquisitions. In 2012 it acquired not-for-profit software maker Convio in a deal valued at about $275 million. The acquisition pairs Blackbaud's strong CRM services with Convio's online fundraising services to create one of the largest Software-as-a-Service (SaaS) software companies in the not-for-profit space. Blackbaud bought Virginia-based Public Interest Data for about $17.5 million in cash in early 2011 to expand its access to the not-for-profit market. Public Interest Data specializes in data management and acquisition list services for customers including the ASPCA and UNICEF. In 2010 it acquired partner NOZA which maintained a database of charitable donations made to not-for-profit organizations primarily in the US. Internationally the company's acquisition of Netherlands-based RLC Customer Centric Technology in 2009 gave it greater ability to expand throughout Europe. The 2011 acquisition of Everyday Hero for about $7 million contributed to its presence in Australia New Zealand and the UK.

HISTORY

The company bought eTapestry a software-as-a-service provider focused on fundraising tools for the not-for-profit sector for about $25 million in 2007 as well as Target Software. The acquisition supplemented Blackbaud's prospect research software for not-for-profits. In 2008 it purchased chief competitor Kintera for $46 million in cash. Blackbaud combined the Target and Kintera businesses and technology with its prospect research division to form a new unit known as Target Analytics. The division offers donor acquisition and related development tools and services including WealthPoint (database screening) and P!N Service (donor screening).

EXECUTIVES

President General Markets Business, Kevin W. Mooney, age 55, $340,000 total compensation
Senior Vice President - Human Resources, John J. Mistretta, age 57
SVP Controller Assistant Treasurer and Assistant Secretary, Heidi H. Strenck, age 43
Director Corporate Relations and Philanthropy, Rachel Hutchisson
President Enterprise Customer Business Unit, Gene Austin, age 54
Chairman, Andrew M. Leitch, age 69
SVP and Chief Scientist, Charles L. (Chuck) Longfield, age 56, $226,667 total compensation
CFO and SVP Finance and Administration, Anthony W. (Tony) Boor, age 50
President CEO and Director, Marc E. Chardon, age 57, $564,000 total compensation
Manager Public Relations, Melanie Mathos

President International Business, Bradley J. (Brad) Holman
CTO, Shawn Sullivan
SVP Products and Marketing, Jana B. Eggers
Senior Vice President - New Business Development, Charlie Cumbaa
VP and General Counsel, Jon Olson
President Enterprise Customer Business, Joe Moye
Vice President of Product Development, Mary Westmoreland
Director, David G. (Dave) Golden, age 55
Director, Timothy C. K. (Tim) Chou, age 58
Director, John P. McConnell, age 58
Director, George H. Ellis, age 64
Director, Carolyn S. Miles, age 51
Director, Sarah E. Nash, age 59
President CEO and Director, Marc E. Chardon, age 57
Auditors: PricewaterhouseCoopersLLP

LOCATIONS

HQ: Blackbaud, Inc.
2000 Daniel Island Drive, Charleston, SC 29492
Phone: 843 216-6200   **Fax:** 843 216-6100
Web: www.blackbaud.com

2012 Sales

	$ mil.	% of total
US	386	86
Europe	23	5
Canada	22	6
Asia/Pacific	15	3
Total	**447**	**100**

PRODUCTS/OPERATIONS

2012 Sales

	$ mil.	% of total
General markets	203	45
Enerprise customers	165	38
International	40	9
Target analytics & other	38	8
Total	**447**	**100**

2012 Sales

	$ mil.	% of total
Subscriptions	162	36
Maintenance	136	30
Services	119	27
Licenses	20	5
Other	9	2
Total	**447**	**100**

Selected Products

Accounting software
Blackbaud Forms (wealth identification)
The Financial Edge (not-for-profit accounting)
Analytical services
Prospect Management (prospect management and research)
Wealth & Affluence Indicators (wealth identification and information)
Business intelligence software
Altru (general admissions management)
The Patron Edge (ticketing management for admissions)
Customer relationship management
Blackbaud Enterprise CRM
eTapestry
Education administration software
The Education Edge (admissions registrar business office and development office software)
Small Colleges (suite for colleges under 300 students)
Student Billing
Total Campus Solution (suite for colleges under 2000 students)
Fundraising management software
The Raiser' s Edge (fundraising management system)

COMPETITORS

Acorn Systems	Microsoft
Advanced Solutions	Oracle
Auctionpay	Sage Software
Campus Management Corp	SunGard
Intuit	salesforce.com
MicroEdge	

HISTORICAL FINANCIALS

Company Type: Public

Income Statement

FYE: December 31

	REVENUE ($ mil.)	NET INCOME ($ mil.)	NET PROFIT MARGIN	EMPLOYEES
12/12	447.4	6.5	1.5%	2,705
12/11	370.8	33.2	9.0%	2,256
12/10	327.0	29.8	9.1%	2,065
12/09	309.3	28.4	9.2%	1,956
12/08	302.5	29.8	9.9%	1,977
Annual Growth	**10.3%**	**(31.5%)**	**—**	**8.2%**

2012 Year-End Financials

Debt ratio: 30.5%
Return on equity: 4.5%
Cash ($ mil.): 13
Current ratio: 0.69
Long-term debt ($ mil.): 205
No. of shares (mil.): 45
Dividends
Yield: 2.1%
Payout: 320.0%
Market value ($ mil.): 1,042

	STOCK PRICE ($) FY Close	P/E High/Low	PER SHARE ($) Earnings	Dividends	Book Value
12/12	22.83	226 141	0.15	0.48	3.24
12/11	27.70	40 28	0.75	0.48	3.12
12/10	25.90	41 30	0.68	0.44	2.77
12/09	23.63	36 14	0.65	0.40	2.61
12/08	13.50	40 15	0.68	0.40	2.07
Annual Growth	**14.0%**		**— —(31.5%)**	**4.7%**	**11.8%**

Blount International, Inc.

Folks at Blount International have their work cut out for them. The manufacturer produces cutting chain guide bars sprockets and accessories for chainsaws concrete-cutting equipment and lawn-mower blades. Blount's lineup is sold under brands Oregon Carlton Tiger and Windsor to outdoor equipment OEMs including Husqvarna and the replacement and retail markets. Other subsidiaries supply log splitters post-hole diggers and other agriculture add-ons. End users are professionals and consumers engaged in forestry lawn and garden farming and construction activities. The company's manufacturing facilities dot the US Canada Brazil and China. About two-thirds of Blount's sales are made outside of the US.

Operations

Blount sells its products across two segments: forestry lawn and garden; and farm ranch and agriculture. The former segment represents about 80% of its total sales each year while the latter accounts for the remainder.

Financial Analysis

With the recession behind it Blount has seen sizable growth over the years. From 2010 to 2011 the company's total sales increased by 36% and it

enjoyed a 5% increase in profits. It attributes the growth to increased sales it received from previous acquisitions and to an increase in the average selling price of its products. The rise in profits was mainly due to a 25% increase in gross profits from 2010 to 2011.

Most notably sales for Blount's farm ranch and agriculture products skyrocketed by more than 300% in 2011 due to its purchase of Woods Equipment Company that year. Total sales for its forestry lawn and garden products jumped by 19%. The company's total sales in the US increased by 59% in 2011 and it also experienced 34% growth in Canada and a 37% surge in total sales in the European Union.

Strategy

Blount has also fueled its momentum by strategically expanding its product portfolio and customer base through acquisitions. In late 2011 the company acquired Woods Equipment Company from Genstar Capital for $185 million. Woods is a manufacturer of attachments for agricultural and construction applications and a large independent distributor of tractor parts. The deal enhanced the scale of Blount's farm ranch and agriculture business and widened its product line of tractor attachments and aftermarket replacement parts including the Woods and TISCO brands. It also extended its North American manufacturing and distribution footprint through the addition of three manufacturing and five distribution facilities.

In 2011 Blount purchased KOX GmbH a German distributor of forestry replacement parts and accessories to professional loggers and consumers. The approximate $20.6 million deal bolstered Blount's European presence. Also that year the company absorbed FinalameSA and its wholly-owned subsidiary PBL SAS. PBL makes lawn-mower blades and agricultural cutting parts based in France and Mexico. Blount bought PBL for about $14 million in cash and assumed $14 million in debt. The acquisition upped Blount's lawn-mower blade capacity and entrenched its presence in the European agriculture market.

EXECUTIVES

SVP General Counsel and Secretary, Richard H. (Dick) Irving III, age 68, $348,005 total compensation
Vice President; Corporate Controller, Mark V. Allred, age 55
SVP and CFO, Calvin E. Jenness, age 58, $348,005 total compensation
Senior Vice President - Supply Chain and Manufacturing Operations, Kenneth O. Saito, age 65, $345,010 total compensation
SVP Business Development; President ICS, James L. (Jake) VanderZanden, age 47, $248,073 total compensation
Advertising and Promotions Manager, David Dugan
VP Corporate Human Resources, Dale C. Johnson Jr., age 63
CEO and Chairman, Joshua L. (Josh) Collins, age 49, $84,615 total compensation
President FRAG Division, Jerry D. Johnson
President Gear Products Inc., William C. Alford
SVP European Operations, Cyrille B. Michel, age 55
VP Finance and Corporate Development, Matthew D. Clark
Vice President; General Counsel; Secretary, Chad E. Paulson
Treasurer, Wendy J. Gilligan
President and COO, David A. Willmott, age 43
SVP Global Sales and Marketing FLAG, Andrew York
President FRAG, Paul Valas
President - Aluminium, Daniel Malchuk

President - Iron Ore, Jimmy Wilson
President - Public Affairs, Karen J. Wood
President - Copper, Peter Beaven
President - Petroleum and Potash, Tim Cutt
Director, Harold E. Layman, age 66
Director, R. Eugene Cartledge, age 82
Director, E. Daniel James, age 48
Director, Thomas J. (Tom) Fruechtel, age 62
Director, Robert E. Beasley Jr., age 67
Director, Ronald Cami, age 46
Independent Director, Andrew Clarke
Independent Director, Nelda Connors
Auditors: PricewaterhouseCoopersLLP

LOCATIONS

HQ: Blount International Inc.
4909 SE International Way, Portland OR 97222-4679
Phone: 503-653-8881   Fax: 503-653-4612
Web: www.blount.com

2011 Sales

US	308	37
China	45	5
Canada	25	3
Russian Federation	23	3
Others	166	20

PRODUCTS/OPERATIONS

2011 Sales

Forestry lawn & garden products	660	79
Farm ranch & agriculture products	147	18
Corporate & other	24	3
Total	**831**	**100**

Selected Mergers and Acquisitions

FY2011
Woods Equipment Company ($185 million; Oregon Illinois; maker of attachments for agricultural and construction applications)
KOX GmbH ($21 million; Germany; distributor of forestry replacement parts and accessories)
FinalameSA ($28 million; France and Mexico; maker of lawnmower blades)

Selected Products

Chain drive sprockets
Chainsaw guide bars
Concrete-cutting chainsaws and circular saws (gasoline and hydraulic powered)
Cutting chain (for chainsaws)
Diamond-segmented chain (for cutting concrete)
Farm accessories
Lawn and garden cutting attachments
Lawnmower and edger cutting blades
Log splitters
Maintenance tools (for chainsaws and mechanical timber harvesting equipment)
Tractor driven post-hole diggers
Tractor three-point linkage parts

COMPETITORS

Alamo Group	Great Plains
Ariens	Manufacturing
Briggs & Stratton	Husqvarna
Caterpillar	Kubota
Champion Cutting Tool	MTD Products
Deere	Metso
Dover Corp.	STIHL Incorporated
Emak Group	Terex

HISTORICAL FINANCIALS

Company Type: Public

Income Statement

FYE: December 31

	REVENUE ($ mil.)	NET INCOME ($ mil.)	NET PROFIT MARGIN	EMPLOYEES
12/12	927.6	39.5	4.3%	4,700
12/11	831.6	49.6	6.0%	4,500
12/10	611.4	47.2	7.7%	3,600
12/09	502.4	22.9	4.6%	3,100
12/08	597.0	38.6	6.5%	3,600
Annual Growth	**11.6%**	**0.6%**	**—**	**6.9%**

2012 Year-End Financials

Debt ratio: 57.0%	No. of shares (mil.): 49
Return on equity: 43.6%	Dividends
Cash ($ mil.): 50	Yield: —
Current ratio: 2.79	Payout: —
Long-term debt ($ mil.): 501	Market value ($ mil.): 777

	STOCK PRICE ($) FY Close	P/E High/Low	PER SHARE ($) Earnings	Dividends	Book Value
12/12	15.82	22 16	0.79	0.00	2.27
12/11	14.52	18 13	1.01	0.00	1.42
12/10	15.76	16 10	0.97	0.00	0.88
12/09	10.10	23 8	0.48	0.00	(0.14)
12/08	9.48	17 9	0.80	0.00	(0.91)
Annual Growth	**13.7%**	**— —**	**(0.3%)**	**—**	**—**

Blucora, Inc.

Why crawl the Web when others can do it for you? Blucora (formerly InfoSpace) operates through two businesses. Its InfoSpace unit consists of online search services that rely on its metasearch search technology. Owned and operated consumer websites include Dogpile.com WebFetch.com and MetaCrawler.com which query such leading search providers as Google and Yahoo! and then collate and rank those search results. InfoSpace also offers a private-label search product for businesses (which it calls distribution partners); it develops hosts and delivers search results for more than 100 distribution partners. Blucora acquired its other primary business online tax solutions provider TaxACT in 2012.

The company has been through several transformations in its more than 15-year history; the latest one occured in 2012 when it changed its name from InfoSpace to Blucora followng its acquisition of TaxACT. Its official reason for adopting the new identity is to distinguish between its InfoSpace and TaxACT holdings which operate as two distinct and separate businesses. However years earlier the InfoSpace brand had been tarnished by an insider trading scandal surrounding its founder and former leader Naveen Jain and with the fresh moniker comes an additional benefit of building a new reputation.

The firm acquired the profitable TaxACT for some $287.5 million to diversify its business beyond Internet search and enter what it considers a growing market. TaxACT provides income tax preparation solutions to consumers and professional preparers. Before the TaxACT purchase the firm primarily generated revenue through paid search results.

About 80% of the company's 2011 search services revenue was generated through its distribution partners many of which are mobile app developers. It has distribution and partnership agreements with search giants Google and Yahoo! ensuring access to search results through at least part of 2013 (Google) and the entirety of 2013 (Yahoo!). The two search giants together accounted for more than 95% of sales in 2011.

InfoSpace reported revenues of about $229 million and net income of nearly $22 million for 2011. The company benefitted from increased distribution revenue and the addition of more than 40 new distribution partners (a result of the recent smartphone boom). However such benefits were offset by a drop in visitors to owned and operated sites such as Dogpile.com. InfoSpace was also negatively affected by a drop in its direct marketing activates. Net income grew thanks to a tax benefit of $19.6 million related to the release of valuation allowance on deferred tax assets.

The company admitted defeat with regards to one of its assets —selling Internet shopping service Mercantila at a loss in 2011 just a year after it acquired the company. It had bought Mercantila for about $8 million plus the assumption of up to $5.9 million in debt in order to diversify beyond Internet search. However after the venture lost money InfoSpace decided e-commerce no longer fit with its core strategy. It divested the business for a "nominal upfront payment" and the right to receive additional payments of up to $3 million.

The Mercantila sale follows a string of other disposals. At one point the company consisted of more than a dozen mobile directory and e-commerce businesses. Key asset sales included online phone-directory service Switchboard.com for $225 million and a mobile-phone platform business for $135 million.

HISTORY

Indian immigrant Naveen Jain a veteran of Microsoft's online services unit set out to create an interactive "people and business finder" in 1996. Eschewing funding from venture capitalists (disdainfully calling them "vulture capitalists") the outspoken Jain launched his new enterprise dubbed InfoSpace with $250000 of his own money. Its online phone directory service debuted in May and a few months later it unveiled an online e-mail directory. Unlike most Internet players InfoSpace wasn't looking to lure users to its own website (though it did have one). Instead the company focused on supplying information to other sites.

By the beginning of 1997 InfoSpace had added industry stalwarts Lycos (now owned by South Korea's Daum Communications) and Microsoft to its customer list. That year it signed up @Home Network Playboy Dow Jones' Wall Street Journal Online and Go2Net. The company's content also found its way to cable TV that year by way of InfoSpace's alliance with Source Media's Interactive Channel. InfoSpace continued expanding beyond traditional Internet customers inking deals to feed its content to Motorola and SkyTel pagers the 3Com PalmPilot and the AT&T PocketNet service.

The company secured two vital customers in 1998 signing America Online (AOL) and Netscape (later acquired by AOL) to content distribution deals. To get the agreements however InfoSpace had to pay AOL and Netscape to carry its content. Also in 1998 the company set up shop in the UK through a joint venture with Thomson Directories. It went public later that year as InfoSpace.com.

After going public the company entered into e-commerce agreements with Cyberian Outpost and

Multiple Zones (now known as just Zones). In 1999 it joined with Quote.com to create a financial content package. It later established a venture capital fund launched its comparison shopping application ActiveShopper and expanded into Canada and India. InfoSpace bolstered its wireless operations in 2000 through acquisitions of Saraide and Millet Software and signed agreements with GTE Wireless (now Cingular) and VeriSign. The company later dropped the ".com" from its name and Jain handed the CEO title to Arun Sarin.

In October InfoSpace expanded its infrastructure services and content offerings when it acquired online content company Go2Net for about $1.5 billion. The company's stock sank into the single digits however and a management shakeup led to the departures of its COO and CFO. Jain took back the CEO title from Sarin (who briefly served as vice chairman before resigning from the board) and realigned the company's focus on its core distribution products. The company later acquired Locus Dialogue a developer of speech recognition technologies. In late 2002 one of the company's directors Jim Voelker replaced Jain as chairman and CEO.

InfoSpace cut about 115 jobs and sold its Silicon Investor site in 2003. It also purchased mobile media company Moviso for some $25 million from the now defunct Vivendi Universal Net USA Group. The company formed a Media Studios business unit in order to house its Moviso acquisition.

Later that year Jain resigned from the board of directors after the company filed a lawsuit against him claiming his new company Intelius violated non-compete clauses. (The suit was dismissed the following year.) Also in 2003 in a separate case a US District Judge ruled that Jain violated federal law when he bought and sold millions of shares of InfoSpace stock within a six-month period. He was later ordered to pay a $247 million penalty. (Up until that point the largest award for that type of insider trading was $20 million.)

InfoSpace sold its payment solutions business to Lightbridge (later renamed Authorize.Net Holdings) in 2004 for $82 million and boosted its local directory offerings with the acquisition of Switchboard for $160 million. It also acquired mobile game creators Atlas Mobile and IOMO Limited.

In 2006 InfoSpace announced a restructuring plan as a response to revenue losses. The plan included 250 job cuts and the closing of its Hamburg Germany facility. Streamlining continued in 2007 with the company's sale of its online directory business including Switchboard to Idearc (now called SuperMedia) for $225 million. Also in 2007 InfoSpace sold Media Studios (including Moviso) to FunMobility Inc. of Pleasanton California for an undisclosed price and its mobile services business for $135 million to Motricity a provider of mobile content.

In 2008 it closed its European facilities. Jim Voelker retired as CEO early in 2009. InfoSpace acquired Internet shopping service Mercantila in 2010 only to divest the business a year later. John Cunningham became chairman in early 2011 and Bill Ruckelshaus was named CEO later that year.

The company changed its name from InfoSpace to Blucora in 2012 followng its acquisition of TaxACT for some $287.5 million.

EXECUTIVES

President Chief Executive Officer, William J. (Bill) Ruckelshaus, age 48
Chief Financial Officer Treasurer, Eric M. Emans, age 39, $170,654 total compensation

Executive Vice President Corporate Development, George Allen
Vice President of Business Development, Mike Glover
Director, Jules Haimovitz, age 61
Director, Steven W. (Steve) Hooper
Director, Elizabeth J. (Liz) Huebner, age 54
Director, Lewis M. Taffer, age 64
Director, Richard D. Hearney, age 72
President CEO and Director, William J. (Bill) Ruckelshaus, age 47
Auditors: Deloitte&ToucheLLP

LOCATIONS

HQ: Blucora Inc.
  601 108th Ave. NE Ste. 1200, Bellevue WA 98004
Phone: 425-201-6100   **Fax:** 425-201-6150
Web: www.blucora.com

PRODUCTS/OPERATIONS

Selected Operations
Infospace
  Owned and operated websites
    Dogpile.com
    InfoSpace.com
    MetaCrawler.com
    WebCrawler.com
  White label search services
TaxACT

COMPETITORS

AOL	Local.com
Answers Corporation	LookSmart
Ask.com	MSN
Daum Communications	Marchex
Google	ValueClick
H&R Block	Vertro
Intuit	Yahoo!
Jackson Hewitt	

HISTORICAL FINANCIALS
Company Type: Public

Income Statement
FYE: December 31

	REVENUE ($ mil.)	NET INCOME ($ mil.)	NET PROFIT MARGIN	EMPLOYEES
12/12	406.9	22.5	5.5%	225
12/11	228.8	21.5	9.4%	198
12/10	246.8	13.7	5.6%	174
12/09	207.6	7.4	3.6%	157
12/08	156.7	(18.7)	—	160
Annual Growth	26.9%	—	—	8.9%

2012 Year-End Financials
Debt ratio: 12.6%   No. of shares (mil.): 40
Return on equity: 5.8%   Dividends
Cash ($ mil.): 68   Yield: —
Current ratio: 3.13   Payout: —
Long-term debt ($ mil.): 69 Market value ($ mil.): 641

	STOCK PRICE ($) FY Close	P/E High/Low		PER SHARE ($) Earnings	Dividends	Book Value
12/12	15.71	33	20	0.54	0.00	10.17
12/11	10.99	21	14	0.56	0.00	8.98
12/10	8.30	31	18	0.37	0.00	8.61
12/09	8.57	42	25	0.21	0.00	7.91
12/08	7.55	—	—	(0.54)	9.00	7.54
Annual Growth	20.1%	—	—	—	—	7.8%

Blue Nile Inc

Blue Nile helps tech-savvy Marc Antonys bejewel their Cleopatras. The leader in online jewelry sales Blue Nile offers luxury-grade jewelry at bluenile.com and sells loose diamonds settings engagement rings as well as non-bridal jewelry made of gold platinum and silver set with diamonds pearls emeralds rubies and sapphires. While engagement rings account for about two-thirds of its sales the e-tailer also sells watches and provides custom jewelry design services. Blue Nile's Web sites serve customers in the US Canada Europe and the Asia-Pacific region —more than 40 countries in all. Chairman Mark Vadon and Ben Elowitz formerly of Fatbrain.com founded the site in 1999.

Blue Nile's sales climbed 4.5% in 2011 vs. 2010 with sales of non-engagement jewelry outperforming growth in other merchandise categories. While 2011 marked the third consecutive year of sales growth —following a recession-related decline in 2008 —net income fell nearly 20% in 2011 as rising diamond and gold prices put the squeeze on profits.

The growth engine for the online jeweler is its international business which saw sales rise 29% in 2011 vs. a sales gain of less than 1% in the US. The company rang up 16% of its sales overseas in 2011 vs. 13% during the prior year. Indeed with half the world market for diamonds outside the US growing its international business is a priority for Blue Nile as is increasing its non-engagement offering. Concurrent with the abrupt resignation of its CEO in late 2011 Blue Nile announced it will focus on non-bridal jewelry going forward. The strategy is a reversal for Blue Nile which made its mark by selling diamond engagement rings online at prices significantly less than brick-and-mortar jewelry stores. Engagement rings are often a customer's first purchase through the site. However declining margins on engagement rings and dim prospects for young consumers many of whom are out of work or lack access to credit led to the change.

Another priority for the e-tailer is building its mobile business. To serve jewelry buyers on the go the company launched a mobile Web site designed for the iPhone iPod touch and Android mobile devices. The mobile version launched in spring 2010 is smaller than the PC site in scope with quick tabs to find diamonds engagement rings and other gift ideas. The company reports that more than 20% of its shoppers are using the mobile site.

Marathon Asset Management owns about 19% of the company. Morgan Stanley T. Rowe Price and Manulife Financial Corp. each hold about 10% of Blue Nile's shares.

EXECUTIVES

Chief Marketing Officer, Engle E. Saez
Chairman, Mark Vadon, $250,000 total compensation
VP Finance Controller and Chief Accounting Officer, Terri K. Maupin, age 49, $159,501 total compensation
SVP, Susan Bell, age 55, $230,001 total compensation
President and CEO, Harvey S. Kanter
CFO, David B. Binder
Director Corporate Communications, John Baird
SVP Operations, Dwight Gaston, $233,751 total compensation
Manager Investor Relations, Eileen Askew
VP Technology Operations, Steven Gire
Secretary and General Counsel, Lauren Neiswender, age 40

SVP, Marianne Marck, age 53
General Manager and President International,
Vijay Talwar
VP Marketing, Jon Sainsbury
Chief Merchandising Officer, Julie Yoakum
Director, Steven L. (Steve) Scheid, age 59
Director, Michael J. Potter, age 51
Director, Mary Alice Taylor, age 63
Director, W. Eric Carlborg, age 49
President CEO and Director, Harvey S. Kanter, age 51
Director, Leslie Lane, age 45
Director, Chris Bruzzo, age 43
Auditors: Deloitte&ToucheLLP

LOCATIONS

HQ: Blue Nile Inc.
705 5th Ave. South Ste. 900, Seattle WA 98104
Phone: 206-336-6700   **Fax:** 206-336-6750
Web: www.bluenile.com

2011 Sales

	$ mil.	% of total
US	292	84
International	55	16
Total	**348**	**100**

PRODUCTS/OPERATIONS

2011 Sales

	$ mil.	% of total
Engagement	231	66
Non-engagement	116	34
Total	**348**	**100**

Selected Products

Accessories
  Cuff links
  Desk accessories
  Frames
  Key rings
  Money clips
  Pens
Bracelets
Earrings
Necklaces and pendants
Watches
  Men's
  Women's
Wedding and anniversary rings

Selected Materials

Diamonds
Gemstones
  Emeralds
  Rubies
  Sapphires
Gold
Pearls
Platinum
Silver

COMPETITORS

Amazon.com	QVC
Bidz.com	Reeds Jewelers
Cartier	Ross-Simons
Christie' s	Saks
Costco Wholesale	Saks Fifth Avenue
Gucci	Samuels Jewelers
H. Stern	Signet
HSN	Sotheby' s
Helzberg Diamonds	Tiffany & Co.
Lazare Kaplan	Union Diamond
Mondera	Wal-Mart
Neiman Marcus	Zale
Nordstrom	eBay
Overstock.com	

HISTORICAL FINANCIALS

Company Type: Public

Income Statement

FYE: December 30

	REVENUE ($ mil.)	NET INCOME ($ mil.)	NET PROFIT MARGIN	EMPLOYEES
12/12*	400.0	8.3	2.1%	253
01/12	348.0	11.3	3.3%	212
01/11	332.8	14.1	4.2%	193
01/10	302.1	12.8	4.2%	188
01/09	295.3	11.6	3.9%	177
Annual Growth	**7.9%**	**(7.8%)**	—	**9.3%**

*Fiscal year change

2012 Year-End Financials

Debt ratio: 0.4%
Return on equity: 34.2%
Cash ($ mil.): 87
Current ratio: 0.98
Long-term debt ($ mil.): 0

No. of shares (mil.): 12
Dividends
  Yield: —
  Payout: —
Market value ($ mil.): 471

	STOCK PRICE ($) FY Close	P/E High/Low	Earnings	PER SHARE ($) Dividends	Book Value
12/12*	37.70	68 37	0.63	0.00	1.13
01/12	40.88	80 38	0.77	0.00	2.54
01/11	57.06	64 42	0.94	0.00	3.37
01/10	63.33	75 21	0.84	0.00	2.95
01/09	24.85	81 27	0.75	0.00	1.33
Annual Growth	**11.0%**	— —	**(4.3%)**	—	**(4.1%)**

*Fiscal year change

BNC Bancorp

BNC Bancorp knows the ABCs of the financial world. The firm is the holding company for Bank of North Carolina which has about 35 locations in both North and South Carolina. The bank offers community-oriented services to local business and retail customers providing checking savings and money market accounts credit cards and certificates of deposit. Its loan portfolio is mainly composed of residential and commercial mortgages and construction loans. Bank of North Carolina also offers insurance retirement planning and other investment products and services. BNC Bancorp is buying First Trust Bank which has three branches in the Charlotte area for some $35 million.

The deal is the latest in a string of acquisitions for BNC Bancorp. In 2010 the company acquired the failed Beach First National Bank in an FDIC-facilitated transaction expanding Bank of North Carolina's branch network into South Carolina. The 2012 acquisitions of Regent Bank further extended the bank's reach in the state. BNC Bancorp acquired another failed bank in 2011 with assistance from the FDIC Blue Ridge Savings Bank in North Carolina. The following year it bought the single-branch KeySource Financial also in North Carolina.

In 2010 Aquiline Capital Partners a private equity firm specializing in the financial services industry invested nearly $35 million in BNC Bancorp. The transaction netted the investor approximately 10% of the bank holding company as well as convertible shares that could equate to an additional 15% stake.

EXECUTIVES

IR Contact, Drema A. Michael
Chairman Emeritus, W. Groome Fulton Jr., age 74
President CEO and Director; President and CEO Bank of North Carolina, W. Swope Montgomery Jr., age 64, $345,200 total compensation
EVP COO and Director; EVP and COO Bank of North Carolina, Richard D. Callicutt II, age 54, $268,650 total compensation
EVP and CFO BNC and Bank of North Carolina, David B. Spencer, age 50, $251,200 total compensation
Secretary and Director, Richard F. Wood, age 69
Chairman of the Board, Thomas R. Sloan, age 68
SVP Bank of North Carolina, Thomas N. Nelson, $172,800 total compensation
SVP Manager, Dave E. White
Senior Vice President of Administration, Kirk Robinson
VP SBA Underwriter, Nisha Desai
VP Business Development Officer, Scott Birkner
President CEO and Director; President and CEO Bank of North Carolina, W. Swope Montgomery Jr., age 64
EVP COO and Director; EVP and COO Bank of North Carolina, Richard D. Callicutt II, age 54
Director, Robert A. Team Jr., age 58
Director, Larry L. Callahan, age 66
Director, Joseph M. Coltrane Jr., age 67
Director, Lenin J. Peters, age 62
Director, Thomas R. Smith, age 65
Director, D. Vann Williford, age 65
Secretary and Director, Richard F. Wood, age 69
Director, Charles T. Hagan III, age 64
Chairman of the Board, Thomas R. Sloan, age 68
Director Emeritus, Bob M. Burleson
Director Emeritus, John J. Collett Jr.
Director Emeritus, Lloyd M. Higgins
Director Emeritus, Carlyle A. Nance Jr.
Auditors: CherryBekaert&HollandLLP

LOCATIONS

HQ: BNC Bancorp
831 Julian Ave., Thomasville NC 27360
Phone: 336-476-9200   **Fax:** 336-476-5818
Web: www.bankofnc.com

PRODUCTS/OPERATIONS

2008 Sales

	$ mil.	% of total
Interest		
Loans including fees	64	85
Debt securities	5	7
Other	0	1
Noninterest		
Service charges	3	4
Mortgage fees	0	1
Other	1	2
Total	**76**	**100**

COMPETITORS

BB&T	NewBridge Bancorp
Bank of America	Piedmont Federal
Bank of the Carolinas	Southern Community
Carolina Bank	Financial
FNB United	Wells Fargo
First Bancorp (NC)	
First Citizens	
BancShares	

HISTORICAL FINANCIALS

Company Type: Public

Income Statement
FYE: December 31

	ASSETS ($ mil.)	NET INCOME ($ mil.)	INCOME AS % OF ASSETS	EMPLOYEES
12/12	3,083.7	10.4	0.3%	564
12/11	2,454.9	6.9	0.3%	455
12/10	2,149.9	7.7	0.4%	372
12/09	1,634.1	6.5	0.4%	262
12/08	1,572.8	3.9	0.3%	222
Annual Growth	18.3%	27.2%	—	26.3%

2012 Year-End Financials

Return on assets: 0.3%
Return on equity: 4.6%
Long-term debt ($ mil.): —
No. of shares (mil.): 24
Sales ($ mil): 146

Dividends
  Yield: 2.5%
  Payout: 41.6%
Market value ($ mil.): 197

	STOCK PRICE ($) FY Close	P/E High/Low		Earnings	PER SHARE ($) Dividends	Book Value
12/12	8.01	18	14	0.48	0.20	11.45
12/11	7.25	20	14	0.45	0.20	18.00
12/10	9.00	17	11	0.61	0.20	16.81
12/09	7.59	13	8	0.62	0.20	17.19
12/08	7.51	32	14	0.52	0.20	16.42
Annual Growth	1.6%	—	—	(2.0%)	(0.0%)	(8.6%)

Boardwalk Pipeline Partners LP

Boardwalk Pipeline Partners walks a fine (pipe) line. The limited partnership owns and operates three US interstate natural gas pipeline systems — totaling 14300 miles —that originate in the Gulf Coast region Arkansas and Oklahoma and extend up toward the Midwest. It provides transportation and storage to customers that include gas producers marketers local distribution companies and interstate and intrastate pipelines. The company operates through Boardwalk Pipelines LP and its subsidiaries Gulf Crossing Pipeline Company Gulf South Pipeline Company and Texas Gas Transmission. In 2011 the company's systems carried 11% of the average daily consumption of natural gas in the US.

Boardwalk Pipeline Partners operates in one business segment but its subsidiaries offer both firm transportation and firm storage services meaning that a customer pays a reservation fee to reserve pipeline capacity at certain receipt and delivery points along the pipeline system as well as a commodity and fuel charge. For firm storage a customer pays for a specific amount of storage capacity. In fiscal 2011 the company's pipeline systems transported about 2.7 trillion cu. ft. of natural gas. Its eleven natural gas storage facilities in four states reported an aggregate gas capacity of 186 billion cu. ft.

Boardwalk Pipeline Partners' 14300 miles of owned and operated interconnected pipelines and numerous interconnections with unaffiliated pipelines serve customers in 12 states throughout the northeastern and southeastern US.

While fiscal year 2011 revenues rose 2% the company's net income decreased 24% for the year compared to a 23% leap in sales and a 78% increase in net income in 2010 over 2009. Net income for 2011 decreased as a result of several factors including charges related to materials and supplies decreased storage revenues and increased operations and maintenance-related expenses. The majority of Boardwalk Pipeline Partners' revenues are derived from capacity reservation charges under firm agreements that are not impacted by volume of gas transported or stored. However changes in natural gas prices can impact the volume of gas transported through its pipeline system.

Boardwalk Pipeline Partners' long-term strategy is to diversify into markets that complement its core natural gas pipeline and storage businesses. It does so organically and through acquisitions. In mid-2012 it formed a joint venture with its general partner which acquired PL Midstream LLC from PL Logistics for $625 million in cash. This acquisition gave Boardwalk entry into the natural gas liquids business. It subsequently bought the remaining 65% of the joint venture it did not already own for $269 million.

HP Storage a joint venture between Boardwalk and BPHC made a significant step toward growing its natural gas storage assets by acquiring Petal Gas Storage and Hattiesburg Gas Storage from Enterprise Products Partners for $550 million in late 2011. Petal and Hattiesburg operate seven salt dome natural gas storage caverns in Mississippi with 29 billion cu. ft. of total storage capacity. The company acquired 100% of these assets in 2012 by acquiring the 80% stake in HP Storage that it did not already own for $285 million.

Boardwalk Pipeline Partners is held by Boardwalk Pipelines Holding Corp. (BPHC) ultimately owned by Loews Corporation.

EXECUTIVES

Chairman Boardwalk GP LLC, Arthur L. Rebell, age 72
Senior Vice President Chief Financial & Administrative Officer, Jamie L. Buskill, age 48, $225,000 total compensation
COO Boardwalk GP LLC, Brian A. Cody, age 55
SVP General Counsel and Secretary, Michael E. McMahon, age 57, $216,346 total compensation
Director Investor Relations, Allison McLean
Senior Vice President - Operations of Boardwalk GP; LLC, Richard Keyser
Chief Executive Officer President Director, Stanley Horton
Director Boardwalk GP LLC, Andrew H. Tisch, age 63
Director Boardwalk GP LLC, William R. (Bill) Cordes, age 64
Director Boardwalk GP LLC, Mark L. Shapiro, age 69
Director, Rolf A. Gafvert, age 59
Director Boardwalk GP LLC, Thomas E. Hyland, age 67
Director, Kenneth I. Siegel, age 55
Auditors: Deloitte&ToucheLLP

LOCATIONS

HQ: Boardwalk Pipeline Partners LP
  9 Greenway Plaza Ste. 2800, Houston TX 77046
Phone: 713-479-8000   **Fax:** -9690
Web: www.rightmove.co.uk

PRODUCTS/OPERATIONS

2011 Sales

	$ mil.	% of total
Gas transportation	1,065	94
Gas storage	49	4
Parking & lending	12	1
Other	11	1
Total	**1,138**	**100**

2011 Sales by Customer

	% of total
Producers	54
Local distribution	22
Marketers	18
Power	5
Industrial end users &	1
Total	**100**

COMPETITORS

Columbia Gulf Transmission
El Paso Corporation
Energy Future
Florida Gas Transmission
Great Lakes Gas Transmission

Kinder Morgan
ONEOK Partners
Southwest Gas
U.S. Transmission
Williams Gas Pipeline

HISTORICAL FINANCIALS

Company Type: Public

Income Statement
FYE: December 31

	REVENUE ($ mil.)	NET INCOME ($ mil.)	NET PROFIT MARGIN	EMPLOYEES
12/12	1,185.0	306.0	25.8%	1,200
12/11	1,138.8	220.0	19.3%	1,170
12/10	1,116.8	289.4	25.9%	1,100
12/09	909.2	162.7	17.9%	1,110
12/08	784.8	294.0	37.5%	1,128
Annual Growth	10.9%	1.0%	—	1.6%

2012 Year-End Financials

Debt ratio: 45.0%
Return on equity: 8.7%
Cash ($ mil.): 3
Current ratio: 0.60
Long-term debt ($ mil.): 3,539

No. of shares (mil.): 230
Dividends
  Yield: 8.5%
  Payout: 155.2%
Market value ($ mil.): 5,742

	STOCK PRICE ($) FY Close	P/E High/Low		Earnings	PER SHARE ($) Dividends	Book Value
12/12	24.90	21	17	1.37	2.13	16.81
12/11	27.67	31	22	1.09	2.10	16.14
12/10	31.13	23	18	1.47	2.03	16.83
12/09	30.03	35	20	0.88	1.95	17.47
12/08	17.78	16	8	1.98	1.87	18.25
Annual Growth	8.8%	—	—	(8.8%)	3.3%	(2.0%)

Body Central Corp.

Body Central likely has something in store for young women who feel that image is everything. The company offers trendy apparel shoes and accessories to women in their late teens and early 20s through about 290 Body Central and Body Shop retail stores. Located primarily in malls in more than 25 states in the South Midwest and Mid-Atlantic the shops carry dresses tops jewelry and shoes sold under its Body Central and Lipstick brands. It also sells its merchandise through catalogs and its e-commerce site. A holding company Body Central operates primarily through its Body Shop of America (not affiliated with The Body Shop) and Catalogue Ventures subsidiaries. Body Central went public in 2010.

IPO

The October IPO raised $65 million which the women's apparel chain used to repay debt and fund expansion in existing and new markets grow its direct catalog and e-commerce businesses and bolster its sales and marketing activities.

Geographic Reach

Body Central has stores in 28 states. Its largest markets are Texas Florida Georgia and Pennsylvania home to more than a third of its stores.

Operations

The multichannel retailer operates stores and a direct (online and catalog) business. Stores account for nearly 90% of total sales while direct sales account for the rest.

Financial Performance

Body Central rang up $311 million in sales in 2012 a 5% increase versus 2011. The increase was driven by the addition of some 35 new stores over the course of the year partially offset by an 8% decline in same-store sales. 2012 marked the fourth consecutive year of increasing sales for the chain. However after three straight years of steeply rising profits net income posted a 39% drop on tighter merchandise margins due to discounting rising freight costs and higher rent and purchasing costs.

Strategy

The fast-growing chain plans to open about 25 new stores in 2013 while boosting same-store sales by keeping up with the latest merchandising trends and focusing on store operations. By keeping inventories tight Body Central hopes to minimize discounting. Another key part of its sales and marketing strategy includes increasing the presence of its Body Central and Lipstick brands in its core markets through advertising initiatives. The company typically does not use traditional advertising channels like print media and television; instead it opts to reach its 18-to-29-year-old target audience through social networking sites like Facebook and Twitter.

Unlike many of its competitors that don't offer a catalog Body Central believes that by sticking with print it can differentiate itself from its rivals. Indeed the retailer has increased the number of catalogs it mails annually to 24.2 million in 2012 from 20.3 million in 2009.

The company is also moving away from using the Body Shop brand name in part because its subsidiary Body Shop of America had sold the exclusive rights to the trademarked "Body Shop" name to beauty and cosmetic retailer The Body Shop years earlier in 1991.

Ownership

Investment firm FMR LLC owns more than 12% of the company's shares.

EXECUTIVES

Chairman, Martin P. Doolan, age 73
Chief Financial Officer, Richard L. Walters, age 61, $304,200 total compensation
President CEO and Director, B. Allen Weinstein, age 66, $134,615 total compensation
CEO, Brian P. Woolf, age 64
SVP General Merchandise Manager, Patti Simigran, age 53
EVP CFO COO and Treasurer, Thomas W. (Tom) Stoltz, age 52

EVP Chief Merchandising Officer and Director, Beth R. Angelo, age 46, $319,230 total compensation
Senior Vice President Stores, Matt Swartwood
Chairman, Donna R. Ecton, age 65
SVP and CIO, Charles Carstens, age 62
SVP of Stores, Michael Millonzi, age 40
President CEO and Director, B. Allen Weinstein, age 66
Director, John K. Haley, age 62
EVP Chief Merchandising Officer and Director, Beth R. Angelo, age 46
Director, Scott M. Gallin, age 41
Director, Jerrold S. Rosenbaum, age 76
Auditors: PricewaterhouseCoopersLLP

LOCATIONS

HQ: Body Central Corp.
6225 Powers Avenue, Jacksonville, FL 32217
Phone: 904 737-0811   **Fax:** 904 730-0638
Web: www.bodycentral.com

2012 Stores

	No.
Alabama	13
Arkansas	5
Delaware	3
Florida	33
Georgia	23
Illinois	12
Indiana	12
Iowa	1
Kansas	5
Kentucky	8
Louisiana	11
Maryland	10
Michigan	1
Mississippi	6
Missouri	8
North	14
New	2
Ohio	14
Oklahoma	4
Pennsylvania	20
South	9
Tennessee	10
Texas	36
Wisconsin	3
Virginia	12
West	1
Total	**276**

PRODUCTS/OPERATIONS

2012 Sales

	% of total
Apparel	76
Accessories	24
Total	**100**

2012 Sales

	$ mil.	% of total
Stores	275	89
Direct	35	11
Total	**311**	**100**

COMPETITORS

Abercrombie & Fitch	Forever 21
Aeropostale	Target Corporation
Amazon.com	The Buckle
American Eagle Outfitters	The Gap
	Wal-Mart
Charlotte Russe	Wet Seal
	rue21

HISTORICAL FINANCIALS

Company Type: Public

Income Statement

FYE: December 29

	REVENUE ($ mil.)	NET INCOME ($ mil.)	NET PROFIT MARGIN	EMPLOYEES
12/12	310.9	11.9	3.8%	3,305
12/11*	296.5	19.7	6.7%	2,869
01/11	243.3	9.8	4.0%	2,410
01/10	198.8	2.7	1.4%	2,300
01/09	191.8	(0.9)	—	0
Annual Growth	**12.8%**	—	—	—

*Fiscal year change

2012 Year-End Financials

Debt ratio: —	No. of shares (mil.): 16
Return on equity: 12.9%	Dividends
Cash ($ mil.): 41	Yield: —
Current ratio: 2.32	Payout: —
Long-term debt ($ mil.): —	Market value ($ mil.): 155

	STOCK PRICE ($) FY Close	P/E High/Low	PER SHARE ($)		
			Earnings	Dividends	Book Value
12/12	9.52	41 11	0.73	0.00	6.16
12/11*	24.96	21 11	1.22	0.00	5.29
01/11	14.27	6 4	0.73	0.00	3.77
Annual Growth	**(18.3%)**	— —	**(0.0%)**	—	**27.7%**

*Fiscal year change

Bofl Holding, Inc.

Bofl Holding owns Bank of Internet USA a savings bank that operates online in all 50 states. The bank offers checking savings and money market accounts CDs and ATM and check cards. Multifamily real estate loans account for nearly two-thirds of the company's loan portfolio although the bank only offers them in selected states; it also acquires them on the secondary market. Offered nationwide single-family residential mortgages make up nearly 30% of its loan portfolio. Bank of Internet USA also issues home equity automobile and recreational vehicle loans. Officers and directors own more than 30% of Bofl Holding's stock.

EXECUTIVES

Chairman, Theodore C. (Ted) Allrich, age 67
Executive Vice President and Chief Financial Officer, Andrew J. Micheletti, age 54, $190,000 total compensation
President and Chief Executive Officer, Gregory Garrabrants, age 42, $243,884 total compensation
Vice Chairman, Nicholas A. Mosich
SVP and Chief Risk Officer, Thomas Williams
Chief Operating Officer; Executive Vice President, Adriaan Zyl
Corporate Secretary & Investor Relations, Angela Lopez
Executive Vice President Residential and Multifamily Lending, Brian Swanson
Executive Vice President; Specialty Finance and Chief Legal Officer, Eshel Bar-Adon
Senior Vice President; Principal Accounting Officer, Michael Sisk
Executive Vice President; Chief Credit Officer, Thomas Constantine
Independent Director, Jerry F. Englert, age 72

Independent Director, Paul Grinberg, age 52
Independent Director, John G. Burke, age 68
Vice Chairman, Nicholas A. Mosich
Independent Director, Edward Ratinoff
Independent Director, James Argalas
Independent Director, James Court
Auditors: CroweHorwathLLP

LOCATIONS

HQ: BofI Holding Inc.
12777 High Bluff Dr. Ste. 100, San Diego CA 92130
Phone: 858-350-6200   **Fax:** 858-350-0443
Web: www.bofiholding.com

COMPETITORS

Bank of America	ISN Bank
Citigroup	Steel Partners
E*TRADE Bank	Holdings
First IB	UnionBanCal
ING DIRECT USA	

HISTORICAL FINANCIALS

Company Type: Public

Income Statement

FYE: June 30

	ASSETS ($ mil.)	NET INCOME ($ mil.)	INCOME AS % OF ASSETS	EMPLOYEES
06/13	3,090.7	40.2	1.3%	312
06/12	2,386.8	29.4	1.2%	230
06/11	1,940.0	20.5	1.1%	173
06/10	1,421.0	21.1	1.5%	90
06/09	1,302.2	7.1	0.5%	57
Annual Growth	24.1%	54.1%	—	53.0%

2013 Year-End Financials

Return on assets: 1.4%	Dividends
Return on equity: 16.9%	Yield: —
Long-term debt ($ mil.): —	Payout: —
No. of shares (mil.): 13	Market value ($ mil.): 629
Sales ($ mil): 163	

	STOCK PRICE ($) FY Close	P/E High/Low		Earnings	PER SHARE ($) Dividends	Book Value
06/13	45.82	16	7	2.89	0.00	19.53
06/12	19.76	8	5	2.33	0.00	17.95
06/11	14.41	9	6	1.87	0.00	14.16
06/10	14.12	8	3	2.22	0.00	12.75
06/09	6.09	10	4	0.78	0.00	11.00
Annual Growth	65.6%	—	—	38.7%	—	15.4%

Boingo Wireless Inc

Boingo keeps travelers with laptops and smartphones connected as they bounce through often unfamiliar locales. The company sells access to a global Wi-Fi network of about 600000 hot spots to about 200000 subscribers through wholesale agreements with wireless network and hot spot operators. Access is offered mainly in such venues as hotels convention centers airports and restaurants including McDonald's and Krispy Kreme. Additionally Boingo offers its roaming network and software to ISPs and managed network service providers. Fiberlink and Verizon Business are among the company's corporate customers. Estab-

lished in 2001 by chairman and Earthlink founder Sky Dayton the company went public in 2011.
IPO
Proceeds from the public offering of stock were slated to fund software development customer acquisition and the expansion of its network.
The company's wholesale network usage partnerships include list of more than 100 global carriers and ISP's which includes BT China Telecom Livedoor Towerstream Corporation and T-Mobile.
Financial Performance
The IPO followed a fiscal year in which Boingo's sales and profits rose significantly due to the company's efforts to boost the profile of its brand and add subscribers both in the US and abroad. Boingo has increased its sales significantly in recent years turning a profit in 2009 after years of losses by keeping costs down capitalizing on the growing numbers of consumers carrying wireless computing devices everywhere they go. Revenue growth continued through 2011.
Strategy
Boingo is looking overseas for growth particularly in Asia. To that end the company began offering services at airports in Bangkok and Milan in 2011. It also forged a wholesale deal with LG that year to provide international Wi-Fi roaming and cellular data services for LG Uplus customers in South Korea and it established a roaming agreement with Wire & Wireless (Wi2) giving Boingo customers access to hotspots operated by the Wi2 300 service in Japan. The company made similar deals with Asian telecom service providers China Telecom KT Corporation and NTT in 2010.
Boingo also continues to grow its international airport portfolio. In 2012 it entered into an agreement to manage and operate Wi-Fi services at three of the most highly-trafficked airports in Norway. Boingo now manages Wi-Fi services at more than 20 European airports.
Mergers and Acquisitions
In 2012 Boingo acquired Cloud Nine Media a provider of Wi-Fi sponsorship and location-based advertising at about 6000 airports hotels bars restaurants and recreational areas in North America. The deal helped Boingo boost its own advertising technology and sales expertise.

EXECUTIVES

Chairman, Sky D. Dayton, age 42
CEO, David (Dave) Hagan, age 53
CFO, Peter (Pete) Hovenier, age 46
President, Nick Hulse
SVP Business and Corporate Development, Luis-Alfonso Serrano
SVP Engineering, Alan Lang
Director of Asia Pacific, Allen J. Pan
SVP Operations, Tom Tracey
SVP Marketing and Sales, Dawn Callahan
General Manager Mobile and Product Management, Johnathan Mendelson
Media Relations, Katie O'Neill
SVP Engineering, Derek Peterson
Director, Chuck Davis, age 53
Director, Charles M. (Chuck) Boesenberg, age 65
President CEO and Director, David (Dave) Hagan, age 52
Director, Marc Geller, age 68
Director, Paul Hsiao, age 41
Director, Shigeyuki Toya, age 43
Auditors: PricewaterhouseCoopersLLP

LOCATIONS

HQ: Boingo Wireless Inc.
10960 Wilshire Blvd. Ste. 800, Los Angeles CA 90024
Phone: 310-586-5180   **Fax:** 770-980-3301
Web: www.ing-usa.com

COMPETITORS

AT&T Mobility	LodgeNet
BT	Orange Business
Cable & Wireless	Services
Cablevision Systems	Sprint Communications
Cellco	T-Mobile HotSpot
Comcast	Vodafone
EarthLink	iBAHN
ICOA	iPass

HISTORICAL FINANCIALS

Company Type: Public

Income Statement

FYE: December 31

	REVENUE ($ mil.)	NET INCOME ($ mil.)	NET PROFIT MARGIN	EMPLOYEES
12/12	102.5	7.3	7.1%	160
12/11	94.5	6.3	6.7%	149
12/10	80.4	15.7	19.6%	135
12/09	65.7	1.0	1.6%	0
12/08	56.7	(5.9)	—	0
Annual Growth	15.9%	—	—	—

2012 Year-End Financials

Debt ratio: 0.0%	No. of shares (mil.): 35
Return on equity: 5.3%	Dividends
Cash ($ mil.): 58	Yield: —
Current ratio: 3.42	Payout: —
Long-term debt ($ mil.): 0	Market value ($ mil.): 268

	STOCK PRICE ($) FY Close	P/E High/Low	Earnings	PER SHARE ($) Dividends	Book Value
12/12	7.55	63 32	0.20	0.00	4.05
12/11	8.60	64 36	0.17	0.00	3.84
Annual Growth	(12.2%)	— —	17.6%	—	5.5%

Boston Beer Co., Inc

A half-pint compared to megabrewers like the world's #1 beer maker Anheuser-Bush InBev The Boston Beer Company holds a distinction all its own –it is the US's largest craft brewer. The company produces more than 50 seasonal and year-round varieties of craft beers at breweries in Boston and four other states. Annually it sells around 2.7 million barrels of lagers and ales (including its flagship Samuel Adams Boston Lager and other Sam Adams brand beers) and Twisted Tea malt beverages. it also brews beer for third parties. Founded in 1984 by its chairman James Koch The Boston Beer Company has grown along with America's increasing thirst for better beer.
Geographic Reach
In addition to Boston The Boston Beer Company owns breweries in Breinigsville Cincinnati Breinigsville Pennsylvania and Los Angeles. The company distributes its brews primarily in the US but they are also sold in Canada the Caribbean Europe Israel Mexico and the Pacific Rim.
Operations

Beyond beer the company makes 10 flavored malt beverages under the Twisted Tea brand name and five hard ciders under the Angry Orchard brand. The Boston Beer Company's A&S Brewing Collaborative (dba Alchemy & Science) subsidiary (formed in 2011) makes five beers under two brand names. A&S recently formed House of Shandy (since renamed Traveler Beer Co.) which brews shandy style beers (beer mixed with citrus flavored soda carbonated lemonade ginger beer or cider).

In addition to production at its own breweries the company contracts some of its production to brewers among them Wisconsin-based City Brewing Company and New York-based Pleasant Valley Wine.

Sales and Marketing

The Boston-based brewer distributes its products through a network of some 340 wholesale distributors who in turn sell its beverages to retailers including pubs restaurants food and liquor stores and stadiums. Boston Beer employs a sales force of approximately 330 people.

The company's media campaigns include TV radio billboards and print. The brewer complements is media buying by sponsoring cultural and community events local beer festivals industry-related trade shows and promotional events at local establishments. Boston Beer reported spending on advertising and promotions of $78.3 million in 2012 versus $73.4 million in 2011 and $66.1 million in 2010.

Financial Performance

The Boston Beer Company's sales topped $580 million in 2012 a 13% increase versus 2011. The double-digit gain was driven primarily by an increase in core brand (Sam Adams Twisted Tea Angry Orchard) shipment volume and price increases levied in 2012 and capped a decade of steady and accelerating sales growth for the company. Indeed Boston Beer's five-year annual revenue growth rate exceeds 11%. Boston Beer shipped 2.7 million barrels during 2012 versus 2.5 million barrels in 2011.

Net income fell 10% in 2012 versus 2011 due to a one-time gain in 2011 related to a product recall.

Strategy

The domestic beer industry is dominated by two major brewers Anheuser-Busch InBev and Miller-Coors which together account for more than 90% of all US domestic beer production (excluding exports). Boston Beer —along with a growing number of craft brewers —competes in the Better Beer (as opposed to mass-produced) category. However with the domestic beer industry excluding Better Beers in decline the beer giants have begun developing their own specialty beers and acquiring craft brewers to compete in this small growth market. To keep adventurous drinkers brand-loyal Boston Beer follows a strategy of frequently offering new beverages and discontinuing others. During 2012 the company launched two specialty variety six-packs under the Samuel Adams IPA Hopology and Samuel Adams Hop Tour names.

Mergers and Acquisitions

In January 2012 the company acquired craft brewer Southern California Brewing Company (dba Angel City Brewing) for nearly $2 million. Tasked with finding unique brewing techniques and ingredients in 2012 A&S acquired Los Angeles-based Southern California Brewing Company a craft brewer doing business as Angel City Brewing Company.

Ownership

Founder and chairman James Koch owns about a third of the company's shares. Investment firm Neuberger Berman owns nearly 13%.

HISTORY

Management consultant James Koch started The Boston Beer Company with his former secretary Rhonda Kallman in 1983. With Koch's $100000 in life savings plus $300000 raised from family and friends the company contracted with Pittsburgh Brewing to make beer using Koch's great-great-grandfather's recipe. (Louis Koch had brewed beer in Germany before opening a St. Louis brewery in 1860.)

Koch and Kallman launched their premium beer in Boston in 1985 and four years later Boston Beer contracted with Blitz-Weinhard Brewing in Oregon to make beer for distribution in the western US.

The company's rise to the top of the small hopmeister heap was driven by Koch's earnest radio spots and by the quality of the product. Boston Beer went public in 1995 while the craft-brewing sector was booming but by 1997 the market stopped growing soggy with competing brands.

Using recipes gleaned from a home-brewing contest the company briefly brewed the LongShot line of beers in 1996. The next year Boston Beer moved into the fledgling alcoholic cider market with HardCore Cider and it purchased a small-batch brewery in Koch's hometown of Cincinnati. In 1998 Boston Beer expanded distribution to Japan and Australia while 1999 saw the introduction of Millennium Ale.

In 2000 Boston Beer launched BoDean's Twisted Tea a malt-and-tea-based beverage. In 2001 president Martin Roper was named CEO succeeding Koch who remains chairman.

Boston Beer began selling its first light beer Sam Adams Light in 2002 in most of its top US markets. The following year the company broke records with its 25% alcohol Utopia brew and in 2004 introduced Chocolate Bock. These offerings joined Millennium and Triple Bock under the heading Extreme Beers. Limited edition Samuel Adams Chocolate Bock which uses Scharffen Berger Chocolate was introduced in 2003.

In 2007 the company announced a brewing agreement with City Brewing to brew some of City's Latrobe brand beer. In order to add to its brewing capacity in 2008 Boston Beer acquired Pennsylvania Brewery from Diageo North America for $55 million.

In December 2010 the company introduced Infinium a limited-edition ale that was developed with Germany's Weihenstephan Brewery —recognized as the world's oldest brewery. Infinium was touted as the first new style of beer created under Reinheitsgebot purity standards in more than a century. (Reinheitsgebot purity laws dictate that only barley hops yeast and water may be used as ingredients in beer.) The ale was described by Boston Beer as tasting crisp and champagne-like.

EXECUTIVES

VP Operations, Thomas W. Lance, age 60, $320,000 total compensation
VP Brewing, David A. Grinnell, age 55
President CEO and Director, Martin F. Roper, age 50, $666,750 total compensation
Chairman, C. James (Jim) Koch, age 63, $273,000 total compensation
VP Sales, John C. Geist, age 52, $300,000 total compensation

CFO and Treasurer, William F. Urich, age 56, $362,000 total compensation
Vice President of Human Resources, Al-Li Lim
Vice President - Legal; Corporate Secretary, Kathleen H. Wade
VP Brand Development, Robert P. Pagano
Vice President - Human Resources, Ai-Li Lim
Director, Pearson C. Cummin III, age 70
President CEO and Director, Martin F. Roper, age 50
Director, Jay M. Margolis, age 62
Director, Jean-Michel Valette, age 52
Director, David A. (Dave) Burwick, age 51
Director, Gregg A. Tanner, age 57
Auditors: Ernst&YoungLLP

LOCATIONS

HQ: Boston Beer Co., Inc
One Design Center Place, Suite 850, Boston, MA 02210
Phone: 617 368-5000   **Fax:** 617 368-5500
Web: www.bostonbeer.com

PRODUCTS/OPERATIONS

Selected Brands and Year Introduced
Barrel Room Collection
  Samuel Adams American Kriek 2009
  Samuel Adams New World Tripel 2009
  Samuel Adams Stony Brook Red 2009
  Samuel Adams Thirteenth Hour 2011
Brewmaster's Collection
  Samuel Adams Black Lager 2005
  Samuel Adams Blackberry Witbier 2009
  Samuel Adams Boston Ale 1987
  Samuel Adams Cherry Wheat 1995
  Samuel Adams Coastal Wheat 2009
  Samuel Adams Cranberry Lambic 1990
  Samuel Adams Cream Stout 1993
  Samuel Adams Irish Red 2008
  Samuel Adams Latitude 48 IPA 2010
  Samuel Adams Pale Ale 1999
Core Focus Beers
  Samuel Adams Boston Lager 1984
  Sam Adams Light 2001
Flavored Malt Beverages
  Twisted Tea Backyard Batch Hard Iced Tea 2009
  Twisted Tea Half Hard Iced Tea & Half Hard Lemonade 2003
  Twisted Tea Hard Iced Tea 2001
  Twisted Tea Light Hard Iced Tea 2007
  Twisted Tea Peach Hard Iced Tea 2005
  Twisted Tea Raspberry Hard Iced Tea 2001
  Twisted Tea Blueberry Hard Iced Tea 2011
Hard Cider
  Angry Orchard Crisp Apple 2011
  Angry Orchard Apple Ginger 2011
  HardCore Crisp Hard Cider 1997
Imperial Series
  Samuel Adams Double Bock 1988
  Samuel Adams Imperial Stout 2009
  Samuel Adams Imperial White 2009
  Samuel Adams Wee Heavy 2011
Limited Edition Beers
  Infinium 2010
  Samuel Adams Utopias 2001
Seasonal Beers
  Samuel Adams Octoberfest 1989
  Samuel Adams Summer Ale 1996
  Samuel Adams Winter Lager 1989
  Samuel Adams Alpine Spring 2011

COMPETITORS

Anchor Brewers	Michigan Brewing
Anheuser-Busch InBev	MillerCoors
Asahi Breweries	New Belgium Brewing
Bacardi	Pabst
Carlsberg	Pyramid Breweries
Craft Brew Alliance	Rogue Ales
Diageo	Shipyard Brewing
Grupo Modelo	Company

Heineken
Kirin Brewery of
 America
Lancaster Brewing Co.
Lion Brewery

Sprecher
Stoudt's Brewing
Victory Brewing
Weyerbacher Brewing

HISTORICAL FINANCIALS
Company Type: Public

Income Statement
FYE: December 29

	REVENUE ($ mil.)	NET INCOME ($ mil.)	NET PROFIT MARGIN	EMPLOYEES
12/12	580.2	59.4	10.2%	950
12/11	513.0	66.0	12.9%	840
12/10	463.8	50.1	10.8%	780
12/09	415.0	31.1	7.5%	780
12/08	398.4	8.0	2.0%	775
Annual Growth	9.9%	64.7%	—	5.2%

2012 Year-End Financials
Debt ratio: 0.1%
Return on equity: 27.7%
Cash ($ mil.): 74
Current ratio: 1.83
Long-term debt ($ mil.): 0

No. of shares (mil.): 12
Dividends
 Yield: —
 Payout: —
Market value ($ mil.): 1,704

	STOCK PRICE ($) FY Close	P/E High/Low		PER SHARE ($) Earnings	Dividends	Book Value
12/12	132.98	30	21	4.39	0.00	19.13
12/11	108.56	22	14	4.81	0.00	14.41
12/10	97.91	27	12	3.52	0.00	12.36
12/09	46.81	21	8	2.17	0.00	12.15
12/08	26.76	86	45	0.56	0.00	9.88
Annual Growth	49.3%	—	—	67.3%	—	18.0%

Bravo Brio Restaurant Group Inc

Standing ovations are welcomed but not required at these restaurants. Bravo Brio Restaurant Group owns and operates more than 100 upscale casual-dining locations in 30 states. The restaurants operate under the names BRAVO! Cucina Italiana and BRIO Tuscan Grille. The company's flagship BRAVO! Cucina Italiana restaurants offer pasta pizza and other affordable Italian-inspired cuisine. The group's BRIO Tuscan Grille concept meanwhile specializes in upscale Tuscan-style ambiance and entrees such as steaks chops and fresh seafood. Bravo Brio Restaurant Group went public in 2010.
IPO
Through its public offering Bravo Brio Restaurant Group raised about $140 million in capital to pay off debt with additional funds earmarked for operational purposes.
Geographic Reach
The restaurants are concentrated somewhat in the Midwest and Southeast regions of the US. The chain's expansion plans call for an additional 50 new restaurants to open through 2015.
Sales and Marketing
BRAVO! Cucina Italiana and BRIO Tuscan Grille locations are primarily in larger metropolitan markets and around suburban retail and entertain-

ment developments. Promoting themselves to the up-market segment of the casual dining sector both chains tout their use of fresh ingredients to offer authentic Italian cuisine. They compete largely against chains such as Maggiano's Little Italy (owned by Brinker International) and The Cheesecake Factory.
The company spends heavily on advertising. Its advertising expenses were $4.1 million in fiscal 2012. It spent $3.1 million on advertising in each of the two previous fiscal years.
Financial Performance
Bravo Brio Restaurant Group has been experiencing steady growth in its year-over-year revenue since fiscal 2008. Its revenue in fiscal 2012 increased 11% compared to fiscal 2011. The company experienced double digit revenue growth of 17% in its BRIO brand and single digit revenue growth of 3% in its BRAVO! brand during fiscal 2012.
Despite the increase in total annual revenue during fiscal 2012 the company's net profit decreased by 79% compared to fiscal 2011. The net loss was largely the result of increased operating and tax expenses.

EXECUTIVES
Chairman, Alton F. (Rick) Doody III, age 54, $186,500 total compensation
President ;Chief Executive Officer; Director, Saed Mohseni, age 51, $518,000 total compensation
Corporate Executive Chef, Philip Yandolino
Chief Operating Officer, Brian O'Malley, age 45, $185,000 total compensation
CFO Treasurer and Secretary, James J. O?Connor, age 51, $206,000 total compensation
SVP Development, Ronald F. Dee, age 48, $165,000 total compensation
Director, James S. Gulmi
Director, Allen J. Bernstein, age 67
Director, David B. Pittaway, age 61
President CEO and Director, Fortunato N. (Nick) Valenti, age 65
President CEO and Director, Saed Mohseni, age 51
Director, Harold O. Rosser II, age 64
Auditors: Deloitte&ToucheLLP

LOCATIONS
HQ: Bravo Brio Restaurant Group Inc.
 777 Goodale Blvd. Ste. 100, Columbus OH 43212
Phone: 614-326-7944   **Fax:** 614-326-7943
Web: www.bbrg.com

COMPETITORS
BJ's Restaurants
BUCA
Benihana
Brinker
California Pizza Kitchen
Cameron Mitchell Restaurants
Carlson Restaurants
Cheesecake Factory

Darden
Houlihan's
J. Alexander's
Landry's
McCormick & Schmick's
OSI Restaurant Partners
P.F. Chang's
Ruby Tuesday

HISTORICAL FINANCIALS
Company Type: Public

Income Statement
FYE: December 30

	REVENUE ($ mil.)	NET INCOME ($ mil.)	NET PROFIT MARGIN	EMPLOYEES
12/12	409.0	16.1	3.9%	9,500
12/11	369.2	76.4	20.7%	8,700
12/10	343.0	(1.2)	—	8,000
12/09	311.7	3.4	1.1%	8,000
12/08	300.7	(61.3)	—	0
Annual Growth	8.0%	—	—	—

2012 Year-End Financials
Debt ratio: 8.7%
Return on equity: 17.1%
Cash ($ mil.): 13
Current ratio: 0.55
Long-term debt ($ mil.): 20

No. of shares (mil.): 19
Dividends
 Yield: —
 Payout: —
Market value ($ mil.): 258

	STOCK PRICE ($) FY Close	P/E High/Low		PER SHARE ($) Earnings	Dividends	Book Value
12/12	13.18	27	15	0.78	0.00	5.12
12/11	15.93	6	4	3.72	0.00	4.34
12/10	18.71	—	—	(0.54)	0.00	0.33
Annual Growth	(16.1%) 292.2%	—	—	—	—	—

Bridge Bancorp, Inc. (Bridgehampton, NY)

Bridge Bancorp wants you to cross over to its subsidiary The Bridgehampton National Bank which operates about 20 branches in eastern Long Island New York. Founded in 1910 the bank offers traditional deposit services to area individuals small businesses and municipalities including checking savings and money market accounts and CDs. Deposits are invested primarily in mortgages which account for some 80% of the bank's loan portfolio. Title insurance services are available through bank subsidiary Bridge Abstract; wealth management services include financial planning estate administration and trustee services. Bridge Bancorp bought Hamptons State Bank in 2011 to fortify its presence on Long Island.

EXECUTIVES
SVP and Chief Lending Officer Bridgehampton National Bank, Kevin L. Santacroce, $180,000 total compensation
Senior Vice President; Chief Information Officer, Thomas H. Simson
Vice Chairperson, Dennis A. Suskind, age 70
SEVP CFO Chief Administrative Officer Secretary and Director, Howard H. Nolan, age 52, $230,000 total compensation
Chairperson Bridge Bancorp and Bridgehampton National Bank, Marcia Z. Hefter, age 69
Executive Vice President; Chief Retail Banking Officer, James Manseau
President; Chief Executive Officer; Director, Kevin OConnor
Director, Thomas J. (Tom) Tobin, age 68
Director, Emanuel (Manny) Arturi, age 67

Director, Charles I. Massoud, age 68
Vice Chairperson, Dennis A. Suskind, age 70
SEVP CFO Chief Administrative Officer Secretary
 and Director, Howard H. Nolan, age 52
Director, Albert E. McCoy Jr., age 49
Director, Rudolph J. Santoro
Independent Director, Antonia Donohue
Auditors: CroweHorwathLLP

LOCATIONS

HQ: Bridge Bancorp Inc.
 2200 Montauk Hwy., Bridgehampton NY 11932
Phone: 631-537-1000   Fax: 631-537-1835
Web: www.bridgenb.com

PRODUCTS/OPERATIONS

2009 Sales

	$ mil.	% of total
Interest		
Loans including fees	29	59
Mortgage-backed securities	11	23
Other	3	6
Noninterest		
Service charges on deposit accounts	3	6
Other customer services fees	1	3
Title fees	0	2
Other	0	1
Total	**49**	**100**

COMPETITORS

Bank of America	JPMorgan Chase
Bank of New York	Suffolk Bancorp
Mellon	

HISTORICAL FINANCIALS

Company Type: Public

Income Statement

FYE: December 31

	ASSETS ($ mil.)	NET INCOME ($ mil.)	INCOME AS % OF ASSETS	EMPLOYEES
12/12	1,624.7	12.7	0.8%	257
12/11	1,337.4	10.3	0.8%	227
12/10	1,028.4	9.1	0.9%	206
12/09	897.2	8.7	1.0%	195
12/08	839.0	8.7	1.0%	175
Annual Growth	18.0%	9.9%	—	10.1%

2012 Year-End Financials

Return on assets: 0.8%	Dividends
Return on equity: 11.2%	Yield: 5.6%
Long-term debt ($ mil.): —	Payout: 75.6%
No. of shares (mil.): 8	Market value ($ mil.): 181
Sales ($ mil): 65	

	STOCK PRICE ($) FY Close	P/E High/Low	PER SHARE ($) Earnings	PER SHARE ($) Dividends	PER SHARE ($) Book Value
12/12	20.34	17 13	1.48	1.15	13.32
12/11	19.90	17 11	1.54	0.69	12.82
12/10	24.65	19 14	1.45	0.92	10.33
12/09	24.04	20 12	1.43	0.92	9.88
12/08	18.50	17 12	1.43	0.92	9.08
Annual Growth	2.4%	— —	0.9%	5.7%	10.1%

Bridgepoint Education, Inc.

Bridgepoint Education invites students from all walks of life to cross on over to the higher-education side. The for-profit company offers some 1400 courses and about 85 graduate and undergraduate degree programs online and at its bricks-and-mortar campuses: Ashford University in Iowa and University of the Rockies in Colorado. Academic disciplines include education business psychology and health and social sciences. Most of the company's campus-based revenues are derived from federal financial aid. About 99% of Bridgepoint Education's more than 90000 students are enrolled exclusively online.

Much like a community college Bridgepoint appeals to students who might find tuition costs credit transfer or work schedules to be barriers to attending traditional universities. Bridgepoint tries to remove those barriers by accepting a maximum number of prior credits to ease transferability by continuously expanding its online course offerings to increase accessibility and by structuring the price of its tuition to fall below Title IV loan limits so most students can afford to attend its schools. Title IV loans such as Stafford loans and Pell grants are generally easier to obtain than private loans and carry lower fixed interest rates. In 2011 both Ashford University and the University of the Rockies derived about 85% of their revenues from Title IV programs.

However Ashford University and University of the Rockies have been facing scrutiny over compliance issues from government agencies including the US Department of Education and two regional accreditation commissions that could put their administration of Title IV funds at risk. The difficulties come as online universities have increasingly been put under the magnifying glass by officials and are being required to enact extra academic integrity initiatives (such as changes in compensation policies and the enactment of student preparedness programs) to meet new regulatory standards. As a result of these changes as well as bad publicity related to government scrutiny of the industry Bridgepoint Education saw a downturn in new student enrollments during the second half of 2011.

Despite its troubles Bridgepoint Education's overall enrollment levels have grown exponentially in recent years including an 11% increase in 2011 causing the company to experience a coinciding rise in revenues. In 2011 for instance sales increase more than 30% to some $933 milllion and net income rose 35% to $173 million. The firm attributes much of its success to an increase in admissions staff and online advertising as well as to strong student satisfaction levels and its ability to balance operational costs as its revenue has grown.

Bridgepoint bases its growth strategy on expanding its academic offerings to attract more students. It identifies new programs by listening to student and faculty feedback as well as by researching macro market trends to identify which job areas will experience demand in coming years and introducing programs to educate students in those fields (such as health care and education).

In addition the firm enhances its technology capabilities to increase the quality and affordability of its programs. It introduced its proprietary Constellation platform in 2010 which allows students to access digital learning materials and textbooks from a variety of mobile devices. To enhance the Constellation platform it added the Thuze cloud-based collaborative learning environment in 2012.

The company also seeks to increase its student base by offering special programs for corporate employees and military personnel. Both of Bridgepoint's universities work with employers offering education reimbursement programs and Ashford University also offers educational opportunities to active-duty personnel and veterans of US armed forces branches with special tuition rates waived fees and free books and shipping costs. Nearly 20% of its students are with the military.

Warburg Pincus owns about two-thirds of the company. CEO and president Andrew Clark owns a 5% stake in Bridgepoint Education which he founded in 2004 with the assistance of other executives of the company and the backing of Warburg Pincus.

HISTORY

Ashford University was founded in 1918 as Mount St. Clare College by the Sisters of St. Francis. It became The Franciscan University in 2002 and was purchased in 2005 by Bridgepoint Education which changed the university's name. In 2007 Bridgepoint acquired University of the Rockies (formerly Colorado School of Professional Psychology) which focuses on offering graduate degrees in psychology.

Hoping to take advantage of the growing market for online and nontraditional schools the company went public in 2009. The IPO filing came on the heels of the public offerings of other education companies China Distance Education Holdings and Grand Canyon Education. Bridgepoint raised roughly $141 million in its IPO; proceeds went to the company's investors as well as towards general corporate purposes. Principal investor Warburg Pincus retained majority ownership of Bridgepoint's shares after the IPO.

EXECUTIVES

SVP General Counsel and Secretary, Diane L. Thompson, age 56
Chairman, Patrick T. (Pat) Hackett, age 51
President CEO and Director, Andrew S. Clark, age 47, $325,000 total compensation
EVP and CFO, Daniel J. (Dan) Devine, age 48, $220,000 total compensation
SVP Human Resources, Charlene Dackerman, age 52
EVP External Affairs and Chief Academic Officer, Jane McAuliffe, age 45, $178,228 total compensation
SVP and Chief Marketing Officer, Ross L. Woodard, age 46, $216,000 total compensation
EVP and Chief Administrative Officer, Rodney T. (Rocky) Sheng, age 46, $227,000 total compensation
SVP and CIO, Thomas (Tom) Ashbrook, age 47
VP Chief Accounting Officer and Controller, Brandon Pope, age 49
VP Learning Resources and Publishing, Elizabeth Aguiar
VP; President University of the Rockies, Charlita Shelton
VP Administrative Services, Sheri Jones
VP Technology Operations, Mike Stansbury
SVP External Affairs, Sheryl Wright
Director Public Relations, Shari Rodriguez
SVP Strategy and Corporate Development, Douglas C. Abts
VP Talent Management, John Higgins
VP Operations, Sean Gousha
VP Marketing, Linda Mignone

SVP Regulatory Affairs, Vickie Schray
VP Corporate Development, Raj Kaji
Director, Robert D. (Bob) Hartman, age 64
Director, Ryan Craig, age 40
President CEO and Director, Andrew S. Clark, age 47
Director, Adarsh Sarma, age 38
Director, Dale Crandall, age 71
Independent Director, Andrew Miller
Independent Director, Marye Fox
Auditors: PricewaterhouseCoopersLLP

LOCATIONS

HQ: Bridgepoint Education, Inc.
13500 Evening Creek Drive North, Suite 600, San Diego, CA 92128
Phone: 858 668-2586
Web: www.bridgepointeducation.com

PRODUCTS/OPERATIONS

2011 Enrollment by Degree Type

Bachelor's	63,962	74
Master's	9,805	11
Other	471	1

Selected Programs

Associate of Arts
  Business
Bachelor of Applied Science
  Accounting
  Computer
  Computer Graphic Design Core
Bachelor of Arts
  Accounting
  Business Administration
  Communication Studies
  Education
  Health Care Administration
  Liberal Arts
  Political Science and Government
  Psychology
  Social and Criminal Justice
  Social Science
  Sociology
  Visual Arts
Bachelor of Science
  Biology
  Clinical Cytotechnology
  Health Science Administration
  Natural Science
Doctorate
  Psychology
Master of Arts
  Education
  Organizational Management
  Psychology
  Teaching and Learning with Technology
Master of Business Administration
Master of Public Administration

COMPETITORS

American Public Education
Apollo Education
Capella Education
Career Education
Corinthian Colleges
DeVry Education Group
Education Management
Grand Canyon Education
ITT Educational
International Scholarship and Tuition Services
Laureate Education
Lincoln Educational Services
Strayer Education

HISTORICAL FINANCIALS

Company Type: Public

Income Statement

FYE: December 31

	REVENUE ($ mil.)	NET INCOME ($ mil.)	NET PROFIT MARGIN	EMPLOYEES
12/12	968.1	127.9	13.2%	5,620
12/11	933.3	172.7	18.5%	8,900
12/10	713.2	127.5	17.9%	3,000
12/09	454.3	47.1	10.4%	5,795
12/08	218.2	26.4	12.1%	1,200
Annual Growth	45.1%	48.3%	—	47.1%

2012 Year-End Financials

Debt ratio: —
Return on equity: 30.0%
Cash ($ mil.): 255
Current ratio: 2.21
Long-term debt ($ mil.): —

No. of shares (mil.): 54
Dividends
  Yield: —
  Payout: —
Market value ($ mil.): 557

	STOCK PRICE ($) FY Close	P/E High/Low		PER SHARE ($) Earnings	Dividends	Book Value
12/12	10.30	11	3	2.29	0.00	9.17
12/11	23.00	9	5	3.02	0.00	6.84
12/10	19.00	12	5	2.14	0.00	4.51
12/09	15.02	25	12	0.74	0.00	2.48
Annual Growth	(11.8%)	—	—	45.7%	—	54.6%

Bristow Group Inc

Bristow Group takes its customers for a ride. The company offers helicopter transportation services for offshore petroleum workers and equipment. Offshore Logistics and Bristow Helicopters units and several international affiliates serve oil and gas exploration and production companies in the world's major offshore oil production zones; 80% of its sales come from international operations. Its main operating areas are the North Sea and the Gulf of Mexico. Bristow operates a fleet of almost 400 aircraft which consists primarily of helicopters and also includes some fixed-wing aircraft. Affiliates operate another 200 or so aircraft. Customers Shell Oil and Chevron generate about 20% of company sales.

Bristow's business is inextricably linked to the oil industry which was plagued by low demand prior to 2010. Bristow runs business units that support its operations based on geographic location including North America Europe West Africa and Australia. The company is expanding its presence in Asia South America and the Middle East through its Other International business segment. Bristow still conducts a hefty business in the North Sea deriving approximately 39% of its revenues from the region. It is the non-US opportunities that have helped the company ride out the economic doldrums better than most of its competitors that are entirely dependent upon the US oil business.

The company set about to reduce its reliance on Gulf operations to only 6% (other US operations still account for more than 10% of company revenues) just in time for the explosion that wiped out British Petroleum's offshore drilling rig Deepwater Horizon in 2010; 11 people were killed off the Louisiana Coast. The catastrophe prompted the US

federal government to call for a moratorium on all new offshore drilling permits pending a federal investigation. Additionally the Obama administration proposed the repeal of many tax incentives in the 2011 federal budget for oil and natural gas exploration legislation that is guaranteed to negatively impact any company involved in oil-related business in the Gulf of Mexico.

Bristow started cutting back on its Gulf of Mexico and the North Sea operations a few years back when it realized that both areas have undergone exploration and drilling activity for so long that potential drilling opportunities are few and far between. Because Bristow proactively expanded into alternative markets it is one of only two helicopter service providers with global operations catering to the offshore energy industry. With about 8700 production platforms and 500 offshore rigs in existence there is a decided market for transportation service providers from rig/platform to shore.

Bristow is also picking up business that other companies may miss through its joint ventures with air transport companies. Because many countries limit foreign ownership of aviation companies Bristow has acquired stakes in several foreign helicopter operations. The strategy of combining Bristow's experience with local ownership allows the company to expand its operations without expending major capital investment. In 2009 the company purchased more than 42% of Lider Aviac?o Holding a Brazilian helicopter and aviation services company for the oil and gas industry. Through the purchase Bristow hopes to capitalize on Brazil's booming oil business. Bristow's strategy is paying off –the company announced in late summer 2010 that it has $1.3 billion in international contracts.

To diversify its offerings the company provides services other than just helicopter transportation and maintenance to the offshore oil and gas industry. It also offers search and rescue as well as helicopter training programs through its Bristow Academy. Additionally the company maintains a competitive edge by offering a helicopter fleet which includes small medium and large helicopters in order to serve customers' needs.

HISTORY

When Burt Keenan founded Offshore Logistics in 1969 the company used boats to transport people and cargo to offshore rigs; it added helicopters in 1972. Due to plunging oil prices in the mid-1980s the company signed over all its domestic supply vessels to the US Maritime Administration by 1985 to help settle its debts. It retained its helicopters and foreign-based ships. Keenan resigned in 1986 and gave up his interest in the company for forgiveness of a large personal loan. James Clement assumed command and revitalized Offshore Logistics during the oil recession by selling the rest of its ships and buying other helicopter companies.

With its purchase of 50% of Seahawk Services in 1993 Offshore Logistics began offering petroleum production management. It soon swapped its Seahawk stake for 27.5% of Grasso Corporation.

In 1996 Offshore Logistics in a key overseas expansion bought 49% of British helicopter company Bristow Aviation. The next year Clement was succeeded by former CFO George Small. Offshore Logistics continued to grow buying 23 new helicopters in 1998 and signing a seven-year helicopter services contract with Shell Exploration UK.

Depressed oil prices and a slowdown in exploration activities forced the company to cut back on its operations in 1999 particularly in the North

Sea. Just a couple of years later however Offshore Logistics began to update its helicopter fleet and it renewed a crucial contract with the US Coast Guard to provide flight services in the Gulf of Mexico for five years.

Between 2002 and 2005 one of Bristow's helicopters crashed on its way to a North Sea oil rig; five people were killed. More catastrophe occurred when the company lost two operating bases on the Louisiana Gulf Coast to hurricanes Katrina and Rita.

Bristow Group's international operations were a source of internal turmoil in 2005. The company conducted an internal investigation and self-reported its finding to the SEC which launched its own investigation into alleged bribery charges and under-reporting of tax liabilities. The company's CFO the president of its Air Logistics unit and other top executives left the company. The case was settled in 2007; no fines or other penalties were imposed but the company agreed not to engage in similar actions in the future; it also took steps to strengthen its financial controls. In December 2005 the company restated its financial reports for fiscal years 2003 through 2005. In 2006 Offshore Logistics changed its name to Bristow Group.

To secure a source of pilots for new aircraft Bristow Group in 2007 acquired flight training provider Helicopter Adventures (renamed Bristow Academy) for $15 million and $5 million in assumed debt. That same year the company also sold its Grasso Production Management subsidiary which offered management services for offshore oil rigs in the Gulf of Mexico to Production Services Network.

EXECUTIVES

Chairman, Thomas C. (Tom) Knudson, age 66
President CEO and Director, William E. (Bill) Chiles, age 64, $749,999 total compensation
SVP Administration, Hilary Ware, age 56
Vice President Treasurer, Joseph A. (Joe) Baj, age 55
Executive Vice President Chief Administrative Officer, Michael A. Flick, age 64
SVP Commercial, Mark B. Duncan, age 51, $325,001 total compensation
CFO, Jonathan E. Baliff
VP and Chief Accounting Officer, Brian J. Allman
Senior Vice President Operations, Jeremy Akel
Senior Vice President General Counsel, Edward Earle
Vice President Strategy and Structured Transactions, Don Miller
Vice President Integration Management, Lori Gobillot
Vice President - Sales and Marketing, Margaret Montaigne
Senior Vice President General Counsel Corporate Secretary, Chipman Earle
Vice President Business Development & Marketing, Maggie Montaigne
Vice President Operations Transformation and CTO, John Cloggie
Vice President Information Technology and CIO, Steve Sidney
Director, Bruce H. Stover, age 64
President CEO and Director, William E. (Bill) Chiles, age 64
Director, Ken C. Tamblyn, age 68
Director, Thomas N. (Tom) Amonett, age 69
Director, Stephen J. Cannon, age 59
Director, Stephen A. King, age 52
Director, Ian Godden, age 59
Director, John M. May, age 56
Director, Michael A. Flick, age 64
Independent Director, Lori Gobillot
Independent Director, Mathew Masters
Auditors: KPMGLLP

LOCATIONS

HQ: Bristow Group Inc.
2103 City West Blvd. 4th Fl., Houston TX 77042
Phone: 713-267-7600 **Fax:** 713-267-7620
Web: www.bristowgroup.com

2011 Sales

	$ mil.	% of total
UK	303	25
US	216	18
Australia	158	13
Trinidad	29	2
Other countries	101	8
Total	**1,232**	**100**

COMPETITORS

CHC Helicopter SEACOR
Evergreen Holdings Tidewater Inc.
PHI Inc.

HISTORICAL FINANCIALS

Company Type: Public

Income Statement

FYE: March 31

	REVENUE ($ mil.)	NET INCOME ($ mil.)	NET PROFIT MARGIN	EMPLOYEES
03/13	1,508.4	130.1	8.6%	3,465
03/12	1,341.8	63.5	4.7%	3,281
03/11	1,232.8	132.3	10.7%	3,289
03/10	1,167.7	112.0	9.6%	3,410
03/09	1,133.8	124.3	11.0%	3,569
Annual Growth	**7.4%**	**1.1%**	**—**	**(0.7%)**

2013 Year-End Financials

Debt ratio: 26.6%
Return on equity: 8.3%
Cash ($ mil.): 215
Current ratio: 2.82
Long-term debt ($ mil.): 764
No. of shares (mil.): 36
Dividends
 Yield: 0.0%
 Payout: 22.4%
Market value ($ mil.): 2,384

	STOCK PRICE ($) FY Close	P/E High/Low	PER SHARE ($) Earnings	Dividends	Book Value
03/13	65.94	19 11	3.57	0.80	44.29
03/12	47.73	30 22	1.76	0.60	42.32
03/11	47.30	14 8	3.60	0.00	41.63
03/10	37.73	12 7	3.10	0.00	37.54
03/09	21.43	15 4	3.60	0.00	41.62
Annual Growth	**32.4%**	**— —**	**(0.2%)**	**—**	**1.6%**

BroadSoft Inc

BroadSoft hopes to remove some of the hard work from the process of supplying voice and data services. The company develops software that more than 500 fixed-line mobile and cable telecommunications service providers use to deliver voice and data services. Its BroadWorks software enables carriers to offer their subscribers unified communications services such as video calling hosted multimedia communications business telephone systems and collaboration tools. A hosted program is sold under the BroadCloud platform while its BroadTouch applications facilitate communica-

tions services for mobile devices. Customers include Rogers Swisscom Telstra and Verizon.

Geographic Reach
BroadSoft has offices in more than a dozen countries in Asia Australia Canada Europe and the US.

While customers come from about 70 countries the US is its largest single market accounting for almost 60% of sales. Customers in Europe make up another quarter of sales.

Sales and Marketing
The company uses a direct sales force and more than 60 distributors for its indirect sales channel. Its distribution partners include many of the world's largest networking and telecommunications equipment vendors which are located outside the US.

Financial Performance
Overall sales grew 19% in 2012 to $165 million driven by increases in licensed software and support fees. Sales for its professional services decreased slightly after deferring revenue for its new call center application Call Center Xpress. BroadSoft has been profitable for the past three years.

Strategy
While many service providers originally developed Internet protocol (IP) networks for the sole purpose of transmitting high speed data they're turning to software providers such as BroadSoft to leverage their IP networks for other purposes. BroadSoft's products are installed on servers typically located in clients' data centers enabling the use of existing IP networks for broader tasks such as delivering video calls providing hosted PBX exchanges and enabling collaboration and conferencing.

Mergers and Acquisitions
BroadSoft has continued to expand with acquisitions that enhance its BroadCloud Software-as-a-Service (SaaS) with additional capabilities. In late 2013 it bought finocom AG to offer BroadCloud in Germany and Eastern Europe. The year before it bought the assets of hosted business VoIP provider Adaptation Technologies which added a Web-based platform that telecom service providers use to manage unified communications services. It also gave BroadSoft the infrastructure needed to add BroadWorks software to its BroadCloud delivery platform.

In 2011 BroadSoft acquired Phoenix-based Web-conferencing provider iLinc Communications. Its SaaS products added enterprise collaboration capabilities to BroadCloud. Also that year it bought Finland-based Movial Applications a developer of user interface and multimedia sharing software for communications devices and IP. The deal helped BroadSoft improve access to unified communications services such as video calling and conferencing instant messaging and online collaboration from its various products particularly its BroadTouch application which gives users access to their unified communications services from mobile devices.

EXECUTIVES

VP and General Counsel, Mary Ellen Seravalli, age 52
Chief Financial Officer, James A. (Jim) Tholen, age 54, $225,865 total compensation
VP BroadCloud PBX, Todd W. Wilkens
VP Cloud Research and Development, Greg E. Pounds
Chairman, Robert P. (Bob) Goodman, age 52
Vice President Global Sales, Patrick Joggerst

President and Chief Executive Officer; Director, Michael (Mike) Tessler, age 52, $276,058 total compensation
Chief Technology Officer, Scott D. Hoffpauir, age 48
Vice President BroadCloud, Ken Rokoff
VP Operations, Geoffrey K. (Geoff) Hicks
VP Sales, Greg Callanan
VP Engineering, Robert (Bob) Weidenfeller
VP Asia/Pacific, Jonathan Reid
VP Sales EMEA, Craig Decker
VP Products, David Bukovsky
Vice President Marketing, Leslie Ferry
Chairman, John D. Markley Jr., age 48
VP Sales Operations, Pamela Coleman-Davis
Director, John J. Gavin Jr., age 57
Director, Douglas L. Maine, age 64
President CEO and Director, Michael (Mike) Tessler, age 52
Director, Charles L. (Charlie) III, age 58
Director, John D. Markley Jr., age 47
Director, David Bernardi, age 50
Auditors: PricewaterhouseCoopersLLP

LOCATIONS

HQ: BroadSoft Inc
9737 Washingtonian Boulevard, Suite 350, Gaithersburg, MD 20878
Phone: 301 977-9440
Web: www.broadsoft.com

2012 Sales

	$ mil.	% of total
US	94	57
EMEA	39	24
APAC	18	11
Other	12	8
Total	**164**	**100**

PRODUCTS/OPERATIONS

2012 Sales

	$ mil.	% of total
License software	89	55
Subscription & maintenance support	58	35
Professional services & other	16	10
Total	**164**	**100**

Mergers and Acquisitio
FY 2,013
finocom AG
FY 2,012
Adaptation Technologi
FY 2,011
iLinc Communicat
Movial Applicatio
FY 2,010
Casabi

COMPETITORS

Alcatel-Lucent	Huawei Technologies
Amdocs	Metaswitch
Avaya	Microsoft
Cisco Systems	Nokia Siemens Networks
Comverse Technology	Sonus Networks
Ericsson	Telcordia
GENBAND	

HISTORICAL FINANCIALS

Company Type: Public

Income Statement

FYE: December 31

	REVENUE ($ mil.)	NET INCOME ($ mil.)	NET PROFIT MARGIN	EMPLOYEES
12/12	164.8	12.0	7.3%	611
12/11	138.0	32.3	23.4%	487
12/10	95.6	7.9	8.4%	372
12/09	68.8	(7.8)	—	340
12/08	61.8	(11.2)	—	0
Annual Growth	**27.8%**	—	—	—

2012 Year-End Financials

Debt ratio: 26.7%
Return on equity: 8.1%
Cash ($ mil.): 90
Current ratio: 3.46
Long-term debt ($ mil.): 86

No. of shares (mil.): 27
Dividends
  Yield: —
  Payout: —
Market value ($ mil.): 1,014

	STOCK PRICE ($) FY Close	P/E High/Low	PER SHARE ($) Earnings	Dividends	Book Value
12/12	36.33	101 46	0.43	0.00	5.78
12/11	30.20	43 20	1.15	0.00	4.92
12/10	23.88	54 16	0.32	0.00	2.06
Annual Growth	**23.3%**	— —	**15.9%**	—	**67.3%**

Brookline Bancorp Inc (DE)

Brookline Bancorp is the holding company for Brookline Bank Bank Rhode Island (BankRI) and The First National Bank of Ipswich which operate more than 40 branches in eastern Massachusetts and Rhode Island. Commercial and multifamily mortgages backed by real estate such as apartments condominiums and office buildings account for the largest portion of the company's loan portfolio followed by indirect auto loans commercial loans and consumer loans. Most of Brookline's commercial loans are offered through Eastern Funding a majority-owned firm that specializes in financing coin-operated laundry dry cleaning and convenience store equipment in the New York City metropolitan area.

Brookline Bancorp has been making acquisitions to grow geographically. In 2011 it acquired The First National Bank of Ipswich a six-branch bank serving Massachusetts' North Shore. The $19.7 million transaction gave First National Bank of Ipswich a much-needed boost as that bank had been struggling with loan losses during the recession. It also expanded Brookline Bancorp's market area as there was no overlap between the two banks.

The following year the company completed the acquisition of Bancorp Rhode Island for $234 million in cash and stock adding 17 branches in that state. BankRI retained its brand and operates as a separate subsidiary of Brookline Bancorp.

The acquisitions helped to boost the company's deposit base. Brookline Bancorp also reported higher earnings in 2011 as interest rate margins improved and the company grew its loan portfolio across all sectors. It plans to continue to increase its commercial lending.

Brookline Bancorp's board rejected a takeover offer by an unnamed suitor in early 2010. Two directors had voted to accept the bid however including former longtime chairman Richard Chapman. Both resigned in the aftermath of the vote.

EXECUTIVES

President; Chief Executive Officer; Director, Paul A. Perrault, age 62
Acting Chairman, Joseph J. Slotnik, age 77
VP and Relationship Manager Brookline Bank, Lori B. Leeth
SVP Commercial Banking Brookline Bank, William R. MacKenzie
VP Commercial Banking Brookline Bank, Warren Ramirez
Senior Vice President, Wesley K. Blair
Chief Operating Officer, James Cosman
Chief Financial Officer; Treasurer, Julie Gerschick
President and Chief Executive Officer of Bank Rhode Island, Mark Meiklejohn
General Counsel; Secretary, Michael McCurdy
Chief Credit Officer, Robert Rose
President and Chief Executive Officer of The First National Bank of Ipswich, Russell Cole
Chief Human Resources Officer, Sarah Merritt
President CEO and Director, Paul A. Perrault, age 61
Director, Charles H. Peck, age 72
Director, David C. Chapin, age 77
Director, John L. Hall II, age 74
Director, Hollis W. Plimpton Jr., age 81
Director, Rosamond B. Vaule, age 76
Director, William V. Tripp III, age 73
Director, Peter O. Wilde, age 74
Director, John A. Hackett, age 73
Director, John J. Doyle Jr., age 81
Independent Director, Bogdan Nowak
Independent Director, Thomas Hollister
Auditors: KPMGLLP

LOCATIONS

HQ: Brookline Bancorp Inc (DE)
131 Clarendon Street, Boston, MA 02117-9179
Phone: 617 425-4600
Web: www.brooklinebank.com

PRODUCTS/OPERATIONS

2011 Sales

	$ mil.	% of total
Interest		
Loans	133	92
Debt securities	6	4
Other	0	-
Noninterest		
Fees charges & other	5	4
Gains on sales of securities	0	-
Investments in affordable housing projects	(0.7)	-
Total	**145**	**100**

COMPETITORS

Bank of America	RBS Citizens Financial
Boston Private	Group
Central Bancorp	Sovereign Bank
Century Bancorp (MA)	TD Bank USA
Eastern Bank	

Company Type: Public

Income Statement

FYE: December 31

	ASSETS ($ mil.)	NET INCOME ($ mil.)	INCOME AS % OF ASSETS	EMPLOYEES
12/12	5,147.5	37.1	0.7%	662
12/11	3,299.0	27.6	0.8%	358
12/10	2,720.5	26.8	1.0%	266
12/09	2,615.8	19.2	0.7%	245
12/08	2,613.0	12.8	0.5%	245
Annual Growth	18.5%	30.4%	—	28.2%

2012 Year-End Financials

Return on assets: 0.8%	Dividends
Return on equity: 6.6%	Yield: 4.0%
Long-term debt ($ mil.): —	Payout: 64.1%
No. of shares (mil.): 70	Market value ($ mil.): 598
Sales ($ mil.): 231	

	STOCK PRICE ($) FY Close	P/E High/Low		PER SHARE ($) Earnings	Dividends	Book Value
12/12	8.50	18	14	0.53	0.34	8.70
12/11	8.44	24	15	0.47	0.34	8.50
12/10	10.85	25	19	0.46	0.34	8.39
12/09	9.91	37	23	0.33	0.54	8.26
12/08	10.65	60	41	0.22	0.74	8.46
Annual Growth	(5.5%)	—	—	24.6%	(17.7%)	0.7%

Bruker Corp

The life sciences research field likes to put Bruker's equipment to the test. The company makes an array of scientific analysis instruments for pharmaceutical biotech industrial academic and government customers through four business units. Its Bruker MAT unit manufactures a portfolio of X-ray analysis products while Bruker CALID makes mass spectrometry equipment and chromatography instruments used for chemical testing and CBRNE detection. Bruker Energy & Supercon Technologies (BEST) offers superconducting systems and magnetic devices used in medical imaging and energy research. The company also makes magnetic resonance equipment through Bruker BioSpin. Bruker is owned by the Laukien family.

IPO

In 2010 the company's BEST subsidiary announced plans to go public through a $100 million IPO with proceeds going toward R&D and production expansion efforts as well as repaying loans to its parent company. Bruker would have remained the majority shareholder of BEST; however the IPO was delayed in 2011 and withdrawn in 2012 due to poor market conditions.

Geographic Reach

Bruker operates major manufacturing plants and technology centers in North America Europe and Japan. It also maintains a direct sales network in these operation regions and it markets its products through independent representatives and wholesale distributors in smaller markets.

Operations

The company operates through four business units: Bruker MAT a manufacturer of X-ray analysis products; Bruker CALID which makes mass spectrometry equipment and chromatography instruments; Bruker Energy & Supercon Technolo-

gies a manufacturer of superconducting systems and magnetic devices; and Bruker BioSpin which makes magnetic resonance equipment.

Sales and Marketing

Bruker maintains a direct sales network in its primary operation regions and it markets its products through independent representatives and wholesale distributors in smaller markets. It targets customers in the pharmaceutical biotechnology proteomics molecular diagnostics industrial agricultural government and academic sectors. Its advertising expenses were $7.5 million during fiscal year 2012.

Financial Performance

Bruker's revenue was up 8.5% in 2012 over 2011. Overall its revenue growth has been on the rise in recent years due to organic growth and acquisitions. The company's net income which has fluctuated in recent years with changes in acquisition-related expenses was up 16% in 2012.

Strategy

Bruker's growth strategy includes ramping up sales in emerging markets like Asia and pursing strategic acquisitions that enable it to sell in new markets and expand and build on its product offerings.

Mergers and Acquisitions

Bruker bolstered its X-ray analysis product offerings with the 2012 acquisition of X-ray analysis equipment maker Hecus X-Ray GmbH. The company also enhanced its imaging technologies business the same year after acquiring SkyScan N.V. a manufacturer of tomography systems for 3D X-ray imaging technologies.

Ownership

Frank Laukien and his brothers and fellow company executives Dirk Laukien and Joerg Laukien together own more than 35% of Bruker.

Company Background

The company was formed in 2008 through the combination of several entities controlled by the Laukien family. Through the transaction publicly traded Bruker (then named Bruker BioSciences which held the AXS Daltonics and Optics units) purchased Bruker BioSpin a private company owned by the Laukiens in a cash and stock deal worth more than $900 million.

EXECUTIVES

President of Bruker CAM, Collin J. D'Silva, age 56
Chairman President and Chief Executive Officer, Frank H. Laukien, age 53, $318,750 total compensation
Secretary and Director, Richard M. Stein, age 61
Executive Vice President and Chief Financial Officer, Charles F. (Charlie) Wagner Jr., age 45
VP Strategic and Financial Planning, Brian P. Monahan, age 41, $193,154 total compensation
Director; COO Bruker BioSpin Group; President BioSpin MRI, Joerg C. Laukien, age 59
Senior Scientific Fellow and Director, Dirk D. Laukien, age 49, $212,283 total compensation
SVP and CFO Advanced Supercon, Thomas M. (Tom) Rosa, age 60
Director Investor Relations, Stacey Desrochers
Co-President BioSpin Division, Bernd Gewiese
Co-President BioSpin Division, Werner Maas
Executive Director Marketing and Business Development, George Goedesky
Director Marketing Communications Bruker BioSpin, Thorsten Thiel
President and Chief Executive Officer of Bruker Energy & Supercon Technologies; Inc, Burkhard Prause
President of Bruker Nano Inc., Mark Munch

Vice President - Finance; Chief Accounting Officer, Michael Knell
Executive Vice President-Order Execution Production & Logistics Bruker Scientific Instruments and, Stephan Westermann
Senior Vice President - Corporate Finance and Accounting, Anthony Mattacchione
Director, Richard A. Packer, age 56
Director, Richard D. Kniss, age 72
Secretary and Director, Richard M. Stein, age 61
Director, William A. (Bill) Linton, age 65
Director, Bernhard Wangler, age 62
Director, Brenda J. Furlong, age 65
Director; COO Bruker BioSpin Group; President BioSpin MRI, Joerg C. Laukien, age 59
Senior Scientific Fellow and Director, Dirk D. Laukien, age 49
Director, Wolf-Dieter Emmerich, age 73
Director, Stephen W. Fesik, age 59
Independent Director, Christopher Ingen
Auditors: Ernst&YoungLLP

LOCATIONS

HQ: Bruker Corporation
40 Manning Rd., Billerica MA 01821
Phone: 978-663-3660   **Fax:** 978-663-5585
Web: www.bruker.com

2012 Sales

	$ mil.	% of total
Europe	706	39
Asia Pacific	570	32
US	377	21
Other regions & countries	137	8
Total	**1,791**	**100**

PRODUCTS/OPERATIONS

2012 Sales

	$ mil.	% of total
Scientific instruments (BioSpin CALID & MAT)	1,666	93
Energy & Supercon Technologies	136	7
Adjustments	(10.9)	-
Total	**1,791**	**100**

COMPETITORS

ABB	PANalytical
AMETEK	PerkinElmer
Affymetrix	Renishaw
Agilent Technologies	Sequenom
Caliper Life Sciences	Shimadzu
Danaher	Smiths Detection
GE Healthcare	Spectris
Hitachi Medical Systems America	Sumitomo
JEOL	Thales
Mettler-Toledo	Thermo Fisher Scientific
Mitsubishi Electric	Toshiba
Olympus	Waters Corp.
Oxford Instruments	Zygo

HISTORICAL FINANCIALS

Company Type: Public

Income Statement

FYE: December 31

	REVENUE ($ mil.)	NET INCOME ($ mil.)	NET PROFIT MARGIN	EMPLOYEES
12/12	1,791.4	77.5	4.3%	6,400
12/11	1,651.7	92.3	5.6%	6,000
12/10	1,304.9	95.4	7.3%	5,400
12/09	1,114.5	81.2	7.3%	4,500
12/08	1,107.1	64.9	5.9%	4,400
Annual Growth	12.8%	4.5%	—	9.8%

Bryn Mawr Bank Corp.

Bryn Mawr Bank Corporation stands atop a "big hill" in Pennsylvania. It is the bank holding company for Bryn Mawr Trust which operates some 25 offices (several are limited-service branches located in retirement communities) in Chester Delaware and Montgomery counties including Philadelphia's tony Main Line suburbs. Founded in 1889 the bank offers traditional services as checking and savings accounts CDs mortgages and business and consumer loans in addition to insurance products equipment leasing investment management retirement planning tax planning and preparation and trust services.

Bryn Mawr (which is Welsh for big hill) has more than $5 billion of assets under administration and management. As part of a strategy to build its wealth management division the company acquired Davidson Trust in 2012. The deal added some $1 billion in assets under management. In 2011 the company bought the private wealth management business of Hershey Trust Company for more than $14.5 million; that deal brought in approximately $1 billion of assets under management. In 2010 the company purchased First Keystone Financial adding about 10 bank branches in Pennsylvania and some $2.7 billion in trust and investment assets.

The latter two acquisitions along with growth in the company's loan and lease portfolio helped Bryn Mawr report record earnings in 2011. Besides acquisitions the company has also grown its wealth management business through marketing campaigns to raise brand awareness.

In 2012 Bryn Mawr continued its growth strategy and announced plans to acquire First Bank of Delaware. The deal includes certain consumer and business deposits and loan accounts as well as a bank branch in Delaware and will help increase the company's brand awareness there. Bryn Mawr also operates Delaware-based Lau Associates a financial planning and investment advisory firm and The Bryn Mawr Trust Company of Delaware.

EXECUTIVES

SVP, June M. Falcone
EVP Community Banking Division Marketing Technology and Information Services and Operations Bryn Mawr Trust, Alison E. Gers, age 55, $206,202 total compensation
Executive Vice President; Chief Lending Officer of the Bank, Joseph G. (Joe) Keefer, age 54, $205,021 total compensation
Secretary; EVP Secretary and Chief Credit Policy Officer Bryn Mawr Trust, Robert J. Ricciardi, age 64, $176,436 total compensation
CFO and Treasurer; EVP CFO and Treasurer Bryn Mawr Trust, J. Duncan Smith, age 54, $202,951 total compensation
Chairman of the Board; President; Chief Executive Officer of the Corporation and the Bank, Frederick C. (Ted) Peters II, age 63, $359,582 total compensation
SVP Bryn Mawr Trust, Lynn S. Mander, age 64
SVP Wealth Management Division Bryn Mawr Trust, Doris P. (Dodie) Theune
SVP Fiduciary Services Group, Karen A. (Kim) Fahrner
SVP, Geoffrey L. Halberstadt
Assistant Secretary, Diane C. McDonald
SVP Commercial Lending, Martin F. Gallagher Jr.
SVP Wealth Management; President Retirement Services, Gilbert B. Mateer
President BMT Leasing, James A. (Jim) Zelinskie Jr.
SVP BMT Leasing, Timothy Westburg
VP and Controller BMT Leasing, Paul Wesolowski
VP Wealth Management Division Bryn Mawr Trust, John S. Harrison
Executive Vice President Wealth Management Division, Matthew G. Waschull, age 51, $208,201 total compensation
VP and Branch Manager Bryn Mawr Trust, Martha Hilty
Vice President & Trust Officer, Jesse S. Ashcroft
Senior Vice President & Senior Trust Officer, Lisa L. Piergallini
Vice President & Investment Officer, Linda B. Dwyer
Vice President Senior Investment Advisor, Ruston J. Wolfe
Vice President Senior Investment Advisor, William A. Reasner
Chairman President and CEO Bryn Mawr Bank Corporation and Bryn Mawr Trust, Frederick C. (Ted) Peters II, age 63
Director, Wendell F. Holland, age 62
Director, Britton H. Murdoch, age 55
Director, Scott M. Jenkins, age 58
Director, Francis J. Leto, age 54
Director, B. Loyall Taylor Jr., age 65
Director, Andrea F. Gilbert
Director, David E. Lees, age 52
Director, Thomas L. Bennett, age 64
Independent Director, Jerry Johnson
Auditors: KPMGLLP

LOCATIONS

HQ: Bryn Mawr Bank Corporation
801 Lancaster Ave., Bryn Mawr PA 19010-3396
Phone: 610-525-1700 **Fax:** 610-526-2450
Web: www.bmtc.com

PRODUCTS/OPERATIONS

2011 Sales

	$ mil.	% of total
Interest		
Interest & fees on loans & leases	69	64
Investment securities	5	5
Cash & cash equivalents	0	.
Noninterest		
Fees for wealth management services	21	20
Net gain on sale of residential mortgages	2	2
Service charges on deposits	2	2
Other	7	7
Total	**108**	**100**

Selected Subsidiaries

Bryn Mawr Advisors Inc.
Bryn Mawr Asset Management Inc.
Bryn Mawr Brokerage Co. Inc.
Bryn Mawr Financial Services Inc.
Bryn Mawr Trust Company of Delaware
Joseph W. Roskos Co. Inc.
Lau Associates LLC
The Bryn Mawr Trust Company
 BMT Leasing Inc.
 BMT Mortgage Services Inc.
 BMT Settlement Services Inc.
 Insurance Counsellors of Bryn Mawr Inc.

COMPETITORS

Alliance Bancorp of Pennsylvania	PNC Financial
Firstrust Savings Bank	Royal Bancshares
Metro Bancorp	Sovereign Bank
National Penn Bancshares	Wells Fargo

HISTORICAL FINANCIALS

Company Type: Public

Income Statement

Buckle, Inc. (The)

The Buckle has done away with the notion that Midwestern kids' fashion sense favors overalls. With some 430 mostly mall-based stores in 40-plus states The Buckle sells fashion-conscious 15- to 30-year-olds the clothes they've just got to have. The company retails a variety of clothing items including mid- to higher-priced casual apparel (pants tops and outerwear) shoes and accessories. Its products portfolio boasts such brands as Lucky Brand Dungarees Hurley Roxy Silver Billabong Fossil and Ed Hardy. The Buckle operates under the names Buckle and The Buckle; it also has an online store. Born in Nebraska in 1948 under the name Mills Clothing the chain has expanded into the South and West.

The Buckle topped a billion in sales in fiscal 2012 (ends January) a 12% increase compared with the prior year. Net income grew by more than 12%and cash flow increased as well over the same period. Indeed the retail chain's sales have doubled over the past five years as it sailed through the deep recession that punished some of its rivals (notably Abercrombie & Fitch). Same-store sales for the fiscal year increased more than 8% as its stores sold more goods at higher prices.

The Buckle is growing by adding stores (135 over the past decade) and entering new markets (most recently Massachusetts and Rhode Island). Another 10 stores are planned for fiscal 2013. Its stores can be found in strip centers enclosed shopping malls and large lifestyle centers as well as free-standing downtown locations. On the merchandise side of the business Buckle and other retailers have grappled with rising costs for labor and commodities —especially cotton. CEO Dennis Nelson expects rising cotton costs to impact sweaters and outerwear more than denim. Denim (47% of fiscal 2012 sales) is increasingly popular with Buckle customers and is a key component of the retailer's merchandising strategy. Unlike competitors Gap and Abercrombie & Fitch the teen retailer relies heavily on hip brand-name clothing which generates about two-thirds of its sales; the rest comes from private labels with BKE being the most notable. Brand names are big among its youthful clientele which tends to be fickle and chases after the "it" brands of the moment. Also because the majority of the company's stores are in smallish markets in middle America The Buckle is the leading edge of fashion for many of its customers. The chain also moving "down market" to appeal to the younger set —children ages 8 to 15 —with apparel only sold online.

Chairman Daniel Hirschfeld the founder's son owns more than a third of The Buckle's shares. The New York-based investment firm Royce & Associates LLC owns nearly 15%.

HISTORY

David Hirschfeld and a partner Ivan Mills founded Mills Clothing in Kearney Nebraska in 1948 with a single men's clothing store. Hirschfeld's son Daniel worked as a clerk there took over the business in the mid-1960s and bought a second store The Brass Buckle in 1967.

Catering to students (like future CEO Dennis Nelson) at nearby Kearney State College The Brass Buckle began offering jeans and more casual clothes later adding women's clothing; it opened its first mall store in 1977. By 1981 it had 17 stores. During the next decade the company expanded beyond Nebraska. It changed its name to The Buckle in 1991 and promoted Nelson who started as a part-time clerk in 1970 to president. The company had 89 stores in 13 states when it went public in 1992.

The Buckle continued to stretch in the 1990s opening scores of stores –including locations in the West and Southeast —and introducing its Primo frequent-shopper card. Nelson became CEO in 1997. The following year as Generation Y flexed its spending power the retailer expanded its distribution center in Kearney enabling it to handle another 250 stores. The Buckle opened about 30 stores and moved into six new states during fiscal 2000 and another two dozen new stores and two new states in 2001.

The company in 2002 kicked off a multiyear expansion plan that includes locating new stores in high-traffic shopping malls. During the period of 2003 (when The Buckle boasted 307 stores) to 2008 (when it operated 371) the retailer has slowly increased its presence in malls through its organic growth.

EXECUTIVES

VP Leasing, Brett P. Milkie, age 53, $315,000 total compensation
Chief Financial Officer; Vice President - Finance; Director, Karen B. Rhoads, age 54, $280,000 total compensation
President; Chief Executive Officer and Director, Dennis H. Nelson, age 63, $900,000 total compensation
Chairman, Daniel J. Hirschfeld, age 71
VP Sales, Kari G. Smith, age 49, $310,000 total compensation
VP Women's Merchandising, Patricia K. Whisler, age 56, $325,000 total compensation
Secretary and General Counsel, Kyle L. Hanson, age 48
VP Men's Merchandising, Robert M. (Bob) Carlberg, age 50
Treasurer and Corporate Controller, Thomas B. (Tom) Heacock
VP Finance CFO Treasurer and Director, Karen B. Rhoads, age 54
President, Dennis H. Nelson, age 63
Director, Robert E. Campbell, age 70
Director, Bill L. Fairfield, age 67
Director, Bruce L. Hoberman, age 66
Director, James E. Shada, age 57
Director, John P. (Jack) Peetz III, age 63
Director, Michael E. Huss, age 58
Auditors: Deloitte&ToucheLLP

LOCATIONS

HQ: The Buckle Inc.
2407 W. 24th St., Kearney NE 68845-4915
Phone: 308-236-8491   **Fax:** 308-236-4493
Web: www.buckle.com

2012 Stores

	No.
Texas	47
Florida	22
Ohio	20
Michigan	19
California	18
Illinois	18
Iowa	17
Kansas	17
Missouri	15
Indiana	14
Washington	14
Nebraska	13
Oklahoma	13
Wisconsin	13
Arizona	12
Colorado	12
Minnesota	12
Tennessee	12
Louisiana	11
North	10
Utah	10
Pennsylvania	9
Georgia	6
Alabama	6
Arkansas	6
Idaho	6
Kentucky	5
Mississippi	5
Montana	5
Nevada	4
New	4
North	4
Oregon	4
Virginia	4
West	4
Maryland	3
New	3
New	3
South	3
South	3
Massachusetts	1
Rhode	1
Wyoming	1
Total	**431**

PRODUCTS/OPERATIONS

2012 Sales

	$ mil.	% of total
		% of total
Denims		47
Tops (including		32
Accessories		8
Footwear		5
Sportswear/fashions		5
Outerwear		2
Casual bottoms &		1
Total		**100**

COMPETITORS

Abercrombie & Fitch	Forever 21
Aeropostale	Hot Topic
American Eagle Outfitters	J. C. Penney
Ascena Retail	J. Crew
Benetton	Macy's
Bon-Ton Stores	Nordstrom
Deb Shops	Pacific Sunwear
Destination XL Group	Saks
Dillard's	The Gap
Eddie Bauer LLC	Urban Outfitters
	Wet Seal
	dELiA*s

HISTORICAL FINANCIALS

Company Type: Public

Income Statement

FYE: February 2

	REVENUE ($ mil.)	NET INCOME ($ mil.)	NET PROFIT MARGIN	EMPLOYEES
02/13*	1,124.0	164.3	14.6%	8,600
01/12	1,062.9	151.4	14.2%	8,600
01/11	949.8	134.6	14.2%	7,600
01/10	898.2	127.3	14.2%	7,000
01/09	792.0	104.4	13.2%	8,225
Annual Growth	9.1%	12.0%	—	1.1%

*Fiscal year change

2013 Year-End Financials

Debt ratio: —	No. of shares (mil.): 48
Return on equity: 49.5%	Dividends
Cash ($ mil.): 117	Yield: 0.1%
Current ratio: 2.15	Payout: 154.0%
Long-term debt ($ mil.): —	Market value ($ mil.): 2,260

	STOCK PRICE ($) FY Close	P/E High/Low		PER SHARE ($) Earnings	Dividends	Book Value
02/13*	47.03	15	11	3.44	5.30	6.03
01/12	43.35	15	11	3.20	3.05	7.66
01/11	35.59	14	8	2.86	3.30	7.33
01/10	30.34	14	8	2.73	2.60	7.64
01/09	21.15	27	6	2.24	2.73	7.35
Annual Growth	22.1%	—	—	11.3%	18.0%	(4.8%)

*Fiscal year change

Buffalo Wild Wings Inc

Hot sauce fuels the flight of this restaurateur. Buffalo Wild Wings (BWW) operates a chain of about 900 Buffalo Wild Wings Grill & Bar quick-casual dining spots that specialize in serving Buffalo-style chicken wings. The eateries found in about 40 states offer more than a dozen unique dipping sauces to go with the spicy wings as well as a complement of other items such as chicken tenders and legs. BWW's menu also features appetizers burgers tacos salads and desserts along with beer wine and other beverages. The company owns and operates more than 380 of the restaurants while the rest are operated by franchisees.

Geographic Reach

Buffalo Wild Wings has locations across 49 states in the US as well as in Canada. The majority of the company's restaurants are located in California Illinois Indiana Michigan Ohio and Texas. Many BWW locations are found in suburban areas typically near established retail and entertainment developments.

Operations

Typical in the casual dining industry the BWW chain comprises a mix of corporate-run and franchised locations. Its large estate of owned and operated eateries accounts for the greatest share of the company's sales (about 93% in fiscal 2012) and allows it to maintain control over the Buffalo Wild Wings dining experience while its franchising efforts help expand the chain with fewer construction and operating costs.

Food and nonalcoholic beverages accounted for about 78% of restaurant sales in fiscal 2012. The remaining 22% of restaurant sales was from alcoholic beverages.

Sales and Marketing

The BWW concept is designed to appeal to a broad mix of customers but the chain promotes itself as a place for groups and families to gather and watch sporting events. (Some locations have as many as 50 TV screens to give everyone a good view of the big game.)

Local franchise operators such as Michigan-based Diversified Restaurant Holdings typically pay the company royalties and other fees in order to use the Buffalo Wild Wings brand and marketing.

BWW competes broadly against other casual dining chains such as Applebee's and T.G.I. Friday's (owned by Carlson Restaurants Worldwide) but within its target audience the chain faces competition from Dave & Buster's the Fox & Hound chain of sports bars and of course Hooters.

Financial Performance

The company's revenue increased by 33% to $1.04 billion in fiscal 2012 up from $784 million in fiscal 2011 while its profits grow by 14% in fiscal 2012 compared to fiscal 2011. The spikes were powered by growth in both its Restaurant sales and Franchise royalties and fees.

Restaurant sales increased by 35% due to a $182.7 million increase associated with 69 company-owned restaurants that opened or acquired in 2012. A same-store sales increase of 7% accounted for $41.6 million of the increase in restaurant sales. Franchise royalties and fees increased by 14% primarily due to royalties related to additional sales at 12 more franchised restaurants in operation at the end of the period compared to prior year and an increase in same-store sales for franchised restaurants of 7% in 2012.

Strategy

The company is working toward the goal of eventually reaching about 1500 locations with plans calling for corporate-owned restaurants to make up about 40% of the chain. BWW opened its first international location in Toronto Canada in 2011 and plans to have 50 Canadian outposts of the restaurant up and running by 2016.

Company Background

Jim Disbrow and Scott Lowery opened the first Buffalo Wild Wings restaurant on the campus of Ohio State University in Columbus in 1982. (Legend has it that they started the eatery because they craved the style of chicken wings they had eaten in Buffalo New York.) Originally called Buffalo Wild Wings & Weck (a reference to the Kimmelweck brand rolls used for sandwiches) the chain became known as BW3 for short. Rapid expansion and financial mismanagement pushed Buffalo Wild Wings to the brink of bankruptcy by the mid-1990s. Sally Smith became CEO in 1996 and helped retool the chain's branding strategy to appeal more to families and non-students.

EXECUTIVES

EVP CFO and Treasurer, Mary J. Twinem, age 52, $350,000 total compensation

President CEO and Director, Sally J. Smith, age 55, $560,000 total compensation

Managing Director International, Mounir N. (Mo) Sawda, age 55

EVP North American Operations, Judith A. (Judy) Shoulak, age 53, $295,000 total compensation

EVP Global Marketing and Brand Development, Kathleen M. (Kathy) Benning, age 50, $252,000 total compensation

Chairman, James M. Damian, age 62

EVP and COO, James M. Schmidt, age 53, $295,000 total compensation

Regional Manager Canada, Robert Stewart

Vice President; General Counsel; Secretary, Emily C. Decker

Senior Vice President - Talent Management, Andrew Block

Senior Vice President - Guest Experience and Innovation, Lee R. Patterson

Director, Michael P. Johnson, age 65

President CEO and Director, Sally J. Smith, age 55

Director, Robert W. MacDonald, age 70

Director, J. Oliver Maggard, age 58

Director, Dale M. Applequist, age 65

Director, Warren E. Mack, age 68

Director, Jerry R. Rose

Auditors: KPMGLLP

LOCATIONS

HQ: Buffalo Wild Wings Inc.
5500 Wayzata Blvd. Ste. 1600, Minneapolis MN 55416
Phone: 952-593-9943 **Fax:** 952-593-9787
Web: www.buffalowildwings.com

PRODUCTS/OPERATIONS

2012 Sales

Restaurants	964	93
Total	**1,040**	**100**

2012 Locations

Franchised	510	
Total	**0**	**891**

COMPETITORS

Applebee's	Hooters
International	Houlihan's
Brinker	Johnny Rockets
Carlson Restaurants	OSI Restaurant
Damon's	Partners
Darden	Rock Bottom
Dave & Buster's	Restaurants
Famous Dave's	Ruby Tuesday
Fox & Hound	
Restaurant	

HISTORICAL FINANCIALS

Company Type: Public

Income Statement

FYE: December 30

	REVENUE ($ mil.)	NET INCOME ($ mil.)	NET PROFIT MARGIN	EMPLOYEES
12/12	1,040.5	57.2	5.5%	25,500
12/11	784.4	50.4	6.4%	21,000
12/10	613.2	38.4	6.3%	15,900
12/09	538.9	30.6	5.7%	14,000
12/08	422.4	24.4	5.8%	12,000
Annual Growth	25.3%	23.7%	—	20.7%

2012 Year-End Financials

Debt ratio: —
Return on equity: 16.0%
Cash ($ mil.): 83
Current ratio: 0.89
Long-term debt ($ mil.): —

No. of shares (mil.): 18
Dividends
  Yield: —
  Payout: —
Market value ($ mil.): 1,340

	STOCK PRICE ($) FY Close	P/E High/Low	PER SHARE ($) Earnings	Dividends	Book Value
12/12	71.94	31 21	3.06	0.00	20.59
12/11	68.24	25 16	2.73	0.00	17.30
12/10	44.97	25 17	2.10	0.00	14.10
12/09	42.92	26 13	1.69	0.00	11.62
12/08	24.72	32 11	1.36	0.00	9.59
Annual Growth	30.6%	— —	22.5%	—	21.0%

Cabot Microelectronics Corp

Cabot Microelectronics sits atop a mountain of slurry. The company is a top maker of slurries (consumables) used in chemical mechanical planarization (CMP). CMP is a wafer polishing process that enables semiconductor manufacturers to produce smaller faster and more complex devices. Cabot Micro's CMP slurries consist of liquids containing abrasives and chemicals that aid in the CMP process. The company is also a leading provider of polishing pads for CMP and it makes slurries used to polish the substrates and magnetic heads of hard-disk drives. TSMC United Microelectronics Samsung and Intel are among its largest customers.

Geographic Reach

Cabot Micro has five manufacturing facilities in Japan Singapore South Korea Taiwan and the US. It has regional sales customer service and technical support offices in Europe Asia and the US. About 80% of sales come from the Asia/Pacific region.

Operations

Sales of various slurries (tungsten dielectric copper and data storage slurries) and polishing pads account for more than 95% of Cabot Micro's revenues. In addition the company's Engineered Surface Finishes (ESF) business develops new polishing techniques and processes that are focused on production efficiency improvements and applications in industries outside of semiconductors. Within the ESF division Cabot Micro's QED Technologies subsidiary makes precision polishing and metrology systems used to shape and surface optical components including lenses mirrors and prisms. Its automated polishing systems use magnetic fluids to polish an array of shapes and finishes. Its metrology systems are based on Subaperture Stitching Interferometer (ASI) which measures non-spherical surfaces.

Sales and Marketing

Cabot Micro serves customers that make or provide logic IC (integrated circuit) devices memory IC devices or IC foundry services. Its five largest customers make up nearly half of sales. Its top two customers are TSMC and Samsung which respectively account for 18% and 13% of annual sales.

The company uses a direct sales force to market its products to customers. It also uses independent distributors in some regional markets.

Financial Performance

Cabot Micro remained profitable throughout the global economic downturn and reported rising sales in 2010 and 2011. Revenues fell 4% in 2012 however due to lower sales volumes and pricing issues. Net income also fell 21% to $40.8 million that year due to lower sales volume recapitalization costs and bad debt expenses (related to one customer's bankruptcy filing).

Strategy

Cabot Micro continues to expand globally particularly in Asia where it can be close to its customers. Cabot Micro completed construction of its new manufacturing and research and development facility in South Korea in 2011 allowing it to better serve its memory customers there. The company also expanded plants in Japan and Singapore that year to increase production capacity and improve customer response times.

To improve product performance quality and consistency Cabot also works to streamline processes and reduce product variation levels. Some product improvement efforts are conducted in collaboration with customers and strategic partners. In addition to R&D efforts on core lines of slurries and pads for CMP processes the ESF business develops new polishing techniques and processes for applications in industries outside of semiconductors such as precision optics and electronic substrates. These efforts aim to reduce Cabot Micro's dependence on one product for most of its sales which increases its vulnerability to competition.

Ownership

Investment firm Royce & Associates owns a 13% stake in Cabot Micro.

HISTORY

The business that became Cabot Microelectronics first came into existence as the Microelectronics Materials Division of Cabot Corp. formed in 1995. Cabot Corp. spun off the division as an independent entity through an IPO in 2000. The former parent company remained Cabot Micro's primary supplier of fumed silica a material which goes into making CMP slurries under an agreement running through 2009. Cabot Corp. also supplied fumed alumina to Cabot Micro.

In 2005 Cabot Microelectronics acquired the assets of Surface Finishes Co. a supplier of precision machining techniques that was established in 1949 for about $2.3 million. The company used Surface Finishes' technology as part of its engineered sur-

face finishes initiative meeting the technical challenges of sub-nanometer atomic-scale manufacturing of semiconductors and other advanced components. Like Cabot Microelectronics Surface Finishes was based in a suburb of Chicago.

Cabot Micro acquired the assets of QED Technologies a supplier of polishing and metrology systems for high-precision optics in 2006. The company made the QED product line part of its engineered surface finishes portfolio. Cabot Micro paid $21.5 million in cash for the assets plus it assumed about $2 million in liabilities.

Also in 2006 it acquired patents and associated rights for CMP slurry technology from IBM. The patents covered manufacturing process applications in copper copper barrier tungsten and dielectrics among other uses.

In mid-2006 President George W. Bush toured Cabot Micro's headquarters promoting his American Competitiveness Initiative.

The company raised prices in late 2006 on its Semi-Sperse and Cab-O-Sperse product lines used for interlayer dielectrics and general-purpose oxide polishing applications. It noted that this represented the first price increase on those products since they were introduced some 15 years earlier. The price boost was said to be necessary to maintain the level of service Cabot Micro provides to its customers.

The company acquired Taiwan-based Epoch Material Co. Ltd. in 2009 for about $66 million. Epoch specializes in the development production and sale of copper CMP slurries and CMP cleaning products for the semiconductor industry as well as color filter slurries for the LCD industry. The deal is in line with Cabot's strategy of growing its core CMP business in one of its strongest geographic markets.

EXECUTIVES

VP Corporate Development, Daniel J. (Dan) Pike, age 49, $267,500 total compensation
VP and CFO, William S. (Bill) Johnson, age 56, $337,825 total compensation
VP Secretary and General Counsel, H. Carol Bernstein, age 52, $300,350 total compensation
VP Global Sales, Daniel S. (Dan) Wobby, age 50, $285,000 total compensation
Chairman President and CEO, William P. (Bill) Noglows, age 55, $545,000 total compensation
VP Marketing, Stephen R. (Steve) Smith, age 54, $217,875 total compensation
VP Business Operations, Adam F. Weisman, age 51, $316,650 total compensation
Corporate Controller and Principal Accounting Officer, Thomas S. Roman, age 52
VP Asia Pacific Region, David H. Li, age 40
VP Japan and Asia Operations, Yumiko Damashek, age 57
Director Investor Relations, Amy Ford
Director Human Resources, Lisa Polezoes
VP Research and Development, Ananth Naman
IR Contact Officer, Trisha Tuntland
Director, H. Laurance (Larry) Fuller, age 74
Director, John P. Frazee Jr., age 68
Director, Barbara A. (Barb) Klein, age 58
Director, Edward J. (Ted) Mooney, age 71
Director, Steven V. Wilkinson, age 71
Director, Robert J. Birgeneau, age 70
Director, Bailing Xia, age 57
Independent Director, Richard Hill
Auditors: PricewaterhouseCoopersLLP

LOCATIONS

HQ: Cabot Microelectronics Corporation
870 N. Commons Dr., Aurora IL 60504
Phone: 630-375-6631   **Fax:** 650-321-2800
Web: www.gunder.com

2012 Sales

	$ mil.	% of total
Asia/Pacific	343	80
US	56	13
Europe	27	7
Total	**427**	**100**

PRODUCTS/OPERATIONS

2012 Sales

	$ mil.	% of total
Tungsten slurries	161	38
Dielectric slurries	119	28
Copper slurries	67	16
Polishing pads	33	8
Engineered surface finishes	24	6
Data storage slurries	20	5
Total	**427**	**100**

Selected Products

CMP Polishing Pads
Polished Surface Finishes
Slurries
  Barrier
  Copper
  Data Storage
  Dielectric
  Emerging Applications
  Silicon Carbide Wafer
  Silicon Wafer
  TSV
  Tungsten

COMPETITORS

3M	Fujimi Corp.
ATMI	Hitachi Chemical
Air Products	Praxair
DuPont	Saint-Gobain Abrasives

HISTORICAL FINANCIALS

Company Type: Public

Income Statement
FYE: September 30

	REVENUE ($ mil.)	NET INCOME ($ mil.)	NET PROFIT MARGIN	EMPLOYEES
09/13	433.1	51.3	11.9%	1,053
09/12	427.6	40.8	9.5%	1,042
09/11	445.4	51.6	11.6%	1,025
09/10	408.2	49.4	12.1%	933
09/09	291.3	11.1	3.8%	882
Annual Growth	**10.4%**	**46.4%**	**—**	**4.5%**

2013 Year-End Financials

Debt ratio: 29.1%	No. of shares (mil.): 23
Return on equity: 16.8%	Dividends
Cash ($ mil.): 226	Yield: —
Current ratio: 5.42	Payout: —
Long-term debt ($ mil.): 150	Market value ($ mil.): 899

	STOCK PRICE ($) FY Close	P/E High/Low		PER SHARE ($) Earnings	Dividends	Book Value
09/13	38.51	18	13	2.14	0.00	14.01
09/12	35.14	29	16	1.75	15.00	12.23
09/11	34.39	23	14	2.20	0.00	24.69
09/10	32.18	20	14	2.13	0.00	22.42
09/09	34.86	75	40	0.48	0.00	20.08
Annual Growth	**2.5%**	**—**	**—**	**45.3%**	**—**	**(8.6%)**

CAI International Inc

Is it bigger than a breadbox? CAI International can pack it. The company leases large steel boxes to ship freight by plane train or truck around the world. More than 65% of its container fleet is owned by CAI and the balance owned by container investors is managed by CAI. The leasing segment offers 280-plus shipping companies short-term and long-term leases with some leases giving the lessees the option to purchase the container. The container management segment provides container investors with the ability to lease re-lease and dispose of their container portfolio; services also include container repair relocation and storage.

Geographic Reach

CAI caters to 280 customers from 16 offices spanning 12 countries. CAI purchases the majority of its containers in China and operates from offices in Belgium Hong Kong Japan Korea Singapore Taiwan the UK and the US among others.

Operations

CAI has two reportable business segments: equipment leasing (92% of sales) and container management (8%). The equipment leasing segment generates revenue from the ownership and leasing of containers to container shipping lines and freight forwarders.

The container management segment draws revenue from management fees earned from portfolios of containers and associated leases which are managed on behalf of container investors. In addition CAI derives revenue from the sale of containers to container investors who in turn enter into management agreements with the company.

Sales and Marketing

The top ten largest lessees accounted for about 60% of its total leasing segment sales (approximately 55% of total sales). Its largest customer CMA CGM accounted for 12% of sales.

Financial Performance

CAI has enjoyed three straight years of unprecedented growth. Revenues climbed 38% from $126 million in 2011 to reach a historic high of $174 million in 2012. Profits also surged 26% from $50 million in 2011 to $63 million 2012 another record high.

The growth was driven by a 45% spike in equipment leasing sales due to an increase in the average number of owned containers on lease. The company was also helped by a 100% surge in finance lease sales. This growth was offset by a 13% decrease in container management sales.

Ownership

Founder Hiromitsu Ogawa owns about 22% of the company while Columbia Wanger Asset Management owns 12%

Company Background

Founded by Hiromitsu Ogawa in 1989 CAI has evolved from solely an intermodal leasing concern to a more ambitious manager of containers owned by investors.

EXECUTIVES

President Chief Executive Officer, Victor M. Garcia, age 45, $323,833 total compensation
VP Operations, Camille G. Cutino, age 54, $164,800 total compensation
Chief Financial Officer, Timothy Page
Senior Vice President Global Marketing, Daniel Hallahan
Vice President Finance and Corporate Controller, David Morris

Vice President Information Technology, Matthew Easton
Director, William W. Liebeck, age 57
President CEO and Director, Victor M. Garcia, age 45
Director, Marvin Dennis, age 75
Auditors: KPMGLLP

LOCATIONS

HQ: CAI International Inc.
1 Market Plaza Ste. 900, San Francisco CA 94105
Phone: 415-788-0100   **Fax:** 415-788-3430
Web: www.capps.com

PRODUCTS/OPERATIONS

2012 Sales

	$ mil.	% of total
Equipment leasing	160	92
Total	**173**	**100**

2012 Sales

	%
Rental revenue	88
Finance lease income	4
Gain on sale of container portfolios	1
Total	**100**

Selected Operations

Container leasing
  Container owned by CAI
  Full benefits of ownership
  Placed on long- and short-term leases to shipping lines
Container management
  Container sold to investors
  Generate cash flow through management fee revenue and trading income
  Managed by CAI over expected life of asset

COMPETITORS

COSCO Group	Seaco
SeaCube Container	Touax
Seacastle	XTRA Corp.

HISTORICAL FINANCIALS

Company Type: Public

Income Statement

FYE: December 31

	REVENUE ($ mil.)	NET INCOME ($ mil.)	NET PROFIT MARGIN	EMPLOYEES
12/12	173.9	63.4	36.5%	91
12/11	125.7	50.1	39.9%	83
12/10	77.9	28.3	36.4%	89
12/09	65.2	13.5	20.8%	83
12/08	83.1	(26.9)	—	89
Annual Growth	**20.3%**	**—**	**—**	**0.6%**

2012 Year-End Financials

Debt ratio: 68.9%
Return on equity: 21.9%
Cash ($ mil.): 17
Current ratio: 0.89
Long-term debt ($ mil.): 894
No. of shares (mil.): 22
Dividends
  Yield: —
  Payout: —
Market value ($ mil.): 484

	STOCK PRICE ($) FY Close	P/E High/Low		PER SHARE ($) Earnings	Dividends	Book Value
12/12	21.95	7	5	3.18	0.00	15.73
12/11	15.46	10	4	2.55	0.00	11.92
12/10	19.60	13	5	1.56	0.00	9.31
12/09	9.03	12	3	0.76	0.00	7.21
12/08	3.17	—	—	(1.55)	0.00	6.35
Annual Growth	**62.2%**	**—**	**—**	**—**	**—**	**25.5%**

Cal-Maine Foods, Inc.

Cal-Maine Foods' more than 26 million laying hens are some of its top performers. The nation's largest shell egg producer and marketer the company sells more than 880 million dozen eggs a year. It is also one of the top suppliers of specialty shell eggs (which are Omega-3 enhanced organic and cage free) that are marketed under the Egg-Land's Best Farmhouse and 4Grain brands. Cal-Maine's operations span all phases of shell egg production: hatching chicks making feed housing hens and distributing eggs. Customers include US grocery stores (such as Publix) superstores the likes of Wal-Mart and warehouse clubs (Sam's Club) as well as foodservice distributors and makers of egg products dotting 29 states.

Geographic Reach

The company's operations extend nationwide across nearly 30 states.

Mergers and Acquisitions

Cal-Maine continues to grow its share of the shell-egg market through acquisitions of existing production and processing operations. It has made nearly 20 acquisitions since 1989. Each added between 600000 to 7.5 million laying hens (called layers) and related facilities as well as expanded the company's portfolio of name brands. Such investments and acquisitions have boosted Cal-Maine's flock of layers pullets and breeders. The flock is likely the largest in the US.

The company acquired certain egg operations from Pilgrim's Pride in 2012. Cal-Maine gained two production facilities in Texas with capacity for some 1.4 million laying hens and stepped up its presence in the Southwest market as a result. Adding to its Texas holdings Cal-Maine in late 2012 acquired Maxim Production Co. The purchases complement its 2009 acquisition of Florida's Tampa Farms' 4Grain brand of specialty shell eggs.

Strategy

Cal-Maine also looks to shore up operations through construction of new more efficient egg production and processing plants paired with a pullet growing facility. It also regularly disposes of older less efficient facilities.

On several separate occasions the company was hit by a nationwide food recall. The 2011 and 2010 recalls were attributable to possible salmonella contamination from eggs produced by Hillandale Farms of Iowa as well as from other outside contractors. In addition Cal-Maine is under pressure from animal welfare advocates who argue for better treatment of its flock of hens including larger cages fewer beak trimmings and decreased forced molting practices (which put chickens under stress to lay more eggs). The Humane Society of the United States and the United Egg Producers agreed in 2011 to press toward new federal legislation which if passed will increase the production costs of housing and feeding hens.

Financial Performance

Net sales rose 18% in fiscal 2012 as compared to 2011 due in part to an 8% increase in total dozens of eggs sold and a boost in the average selling price of shell eggs. Cal-Maine's 48% increase in net income during the same reporting period is primarily attributable to the increase in net sales partially offset by the increase in cost of sales. Contributing to the cost of sales bump were the increase in dozens produced dozens purchased from outside shell egg producers and cost of feed ingredients.

Sales and Marketing

Cal-Maine markets its shell eggs through a distribution network serving a diverse group of customers. It caters to national and regional grocery store chains club stores foodservice distributors and egg product makers. Together Wal-Mart and Sam's Club account for 31% of sales and Publix Super Markets generates 10%.

The company's advertising costs totaled $4245 $5768 and $2098 in fiscal 2012 2011 and 2010 respectively.

Company Ownership

Cal-Maine also faces significant control by a small party. Founder and chairman emeritus Fred Adams Jr. owns about 53% of the company's voting power. The son-in-law of Adams Adolphus "Dolph" Baker is president and CEO and holds a 14% stake.

HISTORY

One can side with the chicken or the egg in the which-came-first argument but it was Fred Adams Jr. who came first at Cal-Maine. A former salesman with pet food giant Ralston Purina (now Nestle Purina PetCare) Adams founded a poultry and egg business in Mendenhall Mississippi in 1957. He focused exclusively on egg sales in 1960 and merged his company in 1969 with Maine Egg Farms and Dairy Fresh Foods in California to form Cal-Maine Foods.

Cal-Maine cracked new markets through internal growth and the acquisition of rival egg firms. The company acquired Egg City (Arkansas 1989) Sunny Fresh Foods (Arkansas 1990) Sunnyside Eggs (North Carolina 1991) Wayne Detling Farms (Ohio 1994) A&G Farms (Kentucky 1995) and Sunbest Farms (Arkansas 1996). After going public in 1996 Cal-Maine bought two Georgia firms: Southern Empire Egg Farm (1997) and J&S Farms (1998).

In 1998 the company sold off its egg products division which provided food makers with egg whites and yolks and accounted for 4% of total sales.

In 1999 Cal-Maine bought two egg producers and processors: Kentucky-based Hudson Brothers and Texas-based Smith Farms. Declining supplies in the cyclical egg market and increasing demand in late 2000 raised the company out of the loss column for the first time in 18 months. In late 2001 Cal-Maine's board of directors voted to explore the possibility of the company becoming privately held but abandoned the idea because of a sagging egg market. Industry-wide overproduction helped to drive down egg prices pecking away at the company's profits in 2002.

In 2003 Cal-Maine's board of directors voted to take the company private. However as demand for eggs shot up so did Cal-Maine stock prices and shareholders were unconvinced such a move would benefit them. Faced with shareholder lawsuits in November of that year the board voted to terminate the proposal to take the company private.

After years of oversupply and weak prices starting in 2003 the entire egg industry enjoyed a boost from the popular protein-heavy Atkins diet. Cal-Maine's sales jumped as people chose hard-boiled eggs as snacks. However by 2004 its popularity had peaked leaving the market (and Cal-Maine) with an egg glut and plunging sales. In 2005 the company acquired egg supplier Hillandale Farms. In 2006 the company formed a 50-50 joint venture (Green Forest Foods) with Pier 44 Properties to lease and operate Green Forest Egg's production assets which included about 1 million laying

hens at facilities located in Arkansas. Cal-Maine's bought of Pier 44's interest in Green Forest in 2007 and purchased the shell-egg division of George's Inc. for which it paid $11 million in cash.

Fred Adams Jr. founder and chairman handed over the title of CEO to former COO Dolph Baker in late 2010.

EXECUTIVES

Vice President Chief Financial Officer Treasurer Secretary and Director, Timothy A. Dawson, age 59, $179,346 total compensation

Chairman of the Board; President; Chief Executive Officer, Adolphus B. (Dolph) Baker, age 56, $243,461 total compensation

Vice President; Controller, Charles F. Collins, age 69, $102,769 total compensation

Vice President - Feed Mill Division, Joe M. Wyatt, age 74, $126,535 total compensation

Chairman, Fred R. Adams Jr., age 81, $250,000 total compensation

Vice President Operations-Production, Jack B. Self, age 85, $109,155 total compensation

VP Sales, Charles J. (Jeff) Hardin, $85,751 total compensation

VP Operations, David Jenkins

Vice President Operations, Bob L. (Bobby) Scott, $118,619 total compensation

VP Operations, Steve Storm

VP Sales, Kyle Morris

Chief Operating Officer; Director, Sherman Miller

Vice President Egg Sales, Matthew Arrowsmith

VP Egg Products, James Hull

Vice President Operations, Marc Ashby

Vice President General Counsel, Rob Holladay

Vice President Operations, Todd Waters

VP Operations, Christopher Myers

Vice President Operations, Kevin Lastowski

Vice President; General Counsel, Robert Holladay

Vice President Sales, Jeff Hardin

Vice President Egg Products, Jim Hull

Vice President Chief Financial Officer Treasurer Secretary and Director, Timothy A. Dawson, age 59

President CEO and Director, Adolphus B. (Dolph) Baker, age 55

Vice Chairman, Richard K. Looper, age 85

Director, Letitia C. (Tish) Hughes, age 61

Director, James E. (Jim) Poole, age 64

Auditors: Ernst&YoungLLP

LOCATIONS

HQ: Cal-Maine Foods Inc.
3320 Woodrow Wilson Ave., Jackson MS 39209
Phone: 601-948-6813 **Fax:** 601-969-0905
Web: www.calmainefoods.com

PRODUCTS/OPERATIONS

2012 Sales

	% of total
Shell eggs	
Non-specialty shell	73
Specialty shell	23
Other shell —	
Egg	3
Incidental feed & feed	1
Total	

Selected Brands

4Grain
Cal-Maine
Egg-Land's Best (licensed from Egg-Land's Best Inc.)
Farmhouse
Rio Grande
Sunny Meadow
Sunups

COMPETITORS

Cargill Kitchen Solutions	Ise America
	Luberski
Chino Valley Ranchers	Michael Foods
ConAgra	Moark
Cooper Farms	National Food
Egg Innovations	Rose Acre Farms
Hickman's Family Farms	Wilson Farms

HISTORICAL FINANCIALS

Company Type: Public

Income Statement

FYE: June 1

	REVENUE ($ mil.)	NET INCOME ($ mil.)	NET PROFIT MARGIN	EMPLOYEES
06/13	1,288.1	50.4	3.9%	2,479
06/12*	1,113.1	89.7	8.1%	2,175
05/11	941.9	60.8	6.5%	2,100
05/10	910.1	67.8	7.5%	1,950
05/09	928.8	79.5	8.6%	2,100
Annual Growth	8.5%	(10.8%)	—	4.2%

*Fiscal year change

2013 Year-End Financials

Debt ratio: 8.7%
Return on equity: 10.1%
Cash ($ mil.): 24
Current ratio: 3.19
Long-term debt ($ mil.): 54

No. of shares (mil.): 24
Dividends
Yield: 0.0%
Payout: 60.6%
Market value ($ mil.): 1,078

	STOCK PRICE ($) FY Close	P/E High/Low		PER SHARE ($) Earnings	Dividends	Book Value
06/13	44.74	22	17	2.10	1.27	21.48
06/12*	34.84	11	7	3.75	0.84	20.03
05/11	28.93	13	10	2.54	1.04	17.55
05/10	32.37	13	8	2.84	0.80	15.85
05/09	24.37	14	5	3.34	1.49	13.96
Annual Growth	16.4%		—	— (11.0%)	(3.8%)	11.4%

*Fiscal year change

CalAmp Corp

CalAmp adds a little boost even to the weakest of TV programs. The former military supplier makes microwave amplification and conversion components that improve reception in satellite television wireless cable and wireless broadband access systems. Its products include antennas amplifiers and transceivers and receivers for broadband wireless transmission. CalAmp's wireless datacom segment provides wireless network and mobile resource management products for state and local governments and industrial utility and transportation companies. The company's largest customer EchoStar accounted for 31% of consolidated annual sales in 2011.

Revenue for the company satellite segment (more than 31% of revenue) was down 34% in fiscal 2011 compared with 2010 while revenue in the wireless datacom segment (accounting for 69% of revenue) was up 37% over the same period. The company believes that an order from EchoStar will bring an increase to satellite revenue in fiscal 2012.

Faced with tough competition and pricing issues CalAmp lost DIRECTV as a customer in 2010 and 2011 after relying on it for more than 10% of revenue in 2009.

CalAmp is tapping into a market that includes more than 250 million registered vehicles with a new product that provides monitoring and messaging services for the auto insurance industry. The LMU-3000 includes GPS for tracking vehicles and even a sensor that detects dangerously aggressive driving behaviors and accidents.

Looking to expand into new market verticals the company in early 2013 purchased Virginia-based Wireless Matrix which provides resource management software for the remote tracking and monitoring of vehicle fleets.

HISTORY

DISH Network substantially reduced its business with CalAmp during fiscal 2007 and fiscal 2008 due to a product quality problem that CalAmp blamed on its supplier of laminate material for printed circuit boards. DISH returned more than 1.2 million units to CalAmp for analysis and rework; it cut off all orders to the company in 2007 until CalAmp's products could be requalified for its use. Later that year CalAmp reached a settlement with DISH; the terms included issuing a $5 million note to the customer a $1 million credit against outstanding receivables 1 million shares of CalAmp's common stock and a warrant to purchase 350000 additional shares of common stock over three years. The company resumed shipments to DISH Network in 2008.

EXECUTIVES

Chairman, Frank Perna Jr., age 75
EVP CFO and Secretary, Richard K. (Rick) Vitelle, age 59, $280,000 total compensation
Vice Chairman, Richard B. (Rick) Gold, age 58, $385,134 total compensation
President and CEO, Michael J. Burdiek, age 53, $280,000 total compensation
Vice President - Corporate Development, Garo Sarkissian, age 46, $210,000 total compensation
VP Operations, Neil Friedlander
Vice President investor relations, Gail Gerono
Vice President Global Procurement & Strategic Initiatives, James C. Coccagno
Senior Vice President General Counsel Secretary, Richard D. Rose
Director, Larry J. Wolfe, age 62
Director, Thomas E. Pardun, age 69
Vice Chairman, Richard B. (Rick) Gold, age 58
President CEO and Director, Michael J. Burdiek, age 53
Director, Albert J. (Bert) Moyer, age 69
Director, Kimberly E. Alexy, age 43
Auditors: SingerLewakLLP

LOCATIONS

HQ: CalAmp Corp.
1401 N. Rice Ave., Oxnard CA 93030
Phone: 805-987-9000   **Fax:** 805-856-3869
Web: www.calamp.com

PRODUCTS/OPERATIONS

2010 Sales

	$ mil.	% of total
Wireless DataCom	78	69
Satellite	35	31
Total	114	100

Selected Products

Satellite components
  Amplifiers
  Downconverters
  Feedhorns

Wireless access equipment
  Antennas
  Broadband analog scrambling/decoding systems
    (MultiCipher)
  Transceivers (passive planar stand-alone)

COMPETITORS

AML Communications
Broadcast Microwave
  Services
COM DEV
Cohu
Enfora
Filtronic
Kratos Defense &
  Security Solutions
Motorola Solutions
Powerwave Technologies
STC Microwave Systems
Sharp Corp.
Sierra Wireless
WebTech
Wistron NeWeb

HISTORICAL FINANCIALS

Company Type: Public

Income Statement

FYE: February 28

	REVENUE ($ mil.)	NET INCOME ($ mil.)	NET PROFIT MARGIN	EMPLOYEES
02/13	180.5	44.6	24.7%	380
02/12	138.7	5.2	3.8%	370
02/11	114.3	(3.2)	—	440
02/10	112.1	(10.8)	—	510
02/09	98.3	(49.6)	—	553
Annual Growth	**16.4%**	**—**	**(9.0%)**	

2013 Year-End Financials

Debt ratio: 3.1%
Return on equity: 62.4%
Cash ($ mil.): 63
Current ratio: 3.69
Long-term debt ($ mil.): 2
No. of shares (mil.): 35
Dividends
  Yield: —
  Payout: —
Market value ($ mil.): 384

	STOCK PRICE ($) FY Close	P/E High/Low		Earnings	PER SHARE ($) Dividends	Book Value
02/13	10.95	7	3	1.49	0.00	3.35
02/12	4.30	27	14	0.19	0.00	0.87
02/11	3.05	—	—	(0.12)	0.00	0.63
02/10	2.81	—	—	(0.43)	0.00	0.69
02/09	0.50	—	—	(2.01)	0.00	0.92
Annual Growth	**116.3%**	—	—	—	—	**38.2%**

Calavo Growers, Inc.

The avocado growers of Calavo Growers might not be a cooperative anymore but they're still friendly folks. Calavo (a combination of "California" and "avocado") began as a growers' marketing cooperative founded in 1924 in order to transform the exotic hobby crop avocados into a culinary staple. And the avocado has become if not a staple a regular in US supermarket shopping carts. Calavo procures and processes avocados papaya pineapple tomatoes and other fresh fruits grown mainly in California but the company also uses fruit from Chile Peru and Mexico. The products are then distributed to retail food outlets food service operators and produce wholesalers throughout the world.

Cavado has two packing houses in California and one in Michoacan Mexico that pack approximately 200 million pounds of fruit per year. (The company also has additional facilities in Califorina

Arizona New Jersey Texas and Mexico.) Some 2000 growers deliver their crops to Calavo for processing. In addition to whole avocados the company manufactures avocado pulp and frozen peeled avocado halves through its Fresh business unit. Meanwhile its Calavo Foods business unit sells guacamole and the Salsa Lisa line of fresh salsas hummus and tortilla chips.

In 2011 Calavo reported a dip in net income earning about $11 million that year versus nearly $18 million in 2010. The decrease in earnings was due to a smaller supply of fresh avocados in the marketplace. In addition the company was negatively impacted by a freeze that limited availability of fresh tomatoes as well as higher Mexican fruit costs at its Calavo Foods business segment.

Calavo Foods represents the company's move beyond fresh avocados and commodity produce into the market for fresh refrigerated packaged foods. It has expanded such holdings through acquisitions. In 2011 it acquired Renaissance Food Group (RFG) of Rancho Cordova California. With six processing plants nationwide RFG's Garden Highway brand supplies fresh-cut fruit ready-to-eat vegetables and grab-and-go salads snacks and sandwiches to retailers deli departments and food service operators. Following completion of the deal RFG became a wholly-owned subsidiary of Calavo Foods. Previous related acquisitions include Minnesota-based Lisa Salsa in 2010 and papaya businesses Hawaiian Sweet and Hawaii Pride in 2008.

EXECUTIVES

Chairman of the Board; President; Chief Executive Officer, Lecil E. (Lee) Cole, age 74, $480,433 total compensation
Vice President - Sales and Fresh Marketing, Robert J. (Rob) Wedin, age 64, $213,497 total compensation
Vice President - Processed Product Sales and Production, Alan C. (Al) Ahmer, age 64, $213,497 total compensation
Chief Financial Officer; Chief Operating Officer; Corporate Secretary, Arthur J. (Art) Bruno, age 63, $266,486 total compensation
Director Operations Calavo de Mexico, Dionisio Ortiz
Vice President - Fresh Operations, Michael A. (Mike) Browne, age 55, $213,497 total compensation
Corporate Marketing Manager, Bibiana Bravo
Los Angeles Produce Sales, Paul Stanke
Manager Sales Nogales AZ, Javier Badillo
Manager Southwest Regional Sales, Dan Kennemur
Northwest Area Sales Manager, Russ Mikolasy
Corporate Controller, James Snyder
Account Executive Fresh Sales, Mark Nolan
Area Sales Manager Fresh Sales, Peter Shore
Areas Sales Manager Fresh Sales, Gordon Breschini
Fresh Sales Representative Fresh Sales, Jaime Padilla
Sales Assistant Fresh Sales, Nick Garcia
Account Executive Santa Paula CA, Liz Inglese
Organic Sales Manager Santa Paula CA, Sandy Eason
Sales Representative Santa Paula CA, Kyla Maxfield
Sales Assistant Santa Paula CA, Angela Tallant
Northeast Area Sales Manager Foodservice and Retail Processed Sales, Rick Joyle
International Sales Manager, Steve Hayworth
National ProRipe Sales Manager, Juan Betancourt
Area Sales Manager Chicago, Fred Annerino
Area Sales Manager Chicago IL, Mark Steffen
Area Sales Manager New Jersey NJ, Peter Szal
Sales Assistant New Jersey NJ, Irene Popyk
Area Sales Manager Southeast, Wayne Beck

Area Sales Manager Midwest and Canada, Mark Schweihs
Director, Egidio Carbone Jr., age 72
Director, George H. Barnes, age 80
Director, Alva V. Snider, age 96
Director, Scott Van Der Kar, age 58
Director, J. Link Leavens, age 61
Director, John M. Hunt, age 56
Director, Harold S. Edwards
Director, Michael D. Hause, age 58
Director, Donald M. Sanders, age 65
Director, Steve W. Hollister, age 55
Director, Marc L. Brown
Independent Director, James Helin
Auditors: Ernst&YoungLLP

LOCATIONS

HQ: Calavo Growers Inc.
1141-A Cummings Rd., Santa Paula CA 93060
Phone: 805-525-1245   **Fax:** 949-789-9300
Web: www.mbk.com

Selected Locations

Mexico
    Uruapan Michoacan packinghouse and processing
        plant
US
    Arizona
        Nogales (Maui Fresh International) packer shipper
            broker and distributor
    California
        Santa Paula corporate headquarters packing house and
            value-added depot
        Temecula packinghouse
    New Jersey
        Swedesboro value-added depot
    Texas
        Garland value-added depot

PRODUCTS/OPERATIONS

2011 Sales

	$ mil.	% of total
Fresh products	420	80
Calavo Foods	101	20
Total	**522**	**100**

Selected Products

Fresh
    Whole avocado
    Avocado halves
    Avocado pulp
    Papaya
    Pineapple
    Tomato
Calavo Foods
    Guacamole
    Salsa Lisa
    Tortilla chips

Selected Services

Growing
Ripening
Packing
Sales
Warehousing
Shipping & distribution

COMPETITORS

Azteca Foods	Gentile Bros.
BC Hot House Foods	Giumarra Companies
Brooks Tropicals	Goya
Caribe Food	Gruma Corporation
Chiquita Brands	Grupo Bimbo
Coast Citrus	H. J. Heinz Limited
Distributors	Hain Celestial
ConAgra	Index Fresh
Dole Food	Interfresh
Don Miguel Mexican	JR Simplot
Foods	La Tortilla Factory

Eastern Fresh Growers Inc.	Oceanside Produce
	Pacific Tomato Growers
Eurofresh	Pinos Produce
Fresh Del Monte Produce	Rancho Mission Viejo
	Shamrock Foods
FreshPoint	

HISTORICAL FINANCIALS

Company Type: Public

Income Statement

FYE: October 31

	REVENUE ($ mil.)	NET INCOME ($ mil.)	NET PROFIT MARGIN	EMPLOYEES
10/13	691.4	17.3	2.5%	1,848
10/12	551.1	17.0	3.1%	1,531
10/11	522.5	11.0	2.1%	1,509
10/10	398.3	17.7	4.5%	1,157
10/09	344.7	7.7	2.2%	1,049
Annual Growth	**19.0%**	**22.4%**	**—**	**15.2%**

2013 Year-End Financials

Debt ratio: 19.6%   No. of shares (mil.): 15
Return on equity: 14.5%   Dividends
Cash ($ mil.): 8   Yield: 2.1%
Current ratio: 1.13   Payout: 55.5%
Long-term debt ($ mil.): 7   Market value ($ mil.): 467

	STOCK PRICE ($) FY Close	P/E High/Low		PER SHARE ($) Earnings	Dividends	Book Value
10/13	29.69	28	19	1.17	0.65	8.17
10/12	23.61	26	19	1.15	0.55	7.42
10/11	22.57	32	24	0.75	0.55	6.48
10/10	21.90	18	13	1.22	0.50	6.00
10/09	17.85	22	7	0.94	0.35	4.79
Annual Growth	**13.6%**	**—**	**—**	**5.6%**	**16.7%**	**14.3%**

Calgon Carbon Corp.

Calgon wants impurities in water and air to be gone. Calgon Carbon makes activated carbons and purification systems and offers purification separation and concentration services to industrial process and environmental markets. It is a global leader in activated carbon ballast water treatment ultraviolet light disinfection and advanced ion-exchange technologies used in the treatment of drinking water wastewater ballast water air emissions and manufacturing processes. Calgon Carbon offers carbon technologies used in more than 700 discrete market applications including air drinking water foods and pharmaceuticals purification and the removal of mercury emissions from coal-powered electrical plants.

Geographic Reach

Calgon Carbon operates in a geographically diverse array of markets. It operates 13 production plants (in Belgium China the UK and the US). It also has 49 warehouses service centers and sales office facilities. Of these 28 are located in the US five in each China and Japan two in Canada and one each in Brazil France Denmark Germany Hong Kong Singapore Sweden Taiwan and the UK. More than half of the company's sales come from outside the US.

Operations

It operates through three segments: Activated Carbon and Service Equipment and Consumer. Its Activated Carbon and Service unit makes granu-

lar and powdered activated carbon to remove organic compounds from water air and gases. The Equipment unit designs and installs carbon adsorption systems for use at treatment sites including equipment to control odors at waste treatment plants. Its Consumer unit makes Zorflex carbon cloth sold to medical military and specialty markets.

Financial Performance

Calgon Carbon's revenues increased by 4% in 2012 due to 43% jump in Equipment revenues driven by ultraviolet light systems principally ballast water treatment which rose by 71%. Consumer revenues went up by 20% thanks to higher demand for activated carbon cloths. The increases were partially offset by 0.15% decrease in the Activated Carbon and Service sales due to the negative impact of foreign currency translation. The company posted a net income of $23.2 million in 2012 (41% down on 2011) due to higher interest expenses and restructuring charges.

Strategy

Calgon Carbon's strategy is to maintain its global coverage while developing or acquiring products and services that complement its existing portfolio. It is also relying on its superior products and services to outpace rising competition from lower cost activated carbon products from Chinese manufacturers.

In 2013 subsidiary Hyde Marine signed a deal with Cammell Laird the largest shipyard in the UK to install chemical-free Hyde GUARDIAN Ballast Water Treatment System at the yard. Cammell Laird had previously been tapped by the UK government to install Hyde GUARDIAN systems onto five naval vessels.

In 2011 the company had a contract to supply 2.9 million pounds of granular activated carbon (GAC) to a municipal water treatment facility in Wuxi City in China's Jiangsu Provice. It also had a GAC contract for sugar purification in India. In Latin America the company forged an alliance with an activated carbon reactivator in Mexico and planned to found a subsidiary in Brazil. In Europe the company is increasing capacity at its facility in Feluy Belgium which it bills as the world's largest reactivation plant. Calgon Carbon also has a leased reactivation plant in New York as well as reactivation facilities in California and Ohio.

All of the company's activated carbon manufacturing plants are in the US except for a facility in Datong China and all are operating at full capacity. The company expects demand for activated carbon to increase by approximately 40% or 1 billion pounds by 2017.

Ownership

In 2012 Shapiro Capital Management owned 13% of Calgon Carbon.

Company Background

In 2010 the company acquired Hyde Marine a maker of ultraviolet light technology systems for eliminating harmful organisms in marine ballast water. The company also completed its acquisitions of Zwicky Denmark and Sweden which distributed its carbon and service products in northern Europe. In a move to consolidate its market position that year Calgon Carbon increased its ownership of joint venture Calgon Carbon Japan from partner Mitsubishi Chemical to an 80% share to take control of the operation. It acquired the rest of the venture in 2011 taking full ownership.

EXECUTIVES

Chief Operating Officer; Executive Vice President, Robert P. (Bob) O'Brien, age 63, $255,856 total compensation

Chairman, Seth E. Schofield, age 73
SVP and CFO, Stevan R. Schott, age 50
Vice President - Investor Relations and
Communications, Gail A. Gerono, age 62
President CEO and Director, Randall S. (Randy)
Dearth, age 50
Vice President - Asia, Allan Singleton
Senior Vice President - Americas, James A. (Jim)
Sullivan, age 48, $184,782 total compensation
SVP General Counsel and Secretary, Richard D.
(Rick) Rose, age 51
Vice President - Europe, Reinier Keijzer
Executive Vice President, Brent Smith
Executive Vice President Chief Operating Officer,
Robert OBrien
Vice President Secretary General Counsel, Richard
D. Rick
Director, Timothy G. Rupert, age 66
Director, William R. (Bill) Newlin, age 72
Director, William J. Lyons, age 64
Director, Robert W. Cruickshank, age 68
Director, Julie S. Roberts, age 58
Director, J. Rich Alexander, age 57
President CEO and Director, Randall S. (Randy)
Dearth, age 50
Auditors: Deloitte&ToucheLLP

LOCATIONS

HQ: Calgon Carbon Corporation
400 Calgon Carbon Dr., Pittsburgh PA 15205
Phone: 412-787-6700   Fax: 412-787-6676
Web: www.calgoncarbon.com

2012 Sales

US	261	45
UK	38	7
Korea	20	4
Canada	17	3
Other countries	102	18

PRODUCTS/OPERATIONS

2012 Sales

Activated Carbon & Service	485	86
Consumer	10	2

COMPETITORS

3M Purification	Norit
ITT Water &	Siemens Water
Wastewater Herford	Technologies
MeadWestvaco	Trojan Technologies
Met-Pro	

HISTORICAL FINANCIALS

Company Type: Public

Income Statement — FYE: December 31

	REVENUE ($ mil.)	NET INCOME ($ mil.)	NET PROFIT MARGIN	EMPLOYEES
12/12	562.2	23.2	4.1%	1,231
12/11	541.4	39.2	7.2%	1,145
12/10	482.3	34.8	7.2%	1,070
12/09	411.9	39.1	9.5%	953
12/08	400.2	38.3	9.6%	943
Annual Growth	8.9%	(11.7%)	—	6.9%

2012 Year-End Financials

Debt ratio: 11.0%
Return on equity: 6.3%
Cash ($ mil.): 18
Current ratio: 2.36
Long-term debt ($ mil.): 44

No. of shares (mil.): 50
Dividends
  Yield: —
  Payout: —
Market value ($ mil.): 710

	STOCK PRICE ($) FY Close	P/E High/Low		PER SHARE ($) Earnings	Dividends	Book Value
12/12	14.18	41	29	0.41	0.00	7.02
12/11	15.71	25	19	0.69	0.00	6.70
12/10	15.12	29	19	0.61	0.00	6.13
12/09	13.90	26	15	0.69	0.00	5.53
12/08	15.36	26	12	0.72	0.00	4.68
Annual Growth	(2.0%)	—	—	(13.1%)	—	10.7%

California Water Service Group (DE)

A big fish in California's water industry pond California Water Service Group is in the swim in three other states as well. The company's main subsidiary regulated utility California Water Service Company (Cal Water) keeps water flowing for 473100 customers in California. California Water Service Group's other water utility subsidiaries include Washington Water (15800 customers) New Mexico Water (7600 water and wastewater customers) and Hawaii Water (4200 customers). The company's CWS Utility Services unit contracts to provide water system operation meter reading and billing services. All told California Water Service Group provides services to about 2 million people in 100 communities.

Geographic Reach
The company has operations in California Hawaii New Mexico and Washington.

Operations
Holding company California Water Service has six operating subsidiaries: California Water Service (Cal Water) New Mexico Water Service Washington Water Service Hawaii Water Service CWS Utility Services and HWS Utility Services. About 95% of the multistate water utility's operations are regulated by state utilities commissions. In 2012 Cal Water owned 629 wells and operates 4 leased wells Hawaii Water owned 20 wells and managed 5 irrigation wells Washington Water owned 341 wells and managed 113 wells and New Mexico Water owned 17 wells.

Financial Performance
California Water Service's revenues increased by 12% in 2012 primarily due to hotter and drier weather which caused increased usage by existing customers. In 2012 residential customers accounted for 68% of sales; business customers 18%. Revenues have grown year-by-year since 2008 thanks to a growth in the number of customers and rate increases.

Net income increased by 29% in 2012 thanks to higher revenues and decreased costs for repairs of mains services meters hydrants and other structures. In addition income tax expense dropped due to lower financing costs on the company's short-term lines of credit.

Strategy
The company has pursued a growth strategy of geographic expansion through organic growth and the acquisition of water and wastewater systems.

California Water Service is exploring opportunities to expand regulated and non-regulated water and wastewater businesses in the western US. Options include buying water systems setting up lease

arrangements similar to the City of Hawthorne and City of Commerce contracts full service system operation and maintenance agreements billing contracts meter reading and other utility-related services.

Company Background
Since 1999 California Water Service Group has established businesses in three new states (Washington New Mexico and Hawaii). Beefing up its Hawaiian operations (which were established in 2003) in 2007 Hawaii Water formed HWS Utility Services LLC which then began non-regulated operations in 2008. Later that year it acquired Waikoloa Resort Utilities Waikoloa Water Company and Waikoloa Sanitary Sewer Company boosting its regulated customer count in Hawaii from 1500 to more than 3700.

EXECUTIVES

Vice President Engineering and Water Quality,
Robert R. Guzzetta, age 55, $261,363 total
compensation
VP and Chief Administrative Officer, Christine L.
McFarlane, age 66
Controller Assistant Secretary and Assistant
Treasurer, Calvin L. Breed, age 56
VP Corporate Development, Francis S. Ferraro, age
60, $314,246 total compensation
Chairman and CEO, Peter C. Nelson, age 64,
$732,760 total compensation
President and Chief Executive Officer, Martin A.
(Marty) Kropelnicki, age 47, $313,862 total
compensation
President Washington Water Service Company,
Michael P. Ireland, age 59
Director Corporate Communications, Shannon C.
Dean
VP of Regulatory Matters and Corporate
Relations, Paul G. Townsley
VP Engineering and Water Quality, Michael J. Rossi,
age 59
Corporate Secretary, Lynne P. McGhee, age 48
VP CFO and Treasurer, Thomas F. Smegal III, age
46
VP Human Resources, Helen Del Grosso
VP Customer Service and Information
Technology, David Karraker
Principal Accounting Officer; Corporate
Controller, David B. Healey
Vice President Human Resources, Helen Grosso
VP Operations, Tim D Treloar
VP Customer Service and Information
Technology, Michael B Luu
Director, George A. Vera, age 67
Director, Edwin A. Guiles, age 61
Director, Linda R. Meier, age 70
Director, Richard P. Magnuson, age 55
Director, Douglas M. Brown, age 73
Director, Bonnie G. Hill, age 71
Director, Lester A. Snow, age 61
Director, Thomas M. Krummel, age 61
Auditors: Deloitte&ToucheLLP

LOCATIONS

HQ: California Water Service Group (DE)
1720 North First Street, San Jose, CA 95112
Phone: 408 367-8200
Web: www.calwatergroup.com

PRODUCTS/OPERATIONS

2012 Sales

	$ mil.	% of total
Residential	394	68
Business	106	18

Public authorities	29	5
Industrial	25	4
Other	26	5
Adjustments	(23.1)	-
Total	**560**	**100**

Selected Subsidiaries

California Water Service Company
CWS Utility Services
Hawaii Water Service Company Inc.
HWS Utility Services LLC
New Mexico Water Service Company
Washington Water Service Company

COMPETITORS

American States Water	SJW
American Water	Siemens Water
Consolidated Water	Technologies
Los Angeles Water and	SouthWest Water
Power	United Water Inc.

HISTORICAL FINANCIALS

Company Type: Public

Income Statement

FYE: December 31

	REVENUE ($ mil.)	NET INCOME ($ mil.)	NET PROFIT MARGIN	EMPLOYEES
12/12	559.9	48.8	8.7%	1,131
12/11	501.8	37.7	7.5%	1,132
12/10	460.4	37.6	8.2%	1,127
12/09	449.3	40.5	9.0%	1,013
12/08	410.3	39.8	9.7%	929
Annual Growth	**8.1%**	**5.2%**	**—**	**5.0%**

2012 Year-End Financials

Debt ratio: 28.5%
Return on equity: 10.5%
Cash ($ mil.): 38
Current ratio: 0.60
Long-term debt ($ mil.): 434

No. of shares (mil.): 41
Dividends
  Yield: 3.4%
  Payout: 57.8%
Market value ($ mil.): 769

	STOCK PRICE ($) FY Close	P/E High/Low		PER SHARE ($) Earnings	Dividends	Book Value
12/12	18.35	16	15	1.17	0.63	11.30
12/11	18.26	42	19	0.90	0.62	10.76
12/10	37.27	44	38	0.91	0.60	10.45
12/09	36.82	48	34	0.98	0.59	10.13
12/08	46.43	48	31	0.95	0.59	9.72
Annual Growth	**(20.7%)**	**—**	**—**	**5.3%**	**1.9%**	**3.8%**

Cantel Medical Corp

Cantel Medical can tell you that cleanliness is second to nothing when it comes to medical and scientific equipment. Through its subsidiaries the firm sells infection prevention and control products to hospitals dentists drugmakers researchers and others in the US and abroad in the field of health care. Its diverse offerings include medical device reprocessing systems and disinfectants for dialyzers and endoscopes water purification equipment masks and bibs used in dental offices specialty packaging of biological and pharmaceutical products and therapeutic filtration systems. Fast-growing Cantel Medical employs an active acquisition strategy.

Geographic Reach

Cantel Medical rings up 85% of its sales in the US. Foreign markets include Canada Europe Africa the Middle East Latin and South America and the Asia-Pacific region.

Operations

Cantel Medical's major subsidiary companies include: Mar Con Purification (water filtration and purification); Medivators (disposables disinfection sterilization); Crosstex (infection control and prevention); and Saf-T-Pak (packaging medical shipping systems). Endoscopy products account for 40% of Cantel's sales followed by water purification/filtration with 27%. Disposable products account for about a fifth of sales followed by dialysis with about 10%.

Financial Analysis

Cantel Medical's fiscal 2012 (ends July) net sales jumped 20% vs. the prior year while net income surged 53% over the same period. The diversified medical products company has seen its sales rise by about 75% over the past five years and its net income steadily climb as a result of an active acquisition schedule and growth in the healthcare sector. Cantel attributed its strong financial performance in fiscal 2012 principally to increased sale of endoscopy products and services stemming from its recent purchase of Byrne Medical a maker of endoscopy products. Indeed sales of endoscopy products have grown to account for 40% of sales up from just 24% two years ago. All of Cantel's product segments with the exception of dialysis logged sales gains. Dialysis product sales have been on the wane for a number of years now.

Strategy

Cantel Medical has grown and diversified by employing an active acquisition strategy. Indeed the company has made more than 15 purchases over the past decade many of them in the field of water purification and filtration. More recently it has focused on endoscopy. The firm focuses on buying companies in the infection prevention and control market healthcare disposable products and water purification and filtration markets among others.

Ownership

Chairman Charles Diker owns about 16% of the company.

EXECUTIVES

Vice Chairman, George L. Fotiades, age 59
President and CEO Minntech Corporation, Roy K. Malkin, age 65, $401,659 total compensation
SVP CFO and Treasurer, Craig A. Sheldon, age 49, $297,847 total compensation
Secretary, Darwin C. Dornbush, age 82
Chairman, Charles M. Diker, age 77, $225,000 total compensation
EVP, Seth R. Segel, age 42, $337,188 total compensation
President and CEO Mar Cor Purification, Curtis (Curt) Weitnauer, age 48
VP and Controller, Steven C. Anaya, age 41
President CEO and Director, Andrew A. Krakauer, age 57, $425,000 total compensation
Assistant Secretary, Joanna Zisa Albrecht
SVP General Counsel and Secretary, Eric W. Nodiff, age 54, $297,847 total compensation
CEO Crosstex, Gary Steinberg
VP Market Development, Matthew J. Conlon
VP Globa Marketing and Business Development Medivators Reprocessing Systems Minntech, Terrence S. Mistalski
VP Supply Chain Logistics Minntech, LuAnn Petersen
VP Therapeutic Technologies Group Minntech, Randal M. Wenthold

Representative Director and Managing Director Minntech Japan, Masaki (Mike) Kitamura
VP and Managing Director Minntech Asia/Pacific Pte Ltd, John Piontkowski
VP Marketing Mar Cor Purification, Christopher Fournier
VP Finance Mar Cor Purification, Kathryn D. McIsaac
VP Sales Medical Mar Cor Purification, John A. Rickert
VP Sales Commercial and Industrial and International Mar Cor Purification, Benjamin J. Roczniak
VP U.S. Field Service Mar Cor Purification, Andrew G. Stitzinger
VP U.S. Operations Mar Cor Purification, Sean J. West
Controller Mar Cor Purification, Jeffrey Conrad
President Crosstex International, Mitchell V. Steinberg
VP Finance and Treasurer Crosstex International, Douglas T. Carpenter
VP Western Region Crosstex International, Sheldon M. Fisher
VP Northeast Region Crosstex International, Les M. Gershon
VP Southeastern Region Crosstex International, Ronald R. Psimas
VP Sales and Marketing Crosstex International, Andrew G. Whitehead
General Manager Saf-T-Pak, David R. Hebrank
VP and Controller Saf-T-Pak, Alex V. Schabel
Vice President - Corporate Development, Seth Yellin
Member of the Management Board, Gennady Yakovlev
General Director, Igor Zabolotnyi
Member of the Management Board; Deputy General Director-Commerce Director, Kirill Karasev
Member of the Management Board; Chief Accountant, Marina Melnik
Executive Vice President Chief Operating Officer, Jorgen Hansen
Vice Chairman, George L. Fotiades, age 59
Director, Robert L. Barbanell, age 81
Director, Alan J. Hirschfield, age 76
Director, Bruce Slovin, age 75
Director, Alan R. Batkin, age 67
Director, Joseph M. Cohen, age 74
Director, Ann E. Berman, age 59
President CEO and Director, Andrew A. Krakauer, age 57
Director, Mark N. Diker, age 45
Director, Peter J. Pronovost
Auditors: Ernst&YoungLLP

LOCATIONS

HQ: Cantel Medical Corp.
  150 Clove Rd. 9th Fl., Little Falls NJ 07424
Phone: 973-890-7220   **Fax:** 973-890-7270
Web: www.cantelmedical.com

2012 Sales

US	329	85
Asia/Pacific	16	4
Canada	15	4
Latin America/South America	3	1

PRODUCTS/OPERATIONS

2012 Sales

Endoscopy	153	40
Water purification & filtration	104	27
Dialysis	35	9
Other	17	4

Selected Acquisitions

FY2012
Byrne Medical Inc. ($100 million; Houston TX; infection control products)

FY2011
ConFirm Monitoring Systems Inc. ($7.5 million; Denver Colorado; sterilization monitoring products)
Gambro Medical Water Systems ($23.7 million; Colorado; production of medical grade water)

Selected Subsidiaries

Biolab Equipment Ltd.
Carsen Group Inc. (Canada)
Crosstex International Inc.
Medivators Inc.
Medivators Japan K.K.
Saf-T-Pak Inc. (Canada)
Strong Dental Products Inc.

COMPETITORS

3M Health Care	Getinge
CONMED Corporation	Johnson & Johnson
DENTSPLY	Kimberly-Clark Health
Danaher	Olympus
Ecolab	STERIS
Fresenius	Siemens AG
GE Water and Process Technologies	TIDI Products

HISTORICAL FINANCIALS

Company Type: Public

Income Statement

FYE: July 31

	REVENUE ($ mil.)	NET INCOME ($ mil.)	NET PROFIT MARGIN	EMPLOYEES
07/13	425.0	39.2	9.2%	1,292
07/12	386.4	31.3	8.1%	1,198
07/11	321.6	20.4	6.4%	1,117
07/10	273.9	19.9	7.3%	883
07/09	260.0	15.5	6.0%	874
Annual Growth	13.1%	26.0%	—	10.3%

2013 Year-End Financials

Debt ratio: 19.4%
Return on equity: 13.1%
Cash ($ mil.): 34
Current ratio: 2.55
Long-term debt ($ mil.): 85

No. of shares (mil.): 41
Dividends
Yield: 0.3%
Payout: 9.7%
Market value ($ mil.): 1,092

	STOCK PRICE ($) FY Close	P/E High/Low		PER SHARE ($) Earnings	Dividends	Book Value
07/13	26.54	39	26	0.95	0.09	7.81
07/12	26.12	42	25	0.77	0.09	6.79
07/11	24.93	53	26	0.52	0.05	6.03
07/10	15.88	41	25	0.52	0.04	5.52
07/09	15.48	39	18	0.42	0.00	5.00
Annual Growth	14.4%	—	—	22.8%	—	11.8%

Capella Education Company

Capella Education is all about the digital age. The fast-growing company operates Capella University an online school that offers more than 45 undergraduate and graduate degree programs with some 150 specializations. Its 35000 students from the US and abroad are primarily composed of working adults 75% of which are pursuing master's or doctoral degrees. Capella Education's faculty members are mostly part-time employees typically teaching one to three courses per semester. The firm's programs range across a variety of subjects including business health human resources information technology and psychology.

Geographic Reach

Capella Education's students come from all 50 states and about 60 countries primarily from urban settings. The company administers its online educational programs from its headquarters in Minneapolis Minnesota.

Operations

Founded in 1991 Capella Education's sales consist principally of tuition application and graduation fees as well as commissions it earns from bookstore and publication sales. Some three-quarters of Capella Education's revenues are derived from federal student financial aid programs.

Financial Analysis

Capella Education's revenues are directly tied to its enrollment levels. In 2011 its revenues increased 1% to $430 million due to higher tuition and a larger proportion of doctoral students. However the company's growth was offset by an overall drop in enrollment numbers that year after several years of double-digit enrollment (and revenue) increases. Net income dropped 15% to some $52 million in 2011 due to increased instructional and marketing expenses. To offset the slowdown in growth in 2011 and 2012 Capella Education enacted workforce reduction programs and other cost-control efforts.

Strategy

Capella Education attracts new students through a variety of strategies including the expansion of its curriculum and program offerings. The firm also targets marketing efforts towards students who are pinpointed as more likely to finish a four-year degree as well as those likely to enroll in masters or doctorate programs. It also boosts enrollment by establishing partnerships with corporations the military and other entities to provide training and professional development for those organizations' workforces as well as by acquiring or developing new educational program platforms.

As consumer acceptance of online education grows Capella Education considers itself to be in a strong competitive position as all of its academic programs are designed specifically for the Internet to promote flexibility and interactivity. Along that same line its classes are also designed to appeal to working adults taking advantage of a growing market of people looking to advance or change careers.

Mergers and Acquisitions

Capella acquired a majority stake in Sophia Learning in 2011 before acquiring full ownership in 2012. Sophia offers users tutorials –called learning packets –focused on helping to teach a specific learning objective. Learning packets are technology based and can be created using virtually any type of media including text images slide shows video and audio.

Capella also bought UK distance learning provider Resource Development International (RDI) for #9.3 million ($14.9 million) in 2011. RDI administers degree courses designed by UK universities and Capella is working to gain direct degree awarding powers for RDI.

EXECUTIVES

Chairman Chief Executive Officer, J. Kevin Gilligan, age 58, $464,423 total compensation

Senior Vice President; General Counsel; Secretary, Gregory W. (Greg) Thom, age 56, $261,692 total compensation

interim President of Capella University, Michael J. (Mike) Offerman, age 65, $294,000 total compensation

senior Vice President Capella University and Capella Education Company, Paul A. Schroeder, age 53

Director Investor Relations, Heide Erickson

SVP Operations and CIO, Scott M. Henkel, age 58, $177,885 total compensation

SVP Strategy and Business Development, Kyle M. Carpenter, age 59

Manager Public Relations, Michael Walsh

President Capella University, Christopher (Chris) Cassirer, age 48

Senior Vice President Chief Financial Officer, Steven L. (Steve) Polacek, age 53

Senior Vice President - Human Resources, Sally B. Chial, age 52, $257,739 total compensation

Vice President of Corporate Communications, Mike Buttry

President Capella University, Scott Kinney

Director, David W. Smith, age 68

Director, Jeffrey W. Taylor, age 59

Director, Michael A. (Mike) Linton

Director, Stephen G. (Steve) Shank, age 69

Director, Jody G. Miller, age 55

Director, Sandra E. Taylor, age 62

Director, Michael L. Lomax, age 65

Director, Andrew M. (Andy) Slavitt, age 46

Director, Darrell R. Tukua, age 59

Auditors: Ernst&YoungLLP

LOCATIONS

HQ: Capella Education Company
Capella Tower 225 S. 6th St. 9th Fl., Minneapolis MN 55402
Phone: -10367   **Fax:** -17279
Web: www.aminex-plc.com

PRODUCTS/OPERATIONS

2011 Students by Program

Master's	17,049	45
Bachelor's	8,489	23
Total	**37,704**	**100**

Selected Academic Programs

Bachelor of Science in Business
Bachelor of Science in Information Technology
Bachelor of Science in Public Safety
Bachelor of Science in Psychology
Doctor of Philosophy in Business
Doctor of Philosophy in Counselor Education and Supervision
Doctor of Philosophy in Education
Doctor of Philosophy in Human Services
Doctor of Philosophy in Information Technology
Doctor of Philosophy in Organization and Management
Doctor of Philosophy in Public Safety
Doctor of Philosophy in Psychology
Doctor of Psychology
Master of Business Administration
Master of Science in Education
Master of Science in Human Resource Management
Master of Science in Human Services
Master of Science in Information Technology
Master of Science in Nursing
Master of Science in Organizational Development
Master of Science in Psychology
Master of Science in Public Health
Master of Science in Public Safety

COMPETITORS

American Public Education	Education Management
Apollo Group	Grand Canyon Education
	ITT Educational

Argosy Education
Bridgepoint Education
Cardean Learning Group
Corinthian Colleges
DeVry

Jones Knowledge
Kaplan
Laureate Education
Strayer Education
The College Network

HISTORICAL FINANCIALS

Company Type: Public

Income Statement

FYE: December 31

	REVENUE ($ mil.)	NET INCOME ($ mil.)	NET PROFIT MARGIN	EMPLOYEES
12/12	421.8	36.4	8.6%	2,829
12/11	430.0	52.1	12.1%	2,883
12/10	426.1	61.2	14.4%	2,968
12/09	334.6	42.6	12.8%	1,277
12/08	272.3	28.7	10.6%	2,383
Annual Growth	11.6%	6.1%	—	4.4%

2012 Year-End Financials

Debt ratio: —
Return on equity: 23.1%
Cash ($ mil.): 93
Current ratio: 3.49
Long-term debt ($ mil.): —

No. of shares (mil.): 12
Dividends
  Yield: —
  Payout: —
Market value ($ mil.): 350

	STOCK PRICE ($) FY Close	P/E High/Low		PER SHARE ($) Earnings	Dividends	Book Value
12/12	28.23	16	9	2.76	0.00	12.27
12/11	36.05	20	8	3.40	0.00	11.71
12/10	66.58	27	14	3.64	0.00	12.79
12/09	75.30	30	18	2.51	0.00	10.99
12/08	58.76	40	21	1.66	0.00	8.45
Annual Growth	(16.7%)	—	—	13.6%	—	9.8%

Carbo Ceramics Inc.

CARBO Ceramics' proppants (tiny alumina-based ceramic beads) are a welcome release for natural gas and oil well operators. To increase well production operators often pump fluids down wells at high pressure to create fractures in the hydrocarbon-bearing rock formation (hydraulic fracturing). Proppants are suspended in the fluid to fill the channels and "prop" up the fissures so that natural gas and oil may flow to the surface. The company's products compete against guar bean and sand-based proppants. CARBO Ceramics also offers related software consulting services and specialty polymers.

Geographic Reach

Headquartered in Houston Texas CARBO Ceramics manufactures its products in Eufaula Alabama; New Iberia Louisiana; Toomsboro and McIntyre Georgia; Luoyang China; and Kopeysk Russia. The company has numerous storage and distribution facilities in North America (US and Canada) Europe and Asia (China).

The US is CARBO Ceramics largest market accounting for 77% of company's revenues in 2012.

Operations

CARBO Ceramics is the world's leading supplier of ceramic proppant the provider of the world's most popular fracture simulation software and a supplier of fracture design and consulting services. The company also offers a broad range

of technologies for spill prevention containment and countermeasures.

The company's ceramic proppants are made from alumina-bearing ores (including clay bauxite bauxitic clay and kaolin). The main deposits of these ores in the US are in Arkansas Alabama and Georgia; other economically viable deposits are found in Australia Brazil China Gabon India Jamaica Russia and Surinam.

In North America the company leased 2100 rail cars to distribute its products and expected to add 250 more railcars by the end of 2013.

Its other operations include Falcon Technologies (high performance polymers) and StrataGen (reservoir stimulation technology).

Sales and Marketing

CARBO Ceramics supplies its customers with products on a just-in-time basis. Continuing sales of products depend on the company's direct customers and the well operators being satisfied with product quality availability and delivery performance. It also provides its software simulation products and consulting services directly to owners and/or operators of oil and gas wells and service companies.

The company's international marketing efforts are conducted through sales offices in Dubai UAE; Aberdeen Scotland; Beijing China; and Moscow Russia and through commissioned sales agents in China and South America.

Halliburton and Schlumberger each accounted for more than 10% of CARBO Ceramics' 2012 and 2011 revenues.

Financial Performance

CARBO Ceramics saw its revenues grow by 3% in 2012 due to 7% increase in proppant sales volume and an increase in sales from some other business units partially offset by a drop in proppant prices as a result of competitive pricing pressures. An increase in the oil rigs lifted North American demand as did the acceptance of the company's products in oily liquids-rich basins. International sales volumes grew led by increases in China Mexico and Russia partially offset by a decrease in Europe.The company reported a $105.9 million net income in 2012 down 18.6% over the previous year primarily due to increased operating expenses. Selling general and administrative expenses rose due to higher administrative spending. Other operating expenses consisted primarily of a loss on disposal of assets as the result of CARBO Ceramics winding down Applied Geomechanics its geotechnical monitoring operation. With the exception of a recession-driven revenue slump in 2009 the company reported an upward trend in revenues from 2008 through 2012.

Strategy

Growing its US manufacturing base in 2012 CARBO Ceramics began construction of a 600 million pound-per-year resin-coating plant in Marshfield Wisconsin. In 2011 the company acquired real estate and submitted environmental permit applications to construct a ceramic proppant plant in the Millen Georgia area. CARBO Ceramics believes this plant (due for completion in 2013) could support a manufacturing capacity of up to 500 million pounds of ceramic proppant per year.

Ownership

William C. Morris owns 12% of CARBO Ceramics.

Company Background

The company was incorporated in 1987.

EXECUTIVES

VP Chief Financial Officer, Ernesto Bautista III, age 42, $267,038 total compensation
VP Operations, Mark L. Edmunds, age 58, $224,250 total compensation
Sales Engineer Southeast Region, Marty Hupp
Director Sales North America, Mark McGill
Sales Engineer Northern Region, John Kullman
Sales Engineer Mid-Continent Region, Jamie Jordan
Sales Manager Latin and South America, Eduardo Velez
Chairman, William C. Morris, age 74
President and Chief Executive Officer, Gary A. Kolstad, age 54, $500,000 total compensation
VP Marketing and Sales, David G. Gallagher, age 55, $234,250 total compensation
Chief Compliance Officer General Counsel and Corporate Secretary, R. Sean Elliott, age 40, $212,750 total compensation
Sales Engineer Southwest Region, Stacy Eschete
Managing Director Asia Pacific, Hongwei Wang
Sales Engineer South Texas Region, Jim Briscoe
Managing Director Europe Middle East Africa, Paul Masseboeuf
Senior Staff Petroleum Engineer Global, Terry Palisch
General Manager, Gary Holzhausen
Sales Engineer, Kean Finnegan
Software Engineer, Jon Eckstein
Service Manager, Billy Peters
Director of Engineering, Bob Shelley
VP of Marketing and Sales, Don P. Conkle
IR Contact Officer, Marlene Owen
Vice President General Counsel, Sean Elliot
Vice President General Counsel, Sean Elliott
Vice President Research and Development, Chad Cannan
Director, Randy L. Limbacher, age 54
Director, James B. (Jim) Jennings, age 72
Director, Robert S. Rubin, age 81
Director, Henry E. (Jack) Lentz Jr., age 68
Director, Sigmund L. (Sig) Cornelius, age 58
President and Chief Executive Officer, Gary A. Kolstad, age 54
Auditors: Ernst&YoungLLP

LOCATIONS

HQ: CARBO Ceramics Inc.
  575 N. Dairy Ashford Ste. 300, Houston TX 77079
Phone: 281-921-6400   **Fax:** 281-921-6401
Web: www.carboceramics.com

2012 Sales

	$ mil.	% of total
US	500	77
Canada	30	5
Other countries	114	18
Total	**645**	**100**

COMPETITORS

China GengSheng Minerals
Core Laboratories
Fairmount Minerals

Halliburton
Hi-Crush
Saint-Gobain
Unimin

HISTORICAL FINANCIALS

Company Type: Public

Income Statement

FYE: December 31

	REVENUE ($ mil.)	NET INCOME ($ mil.)	NET PROFIT MARGIN	EMPLOYEES
12/12	645.5	105.9	16.4%	992
12/11	625.7	130.1	20.8%	961
12/10	473.0	78.7	16.6%	806
12/09	341.8	52.8	15.4%	741
12/08	387.8	110.3	28.4%	648
Annual Growth	13.6%	(1.0%)	—	11.2%

2012 Year-End Financials

Debt ratio: —
Return on equity: 15.7%
Cash ($ mil.): 90
Current ratio: 6.88
Long-term debt ($ mil.): —

No. of shares (mil.): 23
Dividends
  Yield: 1.3%
  Payout: 19.7%
Market value ($ mil.): 1,809

	STOCK PRICE ($) FY Close	P/E High/Low	PER SHARE ($) Earnings	Dividends	Book Value
12/12	78.34	29 13	4.59	1.02	30.88
12/11	123.33	32 17	5.62	0.88	27.27
12/10	103.54	30 17	3.40	0.76	22.59
12/09	68.17	31 12	2.27	0.70	19.82
12/08	35.53	14 7	4.51	0.62	18.72
Annual Growth	21.9%	— —	0.4%	13.3%	13.3%

Cardinal Financial Corp

Cardinal Financial can help you keep out of the red. The holding company owns Cardinal Bank which operates nearly 30 branches in northern Virginia and the Washington DC metropolitan area. Serving commercial and retail customers it offers such deposit options as checking savings and money market accounts; IRAs; and CDs as well as trust services. Commercial real estate loans make up more than 40% of Cardinal Financial's loan portfolio; residential mortgages construction loans business loans and home equity and consumer loans round out the bank's lending activities. Subsidiary Cardinal Wealth Services provides brokerage and investment services through an alliance with Raymond James Financial.

Other units include money manager Wilson/Bennett Capital Management which focuses on value-oriented investing and large-cap stocks and George Mason Mortgage which originates residential mortgages for sale into the secondary market through about 15 branches in Cardinal Bank's market area.

As many of its peers struggled Cardinal Financial reported record earnings for three consecutive years from 2009 to 2011. Net income for the latest period was some $28 million a nearly 35% increase from the previous year. Key factors for the company's results include the relative strength of the Washington DC market (one of the wealthiest regions in the US) and growth in the company's commercial banking and mortgage banking segments.

EXECUTIVES

Executive Vice President; Chief Risk Officer, Christopher W. Bergstrom, age 53, $185,000 total compensation
Regional President of Cardinal Bank, F. Kevin Reynolds, age 53, $155,546 total compensation
Chief Operating Officer; Executive Vice President, Alice P. Frazier, age 47
Chairman of the Board; Chief Executive Officer, Bernard H. Clineburg, age 64, $350,000 total compensation
EVP Real Estate Lending Group Cardinal bank, Dennis M. Griffith, age 64, $154,985 total compensation
VP-Comml Real Estate, Katie L. Golden
Chief Financial Officer; Executive Vice President, Mark A. Wendel, age 54, $185,000 total compensation
VP-Product Dev & Ecommerce, Hilary Blackburn
Vice Chairman, John H. Rust Jr., age 64
Director, George P. Shafran, age 85
Director, James D. Russo, age 65
Director, J. Hamilton Lambert, age 72
Director, Sidney O. (Sid) Dewberry, age 85
Director, B. G. Beck, age 76
Director, Michael A. Garcia, age 53
Director, Alice M. Starr, age 64
Director, William E. Peterson, age 51
Director, William G. Buck, age 66
Director, Alan G. Merten, age 71
Independent Director, Steven Wiltse
Auditors: KPMGLLP

LOCATIONS

HQ: Cardinal Financial Corporation
8270 Greensboro Dr. Ste. 500, McLean VA 22102
Phone: 703-584-3400   **Fax:** 616-554-8608
Web: www.familychristian.com

PRODUCTS/OPERATIONS

2011 Sales

	$ mil.	% of total
Interest		
Loans	89	65
Investment securities	13	10
Other	0	-
Noninterest		
Mortgage banking activities	20	15
Management fees	3	2
Loan fees	2	2
Investment fees	2	2
Net gains on securities available for sale	2	2
Other	2	2
Total	**124**	**100**

COMPETITORS

Access National
BB&T
Bank of America
Burke & Herbert Bank
Capital One

Millennium Bankshares
PNC Financial
SunTrust
United Bankshares
Virginia Commerce Bancorp

HISTORICAL FINANCIALS

Company Type: Public

Income Statement

FYE: December 31

	ASSETS ($ mil.)	NET INCOME ($ mil.)	INCOME AS % OF ASSETS	EMPLOYEES
12/12	3,039.1	45.3	1.5%	706
12/11	2,602.7	28.0	1.1%	510
12/10	2,072.0	18.4	0.9%	417
12/09	1,976.1	10.3	0.5%	368
12/08	1,743.7	0.2	0.0%	352
Annual Growth	14.9%	254.8%	—	19.0%

2012 Year-End Financials

Return on assets: 1.6%
Return on equity: 15.9%
Long-term debt ($ mil.): —
No. of shares (mil.): 30
Sales ($ mil): 178

Dividends
  Yield: 1.2%
  Payout: 12.9%
Market value ($ mil.): 493

	STOCK PRICE ($) FY Close	P/E High/Low	PER SHARE ($) Earnings	Dividends	Book Value
12/12	16.30	11 7	1.51	0.20	10.19
12/11	10.74	13 9	0.94	0.12	8.83
12/10	11.63	19 14	0.62	0.08	7.75
12/09	8.74	24 13	0.37	0.04	7.12
12/08	5.69	965440	0.01	0.04	6.58
Annual Growth	30.1%	—	—250.5%	49.5%	11.6%

Cardtronics Inc

Cardtronics is the largest non-bank owner and operator of automated teller machines (ATMs) and related financial services equipment in the world. It maintains more than 65900 cash machines in the US UK Canada and Mexico. More than 15000 of those machines are branded by banks such as Chase SunTrust and Citibank. The company also leases and sells machines to airports convenience stores supermarkets malls and drug stores. Most clients pay the company to handle some or all of the maintenance services or operational services of their ATMs. Cardtronics also operates Allpoint which is the largest surcharge-free ATM network in the US with 43000 machines.

Cardtronics operates its ATMs under two arrangements with customers. Under the company-owned ATM arrangements (representing about 65% of its network) the firm provides clients with the machines and all related services including cash replenishment telecommunications and maintenance. Most of the company's national and regional customers opt for this plan under which Cardtronics pays a fee to clients to place its machines on their premises. Smaller clients usually enter into the merchant-owned plan in which the merchant owns the ATMs and is responsible for their maintenance and cash replenishment.

Cardtronics operates in the US (including territories of Puerto Rico and the Virgin Islands) the UK Mexico and Canada.

Cardtronics has benefitted from several trends in the market place. The company has seen an increase in revenue and number of transactions as its network has grown and as overall cash usage has increased (and credit availability has decreased). Revenue increased by more than 17% in 2011. Profits also have continued to climb. Net income increased by more than 70% in 2011. The results were driven by the expansion of Cardtronics' network and increase in the total number of transactions conducted on the company's ATMs.

Worldwide ATM network expansion is at the top of Cardtronics' strategy. It continues to seek opportunities in the UK and Mexico which are operated by its Bank Machine and Cardtronics Mexico subsidiaries. Cardtronics also entered Canada with the 2011 purchase of Mr. Cash ATM Network (renamed Cardtronics Canada). The deal added some 600 machines throughout the country. In late 2012 Cardtronics Canada acquired privately-held Can-Do-Cash Ltd. an ATM services company headquartered in Ottawa. Other target growth areas include Central and Eastern Europe Central and South America and the Asia/Pacific region.

Cardtronics also is growing its network in the US. In May 2013 the company acquired Aptus Financial a leader in ATM sales ATM leasing and management services. In 2011 the company expanded its footprint in the Midwestern US with the $145 million purchase of EDC Holding's ATM business. The deal added about 3600 ATMs to Cardtronics' network. Also that year the acquisition of Access to Money added more than 10000 ATMs in the Southeast.

In addition to growing its ATM network the company also is interested in expanding its service capabilities. In another 2011 deal Cardtronics acquired LocatorSearch a provider of search technology to the financial services industry that allows customers to search and find the nearest ATM. In 2012 the company bought Midwest-based machine support provider ATM Network adding some 6200 ATMs to its service network.

Other growth initiatives include building the company's Allpoint surcharge-free network in the US and to introduce it in Cardtronics' international markets. Under the Allpoint model financial institutions pay Cardtronics for participation instead of users paying transaction fees. In 2010 Allpoint entered Australia's market through a partnership with that country's largest ATM operator Customers Limited. The following year Allpoint entered Mexico by adding more than 2500 ATMs across the country.

Cardtronics also has attracted new customers who use prepaid debit cards to make cash withdrawals. These unbanked or underbanked customers previously could not use ATMs. However increased use of prepaid cards have allowed those users access to Cardtronics' kiosks. In 2010 Cardtronics struck a deal with MasterCard to offer free ATM access for prepaid cards. Also that year Univision launched a prepaid card product utilizing the Allpoint Network. The company plans to go after other opportunities to work with financial institutions that issue stored-value debit cards.

EXECUTIVES

President U.S. Business Group, Rick Updyke, age 54, $291,000 total compensation
Managing Director UK and Europe, Ronald (Ron) Delnevo, age 58, $344,698 total compensation
Executive Vice President - Network and Financial Services, Ben Psillas
President Global Services, Michael H. (Mike) Clinard, age 46, $370,800 total compensation
EVP Acquisitions, Thomas E. Upton, age 55, $231,525 total compensation
Chief Compliance Officer Secretary and General Counsel, Michael E. Keller
Chairman, Dennis F. Lynch, age 64
CEO, Steven A. (Steve) Rathgaber, age 60
Chief Information Security Officer, Jerry Garcia

President Enterprise Growth Group, David Dove
Chief Marketing Officer, Tom Pierce
EVP and Division Executive ATM Services, Carleton K. (Tres) Thompson III, age 44, $200,170 total compensation
VP Marketing, Joel Antonini
Executive Vice President - Audit and Risk Management, Randy Rice
Executive Vice President - U.S, Tony Muscarello
Executive Vice President - Product Management, Bill Knoll
SVP Relationship Management, Carl Osterlof
Chief Accounting Officer, E. Brad Conrad, age 40
General Manager Mexico, Scott Abogado
Director Public Relations, Nick Pappathopoulos
Senior Vice President, Jorge A. Fernandez
Sales Director, Manuel Mestre
Operations Director, Marco Beltr+?n
CFO, Chris Brewster, age 64
EVP Corporate Development, Phillip Chin
CIO, Michael McCarthy, age 47
SEVP Sales and Relationship Management, Todd Clark, age 46
EVP Global Operations, Jeffrey B. Keith
Chief Accounting Officer, Brad Conrad
Chief Information Officer, Mike McCarthy
Executive Vice President - Global Operations, Jeffery B. Keith
Executive Vice President - Human Resources, Debra Bronder
Senior Vice President - Planning & Treasurer, Todd Ruden
Executive Vice President - Global Procurement, Ric Davis
Managing Director - Cardtronics Europe, Jonathan SimpsonDent
Director, Juli C. Spottiswood
Director, Mark Rossi, age 56
Director, J. Tim Arnoult, age 64
Director, G. Patrick (Pat) Phillips, age 63
Director, Jorge M. Diaz, age 48
CEO and Director, Steven A. (Steve) Rathgaber, age 60
Director, Robert P. Barone, age 75
Director, Michael A. R. Wilson, age 45
Auditors: KPMGLLP

LOCATIONS

HQ: Cardtronics Inc.
   3250 Briarpark Dr. Ste. 400, Houston TX 77042
Phone: 832-308-4000   **Fax:** 832-308-4001
Web: www.cardtronics.com

2011 Sales by Region

	$ mil.	% of total
US	501	80
UK	97	16
Other international	25	4
Total	**624**	**100**

PRODUCTS/OPERATIONS

2011 Sales

	$ mil.	% of total
ATM operating revenues	597	96
ATM product sales & other	27	4
Total	**624**	**100**

Selected Mergers & Acquisitions

2011
  Mr. Cash ATM Network Inc. (Letherbridge Alberta Canada; ATM network)
  EDC ATM Subsidiary LLC/Efmark Deployment I Inc. ($145 million; Walnut Creek California; ATM network)
  Access to Money Inc. (Cherry Hill New Jersey; merchant-owned ATMs)
  LocatorSearch LLC (New York; location search technology)

COMPETITORS

BBVA Bancomer	HSBC Fianzas
Banamex	Lloyds Banking Group
Bank of America	NYCE Payments Network
Barclays Bank	PNC Financial
DirectCash	PayPoint
Electronic Cash	Payment Alliance
Systems	Payzone
Fifth Third	Royal Bank of Scotland
First Data	U.S. Bancorp
Global Axcess	WRG Services

HISTORICAL FINANCIALS

Company Type: Public

Income Statement

FYE: December 31

	REVENUE ($ mil.)	NET INCOME ($ mil.)	NET PROFIT MARGIN	EMPLOYEES
12/12	780.4	43.2	5.5%	740
12/11	624.5	70.1	11.2%	643
12/10	532.0	41.1	7.7%	535
12/09	493.3	5.2	1.1%	460
12/08	493.0	(70.0)	—	430
Annual Growth	**12.2%**	—	—	**14.5%**

2012 Year-End Financials

Debt ratio: 46.1%	No. of shares (mil.): 44
Return on equity: 33.3%	Dividends
Cash ($ mil.): 13	Yield: —
Current ratio: 0.90	Payout: —
Long-term debt ($ mil.): 353	Market value ($ mil.): 1,060

	STOCK PRICE ($) FY Close	P/E High/Low		PER SHARE ($) Earnings	Dividends	Book Value
12/12	23.74	32	23	0.96	0.00	3.30
12/11	27.06	18	10	1.58	0.00	2.54
12/10	17.70	19	10	0.96	0.00	0.99
12/09	11.06	94	7	0.13	0.00	(0.07)
12/08	1.29	—	—	(1.81)	0.00	(0.47)
Annual Growth	**107.1%**					

Carolina Bank Holdings Inc

Carolina Bank Holdings owns Carolina Bank which serves individuals and small to midsized businesses through some 10 branches in northern portions of North Carolina. The community-oriented financial institution offers standard services such as checking and savings accounts money market and individual retirement accounts CDs ATM and debit cards and online banking and bill payment. Loans secured by commercial properties account for about 40% of the company's portfolio followed by residential mortgages construction and land development loans commercial and industrial loans and consumer loans.

In 2007 Carolina Bank formed a wholesale mortgage division that originates residential home loans through third-party brokers and banks then sells them into the secondary market.

EXECUTIVES

Treasurer and Secretary; EVP CFO and Secretary Carolina Bank, T. Allen Liles, age 60, $155,245 total compensation

President CEO and Director; President and CEO Carolina Bank, Robert T. Braswell, age 61, $283,039 total compensation

EVP and Senior Loan Officer Carolina Bank, Gunnar N. R. Fromen, age 64, $157,175 total compensation

VP Human Resources and Accounting Officer Carolina Bank, Angela J. Nowlin

VP Carolina Bank, Cindi H. Welker

Vice Chairman, Gary N. Brown, age 68

EVP and Chief Credit Officer Carolina Bank, Daniel D. Hornfeck, age 45, $114,766 total compensation

SVP Carolina Bank, Paul L. Kennedy

VP Carolina Bank, John Walters

SVP Carolina Bank, F. Virginia Grimes

VP Carolina Bank, J. Ross Geller

VP Carolina Bank, Wayne J. Handy

VP Carolina Bank, Pamela W. Sparks

Operations Manager Today as Deposit Operations Manager, Sharon A. Williams

VP Carolina Bank, Gail S. Brady

VP Carolina Bank, Jessica L. Gourley

SVP Carolina Bank, W. Keith Strickland

President Carolina Bank Wholesale Mortgage and SVP Carolina Bank, Phillip B. Carmac, age 59, $100,000 total compensation

SVP Carolina Bank, Gerald W. Church

StVP Carolina Bank, H. Dean Sexton

VP Carolina Bank, Bob R. Callicutt

VP Carolina Bank, Chris W. Clemmons

VP Controller, Phyllis D. Rainey

VP Carolina Bank, Michael V. Ruggiero

VP Carolina Bank, Patricia A. Trout

VP Carolina Bank, David A. Woods

VP Carolina Bank, Ron Woody

VP Carolina Bank, G. Georgeanne Wyrick

Assistant VP Carolina Bank, Joy F. Isley

Operations Manager, Heather E. Wallace

Loan Operations Officer, Frances C. Cabe

Credit Administration Officer, Michael G. Church

Deposit Operations Officer, Heather R. Snelling

President CEO and Director; President and CEO Carolina Bank, Robert T. Braswell, age 61

Director, George E. Carr, age 70

Director, James E. Hooper, age 55

Director, J. Alexander S. Barrett, age 56

Director, Stephen K. Bright, age 64

Independent Director, Edward Kitchen

Independent Director, Mary Alt

Independent Director, Kevin Baker

Auditors: CherryBekaert&HollandLLP

LOCATIONS

HQ: Carolina Bank Holdings Inc.
101 N. Spring St., Greensboro NC 27401
Phone: 336-288-1898   **Fax:** 336-286-5553
Web: www.carolinabank.com

COMPETITORS

BB&T
FNB United
First Citizens
BancShares

LifeStore Financial

HISTORICAL FINANCIALS

Company Type: Public

Income Statement

FYE: December 31

	ASSETS ($ mil.)	NET INCOME ($ mil.)	INCOME AS % OF ASSETS	EMPLOYEES
12/12	691.8	7.5	1.1%	208
12/11	673.3	2.4	0.4%	174
12/10	676.7	(2.3)	—	155
12/09	697.0	(0.3)	—	140
12/08	616.6	2.1	0.4%	119
Annual Growth	2.9%	36.0%	—	15.0%

2012 Year-End Financials

Return on assets: 1.1%
Return on equity: 14.9%
Long-term debt ($ mil.): —
No. of shares (mil.): 3
Sales ($ mil): 49

Dividends
Yield: —
Payout: —
Market value ($ mil.): 25

	STOCK PRICE ($) FY Close	P/E High/Low		PER SHARE ($) Earnings	Dividends	Book Value
12/12	7.35	4	1	1.85	0.00	15.90
12/11	2.45	12	6	0.36	0.00	13.75
12/10	3.15	—	—	(1.04)	0.00	13.07
12/09	3.25	—	—	(0.43)	0.00	14.16
12/08	6.15	18	8	0.65	0.00	9.43
Annual Growth	4.6%	—	—	29.9%	—	14.0%

Carpenter Technology Corp.

The Tin Man never would have rusted had he been built with metal from Carpenter Technology. It processes basic raw materials such as cobalt nickel manganese and titanium to make various corrosion-resistant materials. Most sales come from stainless steel products and alloys that provide special heat- or wear-resistance or special magnetic or conductive properties. Finished products come in billet bar rod wire and other forms. Carpenter also produces certain metal powders. Markets include aerospace automotive medical and industrial companies. Aerospace and defense accounted for more than 47% of sales in 2012.

Geographic Reach

Carpenter has manufacturing plants in the US (Florida Ohio Pennsylvania Rhode Island and South Carolina) and in Sweden. In 2012 the US accounted for 68% of company's total revenues.

Operations

The company manufactures fabricates and distributes specialty metals. Its three operating segments are Specialty Alloys Operations (premium alloy and stainless steel manufacturing operations); Latrobe (the manufacturing and distribution operations of the Latrobe businesses acquired in 2012); and Performance Engineered Products (including Dynamet titanium Carpenter Powder Products Amega West and the Specialty Steel Supply distribution business that was gained in connection with the Latrobe Specialty Metals acquisition).

Financial Performance

In fiscal year 2013 Carpenter's revenues increased by 12% thanks to higher sales and the in-

clusion of Latrobe (acquired in 2012). In 2013 Latrobe Business Segment revenues (which are concentrated in aerospace and defense industrial and consumer and energy end-use markets as well as distribution) grew by 145%

The company's net income grew by 21% in fiscal 2013 due to higher revenues and the absence of the acquisition costs it incurred in fiscal 2012.

Strategy

Carpenter grows through strategic partnerships organic expansion and complementary acquisitions.

Expanding its supply position in 2013 the company signed a multi-level agreement with United Technologies Corporation through its Pratt & Whitney Division. The deal includes the production of superalloy powders (and associated licensing technology) and a long-term supply agreement. That year it also signed a supply deal to provide Rolls-Royce with advanced technology materials used in the manufacture of jet engine components including rings blades vanes and airfoils.

Responding to rapid growth in Asia in 2013 the company announced plans to build a bar finishing plant in China.

In order to keep a tight focus on manufacturing and selling specialty materials for the aerospace energy and other high-growth markets Carpenter began trimming in 2012 by announcing that it was commencing the process to sell its distribution businesses: Latrobe Specialty Steel Distribution (LSSD) which it gained as part of its 2012 Latrobe Specialty Metals acquisition and Aceros Fortuna Carpenter's Mexican distribution business. The proceeds will be reinvested into its core product businesses.

Mergers and Acquisitions

In 2012 Carpenter acquired rival Latrobe for $558 million.

(Latrobe which filed for an IPO in 2011 made and distributed specialty metals and alloys used for landing gear oil valves turbine bolts and metal-cutting dies. The deal elevates Carpenter's position in the aerospace and energy markets. To gain approval by US antitrust authorities however Carpenter agreed to sell assets used in making alloys for two aerospace applications (MP159 and MP35N) to French metals manufacturer Eramet).

Prior to that in 2011 Carpenter acquired Amega West Services a Houston-based manufacturer and service provider of components for directional drilling equipment and Oilfield Alloys Pte. a Singapore-based directional drilling equipment company. The acquisitions will help Carpenter expand its presence in the directional drilling equipment market.

HISTORY

Engineer James Henry Carpenter founded Carpenter Steel in Pennsylvania in 1889. The company began making specialty steels after winning a US Navy contract to develop armor-piercing projectiles. Business declined after Carpenter's death in 1898 but former rival Robert Jennings took over and the company rebounded thanks to marketing savvy and the development of new steel grades. Carpenter first produced stainless steel in 1917.

The company went public in 1937 and continued to grow. It made huge expansions in its production capacity to meet the demands spawned by WWII. The company changed its name to Carpenter Technology Corporation in 1968.

Carpenter survived the 1981-82 recession largely because of its lucrative niche in specialty steel. Another recession led to a 1991 reorganization. Robert Cardy a 30-year company veteran became chairman president and CEO the next year.

In 1994 Carpenter established a joint venture in Taiwan with Walsin-Lihwa (a Taiwanese maker of cable and wire). It also acquired Aceros Fortuna (Mexico's largest distributor of specialty steel) and purchased Certech (structural ceramics). In 1997 the company bought Dynamet a producer of titanium bar and wire. It also purchased about 75% of diversified manufacturer Talley Industries for about $312 million acquiring the remainder of Talley the next year. Carpenter formed a joint venture with Kalyani Steels in 1999 to make and distribute specialty steels in India.

High natural gas prices forced the company to increase prices for its nickel- and cobalt-based high-temperature alloys in 2001. The following year Carpenter's sales decreased due to lower stainless steel shipments and an overall weakness in the manufacturing industry.

In 2003 Carpenter's president Robert Torcolini was named to the added positions of chairman and CEO after chairman Dennis Draeger's retirement. Because of broad-based demand on its products Carpenter raised prices primarily on its stainless bar premium-metal alloys and high-speed tool steel products in 2004.

The next year Carpenter sold its Special Products unit a manufacturer of precision engineered metal components and assemblies to investment firm WHI Capital Partners. The former Carpenter Special Products which served customers in the aerospace medical device and nuclear power generation businesses was renamed Veridiam. Carpenter continued to supply alloys to its former subsidiary.

Three years after he took on the added roles of chairman and CEO Torcolini announced his retirement. Carpenter went outside the company to find his replacement tabbing Ford veteran Anne Stevens to take on all three titles.

The company's former Special Products unit sold in 2005 now operates as Veridiam. Carpenter continues to supply alloys to Veridiam which serves customers in the aerospace medical device and nuclear power generation businesses.

William Wulfsohn a former SVP with PPG Industries was named president and CEO of Carpenter in 2010.

To strengthen its presence globally in high-alloy metal powder products Carpenter formed a joint venture in 2010 with Sweden-based Sandvik Powdermet designed to lock in access to each other's goods and services. Each company took a 40% stake in the other assuring Sandvik's supply of powder materials and Carpenter's access to global manufacturing and sales services. The partnership will facilitate joint development of powder metal products particularly for the energy sector.

In fiscal 2011 Carpenter's net revenues increased about 40% as net sales reached nearly $1.7 billion in 2011 compared to less than $1.2 billion in 2010. Carpenter cited improved product mix price increases and better performance for the jump in profit and sales. Net income also soared in 2011 reaching $71.7 million compared to $2.1 million in 2010.

EXECUTIVES

SVP Strategic Business Development and Governmental Affairs, Sunil Y. Widge, age 63, $306,174 total compensation
VP Quality Technical and Customer Service, Russell E. Reber Jr.
President CEO and Director, William A. (Bill) Wulfsohn, age 51

President Asia Pacific, Jaime Vasquez
SVP Commercial Specialty Alloys Operations, Mark S. Kamon, age 59, $345,636 total compensation
Chairman, Gregory A. Pratt, age 65, $296,528 total compensation
VP Human Resources, John L. Rice
SVP Finance and CFO, K. Douglas (Doug) Ralph, age 51, $392,862 total compensation
VP and Treasurer, Michael A. (Mike) Hajost
VP Carpenter Powder Products and Dynamet, Williams B. Kent
SVP and CFO, Tony R. Thene, age 53
VP Premium Engineered Products, Sanjay Guglani
VP and Chief Accounting Officer, Thomas F. Cramsey, age 51
VP and CIO, James A. Johnson II
VP Manufacturing, J. Michael Hom
SVP Commercial Specialty Alloy Operations & Latrobe Operations, Andrew T. Ziolkowski
VP Advanced Engineering, Bernard M. Mara
VP Research and Development, Timothy R. Armstrong
SVP Global Operations, David L. Strobel, age 52
Vice President - Investor Relations Business Development, Dave Christiansen
VP and CIO, Robert C. Martens
VP Forged Bar and Billet Business Group, Stephen Peskosky
SVP Performance Engineered Products, Gary Heasley
Director, Stephen M. Ward Jr., age 57
President CEO and Director, William A. (Bill) Wulfsohn, age 51
Director, Kathryn C. Turner, age 64
Director, Carl G. Anderson Jr., age 68
Director, Jeffrey (Jeff) Wadsworth, age 64
Director, Robert R. McMaster, age 64
Director, I. Martin Inglis, age 63
Director, Philip M. Anderson, age 66
Independent Director, Steven Karol
Independent Director, Thomas Hicks
Auditors: PricewaterhouseCoopersLLP

LOCATIONS

HQ: Carpenter Technology Corporation
2 Meridian Blvd., Wyomissing PA 19610-1339
Phone: 610-208-2000   **Fax:** 610-208-3716
Web: www.cartech.com

2012 Sales

North America		
Mexico	66	3
Europe	382	17
Other regions	34	2

PRODUCTS/OPERATIONS

2012 Sales by Product

Special alloys	989	43
Alloy & tool steel	255	11
Total	**2,271**	**100**

2012 Sales by Market

Aerospace	1,067	47
Energy	337	15
Transportation	138	6
Total	**2,271**	**100**

COMPETITORS

AK Steel Holding Corporation	JFE Holdings
Allegheny Technologies	Nucor
Dofasco	Precision Castparts
Earle M. Jorgensen	RTI International Metals
Eramet	Titanium Metals
Essar Steel Algoma	United States Steel
Gerdau Ameristeel	

HISTORICAL FINANCIALS

Company Type: Public

Income Statement

FYE: June 30

	REVENUE ($ mil.)	NET INCOME ($ mil.)	NET PROFIT MARGIN	EMPLOYEES
06/13	2,271.7	146.1	6.4%	4,800
06/12	2,028.7	121.2	6.0%	4,800
06/11	1,675.1	71.0	4.2%	3,500
06/10	1,198.6	2.1	0.2%	3,000
06/09	1,362.3	47.9	3.5%	3,200
Annual Growth	**13.6%**	**32.2%**	**—**	**10.7%**

2013 Year-End Financials

Debt ratio: 20.9%
Return on equity: 12.1%
Cash ($ mil.): 257
Current ratio: 3.04
Long-term debt ($ mil.): 604

No. of shares (mil.): 52
Dividends
  Yield: 0.0%
  Payout: 26.3%
Market value ($ mil.): 2,378

	STOCK PRICE ($) FY Close	P/E High/Low		PER SHARE ($) Earnings	Dividends	Book Value
06/13	45.07	20	16	2.73	0.72	24.69
06/12	47.84	23	16	2.53	0.72	21.06
06/11	57.68	36	19	1.59	0.72	17.36
06/10	32.83	1063	422	0.04	0.72	13.04
06/09	20.81	40	11	1.08	0.72	14.01
Annual Growth	**21.3%**	**—**	**—**	**26.1%**	**(0.0%)**	**15.2%**

Carrizo Oil & Gas, Inc.

Carrizo Oil & Gas sees its future in 3-D. An independent exploration and production company that explores for oil and gas in a handful of shale plays across the US and in proven onshore fields along the Gulf Coast of Texas and Louisiana Carrizo aggressively acquires 3-D seismic data and arranges land lease options in conjunction with conducting seismic surveys. As part of its shale strategy the company is exploiting the Marcellus play in Appalachia and the Eagle Ford and Barnett plays in Texas. Carrizo has additional properties in the Rockies Arkansas Kentucky Mississippi New Mexico and in the UK North Sea. In 2011 the firm reported proved reserves of 935.6 billion cu. ft. of natural gas equivalent.

Operations

Carrizo's oil and gas exploration and production operations are principally focused on developing proven producing oil and gas plays. In 2011 the company's proved reserves were 78% natural gas and 22% crude oil condensate and natural gas liquids.

Geographic Reach

The company focuses on the Eagle Ford Shale in South Texas the Niobrara Formation in Colorado the Barnett Shale in North Texas the Marcellus Shale in Pennsylvania New York and West Virginia and the Utica Shale in Ohio and Pennsylvania. Outside the US it is working in the UK North Sea in the Huntington Field.

Financial Analysis

Revenues from oil and gas production in 2011 increased 46% to $202.2 million from $138.1 million in 2010. Production volumes for oil and gas in 2011 increased 22% to 45.1 billion cu. ft. equivalent from 36.8 billion cu. ft. equivalent in 2010.

The increase in production from new oil wells in 2011 helped to lift revenues assisted by a jump in oil prices. Average oil prices increased 20% to $94.1 per barrel from $78.6 per barrel in 2010. By contrast average natural gas prices declined 11% to $2.98 per Mcf in 2011 from $3.33 per Mcf in 2010. Natural gas liquids prices increased 31% to $8.4 per Mcf in 2011 from $6.43 per Mcf in 2010 although lower production of NGLs led to a revenue decline in this segment.

In 2011 net income grew by 268% as surging revenues outpaced an increase in operating expenses and Carrizo did not have to carry the $31 million debt-related charge it carried in 2010.

Strategy

The company's strategy is focused on organic growth and to ramp up the development of shale plays (both in the US —Barnett Eagle Ford Marcellus Niobrara and Utica —and in the UK) which have become more commercially viable thanks to advances in drilling technology in recent years. It is pushing to develop higher return crude oil and liquids-rich shale assets (Eagle Ford Niobrara and Utica) to take advantage of high oil oil and NGL prices. The company also seeks capital influx from other companies (inclduing Indian ol companies) through joint ventures to help to develop its cost-intensive shale assets.

In 2012 Carrizo formed a joint venture with subsidiaries of OIL India Ltd. and Indian Oil to exploit Carrizo's assets in the Niobrara Formation oil development in Colorado. Carrizo sold its partners a 30% interest in the Colorado asset for $82.5 million.

In 2011 Carrizo and Avista Capital Partners formed a joint venture to acquire and develop acreage in the liquids rich region of the Utica Shale. In a similar move Carrizo also teamed up with India's GAIL Limited forming a joint venture to exploit assets in the Eagle Ford Shale.

In 2010 the company joined forces with Indian conglomerate Reliance Industries forming a joint venture which acquired 104400 undeveloped leasehold acres in the Marcellus Shale in Appalachia.

Selected Customers

DTE Energy Trading accounted for 43% of Carrizo's revenues in 2011.

EXECUTIVES

Vice President Chief Financial Officer and Secretary, Paul F. Boling, age 59, $229,667 total compensation
Chairman, Steven A. Webster, age 61
President CEO and Director, S. P. (Chip) Johnson IV, age 57, $408,000 total compensation
VP and COO, J. Bradley (Brad) Fisher, age 52, $285,000 total compensation
Vice President of Exploration and Development, Gregory E. Evans, age 63, $226,000 total compensation
Vice President of Land, Richard H. Smith, age 55, $206,667 total compensation
Chief Accounting Officer, David L. Pitts, age 47
VP Business Development (Marcellus), Jim Pritts
General Counsel and VP Business Development, Gerry Morton
VP-IR, Richard Hunter
Director, Frank A. Wojtek, age 57
President CEO and Director, S. P. (Chip) Johnson IV, age 57
Director, Roger A. Ramsey, age 75
Director, F. Gardner Parker, age 71
Director, Thomas L. Carter Jr., age 61
Auditors: KPMGLLP

LOCATIONS

HQ: Carrizo Oil & Gas Inc.
500 Dallas St. Ste. 2300, Houston TX 77002
Phone: 713-328-1000   **Fax:** 713-328-1035
Web: www.crzo.net

PRODUCTS/OPERATIONS

2011 Sales

	$ mil.	% of total
Natural gas	116	58
Oil & condensate	75	37
NGLs	10	5
Total	**202**	**100**

COMPETITORS

Abraxas Petroleum	Forest Oil
Adams Resources	Gastar Exploration
BP	Newfield Exploration
Belden & Blake	Penn Virginia
Brigham Exploration	Petrohawk Energy
Chesapeake Energy	Pioneer Natural
Chevron	Resources
Clayton Williams	Quicksilver Resources
Energy	Samson
Comstock Resources	Shell Oil
Crosstex Energy Inc.	Statoil
Exxon Mobil	TOTAL

HISTORICAL FINANCIALS

Company Type: Public

Income Statement

FYE: December 31

	REVENUE ($ mil.)	NET INCOME ($ mil.)	NET PROFIT MARGIN	EMPLOYEES
12/12	368.1	55.4	15.1%	208
12/11	202.1	36.6	18.1%	169
12/10	139.4	9.9	7.1%	132
12/09	114.0	(204.8)	—	111
12/08	216.6	(17.9)	—	104
Annual Growth	**14.2%**	**—**		**18.9%**

2012 Year-End Financials

Debt ratio: 51.3%
Return on equity: 10.1%
Cash ($ mil.): 52
Current ratio: 0.70
Long-term debt ($ mil.): 967
No. of shares (mil.): 40
Dividends
  Yield: —
  Payout: —
Market value ($ mil.): 840

	STOCK PRICE ($) FY Close	P/E High/Low	PER SHARE ($) Earnings	Dividends	Book Value
12/12	20.92	22 14	1.39	0.00	14.57
12/11	26.35	46 21	0.92	0.00	12.89
12/10	34.49	119 54	0.29	0.00	11.74
12/09	26.51	— —	(6.61)	0.00	7.96
12/08	16.10	— —	(0.60)	0.00	13.84
Annual Growth	**6.8%**	**— —**	**—**	**—**	**1.3%**

Carter's Inc

Carter's has built a big business catering to little ones. Operating through its William Carter Company it's the largest US branded marketer of apparel exclusively for babies and young children. Primary products include newborn layette clothing sleepwear and playwear. It markets its items under the Carter's and OshKosh B'Gosh brands as well as private labels Child of Mine Just One You Genuine Kids and Precious Firsts. While Carter's sells products online and as a wholesaler via 17000 department and specialty stores it also operates some 580 Carter's and OshKosh stores nationwide and 80 stores in Canada thanks to its 2011 acquisition of Bonnie Togs. Carter's was established in 1865 by William Carter.

Geographic Reach

Carter's primarily operates in the US but has gained a foothold in Canada (9% of sales) by acquiring its longtime international licensee there. As a result the manufacturer also boasts a growing retail presence across the nation and into Canada. Across its portfolio the company's apparel and accessories are sold in more than 50 countries worldwide.

Operations

Effective October 2011 the company operates its business through five segments: Carter's wholesale Carter's retail OshKosh retail OshKosh wholesale and international. Following its Bonnie Togs purchase Carter's realigned its reportable segments to include a new international segment to house its Canadian operations existing international wholesale business and royalty income from its international licensees.

Sales and Marketing

The company's brands compete in the $21 billion children's apparel market for children newborn to age 7. Carter's enjoys the #1 branded position and a 14% market share; OshKosh has nearly a 3% market share. Because the company uses a variety of distribution channels it's able to market its products to a more diverse range of consumers and geographic regions. Wal-Mart sells its Child of Mine line while Target offers the Just One You and Precious Firsts brands; the two retailers generate about 15% of sales.

Financial Analysis

Like the children it clothes Carter's is "growing like a weed." Indeed in 2012 Carter's posted record sales of nearly $2.4 billion more than triple its sales in 2003. In 2012 sales increased 13% vs. 2011 while net income rose 41% over the same period. Internaitonal (Bonnie Togs in Canada) and retail sales of its Carter's brand apparel drove growth in 2012. All of the company's business segments grew with the exception of the OshKosh Wholesale business which posted a 3% drop in year-over-year sales. Higher selling prices lower costs and growth in the direct-to-consumer business all contributed to profit growth in 2012.

Strategy

The company has developed a reputation for producing high-quality clothing for children —from the cradle through the early school years. The Carter's brand and private-label collections made for mass-market customers offer apparel in newborn through children's size 7. These lines mostly consist of cotton essentials such as bodysuits and pajamas and collectively typically account for about two-thirds of revenues. Besides apparel Carter's licenses bedding toys furnishings baby gear and gifts that are sold through mass merchandisers. The OshKosh brand acquired in 2005 has extended the company's product range from newborns through children size 12. Known for its rugged playclothes including overalls and T-shirts OshKosh items are marketed at higher price points than the company's traditional Carter's branded products. The company is working to boost its revenues further through expansion of its retail and outlet store operations.

The infant and children's apparel manufacturer is banking on its 2011 acquisition of Bonnie Togs to ultimately provide a network of some 160 stores in Canada that contribute total annual revenues of more than $200 million by 2016.

Mergers and Acquisitions

Carter's extended its reach northward into Canada and added an international segment to its business as a result of the company's 2011 $98 million purchase of Bonnie Togs a Canadian specialty retailer of children's apparel and accessories. Bonnie Togs had been Carter's principal licensee in Canada since 2007.

Ownership

Berkshire Fund VII L.P. owns nearly 16% of the company.

EXECUTIVES

Chairman & Chief Executive Officer, Michael D. (Mike) Casey, age 52, $700,000 total compensation

President Retail Stores, James C. (Jim) Petty, age 54, $425,000 total compensation

Executive Vice President & Brand Leader of OshKosh B?gosh, Lisa A. Fitzgerald, age 50

Executive Vice President & Chief Financial Officer, Richard F. Westenberger, age 44, $376,923 total compensation

Senior Vice President of Marketing, William G. (Greg) Foglesong, age 43

President, Brian J. Lynch, age 50

SVP Human Resources and Talent Development, Jill A. Wilson, age 46

SVP Legal and Corporate Affairs General Counsel and Secretary, Brendan M. Gibbons, age 37

Executive Vice President of Supply Chain, Christopher W. (Chris) Rork

Executive Vice President International, Kevin D. Corning

Executive Vice President and Brand Leader for Carter?s, Lisa C. Evans

Senior Vice President of Retail, Jeffrey B. Williams

Director, Vanessa J. Castagna, age 63

Director, Thomas E. Whiddon, age 60

Director, Paul Fulton, age 78

Director, David Pulver, age 71

Director, Jevin S. Eagle, age 46

Director, A. Bruce Cleverly, age 68

Director, John R. Welch, age 81

Director, William J. Montgoris, age 66

Director, Amy W. Brinkley, age 57

Auditors: PricewaterhouseCoopersLLP

LOCATIONS

HQ: Carter's Inc.
The Proscenium 1170 Peachtree St. NE Ste. 900, Atlanta GA 30309
Phone: 404-745-2700 **Fax:** 404-892-0968
Web: www.carters.com

PRODUCTS/OPERATIONS

2012 Stores

	No.
Carter's	413
OshKosh	168
International	82
Total	**663**

2012 Sales

	$ mil.	% of total
Carter's wholesale	981	41
Carter's retail	818	34
OshKosh retail	283	12
OshKosh wholesale	79	4
International	218	9
Total	**2,381**	**100**

Selected Brands

Carter's
Child of Mine (for Wal-mart)
Genuine Kids from OshKosh
Just One You (for Target)
Little Collections
Little Layette
OshKosh
OshKosh B'Gosh
Precious Firsts (for Target)

COMPETITORS

Babies "R" Us	Levi Strauss
Belk	Macy's
Bon-Ton Stores	Old Navy
Costco Wholesale	Oxford Industries
Disney	Sears Holdings
Fred Meyer Stores	Target Corporation
Fruit of the Loom	The Children's Place
Garan	The Gap
Gerber Childrenswear	Toys ''R'' Us
Gymboree	VF Corporation
J. C. Penney	Wal-Mart
Kohl's	Williamson-Dickie
L.L. Bean	Manufacturing
Lands' End	

HISTORICAL FINANCIALS

Company Type: Public

Income Statement

FYE: December 29

	REVENUE ($ mil.)	NET INCOME ($ mil.)	NET PROFIT MARGIN	EMPLOYEES
12/12	2,381.7	161.1	6.8%	11,786
12/11*	2,109.7	114.0	5.4%	8,684
01/11	1,749.2	146.4	8.4%	8,673
01/10	1,589.6	115.6	7.3%	7,622
01/09	1,490.0	75.0	5.0%	6,548
Annual Growth	**12.4%**	**21.0%**	**—**	**15.8%**

*Fiscal year change

2012 Year-End Financials

Debt ratio: 11.4%
Return on equity: 18.0%
Cash ($ mil.): 382
Current ratio: 3.92
Long-term debt ($ mil.): 186
No. of shares (mil.): 59
Dividends
Yield: —
Payout: —
Market value ($ mil.): 3,207

	STOCK PRICE ($) FY Close	P/E High/Low		PER SHARE ($) Earnings	Dividends	Book Value
12/12	54.24	21	14	2.69	0.00	16.67
12/11*	39.81	21	14	1.94	0.00	13.75
01/11	29.51	13	9	2.46	0.00	11.83
01/10	26.25	14	7	1.97	0.00	9.57
01/09	19.24	17	10	1.29	0.00	7.57
Annual Growth	**29.6%**	**—**	**—**	**20.2%**	**—**	**21.8%**

*Fiscal year change

Cascade Microtech Inc

In the foothills of the Cascade Range Cascade Microtech makes test systems for microelectronics. Semiconductor makers such as Broadcom Fujitsu Semiconductor IBM Intel Samsung and Toshiba use the company's probe cards probe stations and analytical probes to ensure the quality of their integrated circuits (ICs). Many of Cascade's customers use its tools to test their wireless broadband or other communications ICs at the wafer level before the wafers are cut into individual chips. The company has a development alliance with test equipment giant Agilent Technologies. Cascade gets more than 70% of sales from outside the US primarily from customers in Asia.

Cascade bought the semiconductor test equipment business of SUSS MicroTec in 2010 for E4.5 million (about $6 million) in cash and stock plus future payouts. The purchase added a line of wafer probe test systems that expanded Cascade's product portfolio and added 3-D light-emitting diode (LED) and microelectromechanical systems (MEMS) applications —all emerging technologies in the semiconductor test market.

Cascade's sales which have improved since the SUSS acquisition needed the SUSS boost. The company's sales fell by about 40% between 2007 and 2009 primarily due to a downturn in the semiconductor industry. In 2009 alone sales dropped by 30%. Notably in 2010 sales of systems were up 126% compared to 2009. Cascade announced it would restructure late in 2010 as it consolidated the sales organizations and manufacturing operations of the two companies. Post-integration systems are manufactured in Germany while probes are produced at one of its Oregon facilities.

In 2011 the company reported record revenues up 13% over 2010. Systems sales rose 16% on higher average selling prices offset in part by a decrease in unit sales of its more compact systems. The increase in average selling price is attributed to sales of more high-end and special application stations and related probes probe cards and accessories. Cascade managed to trim its net loss to $3.8 million for the year compared to a net loss of $8.1 million in 2010. The company's loss included restructuring charges and factory moving and other project costs in both years. Restructuring costs included employee severance and charges related to abandoned leases.

In 2011 Cascade sold its sockets operation to R&D Sockets for cash and a note receivable due in 2012 as well as the assumption of administrative office and manufacturing facility lease obligations. The company took a $1.5 million loss on disposal of the business.

Co-founders Eric Strid (CTO and former CEO) and K. Reed Gleason own about 12% and 11% respectively of Cascade.

EXECUTIVES

President and CEO; Director, Michael D. (Mike) Burger, age 54

CTO and Director, Eric W. Strid, age 60, $203,231 total compensation

VP Advanced Development and Director Emeritus, K. Reed Gleason, age 67, $152,881 total compensation

VP-Sls & Support, Paul O'Mara

Chairman, F. Paul Carlson, age 74

Vice President Human Resources, Ellen Raim, age 54

Director Sales and Marketing Production Probe Card Division, Russell Schlager

Executive Vice President, Steven L. (Steve) Harris, age 49

VP Marketing, Michael Kondrat, age 63, $163,846 total compensation

Senior Manager Marketing Communications, Laurie Winton

Vice President Finance and Chief Financial Officer, Jeff A. Killian, age 53

Vice President Operations, Steve Mahon, age 53

Vice President - Marketing, Debbora Ahlgren

Vice President - Sales and Customer Service, Paul OMara

VP Sales and Service, Robert Selley

President and CEO; Director, Michael D. (Mike) Burger, age 54

Director, Raymond A. (Ray) Link, age 58

Director, William R. Spivey, age 66

CTO and Director, Eric W. Strid, age 60

Director, George P. O'Leary, age 69

Director, John Y. Chen, age 64

Independent Director, John Delafield

Auditors: KPMGLLP

LOCATIONS

HQ: Cascade Microtech Inc.
2430 NW 206th Ave., Beaverton OR 97006-6461
Phone: 503-601-1000   **Fax:** 503-601-1002
Web: www.cascademicrotech.com

2011 Sales

	$ mil.	% of total
Asia/Pacific	49	48
US	27	26
Europe	24	23
Other regions	2	3
Total	**104**	**100**

PRODUCTS/OPERATIONS

2011 Sales

	$ mil.	% of total
Systems	75	72
Probes	28	28
Total	**104**	**100**

Selected Products

Analytical Probes
  Air coplanar probes and high-performance characterization (HPC) probes (transistors broadband chip packages)
Probe Stations
  Alessi series (general-purpose)
  S300 series (semi-automated with 300mm wafer testing capability)
  Summit series (transistor and chip measurements circuit element modeling)
Production Probe Cards
  LSI Pyramid probe cores (application-specific integrated circuits)
  Pyramid interface boards (all cores)
  RFC Pyramid probe cores (SONET and wireless chips optoelectronic devices)
  VLSR Pyramid probe cores (LCD driver chips)

COMPETITORS

Advantest	Interconnect Devices
Aehr Test Systems	KLA-Tencor
EG Systems	LTX-Credence
Everett Charles Technologies	PDF Solutions
	Teradyne
FormFactor	

HISTORICAL FINANCIALS

Company Type: Public

Income Statement

FYE: December 31

	REVENUE ($ mil.)	NET INCOME ($ mil.)	NET PROFIT MARGIN	EMPLOYEES
12/12	112.9	6.1	5.4%	383
12/11	104.6	(5.8)	—	365
12/10	95.8	(10.3)	—	401
12/09	53.5	(7.6)	—	306
12/08	76.5	(34.5)	—	292
Annual Growth	**10.2%**	**—**	**—**	**7.0%**

2012 Year-End Financials

Debt ratio: —
Return on equity: 9.7%
Cash ($ mil.): 17
Current ratio: 4.49
Long-term debt ($ mil.): —

No. of shares (mil.): 14
Dividends
  Yield: —
  Payout: —
Market value ($ mil.): 80

	STOCK PRICE ($) FY Close	P/E High/Low	Earnings	PER SHARE ($) Dividends	Book Value
12/12	5.60	14 7	0.42	0.00	4.64
12/11	3.41	— —	(0.40)	0.00	4.19
12/10	4.35	— —	(0.72)	0.00	4.52
12/09	4.58	— —	(0.57)	0.00	5.30
12/08	1.95	— —	(2.65)	0.00	5.83
Annual Growth	**30.2%**	**— —**	**—**	**—**	**(5.5%)**

Cash America International, Inc.

If cash is king then Cash America International is king of pawns. Cash America operates more than 960 stores under the banners Cash America Pawn SuperPawn and Pawn X-Change in the US and Cash America casa de empe?o in Mexico. The company is one of the largest providers of secured non-recourse loans (also known as pawn loans). As part of its business Cash America also provides cash advances in half a dozen states through shops operating under the Cashland and Cash America Payday Advance banners. The company offers check cashing money orders and money transfers through about 90 owned and franchised Mr. Payroll stores in about 15 states.

Geographic Reach

Cash America operates through about two dozen US states as well as in Mexico. The US accounts for about 80% of its revenue. Its retail segment operates primarily in Texas and Ohio. Through its e-commerce business Cash America enjoys an extended reach into the UK Australia Canada and Mexico.

Operations

The company operates its business through two segments: Retail Services (63% of revenue) and E-commerce (37%).

Retail Services include pawn lending and consumer lending among other services. Its domestic retail services locations operate under the names Cash America Pawn SuperPawn Cash America Payday Advance Cashland and Mr. Payroll. The domestic retail services locations it has acquired were rebranded in 2013 as Cash America Pawn or SuperPawn. Its foreign retail services locations began operating exclusively under the name Cash America casa de empe?o (previously operating under the name Prenda Facil).

The E-commerce segment comprises its domestic and foreign online lending channels through which Cash America offers consumer loans. The segment operated in more than 30 US states and in three foreign countries. It offers a line of credit product in Mexico that is similar to the micro line of credit (MLOC). Consumer loan fees contribute about 43% of the company's revenue.

Financial Performance

Revenue rose by 17% in 2012 as compared to 2011. Growth in the UK and other foreign markets

helped Cash America log increases primarily due to consumer loan fees from higher average consumer loan balances in the e-commerce segment. Net income meanwhile dropped some 21% during the same reporting period thanks to increases in the cost of revenue from consumer loan loss provisions due to a mix of installment loans and line of credit accounts as a percentage of total consumer loan portfolio. The company's organic growth acquisitions and a $2.4 million spend on employee termination costs related to reorganizing its Mexico operations spurred rising expenses in its operations and administration unit.

Sales and Marketing

Cash America offers loans through retail stores. It offers consumer loans to customers in more than 30 US states through www.cashnetusa.com and www.netcredit.com. In the UK it operates www.quickquid.com.uk and www.pound-stopocket.co.uk. In Australia Cash America runs www.dollarsdirect.com.au and in Canada it provides loans through www.dollarsdirect.ca.

Excluding lead purchase costs Cash America's marketing expenses reached $72.2 million in 2012 up significantly from $41.2 million in 2011 and $30.1 million in 2010. Its 2012 2011 and 2010 lead purchase expenses were $49.7 million $43.2 million and $40.5 million respectively.

The company's pawn and cash advance businesses carry a stigma whether justified or not of preying on the poor or uneducated. (For its part the company claims it attracts consumers who cannot or do not want to deal with traditional banks.) Several states have enacted legislation in recent years that put limits on loan amounts or the interest rates that pawn and payday lenders can charge. In these markets Cash America has either curtailed its operations or is concentrating on credit services such as arranging consumer loans through third-party lenders. The company has also increased it focus on gold-buying services and added stored-value cards.

Strategy

The company is working to expand where it already operates. Strategic markets include Tennessee North Carolina Kentucky and Arizona — states where the company already operates more than 80 pawn lending locations. As part of this push its Nevada subsidiary acquired a nine-store chain of pawn lending locations in Arizona for approximately $15.4 million. Cash America also purchased a 25-store chain of pawn lending locations in Kentucky North Carolina and Tennessee for about $55.1 million.

To streamline its business in Mexico Cash America reorganized its network of stores there to consist of only full-service pawn locations that offer pawn loans based on the pledge of general merchandise and jewelry-based collateral. To this end the company shuttered nearly 150 Mexico-based pawn locations that primarily offered pawn loans based on the pledge of jewelry-based collateral. The move involved buying a 20% minority interest in Creazione Estilo S.A. de C.V. for about $5.6 million and made it a wholly owned subsidiary of Cash America.

HISTORY

When Jack Daugherty was a student he hocked his guitar to finance dates. In 1970 after quitting school he opened a pawnshop that was so successful he used the proceeds to invest in oil. When oil took a downturn he returned to the pawn business incorporating Cash America in 1984; it went public in 1987.

Cash America bought UK-based Harvey & Thompson Ltd. in 1992; two years later the company acquired Sweden's Svensk Pantbel?ning. As part of a low-cost expansion program the firm in 1997 introduced a Cash America franchise plan to independent pawnshop owners.

Over the next two years Cash America expanded further in Texas and Utah. In 1998 Mr. Payroll rolled out automated check-cashing machines that identified customers by their facial features; it formed an alliance with Crestar to supplement the bank's Virginia supermarket branches with the machines. Also that year the company launched its Rent-A-Tire subsidiary in Texas.

In 1999 Cash America expanded its automated check cashing business participating in InnoVentry a joint venture with Wells Fargo (InnoVentry ceased operations in 2001). In 2000 Cash America got lots of publicity (presumably unwanted) when its nine-story headquarters in downtown Fort Worth was slammed by a tornado; the building was later renovated.

In an attempt to focus on lending activities subsidiary Rent-A-Tire was sold off in 2002. The following year Cash America doubled its cash advance operations with the purchase of Cashland Financial Services.

With a desire to concentrate on US operations Cash America sold off its operations in Sweden and the UK in 2004 while at the same time expanding its presence in Southern California with the purchase of UrgentMoney and GoldX.

EXECUTIVES

Executive Vice President and Chief Financial Officer, Thomas A. Bessant Jr., age 54, $375,436 total compensation
President and CEO, Daniel R. Feehan, age 62, $726,000 total compensation
Chairman, Jack R. Daugherty, age 65
EVP General Counsel and Secretary, J. Curtis Linscott, age 47
Director, Albert Goldstein, age 32
President & Chief Operating Officer Retail Services Division, Dennis J. Weese, age 49, $322,650 total compensation
President E-Commerce Division, Timothy S. Ho, age 32
Chief Executive Officer of the E-Commerce Division and CEO of ENOVA Financial, David A. Fisher
VP-Govt Affairs, Alex Vaughn
VP-Customer Support Svcs, Melody Smiley
President and CEO, Daniel R. Feehan, age 61
Director, Daniel E. (Dan) Berce, age 59
Director, Alfred M. Micallef, age 70
Director, James H. Graves, age 64
Director, Buddy (B.D) Hunter, age 83
Director, Timothy J. McKibben, age 64
Auditors: PricewaterhouseCoopersLLP

LOCATIONS

HQ: Cash America International Inc.
1600 W. 7th St., Fort Worth TX 76102-2599
Phone: 817-335-1100   **Fax:** 817-570-1225
Web: www.cashamerica.com

2012 Sales

	% of total
US	78
UK	17
Mexico	4
Other foreign	1
Total	**100**

PRODUCTS/OPERATIONS

Selected Services

Check Cashing & Other Financial Services
Consumer Loan Activities
Merchandise Disposition Activities
Pawn Lending

2012 Sales

	% of total
Retail Services	
Domestic	60
Foreign	3
E-commerce	
Domestic	19
Foreign	18
Total	**100**

2012 Sales

	$ mil.	% of total
Consumer loan fees	781.5	43
Proceeds from disposition of merchandise	703.7	39
Pawn loan fees & service charges	300.9	17
Other	14.2	1
Total	**1800.4**	**100**

COMPETITORS

ACE Cash Express
Advance America
Cash Converters
Cash Plus
Check Into Cash
DFC Global
DGSE Companies

EZCORP
First Cash Financial Services
Winmark
World Acceptance
Xponential

HISTORICAL FINANCIALS

Company Type: Public

Income Statement

FYE: December 31

	REVENUE ($ mil.)	NET INCOME ($ mil.)	NET PROFIT MARGIN	EMPLOYEES
12/12	1,800.4	107.4	6.0%	7,035
12/11	1,540.6	135.9	8.8%	6,619
12/10	1,293.3	115.5	8.9%	6,017
12/09	1,120.3	96.6	8.6%	5,445
12/08	1,030.7	81.1	7.9%	5,587
Annual Growth	**15.0%**	**7.3%**	**—**	**5.9%**

2012 Year-End Financials

Debt ratio: 31.8%
Return on equity: 11.3%
Cash ($ mil.): 63
Current ratio: 4.79
Long-term debt ($ mil.): 534

No. of shares (mil.): 28
Dividends
  Yield: 0.3%
  Payout: 3.6%
Market value ($ mil.): 1,146

	STOCK PRICE ($) FY Close	P/E High/Low		PER SHARE ($) Earnings	Dividends	Book Value
12/12	39.67	13	9	3.42	0.14	34.34
12/11	46.63	13	8	4.25	0.14	30.88
12/10	36.93	11	8	3.67	0.14	26.95
12/09	34.96	11	4	3.17	0.14	23.10
12/08	27.35	17	8	2.70	0.14	19.55
Annual Growth	**9.7%**	**—**	**—**	**6.1%**	**(0.0%)**	**15.1%**

Centerstate Banks, Inc.

CenterState Banks is the holding company for CenterState Bank of Florida which serves the Sunshine State through about 60 branches. The banks offer standard deposit products such as checking and savings accounts money market accounts and CDs. They also sell mutual funds annuities and other investment products. Real estate loans primarily residential and commercial mortgages make up more than three-quarters of the company's loan portfolio. CenterState began offering correspondent banking services in 2008 and the business quickly became one of the company's largest revenue-earning segments.

The correspondent banking division provides bond securities accounting and loans to small and midsized banks throughout the Southeast and Texas. It expanded with the 2011 addition of a correspondent banking team from the failed Silverton Bank in Atlanta.

Bargain purchase gains from acquisitions helped CenterState turn a nearly $8 million profit in 2011 on revenues of nearly $185 million. Hampered by the Florida economy which had been hit particularly hard by the recession the company had posted losses each of the previous two years.

In separate deals CenterState has acquired six failed banks in FDIC-assisted transactions since 2010 adding about 20 branches. In a more traditional deal the company in 2011 bought Federal Trust Corporation parent of Federal Trust Bank in central Florida from insurance group The Hartford adding five branches. CenterState also acquired four branches from TD Bank.

CenterState continues to seek out additional acquisition opportunities and is targeting the Florida markets of Jacksonville Okeechobee and Vero Beach for expansion. In order to simplify its operations the company merged its former Valrico State Bank subsidiary into CenterState Bank in 2012.

EXECUTIVES

SVP CFO and Corporate Secretary, James J. Antal, age 62, $190,000 total compensation
Chairman Emeritus, James H. White, age 87
Chairman President and CEO; Chairman CenterState Bank Central Florida CenterState Bank West Florida and CenterState Bank Mid Florida, Ernest S. (Ernie) Pinner, age 65, $350,000 total compensation
President and CEO Valrico State Bank, Jerry L. Ball, age 57
Chief Credit Officer President CEO, Robert Dodd
EVP and Director; President and CEO Centerstate Bank of Florida, John Corbett, age 45, $230,000 total compensation
President and CEO CenterState Bank Central Florida, Thomas E. White, age 58, $192,000 total compensation
CFO CenterState Bank of Florida, Steve Young
President and CEO CenterState Bank, Timothy A. Pierson, age 53, $178,313 total compensation
Area Executive Winter Haven CenterState Bank of Florida, J. Brett Barnhardt
Area Executive Ridge Centerstate Bank of Florida, Paul W. Gerrard Jr.
EVP and Chief Credit Officer CenterState Bank, Joseph D. Cioppa
SVP and CFO CenterState Bank, John L. Rust
SVP and Chief Credit Oficer CenterState Bank Central Florida, Mark W. Thompson
EVP and Director Lending Valrico State Bank, Donald M. Weaver
SVP and COO, Rodney A. Anthony
Corporate Chief Risk Officer; Executive Vice President of CenterState Bank of Florida; N.A, Daniel Bockhorst
Senior Vice President; Treasurer; Executive Vice President and COO of CenterState Bank of Florida; N.A, Stephen Young
Director, James H. Bingham, age 64
Director, Bryan W. Judge, age 84

Director, Samuel L. (Sam) Lupfer IV, age 56
Director, J. Thomas Rocker, age 70
Chairman President and CEO; Chairman
CenterState Bank Central Florida CenterState
Bank West Florida and CenterState Bank Mid
Florida, Ernest S. (Ernie) Pinner, age 65
Director, Thomas E. Oakley, age 70
Director, George Tierso Nunez II, age 59
EVP and Director; President and CEO Centerstate
Bank of Florida, John Corbett, age 45
Director, G. Robert Blanchard Jr., age 48
Director, Rulon D. Munns, age 62
Director, Gail Gregg-Strimenos, age 64
Director, Charles D. Carlton, age 60
Auditors: CroweHorwathLLP

LOCATIONS

HQ: CenterState Banks Inc.
42745 US Hwy. 27, Davenport FL 33837
Phone: 863-419-7750   Fax: -7762
Web: www.dartgroup.co.uk

PRODUCTS/OPERATIONS

2011 Sales

	$ mil.	% of total
Interest		
Loans	65	36
Investment securities available for sale	15	9
Other	0	-
Noninterest		
Bargain purchase gain	57	31
Correspondent banking & bond sales	24	13
Service charges on deposit accounts	6	3
Net gain on sale of securities	3	2
Other	10	6
Total	**184**	**100**

COMPETITORS

BB&T	JPMorgan Chase
BBX Capital	Regions Financial
Bank of America	SunTrust
Fifth Third	Wells Fargo

HISTORICAL FINANCIALS

Company Type: Public

Income Statement

FYE: December 31

	ASSETS ($ mil.)	NET INCOME ($ mil.)	INCOME AS % OF ASSETS	EMPLOYEES
12/12	2,363.2	9.9	0.4%	689
12/11	2,284.4	7.9	0.3%	655
12/10	2,063.3	(5.5)	—	600
12/09	1,751.3	(6.2)	—	478
12/08	1,333.1	3.4	0.3%	399
Annual Growth	15.4%	30.4%	—	14.6%

2012 Year-End Financials

Return on assets: 0.4%
Return on equity: 3.6%
Long-term debt ($ mil.): —
No. of shares (mil.): 30
Sales ($ mil): 154

Dividends
Yield: 0.4%
Payout: 12.1%
Market value ($ mil.): 257

	STOCK PRICE ($) FY Close	P/E High/Low	PER SHARE ($) Earnings	Dividends	Book Value
12/12	8.53	27 20	0.33	0.04	9.09
12/11	6.62	31 19	0.26	0.04	8.74
12/10	7.92	— —	(0.20)	0.04	8.42
12/09	10.09	— —	(0.47)	0.07	8.90
12/08	16.99	69 37	0.26	0.16	14.36
Annual Growth (15.8%) (10.8%)		— —	6.1%	(29.3%)	

Ceva Inc

CEVA has a fever for semiconductor design. CEVA specializes in technology —both integrated circuit and software designs —used in cell phones handheld computers MP3 players and other wireless devices. It licenses its semiconductor intellectual property (SIP) designs to such industry heavyweights as Broadcom and Sony. The company derives more than 90% of its sales from technology licensing and royalties with the remainder coming from design and consulting services along with maintenance training and technical support fees from licensees. CEVA's SIP is shipped in more than 600 million devices a year.

Revenue for CEVA rose more than 16% in 2010 over 2009.

CEVA operates in a highly competitive sector of the semiconductor industry. The company tries to keep a firm grasp on a limited number of customers —its top five clients accounting for more than 80% of royalty revenues —while competitors lower fees in an attempt to pull them away. The company is also trying to decrease its reliance on Europe and the Middle East responsible for than 40% of revenue by exploring opportunities in such emerging markets as China India and Africa where ultra-low-cost handsets are an attractive solution for communications needs.

More generally CEVA's revenue mix is shifting from primarily licensing to more of royalties. CEVA signed 25 new license agreements in 2010 compared with 34 the year before and 30 in 2008. According to technology consulting firm The Linley Group CEVA held a 78% share of the licensable DSP market in 2010. DSPs are widely used in wireless handsets and other portable electronics.

The company took the name ParthusCeva after Ireland's Parthus Technologies combined its operations with the Ceva unit of DSP Group; the combined company later changed its name to CEVA.

HISTORY

Brian Long and Peter McManamon founded Silicon Systems in 1993. Long's background included a stint at AT&T and 17 years with Digital Equipment; McManamon co-founded a large-screen projector company. Silicon Systems was aided early on by seed capital from Enterprise Ireland a government-run development agency plus its first customer STMicroelectronics. Long took advantage of his previous contact with the Switzerland-based semiconductor giant to secure early contracts.

Over the next five years Silicon Systems honed its design skills in a number of technologies performing contract work for STMicroelectronics and other chip manufacturers. During this period the company retained ownership and licensing rights to its intellectual property which incorporated expertise in digital analog and mixed-signal chips as well as in software design.

Silicon Systems narrowed its focus in 1998 deciding to concentrate on technology for mobile devices. That year Goldman Sachs invested in the company trading $16 million for a 23% stake (reduced to 19% after the company's public offering and subsequently divested).

In 2000 Silicon Systems changed its name to Parthus Technologies and acquired the Global Positioning System (GPS) division of electronics maker Symmetricom. Later that year the company went public listing on both the Nasdaq and the

London Stock Exchange in what was at that time the largest technology float by an Irish company. The offering made the reticent Long (he was often accused of being too modest about the company's achievements) one of the richest men in Ireland.

Parthus secured a number of major contracts in 2000 including licensing deals for its NavStream GPS with ARM Holdings and for its processor design for wireless devices (InfoStream) with Motorola Inc. and Psion. The next year the company bought privately held Chicory Systems (technology for speeding up mobile Internet applications) in a cash and stock deal valued at about $41 million.

In 2002 the company combined its operations with Ceva the IP licensing arm of DSP Group to form a new company called ParthusCeva. Parthus president Kevin Fielding became CEO of the combined company. Fielding stepped down in 2003; Long became interim CEO for a few months until industry veteran Chet Silvestri succeeded him as president and CEO. That same year the company changed its name from ParthusCeva to CEVA. Silvestri added the post of chairman in 2004.

Silvestri resigned as chairman and CEO the following year leaving CEVA's board altogether. Cofounder Peter McManamon replaced him as chairman and EVP/GM Gideon Wertheizer was promoted to CEO.

In 2006 the company sold its Global Positioning System (GPS) technology and associated products to GloNav a fabless semiconductor startup in return for an equity stake of about 20% in the firm. GloNav also licensed the CEVA-TeakLite digital signal processor core for the development of its GPS chipsets. At the end of 2007 however NXP acquired GloNav and CEVA divested its 20% stake.

EXECUTIVES

Chief Executive Officer, Gideon Wertheizer, age 56, $315,655 total compensation
Chairman, Peter McManamon, age 64
Chief Financial Officer, Yaniv Arieli, age 44, $208,410 total compensation
EVP Worldwide Sales, Issachar Ohana, age 47, $248,000 total compensation
CTO, Erez Bar-Niv
VP Research and Development, Menachem Stern
Director Marketing and Investor Relations, Richard Kingston
VP Marketing, Eran Briman
VP Operations, Aviv Malinovitch
CEO and Director, Gideon Wertheizer, age 56
Director, Eliyahu Ayalon, age 70
Director, Bruce A. Mann, age 78
Director, Tzvi Limon, age 55
Director, Louis Silver, age 59
Director, Sven-Christer Nilsson, age 68
Director, Dan Tocatly, age 53
Auditors: Ernst&Young

LOCATIONS

HQ: CEVA Inc.
2033 Gateway Place Ste. 150, San Jose CA 95110-1002
Phone: 408-514-2900   Fax: 408-514-2995
Web: www.ceva-dsp.com

2010 Sales

	$ mil.	% of total
Europe/Middle East	18	42
Asia/Pacific	16	37
US	9	21
Total	**44**	**100**

PRODUCTS/OPERATIONS

2010 Sales

	$ mil.	% of total
Royalties	22	51
Licensing	18	41
Other	3	8
Total	**44**	**100**

COMPETITORS

ARM Holdings	Infineon Technologies
Analog Devices	MIPS Technologies
Axeon	NXP Semiconductors
Fairchild	Patriot Scientific
Semiconductor	Silicon Image
Freescale	Synopsys
Semiconductor	Tensilica
Fujitsu Semiconductor	Texas Instruments
Gennum	VeriSilicon
Imagination	
Technologies	

HISTORICAL FINANCIALS

Company Type: Public

Income Statement

FYE: December 31

	REVENUE ($ mil.)	NET INCOME ($ mil.)	NET PROFIT MARGIN	EMPLOYEES
12/12	53.6	13.6	25.5%	193
12/11	60.2	18.5	30.8%	193
12/10	44.9	11.3	25.3%	181
12/09	38.4	8.3	21.7%	184
12/08	40.3	8.5	21.2%	187
Annual Growth	**7.4%**	**12.4%**	—	**0.8%**

2012 Year-End Financials

Debt ratio: —	No. of shares (mil.): 22
Return on equity: 6.8%	Dividends
Cash ($ mil.): 65	Yield: —
Current ratio: 10.32	Payout: —
Long-term debt ($ mil.): —	Market value ($ mil.): 349

	STOCK PRICE ($) FY Close	P/E High/Low		PER SHARE ($) Earnings	Dividends	Book Value
12/12	15.75	51	22	0.59	0.00	8.84
12/11	30.26	43	26	0.77	0.00	8.53
12/10	20.50	44	20	0.51	0.00	7.48
12/09	12.86	31	12	0.41	0.00	6.81
12/08	7.00	28	13	0.42	0.00	6.23
Annual Growth	**22.5%**	—	—	**8.9%**	—	**9.1%**

Chart Industries Inc

Chart Industries is charting its own miracle on ice campaign. The company designs equipment for low-temperature hydrocarbon and industrial gas production and storage including cryogenic systems that can operate near absolute zero. Chart vessels can process liquefy store and transport gases which are marketed to petrochemical and natural gas processors industrial gas producers satellite testing companies and restaurants and convenience stores. The company also offers engineered bulk gas installations and makes specialty liquid nitrogen end-use equipment used in the hydrocarbon processing and industrial gas industries.

Geographic Reach

Headquartered in Garfield Heights Ohio Chart has about 40 domestic operations located across the US and an international presence in Asia Australia and Europe. Although Chart products are sold worldwide the US generates about 70% of sales.

Operations

The company operates through three chief segments: energy and chemicals (32% of sales); distribution and storage (47%); and biomedical (21%).

The majority of Chart's products –including vacuum insulated containment vessels heat exchangers cold boxes and other cryogenic components — are used throughout the liquid gas supply chain for the purification liquefaction distribution storage and end-use of hydrocarbon and industrial gases.

Sales and Marketing

Chart's primary customers are large multinational producers and distributors of hydrocarbon and industrial gases and their suppliers. It sells its products and services to more than 2000 customers around the globe.

Financial Performance

Chart has successfully bounced back after a period of plunging profits and reduced revenue in 2010 when it was hurt largely by the struggling energy-related construction market. Revenues soared 28% from $795 million in 2011 to pass the $1 billion mark in 2012 the first time in its history.

The growth for 2012 was driven by a 58% spike in energy and chemicals sales due to increased demand across brazed aluminum heat exchanger and process systems product lines which included revenue recognized for several large LNG projects which ramped up production during the year. Distribution and storage sales also spiked 22% in 2012 due to higher volumes shipped from LNG applications including mobile equipment and bulk storage tanks especially in China. Both segments also benefited from acquisitions throughout the year.

Profits also jumped 61% from $44 million in 2011 to $71 million in 2012 as a result of the higher revenue coupled with a decline in interest expense.

Strategy

Acquisitions have helped maintain the momentum of its distribution and storage business now the company's largest in sales. Chart has specifically cast an eye towards expanding the segment's European footprint. To boost its BioMedical segment Chart in 2012 swallowed up AirSep which makes oxygen-generating systems for medical and industrial use for about $170 million in cash and some $10 million in assumed debt. The deal was one of Chart's largest in its history.

In late 2013 Chart announced it was acquiring the brazed aluminum heat exchanger (BAHX) business belonging to Wuxi City Zhongbo Heat Exchanger Co. Ltd in order to augment its energy and chemical segment. The agreement includes the construction of a newly built BAHX manufacturing and cold box fabrication facility in Wuxi China. Chart's existing cold box fabrication facility in Changzhou China will be integrated into the new facility in Wuxi which will open up more capacity for Chart's distribution and storage LNG business in Changzhou. The expansion projects are expected to be completed in the first half of 2014.

HISTORY

In 1986 Arthur Holmes teamed up with his brother Charles to purchase ALTEC International

a struggling maker of brazed aluminum heat exchangers that dated to 1949. The brothers turned ALTEC around and used it to acquire undervalued companies. From 1986 to 1991 they purchased storage and transportation equipment for liquefied gases and high-pressure cryogenic equipment including Greenville Tube Corporation (stainless steel tubing 1987); Process Engineering Inc. (cryogenic tanks 1990); and Process Systems International (cold boxes 1991). The Holmes brothers finally established a public holding company in 1992 and named it Chart Industries (for CHarles and ARThur).

The company ran into trouble over the next few years trying to make its acquisitions profitable. Chart restructured its most troubled unit Process Engineering Inc. in 1994. It bought cryogenic vacuum pumps maker CVI to build systems for NASA. In 1995 the company began supplying vacuum equipment for the Laser Interferometer Gravitational-Wave Observatory project a research program searching for cosmic gravitational waves.

In 1997 Chart bought Cryenco Sciences which makes cryogenic road trailers. The next year the company acquired the Industrial Heat Exchanger division of UK-based IMI Marston (IMI sold the Marston aerospace business in 1999). In a move intended to increase foreign sales Chart in 1999 bought MVE Holding a cryogenic storage and transportation company with facilities in the US and Europe for $240 million in cash. The company also expanded its cryogenic equipment repair services across the US with the purchase of Northcoast Cryogenics.

Chart signed an agreement in 2000 to build and maintain a new liquid natural gas fueling station for Waste Management. The new refueling station will be the world's largest capable of refueling 120 trucks per four hours. In March 2002 the company announced it would place surcharges on its bulk storage tanks to offset the tariffs set by the US government on imported steel products which would increase manufacturing costs.

In 2003 the NYSE suspended trading of the company's shares after the company fell below continued listing standards and fell into bankruptcy protection. Later that year Chart Industries came out of bankruptcy protection with a new board membership and senior management. Chairman Arthur Holmes also resigned his post in 2003 but continued as a board member until 2005.

Chart Industries filed for another IPO in 2006 applying to list on the Big Board once more. The company had to settle for a Nasdaq listing but completed its IPO in mid-2006.

Also in 2006 the company acquired Cooler Service Company of Tulsa Oklahoma for nearly $16 million net of cash. Cooler Service makes custom air-cooled heat exchangers for hydrocarbon petrochemical and industrial gas processing and power generation. The firm became part of the Energy & Chemicals segment. In mid-2007 First Reserve sold its 48% equity stake in Chart Industries through a secondary offering receiving approximately $263 million. In 2009 Chart acquired Covidien's oxygen therapy business including its Companion and HELiOS brands.

In 2011 the company purchased GOFA Gocher Fahrzeugbau a Germany-based cryogenic and non-cryogenic mobile equipment manufacturer. The addition completed Chart's move to widen its liquefied natural gas (LNG) offerings as well as its opportunities in Europe's industrial gas energy chemical and other industries. The deal also helped Chart to capture a sizable share of the German market (the country accounted for 16% of its total sales in 2011).

At home in mid-2011 Chart acquired California-based Cryotech International (formerly VPS International). Cryotech added to its D&S manufacturing capacity for cryogenic injectors vacuum insulated piping systems and manifolds as well as branded design and service offerings. Its global customer base included defense semiconductor pharmaceutical biotechnology solar and electronics industry clients.

EXECUTIVES

Executive Vice President Chief Financial Officer Treasurer, Michael F. Biehl, age 57, $262,150 total compensation

VP-HR, Mark H. Ludwig

President Biomedical Group, Steven T. (Steve) Shaw

Chairman President and CEO, Samuel F. Thomas, age 60, $550,000 total compensation

President Distribution and Storage Group, Thomas M. (Tom) Carey

VP General Counsel and Secretary, Matthew J. Klaben, age 43, $243,000 total compensation

President Chart Asia, Eric M. Rottier

Chairman and Managing Director Chart Ferox, Hans Lonsain, age 56

VP Chief Accounting Officer and Controller, Kenneth J. (Ken) Webster, age 50, $163,800 total compensation

President Energy and Chemicals, Mike Durkin

Chief Executive Officer; Director, Craig Robson

VP of Sales & Marketing, Samuel Komar

Chief Financial Officer; Secretary; Director, Bill Grossholz

Chairman VP, John H. Schwan

Director, W. Douglas Brown, age 67

Director, James M. (Jim) Tidwell, age 66

Director, Steven W. (Steve) Krablin, age 62

Director, Richard E. Goodrich, age 70

Director, Michael W. Press, age 64

Director, Thomas L. (Tom) Williams, age 54

Auditors: Ernst&YoungLLP

LOCATIONS

HQ: Chart Industries Inc.
1 Infinity Corporate Centre Dr. Ste. 300, Garfield Heights OH 44125-5370
Phone: 440-753-1490   **Fax:** 440-753-1491
Web: www.chartindustries.com

2011 Sales

	$ mil.	% of total
US	710	70
Czech Republic	70	7
Other countries	12	1

PRODUCTS/OPERATIONS

2012 Sales by End-User

Energy	54
Biomedical	21

Selected Products

Cold boxes (reduce the temperature of gas mixtures to liquefy and separate them)

Cryogenic components (pumps valves vacuum-jacketed piping systems and specialty components)

Cryogenic storage tanks (tanks trailers intermodal containers and railcars)

Heat exchangers (facilitate cooling and liquefaction of air or hydrocarbons)

Space simulation systems (satellite and spacecraft testing)

Thermal vacuum systems (aerospace and research applications)

Vacuum insulated bulk liquid CO2 containers (beverage carbonation)

COMPETITORS

Air Products	Matrix Service
Cobham	Praxair
Fives	QualMark
Flowserve	Reliance Steel
Graham Corp.	Senior plc
Ingersoll-Rand	Sumitomo Metal
Kobe Steel	Industries
L' Air Liquide	The Linde Group

HISTORICAL FINANCIALS

Company Type: Public

Income Statement

FYE: December 31

	REVENUE ($ mil.)	NET INCOME ($ mil.)	NET PROFIT MARGIN	EMPLOYEES
12/12	1,014.1	71.3	7.0%	4,842
12/11	794.5	44.0	5.5%	3,831
12/10	555.4	20.1	3.6%	3,013
12/09	591.5	61.0	10.3%	2,517
12/08	744.3	78.9	10.6%	2,945
Annual Growth	8.0%	(2.5%)	—	13.2%

2012 Year-End Financials

Debt ratio: 19.2%	No. of shares (mil.): 30
Return on equity: 10.8%	Dividends
Cash ($ mil.): 141	Yield: —
Current ratio: 2.03	Payout: —
Long-term debt ($ mil.): 252	Market value ($ mil.): 2,003

	STOCK PRICE ($) FY Close	P/E High/Low		PER SHARE ($) Earnings	Dividends	Book Value
12/12	66.69	32	23	2.36	0.00	23.18
12/11	54.07	42	22	1.47	0.00	20.63
12/10	33.78	49	20	0.69	0.00	17.31
12/09	16.52	11	2	2.11	0.00	16.70
12/08	10.63	19	2	2.72	0.00	14.23
Annual Growth	58.3%	—	—	(3.5%)	—	13.0%

Chase Corp.

Duct tape is great but when the job calls for higher-tech stuff Chase has it. The company has made and sold Chase & Sons branded protective tape and coatings including conducting and insulating products for cable and wire makers for more than 50 years. Chase processes almost any flexible material produced on a roll —films to fabrics. It makes laminates sealants and coatings for pipeline construction electronics as well as printing markets. Chase pipe coating tapes Tapecoat and Royston are sold to oil companies and gas utilities. The company also offers expansion/control joint systems and asphalt additives for roads bridges and stadiums. US customers represent about 84% of revenues.

Chase operates through two segments Industrial Materials and Construction Materials. Industrial Materials 62% of revenue provides products that are added to another company's products. The company's stalwart Chase & Sons trademark is included in this segment. Major product families in the segment include insulating and conducting materials moisture protective coatings laminated durable papers and flexible composites and laminates. Construction Materials are sold in final form for use in the transportation and architectural as

well as construction markets. This segment's products include protective pipe coating tapes a polymer additive for waterproofing waterproofing sealants and expansion joints.

Revenue rose 4% in 2011 compared with 2010. Industrial Materials headed up 17% thanks mainly to demand from the electrical cable market for wire and cable products and demand from the industrial controls and automotive markets for electronic coatings products. Construction Materials fell 13% over the same period as the segment struggled with pipeline production problems at its UK facility that prevented the fulfillment of demand in the Middle East. The segment also contended with lower demand from the transportation and architectural markets. Lower sales of private label products additionally contributed to the segment's year-over-year revenue decline. The company's consolidated net income fell 13% in 2011 compared with 2010.

To consolidate manufacturing Chase is closing its Industrial Materials plant in Randolph MA which is one of the company's first plants making Chase & Sons electrical cable insulation tapes and other products for the wire and cable industries. The plant's operations are being transferred to other plants. The company had also moved its manufacturing operations at Webster MA to its Oxford MA plant and transferred its HumiSeal Europe manufacturing operations from Camberly in the UK to a more modern plant in Winnersh UK.

Acquisitions are included in Chase's strategy for growth. In 2012 Chase acquired NEPTCO which supplies engineered materials for producing copper cable and electronic packaging products for about $67 million. The acquisition broadens the menu of products offered by Chase and creates synergies between the markets targeted by Chase and Neptco. In 2010 Chase gained a cash infusion by divesting its contract circuit board assembler Chase Electronic Manufacturing Services (EMS) to contract manufacturer MC Assembly.

A trust controlled by heirs of the company's late founder Edward Chase owns about 12% of the company. Chase's son Peter who serves as company chairman and CEO holds nearly 15% of Chase.

HISTORY

Brothers Edward and Francis Chase founded Chase & Sons in 1946 to make rubberized power cable tape fabric. Under Francis' long tenure as president and CEO the company expanded into related markets. Purchases included Columbia Technical Corporation (electrical insulating varnish and laminates 1971) and Royston Laboratories (corrosion-resistant pipeline coating 1972). The company which by 1973 was called Columbia Chase (shortened to Chase in 1988) won a contract in 1975 to protect seams on the Alaska pipeline. Chase stumbled financially in the late 1980s after diversifying into non-petroleum energy markets. In 1988 Francis retired.

Chase sold its elastomeric materials and fuel technology divisions in 1991. Edward's son Peter became president in 1992 and CEO a year later. He oversaw the company's diversification into adhesives for water purification (Fluid Polymers 1995) and formed a joint venture with the Stewart Group to make products for fiber-optic cable production (sold to Owens-Corning 1997).

Chase entered the electronic manufacturing services market in 1996 by purchasing a 20% stake in DC Scientific. The company raised its interest to more than 50% then in 1999 bought DC Scientific and changed its name to Sunburst Electronic Manufacturing Solutions. Other acquisitions that year included RWA which offers electronic manufacturing and Northeast Quality Products (NEQP) a specialty printer of pressure-sensitive labels. The company boosted its electronic manufacturing service operations in 2000 with the addition of Netco Automation.

Late in 2001 Chase purchased the Tapecoat protective coatings assets of TC Manufacturing Co. The acquisition complemented Chase's Royston division a maker of waterproofing membranes asphalt additives tapes and accessories. Declining health forced co-founder Edward Chase to retire from the company in early 2003. Later in the year Chase sold its Sunburst Electronics Manufacturing Solutions subsidiary to the Edward L. Chase Revocable Trust.

In 2005 the company acquired UK-based Concoat Holdings for $9 million. The next year it bought New York-based Capital Services Joint Systems which made waterproofing sealants and expansion joints.

Looking to court global demand in 2007 Chase picked up UK-based Long Products a maker of corrosion protection and waterproofing systems. The acquisition increased Chase's presence in Europe the Middle East and Southeast Asia as well as its manufacturing capacity in weatherproofing and corrosion protection systems (used in the oil gas and water pipeline industries). In the same year Chase formed HumiSeal Europe via an acquisition of certain assets from Metronelec.

In 2009 Chase purchased the ServiWrap lineup of pipeline protection products from Grace Construction Products (a unit of W.R. Grace). The #5.98 million ($9.7 million) deal picked up anticorrosion systems that cater to global oil gas and water pipeline markets. On its heels Chase snatched up C.I.M. Industries a manufacturer of coating and lining systems. C.I.M.'s established presence in the liquid storage and containment industry opens up new avenues in the growing water and wastewater market.

Restructuring in 2009 the company moved work at a flexible composite and laminates manufacturing facility in Paterson New Jersey to locations in Webster Massachusetts and Taylorsville North Carolina. The company consolidated the sales administrative and research and development activities of two offices to one operation too. Also in 2009 NEQP went on the block sold to Label Tech Inc.

EXECUTIVES

Chairman and CEO, Peter R. Chase, age 66, $499,780 total compensation
Secretary and Director, George M. Hughes, age 74, $117,000 total compensation
Shareholder and Investor Relations, Paula Myers
President COO and Director, Adam P. Chase, age 42, $235,405 total compensation
CFO Principle Accounting Officer and Treasurer, Kenneth L. (Ken) Dumas, age 42, $168,656 total compensation
Director, Thomas (Tom) Wroe Jr., age 63
Secretary and Director, George M. Hughes, age 74
Director, Ronald Levy, age 75
Director, Lewis P. Gack, age 69
Director, Mary Claire Chase, age 58
President COO and Director, Adam P. Chase, age 42
Director, J. Brooks Fenno, age 79
Auditors: PricewaterhouseCoopersLLP

LOCATIONS

HQ: Chase Corp.
26 Summer Street, Bridgewater, MA 02324
Phone: 508 819-4200
Web: www.chasecorp.com

2011 Sales

	$ mil.	% of total
US	103	84
Other countries	19	16
Total	**123**	**100**

PRODUCTS/OPERATIONS

2011 Sales

	$ mil.	% of total
Industrial Materials	75	62
Construction Materials	47	38
Total	**123**	**100**

2011 Sales

	$ mil.	% of total
Sales	120	98
Royalties & commissions	2	2
Total	**123**	**100**

Selected Products and Services

Electrical cable insulation tapes
Electrical splicing & terminating & repair tapes
Flexible composites & laminates for wire & cable aerospace & industrial laminate markets
Flexible packaging for industrial & retail use
Fluid applied coating & lining systems for the water & wastewater industry
Insulating & conducting materials for wire and cable manufacturers
Laminated durable papers
Moisture-protective coatings for electronics and printing services
Protectants for highway bridge deck metal supported surfaces
Protective conformal coatings
Protective pipe coating tapes
Slit film for the building wire market & telecommunication cable
Specialty tapes & related products for the electronic and telecommunications industries
Tapecoat for anti-corrosion applications in the gas & oil & marine pipeline markets
Tapes & membranes for roofing & other construction applications
Waterproofing sealants expansion joints & accessories

COMPETITORS

3M	Iracore
American Biltrite	PPG Industries
Benchmark Electronics	Plymouth Rubber
Dow Corning	Praxair
ELANTAS PDG	Saint-Gobain
Flextronics	W. R. Grace

HISTORICAL FINANCIALS

Company Type: Public

Income Statement

FYE: August 31

	REVENUE ($ mil.)	NET INCOME ($ mil.)	NET PROFIT MARGIN	EMPLOYEES
08/13	216.0	17.2	8.0%	666
08/12	148.9	9.3	6.3%	719
08/11	123.0	10.9	8.9%	324
08/10	118.7	12.5	10.5%	305
08/09	107.6	6.3	5.9%	365
Annual Growth	**19.0%**	**28.1%**	**—**	**16.2%**

2013 Year-End Financials

Debt ratio: 28.7%	No. of shares (mil.): 9
Return on equity: 16.3%	Dividends
Cash ($ mil.): 30	Yield: 0.0%
Current ratio: 3.09	Payout: 21.3%
Long-term debt ($ mil.): 58	Market value ($ mil.): 269

	STOCK PRICE ($) FY Close	P/E High/Low		PER SHARE ($) Earnings	Dividends	Book Value
08/13	29.72	16	8	1.87	0.40	12.44
08/12	16.27	17	10	1.03	0.35	10.90
08/11	12.77	16	9	1.22	0.35	10.26
08/10	12.70	10	7	1.38	0.20	9.28
08/09	11.40	22	9	0.73	0.35	8.06
Annual Growth	**27.1%**	**—**	**—**	**26.5%**	**3.4%**	**11.5%**

Chefs' Warehouse Inc (The)

Before a gourmet chef can say "bon appetit" he must first procure his ingredients. A distributor of specialty food products Chefs' Warehouse sells such gourmet food items as artisan charcuterie specialty cheeses hormone-free protein truffles caviar and chocolates as well as basic food ingredients like cooking oils flour butter milk and eggs. The company's core customers include chefs from independent restaurants fine dining establishments culinary schools hotels and country clubs. It is a leading gourmet ingredient distributor in culinary centers like New York City San Francisco Los Angeles and Washington DC. Tracing its roots back to 1985 Chefs' Warehouse went public in 2011.

IPO

Shares climbed following the company's market debut. The supplier for restaurants caterers and other foodservice businesses raised $135 million; the proceeds from the IPO were about $63.1 million after expenses which went to repay debt and fund general corporate activity. Company CEO Christopher Pappas Christopher's brother John Pappas and brother-in-law Dean Facatselis collectively retain control of Chefs' Warehouse.

Geographic Reach

Based in Connecticut Chefs' Warehouse operates in one segment —food product distribution — along the East and West coasts. It serves some of the nation's culinary hot spots including New York California Nevada and Washington as well as in Ohio Maryland Florida and Oregon.

Financial Performance

Except for revenue slump in 2009 due to the global economic recession Chefs' Warehouse has seen an upward trend in revenue from 2008 to 2012. The company has logged rising net income in all fiscal years from 2008-2012 due to increased net sales and decreased operating expenses. Chefs' Warehouse revenue jumped 20% in fiscal 2012 as compared to 2011 thanks to net sales increases resulting from organic sales growth and the acquisitions of Michael's and Praml in 2012 and Provvista in late 2011. The company's net sales growth was negatively impacted by Hurricane Sandy however during the fourth quarter of 2012 and the prior year impact of an extra week in 2011. Chefs' Warehouse reports $14.51 million in 2012 net income —an 88% increase —due to increased net sales in 2012 and reduced interest expenses.

Mergers and Acquisitions

Going forward Chefs' Warehouse's growth strategy continues to include acquisitions of small food distributors that beef up its entree offerings. In 2013 the company purchased Qzina Specialty Foods North America a Florida-based supplier of gourmet chocolate dessert and pastry products that serves pastry chefs in a deal worth some $32.7 million. In 2012 it bought out Michael's Finer Meats a Midwest distributor of meat and seafood for approximately $54.3 million. The deal was one of several; earlier in the year Chefs' Warehouse purchased Praml International a specialty foods importer and foodservice distributor founded in 1987. The acquisition extended the company's reach to some 500 locations in Las Vegas and Reno. Chefs' Warehouse expanded its operations into south Florida after acquiring Monique & Me Inc. (dba Culinaire Specialty Foods) for $3.7 million in 2010. The previous year it bought the San Francisco division of European Imports for $3.8 million. The transaction bolstered its California operations.

Strategy

Besides acquiring other companies Chefs' Warehouse is expanding its customer base in existing markets and bolstering its product offerings to its existing customers. It is also taking steps to control costs by improving its logistics and inventory management systems. In recent years Chefs' Warehouse has experienced significant financial growth due in large part to a rise in revenue generated by sales to both new and existing customers.

Sales and Marketing

Chefs' Warehouse works to cover a number of popular markets including Philadelphia Boston Napa Valley and Seattle. As part of its business the company serves chefs working in country clubs independent restaurants fine dining establishments culinary schools and hotels.

The company distributes its specialty food products to more than 12500 distinct customer locations from distribution centers located in New York San Francisco Los Angeles Las Vegas Miami Portland Columbus Cincinnati and Washington DC. Its products are sourced from more than 2700 different suppliers.

Company Ownership

Chefs' Warehouse is 17% owned by Christopher Pappas; John Pappas retains another 15% stake.

Company Background

The Pappas family originally founded the company in 1985 as Dairyland USA a specialty dairy product distributor that served chefs in the New York metropolitan area. The company later expanded into other large US markets through acquisitions of small specialty food products distributors.

EXECUTIVES

Founder Chairman President Chief Executive Officer, Christopher Pappas, age 53
Vice Chairman, John Pappas, age 49
CFO, Kenneth Clark, age 45
Executive Vice President of Human Resources, Patricia Lecouras, age 57
General Counsel Corporate Secretary, Alexandros Aldous, age 32
Chief Information Officer, Frank ODowd
Chief Financial Officer, John D. Austin
Director, L. Kevin Cox, age 49
Vice Chairman, John Pappas, age 49
Director, Dean Facatselis, age 57
Auditors: BDOUSALLP

LOCATIONS

HQ: Chefs' Warehouse Holdings LLC
100 E. Ridge Rd., Ridgefield CT 06877
Phone: 203-894-1345   **Fax:** -1279
Web: www.diasorin.com

PRODUCTS/OPERATIONS

2012 Sales

	% of total
Center of	27
Dry	25
Cheeses	14
Pastries &	13
Oils &	10
Dairy	9
Kitchen	2
Total	**100**

Selected Products

Baking
Beverages
Caviar
Cheese & dairy
Chocolate
Coffee & tea
Condiments
Dry goods
Foie gras & pate
Fruits & nuts
Gluten-free
Molecular gastronomy
Oil & vinegar
Organic
Pasta
Specialty meats
Specialty seafood
Spices
Regional

COMPETITORS

American Milk Products
DPI Specialty Foods
Dole & Bailey Inc.
Economy Foods
European Imports
World Finer Foods
atalanta

HISTORICAL FINANCIALS

Company Type: Public

Income Statement   FYE: December 28

	REVENUE ($ mil.)	NET INCOME ($ mil.)	NET PROFIT MARGIN	EMPLOYEES
12/12	480.2	14.5	3.0%	780
12/11	400.6	7.7	1.9%	600
12/10	330.1	15.8	4.8%	571
12/09	271.0	8.9	3.3%	0
12/08	281.7	2.2	0.8%	0
Annual Growth	**14.3%**	**60.3%**	**—**	**—**

2012 Year-End Financials

Debt ratio: 59.2%
Return on equity: 46.3%
Cash ($ mil.): 0
Current ratio: 2.21
Long-term debt ($ mil.): 119
No. of shares (mil.): 20
Dividends
Yield: —
Payout: —
Market value ($ mil.): 323

	STOCK PRICE ($) FY Close	P/E High/Low	PER SHARE ($) Earnings	Dividends	Book Value
12/12	15.40	36 18	0.69	0.00	1.87
12/11	17.86	42 27	0.43	0.00	1.13
Annual Growth	**(13.8%)**	**— —**	**60.5%**	**—**	**65.5%**

Chesapeake Utilities Corp.

Chesapeake Utilities gasses up the Chesapeake Bay and then some. Chesapeake's regulated natural gas distribution divisions serve more than 121930 customers in the Northeast and Florida. Another unit distributes power to about 31000 customers in Florida. On the unregulated side the company also serves more than 48820 retail propane customers in Delaware Florida Maryland and Virginia. Another subsidiary Xeron sells propane at wholesale to distributors industrial users and resellers throughout the US. In addition Chesapeake has interstate gas pipeline and gas marketing operations. Through BravePoint the company also offers data services consulting and software development.

Chesapeake Utilities' business strategy is to grow its core energy businesses while diversifying its portfolio to strengthen its range of revenue opportunities. In this regard in 2010 its BravePoint unit introduced ProfitZoom a business profit management software system for the fire and life safety industry. BravePoint introduced a mobile application for this system in 2012.

The growth and expansion of the company's regulated businesses coupled with rate increases and favorable weather conditions (which spiked demand) helped to limit the company's revenues to a 2% dip despite a drag from weak propane and natural gas prices. However lower gas costs and a Florida-related rate relief provision helped to lift net income by 6%.

In 2011 Chesapeake Utilities president and COO Michael McMasters was appointed as CEO replacing John Schimkaitis who retained his role as vice chairman.

The company was founded in 1859 as the Dover Gas Light Company. It became Chesapeake Utilities Corporation in 1947. During 2003 Chesapeake began to exit the water services business selling six of its seven dealerships. The company sold the remaining water dealership in 2004. Chesapeake Utilities expanded into Florida through the acquisition of Florida Public Utilities Company in 2009.

EXECUTIVES

SVP CFO and Corporate Secretary, Beth W. Cooper, age 46, $169,167 total compensation
SVP; President Eastern Shore Natural Gas, Stephen C. (Steve) Thompson, age 52, $260,500 total compensation
Vice Chairman, John R. Schimkaitis, age 65, $386,250 total compensation
President CEO and Director, Michael P. (Mike) McMasters, age 55, $266,125 total compensation
Chairman, Ralph J. Adkins, age 70, $225,000 total compensation
Investor Relations Administrator, Heidi W. Watkins
President and COO BravePoint, John R. Harlow, age 58
President Sharp Energy, S. Robert (Bob) Zola, age 62, $143,750 total compensation
President and COO Xeron, David E. (Dave) Snyder, age 64
Vice President - Strategic Development, Elaine B. Bittner, age 43
VP; President PESCO, Joseph (Joe) Cummiskey, age 40
VP, Jeffrey R. (Jeff) Tietbohl
Communications Manager, Sydney H. Davis

Assistant VP and Controller, Matthew M. Kim
President Florida Public Utilities, Jeffry M.
  Householder
**Vice President Eastern Shore Natural Gas
  Company,** William B. Zipf
Director - Finance; Treasurer, Thomas Mahn
President Xeron, Richard G. Garcia
Director, Calvert A. (Cal) Morgan Jr., age 64
Vice Chairman, John R. Schimkaitis, age 65
President CEO and Director, Michael P. (Mike)
  McMasters, age 55
Director, Thomas J. (Tom) Bresnan, age 60
Director, Dennis S. (Denny) Hudson III, age 58
Director, Richard Bernstein, age 70
Director, Paul L. (Jay) Maddock Jr., age 63
Director, J. Peter Martin, age 73
Director, Joseph E. Moore, age 70
Director, Dianna F. Morgan, age 61
Director, Eugene H. Bayard, age 66
Director, Thomas P. Hill Jr., age 64

LOCATIONS

HQ: Chesapeake Utilities Corporation
  909 Silver Lake Blvd., Dover DE 19904
Phone: 302-734-6799   **Fax:** 302-734-6750
Web: www.chpk.com

PRODUCTS/OPERATIONS

2011 Sales

	$ mil.	% of total
Regulated energy	256	61
Unregulated energy	149	36
Other	11	3
Total	**418**	**100**

Selected Subsidiaries

Chesapeake Service Company
  BravePoint Inc. (formerly United Systems Inc.
    information technology)
Chesapeake Investment Company (real estate
    investments)
Eastern Shore Real Estate Inc. (office building leases)
  Skipjack Inc. (office building leases)
Eastern Shore Natural Gas Company (transmission)
Florida Public Utilities Company (gas power and propane
    distribution)
Flo-Gas Corporation
Peninsula Energy Services Company Inc
Peninsula Pipeline Company Inc.
Sharp Energy Inc. (propane distribution)
  Sharpgas Inc.
Xeron Inc. (propane marketing)

COMPETITORS

Constellation Energy	JEA
Group	New Jersey Resources
Delmarva Power	NextEra Energy
Energy Transfer	Suburban Propane
Ferrellgas Partners	UGI

HISTORICAL FINANCIALS

Company Type: Public

Income Statement

FYE: December 31

	REVENUE ($ mil.)	NET INCOME ($ mil.)	NET PROFIT MARGIN	EMPLOYEES
12/12	392.5	28.8	7.4%	738
12/11	418.0	27.6	6.6%	711
12/10	427.5	26.0	6.1%	734
12/09	268.7	15.9	5.9%	757
12/08	291.4	13.6	4.7%	448
Annual Growth	**7.7%**	**20.7%**	**—**	**13.3%**

2012 Year-End Financials

Debt ratio: 23.3%	No. of shares (mil.): 9
Return on equity: 11.5%	Dividends
Cash ($ mil.): 3	Yield: 3.1%
Current ratio: 0.62	Payout: 51.6%
Long-term debt ($ mil.): 101	Market value ($ mil.): 436

	STOCK PRICE ($) FY Close	P/E High/Low		PER SHARE ($) Earnings	Dividends	Book Value
12/12	45.40	16	13	2.99	1.44	26.74
12/11	43.35	15	13	2.87	1.37	25.17
12/10	41.52	15	10	2.73	1.31	23.75
12/09	32.05	16	10	2.15	1.25	22.33
12/08	31.48	17	12	1.98	1.21	18.03
Annual Growth	**9.6%**	**—**	**—**	**10.9%**	**4.4%**	**10.4%**

Churchill Downs, Inc.

You might say this company has put its money on the sport of champions to win. Churchill Downs is a leading operator of horse racing tracks in the US with four major race courses including its namesake track that hosts the world-famous Kentucky Derby. Other tracks include Arlington Park (Illinois) Calder Race Course (Florida) and Fair Grounds Race Course (Louisiana). In addition to horse racing Churchill Downs has gaming assets. It operates a number of simulcast networks and off-track betting facilities as well as a TwinSpires wagering deposit service that allows punters to place bets online. Richard Duchossois who controls diversified holding company Duchossois Group owns about 20% of Churchill Downs.

Geographic Reach

Churchill Downs operates the racetracks in Florida Illinois Kentucky and Louisiana. The company's off-track betting facilities widen its reach.

Financial Performance

While still grounded in live horse racing Churchill Downs has been actively investing in new ventures —both gaming and non-gaming —to diversify its revenue stream.

The company has enjoyed an upward trend in revenues during recent fiscal years. In fiscal 2012 the company reported about $732.4 million in revenues including more than $300 million from racing operations and $223 million from gaming operations. Revenues in fiscal 2011 were about $696.9 million and back in fiscal 2010 the company claimed roughly $585.3 million.

Strategy

In addition to its emphasis on new technology Churchill Downs is focused on investing in its traditional horseracing and gaming sphere. In 2012 Churchill Downs entered into a 50% joint venture with Delaware North Companies Gaming & Entertainment to develop a new harness racetrack and video lottery terminal gaming facility in Lebanon Ohio. The project will involve the relocation of the current operations of Lebanon Raceway to a new location along the Interstate 75 corridor between Cincinnati and Dayton.

Mergers and Acquisitions

Churchill Downs acquired a Mississippi property —the Riverwalk Casino and Hotel in Vicksburg —for approximately $141 million in 2012. The purchase added to a previous acquisition —Harlow's Casino Resort & Hotel in Greenville Mississippi. It made that deal in 2012 for about $138 million as

part of its geographic diversification strategy and is attracted to Mississippi as a business and gaming location.

Also in 2012 the company acquired the assets of Bluff Media a multimedia poker content brand and publishing company. Bluff Media's assets included the poker periodical BLUFF Magazine; BLUFF Magazine's online counterpart Bluff-Magazine.com; ThePokerDB a comprehensive online database and resource that tracks and ranks the performance of poker players and tournaments; and various other news and content forums.

In 2010 the company acquired interactive-betting technology company Youbet.com for some $127 million. It made the deal in order to expand its online wagering capabilities; soon after the purchase it combined the Youbet site with its Twin-Spires depositing service. TwinSpires is one of Churchill's online businesses which also include Bloodstock Research Information Services (BRIS) a data service provider for the equine industry and a minority stake in horseracing TV channel HRTV.

HISTORY

Inspired by a tour of European horse racing meets Colonel Lewis Clark founded the Louisville Jockey Club in 1874. The next year the first Kentucky Derby debuted at a site that by 1883 was called Churchill Downs (after Clark's uncles the Churchills who leased him the land). The track suffered financially until 1903 when it showed its first profit. Over the next 25 years the Jockey Club added four more tracks but when the Great Depression hit the company began selling and closing its tracks. Churchill Downs incorporated in 1937 and by 1952 the Kentucky Derby was televised. The company had never really prospered since the Depression and company executives thwarted a takeover bid by National Industries in 1969; two other takeovers were attempted in 1984.

Thomas Meeker who once had served as the company's lawyer took over as president and CEO of Churchill Downs in 1984. He sought to turn the track around and pitched a five-year $25 million renovation of the company's facilities. The investment to revitalize Churchill Downs drove earnings up for the company in the late 1980s.

During the 1990s Churchill Downs diversified into different states and media. Its first simulcast wagering facility opened in 1992 and in 1994 the company gained a majority interest in Hoosier Park (sold 2007). The company acquired a third racetrack Ellis Park in 1998. The following year it launched the Kentucky Derby Auction site on the Web which features the buying and trading of memorabilia related to the race. The firm moved into the technical side of gambling when it formed a joint venture (Charlson Broadcast Technologies LLC) with Charlson Industries to provide simulcast graphic software and video services to its racing and off-track betting sites. Also in 1999 Churchill Downs expanded its geographical base with the $86 million purchase of Calder Race Course in Miami and the Hollywood Park Race Track and adjacent card casino in Southern California.

The company bought Arlington International Racecourse near Chicago as well as five related off-track betting and pari-mutuel operations in Illinois from Duchossois Industries (later The Duchossois Group) in 2000. The next year it joined the New York Racing Association in its bid to buy New York City Off-Track Betting but the group failed to snag the OTB operation which was won by a consortium led by Magna Entertainment. Also in

2001 Churchill Downs sold a 15% stake in Hoosier Park to Centaur Racing for $4.5 million (the company still owned 62% of Hoosier Park with Centaur owning the rest). In 2002 Churchill Downs sold its 35% interest in EquiSource a procurer of equine industry supplies and services.

In 2004 Churchill Downs acquired the Fair Grounds Race Course in New Orleans from Fair Grounds Corporation for $47 million. It also acquired Video Services Inc. (VSI) that year. VSI runs the Louisiana poker business. A year later Churchill Downs sold its Hollywood Park track to Bay Meadows Land Company.

The company's Louisiana Fair Grounds and nearby betting facilities were closed in 2005 in the wake of Hurricane Katrina. Horse races scheduled for the Fair Grounds were moved to Bossier City's Louisiana Downs (operated by Harrah's (now Caesars Entertainment). The following year Robert Evans replaced longtime CEO Meeker. In 2007 Churchill Downs sold its stake in Hoosier Park to Centaur.

The company acquired interactive-betting technology company Youbet.com in 2010 in order to expand its online wagering capabilities; it combined the site with its Twinspires wagering deposit service. Later that year Churchill Downs acquired Harlow's Casino Resort & Hotel in Greenville Mississippi for about $138 million

EXECUTIVES

senior Vice President legal affairs and chief compliance officer, Rebecca C. Reed, age 55
Chairman and Chief Executive Officer, Robert L. (Bob) Evans, age 60, $512,019 total compensation
President and COO, William C. (Bill) Carstanjen, age 45, $410,623 total compensation
SVP; President Churchill Downs Racetrack, T. Kevin Flanery, age 47
President Churchill Downs Interactive, James E. (Ted) Gay
SVP Illinois Operations; President Arlington Park Racecourse, Roy A. Arnold, age 57
Executive Vice President and Chief Financial Officer, William E. (Bill) Mudd, age 41, $337,604 total compensation
General Manager Harlow's Casino Resort & Hotel, Reginald Fullwood Jr.
President Calder Casino & Race Course, Austin Miller
EVP Technology Initiatives; President TwinSpires.com, Rohit Thukral, $288,693 total compensation
SVP Corporate and Government Relations, D. Brett Hale
SVP; President Fair Grounds Race Course and Slots, Timothy W. (Tim) Bryant
SVP and CTO, Ben Murr
Executive Vice President General Counsel, Alan K. Tse, age 41
General Manager Arlington Park, Tony Petrillo
senior Vice President corporate affairs, Brett Hale
senior Vice President human resources, Chuck Kenyon
senior Vice President business development, Shawn Bailey
Senior Vice President Churchill Downs Incorporated, Arlington Park
President of the newly established Churchill Downs Entertainment, Steve Sexton
Director, James F. (Jim) McDonald, age 73
Director, Robert L. Fealy
Director, Craig J. Duchossois
Director, Richard L. Duchossois
Director, Darrell R. Wells, age 70
Director, Daniel P. Harrington, age 57

Director, Leonard S. Coleman Jr., age 64
Director, G. Watts Humphrey Jr., age 68
CEO and Director, Robert L. (Bob) Evans, age 59
Director, Michael Brodsky, age 44
Director, R. Alex Rankin, age 58
Auditors: PricewaterhouseCoopersLLP

LOCATIONS

HQ: Churchill Downs, Inc.
600 North Hurstbourne Parkway, Suite 400, Louisville, KY 40222
Phone: 502 636-4400
Web: www.churchilldownsincorporated.com

PRODUCTS/OPERATIONS

Selected Operations
Racetracks
    Arlington Park (Arlington Heights IL)
    Calder Race Course (Miami)
    Churchill Downs (Louisville KY)
    Fair Grounds Race Course and Slots (New Orleans)
Gaming
    Calder Casino (slot machines Florida)
    Harlow's Casino Resort & Hotel (casino Mississippi)
    Video Services (video poker machines Louisiana)
    Fair Ground Slots (slot machines Louisiana)
Online
    Bloodstock Research Information Services (equine industry information)
    Horse Racing TV (HRTV minority stake)
    TwinSpires (deposit wagering service)
Other operations
    Churchill Downs Simulcast Productions
    United Tote Company (pari-mutuel wagering systems)

COMPETITORS

Boyd Gaming	MTR Gaming
Caesars Entertainment	Penn National Gaming
Daily Racing Form	Pinnacle Entertainment
Dover Downs Gaming	Seminole Tribe of
Equibase	Florida
Granite Real Estate	
Jacksonville Greyhound Racing	

HISTORICAL FINANCIALS

Company Type: Public

Income Statement
FYE: December 31

	REVENUE ($ mil.)	NET INCOME ($ mil.)	NET PROFIT MARGIN	EMPLOYEES
12/12	732.3	58.2	8.0%	2,300
12/11	696.8	64.3	9.2%	2,000
12/10	585.3	16.3	2.8%	2,000
12/09	439.7	16.8	3.8%	1,300
12/08	430.5	28.5	6.6%	1,000
Annual Growth	14.2%	19.5%	—	23.1%

2012 Year-End Financials

Debt ratio: 18.8%	No. of shares (mil.): 17
Return on equity: 9.4%	Dividends
Cash ($ mil.): 37	Yield: 1.9%
Current ratio: 0.36	Payout: 36.6%
Long-term debt ($ mil.): —	Market value ($ mil.): 1,159

	STOCK PRICE ($) FY Close	P/E High/Low	PER SHARE ($) Earnings	Dividends	Book Value
12/12	66.45	20 15	3.34	1.32	36.93
12/11	52.13	14 10	3.76	0.60	34.00
12/10	43.40	42 29	1.05	0.50	30.55
12/09	37.35	34 18	1.21	0.50	29.74
12/08	40.42	26 12	2.05	0.50	28.77
Annual Growth	13.2%	— —	13.0%	27.5%	6.4%

Cinemark Holdings Inc

Showing films is where Cinemark Holdings really makes its mark. The third-largest movie exhibitor in the US (following Regal Entertainment and AMC) has more than 5200 screens in some 465 theaters in the US and Latin America. Cinemark operates its multiplex theaters in smaller cities and suburban areas of major metropolitan markets. Some larger theaters operate under the Tinseltown name; others are "discount" theaters showing no first-run films. About 85% of its first-run auditoriums feature stadium seating. The company prefers to build new theaters in midsized markets or in suburbs of major cities where the Cinemark theater is the only game in town.

Geographic Reach
Cinemark operates theaters in 39 US states as well as Argentina Brazil Mexico and 10 other Latin American countries. The company gets about 70% of its sales from the US market.

Financial Performance
Despite a down economy people still flock to the movies. The company's revenue has been trending upwards in recent fiscal years. Cinemark reported about $2.47 billion in revenue for fiscal 2012 up from the roughly $2.28 billion it brought in during fiscal 2011 and the $2.1 billion the company reported in revenue for fiscal 2010.

Strategy
The company's strategy focuses on international expansion primarily in Latin America through construction of modern state-of-the-art theatres in growing urban markets. Cinemark plans to build 13 new theatres with 88 screens during 2013 and three new theatres with 21 screens subsequent to 2013 investing an additional $89 million in Latin American markets.

Its adoption of the 3D format is just one way in which Cinemark focuses on being one of the most modern and technologically advanced movie chains. The company has developed a large screen digital format XD Extreme Digital Cinema or XD. The format includes wall-to-wall and ceiling-to-floor screens wrap-around sound and can play any available digital print. Cinemark has XD screens in more than 50 theatres. The company expanded on this concept with the launch of its first NextGen Cinema location in the Dallas area in 2010. NextGen is a high-tech movie theater that houses XD screens the latest projectors and sound systems and other cutting edge amenities.

The company is able to finance many of its technological advancements by forming partnerships with the other major theater chains. National CineMedia a joint venture with Regal Entertainment and AMC Entertainment delivers digital advertising pre-recorded concerts meetings sporting events and other non-film entertainment content. In addition it is continuing to roll-out digital cinema through its Digital Cinema Implementation Partners another joint venture between Cinemark Regal and AMC.

Mergers and Acquisitions
Cinemark USA a wholly owned subsidiary of Cinemark and Rave Real Property Holdco an affiliate of Rave Cinemas entered into an asset purchase agreement in 2012 in which Cinemark will acquire most of Rave's assets consisting of 32 theaters and more than 480 screens in 12 states. The purchase price is $240 million. This acquisition would further enhance Cinemark's domestic footprint especially adding presence in the New England market.

Ownership

Madison Dearborn Capital Partners owns about a third of Cinemark; chairman and former CEO Lee Roy Mitchell and the Mitchell Special Trust collectively own about 11%. Members of the Syufy family the founders of Century Theatres hold a 5% stake.

HISTORY

Lee Roy Mitchell and partner Paul Broadhead founded Cinemark in 1985 and by the end of 1989 Cinemark had about 660 screens in 18 states. Mitchell set a company goal of 1000 screens by 1992 and in addition to constructing its own theaters Cinemark made acquisitions to achieve its goal.

In 1992 Cinemark built its first megaplex Hollywood USA –featuring 15 movie screens a pizzeria and an arcade. As the multiplex became one of its most profitable theaters the company added more to its portfolio. Cinemark also started developing a Latin American presence in 1992 building theaters in Mexico and Chile.

The company formed a joint venture in 1995 to build theaters in Argentina and in 1996 created three more joint ventures for theaters in Brazil Ecuador and Peru.

Meanwhile Cinemark continued to add megaplexes; it opened 12 theaters with 165 screens (an average of about 14 screens per theater) in 1997. In the first half of 1998 the company added 223 more screens including 64 in Latin America.

Later that year a group of wheelchair users sued the company claiming the front-row spaces reserved for them in Cinemark's stadium-seating theaters were uncomfortably close to screens. A US Court of Appeals sided with the theater chain in 2000 and the US Supreme Court refused to hear the plaintiffs' appeal. The company later agreed to modify some theaters and build future theaters in compliance with a court-approved plan.

Cinemark along with the rest of the movie-theater industry struggled through the late 1990s as numerous bankruptcies abounded thanks to overbuilding. The overall decline of the stock market forced the firm to postpone filing an IPO in 2002.

In 2001 Cinemark introduced the electronic gift card for movie ticket and concessions purchases. During 2002 Cinemark opened seven new theaters with 58 screens. The following year the company opened nine new theaters with 77 screens and added three screens to existing theaters.

In 2004 the company brought in investor Madison Dearborn rather than going public and additional minority investors joined up in the next two years. The following year Cinemark joined Regal Entertainment and AMC Entertainment in National CineMedia a joint venture that delivers ads and pre-movie entertainment to screens throughout the US and Canada via a private digital network.

In 2006 Cinemark expanded significantly with the acquisition of Century Theatres the eighth-largest movie-theater operator. The combination added more than 1000 screens to Cinemark's operations and strengthened its foothold as the third-largest movie-theater operator. Also during 2006 the company grew by building 210 screens. In 2007 it again filed an IPO after a brighter year at the box office.

EXECUTIVES

President and CEO, Timothy (Tim) Warner, age 68, $446,420 total compensation

EVP and CFO, Robert Copple, age 55, $420,160 total compensation
SVP General Counsel and Secretary, Michael (Mike) Cavalier, age 47, $341,380 total compensation
SVP Film Licensing, Steven (Steve) Bunnell, age 53
SVP Real Estate, Tom Owens, age 56
Chairman, Lee Roy Mitchell, age 76, $802,461 total compensation
President Cinemark International, Valmir Fernandes, age 54
Director, Raymond W. (Ray) Syufy, age 51
Director, Roger T. Staubach, age 71
Director, Enrique F. Senior, age 69
Director, Donald G. Soderquist, age 80
Director, Steven P. (Steve) Rosenberg, age 54
Director, Vahe A. Dombalagian, age 40
Director, Carlos M. Sepulveda, age 56
Director, Peter R. Ezersky, age 53
Director, Benjamin D. Chereskin, age 54
Independent Director, Enrique Hernandez
Auditors: Deloitte&ToucheLLP

LOCATIONS

HQ: Cinemark Holdings Inc.
 3900 Dallas Pkwy. Ste. 500, Plano TX 75093-7865
Phone: 972-665-1000   **Fax:** 972-665-1004
Web: www.cinemark.com

PRODUCTS/OPERATIONS

2012 Sales

	$ mil.	% of total
Admissions	1,580	64
Other	121	5

COMPETITORS

AMC Entertainment	Kerasotes ShowPlace
Alamo Drafthouse	Landmark Theatres
Carmike Cinemas	Marcus Corporation
Cineplex	National Amusements
Clearview Cinemas	Pacific Theatres
Hoyts Cinemas	Rave Cinemas
IMAX	Regal Entertainment

HISTORICAL FINANCIALS

Company Type: Public

Income Statement

FYE: December 31

	REVENUE ($ mil.)	NET INCOME ($ mil.)	NET PROFIT MARGIN	EMPLOYEES
12/12	2,473.5	168.9	6.8%	22,500
12/11	2,279.6	130.5	5.7%	14,000
12/10	2,141.1	146.1	6.8%	14,600
12/09	1,976.5	97.1	4.9%	20,700
12/08	1,742.2	(48.3)	—	18,300
Annual Growth	9.2%	—	—	5.3%

2012 Year-End Financials

Debt ratio: 49.5%
Return on equity: 16.0%
Cash ($ mil.): 742
Current ratio: 2.50
Long-term debt ($ mil.): 1,893

No. of shares (mil.): 114
Dividends
 Yield: 3.2%
 Payout: 60.4%
Market value ($ mil.): 2,986

	STOCK PRICE ($) FY Close	P/E High/Low	PER SHARE ($) Earnings	Dividends	Book Value
12/12	25.98	19 12	1.47	0.84	9.43
12/11	18.49	19 15	1.14	0.84	8.87
12/10	17.24	15 10	1.29	0.75	8.98
12/09	14.37	16 8	0.87	0.72	8.11
12/08	7.43	— —	(0.45)	0.72	7.45
Annual Growth	36.7%	— —	—	3.9%	6.1%

Cirrus Logic, Inc.

Cirrus Logic's approach to computing is hardly wispy. The fabless semiconductor company long a leader in audio chips of all kinds develops integrated circuits (ICs) for specialized applications in consumer electronics energy and industrial equipment. Its more than 700 products include audio encoder/decoders (codecs) digital amplifiers digital audio converters and energy management devices. Cirrus Logic's audio chips are used in smartphones tablet and laptop computers Blu-ray Disc players gaming devices and digital TVs. Energy management products include LED driver ICs ADCs and DACs used to make LEDs digital utility meters and power supplies. The company gets most of its sales from customers in China.

HISTORY

Suhas Patil a professor who had developed a chip-level software system for controlling disk drives while at MIT founded Patil Systems in 1981. When his firm failed to find buyers for its advanced products Patil sought advice from semiconductor executive Michael Hackworth. Impressed with the products' possibilities Hackworth joined Patil Systems as CEO. In 1984 the company was renamed Cirrus Logic after the high-flying clouds.

The company initially focused on chips for computer peripherals but during the 1980s it also began making chips for PCs. It debuted the first controller chips small enough to be built directly into a disk drive unit an advance that prompted the PC industry's shift to smaller-profile disk drives. When IBM introduced its Video Graphics Array (VGA) graphics display standard in 1987 Cirrus Logic quickly followed with the market's first VGA controller chip.

Cirrus Logic went public in 1989. Its 1991 acquisitions of Crystal Semiconductor and Pixel Semiconductor provided it with access to audio and video technology for the multimedia and fax/modem markets. It bought PC graphics chip maker Acumos in 1992 and Pacific Communication Sciences (products for cellular communications) in 1993. The next year it bought PicoPower Technology a maker of system controller chips.

In 1996 Cirrus Logic sold its wireless infrastructure equipment unit to ADC Telecommunications. That year the company formed wafer fabrication joint venture Cirent with Lucent's microelectronics unit (which became Agere Systems later acquired by LSI Corp.).

An industry downturn led Cirrus Logic to cut its workforce by 13% in 1996 and by another 15% in 1997. That year Patil stepped away from the company's day-to-day operations (he continued to serve as chairman emeritus and a director) and Hackworth became chairman.

In 1998 continuing to expand its offerings Cirrus Logic debuted products for DVDs. In response to a prolonged slump in the semiconductor industry it eliminated its PC graphics and video accelerator product lines and sold voice compression technology subsidiary Nuera Communications to management. Also that year Cirrus Logic spun off its PC modem business as Ambient Technologies. Analog Devices VP/GM David French was named president and COO in 1998.

In 1999 about 500 more employees were laid off. In an effort to phase out more of its wafer fabrication operations the company that year handed over control of its MiCRUS joint venture (founded in 1994) to partner IBM and transferred its ownership of Cirent to Lucent (now Alcatel-Lucent). Also that year French became CEO; Hackworth remained chairman.

In 2000 Cirrus Logic moved its headquarters from Fremont California to Austin Texas. The next year the company announced that it would focus growth efforts on semiconductors used in consumer entertainment devices. Despite historically dismal conditions in the chip industry Cirrus Logic took steps to pursue this strategy in 2001 when it acquired private chip makers Peak Audio (digital audio hardware and software) LuxSonor ($65 million DVD video processors) ShareWave ($92 million wireless home networking chips and software) and Stream Machine ($110 million digital video encoding chips).

Later in 2001 the company announced that it would lay off about 300 workers –30% of its staff –in the face of continued poor conditions in the global chip market. The next year Cirrus exited the magnetic storage chip business in order to focus on products for the consumer entertainment market. In 2003 the company announced more job cuts and discontinued the wireless product line acquired as part of the ShareWave acquisition. It also sold its chip testing facilities to ChipPAC (now part of STATS ChipPAC) which in turn supplied Cirrus Logic with assembly test and packaging services.

As conditions in the worldwide semiconductor market turned choppy again in 2004 Cirrus Logic had a 7% reduction in force more than 50 workers mostly affecting employees in California and Texas.

In 2005 the company received $25 million from a legal settlement with Amkor Technology Fujitsu and Sumitomo Bakelite. The litigation was over faulty semiconductors sold by Cirrus to Fujitsu. Cirrus and Fujitsu first sued each other in 2001; Amkor and Sumitomo were added as parties to the litigation (which shifted from federal court to state court) in 2003. The insurance carriers for the four vendors reached a settlement through arbitration in 2005.

That same year Cirrus Logic sold its digital video IC product line to Magnum Semiconductor an entity formed by investors led by Investcorp and August Capital Management. The company received a minority equity stake in Magnum Semi for the assets of the digital video line.

In 2006 Cirrus acquired Shanghai-based Caretta Integrated Circuits for about $10 million in cash. Caretta designed power management ICs for the large single-cell lithium-ion battery market.

David French resigned as president and CEO in 2007 after a special committee of the board investigated the company's past practices in granting stock options and found that French was significantly involved in backdating certain option grants. Chairman Michael Hackworth stepped in as acting president and CEO. VP/GM Jason Rhode a Cirrus Logic employee since 1995 was named to succeed French as president and CEO.

In 2007 the SEC's Division of Enforcement informed Cirrus Logic that its informal investigation of the company's historical stock option practices initiated a year earlier was elevated to a formal inquiry. The SEC later notified the company that the inquiry was concluded and the commission's staff was not recommending any enforcement action against the company.

Cirrus acquired Apex Microtechnology for $42 million in cash in 2007. Apex Micro developed precision high-power analog amplifiers for aerospace and industrial applications used in motors piezoelectrics programmable power supplies and

other devices. Founded in 1980 the company (also known as Apex Precision Products) had some 1200 customers with about $20 million in annual sales and employed around 90 people.

In 2008 the company decided that things weren't working out with Caretta Integrated Circuits in terms of its long-term strategic plan. It shut down the subsidiary and laid off about 30 employees in China as a result.

The global financial crisis of 2008 which restricted the worldwide availability of credit destabilized the general economy and triggered a significant slowdown in orders for Cirrus Logic.

EXECUTIVES

Chairman, Michael L. (Mike) Hackworth, age 71
Chairman, Alan R. Schuele
VP Coporate Marketing Communications and Human Resources, Jo-Dee M. Benson, age 53
Manager Public Relations North America and Europe, Bill Schnell
President CEO and Director, Jason P. Rhode, age 43, $390,000 total compensation
SVP; General Manager Mixed-Signal Audio Division, Scott A. Anderson, age 59, $275,000 total compensation
Chief Financial Officer; Vice President; Principal Accounting Officer, Thurman Case
VP General Counsel and Secretary, Gregory S. (Scott) Thomas, age 47, $275,000 total compensation
Senior Marcom Manager Asia, Regina Shum
VP Worldwide Sales, Tim Turk, age 56, $255,000 total compensation
VP Finance CFO and Treasurer, Thurman K. Case, age 55, $245,000 total compensation
VP and General Manager Apex Precision Power, Gregory L. (Greg) Brennan
VP and General Manager EXL, Thomas (Tom) Stein, age 41
VP Corporate Quality, Lewis Venters
Vice President - Supply Chain, Randy Carlson
Vice President - Corporate Marketing Communications and Human Resources, Jo-Benson
Vice President - Worldwide Sales, Timothy Turk
Vice President Chief Culture Officer, Dee M. Benson
Board Member, Robert H. (Bob) Smith, age 75
Board Member, D. James Guzy Sr., age 76
Director, Susan S. Wang, age 62
Director, Al R. Schuele
Director, William D. Sherman, age 70
President CEO and Director, Jason P. Rhode, age 43
Director, John C. Carter, age 58
Director, Timothy R. Dehne, age 47
Auditors: Ernst&YoungLLP

LOCATIONS

HQ: Cirrus Logic Inc.
800 W. 6th St., Austin TX 78701
Phone: 512-851-4000   **Fax:** 512-851-4977
Web: www.cirrus.com

2013 Sales

	$ mil.	% of total
China	700	87
US	38	5
UK	19	2
Taiwan	11	1
Japan	9	1
South Korea	9	1
Hong Kong	8	1
Rest of the World	13	2
Total	**809**	**100**

PRODUCTS/OPERATIONS

2013 Sales

	$ mil.	% of total
Audio products	754	93
Energy products	55	7
Total	**809**	**100**

Selected Products

Amplifier integrated circuits
Analog-to-digital converters
Digital amplifiers
Digital interface integrated circuits
Digital-to-analog converters
Linear amplifiers
Volume controls

COMPETITORS

AMD	Macronix International
Actions Semiconductor	Marvell Technology
Analog Devices	Maxim Integrated
Analogic	Products
Asahi Kasei	NXP Semiconductors
Atmel	O2Micro
Broadcom	ON Semiconductor
Conexant Systems	Power Integrations
Creative Technology	STMicroelectronics
Dialog Semiconductor	Samsung Electronics
Fairchild	Sigma Designs
Semiconductor	Standard Microsystems
Freescale	Sunplus
Semiconductor	Texas Instruments
Infineon Technologies	VIA Technologies
Integrated Device	Wolfson
Technology	Microelectronics
Intel	Yamaha
LSI Corp.	austriamicrosystems
Linear Technology	iWatt

HISTORICAL FINANCIALS

Company Type: Public

Income Statement

FYE: March 30

	REVENUE ($ mil.)	NET INCOME ($ mil.)	NET PROFIT MARGIN	EMPLOYEES
03/13	809.7	136.6	16.9%	652
03/12	426.8	87.9	20.6%	676
03/11	369.5	203.5	55.1%	570
03/10	220.9	38.4	17.4%	505
03/09	174.6	3.4	2.0%	479
Annual Growth	**46.7%**	**150.4%**	**—**	**8.0%**

2013 Year-End Financials

Debt ratio: —
Return on equity: 27.0%
Cash ($ mil.): 66
Current ratio: 4.78
Long-term debt ($ mil.): —

No. of shares (mil.): 63
Dividends
  Yield: —
  Payout: —
Market value ($ mil.): 1,440

	STOCK PRICE ($) FY Close	P/E High/Low		Earnings	PER SHARE ($) Dividends	Book Value
03/13	22.75	21	10	2.00	0.00	8.66
03/12	23.80	18	9	1.29	0.00	7.23
03/11	21.16	8	3	2.82	0.00	6.38
03/10	7.89	14	6	0.59	0.00	3.33
03/09	4.00	151	44	0.05	0.00	2.65
Annual Growth	**54.4%**			**—151.5%**	**—**	**34.4%**

Clean Harbors, Inc

Hazardous-waste management company Clean Harbors does more than its name suggests. Its major business lines are its technical services and industrial services units. Its technical services group which accounts for more than 40% of sales provides for the collection transportation treatment and disposal of hazardous waste including chemical and laboratory waste (but not nuclear waste). Its industrial services unit provides high-pressure and chemical cleaning catalyst handling decoking material processing and industrial lodging services. Clean Harbors also has a field services segment and an exploration services unit and recycles used motor oil through its Safety-Kleen unit.

Geographic Reach

The company's 200 service locations include some 50 waste management facilities located throughout North America in 37 US states seven Canadian provinces Mexico and Puerto Rico. The company also operates locations in Bulgaria China Singapore Sweden Thailand and the UK.

Operations

The company has operations in four reportable segments: Technical Services Field Services Industrial Services and Oil and Gas Field Services. Oil and Gas Field Services consists of the previous Exploration Services segment as well as certain oil and gas related field services departments. Clean Harbors' Field Services segment provides a wide variety of environmental cleanup services on customer sites or other locations on a scheduled or emergency response basis. Its major operating subsidiaries include Clean Harbors Canada Inc. Clean Harbors Environmental Services Inc. Clean Harbors Energy and Industrial Services and Safety-Kleen.

Sales and Marketing

Clean Harbors' serve customers in a range of industries including Chemical Engineering General Manufacturing Healthcare Oil and Gas Petroleum Refining Pharmaceutical Retail Steel Transportation and Utilities. It also has various Government clients. Oil and gas production accounted for 27% of the company's total revenues in 2012; oil and gas exploration (26%).

Financial Analysis

The company's revenue grew by 10% in 2012 thanks to a 24% revenue increase in the Industrial Services segment as the result an increase in the lodging business growth in the oil sands region of Canada and higher demand for specialty services. Oil and Gas Field Services segment revenue jumped by 16% due to higher fluids handling and surface rentals activity stemming from the acquisition of Peak Energy Services in 2011 and from increased exploration activities. The Technical Services Segment revenue grew by 6% as the result of higher volumes of waste being processed through the unit's incinerators and landfills. Net income increased by 2% in 2012 as the result of higher revenues and a benefit from a provision for income taxes due to a drop in unrecognized tax benefits related to an earlier Canadian debt restructuring transaction. The company has reported a year-over-year increase in revenues from 2008 to 2012 as the result of acquisition and the increased global demand for oil and gas production and exploration spurring demand for Clean Harbors' services.

Strategy

The company's strategy for business growth involves both expanding its service offerings and the geographic regions in which it operates; cross-selling its services among its four business segments; pursuing large-scale projects; and grow its business through both organic growth and acquisitions.

Mergers and Acquisitions

In a major move in 2012 the company acquired Safety-Kleen for $1.25 billion.

The deal helps Clean Harbors to expand its portfolio by moving into the recycling of used motor oil. The acquisition of Safety-Kleen which also provides environmental services to motor races allows Clean Harbors to broaden its solvent-recycling capabilities and expand its waste treatment services. Safety-Kleen services more than 200000 customer locations. It operates a fleet of more than 2300 vehicles and 1000 rail cars and collects and processes about 200 million gallons of used oil annually.

In a deal to allow Clean Harbors to expand into key markets in western Canada in 2011 the company acquired Peak Energy Services an oil and gas services firm for $167 million.

That same year however Clean Harbors failed in a bid to acquire Calgary-based Badger Daylighting North America's largest provider of hydrovac services for $248 million. However Badger shareholders rejected the deal.

Ownership

Rowe Price Associates Inc. owns almost 13% of Clean Harbors.

EXECUTIVES

Vice Chairman President and CFO, James M. Rutledge, age 61, $365,000 total compensation
President Clean Harbors Development, William J. (Bill) Geary, age 64, $225,000 total compensation
Chairman and CEO, Alan S. McKim, age 59, $625,000 total compensation
SVP Corporate Controller and Chief Accounting Officer, John R. Beals, age 58
President Environmental Services, Eric W. Gerstenberg, age 45, $275,000 total compensation
EVP Marketing and Oil Re-refining Sales, Curt C. Knapp
EVP Pricing and Proposals, George L. Curtis, age 55
President Energy and Industrial Services, David M. Parry, age 48, $295,833 total compensation
President Safety-Kleen Environmental Services, Jerry E. Correll
SVP Risk Management Clean Harbors Environmental Services, William F. O'Connor, age 62
EVP Corporate Planning and Development, Brian P. Weber, age 45, $247,500 total compensation
EVP Seismic Services, Marvin Lefebvre, age 55
EVP Human Resources, Deirdre J. Evens, age 50
Secretary, C. Michael Malm
SVP Regulatory Affairs Clean Harbors Environmental Services, Phillip G. Retallick, age 60
SVP Internal Audit and Compliance Clean Harbors Environmental Services, Simon R. Gerlin, age 55
VP Marketing Clean Harbors Environmental Services, David N. Proud
Chief Financial Officer; Executive Vice President; Treasurer, Robert E. Gagnon, age 38
SVP and General Counsel, David T. Musselman, age 52
EVP Assest Management, Thomas J. Seeger, age 57
Senior Vice President - Risk Management of Clean Harbors Environmental Services Inc., William OConnor

President Oil and Gas Field Services, Laura Schwinn
EVP and CIO, Steven R. Fusco
EVP Branch Sales and Service, Dave Eckelbarger
Vice Chairman President and CFO, James M. Rutledge, age 61
Director, Eugene G. (Gene) Banucci, age 70
Director, Edward G. (Ed) Galante, age 62
Director, John P. DeVillars, age 64
Director, John F. (Jack) Kaslow, age 81
Director, Daniel J. McCarthy, age 81
Director, Thomas J. (Tom) Shields, age 66
Director, John T. Preston, age 63
Director, Andrea Robertson, age 56
Director, Rod Marlin
Auditors: Deloitte&ToucheLLP

LOCATIONS

HQ: Clean Harbors Inc.
42 Longwater Dr., Norwell MA 02061-9149
Phone: 781-792-5000 **Fax:** 781-792-5900
Web: www.cleanharbors.com

PRODUCTS/OPERATIONS

2012 Sales

	$ mil.	% of total
Technical Services	937	43
Industrial Services	581	27
Oil & Gas Field Services	428	20
Field Services	240	10
Adjustments	(0.4)	-
Total	**2,187**	**100**

2012 Revenues

	% of total
Oil & gas	27
Oil & gas	26
Chemical	14
General	8
Refineries &	7
Brokers	5
Utilities	4
Terminals &	4
Engineering &	3
Government	2
Total	**100**

Selected Services

Chemical Packing
Directional Boring
Emergency Response
Exploration Services
Field Services
Industrial Services
InSite Services
Lodging Services
Production Services
Waste Disposal and Recycling

Selected Industries Served

Chemical and Specialty Chemical
Education
Engineering and Consulting
General Manufacturing
Government
Healthcare
Oil and Gas
Pharmaceutical and Biotechnology
Refinery and Petrochemical
Retail
Steel and Primary Metals
Transportation
Utilities

Selected Mergers and Acquisitions

2012
Safety-Kleen ($1.25 billion; used motor oil recycler)
2011
Peak Energy Services ($167 million; Canada; oil and gas services)

HISTORICAL FINANCIALS

Company Type: Public

Income Statement

FYE: December 31

	REVENUE ($ mil.)	NET INCOME ($ mil.)	NET PROFIT MARGIN	EMPLOYEES
12/12	2,187.9	129.6	5.9%	13,180
12/11	1,984.1	127.2	6.4%	8,320
12/10	1,731.2	130.5	7.5%	6,840
12/09	1,074.2	36.6	3.4%	6,399
12/08	1,030.7	57.4	5.6%	4,804
Annual Growth	20.7%	22.6%	—	28.7%

2012 Year-End Financials

Debt ratio: 36.8%
Return on equity: 11.0%
Cash ($ mil.): 229
Current ratio: 1.91
Long-term debt ($ mil.): 1,402

No. of shares (mil.): 60
Dividends
  Yield: —
  Payout: —
Market value ($ mil.): 3,322

	STOCK PRICE ($) FY Close	P/E High/Low	PER SHARE ($) Earnings	Dividends	Book Value
12/12	55.01	29 20	2.40	0.00	23.72
12/11	63.73	47 19	2.39	0.00	16.94
12/10	84.08	34 22	2.47	0.00	14.80
12/09	59.61	86 56	0.74	0.00	11.70
12/08	63.44	65 39	1.26	0.00	9.04
Annual Growth	(3.5%)	— —	17.6%	—	27.3%

Clearwater Paper Corp

No pulp fiction here —the story of Clearwater Paper is clearly fact. The company produces solid bleach sulfate paperboard consumer tissue products lumber and northern bleached softwood (NBSK) pulp. Business is divided into two primary divisions: Its Pulp and Paperboard segment manufactures paperboard (used to make packaging for foods liquids pharmaceuticals and toiletries) and pulp (consumed internally to make paperboard and tissues). A Consumer Products arm produces a private label tissue largely for grocery chains. Most of Clearwater sales are made in the US.

Geographic Reach

Clearwater has 15 manufacturing locations spanning the US and Canada. The US accounted for 92% of its total revenues in 2012.

Operations

Clearwater's operations are divided into two primary segments: Consumer Products (around 60% of total sales) sells its line of at-home and away-from-home tissue products and Pulp and Paperboard (40%) makes its bleached paperboard used in packaging products.

Sales and Marketing

Clearwater's paperboard is sold to packaging converters domestically through sales offices located throughout the country with a smaller percentage channeled through distribution to commercial printers. International paperboard sales are conducted via sales agents.

Financial Performance

In 2011 Clearwater achieved a historic milestone when it posted $1.9 billion in total revenue the highest in its history. However revenues fell by 3% to $1.87 billion in 2012 while profits surged 62% from $40 million in 2011 to $64 million in 2012.

The revenue decrease was due to the sale of its Lewiston Idaho sawmill it divested in late 2011. Consequently its rise of profits for 2012 was also due to the proceeds of this sawmill sale coupled with lower costs of energy and purchased pulp.

Strategy

Clearwater is continuing to grow its business and streamline its operations through business acquisitions capital investments and plant closings. In mid-2013 it announced the closing of its Thomaston Georgia tissue converting and distribution facility. The closing is part of its strategy to consolidate regional plants to achieve short-term and long-term cost savings. Adhering to this strategy previously the company sold its Lewiston Idaho sawmill in 2011.

To bolster its wood fiber operations in late 2012 Clearwater purchased a wood chipping facility in Clarkston Washington for about $11 million.

Ownership

Royce & Associates owns 10% of Clearwater.

Company Background

Clearwater was spun off from Potlatch Corporation a real estate investment trust in late 2008.

EXECUTIVES

Chairman, Boh A. Dickey, age 68
President CEO and Director, Linda K. Massman, age 46, $103,441 total compensation
Senior Vice President General Counsel Corporate Secretary, Michael S. Gadd, age 48, $170,948 total compensation
SVP Consumer Products, Thomas A. Colgrove, age 61
SVP and CFO, John D. Hertz
President Pulp and Paperboard, Danny G. Johansen
Director, William D. (Bill) Larsson, age 67
Director, Michael T. Riordan, age 62
Director, Fredric W. (Fritz) Corrigan, age 71
Director, William T. Weyerhaeuser, age 69
President CEO and Director, Linda K. Massman, age 46
Auditors: KPMG LLP

LOCATIONS

HQ: Clearwater Paper Corporation
  601 W. Riverside Ste. 1100, Spokane WA 99201-3825
Phone: 509-344-5900   **Fax:** -12124
Web: www.melroseplc.net

2012 Sales

	$ mil.	% of total
US	1,726	92
Canada	29	2
Korea	9	1
Australia	7	-
China	3	-
Other countries	14	-

PRODUCTS/OPERATIONS

2012 Sales

	$ mil.	% of total
Consumer Products	1,134	60

HISTORICAL FINANCIALS

Company Type: Public

Income Statement

FYE: December 31

	REVENUE ($ mil.)	NET INCOME ($ mil.)	NET PROFIT MARGIN	EMPLOYEES
12/12	1,874.3	64.1	3.4%	3,860
12/11	1,927.9	39.6	2.1%	3,710
12/10	1,372.9	73.8	5.4%	3,830
12/09	1,250.0	182.4	14.6%	2,500
12/08	1,255.3	9.7	0.8%	2,460
Annual Growth	10.5%	60.2%	—	11.9%

2012 Year-End Financials

Debt ratio: 33.6%
Return on equity: 12.4%
Cash ($ mil.): 12
Current ratio: 2.68
Long-term debt ($ mil.): 549

No. of shares (mil.): 22
Dividends
  Yield: —
  Payout: —
Market value ($ mil.): 900

	STOCK PRICE ($) FY Close	P/E High/Low	PER SHARE ($) Earnings	Dividends	Book Value
12/12	39.16	15 11	2.72	0.00	23.53
12/11	35.61	48 18	1.66	0.00	21.30
12/10	78.30	26 14	3.12	0.00	20.40
12/09	54.97	7 1	7.75	0.00	16.00
12/08	8.39	52 17	0.43	0.00	7.97
Annual Growth	47.0%	— —	58.6%	—	31.1%

CNB Financial Corp. (Clearfield, PA)

CNB Financial is the holding company for CNB Bank (formerly County National Bank) which provides traditional deposit and loan services through more than 20 branches and two loan production offices in northwestern and central Pennsylvania. In 2005 the company opened ERIEBANK a division of CNB Bank in Erie Pennsylvania. Commercial financial and agricultural loans make up more than 35% of CNB Financial's loan portfolio which also includes residential mortgages (about 30%) and commercial mortgages (more than 25%). Other offerings include credit cards investments life insurance wealth management and merchant credit card processing.

The company established Holiday Financial Services Corporation a consumer financing and discount lending subsidiary in 2005. The unit has since grown to seven locations.

EXECUTIVES

EVP and Chief Credit Officer CNB Bank, Mark D. Breakey, age 54, $125,000 total compensation
President; Chief Executive Officer; Director of the Company and the Bank, Joseph B. Bower Jr., age 49, $175,000 total compensation
Chairman, Dennis L. Merrey, age 64

EVP and Chief Lending Officer CNB Bank,
Richard L. (Rick) Sloppy, age 62, $130,000 total
compensation
Senior Vice President - Administration; Secretary;
Director, Richard L Greslick Jr.
Principal Financial Officer; Principal Accounting
Officer; Interim Treasurer of the Company &
Interim Chief Financial Officer of CNB Bank,
Brian W. Wingard
Senior Vice President - Operations of CNB Bank,
Vincent Turiano
President; Chief Executive Officer; Director of
the Company and the Bank, Joseph B. Bower Jr.,
age 49
Director, William F. Falger, age 65
Director, Jeffrey S. Powell, age 48
Director, Peter F. Smith, age 58
Director, James B. Ryan, age 65
Director, Robert E. Brown, age 70
Director, Deborah Dick Pontzer, age 53
Director, Robert W. Montler, age 61
Director, Charles H. Reams, age 69
Director, William C. Polacek
Independent Director, Joel Peterson
Auditors: CroweHorwathLLP

LOCATIONS

HQ: CNB Financial Corporation
1 S. 2nd St., Clearfield PA 16830
Phone: 814-765-9621   Fax: 814-765-4511
Web: www.bankcnb.com

PRODUCTS/OPERATIONS

2007 Sales

	$ mil.	% of total
Interest		
Loans including fees	44	71
Securities	8	13
Other	0	1
Noninterest		
Service charges on deposit accounts	4	7
Trust & asset management fees	1	2
Other service charges & fees	1	2
Other	2	4
Total	63	100

COMPETITORS

AmeriServ Financial	Northwest Bancshares
CBT Financial	PNC Financial
First Commonwealth	RBS Citizens Financial
Financial	Group
M&T Bank	S&T Bancorp

HISTORICAL FINANCIALS

Company Type: Public

Income Statement

FYE: December 31

	ASSETS ($ mil.)	NET INCOME ($ mil.)	INCOME AS % OF ASSETS	EMPLOYEES
12/12	1,773.0	17.1	1.0%	337
12/11	1,602.2	15.1	0.9%	314
12/10	1,413.5	11.3	0.8%	304
12/09	1,161.5	8.5	0.7%	295
12/08	1,016.5	5.2	0.5%	303
Annual Growth	14.9%	34.5%	—	2.7%

2012 Year-End Financials

Return on assets: 1.0%	Dividends
Return on equity: 12.3%	Yield: 4.0%
Long-term debt ($ mil.): —	Payout: 47.8%
No. of shares (mil.): 12	Market value ($ mil.): 204
Sales ($ mil): 80	

	STOCK PRICE ($) FY Close	P/E High/Low		PER SHARE ($) Earnings	Dividends	Book Value
12/12	16.38	13	10	1.38	0.66	11.65
12/11	15.78	14	9	1.23	0.66	10.66
12/10	14.81	18	10	1.06	0.66	8.96
12/09	15.99	19	9	0.98	0.66	7.92
12/08	11.19	23	15	0.61	0.65	7.27
Annual Growth	10.0%	—	—	22.6%	0.6%	12.5%

Coeur Mining, Inc.

Coeur Mining (formerly Coeur d'Alene Mines) gets to the heart of the matter when it comes to precious metals. A leading primary silver producer the company holds interests in silver and gold properties in Australia North America and South America. It produces 18 million ounces of silver and more than 226490 ounces of gold annually. Coeur has proved and probable reserves of about 220.4 million ounces of silver and almost 2 million ounces of gold. It produces most of its revenue from the San Bartolome mine in Bolivia and Palmarejo mine in Mexico. Sales of silver account for about three-fourths of the company's revenue. Most of the minerals are sold to bullion-trading banks and to smelters.

Geographic Reach

Coeur Mining is a large primary silver producer with growing gold production and has assets located in Argentina Australia Bolivia Mexico and the US. In 2012 Mexico accounted for 49% of company's total revenues.

Sales and Marketing

The company refines its precious metals dore (an alloy of gold and silver) and concentrates using a geographically diverse group of third party smelters and refiners including clients in Australia China Germany Switzerland and the US (such as Valcambi Nyrstar Aurubis China National Gold Sumitomo Republic Metals and Johnson Matthey).

It markets its dore to bullion trading houses market makers and members of the London Bullion Market Association industrial companies and sound financial institutions. The refined metals are sold to end users for use in electronic circuitry jewelry silverware and the pharmaceutical and technology industries. The company's seven trading counterparties include Mitsui Mitsubishi Standard Bank and Auramet). Sales of metals to the seven companies amounted to 91% of Coeur's total metal sales in 2012.

Operations

Coeur Mining's operating segments include Palmarejo (Mexico) San Bartolome (Bolivia) Kensington (Alaska US) Rochester (Nevada US) Martha (Argentina) and Endeavor (New South Wales Australia).

Financial Performance

The company's revenues decreased by 12% in 2012 due to a drop in the quantity of silver and gold ounces sold and a lower realized price per ounce for silver. The lower sale of silver ounces was primarily due to decreases in silver production at the Palmarejo and San Bartolome mines.

Coeur Mining's net income decreased by 48% in 2012 due to lower revenues an increase in administrative and general expenses (due to increased legal and finance-related expenses and

salaries and relocation costs for new employees) and a growth in exploration expenses as a result of increased exploration activity at and around the company's existing properties.

Except for revenue slump in 2012 the company has seen an upward trend in revenues from 2008 to 2011.

Strategy

The company grows through acquisitions. In 2013 it bought Orko Silver for about $350 million. The combination with Orko grows the company's assets and diversifies its geographic portfolio. Orko owns majority stakes in precious metal mines in Mexcio.

In 2012 Coeur Mining completed the acquisition of the remaining 49% interest in the Joaquin silver-gold project that it did not already hold from Mirasol Resources Ltd.

To raise cash Coeur sold its Minera Cerro Bayo subsidiary in Patagonia Chile to Mandalay Resources for cash and stock in 2010. The main asset was the Cerro Bayo silver-gold mine.

Company Background

In 2007 it bought Australian miner Bolnisi Gold and the Canadian Palmarejo in a deal valued at $1.1 billion. Besides its primary operations in the US and Chile Coeur has interests in exploration-stage properties in Argentina Bolivia Chile Tanzania and the US. The combination with Bolnisi and Palmarejo created the world's largest primary silver producer. Those two companies had already been linked in that Bolnisi owned almost three-quarters of Palmarejo whose biggest asset was the Palmarejo silver and gold project in the Mexican state of Chihuahua.

Coeur Mining traces its roots to 1928; it took its present name in 2013.

EXECUTIVES

Chairman President and CEO, Dennis E. Wheeler, age 70, $587,633 total compensation
Chairman, Robert E. (Rob) Mellor, age 69
Senior Vice President Exploration Coeur South America, Alfredo Cruzat
President CEO and Director, Mitchell J. Krebs, age 41, $262,558 total compensation
SVP Chief Administrative Officer General Counsel and Corporate Secretary, Kelli C. Kast, age 46
Senior Vice President - Exploration, Donald J. Birak, age 59, $262,758 total compensation
Senior Vice President; Chief Compliance Officer, Thomas T. (Tom) Angelos, age 57
Director Investor Relations North America, Karli Anderson
Senior Vice President - Environmental; Health; Safety and Social Responsibility, Luther J. Russell, age 57
Director Corporate Communications, Tony Ebersole
VP and General Manager Kensington Project Coeur Alaska, Thomas C. (Tom) Henderson
Vice President Nevada Development, Guy C. Jeske
SVP Operations, K. Leon Hardy, age 58
VP-HR, Larry A. Nelson, age 60
Controller, Kenneth L. (Ken) Koski, age 44
VP and Managing Director Coeur Tanzania, Godfrey B. Mramba
Director Investor Relations Australia and Asia, John Blue
General Manager San Bartolome, Stuart O'Brien
General Manager Martha Mine, Gordon Babcock
General Manager Technical Support Services, Bernie O'Leary
Corporate Mine Engineering Manager, Al Tattersall
President Manquiri, Huberto Rada, age 60
SVP and CFO, Peter Mitchell

Treasurer; Chief Accountant, Elizabeth M. (Beth) Druffel
SVP and COO, Frank Hanagarne
Senior Vice President of Operations, Randy Buffington
Vice President General Counsel, Casey Nault
Vice President Investor Relations, Wendy Yang
Vice President - Human Resources, Keagan Kerr
Senior Vice President; Chief Development Officer, Joe Phillips
Vice President - Health and Safety, William Holder
Vice President of Project Development and Assessments, Hunter Dickinson
Vice President Information Technology, Don Moss
Vice President North American Operations, Terry Smith
Vice President Operations Support, Sandro Ferrarone
Vice President Exploration, Hans Rasmussen
Vice President Business Development, Mike Harrison
Director, James J. Curran, age 73
Director, Robert E. (Rob) Mellor, age 69
Director, John H. Robinson, age 62
Director, Timothy R. Winterer, age 76
President CEO and Director, Mitchell J. Krebs, age 41
Director, Andrew D. Lundquist, age 49
Director, J. Kenneth Thompson, age 62
Director, Prof Sebastian Edwards, age 59
Director, L. Michael Bogert, age 55
Auditors: KPMGLLP

LOCATIONS

HQ: Coeur Mining Inc.
505 Front Ave., Coeur d' Alene ID 83816-0316
Phone: 208-667-3511   **Fax:** 208-667-2213
Web: www.coeur.com

2012 Sales

	$ mil.	% of total
Latin America	.	
Bolivia	178	20
Argentina	13	1
US	243	28
Total	**895**	**100**

PRODUCTS/OPERATIONS

2012 Sales

	% of total
Palmarejo	49
San Bartolome	20
Rochester	15
Kensington	13
Endeavor	2
Martha	1
Total	**100**

COMPETITORS

Agnico-Eagle	Newmont Mining
BHP Billiton	Pan American Silver
Barrick Gold	Pe?oles
Hecla Mining	Sunshine Silver Mines
Kinross Gold	

HISTORICAL FINANCIALS

Company Type: Public

Income Statement

FYE: December 31

	REVENUE ($ mil.)	NET INCOME ($ mil.)	NET PROFIT MARGIN	EMPLOYEES
12/12	895.4	48.6	5.4%	1,898
12/11	1,021.2	93.5	9.2%	1,903
12/10	515.4	(91.3)	—	1,471
12/09	300.6	(31.9)	—	1,294
12/08	189.4	(0.0)	—	1,034
Annual Growth	**47.4%**	**—**	**—**	**16.4%**

2012 Year-End Financials

Debt ratio: 1.8%
Return on equity: 2.2%
Cash ($ mil.): 125
Current ratio: 1.70
Long-term debt ($ mil.): 3

No. of shares (mil.): 90
Dividends
　Yield: —
　Payout: —
Market value ($ mil.): 2,222

	STOCK PRICE ($) FY Close	P/E High/Low	Earnings	Dividends	Book Value
12/12	24.60	59 28	0.54	0.00	24.33
12/11	24.14	35 20	1.04	0.00	23.83
12/10	27.32	— —	(1.05)	0.00	22.85
12/09	18.06	— —	(0.45)	0.00	24.82
12/08	0.88	— —	(0.00)	0.00	30.64
Annual Growth	**129.9%**	**— —**	**—**	**—**	**(5.6%)**

Cognex Corp.

Cognex machines see what the human eye cannot. The company is one of the world's largest producers of systems that linked to a video camera serve as eyes where human vision is insufficient. Semiconductor consumer goods health care and automotive companies among others use the company's machine vision and industrial identification systems to position and identify products gauge sizes and locate defects. Cognex serves three primary markets: factory automation semiconductor and electronics capital equipment and surface inspection. It also offers consulting and educational services as well as tech support for its products. Sales to customers based outside the US account for about two-thirds of sales.

Geographic Reach

The US and Europe each contributed nearly a third of Cognex's $324 million in sales in 2012. Japan accounted for 13%. Internationally Cognex has been expanding in China India Brazil and Eastern Europe.

Operations

Cognex operates two business segments. The largest is its Modular Vision Systems Division (MVSD) which accounts for about 85% of its sales. MVSD develops manufactures and markets modular vision systems and ID products that are used to automate the manufacturing and tracking of discrete items by locating identifying inspecting and measuring them during the manufacturing or distribution process. The smaller Surface Inspection Systems Division (SISD) develops makes and markets surface inspection vision systems that are used to inspect surfaces of materials processed in a continuous fashion such as metals papers plastics and glass to ensure that there are no defects on the surfaces.

Sales and Marketing

Cognex sells its MVSD products through a worldwide direct sales force and via a global network of integration and distribution partners. SISD. which is the smaller of the two businesses and has fewer customers in a concentrated group of industries sells its products primarily through a worldwide direct sales force.

Financial Performance

Cognex reported sales of $324.3 million in 2012 an increase of nearly 1% versus 2011. The modest uptick resulted from increased sales to factory automation and surface inspection customers partially offset by a decrease in sales to semiconductor and electronics capital equipment customers. Cognex's service revenue increased 17% on higher consulting services at MVSD as well as higher revenue from SISD spare part sales training services and maintenance and support contracts. On a geographic basis the US outperformed Europe and Japan. Indeed sales in the US increased 3% year over year while sales in Europe and Japan decreased 5% and 13% respectively. Sales to other countries jumped 17% to account for nearly a quarter of total sales.

Sales to customers in the factory automation market represented 75% of Cognex's total revenue in 2012. In the fourth quarter of 2012 revenue trends in Asia specifically in China were negatively impacted by a slowdown in the consumer electronics industry which overshadowed gains in the factory automation market in the Americas and Europe.

Strategy

Cognex's successful expansion into the factory automation market has significantly widened its customer base. The company is focusing on factory automation because it believes it provides the greatest potential for long-term sustainable revenue growth. To that end it's investing in new product development and functionality to make its machines vision products easier to use and more affordable. Cognex has opened sales offices in emerging markets such as China India and Brazil where it sees ample opportunity for the adoption of its factory automation products. Cognex's business strategy includes selective expansion into new machines vision applications through the acquisition of businesses and technologies.

Meanwhile Cognex has reduced its dependence on the highly-cyclical semiconductor and electronics industries which now account for less than 10% of sales down from 61% in 2000. Surface inspection customers represented 16% of sales in 2012. These customers use machine vision to examine materials including metals paper plastics and glass that are processed at high speeds in a continuous manner.

Ownership

Royce & Associates owns about 11% of Cognex's shares.

HISTORY

Robert Shillman and two MIT colleagues Marilyn Matz and William Silver started Cognex (short for "cognition experts") in 1981 to create vision replacement machines for factories. Competition and inadequate technology forced the firm to reevaluate its distribution strategy in 1986. Cognex began supplying machine vision technology to original equipment manufacturers. The company introduced the first custom vision chip in 1988 and went public the next year.

Cognex found success where human vision fails –in the high-speed detailed repetitive processes required in making semiconductors. The company expanded by purchasing Acumen a developer of machine vision systems for semiconductor wafer identification (1995); Isys Controls a maker of quality control systems (1996); and Mayan Automation a maker of surface inspection systems (1997).

Low demand for semiconductor and printed circuit board manufacturing equipment in Asia hurt sales in 1998. Nonetheless the company boosted R&D by 10% and acquired some of Rockwell Automation's machine vision operations also becoming the preferred global supplier to Rockwell's plants. Orders picked up in early 1999 and Cognex invested $1 million in upstart Avalon Imaging (machine vision for the plastics industry) its first investment in such a company.

In 2000 Cognex acquired Komatsu's machine vision business. The Komatsu unit was one of the largest machine vision system suppliers in Japan. Also that year the company acquired additional machine vision products by purchasing UK-based Image Industries. In 2002 Cognex won an appeal in its ongoing patent lawsuit with the Lemelson Medical Education & Research Foundation. The company legally prevailed over the Lemelson trust again in 2005. In 2004 the company reached a legal settlement and licensing agreement with rival Electro Scientific Industries (ESI) with ESI paying a license fee to Cognex.

In 2003 the company acquired the wafer identification business of Siemens Logistics and Assembly Systems (formerly Siemens Dematic) expanding its presence in Europe. The same year it also bought the industrial parts identification business of Gavitec.

In 2005 Cognex bought DVT Corp. for $104 million in cash; DVT made vision sensors used on factory floors. Cognex celebrated its 25th anniversary in 2006 with a gala celebration at its corporate headquarters and in downtown Boston.

Also in 2006 Cognex acquired AssistWare Technology a developer of lane departure warning systems for vehicles. The experiment was short-lived as Cognex sold the the lane departure warning operations to Takata Corporation in 2008 saying the business did not fit the company's business model.

Reacting to the unfavorable business environment around the world Cognex took cost-cutting measures in 2008 and again in 2009. The latter reductions included laying off about 145 employees and contractors (a 17% cut in workforce) cuts in certain executive salaries adding more mandatory shutdown days and decreases in discretionary spending.

Seeking to expand its surface inspection system products Cognex in 2009 bought the SmartAdvisor web monitoring system product line from Monitoring Technology Corporation (MTC) for $5 million in cash.

EXECUTIVES

SVP and Senior Fellow, William M. (Bill) Silver, age 58

SVP Research and Development, E. John McGarry, age 56

EVP Finance and Administration CFO and Treasurer, Richard A. Morin, age 63, $249,623 total compensation

SVP and Director, Patrick A. Alias, age 67, $233,896 total compensation

Chairman and Chief Culture Officer, Robert J. (Bob) Shillman, age 66, $250,000 total compensation

SVP MVSD Sales Americas, Kris Nelson, age 65

Director Investor Relations, Susan Conway

Secretary, Anthony J. Medaglia Jr.

President CEO and Director, Robert Willett, age 46, $255,981 total compensation

President Surface Inspection Systems Division, Thomas F. Nash

Director and Business Unit Manager Vision Systems, Bhaskar Banerjee

VP and Business Unit Manager ID Products, Carl Gerst

VP Legal Services, Todd Keebaugh

SVP Worldwide Sales and Marketing MVSD, Didier Lacroix

VP Operations, Herbert Lade

VP and Corporate Controller, Laura MacDonald

VP Global Marketing, Peter Neve

President Cognex K.K., Kiyoshi Shima

SVP SISD Cognex K.K., Hisataka Shitara

Treasurer, Sheila DiPalma

VP-Ops, Herb Lade

Director, Jerald G. (Jerry) Fishman, age 67

SVP and Director, Patrick A. Alias, age 67

Director, Anthony (Tony) Sun, age 60

Director, Reuben Wasserman, age 83

Director, Theodor Krantz, age 70

President CEO and Director, Robert Willett, age 45

Director, Jeffrey B. Miller

Auditors: GrantThorntonLLP

LOCATIONS

HQ: Cognex Corporation
1 Vision Dr., Natick MA 01760-2059
Phone: 508-650-3000 **Fax:** 508-650-3344
Web: www.cognex.com

2012 Sales

	$ mil.	% of total
US	101	31
Europe	101	32
Japan	43	13
Other	78	24
Total	**324**	**100**

PRODUCTS/OPERATIONS

2012 Sales

	$ mil.	% of total
Product	295	91
Service	28	9
Total	**324**	**100**

2012 Sales by Segment

	$ mil.	% of total
Modular Vision Systems	273	84
Surface Inspection Systems	50	16
Total	**324**	**100**

Selected Products

DataMan 100 and 200 Series (image-based ID readers)
DisplayInspect (LCD inspection software)
In-Sight 5000 (machine vision system)
SmartAdvisor (web monitoring technology)
SmartView Paper (paper web inspection system)
SmartView Metals (flat-rolled metals surface inspection system)

COMPETITORS

Adept Technology	KLA-Tencor
Camtek	National Instruments
Clemex	Orbotech
CyberOptics	PPT VISION
Data Translation	Panasonic Electric
Elbit Vision	Works UK
Electro Scientific	Perceptron
Industries	RoboGroup T.E.K.
Image Sensing Systems	Scanner Technologies
Integral Vision	

HISTORICAL FINANCIALS

Company Type: Public

Income Statement

FYE: December 31

	REVENUE ($ mil.)	NET INCOME ($ mil.)	NET PROFIT MARGIN	EMPLOYEES
12/12	324.2	68.1	21.0%	984
12/11	321.9	69.8	21.7%	919
12/10	290.6	61.3	21.1%	824
12/09	175.7	(4.8)	—	729
12/08	242.6	27.2	11.2%	832
Annual Growth	**7.5%**	**25.7%**	**—**	**4.3%**

2012 Year-End Financials

Debt ratio: —
Return on equity: 12.0%
Cash ($ mil.): 45
Current ratio: 4.78
Long-term debt ($ mil.): —

No. of shares (mil.): 86
Dividends
 Yield: 2.9%
 Payout: 197.4%
Market value ($ mil.): 3,168

	STOCK PRICE ($) FY Close	P/E High/Low	PER SHARE ($) Earnings	Dividends	Book Value
12/12	36.79	56 38	0.78	1.54	6.65
12/11	35.79	44 30	0.82	0.18	6.55
12/10	29.42	41 21	0.76	0.25	5.76
12/09	17.71	— —	(0.06)	0.30	4.97
12/08	14.80	85 33	0.33	0.47	5.21
Annual Growth	**25.6%**	**— —**	**24.0%**	**34.5%**	**6.3%**

Coherent, Inc.

Coherent lets its lights shine. The company uses light wave manipulation called photonics to manufacture and market a diverse array of lasers. Its products are used in a host of areas: microelectronics (semiconductor fabrication packaging flat-panel display and solar cell manufacturing) scientific and government research in physical and chemical processes OEM components and instrumentation and materials processing. Its specialty lasers and systems segment makes configurable laser products while its commercial lasers and components unit specializes in high-volume products sold in set configurations.

Nearly three-quarters of Coherent's sales come from customers outside the US. The company has manufacturing facilities in Germany Malaysia Scotland Singapore and the US in addition to sales offices worldwide.

Overall sales for Coherent rose 33% to $802.8 million in 2011 while its net income was up more than 150%. Sales to the company's largest market —microelectronics (47% of sales) —rose 64% primarily due to increased sales to the flat-panel semiconductor chip packaging and solar markets. Sales to the materials processing sector increased 27% for the year due to higher sales of lasers for cutting drilling and marking applications. Improved demand drove an 11% increase in sales to the scientific and government research markets. Bio-instrumentation medical and machine vision uses were behind a 9% rise in OEM components and instrumentation sales.

Coherent's strategy includes expanding its portfolio through acquisitions and internal development in order to enter new markets while extending its leadership in existing markets including microelectronics. The company also collaborates with customers to design and development new products as new technologies emerge and looks to increase its market share using both new product development —it spends upwards of 10% of sales on research and development —and acquisitions to spur growth.

In late 2012 the company acquired Germany-based Lumera Laser for about $52 million which enhances its position in the fast-growing market for short-pulse micromaterials processing.

The following year Coherent paid $14.5 million for the assets of Singapore-based Hypertronics a maker of standard and custom laser tools with facilities in both Singapore and Malaysia. It purchased Beam Dynamics for $6 million in 2010 extending its R&D capabilities and expanding into precision laser processing workstations.

HISTORY

In 1966 the six founders of Coherent Radiation Laboratories created their first product a carbon dioxide laser in a laundry room (the only room in the house with a 220-volt outlet to power the laser). In true Silicon Valley fashion the founders were all disgruntled ex-employees of another established company —in this case Spectra-Physics. With a research contract from DuPont and sales to Boeing Coherent's revenues topped $1 million by 1968. In 1970 the company pioneered lasers for ophthalmologic use and completed an IPO. It introduced a carbon dioxide surgical laser in 1976 and the first true excimer laser (which produces a deep ultraviolet light) in 1977 (the same year it became Coherent Inc.). In 1981 the company acquired a stake in Lambda Physik (founded in 1971 as the commercial arm of Germany's renowned Max Planck Institute).

After limping through the recession of the early 1990s Coherent sold its industrial division in 1993. In 1995 the company expanded its semiconductor diode laser business with several acquisitions including the manufacturing operation of laser maker Uniphase (now part of JDS Uniphase). In 1996 Coherent bought telecommunications microchip laser maker Micracor and a controlling stake in Finnish semiconductor wafer maker Tutcore. That year VP Bernard Couillaud was named CEO.

The 1997 acquisition of UK-based Ealing Electro-Optics added assembly capabilities for medical and other systems. Also that year the company formed a telecommunications market-based joint venture with Fiber Optics Network (closed in 1999). In 1999 Coherent bought Star Medical Technologies a maker of laser hair removal equipment in an effort to expand its medical business.

In 2000 the company acquired Crystal Associates a manufacturer of crystals for photonics applications. The next year the company sold its medical products division to Lumenis (formerly ESC Medical Systems) for about $235 million. Also in 2001 Coherent acquired DeMaria Electro-Optics Systems a maker of specialized carbon dioxide lasers. Late the next year the company acquired Molectron Detector a maker of laser-based equipment used to test photonics gear.

Late in 2002 company COO John Ambroseo succeeded Couillaud as CEO; Couillaud remained chairman.

Lambda Physik was organizationally merged into the company's Coherent Japan subsidiary in 2005. During fiscal 2005 Coherent raised its ownership of Lambda Physik from 95% to 100%.

In mid-2005 the company acquired TuiLaser for about E22.5 million net of cash. TuiLaser made excimer and solid-state lasers for industrial med-

ical and scientific applications. In late 2005 Coherent also acquired the assets of iolon a competitor for around $5 million in cash.

A year later Coherent licensed manufacturing and sales rights to iolon's Apollo line of swept tunable lasers to Luna Innovations. Luna also acquired manufacturing equipment and inventory previously used by Coherent to manufacture the lasers.

In early 2006 Coherent agreed to acquire competitor Excel Technology for about $376 million in cash; the deal was blocked by German regulators however.

Closing of the transaction was delayed due to an extended antitrust investigation by the Federal Cartel Office of Germany. Coherent and Excel couldn't meet the conditions set by the German business competition authorities. Their merger agreement called for the transaction to close by the end of October 2006 or one of the parties could unilaterally terminate the agreement which Excel opted to do. The deal was cleared by the Justice Department and the Federal Trade Commission in the US and approved by Excel shareholders.

During fiscal 2006 the company combined its Electro-Optics and Lambda Physik segments into one operating segment. The next year Coherent reorganized its business segments again into Specialty Laser Systems and Commercial Lasers & Components.

Bernard Couillaud resigned as Coherent's chairman in mid-2007. Garry Rogerson the CEO of Varian Inc. and a director since 2004 was elected to succeed him.

Coherent responded to the 2008-2009 global economic downturn by shuttering two US facilities and consolidating its four German plants into two. In addition it announced plans to close its Finland plant but delayed the closure as demand for products manufactured there picked up. The company's Finnish operations were dissolved in the third quarter of 2011.

After restructuring Coherent returned to acquisition mode. In late 2009 the company bought the North American laser assets of StockerYale adding laser diode module and specialty optical fiber product lines manufactured in Canada and New Hampshire.

Coherent acquired Beam Dynamics in 2010 for $6 million adding a line of laser processing workstations. In 2011 the company paid $14.5 million for the assets of Singapore-based Hypertronics a maker of standard and custom laser tools with facilities in both Singapore and Malaysia.

EXECUTIVES

President CEO and Director, John R. Ambroseo, age 52, $602,316 total compensation
Chairman, Garry W. Rogerson, age 61
EVP and CFO, Helene (Leen) Simonet, age 61, $384,221 total compensation
EVP and General Manager Specialty Laser Systems Business Group, Mark Sobey, age 52
EVP and CTO, Luis Spinelli, age 66, $265,853 total compensation
EVP Worldwide Sales Service and Marketing, Paul W. Sechrist, age 53
EVP General Counsel and Corporate Secretary, Bret M. DiMarco, age 45, $311,658 total compensation
VP Human Resources, Mark Rakic
Director, Sandeep S. Vij, age 47
President CEO and Director, John R. Ambroseo, age 51
Director, L. William (Bill) Krause, age 70
Director, Jay T. Flatley, age 60

Director, Lawrence J. (Larry) Tomlinson, age 72
Director, Susan M. James, age 66
Auditors: Deloitte&ToucheLLP

LOCATIONS

HQ: Coherent Inc.
 5100 Patrick Henry Dr., Santa Clara CA 95054
Phone: 408-764-4000   **Fax:** 408-764-4800
Web: www.coherentinc.com

2011 Sales

	$ mil.	% of total
Asia/Pacific		
Japan	166	21
South Korea	117	15
Other countries	71	9
US	208	26
Europe		
Germany	100	12
Other countries	79	10
Other regions	56	7
Total	**802**	**100**

PRODUCTS/OPERATIONS

2011 Sales

	$ mil.	% of total
Specialty laser systems	519	65
Commercial lasers & components	283	35
Total	**802**	**100**

2011 Sales by Market

	$ mil.	% of total
Microelectronics	377	47
OEM components & instrumentation	165	21
Scientific & government programs	156	19
Materials processing	104	13
Total	**802**	**100**

COMPETITORS

Avensys Inc.	New Focus
CVI Laser	Newport Corp.
Cymer	Presstek
GSI Group	Princeton Lightwave
Gemfire	ROFIN-SINAR
II-VI	Roper Industries
IPG Photonics	Schmitt Industries
Isomet	Spectris
JDS Uniphase	TRUMPF
Jenoptik	USHIO
Komatsu	

HISTORICAL FINANCIALS

Company Type: Public

Income Statement

FYE: September 28

	REVENUE ($ mil.)	NET INCOME ($ mil.)	NET PROFIT MARGIN	EMPLOYEES
09/13	810.1	66.3	8.2%	2,514
09/12*	769.0	62.9	8.2%	2,328
10/11	802.8	93.2	11.6%	2,309
10/10	605.0	36.9	6.1%	2,006
10/09	435.8	(35.3)	—	1,712
Annual Growth	**16.8%**	**—**	**—**	**10.1%**

*Fiscal year change

2013 Year-End Financials

Debt ratio: 0.0%	No. of shares (mil.): 24
Return on equity: 9.3%	Dividends
Cash ($ mil.): 110	Yield: 0.0%
Current ratio: 4.31	Payout: 37.0%
Long-term debt ($ mil.): —	Market value ($ mil.): 1,500

STOCK PRICE ($) FY Close	P/E High/Low		PER SHARE ($) Earnings	Dividends	Book Value
09/13	61.32	23 15	2.70	1.00	31.01
09/12*	45.86	22 15	2.62	0.00	28.29
10/11	42.96	17 10	3.66	0.00	26.05
10/10	40.20	27 15	1.47	0.00	24.09
10/09	22.97	— —	(1.45)	0.00	23.54
Annual Growth 27.8%		— —	—	—	7.1%

*Fiscal year change

Collectors Universe Inc

Before you sell that silver dollar or those baseball cards you might want to check with Collectors Universe. The company provides authentication grading and information services for sellers and buyers of trading cards event tickets vintage autographs and other memorabilia. The company charges a fee —usually between $4 and $200 per item —to determine the authenticity quality and worth of the collectible. Coins and sports cards account for most of the company's business; notable offerings include its Professional Coin Grading Service (PCGS). Collectors Universe also publishes price guides market reports rarity reports and other information in print form as well as on its website.

Geographic Reach
Collectors Universe does business primarily in the US. In 2010 the company's Professional Coin Grading Service (PCGS) opened an office in Paris as part of Collectors Universe's international expansion efforts. While expanding its geographic scope and its grading capabilities with an eye on the Asian market the company has also been cutting back in underperforming areas.

Operations
Collectors Universe three reportable service segments are coins trading cards and autographs and other high-end collectibles. The coin authentication and grading business represented about 66% of total revenues in both fiscal 2012 and 2011.

Sales and Marketing
Collectors Universe works directly with individual dealers who submit items to the company for authentication. It also maintains a presence at collectibles trade shows.

The company has enhanced its marketing programs to promote its services directly to the Internet other auction-related businesses and high-volume distributors of modern coins.

Because most collectibles are sold without being authenticated by a third party the company believes it has plenty of room for growth. Collectors Universe estimates that less than 10% of the vintage US coins less than 15% of vintage trading cards and less than 10% of valuable autographs have been authenticated and graded by independent providers of authentication and grading services.

Financial Analysis
The company's total revenue increased about 9% in fiscal 2012 to $48.3 million compared to $44.4 million in 2011 thanks to a boost in the average service fees earned from grading authentication and related services. Except for a slump in 2009 the company has reported an upward trend in revenue from 2008 to 2012.

World coin authentication and grading revenues grew by approximately $1.7 million or 73% in fiscal 2012 compared to 2011. The windfall came from increased submissions of world coins including grading at the company's Paris facility.

Strategy
The company's growth strategy includes both acquisitions and new product launches. In 2010 Collectors Universe launched its PCGS Secure Plus service. The high-tech grading process uses laser scanning to help detect coins that have been artificially enhanced since their last certification. PCGS Secure Plus can also be used to help identify stolen coins.

Mergers and Acquisitions
Collectors Universe expanded its Web presence with the purchase of the precious metal and coin information website Coinflation.com in 2011 for $750000 in cash and stock. The acquisition complemented its existing Web holdings such as PCGSCoinFacts.com a source for historical US numismatic information and other related content.

Ownership
David G. Hall and Richard Kenneth Duncan Sr. each own about 13% and 12% of the company respectively.

EXECUTIVES

Chief Executive Officer, Robert G. (Bob) Deuster, age 62
Chairman, A. Clinton (Clint) Allen, age 69
President; Director, David G. Hall, age 65, $300,000 total compensation
SVP Finance and Chief Compliance Officer, Michael J. Lewis, $168,750 total compensation
Chief Financial Officer, Joseph J. (Joe) Wallace, $212,391 total compensation
President Professional Coin Grading Service, Don Willis
Director, Bruce A. Stevens, age 70
President and Director, David G. Hall, age 64
Director, Deborah A. Farrington, age 62
Director, Albert J. (Bert) Moyer, age 69
Director, Michael J. McConnell, age 47
Auditors: GrantThorntonLLP

LOCATIONS

HQ: Collectors Universe Inc.
1921 E. Alton Ave., Santa Ana CA 92705
Phone: 949-567-1234   **Fax:** 415-644-1401
Web: www.mediaplex.com

PRODUCTS/OPERATIONS

2012 Sales

	$ mil.	% of total
Grading & authentication fees	39	83
Total	48	100

2012 Sales

	$ mil.	% of total
Coins	32	67
Other	4	10

Selected Products & Operations

Coins
  Professional Coin Grading Service (PCGS)
  Certified Coin Exchange (CCE)
Trading Cards & Tickets
  Professional Sports Authenticator (PSA)
Autographs & Memorabilia
  PSA/DNA authentication services
Stamps
  Professional stamp experts
Expos
  Long Beach Expo
  Santa Clara Expo

Selected Mergers & Acquisitions

FY2011
Coinflation.com ($750000 in cash and stock; precious metal and coin information website)

COMPETITORS

Beckett Media	Krause Publications
Christie's	Leland's Auctions
F+W Media	Sotheby's
H.R. Harmer	Spectrum Group

HISTORICAL FINANCIALS

Company Type: Public

Income Statement

FYE: June 30

	REVENUE ($ mil.)	NET INCOME ($ mil.)	NET PROFIT MARGIN	EMPLOYEES
06/13	49.0	5.7	11.7%	256
06/12	48.3	6.7	14.0%	249
06/11	44.4	5.1	11.5%	241
06/10	39.7	16.7	42.0%	231
06/09	35.9	(16.9)	—	216
Annual Growth	8.1%	—	—	4.3%

2013 Year-End Financials

Debt ratio: —	No. of shares (mil.): 8
Return on equity: 25.4%	Dividends
Cash ($ mil.): 18	Yield: 0.1%
Current ratio: 2.40	Payout: 183.1%
Long-term debt ($ mil.): —	Market value ($ mil.): 113

STOCK PRICE ($) FY Close	P/E High/Low		PER SHARE ($) Earnings	Dividends	Book Value
06/13	13.25	21 13	0.71	1.30	2.42
06/12	14.68	21 15	0.84	1.30	3.03
06/11	14.82	25 18	0.66	1.28	3.16
06/10	13.41	7 2	2.19	0.80	3.59
06/09	4.88	— —	(1.85)	0.68	2.71
Annual Growth 28.4%		— —	—	17.5%	(2.8%)

Colony Financial Inc.

While most real estate investors are heading for the nearest exit Colony Financial is knocking on the doors of opportunity. The real estate finance company which formed in June 2009 and immediately filed for an initial public offering (IPO) was established to acquire originate and manage commercial mortgage loans and other commercial real estate related debts. It is externally managed by affiliate Colony Financial Manager a wholly owned subsidiary of Colony Capital. Colony Financial is using the approximately $250 million in proceeds from its IPO to acquire commercial real estate-related loans and assets; it may diversify as opportunities arise.

In 2010 Colony Financial bought some $1.2 billion in discounted commercial mortgages in a structured transaction with the FDIC which has been assuming billions of dollars in loans from failed banks. Colony Financial acquired 40% of the limited liability company formed to hold the loans with the FDIC holding the rest. Early the following year Colony invested in two more discounted loan portfolios with a combined balance of more than $800 million. By focusing on real estate-related assets the company elected to qualify as a real estate investment trust (REIT) a designation that brings tax benefits.

Because Colony Financial has little operating history it is relying on the experience and existing relationships of its management team and Colony Capital. Owned by billionaire Thomas Barrack Colony Capital made headlines in 2008 when it acquired late pop singer Michael Jackson's Neverland Ranch saving the property from foreclosure.

EXECUTIVES

Chairman, Thomas J. (Tom) Barrack Jr., age 62
President CEO and Director, Richard B. Saltzman, age 53
Chief Investment Officer, Kevin P. Traenkle, age 40
Chief Legal Officer and Secretary, Ronald M. Sanders
CFO and Treasurer, Darren J. Tangen, age 39
Chief Compliance Officer, David Palame
Chief Compliance Officer, David A. PalamT
Director, John A. Somers
Director, Prof George G. C. Parker, age 70
President CEO and Director, Richard B. Saltzman, age 53
Director, John L. (Launny) Steffens
Auditors: Ernst&YoungLLP

LOCATIONS

HQ: Colony Financial Inc.
  2450 Broadway 6th Fl., Santa Monica CA 90404
Phone: 310-282-8820   **Fax:** -2267
Web: www.hamworthy.com

COMPETITORS

Arbor Realty Trust	Macerich
Bimini Capital	Newcastle Investment
Management	PS Business Parks
CIFC Deerfield	Pacific Office
Cousins Properties	Properties Trust
Douglas Emmett	Petra Real Estate
Institutional	Redwood Trust
Financial Markets	Starwood Property
JER Investors Trust	Western Asset Mortgage
MPG Office Trust	

HISTORICAL FINANCIALS

Company Type: Public

Income Statement

FYE: December 31

	REVENUE ($ mil.)	NET INCOME ($ mil.)	NET PROFIT MARGIN	EMPLOYEES
12/12	107.1	62.0	57.9%	0
12/11	65.4	43.3	66.2%	0
12/10	27.4	17.7	64.7%	0
12/09	1.0	(0.4)	—	0
Annual Growth	361.4%	—	—	—

2012 Year-End Financials

Debt ratio: 7.5%
Return on equity: 6.7%
Cash ($ mil.): 170
Current ratio: 5.42
Long-term debt ($ mil.): 108

No. of shares (mil.): 53
Dividends
  Yield: 7.3%
  Payout: 105.1%
Market value ($ mil.): 1,035

	STOCK PRICE ($) FY Close	P/E High/Low		PER SHARE ($) Earnings	Dividends	Book Value
12/12	19.50	15	12	1.32	1.44	23.04
12/11	15.71	15	8	1.46	1.31	18.48
12/10	20.02	17	14	1.18	0.97	19.16
12/09	20.37	—	—	(0.06)	0.07	18.68
/0.00	—			—(0.00)	0.00	(0.00)
Annual Growth	—			—	—	—

Columbia Banking System, Inc.

Columbia Banking System (CBS) is the holding company for Columbia State Bank (also known as Columbia Bank). The regional community bank has about 155 branches in Washington from Puget Sound to the timber country in the southwestern part of the state as well as in northern Oregon where it also operates as Bank of Astoria. Targeting retail and small and medium-sized business customers the bank offers standard retail services such as checking and savings accounts CDs IRAs credit cards loans and mortgages. Commercial business and real estate loans make up more than 75% of the company's loan portfolio. CBS is increasing its presence in the Pacific Northwest through acquisitions of other community banks.

Geographic Reach

Tacoma-based Columbia Banking System has bank branches in 38 countries in Washington and Oregon.

Operations

The bank's Columbia Private Banking division offers customized financial services for businesses and affluent families. Subsidiary CB Financial Services provides investment products through a pact with third-party provider PrimeVest.

Financial Performance

Columbia Bank's revenue increased 17% in 2013 versus 2012 to $323.6 million. Net income rose 30% over the same period to $60 million. The bank's merger with West Coast Bank in early 2013 had a positive impact on its financial performance. Columbia's total assets at the end of 2013 were $7.16 billion compared with $4.9 billion at year end 2012 primarily due to the purchase of West Coast.

Strategy

Columbia Banking System has taken advantage of the rash of bank failures in recent years to increase its presence in the region. It added more than 30 branches in 2010 when it acquired most of the deposits and assets of failed banks Columbia River Bank and American Marine Bank a week apart. In similar transactions in 2011 it acquired most of the operations of the failed institutions Summit Bank First Heritage Bank and Bank of Whitman. Those deals added more than a dozen branches in Washington. More recently it acquired its smaller competitor West Coast Bank in spring 2013. Columbia plans to rebrand West Coast under its own name. Also Bank of Astoria will rebrand as Columbia State Bank to create a unified presence in the market.

Mergers and Acquisitions

In April 2013 Columbia acquired West Coast Bancorp –the parent company of West Coast Bank which operates nearly 60 bank branches in Oregon and Washington. The cash-and-stock deal included $264 million in cash and 12.8 million shares of its stock which were paid to West Coast shareholders. The purchase boosted Columbia's total assets to more than $7 billion and furthered Columbia's goal of becoming the leading regional community bank in the Pacific Northwest.

EXECUTIVES

President and CEO; President and CEO Columbia Bank, Melanie J. Dressel, age 60, $420,000 total compensation
Chairman, William T. Weyerhaeuser, age 69, $25,000 total compensation
EVP and COO, Mark W. Nelson, age 61, $235,001 total compensation
VP Corporate Communications and Investor and Community Relations Columbia Bank, JoAnne Coy
EVP and Director Human Resources, Kent L. Roberts, age 61, $180,000 total compensation
EVP and Chief Credit Officer, Andrew L. (Andy) McDonald, age 53, $195,001 total compensation
Vice President & Private Banking Relationship Manager, Scott McVay
EVP and CFO, Clint E. Stein
Vice President & Professional Banking Officer, Dani Collins
Senior Vice President & Professional Banking Relationship Manager, Jerri Pavitt
Senior Vice President and Professional Banking Team Leader, Barbara Cooch
Vice President & Private Banking Relationship Manager, Amy Mullins
Vice President & Private Banking Officer, Chris Sakas
Vice President & Professional Banking Relationship Manager, Chris Frankovich
Vice President & Professional Banking Relationship Manager, Katia Palander
Senior Vice President & Private Banking Team Leader, Megan Sweeters
Vice President and Private Banking Relationship Manager, Neil Zellick
Vice President & Private Banking Relationship Manager, Rebecca Holverson-Cherney
President CEO and Director; President and CEO Columbia Bank, Melanie J. Dressel, age 60
Director, John P. Folsom, age 68
Director, Thomas M. Hulbert, age 66
Director, Thomas L. Matson Sr., age 75
Director, Donald H. Rodman, age 74
Director, James M. Will, age 66
Director, Daniel C. (Dan) Regis, age 73
Director, Frederick M. (Fred) Goldberg, age 73
Independent Director, Mae Numata
Independent Director, Michelle Lantow
Auditors: Deloitte&ToucheLLP

LOCATIONS

HQ: Columbia Banking System Inc.
  1301 A St. Ste. 800, Tacoma WA 98402
Phone: 253-305-1900   **Fax:** 253-305-0317
Web: www.columbiabank.com

2013 Branches

	No.
Washington	86
Oregon	71
Total	**157**

COMPETITORS

BECU	KeyCorp
Bank of America	Sterling Financial
Banner Corp	(WA)
Heritage Financial	U.S. Bancorp
HomeStreet	Washington Federal
JPMorgan Chase	Wells Fargo

HISTORICAL FINANCIALS

Company Type: Public

Income Statement

FYE: December 31

	ASSETS ($ mil.)	NET INCOME ($ mil.)	INCOME AS % OF ASSETS	EMPLOYEES
12/12	4,906.3	46.1	0.9%	1,198
12/11	4,785.9	48.0	1.0%	1,256
12/10	4,256.3	30.7	0.7%	1,092
12/09	3,200.9	(3.9)	—	715
12/08	3,097.0	5.9	0.2%	735
Annual Growth	12.2%	66.8%	—	13.0%

2012 Year-End Financials

Return on assets: 0.9%	Dividends
Return on equity: 6.0%	Yield: 5.4%
Long-term debt ($ mil.): —	Payout: 84.4%
No. of shares (mil.): 39	Market value ($ mil.): 712
Sales ($ mil): 275	

	STOCK PRICE ($) FY Close	P/E High/Low	PER SHARE ($) Earnings	Dividends	Book Value
12/12	17.94	20 14	1.16	0.98	19.25
12/11	19.27	18 11	1.21	0.27	19.22
12/10	21.06	34 22	0.72	0.04	17.97
12/09	16.18	— —	(0.38)	0.07	18.78
12/08	11.93	96 26	0.31	0.58	22.88
Annual Growth	10.7%	— —	39.1%	14.0%	(4.2%)

CommVault Systems Inc

CommVault Systems wants to have a lock on data management. The company provides software that customers use to store and manage enterprise data. Its Simpana software suite handles such tasks as resource management backup archiving data replication disaster recovery and search. The company's customers come from industries that include financial services health care manufacturing and utilities as well as from the public sector. CommVault's strategic partners include systems integrators and professional services firms distributors and resellers and technology providers. About 40% of its revenues are generated outside the US.

During the past two years CommVault has been growing its customer base significantly. Year-over-year revenue rose 16% in 2011. By segment services 52% of revenue was up 21% behind customer support agreements. Software 48% of revenue increased 11% as result mainly of strong demand in Europe Canada Australia and Asia. Year-over-year revenue in 2010 mimicked the previous year with a 16% increase.

The company recorded a net loss in 2007 but has been on a good track since then enjoying net income from 2008 to 2011.

CommVault markets its products worldwide. Maintaining customer support centers in Europe Australia India and China as well as the main one at its headquarters in New Jersey the company counts BT IMG F.N.B. and Sundt Construction among its 14000 end-use customers.

CommVault has identified partnerships as an essential component of its sales strategy. Dell (23% of sales) and Hitachi Data Systems (HDS) are among its key strategic partners.

Serving North American commercial and government customers Arrow Electronics holds a distribution agreement with CommVault and provides around one-quarter of sales. In 2010 the company signed up Avnet to serve North American VARs in addition to customers in overseas markets.

The company also targets the federal government which represented about 8% of revenues for fiscal 2011 down from 9% the previous year. Addressing the cloud computing market CommVault began shipping a cloud-optimized version of Simpana in 2010.

The company was founded as an independent segment of Bell Laboratories in 1988; senior management (backed in part by funding from Sprout Group) purchased the company's assets from Lucent Technologies in 1996.

EXECUTIVES

Chairman President and CEO, N. Robert (Bob) Hammer, age 71, $457,307 total compensation
EVP COO and Director, Alan G. (Al) Bunte, age 60, $338,154 total compensation
VP Services and Technical Support EMEA and APAC, Suresh P. Reddy, age 51
SVP Marketing and Business Development, David R. (Dave) West, age 48, $257,308 total compensation
SVP Finance, Louis F. (Lou) Miceli, age 64, $303,992 total compensation
Press Contact, Dani Kenison
VP Human Resources, William (Bill) Beattie
SVP Worldwide Sales, Ron Miiller, age 47, $269,000 total compensation
VP General Counsel Secretary and Chief Compliance Officer, Warren H. Mondschein
VP Operations, Allen Shoemaker
VP EMEA, Steven Rose, age 56, $260,602 total compensation
VP Worldwide Human Resources, Jane F. Greenman
Senior Director Channel Sales North America, Mark Conley
Chief Financial Officer, Brian Carolan, age 42
VP of Worldwide Customer Support and Training, Robert Brower
VP Worldwide Technical Services, Robert Kaloustian
Senior Director Information Management, Simon Taylor
VP Product Management, Brian Brockway
Director Investor Relations, Michael Picariello
Director Business Development Asia Pacific and Japan, Adam Beavis
Senior Director Cloud Strategy and Alliances, Jeff Echols
Director Professional Services Americas, Bob Carapezzi
Chief Accounting Officer, Gary Merrill, age 38
VP Global Infrastructure and Operations, Gary Simpson
VP-Sls-Americas, Peter Kobs
Director, Gary B. Smith, age 53
Director, Armando Geday, age 51
Director, Keith B. Geeslin, age 60
Director, Frank J. Fanzilli Jr., age 57
EVP COO and Director, Alan G. (Al) Bunte, age 59
Director, David F. Walker, age 59
Director, F. Robert Kurimsky, age 74
Director, Daniel Pulver, age 44
Auditors: Ernst&YoungLLP

LOCATIONS

HQ: CommVault Systems Inc
2 Crescent Place, Oceanport, NJ 07757
Phone: 732 870-4000
Web: www.commvault.com

2011 Sales

	$ mil.	% of total
US	190	61
Other countries	124	39
Total	**314**	**100**

PRODUCTS/OPERATIONS

2011 Sales

	$ mil.	% of total
Services	164	52
Software	149	48
Total	**314**	**100**

COMPETITORS

CA Inc.	Microsoft
EMC	NetApp
Hewlett-Packard	Quantum Corporation
IBM Software	Symantec

HISTORICAL FINANCIALS

Company Type: Public

Income Statement

FYE: March 31

	REVENUE ($ mil.)	NET INCOME ($ mil.)	NET PROFIT MARGIN	EMPLOYEES
03/13	495.8	53.2	10.7%	1,740
03/12	406.6	31.9	7.9%	1,437
03/11	314.7	21.0	6.7%	1,268
03/10	271.0	18.4	6.8%	1,154
03/09	234.5	12.3	5.3%	1,070
Annual Growth	20.6%	44.1%	—	12.9%

2013 Year-End Financials

Debt ratio: —	No. of shares (mil.): 46
Return on equity: 18.2%	Dividends
Cash ($ mil.): 433	Yield: —
Current ratio: 2.62	Payout: —
Long-term debt ($ mil.): —	Market value ($ mil.): 3,805

	STOCK PRICE ($) FY Close	P/E High/Low	PER SHARE ($) Earnings	Dividends	Book Value
03/13	82.00	72 34	1.10	0.00	7.63
03/12	49.64	76 43	0.68	0.00	5.16
03/11	39.88	84 36	0.45	0.00	4.28
03/10	21.35	55 23	0.41	0.00	3.68
03/09	10.97	64 27	0.28	0.00	2.68
Annual Growth	65.3%	— —	40.8%	—	29.9%

Computer Programs & Systems Inc

The general-sounding Computer Programs and Systems Inc. (CPSI) is focused on a very specific market - providing administrative software and hardware systems and outsourcing services to acute care community hospitals. CPSI develops and supports electronic health records (EHR) as well as financial and clinical information management software and IT systems for small and mid-sized hospitals in the US. The company boasts a client base of more than 650 hospitals across 45 states. CPSI's software enables users to manage their patients staff finances and facilities. Subsidiary TruBridge offers manged IT services and business office outsourcing services.

Operations

CPSI products form an integrated data management system so the company markets its various applications as a single system. Among the various functions its electronic health record (EHR) system covers the basic necessary system includes patient management and financial accounting along with the hardware needed to run those programs. The other applications available to customers are patient care clinical record keeping and reporting and enterprise applications. Enterprise applications include such functions as system backups integrated fax document scanning and more.

Sales and Marketing

Nearly all of CPSI's customers are organizations with 100 or fewer acute care beds but its target market includes hospitals with up to 300 such beds. The company serves less than 15% of the estimated size of its larger target market and less than one-quarter of its core market giving it room to continue the growth it has enjoyed so far.

For the most part CPSI lands new customers through referrals from existing customers. It also attracts potential customers with presentations at industry seminars and tradeshows and advertisements in publications for the healthcare industry. The company's typical sales cycle can be anywhere from six to 18 months.

Financial Performance

CPSI continued to grow revenue and profits in 2012 the former rising 5% to $183 million while net income climbed 16% to $29 million. The government incentives for health care organizations to move to electronic records continue to drive sales. It installed systems at 34 new hospitals in 2012 (up from 17 in 2011). The TruBridge business management services segment continued to grow and now accounts for a fifth of total revenue.

Strategy

CPSI named its outsourcing division TruBridge in early 2013. TruBridge offers include network management and monitoring server and storage management hosted email firewall management malware protection data center services and help desk support and more. Business management services include electronic billing patient statement processing payroll processing website hosting and others.

EXECUTIVES

Chairman of the Board; Chief Financial Officer; Treasurer; Secretary, David A. Dye, age 43, $239,731 total compensation

President CEO and Director, J. Boyd Douglas, age 46, $521,154 total compensation

EVP Corporate and Business Development, Victor S. Schneider, age 54, $442,454 total compensation

VP Information Technology Services, Patrick A. Immel, age 42

SVP Software Services, Robert D. Hinckle, age 43

SVP Sales, Troy D. Rosser, age 48, $353,889 total compensation

SVP Product Development Services, Michael K. Muscat Jr., age 39

VP Product Development Services, Robert D. Smith, age 42

President TruBridge, Christopher L. Fowler, age 37

Vice President - Finance; Controller, James Britain

VP Information Technology Services, J. Scott Littrell, age 38

Vice President - Implementation, Lamar Cowart

Vice President - Sales, Lyle Hutchison

Vice President - Financial Support, Pamela Phillips

Vice President - Clinical Support, Stephanie Durkac

Director, Charles P. Huffman, age 59

President CEO and Director, J. Boyd Douglas, age 46

Director, M. Kenny Muscat, age 65

Director, Ernest F. Ladd III, age 72

Director, W. Austin Mulherin III, age 47

Director, William R. Seifert II, age 64

Director, John C. Johnson, age 62

Auditors: GrantThorntonLLP

LOCATIONS

HQ: Computer Programs and Systems Inc.
6600 Wall St., Mobile AL 36695
Phone: 251-639-8100   **Fax:** 251-639-8214
Web: www.cpsinet.com

PRODUCTS/OPERATIONS

2012 Sales

	$ mil.	% of total
System sales	72	40
Support & maintenance	73	40
Business management services	37	20
Total	**183**	**100**

Selected Products

Clinical information systems
  Anatomic pathology
  Cardiopulmonary
  Laboratory information systems
    Blood inventory
    Microbiology
    Quality control
  Laboratory instrument interfaces
  Medical image management systems
  Pharmacy
  Physical therapy
  Radiology information systems
Enterprise applications
Financial accounting applications
  Accounts payable applications
  Budgeting
  Electronic direct deposit
  Executive information
  Fixed asset information
  General ledger applications
  Human resources
  Payroll and personnel
  Time and attendance applications
Home health
Patient care
  Care plans
  Core measures system
  Medication management
  Order entry/results reporting
  Patient activity
Patient management applications
  Contract management
  Electronic file management
  Health information management
  Patient accounting
  Quality improvement applications
  Registration systems

Selected Services

Application services
Internet services
Outsourcing services
  Business office management
  Electronic billing
  Statement processing
Support
System implementation and conversion
Training

COMPETITORS

Cerner	QuadraMed
Global Med	Quality Systems
Healthland	Siemens Healthcare
MEDHOST	Streamline Health
MEDITECH	Solutions
McKesson	

HISTORICAL FINANCIALS

Company Type: Public

Income Statement
FYE: December 31

	REVENUE ($ mil.)	NET INCOME ($ mil.)	NET PROFIT MARGIN	EMPLOYEES
12/12	183.3	29.9	16.4%	1,420
12/11	173.4	25.8	14.9%	1,341
12/10	153.2	18.7	12.2%	1,194
12/09	127.7	15.1	11.9%	1,077
12/08	119.6	15.4	12.9%	886
Annual Growth	**11.3%**	**18.0%**		**12.5%**

2012 Year-End Financials

Debt ratio: —
Return on equity: 52.1%
Cash ($ mil.): 8
Current ratio: 2.76
Long-term debt ($ mil.): —

No. of shares (mil.): 11
Dividends
  Yield: 5.6%
  Payout: 114.5%
Market value ($ mil.): 558

	STOCK PRICE ($) FY Close	P/E High/Low		PER SHARE ($) Earnings	Dividends	Book Value
12/12	50.34	23	17	2.71	2.84	5.16
12/11	51.11	31	18	2.34	1.44	5.19
12/10	46.84	29	21	1.71	1.44	4.24
12/09	46.05	36	16	1.39	1.44	3.89
12/08	26.80	21	12	1.43	1.44	3.72
Annual Growth	**17.1%**	—	—	**17.3%**	**18.5%**	**8.5%**

Concho Resources Inc

Concho Resources has more than a hunch that a lucrative resource lies under its feet in Southeastern New Mexico and West Texas. The company explores and develops properties (more than 626190 net acres) located primarily in the Permian Basin region in which it produces oil and natural gas. The bulk of the company's reported 447.1 million barrels of proved reserves in 2012 is crude oil while the rest is natural gas. Concho Resources gets more than 80% its revenues from crude oil which is priced much higher than natural gas. The company drilled 513 net wells in 2012.

Geographic Reach

The company's core oil and gas exploration and production operating areas are the New Mexico Shelf Delaware Basin and Texas Permian in the Permian Basin region of Southeast New Mexico and West Texas. The New Mexico Shelf represented 50% of Concho Resources' total reserves in 2012; Texas Permian 32%; and the Delaware Basin 18%.

Sales and Marketing

The company's major customers include HollyFrontier Refining and Marketing ConocoPhillips and DCP Midstream which accounted for 26% 14% and 8% respectively of Concho Resources' revenues in 2012.

Financial Performance

The company's revenues increased by 12% in 2012 thanks to higher oil prices and increased production due an expansion in drilling as well as production from 2011 and 2012 acquisitions. Net income dropped by 21% in 2012 primarily due to decreased income from discontinued operations and increased depreciation expenses associated with new wells and acquisitions in 2011 and 2012. Production costs also rose due to increased production and acquisition-related expenses.

Acquisitions and increased demand for oil and gas helped to lift Concho Resources' revenues each year from 2008 through 2012.

Strategy

The company has focused on expanding its holdings through medium- and large-sized complementary acquisitions.

To raise cash to help fund acquisitions in 2012 Concho Resources sold some non-core Permian Basin oil and natural gas properties to Legacy Reserves for $520 million. It also sold its Bakken assets in North Dakota in 2011 to focus on its core Permian properties.

Mergers and Acquisitions

In 2012 the company acquired interests in the Wolfberry trend in the Permian Basin from Petroleum Development Corporation for $189.2 million. The acquisition added about 10200 net acres to Concho Resources' holdings in the region and estimated proved oil reserves of about 10 million barrels of oil equivalent.

The company boosted its Permian holdings further in 2012 by buying all of the oil and gas assets of Three Rivers Operating Company for $1 billion. Three Rivers has estimated proved reserves of 45.5 million barrels of oil equivalent and 200000 net acres in a handful of Permian plays.

Concho Resources acquired three entities affiliated with OGX Holdings II LLC for $252 million. The OGX deal included producing and non-producing acreage in the Delaware Basin of Southeast New Mexico and West Texas representing about 5.7 million barrels of of proved oil equivalent reserves.

EXECUTIVES

Director, Steven L. Beal, age 54
SVP and Chief of Staff, Jack F. Harper, age 41, $225,000 total compensation
SVP CFO and Treasurer, Darin G. Holderness, age 49, $285,000 total compensation
SVP Exploration, Matthew G. Hyde, age 57, $300,000 total compensation
Chairman CEO and President, Timothy A. Leach, age 54, $512,500 total compensation
Manager Investor Relations, Toffee McAlister
SVP General Counsel and Secretary, C. William Giraud
SVP and COO, E. Joseph Wright, age 53, $300,000 total compensation
VP and Chief Accounting Officer, Don O. McCormack, age 51
Vice President Operations and Production, Erick Nelson
Vice President of Administration, Kyle Rose
Senior Vice President of Corporate Development, Steven Pruett
Vice President Treasurer, Ben Rodgers
Senior Vice President General Counsel Corporate Secretary, William Giraud
Director, Steven L. Beal, age 54
Director, Mark B. Puckett, age 61
Director, William H. (Bill) Easter III, age 63
Director, Ray M. Poage, age 65
Director, Tucker S. Bridwell, age 61
Director, A. Wellford Tabor, age 44

Director, W. Howard Keenan Jr., age 62
Independent Director, Gary Merriman
Auditors: GrantThorntonLLP

LOCATIONS

HQ: Concho Resources Inc.
550 W. Texas Ave. Ste. 100, Midland TX 79701
Phone: 432-683-7443   **Fax:** 432-683-7441
Web: www.conchoresources.com/index.html

PRODUCTS/OPERATIONS

2012 Sales

	$ mil.	% of total
Oil	1,483	81
Natural gas	336	19
Total	**1,819**	**100**

COMPETITORS

Abraxas Petroleum	Occidental Petroleum
Apache	PDC Energy
Brigham Exploration	Parallel Petroleum
Chaparral Energy	Permian Basin
Chevron	SM Energy
Cimarex	SandRidge Energy
ConocoPhillips	Treaty Energy
Encore Energy	Vanguard Natural
Exxon Mobil	Resources
Legacy Reserves	Whiting Petroleum
Marathon Petroleum	

HISTORICAL FINANCIALS

Company Type: Public

Income Statement

FYE: December 31

	REVENUE ($ mil.)	NET INCOME ($ mil.)	NET PROFIT MARGIN	EMPLOYEES
12/12	1,819.8	431.6	23.7%	745
12/11	1,739.9	548.1	31.5%	592
12/10	972.5	204.3	21.0%	443
12/09	544.4	(9.8)	—	284
12/08	533.7	278.7	52.2%	245
Annual Growth	35.9%	11.6%	—	32.1%

2012 Year-End Financials

Debt ratio: 36.1%	No. of shares (mil.): 104
Return on equity: 13.3%	Dividends
Cash ($ mil.): 2	Yield: —
Current ratio: 0.62	Payout: —
Long-term debt ($ mil.): 3,101	Market value ($ mil.): 8,425

	STOCK PRICE ($) FY Close	P/E High/Low		Earnings	Dividends	Book Value
12/12	80.56	28	19	4.15	0.00	33.14
12/11	93.75	21	13	5.28	0.00	28.74
12/10	87.67	40	19	2.18	0.00	23.19
12/09	44.90	—	—	(0.12)	0.00	15.56
12/08	22.82	11	4	3.46	0.00	15.62
Annual Growth	37.1%	—	—	4.7%	—	20.7%

Connecticut Water Service, Inc.

A splash from Connecticut Water Service (CWS) might have helped Mark Twain's Yankee wake up from King Arthur's court. CWS's subsidiary Connecticut Water Company through its three operating divisions —Connecticut Water Crystal and Unionville —serves almost 330000 people in 55 Connecticut towns. The non-operating holding company's subsidiaries gather water from wells and reservoirs and produce 49 million gallons daily. They also offer fire protection and other water-related services. CWS's growth strategy is based on acquisitions. In 2012 the company acquired Aqua America's Maine operations for $54 million.

The acquisition of Aqua Maine allows the company to expand into New England. The company will be known as The Maine Water Company and Connecticut Water will receive approximately $33.7 million more in additional rates and increase its customer base by 16000. The transaction also makes Connecticut Water the largest publicly traded water utility company in New England with 106000 customers in Connecticut and Maine.

That year it also acquired Biddeford and Saco Water Company for $11.4 million.

In 2011 the company acquired Green Springs Water Company (Madison Connecticut) which serves about 12000 people.

EXECUTIVES

Director Rates and Forecasting and Assistant Treasurer, Peter J. Bancroft, age 62
VP Customer and Regulatory Affairs, Maureen P. Westbrook, age 54, $198,275 total compensation
VP Service Delivery, Terrance P. O'Neill, age 58, $190,580 total compensation
Chief Financial Officer; Vice President - Finance; Treasurer, David C. Benoit, age 56, $222,041 total compensation
Chairman of the Board; President; Chief Executive Officer, Eric W. Thornburg, age 53, $345,000 total compensation
VP Business Development, Thomas R. Marston, age 60, $181,458 total compensation
Vice President - Human Resources; Corporate Secretary, Kristen A. Johnson, age 46
Corporate Secretary and Director Corporate Communications, Daniel J. Meaney, age 52
Controller and Principal Accounting Officer Connecticut Water Service and Connecticut Water Company, Nicholas A. Rinaldi, age 59
Media Relations, Mary B. Ingarra
Director Technical and Environmental Services, Kevin T. Walsh
Manager Source Protection and Real Estate, Cindy Gaudino
Vice President G?? Service Delivery, Terrance Neill
Division President of The Maine Water Company; Director, Judith Wallingford
Vice President ?? Service Delivery, Terrance ONeill
Director, David A. Lentini, age 66
Director, Mark G. Kachur, age 69
Director, Lisa J. Thibdaue, age 60
Director, Arthur C. Reeds, age 69
Director, Mary Ann Hanley, age 56
Director, Donald B. Wilbur, age 71
Director, Carol P. Wallace, age 58
Director, Heather Hunt, age 47
Auditors: PricewaterhouseCoopersLLP

LOCATIONS

HQ: Connecticut Water Service Inc.
93 W. Main St., Clinton CT 06413
Phone: 860-669-8636 **Fax:** 860-669-5579
Web: www.ctwater.com

PRODUCTS/OPERATIONS

2008 Sales

	$ mil.	% of total
Residential		38
Fire protection		10
Commercial		7
Public authority		2
Industrial		1
Other		1
Total		**61**

COMPETITORS

American Water
Aquarion
Pennichuck

United Water Inc.
Veolia Water North
America

HISTORICAL FINANCIALS

Company Type: Public

Income Statement   FYE: December 31

	REVENUE ($ mil.)	NET INCOME ($ mil.)	NET PROFIT MARGIN	EMPLOYEES
12/12	83.8	13.6	16.3%	259
12/11	69.4	11.3	16.3%	198
12/10	66.4	9.8	14.8%	204
12/09	59.3	10.2	17.2%	225
12/08	61.2	9.4	15.4%	226
Annual Growth	**8.2%**	**9.7%**	**—**	**3.5%**

2012 Year-End Financials

Debt ratio: 31.3%
Return on equity: 8.9%
Cash ($ mil.): 13
Current ratio: 2.29
Long-term debt ($ mil.): 178

No. of shares (mil.): 10
Dividends
Yield: 3.2%
Payout: 62.7%
Market value ($ mil.): 326

	STOCK PRICE ($) FY Close	P/E High/Low	PER SHARE ($) Earnings	Dividends	Book Value
12/12	29.78	21 17	1.53	0.96	17.01
12/11	27.13	22 18	1.29	0.94	13.59
12/10	27.88	24 18	1.13	0.92	13.13
12/09	24.77	21 14	1.19	0.90	12.75
12/08	23.61	26 18	1.11	0.88	12.32
Annual Growth	**6.0%**	**— —**	**8.4%**	**2.2%**	**8.4%**

Constant Contact Inc

Constant Contact makes sure businesses never lose touch with their prospects and customers. The company provides small businesses with Web-based marketing software and services for managing e-mail and social media campaigns as well as offering local deals managing digital storefronts and creating online surveys. Its offerings include tools for creating implementing tracking managing and analyzing marketing materials. Customers include retailers restaurants and other businesses as well as non-profit organizations alumni associations and churches; two-thirds of its clients have fewer than 10 employees. It claims more than 555000 customers for its products.

Geographic Reach Constant Contact has offices in Massachusetts Colorado Florida California and New York as well as in London. It serves clients in some 180 countries although the US accounts for nearly 90% of sales.

Sales and Marketing Of course Constant Contact uses digital marketing techniques to attract customers. Its products are marketed through its own advertising and referral efforts as well as through partnerships with more than 9500 local and national small business service providers.

It focuses on small businesses and organizations most of which pay a fixed monthly subscription fee based on the number of e-mail addresses in their account. Subscriptions to its e-mail marketing tools typically cost between $15-$150 per month which allows Constant Contact to serve a market that is typically ignored by larger CRM and marketing software competitors such as Oracle SAP and salesforce.com. The company has seen rapid organic growth in recent years with its customer base growing 20-fold from the 25000 it reported in 2004.

Financial Performance Constant Contact's revenue has risen steadily along with its customer base. In 2012 sales were up 18% to $252 million driven by a 12% increase in the number of average monthly customers and a 5% rise in revenue per customer. Now in its third year of profitability the company took in $12.7 million in net income for 2012 down 46% from $23 million in 2011. The decrease in profits was due to increases in operating expenses as well as costs for acquisitions the company has made.

Strategy The company continues to enhance its offerings with new services and tools and throughout 2012 it expanded its product suite from three products to six. CardStar provides mobile applications for loyalty cards and coupons. SaveLocal manages group coupons for small businesses and SinglePlatform offers a digital storefront for mobile formats. Previous product launches include online surveys (2007) event marketing (2009) and social media (2010) tools. It is also looking for growth in new geographic markets. Although international operations are a small part of Constant Contact's business today it sees opportunity in international markets. Its email marketing templates are also offered in Spanish and the company opened its first office outside the US in the UK in 2011.

Mergers and Acquisitions In 2012 Constant Contact paid $5.7 million for CardStar which provides mobile applications for loyalty cards and coupons. Also that year the company acquired SinglePlatform a developer of marketing software used by small businesses to improve their visibility to consumers on the Web. SinglePlatform's application enables businesses to use a single interface to distribute content to such online venues as Foursquare YP and UrbanSpoon as well as on social networks and other websites. In 2011 Constant Contact had added social CRM capabilities with the acquisition of Bantam Networks for $15 million in cash. Its Bantam Live application gives small businesses a place to launch and monitor customer engagement campaigns across social media platforms. In 2010 the company acquired NutshellMail giving its customers a tool for engaging social media networks from their e-mail inbox.

EXECUTIVES

EVP CFO and Treasurer, Harpreet S. Grewal, age 46
Vice President Customer Operations, Ellen M. Brezniak, age 54, $200,000 total compensation
VP General Counsel and Secretary, Robert P. (Bob) Nault, age 49, $210,000 total compensation
SVP and Chief Sales and Marketing Officer, Rick W. Jensen, age 53
Chairman President and CEO, Gail F. Goodman, age 52, $350,000 total compensation
SVP Corporate Strategy Development and Innovation, Eric S. Groves, age 49, $200,000 total compensation
Vice President Strategy and Emerging Business, Joel A. Hughes, age 49
VP Constant Contact Labs, Daniel A. (Dan) Richards, age 53, $150,000 total compensation
SVP Customer Operations, Thomas C. (Tom) Howd, age 53, $150,000 total compensation
VP and Chief Marketing Officer, Nancie G. Freitas, age 51, $195,000 total compensation
VP and Chief Human Resources Officer, Robert D. (Bob) Nicoson, age 62
CTO, Stefan Piesche
Senior Vice President Sales and Marketing, Christopher M. Litster, age 43
VP and General Manager SaveLocal, David Gilbertson, age 35
Vice President Product, Ken Surdan
Vice President and Chief Human Resources Officer, Bob Nicoson
Vice President and General Manager SinglePlatform, Wiley Cerilli
Director, Robert P. (Bob) Badavas, age 60
Director, William S. (Bill) Kaiser, age 56
Director, Sharon T. Rowlands, age 54
Director, Daniel T. H. (Dan) Nye, age 46
Director, Michael T. (Mike) Fitzgerald, age 60
Director, Thomas (Tom) Anderson, age 50
Director, John Campbell, age 65
Auditors: PricewaterhouseCoopersLLP

LOCATIONS

HQ: Constant Contact Inc.
1601 Trapelo Rd. 3rd Fl., Waltham MA 02451
Phone: 781-472-8100 **Fax:** 781-472-8101
Web: www.constantcontact.com

PRODUCTS/OPERATIONS

Selected Products
Contact list management tools
Digital storefront (SinglePlatform)
E-mail campaign creation interface (Campaign Creation Wizard)
E-mail delivery management
E-mail message templates
E-mail tracking and reporting tools
Event marketing
Group coupons (SaveLocal)
Image hosting services
Security and privacy compliance services
Social media marketing platform (Flowtown)
Social media notification tool (NutshellMail)
Survey tools

COMPETITORS

Active Network
Alterian
Evite
ExactTarget
Experian CheetahMail
Google
Groupon
LivingSocial
Lyris
MarketTools

Microsoft
Responsys
Silverpop
Topica
VerticalResponse
Vistaprint
Vocus
Yahoo!
j2 Global
yesmail

Company Type: Public

Income Statement
FYE: December 31

	REVENUE ($ mil.)	NET INCOME ($ mil.)	NET PROFIT MARGIN	EMPLOYEES
12/12	252.1	12.7	5.1%	1,162
12/11	214.4	23.6	11.0%	367
12/10	174.2	2.9	1.7%	734
12/09	129.0	(1.2)	—	625
12/08	87.2	(2.0)	—	456
Annual Growth	30.4%	—	—	26.3%

2012 Year-End Financials

Debt ratio: —
Return on equity: 6.7%
Cash ($ mil.): 67
Current ratio: 1.94
Long-term debt ($ mil.): —

No. of shares (mil.): 30
Dividends
  Yield: —
  Payout: —
Market value ($ mil.): 436

	STOCK PRICE ($) FY Close	P/E High/Low	PER SHARE ($) Earnings	Dividends	Book Value
12/12	14.21	75 28	0.41	0.00	6.64
12/11	23.21	45 19	0.77	0.00	5.68
12/10	30.99	319 160	0.10	0.00	4.30
12/09	16.00	— —	(0.04)	0.00	3.70
12/08	13.25	— —	(0.07)	0.00	3.55
Annual Growth	1.8%	— —	—	—	17.0%

Cooper Companies, Inc. (The)

From eye care to lady care The Cooper Companies has its customers covered. The global company makes specialty medical devices in two niche markets: vision care and gynecology. Its CooperVision subsidiary makes specialty contact lenses including toric lenses for astigmatism multifocal lenses for presbyopia and cosmetic lenses. The company also offers spherical lenses for more common vision problems such as nearsightedness and farsightedness. Subsidiary CooperSurgical specializes in women's health care; its wide range of products includes bone densitometers (for diagnosing osteoporosis) contraceptive devices surgery instruments and fetal monitors. Cooper's products are sold in more than 100 countries.

Geographic Reach

California-based Cooper rings up nearly half of its sales in the US and about 30% in Europe. The company has manufacturing and distribution facilities for optical products in the US (New York and Puerto Rico) the UK Australia and Japan. Its medical device and surgical instrument products are manufactured and distributed from facilities in Germany and the US (California Connecticut and Texas).

Sales and Marketing

Cooper markets its products through its own sales representatives in North America and through a mix of direct sales and distributors elsewhere. The company boosted its direct sales presence in international markets through acquisitions in Japan Mexico and the Czech Republic in 2010 and 2011.

Operations

The Cooper Companies operates through two business units: CooperVision the larger of the two (80% of annual sales) is one of the largest contact lens manufacturers in the world: CooperSurgical provides diagnostic and therapeutic products used by obstetricians and gynecologists. It has been a consolidator in the fragmented women's medical device market acquiring more than 30 niche companies since its inception in 1990. Trends that it is taking advantage of include the increase in laparoscopic procedures and a shifting of procedures done in doctor's offices rather than in hospital settings.

Financial Performance

The Cooper Companies' fiscal 2013 (ended October) sales increased 10% versus the prior year to $1.6 billion. Net income grew 19% over the same period to $296.1 million. The smaller of its two businesses CooperSurgical (CSI) out performed its sister company with CSI posting a 25% increase in annual sales while CooperVision's (CVI) sales rose a more modest 7%. Revenue from the acquisition of Origio propelled SCI's growth in fiscal 2013. The sale of more contact lenses and new products primarily silicone hydrogel lenses drove growth at CVI. The Cooper Companies has posted steady and significant growth in sales and profits in recent years as a result of organic growth and the purchase of other companies.

Sales gains in Europe (up 17%) outpaced growth in the US (up 9%) in fiscal 2013 compared with the prior year.

Strategy

CooperVision (CVI)is working to expand internationally by increasing operations in various high-growth geographic markets. It is building a plant in Costa Rica. The lens maker is attempting to expand its market share by launching new products. Its R&D team is working on several new products using its Proclear moisturizing technology. It is also developing new products using silicone hydrogel a more breathable lens material that is healthier and more comfortable for the eye including single-use (throwaway) toric and multifocal lenses. For instance CooperVision launched the new Biofinity multifocal and Avaira toric lens lines in the US in 2011. In 2013 CVI sold Aime its rigid gas-permeable contact lens and solutions business in Japan to Nippon Contact Lens. The sale was consistent with CVI's strategy to focus on its core soft contact lens business.

CSI is growing by acquiring complementary technologies products and businesses.

Mergers and Acquisitions

In July 2012 Cooper acquired Denmark-based Origio an in-vitro fertilization (IVF) medical device company for approximately $189 million.

In 2010 CooperSurgical paid some $20 million for American Medical Systems' Her Option branded line of endometrial ablation products for the treatment of irregular periods and heavy bleeding. Additionally the firm purchased laparoscopic smoke filtration systems maker JLJ Medical Devices. In 2011 CooperSurgical acquired Apple Medical whose products included devices used during cesarean sections and cervical biopsies; it also purchased hand-held ultrasound device maker Summit Doppler Systems that year.

HISTORY

Cooper Labs (medical devices founded in 1958 and dissolved 1985) created CooperVision as a subsidiary in 1980. CooperVision diversified into diagnostic equipment and drugs; by 1987 (when it was renamed The Cooper Companies) debt had increased sixfold and creditors came knocking.

Two scandal-tainted families (the Sturmans and the Singers –fraud/organized crime and Medicaid fraud respectively) then bought their way onto the board. Proxy fights cronyism nepotism indictments and lawsuits ensued. Meanwhile cash-strapped Cooper sold most of its international and part of its US contact lens business as well as its ophthalmic surgical products and medical diagnostics businesses. Co-chairman Gary Singer took a leave of absence after being indicted in 1992.

Cooper bought Hospital Group of America and its hospitals that year. Singer resigned shortly before being convicted on 21 counts including racketeering mail and wire fraud and money laundering in 1994. Pharmaceutical industry veteran Thomas Bender joined the board that year and was named CEO in 1995. He was elected chairman in 2002.

Cooper rebuilt its contact business and turned to the women's health field in the early 1990s. In 1996 it bought a line of disposable gynecological products and worked to boost lens-making capacity. The next year it bought a line of colored contact lenses a minimally invasive gynecological surgical and disposable products company and a UK lens maker.

In 1998 The Cooper Companies discontinued its Hospital Group of America operations. It sold the group's hospitals treatment centers and clinics to Universal Health Services in 1999. In 2000 the company made three acquisitions including two makers of gynecological instruments. In 2002 The Cooper Companies bought Biocompatibles Eye Care one of the world's largest contact lens manufacturers.

The company's acquisitions in 2003 included Avalon Medical Corporation (distributor of female sterilization system) and Prism Enterprises (manufacturer of medical devices for the women's health care markets). The Cooper Companies bought gynecology products manufacturer Milex Products in 2004.

It nearly doubled its revenue with the 2005 acquisition of leading contact lens maker Ocular Sciences. The purchase strengthened its presence in the spheric (non-specialty) lens market; it also opened up new geographic markets particularly Germany and Japan. It also purchased NeoSurg Technologies and Inlet Medical in 2005 both of which made devices used in laparoscopic surgeries.

In 2006 it purchased Lone Star Medical Products adding a line of gynecological surgical products. The following year it added medical instrument maker Wallach Surgical Devices.

CooperVision faced some patent issues with CIBA over its silicone hydrogel Biofinity lenses (first launched in 2006); it settled with CIBA in 2007 agreeing to pay royalties on the lenses.

When chairman Thomas Bender chose to step down as CEO in 2007 company veteran Robert Weiss was tapped to fill that role. The Cooper Companies launched its Proclear daily lens in the US and Europe that year followed by the Avaira sphere two-week silicone hydrogel lens in 2008.

The company discontinued operations at its lens manufacturing plant in Norfolk Virginia in 2009 as part of a restructuring of the CooperVision division. It also relocated some of its Australian lens manufacturing operations to Puerto Rico and the UK to streamline and reduce expenses in the organization.

EXECUTIVES

Vice Chairman and Lead Director, Allan E. Rubenstein, age 69

CEO Cooper Medical Inc., Nicholas J. Pichotta, age 69, $300,000 total compensation

EVP Secretary and Chief Administrative Officer, Carol R. Kaufman, age 64, $350,000 total compensation

President CEO and Director, Robert S. Weiss, age 67, $600,000 total compensation

Chairman, A. Thomas Bender, age 75, $750,000 total compensation

VP Research and Development CooperVision, J. Christopher Marmo, age 43

President and CEO CooperSurgical Inc., Paul L. Remmell, age 56, $295,000 total compensation

Human Resources Director, Ruby Varner

President CooperVision Inc., John A. Weber, age 49, $360,000 total compensation

VP Business Development and CFO CooperVision, John C. Calcagno, age 53

VP and Corporate Controller, Rodney E. Folden, age 66

VP Taxes, Eugene J. (Gene) Midlock, age 69, $380,000 total compensation

Vice President - Investor Relations; Chief Strategic Officer, Albert G. White III, age 44

Executive Vice President General Counsel & Chief Operating Officer, Daniel G. (Dan) McBride, age 49

Vice President Chief Financial Officer & Chief Risk Officer, Gregory W. Matz

IR Contact Officer, Kim Duncan

Vice Chairman and Lead Director, Allan E. Rubenstein, age 69

President CEO and Director, Robert S. Weiss, age 67

Director, Steven Rosenberg, age 64
Director, Michael H. Kalkstein, age 71
Director, Donald Press, age 80
Director, Stanley Zinberg, age 79
Director, Jody S. Lindell, age 61
Auditors: KPMGLLP

LOCATIONS

HQ: Cooper Companies, Inc. (The)
6140 Stoneridge Mall Road, Suite 590, Pleasanton, CA 94588
Phone: 925 460-3600   **Fax:** 925 460-3648
Web: www.coopercos.com

2013 Sales

	$ mil.	% of total
US	742	47
Europe	479	30
Rest of world& other	366	23
Total	**1,587**	**100**

PRODUCTS/OPERATIONS

2013 Sales

CooperVision		
Toric lens	388	24
Multifocal lens	121	8
Non single-use sphere other eye care products& other	487	31
Total	**1,587**	**100**

COMPETITORS

Abbott Medical Optics	Femcare
Alara	Gyrus ACMI
Alcon	Hoya Corp.
Bausch & Lomb	Johnson & Johnson
Boston Scientific	Luxottica
Carl Zeiss	Marchon Eyewear
Covidien	Orthometrix
Essilor International	Shamir Optical

HISTORICAL FINANCIALS

Company Type: Public

Income Statement

FYE: October 31

	REVENUE ($ mil.)	NET INCOME ($ mil.)	NET PROFIT MARGIN	EMPLOYEES
10/13	1,587.7	296.1	18.7%	8,000
10/12	1,445.1	248.3	17.2%	7,800
10/11	1,330.8	175.4	13.2%	7,400
10/10	1,158.5	112.8	9.7%	6,800
10/09	1,080.4	100.5	9.3%	6,600
Annual Growth	**10.1%**	**31.0%**	**—**	**4.9%**

2013 Year-End Financials

Debt ratio: 10.9%	No. of shares (mil.): 48
Return on equity: 12.8%	Dividends
Cash ($ mil.): 77	Yield: 0.0%
Current ratio: 2.33	Payout: 0.9%
Long-term debt ($ mil.): 301	Market value ($ mil.): 6,201

	STOCK PRICE ($) FY Close	P/E High/Low		PER SHARE ($) Earnings	Dividends	Book Value
10/13	129.21	22	15	5.96	0.06	50.10
10/12	95.98	19	11	5.05	0.06	45.27
10/11	69.30	22	13	3.63	0.06	40.49
10/10	49.34	20	11	2.43	0.06	36.37
10/09	28.01	14	5	2.21	0.06	34.05
Annual Growth	**46.6%**	**—**	**—**	**28.1%**	**(0.0%)**	**10.1%**

Copart, Inc.

What happens after cars are totaled in wrecks or natural disasters? How about stolen cars recovered "after" the insurance settlement? Perhaps Copart happens —it takes junked cars and auctions them for insurers auto dealers and car rental agencies. The buyers are mostly rebuilders licensed dismantlers and used-car dealers and exporters. It's replaced live auctions with Internet auctions using a platform known as Virtual Bidding Second Generation (VB2 for short). Copart also provides services such as towing and storage to buyers and other salvage companies as well as an online database and search engine for used parts. Copart has more than 150 storage facilities throughout North America Europe and Brazil.

Geographic Reach

The US is by far Copart's largest market accounting for more than 75% of sales. Europe accounts for about 20%. Copart operates about 135 storage facilities in the US four in Canada and 15 in the UK. It entered Brazil Germany and the Middle East in 2012 via acquisitions.

Sales and Marketing

Copart is going the extra mile to market its brand to car enthusiasts. The company produces Sold in Seconds a weekly TV program that highlights purchases from Copart.com and follows up with buyers to see what they've done with their vehicles. The show which started airing in 2010 complements Copart's racing sponsorships in the NASCAR Nationwide Series and NHRA Top Fuel Series.

Financial Performance

Copart's sales increased 6% in fiscal 2012 (ends July) vs. the prior year while net income grew by more than 9%. The online vehicle auction firm's sales and profits has increased steadily since fiscal 2009 when they slipped due to the falling US dollar-Great Britain pound exchange rate lower unit volumes and declining revenues per transaction. Indeed 2012's $924 million in sales and $182 million in net income were all-time highs for fast-growing Copart. Sales growth was driven by increases in service and vehicle sales up 6% and 5% respectively with growth in the US outpacing growth in Canada and the UK.

Strategy

An aggressive acquisition program at home and abroad has made Copart a leader in its industry. Buoyed by the recovery at home Copart is on a global hunt for junked vehicles and vehicle parts. Indeed in 2012 the company made several acquisitions in international markets including Brazil Canada Germany and Dubai UAE. Indeed the UAE is the second-largest international destination for cars sold at Copart's North American salvage yards.

Copart is also expanding its customer base beyond the traditional salvage market by launching new services such as CopartDirect. Launched in 2008 the program allows the company to sell cars to the general public using its VB2 application so that individuals can avoid the inconvenience of selling a vehicle themselves. Other services include Copart Dealer Services which sells trade-ins for franchises and independent dealerships using VB2 and CoPartfinder which enables customers to bid on a vehicle search for parts from Keystone Automotive Industries and receive e-mail notifications when cars matching their criteria come up for sale.

The majority of the vehicles Copart processes are auctioned under an incentive program in which Copart gets a percentage of the proceeds; the rest are auctioned under a fixed-fee consignment basis (generally $50 to $175). Insurance company suppliers represent the firm's largest customer segment and account for about 80% of the vehicles Copart processes each year.

Mergers and Acquisitions

In 2012 Copart expanded into Germany (the world's fourth largest auto market) with the purchase of WOM Wreck Online Marketing a leading European salvage vehicle auction platform there. Earlier in the year it bought Canada's Diamond Auto Bids and Disposals a privately-held automotive auction that gives Copart a foothold in Western Canada specifically Calgary and Edmonton. It also extended the reach of its business into South America through its purchase of Central de Leiloes LTDA based in Sao Paulo Brazil. Central serves the Brazilian market through five facilities located in Sao Paulo states.

In 2011 Copart also purchased the Indiana-based auto auction firm Barodge Auto Pool expanding its presence in Indiana and surrounding states. The company also broadened its existing range of farming equipment in the UK when it acquired Hewitt International an auctioneer of agricultural vehicles and equipment based in central England in 2011. Copart's previous acquisitions have included D Hales an operator of five auto auction sites and parts centers in England in 2010.

Ownership

Founder and former-CEO Willis Johnson owns about 11% of Copart's shares.

HISTORY

Copart was co-founded in 1982 by Willis Johnson who had owned and operated an auto dismantling business for more than 10 years. After buying out his partner in 1986 he became CEO and used his own money to expand the company into a network of four California salvage yards by 1991.

In the next two years Copart nearly tripled the number of salvage operations it owned by acquiring companies throughout the US. HPB Associates a private investor group came on board in 1993 buying 26% of the firm for $10 million and the company went public the next year.

Copart doubled its total facilities in 1995 with the acquisition of NER Auction Systems the largest privately held salvage auction company in the US. The firm acquired or opened more than 30 facilities between 1995 and 1997. In 1998 the company started an online auction site; expanded through acquisitions into Alabama Iowa Michigan and South Carolina; and opened new locations in California and Minnesota. The next year rival Insurance Auto Auctions spurned its merger overtures.

In 2000 Copart opened three new salvage vehicle auction facilities and acquired eight more. That year the company also signed an agreement to sell Keystone Automotive Industries' parts through its Web site. In 2001 and 2002 the company acquired or opened 13 new locations. Continuing its acquisition strategy the company opened or acquired five more facilities in 2004.

In 2005 the company made two acquisitions for about $4.5 million: Kentucky Auto Salvage Pool a 25-acre salvage facility in Lexington Kentucky; and Insurance Auctions of Missouri. In November Copart acquired the salvage pool assets of Central Penn Sales a vehicle salvage disposal company with four sites in Pennsylvania and Maryland totaling 255 acres. In December the company opened a second salvage facility in Michigan.

In June 2007 Copart acquired Universal Salvage the operator of about 10 salvage yards in the UK and a vehicle remarketer to the insurance and automotive industries for about $120 million. Adding to its UK holdings in August Copart purchased Century Salvage Sales Limited which has three salvage yards and AG Watson which has four salvage yards in England and Scotland.

During 2008 the company launched CopartDirect. The service allows Copart to sell cars to the general public using its VB2 application so that individuals can avoid the inconvenience of selling a vehicle themselves.

In February 2010 Willis Johnson relinquished the CEO's title to A. Jayson Adair who formerly served as president of Copart. Johnson continued as chairman of the company.

EXECUTIVES

SVP General Counsel and Secretary, Paul A. Styer, age 57, $190,000 total compensation

Chief Executive Officer; Director, A. Jayson Adair, age 42, $553,849 total compensation

Chairman, Willis J. Johnson, age 66, $571,155 total compensation

Chief Financial Officer; Senior Vice President, William E. Franklin, age 57, $300,000 total compensation

President; Director, Vincent W. Mitz, age 50, $375,000 total compensation

VP Finance, Simon E. Rote, age 41

Chief Operating Officer; Senior Vice President, Russell D. Lowy, age 54

SVP Human Resources, Thomas E. Wylie, age 62

Senior Vice President - Sales, Robert H. Vannuccini, age 46

Senior Vice President - Marketing, Matthew Burgener

Senior Vice President; Chief Information Officer, Vincent Phillips

Senior Vice President - Business Development, Anthony Cristello

Director, James E. Meeks, age 64

CEO and Director, A. Jayson Adair, age 42
Director, Steven D. Cohan, age 52
Director, Matt Blunt, age 42
Director, Daniel (Dan) Englander, age 43
Director, Thomas W. Smith, age 84
Non-Employee Director, Thomas Tryforos
Auditors: Ernst&YoungLLP

LOCATIONS

HQ: Copart Inc.
4665 Business Center Dr., Fairfield CA 94534
Phone: 707-639-5000   **Fax:** 707-639-5196
Web: www.copart.com

2012 Sales

	$ mil.	% of total
US	724	78
UK	192	21
Canada	6	1
Total	**924**	**100**

PRODUCTS/OPERATIONS

2012 Sales

	$ mil.	% of total
Services	757	82
Vehicles	166	18
Total	**924**	**100**

Selected Services

Copart Access (online vehicle information retrieval)
Copart Dealer Services (online trade-in vehicle sales)
Copart Direct (online used car sales)
CoPartfinder (online used-parts search engine)
DMV processing (title document processing)
Monthly reporting (summary of all vehicles processed by company for suppliers)
Online bidding (online auctions)
Salvage brokerage network (coordination of vehicle disposal outside areas of current operation)
Salvage Lynk (software providing online information on vehicles being processed)
Transportation services (fleet of transport trucks)
Vehicle inspection stations (central locations for insurance companies to inspect vehicles)
Vehicle preparation and merchandising (cleaning and weather protection direct mailings to buyers)

COMPETITORS

ADESA	Insurance Auto
Advance Auto Parts	Auctions
CSK Auto	KAR Auction Services
Columbus Fair Auto	LKQ
Auction	Manheim
Cox Enterprises	Pittsburgh Independent
Ford Motor	Auto Auction

HISTORICAL FINANCIALS

Company Type: Public

Income Statement

FYE: July 31

	REVENUE ($ mil.)	NET INCOME ($ mil.)	NET PROFIT MARGIN	EMPLOYEES
07/13	1,046.3	180.0	17.2%	3,875
07/12	924.1	182.1	19.7%	2,981
07/11	872.2	166.3	19.1%	2,825
07/10	772.8	151.6	19.6%	2,834
07/09	743.0	141.1	19.0%	2,713
Annual Growth	**8.9%**	**6.3%**	**—**	**9.3%**

2013 Year-End Financials

Debt ratio: 27.9%
Return on equity: 27.2%
Cash ($ mil.): 63
Current ratio: 1.28
Long-term debt ($ mil.): 296

No. of shares (mil.): 125
Dividends
  Yield: —
  Payout: —
Market value ($ mil.): 4,080

	STOCK PRICE ($) FY Close	P/E High/Low		PER SHARE ($) Earnings	Dividends	Book Value
07/13	32.51	26	16	1.39	0.00	6.08
07/12	23.76	38	16	1.39	0.00	4.51
07/11	43.45	43	29	1.09	0.00	4.21
07/10	36.44	43	36	0.89	0.00	6.44
07/09	35.31	55	28	0.83	0.00	5.49
Annual Growth	**(2.0%)**	**— —**		**13.8%**	**—**	**2.6%**

Core Molding Technologies Inc

The core business of Core Molding Technologies is fiberglass reinforced plastic and sheet molding composite materials. Through compression molding sprayup hand layup and vacuum-assisted resin infusion molding the company makes truck components (air deflectors fenders hoods) and personal watercraft parts (decks hulls and engine hatches). It divides its operations into two segments: Products and Tooling. Navistar International accounts for a majority of its sales and other major customers include heavy-duty truck manufacturers Daimler Trucks North America and PACCAR (Peterbilt trucks; about one-quarter of sales). The company's sales are confined to North America.

Geographic Reach
Core Molding operates plants in Columbus and Cincinnati Ohio; Gaffney South Carolina; and Matamoros Mexico.

Sales and Marketing
With Navistar and PACCAR representing 80% of sales and the medium and heavy-duty truck market accounting for more than 90% it's an understatement to say that Core Molding Technologies has a limited number of customers.

Financial Analysis
Core Molding has enjoyed significant growth over the years. Sales from 2010 to 2011 increased by 43% while its profits skyrocketed from $2.4 million to $10.5 million. The company attributes the growth to a 54% surge in product sales due to higher demand from North American medium and heavy-duty truck customers as well as new business. It was also able to increase its gross margins from 16% in 2010 to 21% in 2011.

The company also recognized significant sales gains in Mexico. Total sales for this region swelled by more than 150% increasing from $11.7 million in 2010 to $30.2 million in 2011.

Ownership
GAMCO Asset Management owns 14% of the company.

Company Background
Core Molding evolved in 1996 from the Columbus Plastics unit of International Truck & Engine (now Navistar Inc.).

EXECUTIVES

Chairman, Malcolm M. Prine, age 83
Vice President Chief Operating Officer, Stephen J. Klestinec, age 63, $206,154 total compensation

President Chief Executive Officer of Core Molding Technologies, Kevin L. Barnett, age 50, $249,231 total compensation
Chairman, James L. Simonton, age 71
Vice President Secretary Treasurer Chief Financial Officer, Herman F. Dick Jr., age 53, $189,615 total compensation
VP Marketing and Sales, Terrence J. (Terry) O'Donovan, age 53
President Chief Executive Officer of Core Molding Technologies, Kevin L. Barnett, age 50
Director, Thomas R. Cellitti, age 61
Director, James F. Crowley, age 66
Director, Ralph O. Hellmold, age 72
Auditors: CroweHorwathLLP

LOCATIONS

HQ: Core Molding Technologies Inc.
800 Manor Park Dr., Columbus OH 43228-0183
Phone: 614-870-5000 **Fax:** 605-335-0268
Web: www.ravenind.com

2011 Sales

	$ mil.	% of total
US	109	76
Mexico	30	21
Total	**143**	**100**

PRODUCTS/OPERATIONS

2011 Sales

	$ mil.	% of total
Product	138	97
Total	**143**	**100**

Selected Services

Assembly Machining and Paint Products
Closed molding
Compression Molding
Glass Mat Thermoplastic Compound
Open Molded Products
Post Molding
Product Development
Reaction Injection Molding
Resin Transfer Molding
Sheet Molding Compound

COMPETITORS

Clarion Technologies	Magna International
Crane Composites	Molded Fiber Glass
Flex-N-Gate	Primex Plastics
Industrial Molding Corp.	Sigma Industries
Lacks Enterprises	Toledo Molding and Die

HISTORICAL FINANCIALS

Company Type: Public

Income Statement

FYE: December 31

	REVENUE ($ mil.)	NET INCOME ($ mil.)	NET PROFIT MARGIN	EMPLOYEES
12/12	162.4	8.1	5.0%	1,373
12/11	143.4	10.5	7.3%	1,596
12/10	100.2	2.4	2.4%	1,014
12/09	83.3	1.0	1.2%	813
12/08	116.6	5.6	4.8%	933
Annual Growth	**8.6%**	**9.8%**	**—**	**10.1%**

2012 Year-End Financials

Debt ratio: 10.3%	No. of shares (mil.): 7
Return on equity: 15.1%	Dividends
Cash ($ mil.): 7	Yield: —
Current ratio: 1.98	Payout: —
Long-term debt ($ mil.): 5	Market value ($ mil.): 47

	STOCK PRICE ($) FY Close	P/E High/Low		PER SHARE ($) Earnings	Dividends	Book Value
12/12	6.62	9	6	1.11	0.00	8.13
12/11	8.09	6	4	1.44	0.00	7.11
12/10	5.76	17	8	0.34	0.00	5.53
12/09	2.87	26	8	0.15	0.00	4.29
12/08	2.60	9	2	0.81	0.00	4.28
Annual Growth	**26.3%**	—	—	**8.2%**	—	**17.4%**

CorVel Corp.

CorVel has carved out a niche providing medical cost containment for US workers' compensation programs auto insurers and group health plans. CorVel helps insurers third-party administrators and self-insured employers keep down costs associated with workers' compensation and other medical claims and to get employees back on the job as soon as is practicable. Among other things CorVel reviews medical bills to make sure they are in line with state fee schedules using its automated online MedCheck software. It also maintains a health provider network and provides case management and vocational rehabilitation services. Clients access CorVel's range of services through its CareMC web portal.

Geographic Reach
CorVel operates through a network of branch offices to provide customer service to its 2000 clients on a localized basis. Its provider network consists of 750000 health care practices across the US.

Operations
CorVel divides its business into two segments: network solutions and patient management services. Its network solutions encompass its risk management solutions (fee auditing bill review utilization review and independent exams) for workers' compensation auto and group health policy providers. It also manages the company's CorCare preferred provider network and CareIQ directed care network (specialist facilities including imaging and physical therapy centers); these networks are licensed to insurance clients for use under their respective insurance policies. Meanwhile CorVel's patient management services focus on injured employees providing case managers who monitor employees' recovery and their use of health care services.

Sales and Marketing
CorVel focuses on national account marketing conducting sales through its account executives located in its primary geographic markets.

Financial Analysis
Its organic and acquisitive expansion activities have allowed CorVel to experience modest revenue and income growth over the years which in turn helps fund future expansion efforts. Its revenues climbed 8% in 2012 to some $413 million in 2012 paired with a net income rise of 6% to $26 million. Growth in 2012 was due to an increase in claims administration customers within the patient management segment as well as growth in the pharmacy service operations of the network solutions segment.

Strategy
As national health care costs continue to soar and the demand for cost-control programs in-creases the company is working to make its offerings more comprehensive. Internal growth efforts include the broadening of CorVel's managed care and directed care networks as well as its patient case management provisions. It has also upgraded its claims processing capabilities through acquisitions and internal software and infrastructure enhancements.

Ownership
Director Jeffrey Michael owns about 35% of the company through Corstar Holdings which is owned by a Michael family trust. Chairman Gordon Clemons Sr. owns about 10% of the company.

HISTORY

Three small rehabilitation centers owned by Minneapolis investment firm North Star Universal merged to form Fortis in 1987 bringing in former Caremark executive Gordon Clemons to run the company. (Before its 1996 purchase by MedPartners Caremark was one of the US's largest managers of prescription drug benefits for insurers managed care organizations and others.) Clemons moved Fortis into workers' compensation with the 1989 acquisition of VPS Case Management of Virginia. Expenses from ambitious expansion in the late 1980s sent the company into the red in 1990 and 1991 the same year it went public.

The company became CorVel in 1992 when Belgian insurer Fortis contemplating expansion into the US bought that name for $4 million.

In 1999 CorVel expanded its MedCheck software to review medical claims for auto insurers. The company subsequently launched MedCheck 2000 a further enhanced version that allows claims professionals access to real-time reports of claims history.

In 2002 Corvel acquired AnciCare PPO a national provider of diagnostic imaging services. The acquisition allowed Corvel to expand its CorCare Preferred Provider Organization (PPO). The company bought Scan One a provider of scanning and document management services in 2003. The following year the company expanded its directed care network to include physical therapy and chiropractic services.

In 2007 Clemons retired from the company's executive post but remained with CorVel as chairman of the board. Dan Stark was named CEO.

In 2009 the company purchased third-party administrator Eagle Claims Services for $1 million. The acquisition allowed CorVel to move into claims processing and added to its patient management and networks solutions customers.

EXECUTIVES

Director Legal Services, Sharon O'Connor
Secretary, Richard J. Schweppe, age 55, $122,254 total compensation
CIO, Donald C. (Don) McFarlane, age 59, $175,714 total compensation
Chairman President CEO and COO, V. Gordon Clemons Sr., age 68, $350,000 total compensation
CFO, Scott R. McCloud, age 45, $146,426 total compensation
SVP Sales and Account Management, Diane J. Blaha, age 57, $275,000 total compensation
EVP Operations, V. Gordon Clemons Jr.
Director, Jeffrey J. Michael, age 55
Director, Steven J. Hamerslag, age 55
Director, R. Judd Jessup, age 64
Director, Alan R. Hoops, age 64
Director, Jean H. Macino, age 69
Auditors: Haskell&WhiteLLP

LOCATIONS

HQ: CorVel Corporation
2010 Main St. Ste. 600, Irvine CA 92614
Phone: 949-851-1473   **Fax:** 949-851-1469
Web: www.corvel.com

PRODUCTS/OPERATIONS

2011 Sales

	% of total
Network solutions	51
Patient management	49
Total	**100**

Selected Services

Network solutions services
  CareIQ (directed care network)
  CorCareRX (pharmacy management system)
  CorCare (preferred provider organization network)
  Diagnostic imaging review
  Fee schedule audits
  Independent medical exam coordination
  Inpatient bill audits
  MedCheck (medical bill review software)
  Medicare solutions
  Reimbursement
  Utilization reviews in retrospect
Patient management services
  Auto claims management
  Claims administration and management
  Disability management
  Inpatient utilization review
  Liability claims management
  Life care planning
  Medical case management
  Telephone case management
  Utilization management
  Vocational rehabilitation

COMPETITORS

Aetna	Progressive Medical
Coventry Health Care	(Ohio)
ExamWorks	Qmedtrix Systems
GENEX Services	RTW
HMS Holdings	UnitedHealth Group
Hooper Holmes	WellPoint
OptumInsight	WorkWell Systems
PRGX	
Paradigm Management	
Services	

HISTORICAL FINANCIALS

Company Type: Public

Income Statement

FYE: March 31

	REVENUE ($ mil.)	NET INCOME ($ mil.)	NET PROFIT MARGIN	EMPLOYEES
03/13	429.3	26.7	6.2%	3,172
03/12	412.6	26.5	6.4%	3,145
03/11	380.6	24.6	6.5%	2,986
03/10	337.9	26.1	7.7%	2,820
03/09	310.0	19.2	6.2%	2,700
Annual Growth	**8.5%**	**8.5%**	**—**	**4.1%**

2013 Year-End Financials

Debt ratio: —	No. of shares (mil.): 21
Return on equity: 24.1%	Dividends
Cash ($ mil.): 19	Yield: —
Current ratio: 1.76	Payout: —
Long-term debt ($ mil.): —	Market value ($ mil.): 1,065

	STOCK PRICE ($) FY Close	P/E High/Low	PER SHARE ($) Earnings	Dividends	Book Value
03/13	49.49	43 33	1.19	0.00	5.18
03/12	39.89	47 33	1.14	0.00	4.88
03/11	53.18	50 31	1.03	0.00	4.28
03/10	35.75	35 19	1.03	0.00	3.98
03/09	20.22	52 22	0.71	0.00	3.73
Annual Growth	**25.1%**	**— —**	**13.8%**	**—**	**8.6%**

CoStar Group, Inc.

CoStar has all the dirt on the commercial real estate industry. A provider of commercial real estate information CoStar has a proprietary database of some 4 million properties in the US the UK and France. The database contains information on more than 10 billion square feet of sale and lease listings. It also has more than 12 million digital images of buildings floor plans and maps. Its hundreds of data fields include location ownership and tenant names. CoStar additionally offers marketing and analytic services. Clients include government agencies real estate brokerages real estate investment trusts (REITs) and property owners and managers. Most of CoStar's sales come from subscription fees.

Geographic Reach

The company's sales teams are located in 30 field sales offices throughout the US and in offices located in London England; Manchester England; Glasgow Scotland and Paris France. Sales in the US accounted for about 95% of total revenues in fiscal 2012.

Operations

The company employs a team of more than 1000 research professionals and contractors who collect and analyze commercial real estate information. Its subscription-based services consist primarily of CoStar Property Professional (comprehensive inventory) CoStar Tenant (tenant information) CoStar COMPS Professional (comparable sales information) FOCUS (data on UK market) and Propex (UK market info for professional investors). It does business in England through CoStar UK.

Sales and Marketing

The company draws its customers from commercial real estate and related business community. Commercial real estate brokers have traditionally formed the largest portion of CoStar clients. The company also provides services to owners landlords financial institutions retailers vendors appraisers investment banks governmental agencies and other parties involved in commercial real estate.

CoStar sells its products and services through a direct sales force located in field sales offices. Its E-commerce advertising expenses were approximately $3 million in fiscal 2012.

Financial Performance

CoStar's revenue has spiked nearly 40% in fiscal 2012 compared to the previous year. The company brought in almost $350 million in revenue during fiscal 2012 after reporting about $251.7 million in fiscal 2011 and $226.3 million back in fiscal 2010.

The increase in revenues during fiscal 2012 was primarily attributable to additional revenue from the acquisition of LoopNet the penetration of the subscription-based information services and successful cross-selling of the company's services to its customers in existing markets combined with continued high renewal rates.

Net income decreased in fiscal 2012 mainly due to the increase in income tax expense and the impact of costs related to the LoopNet acquisition that are not deductible for tax purposes.

Mergers and Acquisitions

In 2012 the company significantly expanded its holdings with the $860 million purchase of LoopNet a complementary provider of online commercial real estate information. The deal doubled the size of CoStar's paid subscriber base to some 160000. The previous year CoStar enhanced its real estate brokerage offerings when it obtained Virtual Premise a provider of real estate management software and lease abstraction services. Each month Virtual Premise manages over $1 billion in rent payments for its customers.

EXECUTIVES

VP Research, Dean L. Violagis, age 46
President; Chief Executive Officer; Director, Andrew C. Florance, age 49, $456,560 total compensation
Chairman, Michael R. Klein, age 71
VP Research, Craig S. Farrington, age 55, $183,892 total compensation
VP Marketing, Daniel (Dan) Kimball, age 37
Senior Vice President - Research, Jennifer L. (Jenny) Kitchen, age 40, $197,600 total compensation
CIO, Frank Simuro, age 46
General Counsel and Secretary, Jonathan Coleman, age 48
Chief Financial Officer, Brian J. Radecki, age 42, $249,600 total compensation
Senior Vice President - Sales and Customer Service, John L. Stanfill, age 45, $250,000 total compensation
Managing Director CoStar UK, Paul Marples, age 51, $227,999 total compensation
Executive Vice President - Operations, Francis Carchedi
Director, Christopher J. (Chris) Nassetta, age 51
Director, David Bonderman, age 70
President CEO and Director, Andrew C. Florance, age 49
Director, David Steinberg
Director, Warren H. Haber, age 72
Director, Josiah O. Low III, age 73
Director, Michael J. Glosserman, age 67
Independent Director, John Hill
Auditors: Ernst&YoungLLP

LOCATIONS

HQ: CoStar Group, Inc.
1331 L Street, NW, Washington, DC 20005
Phone: 202 346-6500   **Fax:** 877 739-0486
Web: www.costar.com

2012 Sales

	$ mil.	% of total
US	330	95
Adjustments	(1.5)	-

PRODUCTS/OPERATIONS

Selected Subscription Products

CoStar COMPS Professional (comparable sales information)
CoStar Property Professional (flagship real estate database)
CoStar Tenant (tenant information)
FOCUS (UK real estate information)

COMPETITORS

First American	Reed Business
Market Leader	Information
Move Inc.	Reis
PropertyInfo	Zillow

HISTORICAL FINANCIALS

Company Type: Public

Income Statement

FYE: December 31

	REVENUE ($ mil.)	NET INCOME ($ mil.)	NET PROFIT MARGIN	EMPLOYEES
12/12	349.9	9.9	2.8%	1,965
12/11	251.7	14.6	5.8%	1,514
12/10	226.2	13.2	5.9%	1,389
12/09	209.6	18.6	8.9%	1,438
12/08	212.4	24.6	11.6%	1,178
Annual Growth	13.3%	(20.3%)	—	13.6%

2012 Year-End Financials

Debt ratio: 14.6%
Return on equity: 1.3%
Cash ($ mil.): 156
Current ratio: 1.96
Long-term debt ($ mil.): 153

No. of shares (mil.): 28
Dividends
  Yield: —
  Payout: —
Market value ($ mil.): 2,533

	STOCK PRICE ($) FY Close	P/E High/Low		PER SHARE ($) Earnings	Dividends	Book Value
12/12	89.37	242	153	0.37	0.00	29.15
12/11	66.73	116	74	0.62	0.00	25.93
12/10	57.56	89	58	0.64	0.00	18.37
12/09	41.77	47	26	0.94	0.00	17.41
12/08	32.94	45	21	1.26	0.00	15.38
Annual Growth	28.3%	—		(26.4%)	—	17.3%

CPI Aerostructures, Inc.

To build an aircraft some assembly is required and CPI Aerostructures is ready. CPI Aero delivers contract production of structural aircraft subassemblies chiefly for the US Air Force and other US military customers. Military products include skin panels flight control surfaces leading edges wing tips engine components cowl doors and nacelle and inlet assemblies. The lineup is used on military aircraft such as the C-5A Galaxy and C-130 Hercules cargo jets E-3 Sentry AWACs jet and T-38 Talon jet trainer. As a subcontractor to OEMs CPI Aero also makes aprons and engine mounts for commercial aircraft such as business jets. Government prime and subcontracts represent a majority of CPI Aero's sales

The company's performance depends on winning government and military work coupled with commercial contracts. Its position albeit exposed to the industry's boom and bust cycles has produced an increase in revenue and net income since 2006. The achievement is a balance of time and money. In 2009 it garnered about $10.6 million in US government contracts (28% of sales) modestly better than $9.2 million in 2008 but a disappointment compared to $22.7 million in 2007.

CPI Aero's partnerships with kingpin primes such as Northrop Grumman Boeing Lockheed Martin and Sikorsky Aircraft are equally volatile. CPI Aero won $6.9 million in subcontracts (43% of sales) in 2009 down from $36.2 million in 2008 and $9 million in 2007. Subcontract work for prime commercial aircraft makers builds upon CPI Aero's relationship as a subcontractor to defense primes. Serving Sikorsky and Spirit AeroSystems CPI Aero's work in 2009 totalled $5.9 million or 29% of sales versus 21% and 7% of sales in 2008 and 2007 respectively.

Chairman Eric Rosenfeld through investment firm Crescendo Partners controls about 18% of CPI Aero.

EXECUTIVES

President; Chief Executive Officer; Director, Edward J. Fred, age 54, $318,000 total compensation
Non-Executive Chairman, Eric S. Rosenfeld, age 55
Chief Operating Officer, Douglas J. McCrosson, age 50
Chief Financial Officer; Secretary, Vincent (Vince) Palazzolo, age 49, $216,300 total compensation
IR Contact Officer, Lena Cati
President CEO and Director, Edward J. Fred, age 54
Director, Walter Paulick, age 66
Director, Kenneth McSweeney, age 81
Director, Harvey J. Bazaar, age 72
Auditors: J.H.CohnLLP

LOCATIONS

HQ: CPI Aerostructures Inc.
60 Heartland Blvd., Edgewood NY 11717
Phone: 631-586-5200   **Fax:** 631-586-5840
Web: www.cpiaero.com

PRODUCTS/OPERATIONS

Selected Products

Cowl doors
Engine components
Flight control surfaces
Inlet assemblies
Leading edges
Nacelle assemblies
Skin panels
Wing tips

COMPETITORS

Boeing
Lockheed Martin
NORDAM
Northrop Grumman
Triumph Aerostructures - Vought Aircraft Division

HISTORICAL FINANCIALS

Company Type: Public

Income Statement

FYE: December 31

	REVENUE ($ mil.)	NET INCOME ($ mil.)	NET PROFIT MARGIN	EMPLOYEES
12/12	89.2	11.0	12.3%	201
12/11	74.1	7.4	10.0%	157
12/10	43.9	0.5	1.2%	127
12/09	43.9	3.9	9.0%	91
12/08	35.5	2.5	7.3%	85
Annual Growth	25.8%	43.6%	—	24.0%

2012 Year-End Financials

Debt ratio: 22.2%
Return on equity: 16.3%
Cash ($ mil.): 2
Current ratio: 3.01
Long-term debt ($ mil.): 3

No. of shares (mil.): 8
Dividends
  Yield: —
  Payout: —
Market value ($ mil.): 84

	STOCK PRICE ($) FY Close	P/E High/Low		PER SHARE ($) Earnings	Dividends	Book Value
12/12	10.01	11	7	1.40	0.00	9.63
12/11	11.87	14	9	1.04	0.00	7.78
12/10	14.08	177	75	0.08	0.00	6.58
12/09	6.01	12	6	0.64	0.00	6.38
12/08	5.50	20	11	0.42	0.00	5.68
Annual Growth	16.1%	—	—	35.1%	—	14.1%

Cray Inc

Cray makes computers that aren't just good — they're super. Its massively parallel and vector supercomputers provide the firepower behind research ranging from weather forecasting and scientific research to design engineering and classified government projects. The company also provides maintenance and support services and it sells its own and third-party data storage products primarily from NetApp and DataDirect Networks. Cray's largest customer is the US government which accounts for about two-thirds of sales. Cray also targets academic institutions and industrial companies. Around 80% of sales come from customers in the US.

Operations

All of its engineering and manufacturing facilities are located in the US (in California and Wisconsin) though the company uses subcontractors to produce the majority of its components. Of course all of its high-performance computers are built to order.

Cray has supercomputers installed at more than 100 sites worldwide. Its supercomputers run on the company's Cray Linux Environment (CLE) operating system. Cray is one of the only companies left that exclusively makes supercomputers. Competitors such as IBM are traditional PC companies that also custom-design high-performance models for customers.

Sales and Marketing

Cray has a direct sales force that operates from sales and service facilities in Australia Canada China France Germany Hong Kong India Italy Japan South Korea Spain Switzerland Taiwan the UK and the US. Only about 20% of sales come from outside the US.

Financial Performance

With supercomputer price tags often at $10 million and up the company's annual results can fluctuate dramatically. In 2012 overall sales jumped to $421 million up 78% from the $236 million earned in 2011. The increase was due a project with the National Center for Supercomputing Applications (NCSA) at the University of Illinois to build its supercomputer named Blue Waters as well as upgrades to the supercomputer at the Oak Ridge National Laboratory.

After years of losses Cray has been profitable since 2010 and 2012's profits skyrocketed 1000% to $161 million after it sold its interconnect hardware development program and related intellectual property to Intel for $140 million in cash.

Strategy

In 2013 Cray expanded its line of midrange supercomputers which have price tags between $200000 and $500000. The lower priced systems expand the company's market reach and potential for growth. In another strategic move in 2012 Cray formed YarcData a division focused solely on providing systems and services to the big data market. That year it also acquired California-based Appro International for about $21.8 million in cash. Appro International provides supercomputing services.

Company Background

Formerly Tera Computer the company bought Cray Research from Silicon Graphics and changed its name to Cray in 2000. In 2004 Cray acquired Canadian supercomputer developer OctigaBay Systems which became Cray Canada. The company's name comes from the late Seymour R. Cray the "father of supercomputing" although Mr. Cray never worked for Cray Inc.

EXECUTIVES

Chief Financial Officer; Executive Vice President, Brian C. Henry, age 56, $349,038 total compensation
Chairman, Stephen C. Kiely, age 67
President; Chief Executive Officer; Director, Peter J. Ungaro, age 44, $440,385 total compensation
Public Relations, Nick Davis
Vice President - Administration; General Counsel; Corporate Secretary, Michael C. Piraino, age 45
VP Europe Middle East and Africa (EMEA), Ulla Thiel
VP-Govt Programs, Jill Y. Hopper
Senior Vice President; Chief Technology Officer, William C. (Bill) Blake, age 63
SVP and CTO, Steven L. (Steve) Scott, age 47, $323,077 total compensation
Senior Vice President - High Performance Computing Systems, Margaret A. (Peg) Williams, age 54, $323,077 total compensation
VP-HR, Linda J. Howitson
Vice President - Field Operations, Charles A. (Chuck) Morreale, age 51
VP-Sls Ops, Paul C. Ciernia
SVP Operations and Customer Support, Wayne J. Kugel, age 45
VP Asia/Pacific, Andrew Wyatt
President Cray Japan, Mamoru Nakano
Investor Relations, Paul Hiemstra
VP Products Division and Corporate Marketing, Barry C. Bolding
VP Worldwide Sales, Larry Hoelzeman
Director Intelligence Accounts, Robert (Bob) Pencek
Senior Vice President; General Manager - YarcData, Arvind Parthasarathi
Vice President; Chief Accounting Officer; Corporate Controller, Charles Fairchild
Vice President Field Operations, Chuck Morreale

Senior Vice President General Manager of Cluster Solutions, Daniel G.B. Kim
Senior Vice President; General Manager - Cluster Solutions, Geun-Bum Kim
Senior Vice President High Performance Computing Systems, Peg Williams
Director, Frank L. Lederman, age 63
Director, Stephen C. Richards, age 59
Director, Sally G. Narodick, age 67
Director, Daniel C. (Dan) Regis, age 74
President CEO and Director, Peter J. Ungaro, age 44
Director, William C. (Bill) Blake, age 63
Director, John B. Jones Jr., age 68
Auditors: PetersonSullivanP.L.L.C.

LOCATIONS

HQ: Cray Inc.
901 5th Ave. Ste. 1000, Seattle WA 98164
Phone: 206-701-2000   **Fax:** 206-701-2500
Web: www.cray.com

2012 Sales

	% of total
US	82
Other	18
Total	**100**

PRODUCTS/OPERATIONS

2012 Sales

	% of total
High-performance	71
Maintenance &	15
Storage & data	12
Engineering services &	2
Total	**100**

2012 Sales

	% of total
Products	84
Services	16
Total	**100**

COMPETITORS

Bull	Lockheed Martin
California Digital Corp.	NEC
	NetApp
Cirrascale	Northrop Grumman
Dell	Oracle
EMC	Panasas
Fujitsu	Penguin Computing
General Dynamics	SRC Computers
Hewlett-Packard	Silicon Graphics
Hitachi	International
IBM	Teradata
LexisNexis	

HISTORICAL FINANCIALS

Company Type: Public

Income Statement

FYE: December 31

	REVENUE ($ mil.)	NET INCOME ($ mil.)	NET PROFIT MARGIN	EMPLOYEES
12/12	421.0	161.2	38.3%	929
12/11	236.0	14.3	6.1%	860
12/10	319.3	15.0	4.7%	885
12/09	284.0	(0.6)	—	872
12/08	282.8	(31.3)	—	829
Annual Growth	10.5%	—	—	2.9%

2012 Year-End Financials

Debt ratio: —	No. of shares (mil.): 39
Return on equity: 63.3%	Dividends
Cash ($ mil.) 253	Yield: —
Current ratio: 3.06	Payout: —
Long-term debt ($ mil.): —	Market value ($ mil.): 629

	STOCK PRICE ($) FY Close	P/E High/Low		PER SHARE ($) Earnings	Dividends	Book Value
12/12	15.95	4	1	4.27	0.00	8.64
12/11	6.47	20	12	0.40	0.00	4.54
12/10	7.17	17	10	0.43	0.00	4.04
12/09	6.42	—	—	(0.02)	0.00	3.53
12/08	2.08	—	—	(0.96)	0.00	3.53
Annual Growth	66.4%	—	—	—	—	25.1%

Credit Acceptance Corp. (MI)

In the world of Credit Acceptance Corporation (CAC) to purchase a car is not an impossible dream for problem borrowers —just an expensive reality. Working with more than 3000 independent and franchised automobile dealers in the US CAC provides capital for auto loans to people with substandard credit. The company also provides other services to dealers including payment servicing receivables management marketing and service contracts. It typically funds around 1.5 million auto loans per year; Michigan New York Texas Ohio and Pennsylvania are the company's largest markets.

The company funds loans in two ways: It advances money to its dealer-partners in exchange for the servicing rights to the underlying loan or it purchases loans directly from dealers. CAC earns most of its revenues from finance charges servicing fees and monthly program fees it charges its dealer partners.

CAC's revenues and its net income have grown steadily for the past five years. Although lending activity slowed due to lack of access to capital during the financial crisis the company managed to maintain good results. In 2010 the company's loan portfolio began picking up both in size and performance. Its bottom line got a boost from a spike in premiums earned on the reinsurance of vehicle service contracts a new area of emphasis for the company.

Sales grew by more than 18% in 2011. Income also was up by more than 10%. The results benefited from a increase in size of CAC's loan portfolio. As the US economy recovered consumer confidence and the firm's ability to access capital strengthened.

Founder and chairman Donald Foss owns more than 40% of CAC.

HISTORY

Donald Foss was a used-car dealer in Detroit where to make sales he sometimes financed cars out of his own pocket. As Foss' chain of dealerships grew so did his financing business. In 1972 he established it as a separate company and 20 years later took it public.

For most of its history CAC stood alone in the field of subprime auto lending but stagnating salaries made it a competitive growth business in the early 1990s. At mid-decade the company entered Canada and the UK to tap similar markets there. In 1996 CAC acquired Montana Investment Group a credit reporting service.

Even as rising consumer debt and bad credit continued to pump buyers into CAC's loan pipeline the economic boom of the mid-1990s paradoxically made used cars less desirable. The soft used-car market squeezed several of CAC's competitors out of business; a staggering default rate —nearing 40% —also pressured CAC whose auditors insisted it increase reserves to cover losses. The subsequent earnings dive spurred a shareholder lawsuit accusing CAC of hiding its poor fiscal health. Although bad loans had damaged its bottom line the company adopted more stringent lending policies to reduce risk. Consumers filed class-action suits alleging unethical practices in 1998 but many claims were dismissed.

To pay off debt acquired through bad loans CAC sold Montana Investment Group in 1999. In 2000 it launched CAC Leasing to further offset losses from a decrease in subprime lending but in 2002 the company exited that line deciding the lending field was more profitable. CAC stopped originating new loans in the UK and Canada in 2003.

In 2005 the SEC investigated CAC's accounting methods specifically related to its loan portfolio and the company restated portions of its past financial results.

The company found itself in hot water again in 2008 when it agreed to pay some 15000 Missouri customers to settle a class action lawsuit. The lawsuit filed more than a decade prior alleged that CAC overcharged customers for fees and interest on their loans. As part of the settlement CAC said it would write off $39 million in outstanding accounts and distribute another $13 million to customers.

EXECUTIVES

Corporate Secretary; Chief Legal Officer, Charles A. Pearce, age 48

Senior Vice President; Treasurer, Douglas W. Busk, age 52

Chief Executive Officer; Director, Brett A. Roberts, age 46, $800,000 total compensation

Chairman, Donald A. Foss, age 68, $475,000 total compensation

President, Steven M. Jones, age 49, $525,000 total compensation

Chief Financial Officer, Kenneth S. Booth, age 45, $341,250 total compensation

Chief Administrative Officer, John P. Neary, age 36

Director, Glenda J. Flanagan, age 60

CEO and Director, Brett A. Roberts, age 46

Director, Thomas M. Tryforos, age 53

Director, Scott J. Vassalluzzo, age 41

Auditors: GrantThorntonLLP

LOCATIONS

HQ: Credit Acceptance Corporation
25505 W. Twelve Mile Rd., Southfield MI 48034-8339
Phone: 248-353-2700   **Fax:** 817-390-1715
Web: www.drhorton.com

PRODUCTS/OPERATIONS

2011 Sales

	$ mil.	% of total
Finance charges	460	88
Premium income	40	8
Other	24	4
Total	**525**	**100**

Selected Subsidiaries

Arlington Investment Company
Auto Funding America Inc.
Auto Lease Services LLC
AutoNet Finance Company.com Inc.
Buyers Vehicle Protection Plan Inc.
CAC Leasing Inc.
CAC Reinsurance Ltd.
CAC Warehouse Funding Corp. II III IV
Credit Acceptance Motors Inc.
Credit Acceptance Wholesale Buyers Club Inc.
Vehicle Remarketing Services Inc.
VSC Re Company

COMPETITORS

Ally Financial
American Honda Finance
Bank of America
Capital One Auto Finance
First Investors Financial Services
Ford Motor Credit
GM Financial
Mercedes-Benz Credit
Mercedes-Benz Financial Services USA
Toyota Motor Credit
Union Acceptance Company
Volkswagen Financial Services
Volvo Car Finance
Wells Fargo Auto Finance

HISTORICAL FINANCIALS

Company Type: Public

Income Statement

FYE: December 31

	REVENUE ($ mil.)	NET INCOME ($ mil.)	NET PROFIT MARGIN	EMPLOYEES
12/12	609.2	219.7	36.1%	1,264
12/11	525.1	188.0	35.8%	1,037
12/10	442.1	170.0	38.5%	862
12/09	380.6	146.2	38.4%	911
12/08	312.1	67.1	21.5%	1,048
Annual Growth	**18.2%**	**34.5%**	**—**	**4.8%**

2012 Year-End Financials

Debt ratio: 58.6%
Return on equity: 37.7%
Cash ($ mil.): 9
Current ratio: 1.33
Long-term debt ($ mil.): 1,250
No. of shares (mil.): 24
Dividends
Yield: —
Payout: —
Market value ($ mil.): 2,452

	STOCK PRICE ($) FY Close	P/E High/Low		PER SHARE ($) Earnings	Dividends	Book Value
12/12	101.68	12	9	8.58	0.00	25.79
12/11	82.28	13	8	7.07	0.00	21.07
12/10	62.77	11	7	5.67	0.00	17.38
12/09	42.10	9	3	4.62	0.00	15.99
12/08	13.70	14	5	2.16	0.00	11.01
Annual Growth	**65.1%**			**— 41.2%**	**—**	**23.7%**

Cree, Inc.

Cree has its name in lights. Its blue green and near-ultraviolet light-emitting diodes (LEDs) — made from silicon carbide (SiC) and gallium nitride (GaN) —are used in dashboard lights architectural light fixtures market tickers and video screens.

Cree also sells SiC wafers which work better at higher temperatures and voltages than other silicon devices and SiC and GaN materials. In addition it offers lighting systems (both LED and traditional) as well as power and radio-frequency (RF) products such as Schottky diodes and transistors. The company makes most of its products at plants in the US (North Carolina Wisconsin) and China. More than 60% of sales come from outside the US.

OperationsLED products (chips components and SiC wafers) account for about 65% of Cree's sales but that's down from more than 80% in previous years. Boosted by the acquisition of Ruud Lighting the lighting systems segment grew to nearly 30% of sales in fiscal 2012 from single digits in previous years. Power and RF products round out the company's segments.

Geographic ReachThe US is Cree's largest geographic market and its impact has increased substantially having grown from less than 20% of sales in fiscal 2010 to nearly 40% in fiscal 2012. China which has been declining in recent years contributes more than 30%; all Asian countries together represent about 45% of total revenue.

Sales and MarketingSome 40% of Cree's sales are made to distributors; in fiscal 2012 Arrow Electronics and World Peace Industrial accounted for 18% and 10% of total sales respectively.

StrategyCree created the first blue LED which when combined with red and yellow LEDs creates a full spectrum of colors. The technology has become an industry standard and expands the applications of LED lighting. To leverage this core technology Cree has introduced the XLamp family of high-power packaged LEDs for specialty lighting applications hoping to stay one step ahead of the competition. Cree's XLamp products have a wide array of residential and commercial uses including appliance lighting and reading lamps as well as backlighting for large flat-panel and retail displays.The trends towards increased energy-efficient and environmental lighting and the growing number of standard lighting products that use LEDs have helped Cree weather a challenging economic environment better than many in the electronics industry. The company has combined external acquisitions and internal R&D to broaden its offerings —and increase its sales and market reach —into LED lighting fixtures power switching and RF products.

Mergers and AcquisitionsOn the acquisition side it bought Ruud Lighting for about $583 million in 2011. The Ruud acquisition the largest in company history gives Cree more sales channels and more opportunities for product development. Ruud Lighting makes outdoor LED lighting systems the logical complement to Cree's focus on indoor LED products. Shortly after the acquisition the company announced a $25 million expansion of manufacturing facilities at Ruud. The expansion added about 470 jobs.

Financial AnalysisRevenue for fiscal 2012 (ended June 30) rose 18% to $1.2 billion driven by 300% higher sales in its lighting systems segment because of the Ruud acquisitions. That offset a 6% decrease in LED product sales and a 25% decrease in power and RF product sales.Cree's net income fell nearly 70% to $44 million on increased R&D and sales general and administrative expenses as well as costs related to the Ruud acquisition.

HISTORY

Cree started at North Carolina State University where brothers Eric and Neal Hunter and Calvin Carter researched silicon carbide (SiC) applications in part with US government funding. In 1987 the trio founded Cree Research to continue their research. The company shipped its first-to-market blue light-emitting diode (LED) in 1991 and went public in 1993.

In 1995 the company began developing blue lasers –a project that continued for years to follow –via a 1999 pact with Microvision. Also that year Cree and Siemens formed a development and manufacturing agreement for blue and green LEDs. In 1997 Cree began supplying SiC crystals to gemstone manufacturer C3.

Cree in 1998 signed or extended pacts with Kansai Electric Power Siemens and Asea Brown Boveri (now ABB Ltd.). The next year the company shortened its name to Cree Inc. and released its first radio-frequency transistor.

In 2000 Cree acquired semiconductor R&D boutique Nitres for $233 million and to close out the year purchased the UltraRF division of Spectrian (a maker of linear power amplifiers) for $113.5 million. (It later renamed the unit Cree Microwave.)

In 2004 Cree acquired the gallium nitride substrate and epitaxy assets of Advanced Technology Materials a subsidiary of ATMI for about $10 million boosting its materials business and IP portfolio.

Co-founder Neal Hunter who served as CEO of Cree from 1994 to 2001 resigned as chairman in 2005 after a decade in that post and left the company's board of directors. Charles Swoboda who had succeeded Hunter as CEO in 2001 succeeded him as chairman as well.

Cree phased out its silicon-based RF and microwave semiconductor business in 2005 citing losses by its Cree Microwave subsidiary. The company refocused on its wide-bandgap RF and microwave devices fabricated on SiC and GaN substrates.

In 2006 the company opened a new engineering and production facility in Research Triangle Park measuring 230000 sq. ft. for making SiC and GaN devices.

That same year Cree acquired INTRINSIC Semiconductor for around $46 million including $43.6 million in cash. INTRINSIC Semiconductor made low-defect-density SiC substrates enabling high-power semiconductor devices and lower-cost LEDs.

In 2007 Cree acquired Hong Kong-based COTCO Luminant Device for about $200 million giving Cree a broader range of LED components access to a lower cost manufacturing facility and established sales channels in the fast growing China market.

EXECUTIVES

EVP Finance CFO and Treasurer, John T. Kurtzweil, age 56, $364,000 total compensation
Chairman President and CEO, Charles M. (Chuck) Swoboda, age 46, $572,000 total compensation
President Cree LED Lighting, Neal Hunter, age 51, $249,999 total compensation
Executive Vice President - LEDs, Norbert W.G. Hiller, age 53
VP Global Manufacturing, Wayne K. Nesbit, age 49
Secretary, Adam H. Broome
Executive Vice President and Chief Financial Officer, Michael E. McDevitt, age 49
SVP Sales, Robert (Bob) Pollock, age 58
LED Programs Manager, Deb Lovig
Director Sales and Marketing RF Products, Tom Dekker
VP Business Development, Chris James
VP and General Manager Asia/Pacific, Soo Ghee Lee

EVP and COO, Stephen D. (Steve) Kelley, age 50, $350,000 total compensation
VP Corporate Marketing, Greg Merritt
VP and General Manager Power and RF, Cengiz Balkas
Director Business Development Solid State Lighting, Mark McClear
Corporate Communications, Michelle Murray
VP Market Development Cree LED Lighting, Gary Trott
Director Marketing LED Components, Paul Thieken
Director Investor Relations, Raiford Garrabrant
Director RF and Microwave Products, Jim Milligan
Director Advanced Optoelectronics, John Edmond
VP and General Manager Cree LED Lighting, Ty Mitchell
VP Sales LED Lighting, Mike Fallon
Product Line Manager Cree LED Module, Scott Schwab
Product Line Manager Cree Materials, Vijay Balakrishna
Director National Accounts Cree LED Lighting, Craig Lofton
Director Marketing LED Modules, Tom Roberts
Vice Chairman - Lighting, Alan Ruud
Executive Vice President - Lighting, Tyrone D. Mitchell Jr., age 46
Director, Robert L. (Bob) Tillman, age 69
Director, Robert A. (Bob) Ingram, age 70
Director, Dolph W. von Arx, age 78
Director, Harvey A. Wagner, age 72
Director, Thomas H. (Tom) Werner, age 53
Director, Clyde R. Hosein, age 53
Director, Franco Plastina, age 50
Auditors: Ernst&YoungLLP

LOCATIONS

HQ: Cree Inc.
4600 Silicon Dr., Durham NC 27703
Phone: 919-407-5300   **Fax:** 919-313-5558
Web: www.cree.com

2012 Sales

	% of total
US	38
China	32
Europe	14
Japan	8
South	2
Malaysia	2
Taiwan	1
Other	3
Total	**100**

PRODUCTS/OPERATIONS

2012 Sales

	$ mil.	% of total
LED products	757	65
Lighting systems	335	29
Power & RF products	73	6
Total	**1,165**	**100**

Selected Products

Blue and green light-emitting diodes (LEDs; used in displays and indicators)
High-power packaged LEDs (XLamp)
Gallium nitride (GaN) products
 High electron mobility transistors (HEMT)
 Monolithic microwave integrated circuits (MMIC)
LED light fixtures (architectural lay-in bulbs downlights housings narrow beam spotlight)
Silicon carbide (SiC) products
 Radio-frequency and microwave transistors (used in communications applications)
 Rectifiers
 Switches
 Wafers (used in research programs)

COMPETITORS

Acuity Brands
Avago Technologies
Cooper Industries
GE
Hitachi
Hubbell
Infineon Technologies
Kopin
LG Electronics
Lighting Science Group
NEC
Nichia
Nitronex
OSRAM SYLVANIA
Orion Energy Systems
Panasonic Corp
Philips Lumileds
Philips Solid-State Lighting Solutions Inc.
Planar Systems
RF Micro Devices
ROHM
Revolution Lighting Technologies
Samsung Semiconductor
Sanken Electric
Sony
Sumitomo Electric Device Innovations
Toyoda Gosei
TriQuint
Zhejiang BOE Display

HISTORICAL FINANCIALS

Company Type: Public

Income Statement

FYE: June 30

	REVENUE ($ mil.)	NET INCOME ($ mil.)	NET PROFIT MARGIN	EMPLOYEES
06/13	1,385.9	86.9	6.3%	6,120
06/12	1,164.6	44.4	3.8%	5,555
06/11	987.6	146.5	14.8%	4,753
06/10	867.2	152.2	17.6%	4,298
06/09	567.2	30.3	5.3%	3,172
Annual Growth	**25.0%**	**30.1%**	**—**	**17.9%**

2013 Year-End Financials

Debt ratio: —
Return on equity: 3.1%
Cash ($ mil.): 1,023
Current ratio: 7.31
Long-term debt ($ mil.): —
No. of shares (mil.): 119
Dividends
 Yield: —
 Payout: —
Market value ($ mil.): 7,636

	STOCK PRICE ($) FY Close	P/E High/Low	PER SHARE ($) Earnings	Dividends	Book Value
06/13	63.83	88 30	0.74	0.00	23.46
06/12	24.45	95 52	0.39	0.00	22.09
06/11	33.96	56 25	1.33	0.00	20.63
06/10	65.06	56 18	1.45	0.00	18.78
06/09	29.92	93 39	0.34	0.00	13.66
Annual Growth	**20.9%**	**— —**	**21.5%**	**—**	**14.5%**

Crestwood Midstream Partners LP (New)

Inergy Midstream knows the ins and outs of the natural gas business. The company owns the northeastern US midstream assets of propane dealer and former parent Inergy L.P. Inergy Midstream oversees four natural gas storage facilities in New York and Pennsylvania that have a combined storage capacity of 41 billion cu. ft. as well as a 1.5 million-barrel natural gas liquids (NGL) storage facility in western New York. The company also owns a 37-mile natural gas pipeline in New York with a capacity of 30 million cu. ft. per day that transports gas exclusively for electric utility NYSEG. In 2013 the company was acquired by Crestwood Midstream Partners LP.

Inergy Midstream went public through a $320 million IPO in 2011.

Inergy Midstream was organized as a master limited partnership (MLP) a publicly traded legal entity exempt from paying federal income taxes. MLPs are specific to the energy infrastructure industry and enjoy tax-exempt status provided they pay taxable quarterly distributions to shareholders.

Unlike its former parent Inergy Midstream relies on a combination of organic and inorganic growth to expand through investments and development projects. The company has two pipeline projects under development - a 39-mile natural gas pipeline in Pennsylvania and an expansion project to build additional compression facilities in order to move gas in both directions at its largest storage facility that straddles two counties in New York and Pennsylvania. The Pennsylvania pipeline named MARC I is expected to be operational in 2012 at a cost of $315 million.

Other growth projects include spending $65 million to build a second NGL storage facility in New York that can hold 2.1 million barrels of natural gas liquids as well as expanding one of its natural gas storage facilities (purchased in July 2011) by 600 million cu. ft. In addition Inergy Midstream also plans to jointly develop a $120 million 10 billion cu. ft. natural gas storage facility with its parent by 2014.

Growing its portfolio in 2012 the company bought salt maker US Salt from its parent for $192.5 million. It also bought Rangeland Energy LLC the owner and operator of the COLT crude oil rail terminal storage and pipeline facilities for $425 million.

Auditors: Ernst&YoungLLP

LOCATIONS

HQ: Inergy Midstream L.P.
Two Brush Creek Blvd. Ste. 200, Kansas City MO 64112
Phone: 816-842-8181   **Fax:** 713-697-5945
Web: www.sss-steel.com

PRODUCTS/OPERATIONS

2010 Sales

	$ mil.	% of total
Firm storage	81	85
Transportation	12	13
Hub services	1	2
Total	**94**	**100**

COMPETITORS

Access Midstream Partners	Duncan Energy
	El Paso Corporation
AmeriGas Partners	Energy Transfer Equity
Boardwalk Pipeline	Ferrellgas Partners
Copano Energy	Kinder Morgan
DCP Midstream Partners	NiSource
Dominion Resources	Tennessee Gas

HISTORICAL FINANCIALS

Company Type: Public

Income Statement

FYE: September 30

	REVENUE ($ mil.)	NET INCOME ($ mil.)	NET PROFIT MARGIN	EMPLOYEES
09/12	189.8	65.7	34.6%	140
09/11	110.9	41.6	37.5%	0
09/10	94.7	30.6	32.3%	0
09/09	87.5	28.3	32.3%	0
Annual Growth	**29.4%**	**32.4%**	—	—

2012 Year-End Financials

Debt ratio: 40.5%	No. of shares (mil.): 75
Return on equity: —	Dividends
Cash ($ mil.): —	Yield: 0.0%
Current ratio: 0.53	Payout: 136.2%
Long-term debt ($ mil.): 415	Market value ($ mil.): 1,755

	STOCK PRICE ($) FY Close	P/E High/Low	PER SHARE ($) Earnings	Dividends	Book Value
09/12	23.34	41 30	0.58	0.79	7.39
09/11	0.00	— —	(0.00)	0.00	(0.00)
Annual Growth	—	— —	—	—	—

Crocs Inc

Crocs has taken a bite out of the footwear industry. The company's shoe collection has grown by leaps and bounds from its ubiquitous colorful slip-on shoe to mainstream fashion. Branded as Crocs its shoes are made of proprietary closed-cell resin and designed for men women and children; its collection includes 300-plus four-season footwear styles. Jibbitz are their decorative add-on charms. The company sells its products in more than 90 countries operating distribution centers worldwide and manufacturing plants in Mexico and Italy. Crocs sells through retailers such as Dillard's Nordstrom and Dick's Sporting Goods as well as through about 250 of its own stores and kiosks worldwide.

Geographic Reach

Based in Colorado Crocs enjoys a global reach doing business in more than 90 countries. It maintains additional offices in Hong Kong England Brazil and Amsterdam.

Operations

The company has three operating segments: Americas Asia and Europe. Its Other segment comprises its manufacturing operations in Mexico and Italy.

The Americas segment generating 44% of sales consists of product sales in North and South America. Across the US and Canada it operates about 200 stores. Bringing in 41% of sales the Asia segment comprises revenue for product sales throughout Asia Australia New Zealand the Middle East and South Africa. The company's about 240 stores in the segment span Korea Taiwan Japan China and Hong Kong. Revenues and expenses related to product sales throughout Europe and Russia appear in the Europe segment which accounts for 15% of revenue. The segment operates nearly 100 stores in Russia Germany and Great Britain. The remaining stores are located throughout Asia Eu-

rope Australia the Middle East South America and South Africa.

As part of its business Crocs relies on third parties for its distribution centers which are located in the US China Japan Hong Kong Australia Korea Singapore India Taiwan the United Arab Emirates Russia Brazil Argentina Chile Puerto Rico and Italy.

Strategy

For the first time in company history Crocs reached $1 billion in revenue in 2011. Despite a continued difficult selling environment industry-wide it had boosted sales by more than 26% as compared to the same period in 2010.

Crocs has worked in recent years to transform its brand from what Crocs calls its clog silhouette to an all-season footwear brand. It's also looking at licensing to further diversify its revenue. The company's products fall into four categories: Core-Comfort Active Casual and Style. The footwear maker partners with the likes of Disney Marvel and Viacom to sell Crocs-licensed shoes and Jibbitz-branded shoe charms. Crocs in 2011 began to license certain trademarks to third parties.

Sales and Marketing

The company sells its products through three primary channels: wholesale (57% of sales) retail (33%) and Internet (10%). Wholesale customers include national and regional retail chains department stores sporting goods stores independent footwear retailers and family footwear retailers such as Dick's Sporting Goods Famous Footwear Academy Kohls Nordstrom Xebio and Murasaki Sports as well as online retailers the likes of Zappos.com and Amazon.com. Additionally Crocs has nearly 540 branded retail locations worldwide.

Crocs boasts sales offices in the US Canada South America Taiwan Hong Kong Australia Korea China the United Arab Emirates India and Europe.

In 2012 the company spent $39.8 million in total advertising marketing and promotional activities. It taps digital social and traditional media outlets for its campaigns. The company's in-house digital marketing team oversees digital marketing programs and platforms that include paid-and-organic search display re-targeting email and affiliate marketing.

Financial Performance

Crocs logged a 12% increase in sales in 2012 as compared to 2011 benefited by a 5% boost in global footwear unit sales and an 8% rise in footwear average selling price. It attributes most of the gains to its retail channel (a 22% rise) which logged strong demand across its three reportable segments. Crocs also opened an impressive 107 net new stores in 2012 while shuttering some kiosks in favor of branded stores which offer customers its full line. Wholesale sales in the Americas and Asia spurred an 8% increase in 2012 sales. Revenues from its Internet channel also helped Crocs increasing 7% due to stronger brand awareness in the Americas and Asia. The company posted increased profits in both fiscal 2011 and 2012. Profits rose 17% in 2012 due to higher operating results and to a lesser extent a lower effective tax rate.

Mergers and Acquisitions

To reach into the accessories and sports businesses Crocs looks for add-on products (such as its purchase of Jibbitz) and technologies. Buying EXO Italia maker of ethylene vinyl acetate-based finished products has given Crocs the tools to compete in the popular performance footwear market against rivals the likes of Teva.

EXECUTIVES

EVP and Chief Legal and Administrative Officer, Daniel P. (Dan) Hart, age 54, $259,119 total compensation
President; Chief Executive Officer; Director, John P. McCarvel, age 56, $595,833 total compensation
Chairman, Thomas J. Smach, age 52
VP Europe, Vince Gunn, age 42
CIO, Paul Lanham
VP and General Manager Americas, Doug Hayes
Chief Financial Officer; Senior Vice President - Finance; Principal Accounting Officer, Jeffrey (Jeff) Lasher, age 48
Senior Public Relations Manager, Tia Mattson
Investor Relations, Jennifer Almquist
Media Contact, Shelley Weibel
Senior Creative Director, Becky Gebhardt
Chief Marketing Officer, Andrew Davison
SVP World Wide Operations, Scott E. Crutchfield
VP Global Sales, Mike De Bell
VP Asia, Dave Thielen
Chief Product Officer, Dale Bathum
Chief Sales Officer, Mike DeBell
Director, W. Stephen Cannon, age 61
Director, Ronald L. (Ron) Frasch, age 64
Director, Raymond D. Croghan, age 63
Director, Peter A. Jacobi, age 69
Independent Director, Doreen Wright
Auditors: Deloitte&ToucheLLP

LOCATIONS

HQ: Crocs Inc.
7477 E. Dry Creek Pkwy., Niwot CO 80503
Phone: 303-848-7000   **Fax:** 303-468-4266
Web: www.crocs.com

2012 Sales

	$ mil.	% of total
Americas	495	44
Asia	457	41
Europe	169	15
Other	0	—
Total	**1,123**	**100**

PRODUCTS/OPERATIONS

2012 Sales

	% of total
Wholesale	57
Retail	33
Internet	10
Total	**100**

2012 Sales

	$ mil.	% of total
Footwear	1,076	96
Other	47	4
Total	**1,123**	**100**

2012 Stores

	No.
Retail	287
Outlet	129
Kiosk	121
Total	**537**

COMPETITORS

Birkenstock USA	R. Griggs
Columbia Sportswear	S?o Paulo Alpargatas
Deckers Outdoor	Skechers U.S.A.
Heelys	Timberland
L.L. Bean	Wolverine World Wide
NIKE	adidas

HISTORICAL FINANCIALS

Company Type: Public

Income Statement

FYE: December 31

	REVENUE ($ mil.)	NET INCOME ($ mil.)	NET PROFIT MARGIN	EMPLOYEES
12/12	1,123.3	131.3	11.7%	4,900
12/11	1,000.9	112.7	11.3%	4,157
12/10	789.7	67.7	8.6%	4,000
12/09	645.7	(42.0)	—	3,560
12/08	721.5	(185.0)	—	3,700
Annual Growth	**11.7%**	**—**		**7.3%**

2012 Year-End Financials

Debt ratio: 0.8%	No. of shares (mil.): 88
Return on equity: 23.6%	Dividends
Cash ($ mil.): 294	Yield: —
Current ratio: 3.88	Payout: —
Long-term debt ($ mil.): 4	Market value ($ mil.): 1,276

	STOCK PRICE ($) FY Close	P/E High/Low		PER SHARE ($) Earnings	Dividends	Book Value
12/12	14.39	15	8	1.44	0.00	6.96
12/11	14.77	25	11	1.24	0.00	5.48
12/10	17.12	25	7	0.76	0.00	4.27
12/09	5.75	—	—	(0.49)	0.00	3.36
12/08	1.24	—	—	(2.24)	0.00	3.46
Annual Growth	**84.6%**	—	—	—	—	**19.1%**

Crown Castle International Corp

Crown Castle International rules over a kingdom of radio towers. Through subsidiaries it provides broadcast data and wireless communications infrastructure services in the US (including Puerto Rico) and Australia. Wireless carrier customers lease antenna space on Crown Castle's owned or managed towers and distributed antenna systems (DAS); its 30000 sites in the US cover 98 of the top 100 markets and its 1700 Australian sites cover nearly the entire population. The company also designs networks selects and develops sites and installs antennas. Crown Castle is among the nation's largest tower managers and earns most of its revenue in the US.

Geographic Reach The US is Crown Castle's principal market accounting for about 95% of sales; Australia brings in the rest.

Sales and Marketing Crown Castle markets its products directly to customers including leading US wireless carriers Sprint Nextel (24% of sales) AT&T Mobility (22% of sales) Verizon Wireless (17%) and T-Mobile USA (11%). Customers in Australia include Telstra and SingTel Optus.

Financial Performance

Crown Castle has seen steady revenue growth over most of the past decade including 20% growth in 2012 to $2.4 billion as it expands its roster of tenants and focuses on contract renewals and extensions amid a continued boom in demand for wireless services. After years of loss the company returned to profitability in 2011 recording $188 million in profit in 2012. In addition to the increase in sales Crown Castle benefitted from not having losses from interest rate swaps and early retirement of debt as it has had in previous years (the company has nearly $11 billion in long-term debt which is working to reduce).

Mergers and Acquisitions Crown Castle which began in 1994 with 130 towers in Texas has grown organically through investments new site construction and share purchases as well as tower acquisitions. In 2012 it bought a portfolio of ground lease assets from Wireless Capital Partners LLC for $215 million. Next it bought NextG Networks for about $1 billion which expanded its wireless (primarily DAS) coverage. Crown Castle continues to focus on the US market while competitors look to emerging markets for expansion. Fortunately the wireless industry in the US is showing no signs of slowing down as network demand increases for integrated devices such as smartphones that offer data service. Later that year the company acquired rights to more than 7000 T-Mobile USA towers for $2.4 billion.

In 2010 it bought NewPath Networks from Charterhouse Group for about $115 million. NewPath developed and operated distributed antenna system (DAS) networks. Crown Castle's interest in the company stemmed from its strategy of expanding further into the wireless infrastructure equipment space broadening its reach past its core tower business.

Ownership Investment firm T. Rowe Price owns about 10% of the company's stock.

EXECUTIVES

Chairman, J. Landis (Lanny) Martin, age 68
EVP and General Counsel, E. Blake Hawk, age 64, $391,432 total compensation
President and CEO, W. Benjamin (Ben) Moreland, age 50, $504,779 total compensation
SVP CFO and Treasurer, Jay A. Brown, age 40, $356,002 total compensation
SVP and COO, James D. (Jim) Young, age 52, $402,096 total compensation
SVP Sales and Chief Commercial Officer, Patrick (Pat) Slowey, age 56
SVP Corporate Development and Strategy, Philip M. (Phil) Kelley, age 40, $237,923 total compensation
Director, Lee W. Hogan, age 68
Director, Robert E. Garrison II, age 71
Director, John P. Kelly, age 55
Director, Edward C. Hutcheson Jr., age 67
President CEO and Director, W. Benjamin (Ben) Moreland, age 49
Director, Robert F. McKenzie, age 69
Director, Dale N. Hatfield, age 75
Director, Ari Q. Fitzgerald, age 50
Director, David C. Abrams, age 51
Director, Cindy Christy, age 46
Auditors: KPMGLLP

LOCATIONS

HQ: Crown Castle International Corp.
1220 Augusta Dr. Ste. 500, Houston TX 77057-2261
Phone: 713-570-3000   **Fax:** 713-570-3100
Web: www.crowncastle.com

2012 Sales

	$ mil.	% of total
US	2,283	94
Australia	146	6
Other countries	3	-
Total	**2,432**	**100**

PRODUCTS/OPERATIONS

2012 Sales

	$ mil.	% of total
Site rental	2,124	87
Network services & other	308	13
Total	**2,432**	**100**

Selected Services

Antenna and equipment installation
Network design
Site acquisition development and construction

COMPETITORS

American Tower	NextG
CellXion	PlastiComm Industries
Global Tower LLC	SBA Communications
LCC International	TowerCo LLC
Microwave Transmission Systems	VelociTel

HISTORICAL FINANCIALS

Company Type: Public

Income Statement

FYE: December 31

	REVENUE ($ mil.)	NET INCOME ($ mil.)	NET PROFIT MARGIN	EMPLOYEES
12/12	2,432.6	188.5	7.8%	1,600
12/11	2,032.7	171.0	8.4%	1,300
12/10	1,878.6	(310.9)	—	1,200
12/09	1,685.4	(114.3)	—	1,200
12/08	1,526.5	(48.8)	—	1,300
Annual Growth	**12.4%**	**—**	**—**	**5.3%**

2012 Year-End Financials

Debt ratio: 72.1%
Return on equity: 6.6%
Cash ($ mil.): 441
Current ratio: 1.28
Long-term debt ($ mil.): 10,923
No. of shares (mil.): 293
Dividends
 Yield: —
 Payout: —
Market value ($ mil.): 21,155

	STOCK PRICE ($) FY Close	P/E High/Low	PER SHARE ($) Earnings	Dividends	Book Value
12/12	72.16	112 70	0.64	0.00	10.02
12/11	44.80	89 72	0.52	0.00	9.46
12/10	43.83	— —	(1.16)	0.00	9.50
12/09	39.04	— —	(0.47)	0.00	11.11
12/08	17.58	— —	(0.25)	0.00	10.51
Annual Growth	**42.3%**				**(1.2%)**

CSG Systems International Inc.

CSG Systems International tries to make life a little easier for CSRs (customer service representatives). Its customer care and billing software and services are designed for clients handling a high volume of transactions. The company offers outsourced transaction processing and customer service systems that are used to establish customer accounts process orders manage and mail monthly statements and perform marketing analysis among other functions. The company serves primarily North American cable TV direct broadcast satellite

online services and telecom companies such as AT&T Time Warner Comcast and Verizon.

Geographic Reach CSG has some three dozen offices in about 25 countries although most of its sales (about 85%) are generated in the US. The company is seeing strong growth in its European and Asian operations however as those regions grew nearly 1000% and 2000% respectively year-over-year.

Sales and Marketing CSG markets its products directly via dedicated account teams. Its largest customers include Comcast (nearly 20% of sales) DISH Network (13%) and Time Warner (10%).

Financial Performance CSG has seen substantial revenue growth since 2005. In 2011 it reported a nearly 35% jump in sales to $735 million almost entirely the result of the acquisition of UK business services software provider Intec which boosted the company's software and maintenance segment by about 300%. Along with the strong 2011 sales net income nearly doubled to $42 million. Mergers and Acquisitions CSG uses acquisitions as one means of expanding. In 2012 it acquired Swedish software developer Ascade a provider of trading and routing applications to telecommunications companies worldwide for approximately $19 million in cash to extend its reach into the wholesale telecommunications wholesale market and expand its geographic reach. In 2010 the company bought Intec Telecom a UK-based business support systems software provider in a deal valued at about $376 million. CSG used the purchase to expand its customer base into international markets and broaden its portfolio of products used to interact with customers in real-time. By integrating Intec's retail billing mediation and wholesale business management systems with its customer interaction management software suite CSG was able to provide a more complete customer interaction platform to telecommunications companies outside of its core cable and satellite markets.

EXECUTIVES

Chairman, Donald B. (Don) Reed, age 68
President CEO and Director, Peter E. Kalan, age 53, $500,000 total compensation
VP Investor Relations, Elizabeth A. (Liz) Bauer
EVP General Counsel Corporate Secretary and Chief Administrative Officer, Joseph T. (Joe) Ruble, age 52, $280,000 total compensation
EVP CFO and Principal Accounting Officer, Randy R. Wiese, age 53, $335,000 total compensation
CTO and SVP Software Development, Ken Kennedy
EVP and COO, Bret C. Griess, age 44, $325,000 total compensation
SVP Business and New Market Development, Jerry Baker
SVP Product Strategy, Dwayne Ruffin
SVP Strategic Business Units, Jay McCracken
Senior Vice President General Manager Quaero, Naras Eechambadi
EVP Sales and Marketing, Michael Henderson, age 55
SVP Product Management, Sean Brown
Senior Vice President of Investor Relations and Strategic Communications, Liz Bauer
Director, Ronald H. (Ron) Cooper, age 54
Director, Donald B. (Don) Reed, age 67
Director, Edward C. (Ed) Nafus, age 72
President CEO and Director, Peter E. Kalan, age 53
Director, James A. Unruh, age 71
Director, Janice I. Obuchowski, age 61
Director, Bernard W. (Bernie) Reznicek, age 76
Director, Frank V. Sica, age 62
Director, Donald V. Smith, age 70

Independent Director, John Hughes
Auditors: KPMGLLP

LOCATIONS

HQ: CSG Systems International Inc.
 9555 Maroon Cir., Englewood CO 80112
Phone: 303-200-2000　　**Fax:** 303-200-3333
Web: www.csgi.com

2011 Sales

$ mil % of total

Americas	627	85
Europe Middle East and Africa	75	10
Asia Pacific	31	4
Total	**734**	**100**

PRODUCTS/OPERATIONS

2011 Sales

	$ mil.	% of total
Processing & related services	524	71
Software maintenance & services	210	29
Total	**734**	**100**

Selected Services

Revenue Management
　Cable & Satellite Care & Billing
　Convergent Rating & Billing
　Charging & Policy
　Total Service Mediation
　Partner Management Billing & Settlement
Customer Interaction Management
　Customer Communication Center
　Interactive Messaging
　Output Solutions
　Marketing Services
Analytics & Intelligence
　Customer Intelligence

COMPETITORS

Alcatel-Lucent	Huawei Technologies
Amdocs	Oracle
Comverse Technology	Synchronoss
Convergys	Telcordia
DST Systems	

HISTORICAL FINANCIALS

Company Type: Public

Income Statement

FYE: December 31

	REVENUE ($ mil.)	NET INCOME ($ mil.)	NET PROFIT MARGIN	EMPLOYEES
12/12	756.8	48.8	6.5%	3,542
12/11	734.7	42.2	5.8%	3,352
12/10	549.3	22.4	4.1%	3,512
12/09	500.7	43.3	8.7%	2,061
12/08	472.0	61.7	13.1%	2,066
Annual Growth	**12.5%**	**(5.7%)**	**—**	**14.4%**

2012 Year-End Financials

Debt ratio: 32.4%
Return on equity: 16.2%
Cash ($ mil.): 136
Current ratio: 2.08
Long-term debt ($ mil.): 259
No. of shares (mil.): 33
Dividends
 Yield: —
 Payout: —
Market value ($ mil.): 613

	STOCK PRICE ($) FY Close	P/E High/Low	PER SHARE ($) Earnings	Dividends	Book Value
12/12	18.18	15 9	1.51	0.00	9.68
12/11	14.71	17 10	1.28	0.00	8.12
12/10	18.94	35 26	0.67	0.00	6.95
12/09	19.09	15 10	1.26	0.00	6.04
12/08	17.47	11 6	1.85	0.00	4.31
Annual Growth	**1.0%**	**— —**	**(5.0%)**	**—**	**22.4%**

Cubic Corp

Cubic's products and services fit in squarely with the global defense and transportation industries. With business divided into three main segments it provides mission support services which include actual combat rehearsal exercises prior to deployment to national militaries and US security forces and their allies. It manufactures air and ground combat instrumentation systems for live and virtual training as well as communications global asset tracking and cyber security equipment for the defense market. Thirdly it provides automated fare collection (AFC) management systems and services for mass transit (including bus light rail ferry and parking) worldwide.

Mission support services (MSS) 37% of sales operates from more than 130 sites in 20+ nations and provides services for three of the Army's Combat Training Centers the Joint Coalition Warfare Center and the Korea Battle Simulation Center. The segment has driven all Marine Corps simulation-based exercises since 1998. Cubic transportation systems (CTS 32% of sales) has worked on more than 400 projects in 40 major markets including the US Canada Australia Germany Sweden the UK. The segment's services include system design central computer systems equipment design software development and retail point of sale network management.

Defense systems 31% of sales is divided into training systems communications global asset tracking and cyber security. Training systems is divided into air combat and ground combat groups. Communications provides Common Data Link (CDL) products for ships unmanned aerial vehicles and remote video terminals. Global asset tracking is focused on the US Department of Defense (DoD) supply chain. Cyber security is built on the recent acquisitions of Safe Harbor Holdings and Abraxas. The segment maintains market leadership under a 10-year $525 million competitive contract awarded in 2003 to provide an advanced air combat training system called P5 to the US Air Force US Navy and Marine Corps. More than half of Cubic's total business is conducted with various agencies of the US government. The remainder of its revenue comes from local regional and foreign governments and agencies.

Sales grew 8% in 2011 vs. 2010. Organic growth accounted for 50% of the company's revenue uptick while the rest was the result of the 2010 acquisition of Abraxas. Net income attributable to Cubic weighed in at $84.8 million in 2011 compared to $70.6 million in 2010. The improvement is the result of a jump in operating income as well as a lower tax rate and a favorable currency exchange rate between the dollar and the pound.

By segment MSS sales headed up 7% in 2011 compared to 2010 thanks to the contribution of newly acquired Abraxas a contract for homeland security and flight simulators. CTS sales rose 8% in 2011 vs. 2010 due to strong demand in Europe and Australia. More specifically a contract with Transport for London (TfL) and contracts with Sydney and Brisbane Australia as well as a new contract with Vancouver Canada contributed to the increase.

In the defense systems segment training systems sales surged 14% in 2011 compared with 2010 as a result of more demand for air combat training in the US and Far East ground combat training in the UK and Multiple Integrated Laser Engagement Simulation equipment. Communica-

tions fell 33% however due in part to lower demand for data links and power amplifiers. The two other groups in the segment global asset tracking and cyber security were recently added as the result of acquisitions. The company invested in developing and marketing these groups' products.

Cubic's strategy for growth includes leveraging long-term relationships. The company's CTS segment already has a strong track record for long-term relationships starting in 1978 when the company began a trial of magnetic ticketing and gating for TfL and has serviced the company with fare collection equipment and systems ever since.

Expanding services is another part of the company's strategy. Counting 52% of its sales from services the company has positioned CTS to offer more services to meet the growing technical complexities of electronic fare collection systems. MSS is also developing new services to meet the demands of additional work for its US Air Force Research Laboratories contract and a new contract with the US Army Training and Doctrine Command Future Warfare Studies Program.

Another prong in Cubic's general strategy is diversifying business. Relying directly and indirectly on the US government for 56% sales the company notes that this government business fulfills needs for a wide variety of government agencies. The company aims to maintain the diverse mix of business attendant on serving a variety of customer needs.

Growing internationally is another goal. The CTS segment recently expanded in Australia through a contract for Sydney's Electronic Ticketing System. The defense systems segment received a contract to supply the Saudi Arabian National Guard with the Engagement skills Trainer.

In 2011 Cubic acquired XIO Strategies a deal that increased Cubic's proficiency at supply chain management especially in regard to work performed for DoD. In late 2010 the company acquired Virginia-based Abraxas Corp. a provider of national security and cyber security services. The $124 million deal bolstered the capacity of Cubic's MSS division and widened its customer base in the homeland security law enforcement and national security markets.

The defense systems division in 2010 acquired Safe Harbor Holdings a supplier of hardware and software for intelligence and cyber defense applications. Safe Harbor formed a new subsidiary called Cubic Cyber Solutions which fueled Cubic's move into the cyber security marketplace. Prior to that it expanded into the global asset management market with the 2010 purchase of Impeva Labs. Now called Cubic Global Tracking Solutions the subsidiary provides devices that monitor and track high-value assets for the DoD.

HISTORY

The late Walter Zable founded Cubic in 1951 to make military electronics. The company went public in 1959 and in the late 1960s and early 1970s it expanded into revenue collection systems. In 1969 Cubic acquired manufacturer United States Elevator (sold 1993). It formed a joint venture with Westinghouse in 1978 to make AFC equipment for the London Underground and others. Cubic bought Automatic Toll Systems in 1987.

Cubic acquired Titan's army training and simulation service business in 1994. As defense budgets dropped in the 1990s the company began to emphasize other businesses including its transit system operations. In 1995 it bought Danish ticketing system maker Scanpoint Technology and the next year it acquired Westinghouse's stake in their

UK joint venture. Cubic bought EMI Group's Thorn Transit Systems International in 1997. It also formed Cubic VideoComm to commercialize video compression technology that it had developed for military use.

In 1998 Cubic won a contract to supply combat training systems to the British army and as a TranSys consortium partner the company was named to privatize and upgrade the London Underground's AFC system using smart card technology. The next year Cubic agreed to install an AFC system for Puerto Rico's premier rapid transit system. Also to better fund development of video compression products for use in surveillance Cubic transferred its Cubic VideoComm unit to a new company Cubic Video Technologies in which it took a minority interest.

Cubic bought Oscmar International Ltd. (New Zealand) a maker of simulation equipment and instrumentation in 2000. The following year Cubic Defense Systems was awarded a $40 million contract by the US Air Force for air combat training systems. Deals in 2002 included a $12 million US Army contract for the company's Multiple Integrated Laser Engagement System (MILES) and an $8 million contract to integrate smart card technology into Houston's METRO transit system.

Late in 2003 Cubic acquired rival simulator company ECC International in a deal worth about $42 million.

Cubic expanded its transportation business in 2005 by combining two acquisitions —the assets of Lexis Systems and Traf-Park —to form Cubic Parking Systems a provider of revenue collection systems for parking lots. In 2007 the company launched a new subsidiary eAccess LLC to offer regional smart card systems.

In mid-2008 the company expanded its mission support services segment by acquiring Omega Training Group. The Georgia-based company brings experience in training staffing and testing and logistics and new contracts with the US Army and other services.

Significant contracts in 2009 include an award with the US Africa Command for training exercises and another with the Marine Corps for Cubic's fifth-generation air combat training instrument. In the spring Cubic won business to conduct battle simulation training exercises for the US Forces Korea. This contract builds upon a 1991 award and expands the company's toehold in virtual exercises for the US and allied forces.

Also in 2009 Cubic scored the Concord operations center and software licenses from the US subsidiary of Vix ERG Pty Ltd. The acquisition built Cubic's services business with transit agencies in Boston Las Vegas and San Francisco.

EXECUTIVES

President and COO, Bradley H. Feldmann, age 52
EVP and CFO, John D. (Jay) Thomas, age 60, $315,000 total compensation
Chief Executive Officer, William W. Boyle, age 79, $540,800 total compensation
Chairman, Walter C. Zable, age 66, $410,000 total compensation
VP General Counsel and Corporate Secretary, William L. Hoese, age 74
VP Information Technologies, John A. Minteer, age 62
SVP Ground Combat Programs, Joseph K. (Keith) Kellogg Jr., age 64
VP and Corporate Controller, Mark A. Harrison, age 56
VP Ethics and Compliance, Daniel A. Jacobsen, age 60

SVP Worldwide Services Cubic Transportation Systems, David M. (Dave) Lapczynski

VP General Counsel and Corporate Secretary, James R. (Jim) Edwards, age 60

VP and Program Manager Support Operations, Michael W. David

President Mission Support Services, Jimmie L. (Jim) Balentine

VP and General Manager Operations Support Division Mission Support Services, Richard D. Bristow

Executive Vice President General Manager Integrated Training Solutions, Raymond C. Barker

VP and General Manager Information Operations Division Mission Support Services, Alan D. Sargeant

VP and General Manager Simulation Systems Division, Theresa W. Kohl

General Manager Cubic Defense New Zealand, Ernie L. Armijo

Managing Director Cubic Defense Singapore, Thomas Scott

VP and General Manager Threat Technologies Division Mission Support Services, Jon D. Neasham

VP Legislative Affairs, Jack W. Liddle

Program Manager Threat Technologies Division Mission Support Services, Richard L. Dickson

Regional Director England, David A. Williams

Vice President Director Cubic Transportation Systems Chicago, John D. Satterfield

Director Investor Relations, Diane L. Dyer

VP and General Manager Worldwide Technical Services Division, Kevin J. Hayes

VP Government Affairs, Richard Trenery

EVP and President Cubic Transportation Systems, Stephen O. (Steve) Shewmaker

Vice President Strategy and Development, Michael L. Kelly

Program Manager Operations Support Division Mission Support Services, Leonard M. Supko

President Cubic Field Services Canada, Robert T. Reilander

Director International Operations Defense Restructuring & Force Modernization, Larry G. Smith

VP and Program Manager JRTC Mission Support, William C. David

President and Group General Manager Cubic Security Systems, Walt Bonneau Jr.

Senior Vice President & General Manager, Richard Wunderle

Treasurer, Gregory L. Tanner, age 55

SVP Business Operations and Controller Cubic Defense Applications, Thomas A. (Tom) Echols

EVP Cubic Applications and Cubic Worldwide Technical Services, Ruth Van Sickle

VP and General Manager Training and Education Division Mission Support Services, John R. Schmader

President and CEO eAccess, Robert A. Kraft

Manager Marketing Communications, Janet Dayton

VP Business Development Cubic Defense Applications, John Naff

Senior Director Business Development Cubic Defense Applications, Philip J. Fisch

Chief Scientist Advanced Programs Business Development, John Boyd

VP Communications Systems, Grant Palmer

VP Sales and Marketing North America, Jean-Marc Landry

Vice President legislative affairs, Andy Jazwick

Corporate Vice President - Human Resources, John Schierer

General Counsel; Secretary, Ab Jenkins

Vice President - Engineering and Operations, Jim Kilfeather

Senior Vice President Business Development, Michael Creighton

Vice President of Cubic Cyber Solutions, Steven Frenz

Vice President Production Operations, John Madeiros

Vice President Programs, Mike Roll

Vice President Human Resources, Mari McAvoy

Senior Vice President Worldwide Financial Operations, Min Wei

Vice President Director Western Region, Matt Newsome

Vice President Engineering, Pradip Mistry

Vice President Customer Services, Derick Benoit

Vice President Contracts, Carl R. Adrignola

Senior Vice President General Manager Simulations Systems, Terry W. Kohl

Senior Vice President, Dave Lapczynski

Executive Vice President General Manager Airborne Systems and Information Superiority, Donald G. Jacobs

Vice President Director Eastern Region, Steve Brunner

Vice President Business Development, Anthony Verna

Interim President and CEO CFO and Director, William W. Boyle, age 78

Director, John H. Warner Jr., age 72

Director, Edwin A. Guiles, age 62

Director, Robert S. Sullivan, age 69

Director, Bruce G. Blakley, age 67

Auditors: Ernst&YoungLLP

LOCATIONS

HQ: Cubic Corporation
9333 Balboa Ave., San Diego CA 92123
Phone: 858-277-6780   Fax: 228-563-5673
Web: www.hancockbank.com

2011 Sales

	$ mil.	% of total
US	705	55
United Kingdom	266	21
Australia	115	9
Far East	84	7
Middle East	35	2
Canada	26	2
Other	51	4
Total	**1,285**	**100**

PRODUCTS/OPERATIONS

2011 Sales

	$ mil.	% of total
Mission support services	475	37
Transportation systems	415	32
Defense systems	392	31
Other	1	-
Total	**1,285**	**100**

Selected Products & Services

Defense systems
  Asset tracking
  Avionics systems
  Communications
  Customized military range instrumentation
  Cyber security
  Simulators
  Training systems
Mission support services
  Cyber support
  Intelligence support
  Logistics
  Professional military education
  Real-world mission rehearsal exercises
  Training
Transportation systems
  Central computer systems
  Contactless smart card readers
  Passenger gates

Payment media management
Ticket vending machines

COMPETITORS

ACS
BAE Systems Inc.
Boeing
CACI International
CAE Inc.
General Dynamics
L-3 Communications
Leidos
Lockheed Martin
Northrop Grumman
Raytheon Intelligence Information and Services
Thales

HISTORICAL FINANCIALS

Company Type: Public

Income Statement

FYE: September 30

	REVENUE ($ mil.)	NET INCOME ($ mil.)	NET PROFIT MARGIN	EMPLOYEES
09/13	1,360.7	19.8	1.5%	8,200
09/12	1,381.5	91.9	6.7%	8,200
09/11	1,285.2	84.7	6.6%	7,800
09/10	1,194.1	70.6	5.9%	7,700
09/09	1,016.6	55.6	5.5%	7,400
Annual Growth	**7.6%**	**(22.8%)**	**—**	**2.6%**

2013 Year-End Financials

Debt ratio: 9.3%
Return on equity: 2.8%
Cash ($ mil.): 203
Current ratio: 2.86
Long-term debt ($ mil.): 102

No. of shares (mil.): 26
Dividends
  Yield: 0.4%
  Payout: 8.0%
Market value ($ mil.): 1,435

	STOCK PRICE ($) FY Close	P/E High/Low	PER SHARE ($) Earnings	Dividends	Book Value
09/13	53.68	73 55	0.74	0.24	26.36
09/12	50.06	15 11	3.44	0.24	25.07
09/11	39.07	18 12	3.17	0.28	20.65
09/10	40.80	16 12	2.64	0.18	18.26
09/09	39.47	20 9	2.08	0.18	15.74
Annual Growth	**8.0%**	**—**	**—(22.8%)**	**7.5%**	**13.8%**

Cubist Pharmaceuticals Inc.

Fighting infection is a modern art at Cubist Pharmaceuticals. The company develops antimicrobial agents to treat drug-resistant bacterial strains including methicillin-resistant Staphylococcus aureus (MRSA) typically found in hospitals and other health care institutions. Its flagship product Cubicin (daptomycin for injection) is an FDA-approved intravenous antibiotic to fight MRSA infections of the skin and blood. Cubist also markets Entereg a drug to speed patient recovery following bowel resection surgery in the US. Cubist's pipeline includes candidates in various stages of clinical and pre-clinical development.

Geographic Reach

The US accounts for more than 90% of Cubist's annual revenues. Outside the US its products are commercially available in more than 50 countries.

Operations

Third-party manufacturers produce the company's active ingredients and finished products. Cubist also outsources the warehousing and distribution of its products.

Cubicin has been the company's main source of revenue since its launch in 2003. With approval in more than 70 countries sales of the drug have climbed steadily over the years. Other products include Entereg a drug sold to hospitals in the US. Cubist has also co-promoted Optimer Pharmaceuticals' Dificid antibiotic for C. difficile associated diarrhea (CDAD) in the US through an agreement lasting until mid-2013. Anticipating the expiration of the agreement Cubist agreed to acquire Optimer in July 2013 and the purchase closed in October.

Sales and Marketing

The company uses its own hospital-focused sales force to market the drug in the US; internationally it relies upon distribution agreements with such companies as Novartis in Europe the Asia/Pacific region and certain Central American South American and Middle Eastern countries; Merck in Japan; and AstraZeneca in China and other countries; and more.

Major customers include wholesale distributors AmerisourceBergen Cardinal Health and McKesson. The three companies each account for about 20% of annual revenues.

Financial Performance

Cubist's revenues grew 23% to $926 million in 2012 primarily due to a 16% increase in sales of Cubicin in the US and a 38% increase in international Cubicin sales (through marketing partners). Entereg and Dificid sales also rose that year. Net income jumped 367% to $154 million due to higher revenues and interest income. While profits have alternated between growth and decline in recent years the company's revenues have steadily increased over the last five years.

Strategy

The company's primary growth strategy revolves around increasing sales of Cubicin and Entereg both in the US and internationally with the goal of achieving $2 billion in revenues by 2017. Cubicin's sales have increased over the years as Cubist has expanded promotional efforts and territories for the drug. It is also working to expand the number of approved indications for Cubicin.

Cubist also looks to grow by adding new product offerings through internal R&D programs as well as through occasional partnerships and acquisitions. For instance in 2011 it entered the Dificid co-promotion agreement with Optimer.

Cubist's own R&D pipeline includes several drug candidates in various stages of development including one aiming to treat CDAD an IV antibiotic candidate for multi-drug resistant gram-negative infections and pneumonia and a potential treatment for opioid-induced constipation (OIC). The company expanded its R&D capacity at its headquarters location during 2012 by opening a new research lab.

Mergers and Acquisitions

The company added its second commercial product Entereg in 2011 by acquiring struggling drug development firm Adolor. Adolor also had products under development including the OIC candidate in late-stage clinical trials. The $330 million deal included cash and shareholder contingent payment rights on drug candidates.

In 2013 it added the Dificid antibiotic through the $550 million purchase of Optimer Pharmaceu-

ticals. Cubist already marketed Dificid through a distribution agreement.

In 2013 the company entered an option agreement through which Cubist may acquire development firm Adynxx should the entity's lead pain medication reach certain development milestones.

Ownership

Investors include BlackRock which holds a 13% stake in the company and Wellington Management (11%).

EXECUTIVES

Senior Vice President; General Manager - International Business, Patrick Vink

Chief Executive Officer; Director, Michael W. (Mike) Bonney, age 54, $500,000 total compensation

Senior Vice President Scientific Affairs, Barry I. Eisenstein, age 64

SVP and CFO, David W. J. McGirr, age 58, $358,800 total compensation

Chairman, Kenneth M. (Ken) Bate, age 63

SVP Commercial Operations, Gregory (Greg) Stea, age 55

President and COO, Robert J. Perez, age 48, $430,011 total compensation

Senior Vice President Discovery and Pharmaceutical Sciences, Ronald (Ronnie) Farquhar

EVP Research and Development and Chief Scientific Officer, Steven C. (Steve) Gilman, age 60, $387,000 total compensation

SVP General Counsel and Secretary, Tamara L. Joseph, age 50

SVP Program and Portfolio Management, Thomas E. Rollins

Sr. Director - Investor Relations, Eileen C. McIntyre

Senior Vice President Corporate Development and Global Strategy, Praveen Tipirneni

SVP Technical Operations, Charles Laranjeira, age 47

SVP Public Affairs, Timothy D. Hunt

SVP and Deputy CFO, Michael Tomsicek

Senior Vice President Regulatory Affairs, Jennifer Jackson

Senior Vice President; General Counsel; Secretary, Thomas DesRosier

Director, Michael B. Wood, age 69

Director, Martin H. Soeters, age 59

President CEO and Director, Michael W. (Mike) Bonney, age 54

Director, Mark H. N. Corrigan, age 55

Director, J. Matthew (Matt) Singleton, age 61

Director, Martin Rosenberg, age 68

Director, Nancy J. Hutson, age 64

Director, Sylvie Gregoire, age 51

Director, Leon O. (Lonnie) Moulder Jr., age 55

Independent Director, Alison Lawton

Independent Director, Jane Henney

Auditors: PricewaterhouseCoopersLLP

LOCATIONS

HQ: Cubist Pharmaceuticals Inc.
65 Hayden Avenue, Lexington, MA 02421
Phone: 781 860-8660   **Fax:** 781 240-0256
Web: www.cubist.com

PRODUCTS/OPERATIONS

2012 Sales

	$ mil.	% of total
US products	849	92
Service	23	3
Total	**926**	**100**

Selected Products and Pipeline with Indications

Marketed products
Cubacin (daptomycin for injectioncertain gram-positive infections including MRSA)
Dificid (fidaxomicin with strategic partner Optimer - Clostridium difficile-associated diarrhea)
Entereg (alvimopan bowel resection surgery with primary anastomosis)

Clininical pipeline
Bevenopran (CB-5945 opioid-induced constipation)
Ceftolozane/tazobactam (CXA-201 licensed from Astellas Pharma Inc complicated urinary tract infection and complicated intra abdominal infection bacterial pneumonia)
Surotomycin (CB-315 C. diff-associated diarrhea)

COMPETITORS

Abbott Labs	Sanofi
Astellas Pharma	Shionogi & Co.
Eli Lilly	Tetraphase
Forest Labs	Teva
Hospira	The Medicines Company
Johnson & Johnson	Theravance
Merck	Trius Therapeutics
Pfizer	ViroPharma
Ranbaxy Laboratories	

HISTORICAL FINANCIALS

Company Type: Public

Income Statement

FYE: December 31

	REVENUE ($ mil.)	NET INCOME ($ mil.)	NET PROFIT MARGIN	EMPLOYEES
12/12	926.3	154.0	16.6%	762
12/11	753.9	33.0	4.4%	669
12/10	636.4	94.3	14.8%	638
12/09	562.1	79.6	14.2%	600
12/08	433.6	169.8	39.2%	554
Annual Growth	**20.9%**	**(2.4%)**	**—**	**8.3%**

2012 Year-End Financials

Debt ratio: 19.0%	No. of shares (mil.): 64
Return on equity: 17.1%	Dividends
Cash ($ mil.): 104	Yield: —
Current ratio: 4.48	Payout: —
Long-term debt ($ mil.): 367	Market value ($ mil.): 2,721

	STOCK PRICE ($) FY Close	P/E High/Low		PER SHARE ($) Earnings	Dividends	Book Value
12/12	42.05	21	16	2.10	0.00	15.31
12/11	39.62	75	39	0.52	0.00	12.77
12/10	21.40	16	12	1.55	0.00	11.18
12/09	18.97	18	10	1.36	0.00	8.12
12/08	24.16	9	6	2.56	0.00	5.43
Annual Growth	**14.9%**	**—**	**—**	**(4.8%)**	**—**	**29.6%**

Culp Inc.

Culp just wants to keep on ticking. The company is one of the world's largest makers of furniture upholstery fabrics and mattress fabrics (known as ticking). Culp delivers fashion-conscious stylish fabrics with broad appeal to some of the largest home furnishing retailers and manufacturers. Its upholstery fabrics include wovens (jacquards and dobbies) knits screen-prints and velvets (woven and tufted). Its fabrics are used in upholstering residential and commercial furniture such as recliners sofas and love seats. Culp's ticking is used for covering mattresses and box springs. US customers account for nearly 80% of sales.

Geographic Reach

Culp has manufacturing plants and distribution facilities in the US Canada China and Poland.

Sales and Marketing

Major customers include furniture makers La-Z-Boy Bassett and Furniture Brands International as well as mattress makers Sealy and Serta.

Financial Analysis

Culp reported a 17.4% increase in revenues in fiscal 2012 thanks to improved industry demand.

Despite the increase in net sales net income dropped by 18% in FY 2012 because of an increase in raw material costs in the mattress fabrics and upholstery fabrics segments and higher selling general and administrative expenses.

Strategy

The company's strategy includes investing heavily in its mattress fabric business restructuring its upholstery fabrics business to be more competitive and expanding in Europe.

One of the keys to Culp's success has been the shift of manufacturing activities from North America to China and Europe. It is continuing to expand manufacturing facilities in China where the company has operated since 2004. Chinese-made upholstery fabrics accounted for 85% of this segment sales in 2010 and 2011.

Culp is also diversifying its distribution network. In 2012 the company opened a distribution warehouse-cum-manufacturing location in Poznan Poland marking Culp's first entry into the European market. Culp has targeted Europe as its second largest sales territory outside the US.

Ownership

Chairman Robert G. Culp III (son of the founder) owns about 17% of the company; Scott Asen and related entities 12.5%.

HISTORY

A member of the American Furniture Hall of Fame Robert Culp Jr. developed the heat-transfer method of printing cloth and introduced tufting machinery for manufacturing velvet. In 1972 with his life savings and son Rob (Robert III) at his side he founded Culp Inc. as a fabric converter for the upholstered furniture industry. In 1979 it switched to manufacturing.

Culp went public in 1983 and that year purchased an upholstery operation from Cannon Mills. Culp retired as CEO in 1988 and as chairman two years later; his son replaced him in both positions.

The company increased its mattress-ticking production in 1991. In keeping with its acquisition and vertical-integration strategies Culp bought upholstery fabric maker Rossville/Chromatex in 1994 and Canadian fabric manufacturer Rayonese in 1995. The company was listed on the NYSE in 1996. The following year it acquired the fabrics division of High Point company Phillips Industries a maker of woven jacquards prints and velvets.

In 1998 Culp restructured as the upholstery market softened particularly among Culp's newest customers in Eastern Europe and Asia. That year Culp bought Artee Industries a yarn manufacturer.

Culp's sales along with much of its industry's slowed in 2000 in response to high interest rates and a cooling US economy. The company closed several plants and terminated employees as part of a restructuring plan in 2001. Further cuts were announced in 2002 when Culp exited its unprofitable wet printed flock upholstery fabrics operations. The following year Culp established manufactur-

ing and distribution operations in China to curb costs.

EXECUTIVES

President CEO and Director, Franklin N. Saxon, age 61, $266,667 total compensation
Chairman, Robert G. Culp III, age 66, $183,333 total compensation
President Culp Home Fashions, Robert G. Culp IV, age 42, $203,750 total compensation
VP CFO Treasurer and Corporate Secretary, Kenneth R. Bowling, age 51, $160,625 total compensation
Corporate Controller and Assistant Treasurer, Thomas B. Gallagher Jr., age 41, $127,500 total compensation
VP Human Resources, Teresa Huffman
President CEO and Director, Franklin N. Saxon, age 61
Director, Patrick B. Flavin, age 66
Director, Kenneth W. McAllister, age 64
Director, Kenneth R. (Ken) Larson, age 70
Auditors: GrantThorntonLLP

LOCATIONS

HQ: Culp Inc.
1823 Eastchester Dr., High Point NC 27265
Phone: 336-889-5161   **Fax:** 336-889-7246
Web: www.culpinc.com

2012 Sales

	$ mil.	% of total
North America		
US	200	79
Other countries	10	4
Far East/Asia	38	15
Other regions	5	2
Total	**254**	**100**

PRODUCTS/OPERATIONS

2012 Sales

	$ mil.	% of total
Mattress Fabrics	145	57
Upholstery Fabrics	108	43
Total	**254**	**100**

Selected Products

Mattress fabrics
  Knitted fabric
  Specialty
  Woven jacquards
Upholstery fabrics
  Suede fabrics
  Velvets
  Woven dobbies
  Woven jacquards

COMPETITORS

Bekaert Corp.
International Textile Group
Johnston Textiles
Milliken
Pharr Yarns
Standard Textile
Tietex
Titan Textile

HISTORICAL FINANCIALS

Company Type: Public

Income Statement

FYE: April 28

	REVENUE ($ mil.)	NET INCOME ($ mil.)	NET PROFIT MARGIN	EMPLOYEES
04/13	268.8	18.3	6.8%	1,205
04/12*	254.4	13.3	5.2%	1,114
05/11	216.8	16.1	7.5%	1,143
05/10	206.4	13.1	6.4%	1,085
05/09	203.9	(38.8)	—	1,047
Annual Growth	**7.1%**	**—**		**3.6%**

*Fiscal year change

2013 Year-End Financials

Debt ratio: 4.9%	No. of shares (mil.): 12
Return on equity: 19.9%	Dividends
Cash ($ mil.): 23	Yield: 0.0%
Current ratio: 2.69	Payout: 42.1%
Long-term debt ($ mil.): 4	Market value ($ mil.): 199

	STOCK PRICE ($) FY Close	P/E High/Low		PER SHARE ($) Earnings	Dividends	Book Value
04/13	16.25	12	6	1.47	0.62	7.82
04/12*	11.05	11	7	1.03	0.00	7.01
05/11	10.08	11	7	1.22	0.00	6.06
05/10	11.94	16	3	1.01	0.00	4.83
05/09	4.40	—	—	(3.07)	0.00	3.76
Annual Growth	**38.6%**	**—**		**—**		**20.1%**

*Fiscal year change

Cumberland Pharmaceuticals Inc

Cumberland Pharmaceuticals wants to make your search for the right drugs less cumbersome. The specialty pharmaceutical company focuses on acquiring developing and commercializing branded prescription drugs. Targeting the hospital acute care and gastroenterology segments Cumberland's FDA-approved drugs include Acetadote for the treatment of acetaminophen poisoning; Kristalose a prescription strength laxative; and Caldolor (nee Amelior) the first injectable dosage form of ibuprofen. The company also has several projects in early-stage development. Acetadote and Kristalose are marketed through Cumberland's own hospital and gastroenterology sales forces. The company went public in a mid-2009 IPO.

Cumberland's August 2009 public offering was based on a May 2007 filing. It intends to use proceeds from its public offering to fund potential acquisitions drug development programs and sales force expansion efforts including the commercial launch of Caldolor which was approved by the FDA earlier in 2009. Ramping up sales and marketing personnel to support Caldolor and IPO-related costs took a bite out of the company's net income and cash flow respectively for 2009.

Caldolor is designed as an alternative pain and fever treatment for patients unable to ingest oral medication. The product is marketed throughout the US by Cumberland's hospital sales group and internationally through marketing partners.

Acetadote stocked in hospitals nationwide is an injectable formulation of N-acetylcysteine (NAC) used to prevent or lessen potential liver damage resulting from acetaminophen overdose.

Prescription laxative Kristalose is a dry powder crystalline formulation of lactulose developed for the treatment of acute and chronic constipation. Cumberland acquired rights to market Kristalose in the US in 2006 when it signed a licensing agreement with Inalco S.p.A. of Italy and its US division Inalco Biochemicals. Cumberland previously co-promoted Kristalose through an agreement with the product's former owner Bertek Pharmaceuticals.

The company's early-stage product candidates which include a treatment for fluid buildup in cancer patients' lungs and an anti-infective for treating fungal infections in patients with weakened immune systems are developed by its majority-owned subsidiary Cumberland Emerging Technologies (CET). The subsidiary works with Vanderbilt University to commercialize products developed there.

In 2011 for example it acquired the rights to a molecule named ifetroban from Vanderbilt University. Cumberland intends to study ifetroban dubbed Hepatoren as a treatment for critically ill hospitalized patients suffering from progressive kidney failure due to cirrhosis of the liver. There is no drug approved in the US to treat the disease and Cumberland plans to develop Hepatoren as an orphan drug which would give the company seven years of marketing exclusivity. Bristol-Myers Squibb originally developed the molecule for cardiovascular indications and eventually donated it to Vanderbilt University.

EXECUTIVES

Director SVP and Medical Director, Gordon R. Bernard, age 61
SVP Chief Commercial Officer and Director, Martin E. Cearnal, age 68
SVP and Corporate Secretary, Jean W. Marstiller, age 63, $170,000 total compensation
SVP Operations, Leo Pavliv, age 52, $211,000 total compensation
Senior Director National Accounts and Corporate Compliance Officer, James L. Herman, age 58
Senior Director Regulatory and Scientific Affairs, Amy Dix Rock, age 42
Director Medical Affairs, Arthur P. (Art) Wheeler, age 56
Product Director, Barry L. Lee, age 55
Senior Manager SEC Reporting, Doug Jack, age 43
Vice President Chief Financial Officer, Rick S. Greene
Director SVP and Medical Director, Gordon R. Bernard, age 61
SVP Chief Commercial Officer and Director, Martin E. Cearnal, age 68
Director, Robert G. Edwards, age 85
Director, Thomas R. Lawrence, age 73
Director, Jonathan Griggs
Independent Director, Joey Jacobs
Auditors: KPMGLLP

LOCATIONS

HQ: Cumberland Pharmaceuticals Inc
2525 West End Avenue, Suite 950, Nashville, TN 37203
Phone: 615 255-0068
Web: www.cumberlandpharma.com

PRODUCTS/OPERATIONS

2009 Product Sales

	% of total
Acetadote	70
Kristalose	22
Caldolor	8
Total	**100**

COMPETITORS

Ben Venue	Roxane Laboratories
Cadence Pharmaceuticals	SkyePharma
	Sucampo
Hospira	Takeda Pharmaceutical
Merck	

HISTORICAL FINANCIALS

Company Type: Public

Income Statement

FYE: December 31

	REVENUE ($ mil.)	NET INCOME ($ mil.)	NET PROFIT MARGIN	EMPLOYEES
12/12	48.8	5.8	12.0%	106
12/11	51.1	5.6	11.1%	138
12/10	45.8	2.4	5.4%	131
12/09	43.5	3.0	7.1%	108
12/08	35.0	4.7	13.6%	59
Annual Growth	8.6%	5.2%	—	15.8%

2012 Year-End Financials

Debt ratio: 4.4%	No. of shares (mil.): 18
Return on equity: 6.9%	Dividends
Cash ($ mil.): 71	Yield: —
Current ratio: 10.83	Payout: —
Long-term debt ($ mil.): 4	Market value ($ mil.): 80

	STOCK PRICE ($) FY Close	P/E High/Low	Earnings	Dividends	PER SHARE ($) Book Value
12/12	4.20	26 14	0.30	0.00	4.53
12/11	5.38	24 17	0.28	0.00	4.14
12/10	5.99	119 39	0.12	0.00	3.82
12/09	13.59	77 54	0.17	0.00	3.68
Annual Growth	(32.4%)	— —	20.8%	—	7.2%

Cyberonics, Inc.

It may sound futuristic but Cyberonics is all about treating an age-old neurological disorder. The company is the maker of the first medical device to gain clearance from the FDA for treating epilepsy. Its Vagus Nerve Stimulation Therapy system (VNS Therapy) is a pacemaker-like device that is implanted under the collarbone with a lead that connects it to the vagus nerve in the neck. The device delivers intermittent signals to the brain to control epileptic seizures. Physicians can program the signals by computer and patients can start or stop signals with hand-held magnets. VNS Therapy is also used for treating depression that has been treatment-resistant. Cyberonics sells its systems worldwide.

Cyberonics employs a direct sales force in the US and in some European countries and it utilizes distributors elsewhere. Its marketing efforts target neurologists surgeons hospitals insurance companies and patients. The VNS Therapy system has been implanted in more than 72000 patients globally. The company relies on reimbursement from private and government insurance entities for more than three-fourths of its device sales; the Centers for Medicaid & Medicare (CMS) alone account for 25% of sales.

The company's dependence on insurance reimbursement means that shifts in CMS' standard rates which many other insurers follow have the potential to impact revenues in a positive or negative manner. At least that applies to the VNS Therapy system when it is used for treating epilepsy. Medicare has denied coverage for those seeking VNS Therapy for depression although some state Medicaid agencies cover it for depression as do a few private payers. Cyberonics has not given up obtaining more federal and private insurance coverage for VNS Therapy for depression and is engaged in further studies it hopes will convince Medicare and other third-party payers of its efficacy as a therapy for depression that is resistant to medication and other treatment efforts.

Cyberonics has facilities in Houston (manufacturing and corporate offices) and Austin Texas (warehousing and distribution) and administrative and sales offices in Europe China and Hong Kong. It is planning to build a second manufacturing plant in Costa Rica to provide for international markets. The plant is expected to be operational in fiscal year 2015.

In fiscal 2012 Cyberonics achieved net sales of $219 million representing a 15% increase from the $190 million it posted in 2010. The increase was due in large part to a 26% increase in international sales (on a constant currency basis) and a 13% increase in net epilepsy sales in the US. The company's income from operations increased 24% although its net income of $36 million represented an almost 23% decrease from 2011 mainly due to increased operating and other expenses.

As a result of its dependence on reimbursement for its financial health Cyberonics' strategic focus is on widening the use of its products through marketing research and technology enhancement efforts. The company also introduces next-generation versions of its VNS Therapy system. For example in 2011 its fifth-generation of VNS Therapy technology - the AspireHC generator (for use with the VNS Therapy system) - was approved and in fiscal 2012 the device was commercially launched. Each "next-generation" system is meant to incorporate greater functionality and ease of use. Improvements with the AspireHC version include longer battery life improved electronics and simplified programming features.

Other strategic initiatives for Cyberonics are increasing market penetration in the US and increasing international sales; sales outside the US grew to more than 15% of total product sales in 2012 with the largest markets being the UK France and Japan. The company also seeks opportunities for licensing its technology to third parties as an additional source of revenue.

EXECUTIVES

Chairman of the Board, Hugh M. Morrison, age 67
Senior Vice President Finance and Chief Financial Officer, Gregory H. (Greg) Browne, age 61, $275,957 total compensation
SVP Chief Administrative Officer and Secretary, David S. Wise, age 58, $252,404 total compensation
President and Chief Executive Officer, Daniel J. (Dan) Moore, age 53, $474,808 total compensation
VP Operations, Randal L. Simpson, age 54, $236,538 total compensation

SVP and Chief Commercial Officer, James A.
Reinstein, age 49, $298,393 total compensation
Senior VP Research & Development, Milton M.
Morris, age 43
VP Clinical Quality and Regulatory, Bryan D. Olin,
age 46
**VP Corporate Counsel Compliance Officer and
Assistant Secretary,** Darren W. Alch, age 46
VP Global Sales, Mark S. Verratti, age 45
VP Marketing and New Business Development,
Sherrie L. Perkins
VP Emerging Therapy, Bruce H. KenKnight, age 52
Senior Vice President - Strategic Planning, Rohan
Hoare
Director, Jon T. Tremmel, age 67
Director, Joseph E. (Joe) Laptewicz Jr., age 65
Director, Guy C. Jackson, age 71
President and Chief Executive Officer, Daniel J.
(Dan) Moore, age 53
Director, Alfred J. Novak, age 66
Director, Arthur J. Rosenthal, age 67
Auditors: KPMGLLP

LOCATIONS

HQ: Cyberonics Inc.
Cyberonics Building 100 Cyberonics Blvd., Houston
TX 77058-2072
Phone: 281-228-7200   **Fax:** 281-218-9332
Web: www.cyberonics.com

2012 Sales

	$ mil.	% of total
US	183	84
Other countries	35	16
Total	**218**	**100**

PRODUCTS/OPERATIONS

Selected VNS Therapy System Components

Equipment to assist with implant procedures
Equipment to assist treating physicians with setting the
stimulation parameters for each patient
Implantable pulse generator (provides stimulation to the
vagus nerve)
Lead (connects the generator to the vagus nerve)
Magnets (to manually suspend or induce stimulation on
a temporary basi
Other
Instruction manuals

COMPETITORS

Brainsway	Pfizer
Cephalon	Sanofi
EnteroMedics	Shire
GlaxoSmithKline	St. Jude Medical
Meda Pharmaceuticals	Taro
Medtronic	Teva
Novartis	UCB

HISTORICAL FINANCIALS

Company Type: Public

Income Statement

FYE: April 26

	REVENUE ($ mil.)	NET INCOME ($ mil.)	NET PROFIT MARGIN	EMPLOYEES
04/13	254.3	46.3	18.2%	581
04/12	218.5	36.0	16.5%	536
04/11	190.4	46.7	24.5%	484
04/10	167.7	78.4	46.8%	465
04/09	143.6	26.7	18.6%	440
Annual Growth	**15.4%**	**14.8%**	**—**	**7.2%**

2013 Year-End Financials

Debt ratio: —	No. of shares (mil.): 27
Return on equity: 22.5%	Dividends
Cash ($ mil.): 120	Yield: —
Current ratio: 7.14	Payout: —
Long-term debt ($ mil.): —	Market value ($ mil.): 1,181

	STOCK PRICE ($) FY Close	P/E High/Low		PER SHARE ($) Earnings	Dividends	Book Value
04/13	42.99	33	22	1.66	0.00	8.36
04/12	38.58	30	18	1.28	0.00	6.66
04/11	35.59	21	10	1.64	0.00	6.20
04/10	19.53	8	4	2.67	0.00	4.00
04/09	13.52	28	10	0.61	0.00	0.89
Annual Growth	**33.5%**	**—**	**—**	**28.4%**	**—**	**74.9%**

Darling International Inc.

A rather dainty name for a messy and stinky
business Darling International is the largest publicly traded rendering operation in the US; it collects and recycles animal by-products used cooking grease and bakery waste and offers grease-trap
cleaning services. It counts restaurants butcher
shops grocery stores and independent meat and
poultry processors among its customers. Darling's
rendering unit which accounts for most of its sales
produces yellow grease tallow and meat bone and
blood meal. The company sells its products nationwide and overseas to makers of soap rubber oils
pet and livestock feed and chemicals.

Geographic Reach

Texas-based Darling International rings up more
than 85% of its sales in the US. Export markets
include Mexico South America Asia the European
Union North Africa and the Pacific Rim. The company operates more than 120 processing and
transfer facilities in 42 US states.

Operations

Darling operates two business segments: Rendering (more than 80% of sales) and Bakery which
accounts for the rest. The company's rendering
business processes animal by-products and used
cooking oil into fats protein and hides. The Bakery operation collects bakery residual and used
cooking oil from poultry and meat processors commercial bakeries grocery stores butcher shops and
food service establishments and provides grease
trap cleaning services to many of the same establishments.

The company operates a fleet of trucks trailers
and railcars for collection of its raw materials.

Financial Performance

Darling International's 2012 sales dipped 5% vs.
2011 while net income fell 23% over the same period. The sale decline followed a banner year in
2011 when sales rose to nearly $1.8 billion vs.
about $723 million during 2010. The surge re-
sulted from the 2010 acquisition of Griffin Industries the largest purchase in Darling's history. Darling attributed the sale dip in 2012 to a sales
decline in its rendering segment. Price competition
from rivals to Darling's BFT (bleachable fancy tallow) and PG (poultry grease) products depressed
the company's pricing power. Results from the
bakery segment were about flat. Sales in the US

fell nearly 3% in 2012 vs. 2011 while foreign sales
toppled 20%.

Darling's profits have suffered in recent years
due to rising raw-material costs and high fuel
prices. Raw material availability has declined too
amid a weak economy coupled with a drop in US
meat consumption that caused the company's suppliers to reduce slaughter volume. Restaurant
grease volume dropped as well driven by fewer
consumers choosing to dine out.

Strategy

For Darling competition comes mostly from obtaining its raw materials. Large meat-packing companies usually handle their own rendering in-
house. As the meat industry has consolidated fewer
independent meat and poultry processors are left
from whom to collect scraps; however until the
economic recession Darling had been seeing
growth in its restaurant-services division even
though collecting spent grease from restaurants is
highly competitive. When it comes time to sell its
commodity-grade products Darling competes with
vegetable-oil producers as well as other rendering
operations.

Mergers and Acquisitions

Nevertheless Darling has remained true to its
growth through acquisition strategy. In 2012 it
purchased RVO BioPur a provider of grease trap
and used cooking oil collection services. RVO
BioPur's customers are primarily restaurants and
foodservice operators along the East coast. Although relatively small the acquisition followed
Darling's buyout of fellow rendering company Griffin Industries. It picked up the Kentucky-based
company in a deal valued at $840 million in late
2010. The purchase boosted the number of Darling's processing and transfer facilities to 120
adding Griffin's 55 locations that include a dozen
rendering plants about 10 bakery by-product
plants and a lone bio-diesel facility.

Prior to the Griffin buy Darling purchased the
Indiana and Ohio operations of rival renderer Sanimax in 2010. The deal included a number of Sanimax collection routes in Pennsylvania and the
lower part of Michigan. In mid-2010 the renderer
purchased Nebraska By-Products extending its
reach in Nebraska Kansas Colorado and South
Dakota.

EXECUTIVES

EVP and Co-COO, Neil Katchen, age 67, $269,000
total compensation
EVP and Chief Administrative Officer, John O.
Muse, $336,000 total compensation
EVP General Counsel and Secretary, John F.
Sterling, age 49, $258,000 total compensation
Chairman and CEO, Randall C. Stuewe, age 50,
$675,000 total compensation
VP Government Affairs and Technology, C. Ross
Hamilton
EVP and Co-COO, Martin W. Griffin
EVP and CFO, Colin Stevenson
President Griffin Industries, Robert Griffin
Director, John D. March, age 66
Director, Charles Macaluso, age 69
Director, O. Thomas Albrecht, age 66
Director, Michael Urbut, age 64
Director, Marlyn Jorgensen, age 72
Independent Director, Eugene Ewing
Independent Director, Michael Rescoe
Auditors: KPMGLLP

LOCATIONS

HQ: Darling International Inc.
251 O' Connor Ridge Blvd. Ste. 300, Irving TX 75038
Phone: 972-717-0300   **Fax:** 972-717-1588
Web: www.darlingii.com

2012 Sales

	$ mil.	% of total
Domestic	1,485	87
Foreign	216	13
Total	**1,701**	**100**

PRODUCTS/OPERATIONS

2012 Sales

	$ mil.	% of total
Rendering	1,406	83
Bakery	295	17
Total	**1,701**	**100**

Selected Subsidiaries

Craig Protein Division Inc.
Darling Green Energy LLC
Darling National LLC
Griffin Industries LLC

COMPETITORS

ADM
Ag Processing Inc.
Baker Commodities
Birchwood Meat &
  Provision
Maple Leaf Foods
North State Rendering
  Company
Prosper De Mulder
Restaurant
  Technologies
Sanimax
Smithfield Foods
Tyson Foods
Valley Proteins

HISTORICAL FINANCIALS

Company Type: Public

Income Statement

FYE: December 29

	REVENUE ($ mil.)	NET INCOME ($ mil.)	NET PROFIT MARGIN	EMPLOYEES
12/12	1,701.4	130.7	7.7%	3,400
12/11*	1,797.2	169.4	9.4%	3,320
01/11	724.9	44.2	6.1%	3,330
01/10	597.8	41.7	7.0%	1,820
01/09	807.4	54.5	6.8%	1,870
Annual Growth	20.5%	24.4%	—	16.1%

*Fiscal year change

2012 Year-End Financials

Debt ratio: 16.1%
Return on equity: 13.2%
Cash ($ mil.): 103
Current ratio: 2.20
Long-term debt ($ mil.): 250
No. of shares (mil.): 117
Dividends
Yield: —
Payout: —
Market value ($ mil.): 1,831

	STOCK PRICE ($) FY Close	P/E High/Low		PER SHARE ($) Earnings	Dividends	Book Value
12/12	15.54	17	12	1.11	0.00	9.02
12/11*	13.29	13	8	1.47	0.00	7.86
01/11	13.28	26	13	0.53	0.00	5.02
01/10	8.38	16	6	0.51	0.00	3.46
01/09	5.93	26	5	0.66	0.00	2.89
Annual Growth	27.2%	—	—	13.9%	—	32.9%

*Fiscal year change

Datalink Corp

Datalink builds and implements high-end custom-designed data storage systems for large corporations. Its storage systems include disk- and tape-based storage devices storage networking components and data management software. The company employs an open-system standard building networks from products made by leading manufacturers such as Brocade EMC and Hitachi Data Systems. Datalink also provides ongoing support and maintenance services. The company markets its products directly to customers in the US. It has designed systems for clients including AT&T Harris Corporation NAVTEQ and St. Jude Medical. It has about 30 locations across the US.

Datalink is rolling out new products and services to address the booming data center market that is being fueled by increased outsourcing of corporate data storage application hosting and other IT services by enterprises in a variety of industries. In 2012 the company added managed monitoring services tailored for data centers with a need to outsource some of their own processes such as systems monitoring alerting problem identification and performance analysis. Also that year Datalink introduced a new managed backup service intended to free up the in-house IT resources of enterprise clients. The company offers its own technical staff to relieve corporate IT departments from day-to-day data backup activities.

Datalink builds its service expertise and geographic presence through acquisitions. In 2012 it bought North Carolina IT services firm Strategic Technologies (StraTech) for about $13 million; StraTech expands Datalink's presence in the eastern US.

In 2011 the company bought Minneapolis-based Midwave in a $17.6 million cash and stock deal. The addition of Midwave's data center and IT infrastructure services increased Datalink's presence in the Midwest and doubled its Cisco-related revenue and consulting services team.

In 2009 the company bought the networking division of Minneapolis-based Cross Telecom for $2 million; the deal expanded Datalink's expertise in designing implementing and managing network storage and backup products. It also acquired IT systems distributor and managed services provider Incentra for $8.8 million in cash that year. The deal boosted the company's profile in Chicago and the Northeast as well as in several western states.

Datalink pushed it profits up more than 400% in 2011 on sales growth of about 30%. The acquisition of Midwave drove product revenue while sales of services increased mainly due to higher demand for customer support contracts and installation and configuration services. Meanwhile Datalink's operating expenses increased in several areas particularly sales and marketing.

Chairman and former CEO Greg Meland owns about 10% of Datalink.

HISTORY

Founded in 1963 as Stan Clothier Datalink was originally a manufacturers' representative for technology products and components. Its name change to Datalink in 1987 reflected the company's growing role as a distributor of data storage products. Datalink opened a Chicago office in 1989 and expanded beyond the Midwest in 1992 with an office in Seattle. Greg Meland formerly the company's VP of sales was named president and CEO in 1993.

In 1995 with the introduction of its DataCare program the company began to reposition itself as a provider of information management services rather than strictly a value-added distributor. Two years later Datalink began offering its consulting services to customers in the information management industry.

In 1998 Datalink initiated an IPO which it later withdrew. That year the company expanded throughout the US opening offices in Massachusetts New Jersey and California and adding five offices in the Southeast US with the acquisition of Georgia-based rival Direct Connect Systems. Datalink successfully went public in 1999. Its expansion continued in 2000 with additional offices opening in North Carolina and Oregon. In 2001 the company moved its headquarters from Edina Minnesota to Chanhassen a Minneapolis suburb.

Datalink raised more than $5 million in a 2002 private placement of stock with institutional investors buying the shares.

Charlie Westling previously the company's VP of market development was promoted to president and COO in 2003 (he joined Datalink in 2001) and was named CEO of the company in 2005; Meland was made chairman. Director Paul Lidsky took over as CEO in 2009.

Datalink expanded its operations by acquiring systems integrator Midrange Computer Solutions for $14 million in 2007. The purchase extended Datalink's operations in the northeastern and midwestern regions as well as in California.

EXECUTIVES

VP Administration CFO and Secretary, Gregory T. Barnum, age 58, $214,225 total compensation
President CEO and Director, Paul F. Lidsky, age 59
Chief Technology Officer, Scott D. Robinson, age 53
Chairman, Greg R. Meland, age 59, $104,184 total compensation
Vice Chairman, James E. (Jim) Ousley, age 67
Executive Vice President - Field Operations, Shawn O'Grady, age 50
Vice President of technical services, Tom Sylvester
Executive Vice President - Field Operations, Shawn Grady
Executive Vice President - Field Operations, Shawn OGrady
President CEO and Director, Paul F. Lidsky, age 59
Director, Robert M. Price Jr., age 82
Vice Chairman, James E. (Jim) Ousley, age 67
Director, Margaret A. Loftus, age 68
Director, Brent G. Blackey, age 54
Director, J. Patrick O'Halloran, age 55
Independent Director, Patrick Halloran
Independent Director, Patrick OHalloran
Auditors: McGladreyLLP

LOCATIONS

HQ: Datalink Corp
10050 Crosstown Circle, Suite 500, Eden Prairie, MN 55344
Phone: 952 944-3462   **Fax:** 952 944-7869
Web: www.datalink.com

PRODUCTS/OPERATIONS

2012 Sales

	$ mil.	% of total
Products	319	65
Services	172	35
Total	**491**	**100**

Selected Services
Advanced Services
Architecture & Deployment
Capacity Services
Cloud Enablement Services
Cloud Service Management
Data Center Transformation
Managed Services
Reporting & Management
Residency Services
Support Services

COMPETITORS

Cranel	IBM
Dell	InterVision Systems
Dot Hill	Technologies
EMC	NetApp
Forsythe Technology	Presidio Inc.
Fujitsu	Qualstar
Hewlett-Packard	Sirius Computer
Hitachi Data Systems	Solutions

HISTORICAL FINANCIALS

Company Type: Public

Income Statement

FYE: December 31

	REVENUE ($ mil.)	NET INCOME ($ mil.)	NET PROFIT MARGIN	EMPLOYEES
12/12	491.2	10.5	2.1%	459
12/11	380.0	9.8	2.6%	389
12/10	293.6	2.3	0.8%	299
12/09	178.0	(0.5)	—	307
12/08	195.6	3.4	1.7%	208
Annual Growth	25.9%	32.7%	—	21.9%

2012 Year-End Financials

Debt ratio: 1.6%	No. of shares (mil.): 18
Return on equity: 11.9%	Dividends
Cash ($ mil.): 10	Yield: —
Current ratio: 1.15	Payout: —
Long-term debt ($ mil.): —	Market value ($ mil.): 160

	STOCK PRICE ($) FY Close	P/E High/Low		PER SHARE ($) Earnings	Dividends	Book Value
12/12	8.55	18	12	0.60	0.00	5.09
12/11	8.26	17	7	0.61	0.00	4.48
12/10	4.67	27	16	0.18	0.00	3.50
12/09	4.33	—	—	(0.04)	0.00	3.27
12/08	3.20	23	9	0.27	0.00	3.29
Annual Growth	27.9%	—	—	22.1%	—	11.6%

DCP Midstream Partners LP

DCP Midstream Partners is the publicly traded entity of DCP Midstream LLC one of the largest natural gas gatherers in North America and also the top producer and one of the primary marketers of natural gas liquids (NGLs). It also engages in natural gas compressing treating processing transporting and selling. DCP Midstream LLC also transports and sells NGLs and distributes propane wholesale. The company operates natural gas gathering systems (5300 miles of pipe) in eight states (including Arkansas Louisiana Oklahoma and Texas) seven processing plants four NGL

pipelines and nine propane storage terminals. Spectra Energy holds a 50% holding in DCP (ConocoPhillips holds the other 50%).

A consolidator in the fragmented natural gas gathering NGLs and wholesale propane industry segments the company has been expanding its gas supply base and its propane wholesale network in recent years through strategic complementary acquisitions and joint ventures.

In 2012 DCP Midstream Partners acquired the Texas-based Crossroads processing plant and gathering system from Penn Virginia Resource Partners for $63 million. The bolt-on acquisition allows the company to expand its market position in East Texas and provide services to drillers in the Haynesville shale and Cotton Valley regions.

In 2011 DCP Midstream Partners acquired the Seaway Products Pipeline Co. from ConocoPhillips. The pipeline now called Southern Hills Pipeline and being converted to NGL service is expected to be operational by mid-2013. It will provide NGL access from the Midcontinent to the Texas Gulf Coast.

The company agreed to form a joint venture with EQT Corporation to develop natural gas processing and related natural gas liquid (NGL) infrastructure in the Marcellus and Huron shale plays in the Appalachian basin. (However the parties could not come to agreement and dropped the plan in early 2011). In 2010 the company acquired the Liberty gathering system and south Raywood processing plant from Ceritas Energy in southeast Texas. The pipeline system interconnects with DCP Midstream's Centana Intrastate Pipeline system.

Expanding in Michigan in 2009 the company acquired gas gathering and treating assets for $45.1 million. In 2010 it acquired a 350-mile interstate natural gas liquids pipeline system in Colorado's Denver-Julesburg Basin from Buckeye Partners for $22 million.

In 2010 DCP Midstream Partners moved to extend its Northeast wholesale propane business into the MidAtlantic region acquiring UGI's Atlantic Energy for $49 million. That year it also purchased of NGL storage company Marysville Hydrocarbon Holdings (in Michigan) for about $95 million.

Although DCP Midstream Partners' revenues suffered in 2009 as a result of the global recession and lower commodity prices acquisitions and organic growth managed to offset lower natural gas volumes. Acquisitions increased demand higher commodity and propane prices and gains on derivatives help to lift the company's revenues and net income in 2010.

In terms of the company's origins the D in DCP Midstream Partners (formerly Duke Energy Field Services) is for Duke Energy; the CP ConocoPhillips. These two energy majors formed DCP Midstream Partners in 2005. Following the spinoff of Spectra Energy from Duke Energy in 2007 Spectra Energy assumed Duke Energy's 50% holding in DCP.

EXECUTIVES

President CEO and Director, Mark A. Borer, age 59, $386,058 total compensation
SVP and CFO, Rose M. Robeson, age 51
Chairman, Thomas C. (Tom) O'Connor, age 58
Vice President; General Counsel; Secretary of DCP Midstream GP; LLC, Michael S. Richards, age 53, $195,673 total compensation
VP-Bus Dev, Greg K. Smith, age 46
VP Natural Gas and NGL Marketing DCP Midstream LLC, Don Baldridge, age 43, $182,077 total compensation
Investor Relations, Jonni Anwar

Chairman of the Board of DCP Midstream GP; LLC, Thomas OConnor
President, William (Bill) Waldheim
CEO, Wouter van Kempen
Director, Paul F. Ferguson Jr., age 63
President CEO and Director, Mark A. Borer, age 59
Director, Frank A. McPherson, age 79
Director, Stephen R. Springer, age 66
Director, Thomas C. Morris, age 72
Auditors: Deloitte&ToucheLLP

LOCATIONS

HQ: DCP Midstream Partners LP
370 17th Street, Suite 2500, Denver, CO 80202
Phone: 303 633-2900
Web: www.dcppartners.com

PRODUCTS/OPERATIONS

2010 Sales

	$ mil.	% of total
Natural gas services	778	61
Wholesale propane logistics	473	37
NGL logistics	17	2
Total	**1,269**	**100**

COMPETITORS

BP NGL	Magellan Midstream
Crestwood Midstream Partners LP	Martin Midstream Partners
Dynegy	SandRidge Energy
El Paso Corporation	Williams Companies
Enterprise Products	XTO Energy
Kinder Morgan	

HISTORICAL FINANCIALS

Company Type: Public

Income Statement

FYE: December 31

	REVENUE ($ mil.)	NET INCOME ($ mil.)	NET PROFIT MARGIN	EMPLOYEES
12/12	1,720.7	168.0	9.8%	7
12/11	1,569.8	100.4	6.4%	6
12/10	1,269.5	48.0	3.8%	7
12/09	942.4	(19.1)	—	9
12/08	1,285.8	125.7	9.8%	10
Annual Growth	7.6%	7.5%	—	(8.5%)

2012 Year-End Financials

Debt ratio: 54.5%	No. of shares (mil.): 61
Return on equity: —	Dividends
Cash ($ mil.): 1	Yield: 6.3%
Current ratio: 1.32	Payout: 116.6%
Long-term debt ($ mil.): 1,620	Market value ($ mil.): 2,561

	STOCK PRICE ($) FY Close	P/E High/Low		PER SHARE ($) Earnings	Dividends	Book Value
12/12	41.75	22	16	2.28	2.66	17.08
12/11	47.47	27	20	1.72	2.52	14.01
12/10	37.40	43	32	0.86	2.42	12.80
12/09	29.57	—	—	(0.99)	2.40	10.91
12/08	9.40	14	2	3.25	2.36	11.66
Annual Growth	45.2%	—	—	(8.5%)	3.0%	10.0%

Dealertrack Technologies, Inc.

DealerTrack keeps auto dealers lenders and OEMs on track with its Web-based software and services. Using a Software-as-a-Service (SaaS) model the company offers a suite of dealer management system (DMS) vehicle inventory management and merchandising sales and financing compliance and processing (including e-registration and titling application) tools that provide real-time on-demand data for auto dealers to operate more efficiently and cost effectively. DealerTrack also operates the largest online credit application network in the US and Canada.

Geographic Reach

DealerTrack operates in the US and Canada. It derives more than 90% of its revenue from the US.

Operations

The company operates through a number of subsidiaries including DealerTrack AAX Dealer-Track Aftermarket Services DealerTrack Canada DealerTrack Digital Services and DealerTrack Processing Solutions.

Sales & Marketing

DealerTrack primarily sells to franchised and independent auto dealers through subscription agreements. It also sells to a network of lenders including national and regional lenders local banks and credit unions primarily through transactional agreements that run for two years with extension options. Other client pools include aftermarket providers OEMs and other service and information providers.

Financial Analysis

In 2011 DealerTrack's transaction services revenues turned the tables on subscription revenues increasing more than 80% over the previous year to become the dominant segment with more than half of sales. About 70% of that increase came from the company's acquisition of online vehicle titling and registration software provider TriVIN (now DealerTrack Processing Solutions) for $131 million early in the year. DealerTrack's interest was in TriVIN's FDI Collateral Management business which provides electronic lien and title information used to manage vehicles held as collateral.

The rest of the transaction segment's growth came mainly from improved credit availability through its application processing network (about 50% more transactions were processed during the year) a rise in automobile sales and adding Ally to its US network. Customers in Canada had been offered only the credit application and contract processing products but recently DealerTrack has opened up a selection of its subscription products to those clients.

Its subscription revenues climbed nearly 20% on the strength of a nearly 15% increase in subscribing dealers (now at more than 17000) in its network and a nearly 10% increase in average monthly subscription revenue per dealer. Its 2011 acquisition of eCarList a provider of online real-time inventory management and merchandising tools for car dealerships was offset by the divestiture of its ALG subsidiary. ALG was a provider of data about automobile residual values and its sale to TrueCar included a license for DealerTrack to continue using services provided by ALG.

Strategy

The company's growth strategy has included shifting its sales emphasis from individual products to integrated offerings. DealerTrack continues to expand its customer network targeting regional banks credit unions and financing and insurance companies. It also hopes to capitalize on cross-selling opportunities to its dealer customers and its network of lenders.

Mergers & Acquisitions

DealerTrack continues to grow through acquisitions. In 2013 it acquired Louisiana's largest provider of electronic vehicle registration lien and title services Auto Title Express for $21 million. The prior year the company bought 1st Auto Transport Directory a Web-based system for scheduling vehicle transportation and shipping. The $74 million transaction expands DealerTrack's offerings for the automotive retail market with products such as CentralDispatch.com (a subscription network used to facilitate vehicle transport); jTracker.com (a CRM and lead management tools for transportation brokers); and MoveCars.com (online advertising directories for the vehicle transportation industries).

The company bought technology from R. L. Polk & Co. during the year that allows dealerships to offer vehicle comparisons. Polk's US Price and Spec business also includes AutositePro a price and specification application used by OEM marketers for competitive analysis. The Price and Spec business became part of DealerTrack's Chrome Systems subsidiary.

EXECUTIVES

President of DealerTrack, Vincent Passione, age 52

SVP Sales Marketing and International, Rick G. Von Pusch, age 52

Chairman of the Board; President; Chief Executive Officer, Mark F. O'Neil, age 54, $525,000 total compensation

Chief Financial Officer, Eric D. Jacobs, age 47, $278,500 total compensation

CEO Automotive Lease Guide, John A. Blair, age 52, $260,000 total compensation

Senior Vice President - Human Resources, Ana M. Herrera, age 56

EVP and Group President Dealer Solutions, Rajesh (Raj) Sundaram, age 47, $278,500 total compensation

Chief Information Officer; Senior Vice President, Richard McLeer, age 49

VP Aftermarket Network Solutions, Hugh Abernethy, age 53

VP-Lender Solutions, Mark Brown, age 56

VP Finance Solutions, Alan Lehmann, age 54

EVP and Group President Lender Solutions, Mark Furcolo

Secretary, Gary Papilsky

Senior Director and General Manager DealerTrack Inventory Optimization DealerTrack Inc., Bridget Townsend, age 39

Senior Vice President - Processing Solutions Group, Mark Furcolo

Chairman President Chief Executive Officer, Mark ONeil

Senior Vice President - Sales; Marketing and International, Rick Pusch

Director, James D. (Jim) Foy, age 66

Director, John McDonnell Jr., age 75

Director, Howard L. Tischler, age 59

Director, Barry Zwarenstein, age 64

Director, Mary A. Cirillo-Goldberg, age 65

Director, James David Power III, age 81

Director, Ann B. Lane, age 58

Auditors: PricewaterhouseCoopersLLP

LOCATIONS

HQ: DealerTrack Technologies Inc.
1111 Marcus Ave. Ste. M04, Lake Success NY 11042
Phone: 516-734-3600   **Fax:** 516-734-3809
Web: www.dealertrack.com

2011 Sales

	% of total
US	91
Canada	9
Total	**100**

PRODUCTS/OPERATIONS

2011 Sales

	$ mil.	% of total
Transaction services	184	52
Subscription services	146	42
Other	21	6
Total	**353**	**100**

COMPETITORS

ADP	Experian
American Honda Finance	Microsoft Dynamics
Arkona	Reynolds and Reynolds
AutoSoft	RouteOne
Compli	TransUnion
Equifax	

HISTORICAL FINANCIALS

Company Type: Public

Income Statement
FYE: December 31

	REVENUE ($ mil.)	NET INCOME ($ mil.)	NET PROFIT MARGIN	EMPLOYEES
12/12	388.8	20.4	5.3%	2,000
12/11	353.2	65.1	18.4%	1,900
12/10	243.8	(27.8)	—	1,200
12/09	225.6	(4.3)	—	1,200
12/08	242.7	1.7	0.7%	1,100
Annual Growth	12.5%	85.3%	—	16.1%

2012 Year-End Financials

Debt ratio: 17.8%	No. of shares (mil.): 42
Return on equity: 3.8%	Dividends
Cash ($ mil.): 143	Yield: —
Current ratio: 2.93	Payout: —
Long-term debt ($ mil.): 162	Market value ($ mil.): 1,231

	STOCK PRICE ($) FY Close	P/E High/Low		PER SHARE ($) Earnings	Dividends	Book Value
12/12	28.72	66	50	0.46	0.00	13.33
12/11	27.26	18	9	1.53	0.00	11.82
12/10	20.07	—	—	(0.69)	0.00	10.05
12/09	18.79	—	—	(0.11)	0.00	10.41
12/08	11.89	837	229	0.04	0.00	9.95
Annual Growth	24.7%	—	—	84.2%	—	7.6%

Deckers Outdoor Corp.

There's no business like the specialty shoe business for Deckers Outdoor. It designs and markets the iconic UGG brand of luxury sheepskin footwear (58% of sales) and Teva sports sandals —a cross between a hiking boot and a flip-flop used for walking hiking and rafting among other pursuits. Other product lines include Simple TSUBO MOZO and

Ahnu. While imitations flood the market the company distinguishes UGG and Teva from its competitors by avoiding distribution in off-price outlets. Deckers Outdoor's products are made by independent contractors in Asia Australia and New Zealand. The company sells its footwear through about 105 retail stores worldwide independent distributors catalogs and online.

Geographic Reach

Deckers Outdoors boasts a global presence with a foothold in the US Canada Australia Europe Japan and China.

Operations

The company which generates about 69% of its sales in the US boasts manufacturing operations in Asia Australia and New Zealand. Deckers Outdoors sells its products through several channels one of which includes company-owned retail shops that it operates worldwide. Its e-commerce business consists of Uggaustralia.com Teva.com Sanuk.com Tsubo.com Ahnu.com and Mozoshoes.com.

Sales and Marketing

The footwear firm markets its products under three primary brand names: UGG Teva and Sanuk. The UGG brand is one of the industry's most recognized shoe brands. Other brands include TSUBO Ahnu MOZO and Hoka. Deckers Outdoors sells its products through both domestic and international retailers international distributors and directly to end-user customers worldwide. It also uses websites call centers retail concept stores and retail outlets stores to get its products in consumers' hands.

In recent years Deckers Outdoors has increased its investment in advertising to boost brand awareness spending $78.5 million in 2012 up incrementally from $57.2 million in 2011 and $33.1 million in 2010.

Customers include Nordstrom Neiman Marcus Bloomingdale's Dillard's Zappos.com REI Dick's Sporting Goods and The Sports Authority among others. The company's five largest customers accounted for some 23% of its net sales in 2012 compared to 24% in 2011 and 29% in 2010.

Financial Performance

Thanks primarily to its UGG footwear business and its newer Sanuk brand of footwear Deckers Outdoor logged a 3% increase in revenue in fiscal 2012. The UGG shoe unit itself accounted for an impressive 58% of sales. Overall the company sold more UGG brand shoes through its retail and e-commerce channels and gained traction with sales of its Sanuk footwear label. To note Deckers Outdoors posted a 4% increase in footwear volumes for all brands and channels resulting in 23.7 million pairs sold in 2012 vs. 22.8 million pairs sold in 2011.

The company's revenue increases were eroded by a 35% decrease in profit due to the cost of sales; selling general and administrative expenses; and Internet expense.

Mergers and Acquisitions

With its Teva shoe business sliding Deckers Outdoor has been working to fill the gap. To that end in 2011 it acquired the Sanuk brand of sport footwear which is sold in the US Canada and Europe. Valued at roughly $120 million the purchase is expected to enhance the company's design capabilities and strengthen demand in North America and abroad. Previous acquisitions include the Ahnu brand (2009) and TSUBO (2008).

Strategy

While it continues to hone its UGG business to further boost sales Deckers Outdoor continues to develop its heritage Teva brand. Pleased that the brand survived the downturn in the economy

Deckers Outdoor has expanded the Teva product line in both performance and lifestyle markets and introduced shoes at several price points to attract additional men women and children who might be lured away by rival brands such as Chaco and other shoes owned by Wolverine World Wide.

Deckers Outdoors's flagship UGG brand hit the ground running and has remained a cash cow thanks to high-end retailers and China. Positioning the UGG sheepskin boot as upscale the company sells the brand mostly through high-end retailers. UGGs also sell through Neiman Marcus and Zappos.com. The shoe company's joint venture agreement with Stella International Holdings (inked in 2008) has been key for the increase. The venture is 51%-owned by Deckers Outdoor; Stella a major manufacturer for the company in China owns the rest. As a result the UGG brand has secured a foothold in China where Deckers Outdoor has begun to open retail stores and distribute its products as a wholesaler. Soon after the venture was formed the company opened its first UGG Australia-branded concept store in Beijing.

Company Background

A continuing rise in UGG sales has extended debates over whether the name is generic or a trademark that could possibly be defended over international boundaries. Australian makers of the sheepskin boots traditionally called uggs contend that the name is generic akin to trying to protect the name "sneaker" as a trademark.

HISTORY

Douglas Otto and his former partner Karl Lopker founded Styled Steers in 1973. But the small obscure maker of leather sandals gained prominence with a line of multicolored rubber sandals. Surfers in Hawaii called them "deckers" and the company soon adopted the name. In 1985 Deckers Outdoor licensed Teva from river guide Mark Thatcher who invented the Teva strapping system for rafters to ensure sandals remained attached in turbulent waters. Teva sport sandals became a popular form of casual footwear largely through word of mouth. The company is the exclusive licensee of Teva shoes the design of which Thatcher has defended repeatedly against would-be copycats.

In 1994 Deckers Outdoor expanded the Teva line to include closed footwear. With the popularity of Teva sandals seemingly on the wane the next year it diversified acquiring rival shoe companies Alp Sport Sandals and UGG Holdings and expanding into the women's and children's markets. A glut of sports sandals depressed sales the following year but with new products and new marketing Teva sales increased in 1997.

That year targeting international expansion the company acquired German distribution rights to Simple shoes from Vision Warenhandels. Also in 1997 Deckers Outdoor sold its interest in Trukke Winter Sports Products to focus on its core lines.

Thatcher settled with Wal-Mart Stores in 1998 after suing the company over patent and copyright infringement. The firm exited the manufacturing business that year and turned production over to suppliers mainly in China. In mid-1999 Deckers Outdoor renewed its license with Thatcher through 2011. Continuing to divest noncore operations in 2000 the company sold its 50% interest in Heirlooms the makers of the Picante line. The company also hired an ex-adidas exec to help increase Teva's global business (26% in 1999).

In 2000 Otto gave up the president in his title to Peter Benjamin who was charged with rejuvenating and giving each brand more individualized

marketing. In 2001 sales slumped nearly 20% due in part to the weak economy and a bankruptcy filing by one of Deckers Outdoor's largest customers Track n' Trail.

The company purchased Teva's total assets from its inventor and trademarks and patents holder Mark Thatcher in November 2002.

In 2004 Deckers inked licensing agreements for the manufacture of UGG handbags and outerwear as well as gloves hats and scarves. The same year the company signed a separate licensing deal with RMP Athletic Locker for the manufacture of Teva sportswear.

In April 2005 Angel Martinez a former Reebok executive was named president and CEO of the company. (Doug Otto retained his position as chairman of the board.) Martinez became chairman of the board in May 2008.

Continued acquisitions and joint ventures have enabled Deckers Outdoor to ride out the recession that began in 2008.

EXECUTIVES

President Europe Middle East and Africa, Stephen M. (Steve) Murray, age 53
President Deckers Asia-Pacific, Peter K. (Pete) Worley, age 52, $225,000 total compensation
Chairman President and CEO, Angel R. Martinez, age 57, $750,000 total compensation
CFO, Thomas A. George, age 58
COO, Zohar Ziv, age 60, $375,000 total compensation
President UGG Australia, Constance X. (Connie) Rishwain, age 55, $300,000 total compensation
Director PR and Corporate Communications, Errin Cecil-Smith
Vice President Consumer Direct, John A. Kalinich, age 46, $173,000 total compensation
SVP Emerging Brands, Colin G. Clark, age 50, $250,000 total compensation
Senior Vice President Supply Chain, Mark N. Fegley
Chief Human Resources Officer, Graciela Montgomery
President Teva, Joel Heath
President Ahnu and TSUBO, Jim Van Dine
Chief Marketing Officer, Jessica Buttimer
VP Information Technology, Yul Vanek
President Sanuk, Jake Brandman
Vice President IT K-Swiss, Charlotte Russe
Vice President Retail Operations, George Troy
President, Jim Dine
Director of Operations, Ahnu Footwear
IR Contact, Brendon Frey
President Global Direct to Consumer, Dave Powers
Director, Michael F. (Mike) Devine III, age 55
Director, Rex A. Licklider, age 70
Director, Ruth M. Owades, age 64
Director, John M. Gibbons, age 64
Director, John G. Perenchio, age 57
Director, Maureen Conners, age 66
Director, Karyn O. Barsa, age 52
Independent Director, James Quinn
Independent Director, Lauri Shanahan
Auditors: KPMGLLP

LOCATIONS

HQ: Deckers Outdoor Corporation
495-A S. Fairview Ave., Goleta CA 93117
Phone: 805-967-7611   **Fax:** 805-967-7862
Web: www.deckers.com

2012 Sales

	$ mil.	% of total
US	973	69
International	441	31
Total	**1,414**	**100**

PRODUCTS/OPERATIONS

2012 Sales

	$ mil.	% of total
UGG wholesale	819	58
Retail stores	245	17
Teva wholesale	108	8
eCommerce	130	9
Sanuk wholesale	89	6
Other brands wholesale	20	2
Total	**1,414**	**100**

Selected Mergers and Acquisitions

FY2011
Sanuk ($120 million sport footwear sold in the US Canada and Europe)

FY2009
Ahnu (active footwear sold in the US)

FY2008
TSUBO (ergonomic sport and casual shoes boots sandals and heels sold in the US Canada France Australia and Japan)

Selected Brands

Ahnu
MOZO
Sanuk
Simple Shoes
Teva
TSUBO
UGG Australia

COMPETITORS

Birkenstock USA	NIKE
C&J Clark	North Face
Cole Haan	PUMA SE
Columbia Sportswear	Patagonia Inc.
Converse	Phoenix Footwear
Crocs	Quiksilver
Diesel SpA	R. Griggs
Fila USA	Rocky Brands
Guess?	Skechers U.S.A.
Jimlar	Steven Madden
K-Swiss	Timberland
Keds	Vans
Kenneth Cole	Wolverine World Wide
L.L. Bean	adidas
LaCrosse Footwear	

HISTORICAL FINANCIALS

Company Type: Public

Income Statement

FYE: December 31

	REVENUE ($ mil.)	NET INCOME ($ mil.)	NET PROFIT MARGIN	EMPLOYEES
12/12	1,414.4	128.8	9.1%	2,300
12/11	1,377.2	199.0	14.5%	1,900
12/10	1,000.9	158.2	15.8%	1,500
12/09	813.1	116.7	14.4%	1,000
12/08	689.4	73.9	10.7%	780
Annual Growth	**19.7%**	**14.9%**	**—**	**31.0%**

2012 Year-End Financials

Debt ratio: 3.0%
Return on equity: 16.3%
Cash ($ mil.): 110
Current ratio: 2.59
Long-term debt ($ mil.): —

No. of shares (mil.): 34
Dividends
  Yield: —
  Payout: —
Market value ($ mil.): 1,385

	STOCK PRICE ($) FY Close	P/E High/Low		PER SHARE ($) Earnings	Dividends	Book Value
12/12	40.27	26	8	3.45	0.00	21.48
12/11	75.57	23	14	5.07	0.00	21.60
12/10	79.74	40	11	4.03	0.00	16.93
12/09	101.72	35	13	2.96	0.00	12.73
12/08	79.87	82	26	1.87	0.00	9.79
Annual Growth	**(15.7%)**	**—**	**—**	**16.6%**	**—**	**21.7%**

Delta Apparel Inc.

Delta Apparel's wares are a wardrobe basic: the t-shirt. The company manufactures knitted cotton and polyester/cotton t-shirts tank tops sweatshirts and caps for screen printers. Through subsidiary M.J. Soffe Delta Apparel also designs makes and sells branded and private-label activewear apparel to mainly to US distributors sporting goods and specialty stores mass merchants traditional and upscale department stores the US military college bookstores and online. The company's garments are finished at plants in North Carolina and abroad in Mexico El Salvador and Honduras. Delta entered the business of custom apparel design by acquiring Art Gun Technologies and hats by taking over Gekko Brands.

The company organizes its business into two segments: basics and branded. Its basics segment which generated 53% of its 2011 sales comprises unembellished knit apparel branded as Delta Pro Weight Delta Magnum Weight Quail Hollow to name a few. The basics arm also functions as a private-labeler for retailers sports licensors and corporate programs. Delta Apparel's branded segment accounting for 47% of sales focuses on activewear items that are sold under the Soffe Salt Life The Game and Realtree Outfitters labels through boutiques and high-end specialty retailers.

Delta Apparel's sales are fueled by predominantly by domestic demand. International customers in 2011 accounted for 1% of sales.

In 2011 Delta Apparel marked its eighth consecutive year of record sales. Sales increased 12% over the prior year. Growth is driven by higher selling prices coupled with success in winning new customers and expanding relationships with established customers. In addition to boosting its top line earnings jumped 42%. Results reflect relief from the one-time costs incurred in 2009 and 2008. Delta shuttered its manufacturing plant in Fayetteville North Carolina in 2009 and moved its operations to another North Carolina plant in Maiden (its last plant in the US) and Honduras. The shutdown was estimated to drive about $1 million annually in cost savings. In 2008 Delta closed a textiles plant in Alabama.

Delta Apparel's strategy focuses on growth through acquisitions in its branded and private-label businesses; it has acquired seven companies since 2003. Through M.J. Soffe subsidiary TCX LLC Delta Apparel in July 2010 purchased the assets of HPM Apparel doing business as The Cotton Exchange. The North Carolina-based designer and marketer of decorated branded casual apparel expanded Delta Apparel's customer based of college bookstores the US military and other retailers. To accomplish the purchase a month earlier Delta Apparel formed TCX LLC as a subsidiary of M.J. Soffe.

The deal for HPM followed Delta Apparel's late 2009 takeover of Art Gun Technologies a software developer of custom garment designs digital printing and shipping arrangements. Delta Apparel also snagged headwear supplier Gekko Brands a subsidiary of Ashworth for nearly $6 million in early 2009. Gekko known for its Kudzu and The Game brands complemented Delta's activewear offerings and expanded its distribution channels.

Members of the family of Edward Crosby "Ned" Johnson III control 10% of Delta Apparel through FMR LLC. An investor Johnson and his daughter Abigail own and manage FMR better known as Fidelity Investments.

EXECUTIVES

Chairman President and CEO, Robert W. (Bob) Humphreys, age 56, $669,167 total compensation
VP and Secretary, Martha M. (Sam) Watson, age 60, $207,656 total compensation
Chief Financial Officer; Vice President; Treasurer, Deborah H. (Deb) Merrill, age 40, $227,500 total compensation
President M. J. Soffe, Kenneth D. (Ken) Spires, age 55, $294,808 total compensation
President and COO, Steven E. Cochran
Director, William F. Garrett, age 71
Director, James A. (Al) Cochran, age 65
Director, E. Erwin Maddrey II, age 71
Director, Max Lennon, age 72
Director, Buck A. Mickel, age 56
Director, David S. Fraser, age 74
Director, David T. (Dave) Peterson, age 62
Director, G. Jay Gogue
Director, Robert E. Staton Sr., age 67
Director, Elizabeth J. (Betsy) Gatewood, age 68
Director, Sam P. Cortez, age 49
Auditors: Ernst&YoungLLP

LOCATIONS

HQ: Delta Apparel Inc.
322 S. Main St., Greenville SC 29601
Phone: 864-232-5200   **Fax:** 864-232-5199
Web: www.deltaapparelinc.com

2011 Sales

	$ mil.	% of total
US	470	99
Foreign	4	1
Total	**475**	**100**

PRODUCTS/OPERATIONS

2011 Sales

	$ mil.	% of total
Basics	253	53
Branded	221	47
Total	**475**	**100**

Selected Brands

Basics
  Delta Pro Weight
  Delta Magnum Weight
  FunTees
  Healthknit
  Quail Hollow
Branded
  Intensity Athletics
  Junkfood
  Realtree Outfitters
  Salt Life
  Soffe
  The Cotton Exchange
  The Game

COMPETITORS

Alstyle Apparel	Hat World
Anvil Holdings	Jockey International
Broder Bros.	Mainland Headwear
Fruit of the Loom	PremiumWear
Genesco	Reebok
Gildan Activewear	Russell Brands
Greenwood Mills	adidas

HISTORICAL FINANCIALS
Company Type: Public

Income Statement
FYE: June 29

	REVENUE ($ mil.)	NET INCOME ($ mil.)	NET PROFIT MARGIN	EMPLOYEES
06/13	490.5	9.1	1.9%	7,000
06/12*	489.9	(2.4)	—	7,200
07/11	475.2	17.3	3.6%	7,200
07/10	424.4	12.1	2.9%	7,000
06/09	355.2	6.4	1.8%	6,500
Annual Growth	8.4%	9.2%	—	1.9%

*Fiscal year change

2013 Year-End Financials

Debt ratio: 31.5%	No. of shares (mil.): 7
Return on equity: 6.5%	Dividends
Cash ($ mil.): 0	Yield: —
Current ratio: 3.39	Payout: —
Long-term debt ($ mil.): 94	Market value ($ mil.): 112

	STOCK PRICE ($) FY Close	P/E High/Low		PER SHARE ($) Earnings	Dividends	Book Value
06/13	14.10	16	11	1.08	0.00	17.81
06/12*	13.66	—	—	(0.29)	0.00	16.50
07/11	17.27	9	6	1.98	0.00	16.86
07/10	13.94	12	5	1.40	0.00	14.76
06/09	6.85	12	4	0.76	0.00	13.19
Annual Growth	19.8%	—	—	9.2%	—	7.8%

*Fiscal year change

Demand Media Inc

Demand Media knows that Web branding is in demand. Attracting some 125 million unique visitors each month the company operates through a variety of Web-related enterprises that exist to help drive Web traffic to its clients' sites. Subsidiaries include domain-name wholesaler eNom and Pluck a blog syndicator and provider of social media tools used for integrating websites. Other Demand Media websites include online how-to tutorials provider eHow humor site Cracked.com and Trails.com for outdoor enthusiasts. It also produces online video and written articles through its Demand Studios business which employs freelancers to provide content for its websites. Demand Media launched an IPO in early 2011.

IPO

By going public Demand Media raised about $151 million. It has been using the cash to expand internationally and for general corporate purposes such as augmenting its working capital and enhancing its sales and marketing activities.

Geographic Reach

In addition to its headquarters in Santa Monica CA the company has offices in Bellevue Washington; Austin Texas; Chicago Illinois; New York City; and London UK. In fiscal 2012 more than 90% of Demand Media's revenues came from websites and customers located in the US.

Operations

The company earns more than 65% of its revenues through the sale of advertising in connection with its content and media segment. The segment includes Demand's owned and operated websites such as eHow.com as well as more than 375 websites operated by customers such as US-ATODAY.com. The company produces videos through Demand Studios. The videos primarily distributed to YouTube earn revenue via targeted advertising.

Demand Media gets the rest of its revenues from its registrar segment which operates primarily under its eNom brand and earns revenues through domain name registration subscriptions and other related value-added services. Demand manages about 15 million Internet domain names.

Financial Performance

Demand Media's revenues have been steadily increasing in recent fiscal years. Demand Media's revenues increased 17% to $381 million in fiscal 2012 as compared to the $325 million the company reported for revenues in fiscal 2011. The growth was powered by increases in revenues from the company's Content & Media and Registrar segments. Demand Media posted revenues of about $253 million in 2010 and roughly $198 million back in fiscal 2009.

Strategy

Demand Media's business model relies on being ranked highly on search results from Google. Criticism of Demand Media was part of a larger discussion of how Google's search results are increasingly being filled with low-quality results. Such complaints led Google in 2011 to change its search algorithm to give low-content sites less visibility. Demand Media subsequently reported that Google's changes had no impact on its search results.

Ownership

Entities affiliated with Oak Investment Partners own 26% and entities affiliated with Spectrum Equity own about 16% of Demand Media.

Company Background

Demand Media was founded in 2006 by former Myspace.com chairman Richard Rosenblatt and Shawn Colo of Spectrum Equity Investors. Shortly after the company was formed Demand Media purchased the assets of Internet marketing firm Intermix Media which had owned and operated Myspace.

EXECUTIVES

Chairman and CEO, Richard M. Rosenblatt, age 44, $251,000 total compensation
President and CFO, Charles S. Hilliard, age 50
VP European Sales and Business Development, Stephanie Himoff
VP Investor Relations, Julie C. MacMedan, age 48
SVP Sales and Marketing, Erika Nardini
SVP and General Manager Pluck Enterprise, Steve Semelsberger
Chief Revenue and Marketing Officer, Joanne K. Bradford, age 49
Interim President, Shawn J. Colo, age 41
EVP Demand Studios, Steven Kydd
EVP People Operations, Courtney Montpas
SVP Corporate Communications, Quinn Daly
Chief Revenue Officer, Jeff Dossett
EVP Media and Marketplace, Michael L. Blend, age 46
Chief Strategy Officer, David E. (Dave) Panos, age 50
General Manager Demand Studio, Stewart Marlborough
Executive Vice President Media, Dan Brian
General Manager eHow.com, Gregory Boudewijn
Chief Innovation Officer, Byron Reese
EVP & General Counsel, Matthew P. Polesetsky, age 44
SVP and General Manager typeF.com, Lisa Kraynak
EVP Registrar Services, Taryn Naidu
EVP Technology, Jeremy Daw
SVP Ad Solutions, Peter Luttrell
Vice President of Marketing, Carole Walker
Chief Financial Officer, Mel Tang
Director, James R. (Jim) Quandt, age 63
Director, Peter Guber, age 71
Director, Victor E. (Vic) Parker Jr., age 44
Director, John A. Hawkins, age 53
Director, Gaurav Bhandari, age 45
Director, Fredric W. (Fred) Harman, age 53
Director, Joshua G. (Josh) James, age 40
Independent Director, Robert Bennett
Auditors: PricewaterhouseCoopersLLP

LOCATIONS

HQ: Demand Media Inc.
1299 Ocean Ave. Ste. 500, Santa Monica CA 90401
Phone: 310-394-6400 **Fax:** 813-882-0209
Web: www.netwolves.com

PRODUCTS/OPERATIONS

2012 Sales

Content & Media	246	65
Total	**380**	**100**

Selected Holdings

Domain Services
eNom.com
Entertainment
Cracked.com
Games
Grab.com
Knowledge
eHow.com
ExpertVillage.com
SoYouWanna.com
Outdoor Lifestyle
Golflink.com
LIVESTRONG.com
Trails.com
Video Production and Written Content
DemandStudio

COMPETITORS

AOL	Live Current Media
About.com	Marchex
Connected Ventures	Network Solutions
Glam Media	Topica
Go Daddy	Tucows
HSW International	ValueClick
IAC	WebMD Health
IGN Entertainment	Yahoo!
Impulse Communications	iVillage
Jive Software	

HISTORICAL FINANCIALS
Company Type: Public

Income Statement
FYE: December 31

	REVENUE ($ mil.)	NET INCOME ($ mil.)	NET PROFIT MARGIN	EMPLOYEES
12/12	380.5	6.1	1.6%	700
12/11	324.8	(18.5)	—	600
12/10	252.9	(5.3)	—	600
12/09	198.4	(22.4)	—	600
12/08	170.2	(14.9)	—	0
Annual Growth	22.3%	—	—	—

2012 Year-End Financials

Debt ratio: —	No. of shares (mil.): 90
Return on equity: 1.3%	Dividends
Cash ($ mil.): 102	Yield: —
Current ratio: 1.46	Payout: —
Long-term debt ($ mil.): —	Market value ($ mil.): 840

	STOCK PRICE ($)	P/E		PER SHARE ($)		
	FY Close	High/Low	Earnings	Dividends	Book Value	
12/12	9.29	169 85	0.07	0.00	5.22	
12/11	6.65	— —	(0.27)	0.00	5.27	
Annual Growth	39.7%		— —	—	(0.8%)	

Denbury Resources, Inc. (DE)

Denbury Resources is the largest combined oil and natural gas producer in Mississippi and Montana. In 2012 it reported estimated proved reserves of 419.4 million barrels of oil equivalent of which 80% is oil. It owns the largest reserves of carbon dioxide (CO2) used in enhanced (also called tertiary) oil recovery east of the Mississippi River and it holds operating acreage in its two core regions Gulf Coast and Rocky Mountains. Using CO2 in enhanced oil recovery is one of the most efficient tertiary recovery methods for producing crude oil. Denbury Resources generates substantially all of its revenue from sales of oil natural gas and related products.

Geographic Reach

Denbury Resources' oil and gas properties are concentrated in the Gulf Coast and Rocky Mountain regions of the US. Its proved and producing reserves in the Gulf Coast are located in Alabama Louisiana Mississippi and Texas and in the Rocky Mountain region in Montana North Dakota and Wyoming.

Sales and Marketing

The company's oil and gas sales are made on a daily basis under short-term contracts at current area market price. Its oil and gas revenues are dependent on two large purchasers in particular Marathon Petroleum and Plains Marketing LP which accounted for 39% and 17% of Denbury Resources' revenues respectively in 2012.

Financial Performance

Denbury Resources' revenues increased by 6% in 2012 thanks to production increases from its tertiary oil fields (which hit record aggregate production levels that year) offset by normal declines in most of its other oil and gas properties. The year-over-year rise in total production was also due to ibncreased production from Bakken area assets which were sold in late 2012.The company reported net income of $525.4 million in 2012 (more than 8% down on 2011) as the result of higher operating expenses.

Strategy

Denbury Resources' business strategy is to focus on regions where it has a competitive advantage due to its ownership or use of CO2 reserves oil fields and infrastructure. It also seeks to acquire properties and maximize the value of its properties by increasing production and reserves. In 2012 it increased its average tertiary oil production by 14% over 2011 due to contributions from its Texas-based Oyster Bayou and Hastings fields and expansion at its Tinsley (Mississippi) Heidelberg (Mississippi) and Delhi (Louisiana) fields.

Acquisition and disposition of assets are a key part of Denbury Resources' quest to become a nearly pure CO2 enhanced oil recovery company.

Denbury Resources sold its Bakken Shale assets in Montana and North Dakota as well as property in Texas and Wyoming to Exxon Mobil and XTO Energy for $1.3 billion in late 2012. Denbury Resources is using the proceeds to purchase additional oil fields in the Gulf Coast and Rocky Mountain regions. In 2012 the company claimed that its current portfolio of properties give it good growth potential for more than a decade.

Mergers and Acquisitions

Subsequent to the Exxon Mobil deal Denbury Resources in 2013 acquired more than $1 billion in producing property interests in Montana and North Dakota from a subsidiary of ConocoPhillips. The properties are expected to contribute about 7700 barrels of oil equivalent per day to the company's full-year average daily production.

Expanding its assets on the Texas Gulf Coast in 2012 the company bought the Thompson Field in Fort Bend County from a private seller for $366 million. In the prior year it grew its CO2 assets by buying the 57.5% working interest it did not already own in the Riley Ridge Federal Unit in southwestern Wyoming as well as a 33% stake in an additional 28000 acres of leasehold property.

Denbury Resources gained entry to the Rocky Mountain market as a result of a transformational acquisition in 2010. Its $4.8 billion purchase of rival Encore Acquisition gave it major operations that it is developing still today. Denbury Resources is in the midst of constructing the Greencore Pipeline its first CO2 pipeline in the Rocky Mountains. (In 2012 it completed the initial 232-mile segment of the 20-inch pipeline).

Ownership

Capital World Investors owns 11% of Denbury Resources.

Company Background

Denbury was formed as a Canadian public company in 1992. It moved its corporate domicile to the US and has been publicly traded in the US since 1995. It was listed on the New York Stock Exchange in 1997.

EXECUTIVES

SVP CFO Treasurer and Assistant Secretary, Mark C. Allen Sr., age 45, $327,500 total compensation
President and CEO, Phil Rykhoek, age 56, $415,000 total compensation
Chairman, Wieland F. Wettstein, age 63
SVP Commercial Development Government Affairs and Project Management, Robert L. (Bob) Cornelius, age 58, $355,000 total compensation
VP Marketing and Business Development, Dan E. Cole, age 60
SVP Planning Technology and Business Development, Charlie Gibson, age 54
VP North Region, Barry Schneider, age 50
VP and Chief Information Officer, Steve McLaurin
VP and Chief Accounting Officer, Alan Rhoades, age 48
VP Drilling and EOR Facilities Engineering/Construction, Jeff Marcel, age 51
VP CO2 Supply and Pipeline Operations, John Filiatrault
SVP and COO, Craig McPherson
VP West Region, Matt Elmer
VP East Region, J. Phillip (Phil) Webb
Director, Kevin O. Meyers, age 59
Director, Michael B. (Mike) Decker, age 63
President CEO and Director, Phil Rykhoek, age 56
Director, Gareth Roberts, age 60
Director, Ronald G. Greene, age 64
Director, Randy Stein, age 59
Director, David I. Heather, age 70
Director, Gregory L. (Greg) McMichael, age 64

Director, Michael L. Beatty, age 66
Independent Director, Laura Sugg
Auditors: PricewaterhouseCoopersLLP

LOCATIONS

HQ: Denbury Resources Inc.
5320 Legacy Dr., Plano TX 75024
Phone: 972-673-2000   **Fax:** 972-673-2150
Web: www.denbury.com

PRODUCTS/OPERATIONS

2012 Sales

	$ mil.	% of total
Oil natural gas & related product sales	2,409	98
CO2 sales and transportation fees	26	1
Interest income & other income	20	1
Total	**2,456**	**100**

COMPETITORS

Abraxas Petroleum	McMoRan Exploration
Apache	Murphy Oil
BP	Newfield Exploration
Chevron	Occidental Permian
Exxon Mobil	Par Petroleum
Forest Oil	Royal Dutch Shell
Genesis Energy	Swift Energy

HISTORICAL FINANCIALS

Company Type: Public

Income Statement FYE: December 31

	REVENUE ($ mil.)	NET INCOME ($ mil.)	NET PROFIT MARGIN	EMPLOYEES
12/12	2,456.4	525.3	21.4%	1,432
12/11	2,309.3	573.3	24.8%	1,308
12/10	1,921.7	271.7	14.1%	1,195
12/09	882.4	(75.1)	—	830
12/08	1,365.7	388.4	28.4%	797
Annual Growth	15.8%	7.8%	—	15.8%

2012 Year-End Financials

Debt ratio: 28.2%	No. of shares (mil.): 375
Return on equity: 10.5%	Dividends
Cash ($ mil.): 98	Yield: —
Current ratio: 2.50	Payout: —
Long-term debt ($ mil.): 3,104	Market value ($ mil.): 6,084

	STOCK PRICE ($)	P/E		PER SHARE ($)		
	FY Close	High/Low	Earnings	Dividends	Book Value	
12/12	16.20	15 10	1.35	0.00	13.62	
12/11	15.10	17 7	1.43	0.00	12.36	
12/10	19.09	27 19	0.72	0.00	10.95	
12/09	14.80	— —	(0.30)	0.00	7.53	
12/08	10.92	25 4	1.54	0.00	7.43	
Annual Growth	10.4%	— —	(3.2%)	—	16.3%	

DeVry Education Group Inc

It isn't exactly Ivy League but DeVry Education Group is in the big leagues of technical health care and business schools. The for-profit educational company offers professional undergraduate and graduate degrees through subsidiary schools. Flagship DeVry University with about 90 locations in roughly 25 states and Canada specializes in business and technology education. Its Keller Graduate School of Management unit offers MBA and other graduate programs while its Ross University offers medical and veterinary school training. The company also offers health care education through Chamberlain College of Nursing and Carrington College. In all DeVry has about 70000 students through campus and online enrollment.

Geographic Reach

In addition to core US operations the company operates DeVry Brasil which offers business law and engineering programs from about a dozen campuses in Brazil. It also has DeVry University campuses in Canada. Ross University has campuses in the West Indies and Caribbean for coursework; students then complete clinical training at US teaching hospitals and vet colleges. Ross also has Canadian locations. The company's Becker Professional Education provides continuing education programs in the US and several international markets.

Operations

DeVry University's student population is generally older than those at traditional colleges. More than half of its students are older than 25 and represent the school's fastest-growing demographic; many are working adults. The school boasts an enrollment of some 50000 undergraduate students and some 18000 graduate students.

In addition to its graduate and undergraduate degrees in business health care and technical fields the Becker Professional Education subsidiary offers professional exam review and continuing education courses in accounting finance and project management. The company discontinued its Advanced Academics unit which offered middle school and high school programs online in 2013.

Sales and Marketing

DeVry uses online television radio and print advertisements to promote its services as well as direct mail and telemarketing campaigns. Marketing expenses were some $261 million in fiscal 2013 down from $266 million in 2012 but up from $247 million in 2011.

Financial Performance

Discontinuation of the company's Advanced Academics segment operations as well as lower enrollment and higher scholarship figures prompted revenues and profits to decline in fiscal 2013 and 2012. Along with other similar institutions DeVry's enrollment has been impacted in recent years by market factors including regulatory changes and negative press over the practices of for-profit college operators as well as economic conditions and increased competition.

Earnings dropped 6% in 2013 to just under $2 billion and net income fell 25% to $107 million. Profits were impacted not only by lower revenue but also by increased interest expense and a loss on discontinued operations.

The company had experienced climbing enrollment and increased financial success during the economic recession as a higher number of unemployed individuals sought out training and education services.

Strategy

Acquisitions and organic measures to add to or expand upon its offerings are a key part of the company's growth strategy. Part of DeVry's acquisition strategy is to diversify its holdings by purchasing schools in different geographic regions as well as in different educational arenas. By diversifying its offerings DeVry hopes to attract a broader student base and up its enrollment numbers.

Organic measures include opening new campuses and adding new education programs and capacity to existing locations. The company is especially working to expand its health and medical related educational offerings. It is also focused on increasing brand awareness and quality of student outcomes.

While the company continues to offer some online courses it suspended its 100% online certification programs in 2013 to revamp the quality of the programs. DeVry also discontinued its Advanced Academics segment in 2013 to focus on core college-level programs.

Mergers and Acquisitions

Focusing on international growth DeVry expanded its medical training offerings through the $235 million purchase of American University of the Caribbean a physician training school located on St. Maarten in 2011. Then in 2012 the company acquired two schools in northeastern Brazil (Faculdade Boa Viagem and Faculdade do Vale do Ipojuca) to extend its presence in that country. In 2013 it added another Brazilian school Faculdade Diferencial Integral.

In addition in 2011 and 2012 Becker Professional Education acquired ATC International which operates finance and accounting centers in Europe and Asia and Falcon Physician Reviews which provides physician training review programs.

Ownership

Company co-founder and former chairman Dennis Keller now a director emeritus owns about 10% of DeVry Education Group.

HISTORY

DeVry Institutes was founded in 1931 by Herman DeVry as an electronics repair school. It was later acquired by Bell & Howell (now Voyager Learning Company). While working at Bell & Howell Dennis Keller a Princeton graduate met Ronald Taylor who had degrees from Harvard and Stanford. In 1973 they created a private business school targeting working adults. In 1987 Keller and Taylor bought DeVry and combined it with their graduate business school under the DeVry name; the company went public in 1991.

The company acquired Becker CPA Review in 1996. With plans to increase the number of DeVry campuses to 40 by the next decade the company opened DeVry Institutes in New York City and Fremont California in 1998. The following year it bought Denver Technical College which later was integrated into DeVry University. DeVry also began offering classes online.

The Becker Conviser Professional Review segment was bolstered in 2001 with the purchase of Argentum (which did business as Stalla Seminars) a firm engaged in the production of CFA (chartered financial analyst) test prep materials. DeVry Institutes and Keller Graduate School of Management merged to form DeVry University in 2002. DeVry acquired Ross University a medical and veterinary school in 2003.

In 2004 Keller turned over the CEO spot to fellow co-founder Ronald Taylor. He remained chairman for a couple of years before stepping down to become director emeritus.

DeVry's medical credentials were expanded in 2005 with the acquisition of Deaconess College of Nursing renamed Chamberlain College of Nursing. Also that year the company acquired Gearty CPE a provider of continuing education programs in accounting and finance operating in New York and New Jersey.

Ronald Taylor retired as CEO at the end of 2006. He was succeeded by company COO Daniel Hamburger.

Keller Graduate School expanded its degree offerings in 2007 with the addition of a master's degree in educational technology.

DeVry acquired the U.S. Education Company in 2008 which included about 20 Apollo College and Western Career College locations in the western US. The locations were later renamed Carrington College.

DeVry enjoyed a boost in enrollments during the economic recession as many unemployed workers took the opportunity to seek new technical training and at the same time federal student loan purse strings loosened up giving those workers access to loans for tuition.

However the rapid growth in the entire private education industry including DeVry drew attention from lawmakers during 2010 who were concerned that people were adding to their debt with student loans but receiving incomplete or low-quality education services. Still attention from lawmakers didn't hurt revenues and profits in 2011 even as the economy began to recover and people started going back to work (instead of school).

EXECUTIVES

SVP External Relations & Global Responsibility Chief Regulatory Compliance Officer; President DeVry Foundation, Sharon Thomas Parrott, age 63

Chairman, Harold T. Shapiro, age 78

SVP Human Resources, Donna N. Jennings, age 51

Chairman, Connie R. Curran, age 65

Senior Director Investor Relations and Media Relations, Joan Bates

President and CEO, Daniel M. Hamburger, age 49, $751,689 total compensation

SVP CFO and Treasurer, Timothy J. Wiggins, age 56

President DeVry Online Services, Eric Dirst, age 46

EVP; President DeVry University, David J. (Dave) Pauldine, age 56, $400,983 total compensation

President DeVry Medical International; Professional and International Education, Steven P. (Steve) Riehs, age 53, $298,812 total compensation

SVP General Counsel and Secretary, Gregory S. Davis, age 51

Vice President - Finance; Chief Accounting Officer; Controller, Patrick J. Unzicker, age 42

President Chamberlain College of Nursing, Susan L. Groenwald

President Becker Professional Education, John P. Roselli, age 49

SVP; President Healthcare Group, William Hughson, $287,019 total compensation

President Tinley Park, Jamal J. Scott

President Online Services, Christopher Caywood

VP Strategy and Business Development, Adriano Allegrini

President DeVry Brasil, Carlos Filgueiras

President DeVry Medical International, Andrew Jeon

President Carrington Colleges Group, Robert Paul

Senior Vice President External Relations & Global Responsibility Chief Regulatory Compliance Officer DeVry Inc. President DeVry Foundation, Sharon Thomas Parrott

SVP and CIO, Chris Nash

Director, Gary C. Butler, age 66

Director, Ronald L. Taylor, age 70

Director, Fernando Ruiz, age 57

Director, Julie A. McGee, age 70

Director, David S. Brown, age 72

Director, Connie R. Curran, age 65

President CEO and Director, Daniel M. Hamburger, age 49

Director, Darren R. Huston, age 46
Director, William T. (Bill) Keevan, age 65
Director, Lyle L. Logan, age 54
Director, Lisa Pickrum, age 44
Independent Director, Christopher Begley
Auditors: PricewaterhouseCoopersLLP

LOCATIONS

HQ: DeVry Education Group Inc.
3005 Highland Pkwy, Downers Grove IL 60515-5799
Phone: 630-571-7700   **Fax:** 207-556-4346
Web: www.idexx.com

PRODUCTS/OPERATIONS

2013 Sales by Segment

	$ mil.	% of total
Business technology & management	1,096	56
Internet K-12 Other educational services	196	10
Total	**1,964**	**100**

2013 Sales

	$ mil.	% of total
Tuition	1,840	94
Other	124	6
Total	**1,964**	**100**

Selected Divisions and Fields of Study

American University of the Caribbean School of
  Medicine
Becker Professional Education
  CFA exam review
  CPA exam review
Carrington College
  Dental assisting
  Diagnostic medical sonography
  Fitness training
  Medical assisting
  Medical laboratory technician
  Medical radiography
  Physical therapy assisting
  Practical nursing
  Respiratory care
  Veterinary assisting
Chamberlain College of Nursing
  Nursing
DeVry Brasil
  Business management
  Engineering
  Law
DeVry University
  Accounting
  Biomedical engineering technology
  Business administration
  Computer engineering technology
  Computer information systems
  Electrical engineering
  Electronics and computer technology
  Electronics engineering technology
  Game and simulation programming
  Health information technology
  Network and communications management
  Network systems administration
  Technical management
Keller Graduate School of Management
  Accounting and finance
  Business administration
  Human resources
  Project management
  Public administration
  Technology management
Ross University
  Medicine
  Veterinary medicine

COMPETITORS

Apollo Education	Heald College
Bridgepoint Education	ITT Educational
Capella Education	Kaplan
Cardean Learning Group	Laureate Education
Career Education	Lincoln Educational

Concorde Colleges	Services
Corinthian Colleges	National American
Education Management	University
Grand Canyon Education	Strayer Education

HISTORICAL FINANCIALS
Company Type: Public

Income Statement

FYE: June 30

	REVENUE ($ mil.)	NET INCOME ($ mil.)	NET PROFIT MARGIN	EMPLOYEES
06/13	1,964.3	106.7	5.4%	12,668
06/12	2,089.7	141.5	6.8%	13,521
06/11	2,182.3	330.4	15.1%	12,599
06/10	1,915.1	279.9	14.6%	12,117
06/09	1,461.4	165.6	11.3%	10,200
Annual Growth	**7.7%**	**(10.4%)**	**—**	**5.6%**

2013 Year-End Financials

Debt ratio: —
Return on equity: 7.7%
Cash ($ mil.): 196
Current ratio: 1.40
Long-term debt ($ mil.): —

No. of shares (mil.): 62
Dividends
  Yield: 0.0%
  Payout: 20.6%
Market value ($ mil.): 1,953

	STOCK PRICE ($) FY Close	P/E High/Low		Earnings	Dividends	Book Value
06/13	31.02	21	11	1.65	0.34	22.20
06/12	30.97	32	13	2.09	0.30	20.96
06/11	59.13	13	8	4.68	0.24	20.25
06/10	52.49	19	12	3.87	0.20	16.60
06/09	50.04	27	17	2.28	0.16	13.01
Annual Growth	**(11.3%)**	**—**	**—**	**(7.8%)**	**20.7%**	**14.3%**

Diamond Hill Investment Group Inc.

Diamond Hill Investment Group takes a shine to investment management. Operating through flagship subsidiary Diamond Hill Capital Management the firm oversees some $11.5 billion in assets most of it invested in mutual funds. Serving institutional and individual clients the company administers several mutual funds and sells them mainly through independent investment advisers broker-dealers financial planners investment consultants and third-party marketing firms. The firm hews to a value-based investment philosophy and takes a long-term perspective to investing. Formed in 1990 Diamond Hill Investment Group also manages separate accounts and hedge funds.

Operations

Diamond Hill Investment Group operates through its subsidiaries: Diamond Hill Capital Management; and Beacon Hill Fund Services and BHIL Distributors collectively known as Beacon Hill. Beacon Hill provides fund administration and statutory underwriting services to various clients including Diamond Hill Funds.

Financial Performance

Diamond Hill Investment Group's revenue rose 4% in 2012 versus 2011 to $66.6 million. The increase was due to a 13% rise in fees from mutual fund administration while investment advisory fees rose a more modest 3%. Net income rose 18% over

the same period to $16.9 million. Assets under management at the end of 2012 exceeded $9.4 billion an increase of nearly 9% over the prior year. The firm's revenue and profits have increased steadily since 2008 after taking a hit during the financial crisis as investors retreated from the market.

EXECUTIVES

President and CEO; Director, Roderick H. (Ric) Dillon Jr., age 56, $360,000 total compensation
Chief Financial Officer and President of Diamond Hill Funds; Director, James F. (Jim) Laird Jr., age 56, $200,000 total compensation
Portfolio Manager Strategic Income, William P. Zox
Managing Director Strategic Income Diamond Hill Investments, Kent K. Rinker, age 62
Co-Chief Investment Officer, Christopher A. (Chris) Welch
Chairman Diamond Hill Funds, Thomas E. (Tom) Line
Coporate Controller and Chief Compliance Officer Diamond Hills Funds, Gary R. Young
Treasurer, Trent Statczar
Chief Compliance Officer, George Stevens
Managing Director - Investments, Chuck Bath
Co-Chief Investment Officer, Christopher (Chris) Bingaman
Director, David R. Meuse, age 67
President and CEO; Director, Roderick H. (Ric) Dillon Jr., age 56
Director, James G. Mathias, age 59
Director, Donald B. Shackelford, age 78
Director, David P. Lauer, age 71
Independent Director, Bradley Shoup
Independent Director, Frances Skinner
Independent Director, Peter Moran
Auditors: Plante&MoranPLLC

LOCATIONS

HQ: Diamond Hill Investment Group Inc.
325 John H. McConnell Blvd. Ste. 200, Columbus OH 43215
Phone: 614-255-3333   **Fax:** 614-255-3363
Web: www.diamond-hill.com

PRODUCTS/OPERATIONS

2012 Sales

	$ mil.	% of total
Investment advisory	57	87
Mutual fund administration	8	13
Total	**66**	**100**

Selected Products

Diamond Hill Small Cap Fund
Diamond Hill Small-Mid Cap Fund
Diamond Hill Large Cap Fund
Diamond Hill Select Fund Fund
Diamond Hill Long-Short Fund
Diamond Hill Strategic Income Fund

COMPETITORS

AllianceBernstein	GAMCO Investors
American Century	Janus Capital
Calamos Asset	Legg Mason
Management	MFS
Cohen & Steers	Putnam
Columbia Management	Pzena Investment
Davis Advisers	Management
Duncan-Hurst	Raymond James
Eaton Vance	Financial
Edelman Financial	SEI Investments
Edward Jones	T. Rowe Price
Epoch	The Vanguard Group

HISTORICAL FINANCIALS

Company Type: Public

Income Statement

FYE: December 31

	REVENUE ($ mil.)	NET INCOME ($ mil.)	NET PROFIT MARGIN	EMPLOYEES
12/12	66.6	16.9	25.4%	79
12/11	63.8	14.3	22.5%	73
12/10	56.7	12.4	21.9%	77
12/09	43.5	11.3	26.1%	66
12/08	47.0	3.2	7.0%	57
Annual Growth	9.1%	50.8%	—	8.5%

2012 Year-End Financials

Debt ratio: —
Return on equity: 84.8%
Cash ($ mil.): 7
Current ratio: 1.06
Long-term debt ($ mil.): —

No. of shares (mil.): 3
Dividends
  Yield: 11.7%
  Payout: 148.1%
Market value ($ mil.): 215

	STOCK PRICE ($) FY Close	P/E High/Low		PER SHARE ($) Earnings	Dividends	Book Value
12/12	67.86	15	12	5.44	8.00	6.86
12/11	73.98	17	14	4.86	5.00	6.03
12/10	72.34	19	11	4.48	13.00	2.68
12/09	64.23	16	7	4.40	10.00	8.58
12/08	65.00	72	34	1.36	10.00	12.36
Annual Growth	1.1% (13.7%)	—	—	41.4%	(5.4%)	

Digimarc Corp

Digimarc makes its mark on media. The company provides digital watermarking software that embeds code in printed and digital content including photographs music movies and television content as well as currency documents and packages. Customers - which include movie studios record labels broadcasters creative professionals and government agencies —use Digimarc's software to control copyrights deter piracy license online content and manage digital assets. The company generates revenue from software development consulting services and technology licensing and subscription fees. Its licensees include Microsoft Adobe Systems The Nielsen Company and Open Text.

Revenue increased about 14% in 2010 compared with 2009 and the company recorded net income of 13% in 2010 compared with a net loss of 14% the previous year. Digimarc attributes a big part of its healthy operating results to licensing income from Intellectual Ventures and Arbitron (since acquired by Nielsen and renamed Nielsen Audio) which respectively account for 18% and 14% of revenue. Income from these two companies as well as Nielsen (12% of revenue) and government contracts increased domestic income 119% in 2010 over 2009. The company still counts its first successful product launch —counterfeiting prevention technology –as an important source of revenue. Government contracts account for 33% of the company's sales and 90% of that

business involves counterfeiting deterrence for banks.

Though the company first made a name for itself with anticounterfeiting software it has now branched out into new growing markets. One recently launched product the Digimarc Discover platform targets the iTunes and Android markets by offering new media applications for smartphone users. In late 2012 it branched into the fast-growing eBook market via the acquisition of Attributor Corporation which provides software to protect against online piracy.

With more than a thousand US and foreign patents and patent applications in digital watermarking and related technologies Digimarc faces competition primarily from alternative technologies such as encryption radio frequency tags smart cards and bar codes.

Prior to 2008 Digimarc also sold secure ID products used to create identification cards such as driver's licenses and office security badges. The company agreed to sell its ID systems business to L-1 Identity Solutions for $250 million in cash and stock in early 2008. Before the deal closed French aerospace and defense giant SAFRAN offered a competing bid of $300 million for Digimarc. The company then accepted a second offer from L-1 for $310 million; the deal closed in August 2008.

When L-1 acquired Digimarc its digital watermarking business was spun off as a separate entity initially called DMRC. The new independent company later retained the Digimarc name.

EXECUTIVES

EVP Chief Legal Officer and Secretary, Robert P. Chamness, age 61, $285,000 total compensation
Chairman and CEO, Bruce Davis, age 61, $450,000 total compensation
EVP CFO and Treasurer, Michael E. McConnell, age 62, $285,000 total compensation
VP, Jeri Owen
VP of Sales and Marketing, Ed Knudson
Director, James T. (Jim) Richardson, age 65
Director, Bernard J. (Bern) Whitney, age 57
Director, William J. (Bill) Miller, age 67
Director, Peter W. Smith, age 79
Auditors: GrantThorntonLLP

LOCATIONS

HQ: Digimarc Corp
  9405 SW Gemini Drive, Beaverton, OR 97008
Phone: 503 469-4800
Web: www.digimarc.com

2010 Sales

	$ mil.	% of total
US	19	61
Other countries	12	39
Total	31	100

PRODUCTS/OPERATIONS

2010 Sales

	$ mil.	% of total
Service	12	40
License & subscription	18	60
Total	31	100

COMPETITORS

Aware Inc.
Document Security Systems
Irdeto

Nielsen Holdings
Philips Electronics
Widevine Technologies

HISTORICAL FINANCIALS

Company Type: Public

Income Statement

FYE: December 31

	REVENUE ($ mil.)	NET INCOME ($ mil.)	NET PROFIT MARGIN	EMPLOYEES
12/12	44.3	8.2	18.6%	124
12/11	36.0	5.6	15.7%	109
12/10	31.1	4.1	13.4%	98
12/09	19.0	(2.7)	—	93
12/08	7.8	0.0	1.0%	87
Annual Growth	54.3%	223.0%	—	9.3%

2012 Year-End Financials

Debt ratio: —
Return on equity: —
Cash ($ mil.): 6
Current ratio: 10.26
Long-term debt ($ mil.): —

No. of shares (mil.): 7
Dividends
  Yield: 1.5%
  Payout: 31.1%
Market value ($ mil.): 148

	STOCK PRICE ($) FY Close	P/E High/Low		PER SHARE ($) Earnings	Dividends	Book Value
12/12	20.70	27	15	1.12	0.33	7.39
12/11	23.89	51	26	0.76	0.00	5.95
12/10	30.01	53	25	0.55	0.00	6.87
12/09	14.99	—	—	(0.39)	0.00	6.48
12/08	10.02	1068822		0.01	0.00	6.65
Annual Growth	19.9%	—		—225.3%	—	2.7%

Digital Realty Trust, Inc.

Technically Digital Realty Trust puts its chips in real estate. The real estate investment trust (REIT) owns properties that are leased to firms in the technology sector. Its portfolio includes more than 100 properties in the US Europe and Asia including data communications hubs electronic storage and processing centers tech manufacturing facilities and offices of tech companies. All told the REIT owns more than 18 million sq. ft. of rentable space including space held for redevelopment. Digital Realty Trust focuses on hot tech markets such as Chicago Dallas Phoenix New Jersey New York northern Virginia and California's San Francisco Bay area and Silicon Valley (its largest market).

Digital Realty Trust's occupancy rate stood at nearly 95% at the end of 2011. Its largest tenant Century Link accounts for more than 10% of its annualized rent; other major tenants include Equinix AT&T Level 3 Communications and Facebook.

The REIT's growth strategy includes real estate acquisitions and redevelopment of its existing properties. It has approximately 2 million sq. ft. of space under development. The company believes that upgrades to its properties lead to low tenant turnover and longer lease terms.

Digital Realty Trust acquired 15 properties in 2010 (the busiest that the company had been since 2007) including some in new markets. The REIT added its first property in Asia when it bought a data center in Singapore. It entered Massachusetts and Connecticut with the acquisition of three data centers there.

Digital Realty Trust continued its acquisition activity into 2011 and 2012 when it purchased more than a dozen properties including some in new markets such as London and Sydney. The latter deals added to the company's international presence in Dublin Melbourne Paris and Singapore.

The acquisitions in 2010 and 2011 also helped to boost the company's revenues and net income for both years. Digital Realty Trust reported a more than 50% increase in net income from fiscal 2010 to 2011 ($105.4 million to $162.1 million) and a nearly 25% gain in operating income ($865.4 million to nearly $1.1 billion).

EXECUTIVES

CFO Chief Investment Officer and Secretary, A. William Stein, age 59, $386,567 total compensation

Chairman, Dennis E. Singleton, age 68

VP Investor Relations and Corporate Marketing, Pamela Matthews Garibaldi

Senior Vice President General Counsel, Joshua A. Mills

CEO and Director, Michael F. Foust, age 57, $591,000 total compensation

Chief Acquisitions Officer, Scott E. Peterson, age 51, $337,155 total compensation

CTO, Jim Smith

SVP Sales, Brent Behrman

SVP Portfolio Management, David J. Caron

SVP EMEA, Bernard Geoghegan

Senior Vice President; Regional Head; Asia Pacific, Kris Kumar

Senior Vice President - Sales, Matthew Miszewski

Director, Laurence A. Chapman, age 63

Director, Ruann F. Ernst, age 66

Director, Robert H. (Bob) Zerbst, age 66

CEO and Director, Michael F. Foust, age 57

Director, Kathleen Earley, age 61

Auditors: KPMGLLP

LOCATIONS

HQ: Digital Realty Trust Inc.
560 Mission St. Ste. 2900, San Francisco CA 94105
Phone: 415-738-6500   **Fax:** 415-738-6501
Web: www.digitalrealtytrust.com

PRODUCTS/OPERATIONS

2011 Sales

	$ mil.	% of total
Rental	820	77
Tenant reimbursements	211	20
Construction management	29	3
Other	0	-
Total	**1,062**	**100**

COMPETITORS

Brandywine Realty	Mack-Cali
CenterPoint Properties	Mission West
CoreSite	Properties
DuPont Fabros	Prologis
Duke Realty	QTS Realty Trust Inc.
EastGroup Properties	Vornado Realty
First Industrial	
Realty	

HISTORICAL FINANCIALS

Company Type: Public

Income Statement

FYE: December 31

	REVENUE ($ mil.)	NET INCOME ($ mil.)	NET PROFIT MARGIN	EMPLOYEES
12/12	1,279.0	210.3	16.4%	702
12/11	1,062.7	156.2	14.7%	532
12/10	865.4	102.2	11.8%	454
12/09	637.1	87.6	13.8%	264
12/08	527.4	67.6	12.8%	210
Annual Growth	24.8%	32.8%	—	35.2%

2012 Year-End Financials

Debt ratio: 48.5%
Return on equity: 7.0%
Cash ($ mil.): 56
Current ratio: 0.36
Long-term debt ($ mil.): 4,278

No. of shares (mil.): 125
Dividends
Yield: 4.3%
Payout: 200.0%
Market value ($ mil.): 8,496

	STOCK PRICE ($) FY Close	P/E High/Low	PER SHARE ($) Earnings	Dividends	Book Value
12/12	67.89	54 40	1.48	2.92	27.72
12/11	66.67	50 38	1.32	2.72	23.79
12/10	51.54	93 68	0.68	2.02	21.53
12/09	50.28	80 42	0.62	1.47	20.30
12/08	32.85	117 51	0.41	1.26	20.36
Annual Growth	19.9%	— —	37.8%	23.4%	8.0%

DigitalGlobe Inc

DigitalGlobe has its eye on you. The company provides satellite imagery used for a variety of applications including mapping urban planning oil exploration land management and disaster assessment. DigitalGlobe's products include standard images panchromatic images multispectral images and color infrared images as well as mosaics and digital elevation models. Nearly 80% of its revenues come from the US government; commercial customers include oil and gas exploration companies and GPS navigation system makers. DigitalGlobe's images and services are incorporated into popular mapping applications such as Google Maps and Microsoft Virtual Earth as well as into GPS systems from DeLorme and Garmin.

Operations

DigitalGlobe owns and operates three imagery satellites —WorldView-1 WorldView-2 and Quick-Bird --that have collected more than 2.8 billion square kilometers of images. In 2010 it commissioned Ball Aerospace to build a fourth satellite WorldView-3 and for ITT Corporation to design the imaging system. WorldView-3 is scheduled to be ready for launch in 2014.

Geographic Reach

The company serves its largest customer the US government from five US locations. International offices are located in Abu Dhabi the Netherlands Singapore and the UK.

Sales and Marketing

The National Geospatial-Intelligence Agency (NGA) accounts for a majority of DigitalGlobe's sales. The federal agency buys images for use by agencies of the US government for defense intelligence and foreign policy applications. DigitalGlobe has a 10-year $3.5 billion contract that's ex-

pected to provide a serious revenue boost through 2020.

Financial Performance

Overall sales were up 24% in 2012 to $421 million thanks to the NGA contract. After suffering a rare net loss in 2011 the company returned to profitability in 2012 earning $39 million.

Mergers and Acquisitions

In 2013 DigitalGlobe acquired top rival GeoEye in a cash and stock transaction valued at around $1.4 billion. Like DigitalGlobe GeoEye provides satellite imagery of the air land and sea used in applications that include mapping resource management environmental monitoring disaster response national security and the like. GeoEye brings substantial resources to the merger table including satellites and aircraft that provide aerial imagery. (DigitalGlobe has no similar aircraft instead buying the aerial images in its ImageLibrary from suppliers.) Both companies sell primarily to the US government as well as international governments and commercial customers. The combined company will continue to operate under the DigitalGlobe moniker. More importantly they will no longer be competing for the same contracts —giving each a more stable revenue base —and will share the substantial cost of developing and launching new satellites.

Company Background

DigitalGlobe was founded in 1993 as World-View Imaging Corporation when the Commerce Department licensed it to build and operate a satellite system to gather digital images for commercial use.

EXECUTIVES

Executive Vice President Chief Technical Officer Founder, Walter S. Scott, age 55, $270,386 total compensation

SVP and General Manager Defense and Intelligence, Jeffrey S. (Jeff) Kerridge, age 51

President; Chief Executive Officer; Director, Jeffrey R. (Jeff) Tarr, age 50

Chairman, Gen. Howell M. Estes III, age 72

SVP Secretary and General Counsel, J. Alison Alfers, age 46, $252,598 total compensation

EVP Strategy and Product, H. John Oechsle, age 50

Executive Vice President Chief Financial Officer Treasurer, Yancey L. Spruill, age 45, $304,633 total compensation

SVP Commercial Sales, Rafay Khan

SVP and CIO, Scott M. Hicar

VP Government Relations, Dawn Sienicki

VP U.S. Defense Strategy., Jack Hild

VP Investor Relations, David Banks

Senior Vice President - Sales, Bert Turner

Senior Vice President; Chief Human Resources Officer, Grover N. Wray

Senior Vice President Government Relations, Marcy Steinke

Executive Vice President Operations and Customer Experience, Timothy M. Hascall

Senior Vice President Strategy and Corporate Development, Amy Shapero

Senior Vice President General Counsel, Dan Jablonsky

Senior Vice President - Government Relations, Marcy Steinke-Fike

Senior Vice President; General Counsel; Secretary, Daniel Jablonsky

Chief Accounting Officer, Susan Fox

Senior Vice President U.S. Government Sales, Chris Tully

Director, Warren C. Jenson, age 57

President CEO and Director, Jeffrey R. (Jeff) Tarr, age 50

Director, James M. (Jim) Whitehurst, age 46
Director, Paul M. Albert Jr., age 70
Director, Kimberly Till, age 57
Director, Eddy Zervigon, age 44
Director, Nick S. Cyprus
Director, Alden V. (Al) Munson Jr., age 70
Auditors: PricewaterhouseCoopersLLP

LOCATIONS

HQ: DigitalGlobe Inc.
  1601 Dry Creek Dr. Ste. 260, Longmont CO 80503
Phone: 303-684-4000   Fax: 303-682-3848
Web: www.digitalglobe.com

2012 Sales

	$ mil.	% of total
US	295	70
Other countries	125	30
Total	421	100

PRODUCTS/OPERATIONS

2012 Sales

	$ mil.	% of total
Defense & intelligence	321	76
Commercial	100	24
Total	421	100

Selected Products

Crisis Event Service (Web-based access to pre- and post-event images of world disasters)
ImageConnect (downloadable georeferenced aerial and satellite photos)
ImageScape (3D terrain models)
Orthorectified geospatial images
Satellite images (basic standard stereo pair 8-band multispectral)
WorldView Elevation Suite (elevation datasets over rural areas of low vegetation)

COMPETITORS

GeoEye	Orbital Sciences
Google	Trimble Navigation
Microsoft	

HISTORICAL FINANCIALS

Company Type: Public

Income Statement

FYE: December 31

	REVENUE ($ mil.)	NET INCOME ($ mil.)	NET PROFIT MARGIN	EMPLOYEES
12/12	421.4	39.0	9.3%	749
12/11	339.5	(28.1)	—	708
12/10	322.2	4.1	1.3%	629
12/09	281.9	47.4	16.8%	507
12/08	275.2	53.8	19.5%	464
Annual Growth	11.2%	(7.7%)	—	12.7%

2012 Year-End Financials

Debt ratio: 30.6%
Return on equity: 7.5%
Cash ($ mil.): 246
Current ratio: 3.32
Long-term debt ($ mil.): 478

No. of shares (mil.): 47
Dividends
  Yield: —
  Payout: —
Market value ($ mil.): 1,151

	STOCK PRICE ($) FY Close	P/E High/Low		PER SHARE ($) Earnings	Dividends	Book Value
12/12	24.44	31	14	0.84	0.00	11.45
12/11	17.11	—	—	(0.61)	0.00	10.52
12/10	31.71	366	241	0.09	0.00	10.87
12/09	24.20	24	16	1.06	0.00	10.63
Annual Growth	0.3%	—	—	(7.5%)	—	2.5%

Diodes, Inc.

Diodes Incorporated knows how important it is to be discrete in business. The company makes discrete semiconductors —fixed-function devices that are much less complex than integrated circuits. Diodes' products include diodes transistors and rectifiers; they are used by computer and consumer electronics manufacturers in products such as notebooks LCD monitors smartphones and game consoles. Other applications include power supplies climate control systems GPS devices and networking gear. Cisco LG Electronics Samsung Flextronics and Hon Hai are among its 150 OEM and contract manufacturing customers. The company's products are sold throughout Asia Europe and North America.

Geographic Reach

Asia is the Texas-based company's largest market accounting for more than 75% of its annual sales. China is its single largest market contributing 35% of sales followed by Taiwan (20%). Together Germany and the UK contribute about 9% of sales as does the US.

Operations

The semiconductor manufacturer operates design marketing and engineering centers in the US the UK Germany and Taiwan as well as a joint venture manufacturing plants in China and other manufacturing facilities in Neuhaus Germany and Taiwan.

Sales and Marketing

The company markets and sells its products worldwide through direct sales and marketing personnel independent sales representatives and distributors in the US Europe and Asia. Customers include about 150 leading OEMs as well as major electronic manufacturing service (EMS) providers. Additionally Diodes has about 65 distributor customers including Arrow Electronics and Avnet through which it indirectly serves more than 10000 customers worldwide. End users for the company's semiconductors include the: consumer electronics (33% of net sales); computing (28% of sales); Industrial (about 20% of sales); communications (about 15%) and automotive industries.

Financial Performance

The semiconductor maker's sales were flat in 2012 compared with 2011 at about $634 million. The company attributed the weak sales growth to a 10% increase in units sold offset by a 10% decrease in average selling price (ASP). ASP came under pressure from customers competitors and product mix. Asia was Diodes' best performing market in 2012 with sales there up 5% year over year on increased demand from China and South Korea.

Net income declined 52% in 2012 versus 201 to $24.1 million on margin pressure partially offset by a $4 million gain on asset sales in Europe and Taiwan. Manufacturing and raw materials costs particularly gold costs squeezed margins as did lower equipment utilization. 2012 marked the second consecutive year of steeply declining net income.

Strategy

Diodes is under continuous pressure from customers and competitors to reduce the prices of its products which can result in lower sales and profits for the company. The company has countered by expanding into higher-margin proprietary product lines such as high-density arrays and ultra-miniature switching diodes used in mobile applications. It also continues to become more vertically integrated which brings down cost and increases efficiency of operations. Diodes is looking to expand manufacturing capacity R&D capabilities product development and its sales and marketing organization in part through acquisitions. It's also looking to reduce its gold consumption.

In 2013 Diodes enhanced its general-purpose low-voltage CMOS (complementary metal-oxide-semiconductor) logic family for wide application range by adding shift registers. It also expanded its power-circuit densities with integrate high-voltage regulator transistors.

Mergers and Acquisitions

In 2013 the company acquired BCD Semiconductor Manufacturing Limited for about $151 million in an effort to broaden its reach in Asia particularly China where BCD is strong. Previously Diodes purchased Power Analog Microelectronics a provider of advanced analog and high-voltage power ICs for $16 million in 2012. The purchase strengthened its position in analog products.

Ownership

Lite-On Semiconductor a company that is part of Taiwan's Lite-On Technology is Diodes largest shareholder with about 18% the stock. Lite-On Semiconductor is also Diodes' biggest customer and its biggest supplier. Investment firm T. Rowe Price owns about 13% of Diodes' shares.

EXECUTIVES

President; Chief Executive Officer; Director, Keh-Shew Lu, age 67, $343,000 total compensation
Senior Vice President - Operations, Joseph Liu, age 71, $248,000 total compensation
Chairman, Raymond Soong, age 72
Vice Chairman, C. H. Chen, age 70, $62,500 total compensation
Senior Vice President - Sales and Marketing, Mark A. King, age 54, $215,000 total compensation
Senior Vice President - Business Development, Hans Rohrer, age 64
Vice President - Corporate Administration, Edmund (Ed) Tang, age 66
Vice President - Europe Sales and Marketing; President - Europe, Colin Greene, age 57
Vice President - Worldwide Discrete Products, Francis Tang, age 59
Chief Financial Officer; Treasurer; Secretary, Richard D. White, age 66, $170,000 total compensation
Vice President - Worldwide Analog Products, Julie Holland, age 51
VP Packaging Operations, T.J. Lee, age 64
Vice President - Corporate Supply Chain/Planning; Outsourcing and Quality, Clemente Beltran
President CEO and Director, Keh-Shew Lu, age 66
Vice Chairman, C. H. Chen, age 70
Director, Michael R. Giordano, age 67
Director, John M. Stich, age 71
Director, L.P. Hsu, age 74
Director, Michael K. C. Tsai
Auditors: MossAdamsLLP

LOCATIONS

HQ: Diodes Incorporated
  15660 Dallas Pkwy. Ste. 850, Dallas TX 75248
Phone: 972-385-2810   Fax: 800-232-9396
Web: www.dixonticonderoga.com

2012 Sales

	$ mil.	% of total
Asia	497	78
Europe	68	11
North America	67	11
Total	633	100

2012 Sales by Customer Location

	$ mil.	% of total
China	223	35
Taiwan	126	20
Switzerland	57	9
US	54	9
South Korea	50	8
UK	28	5
Singapore	27	4
Germany	24	4
Other countries	40	6
Total	**633**	**100**

PRODUCTS/OPERATIONS

2012 Sales by Market

	% of total
Consumer	33
Computing	28
Industrial	19
Communications	16
Automotive	4
Total	**100**

Selected Products

Diodes
  Schottky diodes
  Switching diodes
  Zener diodes
High-density arrays
Metal oxide semiconductor field-effect transistors
  (MOSFETs)
Rectifiers
  Bridge rectifiers
  Schottky rectifiers
  Standard fast superfast and ultrafast recovery rectifiers
Transient voltage suppressors
  Thyristor surge protection devices
  Zener transient-voltage suppressors
Transistors
  Bipolar transistors
  Darlington transistors
  Prebiased transistors

COMPETITORS

Advanced Photonix
BCD Semiconductor
Fairchild Semiconductor
IXYS
Infineon Technologies
International Rectifier
Microsemi
NXP Semiconductors
ON Semiconductor
ROHM
STMicroelectronics
Sanken Electric
Shindengen Electric Manufacturing
Siliconix
Toshiba Semiconductor & Storage Products
Vishay Intertechnology

HISTORICAL FINANCIALS

Company Type: Public

Income Statement

FYE: December 31

	REVENUE ($ mil.)	NET INCOME ($ mil.)	NET PROFIT MARGIN	EMPLOYEES
12/12	633.8	24.1	3.8%	4,605
12/11	635.2	50.7	8.0%	4,499
12/10	612.8	76.7	12.5%	3,986
12/09	434.3	7.5	1.7%	3,501
12/08	432.7	38.9	9.0%	3,067
Annual Growth	**10.0%**	**(11.3%)**	**—**	**10.7%**

2012 Year-End Financials

Debt ratio: 5.7%
Return on equity: 3.6%
Cash ($ mil.): 157
Current ratio: 4.33
Long-term debt ($ mil.): 44

No. of shares (mil.): 46
Dividends
  Yield: —
  Payout: —
Market value ($ mil.): 798

	STOCK PRICE ($) FY Close	P/E High/Low		PER SHARE ($) Earnings	Dividends	Book Value
12/12	17.35	51	25	0.51	0.00	14.72
12/11	21.30	31	15	1.09	0.00	13.95
12/10	26.99	16	8	1.68	0.00	12.12
12/09	20.41	121	31	0.17	0.00	10.08
12/08	6.06	32	4	0.91	0.00	9.00
Annual Growth	**30.1%**	**—**	**—**	**(13.5%)**	**—**	**13.1%**

Donegal Group Inc.

Risk is Donegal Group's middle name. Through its subsidiaries including Atlantic States Insurance and Southern Insurance Company of Virginia Donegal Group provides clients in 22 mid-Atlantic midwestern and southeastern states with personal farm and commercial property/casualty insurance products. The group's personal insurance offerings range from auto and boat policies to homeowners and fire coverage; its commercial insurance products include business owners multiperil and workers' compensation. Donegal's financial services arm owns Union Community Bank with 13 branches in Pennsylvania. Donegal Mutual Insurance controls two-thirds of the company's voting stock.

Donegal Group's subsidiaries provide insurance cooperatively with Donegal Mutual. The collective insurance businesses target customers in small to midsized regional communities to allow for local market knowledge and more personal services. Pennsylvania is the company's largest market accounting for more than a third of revenues; personal auto policies are account for 40% of its written net premiums. It distributes its products through some 2500 independent agencies.

Donegal Group's growth strategy is to acquire property/casualty insurance companies to augment its organic growth in existing markets and to expand into new markets. The company has completed a half-dozen acquisitions since 1995. In 2011 the company began writing business in Indiana as part of its organic geographic expansion.

While Donegal Group's revenues from premiums and investments have climbed steadily across the years so have its expenses and underwriting losses resulting in a tumbling net income. It brought in revenues of $475 million in 2011 but saw its net income drop from $11.5 million 2010 down to $0.45 million in 2011. Much of that year's loss can be tied to an 80% jump in claims due to adverse weather events and an increase in litigation as a result of the economic recession.

Donegal Group (along with Donegal Mutual) already held Province Bank with three branches in Pennsylvania when it acquired Union National Financial in 2011. Province Bank was merged into Union National's Union Community Bank with more than a dozen branches in Lancaster County Pennsylvania.

To expand in the Midwest the firm also acquired the outstanding stock of property/casualty insurer

Michigan Insurance Company from West Bend Mutual Insurance for some $39 million in late 2010. Previous growth in the region included the 2008 acquisition of Wisconsin-based mutual property/casual insurer Sheboygan Falls Insurance Company. Donegal Group also expanded in the Atlantic states in 2009 by forming an affiliation with Southern Mutual Insurance Company.

EXECUTIVES

SVP Claims Donegal Group and Donegal Mutual, Robert G. Shenk, age 59, $229,000 total compensation
SVP Human Resources, Kevin G. Burke
President CEO and Director Donegal Group and Donegal Mutual, Donald H. Nikolaus, age 70, $555,000 total compensation
Chairman Donegal Group and Donegal Mutual, Philip H. Glatfelter II, age 83
SVP and CFO Donegal Group and Donegal Mutual, Jeffrey D. Miller, age 48, $187,000 total compensation
SVP and Treasurer Donegal Group and Donegal Mutual, Daniel J. Wagner, age 52, $180,000 total compensation
SVP and Chief Underwriting Officer Donegal Group and Donegal Mutual, Cyril J. Greenya, age 68, $180,000 total compensation
SVP Personal Lines Underwriting, Jeffrey A. Jacobsen
VP General Casualty Claims, Steven P. Klipa
VP Marketing and Advertising, David S. Krenkel
VP Bodily Injury Claims, Janet L. Weisberg
SVP Marietta Marketing and Corporate Development Officer Affiliations and Acquisitions, Richard G. Kelley
SVP Underwriting, William H. Shupert
Secretary, Sheri O. Smith
VP and Chief Actuary, Chester J. Szczepanski
SVP Commercial Lines Underwriting, Francis J. Haefner Jr.
VP Claims Recovery, Thomas J. Kovach
SVP and CIO, Sanjay Pandey
VP Personal Lines Underwriting, David W. Sponic
SVP and Chief Investment Officer, V. Anthony Viozzi
SVP Commercial Lines, Ann H. Zaprazny
Senior Vice President Sales and Marketing Field Operations, Randall R. Farless
SVP Business Services, William M. Anderson
VP and Controller, Jason M. Crumbling
VP Commercial Lines Underwriting, George A. Ludwig
VP Internal Audit, Christina M. Springer
VP Claims, Thomas D. Richards
Regional Vice President, James R. Parker
Vice President, David B. Johnson
Regional Vice President Ohio Region, James C. Stiegler
Senior Vice President Manager, Janice L. Tupper
Vice President Quality Assurance, Kari A. Jacobson
Vice President, Kerri R. McNees
President Treasurer, Lee F. Wilcox
Vice President, Michelle A. Zimmerman
Vice President, Ray Z. Haag
Regional Vice President Director of Marketing and Sales, Richard A. Mason
Vice President and House Counsel, Robert R. Long
Vice President Commercial Lines Underwriting, Eric W. Pippen
Vice President Claims, William A. Folmar
Vice President, Andrew G. Fischer
President CEO and Director Donegal Group and Donegal Mutual, Donald H. Nikolaus, age 70
Director, Robert S. Bolinger, age 76
Director, Philip A. Garcia, age 55

Director, R. Richard Sherbahn, age 83
Director, John J. Lyons, age 73
Director, Patricia A. Gilmartin, age 73
Director, S. Trezevant (Trez) Moore Jr., age 59
Director, Richard D. Wampler II, age 71
Director, John M. Mahan, age 43
Director, Kevin M. Kraft Sr., age 60
Independent Director, Jack L. Hess
Auditors: KPMGLLP

LOCATIONS

HQ: Donegal Group Inc.
1195 River Road, P.O. Box 302, Marietta, PA 17547
Phone: 717 426-1931
Web: www.donegalgroup.com

2009 Premiums

Pennsylvania	37
Maryland	9
Georgia	5
Ohio	3
Wisconsin	3
Nebraska	2
Other	2

PRODUCTS/OPERATIONS

2011 Net Written Premiums

Personal	
Homeowners	20
Commercial	
Workers' compensation	11
Other commercial	2

Selected Subsidiaries

Atlantic States Insurance Company
Donegal Financial Services Corporation (48%)
  Union National Financial
    Union Community Bank
Le Mars Insurance Company
Michigan Insurance Company
The Peninsula Insurance Company
  Peninsula Indemnity Company
Sheboygan Falls Insurance Company
Southern Insurance Company of Virginia

COMPETITORS

AIG	Harleysville Group
Allstate	Liberty Mutual
American National	Penn National Mutual
Insurance	Casualty
Berkley Mid-Atlantic	Penn-America
Group	Progressive
COUNTRY Financial	Corporation
Erie Indemnity	RLI
GAINSCO	State Farm
GEICO	

HISTORICAL FINANCIALS

Company Type: Public

Income Statement

FYE: December 31

	ASSETS ($ mil.)	NET INCOME ($ mil.)	INCOME AS % OF ASSETS	EMPLOYEES
12/12	1,336.8	23.0	1.7%	0
12/11	1,290.7	0.4	0.0%	0
12/10	1,174.6	11.4	1.0%	0
12/09	935.6	18.8	2.0%	0
12/08	880.1	25.5	2.9%	0
Annual Growth	11.0%	(2.5%)	—	—

2012 Year-End Financials

Return on assets: 1.7%	Dividends
Return on equity: 5.8%	Yield: 3.4%
Long-term debt ($ mil.): —	Payout: 53.5%
No. of shares (mil.): 25	Market value ($ mil.): 359
Sales ($ mil): 514	

	STOCK PRICE ($) FY Close	P/E High/Low		PER SHARE ($) Earnings	Dividends	Book Value
12/12	14.04	17	13	0.91	0.49	15.63
12/11	14.16	765	576	0.02	0.48	15.01
12/10	14.48	35	24	0.46	0.46	14.86
12/09	15.54	23	16	0.76	0.44	15.12
12/08	16.77	19	12	1.02	0.41	14.29
Annual Growth	(4.3%)	—	—	(2.8%)	4.7%	2.3%

Dorman Products Inc

Got parts? Dorman does. From its stock of more than 130000 products Dorman Products (formerly R&B Inc.) is a leading supplier of automotive replacement parts (including brake parts) fasteners and service line products to the automotive aftermarket. It also provides household hardware and organization items to mass merchants. About 85% of revenue comes from parts sold under Dorman's sub-brands which include AutoGrade FirstStop and OE Solutions. Dorman sells to auto aftermarket retailers and warehouse distributors (such as AutoZone CARQUEST) as well as to parts manufacturers for resale under private labels. Dorman distributes its products in the North America Asia Europe and the Middle East.

Geographic Reach

Pennsylvania-based Dorman Products has about 15 warehouse and office facilities throughout North America and overseas in China and India. Dorman purchases about 80% of its products from international suppliers primarily in China. More than 90% of the company's sale come from customers in North America.

Sales and Marketing

About half of Dorman's products are primarily sold through automotive aftermarket retails such as AutoZone Advance Auto Parts and O'Reilly Automotive. Distributors such as CARQUEST and NAPA account for more than 40% of the company's sales. International customers sales to mass merchants (including Wal-Mart Stores) and salvage yards represent the rest. In 2012 AutoZone Advance Auto Parts O'Reilly and Genuine Parts each accounted for more than 10% of sales and 57% of total sales.

Financial Performance

Dorman's sales grew 8% in 2012 versus 2011 to $570 million. Net income increased 33% over the same period to $71 million. The company credited strong demand for its products and higher new product sales for the gains. Indeed sales profits and cash flow have risen steadily since 2008 as tough economic times across North America drove demand in the automotive aftermarket and in turn Dorman's own business because drivers kept their cars longer and took a do-it-yourself approach to auto maintenance.

Strategy

Introducing new products to the automotive aftermarket has been central to Dorman's strategy. The company attributes its growth over the years to its development of a wide assortment of parts and accessories many of which Dorman believes may not have been easily available otherwise and which improve upon the original parts being replaced. As such the firm has made increased investments in product development resources and

marketing programs to strengthen its ties to customers. Indeed spending on research and development has more than doubled from $4.6 million in 2010 to $10.5 million in 2012.

As its business in North America continues to grow the company cut its losses overseas with the sale of its ScanTech subsidiary in Sweden in late 2011. ScanTech distributed a line of Volvo and Saab replacement parts worldwide.

Mergers and Acquisitions

In October 2013 Dorman acquired North Carolina-base Re-Involt Technologies an aftermarket leader in hybrid battery remanufacturing technology. The purchase enables Dorman to refine its process for remanufacturing hybrid drive batteries develop new hybrid products for the aftermarket and ultimately capture sales of replacement batteries for hybrid vehicles a growing segment of the vehicle market.

Ownership

Chairman and CEO Steven Berman and his family control the company through their ownership of 31% of Dorman's common stock. Formerly COO of the company Steven succeeded his late brother Richard as CEO in 2011. The Berman brothers founded Dorman Products in 1978. Royce & Associates owns about 10% of the shares.

EXECUTIVES

SVP and CFO, Mathias J. Barton, age 53, $306,940 total compensation
President CEO COO Secretary Treasurer and Director, Steven L. Berman, age 54, $529,973 total compensation
SVP Product, Joseph M. Beretta, age 58, $287,174 total compensation
VP General Counsel and Assistant Secretary, Thomas J. Knoblauch, age 57
CFO, Matthew S. Kohnke, age 41
Senior Vice President - Supply Chain, Louis Arace
Senior Vice President - Product, Michael Kealey
Director, Richard T. Riley, age 57
President CEO COO Secretary Treasurer and Director, Steven L. Berman, age 54
Director, Paul R. Lederer, age 74
Director, Edgar W. Levin, age 80
Auditors: KPMGLLP

LOCATIONS

HQ: Dorman Products Inc.
3400 E. Walnut St., Colmar PA 18915-1800
Phone: 215-997-1800   **Fax:** 215-997-8577
Web: www.dormanproducts.com

PRODUCTS/OPERATIONS

2012 Sales

	% of total
Automotive	49
Warehouse	43
International & special markets (includes mass merchants & salvage	8
Total	**100**

2012 Sales

	% of total
Power-train	33
Automotive	30
Chassis	26
Hardware	11
Total	**100**

Selected Subsidiaries

Allparts Inc.
RB Distribution Inc.
RB Management Inc.
RB Vest Inc.

HISTORICAL FINANCIALS

Company Type: Public

Income Statement

FYE: December 29

	REVENUE ($ mil.)	NET INCOME ($ mil.)	NET PROFIT MARGIN	EMPLOYEES
12/12	570.4	70.9	12.4%	1,321
12/11	529.2	53.2	10.1%	1,265
12/10	455.7	46.1	10.1%	1,185
12/09	377.3	26.5	7.0%	997
12/08	342.3	17.8	5.2%	966
Annual Growth	13.6%	41.3%		8.1%

2012 Year-End Financials

Debt ratio: —	No. of shares (mil.): 36
Return on equity: 21.9%	Dividends
Cash ($ mil.): 27	Yield: 0.0%
Current ratio: 5.75	Payout: 77.3%
Long-term debt ($ mil.): —	Market value ($ mil.): 1,246

	STOCK PRICE ($) FY Close	P/E High/Low	PER SHARE ($) Earnings	Dividends	Book Value
12/12	34.15	26 11	1.94	1.50	9.13
12/11	36.93	29 19	1.47	0.00	8.77
12/10	35.99	36 12	1.28	0.00	7.36
12/09	15.76	22 9	0.74	0.00	6.09
12/08	12.69	29 13	0.50	0.00	5.32
Annual Growth	28.1%	— —	40.7%	—	14.4%

Drew Industries, Inc.

Drew Industries is a dream factory; it makes wanderlust —in comfort and style —a possibility. The company manufactures aluminum and vinyl windows and doors and other products (furniture and slide-out walls) for travel trailers and fifth-wheel recreational vehicles (RVs) (some 80% of sales) and manufactured housing (MH). Drew does business via two subsidiaries: Kinro produces windows doors and screens and Lippert Components churns out axles ramps and chassis parts as well as specialty trailers for hauling boats and snowmobiles. Customers include homebuilders Clayton Homes and Cavco Industries and RV makers Thor Industries and Forest River. Drew operates about 25 facilities in roughly a dozen states.

The company has made its mark in the RV and manufactured housing industries primarily by growing through acquisitions. As a result of the economic downturn certain distressed manufacturers have placed their assets and intellectual property rights on the sales block and Drew Industries's subsidiaries have taken advantage of those opportunities. In 2011 Kinro acquired Starquest Products for an unnamed amount. The deal is expected to add more than $70 million in annualized sales.

Earlier in the year Lippert purchased certain assets of Indiana-based M-Tec Corporation for $6 million in cash. M-Tec brings its expertise in bridge beams which are used in certain motorhomes and will complement Lippert's motorhome chassis modification business. Prior to that the company acquired Home-Style Industries for $7.3 million. The Idaho-based manufacturer churns out a line of upholstered furniture and mattresses primarily for the towable RV market in the Northwest US.

Over a five-year period through 2010 Drew Industries acquired more than a dozen manufacturers as well as a slew of patent-pending designs used in manufactured homes RVs and specialty (such as horse cargo and utility) trailers. Deals included the purchase of Sellers Mfg. Inc. The half-a-million dollar deal snagged the assets for retrofitting chassis built by motor home RV bus and commercial truck OEMs and for producing the E-Z Cruise (an enhanced suspension system for motor homes and buses). The largest acquisition of 2010 targeted former rival Schwintek. Its purchase for $20 million included assets for an RV wall slide-out mechanism an aluminum cylinder integral to leveling motor homes and a power roof-lift used in tent campers. Separately Drew Industries spent for $1.4 million to pocket a patent-pending six-point leveling system for towable RVs.

The collapsed market for RVs and manufactured homes however has taken its toll on the company. Drew Industries' sales declined roughly 45% in 2009 from a high in 2006. The company suffered a loss in excess of $34 million in 2009 (following a 70% earnings plunge in 2008); much of the loss was attributable to the unprecedented cost of restructuring including a hefty goodwill impairment charge headcount reductions plant closings and start-ups bad debt and legacy tooling and inventory.

During 2010 demand for RVs and manufactured homes picked up modestly and Drew Industries' sales climbed more than 40% over 2009. The company's bottom line appreciably recovered climbing out of the red to more than $28 million. As a result cash generated from operations slumped under the pressure of carrying larger inventories to meet higher sales and an improved outlook.

HISTORY

Drew Industries was founded as Drew National Corp. in 1962. Drew purchased Kinro a maker of aluminum primary and storm windows for the manufactured-housing industry in 1980. The company reincorporated as Drew Industries in 1984. Under the leadership of Kinro president David Webster investor (and chairman) Edward Rose and CEO Leigh Abrams (who all took up their leadership positions in 1984) Drew pursued a strategy of diversifying within its niche market of supplying components to the RV and manufactured-home industries. Kinro subsequently acquired makers of aluminum windows for manufactured homes and manufacturers of doors and windows for recreational vehicles and in 1993 it began production of vinyl windows in addition to aluminum windows.

In 1996 Drew acquired Shoals a maker of axles and a distributor of refurbished axles and new and refurbished tires for manufactured homes. The next year Drew purchased Lippert which makes chassis and chassis parts and galvanized roofing for manufactured homes. Lippert CEO Douglas Lippert gained about a 19% stake in Drew as part of the deal. Drew bought Coil Clip (specialty steel parts supplier) in 1998. The company added five plants in 2000 to accommodate its booming RV chassis business.

In April 2001 the company gave a boost to its MH sales by acquiring rival Kevco's Better Bath division (bath fixtures). The next year Drew gained higher quarter sales numbers due to its implementation of cost-cutting measures and lower-than-normal product inventories.

Drew's Lippert Tire & Axle subsidiary sold its one remaining operation which engaged in refurbishing used axles and distributing used tires for manufactured homes in January 2003. Mid-year Drew expanded its RV segment through the purchase of LTM Manufacturing; later in the year Drew boosted its chassis manufacturing business into specialty chassis when subsidiary Lippert Components paid $3.6 million to acquire certain business and assets of specialty chassis manufacturer ET&T Frames Inc. of Elkhart Indiana.

Also in 2003 Drew transferred its stock listing to the New York Stock Exchange from the American Stock Exchange and began trading on the NYSE under the ticker DW in December of that year.

In 2004 the company's Better Bath division a part of its Kinro subsidiary entered into an equipment lease and license agreement with the buyer of certain of its intellectual property rights related to a process used in manufacturing a new composite material for use in fiberglass bathtubs. The $4 million sale included a five-year payoff period. Drew also acquired privately held Zieman Manufacturing Company a Whittier California-based manufacturer of trailers for equipment hauling boats personal watercrafts and snowmobiles; chassis and chassis parts for manufactured homes and RVs (mainly travel and fifth-wheel trailers); and specialty chassis for modular offices. Zieman became a part of Drew's Lippert Components business.

Lippert Components acquired the Venture Welding division of Banks Corporation for about $19 million in May 2005. Venture Welding manufactures chassis and chassis parts in Elkhart Indiana.

In 2004 and into 2005 a California state court rendered a verdict in favor of a former employee of Drew's Lippert Components subsidiary in connection with a workplace injury. The former employee was awarded $4 million in punitive damages and compensatory damages of $464000.

The hurricane extravaganza of 2005 was good to Drew Industries. Although not a FEMA supplier the company estimated a 6% increase in sales of both RVs and manufactured homes as dealers sold off inventory to meet demand. The increase offset to a certain extent slowing sales of RVs due to high gas prices.

In 2006 Lippert acquired recreational vehicle and manufactured home chassis supplier SteelCo Inc. for $4.5 million and Happijac which supplies bed-lift systems for RVs for $29.5 million. The following year Lippert purchased sister businesses Trailair and Equa-Flex makers of suspension systems used in towable RVs. In addition it bolted on Coach Step which produces electric steps for motor homes and Extreme Engineering and its affiliate Pivit Hitch specialty trailer makers (primarily for luxury boats).

Kinro expanded in 2008 pocketing Philips Products' inventory and equipment used in fabricating front entry doors for manufactured housing. Lippert also made several acquisitions in 2008 including Seating Technology based in Goshen Indiana and the patent for JT's Strong Arm Jack Stabilizer and other intellectual assets from JT's RV Accessories. In 2009 Lippert unveiled the Tow-N-Stow a first-of-a-kind storable trailer.

EXECUTIVES

President; Chief Executive Officer; Director, Fredric M. (Fred) Zinn, age 62, $450,000 total compensation

Chairman, Leigh J. Abrams, age 70, $400,000 total compensation

Chief Executive Officer, Jason D. Lippert, age 40, $700,000 total compensation

Manager Tax, John F. Cupak, age 62

Chief Financial Officer; Treasurer, Joseph S. Giordano III, age 44, $210,000 total compensation

VP Chief Legal Officer and Secretary, Harvey F. Milman, age 71

President and Chief Operating Officer, Scott T. Mereness, age 41, $360,000 total compensation

Corporate Controller and Assistant Secretary, Christopher L. Smith, age 36

National Director RV Sales Lippert Components and Kinro, Andy Murray

President; Chief Executive Officer; Director, Fredric M. (Fred) Zinn, age 62

Director, David A. Reed, age 65

Director, Frederick B. (Fred) Hegi Jr., age 69

Director, John B. (Jack) Lowe Jr.

Director, Edward W. (Rusty) Rose III, age 72

Director, James F. (Jim) Gero, age 68

Chief Executive Officer, Jason D. Lippert, age 40

Independent Director, Brendan Deely

Auditors: KPMGLLP

LOCATIONS

HQ: Drew Industries, Inc.
200 Mamaroneck Avenue, White Plains, NY 10601
Phone: 914 428-9098
Web: www.drewindustries.com

PRODUCTS/OPERATIONS

2010 Sales

	$ mil.	% of total
Recreational vehicles	477	83
Manufactured housing	95	17
Total	**572**	**100**

Selected Products

Manufactured housing (MH) products
  Aluminum and vinyl patio doors
  Axles
  Entry doors
  Steel and fiberglass entry doors
  Steel chassis
  Steel chassis parts
  Replacement windows doors thermoformed bath products
  Thermoformed bath and kitchen products
  Vinyl and aluminum windows and screens
Recreational vehicle (RV) products (travel trailers and fifth-wheel RVs)
  Aluminum windows and screens
  Chassis components
  Entry and baggage doors
  Entry steps
  Furniture and mattresses
  Manual electric and hydraulic stabilizer and lifting systems
  Patio doors
  Slide-out mechanisms
  Specialty trailers for hauling boats personal watercraft snowmobiles and equipment
  Thermoformed bath kitchen and other products
  Towable axles and suspensions
  Towable steel chassis
  Toy hauler ramp doors

Selected Subsidiaries

Kinro Inc.
Lippert Components Inc.

COMPETITORS

Atwood Mobile	Patrick Industries
Coast Distribution	Quality Trailer
Elixir Industries	Products
Euramax	Tomkins
Featherlite	Tuthill
LaSalle Bristol	Wozniak Industries
Meritor	

HISTORICAL FINANCIALS

Company Type: Public

Income Statement

FYE: December 31

	REVENUE ($ mil.)	NET INCOME ($ mil.)	NET PROFIT MARGIN	EMPLOYEES
12/12	901.1	37.3	4.1%	5,179
12/11	681.1	30.0	4.4%	4,130
12/10	572.7	28.0	4.9%	3,016
12/09	397.8	(24.0)	—	3,054
12/08	510.5	11.6	2.3%	2,223
Annual Growth	**15.3%**	**33.7%**	**—**	**23.5%**

2012 Year-End Financials

Debt ratio: —	No. of shares (mil.): 22
Return on equity: 13.2%	Dividends
Cash ($ mil.): 9	Yield: 6.2%
Current ratio: 2.21	Payout: 123.4%
Long-term debt ($ mil.): —	Market value ($ mil.): 732

	STOCK PRICE ($) FY Close	P/E High/Low	PER SHARE ($) Earnings	Dividends	Book Value
12/12	32.25	20 15	1.64	2.00	12.53
12/11	24.53	20 13	1.34	0.00	12.52
12/10	22.72	22 14	1.26	1.50	11.05
12/09	20.65	— —	(1.10)	0.00	11.11
12/08	12.00	53 18	0.53	0.00	12.03
Annual Growth	**28.0%**	**— —**	**32.6%**	**—**	**1.0%**

Dril-Quip, Inc.

Dril-Quip equips the folks who operate the expensive drills –the global deepwater oil and gas industry. The company specializes in deepwater harsh-environment and/or severe-condition equipment. Its products include drilling and production riser systems subsea and surface wellheads and production trees mudline hanger systems (which support the weight of each casing string at the mudline) and specialty connectors and pipe. Dril-Quip's offshore rig equipment includes drilling and completion riser systems wellhead connectors and diverters. The company also provides reconditioning tool rental and technical advisory services. It had work or service contracts with more than offshore rigs in 2012.

Geographic Reach

Dril-Quip's operations are organized into three geographic segments: Western Hemisphere (including North and South America; headquartered in Houston) Eastern Hemisphere (including Europe and Africa; headquartered in Aberdeen Scotland) and Asia/Pacific (including the Pacific Rim Southeast Asia Australia India and the Middle East; headquartered in Singapore).

Each of these segments sells similar products and services and the company has major manufacturing facilities in all three of its headquarter loca-

tions as well as in Macae Brazil. Dril-Quip has sales service and reconditioning facilities in Australia China Denmark Egypt Ghana the Netherlands Nigeria Norway Qatar and the US. In 2012 the company generated 74% of its total revenues outside of the US.

Sales and Marketing

Dril-Quip markets its products through its offices and sales representatives in the world's major energy markets. It markets its products and services directly through its sales personnel in two US and 19 international locations. In addition in some international markets where the company does not maintain offices it sells through independent sales representatives. The company has sales representatives in Brazil China India Indonesia Malaysia Saudi Arabia and the UAE. Sales are geared at major integrated large independent and foreign national oil and gas companies. A portion of its customer base consists of offshore drilling contractors and engineering and construction companies.

Dril-Quip advertises its products and services in trade and technical publications and participates in industry conferences and trade shows to enhance industry awareness of its products.

The company is not dependent on any one customer; its top 15 customers represented 62% of total revenues in 2012; Brazil's PETROBRAS accounted for about 12%. Keppel Fels is also a major customer.

Financial Performance

Dril-Quip reported 22% rise in revenues in 2012 compared to FY 2011 was primarily as a result of increased revenues in subsea equipment and surface equipment partially offset by lower in offshore rig equipment revenues. The reduction in the number of long-term projects with offshore rig equipment components dragged down offshore rig equipment sales. However product revenues increased in each of is geographic segments reflecting strong industry demand for the company's equipment. Increased service revenues in the Western Hemisphere and the Eastern Hemisphere helped to lift overall service revenues despite a slight decrease in the Asia-Pacific region. The bulk of revenue growith in services came from increased demand for technical advisory services and installation tool rentals.Net income increased by 25% in 2012 primarily due to higher revenues and lower special items expenses. Interest income increased due to good returns from its short-term investments and reduced interest expenses.

In 2012 ATP Oil & Gas filed for bankruptcy owing Dril-Quip $1.4 million in receivables.

Dril-Quip reported a year-over-year increase in revenues between 2008 and 2012 thanks to growing oil and gas industry demand with higher oil prices and growing energy consumption prompting oil and gas companies to make capital expenditures on exploration drilling and production operations offshore.

Strategy

The company continually introduces new products and product enhancements and sees its ability to develop new products and maintain technological advantages as key to its future success. Dril-Quip has introduced multiple new products including liner hangers subsea control systems and subsea manifolds.

Dril-Quip's product development work is conducted at its facilities in Houston Texas and Aberdeen Scotland. The company's application engineering staff provides engineering services to customers in connection with the design and sales of its products. The company's global manufacturing and servicing locations allow it to have short supply lines and delivery times for its clients in far-flung oil and gas fields worldwide.

Taking advantage of its strong manufacturing presence in Brazil in 2012 Dril-Quip secured a $650 million four-year contract from PETROBRAS to supply subsea wellhead systems and associated tools to be used in the drilling of deepwater wells offshore Brazil.

Expanding its manufacturing base in 2011 Dril-Quip opened a new manufacturing plant in Singapore valued at $33.2 million.

Company Background

Dril-Quip was founded in 1981.

EXECUTIVES

VP Finance and CFO, Jerry M. Brooks, age 61, $252,116 total compensation
Chairman, John V. Lovoi, age 52
President and CEO, Blake DeBerry
SVP and COO, James A. Gariepy
Vice President; General Counsel; Secretary, James C. Webster
Co-Chairman, Larry E. Reimert, age 64
Director, Alexander P. Shukis, age 68
Director, John V. Lovoi, age 51
Director, L. H. Dick Robertson, age 78
Auditors: BDOUSALLP

LOCATIONS

HQ: Dril-Quip Inc.
6401 N. Eldridge Pkwy., Houston TX 77041
Phone: 713-939-7711 **Fax:** 713-939-8063
Web: www.dril-quip.com

2012 Sales

	$ mil.	% of total
Western Hemisphere	367	50
Eastern Hemisphere	233	32
Asia/Pacific	131	18
Total	**733**	**100**

PRODUCTS/OPERATIONS

2012 Sales

	$ mil.	% of total
Products		
Subsea equipment	518	71
Offshore rig equipment	53	7
Surface equipment	38	5
Services	122	17
Total	**733**	**100**

Selected Products and Services

Products Group
  Diverters
  Drilling riser systems
  Mudline hanger systems
  Platform production trees
  Platform wellheads
  Production risers
  Specialty connectors
  Subsea production trees
  Subsea wellheads
  Surface wellheads
  Wellhead connectors
  Valves
  Well systems
Services Group
  Field installation
  Reconditioning
  Rental

COMPETITORS

ABB	Hornbeck Offshore
Aker Solutions	McDermott
Atwood Oceanics	Newpark Resources
Cameron International	Oceaneering
FMC Technologies	International

GE Oil	Parker Drilling
Global Power Equipment	Siem Offshore
GulfMark Offshore	Superior Energy
Helix Energy Solutions	Tesco Corporation
Hercules Offshore	

HISTORICAL FINANCIALS

Company Type: Public

Income Statement

FYE: December 31

	REVENUE ($ mil.)	NET INCOME ($ mil.)	NET PROFIT MARGIN	EMPLOYEES
12/12	733.0	119.2	16.3%	2,451
12/11	601.3	95.2	15.8%	2,194
12/10	566.2	102.2	18.1%	2,127
12/09	540.2	105.1	19.5%	2,130
12/08	542.7	105.5	19.5%	2,051
Annual Growth	7.8%	3.1%	—	4.6%

2012 Year-End Financials

Debt ratio: —	No. of shares (mil.): 40
Return on equity: 11.9%	Dividends
Cash ($ mil.): 257	Yield: —
Current ratio: 5.96	Payout: —
Long-term debt ($ mil.): —	Market value ($ mil.): 2,957

	STOCK PRICE ($) FY Close	P/E High/Low		PER SHARE ($) Earnings	Dividends	Book Value
12/12	73.05	26	20	2.94	0.00	26.35
12/11	65.82	34	21	2.36	0.00	23.03
12/10	77.72	32	16	2.55	0.00	20.68
12/09	56.48	22	7	2.66	0.00	17.78
12/08	20.51	24	5	2.62	0.00	14.34
Annual Growth	37.4%	—	—	2.9%	—	16.4%

DSW Inc

While you don't have to watch out for trees in this jungle you may want to watch your back. DSW (short for Designer Shoe Warehouse) sells discounted brand-name footwear for style-conscious men women and kids through nearly 400 stores in 40-plus US states and Puerto Rico as well as online at dsw.com. DSW stores average 22000 square feet and stock about 24000 pair of dress casual and athletic shoes as well as a complementary array of handbags hosiery and accessories. The company also operates about 355 leased departments inside stores operated by other retailers. DSW was founded in 1969 and merged with its majority shareholder Retail Ventures in 2011.

Change in Company Type

In May 2011 DSW bought out its majority shareholder Retail Ventures in an all-stock deal valued at about $773 million. Retail Ventures whose only operating business was its 62% stake in DSW became a subsidiary of DSW following the tax-free exchange of shares. The deal allowed Retail Ventures shareholders to become shareholders in DSW and eliminated the expenses associated maintaining Retail Venture's listing on the New York Stock Exchange.

Geographic Reach

Fast-growing DSW operates shoe stores in 42 US states the District of Columbia and Puerto Rico. Its two largest markets are California and Texas home to about 20% of its stores.

Operations

In addition to its historically-fast-growing retail operation DSW operates leased departments inside more than 260 stores operated by Stein Mart 83 Gordmans stores and one Frugal Fannie's Fashion Warehouse store. Leased departments accounted for 6% of DSW's fiscal 2013 (ended January) sales.

Sales and Marketing

DSW's marketing expenses totaled $55.9 million $50.9 million and $46.5 million in fiscal years 2013 2012 and 2011 respectively.

Financial Performance

DSW's fiscal 2013 (ended January) sales topped $2.2 billion a 12% increase versus the prior year. While sales at its company-owned shoe stores grew by 14% the leased departments posted a 13% decline in annual sales. (Sales at leased departments suffered as a result of the bankruptcy of Filene's Basement in 2011 resulting in the closure of 27 stores.) Sales at DSW stores open for at least one year increased 5.5% with all merchandise categories performing well. Sales also got a boost from the addition of nearly 40 new stores including the company's first in the District of Columbia and Puerto Rico. The company's sales have grown at a compounded annual rate of 10% since fiscal 2009.

Net income declined 16% in fiscal 2013 versus 2012 to $146.4 million because of an income tax provision of $95 million.

Strategy

The historically fast-growing company has returned to a more aggressive growth strategy after a hiatus during the deep recession and its aftermath.(DSW was a relatively-strong performer throughout the recession which left many other retailers struggling with falling sales.) In fiscal 2014 the chain plans to open 25 to 30 new stores with an ultimate goal of 450 to 500 stores. The new locations will be in both new and existing markets. To grow its online business the shoe seller will offer styles sizes and widths not available in local stores. DSW is also looking for new partner retailers for its leased department business. The company targets fashion-focused men and women from wide-ranging socioeconomic and demographic backgrounds. It looks to capture these shoppers by offering a broad selection of in-season styles at prices that rival the sales deals found in department stores.

Ownership

DSW chairman Jay Schottenstein owns nearly 63% of the combined voting power of all classes of DSW's common stock.

EXECUTIVES

Chairman, Jay L. Schottenstein, age 59, $500,000 total compensation
President and Chief Executive Officer; Director, Michael R. (Mike) MacDonald, age 61, $730,769 total compensation
Executive Vice President and Chief Marketing Officer, Derek Ungless, age 64
Executive Vice President and Chief Financial Officer, Douglas J. (Doug) Probst, age 48, $465,385 total compensation
Vice Chairman and Chief Merchandising Officer, Deborah L. Ferree, age 59, $846,764 total compensation
Executive Vice President and General Counsel, William L. Jordan, age 41
Executive Vice President Supply Chain and Merchandise Planning and Allocation, Harris Mustafa, age 59, $536,154 total compensation

Executive Vice President Stores and Operations,
Carrie McDermott
President and Chief Executive Officer; Director,
Michael R. (Mike) MacDonald, age 61
Vice Chairman and Chief Merchandising Officer,
Deborah L. Ferree, age 59
Auditors: Deloitte&ToucheLLP

LOCATIONS

HQ: DSW Inc
810 DSW Drive, Columbus, OH 43219
Phone: 614 237-7100
Web: www.dswinc.com

2013 Stores

	No.
California	37
Texas	32
Florida	25
New	25
Illinois	20
Pennsylvania	18
Michigan	15
New	15
Ohio	15
Georgia	14
Massachusetts	14
Virginia	14
Maryland	13
Colorado	10
Minnesota	9
Indiana	8
Arizona	7
North	7
Washington	7
Connecticut	6
Missouri	5
Tennessee	5
Wisconsin	5
Alabama	4
Oregon	4
Kentucky	3
Nevada	3
District of	2
Kansas	2
Louisiana	2
Nebraska	2
New	2
Oklahoma	2
Rhode	2
Utah	2
Arkansas	1
Delaware	1
Idaho	1
Iowa	1
Maine	1
Mississippi	1
North	1
Puerto	1
Total	**364**

PRODUCTS/OPERATIONS

2013 Sales

	% of total
Women's	65
Men's	16
Athletic	12
Accessories &	7
Total	**100**

2013 Sales

	$ mil.	% of total
DSW stores	2,125	94
Leased departments	132	6
Total	**2,257**	**100**

COMPETITORS

Belk	Rack Room Shoes
Brown Shoe	Ross Stores
Collective Brands	Sears
Dillard's	Shoe Carnival

Foot Locker	Steven Madden
Iconix Brand Group	TJX Companies
J. C. Penney Company	Target Corporation
Kenneth Cole	The Gap
Kohl's	Wal-Mart
Macy's	Zappos.com
Nine West	shoebuy.com
Payless ShoeSource	

HISTORICAL FINANCIALS

Company Type: Public

Income Statement

FYE: February 2

	REVENUE ($ mil.)	NET INCOME ($ mil.)	NET PROFIT MARGIN	EMPLOYEES
02/13*	2,257.7	146.4	6.5%	11,000
01/12	2,024.3	174.7	8.6%	10,800
01/11	1,822.3	107.6	5.9%	10,500
01/10	1,602.6	54.7	3.4%	10,000
01/09	1,462.9	26.9	1.8%	10,000
Annual Growth	**11.5%**	**52.7%**	**—**	**2.4%**

*Fiscal year change

2013 Year-End Financials

Debt ratio: —
Return on equity: 17.5%
Cash ($ mil.): 81
Current ratio: 2.98
Long-term debt ($ mil.): —

No. of shares (mil.): 90
Dividends
Yield: 0.0%
Payout: 88.8%
Market value ($ mil.): 6,081

	STOCK PRICE ($) FY Close	P/E High/Low		PER SHARE ($) Earnings	Dividends	Book Value
02/13*	67.55	43	30	1.62	1.44	9.54
01/12	49.49	22	13	2.27	1.15	9.08
01/11	33.28	33	18	1.20	0.00	7.25
01/10	24.10	43	11	0.62	0.00	5.98
01/09	9.98	67	26	0.31	0.00	5.29
Annual Growth	**61.3%**	**—**	**—**	**51.7%**	**—**	**15.9%**

*Fiscal year change

Ducommun Inc.

Too common? Not at all Ducommun. The company designs and makes aerostructures and electromechanical components for commercial and military aircraft as well as for missile and space programs. Ducommun AeroStructures (DAS) engineers and manufactures structures and assemblies such as aircraft wing spoilers and helicopter blades using aluminum composites and titanium. Ducommun LaBarge Technologies (DLT) makes electromechanical components such as switch assemblies actuators keyboard panels and avionics racks. Its Miltec subsidiary designs missile and aerospace systems. Products for military and space applications account for about 32% of sales. Aircraft giant Boeing represents about 19% of sales.

DAS' production techniques include stretch-forming (the creation of large structural shapes from aluminum sheet metal extrusions) and hot-forming (metal working at high temperature) and computer-controlled machining. The segment also provides chemical milling (the removal of material to reduce weight) services. Commercial aerospace account for 55% of DAS' sales while military and space applications represent the rest.

DLT was created in 2011 when the company's Technologies segment was merged with newly ac-

quired LaBarge a St. Louis-based electronics component manufacturer. Besides making electronic electromechanical and interconnect systems and components DLT offers services that include design integration and testing for advanced weapons and missile defense systems. Military and space applications account for 58% of the segment's sales while commercial aerospace natural resources industrial medical and other markets represent the rest.

With facilities in Alabama Arizona Arkansas California Kansas Mississippi Missouri New York Oklahoma Pennsylvania and Wisconsin Ducommun also operates plants in Mexico and Thailand.

Ducommun's sales surged 42% in 2011 compared with 2010 thanks in part to the contribution of the LaBarge acquisition. By segment DAS' sales rose about 8% over the same period while DLT's soared about 111%. Product sales increased 50% in 2011 vs. 2010 but service sales decreased 30%. The company also weathered a net loss of more than $47 million in 2011 as the result in part of expenses related to its acquisition activity and greater interest demands.

Acquisitions are a major element of Ducommun's strategy. In 2011 the company expanded its capabilities by paying about $325.3 million to acquire LaBarge. LaBarge's products –including circuit board assemblies —served customers in the aerospace and defense industries as well as the medical energy and industrial markets. The deal added more than 10 manufacturing sites in six states to Ducommun's assets.

Considered the oldest company in California with a founding date of 1849 Ducommun is dedicated to new technologies for the aerospace industry. It was the first to make all-composite rotor blades for Sikorsky S-61 helicopters; traditional blades were made of a mixture of metal and composite materials.

HISTORY

Swiss immigrant Charles Ducommun walked from Arkansas to California to take part in the California Gold Rush in 1849. He soon started a small watch-repair shop and then expanded his business to include general supplies. In the early 1900s the firm moved into the metals business as Ducommun Hardware Company and started making parts for California's aviation industry. The firm profited from increased demand during both World Wars and by the 1960s Ducommun had expanded into the electronics industry. It sold its metals business in 1981 and used the proceeds to buy aerospace companies.

The semiconductor business went bust in the early 1980s hurting Ducommun's sales. In 1986 the "Challenger" space shuttle explosion also took its toll on the company as the government scaled back on the space program. In 1987 Ducommun sold its electronics companies to Arrow Electronics the world's leading electronics distributor.

In 1988 the company began cutting costs and restructuring and by 1990 had made a small profit. In 1994 Ducommun began to remake itself as an aerospace component supplier. It bought Brice (aircraft seating 1994) 3dbm (telecommunications 1995) and MechTronics (radar enclosures 1996). A revived aerospace industry took off in 1997 fueling Ducommun's growth. Focusing on the aerospace industry the company sold 3dbm to COM DEV International (1998) and bought Jordan Industries' titanium components unit (1999).

In 2001 Ducommun announced the creation of Ducommun AeroStructures a combination of three of its subsidiaries (AHF-Ducommun Incorporated

Aerochem Inc. and Parsons Precision Products Inc.) in an effort to reduce costs. Later in the year the company combined Ducommun AeroStructures with Composite Structures LLC. Ducommun sold Brice Manufacturing Company its airline seating manufacturer in 2002. The next year Ducommun acquired DBP Microwave a maker of radio frequency and microwave switches and incorporated those operations into its Technologies sector.

Ducommun went on a buying spree in 2006 spending roughly $66 million to acquire three new operations. Those were Miltec which provides missiles and aerospace systems; WiseWave a maker of microwave and millimeter-wave products; and CMP Display Systems a light-emitting diode (LED) edge-lit panel manufacturer. All three acquisitions were incorporated into Ducommun Technologies as part of an effort to bolster sales for that segment which served primarily military customers.

In late 2008 Ducommun paid more than $45 million in cash and notes to acquire privately held DynaBil Industries of Coxsackie New York. DynaBil broadened Ducommun's product line by making titanium and aluminum structural components and assemblies for commercial and military aerospace applications.

EXECUTIVES

VP Controller and Assistant Treasurer, Samuel D. Williams, age 64, $233,679 total compensation
VP General Counsel and Secretary, James S. Heiser, age 56, $301,179 total compensation
VP and CFO, Joseph P. (Joe) Bellino, age 62, $337,025 total compensation
Chairman President and CEO, Anthony J. (Tony) Reardon, age 62, $363,487 total compensation
VP Internal Audit, Kathryn M. Andrus, age 44
VP and Treasurer, Donald C. DeVore Jr., age 49
Vice President - Human Resources, Rosalie F. (Rose) Rogers, age 51
President, James (Mike) Stanfield
VP Sales and Marketing, Michael G. Pollack
EVP and COO, Joel H. Benkie
Director, Jay L. Haberland, age 62
Director, Ralph D. Crosby Jr., age 66
Director, Eugene P. Conese Jr., age 53
Director, Dean M. Flatt, age 62
Director, Robert C. (Bob) Ducommun, age 61
Director, Robert D. Paulson, age 67
Auditors: PricewaterhouseCoopersLLP

LOCATIONS

HQ: Ducommun Incorporated
23301 Wilmington Ave., Carson CA 90745-6209
Phone: 310-513-7200 **Fax:** 310-513-7279
Web: www.ducommun.com

PRODUCTS/OPERATIONS

2011 Sales

	$ mil.	% of total
AeroStructures	292	50
LaBarge Technologies	288	50
Total	**580**	**100**

2011 Sales

	$ mil.	% of total
Products	552	95
Services	28	5
Total	**580**	**100**

2011 Sales

	$ mil.	% of total
Military & space	54	32
Industrial	36	21

Natural resources	35	20
Commercial aerospace	22	13
Medical & other	23	14
Total	**172**	**100**

2011 Sales

	% of total
Boeing	19
Raytheon	9
United	5
Spirit	5
Owen-Illinois	4
Other	58
Total	**100**

Selected Capabilities

Ducommun Aerostructures
  Assembly
  Bonding
  Forming
  Machining
  Tooling
Ducommun LaBarge Technologies
  Assembly
  Prototyping
  System integration
Ducommun Miltec
  Acoustics
  Aerodynamics
  Aviation and UAV sensors
  Configuration design
  Explosives testing & handling
  Infrasound sensor technology
  Mine detection
  Training & logistics

COMPETITORS

AIM Aviation
B/E Aerospace
Barnes Group
CPI Aerostructures
Esterline
GE
Goodrich Corp.
Kreisler Manufacturing
L-3 Avionics
LMI Aerospace
Lockheed Martin
Magellan Aerospace
Orbit International
Spirit AeroSystems
Triumph Aerostructures - Vought Aircraft Division

HISTORICAL FINANCIALS

Company Type: Public

Income Statement

FYE: December 31

	REVENUE ($ mil.)	NET INCOME ($ mil.)	NET PROFIT MARGIN	EMPLOYEES
12/12	747.0	16.4	2.2%	3,294
12/11	580.9	(47.5)	—	3,541
12/10	408.4	19.8	4.9%	1,815
12/09	430.7	10.1	2.4%	1,872
12/08	403.8	13.1	3.2%	2,048
Annual Growth	**16.6%**	**5.8%**	**—**	**12.6%**

2012 Year-End Financials

Debt ratio: 46.5%	No. of shares (mil.): 10
Return on equity: 7.6%	Dividends
Cash ($ mil.): 46	Yield: —
Current ratio: 3.09	Payout: —
Long-term debt ($ mil.): 362	Market value ($ mil.): 171

	STOCK PRICE ($) FY Close	P/E High/Low		PER SHARE ($) Earnings	Dividends	Book Value
12/12	16.17	11	5	1.55	0.00	21.02
12/11	12.75	—	—	(4.52)	0.08	19.38
12/10	21.78	13	9	1.87	0.30	24.19
12/09	18.71	21	12	0.97	0.30	22.38
12/08	16.70	31	11	1.23	0.15	21.35
Annual Growth	**(0.8%)**	**—**	**—**	**6.0%**	**—**	**(0.4%)**

DuPont Fabros Technology Inc

DuPont Fabros Technology owns develops operates and manages wholesale data centers —the facilities that house power and cool computer servers for such technology companies as Facebook Google Microsoft and Yahoo! The company establishes its rental rates based on the amount of power reserved for tenant use and the square footage they occupy. As a wholesale provider the company targets clients with high power requirements and a preference for long-term leases. DuPont Fabros Technology develops its wholesale data centers to compete with more traditional colocation models in which managed services are bundled with power and cooling. Wholesale customers typically install and maintain their own servers.

The company's three largest clients —Facebook Microsoft and Yahoo! —account for about two-thirds of its annualized base rental revenues.

DuPont Fabros Technology owns and operates eight data centers —six in northern Virginia one in suburban Chicago and one in New Jersey. It is developing two more data centers one in Virginia and the other in California.

Depending on outside sources of capital to develop its data centers DuPont Fabros is subject to disruptions and fluctuations in the credit markets. The company carries about $700 million in debt. It operates as a real estate investment trust (REIT) for federal income tax purposes. DuPont Fabros has been profitable from 2008 to 2010 the year it earned a net income of $43.7 million but it has an accumulated deficit of $51.1 million. The company's tenants may choose to develop their own data centers as Google is doing on a significant scale.

EXECUTIVES

Chief Accounting Officer, Jeffrey H. Foster, age 50, $231,750 total compensation
Executive Vice President Chief Financial Officer Treasurer, Mark L. Wetzel, age 54, $275,000 total compensation
Chairman, Lammot J. du Pont, age 46, $250,000 total compensation
President CEO and Director, Hossein Fateh, age 45, $250,000 total compensation
EVP Operations, Scott A. Davis, age 53
Senior Vice President of Finance & Acquisitions, Maria Kenny, age 46
SVP Sales and Leasing, M. Lee Kestler Jr., age 49
EVP General Counsel, Richard A. (Rick) Montfort Jr., age 52, $235,000 total compensation
Chairman of the Board, Lammot Pont

Executive Vice President General Counsel Secretary, Rick Montfort
Director, John T. Roberts Jr., age 49
Director, Frederic V. Malek, age 76
Director, Michael A. (Mike) Coke, age 45
Director, Thomas D. Eckert, age 65
President CEO and Director, Hossein Fateh, age 45
Director, John H. Toole, age 71
Independent Director, Jonathan Heiliger
Chairman of the Board, Lammot Pont
Auditors: Ernst&YoungLLP

LOCATIONS

HQ: DuPont Fabros Technology Inc
1212 New York Avenue N.W., Suite 900, Washington, DC 20005
Phone: 202 728-0044
Web: www.dft.com

PRODUCTS/OPERATIONS

2010 Sales

	$ mil.	% of total
Base rent	154	64
Recoveries from tenant	78	32
Other revenues	9	4
Total	**242**	**100**

COMPETITORS

AT&T	Rackspace
CoreSite	SAVVIS
Digital Realty	Terremark Worldwide
Equinix	Verizon
Internap Network Services	

HISTORICAL FINANCIALS

Company Type: Public

Income Statement FYE: December 31

	REVENUE ($ mil.)	NET INCOME ($ mil.)	NET PROFIT MARGIN	EMPLOYEES
12/12	332.4	53.0	16.0%	93
12/11	287.4	64.9	22.6%	91
12/10	242.5	30.4	12.6%	83
12/09	200.2	1.7	0.9%	70
12/08	173.6	19.0	11.0%	67
Annual Growth	**17.6%**	**29.1%**	**—**	**8.5%**

2012 Year-End Financials

Debt ratio: 27.9%	No. of shares (mil.): 63
Return on equity: 3.1%	Dividends
Cash ($ mil.): 23	Yield: 2.5%
Current ratio: 0.51	Payout: 147.6%
Long-term debt ($ mil.): 707	Market value ($ mil.): 1,530

	STOCK PRICE ($) FY Close	P/E High/Low		PER SHARE ($) Earnings	Dividends	Book Value
12/12	24.16	71	49	0.41	0.62	27.16
12/11	24.22	37	27	0.71	0.48	26.53
12/10	21.27	54	31	0.51	0.44	25.86
12/09	17.99	445	52	0.04	0.08	24.88
12/08	2.07	37	3	0.54	0.71	15.56
Annual Growth	**84.8%**	**—**	**—**	**(6.7%)**	**(3.4%)**	**14.9%**

Durect Corp

DURECT wants your medicine to go DURECTly where it's needed. The company is developing drug delivery systems to provide long-term therapy for such conditions as chronic pain heart disease cancer and neurological disorders. Drug delivery technologies provided by DURECT include SABER a controlled-release injectable; TRANSDUR a transdermal patch; ORADUR a sustained release oral gel-cap; DUROS an osmotic implant; and DURIN a biodegradable implant. DURECT conducts R&D efforts independently and collaboratively. The firm sells biodegradable polymers (Lactel) and osmotic pumps (ALZET) to pharmaceutical and medical research firms. Hospira and Pfizer account for 34% and 16% of sales respectively.

As the company focuses on its R&D programs sales of ALZET and LACTEL support its drug development efforts. The ALZET pumps are used by scientists conducting experimental research on lab animals while the LACTEL polymers are used as raw materials by drug and device manufacturers. ALZET and LACTEL are sold through direct sales representatives in the US and through distributors in international markets. In 2011 sales from the ALZET and LACTEL product lines accounted for 22% and 9% of total sales respectively.

DURECT also strongly relies on partnerships with other drugmakers to help fund its research programs. The company's most promising candidate is Remoxy an oral abuse-resistant oxicodone medication using the ORADUR technology that is being developed through global licensing agreements with Pfizer and Pain Therapeutics; the three companies are also working on abuse-resistant versions of other painkillers. In addition DURECT is working with Pfizer on ELADUR a development-stage TRANSDUR bupivacaine pain patch. All of the company's collaborations with Pfizer were formerly conducted with King Pharmaceuticals which Pfizer acquired in 2011.

Another late-stage candidate POSIDUR is a bupivacaine-based injectable pain medication that uses its SABER technology. POSIDUR is in development for post-operative pain applications through a partnership with Nycomed for the European markets; DURECT also formed a partnership with Hospira to develop and sell POSIDUR in North American markets in 2010.

As with all development-stage companies development candidates are often set aside when clinical trial results are less than promising or when a partner decides to focus on different programs. For instance a partnership with Endo Pharmaceuticals on a TRANSDUR pain candidate Sufentanil was canceled in 2009; DURECT is looking for a new partner for the program which it believes still has potential.

Additional trial programs in proprietary or partnered development stages include an ORADUR candidate for ADHD. DURECT is also investigating potential treatments for schizophrenia and cancer.

To deliver on its strategy of developing and commercializing pharmaceutical systems that address significant medical needs and improve quality of life for patients the company has set several key initiatives. These include focusing on chronic debilitating medical conditions and certain local pain conditions; minimizing risks in product development; enabling the development of pharmaceutical systems based on biotechnology and other new compounds; diversifying risk by pursuing multiple programs in development; enabling product development through strategic collaborations; and building its own commercial organization.

Another drug delivery firm ALZA (a subsidiary of Johnson & Johnson) owns an 8% stake in the company. DURECT licenses the DUROS technology from ALZA which was also the original developer of the ALZET pumps.

EXECUTIVES

Chief Financial Officer, Matthew J. (Matt) Hogan, age 54, $283,588 total compensation
Chairman and Chief Scientific Officer, Felix Theeuwes, age 76, $473,660 total compensation
President; Chief Executive Officer; Director, James E. Brown, age 57, $461,965 total compensation
SVP General Counsel and Secretary, Jean I. Liu, age 44, $253,000 total compensation
Executive Vice President - Pharmaceutical Systems Research and Development, Su Il Yum, age 74, $301,600 total compensation
Vice President Finance and Corporate Controller, Jian I. Li, age 42, $220,000 total compensation
EVP Operations and Administration, Paula Mendenhall, age 69
VP Engineering and Safety, Harry Guy
Vice President Pharmaceutical Research and Development, Andrew R. (Andy) Miksztal, age 61
VP-Biostatistics, Nacer E. Dean Abrouk
Chief Medical Officer and EVP Corporate Strategy, Joseph W. (Joe) Stauffer, age 47, $203,125 total compensation
Vice President Birmingham Operations and Principal Scientist, John W. Gibson
Senior Vice President Corporate and Business Development, Michael H. Arenberg
Vice President Clinical and Regulatory Affairs, David J. Ellis
VP of Operations and Corp, Judy Joice
Vice President R&D Business Development & Principal Scientist, WeiQi Lin
Vice President Chief Patent Counsel, Steve Helmer
VP Sales and Marketing, Tracy Maida
Director, Michael D. (Mike) Casey, age 67
Director, David R. Hoffmann, age 68
Director, Terrence F. Blaschke, age 71
President CEO and Director, James E. Brown, age 56
Director, Jon S. Saxe
Director, Armand P. Neukermans, age 72
Director, Simon X. Benito, age 68
Auditors: Ernst&YoungLLP

LOCATIONS

HQ: DURECT Corporation
2 Results Way, Cupertino CA 95014-4166
Phone: 408-777-1417   **Fax:** 408-777-3577
Web: www.durect.com

2011 Sales

	$ mil.	% of total
US	27	83
Europe	3	11
Japan	1	3
Other countries	0	3
Total	**33**	**100**

PRODUCTS/OPERATIONS

2011 Sales

	$ mil.	% of total
Collaborative R&D & other	22	67
Product revenue	11	33
Total	**33**	**100**

COMPETITORS

Abbott Labs	Hospira
Acura Pharmaceuticals	I-Flow
Alexza	Janssen
Alkermes plc	Pharmaceuticals
AstraZeneca	Johnson & Johnson
Bristol-Myers Squibb	Medtronic
Cadence	Nektar Therapeutics
Pharmaceuticals	NeurogesX
Celgene	Novartis
Covidien	Noven Pharmaceuticals
Cumberland	Pacira Pharmaceuticals
Pharmaceuticals	Pfizer
Eli Lilly	Purdue Pharma
Endo	Shire
EpiCept	Teleflex
Flamel Technologies	UCB

HISTORICAL FINANCIALS

Company Type: Public

Income Statement

FYE: December 31

	REVENUE ($ mil.)	NET INCOME ($ mil.)	NET PROFIT MARGIN	EMPLOYEES
12/12	53.0	16.2	30.5%	102
12/11	33.4	(18.7)	—	106
12/10	31.5	(22.9)	—	131
12/09	24.2	(30.2)	—	127
12/08	27.1	(43.9)	—	171
Annual Growth	18.3%	—	—	(12.1%)

2012 Year-End Financials

Debt ratio: —	No. of shares (mil.): 101
Return on equity: 81.1%	Dividends
Cash ($ mil.): 11	Yield: —
Current ratio: 5.25	Payout: —
Long-term debt ($ mil.): —	Market value ($ mil.): 94

	STOCK PRICE ($) FY Close	P/E High/Low		PER SHARE ($) Earnings	Dividends	Book Value
12/12	0.92	9	4	0.18	0.00	0.36
12/11	1.18	—	—	(0.21)	0.00	0.04
12/10	3.45	—	—	(0.26)	0.00	0.17
12/09	2.47	—	—	(0.36)	0.00	0.32
12/08	3.39	—	—	(0.56)	0.00	0.46
Annual Growth	(27.8%)			—	—	(6.1%)

DXP Enterprises, Inc.

DXP Enterprises (DXP) knows that distribution is the quickest way to a customer's doorstep. The company is a distributor of industrial products and services through its three main segments Service Centers Supply Chain Services and Innovative Pumping Solutions. Generating the majority of sales the company's service centers offer bearing rotating fluid power and power transmission products and safety equipment as well as technical design and logistics services. Industries served include agriculture chemical construction food and beverage mining and municipal government. DXP operates from about 150 locations throughout North America.

Geographic Reach

DXP serves 50000 customers from more than 150 locations in 38 states seven provinces from Canada and one state in Mexico. The US generates 95% of its total sales while Canada accounts for the remainder.

Operations

The Service Centers segment 71% of sales operates more than 120 outlets and seven distribution centers. The segment distributes more than a million primarily MRO (maintenance repair operating) items. More than 60000 of them are stock keeping units.

Managing customers' supply chains including inventory the Supply Chain Services segment 15% of sales operates through outlets at more than 50 of its customers' facilities. It offers several software programs to help customers manage their supply chains including SmartAgreement for procuring items from service centers and Smart-Store an e-Catalog.

With eight facilities in Arizona Colorado Louisiana Nebraska and Texas the Innovative Pumping Solutions segment 14% of sales helps clients with capital equipment by offering such services as fabrication and technical design.

Financial Performance

DXP has enjoyed unprecedented growth over the years. Revenues increased 36% in 2012 to reach the $1 billion mark for the first time in its history. Profits also skyrocketed 62% from $31 million in 2011 to peak at a record high of $51 million in 2012.

The growth for 2012 was fueled by a 58% rise in Supply Chain Services sales. Services Centers also experienced growth of 30%; Innovative Pumping Solutions 8%. The company also generated an additional 5% of its total revenue from Canada marking the first time it had ever generated sales from that country.

These rises were the result of previous acquisitions the company has made coupled with a surge in sales of pumps bearings safety products and industrial supplies for customers in the oil and energy sectors.

Strategy

Unlike many of its smaller competitors DXP benefits from having a comprehensive product inventory. It operates as a first-tier distributor getting its products directly from manufacturers which typically allows it to offer very competitive pricing on the goods that it distributes. With more product offerings the company is able to serve a diverse range of industries and to reduce dependence on any one customer base.

Mergers and Acquisitions

DXP acquires smaller niche businesses that strengthen its offerings geographic presence and profitability. The company quickly integrates acquired products and reaps their accretive earnings. Since 2004 DXP has completed more than 25 acquisitions ranging in value from $2.2 million to $106 million and it continues to gobble up market share in Canada.

In 2013 DXP entered a new market for rotating equipment through the purchase of Alaska Pump & Supply a provider and distributor of pump products and process equipment based in Alaska. The company also purchased National Process Equipment (Natpro) a Canadian distributor of pumps and Tucker Tool Company a distributor of abrasives coolants and machine shop supplies.

In 2012 DXP expanded its offerings by acquiring Canadian industrial safety services company HSE Integrated for about $85 million. HSE provides such services as gas detection air quality monitoring and fire protection. Other 2012 purchases included the acquisitions of Pump & Power Equipment Aledco and Force Engineered Products. All three firms are distributors of pump products process equipment and related services and

the buy-outs allowed DXP to boost its rotating equipment product division.

Ownership

DXP executive David Vinson owns more than 20% of the company. Chairman and CEO David Little and FMR LLC each own 10%.

EXECUTIVES

SVP Finance; CFO; and Secretary, Mac McConnell, age 59, $170,000 total compensation

Chairman of the Board; President; Chief Executive Officer, David R. Little, age 61, $448,000 total compensation

SVP Innovative Pumping Solutions, David C. Vinson, age 62, $140,000 total compensation

Senior Vice President - Supply Chain Services and Marketing, John J. Jeffery, age 45, $140,000 total compensation

Senior Vice President - Service Centers, Todd Hamlin

Senior Vice President - Corporate Development, Kent Yee

Senior Vice President - Information Technology, Wayne Crane

Senior Vice President; General Counsel, Gary Messersmith

Director, Timothy P. Halter, age 46

Director, Cletus Davis, age 83

Director, Kenneth H. Miller, age 73

LOCATIONS

HQ: DXP Enterprises Inc.
7272 Pinemont, Houston TX 77040
Phone: 713-996-4700   **Fax:** 713-996-4701
Web: www.dxpe.com

2012 Sales

US	95

PRODUCTS/OPERATIONS

2012 Sales

	$ mil.	% of total
Service Centers	779	71
Innovative Pumping Solutions	156	14

COMPETITORS

Applied Industrial	Kaman
Technologies	MSC Industrial Direct
Dillon Supply	Production Tool Supply
DoALL	W.W. Grainger
Industrial	
Distribution Group	

HISTORICAL FINANCIALS

Company Type: Public

Income Statement

FYE: December 31

	REVENUE ($ mil.)	NET INCOME ($ mil.)	NET PROFIT MARGIN	EMPLOYEES
12/12	1,097.1	50.9	4.6%	2,817
12/11	807.0	31.4	3.9%	2,093
12/10	656.2	19.3	3.0%	1,772
12/09	583.2	(42.4)	—	1,697
12/08	736.8	25.8	3.5%	1,884
Annual Growth	10.5%	18.5%	—	10.6%

2012 Year-End Financials

Debt ratio: 41.8%	No. of shares (mil.): 13
Return on equity: 27.8%	Dividends
Cash ($ mil.): 10	Yield: —
Current ratio: 2.30	Payout: —
Long-term debt ($ mil.): 216	Market value ($ mil.): 686

STOCK PRICE ($) FY Close	P/E High/Low		PER SHARE ($) Earnings	Dividends	Book Value
12/12	49.07	14	9	3.35	0.00	14.92
12/11	32.20	15	8	2.08	0.00	11.10
12/10	24.00	17	8	1.32	0.00	8.82
12/09	13.07	—	—	(3.24)	0.00	6.97
12/08	14.61	33	5	1.89	0.00	10.12
Annual Growth	35.4%		— —	15.4%	—	10.2%

Dycom Industries, Inc.

The telecommunications industry dials up Dycom Industries for construction and engineering assistance. Operating through more than 30 subsidiaries the company primarily designs builds and maintains coaxial copper and fiber-optic cable systems for local and long-distance phone companies and cable television operators. Dycom also provides wiring services for businesses and government agencies installs and maintains electrical lines for electric and gas utilities and locates underground wires and pipelines for excavators. Dycom operates in the US and Canada.

Sales and Marketing As a specialty contractor Dycom is dependent upon the needs of telecom and utility companies. It has a limited number of customers with the top five representing about 60% of sales. AT&T CenturyLink and Comcast are its top customers together accounting for 40% of sales. Work for telecom companies make up the majority of revenue; utility companies account for about 10%.

Financial Performance Revenue in fiscal 2012 (ended July) rose 16% to $1.2 billion the second consecutive year of growth for Dycom after the recession led to a decline in sales in 2009 and 2010. Net income also grew that year jumping about 145% to $39 million. The company's largest segment construction services to telecommunications providers increased nearly 20% due to some significant new customer contracts and enhancements to existing contracts. It also saw an increase in sales to utility and other customers. Dycom reported a drop in the underground facility locating segment (as it has the past several years) amid a planned pullback on technician intensive customer contracts.

Strategy Dycom has benefited from the growing demand for converged voice video and data services a trend that requires the expansion and enhancement of telecommunications networks. It is also poised to take advantage of the continued need for mobile broadband as more consumers turn to smartphones and tablets.

Mergers and Acquisitions Dycom has a history of growth through strategic acquisitions. In late 2012 the company purchased the telecommunications infrastructure services business of Quanta Services for $275 million. The deal expands its rural engineering and construction operations and enhances its technical services customer roster and geographic scope. In 2010 Dycom acquired Georgia-based NeoCom Solutions for $27.5 million in cash. NeoCom provided engineering services such as tower construction for telecom government and energy companies.

HISTORY

Floyd Younkin (who died in 1997) founded Mobile Home Dynamics in 1969 to sell mobile homes. In 1981 Thomas Pledger who had a background in utility services joined the firm which began providing services to the electrical and telecommunications industries. The shift prompted the firm to change its name to Dycom short for "dynamic communications." Pledger was named president and CEO in 1984.

Dycom grew through acquisitions in the 1980s when it mainly installed fiber-optic cable for long-distance carriers. During the early 1990s the company suffered from management feuding lost contracts and shareholder lawsuits. However it continued to make acquisitions including North Carolina-based Globe Communications (1992). In 1993 a $24.3 million write-off for the earlier acquisitions of Ansco and Ivy H. Smith Company led to a loss and massive layoffs.

In 1997 Dycom acquired the Communications Construction Group bringing the company more business in the cable TV industry. The purchase also strengthened Dycom's presence in the Midwest Northeast and Mid-Atlantic states. The next year the firm bought Missouri-based Installation Technicians and Georgia-based Cable Com. In 1999 Steven Nielsen took the helm as CEO (Pledger became chairman then retired in 2001). Also that year Dycom acquired companies in Kentucky North Carolina and Washington.

Dycom's business expanded in the late 1990s mainly as a result of telecom deregulation and the rise of the Internet. But the new millennium brought new challenges.

Acquiring telecommunication infrastructure and construction services companies across the US Dycom broadened its customer base in 2000. The purchase of Louisiana-based Point to Point Communications gave Dycom access to Point's two biggest customers: WorldCom and Genuity. Also that year the company acquired Utah-based Niels Fugal Sons which serves the western US.

Despite making five acquisitions during its 2001 fiscal year a slowing economy forced Dycom to temporarily ease off its aggressive buying spree. Nielsen took on the additional title of chairman the next year following Pledger's retirement. After a few of its top customers reduced spending Dycom was forced to reduce its 7200-member workforce by 1000 in an effort to cut costs. In 2002 the company acquired Arguss Communications.

Later that year however Adelphia Communications which was one of Dycom's largest customers filed for bankruptcy protection and halted construction adding to Dycom's financial woes. To cut costs after its top customers pulled back on spending it once again looked to workforce reductions. The company continued to make acquisitions though purchasing Arguss Communications in 2002 and First South Utility Construction and underground utility locator UtiliQuest in 2003. In 2005 it bought customer premise equipment (CPE) installer Prince Telecom and in 2006 it acquired CPE installer Cable Express Holding from H.I.G. Capital for about $63 million.

In late 2010 Dycom bought the assets of Communications Services Inc. (CSI) a provider of outside plant construction services for around $10 million. CSI primarily provides its services to telecom companies in the southeastern and south central US.

EXECUTIVES

Chairman of the Board; President; Chief Executive Officer, Steven E. Nielsen, age 50, $750,000 total compensation
Chief Operating Officer; Executive Vice President, Timothy R. Estes, age 59, $512,500 total compensation
Vice President; General Counsel; Corporate Secretary, Richard B. (Rick) Vilsoet, age 60, $333,125 total compensation
Chief Financial Officer; Senior Vice President, H. Andrew (Drew) DeFerrari, age 44, $340,000 total compensation
Senior Vice President Business Operations, Dwight B. Duke
Director, Charles B. (Charlie) Coe, age 64
Director, Charles M. Brennan III, age 71
Director, Patricia L. Higgins, age 63
Director, Thomas G. Baxter, age 65
Director, James A. (Jim) Chiddix, age 67
Director, Stephen C. Coley, age 68
Auditors: Deloitte&ToucheLLP

LOCATIONS

HQ: Dycom Industries Inc.
11770 US Hwy. 1 Ste. 101, Palm Beach Gardens FL 33408
Phone: 561-627-7171   **Fax:** 561-627-7709
Web: www.dycomind.com

PRODUCTS/OPERATIONS

2012 Sales

	$ mil.	% of total
Telecommunications	1,015	84
Underground facility locating	131	11
Electric utilities & other	55	5
Total	**1,201**	**100**

Selected Services

Construction maintenance and installation
Electric and gas utilities and other construction and maintenance
Engineering
Premise wiring
Underground facility locating

Selected Subsidiaries

Ansco & Associates LLC (North Carolina)
Broadband Express LLC (Ohio)
C-2 Utility Contractors LLC (Oregon)
CableCom LLC (Washington)
Cable Connectors LLC (South Carolina)
Can-Am Communications Inc. (Washington)
CAVO Broadband Communications LLC (Illinois)
Communications Construction Group LLC (Pennsylvania)
Ervin Cable Construction LLC (Kentucky)
Globe Communications LLC (South Carolina)
Installation Technicians LLC (Tennessee)
Ivy H. Smith Company LLC (North Carolina)
Lambert's Cable Splicing Company LLC (North Carolina)
Locating Inc. (Georgia)
Midtown Express LLC (New York)
Nichols Construction LLC (Virgina)
Niels Fugal Sons Company LLC (Utah)
Point to Point Communications Inc. (Florida)
Precision Valley Communications of Vermont LLC (Vermont)
Prince Telecom LLC (Delaware)
RJE Canada ULC (Alberta Canada)
RJE Telecom LLC (Florida)
Star Construction LLC (Tennessee)
Stevens Communications LLC (Georgia)
S.T.S. LLC (Georgia)
TCS Communications LLC (Colorado)
Tesinc LLC (Florida)
Triple-D Communications LLC (Kentucky)
Underground Specialties LLC (Oregon)
UtiliQuest LLC (Georgia)

White Mountain Cable Construction LLC (New Hampshire)

COMPETITORS

Comm-Works	MYR Group
EMCOR	MasTec
Fortress International Group	Pike Electric Corporation
Goldfield	Quanta Services
Henkels & McCoy	Sirti
Integrated Electrical Services	WPCS International Willbros
LCC International	
MDU Construction Services	

HISTORICAL FINANCIALS

Company Type: Public

Income Statement
FYE: July 27

	REVENUE ($ mil.)	NET INCOME ($ mil.)	NET PROFIT MARGIN	EMPLOYEES
07/13	1,608.6	35.1	2.2%	10,822
07/12	1,201.1	39.3	3.3%	8,111
07/11	1,035.8	16.1	1.6%	8,320
07/10	988.6	5.8	0.6%	8,897
07/09	1,106.9	(53.1)	—	9,231
Annual Growth	9.8%	—	—	4.1%

2013 Year-End Financials

Debt ratio: 39.1%
Return on equity: 8.5%
Cash ($ mil.): 18
Current ratio: 2.71
Long-term debt ($ mil.): 444

No. of shares (mil.): 33
Dividends
 Yield: —
 Payout: —
Market value ($ mil.): 881

	STOCK PRICE ($) FY Close	P/E High/Low		PER SHARE ($) Earnings	Dividends	Book Value
07/13	26.48	25	12	1.04	0.00	12.88
07/12	17.68	20	11	1.14	0.00	11.70
07/11	17.04	40	16	0.45	0.00	10.51
07/10	9.05	95	52	0.15	0.00	10.21
07/09	12.10	—	—	(1.35)	0.00	10.02
Annual Growth	21.6%	—	—	—	—	6.5%

Dynex Capital, Inc.

Dynex Capital is a real estate investment trust (REIT) that invests in loans and fixed-income securities backed by single-family residential and commercial mortgage loans. The company isn't too picky investing in both investment-grade and subprime loans and adjustable-rate and fixed-rate loans. However citing competition and a "lack of compelling opportunities" in a volatile marketplace the company makes few new investments and has been slimming down its balance sheet by selling off assets including all of its manufactured home lending and delinquent property-tax receivable portfolios.

EXECUTIVES

EVP COO Secretary and Treasurer, Stephen J. Benedetti, age 51, $236,000 total compensation
Vice President Investor Relations Todd Kuimjian, Alison G. Griffin

VP Portfolio, Wayne E. Brockwell
VP Risk Management, Robert M. Nilson Jr.
Assistant Controller, Kevin J. Sciuk
Chairman, Thomas B. (Tom) Akin, age 62, $277,429 total compensation
VP Information Systems and Technology, John L. Goodhue
VP Controller and Principal Accounting Officer, Jeffrey L. Childress
President CEO and Co-Chief Investment Officer, Byron L. Boston, age 54
EVP and Co-Chief Investment Officer, Smriti L. Popenoe
President Chief Executive Officer, Michael Boguski
Director, Daniel K. Osborne, age 49
Director, Barry Igdaloff, age 58
Director, James C. Wheat III, age 60
Director, Michael R. Hughes
Auditors: BDOSeidmanLLP

LOCATIONS

HQ: Dynex Capital Inc.
 4551 Cox Rd. Ste. 300, Glen Allen VA 23060-6740
Phone: 804-217-5800 **Fax:** 804-217-5860
Web: www.dynexcapital.com

PRODUCTS/OPERATIONS

2012 Sales
% mil. % of total

Agency MBS	77	64
Non Agency MBS	30	25
Gain on sale of investments	8	7
Securitized mortgage loans & others	6	4
Total	**122**	**100**

COMPETITORS

BRT Realty	Redwood Trust
Capstead Mortgage	iStar Financial Inc
Impac Mortgage Holdings	

HISTORICAL FINANCIALS

Company Type: Public

Income Statement
FYE: December 31

	REVENUE ($ mil.)	NET INCOME ($ mil.)	NET PROFIT MARGIN	EMPLOYEES
12/12	113.5	74.0	65.2%	17
12/11	83.3	39.8	47.7%	15
12/10	48.7	29.4	60.4%	15
12/09	39.2	17.5	44.8%	13
12/08	29.6	15.1	51.0%	13
Annual Growth	39.9%	48.8%	—	6.9%

2012 Year-End Financials

Debt ratio: 0.7%
Return on equity: 14.9%
Cash ($ mil.): 55
Current ratio: 0.03
Long-term debt ($ mil.): 30

No. of shares (mil.): 54
Dividends
 Yield: 12.1%
 Payout: 83.3%
Market value ($ mil.): 512

	STOCK PRICE ($) FY Close	P/E High/Low		PER SHARE ($) Earnings	Dividends	Book Value
12/12	9.44	8	7	1.35	1.15	11.36
12/11	9.13	11	7	1.03	1.09	9.20
12/10	10.92	7	6	1.41	0.98	9.64
12/09	8.73	9	6	1.02	0.92	12.11
12/08	6.54	11	6	0.91	0.71	11.54
Annual Growth	9.6%	—	—	10.4%	12.8%	(0.4%)

Eagle Bancorp Inc (MD)

For those nest eggs that need a little help hatching holding company Eagle Bancorp would recommend its community-oriented EagleBank subsidiary. The bank serves businesses and individuals through more than 15 branches in Washington DC and its suburbs. Deposit products include checking savings and money market accounts; certificates of deposit; and IRAs. Commercial real estate and construction real estate loans combined represent about 70% of its loan portfolio. The bank which has significant expertise as a Small Business Administration lender also writes business consumer and home equity loans. EagleBank offers insurance products through an agreement with The Meltzer Group.

The company has been focused on growing within its existing markets. After launching three new branches in 2011 it opened its 16th branch in Virginia in early 2012 and has another new branch on the way. In the past it has also expanded by buying other banks. In 2011 Eagle Bancorp planned to acquire Alliance Bankshares for some $31 million but the two firms terminated the agreement citing irreconcilable differences.

The company reported record net income for the third straight year in 2011 despite the difficult economic conditions that wrecked many banks' results. Profits increased by some 47% from 2010 to 2011. That year the company received a $56.6 million capital infusion due to its participation in the Small Business Lending Fund a recently formed Treasury program designed to encourage small business lending. To further fund its lending activities the company has been pushing such products as its money market accounts in its market.

In 2010 Eagle expanded its residential mortgage lending division in efforts to increase mortgage production volume. The expansion also helped raise the company's noninterest income by nearly half in 2011 as it sold most of the mortgages on the secondary markets rather than holding them on its books.

The company's strategy for further growth includes continuing to seek opportunities to open or acquire new banking locations while waiting out record low interest rates. Eagle's strict loan underwriting standards —it didn't write subprime residential mortgages and didn't buy securities backed by subprime mortgages —has helped it have fewer problem loans the downfall for many banks.

EXECUTIVES

Vice Chairman, Robert P. Pincus, age 66
Chief Financial Officer; Executive Vice President of the Company and Bank, James H. Langmead, age 65, $243,100 total compensation
Senior Executive Vice President; Chief Operating Officer of the Bank, Susan G. Riel, age 64, $243,100 total compensation
President - Community Banking of the Bank, Thomas D. Murphy, age 66, $243,100 total compensation
Chairman President and CEO; Chairman and CEO EagleBank, Ronald D. (Ron) Paul, age 58, $350,000 total compensation
EVP EagleBank, Martha Foulon-Tonat, age 58, $243,100 total compensation
EVP and COO, Michael T. (Mike) Flynn, age 66, $236,080 total compensation
Executive Vice President; Chief Credit Officer of the Bank, Janice L. Williams, age 56

SVP and Group Leader Commercial Real Estate Lending Maryland, Thomas A. Mee
VP and Manager Wiire and Cash Room, Joan M. Grant
VP and Commercial Real Estate Loan Officer, Ryan A. Riel
Executive Vice President; General Counsel of the Company and Bank, Laurence E. (Larry) Bensignor
Executive Vice President; Chief Commercial Real Estate Lending Officer, Antonio Marquez
Vice Chairman, Robert P. Pincus, age 66
Director, Leonard L. Abel, age 85
Director, Neal R. Gross, age 69
Director, Dudley C. Dworken, age 64
Director, Leslie M. Alperstein, age 71
Director, Philip N. Margolius, age 72
Director, Leland M. Weinstein, age 51
Director, Harvey M. Goodman, age 58
Director, Donald R. Rogers, age 68
Director, Norman R. Pozez, age 58
Auditors: Stegman&Company

LOCATIONS

HQ: Eagle Bancorp Inc.
7815 Woodmont Ave., Bethesda MD 20814
Phone: 301-986-1800   Fax: 301-986-8529
Web: www.eaglebankmd.com

PRODUCTS/OPERATIONS

2011 Sales

	$ mil.	% of total
Interest		
Loans including fees	112	85
Securities	6	5
Other	0	-
Noninterest		
Gain on sale of loans	6	5
Service charges on deposits	3	2
Gain on sale of investment securities	1	1
Other	2	2
Total	132	100

Selected Subsidiaries

EagleBank
Bethesda Leasing LLC
Eagle Insurance Services LLC
Fidelity Mortgage Inc.
Eagle Commercial Ventures LLC

COMPETITORS

BB&T	OBA Financial Services
Bank of America	PNC Financial
Capital One	Sandy Spring Bancorp
First Mariner Bancorp	SunTrust
M&T Bank	

HISTORICAL FINANCIALS

Company Type: Public

Income Statement

FYE: December 31

	ASSETS ($ mil.)	NET INCOME ($ mil.)	INCOME AS % OF ASSETS	EMPLOYEES
12/12	3,409.4	35.2	1.0%	393
12/11	2,831.2	24.5	0.9%	338
12/10	2,089.3	16.6	0.8%	292
12/09	1,805.5	10.4	0.6%	235
12/08	1,496.8	7.4	0.5%	235
Annual Growth	22.9%	47.6%	—	13.7%

2012 Year-End Financials

Return on assets: 1.1%	Dividends
Return on equity: 11.4%	Yield: —
Long-term debt ($ mil.): —	Payout: —
No. of shares (mil.): 25	Market value ($ mil.): 504
Sales ($ mil): 163	

	STOCK PRICE ($) FY Close	P/E High/Low	PER SHARE ($) Earnings	Dividends	Book Value
12/12	19.97	14 10	1.46	0.00	13.86
12/11	14.54	14 11	1.04	0.00	12.15
12/10	14.43	21 14	0.70	0.00	9.45
12/09	10.47	22 11	0.50	0.00	8.76
12/08	5.75	25 10	0.56	0.16	10.18
Annual Growth	36.5%	— —	26.9%	—	8.0%

EarthLink Holdings Corp

Some of us spend way too much time online and EarthLink is OK with that. The company provides Internet connections to more than 1 million consumers and about 150000 businesses in the US. About two-thirds of those are broadband users. It also offers such services as VoIP computer telephony and Web hosting. EarthLink provides broadband access over cable lines through agreements with network operators including Time Warner Cable Bright House and Comcast while DSL and dial-up connections are made possible over phone lines owned by AT&T and Verizon among others. The company enterprise segment implements and manages private data networks in addition to providing Internet access and Web hosting for businesses.

Operations

The company operates in two segments - business services and consumer services. Its business customers account for three-quarters of sales. Residential customers make up the other 25%. While it serves fewer business customers (150000 vs. 1 million residential customers) EarthLink offers more robust services to business customers and is able to charge more.

Geographic Reach

EarthLink serves residential and business customers nationwide.

Sales and Marketing

The company scouts for new business customers through direct inside and independent sales channels such as resellers and IT consulting firms. It doesn't use a dedicated sales force for residential customers; they're targeted through call centers online ads and resellers such as Time Warner Cable and Dish Network.

EarthLink is reducing its direct sales presence in smaller markets to focus on larger geographic areas in order to accelerate its transition into an IT services company.

Financial Performance

EarthLink became a billion-dollar company again in 2011 after making several acquisitions. Overall sales increased a scant 3% in 2012 to $1.3 billion. While its business services segment grew 10% for the year residential service revenues fell 15% as the number of subscribers fell from 1.5 million in 2011 to 1.2 million in 2012. The company expects its residential service business to continue to decline from competition from other providers that offer bundled services (such as cable TV and phone). Profits fell 78% in 2012 to $7.5 million due to increased operating costs.

Mergers and Acquisitions

In mid-2013 EarthLink bought CenterBeam for $22 million and added CenterBeam's remote managed IT services and help desk capabilities to its EarthLink Business division.

2011 was an active year for acquisitions as EarthLink bought five companies. The largest was One Communications for $370 million. It provided fixed-line traditional and digital phone service to more than 100000 businesses. Then came Saturn Telecommunications Services (STS Telecom) for $28 million. STS Telecom provided voice data and Internet services to small and mid-sized business clients in Florida and Georgia. It also bought two managed IT services providers Business Vitals and xDefenders. Finally its acquisition of the cloud-based application services business of Synergy Global Solutions expanded its IT support services business and added a hosted applications service for the environmental services market.

In 2010 it bought business communications and technology services provider ITC^DeltaCom for $524 million. Three years later in 2013 it sold the business to an unknown buyer for an undisclosed amount.

Strategy

EarthLink's growth plan involves becoming an IT services player for small and mid-sized businesses with IT and network security needs not just an Internet provider. The company is investing capital to extend its core fiber IP network adding data centers and decreasing investments in legacy products.

HISTORY

After his first attempt to log onto the Internet took 80 hours in 1993 a frustrated 23-year-old Sky Dayton had an idea for a new business: an ISP focused on customer service. Dayton who had already co-founded Los Angeles coffeehouse Cafe Mocha and graphics firm Dayton Walker Design persuaded investors Reed Slatkin and Kevin O'-Donnell to contribute $100000. EarthLink Network was launched in Glendale California in 1994.

Dayton an Ayn Rand fan who graduated from high school at 16 and never attended college first tried to do everything —from sales to software — himself. He ultimately decided to concentrate on customer service correctly betting that such elements as browser software and backbone networks would emerge from other providers. Offering phone help and a flat monthly rate of $19.95 EarthLink sold its first account by the end of 1994.

The next year EarthLink released TotalAccess a package of leading Internet software that included the popular Netscape Navigator browser and QUALCOMM's Eudora the oft-used e-mail program. Viacom's Macmillan Publishing agreed to sell TotalAccess disks in its Internet books. EarthLink was to gain similar deals with about 90 other partners.

By 1996 EarthLink had won 30000 subscribers. The company signed a deal with PSINet giving EarthLink customers dial-up access through PSINet's more than 230 locations in the US and Canada. The next year EarthLink went public.

In 1998 EarthLink teamed with Sprint in a 10-year deal that combined the companies' Internet access services and gave Sprint 29.5% of the firm. As EarthLink passed the 1 million-subscriber mark in 1999 it agreed to offer a co-branded version of America Online's instant messaging service.

EarthLink Network agreed to merge with Mind-Spring in 1999 in a $1.4 billion deal (closed in 2000). The new company EarthLink Inc. moved to MindSpring's Atlanta headquarters. MindSpring founder Charles Brewer took over as chairman and Dayton remained a director. Brewer left EarthLink later in 2000 however and Dayton stepped back in as chairman.

Investments in EarthLink during 2000 included $200 million from Apple (which made EarthLink the default ISP on Macintoshes) and another $431 million from Sprint (which boosted its stake after heavy dilution from the MindSpring deal). That year EarthLink gained 700000 subscribers by buying OneMain.com an ISP focused on small cities and rural communities for $262 million.

EarthLink and Sprint stepped back from their co-branding arrangement in 2001 and Sprint sold about 40% of its stake in the company. That year EarthLink agreed to acquire Cidco a California-based maker of personal e-mail appliances in a $5 million deal (completed in 2002). Also in 2002 EarthLink acquired the assets of wireless Internet access provider OmniSky as well as PeoplePC which used to sell computers with bundled Internet access and now sells value-priced narrowband Internet access (sans computer).

In 2005 Robert Kavner replaced Dayton as EarthLink's chairman of the board. Two years later the company tapped Mpower Communications chairman Rolla Huff as its new president and CEO.

Spurred by mounting costs and dwindling subscribers EarthLink in 2007 initiated a restructuring plan that included the closure of four offices and workforce cuts of roughly half.

As its subscriber numbers continued to decline (down by about half from 2006 to 2008) EarthLink took steps to refocus on its core wireline Internet business in 2008 when it sold its stake in mobile virtual network operator HELIO to Virgin Mobile USA in exchange for a small stake in Virgin Mobile USA. EarthLink had announced previously that it would no longer make additional investments in the loss-making joint venture which it formed in 2005 with South Korea's SK Telecom to market wireless voice and data services in the US.

EXECUTIVES

EVP and CFO, Bradley A. (Brad) Ferguson, age 42, $278,846 total compensation
Chairman President and CEO, Rolla P. Huff, age 56, $830,769 total compensation
President of Premier Business Solutions, Mae S. Squier-Dow, age 51
EVP General Counsel and Secretary, Samuel R. (Sam) DeSimone Jr., age 53, $306,346 total compensation
President and COO, Joseph M. (Joe) Wetzel, age 57, $432,000 total compensation
President of Advanced Services, Vikram (Vik) Desai
EVP Sales and Marketing, Cardi Prinzi, age 56
EVP Service Delivery & Corporate Processes, Stacie Hagan, age 46, $270,000 total compensation
EVP and CTO, Brian Fink
EVP Customer Delivery and Care, Kevin F. Brand, age 54
EVP Infrastructure Engineering and Operations, James P. O'Brien
Chief Information Officer, Robert Scott
Executive Vice President Infrastructure Engineering and Operations, James Brien
Senior Vice President - Marketing and Chief Marketing Officer, Barbara Dondiego
EVP Infrastructure Engineering and Operations, James P. (Jim) O'Brien
EVP Sales and Marketing, Michael D. Toplisek
VP-Natl Acct Support Svcs, Roy Frederickson
Brand Executive Vice President - Customer Delivery and Care, Kevin F

Director, Susan D. Bowick, age 64
Director, Nathaniel A. (Nate) Davis, age 57
Director, Garry K. McGuire
Director, Marce Fuller, age 52
Director, Thomas E. (Tom) Wheeler, age 66
Director, David Koretz, age 33
Director, M. Wayne Wisehart, age 67
Auditors: Ernst&YoungLLP

LOCATIONS

HQ: EarthLink Holdings Corp.
1375 Peachtree St., Atlanta GA 30309
Phone: 404-815-0770   **Fax:** 404-892-7616
Web: www.earthlink.net

PRODUCTS/OPERATIONS

2012 Sales

	% of sales
Business services	76
Consumer services	24
Total	**100**

Selected Services

Retail Services
  Data
  Voice
  Mobile Data and Voice
  Cloud
  Managed security
  Data center
  Application
  IT support
Wholesaler services
Residential Services
  Dial-Up Internet
  Broadband Cable Internet
  High-Speed DSL
  Freestanding DSL
  Web Hosting
  Wireless Internet
Business Services
  MPLS Networks
  Internet Access
  Managed Voice
  Integrated Voice & Data
  Cloud Hosting
  Carrier/Wholesale

COMPETITORS

AOL	MegaPath
AT&T	Microsoft
Aplus.net	ReaLLinx
Charter Communications	Shenandoah
Cincinnati Bell	Telecommunications
Comcast	Sprint Communications
Covad Communications	Time Warner Cable
Group	United Online
Cox Communications	Verizon
Google	Vonage
ITC^DeltaCom	XO Holdings
Internet America	Yahoo!
Level 3 Communications	

HISTORICAL FINANCIALS

Company Type: Public

Income Statement

				FYE: December 31
	REVENUE ($ mil.)	NET INCOME ($ mil.)	NET PROFIT MARGIN	EMPLOYEES
12/12	1,348.9	7.5	0.6%	3,034
12/11	1,314.1	34.5	2.6%	3,241
12/10	622.2	81.4	13.1%	1,870
12/09	723.7	287.1	39.7%	623
12/08	955.5	189.6	19.8%	754
Annual Growth	**9.0%**	**(55.4%)**	**—**	**41.6%**

2012 Year-End Financials

Debt ratio: 38.5%
Return on equity: 1.0%
Cash ($ mil.): 157
Current ratio: 1.58
Long-term debt ($ mil.): 614
No. of shares (mil.): 102
Dividends
  Yield: 0.0%
  Payout: 285.7%
Market value ($ mil.): 664

	STOCK PRICE ($) FY Close	P/E High/Low		PER SHARE ($) Earnings	Dividends	Book Value
12/12	6.46	122	87	0.07	0.20	7.00
12/11	6.44	28	19	0.32	0.20	7.09
12/10	8.60	12	10	0.74	0.62	6.99
12/09	8.31	3	2	2.66	0.28	6.85
12/08	6.76	6	3	1.71	0.00	4.13
Annual Growth	**(1.1%)**	**—**	**—**	**(55.0%)**	**—**	**14.1%**

East West Bancorp, Inc

East West Bancorp is the holding company for East West Bank which operates more than 120 branches worldwide mainly in California (in and around Los Angeles the San Francisco Bay area Orange County and Silicon Valley) and in the Atlanta Boston Houston New York and Seattle metropolitan areas as well in China Hong Kong and Taiwan. Catering to the Asian-American community it provides international banking and trade financing to importers/exporters doing business in the Asia/Pacific region. East West Bank offers multilingual service in English Cantonese Mandarin Vietnamese and Spanish.

Operations

The bank also offers standard services such as personal and business loans checking and savings accounts insurance and merchant credit card processing services. Catering to the manufacturing wholesale trade and service sectors East West Bank focuses its lending activities on commercial and industrial real estate loans which account for the majority of the company's loan portfolio. The bank also writes multifamily real estate residential mortgage construction business and consumer loans.

The retail banking segment focuses primarily on retail operations through the East West Bank's branch network. The commercial banking segment which includes commercial industrial and commercial real estate primarily generates commercial loans through the efforts of the commercial lending offices located in the Bank's production offices in California New York Texas and New England region among others. In addition the bommercial banking segment also offers a wide variety of international finance and trade services and products.

In addition to the bank East West Bancorp's subsidiaries are West Capital Statutory Trust III East West Capital Trust IV East West Capital Trust V East West Capital Trust VI East West Capital Trust VII East West Capital Trust VIII and East West Capital Trust IX.

Financial Performance

In 2011 East West Bancorp reported a 4% decrease in revenues due to a drop in total interest income and dividend income (resulting from lower loans receivable including fees) and a decrease in non-interest income resulting from a decline in total fees and other operating income and a decrease in FDIC indemnification assets and receivables.

However net income increased by 49% in 2011 thanks to a decrease in non-interest expenses loan-related expenses deposit insurance premiums and regulatory assessments.

That year East West Bancorp had $21.97 billion in total consolidated assets $14.26 billion in net consolidated loans and $17.45 billion in total consolidated deposits.

Strategy

Although East West Bancorp is highly involved in California's commercial real estate market the company's strong liquidity and reserves help it to weather economic downturns.

East West Bancorp has expanded its market area through acquisitions. In a 2010 deal East West Bancorp acquired the failed Washington First International Bank adding six branches in Seattle; the transaction also included a loss-sharing agreement with the FDIC.

Company Background

East West Bancorp was founded in 1998.

In 2009 the company acquired more than 60 branches and most of the banking operations of larger rival United Commercial Bank which had been seized by regulators. The deal gave East West Bank about 40 more California branches plus some 20 additional US locations beyond the state.

EXECUTIVES

EVP Chief Risk Officer General Counsel and Secretary East West Bancorp and East West Bank, Douglas P. Krause, age 56, $217,005 total compensation

President and COO East West Bancorp and East West Bank, Julia S. Gouw, age 53, $286,654 total compensation

Chairman and CEO East West Bancorp and East West Bank, Dominic Ng, age 54, $800,000 total compensation

Executive Vice President; Chief Credit Officer of the Bank, John Hall, age 57, $205,004 total compensation

EVP and Head North California Commercial Lending Division, William H. Fong, age 65

Vice Chairman East West Bancorp and East West Bank, John Lee, age 81

Executive Vice President; Director - Business Banking Division of the Bank, Andy Yen, age 55

Executive Vice President; Head - Retail Banking Division of the Bank, Karen Fukumura, age 48

EVP and CFO, Irene Oh

EVP and Director Credit Risk Management, Lawrence B. Schiff

Executive Vice President; Chief Human Resources Officer of the Bank, James T. Schuler

Chief Risk Officer VP Gen. Counsel, Douglas Esq

Executive Vice President; Head - Commercial Banking Services of the Bank, Marty Newton

Executive Vice President; Head - Greater China and Corporate Strategy of the Bank, Sue Yang

Director, Peggy Tsiang Cherng, age 64

Vice Chairman; President and COO East West Bancorp and East West Bank, Julia S. Gouw, age 52

Director, Rudolph I. (Rudy) Estrada, age 65

Director, Herman Y. Li, age 60

Director, Jack C. Liu, age 54

Director, Keith W. Renken, age 78

Director, Paul H. Irving

Director, Iris S. Chan

Vice Chairman East West Bancorp and East West Bank, John Lee, age 81

Director, Andrew S. Kane, age 60

EVP and Director Credit Risk Management, Lawrence B. Schiff

Auditors: KPMGLLP

LOCATIONS

HQ: East West Bancorp Inc.
135 N. Los Robles Ave. 7th Fl., Pasadena CA 91101
Phone: 626-768-6000 **Fax:** 626-799-3167
Web: www.eastwestbank.com

PRODUCTS/OPERATIONS

2011 Sales

	$ mil.	% of total
Commercial lending	619	57
Retail banking	358	33
Other & adjustments	112	10
Total	**1,091**	**100**

COMPETITORS

BBCN	Comerica
Bank of America	Hanmi Financial
Bank of East Asia	JPMorgan Chase
Cathay General Bancorp	U.S. Bancorp
Citibank	Wells Fargo
City National	Wilshire Bancorp

HISTORICAL FINANCIALS

Company Type: Public

Income Statement

FYE: December 31

	ASSETS ($ mil.)	NET INCOME ($ mil.)	INCOME AS % OF ASSETS	EMPLOYEES
12/12	22,536.1	281.6	1.2%	2,306
12/11	21,968.6	245.2	1.1%	2,329
12/10	20,700.5	164.5	0.8%	2,131
12/09	20,559.2	76.6	0.4%	2,667
12/08	12,422.8	(49.6)	—	1,346
Annual Growth	**16.1%**	**—**	**—**	**14.4%**

2012 Year-End Financials

Return on assets: 1.2%	Dividends
Return on equity: 11.9%	Yield: 1.8%
Long-term debt ($ mil.): —	Payout: 21.1%
No. of shares (mil.): 140	Market value ($ mil.): 3,015
Sales ($ mil): 1,045	

	STOCK PRICE ($) FY Close	P/E High/Low	Earnings	Dividends	Book Value
12/12	21.49	13 10	1.89	0.40	16.98
12/11	19.75	15 9	1.60	0.16	15.48
12/10	19.55	23 16	0.83	0.04	14.23
12/09	15.80	49 9	0.33	0.05	20.78
12/08	15.97	— —	(0.94)	0.40	24.33
Annual Growth	**7.7%**	**— —**	**—**	**(0.0%)**	**(8.6%)**

Eaton Vance Corp

A veritable supermarket of investing Eaton Vance offers more than 100 mutual funds and manages investments for retail high-net-worth and institutional clients. Its investment specialties include tax-managed equity funds municipal bond funds floating-rate bank-loan funds income and value equity funds global and high-yield bonds closed-end funds and alternative investments such as private equity funds commodity-based investments and absolute return strategies. Its Eaton Vance Distributors unit markets and sells its products through sales associates in the US Europe the Asia-Pacific region and Latin America as well as a network of brokers independent financial advisors banks and insurance firms.

Operations

The company's institutional investment and retail account management units include Atlanta Capital Management (equity value investing) Boston Management and Research (fund management) Fox Asset Management (value-oriented investments) Parametric Portfolio Associates (tax-managed portfolios) and Tax Advantaged Bond Strategies (TABS). Altogether Eaton Vance and its affiliates have approximately $281 billion of assets under management.

Financial Performance

Eaton Vance's fiscal 2013 (ended October) revenue increased 12% versus the prior year to $1.36 billion. Net income declined 5% over the same period to $193.8 million primarily due to a loss related to debt extinguishment. The recovery in the financial markets and increased investor confidence lead to an increase in assets under management (AUM) which stood at nearly $281 billion at the end of fiscal 2013. Driving the increase in revenue was a 15% increase in investment advisory and administration fees as a result of the 30% increase in AUM as well as increase in revenue from the firm's acquisition of Hexavest in 2012.

Strategy

The investment management firm is looking beyond the US for expansion. In fiscal 2013 Eaton Vance launched a dozen new funds to capitalize on its expanding investment capabilities and continued to develop its exchange-traded managed funds business. In 2012 the firm opened its first Asian office in Singapore and joined forces with Canada-based AGF Management to launch two new mutual funds. Eaton Vance is continuing to grow its assets under management and menu of investment capabilities through acquisitions.

Mergers and Acquisitions

In December 2012 the firm's Parametric Portfolio Associates subsidiary acquired The Clifton Group Investment Management Company which specializes in providing futures- and options-based overlay services and custom risk management products for institutional investors. Operating as a division of Parametric Clifton's assets under management have grown from about $33 billion at the time it was acquired to more than $45 billion as of October 2013.

In August 2012 Eaton Vance acquired 49% of Montreal-based Hexavest and assume primary responsibility for Hexavest's new business development outside of Canada. (Eaton Vance has an option to acquire an additional 26% interest in the firm in fiscal 2017). The deal expanded Eaton Vance's international investment capabilities. Hexavest manages around $10.6 billion of assets for clients.

Eaton Vance purchased assets and intellectual property of Managed ETFs LLC in 2010 in order to expand its capabilities in the trading and management of exchange-traded funds (ETFs). That year also was one of the most prolific in the company's history in terms of new product launches. It introduced nearly ten new mutual funds two off-shore funds and a closed-end fund. The company bolstered its ETF business in 2011 with the formation of a new subsidiary Navigate Fund Solutions to develop and trade such funds.

HISTORY

In 1924 Harvard graduate Charles F. Eaton Jr. founded the investment firm Eaton & Howard which created and managed investment funds throughout the next several decades. The company went public in 1978; the next year it was purchased by Vance Sanders & Company and did business under the moniker Eaton & Howard Vance Sanders. By 1983 the company had $2.3 billion under management.

After 1987's stock market dive the company's tax-free low-interest bond funds made it an industry leader. Early in the 1990s it began to market its funds through more than 60 banks; the company also partnered with Lloyd George Management a move that allowed its mutual funds to be sold internationally.

EXECUTIVES

Chairman President and CEO, Thomas E. (Tom) Faust Jr., age 55, $500,000 total compensation
Chief Financial Officer; Vice President; Chief Accounting Officer, Laurie G. Hylton, age 47
VP and Chief Administrative Officer, Jeffrey P. Beale, age 57, $320,000 total compensation
Treasurer, Daniel C. (Dan) Cataldo
Head Institutional, Scott P. Ruddick
Co-Director Municipal Investments, Cynthia J. (Cindy) Clemson
Portfolio Manager; VP Eaton Vance Management, William H. Ahern Jr., age 54
Portfolio Manager; VP Eaton Vance Management, Craig R. Brandon
Co-Director Municipal Investments, Thomas M. (Tom) Metzold
EVP Chief Equity Investment Officer and Director, Duncan W. Richardson, age 56, $375,000 total compensation
VP Eaton Vance Management, Nancy B. Tooke
Director of Product Management and Client Service, Susan Brengle
Vice President; Chief Legal Officer; Secretary, Frederick S. Marius, age 50
President Eaton Vance Distributors, Matthew J. (Matt) Witkos, age 47, $305,000 total compensation
Chief Income Investment Officer; Vice President, Payson F. Swaffield, age 59
Head Eaton Vance Bank Loan Group, Scott H. Page, age 55
Co-Portfolio Manager of Eaton Vance?s Bank Loan Funds, Craig R. Russ, age 52
VP Consultant Relations, Sarah Morton
VP Institutional Business Development, Joseph Furey
VP Family Office Services Eaton Vance Investment Counsel, Antoinette Russell
Head Business Development Europe, Pepijn Heins
VP-Eaton Vance Investment Counsel, Robert C. Quinn
VP and Investment Counselor Eaton Vance Investment Counsel, Duke Laflamme
President Eaton Vance Investment Counsel, David C. McCabe
Vice President - Institutional Business Development, Rodrigo Soto
Vice President of Eaton Vance Management, John Croft
Director, Dorothy E. Puhy, age 61
Director, Leo I. (Lee) Higdon Jr., age 66
Director, Ann E. Berman, age 60
Director, Winthrop H. Smith Jr., age 64
EVP Chief Equity Investment Officer and Director, Duncan W. Richardson, age 56
Director, Richard J. (Rick) Spillane Jr., age 62
Auditors: Deloitte&ToucheLLP

LOCATIONS

HQ: Eaton Vance Corp.
2 International Pl., Boston MA 02110
Phone: 617-482-8260   **Fax:** 734-761-5368
Web: www.arotech.com

Selected Offices

Atlanta
Boston
London
New York City
Red Bank NJ
Seattle
Singapore
Westport CT

PRODUCTS/OPERATIONS

2013 Sales

	$ mil.	% of total
Investment advisory & administration fees	1,135	84
Service fees	126	9
Distribution & underwriter fees	89	7
Other	6	-
Total	**1,357**	**100**

Selected Subsidiaries

Atlanta Capital Management Company LLC
Boston Management and Research
Eaton Vance Distributors Inc.
Eaton Vance Management
Eaton Vance Management Canada Ltd. (British Columbia)
Eaton Vance Management (International) Limited
Fox Asset Management LLC (UK)
Hexavest (49% Canada)
Parametric Portfolio Associates LLC

COMPETITORS

Affiliated Managers Group	Invesco
AllianceBernstein	Janus Capital
BlackRock	Legg Mason
Capital Group	MFS
Diamond Hill Investment	Nuveen
FMR	PIMCO
Federated Investors	Putnam
Franklin Templeton	T. Rowe Price
	The Vanguard Group

HISTORICAL FINANCIALS

Company Type: Public

Income Statement

FYE: October 31

	REVENUE ($ mil.)	NET INCOME ($ mil.)	NET PROFIT MARGIN	EMPLOYEES
10/13	1,357.5	193.8	14.3%	1,330
10/12	1,209.0	203.4	16.8%	1,197
10/11	1,260.0	214.9	17.1%	1,155
10/10	1,121.6	174.3	15.5%	1,094
10/09	890.3	130.1	14.6%	1,059
Annual Growth	**11.1%**	**10.5%**	**—**	**5.9%**

2013 Year-End Financials

Debt ratio: 45.7%	No. of shares (mil.): 121
Return on equity: 30.2%	Dividends
Cash ($ mil.): 498	Yield: 4.3%
Current ratio: 2.62	Payout: 120.5%
Long-term debt ($ mil.): 1,100	Market value ($ mil.): 5,085

	STOCK PRICE ($) FY Close	P/E High/Low	PER SHARE ($) Earnings	Dividends	Book Value
10/13	41.81	28 18	1.53	1.82	5.51
10/12	28.14	17 12	1.72	0.77	5.26
10/11	26.29	19 11	1.75	0.73	3.98
10/10	28.77	24 18	1.40	0.66	3.47
10/09	28.39	27 11	1.08	0.63	2.95
Annual Growth	**10.2%**	**— —**	**9.1%**	**30.6%**	**16.9%**

Ebix Inc

Ebix knows a lot about the insurance biz. The company sells insurance industry software products and professional services to property/casualty insurers brokerages and individuals in Asia Australia Europe and North America. The company's EbixExchange service acts as an online auction house where buyers and carriers can exchange bids for auto home health life and other types of insurance while paying Ebix a fee on each transaction. Ebix also provides agency management software that includes workflow and customer relationship management (CRM) capabilities as well as other back-office functions for insurance brokers and insurance carriers. The company generates most of its sales in North America.

Geographic Reach

Atlanta-based Ebix's #1 market is the US accounting for about 70% of its sales. Australia accounts for nearly 20%. The firm's international operations are managed from Singapore. The Company has more than 30 offices across the US Australia Singapore New Zealand Canada China Japan and India.

Operations

About 80% of Ebix's revenue is generated by on-demand insurance Exchanges including life insurance annuity employee benefits and property and casualty exchanges. In addition to its insurance exchanges and software products Ebix also offers custom software development and business process outsourcing (BPO) services.

Financial Performance

Ebix has experienced impressive growth over the past decade with its revenue more than doubling since 2009. The company reported sales of more than $199 million in 2012 an 18% increase versus 2011. Net income declined by 1% over the same period to $70.5 million. The double-digit increase in revenue was driven by acquisitions completed in 2012 and 2011 and continued growth generated by its insurance Exchange channel partially offset by a decline in BPO revenue due to the downturn in the construction industry and a drop off in health revenues because of uncertainty associated with the health reform movement.

The company has always been profitable and a handful of recent acquisitions have expanded its service offerings and geographic footprint as well as nearly tripling its headcount since 2008. In 2012 Forbes ranked Ebix as the sixth fastest-growing technology company in the US with three-year average sales growth of 32% per year.

Strategy

The company has used selective acquisitions throughout its history to expand its product lines customer base and geographic footprint in countries including India and Singapore.

Mergers and Acquisitions

In April 2012 Ebix entered the medical education software market with the acquisition of Montreal-based Taimma Communications a developer of applications used by the pharmaceutical and biotechnology industries among others for medical training purposes. Also that year the company acquired Fintechnix a supplier of Web-based e-commerce applications for the life insurance and wealth management industries in Australia to boost its profile in the Asia/Pacific region. Additionally it bought PlanetSoft a developer of data exchange applications for the insurance industry for $40 million in June 2012. The deal added such customers as MassMutual Liberty Mutual and Desjardins as well as operations in India and the US. Ebix also acquired London-based TriSystems an online insurance trading hub that enables commercial insurance and reinsurance transactions between London intermediaries and insurance companies expanding its presence in Europe. TriSystems' products and services became part of the EbixExchange division in Europe.

In 2011 Ebix paid about $66 million to buy Atlanta-based A.D.A.M. The deal gave it a boost in the health care and insurance markets. Later that year the company bought Connecticut-based health insurance and benefits online network exchange HealthConnect Systems which it integrated into the EbixHealth division. The purchase furthered Ebix's strategy to become a health information exchange (HIE).

Ownership

CEO Robin Raina owns about 10% of the company's stock.

EXECUTIVES

Chairman of the Board; President; Chief Executive Officer, Robin Raina, age 47, $550,000 total compensation
SVP Infinity Carrier, Kathryn S. Cay
SVP Ebix P&C, Christine M. Denham
VP System Development Group Infinity Carrier, John L. Schmitt
Chief Financial Officer; Corporate Secretary, Robert (Bob) Kerris, age 59, $135,000 total compensation
SVP International Business and Intellectual Poperty, Graham Prior
SVP EbixExchange, Dan Delity
SVP Ebix Health, Jim Senge
Managing Director Ebix Singapore, Andy Wakefield
Managing Director Ebix New Zealand, Anthony (Tony) Wisniewski
Sr. VP of Exchange Sales, Michael Sladek
Director, Pavan Bhalla, age 50
Director, Hans U. Benz, age 67
Auditors: HabifArogeti&WynneLLP

LOCATIONS

HQ: Ebix Inc
5 Concourse Parkway, Suite 3200, Atlanta, GA 30328
Phone: 678 281-2020
Web: www.ebix.com

2012 Sales

	$ mil.	% of total
US	140	71
Canada	6	3
Latin America	8	4
Australia	36	18
Singapore	2	2
New Zealand	2	1
India	0	1
Europe	2	1
Total	**199**	**100**

PRODUCTS/OPERATIONS

2012 Sales

	$ mil.	% of total
Exchanges	159	80
Broker systems	18	9
Business processoutsourcing	16	8
Carrier systems	4	3
Total	**199**	**100**

COMPETITORS

Answer Financial	Guidewire Software
Applied Systems	InsWeb
BenefitMall	Intuit
CCC Information	Life Quotes
Computer Sciences Corp.	SunGard
	The Hartford
Cover-All	TriZetto
Crawford & Company	Vertafore
Datamonitor	

HISTORICAL FINANCIALS

Company Type: Public

Income Statement

FYE: December 31

	REVENUE ($ mil.)	NET INCOME ($ mil.)	NET PROFIT MARGIN	EMPLOYEES
12/12	199.3	70.5	35.4%	1,903
12/11	168.9	71.3	42.2%	1,426
12/10	132.1	59.0	44.6%	1,179
12/09	97.6	38.8	39.7%	958
12/08	74.7	27.3	36.5%	637
Annual Growth	**27.8%**	**26.8%**	**—**	**31.5%**

2012 Year-End Financials

Debt ratio: 15.8%
Return on equity: 20.6%
Cash ($ mil.): 36
Current ratio: 1.44
Long-term debt ($ mil.): 69
No. of shares (mil.): 37
Dividends
  Yield: 1.1%
  Payout: 10.7%
Market value ($ mil.): 598

	STOCK PRICE ($) FY Close	P/E High/Low		PER SHARE ($) Earnings	Dividends	Book Value
12/12	16.12	14	8	1.80	0.19	9.90
12/11	22.10	16	7	1.75	0.00	8.69
12/10	23.67	30	8	1.51	0.00	6.42
12/09	48.83	53	14	1.03	0.00	4.96
12/08	23.90	124	21	0.76	0.00	2.35
Annual Growth	**(9.4%)**	**—**	**—**	**24.1%**	**—**	**43.3%**

Echo Global Logistics Inc

By land air or sea Echo Global Logistics can help you deliver the goods. The company provides a wide range of transportation and logistics services such as carrier management rate negotiation freight bill audit and payment routing compliance and shipment execution and tracking. In addition its Evolved Transportation Manager (ETM) software analyzes clients' transportation needs and helps reduce costs as well as manages all procedures in shipping. Established in 2005 Echo Global Logistics customer base are primarily companies in the manufacturing and consumer products industries.

Geographic Reach

Echo is stationed in Chicago and has about 20 business development locations spanning 15 US states.

Operations

About 24000 transportation providers make up Echo's carrier network which consists of small and midsized fleets trucking companies and single-truck owners. Less-than-truckload and truckload services collectively account for about 90% of its total revenue.

Sales and Marketing

The company caters to nearly 28500 clients which are divided into two types: enterprise (under multiyear contracts) and transactional (services provided on a shipment-by-shipment basis). For 2012 transactional clients represented 70% of its total revenue.

Financial Performance

Echo has experienced unprecedented growth over the last few years. Revenues jumped 26% from $603 million in 2011 to reach $758 million in 2012 a historical milestone.

The growth was attributed to a major increase in its number of customers coupled with the uptick in shipment volumes. Revenue from enterprise clients jumped 19% in 2012 while revenue from transactional clients spiked 29%. Echo was also helped by $41 million in additional revenue generated in from acquisitions.

Profits also spiked 2% to reach a record high of $12.3 million in 2012 due to the recent surge in revenues and lower interest expenses.

Strategy

Although Echo's focus is on truckload (TL) less than truckload (LTL) and small parcel delivery; the company also offers intermodal (combination of rail and truck) air delivery. The company will continue to expand its geographic reach both through air and ocean modes of delivery; this strategy involves both the launching of new services and the purchasing of other businesses.

In 2013 Echo obtained Open Mile a truckload brokerage stationed in Boston. Echo enhanced its expertise in cloud computing as a result of the purchase. Throughout 2012 the company made several acquisitions including Sharp Freight Systems Purple Plum Logistics and Shipper Direct Logistics.

In 2011 the company gobbled up Rochester New York-based Trailer Transport Systems (TTS). TTS is a non-asset provider of intermodal transportation management and freight brokerage services. Its operations were integrated into the Echo Global Logistics as a regional hub.

Ownership

A group of company executives including directors Richard Heise Eric Lefkofsky and Bradley Keywell control 32% of Echo Global Logistics.

EXECUTIVES

CFO, David B. (Dave) Menzel, age 51
CEO and Director, Douglas R. (Doug) Waggoner, age 54, $223,106 total compensation
Non-Executive Chairman, Samuel K. Skinner, age 74
Regional Branch Manager Dallas, Mike Bryan
Regional Branch Manager Atlanta, Anne Wyrsch
EVP Operations, Tyler Ellison
EVP Sales, Scott Boyer
CTO, Michael E. Reed
Auditors: Ernst&YoungLLP

LOCATIONS

HQ: Echo Global Logistics Inc
600 West Chicago Avenue, Suite 725, Chicago, IL
60654
Phone: 800 354-7993   **Fax:** 888 796-4445
Web: www.echo.com

PRODUCTS/OPERATIONS

2012 Sales

	% of total
LTL	45
TL	44
Small	5
Intermodal	5
Other	1
Total	**100**

Selected Services

Domestic Air and Expedited Services
Flex TMS (a fee-based " software-as-a-service"
    transportation management system)
Inter-Modal
International air and ocean transportation services
Less than Truckload (LTL)
Small Parcel
Truckload

COMPETITORS

ABF Freight System
C.H. Robinson Worldwide
Con-way Inc.
Expeditors
FedEx
J.B. Hunt
MIQ Logistics
Ozburn-Hessey Logistics
Roadrunner Transportation Systems
Ryder System
Schneider Logistics
Total Quality Logistics
Transplace
UPS

HISTORICAL FINANCIALS

Company Type: Public

Income Statement

FYE: December 31

	REVENUE ($ mil.)	NET INCOME ($ mil.)	NET PROFIT MARGIN	EMPLOYEES
12/12	757.6	12.3	1.6%	1,364
12/11	602.7	12.0	2.0%	913
12/10	426.3	8.4	2.0%	709
12/09	259.5	5.2	2.0%	663
12/08	202.8	2.8	1.4%	553
Annual Growth	**39.0%**	**43.9%**	**—**	**25.3%**

2012 Year-End Financials

Debt ratio: 2.5%
Return on equity: 9.4%
Cash ($ mil.): 41
Current ratio: 2.00
Long-term debt ($ mil.): 5

No. of shares (mil.): 22
Dividends
  Yield: —
  Payout: —
Market value ($ mil.): 408

	STOCK PRICE ($) FY Close	P/E High/Low		PER SHARE ($) Earnings	Dividends	Book Value
12/12	17.97	35	29	0.54	0.00	6.21
12/11	16.15	33	21	0.53	0.00	5.39
12/10	12.04	42	26	0.38	0.00	4.76
12/09	12.69	51	40	0.29	0.00	4.31
Annual Growth	**12.3%**	**—**	**—**	**23.0%**	**—**	**13.0%**

Edwards Lifesciences Corp

Edwards Lifesciences has its heart in the right place. Named for the co-inventor of the first artificial heart valve Miles "Lowell" Edwards its main products are still heart valve devices including valves made from animal tissue annuloplasty rings that repair damaged valves and transcatheter heart valves for minimally invasive procedures. The company also makes monitoring systems that measure heart function during surgery; embolectomy catheters that remove blood clots from peripheral arteries; and various types of cannulae (surgical tubes used for drainage delivery or filtration) and other surgical supplies. Edwards Lifesciences markets its products worldwide.

Geographic Reach

Edwards Lifesciences sells its products in roughly 100 countries worldwide with key operations in Australia Canada China Japan the US and numerous countries in Europe (including France Germany Italy the Netherlands Spain and the UK). The company makes most of its sales in the US (more than 40%) Europe and Japan.

Manufacturing plants are located in Irvine California and Draper Utah in the US as well as in the Dominican Republic Puerto Rico Singapore and Switzerland. Research labs are located in Israel the Netherlands and the US.

Operations

Edwards Lifesciences' products fall into three main categories. Its surgical heart valve therapy segment makes tissue valve and valve repair items and accounts for more than 40% of sales. The division also offers various items used in minimally invasive surgeries; cannulae and embolectomy catheters used to treat peripheral vascular disease; and disposable items used in cardiac and other major surgeries.

The critical care products segment includes patient monitoring systems such as the EV1000 for hemodynamic monitoring (cardiovascular performance heart pressure and oxygen saturation) using integrated sensors and catheters during and after surgeries. Other critical care offerings include disposable pressure transducers and various catheters (including central venous pulmonary artery and balloon). The rapidly growing transcatheter heart valve segment makes catheter-based treatment systems for heart valve disease that negate the need for open-heart surgery. The critical care and transcatheter divisions each account for about 30% of sales.

Sales and Marketing

Edwards Lifesciences markets its products around the globe through a direct sales force and distributors. The company's clients include doctors nurses and other hospital or medical facility staff members (such as purchasing managers and administrators).

Financial Performance

Despite challenges in the medical device market due to regulatory and economic factors Edwards Lifesciences has managed to steadily increase revenues and profits over the years by providing innovative products that are essential to modern cardiovascular procedures. (Such products are typically not subject to negative spending or coverage decisions by consumers or insurers.) Revenues increased 13% in 2012 to some $1.9 billion due to a 65% jump in transcatheter heart valve

sales (primarily in the US). Net income also increased by about 24% that year to some $293 million on higher revenues and interest income.

Strategy

Much of the firm's growth can be attributed to a key aspect of its business strategy: The development of new and next-generation medical devices. Over the past few years Edwards Lifesciences has increased its R&D spending. The company invested $291 million (or about 15% of net sales) in R&D during 2012 up from $246 million in 2011 with a special focus on the high-growth field of minimally-invasive devices which aim to treat and monitor patients in a less traumatic way.

Edwards Lifesciences is focused on the development of next-generation transcatheter heart valves (designed to provide less invasive surgical options). The successful launch of the Edwards SAPIEN transcatheter heart valve in 2011 led Edwards Lifesciences to form a new transcatheter heart valve operating segment in fiscal 2012. The company is developing additional transcatheter systems; in 2012 it received approval to market the next-generation SAPIEN XT product in Europe and it expanded uses of the original SAPIEN product in the US.

The company is also creating new versions of its core Carpentier-Edwards PERIMOUNT pericardial tissue valves (for aortic and mitrial valve replacement). It gained approval for its Edwards INTUITY minimally invasive aortic heart valve system in Europe in 2012.

In the critical care segment Edwards Lifesciences is focused on the development of new hemodynamic monitoring systems. The firm is also developing minimally invasive automated glucose monitoring systems.

Alongside its growth measures the company has also chosen to downsize product segments that have been slow to grow. For instance it discontinued two of its vascular product lines the artificial graft implants and the LifeStent non-coronary stent offerings during 2011 and 2009.

Mergers and Acquisitions

Acquisitions can also serve as an effective way for the company to feed its development pipeline and expand its product offerings. In 2011 Edwards Lifesciences expanded its pipeline by purchasing Embrella Cardiovascular for $43 million. The acquisition gave Edwards Lifesciences a development-stage device designed to keep blood flowing to the brain during transcatheter heart valve procedures. The acquisition provides a novel new technology to support its minimally invasive heart valve development efforts.

In 2012 the company moved to expand further by acquiring BMEYE a Dutch maker of hemodynamic monitoring systems for some ?32 million ($42 million). The purchase expanded Edwards Lifesciences' offerings for the clinical market by providing an option that helps reduce complications and reduce the length of patients' hospital stays.

Ownership

Capital Research Global Investors and T. Rowe Price Associates each own a 10% stake in Edwards Lifesciences.

Company Background

Edwards Lifesciences' roots can be traced back to about 1960 when the invention of the artificial heart helped spawn a company that was then called Edwards Laboratories. The company was spun off from former parent Baxter International in 2000.

EXECUTIVES

Chairman and CEO, Michael A. Mussallem, $819,231 total compensation

Corporate VP Public Affairs and Special Counsel, Bruce P. Garren, age 66

Corporate VP Human Resources, Robert C. Reindl, age 58

Corporate VP and General Counsel, Aimee S. Weisner, age 44

Corporate VP Heart Valve Therapy, Donald E. Bobo Jr., $323,077 total compensation

Corporate VP Japan and Asia Pacific, Huimin Wang

Corporate VP Strategy and Corporate Development, John H. Kehl Jr., age 59

VP Investor Relations, David K. Erickson

Corporate VP and CFO, Thomas M. Abate, $394,231 total compensation

Corporate VP EMEA Canada and Latin America, Patrick B. Verguet, $465,278 total compensation

Corporate VP Critical Care and Vascula, Carlyn D. Solomon, $369,231 total compensation

Corporate VP Advanced Technology and Chief Scientific Officer, Stanton J. Rowe

Corporate VP Quality, John P. McGrath, age 52

Director Global Communications, Nolan Taira

Corporate VP Global Corporate Operations, Paul C. Redmond, age 49

Corporate VP Transcatheter Heart Valves, Larry L. Wood

Senior Manager Investor Relations, Elizabeth O'Hare

Senior Manager Global Communications, Amanda Fowler

Manager Global Communications, Janet Kim

Senior Analyst Investor Relations, Laci Smith

Corporate VP Cardiac Surgery Systems, Rich Lunsford

Corporate Vice President Human Resources, Christine McCauley

Director, William J. (Bill) Link, age 67

Director, David E. I. Pyott, age 59

Director, Mike R. Bowlin, age 70

Director, Wesley W. von Schack, age 67

Director, Robert A. (Bob) Ingram, age 70

Director, Barbara J. McNeil, age 71

Director, John T. Cardis, age 71

Presiding Independent Director, Wesley Schack

Auditors: PricewaterhouseCoopersLLP

LOCATIONS

HQ: Edwards Lifesciences Corp
One Edwards Way, Irvine, CA 92614
Phone: 949 250-2500
Web: www.edwards.com

2012 Sales

	$ mil.	% of total
US	812	43
Japan	294	16
Total	**1,899**	**100**

PRODUCTS/OPERATIONS

2012 Sales

	$ mil.	% of total
Surgical heart valve therapy	787	41
Transcatheter heart valves	552	29
Total	**1,899**	**100**

Selected Products

Surgical heart valve therapy
 Carpentier-Edwards Physio (mitral valve)
 Carpentier-Edwards Physio Tricuspid (annuloplasty ring)
 Carpentier-Edwards Perimount (aortic ease and mitral ease surgical heart valves)
 Cosgrove-Edwards (mitral valve)
 Edwards Intuity (minimally invasive aortic valve surgery system)
Critical care (for hemodynamic monitoring)
 Closed-loop blood sampling systems
 Disposable pressure monitors
 EV1000 (clinical monitoring platform)
 FloTrac (continuous cardiac output monitoring system)
 PediaSat (oximetry catheter)
 PreSep (central venous oximetry catheter)
 Swan-Ganz (pulmonary artery catheter)
 VolumeView (sensor-catheter set)
Transcatheter heart valves
 Edwards Sapien (transcatheter heart valve)
 Edwards Sapien XT (transcatheter heart valve)
Cardiac surgery systems
 IntraClude (aortic occlusion device)
 Protection cannulae (for drainage venting and cardioplegia delivery)
 ThruPort (minimal incision valve surgery platform)
Vascular
 Fogarty embolectomy catheters
 Surgical clips and clamps

COMPETITORS

ABIOMED	Johnson & Johnson
B. Braun Melsungen	LeMaitre Vascular
Becton Dickinson	LiDCO
Boston Scientific	Medtronic
CAS Medical	Sorin
Cook Group	St. Jude Medical
CryoLife	Stereotaxis
Hospira	Terumo
ICU Medical	W.L. Gore

HISTORICAL FINANCIALS

Company Type: Public

Income Statement

FYE: December 31

	REVENUE ($ mil.)	NET INCOME ($ mil.)	NET PROFIT MARGIN	EMPLOYEES
12/12	1,899.6	293.2	15.4%	8,200
12/11	1,678.6	236.7	14.1%	7,800
12/10	1,447.0	218.0	15.1%	7,000
12/09	1,321.4	229.1	17.3%	6,400
12/08	1,237.7	128.9	10.4%	6,200
Annual Growth	**11.3%**	**22.8%**	**—**	**7.2%**

2012 Year-End Financials

Debt ratio: 8.5%	No. of shares (mil.): 114
Return on equity: 20.7%	Dividends
Cash ($ mil.): 310	Yield: —
Current ratio: 3.72	Payout: —
Long-term debt ($ mil.): 189	Market value ($ mil.): 10,306

	STOCK PRICE ($) FY Close	P/E High/Low	PER SHARE ($) Earnings	Dividends	Book Value
12/12	90.17	43 27	2.48	0.00	12.94
12/11	70.70	44 30	1.98	0.00	11.73
12/10	80.84	55 26	1.83	0.00	11.38
12/09	86.85	43 26	1.95	0.00	10.19
12/08	54.95	57 37	1.10	0.00	7.86
Annual Growth	**13.2%**	**— —**	**22.7%**	**—**	**13.3%**

eHealth Inc

eHealth brought e-commerce to the insurance business. Through its eHealthInsurance subsidiary the company sells health insurance online to more than 3 million individual family Medicare and small business members. The company is licensed to sell insurance policies throughout the US. It has partnerships with more than 180 health insurance carriers for which it processes and delivers potential members' applications in return for commission on policy sales. It lets consumers compare some 10000 products online —including health dental and vision insurance products from the likes of Aetna Humana UnitedHealth and Wellpoint.

Geographic Reach

Though the company operates a technology center in China where more than half of its IT staff resides almost all its revenues come from the US. However it has launched a pilot program in China to sell insurance online in select markets within the country.

Operations

eHealth fills a gap in the health insurance brokerage business left by large brokers who cater to large and midsized companies and local agents who sell to individuals and small businesses but offer plans from a limited number of carriers. eHealth's technology platform and nationwide presence allow customers to get online rate quotes and side-by-side plan comparisons from a much wider range of providers. The company's online applications are delivered electronically to insurance carriers' information systems reducing the time it takes to process and enroll new members.

Sales and Marketing

In 2012 Humana accounted for 18% of the company's revenues; WellPoint 13%; and UnitedHealth 12%.

Financial Performance

eHealth gets most of its revenues from commissions off sales of policies. A much smaller amount comes from advertising sponsorships on its website; licensing agreements with agents and carriers who use the company's e-commerce technology; and fees for referrals for Medicare clients. Following health reform laws passed in the US however commission sales fell 11% in 2011 as insurance carriers reduced their commission rates due to new medical loss ratio requirements.

The company's revenues increased by 3% in 2012 thanks to a $12.6 million (9%) rise in commission revenues (primarily Medicare-related commission revenues) partially offset this increase was a $2.2 million decline in non-Medicare commission revenues due to a reduction in commission rates as a result of the implementation of the medical loss ratio requirements by insurance carriers beginning in 2011.

The growth was also partially offset by a $10.8 million decrease in Medicare lead referral revenues and a $5.9 million decrease in revenues related to government systems. The decrease in lead referral revenue was the result of eHealth's decision to cut the number of Medicare leads sold to third parties and to instead act as a health insurance agent to those leads. Government systems revenues were hurt by the expiration of the company's technology licensing contract with the federal government in early 2012. These decreases were partially offset by a $10.3 million rise in online sponsorship and advertising revenues (mainly related to Medicare plan carriers). eHealth's net income increased by 5% in 2012 due to higher revenues partially offset by a rise in operating expenses stemming from higher customer care and enrollment costs.

Strategy

As it strives to attract customers by providing more products from an ever-growing network of carriers eHealth has especially been focused on growing its Medicare business.

eHealth uses direct marketing and other means to build brand awareness and attract new customers to its website with the hopes of increasing commission payouts from its insurance partners. The company has marketing partnerships with online financial services firms and medical information providers to help get potential customers to its site. It is also enhancing its technologies to keep pace with competitive pressures aiming to provide the highest level of reliability and functionality.

In addition eHealth is working to increase the number of partners who license its online sales platform to sell policies on their own websites. The company is also looking to benefit from licensing opportunities from federal health reform laws that will require states to provide online health exchanges for consumers by 2014.

In 2013 the company partnered with Aon Hewitt to provide enrollment services to employees of Aon Hewitt's clients who choose to enroll in individual health insurance coverage.

In 2012 eHealth began offering individual and family health insurance plans from Blue Cross and Blue Shield plans in Illinois Oklahoma and Texas through the company's primary retail website.

Ownership

Entities affiliated with RS Investment Management own 15% of eHealth; Wellington Management 13%; and entities affiliated with HealthCor Management 12%.

Company Background

The company was founded in 1997.

It began actively marketing Medicare policies through its eHealthMedicare and PlanPrescriber websites following the 2010 acquisition of privately-held PlanPrescriber for roughly $30 million. PlanPrescriber provides online and pharmacy-based tools to help seniors navigate Medicare health insurance options. The acquisition has helped accelerate eHealth's penetration of the large and steadily growing senior market. eHealth intends to continue to expand its online Medicare enrollment capabilities as the Baby Boomer generation continues to shift into the Medicare bracket.

EXECUTIVES

Chairman of the Board of Directors and Chief Executive Officer, Gary L. Lauer, age 60, $412,500 total compensation

Senior Vice President Chief Financial Officer, Stuart M. Huizinga, age 51, $263,846 total compensation

EVP Business and Corporate Development, Bruce A. Telkamp, age 45, $284,954 total compensation

EVP Technology and CTO, Sheldon X. Wang, age 54, $284,954 total compensation

Senior Vice President of Sales, Samuel C. (Sam) Gibbs III, age 56, $191,461 total compensation

Senior Vice President - Sales and Operations, Robert S. Hurley, age 54, $200,523 total compensation

Senior Media Consultant, Sande Drew

VP Public Policy and Government Affairs, John D. Desser

VP Communications, Brian Mast

Director Public Relations, Nate Purpura

IR Contact Officer, Kate Sidorovich

President Chief Operating Officer, Bill Shaughnessy

Senior Vice President Engineering, Jiang Wu

Senior Vice President Product Management, Tom Tsao

Director, Lawrence M. Higby, age 67

Director, Scott N. Flanders, age 56

Director, Randall S. (Randy) Livingston, age 59

Director, Michael D. Goldberg, age 55

Director, Jack L. Oliver III, age 44

Independent Director, Ellen Tauscher
Auditors: Ernst&YoungLLP

LOCATIONS

HQ: eHealth Inc.
440 E. Middlefield Rd., Mountain View CA 94043
Phone: 650-584-2700   **Fax:** 650-961-2153
Web: https://www.ehealthinsurance.com

PRODUCTS/OPERATIONS

2012 Sales

Commissions	130	84
Total	**155**	**10**

Selected Insurance Carriers

Aetna
Altius
Anthem Blue Cross and Blue Shield
Assurant Health
BlueCross BlueShield of Texas
Blue Shield of California
CareFirst BlueCross BlueShield
Celtic Insurance Company
CIGNA
ConnectiCare
Coventry Health Care
Delta Dental
EmblemHealth
HealthNet
Highmark
Humana
IHC Group
Kaiser Permanente
LifeWise Health Plans
Regence BlueCross BlueShield
Scott & White Health Plan
Security Life Insurance Company of America
UniCare
UnitedHealth
WellPath Select
WellPoint

Selected Products

Health Insurance
Medicare
Maternity Coverage
PPO Plans
HMO Plans
Individual and Family
Individual Health Insurance
Family Health Insurance
Medicare
Short-term Health Insurance
Student Health Insurance
Health Savings Accounts
International Health Insurance
Individual Dental Insurance
Discount Cards
Vision Insurance
Life Insurance
Accident Insurance
Critical Illness Insurance
Travel Health Insurance
FSmall Business
Group Health Insurance
Group Dental Insurance
Group Vision Insurance
Medicare
Medicare Insurance Plans
Medicare Supplement
Medicare Advantage
Medicare Part D
Short Term
Short-term Health Insurance
Dental
Individual Dental Insurance
Group Dental Insurance
Vision
Individual Vision Insurance
Group Vision Insurance
Life
Life Insurance
Other

Travel Health Insurance
International Health Insurance
Pet Insurance
Prescription Discount Card
Telemedicine

COMPETITORS

Aflac	InsWeb
Answer Financial	Life Quotes
Aon	Marsh Inc.
BenefitMall	Matrix Direct
Bollinger Inc.	Wells Fargo Insurance
Ebix	Services
Health Insurance	
Innovations	

HISTORICAL FINANCIALS

Company Type: Public

Income Statement

FYE: December 31

	REVENUE ($ mil.)	NET INCOME ($ mil.)	NET PROFIT MARGIN	EMPLOYEES
12/12	155.4	7.0	4.6%	772
12/11	151.6	6.7	4.4%	635
12/10	160.4	17.4	10.9%	641
12/09	134.8	15.3	11.4%	520
12/08	111.7	14.1	12.7%	482
Annual Growth	8.6%	(15.9%)	—	12.5%

2012 Year-End Financials

Debt ratio: —	No. of shares (mil.): 20
Return on equity: 4.3%	Dividends
Cash ($ mil.): 140	Yield: —
Current ratio: 7.50	Payout: —
Long-term debt ($ mil.): —	Market value ($ mil.): 562

	STOCK PRICE ($) FY Close	P/E High/Low		PER SHARE ($) Earnings	Dividends	Book Value
12/12	27.48	77	39	0.34	0.00	8.36
12/11	14.70	48	36	0.31	0.00	7.83
12/10	14.19	25	13	0.73	0.00	7.52
12/09	16.43	30	19	0.61	0.00	6.47
12/08	13.28	62	15	0.55	0.00	6.19
Annual Growth	19.9%	—	—(11.3%)	—	7.8%

El Paso Pipeline Partners LP

El Paso Pipeline Partners is a natural gas pipeline and storage company with interests that extend far beyond its West Texas roots. The firm which consists primarily of Wyoming Interstate Company (WIC) Cheyenne Plains Gas (CPG) Colorado Interstate Gas Company (CIG) Elba Express and Southern Natural Gas Company (SNG) has 12900 miles of pipeline and storage facilities totaling 97 billion cu. ft. El Paso Pipeline Partners' customers include local distribution companies industrial users electricity generators and natural gas marketing and trading companies. Kinder Morgan controls the company.

Geographic Reach

El Paso Pipeline Partners' pipelines criss-cross the US. SNG's pipelines extend from natural gas supply basins in Texas Louisiana Mississippi Alabama and the Gulf of Mexico to end users in Louisiana Mississippi Alabama Florida Georgia South Carolina and Tennessee. CIG delivers natural gas from the Rocky Mountains and the Anadarko Basin to customers in Colorado Wyoming and indirectly to the Midwest Southwest California and Pacific Northwest. WIC owns interstate natural gas pipelines serving gas producers in the Overthrust Piceance Uinta Powder River and Green River basins. The Elba Express pipeline ships natural gas from the Elba Island LNG terminal (owned by Southern LNG) near Savannah Georgia to markets in the southeastern and eastern US.

Sales and Marketing

The company sells its products and services to natural gas distribution and industrial companies electric generation companies natural gas producers other natural gas pipelines and natural gas marketing and trading companies. Shell Oil Company PSCo and AGL Resources each generated more than 10% of El Paso Pipeline Partners' revenues in 2012.

Financial Performance

Revenues decreased by 1% in 2012 due to the acquisition of CPG. SNG's revenues grew due to the completion of two phases of an expansion project in 2011 and 2012. WIC reported additional revenues due to higher expenses related to compressor station repairs performed in 2011 that were not on its books in 2012. CIG added revenues thanks to favorable property tax adjustments and lower pipeline maintenance payroll and contractor costs and increased reservation revenues related to an expansion project which went into service in late 2011.

El Paso Pipeline Partners' net income increased by 13% in 2012 thanks to decreased operating and maintenance costs and lower net income attributable to noncontrolling interests due to the company's acquisition of additional stakes in SNG and CIG.

Strategy

The partnership's strategy is to increase the efficiency of its pipelines while making complementary asset acquisitions from its parent and from third parties and via strategic partnerships.

To take advantage of a growing gas supply in the US in 2013 subsidiary Southern Liquefaction Company LLC and Shell US Gas & Power agreed to form a limited liability company to develop a natural gas liquefaction plant (to produce liquefied gas for export) at Southern LNG Company LLC's Elba Island LNG Terminal.

Expanding its pipeline assets in 2012 El Paso Pipeline Partners bought the 14% stake in CIG that it did not already own and CPG both from El Paso Corp. for $635 million in cash and $242 million in debt. (El Paso Corp. was acquired by Kinder Morgan that year.)

In 2010 it expanded its liquefied natural gas (LNG) assets acquiring from its parent a 51% stake in Southern LNG Company and El Paso Elba Express Company for $810 million. It subsequently acquired the remaining stakes in these companies plus an additional 15% stake in SNG for $1.1 billion. After further purchases in 2011 El Paso Pipeline Partners held 100% of Southern LNG and El Paso Elba Express 100% of SNG and 86% of CIG.

Ownership

El Paso Pipeline Partners is controlled by Kinder Morgan which holds a 42% of the company.

EXECUTIVES

SVP, James J. Cleary, age 58
Chairman, Ronald L. Kuehn Jr., age 77
Executive Vice President General Counsel, Robert W. Baker, age 56
SVP, Norman G. Holmes, age 57
SVP, Daniel B. (Dan) Martin, age 56
Vice President CFO, Kimberly Dang
President; Director of the General Partner, Park Shaper
Chief Executive Officer; Director of the general partner, Richard Kinder
President COO, Steven Kean
Vice President Human Resources, James E. Street
Vice President General Counsel, David R. DeVeau
Vice President Controller, Debra M. Witges
Vice President CIO, Henry W. Neumann
Vice President Corporate Strategy, Jeffrey R. Armstrong
President Terminals, John W. Schlosser
Vice President Chief Tax Officer, Jordan H. Mintz
Vice President Internal Audit, Patrick Bourgoyne
President Natural Gas Pipelines, Tom Martin
Director, Douglas L. (Doug) Foshee, age 53
Director, William A. Smith, age 68
Director, Arthur C. Reichstetter, age 66
Auditors: Ernst&YoungLLP

LOCATIONS

HQ: El Paso Pipeline Partners L.P.
  1001 Louisiana St., Houston TX 77002
Phone: 713-420-2600   **Fax:** 713-420-4417
Web: www.eppipelinepartners.com

COMPETITORS

ANR Pipeline	Southern Union
Bridgeline	Transcontinental Gas
Duncan Energy	Pipe Line
Gulf South Pipeline	U.S. Transmission

HISTORICAL FINANCIALS

Company Type: Public

Income Statement

FYE: December 31

	REVENUE ($ mil.)	NET INCOME ($ mil.)	NET PROFIT MARGIN	EMPLOYEES
12/12	1,515.0	579.0	38.2%	0
12/11	1,425.0	472.0	33.1%	0
12/10	1,344.1	378.5	28.2%	0
12/09	537.6	213.5	39.7%	0
12/08	141.1	114.5	81.1%	0
Annual Growth	81.0%	50.0%	—	—

2012 Year-End Financials

Debt ratio: 65.9%	No. of shares (mil.): 220
Return on equity: 6,415.7%	Dividends
Cash ($ mil.): 114	Yield: 5.7%
Current ratio: 1.26	Payout: 104.9%
Long-term debt ($ mil.): 4,246	Market value ($ mil.): 8,141

	STOCK PRICE ($) FY Close	P/E High/Low	PER SHARE ($) Earnings	Dividends	Book Value
12/12	36.97	18 14	2.15	2.14	9.02
12/11	34.62	19 16	2.03	1.87	9.23
12/10	33.45	19 12	1.90	1.55	7.90
12/09	25.96	16 10	1.64	1.33	8.38
12/08	15.60	21 11	1.22	1.01	7.47
Annual Growth	24.1%	— —	15.2%	20.6%	4.9%

Electro Rent Corp.

Electro Rent isn't the electronic version of the popular Broadway musical but it is a company that rents leases and resells electronic test and measurement equipment computers servers and related equipment. The company's test instruments come from suppliers that include Agilent Technologies and Tektronix while its computers and workstations are primarily sourced from from such manufacturers as Apple Dell Hewlett-Packard and Toshiba. Electro Rent provides new and used equipment to government agencies and companies in the aerospace and defense electronics semiconductor and telecommunications industries.

True to its name Electro Rent gets more than half of its revenues from rentals and leases; the rest comes from selling equipment. The company's test and measurement unit accounts for some 90% of sales.

The company gets more than 85% of its sales in the US but also has key operations in Canada China and Europe.

Overall sales for Electro Rent were $248 million in fiscal 2012 about an 8% increase over the prior year. The higher sales were due to rental and lease revenues that were up nearly 10% on increased demand and rental rates for test and measurement equipment in North America and Europe partially offset by a decline in revenues related data products for the year also related to demand. Equipment sales and other revenues were up 7% for the year on increases in sales of new equipment and finance leases offset by lower sales of used equipment. Electro Rent is looking to flexible financing alternatives to drive growth in its lease and rental business. The company's net income was also 8% higher for the year due in part to bargain purchase gains related to acquisitions even though operating profit was lower on higher operating expenses.

In 2011 Electro Rent acquired Las Vegas-based Equipment Management Technology (EMT) which specializes in the sale and rental of electronic test equipment to companies in the aerospace and defense sectors. In 2010 the company bought the assets of Telogy for nearly $25 million in cash. Telogy (which had filed for bankruptcy protection from creditors) leased rented and sold electronic test equipment.

Chairman and CEO Daniel Greenberg and his brother Phillip own about 30% of Electro Rent outright and through a family trust.

HISTORY

Formed in 1965 to lease high-tech instruments Electro Rent was bought in 1973 by Telecor. That year Daniel Greenberg joined Electro Rent; he became chairman and CEO in 1979. Electro Rent was spun off and went public in 1980 and continued to thrive during the growth of the defense industry in the early 1980s. In 1985 the company formed a joint venture in Japan. Then sales began to slip as a result of cutbacks in federal spending for defense and aerospace. Greenberg overhauled the company which branched into the leasing of PCs and workstations in 1987. It worked. A surge in demand for PCs and workstations helped to offset the decline in revenues from test and measurement equipment.

Electro Rent's revenues rebounded in 1994 as growth in the communications industry helped boost demand for complex test equipment. Also that year Electro Rent bought rival Genstar Rental

Electronics of Canada. In 1996 the company bought LDI Computer Rentals and the following year it doubled in size when it acquired General Electric Technology Management Services another computer and test equipment rental business. To cut costs the company reduced its workforce by 8% in 1998 and sold its Japanese operations.

Because of slipping demand for PC rentals in 2000 the company shifted focus to its test and measurement equipment rentals and began to offer telecommunications and fiber-optic test equipment in 2001.

It opened its rental center in China in 2005. That same year the company established a European outpost through its relationship with a Belgian rental firm Everest ES. Electro Rent later acquired Everest ES and made it part of its ER Europe subsidiary.

Electro Rent completed its acquisition of Rush Computer Rentals in 2006 and its acquisition of Telogy in 2010. In 2011 Electro Rent acquired Las Vegas-based Equipment Management Technology (EMT) which specializes in the sale and rental of electronic test equipment to companies in the aerospace and defense sectors.

EXECUTIVES

VP Sales Western Region, John Hart, age 61
VP Sales Eastern Region and Canada, Thomas A. Curtin, age 57, $138,000 total compensation
VP-Ops, Craig R. Burgi, age 58
VP Human Resources, Peter M. Shapiro, age 66
Chief Financial Officer; Vice President, Craig R. Jones, age 68, $215,000 total compensation
VP-Product Mgmt, Richard E. Bernosky, age 55
President; Chief Operating Officer, Steven Markheim, age 61, $300,000 total compensation
Chairman of the Board; Chief Executive Officer, Daniel Greenberg, age 73, $450,000 total compensation
VP; General Manager Computer Products and Services Group Rush Computer Rentals, Dennis M. Clark, age 57, $135,000 total compensation
VP Distribution and Technical Services, Ronald J. Deming, age 61
VP Administrative and Information Services, Meryl D. Evans, age 53
General Manager Electro Rent Europe, David Saeys
Sales Manager Distribution Products Group, Scott Wrinkle
General Manager Electro Rent (Tianjin) China, Paul Pang
VP Sales Rush Computer Rentals, Peter Oman
Senior Vice President - North American Sales, Herb Ostenberg, age 64
Director, James S. Pignatelli, age 70
Director, Gerald D. Barrone, age 83
Director, Nancy Y. Bekavac, age 61
Director, Joseph J. Kearns, age 72
Director, Karen J. Curtin, age 59
Director, Theodore E. (Ted) Guth, age 58
Auditors: Deloitte&ToucheLLP

LOCATIONS

HQ: Electro Rent Corporation
6060 Sepulveda Blvd., Van Nuys CA 91411-2512
Phone: 818-787-2100   **Fax:** 818-786-4354
Web: www.electrorent.com

2012 Sales

	$ mil.	% of total
US	214	86
Other countries	34	14
Total	**248**	**100**

PRODUCTS/OPERATIONS

2012 Sales

	$ mil.	% of total
Rentals & leases	129	52
Sales of equipment & other	118	48
Total	**248**	**100**

2012 Sales

	$ mil.	% of total
Test & measurement	230	93
Data products	18	7
Total	**248**	**100**

Selected Products

Test and Measurement
  Cellular mobile and satellite
  Data acquisition
  Digital design
  Electronic
  Insulation
  Network analyzers
  Optical spectrum analyzers
  Power monitors
  Synthesized signal sources
  Telecommunications
  Test equipment calibration
  Transformer
  Video broadcasts
  Wavelength meters
Data Products
  Desktop computers
  Hubs routers and switches
  Peripherals
  PCs
  PC displays
  Projection devices
  Network devices
  Notebook computers
  Servers
  UNIX workstations

COMPETITORS

CalFirst	ORIX
Continental Resources	Transcat
McGrath RentCorp	Trek Equipment
MetricTest	

HISTORICAL FINANCIALS

Company Type: Public

Income Statement

FYE: May 31

	REVENUE ($ mil.)	NET INCOME ($ mil.)	NET PROFIT MARGIN	EMPLOYEES
05/13	248.7	22.7	9.1%	417
05/12	248.5	25.7	10.4%	393
05/11	228.7	23.7	10.4%	371
05/10	145.8	11.6	8.0%	335
05/09	130.4	11.7	9.0%	296
Annual Growth	**17.5%**	**18.0%**	**—**	**8.9%**

2013 Year-End Financials

Debt ratio: 3.1%
Return on equity: 9.5%
Cash ($ mil.): 10
Current ratio: 1.34
Long-term debt ($ mil.): —

No. of shares (mil.): 24
Dividends
  Yield: 10.5%
  Payout: 191.4%
Market value ($ mil.): 408

	STOCK PRICE ($) FY Close	P/E High/Low		PER SHARE ($) Earnings	Dividends	Book Value
05/13	17.01	20	15	0.94	1.80	9.52
05/12	13.84	18	12	1.07	0.80	10.34
05/11	15.34	18	12	0.99	0.60	10.02
05/10	13.59	31	18	0.48	0.60	9.60
05/09	9.65	34	15	0.47	0.60	9.55
Annual Growth	**15.2%**		**—**	**18.9%**	**31.6%**	**(0.1%)**

Ellie Mae Inc

Ellie Mae might sound like Fannie Mae's backwoods cousin but they're just in related industries not bloodlines. The company provides automation software and operates the Ellie Mae Network that facilitates the residential mortgage origination and funding process. Its Encompass software suite combines loan origination with CRM (customer relationship management) to gather review and verify data from a single database. Other programs handle regulatory compliance appraisal and title services underwriting tax transcripts and document preparation and management. More than 90000 mortgage professionals use its software and network to process more than 3 million new mortgages an estimated 20% of its addressable market.

Geographic Reach
Ellie Mae only operates in the US from offices in California Nebraska (technical support) and New Jersey.

Sales and Marketing
The company's sales force is divided into four teams that handle account management new account acquisition sales development and solution engineering. Customers include American Home Bank HighTechLending Skyline Financial and Supreme Lending.

Mortgage originators that use Encompass software pay for it either as a service with monthly fees based on the number of users and mortgages funded or through licensing and recurring subscription fees. Lenders and service providers that use the Ellie Mae Network pay fees per transaction for business received from Encompass users.

Financial Performance
Sales grew more than 80% in 2012 jumping from $55 million to $101 million year-over-year. The substantial increase was primarily due to Encompass users adopting the on-demand Software-as-a-Service model. The company has grown its base of active SaaS users from about 24000 in 2011 to 41000 in 2012. Profits jumped from $3 million in 2011 to almost $20 million in 2012.

Mergers and Acquisitions
In 2013 the company offered to buy Massachusetts-based MortgageCEO which offers on-demand CRM and marketing automation software with marketing software being a new product in its software suite. In 2011 it bought Mortgage Pricing System with which it created its product and pricing service. Also that year it picked up Del Mar Datatrac which made the DataTrac origination software.

Strategy
A major part of Ellie Mae's SaaS focus is its "success-based" pricing model that allows customers to pay at the time loans are closed. Besides its objectives to add new Encompass users and cross-sell to existing ones the company plans to enhance its Ellie Mae Network with increased functionality and services and expand the use of settlement services on the system. Industry trends are also influencing strategy. The software industry has gone cloud crazy over the past few years and Ellie Mae has not been immune. A key part of its strategy is to emphasize the software-as-a-service (SaaS) incarnations of its Encompass offerings.

Company Background
Ellie Mae was founded in 1997 and launched the first version of its transaction network in 2000. The Encompass software suite came out in 2003.

EXECUTIVES

Chief Technology Officer Vice President of Technology and Operations, Limin Hu, age 51, $200,000 total compensation

SVP Sales and Client Services, Cathleen Schreiner Gates

EVP Finance Administration and CFO, Edgar A. (Ed) Luce, age 61, $200,000 total compensation

COO, Jonathan H. Corr, age 46, $200,000 total compensation

senior Vice President of technology, Ting Wu

SVP Business Development, Richard Roof

senior Vice President Vice President of human resources and operations, Lisa Bruun

VP General Counsel and Secretary, Elisa Lee, age 38

SVP Human Resources, Lisa Brunn

Vice President product strategy, Jonas Moe

Chief Information Officer Vice President, David Robbins

Vice President Controller, Matt LaVay

Vice President of financial planning and analysis, Michelle Gable

senior Vice President of marketing, Philip Yee

Managing Director, Lisa Laukkanen

senior Vice President business development, Richard Roof??s

senior Vice President of marketing, Susan Scarth

senior Vice President of software development, Vivian Wong

President Dover Mortgage, Harvey Goldberg

Director, Robert J. (Rob) Levin, age 57

Director, Craig S. Davis, age 62

Director, A. Barr Dolan, age 63

Director, Carl Buccellato, age 71

Director, Bernard M. Notas, age 62

Director, Alan S. Henricks, age 62

Auditors: GrantThorntonLLP

LOCATIONS

HQ: Ellie Mae Inc.
4155 Hopyard Rd. Ste. 200, Pleasanton CA 94588
Phone: 925-227-7000   **Fax:** 925-227-9030
Web: www.elliemae.com

PRODUCTS/OPERATIONS

2012 Sales

	% of total
On-demand	87
On-premise	13
Total	**100**

Selected Products

Ellie Mae Network
Encompass 4506 T-Service (income verification)
Encompass Appraisal Service (appraisals)
Encompass CenterWise (web and electronic document management)
Encompass Compliance Service (compliance)
Encompass EDM (electronic document management)
Encompass Flood Service (flood certifications)
Encompass WebCenter (creates customized websites)

COMPETITORS

Davis + Henderson	McCracken Financial
Dexma	Solutions
FirstPoint Inc	Prommis
Fiserv	Prymak
Harland Financial	Verisk
Solutions	Wolters Kluwer
ISG Novasoft	WowTools
Lender Processing	Xerox
Services	eLynx
MGIC Investment	

HISTORICAL FINANCIALS

Company Type: Public

Income Statement

FYE: December 31

	REVENUE ($ mil.)	NET INCOME ($ mil.)	NET PROFIT MARGIN	EMPLOYEES
12/12	101.8	19.4	19.1%	308
12/11	55.4	3.6	6.5%	270
12/10	43.2	0.7	1.8%	190
12/09	37.7	1.6	4.4%	0
12/08	33.5	(1.0)	—	0
Annual Growth	32.0%	—	—	—

2012 Year-End Financials

Debt ratio: —
Return on equity: 15.8%
Cash ($ mil.): 44
Current ratio: 4.69
Long-term debt ($ mil.): —

No. of shares (mil.): 26
Dividends
  Yield: —
  Payout: —
Market value ($ mil.): 723

	STOCK PRICE ($) FY Close	P/E High/Low		PER SHARE ($) Earnings	Dividends	Book Value
12/12	27.75	35	7	0.76	0.00	6.40
12/11	5.65	32	17	0.18	0.00	3.75
Annual Growth	391.2%	—	—	—322.2%	—	70.7%

Ellington Financial LLC

Mortgage-related assets are music to Ellington Financial's ears. The specialty finance company manages a portfolio of primarily non-agency residential mortgage-backed securities valued at more than $366 million. It also seeks to acquire other target assets such as residential whole mortgage loans commercial mortgage-backed securities commercial real estate debt and asset-backed securities. Riskier residential whole mortgage loans which are generally not guaranteed by the US government include subprime non-performing and sub-performing mortgage loans. Founded in 2007 Ellington Financial went public in 2010 in hopes of taking advantage of the current credit environment.

The company is using a substantial portion of the proceeds from its initial public offering to acquire more target assets. It plans to use the balance for interest-bearing short-term investments — such as money market accounts —as well as for working capital and general corporate expenses.

In its attempt to acquire target assets Ellington Financial will compete with other specialty finance companies mortgage REITs public and private funds and commercial and investment banks. Keeping its portfolio diverse may help it weather downturns among certain geographic regions or property types that are subject to higher risk of foreclosure.

Ellington Financial executive officers and directors together own about a quarter of the company's stock.

EXECUTIVES

Director, Edward (Ed) Resendez, age 56
Chairman and Co-Chief Investment Officer, Michael W. Vranos, age 51
President CEO and Director, Laurence E. Penn
Co-Chief Investment Officer, Mark Tecotzky

Chief Financial Officer, Lisa Mumford
Director, Ronald I. Simon, age 75
Director, Thomas F. Robards, age 66
Director, Edward (Ed) Resendez, age 56
President CEO and Director, Laurence E. Penn
Auditors: PricewaterhouseCoopersLLP

LOCATIONS

HQ: Ellington Financial LLC
53 Forest Ave., Old Greenwich CT 06870
Phone: 203-698-1200   **Fax:** 203-698-0869
Web: www.ellingtonfinancial.com

COMPETITORS

Annaly Capital	MFA Financial
Management	MFResidential
Chimera	Sutherland
Galiot Capital	Western Asset Mortgage

HISTORICAL FINANCIALS

Company Type: Public

Income Statement

FYE: December 31

	REVENUE ($ mil.)	NET INCOME ($ mil.)	NET PROFIT MARGIN	EMPLOYEES
12/12	63.8	24.1	37.9%	100
12/11	63.5	44.7	70.3%	100
12/10	45.6	24.7	54.3%	100
12/09	51.7	18.3	35.5%	0
12/08	29.9	12.8	42.9%	0
Annual Growth	20.9%	17.2%	—	—

2012 Year-End Financials

Debt ratio: 0.0%
Return on equity: 5.5%
Cash ($ mil.): 59
Current ratio: 0.43
Long-term debt ($ mil.): 1

No. of shares (mil.): 20
Dividends
  Yield: 11.1%
  Payout: 129.5%
Market value ($ mil.): 458

	STOCK PRICE ($) FY Close	P/E High/Low		PER SHARE ($) Earnings	Dividends	Book Value
12/12	22.46	17	13	1.35	2.50	24.86
12/11	17.17	9	6	2.71	2.51	22.55
12/10	22.24	12	11	1.91	0.80	24.47
Annual Growth	0.5%	—	—	(15.9%)	76.8%	0.8%

Emergent BioSolutions Inc

Emergent BioSolutions is preparing for a bioterrorism or pandemic worst-case scenario. The company develops and produces vaccines that treat or protect against infectious diseases and bio-agents. The company supplies BioThrax (the US's only FDA-approved anthrax vaccine) primarily to the US Department of Defense (DOD) Centers for Disease Control (CDC) and the US Department of Health and Human Services (HHS). Its biodefense unit is also developing a post-exposure treatment for anthrax. The company's biosciences division is working on therapies for leukemia and lymphoma and vaccines for such infectious as influenza.

Operations

The company manufactures BioThrax at its production facility in Lansing Michigan. The company also operates offices and laboratories in Maryland and Washington as well as in Germany. Emergent BioSolutions contracts with a third-party filling laboratory to measure BioThrax into dosage vials.

Sales and Marketing

The company markets its products primarily to US state and local governments. It also markets to international customers including governments in the Middle East India Australia Europe and Southeast Asia. through third parties.

Financial Performance

The company's revenue up 3% in 2012 over 2011 due in part to an increases in sales of its core BioThrax product. The company's profits rose slightly in the same period. Substantially all of Emergent BioSolutions' revenue comes from sales of its biodefense products to its US government customers.

Strategy

While Emergent BioSolutions dominates the anthrax vaccine niche its focus on a single niche product can leave it vulnerable to fluctuations in demand from a relatively narrow customer base. To reduce its vulnerability the company has broadened its customer base in recent years to include state and local governments (who might want their own stockpiles for first responders) as well as foreign governments. It has also built up its non-anthrax pipeline through acquisitions.

The company's overall product development strategy includes acquiring new candidates through company acquisitions. In 2013 it bought the Healthcare Protective Products Division of Bracco Diagnostics Inc. and added the division's Reactive Skin Decontamination Lotion (RSDL) to its product offerings. In addition to its acquisitions the company has also divested its stake in a tuberculosis vaccine candidate and saw Pfizer terminate a collaboration agreement related to the development of a rheumatoid arthritis treatment and Abbott Laboratories terminate a collaboration for development of a leukemia treatment.

Ownership

Chairman Fuad El-Hibri holds a 19% interest in the compan.

EXECUTIVES

Chairman, Fuad El-Hibri, age 55, $585,628 total compensation

SVP and Chief Scientific Officer, W. James Jackson, age 52

President and Chief Executive Officer, Daniel J. Abdun-Nabi, age 58, $411,485 total compensation

Executive Vice President Corporate Services Division Chief Financial Officer Treasurer, Robert G. (Bob) Kramer Sr., age 55

IR Contact Officer, Robert G. Burrows

SVP and Chief Quality Officer, Denise Landry

SVP Product Development, Stephen Lockhart, age 56, $295,604 total compensation

Executive Vice President Corporate Affairs Division, Allen Shofe

VP Corporate Communications, Tracey Schmitt

Executive Vice President Strategic Investments Division, Steven N. Chatfield, age 56

Executive Vice President and President BioDefense Division, Adam R. Havey, age 42

Director, Louis W. Sullivan, age 77

President and Chief Executive Officer, Daniel J. Abdun-Nabi, age 58

Director, Jerome M. (Jerry) Hauer, age 60

Director, Ronald B. Richard, age 57

Director, Zsolt Harsanyi, age 69

Director, John E. Niederhuber

Director, Sue Bailey, age 69

Director, Marvin L. White

Auditors: Ernst&YoungLLP

LOCATIONS

HQ: Emergent BioSolutions Inc.
2273 Research Blvd. Ste. 400, Rockville MD 20850
Phone: 301-795-1800   **Fax:** 301-795-1899
Web: www.emergentbiosolutions.com

PRODUCTS/OPERATIONS

2012 Sales

Products	215	77
Total	**281**	**100**

Selected Acquisitions and Ventures

2013
Bracco Diagnostics' Healthcare Protective products Division ($26 million Reactive Skin Decontamination Lotion)
2011
TenX BioPharma ($2.5 million late-stage biopharmaceutical candidate zanolimumab)
2010
Trubion Pharmaceuticals ($135 million biopharmaceutical development)
EPIC Bio Pte Limited (joint venture with Temasek Life Sciences influenza vaccine development)

Selected Products & Candidates

Licensed
BioThrax (Anthrax Vaccine Adsorbed)
Investigational
Infectious Disease
Anthrivig
NuThrax
PreviThrax
Thravixa
Oncology
Zanolimumab (T-cell lymphoma)

COMPETITORS

Amgen	Human Genome Sciences
Biogen Idec	Panacea
Cangene	Pharmaceuticals
Crucell	Pfizer
DiagnoCure	PharmAthene
Elusys Therapeutics	Roche Holding
Genentech	Soligenix

HISTORICAL FINANCIALS

Company Type: Public

Income Statement

FYE: December 31

	REVENUE ($ mil.)	NET INCOME ($ mil.)	NET PROFIT MARGIN	EMPLOYEES
12/12	281.8	23.5	8.3%	877
12/11	273.3	23.0	8.4%	811
12/10	286.1	51.7	18.1%	767
12/09	234.7	31.1	13.3%	652
12/08	178.5	20.6	11.6%	587
Annual Growth	**12.1%**	**3.3%**	**—**	**10.6%**

2012 Year-End Financials

Debt ratio: 11.1%	No. of shares (mil.): 35
Return on equity: 5.4%	Dividends
Cash ($ mil.): 141	Yield: —
Current ratio: 4.25	Payout: —
Long-term debt ($ mil.): 58	Market value ($ mil.): 575

	STOCK PRICE ($) FY Close	P/E High/Low		PER SHARE ($) Earnings	Dividends	Book Value
12/12	16.04	28	20	0.65	0.00	12.30
12/11	16.84	38	23	0.64	0.00	11.51
12/10	23.46	15	8	1.59	0.00	10.55
12/09	13.59	26	9	0.99	0.00	7.82
12/08	26.11	38	7	0.68	0.00	6.61
Annual Growth	**(11.5%)**	**—**	**—**	**(1.1%)**	**—**	**16.8%**

Employers Holdings Inc

Because workers' compensation is nothing to gamble with small business owners can turn to Employers Holdings. The Reno-based holding company provides workers' compensation services including claims management loss prevention consulting and care management to small businesses in low hazard industries including retailers and restaurants. The company provides workers' compensation through its Employer Insurance Company of Nevada (EICN) and Employers Compensation Insurance Company. Employers Holdings also operates Employers Assurance and Employers Preferred Insurance Company both of which also offer workers' compensation.

While it distributes its products through independent agents and brokers in more than 30 states and the District of Columbia more than half of its premiums come from California. It also markets its products along with ADP's payroll services in several states and with Anthem Blue Cross of California's group health insurance products in California. Employers Holdings is forging additional distribution partners in other markets.

Employers Holdings maintains a strategy of engaging in low-to-medium hazard industries in order to try to keep its losses under control. Its top types of insureds include restaurants the clerical side of physician offices automobile service or repair centers and colleges (professional employees and clerical). The company also spreads its risk around and is not dependent upon any one customer for a significant portion of its income.

Along with spreading its risk among many customers the company also grows geographically. In 2011 Employers Holdings expanded its discounted workers' compensation coverage to small businesses in four additional states through the National Federation of Independent Business (NFIB). It launched NFIB-endorsed programs in eight more states later in 2011. The NFIB is focused largely on small businesses about 97% of its members have 50 or fewer employees.

Like all workers compensation insurers Employers Holdings has been hurt by the economic recession. (As employers cut their workforces they also cut the amount of workers' comp coverage they need). The company's net income has dropped by nearly half since 2008. In response the company restructured during 2009 and 2010 by cutting its workforce consolidating its claims system and combining its four regional operating units into two. It also cozied up to its distribution partners to keep warm by offering bundled products in bulk.

In fiscal 2011 Employers Holdings' revenues increased by 10% from the previous year to $464.2 million reflecting an 11% increase in premiums earned (attributable to increased policy count) and doubled gains on investments as a result of the company's strategic rebalancing of its investment portfolio. Its net income dropped 23% however to $48.3 million or $1.29 per diluted share compared with $62.8 million or $1.51 per diluted share for 2010. This was primarily due to a 16% increases in expenses including losses and loss adjustment expenses.

HISTORY

EICN was the successor to Nevada's public workers' compensation fund. The state-run system which was deeply in debt and on the verge of collapse was officially privatized in 2000 under the guidance of CEO Douglas Dirks. In 2004 EICN reorganized into a mutual insurance company which took the name EIG Mutual Holdings and included EICN as its subsidiary.

In 2006 EIG Mutual Holdings filed its initial public offering to convert from a mutual insurance holding company to a publicly traded corporation. When the company's members approved the conversion in early 2007 the name changed to Employers Holdings Inc. Eligible members received shares of the new company; non-eligible members took home just their share of the proceeds raised.

EXECUTIVES

President CEO and Director, Douglas D. Dirks, age 54, $575,509 total compensation
Executive Vice President Chief Legal Officer General Counsel, Lenard T. Ormsby, age 60, $320,665 total compensation
Executive Vice President Corporate & Public Affairs, Ann W. Nelson, age 52, $218,963 total compensation
Executive Vice President Chief Administrative Officer, John P. Nelson, $210,392 total compensation
Senior Vice President Chief Claims Officer, Stephen V. Festa
Executive Vice President Chief Financial Officer, William E. Yocke, age 62, $313,236 total compensation
Chairman, Robert J. Kolesar, age 69
Senior Vice President Manager Eastern Region, Timothy J. Spear, age 46
Senior Vice President Manager Western Region, T. Hale Johnston
Senior Vice President General Manager Strategic Partnerships & Alliances, David M. Quezada
VP and Corporate Controller and Chief Accountant EICN and ECIC, Cynthia M. Morrison
Senior Vice President Chief Information Officer, Richard P. Hallman
VP Corporate Marketing, Ty Vukelich
VP Investor Relations, Vicki Erickson
Vice President - Investor Relations, Vicki Mills
VP-Sls-Western Reg, Zac Taylor
Senior Vice President Chief Actuary, Bryan Ware
Senior Vice President Chief Underwriting Officer, Cecelia M. Abraham
Senior Vice President Manager Eastern Region, Mark R. Hogle
Director, Michael D. (Mike) Rumbolz, age 60
President CEO and Director, Douglas D. Dirks, age 54
Director, Richard W. Blakey, age 63
Director, Valerie R. Glenn, age 58
Director, Rose E. McKinney-James, age 61
Director, Ronald F. Mosher, age 69
Director, Katherine W. Ong, age 55
Director, John P. Sande III, age 63
Auditors: Ernst&YoungLLP

LOCATIONS

HQ: Employers Holdings Inc.
10375 Professional Circle, Reno NV 89521
Phone: 775-327-2700   **Fax:** 888-527-3422
Web: www.eig.com

2011 Premiums In-force

	% of total
California	56
Illinois	6
Georgia	4
Nevada	4
Other states	26

PRODUCTS/OPERATIONS

2011 Sales

	$ mil.	% of total
Net premiums earned	363	78
Realized gains on investments & adjustment	20	5
Other income	0	-
Total	**464**	**100**

Selected Subsidiaries

AmSERV Inc.
EIG Services Inc.
Elite Insurance Services Inc.
Employers Assurance Company
Employers Compensation Insurance Company
Employers Group Inc.
Employers Insurance Company of Nevada
Employers Occupational Health Inc.
Employers Preferred Insurance Company
Pinnacle Benefits Inc.

COMPETITORS

AMERISAFE	RLI
AmTrust Financial	Republic Indemnity
Baldwin & Lyons	Safety Insurance
Berkshire Hathaway	SeaBright Insurance
CNA Financial	Selective Insurance
Donegal	State Auto Financial
EMC Insurance	State Compensation
Harleysville Group	Insurance Fund
Liberty Mutual	The Hartford
Meadowbrook Insurance	TowerGroup
Navigators	Travelers Companies
PMA Insurance Group	United Fire
ProAssurance	Zenith National

HISTORICAL FINANCIALS

Company Type: Public

Income Statement

FYE: December 31

	ASSETS ($ mil.)	NET INCOME ($ mil.)	INCOME AS % OF ASSETS	EMPLOYEES
12/12	3,511.3	106.8	3.0%	667
12/11	3,481.7	48.3	1.4%	651
12/10	3,480.1	62.8	1.8%	699
12/09	3,676.6	83.0	2.3%	941
12/08	3,756.7	101.7	2.7%	1,040
Annual Growth	**(1.7%)**	**1.2%**	**—**	**(10.5%)**

2012 Year-End Financials

Return on assets: 3.0%	Dividends
Return on equity: 21.0%	Yield: 1.1%
Long-term debt ($ mil.): —	Payout: 20.6%
No. of shares (mil.): 30	Market value ($ mil.): 633
Sales ($ mil): 579	

	STOCK PRICE ($) FY Close	P/E High/Low		PER SHARE ($) Earnings	Dividends	Book Value
12/12	20.58	6	5	3.37	0.24	17.53
12/11	18.09	16	8	1.29	0.24	14.37
12/10	17.48	12	8	1.51	0.24	12.58
12/09	15.34	9	5	1.80	0.24	11.62
12/08	16.50	10	5	2.07	0.24	9.11
Annual Growth	**5.7%**	**—**	**—**	**13.0%**	**(0.0%)**	**17.8%**

Encore Capital Group Inc

Credit junkies beware: Encore Capital Group has your number. The firm and its Midland Credit Management subsidiary purchase at a discount defaulted consumer receivables that banks credit unions consumer and auto finance companies credit card issuers telecommunications firms retailers and other lenders have given up on. The group then does its best to collect the money via phone direct mail third-party collection agencies and legal action; it employs skip-tracing to track down stubborn debtors. Subsidiary Ascension Capital Group provides bankruptcy support services to the financial services industry. Encore Capital acquired Propel Financial Services which specializes in tax lien transfers in 2012.

Encore Capital has ramped up its acquisition of new portfolios of card telecom and consumer bankruptcy charge-offs amid continued stagnant job growth in the aftermath of the recession. As Encore grew its portfolio its gross collections also increased (by more than 25% in 2011 alone); not coincidentally its revenue and income were up as well.

The company's consumer database comprises more than 25 million accounts. Volume is important for Encore Capital as the company pursues collections on only a fraction of accounts and generates payments from less than 1% of them. Practicing a "friendly but firm approach" its account managers evaluate customers' ability to pay then develop tailored payment programs. The company utilizes proprietary statistical and behavioral models account-level valuation methods customized software applications and purchased credit bureau information to determine its collection strategies.

Encore Capital operates call centers in California Arizona Minnesota Texas and another in India. The company considers its operations in India where the annual attrition rate for experienced account managers is well the below industry average in the US key to its future growth. It is building its software development IT infrastructure analytics operations and back-office functions there. Encore Capital opened a call center in Costa Rica in 2012 and may consider business acquisitions to expand its geographic presence in other parts of the world.

In 2011 Encore Capital agreed to pay up to $5.7 million to settle several class-action lawsuits that accused the company of using falsified affidavits to collect money. Later that year Encore Capital resolved litigation initiated by the Texas Attorney General's office which had investigated the company's collection methods.

EXECUTIVES

President CEO and Director, J. Brandon Black, age 45, $414,260 total compensation
EVP CFO Treasurer and Secretary, Paul J. Grinberg, age 52, $291,200 total compensation
Executive Chairman, George Lund, age 49, $405,769 total compensation
SVP Human Resources, Steven B. (Steve) Gonabe, age 60
Senior Vice President Chief Marketing Officer, Jim Syran
SVP Information Technology and CIO, Carl Eberling
Senior Vice President Chief Scientific Officer, Christopher Trepel
President Propel Financial Services, Jack Nelson
Senior Vice President Business Development, Amy Anuk
Senior Vice President Global Operations, Brandon Homuth
Senior Vice President Indian Operations, Manu Rikhye
Senior Vice President Legal Collections Operations, Ashish Masih
Senior Vice President Corporate & Government Affairs, Sheryl Wright
Senior Vice President Human Resources, Steve Gonabe
President CEO and Director, J. Brandon Black, age 45
Director, Warren Wilcox, age 55
Director, Willem (Will) Mesdag, age 60
Director, J. Christopher (Chris) Teets, age 40
Director, H. Ronald Weissman, age 68
Independent Director, Francis Quinlan
Independent Director, Norman Sorensen
Auditors: BDOUSALLP

LOCATIONS

HQ: Encore Capital Group Inc
3111 Camino Del Rio North, Suite 1300, San Diego, CA 92108
Phone: 877 445-4581
Web: www.encorecapital.com

PRODUCTS/OPERATIONS

2011 Sales

	$ mil.	% of total
Receivable portfolios net	448	96
Servicing fees & other	18	4
Total	**381**	**100**

Selected Subsidiaries

Ascension Capital Group Inc.
MCM Midland Management Costa Rica S.r.l.
Midland Credit Management Inc.
Midland Credit Management India Private Limited
Midland Funding LLC
Midland Funding NCC-2 Corporation
Midland India LLC
Midland International LLC
Midland Portfolio Services Inc.
MRC Receivables Corporation

COMPETITORS

Asset Acceptance Capital
Asta Funding
Expert Global Solutions
FirstCity Financial
GC Services
Genesis Financial Solutions
Leland Scott & Associates
Nationwide Recovery Systems
Portfolio Recovery

HISTORICAL FINANCIALS

Company Type: Public

Income Statement

FYE: December 31

	REVENUE ($ mil.)	NET INCOME ($ mil.)	NET PROFIT MARGIN	EMPLOYEES
12/12	555.8	69.4	12.5%	2,800
12/11	467.3	60.9	13.0%	2,200
12/10	381.3	49.0	12.9%	1,900
12/09	316.4	33.0	10.4%	1,500
12/08	255.8	18.8	7.4%	1,100
Annual Growth	**21.4%**	**38.6%**	**—**	**26.3%**

2012 Year-End Financials

Debt ratio: 60.2%	No. of shares (mil.): 23
Return on equity: 17.8%	Dividends
Cash ($ mil.): 17	Yield: —
Current ratio: 3.23	Payout: —
Long-term debt ($ mil.): 706	Market value ($ mil.): 710

	STOCK PRICE ($) FY Close	P/E High/Low		PER SHARE ($) Earnings	Dividends	Book Value
12/12	30.62	11	8	2.80	0.00	17.50
12/11	21.26	13	8	2.37	0.00	15.15
12/10	23.45	12	7	1.95	0.00	12.61
12/09	17.40	14	2	1.37	0.00	10.41
12/08	7.20	17	8	0.80	0.00	8.50
Annual Growth	**43.6%**	**—**	**—**	**36.8%**	**—**	**19.8%**

Ensign Group Inc

The Ensign Group hangs its insignia at dozens of senior living facilities. Most of its facilities are skilled nursing homes but it also operates a number of assisted-living and independent-living facilities as well as combination nursing assisted and independent-living centers. Some locations also offer rehabilitation hospice and physical therapy services. Ensign's facilities are either owned by the company or operated under lease agreements. The medical group operates some 120 long-term care centers (it owns three-fourths of them) with a capacity of some 11700 beds in 11 states in the southwestern and western US. Ensign also operates home health and hospice agencies.

Geographic Reach

Ensign has a presence in several US states including California Arizona Texas Washington Utah Idaho Colorado Nevada Iowa Nebraska and Oregon.

Operations

Ensign is a holding company that counts among its operations nearly 120 facilities half a dozen hospice companies and about 10 home health businesses. The company has a decentralized operating structure with its portfolio of homes organized into five regional operating companies. Each home operates under local –and largely independent –management. As part of its business the company relies on reimbursement from government and commercial health insurance plans as well as sales to private pay customers. It generates about three-fourths of its revenues from Medicaid and Medicare programs.

Financial Analysis

The company's growth strategy has led to double-digit revenue and income growth over the years. Ensign's net revenue rose 17% in 2011 vs.

2010 due to an increase in Medicare and managed care revenue Medicaid revenue and other revenue. Acquired facilities also helped to boost its bottom line. Ensign continues to rely on growth in its managed care rates. Net income during the same period rose some 18% thanks to income increases that eclipsed expenses.

Strategy

Ensign primarily expands its operations by snapping up underperforming nursing homes in existing or new territories and turning them around both in terms of operating performance and clinical quality.

Ensign branched out into a new area of operations in 2012 when it formed a joint venture with a group of physicians to establish or acquire urgent care centers in select communities. The Immediate Clinic venture intended to provide walk-in medical care to fill the gap between primary care doctor's offices and hospital emergency rooms which the company sees as a growing area of need as health reform measures take effect in the US. Its first acquisition in 2012 was Doctors Express which boasts about 50 franchised urgent care centers nationwide. However Immediate Clinic turned around and sold the Doctors Express business to American Family Care in 2013 while retaining five urgent care clinics in the greater Seattle area; Immediate Clinic plans to expand in that market.

Mergers and Acquisitions

In 2012 and 2013 Ensign added skilled nursing facilities assisted living facilities and independent living facilities in Idaho Texas Nevada Arizona and Washington.

Ensign extended its reach in 2011 by acquiring about 20 skilled nursing assisted-living independent-living and combination facilities in Arizona California Nevada Texas Idaho and Utah. It also added new territories in Nebraska and Iowa. To expand its home health and hospice operations held by subsidiary Cornerstone Health it has purchased agencies in Colorado Iowa Idaho Texas Oregon and Utah.

Strategy

In addition to acquiring new facilities and establishing local leadership teams the company works to boost patient occupancy at its existing facilities especially those facing financial troubles and extremely low occupancy rates. It does this by developing quality staff and clinical processes and through facility upgrades as well as by adding services such as outpatient therapy services. It is also focused on attracting more high-acuity patients who require higher levels of medical and rehabilitative care and for whom the company is generally reimbursed at higher rates.

Ownership

Chairman Roy Christensen and his son CEO Christopher Christensen together own about 20% of the company.

EXECUTIVES

President CEO and Director, Christopher R. Christensen, age 45, $410,531 total compensation
EVP and Secretary, Gregory K. Stapley, age 54, $342,552 total compensation
VP Organizational Development, David M. Sedgewick, age 37, $227,103 total compensation
President Northern Pioneer Healthcare, Cory R. Monette, age 43
President Keystone Care, Barry R. Port, age 39, $185,986 total compensation
President Bandera, John P. Albrechtsen, age 36
President Bandera, Michael C. Dalton, age 37, $183,849 total compensation

Chairman, Roy E. Christensen, age 80, $354,935 total compensation
President The Flagstone Group, Covey Christensen, age 39, $185,159 total compensation
CFO, Suzanne D. Snapper, age 39, $232,100 total compensation
VP and General Counsel, Beverly B. Wittekind, age 48, $234,400 total compensation
President Cornerstone, Daniel H. (Danny) Walker
President Touchstone Care, Brian Hulse
President Touchstone Care, Matthew Hueffner
President Northern Pioneer Healthcare, Matt Rutter
President Pennant, Owen Hammond
President Milestone Healthcare, Brian Newberry
President Gateway Healthcare, Michael Clegg
President Bridgestone Living, John Guerreri
President Keystone North, Rick Forscutt
President Keystone South, Jorge Rojas
President Paragon, Steve Burningham
Director, Van R. Johnson, age 68
Director, Thomas A. Maloof, age 62
Director, Antoinette T. Hubenette, age 64
President CEO and Director, Christopher R. Christensen, age 45
Director, John G. Nackel, age 61
Independent Director, Daren Shaw
Auditors: Deloitte&ToucheLLP

LOCATIONS

HQ: The Ensign Group Inc.
27101 Puerta Real Ste. 450, Mission Viejo CA 92691
Phone: 949-487-9500   **Fax:** 212-750-5505
Web: www.golubcapital.com

2011 Beds

	No.
California	3,876
Texas	2,662
Arizona	1,923
Utah	1,364
Colorado	463
Iowa	356
Nebraska	296
Washington	274
Idaho	246
Nevada	242
Total	**11,702**

PRODUCTS/OPERATIONS

2011 Facilities

No.	% of total		
Owned		77	74
Leased (without a purchase option)		20	20
Leased (with a purchase option)		5	6
Total		**102**	**100**

2011 Facilities

	No.
Skilled	9,952
Assisted	1,262
Independent	488
Total	**11,702**

2011 Sales

	% of total
Medicaid -	37
Medicare	36
Medicaid -	3
Managed	12
Private &	12
Total	**100**

COMPETITORS

Amedisys
American Baptist Homes of the West
Five Star Quality Care
Golden Horizons
HCR ManorCare

Apria Healthcare
Assisted Living Concepts
Brookdale Senior Living
Covenant Care
Dignity Health
Diversicare Healthcare Services
HealthSouth
Kindred Healthcare
Life Care Centers
RehabCare
SavaSeniorCare
Skilled Healthcare Group
Sun Healthcare
Sunrise Senior Living

HISTORICAL FINANCIALS

Company Type: Public

Income Statement

FYE: December 31

	REVENUE ($ mil.)	NET INCOME ($ mil.)	NET PROFIT MARGIN	EMPLOYEES
12/12	824.7	40.5	4.9%	10,371
12/11	758.2	47.6	6.3%	9,433
12/10	649.5	40.5	6.2%	8,382
12/09	542.0	32.4	6.0%	7,718
12/08	469.3	27.5	5.9%	6,153
Annual Growth	**15.1%**	**10.2%**	**—**	**13.9%**

2012 Year-End Financials

Debt ratio: 30.0%
Return on equity: 13.4%
Cash ($ mil.): 40
Current ratio: 1.38
Long-term debt ($ mil.): 200
No. of shares (mil.): 21
Dividends
Yield: 0.9%
Payout: 10.9%
Market value ($ mil.): 590

	STOCK PRICE ($) FY Close	P/E High/Low		PER SHARE ($) Earnings	Dividends	Book Value
12/12	27.15	16	13	1.85	0.25	15.03
12/11	24.50	15	9	2.21	0.23	13.10
12/10	24.87	13	8	1.92	0.21	10.96
12/09	15.37	12	8	1.55	0.19	9.09
12/08	16.74	14	6	1.33	0.17	7.59
Annual Growth	**12.9%**	**—**	**—**	**8.6%**	**10.4%**	**18.6%**

Epam Systems, Inc.

How do you say "offshoring" in Russian? Just ask EPAM. The IT outsourcing company provides software development and other IT services to US and European customers primarily from development centers in Russia Belarus Hungary Ukraine Kazakhstan and Poland. In addition to software product development the company offers services in such areas as e-commerce support data warehousing customer relationship management and application integration. EPAM also offers its own hosted and stand-alone enterprise software for sales force automation content management order management and other business processes. More than half of sales come from North America. EPAM went public in 2012.

IPO

The company plans to use the proceeds from its IPO to acquire facilities and to make acquisitions of businesses or technologies that complement its expansion strategies.

Strategy

The company is looking to extend its expertise in targeted industry verticals which include independent software vendors banking and financial services business information and media hospitality and travel and retail and consumer. To do this EPAM continues to recruit IT professionals with specific industry knowledge and to pursue acquisitions that add to its service portfolio and customer base. Another part of EPAM's growth strategy is to make acquisitions of companies that have a significant presence in China Latin America and other emerging markets.

Mergers and Acquisitions

It found an acquisition in 2012 to further its expansion plans when it agreed to buy Toronto-based IT consultancy and software provider Thoughtcorp in a deal worth more than $17 million. The acquisition ticks a number of boxes: it bolsters EPAM's presence in North America improves the company's opportunities for growth in the telecommunications sector and brings in greater delivery capabilities in areas such as agile development enterprise mobility and business intelligence.

EPAM strengthened its presence in the business information and media industry when it bought New York-based Web data management services provider Instant Information in 2010. The purchase expanded its operations in Belarus. The acquisition of Rodmon Systems in 2009 added a large client in the business information and media industry along with operations in Belarus.

Financial Analysis

In 2010 revenues were up 48% over 2009 driven by a more than 150% increase in sales to the banking and financials services market and revenues from the business information and media industry that were 60% higher. Geographically most of EPAM's growth was from clients in Europe. In Switzerland revenues were up more than 300% and the UK saw a 74% increase in sales; both countries have strong banking and financial services industries. Though its profits dipped somewhat during the global economic downturn the company's net income in 2010 was double that reported in 2009.

Geographic Reach

The company has expanded geographically by adding client management offices in locations that are close to customers –including the US UK Germany Sweden Switzerland Russia and Kazakhstan –and by adding new development centers. Its development center in Poland was opened in 2011. The company's acquisition of PLUS MICRO in 2008 expanded EPAM's operations in Kazakhstan. In certain cases (such as Russia and Kazakhstan) EPAM has both development centers and client management offices in the same country.

Ownership

EPAM's investors include Renaissance Investment Management and Da Vinci Capital. Its clients include Barclays Thomson Reuters The Coca-Cola Company Expedia Google and Sberbank.

EXECUTIVES

SVP Marketing, John J. Mahoney
SVP Business Information Services, Isaak Karaev
CEO President, Arkadiy Dobkin, age 53
President EPAM Systems Europe, Karl Robb, age 51
CTO, Balazs Fejes, age 38
Chief Financial Officer, Ilya Cantor, age 44
Managing Director, Donald P. Spencer, age 58
Vice President General Counsel Corporate Secretary, Ginger Mosier, age 49
VP Cloud Services, Eli Feldman
Chief Technology Officer, Sam Rehman
EVP and Director; President EU Operations, Karl Robb, age 51
Director, Andrew J. (Drew) Guff, age 52
Managing Director, Donald P. Spencer, age 58

Director, Ross Goodhart, age 33
Auditors: Deloitte&ToucheLLP

LOCATIONS

HQ: EPAM Systems Inc.
41 University Dr. Ste. 202, Newtown PA 18940
Phone: 267-759-9000 **Fax:** 267-759-8989
Web: www.epam.com

2010 Sales by Customer Location

	$ mil.	% of total
North America	117	53
Europe		
UK	32	14
Other countries	26	12
CIS		
Russia	31	14
Other countries	10	5
Reimbursable expenses & other revenues	3	1
Total	**221**	**100**

PRODUCTS/OPERATIONS

2010 Sales

	$ mil.	% of total
Software development	149	67
Application testing services	44	20
Application maintenance & support	19	9
Infrastructure services	2	1
Licensing	1	1
Reimbursable expenses & other revenues	3	2
Total	**221**	**100**

2010 Sales by Industry

	$ mil.	% of total
Independent software vendors & technology	68	31
Business information & media	45	21
Banking & financial services	42	19
Travel & hospitality	18	8
Retail & consumer	17	8
Other verticals	24	11
Reimbursable expenses & other revenues	3	2
Total	**221**	**100**

Selected Services

Application development
Application maintenance and support
Application testing
Business intelligence
Business process management
Content management
Customer Relationship Management (CRM)
Data warehousing and business intelligence
E-commerce
Enterprise application integration
Enterprise resource planning
Infrastructure and hosting
Knowledge management
Localization
Offshore software development
Quality assurance consulting and testing strategy
    transformation
Server and network management

COMPETITORS

Accenture	Infosys
Atos	MindTree
Camelot Information	Pactera
Capgemini	Sapient
Cognizant Tech	Satyam
Solutions	Symphony Technology
Computer Sciences	Group LLC
Corp.	Tata Consultancy
GlobalLogic	VanceInfo
HCL Technologies	Wipro
IBM Global Services	iSoftStone

HISTORICAL FINANCIALS

Company Type: Public

Income Statement

FYE: December 31

	REVENUE ($ mil.)	NET INCOME ($ mil.)	NET PROFIT MARGIN	EMPLOYEES
12/12	433.8	54.4	12.6%	10,043
12/11	334.5	44.3	13.3%	8,125
12/10	221.8	28.3	12.8%	6,168
12/09	149.9	13.5	9.0%	4,432
12/08	160.6	4.0	2.5%	0
Annual Growth	**28.2%**	**91.5%**	—	—

2012 Year-End Financials

Debt ratio: —
Return on equity: 23.2%
Cash ($ mil.): 118
Current ratio: 4.23
Long-term debt ($ mil.): —
No. of shares (mil.): 44
Dividends
  Yield: —
  Payout: —
Market value ($ mil.): 804

	STOCK PRICE ($) FY Close	P/E High/Low	PER SHARE ($) Earnings	Dividends	Book Value
12/12	18.10	18 11	1.17	0.00	6.44
Annual Growth	—	— —	—	—	—

EPIQ Systems Inc

Epiq Systems wants to make legal discovery and bankruptcy proceedings as quick and painless as possible (for attorneys that is). The company provides case and document management software for bankruptcy class action mass tort and other legal proceedings. Its software automates tasks including electronic discovery legal notice claims management and government reporting. Epiq's software line includes products for Chapter 7 liquidations as well as Chapter 13 and 11 reorganizations. The company which caters to law firms and bankruptcy trustees also offers consulting and case management services and software for class action mass tort and bankruptcy case administration. Epiq operates primarily in the US.

Geographic Reach

Kansas City-based Epiq Systems' primary market is the US representing more than 90% of its sales. The firm has offices in about 10 US cities including New York Chicago Dallas and Los Angeles. Overseas it has offices in London and Hong Kong.

Operations Epiq's largest and fastest-growing segment is electronic discovery or eDiscovery which provides collections and forensics processing search and review and document review services for corporate legal departments and law firms. Its bankruptcy division focuses on products for Chapter 7 and 13 filings as most bankruptcies fall under these models. As part of an effort to cover the entire bankruptcy spectrum however Epiq maintains its services to the Chapter 11 market. The company's smallest segment is settlement administration services which includes corporations administering the settlement of class action cases.

Financial Performance Revenue increased 32% in 2012 versus 2011 to $373 million on the strength of Epiq's eDiscovery business which posted a year-over-year gain of 48% as a result of the Encore and De Novo acquisitions in 2011. The

firm's Settlement Administration businesses grew 64% due to a large legal notification engagement in 2012. The bankruptcy unit posted a 4% decline in annual sales. Net income rose 86% in 2012 versus 2011 to $22.4 million on higher sales and acquisition-related income from Encore. Mergers and Acquisitions Epiq which has traditionally grown organically acquired two eDiscovery businesses in 2011 to strengthen that segment. It purchased De Novo Legal in late 2011 for $68 million and Encore Discovery Solutions for $100 million earlier in the year. The company also made an acquisition in 2010 with the $60 million purchase of Jupiter eSources. Jupiter specializes in software (known as AACER) used by creditors to automate the processing of loans in bankruptcy cases. With the acquisition Epiq expanded its product line and added clients in such segments as banking and mortgage lending. Ownership The company was founded in 1988 by chairman and CEO Tom W. Olofson. He and his family own (both directly and through a family foundation) a 13% stake in the company. President and COO Christopher Olofson owns about 5% of the shares. St. Denis J. Villere & Co. owns 13% of the company's shares while investment firm T. Rowe Price holds 11%.

EXECUTIVES

President; Chief Operating Officer; Director, Christopher E. Olofson, age 43, $850,000 total compensation
Chairman and CEO, Tom W. Olofson, age 71, $850,000 total compensation
Chief Financial Officer; Executive Vice President - Operations; Treasurer; Corporate Secretary, Elizabeth M. (Betsy) Braham, age 54, $700,000 total compensation
President Bankruptcy Solutions, Ron Jacobs, age 56
Controller, David Wright
Managing Director Bankruptcy, Lorenzo Mendizabal, age 53, $515,000 total compensation
SVP Sales, Myriam Schmell
Investor Relations, Lew P. Schroeber
Media Relations, Cindy Morgan-Olson
Managing Director Expert & Professional Services, Laura Kibbe
Managing Director International eDiscovery, Greg Wildisen
SVP eDiscovery, Paul Brabant
SVP eDiscovery, Lisa Schofield
Managing Director, Dan McElhinney
SVP, Patty Radovan
Relationship Manager Bankrupcty Services, Christel Hockett
VP Sales and Marketing, Lance Wickel
EVP Bankruptcy Solutions, Jane Sullivan
VP and Director Client Services, Bob Saraceni
VP and Director Solicitation Services, Christina Pullo
Executive Vice President Bankruptcy Services, James Katchadurian
Senior Vice President General Manager Class Action and Claims Solutions, Andrew Shimek
Vice President Manager eDiscovery Solutions, James Ramsey
Senior Vice President Information Technology & Development, George Tsounis
Managing Director Sales, Robert Hopen
Managing Director Operations eDiscovery, Adam Seskis
Chief HR Officer VP N/A, Brad D. Scott
President COO and Director, Christopher E. Olofson, age 43
Director, W. Bryan Satterlee, age 78
Director, Edward M. Connolly Jr., age 70

Director, James A. Byrnes, age 66
Director, Joel Pelofsky, age 74
Director, Terry C. Matlack, age 55
Auditors: Deloitte&ToucheLLP

LOCATIONS

HQ: Epiq Systems Inc.
501 Kansas Ave., Kansas City KS 66105-1309
Phone: 913-621-9500   Fax: 678-638-0466
Web: www.neom.com

2012 Sales

	$ mil.	% of total
US	346	93
Other countries	26	7
Total	**373**	**100**

PRODUCTS/OPERATIONS

2012 Sales

	$ mil.	% of total
Electronic discovery	197	57
Bankruptcy	88	26
Settlement administration	59	17
Reimbursed expenses	28	-
Total	**373**	**100**

Selected Products

Case Power (Chapter 13 administration)
ClaimsMatrix (case management software to administer class action settlements)
DebtorMatrix (Chapter 11)
DocuMatrix (Hosted discovery management platform)
eDataMatrix (electronic discovery)
IQ Review (document indexing)
TCMS (Chapter 7 trustee case management system)
TCMSWeb (Web-based trustee case management system)

COMPETITORS

Applied Discovery	Kurtzman Carson
Clearwell Systems	Consultants
Cricket Technologies	LexisNexis
Daegis	Misys
Dolan Company	Recommind
FTI Consulting	Stratify
Fios	SunGard
Fiserv	Symantec
Hewlett-Packard	West Publishing
Huron Consulting	Corporation
JPMorgan Chase	Xerox
Kroll Ontrack	

HISTORICAL FINANCIALS

Company Type: Public

Income Statement

FYE: December 31

	REVENUE ($ mil.)	NET INCOME ($ mil.)	NET PROFIT MARGIN	EMPLOYEES
12/12	373.0	22.4	6.0%	1,000
12/11	283.3	12.0	4.3%	1,000
12/10	247.1	13.9	5.6%	550
12/09	239.0	14.6	6.1%	550
12/08	236.1	13.8	5.9%	550
Annual Growth	**12.1%**	**12.8%**	**—**	**16.1%**

2012 Year-End Financials

Debt ratio: 32.4%
Return on equity: 6.6%
Cash ($ mil.): 3
Current ratio: 1.98
Long-term debt ($ mil.): 203
No. of shares (mil.): 35
Dividends
 Yield: 2.7%
 Payout: 56.5%
Market value ($ mil.): 458

	STOCK PRICE ($) FY Close	P/E High/Low		PER SHARE ($)		
			Earnings	Dividends	Book Value
12/12	12.75	22 17	0.61	0.35	9.56
12/11	12.02	45 31	0.33	0.16	9.31
12/10	13.73	37 30	0.36	0.07	9.18
12/09	13.99	45 30	0.38	0.00	9.02
12/08	16.71	46 27	0.36	0.00	8.43
Annual Growth	**(6.5%)**	**— —**	**14.1%**	**—**	**3.2%**

EPL Oil & Gas Inc

It pays for EPL Oil & Gas (formerly Energy Partners) to have friends in the oil and gas business. The independent explorer and producer focuses on the waters of the Gulf of Mexico off the Gulf Coast. It partners with big oil companies to explore for reserves on properties the majors have left behind; EPL Oil & Gas earns an interest in the new reserves and production. The company has grown through a combination of exploration exploitation and development drilling as well as strategic acquisitions of oil and natural gas fields. It changed its corporate name in 2012 to reflect its oil and gas focus.

Geographic Reach

The company's operations are focused in the US Gulf of Mexico shelf primarily in state and federal waters offshore Louisiana.

Operations

In 2012 EPL Oil and Gas reported estimated proved reserves of 77.4 million barrels of oil equivalent of which 61% were oil and 75% were proved developed. Of its proved developed reserves some 65% were oil reserves.

Sales and Marketing

The company's main customers include ConocoPhillips Chevron USA and Shell Trading (US) which accounted for 45% 31% and 11% of company's 2012 revenues respectively.

Financial Performance

Revenues increased by 22% in 2012 thanks to a 29% increase in the oil production. EPL Oil and Gas' Gulf of Mexico shelf production (excluding the recently acquired Hilcorp Properties) grew primarily to production increases in the company's West Delta field and production from other properties.

Net income jumped by 121% in 2012 primarily due to higher revenues decreased impairment charges (due to decline in future natural gas prices) which affected three of its natural gas producing fields and reservoir performance at two of those fields and increased interest income in 2012.

Strategy

The company is beefing up its its shallow water shelf assets to take advantage of higher oil prices. In 2012 EPL Oil and Gas bought producing oil and natural gas assets in the central Gulf of Mexico from Hilcorp Energy for $550 million. It also bought shallow-wateroil and natural gas interests from W&T Offshore in its South Timbalier 41 field in the Gulf of Mexico for $32.4 million.

The company acquired shallow-water Gulf of Mexico shelf oil and natural gas interests surrounding the Mississippi River delta in 2011 from privately-owned Anglo-Suisse Offshore Partners LLC for $200.7 million. The assets produce about 3000 net barrels of oil equivalent per day. That year it also acquired producing oil and natural gas assets

in the shallow-water central Gulf of Mexico shelf from Stone Energy Offshore L.L.C. for $38.6 million.

To raise cash to help defray some of the cost of its recent acquisitions in 2013 EPL Oil and Gas sold certain non-operated shallow water Gulf of Mexico shelf oil and natural gas assets located in the Bay Marchand field area to the property operator for $51.5 million.

Ownership

Marc McCarthy a director of Wexford Capital LP owns 14.4% of EPL Oil & Gas.

Company Background

Buffered by a major economic downturn and by 2008 hurricanes that damaged Energy Partners' oil and gas pipelines disrupting production in May 2009 the company filed for Chapter 11 bankruptcy protection. It emerged from Chapter 11 in September 2009.

In 2009 the company announced its first deep-water Gulf of Mexico production from its Raton gas well in the Mississippi Canyon field.

EXECUTIVES

Chairman of the Board; President; Chief Executive Officer, Gary C. Hanna, age 55, $112,308 total compensation
SVP Treasurer and CFO, Tiffany J. Thom, age 41
Chief Accounting Officer; Senior Vice President; Treasurer; Corporate Secretary, David P. Cedro, age 45
VP Geosciences (Houston), Paul B. Jones
Senior Vice President - Production, Chad E. Williams
Chairman, Marc McCarthy, age 41
Senior Vice President - Geosciences, Andre J. Broussard
Senior Vice President - Business Development, Mac Jensen
Director, Scott A. Griffiths, age 59
CEO and Director, Gary C. Hanna, age 54
Director, Steven J. Pully, age 53
Director, Charles O. (Chuck) Buckner, age 69
Director, John F. Schwarz, age 75
Auditors: KPMGLLP

LOCATIONS

HQ: EPL Oil & Gas Inc.
201 St. Charles Ave. Ste. 3400, New Orleans LA 70170-3400
Phone: 504-569-1875   Fax: 504-569-1874
Web: www.eplweb.com

PRODUCTS/OPERATIONS

2012 Sales

	$ mil.	% of total
Oil	403	95
Natural gas	18	4
Other	1	1
Total	**423**	**100**

COMPETITORS

ATP Oil & Gas	McMoRan Exploration
BP	Murphy Oil
Chevron	Newfield Exploration
El Paso Corporation	Pioneer Natural
Exxon Mobil	Resources
Forest Oil	Stone Energy
Marathon Oil	W&T Offshore

HISTORICAL FINANCIALS

Company Type: Public

Income Statement

FYE: December 31

	REVENUE ($ mil.)	NET INCOME ($ mil.)	NET PROFIT MARGIN	EMPLOYEES
12/12	423.6	58.8	13.9%	173
12/11	348.3	26.6	7.6%	108
12/10	239.9	(8.4)	—	100
12/09*	56.7	(21.0)	—	101
09/09	134.8	(36.1)	—	0
Annual Growth	33.1%			

*Fiscal year change

2012 Year-End Financials

Debt ratio: 40.4%
Return on equity: 11.3%
Cash ($ mil.): 1
Current ratio: 0.45
Long-term debt ($ mil.): 689

No. of shares (mil.): 39
Dividends
  Yield: —
  Payout: —
Market value ($ mil.): 882

	STOCK PRICE ($) FY Close	P/E High/Low		PER SHARE ($) Earnings	Dividends	Book Value
12/12	22.55	15	10	1.50	0.00	13.96
12/11	14.60	28	16	0.66	0.00	12.46
12/10	14.86	—	—	(0.21)	0.00	11.80
12/09*	8.55	—	—	(0.53)	0.00	12.00
09/09	7.46	—	—	(1.12)	0.00	(0.00)
Annual Growth	31.9%			—	—	—

*Fiscal year change

ePlus Inc

ePlus wants to rate an A-plus from its customers by meeting their hardware and software needs. ePlus is a holding company and operates through two business segments that deal in technology sales and financing. Its ePlus Technology subsidiary resells and leases products from top IT infrastructure providers. Offerings include security storage and networking products as well as consulting and systems integration services. It also offers supply chain management software and services; its proprietary applications include procurement asset management spend analytics and document management tools. The company's Leasing and Financial Services arm offers lease financing and leases IT and medical equipment.

The company markets its products and services to midsized and large businesses government agencies and schools. ePlus gets nearly all of its sales in the US. The majority of sales of product and services derived from sales of Cisco Systems and HP products which represented 43% and 16% of sales of product and services in 2011.

ePlus' strategy includes expanding its professional services offerings. Since going public it has acquired more than a dozen businesses including most recently California-based Pacific Blue Micro (PBM) in 2012 thereby expanding its IT services business in Southern California. Previously it purchased NCC Networks a provider of managed security services with a Security Operations Center (SOC) located in Chicago in 2011. With the acquisition ePlus extended its security offerings for cloud-based networks and data centers adds a sales branch in Chicago and expands its customer base.

The company also developed and began offering eCloud a private cloud computing service which can be tailored to the needs of customers in 2011. ePlus believes customers will continue to focus on costs savings and will utilize technologies such as virtualization and cloud computing.

Chairman president and CEO Phillip Norton owns more than a quarter of ePlus.

EXECUTIVES

SVP and Assistant Secretary, Kleyton L. (Kley) Parkhurst, age 49, $225,000 total compensation
SVP Business Operations, Steven J. (Steve) Mencarini, age 57, $286,458 total compensation
EVP; President ePlus Group, Bruce M. Bowen, $330,000 total compensation
Chairman President and CEO, Phillip G. Norton, $454,167 total compensation
COO; President ePlus Technology, Mark P. Marron, $407,597 total compensation
President ePlus Systems and ePlus Content Services, Kenneth G. Farber
General Counsel, Erica S. Stoecker
CFO, Elaine D. Marion
CTO, Mark C. Melvin
senior Vice President of ePlus Group, Chad Fredrick
Regional VP Sales Metro New York, Tony DiBenedetto
VP-Sls-Pub Sector, Darren Raiguel
Director, Milton E. (Milt) Cooper Jr., age 74
Director, Eric D. Hovde, age 49
Director, C. Thomas (Tom) Faulders III, age 63
EVP and Director; President ePlus Group, Bruce M. Bowen, age 61
Director, Terrence (Terry) O'Donnell, age 68
Director, Lawrence S. (Larry) Herman, age 69
Director, John E. Callies, age 59
Independent Director, Terrence Donnell
Independent Director, Terrence ODonnell
Auditors: Deloitte&ToucheLLP

LOCATIONS

HQ: ePlus inc.
13595 Dulles Technology Dr., Herndon VA 20171-3413
Phone: 703-984-8400   **Fax:** 703-984-8600
Web: www.eplus.com

PRODUCTS/OPERATIONS

2011 Sales

	$ mil.	% of total
Technology sales	825	96
Financing	37	4
Total	863	100

Selected Subsidiaries

ePlus Canada Company
ePlus Capital inc.
ePlus Document Systems inc.
ePlus Group inc.
ePlus Iceland inc.
ePlus Jamaica inc.
ePlus Technology inc.

COMPETITORS

American Express
CDW
CSI Leasing
Citibank
CompuCom
Dell
Deutsche Bank
En Pointe
FAEF
Forsythe Technology

General Dynamics Information Technology
Hewlett-Packard
IBM Global Financing
IBM Global Services
Insight Enterprises
JPMorgan Chase
Leidos
Meridian Group
Microsoft
PC Connection
PC Mall
Pomeroy IT
Red River Computer
Systemax
UNICOM Government
Unisys
Zones

HISTORICAL FINANCIALS

Company Type: Public

Income Statement

FYE: March 31

	REVENUE ($ mil.)	NET INCOME ($ mil.)	NET PROFIT MARGIN	EMPLOYEES
03/13	983.1	34.8	3.5%	904
03/12	825.5	23.3	2.8%	833
03/11	863.0	23.7	2.7%	725
03/10	684.2	12.7	1.9%	661
03/09	698.0	12.8	1.8%	656
Annual Growth	8.9%	28.4%	—	8.3%

2013 Year-End Financials

Debt ratio: 9.5%
Return on equity: 15.2%
Cash ($ mil.): 53
Current ratio: 2.53
Long-term debt ($ mil.): 41

No. of shares (mil.): 8
Dividends
  Yield: 0.0%
  Payout: 57.8%
Market value ($ mil.): 377

	STOCK PRICE ($) FY Close	P/E High/Low		PER SHARE ($) Earnings	Dividends	Book Value
03/13	46.21	11	7	4.32	2.50	29.23
03/12	31.97	12	8	2.84	0.00	27.45
03/11	26.61	10	6	2.82	0.00	24.93
03/10	17.55	11	7	1.50	0.00	22.83
03/09	11.69	9	5	1.52	0.00	21.57
Annual Growth	41.0%	—	—	29.8%	—	7.9%

Equinix Inc

Equinix provides data and network hosting and colocation facilities (it calls them Internet Business Exchanges or IBXs) where ISPs telecommunications carriers and content providers can locate equipment and interconnect networks and operations. The company also offers colocation-related services to provide clients with cabinets operating space and storage. Customers include network and mobility providers (such as AT&T BT and Comcast); cloud and IT services (Amazon.com Microsoft and Salesforce.com); and content providers (DIRECTV Facebook). Altogether Equinix operates almost 100 IBXs around the world and international customers make up about one-third of sales.

Operations

The market for colocation facilities has been served by large telecom carriers that bundle telecommunications and managed services with their colocation offerings. But telecom customers still outsource their critical interconnection relationships to Equinix especially as more companies need data center space for bandwidth-intensive services such as video voice over IP (VoIP) social media mobile data gaming data-rich media Ethernet and wireless services. In addition the company has gained many customers that have outgrown their existing data centers.

Geographic Reach

Equinix has 95 data centers located in 15 countries around the world. Customers in the Americas however account for more than half of sales. The EMEA region makes up another quarter while Asian customers account for the remaining 15% of revenues.

Sales and Marketing

The company employs a direct sales force to serve its 4000 existing customers and attract new ones. It also actively promotes the brand around the world through industry conferences business and trade publications online media and sponsored activities.

Financial Performance

Equinix has enjoyed consistent revenue growth every year and overall sales increased almost 20% in 2012 reaching $1.9 billion. The boost was attributable to a growing international customer base driven by acquisitions and organic expansion of its global facilities network. The company has also been consistently profitable; net income climbed more than 50% in 2012 to $145 million despite higher operating costs in most areas of the business.

Strategy

In anticipation of a steady demand for commercial data center services Equinix is expanding its infrastructure around the world. In 2012 it bought the assets including five data centers and a disaster recovery center of Asia Tone for about $230 million in cash. The facilities are located in Hong Kong Shanghai and Singapore and will expand Equinix's footprint in China.

Also that year it completed its acquisition of Germany-based colocation and interconnection services provider ancotel GmbH which tacked on one more data center to Equinix's existing four in Frankfurt. With edge nodes (smaller more mobile data centers) not only in London but also Hong Kong and Miami the deal also expanded Equinix's geographical reach and it added 400 new customers.

As it focuses on core markets the company is also divesting some data centers. In late 2012 it sold more than a dozen centers exiting such markets as Cleveland Detroit and St. Louis.

In 2011 the company acquired 90% of ALOG Data Centers of Brazil for $83 million in cash $15 million of which was slated for future data center expansion. The deal extended the company's reach to South America bringing its total number of data centers to about 100 in 38 markets in 13 countries worldwide. ALOG has data centers in Rio de Janeiro and Sao Paolo.

As part of an ongoing effort to deploy new resources internationally as it works to solidify the presence of its brand the company announced an investment of about $100 million in 2012 to build an additional data center in Washington DC to support expansion in the area. Late the previous year Equinix expanded its presence in Hong Kong spending $63 million to establish second data center there in support of growing demand in the region. This was part of a pattern of Asia-Pacific investment that also saw the company opening a third data center in both Sydney and Tokyo in 2011.

EXECUTIVES

Chief Sales Officer, Peter T. Ferris, age 55, $308,333 total compensation

Executive Chairman, Peter F. Van Camp, age 58, $213,500 total compensation

Chief Financial Officer, Keith D. Taylor, age 52, $342,500 total compensation

General Counsel and Corporate Secretary, Brandi L. Galvin Morandi

Managing Director United Kingdom, Russell Poole

Senior Director Investor Relations, Jason Starr

SVP Global Human Resources, Garry Ronco

VP Sales Equinix Asia-Pacific, Doug Oates

President Equinix Asia-Pacific, Samuel Lee

COO, Charles Meyers, age 43

Managing Director France, Michel Brignano

Chief Global Operations Officer, Sushil (Sam) Kapoor, age 67, $256,833 total compensation

President EMEA, Eric Schwartz, age 46, $285,000 total compensation

Managing Director Equinix South Asia, Clement Goh

CEO & President; Director, Stephen M. (Steve) Smith, age 57, $490,000 total compensation

Managing Director Equinix Greater China, Jonathan Leung

Chief Information Officer, Brian Lillie

Chief Development Officer, Mark Adams

SVP Global Real Estate, Howard B. Horowitz

Managing Director Equinix Australia, Darren Mann

Managing Director Germany, Jorg Rosengart

CTO, Lane Patterson

VP Sales North America, Dan Walker

Managing Director The Netherlands, Michiel Eielts

Managing Director Equinix Japan, Kei Furuta

Executive Chairman of the Board, Peter Camp

Chief Marketing Officer, Sara Baack

VP-Facility Design & Construction, Glenn Todd

VP-SIs, John Hardie

Vice President of Sales, Michael Winterson

Managing Director Switzerland, Marco Dottarelli

Managing Director Australia, Tony Simonsen

Managing Director Equinix Greater China, Alex Tam

Director, Irving F. (Bud) Lyons III, age 63

Director, Scott G. Kriens, age 54

Director, Christopher B. (Chris) Paisley, age 61

Director, Steven T. (Terry) Clontz, age 62

Director, William (Bill) Luby, age 52

President CEO and Director, Stephen M. (Steve) Smith, age 57

Auditors: PricewaterhouseCoopersLLP

LOCATIONS

HQ: Equinix Inc.
1 Lagoon Dr. 4th Fl., Redwood City CA 94065
Phone: 650-598-6000   **Fax:** 650-598-6900
Web: www.equinix.com

2012 Sales

	$ mil.	% of total
Americas	1,160	61
Europe Middle East & Africa	433	23
Asia-Pacific	301	16
Total	**1,895**	**100**

PRODUCTS/OPERATIONS

Selected Mergers and Acquisitions

FY 2012
ancotel (Germany $85 million)
Asia Tone ($230 million)
FY 2011
ALOG Data Centers (Brazil $83 million)
FY 2010
Switch and Data Facilities ($683 million)

COMPETITORS

AT&T	NaviSite
AboveNet	Rackspace
COLT Group	SAVVIS
CenturyLink	SingTel
CyrusOne	SunGard Availability
Digital Realty	Services
DuPont Fabros	TeleCity
Everest Interlink	Telx Group
Broadband	Terremark Worldwide
Hostway	Verio
Internap Network	Verizon Enterprise
Services	Solutions
Level 3 Communications	Zayo Group
NTT	

HISTORICAL FINANCIALS

Company Type: Public

Income Statement

FYE: December 31

	REVENUE ($ mil.)	NET INCOME ($ mil.)	NET PROFIT MARGIN	EMPLOYEES
12/12	1,895.7	144.6	7.6%	3,153
12/11	1,606.8	94.0	5.9%	2,709
12/10	1,220.3	36.8	3.0%	1,921
12/09	882.5	69.4	7.9%	1,301
12/08	704.6	131.5	18.7%	1,115
Annual Growth	28.1%	2.4%	—	29.7%

2012 Year-End Financials

Debt ratio: 49.0%
Return on equity: 6.7%
Cash ($ mil.): 252
Current ratio: 1.19
Long-term debt ($ mil.): 2,943
No. of shares (mil.): 48
Dividends
  Yield: —
  Payout: —
Market value ($ mil.): 10,058

	STOCK PRICE ($) FY Close	P/E High/Low	PER SHARE ($) Earnings	Dividends	Book Value
12/12	206.20	68 34	2.92	0.00	47.88
12/11	101.40	60 46	1.72	0.00	41.83
12/10	81.26	130 84	0.82	0.00	40.73
12/09	106.15	60 23	1.75	0.00	30.08
12/08	53.19	28 10	3.31	0.00	23.65
Annual Growth	40.3%	— —	(3.1%)	—	19.3%

Equity Lifestyle Properties Inc

Snow birds and empty nesters flock to communities developed and owned by Equity LifeStyle Properties. The real estate investment trust (REIT) owns and operates lifestyle-oriented residential properties aimed at retirees vacationers and second home owners. Other properties provide affordable housing for families. Equity LifeStyle Properties leases lots for factory-built homes cottages cabins and recreational vehicles. Available homes range in size and style. The REIT's portfolio includes more than 380 properties containing some 141000 lots in about 30 states and Canada. Properties are similar to site-built residential subdivisions with centralized entrances utilities gutters curbs and paved streets.

Many of Equity LifeStyle's communities include club houses swimming pools game courts and other amenities. The company mainly focuses on developing properties in large metro areas near retirement and vacation spots.

Subsidiary Realty Systems leases or finances homes at communities owned by Equity LifeStyle Properties. While home sales have dropped in recent years more customers are choosing to lease a home in light of uncertain economic conditions. The company has adjusted its strategy accordingly and significantly reduced its new home sales activities. Instead of selling new manufactured homes it rents them. Equity LifeStyle Properties also has bumped up rental rates in order to boost revenues. The company hopes to convert its home renters to buyers in the future as the economy recovers. Equity LifeStyle also is focused on offering smaller more energy efficient and affordable homes which are in high demand.

The REIT which was founded in 1992 has significantly grown its portfolio over the years and continues to acquire properties located in high growth urban and resort areas such as Florida (which accounts for about 38% of revenues) Arizona and California. In 2011 the company acquired 74 manufactured home communities and one RV resort from Hometown America for some $1.5 billion. The deal added more than 31000 home sites in 16 states mostly in Florida and the northeastern US.

The company also looks to expand existing properties to accommodate more tenants. It focuses on attracting customers and extending their stays by providing attractive amenities (cable TV laundry rooms) and common facilities (swimming pools tennis courts clubhouses) that foster a social atmosphere for tenants and keep occupancy turnover low.

Equity LifeStyle Properties has been working to improve its membership business which gives members passes to certain properties within geographic zones in exchange for an annual fee. In 2008 it acquired Privileged Access an RV and vacation membership business which helped grow Equity LifeStyle Properties' client base. The deal added to Equity LifeStyle's other membership-based subsidiary Thousand Trails which has more than 130000 dues-paying members that have special access to campgrounds.

Chairman Sam Zell (the so-called "Grave Dancer" of Equity Office Properties and Equity Residential fame) controls about 9% of the REIT.

EXECUTIVES

Chairman, Samuel Zell, age 71
Vice Chairman, Howard Walker, age 73, $500,000 total compensation
EVP Property Management, Ellen Kelleher, age 51, $311,428 total compensation
President CEO and Director, Thomas P. Heneghan, age 49, $382,454 total compensation
Executive Vice President - Asset Management, Roger A. Maynard, age 55, $311,428 total compensation
SVP Sales and Marketing, Seth Rosenberg, age 44
Senior Vice President- East Operations, Brad Nelson
Vice President - Customer Relations, Dave Kozy
Senior Vice President - Sales, Jim Phillips
Chief Financial Officer; Senior Vice President; Treasurer, Paul Seavey
Senior Vice President - Revenue Management, Peter Underhill
Senior Vice President - West Operations, Ron Bunce
Senior Vice President; Principal Accounting Officer, Thomas Novosel

Director, David J. Contis, age 54
Director, Philip C. Calian, age 50
Vice Chairman, Howard Walker, age 73
President CEO and Director, Thomas P. Heneghan, age 49
Director, Sheli Z. Rosenberg, age 70
Director, Thomas E. Dobrowski, age 69
Director, Gary L. Waterman, age 71
Auditors: Ernst&YoungLLP

LOCATIONS

HQ: Equity LifeStyle Properties Inc.
2 N. Riverside Plaza Ste. 800, Chicago IL 60606
Phone: 312-279-1400   **Fax:** 312-279-1710
Web: www.equitylifestyle.com

2011 Properties

	No.
US	
Florida	119
California	49
Arizona	41
Michigan	15
Texas	15
Washington	15
Pennsylvania	15
Colorado	10
Oregon	9
North	8
Delaware	7
Indiana	7
New	7
Nevada	7
Virginia	7
Maine	5
Massachusetts	5
Wisconsin	5
Idaho	4
Illinois	4
New	4
Minnesota	4
South	3
Utah	3
Maryland	2
Ohio	2
Tennessee	2
New	2
North	2
Ohio	2
Alabama	1
Connecticut	1
Kentucky	1
Canada	
British	1
Total	**382**

PRODUCTS/OPERATIONS

2011 Sales

	$ mil.	% of total
Resort base rentals	130	22
Utility and other	53	9
Right-to-use contracts current period gross	17	3
Home sales	6.1	1
Right-to-use contracts defeered net of prior period amortization	(11.9)	-
Other	15	3

COMPETITORS

American Land Lease	Outdoor Resorts
Hometown America	Sun Communities
International Leisure	UMH Properties
Kampgrounds of America	

HISTORICAL FINANCIALS

Company Type: Public

Income Statement

FYE: December 31

	REVENUE ($ mil.)	NET INCOME ($ mil.)	NET PROFIT MARGIN	EMPLOYEES
12/12	709.8	74.4	10.5%	3,600
12/11	580.0	42.5	7.3%	3,500
12/10	511.3	60.4	11.8%	3,600
12/09	489.9	56.2	11.5%	3,200
12/08	443.4	18.3	4.1%	3,000
Annual Growth	12.5%	42.0%	—	4.7%

2012 Year-End Financials

Debt ratio: 66.8%
Return on equity: 8.3%
Cash ($ mil.): 37
Current ratio: 0.57
Long-term debt ($ mil.): 2,269

No. of shares (mil.): 83
Dividends
  Yield: 5.2%
  Payout: 265.1%
Market value ($ mil.): 5,598

	STOCK PRICE ($) FY Close	P/E High/Low	PER SHARE ($) Earnings	Dividends	Book Value
12/12	67.29	110 96	0.66	1.75	10.33
12/11	66.69	225 171	0.32	0.75	11.28
12/10	55.93	94 74	0.63	1.20	3.67
12/09	50.47	83 49	0.61	1.10	3.60
12/08	38.36	145 64	0.38	0.80	1.57
Annual Growth	15.1%	—	15.2%	21.6%	60.1%

Essex Property Trust, Inc.

Essex Property Trust acquires develops redevelops and manages apartment communities focusing on the metropolitan areas of Los Angeles San Diego San Francisco and Seattle. The self-managed and self-administered real estate investment trust (REIT) owns about 160 residential communities with more than 32000 apartment units; about half are located in Southern California. Essex also owns a handful of office buildings in its home state and has partial stakes in several apartment communities through joint ventures. The REIT adds to its portfolio through acquisition and through the development and renovation of properties.

When making acquisitions Essex usually targets multifamily properties with more than 100 units and spends from $300 million to $500 million per transaction. It likes to be active in supply-constrained markets with populations of at least one million and drives rent growth through high occupancy rates (approximately 96% at year-end 2011). The REIT continually monitors its existing markets and isn't afraid to exit if the housing supply increases too much. The company sells off assets if they no longer fit into its strategy and often uses the money raised to buy newer communities.

As the economic recession settled over the US West Coast Essex remained flexible and began pursuing non-traditional investments such as parcels of land. In 2009 the company shifted its focus from building and acquiring apartments to resident retention and occupancy. However as rental income dipped during the economic downturn Essex looked again towards acquisitions to pick up the slack. Since the beginning of 2010 it has invested some $1.2 billion to acquire about 20 apartment communities in its key markets in several separate transactions.

The acquisitions contributed to a nearly 20% rise in net income for Essex in 2011. The REIT also benefitted from an increase in scheduled rents at its existing properties.

Insiders and unrelated institutional investors own almost half of Essex's stock.

EXECUTIVES

VP Human Resources, Suzanne M. Golden
SVP Asset Management, Mark J. Mikl
SVP and General Counsel, Jordan E. Ritter
EVP Acquisitions, Craig K. Zimmerman, age 61, $300,000 total compensation
EVP Development, John D. Eudy, age 57, $300,000 total compensation
President CEO and Director, Michael J. (Mike) Schall, age 54, $295,000 total compensation
Vice Chairman, Keith R. Guericke, age 63, $350,000 total compensation
SVP Fund Management, John F. Burkart
First VP Development, Bruce Knoblock
First VP Acquisitions, Bryan W. Meyer
SVP Property Operations, Erik J. Alexander
VP Information Technology, Jamie Williams
Chairman, George M. Marcus, age 70
First VP Manager Regional Development, Maura Lederer
First VP Acquisitions, Jeff S. Rowerdink
Director Finance, Lisa C. Burton
VP and Economist, John D. Lopez
VP Development and Redevelopment Controller, Les Filler
Director Ancillary Income, Karen C. Seemann
VP Internal Audit, Gale H. Hansrajh
EVP and CFO, Michael T. Dance, age 56, $225,000 total compensation
VP and Manager Senior Development, Josh Corzine
VP Acquisitions, Adam Berry
Collections Manager, Lisa Demeter
Regional Portfolio Manager Pacific Nortwest Region, Carol Swanson
Regional Portfolio Manager Pacific Northwest Region, Sherri Clevenger
Regional Portfolio Manager Pacific Northwest Region, Mike Ashbrook
Divisional Manager Northern California/Pacific Northwest, Shawnee Tharp
Regional Portfolio Manager Southern California Region, Don Kinney
Regional Portfolio Manager Southern California, Jo Bonnet
Divisional Manager Southern California, Connie White
VP and Chief Accounting Officer, Bryan G. Hunt
Director Marketing, Darcey Forbes
VP Construction, Jeff Lambert
Investor Relations, Nicole Christian
First VP Fund Management, Angela L. Kleiman
Vice President Development, Andrew Baker
IR Contact Officer, Barb Pak
Executive Vice President Asset Management, John Burk
Director Information Technology, Matt Clark
President CEO and Director, Michael J. (Mike) Schall, age 54
Vice Chairman, Keith R. Guericke, age 63
Director, Willard H. Smith Jr., age 75
Director, David W. Brady, age 71
Director, Robert E. Larson, age 73
Director, Gary P. Martin, age 64
Director, Issie N. Rabinovitch, age 66
Director, Thomas E. (Tom) Randlett, age 69
Independent Director, Byron Scordelis
Independent Director, Claude Zinngrabe
Independent Director, Janice Sears
Auditors: KPMGLLP

LOCATIONS

HQ: Essex Property Trust Inc.
925 E. Meadow Dr., Palo Alto CA 94303
Phone: 650-494-3700   **Fax:** 650-494-8743
Web: www.essexpropertytrust.com/

PRODUCTS/OPERATIONS

2011 Sales

	$ mil.	% of total
Rental & other property revenues		
Southern California	226	48
Northern California	149	32
Seattle Metro	82	17
Other real estate assets	11	2
Management & other fees from affiliates	6	1
Total	**475**	**100**

COMPETITORS

Apartment Investment and Management	Colonial Properties
Archstone	Equity Residential
AvalonBay	Fairfield Residential
BRE Properties	Irvine Apartment Communities
Camden Property	UDR

HISTORICAL FINANCIALS

Company Type: Public

Income Statement

FYE: December 31

	REVENUE ($ mil.)	NET INCOME ($ mil.)	NET PROFIT MARGIN	EMPLOYEES
12/12	543.4	125.2	23.1%	1,144
12/11	475.5	47.0	9.9%	1,099
12/10	415.7	35.9	8.6%	1,039
12/09	411.3	37.1	9.0%	938
12/08	412.9	65.3	15.8%	930
Annual Growth	**7.1%**	**17.7%**	**—**	**5.3%**

2012 Year-End Financials

Debt ratio: 58.1%
Return on equity: 7.7%
Cash ($ mil.): 42
Current ratio: 1.74
Long-term debt ($ mil.): 2,818
No. of shares (mil.): 36
Dividends
Yield: 3.0%
Payout: 129.0%
Market value ($ mil.): 5,344

	STOCK PRICE ($) FY Close	P/E High/Low		PER SHARE ($) Earnings	Dividends	Book Value
12/12	146.65	47	40	3.41	4.40	48.55
12/11	140.51	118	89	1.24	4.16	42.55
12/10	114.22	103	68	1.14	4.13	36.85
12/09	83.65	29	17	2.91	4.12	36.65
12/08	76.75	58	29	2.21	4.08	37.54
Annual Growth	**17.6%**	**—**	**—**	**11.5%**	**1.9%**	**6.6%**

Esterline Technologies Corp

Esterline Technologies has a trio of aerospace defense and commercial business segments: Avionics & Controls Sensors & Systems and Advanced Materials. Avionics & Controls makes interface systems (switches indicators keyboards displays GPS systems) for aircraft and military vehicles communications systems and medical equipment. Sensors & Systems operations include temperature and pressure sensors as well as power switching data communications and fluid control devices. Advanced Materials makes elastomer products and through the defense group ordnance and military countermeasures. Esterline also offers aftermarket parts and service which have higher sales margins than OEM sales.

HISTORY

Esterline Technologies Corporation formed in 1967 as Boyar-Schultz. The company adopted its current name later that year after it merged with Esterline Angus Instrument. Esterline went public in 1968. It soon began a major period of expansion through acquisitions including Federal Products (industrial automation 1969) Auxitrol (precision measuring devices 1972) and Excellon Automation (drilling systems 1977). By the end of 1986 Esterline had acquired some 20 companies.

In 1987 Esterline turned over its operations to a management team from aerospace company Criton Technologies (the two shared a major investor Dyson-Kissner-Moran or DKM). The new management moved Esterline's headquarters from Darien Connecticut to Bellevue Washington. Esterline bought back DKM's shares in its business in 1989.

Esterline encompassed 22 subsidiaries in six countries by 1990. Following a 1993 restructuring the company began selling its smaller businesses including Republic Electronics. It sold its Angus Electronics subsidiary to Thermo Instruments in 1997; later that year it made three strategic acquisitions including hydraulic controls manufacturer Fluid Regulators to bolster its aircraft offerings.

The company continued to expand through acquisitions in 1998. Among its seven purchases made that year were Kirkhill Rubber (aerospace components) Memtron Technologies (membrane switches used in instrumentation) and Korry Electronics (lighted switches and panels for the aerospace market). In 1999 the company opened an office in Hong Kong to boost sales in Asia. Esterline sold its Federal Products (automotive metrology technology) subsidiary and later that year it acquired privately held Advanced Input Devices (custom keyboards and multifunction data-input subsystems) and UK-based Muirhead Aerospace (motion-control devices sold in 2008).

In 2001 Esterline received a contract potentially worth $40 million to produce combustible cases for US Army 155mm artillery rounds. The next year the company paid about $68 million for BAE SYSTEMS' Electronic Warfare Passive Expendables Division a maker of defensive countermeasures such as chaff. Chaff confuses radar and flares which draw off heat-seeking weapons. In 2003 Esterline acquired Weston Group (speed temperature and rotational sensors) and BVR Aero Precision Corporation (gears and data concentrators).

Esterline in 2004 acquired Leach Holding Company a maker of relays power distribution assemblies and switching devices in a deal worth about $145 million. Acquisitions continued in 2005 with the addition of secure military communication product manufacturer Palomar Products Inc. which enhanced the company's Avionics & Controls segment.

In 2005 the company paid about $120 million for UK-based Darchem a maker of thermally engineered components such as insulation for jet exhaust ducting nacelle and thrust reverser units as well as environmental control ducting and heat shields. Darchem which had annual sales of about $70 million became part of Esterline's Advanced Materials segment.

The company bought UK-based Wallop Defense Systems for about $59 million in 2006. Wallop a maker of military countermeasure flares became part of the Esterline Defense Group. CMC Electronics (aerospace and defense avionics) a $335 million acquisition in 2007 yielded a dynamic financial performance in 2009. In 2008 Esterline picked up Nylon Molding Corporation (NMC) Group which brought specialized fasteners for aviation applications to Esterline's product portfolio. Also that year it sold Traxsys Input Products (sensors) as well as UK motion technology maker Muirhead Aerospace. Muirhead was sold to AMETEK an electrical motor and monitoring equipment firm.

The company took advantage of the global economic recession by enacting cost-saving measures to generate more operational efficiency in preparation for the market turnaround. After spending higher-than-industry-average on research and technology from 2005 to 2008 which resulted in Esterline's prominent foothold in high-profile programs the company began reducing that expenditure in 2009.

Some of the high-profile programs include the use of Esterline's avionics systems on the Joint Strike Fighter the Hawker Beechcraft T-6B Texan Trainer (however this company filed for bankruptcy protection in 2012) the Trent XWB (30 separate components and sensors package) the Boeing 787 Dreamliner (pilot controls and cockpit environmental sensors) the Airbus A-350 and the UH-60 Black Hawk (cockpit retrofit program). Esterline's Avionics & Controls division provides components to every Boeing commercial aircraft currently in production.

A couple years prior in 2009 Esterline increased production capacity by upgrading several of its US operations and making strategic acquisitions that positively impacted the year's results. Also that year it bought UK-based Racal Acoustics for about $172 million; Racal makes ruggedized communications equipment such as protective headphones for military applications.

EXECUTIVES

Vice President Chief Financial Officer & Corporate Development, Robert D. George, age 57, $415,207 total compensation

President CMC Electronics, Gregory A. (Greg) Yeldon

Director Corporate Communications, Brian D. Keogh

Group VP, Alain Durand

Senior Group VP, Frank E. Houston, age 61, $351,346 total compensation

Executive Chairman, R. Bradley (Brad) Lawrence, age 66, $349,615 total compensation

Vice President Corporate Marketing & Strategy, Michel Potvin

Group VP and Treasurer, Albert S. (Al) Yost, age 47

President Esterline Communications Systems and Palomar Products, Kevin Moschetti

VP Human Resources, Marcia J. Mason, age 61

VP Customer Support and Strategic Development, Claude Chidiac

VP Human Resources, Tom Heine

President and Chief Executive Officer; Director, Curtis C. Reusser

Vice President of Engineering, Mitch Iverson

Director, LeRoy D. Nosbaum, age 65

Director, Robert W. Cremin, age 72

Director, Mary L. Howell, age 60

Director, Jerry D. Leitman, age 70

Director, Gary E. Pruitt, age 63

Director, Anthony P. (Tony) Franceschini, age 61

Director, Paul V. Haack, age 62

Director, Delores M. Etter, age 64

Director, James J. Morris, age 64

Auditors: Ernst&YoungLLP

LOCATIONS

HQ: Esterline Technologies Corporation
500 108th Ave. NE Ste. 1500, Bellevue WA 98004
Phone: 425-453-9400   **Fax:** 425-453-2916
Web: www.esterline.com

2012 Sales

	$ mil.	% of total
US	1,046	49
France	452	21
Canada	270	13
UK	255	12
Other countries	105	5
Adjustments	(137.1)	-
Total	**1,992**	**100**

PRODUCTS/OPERATIONS

2012 Sales

	$ mil.	% of total
Avionics & Controls	790	40
Sensors & Systems	702	35
Advanced Materials	499	25
Total	**1,992**	**100**

Selected Products

Avionics & Controls
  Electronic flight management systems
  Enhanced vision systems
  Global positioning systems
  Head-up displays
  Keyboards
  Lighted indicators
  Lighted push-button and rotary switches
  Panels and displays
Sensors & Systems
  Fluid control components
  Micro-motors
  Motion-control sensors
  Pressure-sensing devices
  Temperature-sensing devices
Advanced Materials
  Chaff
  Combustible ammunition components
  Elastomer products
  Flares
  Igniter tubes
  Molded fiber cartridge cases (120mm tank rounds and 60mm 81mm and 120mm mortar rounds)
  Mortar increments
  Thermal insulation

Selected Brands

Advanced Materials
  Armtec
  Darchem
  Hytek
  Kirkhill-TA
  NMC Aerospace
  Wallop
Avionics & Controls
  Advanced Input Systems

Avista
BVR
CMC Electronics
Korry
LRE Medical
Mason
Memtron
Palomar
Racal Acoustics
Sensors & Systems
  Auxitrol
  Leach
  Norwich Aero
  Pressure Systems
  Weston

COMPETITORS

AMETEK	L-3 Avionics
Astronautics	L. S. Starrett
BAE Systems Inc.	Labfacility
BNS Holding	Meggitt
Bose	Renishaw
Chemring	Rheinmetall
Doncasters	Rockwell Collins
Ducommun	SELEX SI
EMS Technologies	Sypris Solutions
Eaton	Telephonics
Elbit Systems	Thales
Electro Scientific	Trelleborg
Industries	Tyco
GE Aviation	Ultra Electronics
Goodrich Corp.	Universal Avionics
Hamilton Sundstrand	Woodward Governor
Honeywell Aerospace	Yokogawa Electric
Israel Aerospace	Zodiac Aerospace
Industries	

HISTORICAL FINANCIALS

Company Type: Public

Income Statement

FYE: October 25

	REVENUE ($ mil.)	NET INCOME ($ mil.)	NET PROFIT MARGIN	EMPLOYEES
10/13	1,969.7	164.7	8.4%	12,049
10/12	1,992.3	112.5	5.6%	12,185
10/11	1,717.9	133.0	7.7%	12,114
10/10	1,526.6	141.9	9.3%	8,976
10/09	1,425.4	119.8	8.4%	8,901
Annual Growth	**8.4%**	**8.3%**	**—**	**7.9%**

2013 Year-End Financials

Debt ratio: 21.1%
Return on equity: 9.4%
Cash ($ mil.): 179
Current ratio: 2.68
Long-term debt ($ mil.): 667

No. of shares (mil.): 31
Dividends
  Yield: —
  Payout: —
Market value ($ mil.): 2,541

	STOCK PRICE ($) FY Close	P/E High/Low		PER SHARE ($) Earnings	Dividends	Book Value
10/13	80.80	16	10	5.19	0.00	59.59
10/12	56.44	21	13	3.60	0.00	52.17
10/11	57.03	19	11	4.27	0.00	51.05
10/10	60.44	13	8	4.66	0.00	46.66
10/09	42.11	11	5	4.00	0.00	42.08
Annual Growth	**17.7%**	**—**	**—**	**6.7%**	**—**	**9.1%**

Evercore Partners Inc

Evercore Partners provides advisory services on mergers and acquisitions restructurings divestitures and financing to corporate clients. The firm's investment management business principally manages and invests capital for clients including institutional investors such as corporate and public pension funds endowments insurance companies and high net-worth individuals. Evercore also makes private equity investments. All told Evercore Partners has some $13 billion of assets under management. In addition to its US operations the company is active around the world through subsidiaries such as Protego in Mexico and Evercore Europe in London. Evercore also has offices in Brazil Hong Kong and Scotland.

Geographic Reach

While Evercore Partners operates globally the US accounts for more than 70% of the firm's revenue. Europe contributes about a fifth while Latin America accounted for 6% in 2011.

Operations

Investment banking is the company's core business accounting for about 80% of its revenue in 2011. (Evercore's Institutional Equities services offering equity research and securities trading for institutional clients resides under the Investment banking umbrella.) The firm's Investment Management segment which focuses on asset management for institutions wealthy individuals and private equity clients accounts for most of the remainder. Evercore Trust (formed via the 2009 purchase of Bank of America's Special Fiduciary Services division) provides investment management and trustee services to employee benefits plans.

Financial Analysis

Evercore's revenue increased by about 35% in 2011 vs. 2010 to a record $543 million. Net income fell 22% over the same period while cash flow increased by more than 100%. The firm's investment banking activities generated more than $430 million and included about $15 million and nearly $9 million in commissions and underwriting revenues respectively. Evercore served 245 advisory clients in 2011 94 of which exceeded $1 million in revenue compared with 183 clients in 2010. Fee-based revenues earned from the management of client portfolios and other investment advisory services increased by a third vs. the prior year. The decline in net income was due to increased operating expenses related to higher compensations costs and other expenses.

Strategy

As an independent investment banking firm that isn't involved in commercial banking or proprietary trading Evercore has avoided the controversy swirling around competitors such as Goldman Sachs that results from the conflicts of interest that may occur at larger firms that both underwrite and invest in their clients. Evercore also appears to be capitalizing on the turmoil in the financial industry that has seen some of its bulge-bracket competitors go bankrupt (Lehman Brothers) or get acquired (Merrill Lynch Bear Stearns). Recent high-profile transactions include the 2012 breakup of Kraft Foods (now Mondelez International) the recapitalizations of GM and CIT Group and the acquisition of Lubrizol by Berkshire Hathaway.

Evercore is expanding its Investment Banking business by diversifying geographically and through sectors served. Indeed in 2012 it formed a partnership with VTB Capital to develop cross-border transactions between Russia and North America. In 2011 the firm bought UK-based investment bank Lexicon Partners which provides advisory services for large and midsize corporations from offices in London Hong Kong New York and Aberdeen Scotland. Evercore also acquired a 45% stake in ABS Investment Management.

Evercore has also been growing internally expanding its coverage of the chemicals and energy and mining minerals and materials sectors and adding financial institutions and technology telecommunications and media groups.

Ownership

Investment firm FMR LLC owns about 10% of the shares of Evercore Partners.

Company Background

Evercore was launched in 1996 (it went public 10 years later) by Roger Altman who formerly led investment banking and merger advisory practices at Lehman Brothers and The Blackstone Group. Altman resigned as CEO in 2009 and was succeeded by Ralph Schlosstein co-founder of asset management giant BlackRock; Altman remained executive chairman.

EXECUTIVES

Executive Chairman and Co-Chairman, Roger C. Altman, age 68, $500,000 total compensation
Senior Managing Director and Co-Head Private Equity, James R. Matthews
Senior Managing Director Evercore Europe, Philippe Camus, age 65
Senior Managing Director Mexico, Pedro Aspe, age 62, $500,000 total compensation
CEO Evercore Wealth Management, Jeffrey S. (Jeff) Maurer
General Counsel, Adam B. Frankel, age 45
Senior Managing Director Strategy and Business Development, Ciara A. Burnham
Senior Managing Director and Co-Head Private Equity, Neeraj Mital
Senior Managing Director and COO Private Equity, Kathleen G. Reiland, age 48
Co-Vice Chairman Corporate Advisory Business, Eduardo G. Mestre, age 65, $500,000 total compensation
Senior Managing Director and COO Corporate Advisory Business, Timothy G. LaLonde
Client Services Manager Evercore Wealth Management, Karen Francois
Director Protego, Fernando Aportela
Director Protego, Augusto Arellano
Director Protego, Hugo Garza
Director Protego, Jorge Marcos
Director Protego, Antonio Souza
CEO and Director Protego Asset Management Business, Sergio Sanchez
Chief Financial Officer, Robert B. Walsh, age 57, $500,000 total compensation
Senior Managing Director and Head Equities Division, Charles Myers
VP Evercore Europe and Corporate Advisory, Tiarnan O'Rourke
VP Privatge Equity, Justin W. Steil
Managing Director Restructuring Advisory, Stephen Hannan
VP Corporate Advisory, Jeffrey M. Reisenberg
VP Corporate Advisory, Rafael Polanco
VP Corporate Advisory, Brendan Panda
VP Corporate Advisors, Gus Christensen
Senior Managing Director Corporate Advisory, Naveen Nataraj
CEO of Evercore Partners International LLP, Andrew Sibbald, age 46
Senior Managing Director and Head Real Estate Advisory, Martin J. Cicco, age 57

Senior Managing Director Mining Metals and Materials Advisory, F. Perkins (Perk) Hixon, age 54
COO Equities Division, Terri Fortuna
Vice President and Wealth Advisor, Paulo Coelho
Senior Vice President Sales and Service, Peter Collingwood
General Partner, Richard A. DAmore
Executive Vice President Process Equipment, William J. Miller
Executive Vice President Chief Financial Officer, David D. Glass
Managing Director, Mark Finkelstein
Senior Managing Director, Angus Winther
Senior Vice President Finance and Corporate Controller, John P. Kiernan
Chief Information Officer, Dean A. Ward
Chief Operating Officer for the Equity Research business, Morgan Stanley
Director, Richard I. (Dick) Beattie, age 74
Co-Chairman; Chairman and CEO Protego, Pedro Aspe, age 61
Director, Curt Hessler, age 70
Director, Francois de Saint Phalle, age 65
Director, Gail B. Harris, age 59
Director, Anthony N. Pritzker, age 53
Independent Director, Francois Phalle
Auditors: Deloitte&ToucheLLP

LOCATIONS

HQ: Evercore Partners Inc.
55 E. 52nd St., New York NY 10055
Phone: 212-857-3100 **Fax:** 212-857-3101
Web: www.evercore.com

2011 Sales

	% of total
US	73
Europe &	21
Latin	6
Total	**100**

PRODUCTS/OPERATIONS

2011 Sales

	$ mil.	% of total
Investment banking	430	80
Investment management	99	18
Other	13	2
Total	**543**	**100**

COMPETITORS

Allen & Company	Greenhill
Bank of America	JPMorgan Chase
Barclays Capital	Lazard
Blackstone Group	Merrill Lynch
Citigroup Global	Morgan Stanley
Markets	Rothschild North
Credit Suisse	America
Deutsche Bank	UBS Investment Bank
Goldman Sachs	

HISTORICAL FINANCIALS

Company Type: Public

Income Statement

FYE: December 31

	REVENUE ($ mil.)	NET INCOME ($ mil.)	NET PROFIT MARGIN	EMPLOYEES
12/12	642.3	28.8	4.5%	900
12/11	524.2	6.9	1.3%	800
12/10	378.9	8.9	2.4%	610
12/09	313.1	(1.5)	—	443
12/08	194.6	(4.7)	—	335
Annual Growth	**34.8%**	**—**	**—**	**28.0%**

2012 Year-End Financials

Debt ratio: 8.8%
Return on equity: 6.8%
Cash ($ mil.): 259
Current ratio: 1.64
Long-term debt ($ mil.): 101

No. of shares (mil.): 29
Dividends
  Yield: 2.7%
  Payout: 303.7%
Market value ($ mil.): 893

	STOCK PRICE ($) FY Close	P/E High/Low	Earnings	PER SHARE ($) Dividends	Book Value
12/12	30.19	31 21	0.89	0.82	14.49
12/11	26.62	142 81	0.23	0.74	14.59
12/10	34.00	85 49	0.39	0.63	15.05
12/09	30.40	— —	(0.10)	0.51	16.30
12/08	12.49	— —	(0.36)	0.48	17.07
Annual Growth	24.7%	— —	—	14.3%	(4.0%)

Evolution Petroleum Corp

Petroleum evolved from old living forms and Evolution Petroleum evolved from Natural Gas Systems (which was formed in 2003). The crude oil and natural gas exploration company operates oil and gas producing fields in Louisiana. Its strategy is to acquire already-established properties and to redevelop them thereby making the fields more profitable. One method it uses is gas flooding which uses carbon dioxide to free up trapped oil deposits. In 2007 the company reported proved reserves of 1.7 million barrels of oil equivalent and probable reserves of up to 16 million barrels of oil equivalent

In 2008 in order to raise cash Evolution Petroleum sold its working interests in some oil fields in LaSalle and Winn Parishes Louisiana to a private buyer for $4.6 million.

EXECUTIVES

Chairman of the Board; President; Chief Executive Officer, Robert S. Herlin, age 58, $269,167 total compensation
Chief Financial Officer; Vice President; Treasurer, Sterling H. McDonald, age 64, $201,083 total compensation
VP Operations, Daryl V. Mazzanti, age 51, $201,083 total compensation
Controller and Corporate Secretary, David Joe
General Manager Drilling and Unconventional Gas, Eddie Schell
Principal Accounting Officer, Greg Goodale
Independent Director, William E. (Bill) Dozier, age 61
Independent Director, Edward J. DiPaolo, age 59
Director Co-Founder, Laird Q. Cagan, age 55
Independent Director, Gene Stoever, age 75
Independent Director, Kelly W. Loyd

LOCATIONS

HQ: Evolution Petroleum Corp
2500 CityWest Blvd., Suite 1300, Houston, TX 77042
Phone: 713 935-0122   **Fax:** 713 935-0199
Web: www.evolutionpetroleum.com
Evolution Petroleum owns interests in oilfields located in Louisiana.

PRODUCTS/OPERATIONS

Selected Operations

CO2-based enhanced oil recovery
Low-permeablitiy reservoir development
Technology-based redevelopment of old oil and gas fields

COMPETITORS

Anadarko Petroleum
Callon Petroleum
Carrizo Oil & Gas
Midstates Petroleum

HISTORICAL FINANCIALS

Company Type: Public

Income Statement

FYE: June 30

	REVENUE ($ mil.)	NET INCOME ($ mil.)	NET PROFIT MARGIN	EMPLOYEES
06/13	21.3	6.6	31.0%	11
06/12	17.9	5.1	28.6%	10
06/11	7.5	(0.2)	—	11
06/10	5.0	(2.3)	—	10
06/09	6.1	(2.6)	—	11
Annual Growth	36.8%	—	—	0.0%

2013 Year-End Financials

Debt ratio: —
Return on equity: 13.0%
Cash ($ mil.): 25
Current ratio: 10.42
Long-term debt ($ mil.): —

No. of shares (mil.): 28
Dividends
  Yield: —
  Payout: —
Market value ($ mil.): 312

	STOCK PRICE ($) FY Close	P/E High/Low	Earnings	PER SHARE ($) Dividends	Book Value
06/13	10.91	54 36	0.19	0.00	1.92
06/12	8.34	62 38	0.14	0.00	1.67
06/11	7.10	— —	(0.01)	0.00	1.21
06/10	5.01	— —	(0.09)	0.00	1.16
06/09	2.60	— —	(0.10)	0.00	1.20
Annual Growth	43.1%	— —	—	—	12.5%

Exactech, Inc.

Exactech has joint replacement technologies down to an exact science. Health professionals worldwide use the company's orthopedic devices to replace joints weakened by injury or disease. Its Optetrak knee implants Equinoxe shoulder systems and Novation hip implants either partially or totally replace patients' damaged joints. It also markets Opteform and Optefil bone allograft materials used to correct bone defects and damage. Exactech markets its products through direct sales representatives and independent dealers in the US as well as through affiliated and independent distributors in about 35 other countries. Customers include hospitals clinics surgeons and physicians.

Operations

Exactech's largest business segment is its knee replacement systems which account for about 40% of annual revenues followed by shoulder and knee implants (each accounting for about 20% of sales).

While the company manufactures most of its joint replacement systems at its own facilities some of the components are made by third parties. In addition several of Exactech's biologic bone matrix and bone graft products are licensed from RTI Bi-

ologics. The company also has a licensing agreement with Italian manufacturer Tecres through which it distributes Cemex a bone cement product used during joint procedures in the US and Canada.

Geographic Reach

The company sells its products in North and South America the Asia Pacific region and Europe. Sales in the US market account for about two-thirds of revenues.

Exactech manufactures some of its devices at its Gainesville Florida plant. It has subsidiaries in China Japan France Germany Switzerland Spain Taiwan and the UK and a branch office in Canada.

Sales and Marketing

In the US the company conducts sales and distribution through a subsidiary which engages independent sales agencies and direct sales representatives. International are conducted through independent distributors coordinated out of Exactech's Swiss office.

Financial Performance

Revenue saw a slight bump 9% for 2012 as all sectors saw an increase in sales except international surgical instrument sales. Net income rose 44% as the company had lower legal fees after settling some legal matters. Exactech continues to spend heavily on sales and marketing as well as R&D like most others in its industry.

Strategy

Exactech's strategy involves reducing R&D costs while continuing to roll out new products. To that end it has brought more manufacturing in-house in the last few years and works to keep those costs down through automation. It also takes some of the pressure off manufacturing by distributing products and services for third parties.

For new and improved products the company has added functionality to its knee replacement system for international markets developed the Gibralt cervical thoracic spine system and worked with CONMED to develop medical education materials.

Background and ownership

Chairman and CEO William Petty and his family own about 30% of Exactech primarily through their Prima Investments vehicle. Exactech was founded in 1985 by William Petty and executive Gary Miller (who also owns a small stake in the firm) both of whom had backgrounds in orthopedic surgery as well as Petty's wife Betty Petty who also serves as an officer of the company.

EXECUTIVES

President; Director, David W. Petty, age 46, $314,709 total compensation
Executive Vice President - Research and Development, Gary J. Miller, age 65, $261,816 total compensation
VP Administration and Corporate Secretary, Betty B. Petty, age 70, $205,032 total compensation
Chief Financial Officer; Treasurer, Joel C. (Jody) Phillips, age 45, $287,110 total compensation
Senior Vice President; General Manager - Biologics and Spine Division, Bruce Thompson, age 55, $347,292 total compensation
VP Sales, Bob Purcell
VP International Sales and Marketing, Daniel Berdat
VP-Engrg & Dev, Raymond Cloutier
Director of Sales and Marketing, Grant Boyle
Vice President - Legal, Donna Edwards
President; Director, David W. Petty, age 46
Director, James G. (Jim) Binch, age 64
Director, Richard C. Smith, age 51
Director, R. Wynn Kearney Jr., age 69

Director, Albert H. Burstein, age 75
Director, Paul E. Metts, age 69
Director, William B. Locander, age 69
Auditors: Deloitte&ToucheLLP

LOCATIONS

HQ: Exactech Inc.
2320 NW 66th Ct., Gainesville FL 32653
Phone: 352-377-1140   **Fax:** 352-378-2617
Web: www.exac.com

2012 Sales

US	145	65
Other countries	78	35

PRODUCTS/OPERATIONS

2012 Sales

Knee implants	81	36
Extremities	52	23
Hip implants	40	18
Other products	25	12

Selected Products

Knee implants
  Optetrak CR Slope PCL referencing system
  Optetrak Cruciate Retaining
  Optetrak Hi-Flex
  Optetrak Logic knee system
  Optetrak Non-Modular Constrained Condylar
  Optetrak Unicondylar
Extremities
  Equinoxe Fracture Shoulder System
  Equinoxe Cage Glenoids
  Equinoxe Platform Shoulder System
  Equinoxe Stem Positioning Device
Hip implants
  AcuMatch Bipolar Endoprosthesis
  AcuMatch M-series
  AcuMatch Unipolar Endoprosthesis
  Novation CFS cemented
  Novation Crown Cup
  Novation Element
Biologics and spine
  Accelerate platelet/bone marrow concentration system
  HydraLok
  Optefil and Opteform bone matrix
  OpteMx and Optecure bone graft substitute
  Ossigen bone matrix
  Proliant and Gibralt spinal systems
  Regenafil and Regenaform
  Silverbolt spinal system
Other products
  AcuDriver Automated Osteotome System (handpiece for implant revision procedures)
  Cemex bone cement
  InterSpace spacers

COMPETITORS

Bacterin	Orthofix
BioMimetic	Smith & Nephew
Biomet	Stryker
DJO Global	Symmetry Medical
DePuy	Synthes
Integra LifeSciences	Tornier
Kensey Nash	Wright Medical Group
MAKO Surgical	Zimmer Holdings
Medtronic	

HISTORICAL FINANCIALS

Company Type: Public

Income Statement

FYE: December 31

	REVENUE ($ mil.)	NET INCOME ($ mil.)	NET PROFIT MARGIN	EMPLOYEES
12/12	224.3	12.7	5.7%	590
12/11	205.4	8.8	4.3%	574
12/10	190.4	10.4	5.5%	553
12/09	177.3	8.3	4.7%	408
12/08	161.7	11.0	6.9%	390
Annual Growth	8.5%	3.5%	—	10.9%

2012 Year-End Financials

Debt ratio: 16.7%
Return on equity: 7.7%
Cash ($ mil.): 5
Current ratio: 4.13
Long-term debt ($ mil.): 38
No. of shares (mil.): 13
Dividends
  Yield: —
  Payout: —
Market value ($ mil.): 226

	STOCK PRICE ($) FY Close	P/E High/Low	PER SHARE ($) Earnings	Dividends	Book Value
12/12	16.95	19 15	0.96	0.00	12.82
12/11	16.47	29 19	0.67	0.00	11.81
12/10	18.82	27 17	0.80	0.00	11.16
12/09	17.31	29 17	0.65	0.00	10.27
12/08	16.84	35 15	0.87	0.00	9.57
Annual Growth	0.2%	— —	2.5%	—	7.6%

ExlService Holdings Inc

Have an extra-large task you'd rather not take on? Outsource it to ExlService Holdings. The company known as EXL offers business process outsourcing (BPO) research and analytics and consulting services. EXL's BPO offerings which generate most of its sales include claims processing collections customer support and finance and accounting. Customers come mainly from the banking financial services and insurance industries as well as from the utilities and telecommunications sectors. EXL operates offices around the world including the US and countries in Eastern Europe and Asia. The company was established in 1999.

Geographic Reach

EXL operates through six offices in the US 15 offices in India as well as through a half-a-dozen locations in the Czech Republic Bulgaria Romania Malaysia and the Philippines. The company also has a sales office in the UK and networking and telecommunications centers in California New Jersey and New York.

Sales and Marketing

EXL earned revenue from more than 270 clients in 2012 with its top three clients generating 26% of its revenue. Major clients include The Travelers Indemnity Company which accounted for 10% of the company's total revenue in 2012 and natural gas supplier Centrica. The company hopes to grow primarily by selling more services to existing customers and by adding more Global 1000 companies to its client list.

Financial Performance

Revenue growth in its outsourcing services segment combined with revenue from its Landacorp and other acquisitions helped drive the company's profits up 20% in 2012 over 2011 results. EXL's overall revenue was up 23% during the same period.

Mergers and Acquisitions

EXL continues to evaluate acquisition opportunities; it has its eye fixed on BPO firms in Eastern Europe or the US with capabilities in insurance utilities compliance and risk management. In 2012 it acquired collaborative care management software subsidiary Landacorp from SHPS to strengthen its capabilities in healthcare process analytics and technology.

In 2011 EXL acquired Outsource Partners International (OPI) a provider of finance and accounting outsourcing services serving about 80 clients. OPI has expertise in such areas as payroll and tax compliance SEC financial reporting and risk management. The deal substantially bolstered EXL's existing finance and accounting offerings and allowed it to better cater to CFOs. It also enhanced its footprint in the Asia/Pacific and in Europe.

Ownership

FMR LLC owns a 13% stake in of EXL Blackrock Inc owns 12% and Columbia Wanger Asset Management LLC owns 10%.

EXECUTIVES

Chairman, Vikram Talwar, age 63, $420,000 total compensation
Vice Chairman of the Board; Chief Executive Officer, Rohit Kapoor, age 48, $420,000 total compensation
President; Chief Operating Officer, Pavan Bagai, age 51, $224,719 total compensation
Executive Vice President; Head - Outsourcing Services, Vikas Bhalla, age 41
Executive Vice President; Chief Compliance Officer; General Counsel; Corporate Secretary, Amit Shashank, age 43, $297,000 total compensation
Executive Vice President; Global Head - Client Management and Chief Strategy Officer, Rembert de Villa, age 56, $350,000 total compensation
EVP Global Client Services, Bill Bloom
Executive Vice President; Global Head - Human Resources, Mohan A.V.K.
Executive Vice President; Global Head - Finance and Accounting, Tyler Largey
Executive Vice President; Global Head - Human Resources, Mohan V
Executive Vice President; Global Head - Client Management and Chief Strategy Officer, Rembert Villa
Director, David B. Kelso, age 60
Director, Clyde W. Ostler, age 67
Director, Garen K. Staglin, age 68
Director, Mohanbir Sawhney, age 49
Director, Kiran Karnik, age 66
Auditors: Ernst&YoungLLP

LOCATIONS

HQ: ExlService Holdings Inc.
280 Park Ave. 38th Fl., New York NY 10017
Phone: 212-277-7100   **Fax:** 212-277-7111
Web: www.exlservice.com

2012 Sales

	$ mil.	% of total
US	320	72
Other countries	33	8

PRODUCTS/OPERATIONS

2012 Sales

Outsourcing services	366	83
Total	**442**	**100**

COMPETITORS

Accenture	IBM Global Services
Affiliated Computer	Infosys
Services	Tata Consultancy
Genpact	WNS (Holdings)
HP Enterprise Services	Wipro

HISTORICAL FINANCIALS

Company Type: Public

Income Statement

FYE: December 31

	REVENUE ($ mil.)	NET INCOME ($ mil.)	NET PROFIT MARGIN	EMPLOYEES
12/12	442.9	41.8	9.4%	21,000
12/11	360.5	34.7	9.6%	18,900
12/10	252.7	26.5	10.5%	12,700
12/09	191.0	15.6	8.2%	10,700
12/08	181.7	14.4	7.9%	9,995
Annual Growth	25.0%	30.5%	—	20.4%

2012 Year-End Financials

Debt ratio: 1.0%
Return on equity: 13.4%
Cash ($ mil.): 109
Current ratio: 2.80
Long-term debt ($ mil.): 2

No. of shares (mil.): 32
Dividends
 Yield: —
 Payout: —
Market value ($ mil.): 853

	STOCK PRICE ($) FY Close	P/E High/Low	PER SHARE ($) Earnings	Dividends	Book Value
12/12	26.50	23 16	1.26	0.00	10.70
12/11	22.37	23 16	1.10	0.00	8.93
12/10	21.48	24 17	0.88	0.00	8.44
12/09	18.15	34 11	0.53	0.00	7.09
12/08	8.57	51 11	0.49	0.00	5.95
Annual Growth	32.6%	— —	26.6%	—	15.8%

Exterran Partners LP

Exterran Partners is the largest operator of contract compression equipment in the US. Its services include designing installing operating repairing and maintaining compression equipment. The company operates a fleet of more than 3950 compressor units comprising almost 1.6 million horsepower. Exterran Holdings a global leader in full-service natural gas compression equipment and services controls Exterran Partners. Exterran Partners and Exterran Holdings manage their respective US compression fleets as one pool of compression equipment in order to more easily fulfill their respective customers' needs. (North American contract sales accounted for about 25% of Exterran Holdings' total revenues in 2010.)

Exterran Partners grows through accretive acquisitions of compression assets (including business lines and contracts) from its parent company third-party compression providers and natural gas producers or transporters.

In 2009 the company reported a growth in revenues as the properties gained from earlier acquisitions came into service. However increased costs brought down income that year.

Growing its portfolio in 2010 Exterran Partners acquired contracts serving 43 customers and 580 related compressor units from Exterran Holdings for $214 million. The growth in assets (a 21% increase in horsepower over 2009) lifted the com-

pany's revenues in 2010 but lower pricing and increased field operating expenses resulted in a net loss for the year.

In 2011 Exterran Partners acquired compression and processing assets (contracts serving 34 customers and 407 compressor units) from its parent for $228 million. It follow this up in 2012 buying another contract serving 40 customers (400 compressor units) for about $183 million.

Universal Compression Holdings held a 50% stake in the company (spun off in 2006) until Universal Compression merged with Hanover Compressors to form Exterran Holdings in 2007.

EXECUTIVES

SVP General Counsel and Secretary, Donald C. Wayne, age 47, $250,000 total compensation
SVP and Director, Daniel K. Schlanger, age 40, $265,192 total compensation
VP Finance and Accounting, Kenneth R. Bickett, age 52
Director; VP and CFO Eastern Hemisphere, David S. Miller, age 49
Executive Vice Chairman of the Board, Mark Sotir
Senior Vice President, Robert Rice
Senior Vice President, Ronaldo Reimer
Chief Financial Officer; Executive Vice President, William Austin
Independent Chairman of the Board, Gordon Hall
Senior Vice President, Joseph Kishkill
Director, Edmund P. (Ed) Segner III, age 59
Director, Mark A. McCollum, age 54
Director, James G. Crump, age 73
SVP and Director, Daniel K. Schlanger, age 40
Director, George Stephen Finley, age 63
Director; VP and CFO Eastern Hemisphere, David S. Miller, age 49
Independent Director, Stephen Pazuk
Independent Director, Uriel Dutton
Independent Director, William Pate
Independent Director, Christopher Seaver
Independent Director, J. Honeybourne
Auditors: Deloitte&ToucheLLP

LOCATIONS

HQ: Exterran Partners L.P.
 16666 Northcase Dr., Houston TX 77060
Phone: 281-836-7000 **Fax:** 717-772-8284
Web: www.governor.state.pa.us

COMPETITORS

Cameron International	Enerflex
Compressor Systems	J-W Operating
Dresser-Rand	

HISTORICAL FINANCIALS

Company Type: Public

Income Statement

FYE: December 31

	REVENUE ($ mil.)	NET INCOME ($ mil.)	NET PROFIT MARGIN	EMPLOYEES
12/12	387.4	10.5	2.7%	0
12/11	308.2	6.0	2.0%	0
12/10	237.6	(23.3)	—	0
12/09	181.7	14.7	8.1%	0
12/08	163.7	29.8	18.2%	0
Annual Growth	24.0%	(23.0%)	—	—

2012 Year-End Financials

Debt ratio: 58.4%
Return on equity: —
Cash ($ mil.): 0
Current ratio: 1.05
Long-term debt ($ mil.): 680

No. of shares (mil.): 43
Dividends
 Yield: 9.8%
 Payout: 1,428.5%
Market value ($ mil.): 874

	STOCK PRICE ($) FY Close	P/E High/Low	PER SHARE ($) Earnings	Dividends	Book Value
12/12	20.27	179133	0.14	2.00	10.18
12/11	20.15	345202	0.09	1.92	11.14
12/10	26.86	— —	(0.90)	1.86	10.71
12/09	22.22	33 16	0.68	1.85	10.61
12/08	11.23	21 5	1.61	1.74	9.01
Annual Growth	15.9%	—	(45.7%)	3.6%	3.1%

Extra Space Storage Inc

When closets are bursting at the seams and garages are overflowing Extra Space Storage gives its customers room to breathe. One of the largest operators and managers of self-storage properties in the US the self-administered self-managed real estate investment trust (REIT) wholly owns owns in joint-venture partnerships or operates for third parties more than 900 facilities with some 610000 units totaling nearly 67 million sq. ft. of rentable space. Active in metropolitan areas in nearly 35 states and Washington DC the company also offers business boat and RV storage and leases to nearly 450000 tenants nationwide.

In late 2012 Extra Space Storage added more extra space to its holdings with the acquisition of 21 properties in about a dozen states from a joint venture partner.

In 2009 Extra Space Storage announced that it would finish up its existing development projects and wind down those activities due to a lack of reasonably priced development financing during the economic recession. Since then the REIT has turned to acquisitions in growing markets. It acquired 55 properties in 2011 and has a deal in place to acquire outright 36 properties from a joint venture with Prudential Real Estate Investment. Extra Space is also looking to expand Extra Space Management its third-party property management subsidiary.

The company reported revenues of nearly $330 million and net income of some $50.5 million in 2011; the latter figure was nearly double that of the prior year. Extra Space Storage's results were boosted by an increase in rental income from its acquisitions more third-party properties under management and greater customer participation in tenant insurance.

EXECUTIVES

EVP and COO, Karl T. Haas, age 61, $315,000 total compensation
Chairman, Kenneth M. Woolley, age 66, $210,000 total compensation
CEO, Spencer F. Kirk, age 51, $387,500 total compensation
EVP Chief Legal Officer and Secretary, Charles L. Allen, age 63, $290,000 total compensation
EVP and CFO, Scott Stubbs
SVP Marketing and Corporate Communications, James Overturf
IR Contact Officer, Clint Halverson
Director Marketing, Jessica Johnson

LOCATIONS

HQ: Extra Space Storage Inc.
2795 E. Cottonwood Pkwy. Ste. 400, Salt Lake City UT 84121
Phone: 801-562-5556   **Fax:** 801-562-5579
Web: www.extraspace.com

PRODUCTS/OPERATIONS

2011 Sales

	$ mil.	% of total
Property rental	268	82
Tenant reinsurance	31	9
Management & franchise fees	29	9
Total	**329**	**100**

2011 Properties

	No.
Wholly	356
Owned through joint venture	341
Managed	185
Total	**882**

COMPETITORS

AMERCO	PODS Enterprises
CubeSmart	Public Storage
Mobile Mini	Sovran

HISTORICAL FINANCIALS

Company Type: Public

Income Statement

FYE: December 31

	REVENUE ($ mil.)	NET INCOME ($ mil.)	NET PROFIT MARGIN	EMPLOYEES
12/12	409.4	127.6	31.2%	2,283
12/11	329.8	58.4	17.7%	2,239
12/10	281.5	33.3	11.9%	2,125
12/09	280.4	39.0	13.9%	2,001
12/08	273.2	46.8	17.2%	1,947
Annual Growth	**10.6%**	**28.5%**	**—**	**4.1%**

2012 Year-End Financials

Debt ratio: 49.0%	No. of shares (mil.): 110
Return on equity: 10.1%	Dividends
Cash ($ mil.): 30	Yield: 2.3%
Current ratio: 0.57	Payout: 74.5%
Long-term debt ($ mil.): 1,496	Market value ($ mil.): 4,030

	STOCK PRICE ($) FY Close	P/E High/Low		PER SHARE ($) Earnings	Dividends	Book Value
12/12	36.39	32	21	1.14	0.85	13.47
12/11	24.23	45	32	0.54	0.56	10.75
12/10	17.40	59	37	0.30	0.40	10.06
12/09	11.55	33	14	0.37	0.38	10.20
12/08	10.32	29	11	0.61	1.00	10.17
Annual Growth	**37.0%**			**16.9%**	**(4.0%)**	**7.3%**

EZCORP, Inc.

No mere pawn in the game EZCORP is one of the nation's largest operators of pawnshops. The company operates about 500 EZPAWN and Value Pawn locations in the US and almost 250 stores in Mexico under the Empe?o Facil brand. EZCORP also offers customers unsecured loans commonly referred to as payday loans or payroll advances through some of its pawnshops and from almost 500 EZMONEY stores in the US and 40 locations in Canada under the CASHMAX and Cash Converters banners. EZCORP also issues larger longer-term consumer installment loans and loans secured by automobile titles and loans money via the Internet through its 2013 acquisition of online lender Go Cash.

Operations

EZCORP's pawnshops feature a retail ambience intended to dispel the industry's seedy image. The stores offer standard pawnshop fare such as second-hand jewelry tools electronics sports equipment and musical instruments. Their inventory is built from items forfeited by customers who used them as collateral for small short-term high-interest loans.

The stores' services come at a price: monthly interest rates of up to 20% on loans that typically range from $130 to $135 and reach maturity in four months. Some three in four borrowers redeem their property or renew or extend the terms of their loans. About a third of the company's revenues come from reselling forfeited merchandise.

Its financial services stores attempt to resemble a bank. Its EZMONEY CASHMAX and Cash Converters are located in retail strip centers and many are adjacent to a pawnshop. Most of its EZMONEY stores are not allowed to market payday loans but instead offer fee-based advice and third-party loans. The company doesn't actually make or fund the loans but typically earns a fee of 20% on each loan amount. If a borrower defaults EZCORP pays the lender the principal and accrued interest plus an insufficient funds fee. The company then attempts to collect from the borrower.

Geographic Reach

EZCORP has about 1350 stores in the US Mexico and Canada. Most of its EZMONEY stores are located in Texas the company's largest market by far. It also owns a 30% stake in international pawnshop operators Albemarle & Bond (UK) and Cash Converters International (Australia).

Financial Performance

EZCORP became a billion-dollar company in fiscal 2013 (year-end September) after opening several new stores mostly in Mexico. The company makes about 35% of sales from merchandise sold in its pawnshops. Service charges for pawnshop items and interest charges on loans each account for 25% of sales. Jewelry scrapping (buying gold for the resale market) now accounts for nearly 15% of revenue.

The company's bottom line however fell for the first time in history to $34 million due to higher operating expenses (running all its new stores) as well as pre-tax impairment charges related to Albermale & Bond.

Strategy

Since regulation of payday lending is in flux and varies from state to state EZCORP is often compelled to exit or reduce its presence in states when new laws that restrict the company's activities are enacted. In order to reduce its reliance on payday lending the company has added services in recent years such as auto title lending fee-based credit consulting and jewelry scrapping.

Mergers and Acquisitions

EZCORP has targeted Mexico for growth and structures its product offerings and channels based on local custom and regulation. In 2012 the company acquired 60% of Crediamigo a provider of payroll deduction loans in Mexico and a 51% stake in Renueva Commercial (doing business as TUYO) which owns and operates buy/sell stores in Mexico City and the surrounding metropolitan area.

Across the pond in 2013 it bought a 95% stake in Cash Genie a UK-based Internet loan provider.

EZCORP also continues to build its US pawnshop empire through acquisitions. Buying online lender Go Cash in 2013 gave it a leg up in Internet lending while it works to expand its stores network in Arizona through its purchase of a dozen USA Pawn & Jewelry shops there. Previous purchases include its 2011 acquisition of 30 Mister Money pawn stores in Iowa Illinois Wisconsin and Texas; and seven Jumping Jack Cash stores in Salt Lake City. In 2010 the company bought some 15 pawnshops in Florida Illinois Nevada and Texas from separate sellers including its first five locations in Chicago.

HISTORY

Courtland Logue opened the first EZ Pawn in Austin Texas in 1974. By 1989 there were 16 U-Pawn-It and EZ Pawn stores. (All of them took the latter name in 1991.) Bankrolled by private investors Logue began expanding nationally.

After going public in 1991 EZCORP tightened loan valuation standards beefed up internal audit procedures to decrease shrinkage set up a centralized jewelry center to refurbish forfeited collateral and expanded retail sales.

In 1995 inventory reductions contributed to plummeting earnings. EZCORP closed 15 stores and combined 17 units with others; it also instituted a more restrictive lending policy to boost the number of repaid loans. Amid the turmoil Logue was ousted as chairman and succeeded by Sterling Brinkley.

The company's first JewelryLand Outlet a low-priced jewelry store opened in Georgia in 1996. Four new EZ Pawns opened in 1997 and 1998 saw EZCORP go international buying about 30% of Albemarle & Bond Holdings a pawnshop operator in the UK.

EZCORP made headlines in 1998 and 1999 with its bid to keep small-caliber handguns off the streets; it gave guns from its stores to local police departments (although it continues to sell such "sporting long guns" as rifles and shotguns). As the booming US economy made it easier for the company's traditional clients to get mainstream credit the company eyed expansion of its retail business launching website EZPAWN.com.

In 2000 the company decided to shut down more than 50 underperforming stores. By year's end almost 25 had been closed and an additional 15 were closed in 2001.

EZCORP began expanding again in 2006. It opened its first Mexico location that year and in 2007 acquired 15 Colorado pawnshops operating under the name Jumping Jack Cash.

The company gained about 70 locations with its 2008 acquisition of Value Financial Services. Also that year it acquired about a dozen Pawn Plus and ASAP Pawn pawnshops in Nevada. That deal expanded its presence in Las Vegas which is considered a good pawn market.

EZCORP ran into legal problems in 2008. It was forced to close 11 EZMONEY stores in Florida after state regulators filed action against EZCORP alleging that its stores violated state law. (The company's Florida pawn shops were not affected.) Also that year EZCORP paid a $600000 settlement with the Texas attorney general who'd charged that the company failed to adequately protect customers' private information. EZCORP disputed the claims.

EXECUTIVES

Chairman, Sterling B. Brinkley Jr., age 62, $649,038 total compensation
Principal Financial Officer; Senior Vice President, Stephen A. Stamp, age 51
EVP, Mark E. Kuchenrither, age 51
VP-Strategic Dev, John R. Kissick, age 71
VP and CIO, Robert Jackson, age 58
President CEO and Director, Paul E. Rothamel, age 49
President of North American Operations of EZCORP, Eric Fosse, age 50, $250,769 total compensation
SVP General Counsel and Secretary, Thomas H. (Tom) Welch Jr.
SVP Human Resources, Anthony (Tony) Sanders
President; U.S. Retail Operations, Barry Guest
Vice President; Chief Accounting Officer; Principal Accounting Officer; Controller, Jeffrey Byal
President - e-Commerce Division, Brent Turner
President & General Director; Empeno Facil, Rodrigo Garcia-Romo
President; Cash Converters Canada, Shanna Munro
Senior Vice President - Communications and Public Affairs, Rick Bluntzer
President US Financial Services, Jimmy Whatley
Director, Joseph J. (Joe) Beal
Director, John Farrell, age 55
Director, Richard D. Sage, age 72
President CEO and Director, Paul E. Rothamel, age 49
Director, Pablo Lagos Espinosa, age 58
Director, Thomas C. Roberts, age 71
Director, William (Bill) Love, age 65
Independent Director, Pablo Espinosa
Auditors: BDOUSALLP

LOCATIONS

HQ: EZCORP Inc.
1901 Capital Pkwy., Austin TX 78746
Phone: 512-314-3400   **Fax:** 512-314-3404
Web: www.ezcorp.com

2013 Stores

	No.
US	991
Mexico	331
Canada	39
Total	**1,342**

PRODUCTS/OPERATIONS

2013 Sales

	$ mil.	% of total
Merchandise sales	368	36
Pawn service charges	251	25
Consumer loan fees & interest	248	25
Jewelry scrapping sales	131	13
Other	10	1
Total	**1,010**	**100**

Selected Subsidiaries

EZCORP International Inc.
EZCORP Online Inc.
EZMONEY Alabama Inc.
EZMONEY Canada Inc.
EZMONEY Colorado Inc.

EZMONEY Holdings Inc.
EZMONEY Idaho Inc.
EZMONEY Kansas Inc.
EZMONEY Management Inc.
EZMONEY Missouri Inc.
EZMONEY Nebraska Inc.
EZMONEY Nova Inc.
EZMONEY South Dakota Inc.
EZMONEY Tario Inc.
EZMONEY Toba Inc.
EZMONEY Utah Inc.
EZMONEY Wisconsin Inc.
EZPAWN Alabama Inc.
EZPAWN Arkansas Inc.
EZPAWN Colorado Inc.
EZPAWN Florida Inc.
EZPAWN Holdings Inc.
EZPAWN Illinois Inc.
EZPAWN Indiana Inc.
EZPAWN Louisiana Inc.
EZPAWN Mexico Holdings Inc.
EZPAWN Mexico Ltd. Inc.
EZPAWN Nevada Inc.
EZPAWN Oklahoma Inc.
EZPAWN Services Mexico SRL de CV (Holdings)
EZPAWN Tennessee Inc.
Payday Loan Management Inc.
Texas EZPAWN Management Inc.

COMPETITORS

ACE Cash Express	DGSE Companies
Advance America	First Cash Financial
Cash America	Services
Cash Plus	World Acceptance
Check Into Cash	Xponential
DFC Global	

HISTORICAL FINANCIALS

Company Type: Public

Income Statement

FYE: September 30

	REVENUE ($ mil.)	NET INCOME ($ mil.)	NET PROFIT MARGIN	EMPLOYEES
09/13	1,010.3	34.0	3.4%	7,500
09/12	992.4	143.7	14.5%	7,200
09/11	869.3	122.1	14.1%	5,600
09/10	733.0	97.2	13.3%	4,900
09/09	597.4	68.4	11.5%	4,350
Annual Growth	**14.0%**	**(16.0%)**	**—**	**14.6%**

2013 Year-End Financials

Debt ratio: 18.3%	No. of shares (mil.): 54
Return on equity: 3.9%	Dividends
Cash ($ mil.): 39	Yield: —
Current ratio: 3.78	Payout: —
Long-term debt ($ mil.): 216	Market value ($ mil.): 915

	STOCK PRICE ($) FY Close	P/E High/Low		PER SHARE ($) Earnings	Dividends	Book Value
09/13	16.87	37	26	0.63	0.00	16.86
09/12	22.93	12	8	2.81	0.00	16.30
09/11	28.54	16	8	2.43	0.00	13.23
09/10	20.04	12	7	1.96	0.00	10.55
09/09	13.66	13	7	1.42	0.00	8.54
Annual Growth	**5.4%**	**—**	**—**	**(18.4%)**	**—**	**18.6%**

F5 Networks, Inc.

F5 Networks wants to help your network take a load off. The company's products include application delivery controllers (ADC) and software that are used for network load balancing availability assurance and security assessment. The company also provides file virtualization WAN optimization and remote access products. It additionally offers such services as network monitoring performance analysis and training. F5 targets a variety of industries including telecommunications manufacturing and financial services. The company gets more than half of its sales from the Americas.

Geographic Reach The company saw solid growth of between 15%-25% across all geographic regions in fiscal 2012. The Americas accounts for nearly 60% of sales with the EMEA and Asia-Pacific (including Japan) regions contributing about 20% each. Sales and Marketing The company sells primarily through distributors systems integrators and resellers although it also maintains a direct sales force for major enterprise accounts. Distribution giants Avnet Technology Solutions and Ingram Micro together account for more than 30% of the company's sales.

Financial Analysis Revenue rose 20% in fiscal 2012 (ended September 30) to $1.4 billion thanks primarily to strong demand for the application delivery networking products that comprise the majority of the company's sales. F5 Networks' net income has also been rising steadily over the past few years; it grew 14% to $275 million in 2012.

Strategy F5 Networks operates in a highly competitive market bumping up against tech powerhouses Cisco Systems and EMC. F5 outsources the majority of its hardware manufacturing with Flextronics International making its ADC product line and Sanmina-SCI producing the ARX line. The company's broader strategy for growing sales includes delivering products as integrated software modules; focusing product development on software as well as hardware and keeping an eye out for gaining new technologies through acquisitions; developing strategic technology partnerships with such vendors as Oracle and SAP; and using the company's online community of network architects and developers known as DevCentral for product development.

In 2013 it formed a long-term partnership with Websense to develop a suite of network security products.

Mergers and Acquisitions To bolster its product line against the challenges of exponential Internet growth and a rise in sophisticated security attacks F5 in 2011 acquired the intellectual property assets of Crescendo Networks which recently went through liquidation proceedings. Crescendo Networks provided field programmable gate array (FPGA) enhancements for hardware and security products. In another strategic move in 2012 F5 bought Traffix Systems which provides Diameter signaling products used by telecom service providers in 4G/LTE networks. The Diameter protocol is gaining acceptance as the standard for network signaling. The acquisition combines F5's IP expertise with Traffix's leadership in Diameter signaling products to enable customers to make the transition from 3G to 4G more cost effective and less disruptive to carriers.

EXECUTIVES

President CEO and Director, John McAdam, age 61, $595,606 total compensation
SVP Corporate Compliance Officer, John Rodriguez, age 52, $233,991 total compensation
Chairman, Alan J. Higginson, age 66
EVP Business Operations, Edward J. Eames, age 54, $303,723 total compensation
EVP Product Development and CTO, Karl D. Triebes, age 45, $389,623 total compensation

Executive Vice President - Marketing and Business Development, Dan Matte, age 46, $241,214 total compensation

EVP and CFO, Andy Reinland, age 48, $191,180 total compensation

VP Product Management and Marketing, Erik Giesa

EVP and General Counsel, Jeffrey A. (Jeff) Christianson, age 55, $340,772 total compensation

EVP Worldwide Sales, Mark Anderson, age 50

Senior Vice President - Security and Strategic Solutions, Manny Rivelo, age 48

SVP Marketing, Dean Darwin

VP North America Channel Sales, Gary Abad

Corporate Communications Americas, Alane Moran

Corporate Communications EMEA, Nick Bowman

VP Business Development, James (Jim) Ritchings

Investor Relations, John Eldridge

VP-WW Data Solution Sls, John Dionne

VP Product Management and Product Marketing Data Solutions, Kathleen Ferraro

VP Sales Asia Pacific and Japan, Christian Hentschel

EVP Worldwide Sales, David Feringa

EVP Strategic Solutions, Manuel F. Rivelo

Director, A. Gary Ames, age 69

President CEO and Director, John McAdam, age 61

Director, Deborah L. Bevier, age 62

Director, Karl D. Guelich, age 69

Director, Scott Thompson, age 55

Independent Director, Jonathan Chadwick

Director, Michael Dreyer

Auditors: PricewaterhouseCoopersLLP

LOCATIONS

HQ: F5 Networks Inc.
401 Elliott Ave. West, Seattle WA 98119
Phone: 206-272-5555   **Fax:** 206-272-5556
Web: www.f5.com

2012 Sales

	$ mil.	% of total
Americas	793	58
Europe Middle East & Asia	294	21
Asia/Pacific		
Japan	90	7
Other Asia/Pacific	199	14
Total	**1,377**	**100**

PRODUCTS/OPERATIONS

2012 Sales

	$ mil.	% of total
Products	818	59
Services	558	41
Total	**1,377**	**100**

Selected Products

Application delivery controllers (BIG-IP)
File virtualization (ARX)
Management console (Enterprise Manager)
SSL/VPN access appliances (FirePass)
WAN optimization (WANJet)

COMPETITORS

Acme Packet	Fortinet
Array Networks	Imperva
Barracuda Networks	Juniper Networks
Blue Coat	NetApp
Brocade Communications	Nokia
Checkpoint Systems	Radware
Cisco Systems	Riverbed Technology
Citrix Systems	SonicWALL
EMC	Symantec
Extreme Networks	Tekelec

HISTORICAL FINANCIALS
Company Type: Public

Income Statement
FYE: September 30

	REVENUE ($ mil.)	NET INCOME ($ mil.)	NET PROFIT MARGIN	EMPLOYEES
09/13	1,481.3	277.3	18.7%	3,356
09/12	1,377.2	275.1	20.0%	3,029
09/11	1,151.8	241.4	21.0%	2,488
09/10	881.9	151.1	17.1%	2,012
09/09	653.0	91.5	14.0%	1,646
Annual Growth	**22.7%**	**31.9%**	**—**	**19.5%**

2013 Year-End Financials

Debt ratio: —	No. of shares (mil.): 78
Return on equity: 19.3%	Dividends
Cash ($ mil.): 189	Yield: —
Current ratio: 1.48	Payout: —
Long-term debt ($ mil.): —	Market value ($ mil.): 6,701

	STOCK PRICE ($) FY Close	P/E High/Low	PER SHARE ($) Earnings	Dividends	Book Value
09/13	85.81	30 19	3.50	0.00	19.70
09/12	104.64	40 20	3.45	0.00	16.89
09/11	71.05	48 23	2.96	0.00	13.97
09/10	103.81	55 20	1.86	0.00	12.49
09/09	39.63	34 16	1.14	0.00	10.20
Annual Growth	**21.3%**	**— —**	**32.4%**	**—**	**17.9%**

FactSet Research Systems Inc.

Analysts portfolio managers and investment bankers know FactSet Research Systems has the facts down pat. The company offers global financial and economic information for investment analysis. FactSet also offers software for use in downloading and manipulating the data. (Its products can be fully integrated with Microsoft applications such as Excel and PowerPoint.) Among the company's applications are tools for presentations data warehousing portfolio analysis and report writing. Revenues are derived from month-to-month subscriptions to services databases and financial applications. More than 80% of revenue comes from investment managers; investment banking clients account for the rest.

Geographic Reach

About 30% of the company's revenues come from outside the US. Recent geographic growth efforts include the build out of new space in Paris and New York as well as the continued expansion of offices in India and the Philippines. It opened its 24th office located in Dubai in 2011. In addition to those locations FactSet has international offices in Australia Germany Italy Japan Hong Kong and the Netherlands.

Financial Analysis

FactSet has managed to achieve several years of consecutive growth in profits and revenues including in 2011 despite a weak economy. In 2011 the company reported a 13% growth in revenues due to a number of factors: broad-based growth across geographical segments; clients continued use of advanced applications such as Portfolio Analysis;

growth in the number of clients and users; new functionality within FactSet that improves clients' workflows by consolidating multiple services into one platform; the expanded deployment of proprietary data; $17 million of incremental revenues from the acquisition of Market Metrics in 2010; an increase in the client retention rate; and annual price increases.

Net income grew by 14% in 2011 thanks to higher revenues offset by a 14% increase in selling general and administrative costs due to higher travel and entertainment expenses increased stock-based compensation from performance-based stock options and a full year of expenses from the acquisition of Market Metrics.

Strategy

The company's success is in part due to its focus on growing its proprietary content collection efforts as well as investing in products and applications. Such efforts in 2011 include the launch of new reports and analytical tools including Interactive Charting FactSet Market Aggregates Debt Capital Structure Analysis and Idea Screening. In 2012 it added StreetAccount a provider of news managment services for investment professionals to its holdings.

FactSet has also benefitted from the launch of wireless applications to allow for mobile access to its offerings as well as from its 2010 acquisition of Market Metrics a US-based market research firm.

Concurrent with the growth of its products and services the company has gained new clients and users both in the US and internationally. By 2011 more than 48000 financial professionals from some 2200 corporate clients used the company's services (compared with some 42000 financial professionals from approximately 2100 corporate clients the previous year). As a result of its growth in 2011 FactSet made capital expenditures that included investing in computer equipment and other technology and hiring more more consultants and software engineers.

Ownership

In 2012 Brown Capital Group and T. Rowe Price Associates owned 10% and 9% of FactSet respectively.

HISTORY

Howard Wille and Charles Snyder founded FactSet in 1978. Both had previously worked for Wall Street investment firm Faulkner Dawkins & Sullivan (acquired by Shearson Hayden Stone in 1977). The company spent the 1980s building its client base and developing software that allowed clients to manipulate data on their own PCs.

FactSet opened an office in London in 1993 and one in Tokyo the next year. In 1994 the company added Morgan Stanley Capital International and EDGAR SEC filings to its database offerings. It added World Bank subsidiary International Finance Corp. in 1995 and the Russell U.S. Equity Profile report and Toyo Keizai a Japanese company database the next year. FactSet went public in 1996. Market Guide's information on US firms and ADRs (American depositary receipts) as well as the economic and financial databases of DRI/McGraw-Hill were added in 1997.

Snyder retired in 1999 but remained vice chairman. The following year Wille retired and Philip Hadley became chairman and CEO. The company made its first acquisition in 2000 when it bought Innovative Systems Techniques (Insyte) a maker of database management and decision support systems.

The company then began acquiring several content businesses. Its 2003 purchase of Mergerstat gave the company a database of global merger and acquisition and related information. In 2004 the company purchased JCF Group a provider of broker estimates and other financial data to institutional investors and CallStreet a provider of quarterly earnings call transcripts to the investment community. The following year the company purchased TrueCourse a provider of corporate competitive intelligence.

FactSet continued its acquisition spree with the 2005 purchase of Derivative Solutions (DSI) which offers fixed income analytics portfolio management and risk management services to financial institutions and the 2006 purchase of AlphaMetrics which provides institutional clients with software for capturing measuring and ranking financial information.

FactSet in 2007 released its ExcelConnect offering which enables data and analytics to be compatible with Microsoft Excel. Also that year the company enhanced its wireless capabilities giving users access to market company and portfolio information via PDAs and other wireless devices.

In 2008 FactSet expanded with the acquisition of the Thomson Fundamentals business which includes a global financial database with coverage of more than 43000 companies. The company also purchased investment banking workflow tool DealMaven reflecting its strategy of developing tools to make client workflows more efficient.

The company expanded in 2010 with the purchase of Market Metrics a US-based market research firm focused on advisor-sold investments and insurance products. FactSet used the acquisition to increase its global sales leveraging its own international network to sell Market Metrics products outside the US.

In 2011 FactSet expanded its presence in the Middle East when it opened an office in Dubai.

EXECUTIVES

SVP and Director Global Sales Operations, Kieran M. Kennedy, age 48, $235,000 total compensation
EVP and Director Global Sales, Michael D. Frankenfield, age 48, $265,000 total compensation
SVP and Chief Content Officer, Townsend Thomas, $184,615 total compensation
Vice Chairman, Charles J. Snyder, age 71
Chairman and CEO, Philip A. Hadley, age 51, $275,000 total compensation
SVP and Director Banking and Brokerage Sales, Scott L. Beyer
SVP and Director Product Development FactSet Analytics, Christopher (Chris) Ellis
SVP Director Finance and Principal Financial Officer, Maurizio Nicolelli, age 45, $190,000 total compensation
EVP and COO, Peter G. Walsh, age 48, $265,000 total compensation
SVP and Director Content Operations, Mark J. Hale
SVP and Director Product Development FactSet Platform, Goran Skoko
SVP General Counsel and Secretary, Rachel R. Stern
SVP and CTO, Jeff Young
SVP and Director Software Engineering, Gavin Rush
Director Portfolio Risk Research, Steve Greiner
SVP and Director U.S. Investment Management Sales, Meghan Garrity
SVP and Director International Investment Management Sales, Martin Gijssel
Senior Vice President FactSet Fundamentals, Justin Strand
Director, Michael F. DiChristina, age 51
Vice Chairman, Charles J. Snyder, age 71

Director, James J. (Jay) McGonigle, age 50
Director, Joseph R. Zimmel, age 60
Director, Scott A. Billeadeau, age 52
Director, Joseph E. (Jed) Laird Jr., age 68
Director, Walter F. Siebecker, age 72
Independent Director, Robin Abrams
Auditors: PricewaterhouseCoopersLLP

LOCATIONS

HQ: FactSet Research Systems Inc.
601 Merritt 7, Norwalk CT 06851
Phone: 203-810-1000   **Fax:** 203-810-1001
Web: www.factset.com

2011 Sales

	$ mil.	% of total
US	497	69
Europe	178	25
Asia/Pacific	50	6
Total	**726**	**100**

PRODUCTS/OPERATIONS

Selected Applications

Company Analysis
Data Warehousing
Economic Analysis
Fixed Income Analysis
Pitchbook Building
Portfolio Analysis
Quantitative Analysis
Real-time Market Data

Selected Content Providers

Dow Jones & Company
Global Insight
Interactive Data Corporation
Merrill Lynch
Morningstar
Standard and Poor' s
Thomson Reuters

Selected Product and Service Offerings:

Investment Managers
Equity Analysis
Quant and Risk Analysis
Portfolio Analysis
Markets and Economics
Fixed Income Analysis
Data Integration
Charting
Wireless Connectivity
Global Banking & Brokerage Professionals
Models and Presentations
Company and Industry Analytics
Deal Analytics
Idea Screening
People Intelligence
Accountability
Corporate Governance
Wireless Connectivity
Other Global Professionals
Hedge Funds
Private Equity and Venture Capital
Sell-Side Research
Equity Sales
Trading and Managing Market Data
Consultants and Advisors
Investor Relations and Corporate Strategy
Legal Accounting Management Consulting and Other Professionals
Academia - Professors and Students

COMPETITORS

Bloomberg L.P.	MSCI
CME	OneSource
Capital IQ	Pearson plc
Dealogic	Telvent DTN
Hoover' s Inc.	Thomson Reuters
Interactive Data	Track Data
LexisNexis	thinkorswim

HISTORICAL FINANCIALS

Company Type: Public

Income Statement

FYE: August 31

	REVENUE ($ mil.)	NET INCOME ($ mil.)	NET PROFIT MARGIN	EMPLOYEES
08/13	858.1	198.6	23.1%	6,258
08/12	805.7	188.8	23.4%	5,735
08/11	726.5	171.0	23.5%	5,251
08/10	641.0	150.2	23.4%	4,116
08/09	622.0	144.9	23.3%	2,962
Annual Growth	**8.4%**	**8.2%**	**—**	**20.6%**

2013 Year-End Financials

Debt ratio: —	No. of shares (mil.): 43
Return on equity: 36.3%	Dividends
Cash ($ mil.): 196	Yield: 0.0%
Current ratio: 2.69	Payout: 29.6%
Long-term debt ($ mil.): —	Market value ($ mil.): 4,434

	STOCK PRICE ($) FY Close	P/E High/Low	PER SHARE ($) Earnings	Dividends	Book Value
08/13	102.35	25 19	4.45	1.32	12.51
08/12	92.27	26 19	4.12	1.16	12.47
08/11	87.90	30 20	3.61	1.00	11.43
08/10	73.55	24 17	3.13	0.86	10.92
08/09	55.04	21 11	2.97	0.76	10.72
Annual Growth	**16.8%**	**— —**	**10.6%**	**14.8%**	**3.9%**

Federal Agricultural Mortgage Corp.

Farmer Mac (Federal Agricultural Mortgage Corporation) is Fannie Mae and Freddie Mac's country cousin. Like its city-slicker kin it provides liquidity in its markets (agricultural real estate and rural housing mortgages) by buying loans from lenders and then securitizing the loans into Farmer Mac Guaranteed Securities. Farmer Mac buys both conventional loans and those guaranteed by the US Department of Agriculture. About 40% of Farmer Mac's outstanding loans are secured by real estate in the southwestern US; the Northwest and the Upper Midwest account for nearly 20% apiece. More than 40% of its loans are for crops some 25% for livestock facilities and about another 20% for permanent plantings.

In 2007 the company was affected by the credit crisis that afflicted most loan buyers but not because of subprime loans; rising interest rates caused a $40 million loss in its derivatives and other trading assets. In 2008 several lenders in the Farm Credit System as well as Zions First National Bank invested $65 million into Farmer Mac to help alleviate its investment losses. Long-time CEO Henry Edelman was replaced by Michael Gerber the head of Farm Credit of Western New York.

The US Congress created Farmer Mac in 1987 at a time when agricultural lending had slowed due to defaults; the Farm Credit Administration oversees Farmer Mac. Zions First National Bank is Farmer Mac's largest stockholder controlling more than 20% the firm; AgribBank FCB controls 13%.

EXECUTIVES

Chief Operating Officer; Executive Vice President, Tom D. Stenson, age 62, $346,716 total compensation

Chairman, Lowell L. Junkins, age 69

President; Chief Executive Officer, Timothy L. (Tim) Buzby, age 44, $253,591 total compensation

President CEO and Director, Michael A. Gerber, age 53, $131,712 total compensation

Senior Vice President; General Counsel; Secretary, Stephen Mullery

Director, Dennis L. Brack, age 60

Director, Paul A. DeBriyn, age 57

Director, Mitchell A. Johnson, age 71

Director, John D. Raines Jr., age 69

Director, Dennis A. Everson, age 62

Director, Julia Bartling, age 53

Director, Glen O. Klippenstein, age 74

Director, Ernest M. Hodges, age 64

Director, James R. Engebretsen

Director, Brian P. Jackson, age 55

Director, Brian J. O'Keane, age 44

Director, Clark Maxwell, age 42

President CEO and Director, Michael A. Gerber, age 53

Director, Sarah L. Faivre-Davis

Director, Myles Watts

Independent Director, Bruce Sherrick

Independent Director, Chester Culver

Independent Director, Richard Davidson

Independent Director, Sara Davis

Auditors: Deloitte&ToucheLLP

LOCATIONS

HQ: Federal Agricultural Mortgage Corporation
  1133 21st St. NW Ste. 600, Washington DC 20036
Phone: 202-872-7700 **Fax:** 202-872-7713
Web: www.farmermac.com

PRODUCTS/OPERATIONS

2007 Sales

	$ mil.	% of total
Interest		
Investments & cash equivalents	174	54
Farmer Mac Guaranteed Securities	77	24
Loans	45	14
Noninterest		
Guarantee & commitment fees	25	8
Losses on financial derivatives & trading assets	(40.3)	-
Other	1	-
Total	**324**	**100**

Selected Programs

Farmer Mac I (purchase of loans not guaranteed by any US agency)

Farmer Mac II (purchase of loans guaranteed by US Department of Agriculture)

COMPETITORS

AgFirst	Fannie Mae
AgStar	Farm Credit Services
AgriBank	of Mid-America
Bank of America	Freddie Mac
Citigroup	

HISTORICAL FINANCIALS

Company Type: Public

Income Statement

FYE: December 31

	ASSETS ($ mil.)	NET INCOME ($ mil.)	INCOME AS % OF ASSETS	EMPLOYEES
12/12	12,622.2	46.7	0.4%	64
12/11	11,883.5	16.6	0.1%	62
12/10	9,479.9	31.9	0.3%	58
12/09	6,138.8	99.6	1.6%	53
12/08	5,107.3	(150.3)	—	43
Annual Growth	25.4%	—	—	10.5%

2012 Year-End Financials

Return on assets: 0.3%
Return on equity: 14.0%
Long-term debt ($ mil.): —
No. of shares (mil.): 10
Sales ($ mil): 268

Dividends
  Yield: 0.0%
  Payout: 10.0%
Market value ($ mil.): 348

	STOCK PRICE ($) FY Close	P/E High/Low		Earnings	PER SHARE ($) Dividends	Book Value
12/12	32.50	8	4	3.98	0.40	32.81
12/11	18.02	17	11	1.28	0.20	30.19
12/10	16.32	11	3	2.08	0.20	23.05
12/09	7.01	1	0	8.04	0.20	33.56
12/08	3.50	—	—	(15.40)	0.40	15.75
Annual Growth	74.6%	—	—	—	(0.0%)	20.1%

FEI Co.

FEI makes instruments to find very small defects. The company makes structural process management systems that use ion beams to analyze and diagnose submicron structures in integrated circuits (ICs) data storage components and biological and industrial compounds. FEI makes focused ion beam and dual beam electron microscopes that analyze ICs. It also makes scanning and transmission electron microscopes that detect defects in ICs and analyze biological specimens and materials. FEI targets applications in nanotechnology R&D but still gets significant sales from the semiconductor and data storage markets.

Operations

The company's products include transmission electron microscopes (TEMs) scanning electron microscopes (SEMs) focused ion beam system (FIBs) DualBeam systems that combine a SEM and a FIB and high-performance optical microscopes. Its products range in price from $100000 to more than $5 million.

Its operations focus on three areas in nanotechnology: nanobiology nanoelectronics and nanoresearch. Nanotech essentially means making things that have dimensions as small as 1 to 100 nanometers with a nanometer being one-billionth of a meter or about one-80000th the thickness of a human hair. Nanotech has applications in a variety of industries from consumer products like clothing and golf balls to electronics and health care.

Geographic Reach

In addition to sales and service offices located in some 50 countries FEI has R&D and manufacturing facilities in the Czech Republic Germany the Netherlands and the US (in Oregon).

Sales and Marketing

FEI sells its products through independent agents and distributors. Its sales cycle typically ranges from three months to a year and a half.

Financial Performance

Overall sales grew 4% in 2013 to $927 million despite cyclical downturns in the semiconductor capital equipment industry. (Because its equipment is used in labs for new process development and yield improvement FEI is less affected by cyclical swings than some other equipment suppliers.) Profits were up 10% to a record $126 million.

Strategy

FEI expects to see continued growth in 2014 driven by several factors. Emerging economies in Asia/Pacific (particularly China) continue to invest in the equipment that will make them more competitive in global technology and research offsetting some weakness in the US and European markets.

Mergers and Acquisitions

FEI periodically makes acquisitions to expand its product offerings and international presence. In 2013 it bought its Australian distributor nanoTechnology Systems Pty. Ltd.

In 2012 it made three acquisitions —ASPEX Corporation AP Tech and Visualization Sciences Group. It paid $30 million for ASPEX Corporation which makes rugged scanning electron microscopes for the materials science and natural resources business. It established a direct sales presence in South Korea with the $12 million purchase of sales and service agent AP Tech. Finally it bought France-based Visualization Sciences Group (VSG) for $55 million. VSG provides high-performance 3D visualization software products and tools to a range of markets.

Late in 2011 the company bought TILL Photonics a maker of digital light microscopes and imaging systems used for live-cell microscopy. FEI paid about $20 million for the German company to expand its products for life sciences market and extend its reach in Europe.

Company Background

The company was founded in 1971 as Field Emission Inc. referring to its use of field emission and ion technology.

EXECUTIVES

Chairman, Gerhard H. (Gerry) Parker, age 69

President CEO and Director, Don R. Kania, age 58, $577,500 total compensation

EVP and CFO, Raymond A. (Ray) Link, age 58, $310,000 total compensation

SVP General Counsel and Secretary, Bradley J. (Brad) Thies, age 53, $255,000 total compensation

Treasurer and Director Investor Relations, Fletcher C. Chamberlin

VP Human Resources, Timothy (Tim) Ashcroft

COO, Benjamin Loh, age 49, $310,000 total compensation

VP Science Group, Paul Scagnetti

EVP Business Development and CTO, Michael R. (Mike) Scheinfein

VP; General Manager Life Sciences, Dominique Hubert

VP Worldwide Service, Jim Fetterman

VP Industry Group, Rudy Kellner

Director, Ad Huijser, age 67

Director, Thomas F. (Tom) Kelly, age 60

Director, Richard H. (Rick) Wills, age 58

Director, Wilfred J. (Wilf) Corrigan, age 73

President CEO and Director, Don R. Kania, age 58

Director, James T. (Jim) Richardson, age 65

Director, William W. (Bill) Lattin, age 71

Director, Jan C. Lobbezoo, age 66

Director, Lawrence A. (Larry) Bock, age 52

Director, Homa Bahrami
Director, Jami Nachtsheim
Auditors: KPMGLLP

LOCATIONS

HQ: FEI Company
5350 NE Dawson Creek Dr., Hillsboro OR 97124-5793
Phone: 503-726-7500   **Fax:** 503-726-2570
Web: www.feicompany.com

2012 Sales

	$ mil.	% of total
North America	291	33
Europe	244	27
Asia/Pacific & other	355	40
Total	**891**	**100**

PRODUCTS/OPERATIONS

2012 Sales

	$ mil.	% of total
Materials science	315	35
Electronics	293	33
Service & components	200	22
Life sciences	82	9
Total	**891**	**100**

Selected Products

Dual beam defect characterization workstations
Electron and ion emitters
Focusing columns
Focused ion beam (FIB) workstations
Scanning electron microscopes (SEMs) and
  environmental SEMs
Transmission electron microscopes (TEMs)

COMPETITORS

Applied Materials	KLA-Tencor
Carl Zeiss	Rudolph Technologies
Dainippon Screen	Seiko Instruments
Hitachi	Tokyo Electron
High-Technologies	Veeco Instruments
JEOL	

HISTORICAL FINANCIALS

Company Type: Public

Income Statement

FYE: December 31

	REVENUE ($ mil.)	NET INCOME ($ mil.)	NET PROFIT MARGIN	EMPLOYEES
12/12	891.7	114.9	12.9%	2,518
12/11	826.4	103.6	12.5%	2,074
12/10	634.2	53.5	8.4%	1,813
12/09	577.3	22.6	3.9%	1,781
12/08	599.1	24.3	4.1%	1,830
Annual Growth	**10.5%**	**47.5%**	**—**	**8.3%**

2012 Year-End Financials

Debt ratio: 7.2%	No. of shares (mil.): 38
Return on equity: 14.9%	Dividends
Cash ($ mil.): 266	Yield: 0.2%
Current ratio: 2.53	Payout: 5.7%
Long-term debt ($ mil.): —	Market value ($ mil.): 2,134

	STOCK PRICE ($) FY Close	P/E High/Low		PER SHARE ($) Earnings	Dividends	Book Value
12/12	55.47	19	14	2.80	0.16	21.83
12/11	40.78	16	10	2.51	0.00	18.40
12/10	26.41	19	12	1.34	0.00	16.54
12/09	23.36	44	19	0.60	0.00	14.99
12/08	18.86	44	25	0.61	0.00	13.92
Annual Growth	**31.0%**	**—**	**—**	**46.4%**	**—**	**11.9%**

Fidelity Southern Corp

Fidelity Southern Corp. is the holding company for Fidelity Bank which operates more than 25 branches mostly in and around Atlanta and another location in Jacksonville Florida. The bank offers traditional deposit services such as checking and savings accounts CDs and IRAs. Consumer loans primarily indirect auto loans which the company purchases from auto franchises and independent dealers throughout the Southeast make up more than 50% of its loan portfolio. Real estate construction commercial real estate business residential mortgage and other consumer loans round out Fidelity Southern's lending activities. Subsidiary LionMark Insurance Company offers consumer credit-related insurance products.

Financial Analysis

Fidelity Southern Corp. (FSC) saw its revenue increase by 5% in 2011 vs. 2010 while net income was up 12% for the year. It was the third consecutive year of rising revenue for FSC which does business in one of the regions hit hardest by the financial crisis that reached its peak in 2008. FSC reported some $12 million in net losses that year largely due to bad loans. The bank has worked to unload some of those loans and raise capital through investment and other asset sales; it also received a $48 million injection of Troubled Asset Relief Program money from the government.

FSC attributed the rise in revenue in 2011 to an increase in noninterest income of more than 15% due to an increase in revenues from Small Business Administration (SBA) lending and other income. Loan income fell by nearly 2%.

Strategy

Fidelity Southern has focused on building and diversifying its loan portfolio including originating more residential mortgages and consumer installment loans. It has added more than 100 loan officers to its staff to increase its origination activity. Loan losses and charge-offs have declined and in 2010 FSC netted its first gains in three years. The following year the company acquired five branches as well as most of the loans and deposits of the shuttered Decatur First Bank. In 2012 Fidelity Southern acquired the assets and branches of Security Exchange Bank in an FDIC-assisted transaction. The deal added two branches in Marietta Georgia.

Ownership

Chairman and CEO James Miller Jr. owns about 24% of Fidelity Southern.

HISTORY

WWII veteran Clark Harrison and five others founded Fidelity National Bank in 1973. The first office opened in downtown Decatur Georgia the next year. Fidelity National Bank opened its second branch and formed Fidelity Southern Corporation as a holding company in 1979; it formed Fidelity National Mortgage a year later. In 1984 the company received trust powers opened two new branches and began a major credit card marketing program.

The acquisition of two branches from the Resolution Trust Corporation in 1992 brought the number of branches to 10 and increased assets to $257 million. Fidelity National Capital Investors a retail brokerage was incorporated that year. In 1993 Fidelity National Bank began a consumer sales finance department to buy auto loans from car dealers.

The company opened an office in Jacksonville in 1995 to offer mortgage car and construction lending. Also that year the firm changed the name of its holding company to Fidelity National Corporation.

Fidelity National acquired Friendship Community Bank in Florida and bought six branches from First Union and NationsBank in 1996; rapid expansion and unexpectedly high credit card chargeoffs that year slashed earnings and prevented Fidelity National from opening three of its newly acquired branches. Under the scrutiny of federal regulators the bank discontinued its high-default card program the next year and shored up its finances raising capital through a stock offering.

In 1998 Fidelity National focused on maintaining capital levels and recovering from its losses while other banks expanded. Fidelity National Bank finally gained regulatory approval to open the three remaining branches acquired from NationsBank and First Union later that year. Regulators released the bank from capital and dividend restrictions in 1999 but Fidelity National had to restate its earnings for 1997 citing overestimation of an asset's value.

Fidelity National experienced moderate growth in 2001. Inspections by the Federal Reserve Board in 2000 and 2001 led to Fidelity National's adoption of a resolution that prohibits Fidelity National from redeeming its capital stock paying dividends on its common stock or incurring debt without prior approval of the Federal Reserve Board. In light of a softening economy in 2001 Fidelity National placed greater significance on credit risk management and building the secured portion of its consumer loan portfolio. The company sold its credit card business to Bank One in December.

In 2003 the company changed its name back to Fidelity Southern Corporation and its branches converted to the shortened Fidelity Bank; the bank also switched from a national to a state charter.

EXECUTIVES

President and Director; President Fidelity Bank, H. Palmer Proctor Jr., age 45, $360,000 total compensation
Chairman and CEO Fidelity Southern and Fidelity, James B. Miller Jr., age 73, $600,000 total compensation
VP; EVP Fidelity Bank, David Buchanan, age 55, $260,000 total compensation
CFO, Stephen H. Brolly, age 50, $184,667 total compensation
President and Director; President Fidelity Bank, H. Palmer Proctor Jr., age 45
Director, William Millard Choate, age 60
Director, Rankin M. Smith Jr., age 65
Director, David R. Bockel, age 68
Director, Edward G. Bowen, age 76
Director, Kevin S. King, age 65
Director, W. Clyde Shepherd III, age 52
Director, Donald A. Harp Jr., age 74
Director, William C. Lankford Jr., age 63
Auditors: Ernst&YoungLLP

LOCATIONS

HQ: Fidelity Southern Corporation
3490 Piedmont Rd. NE Ste. 1550, Atlanta GA 30305
Phone: 404-639-6500   **Fax:** 404-814-8060
Web: www.lionbank.com

PRODUCTS/OPERATIONS

2011 Sales

	$ mil.	% of total
Interest		
Loans including fees	86	60
Investment securities	6	5
Federal funds sold & bank deposits	0	-
Noninterest		
Mortgage banking activities	24	17
SBA lending activities	8	6
Indirect lending activities	5	4
Service charges on deposit accounts	4	3
Bank owned life insurance	1	1
Securities gains	1	1
Other fees & charges	2	2
Other	3	2
Total	**145**	**100**

COMPETITORS

BB&T	SunTrust
Bank of America	Synovus
Citizens Bancshares	Wells Fargo
Regions Financial	

HISTORICAL FINANCIALS

Company Type: Public

Income Statement

FYE: December 31

	ASSETS ($ mil.)	NET INCOME ($ mil.)	INCOME AS % OF ASSETS	EMPLOYEES
12/12	2,477.2	25.3	1.0%	774
12/11	2,234.8	11.4	0.5%	174
12/10	1,945.3	10.1	0.5%	559
12/09	1,851.5	(3.8)	—	488
12/08	1,763.1	(12.2)	—	366
Annual Growth	**8.9%**	—		**20.6%**

2012 Year-End Financials

Return on assets: 1.0%	Dividends
Return on equity: 14.0%	Yield: —
Long-term debt ($ mil.): —	Payout: 24.5%
No. of shares (mil.): 14	Market value ($ mil.): 141
Sales ($ mil): 185	

	STOCK PRICE ($) FY Close	P/E High/Low		PER SHARE ($) Earnings	Dividends	Book Value
12/12	9.55	7	4	1.34	0.00	13.05
12/11	6.08	13	9	0.59	0.02	12.56
12/10	6.98	14	5	0.57	0.00	13.04
12/09	3.60	—	—	(0.71)	0.00	12.89
12/08	3.61	—	—	(1.30)	0.19	14.14
Annual Growth	**27.5%**	—	—	—	—	**(2.0%)**

Fifth Street Finance Corp

Fifth Street Finance works to put the companies it lends money to on easy street. A business development firm Fifth Street lends capital to and invests in small and midsized firms with annual revenues between $25 million and $250 million. The company typically invests $10 million to $100 million in the form of senior debt or equity per transaction. It favors established firms over start-ups and prefers to participate actively in its investments

as advisors. Fifth Street's portfolio comprises more than 85 companies many of which operate in the health care manufacturing IT services and business services sectors. Formed in 2007 the specialty finance company boasts about $2 billion in assets under management.

Geographic Reach

Based in New York Fifth Street Finance operates in Connecticut Illinois California and Texas.

Sales and Marketing

Fifth Street Finance serves several customer types including financial advisors individual investors institutional investors and corporate finance professionals.

The firm has focused on advertising having spent $155 million in 2013 up significantly from $54 million in 2012.

Operations

Since inception Fifth Street Finance has originated $3.3 billion of funded debt and equity investments. Its portfolio which comprises $1.9 billion at fair value effective September 30 2013 consists of 99 investments 86 of which are in operating companies and 13 of which are in private equity funds. Additionally Fifth Street Finance holds equity investments consisting of common stock preferred stock or other equity interests in nearly half of its portfolio companies.

Fifth Street Finance is externally managed and advised by Fifth Street Management LLC.

Strategy

As a business development company Fifth Street Finance's overarching strategy includes infusing debt capital in businesses that show growth potential and then exiting its investments after businesses repay their debt or go through recapitalization.

As part of its own growth strategy the company intends to continue doing what has helped it grow so far: Focusing its lending activity on small and midsized companies which it believes to be underserved by many finance companies. Fifth Street Finance will also continue to originate its own loans to maintain control over the structuring of its investments and generate revenue from origination and exit fees.

Financial Performance

Fifth Street Finance has posted increases in both revenue and net income during the past five years.

Thanks to logging nearly $174 million in interest income from its portfolio investments and about $46 million in fee income Fifth Street Finance's 2013 revenue rose some 40% to nearly $222 million in fiscal 2013 as compared to $165 million in 2012. Increases in the firm's total investment income came from higher average levels of outstanding debt investments helped by a net increase of 18 debt investments and fees related to debt payoffs. Net income also increased by 28% to $102 million in 2012 vs. $79 million in 2012.

Mergers and Acquisitions

In 2013 the investment firm agreed to acquire Healthcare Finance Group planning to invest some $110 million.

EXECUTIVES

President, Bernard D. Berman, age 42
Partner and Co CIO Fifth Street Management LLC, Ivelin M. Dimitrov
Managing Director Origination Fifth Street Management LLC, Sunny K. Khorana
Executive Director and Controller, Steven M. Noreika
Chief Marketing Officer, James F. Velgot
Managing Director, Greg M. Browne
Chief Financial Officer, Alexander Frank

Senior Vice President, Brian A. Miazga
Chief Compliance Officer, David H. Harrison
Vice President Marketing, Jessica K. Tannenbaum
Director, Richard P. (Rick) Dutkiewicz
Director, Frank C. Meyer, age 70
Director, Byron J. Haney, age 53
Director, Brian S. Dunn, age 41
Independent Director, Douglas Ray
Auditors: PricewaterhouseCoopersLLP

LOCATIONS

HQ: Fifth Street Finance Corp.
   10 Bank St. 12th Fl., White Plains NY 10606
Phone: 914-286-6800   **Fax:** 914-328-4214
Web: www.fifthstreetfinance.com

PRODUCTS/OPERATIONS

Selected Portfolio Companies

ADAPCO
Advanced Pain Management Holdings Inc.
Caregiver Services
Cenegenics
CRGT Inc.
DISA Inc.
Dominion Diagnostics LLC
Eagle Hospital Physicians
Enhanced Recovery Corporation
Epic MedStaff Services Inc.
Filet of Chicken
Fitness Edge
Flatout
HealthDrive
idX
IZI
JTC Education Holdings
Lighting by Gregory
MedKnowledge Group
Miche Bag LLC
NDS Surgical Imaging
Nicos Polymers & Ginding
O'Currance Teleservices
Pacific Production Technologies
Premier Trailer Leasing
Rail Acquisition Corp.
ReBath
Specialty Bakers LLC
Tegra
Traffic Control and Safety Corporation
Trans-Trade
Welocalize Inc.
Western Emulsions
WhatCounts

COMPETITORS

American Capital	MCG Capital
Ares Capital	MVC Capital
Gladstone Capital	Solar Capital

HISTORICAL FINANCIALS

Company Type: Public

Income Statement

FYE: September 30

	REVENUE ($ mil.)	NET INCOME ($ mil.)	NET PROFIT MARGIN	EMPLOYEES
09/13	221.6	114.9	51.9%	0
09/12	165.1	88.0	53.3%	0
09/11	125.1	67.1	53.6%	0
09/10	70.5	43.0	61.0%	0
09/09	49.8	31.3	62.9%	0
Annual Growth	**45.2%**	**38.4%**	—	—

2013 Year-End Financials

Debt ratio: 22.1%	No. of shares (mil.): 139
Return on equity: 10.1%	Dividends
Cash ($ mil.): 147	Yield: 11.1%
Current ratio: 0.65	Payout: 108.4%
Long-term debt ($ mil.): 458	Market value ($ mil.): 1,430

STOCK PRICE ($)		P/E		PER SHARE ($)		
	FY Close	High/Low		Earnings	Dividends	Book Value
09/13	10.29	11	9	1.01	1.15	9.85
09/12	10.98	10	8	1.07	1.18	9.92
09/11	9.32	13	8	1.01	1.28	10.07
09/10	11.14	14	10	0.95	0.99	10.43
09/09	10.93	9	4	1.27	1.20	10.84
Annual Growth	(1.5%)	—	—	(5.6%)	(1.1%)	(2.4%)

Financial Engines Inc

Like the little engine that could Financial Engines does. What it does is provide financial advice portfolio management and retirement assessment services. The company serves US retirement-plan participants sponsors and service providers across a wide range of industries that includes more than 100 FORTUNE 500 companies and several of the largest retirement plan operators. It delivers its services online as well as by telephone. Financial Engines has more than $47 billion in assets under management and serves some 8 million individual retirement-plan participants. The company went public in 2010 with an offering worth $127.2 million.

Financial Engines generates revenue from professional management fees and subscription-based platform fees –that is fees paid for access to its online information and services. It markets itself to new employers through existing relationships with plan administrators. Financial Engines also markets its management services to passive plan participants to beef up fee revenues. The company used funds from its public offering to help pay operating costs which have increased as it has ramped up marketing hired personnel and set up new clients.

As more employers begin offering and the demand for retirement planning increases as the population ages the company has seen its business expand. As such revenues have more than doubled in the past five years. In 2011 Financial Engines' earnings increased 29% from the year before to $144.1 million primarily driven by the company's professional management services. Market appreciation of assets under management which grew some 26% year over year also helped boost the company's revenues. However investment in growth (with such aforementioned expenses as wages and sales and marketing costs) cut into the bottom line and the company's profits fell 76% to $15.2 million.

In addition to adding new clients through its marketing push Financial Engines plans to grow by adding new services. It is investing in R&D (the cost of which grew some 10% in 2011 to $21.2 million) to expand its investment research capabilities.

Co-founder Bill Sharpe is a notable innovator in the analysis and valuation of investments and has written books on topics including portfolio theory and investment fundamentals. He received the Nobel Prize in Economics in 1990.

HISTORY

Financial Engines was founded in 1996 by Nobel laureate William (Bill) Sharpe (Sharp was

the recipient of the 1990 Nobel Prize in Economic Sciences); former SEC Commissioner Joseph Grundfest; and the late Craig Johnson then chairman of the Venture Law Group.

Its initial services included providing individual investors with online advice regarding tax-deferred accounts and taxable investments. In 1998 the company began providing advice and assessment on retirement portfolios which consisted of a personalized printed retirement assessment. In 2004 it expanded to offer professional management services to retirement-plan participants

EXECUTIVES

Executive Vice President of Investment Management and Chief Investment Officer, Christopher L. (Chris) Jones, age 46, $193,750 total compensation
CEO and Director, Jeffrey N. (Jeff) Maggioncalda, age 44, $237,500 total compensation
Executive Vice President of Technology and Service Delivery, Garry W. Hallee, age 52, $193,750 total compensation
Executive Vice President and Chief Financial Officer, Raymond J. (Ray) Sims, age 63, $193,750 total compensation
Chairman of the Board, Paul G. Koontz, age 52
President, Lawrence M. (Larry) Raffone, age 50, $200,000 total compensation
Executive Vice President and General Counsel, Anne S. Tuttle, age 52
EVP Marketing, Kenneth M. (Ken) Fine, age 45
EVP Service Delivery, Manjari Lewis
Consultants and ERISA Relations, Joe Parlavecchio
Media Relations, Asma Emneina
Managing Director Retiree Research Center, Jason Scott
Director of Investor Services, David Ankrom
VP Risk and Technical Operations and Chief Security Officer, Matthew Todd
EVP Human Resources, Mary Lee Sharp
Vice President; Principal Accounting Officer; Controller, Jeffrey C. Grace, age 49
Executive Vice President - Marketing, June Bower
Executive Vice President of Human Resources, Mary Sharp
Executive Vice President of Marketing, Kelly S. O'Donnell, age 45
Executive Vice President of Human Resources, Mary Lee, age 52
CEO and Director, Jeffrey N. (Jeff) Maggioncalda, age 44
Independent Director, John B. Shoven, age 65
Independent Director, Prof David B. Yoffie, age 57
Director, Joseph A. (Joe) Grundfest, age 62
Director, Mark A. Wolfson, age 59
Independent Director, Blake R. Grossman
Director, Robert A. (Bob) Huret, age 66
Director, E. Olena Berg-Lacy, age 63
Auditors: KPMGLLP

LOCATIONS

HQ: Financial Engines Inc.
1804 Embarcadero Rd., Palo Alto CA 94303
Phone: 650-565-4900   **Fax:** 650-565-4905
Web: www.financialengines.com

PRODUCTS/OPERATIONS

2011 Sales

	$ mil.	% of total
Professional management	108	75
Platform fees	32	23
Other	3	2
Total	**144**	**100**

COMPETITORS

Ameriprise	Fidelity Financial
BlackRock	Merrill Lynch
Charles Schwab	Morningstar
FMR	The Vanguard Group

HISTORICAL FINANCIALS

Company Type: Public

Income Statement

FYE: December 31

	REVENUE ($ mil.)	NET INCOME ($ mil.)	NET PROFIT MARGIN	EMPLOYEES
12/12	185.8	18.5	10.0%	380
12/11	144.0	15.1	10.5%	355
12/10	111.7	63.5	56.9%	303
12/09	84.9	5.6	6.7%	264
12/08	71.2	(3.6)	—	0
Annual Growth	27.1%	—	—	—

2012 Year-End Financials

Debt ratio: —	No. of shares (mil.): 47
Return on equity: 7.6%	Dividends
Cash ($ mil.): 181	Yield: —
Current ratio: 7.01	Payout: —
Long-term debt ($ mil.): —	Market value ($ mil.): 1,329

STOCK PRICE ($)		P/E		PER SHARE ($)		
	FY Close	High/Low		Earnings	Dividends	Book Value
12/12	27.74	70	45	0.37	0.00	5.50
12/11	22.33	84	47	0.31	0.00	4.80
12/10	19.83	12	7	1.30	0.00	4.30
Annual Growth	18.3%	—	—	(46.7%)	—	13.1%

Financial Institutions Inc.

Financial Institutions may not have a luxurious name but they specialize in five star service. The holding company owns Five Star Bank which serves western and central New York through some 50 branches. Serving area businesses and consumers it offers standard deposit products such as checking and savings accounts CDs and IRAs. Subsidiary Five Star Investment Services offers brokerage and financial planning services. An area of growth for Five Star Bank indirect consumer loans originated through agreements with area franchised car dealers account for the largest percentage of the company's loan portfolio followed by commercial mortgages.

Growth in the bank's commercial and auto loan portfolios coupled with its conservative underwriting standards contributed to a 7% increase in earnings for Financial Institutions in 2011. The bank also writes direct-to-consumer and home equity loans business loans residential mortgages and agricultural loans.

In 2012 Five Star Bank acquired four retail branches owned by HSBC Bank and four owned by First Niagara Bank in upstate New York. The divestitures were made to satisfy antitrust concerns regarding First Niagara's purchase of 195 branches from HSBC.

Five Star Bank was formed in 2005 when the company consolidated its four banking subsidiaries

(First Tier Bank & Trust National Bank of Geneva Wyoming County Bank and Bath National Bank) into a single entity. First Tier Bank & Trust absorbed the other three banks and changed its name to Five Star Bank.

EXECUTIVES

President and CEO Financial Institutions and Five Star Bank, Peter G. Humphrey, age 58, $398,169 total compensation
EVP and CFO, Kevin B. Klotzbach, age 60
Chairman, John E. Benjamin, age 71
Chairman, Erland E. (Erkie) Kailbourne, age 71
SVP, Martin K. Birmingham, age 49, $195,732 total compensation
Chief Operating Officer, Richard J. Harrison, age 67
Senior Vice President; Corporate Secretary of the Company and the Bank, John L. Rizzo
Chief Financial Officer; Executive Vice President of the Company and the Bank, Karl Krebs
Executive Vice President; Chief Risk Officer of Company and Bank, Kenneth Winn
Executive Vice President and Chief Information Officer of the Bank, Mitchell McLaughlin
Senior Vice President; Director - Human Resources of the Company & the Bank, Rita Bartol
President and CEO, Martin Birmingham
President and CEO Financial Institutions and Five Star Bank, Peter G. Humphrey, age 58
Director, Samuel M. Gullo, age 64
Director, Barton P. Dambra, age 71
Director, James H. Wyckoff, age 61
Director, John E. Benjamin, age 71
Director, Susan R. Holliday, age 57
Director, Robert N. Latella, age 70
Director, Karl V. Anderson Jr., age 66
Director, James L. Robinson, age 70
Auditors: KPMGLLP

LOCATIONS

HQ: Financial Institutions Inc.
220 Liberty St., Warsaw NY 14569
Phone: 585-786-1100   **Fax:** 585-786-5254
Web: www.fiiwarsaw.com

PRODUCTS/OPERATIONS

2011 Sales

	$ mil.	% of total
Interest income		
Loans including fees	77	65
Investment securities	18	15
Noninterest income		
Service charges on deposits	8	7
ATM & debit card	4	4
Sales & calls of investment securities net	3	2
Other	7	7
Total	**119**	**100**

COMPETITORS

Astoria Financial	First Niagara
Citibank	Financial
Community Bank System	HSBC USA
ESL Federal Credit	KeyCorp
Union	M&T Bank

HISTORICAL FINANCIALS

Company Type: Public

Income Statement

FYE: December 31

	ASSETS ($ mil.)	NET INCOME ($ mil.)	INCOME AS % OF ASSETS	EMPLOYEES
12/12	2,764.0	23.4	0.8%	662
12/11	2,336.3	22.8	1.0%	613
12/10	2,214.3	21.2	1.0%	616
12/09	2,062.3	14.4	0.7%	620
12/08	1,916.9	(26.1)	—	665
Annual Growth	9.6%	—	—	(0.1%)

2012 Year-End Financials

Return on assets: 0.9%	Dividends
Return on equity: 9.5%	Yield: 3.0%
Long-term debt ($ mil.): —	Payout: 35.6%
No. of shares (mil.): 13	Market value ($ mil.): 257
Sales ($ mil): 122	

	STOCK PRICE ($) FY Close	P/E High/Low		PER SHARE ($) Earnings	Dividends	Book Value
12/12	18.63	12	10	1.60	0.57	18.41
12/11	16.14	13	9	1.49	0.47	17.18
12/10	18.97	12	7	1.61	0.40	19.40
12/09	11.78	15	3	0.99	0.40	18.33
12/08	14.35	—	—	(2.56)	0.54	17.62
Annual Growth	6.7%	—	—	—	1.4%	1.1%

First Cash Financial Services Inc

First Cash Financial Services is the original pawn star. The company operates more than 775 pawnshops and cash advance stores in Mexico (about 55% of sales) and about a dozen US states. First Cash lends money secured by such personal property as jewelry electronics tools sporting goods and musical equipment. Its First Cash Pawn and Famous Pawn shops sell merchandise forfeited by borrowers. The company also offers short-term loans payday loans check cashing money orders and other financial services through First Cash Advance and Cash & Go a partnership that operates about 40 kiosks inside convenience stores.

First Cash Financial earns most of its revenue from pawn operations (about 90%) while short term loans account for about 10%. The money-making pawn business is driven by pawn merchandise sales in addition to statutory service charges on pawns which reach up to 300% of the loan amount. However those service fees vary from state to state depending on the law. The company's average pawn loan amount in the US is about $178 and $66 in Mexico.

To reduce its risk to new regulations associated with payday lending First Cash is moving away from its short term loan and credit business in the US. The company has been selling or closing many of its payday/consumer loan stores across the country. The company now only operates short-term loan locations in Texas and has no plans in the near future to open new short-term loan stores in the US.

The company is looking south of the border to grow business. First Cash operates about 515 pawn shops and payday advance stores in Mexico and it is looking to increase that number by opening new stores and through acquisitions. The company first expanded its presence in the country in 2008 with the acquisition of Presta Max a chain of 16 pawn shops in southern Mexico. In early 2012 it acquired a 29-store chain in western Mexico. First Cash is also looking to open new stores in Mexico where many people don't have bank accounts and have limited access to credit. The company also continues grow in the US by opening new shops or buying two or three individual pawn shops at a time.

In 2012 First Cash announced a larger US deal with the acquisition of a 24-store chain of pawn stores operating under the Mister Money brand. The $25.5 million transaction expanded First Cash's geographic footprint in Colorado Kentucky Wyoming and Nebraska. The company later arranged to purchase 16 pawn stores operating as Fast Cash Pawn in the Denver area. That deal carried an approximately $46 million price tag.

As First Cash has grown so has its revenue. Sales climbed by more than 20% in 2011 to about $520 million and net income increased by about 35% that year (the company saw double-digit revenue and net income growth in 2010 too). Unlike some business sectors the poor economy has done wonders for the pawn business. Consumer demand for pawn products as well as people's need for easy credit has benefited companies such as First Cash. High gold prices also have helped increase wholesale scrap jewelry revenues.

HISTORY

First Cash grew from a single pawnshop in Dallas. John Payne traded some land in Colorado for the store after selling his Dallas bank in 1979. He and his wife ran the shop until 1985 when they sold it and built a new shop in the suburbs aiming to achieve the ambience of a video store.

It was an opportune moment: The Texas economy particularly the banking industry was just beginning its slide. Payne (who later left the company) incorporated First Cash in 1988 and brought in professional management under former banker Rick Powell in 1990.

Eight-store First Cash went public in 1991. Acquisitions and expansions included the 1994 purchase of a Baltimore/Washington DC area chain. The next year First Cash upgraded its computers to improve inventory control and loan valuations and became the first major pawn chain to stop selling or making loans on handguns.

In 1996 and 1997 First Cash added stores in Maryland and Texas. The next year it bought 10-store chain JB Pawn (from a brother of First Cash director Richard Burke) and about 20 individual shops. First Cash also moved into check-cashing buying 11-store Miraglia.

To reflect the diversification the company changed its name to First Cash Financial Services in early 1999. That year First Cash joined other pawnbrokers and short-term lenders in moving into Mexico. In 2000 First Cash partnered with Pawnbroker.com to provide online financial and support services to pawn shops.

First Cash discontinued its auto loan operations in 2008 two years after purchasing dealer and lender Auto Master. In the midst of a worldwide credit crunch First Cash sold Auto Master to Minneapolis-based Interstate Auto Group (dba CarHop).

EXECUTIVES

Chairman of the Board; President; Chief Executive Officer, Rick L. Wessel, age 54, $728,584 total compensation
Chief Financial Officer; Executive Vice President; Treasurer; Secretary, R. Douglas (Doug) Orr, age 52, $330,000 total compensation
Chief Operating Officer, Stephen O. Coffman, age 51, $396,000 total compensation
Vice President - Domestic Operations, Jim Motley
General Counsel, Peter Watson
Investor Relations Officer, Gar Jackson
Vice President of Operations, Christopher J. Lee
Director, Mikel D. Faulkner, age 63
Director, Randel G. (Randy) Owen, age 54
Director, Jorge Monta?o, age 67
Independent Director, Jorge Montano

LOCATIONS

HQ: First Cash Financial Services Inc.
690 E. Lamar Blvd. Ste. 400, Arlington TX 76011
Phone: 817-460-3947   **Fax:** 817-461-7019
Web: www.firstcash.com

2011 Sales

	$ mil.	% of total
$ in mil. % of total		
Mexico	281	54
US	240	46
Total	**521**	**100**

2011 Locations

	No.
Mexico	447
US	
Texas	178
Maryland	26
Indiana	9
South	6
Missouri	4
Washington	3
Oklahoma	3
Virginia	2
Total	**678**

PRODUCTS/OPERATIONS

2011 Sales

	$ mil.	% of total
Pawn merchandise sales	344	66
Pawn loan fees	122	24
Consumer loan and credit service fees	53	10
Other	1	-
Total	**521**	**100**

Selected Subsidiaries

All Access Special Events LLC
American Loan Employee Services S.A. de C.V. (Mexico)
Cardplus Inc.
Cash & Go Inc.
Cash & Go Ltd. (49.5%)
Cash & Go Management LLC (50%)
Cash & Go S.A. de C.V.
College Park Jewelers Inc.
Famous Pawn Inc.
FCFS MO Inc.
FCFS OK Inc.
FCFS SC Inc.
First Cash Corp.
First Cash Credit Ltd.
First Cash Inc.
First Cash Credit Management LLC
First Cash Ltd.
First Cash Management LLC
First Cash S.A. de C.V. (Mexico)
King Pawn Inc.
King Pawn II Inc.
Maryland Precious Metals Inc.
SHAC LLC
T.J. Unlimited LLC

COMPETITORS

ACE Cash Express	EZCORP
Cash America	World Acceptance
Check Into Cash	Xponential

HISTORICAL FINANCIALS

Company Type: Public

Income Statement

FYE: December 31

	REVENUE ($ mil.)	NET INCOME ($ mil.)	NET PROFIT MARGIN	EMPLOYEES
12/12	595.9	80.3	13.5%	6,400
12/11	521.3	77.7	14.9%	5,300
12/10	431.1	57.6	13.4%	4,700
12/09	365.9	49.7	13.6%	4,200
12/08	333.5	(21.5)	—	3,800
Annual Growth	**15.6%**	**—**	**—**	**13.9%**

2012 Year-End Financials

Debt ratio: 22.4%
Return on equity: 24.0%
Cash ($ mil.): 50
Current ratio: 7.75
Long-term debt ($ mil.): 110

No. of shares (mil.): 29
Dividends
Yield: —
Payout: —
Market value ($ mil.): 1,444

	STOCK PRICE ($) FY Close	P/E High/Low	PER SHARE ($) Earnings	Dividends	Book Value
12/12	49.62	18 12	2.70	0.00	12.11
12/11	35.09	20 12	2.47	0.00	10.48
12/10	30.99	17 11	1.86	0.00	9.56
12/09	22.19	14 7	1.65	0.00	7.12
12/08	19.06	— —	(0.71)	0.00	5.28
Annual Growth	**27.0%**	**—**	**—**	**—**	**23.1%**

First Financial Bancorp (OH)

First Financial Bancorp spreads itself thick. The holding company's flagship subsidiary First Financial Bank operates more than 120 branches in Ohio Indiana and Kentucky. Founded in 1863 the bank offers checking and savings accounts money market accounts CDs credit cards private banking and wealth management services (through its First Financial Wealth Management). Commercial loans including real estate and construction loans make up more than 50% of First Financial's total loan portfolio; the bank also offers residential mortgage and consumer loans. First Financial Bancorp has some $6.2 billion in assets and $43.9 billion in loans.

Financial Analysis

First Financial Bancorp's 2011 sales declined by 8% vs. 2010 on falling interest and non-interest income. The decrease in interest income was due to decrease in income from loans including fees resulted from lower interest income earned on loans and other earning assets. The decrease in non-interest income was due to decrease in income from service charges on deposit accounts net gains from sales of loans and decrease in income from accelerated discount on covered loans. Indeed the bank has seen its sales slump steeply: from nearly $675 million in 2009 to $451 million in 2011. The com-

pany net income increased more than 12% over the same period.

Strategy

First Financial recently quit the Michigan and Louisville Kentucky markets (leaving it with only a handful of branches in Kentucky) in order to focus on three core metropolitan markets: Cincinnati Dayton and Indianapolis. To that end it acquired 16 branches in western Ohio from Liberty Savings Bank and bought 22 Indianapolis-area branches from Flagstar Bank in 2011. Together the two acquisitions furthered the bank's growth strategy for the key markets of Dayton and Indianapolis. Also in 2011 First Financial dissolved two subsidiaries: investment advisory group First Financial Capital Advisors; and First Financial (OH) Statutory Trust II.

EXECUTIVES

EVP and COO, C. Douglas (Doug) Lefferson, age 48, $262,404 total compensation
President CEO and Director; Chairman President and CEO First Financial Bank, Claude E. Davis, age 52, $420,000 total compensation
Chairman, Murph Knapke, age 65
VP and Controller, Elizabeth E. Fontaine, age 47
EVP and CFO, J. Franklin (Frank) Hall, age 44, $220,673 total compensation
SVP Chief Accounting Officer and Controller, Anthony M. Stollings, age 57
Market President Northwestern Indiana First Financial Bank, David S. Harvey
EVP Banking Markets, Samuel J. (Sam) Munafo, age 62, $228,461 total compensation
SVP Retail Credit and Product Management, John C. Hoying
Chairman President and CEO First Financial Insurance, Mark A. Willis
Market President North Manchester First Financial Bank, Michael R. Terrone
Market President Hartford City First Financial Bank, James M. (Jim) Weiseman
SVP Sales and Marketing, Jill L. Wyman, age 50
SVP and Chief Credit Officer, Richard S. Barbercheck, age 53
Assistant VP Investor Relations; Secretary First Financial Bancorp and First Financial Bank, Terri J. Ziepfel
Market President Butler and Warren First Financial Bank, Adrian O. Breen
Market President Southeastern Indiana First Financial Bank, Michael A. Sorrells
SVP and General Counsel, Gregory A. Gehlmann, age 51, $219,327 total compensation
Market President Cincinnati First Financial Bank, John Marrocco
Market President Northern Kentucky First Financial Bank, Thomas R. Saelinger
VP and Retail Market Manager Dayton and Middletown, Jason Newport
VP Commercial Lending Clark and Greene Counties First Financial Bank, Herb Greer
VP and Commercial Bank Manager First Financial Bank, Dan Kane
Market President Lafayette First Financial Bank, Bradley W. (Brad) Marley
Market President Celina and Van Wert First Financial Bank, George Brooks
Market President Clyde First Financial Bank, John Christman
Market President Hastings First Financial Bank, Cortney Collison
Market President Dayton and Middletown First Financial Bank, Roger Furrer
SVP and Managing Director Wealth Resource Group First Financial Bank, David C. Brooks

SVP and Chief Investment Officer First Financial Capital Advisors, Alfred Shepard
SVP and Chief Risk Officer, John Sabath
SVP and President Indiana First Financial Bank, Al Roszczyk
VP Investor Relations and Corporate Development, Kenneth Lovik
First Vice President; Principal Accounting Officer; Controller, John Gavigan
President CEO and Director; Chairman President and CEO First Financial Bank, Claude E. Davis, age 52
Director, Maribeth S. Rahe
Director, Donald M. Cisle, age 58
Director, Corinne R. Finnerty, age 56
Director, Steven C. Posey, age 61
Director, Mark A. Collar, age 60
Director, Susan L. Knust, age 59
Director, William J. Kramer, age 52
Director, Richard E. Olszewski, age 63
Director, J. Wickliffe Ach, age 64
Director, David S. Barker
Independent Director, Cynthia Booth
Auditors: Ernst&YoungLLP

LOCATIONS

HQ: First Financial Bancorp
4000 Smith Rd. Ste. 400, Cincinnati OH 45209
Phone: 877-322-9530   Fax: 843-529-5883
Web: www.firstfinancialholdings.com

PRODUCTS/OPERATIONS

2011 Sales

	$ mil.	% of total
Interest		
Loans including fees	285	63
Investment securities	29	6
(Adjustment) (5.9) (1)		
Noninterest		
FDIC loss-sharing income	60	13
Accelerated discount on covered loans	20	5
Service charges on deposit accounts	19	4
Trust & wealth management fees	14	3
Bankcard income	9	2
Net gains from sales on loans	4	1
Gains of sales of investment securities	2	1
Other	11	3
Total	**451**	**100**

COMPETITORS

AMB Financial	Logansport Financial
Commercial Bancshares	MutualFirst Financial
Farmers National	PNC Financial
Fifth Third	Peoples Community
First Defiance	Bancorp
Financial	Peoples-Sidney
First Franklin	SB Financial Group
LCNB	U.S. Bancorp
Liberty Capital	

HISTORICAL FINANCIALS

Company Type: Public

Income Statement
FYE: December 31

	ASSETS ($ mil.)	NET INCOME ($ mil.)	INCOME AS % OF ASSETS	EMPLOYEES
12/12	6,497.0	67.3	1.0%	1,547
12/11	6,671.5	66.7	1.0%	1,656
12/10	6,250.2	59.2	0.9%	1,664
12/09	6,681.1	246.5	3.7%	1,748
12/08	3,699.1	22.9	0.6%	1,127
Annual Growth	**15.1%**	**30.8%**	**—**	**8.2%**

2012 Year-End Financials

Return on assets: 1.0%	Dividends	
Return on equity: 9.4%	Yield: 7.0%	
Long-term debt ($ mil.): —	Payout: 103.5%	
No. of shares (mil.): 58	Market value ($ mil.): 849	
Sales ($ mil): 403		

	STOCK PRICE ($) FY Close	P/E High/Low		PER SHARE ($) Earnings	Dividends	Book Value
12/12	14.62	16	12	1.14	1.18	12.24
12/11	16.64	16	12	1.14	0.78	12.22
12/10	18.48	21	14	0.99	0.40	12.01
12/09	14.56	3	1	5.33	0.40	13.13
12/08	12.39	24	13	0.61	0.68	9.29
Annual Growth	**4.2%**	**—**	**—**	**16.9%**	**14.8%**	**7.1%**

First Niagara Financial Group, Inc.

A lot of water and a few barrels have gone over Niagara Falls since First Niagara Bank was founded. Tracing its roots to 1870 the flagship subsidiary of acquisitive First Niagara Financial operates about 430 branches in upstate New York Connecticut Massachusetts and Pennsylvania. The bank offers financial services like deposits loans insurance investments and wealth management. Commercial real estate loans business loans and residential mortgages account for most of the bank's loan portfolio. Subsidiary First Niagara Risk Management offers risk management employee benefits consulting and investment services while First Niagara Commercial Bank accepts municipal deposits.

First Niagara has been expanding rapidly via transformative acquisitions. In 2012 the company bought nearly 200 HSBC branches in upstate New York and Connecticut for some $1 billion. To satisfy antitrust concerns it is selling more than 35 locations included in the deal to KeyCorp and nearly 30 more to Community Bank System and Financial Institutions in separate transactions. The company is also consolidating 35 branches with nearby locations. In addition to expanding First Niagara's branch network the HSBC acquisition will boost the company's commercial business and credit card portfolio as well.

First Niagara previously entered Pennsylvania in a big way acquiring more than 50 branches from PNC Financial in 2009 and buying bank holding company Harleysville National the next year. The PNC acquisition which expanded First Niagara's operations into western Pennsylvania included locations that PNC was compelled to divest to satisfy antitrust concerns regarding its takeover of National City. The purchase of Harleysville National Bank added some 80 branches in central and eastern Pennsylvania.

First Niagara expanded its insurance business in Pennsylvania in 2010 with the acquisitions of employee benefits risk management and investment services firm Banyan Consulting and Summit Insurance Group's operations in the state. The new businesses were combined with previous acquisitions RTI Insurance Services and Three Rivers Financial Services and took the First Niagara Risk Management name.

To facilitate its expansion First Niagara Financial converted from a thrift holding company to a bank holding company and First Niagara Bank converted from a savings institution to a commercial bank in 2010 moves that gave the company more flexibility in making acquisitions.

In 2011 the company completed its $1.5 billion acquisition of NewAlliance Bancshares adding some 90 bank branches and extending its franchise into Connecticut and Massachusetts. The addition along with organic growth in First Niagara's commercial loan portfolio contributed to a nearly 25% increase in net income for the company that year.

Prior to its latest round of acquisitions First Niagara Financial had already more than doubled its size with an earlier spree of smaller deals. It had fewer than 50 branches operating under its banner at the end of 2003. That year the company acquired Finger Lakes Bancorp. It bought Troy Financial in 2004 and Hudson River Bancorp the following year. In 2008 the company bought Great Lakes Bancorp the parent of Greater Buffalo Savings Bank.

EXECUTIVES

Senior Executive Vice President and Chief Banking Officer, Daniel E. Cantara III, age 54, $326,539 total compensation
Chairman, G. Thomas Bowers, age 70
Interim President and Chief Executive Officer, Gary M. Crosby, age 59
Executive Vice President Retail Banking, Mark R. Rendulic
Senior Executive Vice President and Chief Financial Officer, Gregory W. Norwood
Executive Vice President - Corporate Development, Oliver H. Sommer, age 44
Executive Vice President; Chief Risk Officer, Richard M. Barry
Executive Vice President Consumer Finance, Andrew D. Fornarola
Director, Barbara S. Jeremiah, age 61
Independent Director, Nathaniel D. (Nat) Woodson, age 68
Independent Director, Carlton L. Highsmith, age 59
President CEO and Director, John R. Koelmel, age 60
Director, Carl A. Florio, age 64
Director, Peter B. Robinson, age 63
Director, William H. (Tony) Jones, age 70
Director, Louise Woerner, age 69
Vice Chairman, David M. Zebro, age 61
Director, George M. Philip, age 65
Independent Director, Roxanne J. Coady, age 60
Director, Thomas E. Baker, age 69
Auditors: KPMGLLP

LOCATIONS

HQ: First Niagara Financial Group Inc.
726 Exchange St. Ste. 618, Buffalo NY 14210
Phone: 716-819-5500   Fax: 952-829-2743
Web: www.surmodics.com

PRODUCTS/OPERATIONS

2011 Sales

	$ mil.	% of total
Interest		
Loans & leases	704	54
Investment securities & other	360	28
Noninterest		
Banking services	92	7
Insurance commissions	65	5
Wealth management services	30	2
Mortgage banking	15	1

Lending & leasing	13	1
Other	28	2
Total	**1,310**	**100**

COMPETITORS

Capital One	NBT Bancorp
Citigroup	PNC Financial
Community Bank System	RBS Citizens Financial
HSBC USA	Group
JPMorgan Chase	SEFCU
KeyCorp	TD Bank USA
M&T Bank	

HISTORICAL FINANCIALS
Company Type: Public

Income Statement
FYE: December 31

	ASSETS ($ mil.)	NET INCOME ($ mil.)	INCOME AS % OF ASSETS	EMPLOYEES
12/12	36,806.2	168.4	0.5%	5,927
12/11	32,810.6	173.9	0.5%	4,827
12/10	21,083.8	140.3	0.7%	3,791
12/09	14,584.8	79.3	0.5%	3,000
12/08	9,331.3	88.4	0.9%	1,909
Annual Growth	**40.9%**	**17.5%**	**—**	**32.7%**

2012 Year-End Financials

Return on assets: 0.4%	Dividends
Return on equity: 3.4%	Yield: 4.0%
Long-term debt ($ mil.): —	Payout: 80.0%
No. of shares (mil.): 352	Market value ($ mil.): 2,796
Sales ($ mil): 1,535	

	STOCK PRICE ($) FY Close	P/E High/Low	PER SHARE ($) Earnings	Dividends	Book Value
12/12	7.93	26 18	0.40	0.32	13.97
12/11	8.63	24 13	0.64	0.64	13.64
12/10	13.98	21 16	0.70	0.57	13.22
12/09	13.91	35 21	0.46	0.56	12.61
12/08	16.17	23 12	0.81	0.56	14.57
Annual Growth (16.3%)	(1.0%)	— —	(16.2%)	(13.1%)	

Flagstar Bancorp, Inc.

Flagstar Bancorp is the holding company for Flagstar Bank which operates about 115 branches (including some in retail stores) in Michigan. Home loans are a major focus for Flagstar. The thrift originates purchases and services residential mortgages in all 50 states through a network of brokers and correspondents as well as nearly 30 of its own loan offices in more than a dozen states. More than three-quarters of the company's revenue (after interest expenses) is linked to residential lending but the reliance on this business hurt Flagstar during the housing bust. Expanding its commercial lending operations the firm in 2011 opened four full-service branches in Massachusetts Connecticut and Rhode Island.

Flagstar is broadening its reach beyond mortgage lending. The company is transforming its branches into full-service community banks and focusing on cross-selling an expanded suite of retail commercial and government banking services. It has also recently introduced a line of consumer loans such as credit cards and home equity lines of credit and added services for small and midsized businesses like treasury management and specialty lending. Additionally the bank formally expanded its commercial lending business into New England. While home mortgage lending remains key to Flagstar the company hopes to diversify its revenue streams so the business eventually accounts for about a third of sales.

The shift likely has something to do with the company's exposure to the miserable mortgage market. Flagstar has reported annual losses every year since 2007 since which it has lost a total of nearly $1.4 billion. Revenues fell 11% to $851 million in 2011 while losses that year totaled $182 million. Both interest and noninterest earnings declined that year as as the credit markets remained challenged. The company has been slowing its losses down though and despite reporting another quarter in the red in 2012 expects to return to profitability for the year. Flagstar has also lowered its provision for loan losses thanks to a decline in charge-offs.

To raise capital the company sold 27 bank branches in the suburbs north of Atlanta along with their deposits to PNC in 2011. The company also sold its 22 Indiana branches to First Financial Bancorp in late 2011. In addition to bringing in some cash the divestitures help Flagstar focus on its Michigan operations.

MP Thrift an affiliate of private equity firm MatlinPatterson Global Advisors assumed a controlling stake of Flagstar in 2009. Today it owns 64% of the company.

EXECUTIVES

Chairman, John D. Lewis
EVP Human Resources, Laura C. Anger
President Chief Executive Officer and Director, Alessandro P. DiNello, age 58
EVP and Managing Director Commercial Banking, Steven J. (Steve) Issa
Executive Vice President Chief Financial Officer, Paul D. Borja, age 52, $464,243 total compensation
EVP and Director Corporate Services, Marshall P. Soura, age 73
Chief Legal Officer, Matthew I. Roslin, age 45, $443,269 total compensation
EVP and COO, Salvatore J. Rinaldi, age 58
Executive Vice-President President Mortgage Banking Division, Matthew A. Kerin, age 58
Manager Editorial Services Marketing Advertising and Promotions, Susan Cherry
Executive Vice President; Chief Risk Officer of the Company and the Bank, Todd McGowan
Executive Vice President Personal Financial Services, Michael J. Tierney
Executive Vice President General Counsel, Michael C. Flynn
Executive Vice President Chief Risk Officer, Hugh F. Boyle
Vice President Director, Pam Hardy
Vice President Manager of the funds management department, Smith Barney
President Manager, Annette Devereaux
Vice President Manager Treasury Management Team Lead, Kim GoetheFirst
Director, David L. Treadwell, age 58
EVP and Chief Investment Officer Flagstar Bancorp and Flagstar Bank; President of Flagstar Capital Markets, Kirstin A. Hammond, age 46
Director, James D. Coleman, age 65
Director, Mark R. Patterson, age 60
Director, James A. Ovenden, age 49
Director, Walter N. (Walt) Carter, age 62
Director, Jay J. Hansen, age 50
Director, David J. Matlin, age 50
Director, Gregory Eng, age 46
President CEO and Director, Michael J. Tierney
Independent Director, Michael J. Shonka
Auditors: BakerTillyVirchowKrauseLLP

LOCATIONS

HQ: Flagstar Bancorp Inc.
5151 Corporate Dr., Troy MI 48098-2639
Phone: 248-312-2000   **Fax:** 248-312-6704
Web: www.flagstar.com

PRODUCTS/OPERATIONS

2011 Sales

	$ mil.	% of total
Interest income		
Loans	427	41
Securities	35	3
Other	2	-
Noninterest income		
Net gain on loan sales	300	29
Loan administration	94	9
Loan fees & charges	77	8
Deposit fees & charges	29	3
Other	76	7
Adjustments	(194.1)	-
Total	**850**	**100**

COMPETITORS

Bank of America	Harris
Capitol Bancorp	Huntington Bancshares
Citizens Republic	JPMorgan Chase
Bancorp	KeyCorp
Comerica	Northern Trust
Fifth Third	PNC Financial

HISTORICAL FINANCIALS
Company Type: Public

Income Statement
FYE: December 31

	ASSETS ($ mil.)	NET INCOME ($ mil.)	INCOME AS % OF ASSETS	EMPLOYEES
12/12	14,082.0	68.3	0.5%	3,328
12/11	13,637.4	(181.7)	—	3,136
12/10	13,643.5	(374.8)	—	3,279
12/09	14,013.3	(496.6)	—	3,411
12/08	14,203.6	(275.4)	—	3,920
Annual Growth	**(0.2%)**	**—**	**—**	**(4.0%)**

2012 Year-End Financials

Return on assets: 0.4%	Dividends
Return on equity: 6.0%	Yield: —
Long-term debt ($ mil.): —	Payout: —
No. of shares (mil.): 55	Market value ($ mil.): 1,084
Sales ($ mil): 1,502	

	STOCK PRICE ($) FY Close	P/E High/Low	PER SHARE ($) Earnings	Dividends	Book Value
12/12	19.40	22 1	0.87	0.00	20.75
12/11	0.51	— —	(3.60)	0.00	19.43
12/10	1.63	— —	(24.40)	0.00	22.77
12/09	0.60	— —	(162.00)	0.00	127.30
12/08	0.71	— —	(382.00)	0.00	564.76
Annual Growth 128.6% (56.2%)		— —	—	—	

FleetCor Technologies Inc

Helping companies manage motor fleets is at the core of FleetCor's mission. The company is a leading provider of fleet cards and payment processing services aimed at commercial and government fleets. Its cards carry the names Fuelman CFN Mannatec Keyfuels CCS and Fuelcard. The fleet cards function like typical charge cards and can be used to purchase fuel and lodging. FleetCor tracks purchases in order to help manage employee spending. The company serves more than 500000 accounts and has more than 2 million cards active in Africa Asia Europe and North America. Chevron is FleetCor's largest customer accounting for about 11% of sales. Other major customers include such BP Citgo and Shell.

IPO

Founded in 2000 FleetCor went public in December 2010 via an initial public offering that raised nearly $300 million. The proceeds went to FleetCor's private equity shareholders Advent International Bain Capital and Summit Partners.

Geographic Range

The US accounts for about two-thirds of FleetCor's sales. Outside the US the firm does business in Europe and Latin America. The firm is intent on growing its international presence.

Financial Analysis

In its first year as a public company FleetCor's sales climbed 20% vs. 2010 while net income rose by about 36%. North America outperformed International with year-to-year sales up 21% and 17% respectively. FleetCor credited the growth in its domestic business to organic growth in some of its payment programs higher average retail fuel prices in 2011 compared with 2010 and the spread between wholesale fuel costs and retail fuel costs. The overseas business also got a boost from organic growth as well as acquisitions in 2011.

Indeed 2011 was a year of record sales for FleetCor which has seen sales nearly double since 2007. Profits and cash flow from operations have also steadily risen with the exception of a dip in 2009.

Strategy

FleetCor has built itself into an industry leader mostly through acquisitions. The company plans to consolidate the industry further by targeting smaller and regional fleet service providers in the markets it serves. It also is eyeing expansion into such growing markets as Asia and Latin America and diversifying into new service offerings. To that end in 2011 the company purchased prepaid fuel card and food voucher companies in Mexico and the UK. The purchase of the Mexico firm marked FleetCor's entry into Latin America. In 2012 FleetCor furthered expanded its presence in Mexico with another acquisition of a fuel card client portfolio. Also in 2012 the company entered the Brazil market with its acquisition of CTF Technologies for $180 million. CTF provides fuel payment processing in Brazil.

Ownership

Summit Partners L.P. owns 28% of FleetCor's shares. Other significant shareholders include BCIP Associates III LLC and Chestnut Hill Ventures LLC with about 14% and 11% of the company's shares respectively.

EXECUTIVES

Chief Financial Officer, Eric R. Dey, age 53
President - North American Partner Business, William J. (Bill) Schmit, age 56
CIO, Van E Huff, age 52
President Petroleum Marketer Private Label Programs, Benton C. Routh
President - International Corporate Development, Andrew Blazye
Chief Operating Officer; President - U.S. Direct Business, Todd W. House, age 41
Executive Vice President Global Universal ProductsRobert, Robert P. Brandes, age 52
President - Corporate Lodging Consultants, Timothy J. Downs, age 55
President, Charles R. Freund
Executive Vice President - Global Products, Jeffrey D. Lamb
Executive Vice President Corporate Development, John S. Coughlin
Global Chief Information Officer, Donovan Williams
Director, Glenn W. Marschel Jr., age 66
Director, Richard Macchia, age 61
Director, Bruce R. Evans, age 54
Director, Mark A. Johnson, age 60
Director, John R. Carroll, age 45
Director, Steven Stull, age 54
Auditors: Ernst&YoungLLP

LOCATIONS

HQ: FleetCor Technologies Inc.
655 Engineering Dr. Ste. 300, Norcross GA 30092-2830
Phone: 770-449-0479   **Fax:** 770-449-3471
Web: www.fleetcor.com

2011 Sales

	$ mil.	% of total
North America	348	67
Other	170	33
Total	**519**	**100**

PRODUCTS/OPERATIONS

Selected Brands and Subsidiaries
CCS
CFN Holding Co.
CLC Group
Corporate Lodging Consultants Inc.
FleetCards
FleetNet
Fuelman
The Fuelcard Company
Fuel Vend Limited
Keyfuels
Mannatec Inc.
Transit Card

COMPETITORS

Arval	Retail Decisions
Comdata	Sodexo USA
Edenred	U.S. Bancorp
Multi Service	WEX

HISTORICAL FINANCIALS
Company Type: Public

Income Statement
FYE: December 31

	REVENUE ($ mil.)	NET INCOME ($ mil.)	NET PROFIT MARGIN	EMPLOYEES
12/12	707.5	216.2	30.6%	2,650
12/11	519.5	147.3	28.4%	2,130
12/10	433.8	107.9	24.9%	1,197
12/09	354.0	89.0	25.2%	1,130
12/08	341.0	97.2	28.5%	0
Annual Growth	20.0%	22.1%	—	—

2012 Year-End Financials

Debt ratio: 23.7%	No. of shares (mil.): 81
Return on equity: 24.9%	Dividends
Cash ($ mil.): 283	Yield: —
Current ratio: 1.05	Payout: —
Long-term debt ($ mil.): 485	Market value ($ mil.): 4,348

	STOCK PRICE ($) FY Close	P/E High/Low		Earnings	PER SHARE ($) Dividends	Book Value
12/12	53.65	21	12	2.52	0.00	11.28
12/11	29.87	20	14	1.76	0.00	9.91
12/10	30.92	10	9	1.34	0.00	7.86
Annual Growth	31.7%	—	— 37.1%		— 19.8%	

Flotek Industries Inc

Flotek Industries works to keep oil and gas flowing. The company provides the chemicals and logistical services required in the cementing and stimulation of oil and gas wells. (Cementing holds well casings in place; stimulation opens up cracks in the earth to allow for the easier flow of oil.) Flotek also provides drilling equipment used in cementing and stimulation as well as Petrovalve downhole pump valves (used to pump off the liquids in gas wells in a process known as artificial lift) and Spidle Turbeco (drilling tools motors and casing accessories). The company markets its products throughout the US and is expanding into international markets.

Geographic Reach

The company operates 30 manufacturing and warehouse facilities in eight US states. The US is Flotek's largest single market accounting for 87% of the company's revenue in 2012.

Operations

Flotek operates in three segments: Chemical and Logistics Drilling Products and Artificial Lift. In the Chemical and Logistics segment Specialty Chemicals makes and markets specialty chemicals used in oil and gas well cementing stimulation acidizing drilling and production. The Logistics unit manages automated material handling loading facilities and blending capabilities for oilfield services firms.

The Drilling segment rents inspects makes and markets downhole drilling equipment used in energy mining water well and industrial drilling activities.

Artificial Lift sells artificial lift equipment including rod pump components electric submersible pumps gas separators valves and services that support oil and gas production.

Sales and Marketing

Products are marketed directly to customers through Flotek's own direct sales force and contractual agency arrangements. The company markets products and services through third party agents as well as via direct sales in Asia Canada Central America Mexico the Middle East and South America.

Financial Performance

Flotek's revenues increased by 21% in 2012 due to increased sales to new and existing chemical customers of patented complex nano-fluid? (CnF?) technologies (which increased sales volumes of stimulation additives) and a growth in market share of centralizer products and float equipment. A key driver in the increase of sales was growing customer demand for Flotek's oil tools resulting from the continued shift away from gas-focused drilling in North America to oil-directed drilling in response to low gas prices.

Net income grew by 88% in 2012 primarily due to higher sales a gain on the disposal of long-lived assets and increased interest expense.

With the exception of a recession-driven revenue slump in 2009 Flotek saw an upward trend in revenues from 2008 to 2012.

Strategy

With a eye towards growing its position as a global provider of oilfield specialty chemicals and logistics drilling and production tools to the energy and mining industries Flotek seeks to expand into new geographic markets and keep offering innovative products.

In 2013 the company signed a Letter of Intent with an affiliate of Gulf Energy LLC a leading Oman-based diversified oil and gas entity to build an advanced oilfield chemistry production plant and create a modern research and development organization to address the growing need for advanced oilfield chemistry and analysis in the Middle East and North Africa.

In 2011 Flotek introduced a hydraulic fracturing chemical (in strong demand in the burgeoning shale oil and gas developments across the US) that replaces traditional chemicals with an extract from orange peels turning the toxins/water mixture into a sweet-smelling blend.

Growing its international profile in 2011 Flotek chemicals were used in unconventional gas completions in France Poland and Turkey.

EXECUTIVES

Chairman President Chief Executive Officer, Jerry D. Dumas Sr., age 78

Technology Director, Glenn S. Penny, age 63

President, John W. Chisholm, age 58

Executive Vice President - Operations, Steven A. (Steve) Reeves, age 62, $331,549 total compensation

VP and Treasurer, Glenn Neslony

President of the Chemical and Logistics segment of Flotek, Todd Sanner

VP Sales and Marketing CESI Chemical, Richard Fox

President Downhole Tool Group, Randy Merritt

VP Sales Downhole Tool Group, Beth Thibodeaux

Vice-President of Chemical Technology, Keith Dismuke

EVP Global Business Development, Kevin Fisher

EVP and CFO, H. Richard Walton

Director, Richard O. (Dick) Wilson, age 82

Director, John S. Reiland, age 63

Director, Kenneth T. Hern, age 75

Director, L. V. (Bud) McGuire, age 70

Director, L. Melvin (Mel) Cooper, age 58

Auditors: UHYLLP

LOCATIONS

HQ: Flotek Industries Inc.
2930 W. Sam Houston Pkwy. North Ste. 300, Houston TX 77043
Phone: 713-849-9911   **Fax:** 713-896-4511
Web: www.flotekind.com

2012 Sales

	$ mil.	% of total
US	272	87
Other countries	39	13
Total	**312**	**100**

PRODUCTS/OPERATIONS

2012 Sales

Chemicals & Logistics	184	59
Drilling Products	116	37
Artificial Lifts	12	4

Selected Products

Specialty Chemicals
  Acidizing cementing and fracturing chemicals for oil and gas wells
Equipment Manufacturing
  Acid pump vehicles
  Bulk material handling facilities contracting
  Cement mixing units
  Hydraulic fracturing blenders
  Nitrogen equipment units
Downhole Equipment
  Downhole pumps valves
  Rigid centralizers
Chemical and Logistics
CESI Chemical
  Stimulation Chemicals
  Cementing Chemicals
  IOR
Sooner Energy Services
  Production Chemicals
  Drilling Chemicals
  Coil Tubing Chemicals
MTI
  Logistics Management
Drilling Products
Teledrift
  Survey & Measurement Drilling Tools
Spidle Turbeco
  Downhole Drilling Tools
  CAVO Drilling Motors
  Casing Accessories
Galleon Turbeco
  Blast Hole Drilling Tools
  Underground
Artificial Lift
Flotek Pump Services
  Electrical Submersible Pumps
  Sucker Rod Pumps
  Oilfield Products
Petrovalve
  Rod Pump Valve
  Traveling Valve
  Cages
  Standing Valve

COMPETITORS

Baker Hughes	Lubrizol
CARBO Ceramics	Nalco Energy Services
Cameron International	Natural Gas Services
Champion Technologies	Schlumberger
FMC Technologies	Weatherford
FTS International	International
GE Oil	

HISTORICAL FINANCIALS

Company Type: Public

Income Statement

FYE: December 31

	REVENUE ($ mil.)	NET INCOME ($ mil.)	NET PROFIT MARGIN	EMPLOYEES
12/12	312.8	49.7	15.9%	405
12/11	258.7	31.4	12.1%	379
12/10	146.9	(43.4)	—	312
12/09	112.5	(50.7)	—	320
12/08	226.0	(31.9)	—	500
Annual Growth	8.5%	—	—	(5.1%)

2012 Year-End Financials

Debt ratio: 14.5%
Return on equity: 42.6%
Cash ($ mil.): 2
Current ratio: 2.29
Long-term debt ($ mil.): 22
No. of shares (mil.): 49
Dividends
  Yield: —
  Payout: —
Market value ($ mil.): 605

	STOCK PRICE ($) FY Close	P/E High/Low		PER SHARE ($) Earnings	Dividends	Book Value
12/12	12.20	14	8	0.97	0.00	3.12
12/11	9.96	18	7	0.56	0.00	1.59
12/10	5.45	—	—	(1.94)	0.00	(0.10)
12/09	1.34	—	—	(2.70)	0.00	1.35
12/08	2.52	—	—	(1.69)	0.00	2.23
Annual Growth	48.3%	—	—	—		8.8%

Fortegra Financial Corp

Fortegra Financial foresees a fortuitous future in specialty insurance. The company's payment protection division offers credit insurance debt protection and warranties under the Life of the South brand to consumer finance firms banks retailers and other lenders; it also operates several car club membership groups. Fortegra Financial's brokerage units (including Bliss & Glennon eReinsure and South Bay Acceptance) provide wholesale placement of insurance and reinsurance policies while its business process outsourcing (BPO) subsidiaries provide billing collections underwriting and call center management services for insurers.

The company completed an IPO in late 2010. At that time Fortegra's majority owner investment firm Summit Partners reduced its stake in the firm from 88% to about 62%. Fortegra Financial used net proceeds from its public offering (about $43 million) to redeem shares of preferred stock and pay down debt and credit obligations.

Fortegra Financial's payment protection segment is its largest revenue generator. The division's Life of the South policies essentially protect consumer lenders from borrowers unable to repay debt; it also allows lenders to offer protection policies to consumers. Life of the South is a leading provider of credit life insurance where a person's debts are paid off upon death. The wholesale brokerage segment —which includes the Bliss & Glennon (a top 20 US wholesaler) eReinsure and South Bay Acceptance subsidiaries —enables retail agents to sell various specialty commercial policies to consumers. The smaller BPO division includes the Consecta and Pacific Benefits Group (PBG) units.

In 2011 Fortegra Financial increased revenues by 10% to $225 million largely due to higher premiums commissions and fees earned within the payment protection and brokerage segments. The jump was primarily related to acquisitions conducted in 2010 and 2011. However net income decreased that year by 10% to $14 million due to higher operating costs including personnel costs and other acquisition-related expenses.

Over the years Fortegra Financial has diversified and expanded its offerings through acquisitions especially in its wholesale brokerage and payment protection segments. It expanded its auto-related payment protection services by acquiring new car clubs (United Motor and Auto Knight) in both 2010 and 2011 allowing it to provide roadside assistance and car club memberships to consumer finance companies and automobile dealers among others. The brokerage segment also entered the premium finance market in 2010 through the purchase of South Bay Acceptance and it enhanced its online technology offerings through the purchase of eReinsure in 2011.

The company's organic growth strategy is focused on retaining and expanding service provision to existing clients while at the same time adding new clients in established and exploratory geographic markets. Fortegra's operating model allows it to establish long-term client relationships by deploying its technologies within client systems and providing value-added services to its clients' respective customers a model that the company hopes will help it increase recurring transaction volumes.

Fortegra Financial was incorporated in 1981 as a provider of credit life and disability insurance for financial institutions primarily small community banks in Georgia. Summit Partners acquired more than 90% of the company in 2007; Summit currently owns a 62% stake.

EXECUTIVES

Executive Vice President and President - Motor Clubs, W. Dale Bullard, age 54, $264,807 total compensation

EVP and President Consecta, Robert S. Fullington, age 66, $264,807 total compensation

EVP and President Bliss & Glennon, Daniel A. Reppert, age 53, $259,615 total compensation

Executive Vice President; President - Payment Protection, Joseph R. McCaw, age 61

SVP Corporate Development, Paul S. Romano, age 53

SVP General Counsel and Secretary, John G. Short, age 50

EVP Universal Equipment Recovery Group, Chris Kinnett

Chairman CEO of Fortegra Financial, Richard S. Kalbaugh

Chief Financial Officer; Executive Vice President, Walter P. Mascherin

Senior Vice President General Counsel Secretary, Christopher Romaine

Senior Vice President of Human Resources, Melissa Circelli

Director, Francis M. (Frank) Colalucci, age 68
Director, Frank P. Filipps, age 66
Director, John R. Carroll, age 45
Director, J.J. Kardwell, age 37
Director, Ted W. Rollins, age 50

LOCATIONS

HQ: Fortegra Financial Corporation
100 W. Bay St., Jacksonville FL 32202
Phone: 866-961-9529   **Fax:** 201-818-0807
Web: www.dohertyinc.com

PRODUCTS/OPERATIONS

2011 Sales

	$ mil.	% of total
Operating segments		
Payment protection	60	27
Brokerage	37	16
BPO	15	7
Commissions	74	33
Other	38	17
Total	**225**	**100**

Selected Acquisitions

2011
   Auto Knight Motor Club Inc. (Palm Springs California; motor club membership and service plans in US and Canada)
   eReinsure.com Inc. (web-hosted applications for reinsurance broker/customer transactions)
   Magna Insurance Company (credit annuity and mortgage life insurance policies)
   Pacific Benefits Group Northwest LLC (PBG; Beaverton Oregon; health & life insurance agency in 40 states)
2010
   Continental Car Club (payment protection entry into roadside assistance market)
   South Bay Acceptance Corporation (wholesale brokerage entry into premium finance market)
   United Motor Club (car club in Kentucky)
2009
   Bliss & Glennon (market entry into wholesale brokerage business)

Selected Products and Services

Payment protection
   Accidental death and dismemberment
   Captive reinsurance management
   Car club membership
   Collateral protection
   Credit life and disability
   Credit property
   Debt cancellation
   Involuntary unemployment
   Policy and claims administration
   Policy tracking
   Single interest auto
   Training in products sales and compliance
   Transition management
   Warranty and extended service plans
Wholesale brokerage
   Casualty
   Commercial property
   Construction
   Environmental and pollution
   Personal lines
   Premium finance
   Professional and management liability
   Transportation
BPO
   Asset recovery and commercial collections
   Billing and premium processing
   Campaign execution
   Claims and benefit adjudication
   Commissions processing and recoupment
   Customer care and support
   Customer communications
   Enrollment and new business processing
   Marketing consulting
   Reporting and business intelligence
   Statistical modeling and segmentation

COMPETITORS

Alliant	Coface
AmWINS Group	Computer Sciences
American Modern	Corp.
Insurance	Euler Hermes
Aon	Gallagher
Assurant	Investors Heritage
Asurion	Marsh & McLennan
BB&T	Service Group
BMI Financial Group	Swett & Crawford
Brown & Brown	Unisys
CSO	Willis Group Holdings

HISTORICAL FINANCIALS

Company Type: Public

Income Statement

FYE: December 31

	REVENUE ($ mil.)	NET INCOME ($ mil.)	NET PROFIT MARGIN	EMPLOYEES
12/12	291.6	15.1	5.2%	700
12/11	225.3	14.5	6.4%	545
12/10	204.2	16.2	7.9%	460
12/09	186.1	11.5	6.2%	447
12/08	167.0	8.0	4.8%	0
Annual Growth	**14.9%**	**17.2%**	**—**	**—**

2012 Year-End Financials

Debt ratio: 12.2%	No. of shares (mil.): 19
Return on equity: 11.1%	Dividends
Cash ($ mil.): 15	Yield: —
Current ratio: 2.38	Payout: —
Long-term debt ($ mil.): 89	Market value ($ mil.): 175

	STOCK PRICE ($) FY Close	P/E High/Low		PER SHARE ($) Earnings	Dividends	Book Value
12/12	8.89	12	8	0.74	0.00	7.13
12/11	6.68	17	7	0.68	0.00	6.57
12/10	11.05	11	11	0.94	0.00	6.09
Annual Growth	**(10.3%)**	**—**	**—**	**(11.3%)**	**—**	**8.2%**

Fortinet Inc

Fortinet secures the fortress against Internet marauders. The company makes network security appliances (sold under its FortiGate line) and software that integrate antivirus firewall content filtering intrusion prevention systems (IPS) and anti-spam functions to protect against computer viruses worms and inappropriate Web content. Its Forti-Guard subscription services offer continuous updates on all new threats to provide real-time network protection. The company also offers complementary products that include its FortiManager security management and FortiAnalyzer event analysis systems.

Geographic Reach

Fortinet's largest geographic segment is the Americas which accounts for about 40% of revenues. The EMEA (Europe Middle East and Africa) segment accounts for about 35% of sales while the Asia/Pacific region accounts for the remainder. The company operates sales and service offices in about 30 countries worldwide.

Operations

While service revenues –an important source of recurring income –account for a little more than half of sales product revenues have taken an increasingly important place in Fortinet's earnings as well. The company's products and services are used by companies in a variety of industrise including retail education telecom health care manufacturing and financial services.

Sales and Marketing

Through more than 10000 channel partners (distributors and resellers) Fortinet estimates that it has shipped more than 1.1 million appliances to 150000 end-user customers (including small businesses enterprises government entities and service providers) from its inception through the end of 2012. The company directly sells its products to distributors including Arrow Electronics Ingram Micro and Tech Data.

Financial Performance

Fortinet has experienced exponential revenue growth in recent years due to increased sales within its services and product segments. A 23% increase in revenues to $534 million in 2012 was driven by higher sales of the FortiGate products due to increased demand from small businesses large enterprises and service providers. Service revenues also increased due to Fortinet's larger customer base for subscription and support contracts.

Fortinet which first achieved profitability in 2008 has grown net income alongside revenues in the year since. Profits in 2012 increased 7% to $67 million on higher revenues and interest income.

Strategy

Fortinet sells its products to distributors and resellers who have significant purchasing power and deployment capabilities while at the same time strengthening its customer support network in high-growth regions. It also works to build a solid base of subscription and service customers.

In addition to expand its product offerings Fortinet conducts research and development efforts to create new software and hardware offerings for customers. The company employs about 600 R&D employees in Canada China and the US and spends some $80 million annually on research projects.

Mergers and Acquisitions

Fortinet acquired enterprise Internet telephony systems maker TalkSwitch in 2011 to expand its product selection and boost its profile in the multiservice gateway market. The company also extended the reach of its sales organization with the purchase; TalkSwitch has relationships with resellers and distributors worldwide. Past acquisitions included the purchase of the assets of IPLocks in 2008 a deal that expanded Fortinet's database security and compliance technologies.

Ownership

Fortinet was founded in 2000 by CEO Ken Xie who also founded leading firewall appliance provider NetScreen Technologies (acquired in 2004 by Juniper Networks). Xie holds an equity stake of nearly 16% in the company. CTO Michael Xie a co-founder of Fortinet and Ken Xie's younger brother owns about 11% of the company.

Fortinet used the proceeds from a 2009 IPO for general corporate purposes product development and to pursue potential acquisitions.

EXECUTIVES

Chairman, John L. Walecka, age 53
COO and CFO, Ahmed Rubaie, age 47
VP Products, Anthony James
Chairman and CEO, Ken Xie, age 50, $319,300 total compensation
President and CTO, Michael Xie, age 44, $283,250 total compensation
VP Americas Sales and Support, Michael Valentine
VP Strategy and New Technology, Jens Andreassen
VP and CFO, Kenneth A. Goldman, age 63, $309,000 total compensation
VP Corporate Development Strategic Alliances General Counsel and Corporate Secretary, John Whittle, age 45, $252,000 total compensation
VP Marketing, John Maddison
Vice President Corporate Communications & Investor Relations, Michelle Spolver
VP Human Resources, Sherry Pulvers
VP International Sales and Support, ɾatrice Perche
VP Channel Sales, Kendra Krause
Media Contacts Americas, Rick Popko

Analyst Contact, Jennifer Leggio
Vice President Product and Solution Management, Hendrik Velde
Senior Director of Information Technology and Facilities, Larry Havlik
Vice President of Sales EMEA, Luca Simonelli
Vice President of product marketing for Fortinet, Patrick Bedwell
Vice President of Federal Operations, Phil Fuster
Vice President of Technology, Cary Westmark
Vice President of Worldwide Corporate Marketing, Gregory S. Fitzgerald
Interim Chief Financial Officer, Nancy Bush
Vice President Americas Sales, Peter Brant
Vice President Human Resources, Amanda Mallow
Vice President Services, Michael Anderson
Director, Pehong Chen, age 56
Director, Christopher B. (Chris) Paisley, age 61
Chairman and CEO, Ken Xie, age 50
Director, Hong Liang Lu, age 57
Director, Greg Myers, age 62
Auditors: Deloitte&ToucheLLP

LOCATIONS

HQ: Fortinet Inc.
1090 Kifer Rd., Sunnyvale CA 94086
Phone: 408-235-7700   **Fax:** 408-235-7737
Web: www.fortinet.com

2012 Sales

	$ mil.	% of total
Americas	217	41
Europe Middle East & Africa (EMEA)	184	34
Asia/Pacific	132	25
Total	**533**	**100**

PRODUCTS/OPERATIONS

2012 Sales

	$ mil.	% of total
Services	274	51
Product	249	47
Ratable & other	10	2
Total	**533**	**100**

Selected Products

Database security appliance (FortiDB)
E-mail antispam (FortiMail)
Endpoint security software (FortiClient)
Endpoint vulnerability management appliance (FortiScan)
Network event correlation and content archiving (FortiAnalyzer)
Network security appliances (FortiGate)
Secure wireless access product (FortiAP)
Security management (FortiManager)
Spam and virus control subscription (FortiGuard)
Support (FortiCare)
Web application firewall appliance (FortiWeb)

COMPETITORS

Bivio Networks	NetWolves
Blue Coat	Palo Alto Networks
CA Inc.	SRA International
Check Point Software	SonicWALL
Cisco Systems	SteelCloud
Crossbeam	Symantec
F5 Networks	Trend Micro
Fortrex	VeriSign
Infoblox	WatchGuard
Juniper Networks	Technologies
McAfee	e-DMZ Security
Microsoft	zvelo

HISTORICAL FINANCIALS

Company Type: Public

Income Statement

FYE: December 31

	REVENUE ($ mil.)	NET INCOME ($ mil.)	NET PROFIT MARGIN	EMPLOYEES
12/12	533.6	66.8	12.5%	1,954
12/11	433.5	62.4	14.4%	1,583
12/10	324.7	41.2	12.7%	1,336
12/09	252.1	60.1	23.9%	1,223
12/08	211.7	7.3	3.5%	1,196
Annual Growth	**26.0%**	**73.6%**	**—**	**13.1%**

2012 Year-End Financials

Debt ratio: —	No. of shares (mil.): 160
Return on equity: 15.3%	Dividends
Cash ($ mil.): 122	Yield: —
Current ratio: 1.78	Payout: —
Long-term debt ($ mil.): —	Market value ($ mil.): 3,371

	STOCK PRICE ($) FY Close	P/E High/Low	PER SHARE ($) Earnings	Dividends	Book Value
12/12	21.02	68 42	0.40	0.00	3.19
12/11	21.81	121 40	0.38	0.00	2.31
12/10	32.35	113 51	0.27	0.00	1.56
12/09	17.57	19 17	0.39	0.00	1.07
Annual Growth	**6.2%**	**— —**	**0.8%**	**—**	**44.0%**

Fortress Investment Group LLC

Fortress Investment Group protects its investments. The global investment firm manages private equity and hedge funds for institutional investors wealthy individuals and on its own behalf. Its private equity arm buys long-term controlling stakes in undervalued or distressed companies and credit assets; it also manages real estate investors Newcastle Investment and Eurocastle Investment. The hedge fund arm invests in liquid markets. Fortress offer traditional asset management through Logan Circle Partners. Fortress earns fees performance-based incentive revenues and investment income on its own investments. The firm has more than $43 billion in assets under management.

Formerly focused solely on alternative investment vehicles Fortress diversified in 2010. It entered the fixed income asset management business when it acquired bond investor Logan Circle Partners. The deal added some $12 billion in assets under management; and allowed Fortress to begin offering its clients a broader range of investments. Now Logan Circle is considered Fortress' traditional asset management arm. It is focused on the organic growth of its existing fixed income business.

Fortress in late 2013 agreed to buy more than 50 senior-housing properties from Holiday Acquisition Holdings for more than $1 billion. It anticipates that rent for the portfolio of 5885 units will equal 6.5% of the purchase price.

In the private equity segment Fortress is known as a garbage collector of sorts; picking up the pieces of companies and assets that no one really wants. Fortress has taken advantage of opportunities to buy bargain assets from troubled firms during the economic downturn. In 2010 alone it purchased the European mortgages and operations of Ally Financial subsidiary ResCap including some 6000 good and bad loans; and about 80% of consumer lender American General Finance from AIG. Fortress also acquired commercial real estate loan servicer CW Financial Services in the hopes of profiting from a recovery in the US real estate market. It then purchased a $7 billion distressed portfolio of life settlement insurance policies from KBC. Fortress is eyeing new investments in the transportation senior living and financial services sectors.

In addition to buying assets Fortress also has been selling. Improvements in the equity markets have allowed Fortress Private Equity to spin off a few of its portfolio companies through IPOS. Nationstar SeaCube Container Leasing and RailAmerica recently entered the public markets. Fortress also has sold its positions in other publicly traded securities as the market improved. The proceeds helped Fortress refinance exisiting debt and obtain other debt financing.

The firm's growth strategy is centered on global expansion. Fortress which was founded in 1998 has 15 offices in North America Europe Australia and Asia. Most recently Fortress has grown in Asia. It has launched new private equity funds there and opened new offices in Singapore and Shanghai.

Fortress weathered the recession and in 2010 it reported strong results thanks to its diversification efforts and improved incentive fee income based on better fund performance. It has been raising capital across all of its funds and in 2011 invested in the regional aircraft asset management operations of defense manufacturer BAE Systems. The deal included 151 regional aircraft and is valued at $187 million.

However market volatility had an impact on Fortress' performance in 2011. Revenues declined by nearly 10% due to lower incentive income and a decrease in other revenues. Profits also declined. But Fortress is focused on the long term. Despite the challenging market the company continued to attract new capital commitments and new clients thanks to its diversified business model. In 2011 Fortress invested more than $3.5 billion on its investors' behalf and began marketing new funds in each of its business lines.

In addition to the challenging market Fortress' walls have been shaken by personnel troubles. Former CEO and board member Daniel Mudd resigned from Fortress in early 2012 while fighting SEC allegations that he'd misled investors during his prior position as CEO of Fannie Mae. The SEC alleged that Mudd hadn't sufficiently disclosed Fannie Mae's risky investments in the subprime market leading up to the housing crash. Mudd had taken the helm of Fortress in 2009 shortly after being ousted from Fannie Mae. Mudd took a leave of absence in late 2011 but stepped down a month later to dedicate his time to the lawsuit.

Fortress' core principals and founders remain at the helm. Co-chairmen Peter Briger and Wesley Edens each own around 13% of the company. Principal and director Michael Novogratz owns more than 12% of Fortress. While interim Interim CEO Randal Nardone and principal and director Robert Kauffman each own about 10%

EXECUTIVES

Principal and Co-Chairman, Wesley R. (Wes) Edens, age 51, $200,000 total compensation

Co-Founder Director, Robert I. Kauffman, age 50, $200,000 total compensation

Principal and Co-Chairman, Peter L. Briger Jr., age 50, $200,000 total compensation

Managing Director Fortress Investment Group LLC Chief Executive Officer and Chief Investment Officer Logan Circle Partners, Jude T. Driscoll, age 49

Managing Director Fortress Investment Group LLC (UK), Jonathan Ashley, age 47

Managing Director Shanghai, Lilly H. Donohue

Chief Executive Officer Co-Founder Principal and Director, Randal A. Nardone, age 58, $200,000 total compensation

Principal and Director; Co-Chief Investment Officer of the Fortress Macro Fund and the Drawbridge Global Macro Fund, Michael E. Novogratz, age 49, $200,000 total compensation

President Liquid Markets; Senior Managing Director Strategy, Stuart H. (Stu) Bohart, age 46

Managing Director Private Equity Group, Joseph P. Adams Jr., age 55

CFO, Daniel N. Bass, age 47, $200,000 total compensation

VP General Counsel and Secretary, David N. Brooks, age 42, $200,000 total compensation

Chief Investment Officer Commodities Funds, Bill Callanan

Managing Director, Adam Levinson

Chief Risk Officer, Hilmar Schaumann

Managing Director Chief Executive Officer and Chief Investment Officer Fortress Partners Funds Fortress Investment Group LLC, Alexander M. Cook

Managing Director Co-Chief Investment Officer of the Credit Funds at Fortress Investment Group LLC, Constantine M. (Dean) Dakolias

Managing Director Private Equity and Chief Operating Officer Permanent Capital Business Group, Andrew P. Dempsey

Managing Director President and Chief Operating Officer Credit Funds at Fortress Investment Group LLC, Marc K. Furstein

Managing Director Capital Formation Group, A. Todd Ladda

Managing Director Singapore and Chief Investment Officer Fortress Asia Macro Funds Co-Chief Investment Officer Fortress Macro Funds and Chief Executive Officer Fortress Investment Group (Singapore) Pte. Ltd., Adam J. Levinson

Managing Director San Francisco, Andrew A. McKnight

Managing Director Tokyo Chief Investment Officer Fortress Real Estate (Asia) GK, Thomas W. Pulley

Managing Director Deputy President and Chief Risk Officer Fortress Liquid Markets, Sherif Sweillam

Managing Director Global Chief Operating Officer Liquid Markets Hedge Fund, Louis D. Thorne

Managing Director Credit Funds, Anthony B. Tufariello

Director, Douglas L. Jacobs, age 65

Director, Takumi Shibata, age 61

Principal and Co-Chairman, Wesley R. (Wes) Edens, age 51

Co-Founder Director, Robert I. Kauffman, age 50

Principal and Co-Chairman, Peter L. Briger Jr., age 50

Independent Director, Richard N. Haass, age 60

Chief Executive Officer Co-Founder Principal and Director, Randal A. Nardone, age 58

Principal and Director; Co-Chief Investment Officer of the Fortress Macro Fund and the Drawbridge Global Macro Fund, Michael E. Novogratz, age 49

Director, George W. Wellde, age 60

Director, David Berry

Independent Director, David Barry

Auditors: Ernst&YoungLLP

LOCATIONS

HQ: Fortress Investment Group LLC
1345 Avenue of the Americas, New York NY 10105
Phone: 212-798-6100   **Fax:** 309-346-0742
Web: www.aventinerei.com

PRODUCTS/OPERATIONS

2012 Sales

Management fees	501	52
Expense reimbursements from affiliates	189	19
Total	**969**	**100**

COMPETITORS

American Capital	Investcorp
Apollo Investment	PineBridge Investments
Bessemer Trust	RREEF Funds
Blackstone Group	Schroders
Integrated Asset Management	Soros Fund Management

HISTORICAL FINANCIALS

Company Type: Public

Income Statement

FYE: December 31

	ASSETS ($ mil.)	NET INCOME ($ mil.)	INCOME AS % OF ASSETS	EMPLOYEES
12/12	2,161.4	78.2	3.6%	1,996
12/11	2,220.6	(431.5)	—	979
12/10	2,076.7	(284.6)	—	900
12/09	1,660.2	(254.6)	—	819
12/08	1,577.7	(322.2)	—	850
Annual Growth	**8.2%**	—	—	**23.8%**

	STOCK PRICE ($) FY Close	P/E High/Low		Earnings	PER SHARE ($) Dividends	Book Value
12/12	4.39	16	10	0.27	0.20	1.35
12/11	3.38	—	—	(2.36)	0.00	0.98
12/10	5.70	—	—	(1.83)	0.00	0.88
12/09	4.45	—	—	(2.08)	0.00	0.58
12/08	1.00	—	—	(3.50)	0.68	0.20
Annual Growth	**44.7%**	—	—	—	**(26.2%)**	**60.4%**

Forum Energy Technologies Inc

There is a proper forum for everything; for oil and natural gas drilling and control equipment it would be Forum Energy Technologies. The company designs makes and sells equipment for global customers including drilling contractors oilfield service businesses equipment rental companies and assemblers of drilling and well servicing equipment. Drilling products include tubular handling equipment and drilling data-management systems. Flow control products include expendable fluid end-components for mud and centrifugal pumps valves choke and kill manifolds and pressure control equipment. It also makes remote operating vehicles (ROVs) for subsea work.

IPO

Forum Energy Technologies went public in 2012 raising $258 million to pay down debt. Concurrently with the IPO Company sold 2.7 million shares of stock in a private placement to Tinicum L.P. a private equity fund for $50 million. Prior to the conclusion of the IPO L. E. Simmons controlled 75% of Forum Energy Technologies through investment entity SCF Partners. Following the IPO it held 47% through SCF-V L.P. and related entities.

Geographic Reach

A global player Forum Energy Technologies has manufacturing operations in Texas. It has sales and distribution centers in the US and Canada as well in Singapore the UAE and the UK. It also has regional representative offices in Chile Colombia Mexico and Peru.

The US accounted for 63% of the company's revenues in 2012; Europe & Africa 14%.

Operations

The company operates in two segments: Drilling and Subsea (drilling subsea and well construction completion and intervention product design and manufacture and related services); and Production and Infrastructure (the provision of equipment and services to the well stimulation completion production and infrastructure markets).

Financial Performance

Forum Energy Technologies' revenues increased by 25% in 2012 largely due to a Drilling and Subsea revenues jump of 25% as a result of increased sales of hydraulic catwalk units and blowout preventers (Drilling Technologies product line) and higher sales of ROVs in the Subsea Technologies product line. Production and Infrastructure revenues grew by 26% due to higher market demand for production equipment and valves as well as because of orders from new customers. The 2011 expansion of existing facilities and the addition of new facilities in Pennsylvania enabled higher shipments in the Production Equipment segment in 2012. Net income increased by 62% in 2012 thanks to higher revenues and decreased interest expenses due to lower debt levels as a result of repaying a portion of Forum Energy Technologies' debt from the net proceeds of the IPO and concurrent private placement.With the exception of 2009 when the global economic recession stymied demand and caused revenues to slump the company saw an upward trend in revenues from 2008 to 2012.

Strategy

The company has forged a strategy centered on acquiring complementary companies to enable its its ability to supply both expendable drilling products and capital products for the drilling rig refurbishment market to a global client base.

In 2013 Forum Energy Technologies' signed deals with Helix Energy Solutions Group's Canyon Offshore subsea robotics business unit to supply it with a PerryTM XT1500 Trenching system and two PerryTM XLX 200HP ROVs.In 2012 it signed a deal with Technip Odebrecht PLSV CV to supply that company with four PerryTM XLX Generation 2 150 horsepower ROVs.

Boosting its subsea assets in 2012 Forum Energy Technologies acquired Syntech Technology Inc. a Virgina-based manufacturer of syntactic foam buoyancy materials used for ROVs and other deepwater flotation applications and Dynacon Inc. a Bryan Texas-based provider of launch and recovery systems used for the deployment of ROVs and specialized cable and umbilical handling equip-

ment. (In 2011 it acquired UK-based Specialist ROV Tooling Services Ltd. a provider of intervention tooling and custom engineered products).

Expanding its production and infrastructure portfolio in 2012 the company acquired Texas-based Wireline Solutions LLC a manufacturer of downhole completion tools including composite plugs used for plug perforate and fracture applications and wireline flow control products and Merrimac Manufacturing Inc. a maker of consumable parts for drilling well servicing and pressure pumping applications including mud pump parts power swivel parts and valves and seats for hydraulic fracturing pumps. In 2011 it acquired high pressure flow control equipment maker Phoinix Global.

Moving into the downhole product market in 2011 the company acquired downhole completion control lines and cable protection systems maker Cannon Services and SVP Products a provider of high-pressure flow control equipment for oil and gas wells. In a related move that year it acquired downhole cementing and casing products maker Davis-Lynch.Other accretive purchases in 2011 included Wood Flowline Products LLC (pressure control and flow equipment products) base in Oklahoma and Arkansas; and UK-based AMC Global Group Ltd. (specialized torque equipment for tubular connections) and PQuip Ltd. a leading manufacturer of proprietary mud pump fluid end assemblies.

Company Background

Seeking to grow in 2010 Forum Oilfield Technologies merged with a handful of other oilfield equipment and services companies (Subsea Services International Global Flow Technologies Allied Technology all based in Houston and Triton Group of the UK) to form Forum Energy Technologies. The $750 million in annual revenue business is led by former Halliburton executive Chris Gaut who is the managing director of SCF Partners a Houston-based private equity fund that was majority owner of all five companies.

EXECUTIVES

Senior Vice President General Counsel, James L. McCulloch, age 60
Executive Vice President; President - Drilling and Subsea Division, Charles E. (Charlie) Jones, age 54
EVP and President Production and Infrastructure, Wendell R. Brooks, age 63
Senior Vice President and Chief Financial OfficerJames W, James W. Harris, age 54, $171,692 total compensation
Chairman President and CEO, C. Christopher ("Cris) Gaut, age 57
Senior Vice President General Counsel, Jim McCulloch
Director, John A. Carrig, age 61
Director, Michael McShane, age 59
Director, Franklin Myers, age 60
Director, Andrew L. Waite, age 52
Director, Evelyn M. Angelle, age 46
Director, David C. Baldwin, age 50
Director, John Schmitz, age 53
Auditors: PricewaterhouseCoopersLLP

LOCATIONS

HQ: Forum Energy Technologies Inc.
920 Memorial City Way Ste. 800, Houston TX 77024
Phone: 281-949-2500   **Fax:** 281-949-2554
Web: www.f-e-t.com

2012 Sales

	$ mil.	% of total
North America		
US	895	63
Canada	114	8
Europe & Africa	196	14
Asia/Pacific	100	7
Latin America	58	4
Middle East	49	4
Total	**1,414**	**100**

PRODUCTS/OPERATIONS

2012 Sales

	$ mil.	% of total
Drilling & Subsea	826	58
Total	**1,414**	**100**

2012 Sales

	% of total
Drilling	30
Subsea	18
Production	16
Vale	15
Flow	11
Downhole	10
Total	**100**

Selected Mergers and Acquisitions

2012
Syntech Technology Inc. (Virgina; syntactic foam buoyancy materials used for ROVs and other deepwater flotation applications)
Dynacon Inc. (Bryan Texas; launch and recovery systems used for the deployment of ROVs and specialized cable and umbilical handling equipment)
Wireline Solutions LLC (Texas; downhole completion tools including composite plugs used for plug perforate and fracture applications and wireline flow control products)
2011
Specialist ROV Tooling Services Ltd (UK; intervention tools and custom engineered products)
Cannon Services (downhole completion control lines and cable protection systems)
Wood Flowline Products LLC (pressure control and flow equipment products)
AMC Global Group Ltd. (UK; specialized torque equipment for tubular connections).

COMPETITORS

Cameron International	Halliburton
Canrig Drilling	National Oilwell Varco
Technology	Pason Systems
Double Life	Schlumberger
Exterran	Weatherford
FMC Technologies	International
Fugro	Weir SPM

HISTORICAL FINANCIALS

Company Type: Public

Income Statement

FYE: December 31

	REVENUE ($ mil.)	NET INCOME ($ mil.)	NET PROFIT MARGIN	EMPLOYEES
12/12	1,414.9	151.4	10.7%	3,400
12/11	1,128.1	93.3	8.3%	3,150
12/10	747.3	23.9	3.2%	0
12/09	677.3	19.3	2.9%	0
Annual Growth	27.8%	98.6%	—	—

2012 Year-End Financials

Debt ratio: 22.2%	No. of shares (mil.): 84
Return on equity: 16.6%	Dividends
Cash ($ mil.): 41	Yield: —
Current ratio: 2.76	Payout: —
Long-term debt ($ mil.): 400	Market value ($ mil.): 2,083

	STOCK PRICE ($) FY Close	P/E High/Low	PER SHARE ($) Earnings	Dividends	Book Value
12/12	24.75	14 10	1.74	0.00	13.80
12/11	0.00	— —	1.38	0.00	9.63
Annual Growth	—	— —	26.1%	—	43.3%

Franklin Covey Co.

Franklin Covey publisher of the popular book The 7 Habits of Highly Effective People knows a thing or two about performance improvement. Targeted at individuals teams and organizations the company is a global provider of training programs consulting services books and planning products designed around seven practice areas: leadership productivity trust execution sales performance education and customer loyalty. Franklin Covey's more than 4200 clients include about 90% of the FORTUNE 100 75% of the FORTUNE 500 and thousands of small and midsized businesses. In addition to companies it serves government entities and educational institutions mostly in the US.

Geographic Reach

Franklin Covey has some 46 direct and licensee offices providing professional services in more than 140 countries. It has subsidiaries in Australia Japan and the UK.

Operations

The company delivers its services and products through professional Franklin Covey consultants that offer training on site at client locations. Client employees that have received specialized training can also deliver content as certified Franklin Covey facilitators. The company additionally provides its services through international licensees public workshops and a series of online offerings.

Financial Performance

In 2011 the firm reported revenue of $160.8 million a 17% increase over the $137 million it earned in 2010. Revenue increases were the result of higher sales across all key channels and practices. Franklin Covey's net income also grew to $4.8 million compared with a net loss of $0.5 million in fiscal 2010. Net income benefited from a decrease in the effective tax rate from 210% in fiscal 2010 to 43% in fiscal 2011 primarily due to foreign tax credits it received in 2011.

Strategy

The company continues to expand its offerings beyond its flagship 7 Habits of Highly Effective People introducing new programs in order to boost sales. In 2011 it launched "5 Choices to Extraordinary Productivity" and The 3rd Alternative: Solving Life's Most Difficult Problems. Also that year it signed an agreement with Simon and Schuster for a new book based on the Four Disciplines. (The book The 4 Disciplines of Execution is a companion work to 7 Habits focusing on the execution process of that program.)

Mergers and Acquisitions

In March 2013 Franklin Covey acquired Florida-based NinetyFive 5 LLC adding its Sales Enablement Consulting and Coaching Execution System (SUCCESS) which includes a subscription-based online tool set sales coaching and live and virtual training to Franklin Covey's Sales Performance Practice —doubling that business' size. The deal also brings NinetyFive 5's social media assets a cloud-based learning practice and execution platform called 5 Online and a client base of FORTUNE 1000 companies.

Ownership

Donald McNamara a director on the company's board owns a 27% stake in Franklin Covey. Private equity firm The Hampstead Group LLC of which McNamara is the founder and principal controls another 26% of the company.

HISTORY

Hyrum Smith a former insurance agent founded H.W. Smith and Associates in 1982 to give time-management seminars. With help from Dennis Webb the business became the Franklin Institute (named after efficiency proponent Benjamin Franklin) in 1983. The next year it introduced the Franklin Day Planner. The company was renamed Franklin Quest and went public in 1992. It added new product lines through acquisitions including Productivity Plus (planning materials for military customers) and TrueNorth (corporate training) in 1996 and Premier Agendas (planners for students) in 1997.

That year Franklin Quest acquired Covey Leadership Center for $160 million. Stephen Covey a former professor at Brigham Young University formed his company in 1980. He wrote best-seller "The 7 Habits of Highly Effective People" in 1989 and followed it up with "The 7 Habits of Highly Effective Families" in 1997.

Renamed Franklin Covey Co. in 1998 the company dropped its fitness seminars teamed up with planner competitor At-A-Glance to sell products directly to employers and began a short-lived unsuccessful attempt at selling products through retail giant Office Depot.

Jon Rowberry named CEO in 1998 left the company just 15 months later as it struggled to integrate the operations of Franklin Quest and Covey Leadership Center. Robert Whitman became chairman in 1999 when Franklin Covey sold $75 million in stock to his Dallas investment company; Franklin Covey earmarked the proceeds for online ventures and acquisitions. Under Whitman Franklin Covey cut about 600 jobs and shut its Provo Utah office taking a restructuring charge of $16.3 million for fiscal 1999.

Whitman became CEO in 2000. Also that year the company simplified its product lines eliminating thousands of redundant offerings and sold its commercial printing division. In 2001 Franklin Covey sold its Premier Agendas and Premier School Agendas subsidiaries to School Specialty. In 2002 Mellon Financial's HQ Solutions group acquired a Franklin Covey unit that provides outsourced training operations. Also that year the company discontinued its online planning services unit (FranklinPlanner.com) and terminated a joint venture (Franklin Covey Coaching).

Continuing its strategy of closing unprofitable operations the company shuttered 22 US and 10 international retail stores during 2003 about 20 in 2004 and another 30 in 2005.

Wanting to focus on its consulting and training side of the business Franklin Covey sold its unprofitable Consumer Solutions business (including about 90 stores catalogs a website and licensed operations) to Peterson Partners in 2008 for $32 million. Peterson Partners controls the consumer business now called Franklin Covey Products while Franklin Covey retained a 20% stake.

EXECUTIVES

Vice Chairman, Stephen R. Covey, age 81

Chief Financial Officer; EVP - Finance; Chief Accounting Officer; Corporate Secretary, Stephen D. (Steve) Young, age 59, $250,000 total compensation

EVP Global Solutions and Partnerships Practice Leader Education and Chief Innovation Officer, M. Sean Covey, age 49, $270,000 total compensation

Executive Vice President Chief People & Operations Officer, C. Todd Davis, age 55

Executive Vice President - Operations, Colleen Dom

Vice President Global Sales, Peter Kasic

Corporate Controller, Derek Hatch

President General Manager, Brian Martini

Executive Vice President - Global Sales and Delivery, Shawn D. Moon, age 45, $250,000 total compensation

General Manager, Elise Roma

Vice President Global Accounting, Scott Sumsion

Executive Vice President - Business Development and Marketing, Scott Miller

Managing Director, Sandy Rogers

Vice President Global Finance, Boyd Roberts

Head of Corporate and Global Marketing, Curtis J. Morley

Vice Chairman, Stephen R. Covey, age 79

Director, E. Kay Stepp, age 68

Director, Donald J. McNamara, age 60

Director, Dennis G. Heiner, age 70

Director, Robert H. Daines, age 79

Director, Prof Clayton M. Christensen, age 61

Independent Director, Michael Fung

Auditors: KPMGLLP

LOCATIONS

HQ: Franklin Covey Co.
2200 W. Parkway Blvd., Salt Lake City UT 84119-2331
Phone: 801-817-1776　　**Fax:** 801-817-8069
Web: www.franklincovey.com

2011 Sales

	$ mil.	% of total
US & Canada	118	74
International	40	25
Corporate & eliminations	2	1
Total	**160**	**100**

PRODUCTS/OPERATIONS

2011 Sales

	$ mil.	% of total
Training & consulting services	151	94
Leasing	2	1

Selected Programs

Core Program Offerings
　The 7 Habits of Highly Effective People Signature Program
　Leadership: Great Leaders Great Teams Great Results
　FOCUS: Achieving Your Highest Priorities
　The 4 Disciplines of Execution
　The xQ Service

Publications
　The 7 Habits of Highly Effective People by Dr. Stephen R. Covey
　The 8th Habit: From Effectiveness to Greatness by Dr. Stephen R. Covey
　Everyday Greatness by Dr. Stephen R. Covey
　The Ten Natural Laws of Successful Time and Life Management by Hyrum W. Smith
　The 7 Habits of Highly Effective Families by Dr. Stephen R. Covey
　The 7 Habits of Highly Effective Teens by Sean Covey
　The 6 Most Important Decisions You'll Ever Make by Sean Covey
　Principle-Centered Leadership by Dr. Stephen R. Covey
　First Things First by Dr. Stephen R. Covey
　The Power Principle: Influence with Honor by Blaine Lee

COMPETITORS

American Management Association	Maritz
Bain & Company	Mission Control Productivity
Booz Allen	Organizational Dynamics
CCL	
Dale Carnegie	PRTM Management
Development Dimensions International	The Forum Corporation Thomas Group
IIR	Wilson Learning

HISTORICAL FINANCIALS

Company Type: Public

Income Statement

FYE: August 31

	REVENUE ($ mil.)	NET INCOME ($ mil.)	NET PROFIT MARGIN	EMPLOYEES
08/13	190.9	14.3	7.5%	660
08/12	170.4	7.8	4.6%	630
08/11	160.8	4.8	3.0%	590
08/10	136.8	(0.5)	—	600
08/09	130.1	(10.8)	—	600
Annual Growth	**10.1%**	**—**	**—**	**2.4%**

2013 Year-End Financials

Debt ratio: 15.0%
Return on equity: 14.5%
Cash ($ mil.): 12
Current ratio: 1.89
Long-term debt ($ mil.): 27

No. of shares (mil.): 16
Dividends
  Yield: —
  Payout: —
Market value ($ mil.): 256

	STOCK PRICE ($) FY Close	P/E High/Low		Earnings	PER SHARE ($) Dividends	Book Value
08/13	15.71	20	12	0.80	0.00	6.54
08/12	10.35	24	15	0.43	0.00	5.12
08/11	9.52	43	22	0.27	0.00	4.49
08/10	6.10	—	—	(0.04)	0.00	4.17
08/09	5.54	—	—	(0.81)	0.00	4.06
Annual Growth	**29.8%**	**—**	**—**	**—**	**—**	**12.6%**

Franklin Street Properties Corp

A real estate investment trust (REIT) Franklin Street Properties acquires finances leases and manages office properties in about 15 states throughout the US. It owns some 30 properties located mainly in suburban areas and manages about a dozen others; Dallas Denver Houston and Washington DC are its largest markets. The company's FSP Investment unit is an investment bank and brokerage that organizes REITs that invest in single properties and raises equity for them through private placements. Another subsidiary FSP Management manages properties for Franklin Street as well as for some of the REITs sponsored by FSP Investment.

Franklin Street's properties consist of approximately six million sq. ft. of leasable space. The company serves a diverse mix of tenants: financial services firm Capital One oil company CITGO testing equipment maker Tektronix and Burger King are among its largest clients.

Institutional investors and insiders own a majority of Franklin Street's stock.

EXECUTIVES

Executive Vice President Chief Financial Officer, John G. Demeritt, age 52, $204,750 total compensation

CEO President Chairman of the Board, George J. Carter, age 64, $225,000 total compensation

EVP COO Treasurer Secretary and Director; COO FSP Investments, Barbara J. Fournier, age 57, $227,500 total compensation

Executive Vice President Director, Janet Prier Notopoulos, age 65, $193,375 total compensation

Executive Vice President General Counsel Secretary, Scott H. Carter, age 42

Executive Vice President Chief Investment Officer, Jeffrey B. Carter

VP; VP and Regional Director Southeast Asset Management, Leo H. (Toby) Daley

VP; VP and Regional Director West & Southwest Asset Management, John F. Donahue

VP; VP and Regional Director Mountain & Midwest Asset Management, William S. Friend

VP; VP and Regional Director Northeast & Northwest Asset Management, Patricia A. McMullen

Assistant Vice President Director of Investor Services, Georgia Touma

Assistant Vice President Financial Reporting, Yi-Chin Huang

Jr. Vice President, Leo H. Toby

Director, Georgia Murray, age 62

EVP COO Treasurer Secretary and Director; COO FSP Investments, Barbara J. Fournier, age 57

Director, Dennis J. McGillicuddy, age 71

Director, Barry Silverstein, age 81

Director, John N. Burke, age 51

EVP and Director; President FSP Property Management, Janet Prier Notopoulos, age 65

Auditors: Ernst&YoungLLP

LOCATIONS

HQ: Franklin Street Properties Corp
401 Edgewater Place, Suite 200, Wakefield, MA 01880
Phone: 781 557-1300
Web: www.franklinstreetproperties.com

PRODUCTS/OPERATIONS

2009 Sales

	$ mil.	% of total
Rent	122	95
Syndication fees	2	2
Transaction fees	2	2
Other	1	1
Total	**128**	**100**

COMPETITORS

Brandywine Realty	Investors Real Estate Trust
Corporate Office Properties Trust	Liberty Property Trust
Cousins Properties	Washington Real Estate

HISTORICAL FINANCIALS

Company Type: Public

Income Statement

FYE: December 31

	REVENUE ($ mil.)	NET INCOME ($ mil.)	NET PROFIT MARGIN	EMPLOYEES
12/12	162.8	7.6	4.7%	35
12/11	139.4	43.5	31.2%	32
12/10	123.1	22.0	17.9%	42
12/09	128.3	27.8	21.7%	43
12/08	120.4	31.9	26.5%	40
Annual Growth	**7.8%**	**(30.1%)**	**—**	**(3.3%)**

2012 Year-End Financials

Debt ratio: 40.3%
Return on equity: 0.8%
Cash ($ mil.): 21
Current ratio: 1.66
Long-term debt ($ mil.): 616

No. of shares (mil.): 82
Dividends
  Yield: 6.1%
  Payout: 844.4%
Market value ($ mil.): 1,021

	STOCK PRICE ($) FY Close	P/E High/Low		Earnings	PER SHARE ($) Dividends	Book Value
12/12	12.31	137	106	0.09	0.76	10.43
12/11	9.95	29	19	0.53	0.76	11.11
12/10	14.25	56	39	0.28	0.76	11.32
12/09	14.61	40	27	0.38	0.76	11.76
12/08	14.75	36	19	0.45	1.00	12.05
Annual Growth	**(4.4%)**	**—**	**—**	**(33.1%)**	**(6.6%)**	**(3.5%)**

Fresh Market, Inc.

When it comes to food fresh is best. The Fresh Market operates about 150 full-service upscale specialty grocery stores in some 25 US states from Florida to Wisconsin. As the name suggests the chain specializes in perishable goods (two-thirds of sales) including fruits and vegetables meat and seafood. The stores average 21000 square feet about a third to half the size of a conventional supermarket. However customers won't find the non-food items sold in most grocery stores these days such as cleaning and cooking supplies. Founded by husband-and-wife team Ray and Beverly Berry who opened their first store in 1982 The Fresh Market went public in 2010.

IPO

The Berry family and other company officers were the selling shareholders and received all the proceeds from the November 2010 initial public offering which raised about $290 million. With the economy rebounding the Berrys apparently felt it was time to cash out.

Geographic Reach

The fast-growing chain operates grocery stores in 26 states primarily located in the Southeast Midwest Northeast and Mid-Atlantic region. New markets include California and Texas. However established markets Florida North Carolina and Georgia are home to more than half of The Fresh Market's stores.

Sales and Marketing

The Fresh Market spends far less on advertising than its conventional competitors relying primarily on word-of-mouth publicity to attract customers. Indeed the grocery chain reported advertising costs of only $3862 in fiscal 2013 (ended January) or just 0.3% of annual sales up from $2652 in the previous year. In-store marketing activities include cooking classes and demonstrations tours and product demonstrations. It also distributes a weekly online newsletter named "Fresh Idea" to promote new products seasonal produce recipes and weekly specials.

Financial Performance

Fueled by the addition of new stores The Fresh Market's fiscal 2013 (ended January) sales increased 20% versus the prior year to more than $1.3 billion. Net income rose 25% over the same period to about $64 million due to higher sales and decreased interest expanse. Same-store sales at Fresh Market stores increased 6% year over year. Indeed fiscal 2013 marked the fifth consecutive year of rising sales and the second consecutive year of rising profits (since the 2010 IPO).

Strategy

The Fresh Market's recipe for growth is to continue to open stores at a rapid pace in new and existing markets and to increase sales at older stores. Indeed in fiscal 2013 the chain added 16 stores including its first in California and Iowa. In fiscal 2014 it plans to open a record 22 locations. Ultimately management believes the US can support at least 500 of its upscale grocery stores. The Fresh Market is forecasting same-store sales to increase 4% to 6% in the coming year. The chain caters to its affluent customers by offering high-margin specialty foods such as hand-trimmed aged steaks fresh seafood hand-stacked fresh produce and a high level of customer service. Its smaller store footprint gives the retailer more flexibility in picking locations.

Ownership

The investment firms FMR LLC and Wells Fargo & Company each own about 11% of the company's shares. T. Rowe Price Associates owns about 10%. Founder and company chairman Ray Berry and his son vice chairman Brett Berry together own about 7% of the company stock.

EXECUTIVES

Chairman, Ray Berry, age 72
Vice Chairman, Brett Berry, age 46
EVP and CFO, Lisa K. Klinger, age 46
President and CEO, Craig Carlock, age 46
SVP Real Estate and Development, Randy Kelley, age 42
EVP and COO, Sean Crane, age 45
SVP Merchandising and Marketing, Marc Jones, age 41
SVP Human Resources, Matt Argano
Senior Vice President General Counsel, Scott Duggan
EVP and CFO, Jeffrey (Jeff) Ackerman
Vice Chairman, Brett Berry, age 46
Independent Director, Bob Sasser
Independent Director, David Rea
Independent Director, Jeffrey Naylor
Independent Director, Michael Tucci
Independent Director, Richard Noll
Auditors: Ernst&YoungLLP

LOCATIONS

HQ: The Fresh Market Inc.
628 Green Valley Rd. Ste. 500, Greensboro NC 27408-7041
Phone: 336-272-1338   **Fax:** 310-806-4540
Web: www.buzztone.com

2013 Stores

	No.
Florida	31
North	15
Georgia	12
Virginia	8
Illinois	7
Tennessee	7
Ohio	6
Alabama	5
South	5
Indiana	4
Louisiana	4
Maryland	4
Kentucky	3
Pennsylvania	3
Arkansas	2
Connecticut	2
New	2
Wisconsin	2
California	1
Kansas	1
Massachusetts	1

Mississippi	1
New	1
New	1
Oklahoma	1
Total	**129**

PRODUCTS/OPERATIONS

2013 Sales

	% of total
Perishable	66
Nonperishable	34
Total	**100**

COMPETITORS

Earth Fare	Target Corporation
Food Lion	Trader Joe's
Harris Teeter	Wal-Mart
Kroger	Wegmans
Publix	Weis Markets
Safeway	Whole Foods
Sprouts	Winn-Dixie

HISTORICAL FINANCIALS

Company Type: Public

Income Statement

FYE: January 27

	REVENUE ($ mil.)	NET INCOME ($ mil.)	NET PROFIT MARGIN	EMPLOYEES
01/13	1,329.1	64.1	4.8%	10,000
01/12	1,108.0	51.4	4.6%	8,500
01/11*	78.1	2.6	3.4%	7,300
12/10	974.2	22.9	2.4%	7,300
12/09	861.9	49.2	5.7%	7,500
Annual Growth	**11.4%**	**6.9%**	**—**	**7.5%**

*Fiscal year change

2013 Year-End Financials

Debt ratio: 10.9%
Return on equity: 39.6%
Cash ($ mil.): 8
Current ratio: 0.79
Long-term debt ($ mil.): 42

No. of shares (mil.): 48
Dividends
  Yield: —
  Payout: —
Market value ($ mil.): 2,294

	STOCK PRICE ($) FY Close	P/E High/Low	PER SHARE ($) Earnings	Dividends	Book Value
01/13	47.64	47 32	1.33	0.00	4.11
01/12	44.74	43 29	1.07	0.00	2.64
01/11*	36.29	737534	0.06	0.00	1.50
12/10	41.20	92 67	0.48	1.00	1.44
Annual Growth	**5.0%**	**— —**	**40.5%**	**—**	**41.8%**

*Fiscal year change

Full House Resorts, Inc.

When it comes to gaming outside Sin City nothing beats a Full House. Full House Resorts owns Stockman's Casino in Fallon Nevada featuring 260 slot and gaming machines four table games and keno. In addition its Rising Star Casino Resort in Rising Son Indiana includes a riverboat casino with 40000 square feet of gaming space a 200-room hotel a theater and several restaurants. The company also operates the Grand Lodge Casino at the Hyatt Regency Lake Tahoe Resort Spa and Casino

in Incline Village Nevada through a five-year lease agreement with Hyat Hotels Corporationt.

Mergers & Acquisitions

Full House Resorts pursues acquisitions in regional gaming markets and its business has significantly expanded through a few key recent purchases and partnerships. In 2012 the company completed the purchase of the Silver Slipper Casino in Hancock County Mississippi for approximately $70 million.

The previous year Full House acquired the Grand Victoria Casino & Resort in Rising Son Indiana for approximately $19 million in cash and $33 million in credit and subsequently changed the name of Grand Victoria to Rising Star Casino Resort.

Strategy

In 2012 the company sold its interest in the FireKeepers management agreement. Full House had collaborated with a Native American tribe in Battle Creek Michigan to manage the FireKeepers Casino. The property opened in 2009 and included slot machines table games restaurants and lounges. Full House is using a portion of the proceeds from the sale to pay off its remaining outstanding debt.

HISTORY

s

EXECUTIVES

SENIOR Vice President OF OPERATIONS AND PROJECT MANAGEMENT, T. Wesley (Wes) Elam, age 59, $216,295 total compensation
CFO COO Treasurer and Director, Mark J. Miller, age 56, $288,750 total compensation
Chairman and CEO, Andre M. Hilliou, age 65, $288,750 total compensation
Secretary and General Counsel, Barth F. Aaron, age 64
VP Finance, James D. Meier, age 48, $94,583 total compensation
Vice Chairman, Carl G. Braunlich, age 60
VP Development, Jim Dacey
General Manager FireKeepers Casino, R. Bruce McKee
Integrated Corporate Relations, William Schmitt
General Manager, Marie Pierson
Chief Financial Officer, Deborah Pierce
Director, Lee A. Iacocca, age 88
CFO COO Treasurer and Director, Mark J. Miller, age 56
Director, Kathleen M. (Kathy) Caracciolo, age 57
Vice Chairman, Carl G. Braunlich, age 60
Director, Kenneth R (Ken) Adams, age 70
Auditors: PiercyBowlerTaylor&Kern

LOCATIONS

HQ: Full House Resorts Inc.
4670 S. Fort Apache Rd. Ste. 190, Las Vegas NV 89147
Phone: 702-221-7800   **Fax:** 702-221-8101
Web: www.fullhouseresorts.com

COMPETITORS

Boyd Gaming	MGM Resorts
Caesars Entertainment	Mashantucket Pequot
Dover Downs Gaming	Pinnacle Entertainment

HISTORICAL FINANCIALS

Company Type: Public

Income Statement

FYE: December 31

	REVENUE ($ mil.)	NET INCOME ($ mil.)	NET PROFIT MARGIN	EMPLOYEES
12/12	128.7	27.8	21.6%	1,985
12/11	105.4	2.3	2.2%	2,508
12/10	32.9	7.6	23.3%	2,069
12/09	19.0	4.7	25.1%	110
12/08	9.6	1.6	16.7%	106
Annual Growth	91.0%	103.6%	—	108.0%

2012 Year-End Financials

Debt ratio: 42.2%	No. of shares (mil.): 18
Return on equity: 42.2%	Dividends
Cash ($ mil.): 20	Yield: —
Current ratio: 2.11	Payout: —
Long-term debt ($ mil.): 66	Market value ($ mil.): 64

	STOCK PRICE ($) FY Close	P/E High/Low		PER SHARE ($) Earnings	Dividends	Book Value
12/12	3.45	3	2	1.49	0.00	4.34
12/11	2.63	38	18	0.13	0.00	2.69
12/10	3.39	9	6	0.43	0.00	2.62
12/09	3.44	14	3	0.26	0.00	2.19
12/08	1.12	35	13	0.08	0.00	1.91
Annual Growth	32.5%	—	—107.7%		—	22.9%

Fuller (H.B.) Company

H.B. Fuller has stuck with glue for more than a century. Long known for making adhesives sealants and specialty chemicals the company markets its products in some 40 countries. Industrial adhesives are its core product offering and customers include companies in the assembly packaging automotive woodworking and nonwoven textiles industries. Other products include construction materials principally ceramic tile installation products (such as grouts mortars and sealers) and HVAC insulating coatings (duct sealants fungicidal coatings and weather barriers).

HISTORY

In 1887 armed with a wood stove and an iron kettle Harvey Benjamin Fuller Sr. began making wet paste to sell to paperhangers in St. Paul Minnesota. The company became incorporated as the Fuller Manufacturing Company with $600 in capital from three Minneapolis lawyers. It began marketing glue to shoe companies bookbinders and other customers and producing ink for the city's schools. In 1888 Fuller's son Albert joined his father instantly doubling the firm's workforce.

After the 1892 acquisition of competitor Minnesota Paste Company Fuller grew largely through sales spurred by a series of inventions. Fuller's two cold-water products a dry wall cleaner and dry paste proved wildly successful. In 1905 the company was shipping to Australia Germany and the UK. Fuller's son Harvey Jr. joined the company in 1909.

In 1915 Fuller reincorporated as the H.B. Fuller Company. During WWI it supplied adhesives for canned goods shipped to the troops but business fell off after the war. Harvey Sr. died in 1921. Despite facing possible bankruptcy Harvey Jr. made a fateful decision to hire a full-time chemist. With Ray Burgess' inventions the company achieved record sales by the end of the 1920s.

After the stock market crashed Fuller acquired the Selvasize Company makers of a combination wallpaper- and plaster-adhesive. Fuller rode out the Depression with the success of new products such as Ice Proof (a glue resistant to cold water) and Nu-Type Hot Pick-Up (used in automated labeling). However in 1937 the company learned that three salespeople had been undercutting orders through a phantom firm which they then claimed to represent. Fuller's sales dropped almost $50000 the following year. In 1939 Harvey Jr. suffered a stroke.

In 1941 competitor Paisley Products of Chicago offered to buy the company for $50000. Instead Elmer Andersen (a business whiz who had joined the company as a salesman in the mid-1930s) persuaded Harvey to turn the reins over to him and give him a majority stake. WWII began bringing numerous government contracts to the company. During and after the war H.B. Fuller decentralized operations by opening branch plants beginning with Kansas City in 1943. By 1950 H.B. Fuller was the fourth-largest adhesives company in the US.

Andersen went on to become a state senator and eventually governor of Minnesota. Under the leadership of Al Vigard in the 1950s and 1960s the company expanded into Canada Costa Rica Panama and other countries. H.B. Fuller went public in 1968. In 1971 Tony Andersen (Elmer's son) took over and further pushed international sales. From 1971 to 1980 the company made some two dozen acquisitions –about half in foreign countries –and increased sales fivefold. In 1980 Andersen began revamping the company which had become inefficient because of its geographic expansion. By 1985 earnings were solid again.

In 1991 the company suffered adverse publicity after social activists accused it of marketing its Resistol glue in Latin America while knowing that street kids were sniffing the glue. In 1997 H.B. Fuller entered a joint venture with Switzerland's EMS-Chemie Holding AG to combine their automotive coatings sealants and adhesives businesses. CEO Walter Kissing whose efforts to reduce costs in the 1990s failed to improve margins retired in 1998.

The next year Andersen retired as chairman and Al Stroucken a former Bayer executive took the helm. Stroucken quickly announced a restructuring that would reduce the company's plant operations and lay off 10% of its workforce. From 2001-2003 the company eliminated 20% of its manufacturing plants and cut more than 550 employees. It restructured its adhesives business which was run through four geographic regions into one global unit. The company also reduced its product offerings by half allowing it to deliver products on time more consistently.

While H.B. Fuller did increase sales in 2003 over the previous year that improvement was due mainly to the weakened dollar (against the Euro and other foreign currencies) and the resulting exchange differences. Sales volume decreased as did prices. Revenues increased again in 2004 partly due to the same trend; however the company also benefited from the increased sales volume of global adhesives and specialty products and from its February 2004 acquisition of the adhesives business of Portugese chemical firm Probos.

Due to accounting irregularities during 1999 through 2004 H.B. Fuller conducted an internal investigation into the finances of its Chilean operations in 2005. As a result the company made minor adjustments in its 2004 financial statements.

Also in 2005 the firm combined its Chinese and Japanese adhesives businesses with those of Sekisui Chemical through joint ventures. Three years later H.B. Fuller acquired a business in Egypt called Egymelt to establish a presence in North Africa.

The company reorganized its business segments in 2007. H.B. Fuller rearranged its operations along geographic lines merging the former Global Adhesives and Full Valu/Specialty segments into regional operations. The new segments are Asia/Pacific Europe Latin America and North America. The move followed a gradual coming-together of the company's product groups. Fuller had worked to make its adhesive products more specialized and less of a commodity.

Jim Owens was named president and CEO of H.B. Fuller in 2010. He replaced Michele Volpi who resigned from the company. Owens was previously SVP of H.B. Fullers' Americas operations.

EXECUTIVES

EVP and CFO, James R. (Jim) Giertz, age 56, $428,095 total compensation
Chairman, Lee R. Mitau, age 65
VP and Corporate Controller, James C. (Jim) McCreary Jr., age 56, $277,980 total compensation
VP General Counsel and Corporate Secretary, Timothy J. (Tim) Keenan, age 55, $257,801 total compensation
VP Global Operations, Kevin M. Gilligan, age 47
VP and Treasurer, Cheryl A. Reinitz, age 53
VP Human Resources, Ann B. Parriott, age 54, $322,331 total compensation
Vice President; Asia Pacific, Joan A. Schuller
President and CEO, James J. (Jim) Owens, age 49, $419,130 total compensation
SVP EMEA and India, Steven Kenny, age 52
SVP Construction Materials, Pat Trippel
SVP Americas Adhesives, Traci L. Jensen
Chairman of the Board; President; Chief Executive Officer, John Stuart
Chief Financial Officer; Treasurer; Secretary, William Vastardis
SVP Market Development, Patrick J. (Pat) Trippel, age 53
VP Asia, Heather Campe
Director, J. Michael (Mike) Losh, age 66
Director, John C. van Roden Jr., age 63
Director, R. William Van Sant, age 73
Director, Alfredo L. Rovira, age 67
Director, Thomas W. Handley
Director, Juliana L. Chugg, age 45
President CEO and Director, James J. (Jim) Owens, age 47
Independent Director, Edward Cohen
Independent Director, Thomas Ortwein
Independent Director, Dante Parrini
Independent Director, John Roden
Independent Director, William Sant
Auditors: KPMGLLP

LOCATIONS

HQ: H.B. Fuller Company
1200 Willow Lake Blvd., St. Paul MN 55110-5101
Phone: 651-236-5900   **Fax:** 205-969-3543
Web: www.healthsouth.com

2012 Sales

	$ mil.	% of total
US	802	43
Other countries	1,083	57
Total	**1,886**	**100**

PRODUCTS/OPERATIONS

2012 Sales

North America Adhesives	683	36
Asia/Pacific	228	12
Construction Products	147	8
Total	**1,886**	**100**

Markets and Applicatio
Packaging
Building and Constructi
Paper Converting
Woodworking Adhesives
General Assembly Adhesives and Laminates
Personal Hygiene and Nonwovens
Tile and Floor Adhesive Products
Polymers
Adhesive Technologi
H.B. Fuller Hot Melt Technology
H.B. Fuller Solvent-Based Technology
H.B. Fuller Urethane's Epoxies and other Reactive Chemistrie
H.B. Fuller Water-Based Adhesive Technology
Innovative Solutions
Advantra Encore Packaging Adhesive
New Liquamelt packaging adhesive system
New Flextra Quiet flexible packaging adhesive
Patent Informatio
Flextra Fast Solventless Laminating Adhesive System
PlyABLE Adhesive
Performance Products
Products: Liquamelt Packaging Adhesive System
Products: Advantra Encore
Products: Advantra
Brands and Affiliates
Advantra Encore
Advantra
Clarity
Clean Melt
Flextra
Full-Care
Liquamelt
LiquiLoc
Rakoll
Rapidex

COMPETITORS

3M	Henkel
ADCO Global	SABIC Innovative
ADM Tronics	Plastics
Akzo Nobel	Sherwin-Williams
Bostik	Super Glue
Cytec	Valspar
Dow Corning	

HISTORICAL FINANCIALS

Company Type: Public

Income Statement

FYE: November 30

	REVENUE ($ mil.)	NET INCOME ($ mil.)	NET PROFIT MARGIN	EMPLOYEES
11/13*	2,046.9	96.7	4.7%	3,700
12/12	1,886.2	125.6	6.7%	3,700
12/11	1,557.5	89.1	5.7%	3,500
11/10	1,356.1	70.8	5.2%	3,300
11/09	1,234.6	83.6	6.8%	3,100
Annual Growth	**13.5%**	**3.7%**	**—**	**4.5%**

*Fiscal year change

2013 Year-End Financials

Debt ratio: 26.3%
Return on equity: 11.3%
Cash ($ mil.): 155
Current ratio: 2.20
Long-term debt ($ mil.): 472

No. of shares (mil.): 50
Dividends
  Yield: 0.0%
  Payout: 20.3%
Market value ($ mil.): 2,573

STOCK PRICE ($) FY Close	P/E High/Low		PER SHARE ($) Earnings	Dividends	Book Value
11/13*	51.23	26	17	1.89	0.39	18.52
12/12	32.85	13	8	2.48	0.33	15.60
12/11	22.37	14	9	1.79	0.30	14.26
11/10	21.07	17	13	1.43	0.28	12.85
11/09	20.19	13	6	1.70	0.27	12.15
Annual Growth	**26.2%**	**—**	**—**	**2.7%**	**9.3%**	**11.1%**

*Fiscal year change

FutureFuel Corp

FutureFuel's future may be in biofuels but for now it still relies on chemicals. The company manufactures biodiesel and other biofuels; however its core business is specialty chemicals which include a bleach activator and detergent additives a proprietary herbicide and chlorinated polyolefin adhesion promoters (used in coatings for the automotive industry). It synthesizes custom chemicals for a variety of industries and applications. Selling its products primarily in North America FutureFuel markets to customers that include industrial and consumer goods manufacturers as well as pharmaceutical companies and agribusinesses. It manufactures its biofuels and chemicals at a single plant in Arkansas.

Geographic Reach

Missouri-based FutureFuel has manufacturing plants laboratories an on-site liquid waste treatment site and other infrastructure and a warehouse in Batesville Arkansas. It sells primarily to customers in the US and Mexico.

Operations

FutureFuel divides its operations into two main segments: Biofuels and Chemicals. It splits its Chemicals segment further into Custom Manufacturing and Performance Chemicals (which include its own brands of specialty chemical products).

Its Biofuels segment produces biodiesel from feedstock with high fatty acids. The company which makes its biodiesel from organic products like soybean oil animal lard and cooking oils intends to continue growing its biofuels business by broadening its production and distribution capabilities. In 2011 the company redesigned its production line to achieve a capacity of about 35 million gallons of biodiesel per year. Additional debottlenecking increased the capacity to more than 45 millions gallons per year. The redesigned line enables it to make biodiesel from lower quality and less expensive feedstock. FutureFuels distributes its biofuels as well as its chemical products through its own tanker-truck fleet as well as leased vehicles.

The company's chemical products are used in a range of end uses including agrochemical automotive coatings detergents nutrition photographic imaging and polymer additives. About half of its total revenues comes from custom manufacturing specialty or performance chemicals for specific customers and a smaller portion comes from producing specialty chemicals or performance chemicals for several customers. The company also sells an intermediate anode powder which is used to produce lithium-ion batteries. Its Performance Chemicals unit includes polymer (nylon and polyester) modifiers and some specialty chemicals and solvents for various applications.

Financial Performance

FutureFuel's revenues grew by 14% in 2012 due to a 35% increase in the Biofuels results caused by higher biodiesel production ans sales Revenues from their biofuels also been benefited by sales to a refined petroleum products shipper on a common carrier pipeline. These gains were offset by 5% decline in chemical segment revenues. The company's net income of $351.8 million (14% up on 2011) was the result of higher net sales increased interest and dividend income and a gain on marketable securities.

With the exception of the revenue slump in 2009 (when the global recession and weakened demand for oil and gas products) FutureFuel has reported an upward trend in revenue between 2008 and 2012.

Strategy

FutureFuel's long-term strategy seeks to grow both its chemicals and biofuels businesses. The company also wants to commercialize other products such as building block chemicals. It is seeking to establish new markets for its biofuels business and hopes to accelerate marketing efforts to serve fleets and regional/national customers.

FutureFuel has had a multiyear contract with The Procter & Gamble Co. (which ends in 2016) to sell all of its bleach activator product. However Procter & Gamble notified FutureFuels in 2011 that it was reducing the quantities of bleach activator it purchases. FutureFuel also sells its proprietary herbicide and certain intermediates used in its production to Arysta LifeScience North America. Arysta reduced its purchase volumes of the herbicide by half in 2012.

Ownership

Paul A. Novelly who has been the company's chairman since its formation owns about 44% of the company. He is also chairman and CEO of Apex Oil.

EXECUTIVES

CEO and Director, Lee E. Mikles, age 58
Chairman, Paul A. (Tony) Novelly, age 69
Principal Financial Officer EVP secretary and treasurer, Douglas D. Hommert, age 57
Chief Operating Officer; Director, Paul G. Lorenzini, age 73
SVP Operations Support FutureFuel Chemical, David Baker, age 66
SVP Commercial Operations FutureFuel Chemical, Gary Hess, age 61
Executive Vice President General Manager, Samuel W. Dortch, age 64
Principal Financial Officer And Principal Accounting Officer, Rose Sparks
Corporate Secretary, Ann Faitz
CEO and Director, Lee E. Mikles, age 58
Director, Edwin A. Levy, age 75
Director, Richard L. Knowlton, age 80
COO and Director, Paul G. Lorenzini, age 73
Director, Thomas R. Evans, age 59
Director, Donald C. Bedell, age 71
Independent Director, Paul Manheim
Auditors: RubinBrownLLP

LOCATIONS

HQ: FutureFuel Corp.
  8235 Forsyth Blvd. 4th Fl., Clayton MO 63105
Phone: 805-565-9800   **Fax:** 805-565-0800
Web: www.futurefuelcorporation.com

2012 Sales

US	338	96
Total	**351**	**100**

PRODUCTS/OPERATIONS

2012 Sales

Biofuels	191	54
Total	**351**	**100**

COMPETITORS

ADM	Ecolab
BASF SE	Exxon Mobil
BioFuel Energy	Louis Dreyfus
Cargill	Commodities
Chemtura	Renewable Energy Group
Dow Chemical	UOP
DuPont	

HISTORICAL FINANCIALS

Company Type: Public

Income Statement

FYE: December 31

	REVENUE ($ mil.)	NET INCOME ($ mil.)	NET PROFIT MARGIN	EMPLOYEES
12/12	351.8	34.3	9.8%	500
12/11	309.8	34.5	11.1%	500
12/10	219.1	23.0	10.5%	500
12/09	196.7	16.9	8.6%	464
12/08	198.3	22.6	11.4%	0
Annual Growth	**15.4%**	**10.9%**	—	—

2012 Year-End Financials

Debt ratio: —	No. of shares (mil.): 41
Return on equity: 12.4%	Dividends
Cash ($ mil.): 58	Yield: 13.5%
Current ratio: 5.90	Payout: 173.9%
Long-term debt ($ mil.): —	Market value ($ mil.): 494

	STOCK PRICE ($) FY Close	P/E High/Low		PER SHARE ($) Earnings	Dividends	Book Value
12/12	11.84	15	11	0.83	1.60	6.24
12/11	12.42	16	11	0.84	0.40	6.98
12/10	9.95	16	10	0.62	0.80	6.31
12/09	6.70	12	7	0.58	0.30	6.75
12/08	5.60	9	6	0.82	0.70	6.44
Annual Growth	**20.6%**	—	—	**0.3%**	**23.0%**	**(0.8%)**

G-III Apparel Group Ltd.

G-III Apparel Group is into leather but not exclusively. The company is best known for making leather jackets under the G-III Marvin Richards Black Rivet Winlit Siena Studio and other labels (such as Andrew Marc) as well as under licensed names. It also makes pants skirts and sportswear from leather and other materials. More than two-thirds of G-III's sales are generated from licensed apparel it makes for the NFL NBA NHL and MLB teams as well as for Jones New York Nine West and Kenneth Cole. The company's customers include department stores such as Macy's Nordstrom Lord & Taylor and Kohl's.

Additionally Buckingham Capital Management and FMR each hold about a 12% stake.

The company formed a joint venture with The Camuto Group to develop a chain of stores devoted to footwear and accessories operating under the Vince Camuto banner. The chain leverages G-III's retail infrastructure (real estate distribution infor-

mation and administrative systems) with Camuto providing its growing family of big-name brands including Vince Camuto Jessica Simpson BCBG Max Azria BCBGeneration Kensiegirl Lucky Brand and Arturo Chiang. The first Vince Camuto store opened in early 2011.

Having been big in licensing for a decade the company has inked several deals that maintain its strategy and revenue mix of licensed and non-licensed products. A particular purchase it has used as a foundation for this effort is its acquisition of Andrew Marc for $42 million in 2008. The deal gave G-III handbags and upscale specialty and department store distribution. Andrew Marc then entered a licensing agreement with Camuto to make and market women's footwear under the Andrew Marc and Marc New York brands. G-III's Jessica Howard license extends its reach into dresses with its Jessica Howard and Eliza J names. G-III's purchase of Industrial Cotton also expanded its junior denim products. The purchases also gave G-III a foothold in new retail outlets with the brands selling in Dillard's Nordstrom Sears Kohl's and Coldwater Creek among others.

Beyond the department store channel G-III operates about 120 retail stores most of which are outlet stores. The company's retail business generated about 16% of its sales in 2010. G-III had extended its reach into retail in 2008 when the apparel wholesaler acquired the Wilsons The Leather Experts' outlet stores as well as the Wilsons brand name and distribution center operations for about $22 million. The move represented G-III's effort to boost its retail presence.

G-III conducts most of its business in the US with 98% of its revenue generated within the country's borders. Its products are produced by independent manufacturers however located primarily in China as well as in India Indonesia Sri Lanka Taiwan Thailand Vietnam and Central and South America. Some of its garments are made in the US.

Ownership

Chairman and CEO Morris Goldfarb and investment firm FMR LLC each own about 15% of G-III's shares. Royce & Associates owns about 10%.

EXECUTIVES

Chief Operating Officer; Secretary, Wayne S. Miller, age 55, $500,000 total compensation
Group President Women's Leather Fashions, Deborah Gaertner, age 57, $275,000 total compensation
President, Jeanette Nostra, age 61, $500,000 total compensation
Chairman of the Board; Chief Executive Officer, Morris Goldfarb, age 63, $854,167 total compensation
Chief Financial Officer; Treasurer, Neal S. Nackman, age 53, $325,000 total compensation
Vice Chairman, Sammy Aaron, age 53, $600,000 total compensation
Investor Relations, James Palczynski
Director, Carl Katz, age 72
Director, Thomas J. Brosig, age 63
Director, Alan Feller, age 71
Director, Willem van Bokhorst, age 67
Director, Laura H. Pomerantz, age 65
Director, Richard White, age 59
Vice Chairman, Sammy Aaron, age 53
Director, Jeffrey Goldfarb, age 36
Independent Director, Cheryl Vitali
Independent Director, Willem Bokhorst
Auditors: Ernst&YoungLLP

LOCATIONS

HQ: G-III Apparel Group Ltd.
512 7th Ave., New York NY 10018
Phone: 212-403-0500   **Fax:** 212-403-0551
Web: www.g-iii.com

2012 Sales

	$ mil.	% of total
US	1,185	96
Other countries	45	4
Total	**1,231**	**100**

PRODUCTS/OPERATIONS

2012 Sales

	$ mil.	% of total
Wholesale licensed apparel	840	68
Wholesale non-licensed apparel	277	23
Retail	164	13
Adjustments (51.4) (4)		
Total	**1,231**	**100**

Selected Divisions

Outerwear
  Andrew Marc
  Black Rivet
  Calvin Klein
  Cole Haan
  Dockers
  Ellen Tracy
  Guess
  Jones New York
  Kenneth Cole
  Levi' s
  Marc New York
  Nine West
  Sean John
  Tommy Hilfiger
Ready to Wear
  Andrew Marc Dresses
  Calvin Klein Dresses
  Calvin Klein Performance Wear
  Calvin Klein Sportswear
  Calvin Klein Women Suits
  Eliza J Dresses
  Ellen Tracy Dresses
  Jessica Howard Dresses
  Jessica Simpson Dresses
  Marc New York Dresses
Sports
  G-III for Her
  G-III Sports by Carl Banks
  Major League Baseball
  National Basketball Association
  National Football League
  National Hockey League
  Officially Licensed Collegiate Products
  Touch by Alyssa Milano
Retail
  Wilsons Outlets

Selected Licenses

Men's and Women's
  Calvin Klein
  Cole Haan
  Guess?
  Jessica Simpson
  Kenneth Cole NY
  Levi's
  Vince Camuto
Sports
  Major League Baseball
  Major League Soccer
  National Basketball Association
  National Football League
  National Hockey League

COMPETITORS

Amerex	L.L. Bean
Armani	NIKE
Burberry	North Face
Burlington Coat Factory	Phat Fashions
	Roc Apparel

Columbia Sportswear   Sean John
Diesel SpA   Tandy Leather
FUBU   The Gap
J. Crew   Wal-Mart

HISTORICAL FINANCIALS
Company Type: Public

Income Statement
FYE: January 31

	REVENUE ($ mil.)	NET INCOME ($ mil.)	NET PROFIT MARGIN	EMPLOYEES
01/13	1,399.7	56.8	4.1%	3,109
01/12	1,231.2	49.6	4.0%	2,592
01/11	1,063.4	56.6	5.3%	2,154
01/10	800.8	31.7	4.0%	1,880
01/09	711.1	(14.0)	—	1,245
Annual Growth	18.4%	—	—	25.7%

2013 Year-End Financials

Debt ratio: 11.8%	No. of shares (mil.): 20
Return on equity: 14.4%	Dividends
Cash ($ mil.): 27	Yield: —
Current ratio: 2.22	Payout: —
Long-term debt ($ mil.): 19	Market value ($ mil.): 722

	STOCK PRICE ($) FY Close	P/E High/Low		PER SHARE ($) Earnings	Dividends	Book Value
01/13	35.89	14	8	2.80	0.00	21.34
01/12	22.86	18	7	2.46	0.00	18.09
01/11	34.89	12	6	2.88	0.00	15.41
01/10	17.41	12	2	1.83	0.00	12.33
01/09	5.50	—	—	(0.85)	0.00	9.72
Annual Growth	59.8%	—	—	—	—	21.7%

GAMCO Investors Inc

Investing is anything but a game for "Super Mario" Gabelli the self-made billionaire investor and founder and CEO of GAMCO Investors. The firm oversees the mutual fund- and securities-related portion of Gabelli's financial empire. It provides advisory services to some 20 mutual funds and 10 closed-end funds under the Gabelli GAMCO and Comstock brands. Most of the company's approximately $34 billion in assets under management are invested in stocks though company also has a well-performing money-market fund. GAMCO also offers wealth management services for private clients and institutional investors such as pension plans endowments and municipalities. Gabelli controls the firm.

Geographic Reach

The company has five research offices in the US as well as offices overseas in London Hong Kong Shanghai and Tokyo.

Operations

As with many money managers GAMCO derives most of its revenue from investment advisory and incentive fees (82% in 2011) which are directly linked to its assets under management. Despite market uncertainty the company was able to grow its assets under management in most of its segments during 2011 including mutual funds closed-end funds institutional and private wealth management and investment partnerships. As a result its revenues and net income were up as well.

Financial Analysis

GAMCO's revenue increased by nearly 17% in 2011 vs. 2010 while net income was up about 1% over the same period. 2011 marked the second consecutive year of rising revenue following two years of decline during the financial crisis. Indeed GAMCO's $327 million in revenue in 2011 was an all-time high for the firm.

GAMCO's investment advisory business posted a 16% increase in revenue in 2011 vs. 2010 while distribution fees and other income rose nearly 38% over the same period. The firm's institutional research services segment posted a 14% decline.

Strategy

GAMCO which strives for long-term returns based on proprietary fundamental research is dependent on its flamboyant founder and his legendary gift for picking stocks particularly those of media and communications companies. A brand unto himself Gabelli is the chief investment officer for the firm's Value Portfolios which represent nearly 90% of GAMCO's assets under management and he gets paid tens of millions of dollars per year for his troubles. Gabelli is also the portfolio manager of Teton Advisors; GAMCO spun off the asset management firm in 2009 but retained ownership of more than 40% of the company.

GAMCO is expanding its mutual fund distribution network through agreements with brokerage firms and other third-party channels. It has traditionally reached out to prospective clients through direct marketing but is increasingly courting financial consultants who in turn offer GAMCO funds to their clients. The company focuses on households with more than $1 million to invest.

GAMCO also grows through acquisitions of and alliances with other asset managers. In 2010 the company's institutional and private wealth operations absorbed the client base of NMF Asset Management in Florida. It continues to seek out additional acquisition opportunities.

Ownership

Frederick J. Mancheski owns about 26% of GAMCO's class A shares. Gabelli owns 99% of the firm's class B shares.

HISTORY

Mario Gabelli displayed his flair early. He bought his first stocks when he was 13 years old and read stock market reports in his free time. After college he worked at Wall Street firms Loeb Rhodes and William D. Witter.

He founded institutional broker/dealer Gabelli & Company in 1976 and moved into separate account management —today the nucleus of the company's business —in 1977. Gabelli's first mutual fund debuted in 1986. Gabelli Fund affiliates acquired diversified holding company (now LGL Group) with operations in manufactured housing telecommunications services and TV stations. Through the 1980s the firm added investment vehicles. In 1988 it incorporated as Alpha G. By the 1990s assets had grown enormously but Alpha G suffered management turmoil frequently attributed to Gabelli's temper. By 1995 the Gabelli funds were in a slump; some analysts thought Gabelli was overextended.

He roared back with the Gabelli Global Opportunity Fund (global equities) and the Gabelli/Westwood Mighty Mites Fund (micro cap equities). To boost his funds' investment clout Gabelli used "rights offerings" asking investors to buy more fund shares at a discount —in effect forcing them to pony up or face dilution.

After trying to sell 25% of his firm in 1996 and 1997 Gabelli planned a 1998 IPO of the mutual fund businesses. But it was delayed until the next year because of issues relating to Gabelli's pay. In 1999 Gabelli halved his salary (putting the company on the hook for a compensatory $50 million payout in 2002). In 1999 and 2000 Gabelli Asset Management widened distribution of the funds and despite a static stock price bought up others including the Comstock family of funds. The company also opened a London office to boost its European presence.

The company adopted the name of one of its subsidiaries GAMCO Investments in 2005 and renamed that subsidiary GAMCO Asset Management.

EXECUTIVES

Chairman CEO and Chief Investment Officer Value Portfolios, Mario J. Gabelli, age 70

SVP; EVP and COO Gabelli Funds, Bruce N. Alpert, age 61, $300,000 total compensation

President; Chief Operating Officer, Douglas R. Jamieson, age 58, $300,000 total compensation

Chief Financial Officer; Executive Vice President, Robert S. Zuccaro, age 56

SVP; SVP Gabelli Funds and GAMCO Asset Management, Henry G. Van der Eb, age 67, $300,000 total compensation

President and COO Open-End Fund, Agnes Mullady

President CEO of Teton Advisors, Nicholas F. Galluccio

Co-Portfolio Manager The Gabelli US Treasury Money Market Fund, Ronald S. Eaker

Manager Institutional Sales, Gino Torretta, age 42

Senior Vice President, Henry Eb

Chief Administrative Officer, Scott Long

Director, Richard L. Bready, age 69

Director, Robert S. (Bob) Prather Jr., age 68

Director, Edwin L. Artzt, age 82

Director, Raymond C. (Skip) Avansino Jr., age 69

Director, Eugene R. McGrath, age 71

Director, Elisa M. Wilson, age 40

Auditors: Deloitte&ToucheLLP

LOCATIONS

HQ: GAMCO Investors Inc.
1 Corporate Center, Rye NY 10580-1422
Phone: 914-921-5100   **Fax:** 914-921-5392
Web: www.gabelli.com

Selected Offices
Chicago
Greeenwich CT
Hong Kong
London
Minneapolis
New York
Palm Beach FL
Reno NV
Shanghai
St. Louis

PRODUCTS/OPERATIONS

2011 Sales

Investment advisory & incentive fees	268	82
Institutional research services	14	4
Total	**327**	**100**

Selected Funds
Comstock Capital Value Fund
Gabelli ABC Fund
Gabelli Asset Fund
Gabelli Dividend Growth Fund
Gabelli Equity Income Fund
Gabelli Small Cap Growth Fund
Gabelli SRI Green Fund
Gabelli U.S. Treasury Money Market Fund
Gabelli Utilities Fund

Gabelli Value Fund
Gabelli Woodland Small Cap Value Fund
GAMCO Global Growth Fund
GAMCO Global Opportunity Fund
GAMCO Global Telecommunications Fund
GAMCO Gold Fund
GAMCO Growth Fund
GAMCO International Growth Fund
GAMCO Mathers Fund
GAMCO Vertumnus Fund
GAMCO Westwood Balanced Fund
GAMCO Westwood Equity Fund
GAMCO Westwood Income Fund
GAMCO Westwood Intermediate Bond Fund
GAMCO Westwood Mighty Mites Fund
GAMCO Westwood SmallCap Equity Fund

COMPETITORS

AllianceBernstein	Prudential
Capital Group	Raymond James
FMR	Financial
Franklin Templeton	T. Rowe Price
Legg Mason	The Vanguard Group
Old Mutual (US)	

HISTORICAL FINANCIALS

Company Type: Public

Income Statement

FYE: December 31

	REVENUE ($ mil.)	NET INCOME ($ mil.)	NET PROFIT MARGIN	EMPLOYEES
12/12	344.2	75.5	21.9%	224
12/11	327.1	69.6	21.3%	218
12/10	280.3	68.7	24.5%	222
12/09	218.1	55.5	25.5%	194
12/08	245.0	24.8	10.1%	214
Annual Growth	8.9%	32.0%	—	1.1%

2012 Year-End Financials

Debt ratio: 32.0%
Return on equity: 19.5%
Cash ($ mil.): 190
Current ratio: 5.41
Long-term debt ($ mil.): 221

No. of shares (mil.): 25
Dividends
Yield: 5.3%
Payout: 100.7%
Market value ($ mil.): 1,366

	STOCK PRICE ($) FY Close	P/E High/Low		PER SHARE ($) Earnings	Dividends	Book Value
12/12	53.07	18	14	2.86	2.88	14.28
12/11	43.49	20	14	2.61	1.15	15.10
12/10	48.01	20	13	2.52	1.82	14.27
12/09	48.29	27	13	2.02	2.12	15.93
12/08	27.32	80	25	0.89	2.02	15.86
Annual Growth	18.1%	—	—	33.9%	9.3%	(2.6%)

Geeknet Inc

Geeknet is tuned in to what hipster techies crave. The company operates through its wholly-owned subsidiary ThinkGeek an online retailer of goodies for the global geek community. The company (formerly SourceForge) exited the business of producing websites for software developers to focus entirely on its ThinkGeek website which offers a broad range of apparel edibles electronics gadgets and other geek-themed merchandise for fans of movies and TV programs such as Star Wars Star Trek Dr. Who and Game of Thrones. Founded by former chairman Larry Augustin in 1993 Geeknet

sold its Media business including the SourceForge Slashdot and Freecode websites in 2012 to focus on online retail.

Geographic Reach

Virginia-based Geeknet rings up about 85% of its sales in the US.

Sales and Marketing

Notable customers include Urban Outfitters Books-A-Million in the US and HMV in Canada. The company's international wholesale channel includes distributors in Australia Germany Japan and the UK.

Strategy

After fanning the flames of the open source software movement by producing websites aimed primarily at software developers and other technology enthusiasts the company in late 2012 sold its SourceForge.net (an online collaborative development site) Slashdot.org (peer-produced and -moderated technology news) and Freecode (formerly freshmeat) websites to Dice Holdings for $20 million. The deal had been in the mix since May 2012. Geeknet cashed in on its website communities to concentrate on its e-commerce sales which had been rising despite the economic downturn as its media business declined. Geeknet has been struggling to squeeze profits out of its primary media businesses even enlisting the help of select executives to make it happen.

Financial Performance

Geeknet rang up nearly $119 million in sales in 2012 an essentially flat comparison with the prior year. (On a continuing operations basis sales increased 20% year over year.) While the number of orders received on theThinkGeek.com site rose 62% between 2010 and 2012 the average order value fell from $63.74 in 2010 to $61.10 in 2012. Net income totaled $13.9 million in 2012 compared with a loss in 2011. Indeed 2012 was the company's first profitable year since 2007.

HISTORY

Unable to afford a high-end Sun Microsystems workstation in 1991 Larry Augustin decided to build a Linux-based version in his living room so he could finish his dissertation at Stanford. When his experiment yielded a machine that was a third the price and twice as fast as Sun's his fellow graduate students took notice. Instead of pursuing the business model Augustin co-wrote with friends Jerry Yang and David Filo (which eventually became Yahoo!) Augustin stuck to his engineering roots and continued to build workstations out of his house.

In 1993 still a doctoral student in electrical engineering he started VA Research along with pal James Vera (VA comes from the initials of their surnames) with financing from their credit cards. The company incorporated in 1995. (Vera remained a researcher at Stanford.)

Because VA Research designed and built its systems from the ground up (and because Linux itself was continuously morphing into something else) it wasn't until 1997 that the company released its first high-end workstations. With funding from venture investment firm Sequoia Capital in 1998 VA Research began building its staff by hiring Linux veterans such as Leonard Zubkoff whom Augustin lured away from Oracle to be his CTO. The company also began to target the high-end server market offering $200000 systems to ISPs.

In 1999 VA Research changed its name to VA Linux Systems and formed alliances with Linux software vendors Red Hat and SuSE Linux to preinstall their software on its systems. The company

also bought out its closest rival Linux Hardware Solutions as well as a Linux consulting company and a graphical user interface specialist. VA Linux went public that December —its stock price soaring a record 698% during its first day of trading.

The company acquired Linux information portal Andover.Net in 2000 and later launched the Open Source Development Network (OSDN). It also bought privately held TruSolutions and NetAttach in two deals with a combined value of about $230 million.

The next year —citing sluggish hardware spending and high costs —VA Linux announced that it would cut about 35% of its workforce and exit its core server and workstation business in order to focus on Linux-based development software and services. The company changed its name to VA Software late in 2001.

Company president and COO Ali Jenab was promoted to CEO the next year while Augustin remained chairman (he left in 2007). In 2004 the company renamed OSDN the Open Source Technology Group and redesigned many of its online publications in an effort to expand the audience for its Web sites.

In December 2005 VA Software sold its Animation Factory subsidiary to WebMediaBrands for about $9.4 million. Two years later VA Software changed its name to SourceForge.

In April 2007 the company sold its SourceForge software development suite which offered a Web-based environment for collaborative programming teams to manage their work. CollabNet a fellow collaboration facilitator picked up the software for an equity stake in that company. The software business accounted for about 23% of the firm's sales. While a graduate student at Stanford in 1993 Augustin (who owns 5% of the company) chose to help start VA Software rather than become a co-founder of Yahoo!. The company changed its name from VA Software to SourceForge in May 2007.

In June 2008 Robert Neumeister succeeded Jenab as president and CEO of the firm on an interim basis in June 2008. In January 2009 Scott Kauffman succeeded Neumeister who remained chairman of the company. In May the firm bought privately held Ohloh Corporation a provider of open source data based in Bellevue Washington. In November 2009 the company changed its name from SourceForge to Geeknet Inc. to better communicate its mission as the online network for the global geek community.

In May 2010 Geeknet acquired Geek.com for $1 million. Kauffman resigned in August 2010 amid lukewarm 2Q results and Ken Langone chairman assumed the title of interim CEO. The company moved from California to Virginia in 2011.

EXECUTIVES

Chairman President and CEO, Kenneth G. (Ken) Langone, age 77
President Chief Executive Officer, Kathryn K. (Katy) McCarthy, age 44
President Chief Executive Officer of ThinkGeek, Caroline Offutt, age 50
Executive Vice President; Chief Administrative Officer; General Counsel, Carol DiBattiste
President and Chief Executive Officer of ThinkGeek; Inc., Colon Washburn
Lead Independent Director, Derek Smith
EVP General Counsel Chief Administrative Officer, Kirk Somers
Chief Information Officer, Steven J. Weiskircher
Chief Marketing Officer, Jim O'Brien
Chief Financial Officer, Julie Pangelinan

LOCATIONS

HQ: Geeknet Inc.
11216 Waples Mill Rd. Ste. 100, Fairfax VA 22030
Phone: 650-694-2100   **Fax:** 650-694-2111
Web: geek.net

COMPETITORS

AOL	MSN
Amazon.com	Newegg
Bed Bath & Beyond	Office Depot
Best Buy	PC Connection
Bloomberg Businessweek	PC Mall
Brookstone	Provide Gifts
CBS Interactive	Spencer Gifts
Costco Wholesale	Staples
Dell	Tucows
Forbes	Wal-Mart
Fry' s Electronics	Yahoo!
Google	Ziff Davis Media
International Data	
Group	

HISTORICAL FINANCIALS

Company Type: Public

Income Statement

FYE: December 31

	REVENUE ($ mil.)	NET INCOME ($ mil.)	NET PROFIT MARGIN	EMPLOYEES
12/12	118.9	13.9	11.7%	76
12/11	119.4	(1.1)	—	143
12/10	94.6	(4.4)	—	122
12/09	65.5	(14.0)	—	127
12/08	32.4	1.0	3.3%	0
Annual Growth	**38.3%**	**89.4%**	**—**	**—**

2012 Year-End Financials

Debt ratio: —	No. of shares (mil.): 6
Return on equity: 23.1%	Dividends
Cash ($ mil.): 57	Yield: —
Current ratio: 4.89	Payout: —
Long-term debt ($ mil.): —	Market value ($ mil.): 106

	STOCK PRICE ($) FY Close	P/E High/Low		PER SHARE ($) Earnings	Dividends	Book Value
12/12	16.10	10	6	2.12	0.00	10.54
12/11	17.05	—	—	(0.19)	0.00	8.02
12/10	25.03	—	—	(0.73)	0.00	7.63
12/09	1.19	—	—	(2.30)	0.00	7.97
12/08	0.90	12	3	0.20	0.00	10.35
Annual Growth	**105.7%**	—	—	**80.4%**	—	**0.5%**

Generac Holdings Inc

Perfect storms make good business for Generac Power Systems. That's because the company manufactures engine-driven standby and portable generators for homes businesses hospitals and recreational vehicles. The company also makes industrial power generation equipment automatic transfer switches switch gear and controls and remote monitoring software. Generac sells its products through retailers such as Home Depot as well as through wholesale distributors. The US and Canada represent over 99% of company sales. Established in 1959 Generac was purchased by private equity firm CCMP Capital Advisors in 2006 and went public in 2010.

Generac whose media campaign is "Never Feel Powerless" initiated its IPO to raise cash to pay down debt and to power future growth opportunities in development innovative product offerings and international market expansion. CCMP still owns about 59% of the company's voting shares.

The company is gung ho to expand its presence in underserved North American regions by continuing to build its dealer network. Latin America Russia and China represent favorable opportunities for the company and have piqued Generac's interest in seizing growth opportunities in international markets. The company is pursuing partnerships with established international companies and has built a network of 34 distributors in 16 international markets —primarily in Central and South America and Mexico —to handle its industrial and light-commercial generators.

Boasting a North American market share of 70% for residential standby generators a broad distribution network (direct dealers catalog wholesale and retail) a comprehensive product line and specialized engineering and manufacturing capabilities Generac continues to invest in innovation and product development as well as technician training to ensure the repair and maintenance of its products. To that end the company acquired Magnum Products a Wisconsin manufacturer of light towers mobile generators trash pumps and other portable equipment. The 2011 deal valued at $80 million in cash adds heft to its commercial and industrial product portfolio. Generac followed that deal with the acquisition of Gen-Tran in 2012. The acquisition adds transfer switches and portable generator accessories to round out Generac's portable products offerings.

EXECUTIVES

COO and Secretary, Dawn Tabat, age 59, $450,000 total compensation
President CEO and Director, Aaron Jagdfeld, age 39, $400,000 total compensation
CFO, York A. Ragen, age 40, $153,740 total compensation
SVP Engineering, Allen Gillette, age 55
SVP Service Operations, Roger Schaus Jr., age 57, $200,377 total compensation
SVP Operations, Roger Pascavis, age 51
Director, Barry J. Goldstein, age 69
Director, Stephen P. Murray, age 49
Director, John D. Bowlin, age 61
Director, David Ramon, age 55
Director, Timothy J. Walsh, age 49
President CEO and Director, Aaron Jagdfeld, age 39
Auditors: Ernst&YoungLLP

LOCATIONS

HQ: Generac Holdings Inc.
S45 W29290 Hwy. 59, Waukesha WI 53187
Phone: 262-544-4811   **Fax:** 262-968-3791
Web: www.generac.com

PRODUCTS/OPERATIONS

2011 Sales

	$ mil.	% of total
Residential power products	491	62
Industrial and commercial products	250	32
Other	50	6
Total	**792**	**100**

Selected Products and Brands

Generators
  Commercial (QuietSource)
  Industrial (gaseous diesel bi-fuel modular power systems (MPS) Gemini)
  Portable (GP XG XP iX)
  Recreational vehicle (gasoline propane diesel)
  Residential (QuietSource Guardian)

Selected Markets

Agricultural/mining
Business office
Commercial/retail
Data center
Education
Healthcare
Manufacturing
Municipal
Research
Residential
Telecom

COMPETITORS

Aggreko	Honda
Briggs & Stratton	Kohler
Power Products	Taylor Group
Caterpillar	Techtronic
Cummins Power	Westerbeke Corp.
Generation	

HISTORICAL FINANCIALS

Company Type: Public

Income Statement

FYE: December 31

	REVENUE ($ mil.)	NET INCOME ($ mil.)	NET PROFIT MARGIN	EMPLOYEES
12/12	1,176.3	93.2	7.9%	3,048
12/11	791.9	324.6	41.0%	2,223
12/10	592.8	56.9	9.6%	1,444
12/09	588.2	43.0	7.3%	1,354
12/08	574.2	(555.9)	—	1,486
Annual Growth	**19.6%**	**—**	**—**	**19.7%**

2012 Year-End Financials

Debt ratio: 55.7%	No. of shares (mil.): 68
Return on equity: 15.0%	Dividends
Cash ($ mil.): 108	Yield: 17.4%
Current ratio: 1.77	Payout: 444.4%
Long-term debt ($ mil.): 799	Market value ($ mil.): 2,343

	STOCK PRICE ($) FY Close	P/E High/Low		PER SHARE ($) Earnings	Dividends	Book Value
12/12	34.31	28	15	1.35	6.00	6.79
12/11	28.03	6	3	4.79	0.00	11.37
12/10	16.17	—	—	(1.65)	0.00	6.53
Annual Growth	**45.7%**	—	—	—	—	**1.9%**

Genesee & Wyoming Inc.

Genesee & Wyoming (GWI) once relied on the salt of the earth —hauling salt on a 14-mile railroad for one customer. Now however the company owns stakes in more than 65 short-line and regional freight railroads that operate over a total of about 9000 miles of track including about 7600 miles of track owned and leased by the company and another 1400 miles belonging to other railroads and service to 17 ports in North America and Europe. Freight transported by GWI railroads includes coal forest products and pulp and paper. Outside North America the company has operations in Australia and the Netherlands. In late 2012 it acquired rival RailAmerica for almost $1.4 billion.

Besides its railroad operations GWI provides freight car switching and related services for industrial companies that own railroad facilities.

GWI's average freight revenues per carload increased nearly 8% in 2010 when compared to the previous year. Although revenues from the transportation of coal and coke which accounts for nearly 20% of GWI's freight revenues was relatively flat shipments of farm and food products improved by about 50%. The company is also looking to expand its intermodal operations. (Intermodal involves the shipment of freight in a container using multiple modes of transportation.) Intermodal revenues jumped from $411000 in 2009 to $ 7.8 million in 2010.

The company which has expanded over the years via acquisitions (about 35 between 1985 and 2010) hopes to continue to grow by buying railroads not only in North America and Australia but also in European markets. Its $1.4 billion milestone deal to purchase RailAmerica created the largest short-line railroad operator in the US with about 110 railroads and 15100 miles of track. The transaction is expected to more than triple GWI's debt but it hopes the newly integrated entity's increased cash flow will allow it to quickly recover.

In addition to that significant deal GWI expects freight business in Australia to pick up as the grain harvest in that country increased over the previous year's totals. To that end GWI purchased Australia's FreightLink rail network for about $332 million Australian dollars ($319 million). FreightLink which serves general freight and mining customers in South Australia will operate as part of Genesee & Wyoming Australia (GWA). GWA has managed FreightLink's rail services and operations and provided it with locomotives and crews since its inception.

Chairman Mortimer Fuller great-grandson of founder Edward L. Fuller owns a 28% stake in the company.

EXECUTIVES

Senior Vice President Midwest Region, Spencer D. White
SVP Oregon Region, Ronald G. (Ron) Russ, age 58
Senior Vice President Business Technology, David J. Collins
COO, James W. Benz, age 64, $348,000 total compensation
VP Organizational Effectiveness, Shayne L. Magdoff

Executive Vice President International Business Development, Mark W. Hastings, $252,000 total compensation
Chairman, Mortimer B. Fuller III, age 70, $708,923 total compensation
President Chief Executive Officer, John C. Hellmann, age 42, $703,000 total compensation
Senior Vice President Customer Service, Andrew T. Chunko, age 44
Senior Vice President Canada Region, Mario Brault
VP Government and Industry Affairs, Jerry E. Vest
SVP Corporate Development and Treasurer, Matthew O. Walsh
VP Information Technology, Mike Meyers
Vice President Finance and Administration, Gerald A. Sattora
VP Motive Power, David L. Powell
Chief Financial Officer, Timothy J. Gallagher, age 50, $405,000 total compensation
Senior Vice President Operations Support, Tony Long
VP Operations Services Rail Link, William A. (Bill) Jasper
VP-Compliance & Security, Jack N. Brown
Chief Accounting Officer; Global Controller, Christopher F. Liucci, age 44, $194,580 total compensation
SVP Southern Region, Gerald T. Gates
General Counsel; Secretary, Allison M. Fergus, age 39, $300,000 total compensation
Chief Human Resources Officer, Matthew C. Brush
Managing Director Australia Region, Robert (Bert) Easthope
Director Corporate Communications, Michael E. Williams
Director of Human Resources, Lynn Adams
Senior Vice President Northeast Region, Raymond A. (Ray) Goss
VP Employee and Labor Relations, Niels Hansen
Chief Commercial Officer North America, Michael O. Miller
Managing Director Netherlands Region, Arnoud de Rade
VP Safety and Compliance, Tyrone C. James
Vice President Transportation, Leonard Wagner
Vice President Commercial, Martin Pohlod
Director of Marketing, John Aternali
Customer Service Manager, Keenan Mitchell
Director of Operations, Kenny Bryant
Vice President Marketing Customer Service, Kevin Bowser
Director of Finance, Lauren Gray
Assistant Vice President Sales & Marketing, Sherrie Ralph
Vice President Sales & Marketing, Sherrie Motley
Office Manager, Sophie Skrobialowski
Vice President Finance & Administration, Wendy Hill
Vice President Regional Operations Support, Hoffman Lijeron
General Manager - SL&A, Edward J. Foley
Director Human Resources, Cynthia Strawn
Vice President Engineering, David Baer
Vice President Engineering, Jeff Watson
Vice President Safety and Regulatory Vice-pr+-sident S+-curit+, Jean-Marc Montigny
Marketing Manager, Clint Ashmead
Director Marketing and Sales, David Anzur
Human Resource Director, Bridget Shepard
Vice President Railroads North, Dave Bordner
Vice President Maintenance of Way, Jerry Herndon
Vice President Transportation, Tim Ercanbrack
Vice President Transportation, Eric Hosey
Vice President Mechanical, Donald Robey
General Manager - QGRY CFGQ & SFE, Louis-Rene Pelletier
Vice President Railroads South, Don Vincent

Marketing Manager - SL&A, Laurie Therrien
General Manager, Josh Connell
Vice President Transportation, John Cyrus
Vice President Mechanical, Jim Wineland
Vice President Industrial Switching, Ken Dziwulski
Senior Vice President Oregon Region, James E. Irvin
Vice President Safety, Jeffrey Andrews
Vice President Transportation, Allen Swindall
Vice President Engineering, Woody Ehrh
Vice President Ta, Richard T. ODonnell
Vice President - Taxes, Richard T. T.
Marketing Manager, Peter Valade
Vice President Railroads Central, Michael Erwin
Vice President Compliance and Safety, Michael F. Lundell
Vice President Human Resources, Roberta J. Kane
General Manager, Shannon Elston
Vice President Mechanical, Brad Landers
VP-Sls & Mktg-Georgia, Tracy Stockdale
Director, Robert M. Melzer, age 72
Director, Philip J. Ringo, age 71
President Chief Executive Officer, John C. Hellmann, age 42
Director, Michael Norkus, age 66
Director, Mark A. Scudder, age 50
Director, Louis S. Fuller, age 71
Director, James M. Fuller, age 72
Director, John M. Randolph, age 87
Director, ?ivind Lorentzen III, age 62
Director, Peter O. Scannell, age 52
Director, David C. Hurley, age 71
Independent Director, Ann Reese
Independent Director, Richard Allert
Auditors: PricewaterhouseCoopersLLP

LOCATIONS

HQ: Genesee & Wyoming Inc.
66 Field Point Rd., Greenwich CT 06830
Phone: 203-629-3722 **Fax:** 203-661-4106
Web: www.gwrr.com

2010 Sales

	$ mil.	% of total
North America		
US	434	69
Australia	135	21
The Netherlands	11	2

PRODUCTS/OPERATIONS

2010 Sales

	$ mil.	% of total
Freight		
Farm & food products	56	9
Minerals & stone	41	7
Metals	36	6
Petroleum products	20	3
Metallic ores	8	1
Intermodal	7	1
Non-freight		
Car hire & rental income	24	4
Fuel sales to third parties	18.7	3
Other	52	8

COMPETITORS

Anacostia Rail Holdings
Arkansas & Missouri Railroad
Burlington Northern Santa Fe
CSX
Canadian National Railway
Canadian Pacific Railway
Dakota Minnesota &

Kansas City Southern
Montana Rail Link
Norfolk Southern
OmniTRAX
Pan Am Railways
Pinsly Railroad
Pioneer Railcorp
Providence and Worcester Railroad
RailAmerica
Union Pacific
Watco Companies

Eastern Railroad
Iowa Interstate
Railroad

HISTORICAL FINANCIALS
Company Type: Public

Income Statement
FYE: December 31

	REVENUE ($ mil.)	NET INCOME ($ mil.)	NET PROFIT MARGIN	EMPLOYEES
12/12	874.9	52.4	6.0%	4,600
12/11	829.1	119.4	14.4%	2,620
12/10	630.2	81.2	12.9%	2,502
12/09	544.8	61.3	11.3%	2,481
12/08	601.9	72.2	12.0%	2,647
Annual Growth	9.8%	(7.7%)	—	14.8%

2012 Year-End Financials

Debt ratio: 35.5%
Return on equity: 3.6%
Cash ($ mil.): 64
Current ratio: 1.12
Long-term debt ($ mil.): 1,770

No. of shares (mil.): 47
Dividends
Yield: —
Payout: —
Market value ($ mil.): 3,582

	STOCK PRICE ($) FY Close	P/E High/Low		PER SHARE ($) Earnings	Dividends	Book Value
12/12	76.08	68	43	1.02	0.00	40.23
12/11	60.58	21	15	2.79	0.00	22.63
12/10	52.95	25	14	1.94	0.00	19.53
12/09	32.64	20	10	1.57	0.00	16.79
12/08	30.50	20	10	1.99	0.00	13.27
Annual Growth	25.7%	—	—	(15.4%)	—	32.0%

Genomic Health Inc

Genomic Health believes the genome is key to good health. The company conducts genomic research to develop molecular diagnostics and assays that can predict the likelihood of disease recurrence and response to therapy and treatments. Genomic Health's Oncotype DX breast cancer test predicts the likelihood of chemotherapy effectiveness and cancer recurrence in women with newly diagnosed early stage invasive breast cancer. Genomic Health's research efforts are targeted at providing a wider base of cancer-related tests and in 2010 it launched a new Oncotype DX colon cancer test to predict recurrence rates for stage II colon cancer patients. The company generates more than 90% of sales in the US.

Geographic Reach Although most of its sales come from the US Genomic Health is widening its distribution network into international markets by establishing partnerships with regional drug representatives. International sales accounted for 9% of revenue in 2011 up from 6% in 2010 and 4% in 2009. The company is focused on the Americas Europe and Asia.

Sales and Marketing Genomic Health uses a direct sales force to market its products in the US; internationally it operates through a network of nearly 20 distributors covering some 30 countries. The company relies heavily on reimbursements from health plans and managed care companies to pay for its products and services and as such is dependent on insurance companies' reimbursement approvals of its products. Its largest customer is Centers for Medicare and Medicaid Services (CMS) which accounts for more than 20% of sales.

Financial Analysis Genomic Health has a solid history of revenue growth and 2011 is no exception; sales rose 16% that year to $206 million as adoption of its Oncotype DX tests continues to increase. The company achieved its first profitable year in 2010 and continued in 2011 with net income jumping nearly 85% to about $8 million. As a result it is increasing investments in marketing expansion and research and development efforts.

Strategy In early 2012 the company created a new subsidiary focused on commercializing human genome applications. Now that DNA sequencing has grown faster and cheaper the new subsidiary's commercial efforts will emphasize the clinical use of bioinformatics for diagnosing and making treatment plans for both common and rare genetic conditions. Genomic Health intends to invest up to $20 million into the subsidiary which will draw upon its internal research and development efforts as well as that of third parties. The company is working to apply its breast cancer product to late-stage breast cancer patients as well as to evaluate the effectiveness of other treatment methods besides chemotherapy. It also plans to expand the patient applications for its colon cancer test and it is developing additional tests for prostate lung and renal cell cancer and melanoma patients. Research partnerships also play an important role in Genomic Health's strategy. Major partnerships include an agreement with Bristol-Myers Squibb and ImClone Systems to develop a test evaluating the effectiveness of the companies' Erbitux colorectal treatment and an affiliation with Sanofi-Aventis to predict the likelihood of benefit for Aventis' Taxotere breast cancer treatment. In 2012 it entered into a strategic alliance with OncoMed Pharmaceuticals that calls for OncoMed to provide tumor samples to Genomic Health so that its Next Generation Sequencing (NGS) technology can be used in OncoMed's clinical development of novel anti-cancer stem cell therapeutics. Ownership Investment firm Baker Brothers Advisors owns about 35% of the company's stock.

EXECUTIVES
Chief Scientific Officer, Joffre B. Baker, age 65, $365,000 total compensation
Senior Vice President Corporate Communications, Laura Leber, age 48
Senior Vice President General Counsel, Kathy L. Hibbs, age 50
EVP Worldwide Commercialization, David Logan
Chairman, Randal W. (Randy) Scott, age 55, $290,000 total compensation
Chairman of the Board; President; Chief Executive Officer, Kimberly J. (Kim) Popovits, age 54, $420,000 total compensation
Executive Vice President - Research and Development; Chief Medical Officer, Steven (Steve) Shak, age 62, $380,000 total compensation
Chief Operating Officer, G. Bradley (Brad) Cole, age 57, $360,000 total compensation
SVP Human Resources, Tricia Tomlinson
Chief Financial Officer, Dean Schorno, age 49
Senior Vice President Chief Information Officer, Paul Aldridge
Senior Vice President Human Resources, Kim McEachron
Vice President Operations, Jon Cassel
Senior Vice President Worldwide Commercial, Jim Vaughn
Senior Vice President Biostatistics, Drew Watson
Chief Scientific Officer, Samuel Levy
Director, Ginger L. Graham, age 57

Director, Fred E. Cohen, age 56
Director, Woodrow A. Myers Jr., age 59
Director, Samuel D. (Sam) Colella, age 72
Director, Julian C. Baker, age 46
Director, Randall S. (Randy) Livingston, age 59
Auditors: Ernst&YoungLLP

LOCATIONS
HQ: Genomic Health Inc.
301 Penobscot Dr., Redwood City CA 94063
Phone: 650-556-9300 **Fax:** 650-556-1132
Web: www.genomichealth.com

2011 Sales

	$ mil.	% of total
US	187	91
International	18	9
Total	206	100

PRODUCTS/OPERATIONS

2011 Sales

	$ mil.	% of total
Product revenues	204	99
Contract revenues	1	1
Total	206	100

COMPETITORS

Celera	Myriad Genetics
Foundation Medicine	NanoString
GE Healthcare	Novartis
Genoptix	Precision Therapeutics
Genzyme	QIAGEN
Hologic	Quest Diagnostics
Johnson & Johnson	Response Genetics
LabCorp	Roche Diagnostics
Life Technologies Corporation	Siemens Healthcare
Med BioGene	deCODE genetics

HISTORICAL FINANCIALS
Company Type: Public

Income Statement
FYE: December 31

	REVENUE ($ mil.)	NET INCOME ($ mil.)	NET PROFIT MARGIN	EMPLOYEES
12/12	235.1	8.2	3.5%	612
12/11	206.1	7.8	3.8%	511
12/10	178.1	4.2	2.4%	472
12/09	149.5	(9.4)	—	453
12/08	110.5	(16.0)	—	387
Annual Growth	20.8%	—	—	12.1%

2012 Year-End Financials

Debt ratio: —
Return on equity: 6.8%
Cash ($ mil.): 18
Current ratio: 5.14
Long-term debt ($ mil.): —

No. of shares (mil.): 29
Dividends
Yield: —
Payout: —
Market value ($ mil.): 816

	STOCK PRICE ($) FY Close	P/E High/Low		PER SHARE ($) Earnings	Dividends	Book Value
12/12	27.24	137	95	0.26	0.00	4.22
12/11	25.39	107	72	0.26	0.00	3.88
12/10	21.39	157	82	0.15	0.00	2.97
12/09	19.56	—	—	(0.33)	0.00	2.39
12/08	19.48	—	—	(0.57)	0.00	2.33
Annual Growth	8.7%	—	—	—	—	16.1%

Gentex Corp.

Gentex would agree that competitors never look better than when they are in the rearview. The company focuses on designing making and marketing interior and exterior auto-dimming rearview mirrors and camera-based driver-assist systems for the automotive market. It serves customers worldwide but its largest base includes big carmakers such as Toyota General Motors and Volkswagen. Its products are found as standard or optional features on hundreds of vehicle models. To a lesser degree Gentex also makes dimmable aircraft windows found on commercial aircraft and fire protection products —including smoke detectors fire alarms and signaling devices —primarily for commercial buildings.

Geographic Reach Operating through five manufacturing facilities in Michigan Gentex has additional offices in the US Korea Canada France Mexico China Japan Sweden Hungary and the UK. Unsurprisingly the company's largest markets are the leading car production countries of the US (a third of sales) Germany (about a quarter) and Japan (nearly 10%).

Operations

The company's fire protection products are primarily sold to domestic distributors and OEMs of fire and security systems. Within the aerospace industry Gentex has delivered dimmable aircraft windows to the production line of Boeing's new 787 Dreamliner series and to Hawker Beechcraft for its business-class Beechcraft King Air 350i airplane. Gentex's dimmable window systems are marketed by PPG Aerospace under the brand name Alteos Interactive Window Systems.

Sales and Marketing The company's top customers are Volkswagen (15% of sales) General Motors and Toyota (each accounting for 12%) and Hyundai and Mercedes (both coming in at 11%). Other clients include BMW Ford Chrysler and Nissan. Gentex markets its products directly to OEMs as well as through Tier 1 suppliers.

Financial Performance The company's revenue jumped 25% in 2011 surpassing $1 billion for the first time in its history. It kept this momentum going in 2012 when revenue jumped by 7% from $1.02 billion to $1.1 billion. On the strength of the company's rising revenue net income increased by 2% in 2012 to hit $169 million the highest in the company's history.

Gentex was helped by a 32% surge in sales in Japan for 2012 and a 14% spike in sales in the US. It also experienced an 11% rise in auto-dimming mirror shipments reflecting the increase in light vehicle production in the North American market and increased penetration of those products on 2012 and 2013 model year vehicles.

Strategy To boost production capacity and support growth in its core geographic territories Gentex is busy making investments in its facilities. It constructed a new technology center adjacent to its headquarters in Zeeland Michigan and it is making a number of facility upgrades and renovations. The investments support the company's optimistic sales forecast and anticipated growing demand for high-tech camera-based automotive products such as Gentex's rear camera displays which consist of a liquid crystal display (LCD) that works with a rear-mounted video camera to provide a rear view while backing up and its SmartBeam high-beam assist system which uses a camera-on-a-chip to maximize forward lighting while eliminating the task of turning the high beams on and off manu-

ally. Both are integrated into Gentex auto-dimming mirrors.

HISTORY

At 23 Fred Bauer had already started and sold one company before founding Gentex in 1974. A maker of dual-cell photoelectric smoke detectors Gentex found its niche with products that had fewer false alarms and could detect slow smoldering fires. The company went public in 1981.

The next year Gentex entered the automotive market with the first electromechanical dimming mirror to beat the glare of nighttime driving. (Electrochromic technology uses electricity to darken a material.) The product was soon snapped up by Ford and General Motors to the tune of 200000 units a year. Five years later Gentex debuted the interior Night Vision Safety (NVS) electrochromic automatic-dimming mirror. Exterior NVS mirrors were introduced in 1991.

Gentex entered an agreement in 1992 with Japan's Ichikoh Industries to market mirrors in Asia. The following year it established a European office. Returning to its roots Gentex in 1993 introduced an AC/DC smoke detector. That year rival Donnelly paid $3.6 million in damages for infringing on Gentex's electrochromic mirror patent. Gentex formed a German subsidiary Gentex GmbH in 1994 and two years later opened an $8 million plant near its Michigan headquarters.

In 1997 Gentex developed a compass mirror a headlamp control mirror and a mirror that displays outside temperature. The next year it bought a stake in Photobit a developer of pixel sensor technology and sold more than 3.3 million NVS mirrors. In 1999 DaimlerChrysler agreed to equip all its models with Gentex mirrors.

Adding to its manufacturing capacity Gentex in 2000 completed the construction of a $12 million mirror manufacturing plant in Zeeland Michigan and made plans to build a factory in Europe. Adding more equipment to rearview mirrors paid off when GM announced that it would place the OnStar communications system in Gentex's interior mirrors in 1 million automobiles.

In 2002 Gentex announced that it would bring its new SmartBeam product to market by mid-2004. SmartBeam allowed drivers to use their bright lights more easily because the high beam self-dimmed when it detected an oncoming car. SureBeam came to market in 2004 the same year Gentex finished constructing a sales and engineering facility in Erlenbach Germany. The facility was intended to help Gentex better serve its European customers by offering greater logistics sales and engineering support.

EXECUTIVES

SVP International, James A. (Jim) Hollars, age 68
VP Fire Protection Products, Scott Edwards, age 58
VP-Mechanical Engrg, John Carter, age 65, $215,932 total compensation
VP Investor Relations Corporate Communications and Corporate Secretary, Connie Hamblin, age 52
VP Sales General Motors, Dennis Alexejun, age 60, $222,335 total compensation
Chairman and CEO, Fred T. Bauer, age 71, $428,979 total compensation
VP Business Development Japan Automakers, Robert (Bob) Vance, age 41
VP Operations, John Arnold, age 59
VP Human Resources, Bruce Los, age 58
VP Advanced Materials and Process Development, William (Bill) Tonar, age 60
VP Chemical Research, Tom Guarr, age 54

VP Finance and CFO, Steve Dykman, age 47, $163,586 total compensation
SVP, Enoch Jen, age 60, $242,896 total compensation
SVP, Mark Newton, age 54, $193,183 total compensation
VP Mechanical Engineering and Program Management, Jeremy Fogg
VP Operations, Paul Flynn
VP Europe, Brad Bosma
VP Quality, Ken Horner
CFO and VP of Finance, Steve Downing
Director, John Mulder, age 77
Director, Kenneth La Grand, age 71
Director, Wallace K. Tsuha Jr., age 70
Director, James H. (Jim) Wallace, age 70
Director, Rande S. Somma, age 60
Director, Arlyn Lanting, age 73
Director, Frederick (Fred) Sotok, age 79
Director, Gary F. Goode, age 68
SVP and Director, Mark Newton, age 53
Independent Director, Richard Schaum
Auditors: Ernst&YoungLLP

LOCATIONS

HQ: Gentex Corp.
600 N. Centennial Street, Zeeland, MI 49464
Phone: 616 772-1800   **Fax:** 616 772-7348
Web: www.gentex.com

2012 Sales

	$ mil.	% of total
Automotive products		
Germany	239	22
Other countries	355	32
Total	**1,099**	**100**

PRODUCTS/OPERATIONS

2012 Sales

	$ mil.	% of total
Automotive products	1,077	98
Total	**1,099**	**100**

Selected Products

Automotive
  Auto-dimming mirrors
  Curved glass mirrors
  Custom sensors (for detecting velocity rain and humidity)
  Interior lighting
  Microphones
  Mirror-based displays
  Side blind zone indicators
  SmartBeam (automatic high beam system integrated into auto-dimming mirror)
  Telematics systems
  Razor (turn signal lights)
  Rear camera display (LCD display integrated into auto-dimming mirror that works with a video camera mounted at rear of vehicle)
Fire protection
  Audio and visual signaling appliances
  Bells and speakers
  Carbon monoxide alarms
  Photoelectric smoke alarms and detectors
Other
  Dimmable aircraft windows

COMPETITORS

Ficosa
Guardian Industries
Ichikoh
Ingersoll-Rand Security Technologies
Magna Mirrors
Murakami Corp.
Safety Vision
SimplexGrinnell
UTC Climate Controls & Security
Universal Security Instruments
Visteon

Income Statement
FYE: December 31

	REVENUE ($ mil.)	NET INCOME ($ mil.)	NET PROFIT MARGIN	EMPLOYEES
12/12	1,099.5	168.5	15.3%	3,605
12/11	1,023.7	164.6	16.1%	3,481
12/10	816.2	137.7	16.9%	2,908
12/09	544.5	64.6	11.9%	2,371
12/08	623.8	62.0	10.0%	2,279
Annual Growth	15.2%	28.4%	—	12.1%

2012 Year-End Financials

Debt ratio: —	No. of shares (mil.): 143
Return on equity: 15.6%	Dividends
Cash ($ mil.): 389	Yield: 2.7%
Current ratio: 8.47	Payout: 43.5%
Long-term debt ($ mil.): —	Market value ($ mil.): 2,697

	STOCK PRICE ($) FY Close	P/E High/Low	PER SHARE ($) Earnings	Dividends	Book Value
12/12	18.85	26 13	1.17	0.51	7.83
12/11	29.59	29 19	1.14	0.47	7.13
12/10	29.56	30 17	0.98	0.44	6.28
12/09	17.85	39 15	0.47	0.44	5.32
12/08	8.83	44 15	0.44	0.43	5.08
Annual Growth	20.9%	— —	27.7%	4.7%	11.5%

Gentherm Inc

If Bob Carol TED and Alice are in your bed chances are TED is keeping the mattress cool ... or warm. Gentherm (formerly Amerigon) developed thermoelectric device (TED) technology and has incorporated it into the company's branded Climate-Control Seat (CCS) which allows year-round temperature control and ventilation of car seats on more than 40 vehicle models available in North America and Asia that are made by Ford General Motors and Nissan; the three customers collectively account for more than 70% of the company's sales. Gentherm provides the CCS under contracts with auto industry suppliers such as Lear and NHK Spring. In late 2012 the company changed its name from Amerigon to Gentherm.

The company has transformed its business structure in the wake of its 2011 milestone purchase of W.E.T. Automotive Systems a German-based firm that manufactures thermal systems for automotive seat applications. In June 2012 Amerigon began doing business as Gentherm and updated its trading symbol to better represent its new capabilities and extensive global reach now that W.E.T. Automotive Systems and itself have been officially integrated. (The name change became official after the company's shareholder meeting later in September 2012.)

Not just automotive seats cups and mattresses are warming up —so have Gentherm's revenues. The company reported a sales increase of 84% for 2010 over 2009. The company was slammed a couple of years prior when automotive production was at an all-time low but since North American manufacturers increased vehicle output by almost 40% in 2010 and Gentherm's sales have been on the rise.

Gentherm's bottom line was also helped with the launch of a couple of new products. In late 2010 it debuted its heated and cooled dual cup holder for vehicles with Chrysler's Dodge Charger being the first recipient. Also in 2010 the company premiered its heated and cooled suite of mattresses using Gentherm's thermoelectric technologies. The branded YuMe mattresses are sold through retailer Mattress Firm the retail subsidiary of Mattress Holding.

EXECUTIVES

Chairman, Oscar B. (Bud) Marx III, age 74, $75,000 total compensation
VP Quality and Operations, James L. Mertes, age 60, $194,293 total compensation
President Chief Executive Officer, Daniel R. Coker, age 60, $291,200 total compensation
President Ford Motor Company, James J. Paulsen, age 74
VP Finance CFO Secretary and Treasurer, Barry G. Steele, age 42, $192,611 total compensation
VP Sales and Marketing, Daniel J. Pace, age 62, $188,424 total compensation
President PurchasingNorthville MIBrent, Brent W. Jump, age 39
Executive Vice President Chief Financial Officer, Lewis BoothFormer
Vice President Strategic Marketing, Sophie DesormiereGroup
President Human ResourcesNorthville, David Bomzer
Vice President of Engineering and Product Development, Steve Davis
President & General CounselNorthville, Kenneth Phillips
President Chrysler International OperationsFrancois, Francois J. CastaingFormer
President Chief Executive Officer, Carlos E. MazzorinFormer
President Advanced Products and Managing Director for EuropeOdelzhausen, Marco Ranalli
President of our Automotive Business Unit, Frithjof Oldorff
Vice President Strategic Marketing, Sophie Desormiere
President of our Technologies Business Unit, Thomas Liedl
President Chief Executive Officer, Daniel R. Coker, age 60
Director, John M. Devine, age 69
Director, James J. Paulsen, age 72
Director, Francois J. Castaing, age 67
Director, Lon E. Bell, age 73
Director, Maurice E. P. Gunderson, age 62
Auditors: GrantThorntonLLP

LOCATIONS

HQ: Gentherm Incorporated
21680 Haggerty Rd. Ste. 101, Northville MI 48167
Phone: 248-504-0500 **Fax:** 248-348-9735
Web: www.gentherm.com

2010 Sales

	$ mil.	% of total
US	41	37
Japan	21	19
South Korea	18	16
Mexico	16	14
UK	8	8
Canada	4	4
China	1	1
Germany	0	1
Taiwan	-	-
Total	**112**	**100**

PRODUCTS/OPERATIONS

2010 Sales by Customer

	% of total
Ford Motor	32
General	22
Nissan	17
Hyundai	16
Jaguar/Land	8
Toyota	5
Total	**100**

Selected Capabilities
Advancing core technology
Noise vibration and airflow management
Program management
Testing
Thermoelectric applications

COMPETITORS

Delphi Automotive Systems
Leggett & Platt
Magna International
Robert Bosch
Toyota Boshoku
Visteon

HISTORICAL FINANCIALS
Company Type: Public

Income Statement
FYE: December 31

	REVENUE ($ mil.)	NET INCOME ($ mil.)	NET PROFIT MARGIN	EMPLOYEES
12/12	554.9	17.8	3.2%	116
12/11	369.5	10.3	2.8%	110
12/10	112.4	9.9	8.9%	93
12/09	60.9	0.7	1.2%	68
12/08	63.6	3.5	5.6%	78
Annual Growth	71.9%	49.6%	—	10.4%

2012 Year-End Financials

Debt ratio: 12.9%	No. of shares (mil.): 29
Return on equity: 11.9%	Dividends
Cash ($ mil.): 58	Yield: —
Current ratio: 2.07	Payout: —
Long-term debt ($ mil.): 39	Market value ($ mil.): 397

	STOCK PRICE ($) FY Close	P/E High/Low	PER SHARE ($) Earnings	Dividends	Book Value
12/12	13.30	45 26	0.39	0.00	6.18
12/11	14.26	200 113	0.09	0.00	4.83
12/10	10.88	25 15	0.44	0.00	2.61
12/09	7.94	307 75	0.03	0.00	2.24
12/08	3.26	132 16	0.16	0.00	2.12
Annual Growth	42.1%	— —	25.0%	—	30.6%

Gentiva Health Services Inc

Gentiva Health Services is a gentle giant. As one of the nation's largest home health care and hospice services firms the company provides home nursing care through a network of about 270 agency locations in some 40 states. Gentiva's home care nurses provide services ranging from acute-care treatment to housekeeping for the elderly or disabled. Its hospice services are offered through 150 locations in 30 states. Gentiva also offers consulting services to the home care industry to help with regulatory and reimbursement issues. Gentiva also provides hospice operations through subsidiary Odyssey HealthCare.

Operations

The company's home health services segment accounts for more than 50% of its sales. Hospice contributes about 45%.

Sales and Marketing

Medicare contracts account for more than 75% of Gentiva's home health sales and more than 90% of its hospice sales. The company also receives reimbursement from local governments other insurance entities and private payers.

Financial Performance

Gentiva Health Services (GHS) posted a 27% gain in sales in 2011 vs. 2010 buoyed by a 123% gain at its hospice operation from the Odyssey acquisition (completed in 2010). Home health saw its revenues decline by nearly 5%. The divestiture of 34 home health and nine hospice branches in late 2011 negatively impacted 2011 sales. Despite the double-digit sales gain GHS was unprofitable in 2011.

Strategy

While it is focused on making Odyssey at home figuring out its next acquisition target and keeping its operations slim and trim Gentiva also has to keep its eyes on the Health Care Reform Act and other state and federal measures that could adversely impact hospice providers. Reductions or changes in Medicare or Medicaid funding would obviously significantly reduce Gentiva's patient service revenue and profitability.

Mergers and Acquisitions

Gentiva's growth has primarily come from purchases of smaller providers and agencies in high-growth regions over the past decade. As a big player in the highly-fragmented health market Gentiva has plenty of small- to-mid-size regional home health agencies from which to choose. Many recent purchases have focused on strengthening operations in the Southwest.

The company also occasionally makes larger purchases. It spent about $1 billion to acquire hospice provider Odyssey in mid-2010. The deal boosted its position in the hospice industry and made Gentiva the largest combination home health and hospice care provider in the US. In 2013 Gentiva acquired Harden Healthcare a provider of home health hospice and community care operations. The $409 million purchase excluded the Harden long-term care operations which were retained by Harden's shareholders.

Ownership

Wells Fargo & Co. owns about 10% of Gentiva's shares.

Company Background

Gentiva Health Services was formed a decade ago when staffing firm Olsten spun off its health services unit after being acquired by Adecco.

EXECUTIVES

EVP CFO and Treasurer, Eric R. Slusser
SVP Chief Compliance Officer General Counsel and Secretary, John N. Camperlengo, $243,863 total compensation
President and CEO, H. Anthony (Tony) Strange, $634,247 total compensation
Chairman, Rodney D. Windley
SVP and Chief Clinical Officer, Charlotte A. Weaver, $259,068 total compensation
SVP and President Home Health, David A. Causby
SVP and President Hospice, Jeff Shaner
Vice President - Treasury and Investor Relations, John Mongelli

Director, Stuart Olsten, age 59
Director, Victor F. Ganzi, age 66
Director, Ronald A. (Ron) Malone, age 57
Director, Philip R. Lochner Jr., age 69
Director, Raymond S. Troubh, age 85
Director, Sheldon M. Retchin, age 62
Vice Chairman, Rodney D. Windley, age 64
Director, Robert S. Forman Jr., age 72
Auditors: PricewaterhouseCoopersLLP

LOCATIONS

HQ: Gentiva Health Services Inc.
3350 Riverwood Pkwy. Ste. 1400, Atlanta GA 30339-3314
Phone: 770-951-6450   **Fax:** 800-823-8819
Web: www.savvydiner.com

PRODUCTS/OPERATIONS

2011 Sales

	$ mil.	% of total
Home Health	1,012	56
Total	**1,798**	**100**

2011 Sales by Payer

Medicare		
Hospice	729	41
Commercial insurance & other	187	10

Selected Services

Cardiopulmonary health management
Consulting and support for home health agencies
Disease and pain management
Homemaker services
Hospice
Injury or immobility therapy
Infusion therapy
Medication management and education
Neurological rehabilitation
Orthopedic rehabilitation
Personal care aides
Physical occupational and speech therapy
Respiratory therapy
Skilled nursing
Wound care

Selected Acquisitions

2012
Advocate Hospice (hospice; Danville Indiana)
Family Home Care Corporation (home health and hospice; Spokane Washington)
North Mississippi Hospice (hospice; Oxford Mississippi)
2010
Heart to Heart Hospices (hospice; Starkville and Tupelo Mississippi)
Odyssey HealthCare Inc. ($1 billion home health and hospice services Dallas)
United Home Care Group (home health services Louisiana)
2009
Coordinated Home Health Care Inc.'s Medicare certified assets (home health services; Las Cruces and Silver City New Mexico and in El Paso Texa)
Mid-State Home Health (home health services; Alexandria Louisiana)
Rush Home Care Inc. - d/b/a Magna Home Health (home health services; Meridian Mississippi and Gilbertown Alabama)
2008
Home Health Care Affiliates Inc. - dba Gilbert's Home Health and Gilbert's Hospice Care ($55 million home health and hospice services Mississippi)
Hospice of Charleston (home health and hospice services South Carolina)
Physicians Home Health Care (home health services; Colorado)

COMPETITORS

Addus HomeCare	HCR ManorCare
Almost Family	Home Instead

Amedisys	LHC Group
American HomePatient	Lincare Holdings
Apria Healthcare	NHC
Arcadia Resources	National Home Health
Chemed	Personal-Touch Home
Coram	Care
Critical Homecare	Star Multi Care
Solutions	VITAS Healthcare
DaVita	
Guardian Home Care	
Holdings	

HISTORICAL FINANCIALS

Company Type: Public

Income Statement

FYE: December 31

	REVENUE ($ mil.)	NET INCOME ($ mil.)	NET PROFIT MARGIN	EMPLOYEES
12/12	1,712.8	26.8	1.6%	14,600
12/11	1,798.7	(450.5)	—	14,800
12/10*	1,447.0	52.1	3.6%	9,600
01/10	1,152.4	59.1	5.1%	5,200
12/08	1,300.4	153.4	11.8%	15,450
Annual Growth	7.1%	(35.4%)	—	(1.4%)

*Fiscal year change

2012 Year-End Financials

Debt ratio: 61.8%	No. of shares (mil.): 30
Return on equity: 12.3%	Dividends
Cash ($ mil.): 207	Yield: —
Current ratio: 1.78	Payout: —
Long-term debt ($ mil.): 910	Market value ($ mil.): 309

	STOCK PRICE ($) FY Close	P/E High/Low		PER SHARE ($) Earnings	Dividends	Book Value
12/12	10.05	14	6	0.87	0.00	7.58
12/11	6.75	—	—	(14.85)	0.00	6.50
12/10*	26.60	17	11	1.71	0.00	21.08
01/10	27.01	14	6	1.98	0.00	19.38
12/08	26.96	5	3	5.21	0.00	17.15
Annual Growth	(21.9%) (18.5%)	—	—	(36.1%)	—	

*Fiscal year change

GEO Group, Inc.

The GEO Group sticks to its convictions and it relies on them to generate business. With locations in about 25 states the company one of the largest operators of private correctional facilities in the US (along with Corrections Corporation of America) operates more than 115 correctional detention and mental health facilities with some 81000 beds. Besides incarceration GEO offers educational rehabilitative and vocational training programs at its facilities. The firm offers mental health and residential treatment services through its GEO Care subsidiary.

HISTORY

The company that became The Geo Group began as part of the Wackenhut Corporation (now known as G4S Secure Solutions (USA)) which was founded in 1954 as an investigation firm and moved into the security guard business the next year. When the prison population began to grow in the late 1970s and early 1980s (because of tougher sentences and new federal drug laws) Wackenhut established its Wackenhut Corrections division in 1984 to focus on prison management.

In 1986 the division won its first contract to construct a Colorado facility for the Immigration and Naturalization Service. Two years later Wackenhut Corrections became a full-fledged subsidiary of its parent. Wackenhut Corrections ventured overseas in 1992 when it began operating a prison in Australia and formed a joint venture Premier Prison Services with Serco Group to provide prison management services in the UK.

The company's next step was to go public which it did in 1994 when Wackenhut Corporation sold a minority stake. Also that year Premier Prison Services won its first contract to operate a prison in the town of Doncaster in the UK. The joint venture won another deal in 1997 to manage a 500-bed prison in Kilmarnock Scotland. However Wackenhut Corrections was forced to change policies after violence at some of its foreign prisons. To solve the problem the company replaced American guards with native hires and began paying more attention to troublesome inmates.

Wackenhut Corrections moved beyond prisons in 1997 buying an 86-bed psychiatric hospital in Fort Lauderdale Florida. The next year Wackenhut Corrections spun off a real estate investment trust (REIT) Correctional Properties Trust to buy and build prison facilities and lease them back to the company. (The REIT was later renamed CentraCore Properties Trust.)

Wackenhut Corrections stumbled in 1999 when the state of Texas took over control of a Wackenhut-operated prison in Austin after allegations that guards had had sex with female inmates. In addition a riot at a New Mexico prison sparked bad publicity. But business continued to roll in and the company gained contracts to run a prison in New Zealand and a hospital in Florida.

After its closure in 2000 Wackenhut's juvenile facility in Jena Louisiana was named in a lawsuit brought by the US Justice Department against Louisiana prisons. The company shifted focus to its international operations in 2001 —it expanded existing prisons in Australia and opened prisons in South Africa and the UK.

Danish security firm Group 4 Falck gained control of Wackenhut Corrections in 2002 when it acquired Wackenhut Corporation. Late in the year Wackenhut Corrections acquired four additional facilities in Michigan New Mexico North Carolina and Texas.

In an effort to raise capital needed to expand its prison systems Wackenhut Corrections sold its 50% stake in Premier Custodial Group to Serco in 2003. Also that year Wackenhut Corrections bought back the 57% stake that Group 4 Falck held in the company. As a condition of the purchase the company changed its name to The GEO Group and abandoned its connection to the Wackenhut trademark and name.

GEO expanded in 2005 by buying smaller US rival Correctional Services Corporation. GEO paid about $62 million in cash for Correctional Services and assumed about $124 million of the company's debt. Upon the deal's closing GEO sold Correctional Services' juvenile operations to Correctional Services CEO James Slattery. Correctional Services' adult operations —16 facilities with an overall capacity of about 8000 beds —were absorbed into those of GEO.

In 2006 the company sold its mental health subsidiary Atlantic Shores Healthcare (ASH) which included a 72-bed mental health hospital for approximately $11.5 million. Also that year GEO renewed its contract (for an additional five years)

with the US Department of State and the US Department of Homeland Security to operate the Migrant Operations Center (MOC) at Guantanamo Bay. The MOC a separate facility from the controversial GITMO detention center is intended for immigrants caught at sea without US entry documents.

In 2009 GEO opened a new $62 million Florida Civil Commitment Center (FCCC) in Arcadia Florida. The facility has a capacity of 720 residents and provides treatment services to sexually violent predators. FCCC is operated by GEO Care under a management contract with the Florida Department of Children and Families. Also that year GEO purchased Just Care a provider of medical and mental health services to detainees primarily in Georgia and South Carolina for about $40 million.

Events in 2010 included the company's $730 million acquisition of rival Cornell Companies a private provider of educational treatment and correctional services. Cornell's business which comprises outsourced-contracts with federal state and local governmental agencies is included in GEO's US Detention & Corrections and GEO Care segments which due to the Cornell acquisition generated sales of about $85 and $66 million respectively. The Cornell investment came subsequent to GEO's

GEO also wrapped up a number of projects in 2010 including the completion of the Aurora ICE Processing Center (Colorado) Blackwater River Correctional Facility (Florida) and Harmondsworth Immigration Removal Centre (London). Additionally it landed a new management contract with the D. Ray James Correctional Facility (Georgia).

EXECUTIVES

Chairman and CEO; Chairman GEO Care, George C. Zoley, age 63, $1,017,962 total compensation
Senior Vice President Human Resources, Stephen V. (Steve) Fuller
SVP General Counsel and Secretary, John J. Bulfin, age 59, $391,846 total compensation
SVP; President U.S. Corrections, John M. Hurley, age 65, $409,423 total compensation
SVP Residential Treatment Services; President GEO Care, Jorge A. Dominicis, age 50
SVP and CFO, Brian R. Evans, age 45, $360,577 total compensation
VP Corporate Relations, Pablo E. Paez
Senior Vice President Project Development, Thomas M. (Tom) Wierdsma, age 62
VP Chief Accounting Officer and Controller, Ronald A. Brack, age 51
Vice President Finance, Craig A. Jenkins
VP Finance and Treasurer, Shayn P. March, age 47
Vice President Business Development, David O. Meehan
Director, Richard H. Glanton, age 66
Director, Anne N. Foreman, age 65
Director, Norman A. Carlson, age 79
Director, Clarence E. Anthony, age 53
Director, Christopher C. Wheeler, age 66
Auditors: GrantThorntonLLP

LOCATIONS

HQ: The GEO Group Inc.
1 Park Place Ste. 700 621 NW 53rd St., Boca Raton FL 33487-8242
Phone: 561-893-0101   **Fax:** 561-443-6028
Web: www.geogroup.com

2012 Sales

	$ mil.	% of total
US	1,267	86
UK	32	2
Total	**1,479**	**100**

PRODUCTS/OPERATIONS

2012 Sales

	$ mil.	% of total
US Corrections	975	66
International services	211	14
Total	**1,479**	**100**

Selected Products and Services

Adult inmate management
Behavioral health and residential treatment services for youthful offenders
Community-based residential re-entry services
Construction management
Correctional health care services
Electronic monitoring devices
Facility design
Facility maintenance
Facility management
Facility operation
Infrastructure financing
Pre-trial and immigration custody services
Residential mental health / special needs services
Secure prisoner escort

Selected Facilities

Allen Correctional Center (Kinder Louisiana)
Arizona State Prison - Phoenix West (Phoenix Arizona)
Aurora ICE Processing Center (Aurora Colorado)
Blackwater River Correctional Facility (Milton Florida)
Bronx Community Re-Entry Center (Bronx New York)
Brooklyn Community Correctional Center (Brooklyn New York)
Broward Transition Center (Deerfield Beach Florida)
D. Ray James Correctional Facility (Folkston Georgia)
Harmondsworth Immigration Removal Centre (London England)
Lawrenceville Correctional Center (Lawrenceville Virginia)
South Bay Correctional Facility (South Bay Florida)

COMPETITORS

3M
Avalon Correctional Services
Corizon
Corrections Corporation of America
G4S
MHM Services
Management & Training
Res-Care
Sodexo

HISTORICAL FINANCIALS

Company Type: Public

Income Statement

FYE: December 31

	REVENUE ($ mil.)	NET INCOME ($ mil.)	NET PROFIT MARGIN	EMPLOYEES
12/12*	1,479.0	134.7	9.1%	18,733
01/12	1,612.9	78.6	4.9%	18,894
01/11	1,269.9	63.4	5.0%	19,352
01/10	1,141.0	65.9	5.8%	13,026
12/08	1,043.0	58.9	5.6%	12,378
Annual Growth	9.1%	23.0%	—	10.9%

*Fiscal year change

2012 Year-End Financials

Debt ratio: 52.4%	No. of shares (mil.): 71
Return on equity: 13.0%	Dividends
Cash ($ mil.): 31	Yield: 21.5%
Current ratio: 1.30	Payout: 519.6%
Long-term debt ($ mil.): 1,434	Market value ($ mil.): 2,014

	STOCK PRICE ($) FY Close	P/E High/Low		PER SHARE ($) Earnings	Dividends	Book Value
12/12*	28.20	14	8	2.20	6.08	14.66
01/12	16.75	22	13	1.23	0.00	21.63
01/11	24.66	23	16	1.13	0.00	15.81
01/10	21.88	17	9	1.27	0.00	12.87
12/08	18.13	25	11	1.14	0.00	11.32
Annual Growth	11.7%	—	—	17.9%	—	6.7%

*Fiscal year change

Geospace Technologies Corp

Geospace Technologies (formerly OYO Geospace) analyzes the spaces below the earth's surface to help companies find gas and oil. It makes instruments and equipment used by seismic contractors and oil and gas companies to gather and process seismic data to zero in on hydrocarbons. The company's geophones detect energy from the earth's subsurface and its hydrophones detect changes in pressure and gather seismic data in water. Other products include seismic leader wire geophone string connectors seismic telemetry cable and thermal imaging equipment; all are compatible with most seismic data-acquisition systems. Geospace also makes its thermal printers available for the commercial graphics industry.

Operations

The company has two business lines: seismic products (its largest segment) and thermal solutions products. Geospace's seismic product lines consist of land and marine nodal seismic data acquisition systems high-definition reservoir characterization products and services geophones and hydrophones (including multi-component geophones and hydrophones) seismic leader wire geophone string and acquisition system connectors seismic telemetry cables marine seismic cable retrieval and steering devices and specialized data acquisition systems targeted at conventional and niche markets.

Geospace's thermal printers include both thermal imagesetters for graphics applications and thermal plotters for seismic applications. In addition its thermal solutions products include direct-to-screen systems thermal printheads dry thermal film thermal transfer ribbons and other thermal media. The company also distributes private label high-quality dry thermal media for use in its thermal printers and direct-to-screen systems.

Geographic Reach

Geospace sells products to customers around the world. It is headquartered in Houston Texas. International offices are located in Canada China Russia and the UK. International manufacturing facilities are located in Canada and Russia.

Sales and Marketing

The company's principal seismic customers are seismic contractors and major independent and government-owned oil and gas companies that either operate their own seismic crews or specify seismic instrument and equipment preferences to contractors. Geospace's customers deepwater reservoir characterization products are generally large international oil and gas companies that op-

erate long-term offshore oil and gas producing properties. The company's thermal imaging customers are direct users of its equipment as well as specialized resellers that focus on the newsprint silkscreen and corrugated box printing industries.

Financial Performance

Revenue increased by 11% in fiscal year 2012 due to higher customer demand for seismic products and particularly robust demand for sales and rentals of land-based wireless (or nodal) data acquisition systems driven by strong oil and gas exploration activities throughout the world.

Geospace's net income grew by 18% in fiscal year 2012 thanks to higher revenues and an increase in gross profits resulting from improved sales and rentals of seismic products.

Except for the revenue slump in 2009 the company saw an upward trend in revenues from fiscal year 2008 to 2012. The slump in 2009 was because of a decrease in sales stemming from the decline in customer demand for seismic products as a result of the effects of the worldwide economic slowdown and its impact on energy exploration activities.

Strategy

Geospace relies on a broad base of customers in a wide swath of countries to protect it from dramatic downturns in particular markets. While it has about 50 seismic contracting companies (about 20 of which specialize in marine activities) it also sells thermal printer products as part of its product diversification strategy.

In 2011 the company sold to Dawson Geophysical Company 14850 channels of its galvanic skin response (GSR) wireless data acquisition system for $15.6 million. This transaction aids Geospace's plans of making GSR wireless technology available to their customers under a rent-to-own strategy.

The company dropped OYO from its corporate name in 2012 following the sale of Japanese conglomerate OYO Corporation's 21% stake in the company.

Ownership

Eagle Asset Management owns 18% of Geospace.

EXECUTIVES

CFO, Thomas T. McEntire, age 53, $220,000 total compensation
SVP and CTO, Michael J. Sheen, age 65, $247,500 total compensation
Chairman President and CEO, Gary D. Owens, age 66, $275,000 total compensation
VP Human Resources, Lacey C. Rice, age 57, $96,300 total compensation
EVP and Chief Project Engineer, Robbin B. Adams
EVP and COO, Walter R. Wheeler
Director, Richard C. White, age 58
SVP CTO and Director, Michael J. Sheen, age 64
Director, Thomas L. Davis, age 65
Director, Charles H. (Hank) Still, age 70
Director, William H. (Hank) Moody, age 73
Director, Takashi Kanemori
Auditors: UHYLLP

LOCATIONS

HQ: Geospace Technologies Corporation
7007 Pinemont Dr., Houston TX 77040-6601
Phone: 713-986-4444   **Fax:** 713-986-4445
Web: www.geospace.com

2012 Sales

	$ mil.	% of total
North America		
US	216	85
Canada	23	9

Russian Federation	9	4
Europe		
UK	4	2
Adjustments (62.7)		
Total	**191**	**100**

PRODUCTS/OPERATIONS

2012 Sales

	$ mil.	% of total
Seismic	178	92
Thermal Solutions	12	7
Corporate	0	1
Total	**191**	**100**

Selected Products

Seismic
 Data-acquisition systems
 Geophone string connectors
 Geophones
 High-definition reservoir characterization equipment
 Hydrophones
 Marine seismic cable retrieval devices
 Seismic leader wire
 Seismic telemetry cable
Thermal Solutions
 Dry thermal film (distribution)
 Thermal imaging equipment (wide-format thermal printers for newsprint and other commercial applications)

COMPETITORS

Amphenol	Mitcham Industries
Bolt Technology	Petroleum Geo-Services
CGG	Ricoh Company
Core Laboratories	ShawCor
Dawson Geophysical	WesternGeco
ION Geophysical	Xante

HISTORICAL FINANCIALS

Company Type: Public

Income Statement

FYE: September 30

	REVENUE ($ mil.)	NET INCOME ($ mil.)	NET PROFIT MARGIN	EMPLOYEES
09/13	300.6	69.5	23.1%	1,333
09/12	191.6	35.1	18.3%	1,164
09/11	172.9	29.7	17.2%	1,008
09/10	128.5	14.0	11.0%	891
09/09	92.8	1.7	1.9%	836
Annual Growth	34.1%	150.7%	—	12.4%

2013 Year-End Financials

Debt ratio: 0.2%	No. of shares (mil.): 12
Return on equity: 27.6%	Dividends
Cash ($ mil.): 2	Yield: —
Current ratio: 6.73	Payout: —
Long-term debt ($ mil.): 0	Market value ($ mil.): 1,091

	STOCK PRICE ($) FY Close	P/E High/Low		PER SHARE ($) Earnings	Dividends	Book Value
09/13	84.29	26	12	5.38	0.00	22.33
09/12	122.41	44	19	2.74	0.00	16.79
09/11	56.29	46	24	2.37	0.00	13.94
09/10	57.88	48	20	1.14	0.00	11.16
09/09	25.83	262	62	0.15	0.00	9.90
Annual Growth	34.4%	—	—146.8%		—	22.6%

Global Payments, Inc.

Go ahead —Chaaaaaarge! And when you do Global Payments will do what it does to ensure a seamless transaction. The company provides credit and debit card processing check authorization and other electronic payment processing services for more than 1 million merchant and business locations worldwide including financial institutions governments gaming locations and multinational corporations. It targets small and midsized merchants who are often overlooked by other payment processors. Global Payments also offers electronic tax payment and benefits transfer processing. The company operates throughout North America Europe and the Asia/Pacific region.

Geographic Reach

Atlanta-based Global Payments has operations in the US Canada Brazil Central Europe Russia the UK and the Asia-Pacific Region. The company's North American (US Canada and Brazil) merchant services business accounts for more than 70% of its sales. International brings in the rest.

Sales and Marketing

The company targets customers in a variety of industries including finance gaming (casinos) health care professional services restaurants and retail as well as government universities utilities and non-profit organizations.

Financial Performance

Global Payments' sales increased 8% in fiscal 2013 (ended May) versus the prior year to almost $2.4 billion. Net income increased 15% over the same period to $216 million. Driving sales growth in 2013 was the company's US independent sales organizations (ISO) channel growth from the direct sales channels and gaming business and growth in Europe. Canada logged a 6% decline in annual sales while sales in Asia-Pacific were flat. Net income was lifted by the increase in sales and lower processing costs. As credit and debit cards and other forms of electronic payment displace cash at the register Global Payments has seen its business increase. Indeed over the past decade the company's revenue and profits have more than tripled.

Strategy

The company has been really pushing to put the "global" in "global payments." The payment processor has expanded its international merchant services arm over the years through numerous acquisitions and alliances. In 2014 Global Payments inked a deal to acquire Payment Processing Inc. for $420 million in cash as it works to expand its direct distribution efforts.

In late 2012 the company bought the remaining 44% interest in its merchant services joint venture (formed in 2006) in Asia-Pacific from The Hongkong and Shanghai Banking Corporation Limited ("HSBC"). In all Global Payments operates in about a dozen nations in the region. The company became the first foreign card processor to launch card acquiring services in China in 2010. Global Payments teamed with Shanghai Banking Corporation to start China UnionPay which processes domestic and foreign card transactions via a common point-of-sale system.

In a similar fashion in 2010 the firm took full control of its joint venture with HSBC Merchant Services the UK-based processing operations of international bank HSBC thereby doubling its international revenue. The company maintains a marketing agreement with HSBC for the venture.

The company intends to further diversify in international markets that have potential for industry growth. Key areas include Europe the Asia/Pacific region and South America. In late 2010 it established a payments processing joint venture with Spanish bank La Caixa in a deal which has already brought the company an increase in earnings. The following year it acquired a merchant processing business in Malta.

Additionally the company has targeted Central and Eastern Europe as key growth markets. It operates in the Czech Republic the Balkans and Russia providing credit scoring card personalization and card database management services in addition to payment processing. Its ZAO United Card Service unit provides direct merchant acquisitions and indirect payment processing throughout Russia.

On the mobile payment front Global Payments in 2013 entered into an agreement with ShopKeep POS an iPad point-of-sale (POS) product for brick-and-mortar businesses to offer an iPad POS to its merchants throughout the US. The firm also teamed with three major UK mobile payments providers to enable merchants to accept card payments using a smartphone or tablet. The deal helps foster the acceptance of mobile payments among small businesses in the UK.

Mergers Acquisitions and Divestments

In the US Global Payments acquired payment technology provider Accelerated Payment Technologies (APT) in late 2012 from Great Hill Partners. APT produces some $8 billion in annual card volume catering to small- to medium-sized merchants. The company markets its products and services to a network of 700 value-added resellers spanning more than 30 different vertical markets. The firm also purchased the US merchant portfolio of CyberSource from Visa for $14.9 million.

In late 2011 Global Payments acquired the merchant acquiring business of Alfa-Bank Russia's largest privately owned bank.

Global Payments sold its former international money transfer businesses DolEx and Europhil in 2010 to Palladium Equity Partners for $85 million. The divested units specialized in offering money transfer services to immigrants sending funds to their home countries. The money transfer business suffered in the economic downturn and Global Payments responded by closing underperforming stores selling certain operations and ultimately exiting the business. The sale allowed the company to concentrate on its core merchant services operations.

EXECUTIVES

SEVP and CFO, David E. Mangum, age 47, $230,769 total compensation
Chairman, Paul R. Garcia, age 60, $950,000 total compensation
SVP Strategic Planning and Investor Relations, Jane M. Elliott
EVP and General Counsel, Suellyn P. Tornay, age 53, $350,000 total compensation
Advisor Business Development and International Operations, Carl J. Williams, age 61, $500,000 total compensation
President International, Morgan M. (Mac) Schuessler Jr., age 43
President Global Payments Canada, Jordan E. Cohen
President International, Joseph C. Hyde, $400,000 total compensation
President Global Payments Asia Pacific, James R. Hicks

President and Chief Executive Officer; Director, Jeffrey S. Sloan
Media Relations, Christine Li
VP Corporate Marketing, Amy Corn
Senior Vice President; Chief Accounting Officer, Daniel Keefe
Senior Vice President; Chief Accounting Officer, Daniel OKeefe
Chief Human Resource Officer; Senior Vice President, Thomas Balas
Director, Raymond L. (Ray) Killian, age 76
Director, Gerald J. Wilkins, age 55
Director, Alan M. Silberstein, age 65
Director, William I. Jacobs, age 71
Director, Alex W. (Pete) Hart, age 72
Director, Edwin H. Burba Jr., age 76
Director, Michael W. (Mike) Trapp, age 73
Director, Ruth Ann Marshall, age 59
Auditors: Deloitte&ToucheLLP

LOCATIONS

HQ: Global Payments Inc.
10 Glenlake Pkwy. NE North Tower, Atlanta GA 30328-3473
Phone: 770-829-8000   **Fax:** -10197
Web: www.tecnocom.biz

2013 Sales

	$ mil.	% of total
North America		
US	1,394	59
Canada	311	13
Europe	522	22
Asia/Pacific	147	6
Total	**2,375**	**100**

PRODUCTS/OPERATIONS

Selected Subsidiaries and Affiliates

Comercia Global Payments Entidad de Pago S.L. (51% Spain)
DolEx Belgium S.P.R.L.
DolEx Europe S.L. (Spain)
Global Payment Holding Company
Global Payment Systems of Canada Ltd.
Global Payments Asia-Pacific (Hong Kong) Limited
Global Payments Asia-Pacific (Hong Kong Holding) Limited
Global Payments Asia-Pacific Processing Company Limited (Hong Kong)
Global Payments Canada Inc.
Global Payments Europe s.r.o. (Czech Republic)
Global Payments Gaming Canada Inc.
Global Payments Gaming International Inc.
GPS Holding Limited Partnership
Sabir Invest S.L.U. (Spain)

COMPETITORS

Banc of America Merchant Services
Barclays
Chase Paymentech Solutions
Elavon
Euronet
First Data
Global Cash Access
Heartland Payment Systems
Moneris Solutions
MoneyGram International
Royal Bank of Scotland
Standard Chartered
Total System Services
Western Union
WorldPay

HISTORICAL FINANCIALS

Company Type: Public

Income Statement

FYE: May 31

	REVENUE ($ mil.)	NET INCOME ($ mil.)	NET PROFIT MARGIN	EMPLOYEES
05/13	2,375.9	216.1	9.1%	3,954
05/12	2,203.8	188.1	8.5%	3,796
05/11	1,859.8	209.2	11.3%	3,753
05/10	1,642.4	203.3	12.4%	3,592
05/09	1,601.5	37.2	2.3%	5,844
Annual Growth	10.4%	55.2%	—	(9.3%)

2013 Year-End Financials

Debt ratio: 36.8%	No. of shares (mil.): 75
Return on equity: 18.6%	Dividends
Cash ($ mil.): 680	Yield: 0.1%
Current ratio: 1.72	Payout: 3.4%
Long-term debt ($ mil.): 891	Market value ($ mil.): 3,617

	STOCK PRICE ($) FY Close	P/E High/Low	PER SHARE ($) Earnings	Dividends	Book Value
05/13	47.96	18 14	2.76	0.08	15.19
05/12	42.48	22 16	2.37	0.08	14.92
05/11	51.96	20 14	2.60	0.08	14.74
05/10	42.19	22 14	2.48	0.08	10.81
05/09	35.96	106 59	0.46	0.08	13.02
Annual Growth	7.5%	— —	56.5%	(0.0%)	3.9%

GNC Holdings Inc

What's good for the GNC customer is great for the company's bottom line. GNC Holdings operates the world's leading nutritional-supplements retail chain devoted to items such as vitamins supplements minerals and dietary products. The firm manufactures private-label products for Rite Aid Sam's Club and PetSmart and drugstore.com. Altogether GNC has more than 7700 stores consisting of some 3200 company-owned stores in the US Canada and Puerto Rico followed by 2780 franchised stores in 50-plus countries and 2180 store-within-a-store sites in Rite Aid locations. Founded as a health food store in Pittsburgh in 1935 fast-growing GNC Holdings went public in 2011.

HISTORY

David Shakarian the son of a dairyman founded General Nutrition Companies (GNC) in 1935 as a small Pittsburgh health store called Lackzoom which specialized in selling yogurt and offered honey grains and "health sandwiches." The store prospered and six months later Shakarian opened a second location also in Pittsburgh.

By the early 1940s Shakarian operated six Pittsburgh-area stores. In 1947 the company began its first advertising initiatives using both newspapers and radio. In the 1950s it began selling through mail-order catalogs gaining access to less-populated areas and increasing brand recognition.

The stores benefited from the newly popular alternative approaches to health and medicine in the 1960s. Shakarian decided to expand into other states and changed the chain's name to General Nutrition Centers. GNC continued to add stores and expanded its offerings by adding its own vitamin and mineral supplements as well as health

drinks and foods and cosmetics. The company also began placing stores in malls as those venues became prevalent.

The company experienced a number of changes in its management in the mid-2000s. Former Family Dollar executive Bruce Barkus was named president and CEO in the summer of 2005 after the departure of Louis Mancini in late 2004. In November 2005 Joseph Fortunato (former EVP and COO) took the helm.

Aggressive marketing helped the company prosper. GNC clerks could be found outside stores hawking trendy products and free samples of health foods. By the late 1970s about 50% of sales were from vitamins and other supplements. By the early 1980s the company ran a national network of 1300 stores.

Although GNC benefited from the sale of diet-craze products such as starch blockers it struggled with new competition as supermarkets added health foods and drugstores improved their health supplements' selections. As the company reached a nadir in 1984 Shakarian died igniting a power struggle. It ended in the firing of longtime president Gary Daum; the ouster of Bart Shakarian (David's brother) from the company's board; and the hiring of Jerry Horn who had revitalized Recreational Equipment Inc. (REI) a sporting goods retailer. Horn changed the focus of the company's product line sold GNC's mail-order business and dumped poorly performing stores (by 1989 it had closed more than 300 stores). In 1987 GNC began franchising outlets to help finance expansion plans.

GNC executives teamed with the Thomas H. Lee investment group in 1987 and took the company private in a $361 million LBO. William Watts became CEO in 1991. Lee took the company public again in 1993 eliminating much of its debt and giving it more capital to pursue expansion. Expansion included several acquisitions such as Nature Food Centres (1994) and the Health & Diet Group (UK 1995). In 1996 the company bought the Nature's fresh grocery chain (sold to Wild Oats in 1999). By 1997 81 of the Nature Food Centres had been absorbed into GNC stores; the rest were closed.

GNC opened the first Value Nutrition outlet stores the next year. In 1999 the company agreed to open at least 1000 new stores within Rite Aid drugstores; drugstore.com later became their online partner. Also in 1999 Netherlands-based Royal Numico bought GNC in a deal worth $2.5 billion (about $1.7 billion and debt) giving Numico access to the US retail market. In 2000 the company announced a joint venture with soy cheese wizard Galaxy Nutritional Foods to develop a chain of healthy food cafes. GNC opened 22 Smoothie Bars in existing stores. Also in 2002 the retailer redesigned its stores and cut prices on GNC-branded products to boost sales. In January 2003 the company launched Total Lean an ephedra-free dietary supplement. However by mid-2003 in response to safety concerns GNC stopped selling ephedra-based products.

Following years of rapid growth sales slumped and finally in December 2003 Royal Numico sold GNC to New York's Apollo Advisors for the fire-sale price of $750 million in cash. Apollo announced —a mere five months after acquiring the company —that it intended to sell shares to the public. However the company citing unfavorable market conditions reversed that decision in November 2004 and withdrew its proposed IPO.

In October 2004 Peter P. Copses resigned as chairman of the board of directors and was succeeded by Robert J. DiNicola a director of the company since December 2003. Another top level de-

parture occurred in December when president and CEO Louis Mancini resigned from the company.

The company has experienced a number of changes in its management in recent years. Former Family Dollar executive Bruce Barkus was named president and CEO in mid-2005 after the departure of Louis Mancini in late 2004. In November 2005 Joseph Fortunato (former EVP and COO) took the helm.

In mid-2006 a second attempt by Apollo to take the company public failed. (GNC had filed to go public in June but withdrew the offering two months later citing unfavorable market conditions.) Instead in March 2007 Apollo sold GNC to Ontario Teachers' Pension Plan and Ares Management a US private equity firm for about $1.65 billion.

In September 2010 GNC filed to go pubic. It began trading in April 2011. In August 2011 the company acquired LuckyVitamin.com.

EXECUTIVES

President and CEO, Joseph Fortunato, $860,000 total compensation

EVP Chief Merchandising Officer and General Manager, Thomas Dowd, $330,154 total compensation

SVP Chief Legal Officer and Secretary, Gerald J. Stubenhofer Jr., $294,310 total compensation

SVP and Chief Innovation Officer, Guru Ramanathan

EVP and CFO, Michael M. Nuzzo, $400,000 total compensation

CEO and Director, Joseph (Joe) Fortunato, age 59

Director, David B. Kaplan, age 45

Director, Carmen Fortino, age 54

Director, Romeo Leemrijse, age 41

Director, Andrew Claerhout, age 41

Director, Michael F. Hines, age 56

Director, Richard J. Wallace, age 61

Director, Brian Klos, age 31

Auditors: PricewaterhouseCoopersLLP

LOCATIONS

HQ: GNC Holdings Inc.
300 6th Ave., Pittsburgh PA 15222
Phone: 412-288-4600   **Fax:** 412-288-4764
Web: www.gnc.com

2012 Sales

	$ mil.	% of total
US	2,311	95
Foreign	118	5
Total	**2,430**	**100**

PRODUCTS/OPERATIONS

2012 Sales

	$ mil.	% of total
Retail	1,785	73
Franchise	408	17
Manufacturing/wholesale	236	10
Total	**2,430**	**100**

2012 US Retail Product Sales

	$ mil.	% of total
Sports nutrition	686	43
Vitamins minerals & herbal supplements	624	39
Diet	192	12
Other wellness	105	7
Total	**1,609**	**100**

Selected Brand Names

Mega Men
Pro Performance
Pro Performance AMP
Total Lean
Ultra Mega

COMPETITORS

Alticor	Nature' s Sunshine
Amazon.com	Nu Skin
Bactolac	Pfizer
Pharmaceutical	Safeway
Bayer AG	Shaklee
CVS Caremark	Slim-Fast
Costco Wholesale	Sunrider
Forever Living	Trader Joe' s
Jenny Craig	United Natural
Kroger	Vitamin Shoppe
Mannatech	Wal-Mart
Medicine Shoppe	Walgreen
NAI	Whole Foods
NBTY	
Natural Grocers by	
Vitamin Cottage	

HISTORICAL FINANCIALS

Company Type: Public

Income Statement
FYE: December 31

	REVENUE ($ mil.)	NET INCOME ($ mil.)	NET PROFIT MARGIN	EMPLOYEES
12/12	2,429.9	240.2	9.9%	14,500
12/11	2,072.1	132.3	6.4%	13,800
12/10	1,822.1	96.5	5.3%	13,086
12/09	1,707.0	69.5	4.1%	0
12/08	1,656.7	54.6	3.3%	0
Annual Growth	10.0%	44.8%	—	—

2012 Year-End Financials

Debt ratio: 43.0%
Return on equity: 25.7%
Cash ($ mil.): 158
Current ratio: 3.34
Long-term debt ($ mil.): 1,094

No. of shares (mil.): 99
Dividends
  Yield: 1.3%
  Payout: 20.3%
Market value ($ mil.): 3,303

	STOCK PRICE ($) FY Close	P/E High/Low		PER SHARE ($) Earnings	Dividends	Book Value
12/12	33.28	18	11	2.29	0.44	8.89
12/11	28.95	23	13	1.24	0.00	9.31
Annual Growth	15.0%	—	—	84.7%	—	(4.6%)

Goldfield Corp.

The Goldfield Corporation earns more laying cable now than it used to digging for mother lodes. Through subsidiary Southeast Power Goldfield builds and maintains electrical facilities in the Southeast West and Mid-Atlantic regions for utilities and industrial customers including Florida Power & Light Company and Duke Energy. The unit also installs transmission lines and fiber-optic cable. Goldfield's Bayswater Development subsidiary maintains real estate operations in Florida specializing in developing waterfront condominiums for retirees. The company which had been in the mining industry since 1906 divested those operations in 2002 after deciding that it had become economically unfeasible.

Opting for a less-is-more approach The Goldfield Corporation generally prefers to take on only a handful of customers and electrical construction projects per year. Its top customers often change from year to year and typically account for more than half of the company's total revenues.

On the real estate front Goldfield has delayed sales and new construction until the market improves particularly as Florida is among the hardest-hit areas as homebuilders nationwide struggle. When the economy rebounds the company plans to resume building two condominiums as part of its luxury Pineapple House project.

EXECUTIVES

President Southeast Power, Robert L. Jones, age 64, $146,655 total compensation
SVP Treasurer and CFO, Stephen R. Wherry, age 55, $205,560 total compensation
Chairman President and CEO, John H. Sottile, age 65, $438,728 total compensation
Secretary, Mary L. Manger
Director, Dwight W. Severs, age 68
Director, Thomas E. Dewey Jr., age 80
Director, Harvey C. Eads Jr., age 67
Director, John P. Fazzini, age 68
Director, Danforth E. Leitner, age 72
Director, Al Marino, age 55
Auditors: KPMGLLP

LOCATIONS

HQ: The Goldfield Corporation
1684 W. Hibiscus Blvd., Melbourne FL 32901
Phone: 321-724-1700   **Fax:** 321-724-1163
Web: www.goldfieldcorp.com
The Goldfield Corporation operates primarily in Florida and South Carolina.

PRODUCTS/OPERATIONS

2009 Sales

	$ mil.	% of total
Electrical construction	27	95
Real estate development	1	5
Total	29	100

Selected Subsidiaries
Bayswater Development Corporation
  Cape Club of Brevard Inc.
  Country Club Point of Brevard Inc.
  Florida Coastal Homes Inc.
  Oak Park of Brevard Inc.
  Pineapple House of Brevard Inc.
  Pineapple House Condominium Association Inc.
  Riomar of Brevard Inc.
Florida Transport Corporation
Southeast Power Corporation

COMPETITORS

Dycom	MYR Group
EMCOR	MasTec
Henkels & McCoy	Pike Electric
Integrated Electrical	Corporation
Services	Quanta Services

HISTORICAL FINANCIALS

Company Type: Public

Income Statement
FYE: December 31

	REVENUE ($ mil.)	NET INCOME ($ mil.)	NET PROFIT MARGIN	EMPLOYEES
12/12	81.6	11.9	14.7%	226
12/11	32.8	0.8	2.7%	163
12/10	33.3	(0.2)	—	122
12/09	29.2	(1.9)	—	125
12/08	31.4	(5.3)	—	121
Annual Growth	26.9%	—	—	16.9%

2012 Year-End Financials

Debt ratio: 31.0%
Return on equity: 55.9%
Cash ($ mil.): 7
Current ratio: 2.54
Long-term debt ($ mil.): 13

No. of shares (mil.): 25
Dividends
  Yield: —
  Payout: —
Market value ($ mil.): 48

	STOCK PRICE ($) FY Close	P/E High/Low		PER SHARE ($) Earnings	Dividends	Book Value
12/12	1.88	5	1	0.47	0.00	1.07
12/11	0.25	15	8	0.03	0.00	0.60
12/10	0.31	—	—	(0.01)	0.00	0.57
12/09	0.45	—	—	(0.08)	0.00	0.58
12/08	0.38	—	—	(0.21)	0.00	0.65
Annual Growth	49.1%	—	—	—	—	13.2%

Government Properties Income Trust

If Government Properties Income Trust had one request of Uncle Sam it would be this: "I want you to lease our properties." As a real estate investment trust (REIT) Government Properties Income Trust invests in properties that are leased to government tenants. It owns 10 million sq. ft. of leasing space at some 80 properties. The company leases mostly to federal agencies (such as the FBI IRS and FDA) but it does lease to some state-run agencies as well. Government Properties Income Trust went public in 2009. Former majority owner HRPT Properties Trust owns about 30% of the company following the IPO.

Geographic Reach

Although the company has It does have properties in 31 states many of its properties are located in the Washington DC area.

Financial Performance

Government Properties Income Trust's revenue has been steadily increasing year-over-year. It reported $211.1 million in revenue for fiscal 2012 after claiming $179 million in fiscal 2011 and $116.8 million in fiscal 2010.

EXECUTIVES

Secretary, Jennifer B. Clark, age 52
Independent Trustee, John L. Harrington, age 77
Treasurer Chief Financial Officer, Mark L. Kleifges, age 52
Independent Trustee, Barbara D. Gilmore, age 62
VP Investor Relations, Timothy A. (Tim) Bonang
Independent Trustee, Jeffrey P. Somers, age 70
President Chief Operating Officer, David M. Blackman, age 51
Auditors: Ernst&YoungLLP

LOCATIONS

HQ: Government Properties Income Trust
Two Newton Place, 255 Washington Street, Suite 300, Newton, MA 02458-1634
Phone: 617 219-1440   **Fax:** 617 219-1441
Web: www.govreit.com

COMPETITORS

Boston Properties	First Potomac Realty
CapLease	Piedmont Office Realty

Corporate Office   Trust
Properties Trust   USFP Trust

HISTORICAL FINANCIALS
Company Type: Public

Income Statement
FYE: December 31

	REVENUE ($ mil.)	NET INCOME ($ mil.)	NET PROFIT MARGIN	EMPLOYEES
12/12	211.0	49.9	23.7%	0
12/11	178.9	46.0	25.7%	0
12/10	116.7	27.8	23.8%	0
12/09	78.9	25.9	32.9%	0
12/08	75.4	31.8	42.2%	0
Annual Growth	29.3%	12.0%	—	—

2012 Year-End Financials

Debt ratio: 31.5%
Return on equity: 5.1%
Cash ($ mil.): 5
Current ratio: 0.31
Long-term debt ($ mil.): 399

No. of shares (mil.): 54
Dividends
  Yield: 7.0%
  Payout: 157.9%
Market value ($ mil.): 1,310

	STOCK PRICE ($) FY Close	P/E High/Low	PER SHARE ($) Earnings	Dividends	Book Value
12/12	23.97	24 20	1.03	1.69	18.80
12/11	22.55	26 19	1.06	1.67	18.95
12/10	26.79	35 27	0.81	1.62	18.70
12/09	22.98	15 11	1.72	0.90	16.39
Annual Growth	1.4%	— —	(15.7%)	23.4%	4.7%

Gran Tierra Energy Inc

Gran Tierra Energy hopes the earth still holds a wealth of oil and gas to be tapped especially in South America. Headquartered in Canada and incorporated and trading in the US this oil and gas exploration and production company holds interests in producing and prospective properties primarily in Argentina Brazil Colombia and Peru and is moving into the next phase which is focused on production growth through drilling. It has estimated proved reserves of about 24 million barrels of oil equivalent thanks in large part to increasing production at Costayaco in the Putumayo Basin in Colombia. Colombian oil and gas sales generate a lion's share of Gran Tierra Energy's revenues.

Colombian state-owned oil company Ecopetrol is a major customer and currently buys most of Gran Tierra Energy's crude oil. With a small and not very diverse customer base the company has been embarking on a strategy to expand into other South American regions through acquisition. It marked a major milestone in 2011 when it purchased Petrolifera Petroleum which added substantially to its asset base in Colombia Peru and Argentina. The deal added undeveloped oil and gas reserve potential in Colombia exploration opportunities in Colombia and Peru and additional oil production and reserves in Argentina where oil prices are rising.

Subsequent to the acquisition Gran Tierra Energy announced a capital program to use more than $355 million from existing cash reserves and cash flow to fund the development of these acquired assets. Approximately $14 million will be spent on drilling in Colombia for the purpose of

evaluating a potential production platform in the Lower Magdalena Basin. Another $14 million will be focused on reversing production declines in the Neuquen Basin in Argentina while $13 million will be spent on preparation for drilling in Peru in 2012. With combined assets Gran Tierra Energy expects average production in 2011 to range between 17500 and 19000 barrels of oil equivalent per day.

EXECUTIVES

Chairman, Jeffrey Scott, age 49
President Gran Tierra Energy Argentina, Rafael Orunesu
President Gran Tierra Energy Colombia, Julian Garcia
President Gran Tierra Energy Brasil, Julio Cesar Moreira
VP Legal General Counsel and Secretary, David Hardy
Director Investor Relations, Jason Crumley
President, Duncan Nightingale
Acting Chief Financial Officer; Principal Financial and Accounting Officer, James Rozon
Chief Operating Officer, Shane OLeary
Director, Verne G. Johnson, age 69
Director, Gerry Macey
Director, Ray Antony, age 59
Director, Nicholas G. Kirton, age 67
Director, J. Scott Price, age 49
Auditors: Deloitte&ToucheLLP

LOCATIONS

HQ: Gran Tierra Energy Inc
  300, 625 11th Avenue S.W., Calgary, Alberta T2R 0E1
Phone: 403 265-3221   **Fax:** 403 265-3242
Web: www.grantierra.com

2010 Sales

	$ mil.	% of total
Colombia	359	96
Argentina	13	4
Total	**374**	**100**

COMPETITORS

Emerald Energy
Global Energy Development
HKN
Houston American Energy

Pacific Rubiales
Petrobras Argentina
Woburn Energy
YPF

HISTORICAL FINANCIALS
Company Type: Public

Income Statement
FYE: December 31

	REVENUE ($ mil.)	NET INCOME ($ mil.)	NET PROFIT MARGIN	EMPLOYEES
12/12	585.1	99.6	17.0%	485
12/11	597.4	126.9	21.2%	446
12/10	374.4	37.1	9.9%	307
12/09	263.7	13.9	5.3%	269
12/08	114.0	23.5	20.6%	214
Annual Growth	50.5%	43.5%	—	22.7%

2012 Year-End Financials

Debt ratio: —
Return on equity: 8.0%
Cash ($ mil.): 212
Current ratio: 2.16
Long-term debt ($ mil.): —

No. of shares (mil.): 281
Dividends
  Yield: —
  Payout: —
Market value ($ mil.): 1,553

	STOCK PRICE ($) FY Close	P/E High/Low	PER SHARE ($) Earnings	Dividends	Book Value
12/12	5.51	19 12	0.35	0.00	4.58
12/11	4.80	21 10	0.45	0.00	4.21
12/10	8.05	56 31	0.14	0.00	3.44
12/09	5.73	100 34	0.05	0.00	3.34
12/08	2.80	43 10	0.16	0.00	3.32
Annual Growth	18.4%	—	21.6%	—	8.4%

Grand Canyon Education Inc

Grand Canyon Education (dba Grand Canyon University) spans a broad educational horizon. The regionally accredited educator offers graduate and undergraduate degrees online at its bricks-and-mortar campus in Phoenix and onsite at corporate facilities. Grand Canyon University offers career-oriented degree programs focused on the core disciplines of business education health care and liberal arts. Working adults make up most of the school's student body. Grand Canyon University enrolls almost 44000 students annually; about 90% are enrolled in online programs and about 45% of those pursue master's or doctorate degrees. Most classes have a student-teacher ratio of about 25:1.

Grand Canyon University keeps its enrollment numbers up by marketing itself to working adults (whom the company defines as 25 years and older) seeking to complete their education switch careers or earn a higher degree in the field in which they already work. Grand Canyon University attracts adult students with the flexibility and convenience of online classes and conversely adult students are attractive to Grand Canyon University because they are generally more stable able to finance their education and have higher completion rates than younger students.

To enhance its brand and continue to attract students Grand Canyon University invests in technology to update its infrastructure and expanding its physical campus. In 2012 it will begin constructing its first parking garage. Other improvements have included constructing a basketball and entertainment arena a new dorm an activity center and an Arts and Sciences classroom building. The university also keeps tabs on industry trends and adjusts its course offerings accordingly. For example increased demand for nursing programs led the school to establish satellite locations at multiple hospitals where nursing students can complete their clinical education while also completing other course work online. It has similar onsite arrangements with certain employers such as schools and school districts through which students can pursue a profession in teaching.

Grand Canyon University derives about 80% of its income from tuition that is financed under Title IV programs (federal grants and loans to students awarded on the basis of their financial need). Other sources of income come from self-funding private loans other financial aid programs and employer tuition reimbursements.

During 2011 the school's ground enrollment increased by 33% and online enrollment rose by

3% over 2010 levels. Grand Canyon University attributes these gains to brand recognition and affordability. Costs for its ground traditional campus learning experience compare to the price a student would pay as an in-state resident attending a public college. Grand Canyon University's operating income also increased that year by more than 40% over 2010 mainly due to increased revenue from room and board and student fees.

In 2010 the university transitioned from a calendar-year term based financial aid system to a "borrower-based non-term (BBAY) system to provide flexibility and rolling start dates for its students.

Originally founded as Grand Canyon College a private not-for-profit college in 1949 the university moved to its existing campus in Phoenix in 1951. In 2004 several of its stockholders acquired Grand Canyon University and converted it to a for-profit institution. The company then raised about $126 million through a public offering which was completed in 2008 after a four-month-long IPO drought in the US.

Through venture finance firm Endeavour Capital directors Chad Heath and D. Mark Dorman together own less than 5% of the firm. FMR owns almost 7% and chairman and former CEO Brent Richardson owns about 3% of Grand Canyon Education.

EXECUTIVES

Chief Financial Officer, Daniel E. Bachus, age 42, $132,212 total compensation
Chairman, Brent D. Richardson, age 51, $297,500 total compensation
General Counsel and Director, Christopher C. Richardson, age 41, $297,500 total compensation
President Grand Canyon University, Kathy Player, age 50, $230,000 total compensation
Chief University Relations and Student Success Officer, Faith A. Weese
CEO and Director, Brian E. Mueller, age 59, $246,154 total compensation
EVP, W. Stan Meyer, age 52, $147,692 total compensation
Vice President of Marketing, Christel Mosby
Executive Director of Education Outreach, Marjaneh Gilpatrick
Chief Information Officer, Joseph Mildenhall
Director, Jack A. Henry, age 70
General Counsel and Director, Christopher C. Richardson, age 41
Director, Chad N. Heath, age 38
CEO and Director, Brian E. Mueller, age 59
Independent Director, Bradley Casper
Auditors: Ernst&YoungLLP

LOCATIONS

HQ: Grand Canyon Education Inc
3300 W. Camelback Road, Phoenix, AZ 85017
Phone: 602 639-7500
Web: www.gcu.edu

PRODUCTS/OPERATIONS

2011 Student Enrollment by Degree Type

No. of students % of total

Undergraduate degree	26,742	61
Graduate degree	17,175	39
Total	**43,917**	**100**

2011 Enrollment by Instructional Delivery Method

	# of students	% of total
Online	38,918	89
Ground (Phoenix campus corporate studies)	4,999	11
Total	**43,917**	**100**

COMPETITORS

American Public Education
Apollo Education
Arizona State University
Azusa Pacific University
Baylor University
Bridgepoint Education
Capella Education
Career Education
Corinthian Colleges
DeVry Education Group
Education Management
ITT Educational
Northern Arizona University
Strayer Education
UTI
University of Arizona

HISTORICAL FINANCIALS

Company Type: Public

Income Statement

FYE: December 31

	REVENUE ($ mil.)	NET INCOME ($ mil.)	NET PROFIT MARGIN	EMPLOYEES
12/12	511.2	69.4	13.6%	2,655
12/11	426.7	50.5	11.8%	2,550
12/10	385.8	44.3	11.5%	2,600
12/09	261.9	27.3	10.4%	1,899
12/08	161.3	6.6	4.1%	3,174
Annual Growth	**33.4%**	**79.5%**	**—**	**(4.4%)**

2012 Year-End Financials

Debt ratio: 20.2%
Return on equity: 34.8%
Cash ($ mil.): 105
Current ratio: 1.40
Long-term debt ($ mil.): 93
No. of shares (mil.): 44
Dividends
  Yield: —
  Payout: —
Market value ($ mil.): 1,049

	STOCK PRICE ($) FY Close	P/E High/Low	PER SHARE ($) Earnings	Dividends	Book Value
12/12	23.47	16 10	1.53	0.00	5.23
12/11	15.96	18 11	1.12	0.00	3.69
12/10	19.59	28 16	0.96	0.00	2.99
12/09	19.01	34 22	0.60	0.00	1.88
12/08	18.78	71 46	0.17	0.00	1.18
Annual Growth	**5.7%**	**— —**	**73.2%**	**— 45.2%**	

Great Plains Energy, Inc.

Great Plains Energy is sweeping the fruited plains with electric power. The holding company serves about 826000 electricity customers in Missouri and Kansas through regulated utility Kansas City Power & Light (KCP&L) and KCP&L Greater Missouri Operations Company which both operate under the KCP&L brand. The utility company has more than 6600 MW of primarily coal-fired generating capacity. Great Plains Energy has exited most of its deregulated businesses in order to focus on its utility operations.

Geographic Reach
Great Plains Energy serves about 826000 electricity customers in 47 counties in western Missouri and eastern Kansas.

Operations
Great Plains Energy's power supply operations consist of its electric utilities that generate a capacity of more than 6600 MW. Its electric transmission business interconnects with systems of other utilities for reliability and to permit wholesale trans-

actions with other electricity suppliers. The electric utility operations have about 3600 circuit miles of transmission lines 15600 circuit miles of overhead distribution lines and 6700 circuit miles of underground distribution lines in Missouri and Kansas.

Financial Performance
Great Plains Energy has maintained consistent revenues over the last few years. Revenues hovered around the $2.3 billion mark for both 2011 and 2012. Its profits surged by 15% over that same time period due to new retail rates in Missouri and more favorable weather as well as the fact that 2011 net income was impacted by flooding along the Missouri River and a refueling outage at its Wolf Creek operation.

Strategy
The company is seeking to expand its generating capacity to meet growing demand while meeting green energy regulations through retrofitting its older coal-fired plants and expanding renewable energy and conservation initiatives.

EXECUTIVES

SVP Finance and Strategic Development; CFO, James C. (Jim) Shay
Chairman President and CEO, Terry Bassham, $420,000 total compensation
Chairman Great Plains Energy and KCP&L, Michael J. (Mike) Chesser, age 63, $800,000 total compensation
VP Transmission and Distribution Operations KCP&L, William P. (Bill) Herdegen III, age 56, $175,000 total compensation
VP Business Planning and Controller Great Plains Energy and KCP&L, Lori A. Wright, age 50
VP Strategy and Risk Management Kansas City Power & Light, Todd A. Kobayashi, age 43
VP Strategic Operations Support Kansas City Power & Light, F. Dana Crawford, age 55
SVP Corporate Services Kansas City Power & Light, Michael L. Deggendorf, age 51
VP Safety and Corporate Services KCP&L, Marvin L. Rollison, age 59
Assistant General Counsel and Assistant Secretary, Mark G. English, age 59
VP Investor Relations and Strategic Planning and Treasurer Great Plains Energy and KCP&L, Kevin E. Bryant, age 37
EVP and COO KCP&L, Scott H. Heidtbrink
VP Information Technology KCP&L, Chuck Tickles
VP Customer Service KCP&L, Jim Alberts
VP Corporate Secretary and Chief Compliance Officer Great Plains Energy Inc. and KCP&L, Ellen E. Fairchild, age 51
Director Corporate Communications, Katie McDonald
VP Supply Chain KCP&L, Maria Jenks
SVP Human Resources and General Counsel Great Plains Energy Inc. and KCP&L, Heather Humphrey
Investor Relations Manager, Calvin Girard
VP Marketing and Public Affairs KCP&L, Charles A. (Chuck) Caisley, age 40
VP Generation KCP&L, Kevin Noblet
VP Information Technology KCP&L, Charles King
VP Marketing and Public Affairs KCP&L, Chuck Caisley
Chairman of the Board President and CEO Great Plains Energy and KCP&L, Terry Bassham, age 52
Director, Gary D. Forsee, age 63
Director, John J. Sherman, age 58
Director, Robert H. West, age 74
Director, William C. Nelson, age 74
Director, David L. Bodde, age 70
Director, Linda H. Talbott, age 72
Director, Randall C. Ferguson Jr., age 61

Director, James A. Mitchell, age 71
Independent Director, Thomas Hyde
Auditors: Deloitte&ToucheLLP

LOCATIONS

HQ: Great Plains Energy Incorporated
1200 Main St., Kansas City MO 64105
Phone: 816-556-2200 **Fax:** 816-556-2992
Web: www.greatplainsenergy.com

COMPETITORS

Alliant Energy	NV Energy
Ameren	PNM Resources
Associated Electric	Pinnacle West
Avista	Portland General
Black Hills	Electric
Empire District	Southern Union
Electric	TECO Energy
GenOnEnergy	Westar Energy
IDACORP	Wisconsin Energy
Laclede Group	Xcel Energy

HISTORICAL FINANCIALS

Company Type: Public

Income Statement
FYE: December 31

	REVENUE ($ mil.)	NET INCOME ($ mil.)	NET PROFIT MARGIN	EMPLOYEES
12/12	2,309.9	199.9	8.7%	3,090
12/11	2,318.0	174.4	7.5%	3,053
12/10	2,255.5	211.7	9.4%	3,188
12/09	1,965.0	150.1	7.6%	3,197
12/08	1,670.1	154.5	9.3%	3,259
Annual Growth	8.4%	6.7%	—	(1.3%)

2012 Year-End Financials

Debt ratio: 36.8%
Return on equity: 6.2%
Cash ($ mil.): 10
Current ratio: 0.50
Long-term debt ($ mil.): 2,756

No. of shares (mil.): 153
Dividends
  Yield: 4.2%
  Payout: 65.7%
Market value ($ mil.): 3,118

	STOCK PRICE ($) FY Close	P/E High/Low	PER SHARE ($) Earnings	Dividends	Book Value
12/12	20.31	17 14	1.35	0.86	22.01
12/11	21.78	17 13	1.25	0.84	22.03
12/10	19.39	13 11	1.53	0.83	21.55
12/09	19.39	18 10	1.14	0.83	20.91
12/08	19.33	19 11	1.51	1.66	21.71
Annual Growth	1.2%	— —	(2.8%)	(15.3%)	0.3%

Great Southern Bancorp, Inc.

Despite its name Great Southern Bancorp is firmly entrenched in the heartland. It is the holding company for Great Southern Bank which operates more than 75 branches in Missouri plus more than two dozen locations in Iowa Kansas Nebraska and Arkansas. Founded in 1923 the bank offers checking and savings accounts CDs IRAs and credit cards. The firm's Great Southern Travel division is one of the largest travel agencies in Missouri. It serves both leisure and corporate travel-

ers through about a dozen offices. Among other units Great Southern Insurance offers property/casualty and life insurance while Great Southern Financial provides investment products and services through an agreement with Ameriprise.

The company in late 2012 agreed to sell its Great Southern Travel division to Adelman Travel.

Great Southern's lending activities primarily consist of originating and buying real estate loans: Commercial real estate mortgages and construction and land development loans account for around half of its loan portfolio while single-family residential mortgages make up another 15%. The bank also writes consumer (including home equity) construction and business loans.

The bank expanded into new markets in 2009 nearly doubling its branch network with the FDIC-assisted transactions of the failed TeamBank and deposits of Vantus Bank. It made a similar deal in 2011 when it acquired assets and deposits of the troubled Sun Security Bank. That transaction added another 27 banking locations in Missouri. In a smaller FDIC-assisted deal Great Southern acquired the deposits and loans of Inter Savings Bank in 2012 adding four branches in the Minneapolis/St. Paul market.

The company has also grown by opening new branches. In 2010 it opened three locations including its first in northwest Arkansas and it opened two new branches in 2011. Great Southern strategy for growth includes plans to continue opening two or three new branches per year which will help diversify the bank's loan portfolio beyond its core market of Springfield. Great Southern Travel has also made acquisitions in the bank's expanded market areas.

Despite the tough economic environment in the Midwest Great Southern's revenues and income saw growth in 2011. Adding loans through the FDIC-related acquisitions as well as by operating in new markets such as St. Louis has helped bring up the company's interest income. The company's portfolio of nonperforming loans and foreclosed assets —much of which were acquired in the FDIC purchases —dropped by about 2% each in 2011 (to $27.5 million and $46.9 million respectively) and are performing better than the company had originally expected. Potential problem loans have also decreased for Great Southern.

The bank introduced a smartphone banking application in early 2012. The addition of mobile banking services allows it to better compete with larger technologically advanced banks.

The Turner family including CEO Joseph Turner controls about a quarter of Great Southern Bancorp.

EXECUTIVES

Director Human Resources Great Southern Bank, Matt Snyder
VP Operations and Secretary Great Southern Bank, Douglas W. (Doug) Marrs, age 55, $110,251 total compensation
SVP and Chief Lending Officer of the Bank, Steven G. Mitchem, age 61, $195,215 total compensation
President CEO and Director Great Southern Bancorp and Great Southern Bank, Joseph W. (Joe) Turner, age 48, $258,869 total compensation
SVP and CFO Great Southern Bank, Rex A. Copeland, age 48, $186,640 total compensation
Chairman Great Southern Bancorp and Great Southern Bank, William V. Turner, age 80, $237,269 total compensation
VP Information Systems, Linton J. (Lin) Thomason, age 56

Director Marketing Great Southern Bank, Teresa Chasteen-Calhoun
Director Retail Banking Great Southern Bank, Barby Pohl
Director Corporate Communications Great Southern Bank, Kelly Polonus
Controller Great Southern Bank, Tammy Baurichter
Director Retail Services, Kris Conley
Director Credit Risk Management Great Southern Bank, Debbie Flowers
Insurance Agency Manager Great Southern Insurance, Byron Robison
Compliance Officer Great Southern Bank, Shannon Thomason
Director Risk Management Great Southern Bank, Bryan Tiede
President CEO and Director Great Southern Bancorp and Great Southern Bank, Joseph W. (Joe) Turner, age 48
Director, William E. Barclay, age 83
Director, Larry D. Frazier, age 75
Director, Thomas J. Carlson, age 60
Director, Julie Turner Brown, age 51
Director, Earl A. Steinert Jr., age 76
Director, Grant Q. Haden
Auditors: BKDLLP

LOCATIONS

HQ: Great Southern Bancorp Inc.
1451 E. Battlefield, Springfield MO 65804
Phone: 417-887-4400 **Fax:** 858-550-7506
Web: www.ligand.com

PRODUCTS/OPERATIONS

2011 Sales

	$ mil.	% of total
Interest		
Loans	171	69
Securities & other	27	11
Noninterest		
Service charges & ATM fees	18	7
Gain recognized on business acquisitions	16	7
Commissions	8	4
Net gains on loan sales	3	1
Other	3	1
Adjustments	(38.4)	-
Total	210	100

COMPETITORS

BancorpSouth	Hawthorn Bancshares
Bank of America	NASB Financial
Commerce Bancshares	U.S. Bancorp
First Bancshares (MO)	UMB Financial
Guaranty Federal	Wells Fargo

HISTORICAL FINANCIALS

Company Type: Public

Income Statement
FYE: December 31

	ASSETS ($ mil.)	NET INCOME ($ mil.)	INCOME AS % OF ASSETS	EMPLOYEES
12/12	3,955.1	48.7	1.2%	1,164
12/11	3,790.0	30.2	0.8%	1,256
12/10	3,411.5	23.8	0.7%	1,086
12/09	3,641.1	65.0	1.8%	1,047
12/08	2,659.9	(4.4)	—	741
Annual Growth	10.4%	—	—	12.0%

2012 Year-End Financials

Return on assets: 1.2%
Return on equity: 13.9%
Long-term debt ($ mil.): —
No. of shares (mil.): 13
Sales ($ mil): 239

Dividends
  Yield: 3.5%
  Payout: 25.4%
Market value ($ mil.): 346

STOCK PRICE ($) FY Close	P/E High/Low		PER SHARE ($) Earnings	Dividends	Book Value
12/12	25.45	9 6	3.54	0.90	27.20
12/11	23.59	12 8	1.93	0.72	24.08
12/10	23.59	17 13	1.46	0.72	22.60
12/09	21.36	5 2	4.44	0.72	22.30
12/08	11.44	— —	(0.35)	0.72	17.49
Annual Growth	22.1%	— —	—	5.7%	11.7%

Green Dot Corp

If you've got the green but not the plastic Green Dot would like to help. The company offers prepaid debit cards through approximately 59000 retail locations in the US. The MasterCard- and Visa-branded reloadable cards function like credit cards for purchases and cash withdrawals. Green Dot which has more than 4 million cards in circulation partners with PayPal Wal-Mart Walgreens 7-Eleven and other retailers to enable its customers to add funds to their accounts. The company's products are designed for people who aren't able or choose not to utilize traditional credit card and banking services. It makes most of its money from new card monthly maintenance and ATM fees. Green Dot went public in 2010.

The company's debut on the market exceeded its own expectations raising nearly $165 million. Although the initial public offering (IPO) of secondary shares raised a significant amount Green Dot did not keep any of the money for itself. Instead the money was distributed to existing shareholders the most prominent being Wal-Mart. Prior to the IPO the retail giant took a minority stake in Green Dot –a move that cemented the pair's partnership. Green Dot gets more than 60% of its revenues through sales at Wal-Mart for which it is the exclusive provider of the store-branded Money-Card product. In 2013 Green Dot announced plans to purchase the Wal-Mart-branded pre-paid debit card business from General Electric Co.'s GE Capital unit.

Unlike its nearest competitors which focus on check cashing and payday loans Green Dot has partnered with three of the top five retailers and other mainstream companies such as Radio Shack Kmart and Rite Aid. It also offers co-branded cards. The company's growth has stemmed by an increase in both its network and customer usage by offering improved services.

In addition to serving the underbanked community electronic payments companies have also attracted fully banked consumers seeking to safely shop online using separate accounts. Using prepaid cards as a companion to their primary accounts also allows users to control spending and prevent overdrafts. As the electronics payments industry evolves and competitors continue to introduce new products such as contactless cards Green Dot is exploring its various technological options. In addition to technological innovations card companies like Green Dot are also focusing on maintaining a stable and secure technology infrastructure.

The company makes about half of its money in card revenues which include new card and monthly maintenance fees optional extras including additional cards and ATM fees. Interchange fees (charges paid to the company when its cards

are used) and cash transfer fees make up the rest of Green Dot's revenues. The company saw growth in all three areas in 2010 and 2011.

Green Dot converted to a bank holding company through its 2011 acquisition of Bonneville Bank (now Green Dot Bank) which operates a single branch in Utah. As a bank holding company Green Dot could cut operating costs by issuing cards directly to customers rather than going through third-party banks. However the company has no plans to pursue lending beyond the bank's pre-acquisition levels. Green Dot is also participating in a pilot program through which it distributes federal tax refunds to prepaid debit cards through the bank.

In another move to become more vertically integrated the company in 2012 acquired certain processing and hardware assets of eCommLink for some $2.5 million. The move will allow Green Dot to bring its transaction processing in house rather than rely on third-parties such as TSYS with whom the company has an outsourced processing agreement that expires in 2013. In another deal Greent Dot acquired mobile app startup Loopt for some $43 million. The deal will help Green Dot attract and retain customers and help advance the company's technology capabilities.

Chairman and CEO Steven Streit owns 12% of the company's stock.

EXECUTIVES

Chairman President CEO and Acting CFO, Steven W. Streit, $450,000 total compensation

CFO, John L. Keatley, age 39, $289,231 total compensation

General Counsel; Secretary, John C. Ricci, age 47, $269,615 total compensation

Chief Revenue Officer, Konstantinos (Kostas) Sgoutas

Chief Technology Officer; Executive Vice President - Product Development, Kuan Archer

President and Chief Executive Officer of Green Dot Bank, Lewis Goodwin

Director, Michael J. (Mike) Moritz, age 59

Director, William H. (Bill) Ott Jr., age 60

Director, Kenneth C. Aldrich, age 74

Director, Timothy R. Greenleaf, age 56

Director, Virginia L. Hanna, age 62

Independent Director, Ross Kendell

Auditors: Ernst&YoungLLP

LOCATIONS

HQ: Green Dot Corporation
605 East Huntington Dr. Ste. 205, Monrovia CA 91016
Phone: 626-775-3400   **Fax:** -9812
Web: www.almamaritime.com

PRODUCTS/OPERATIONS

2011 Sales

	$ mil.	% of total
Card revenues & other fees	209	43
Interchange revenues	141	29
Cash transfer revenues	134	28
Adjustments	(17.3)	-
Total	**467**	**100**

COMPETITORS

American Express	NetSpend
Blackhawk Network	PreCash
DFC Global	Western Union
FSV Payment Systems	nFinanSe
First Data	
MoneyGram International	

HISTORICAL FINANCIALS

Company Type: Public

Income Statement

FYE: December 31

	REVENUE ($ mil.)	NET INCOME ($ mil.)	NET PROFIT MARGIN	EMPLOYEES
12/12	546.2	47.2	8.6%	596
12/11	467.4	52.0	11.1%	464
12/10	363.8	42.2	11.6%	352
12/09*	112.7	13.6	12.1%	0
07/09	234.8	37.1	15.8%	289
Annual Growth	23.5%	6.2%		19.8%

*Fiscal year change

2012 Year-End Financials

Debt ratio: —
Return on equity: 16.2%
Cash ($ mil.): 296
Current ratio: 1.40
Long-term debt ($ mil.): —

No. of shares (mil.): 36
Dividends
  Yield: —
  Payout: —
Market value ($ mil.): 439

	STOCK PRICE ($) FY Close	P/E High/Low		PER SHARE ($) Earnings	Dividends	Book Value
12/12	12.20	29 8		1.07	0.00	9.11
12/11	31.22	52 21		1.19	0.00	7.14
12/10	56.74	61 41		0.98	0.00	3.95
Annual Growth	(53.6%)	— —		4.5%	—	51.9%

Guidewire Software Inc

Guidewire Software has staked its claim on providing software to the insurance industry. The company's InsuranceSuite offers applications to the property and casualty insurance industry for underwriting policy administration (PolicyCenter) claims management (ClaimsCenter) and billing (BillingCenter). Its software is intended to replace paper-based processes and legacy systems built around outdated programming languages. Guidewire counts about 100 customers in a dozen countries. It customers include Tokio Marine Nationwide Mutual and Zurich Financial Services.

Geographic Reach

Guidewire's corporate headquarters is in Foster City California. It also leases facilities for distributed sales and international operations in Dublin Ireland; Edina Minnesota; London United Kingdom; Mississauga Ontario Canada; Munich Germany; Paris France; Sydney Australia; and Tokyo Japan.

In 2012 the US accounted for 55% of Guidewire's revenues.

Sales and Marketing

The company has more than 120 employees in a sales and marketing capacity including 23 direct sales representatives organized by geographic region across Australia Canada France Germany Hong Kong Japan the UK and the US.

Operations

The company generates revenue through licensing its software providing professional services and maintenance. Its software is generally licensed over a five-year contract and is priced according to the number of the insurance provider's written premiums. Guidewire charges customers in advance for both term license and maintenance fees.

Financial Performance

Guidewire's revenues increased by 35% in 2012 driven by continued adoption of the company's Claim Center software increasing adoption of itsPolicy Center and Suite software and increased sales and marketing efforts in North America and Europe. The rise in maintenance revenues was primarily driven by new orders. Service revenues increased due to increase use of the company's software.

Net income decreased by 57% in 2012 due to an increase in operating expenses such as an increase in research and development expenses and Sales and Marketing and General Administrative expenses primarily due to an increase in personnel-related expenses (as a result of adding 45 employees). Other factors included an increase in administrative and other professional services expenses and an increase in stock-based compensation.

Strategy

The company has extensive relationships with system integration consulting and industry partners. It encourages partners to co-market pursue joint sales initiatives and drive broader adoption of their technology. Its leading system integrator partners include Capgemini Ernst & Young IBM Global Services and PricewaterhouseCoopers.

In 2012 Guidewire's customer base in Europe increased by 20%. Guidewire has 19 customers in seven countries across Europe. Ten insurers across the region are using a Guidewire system. These include Beazley Direct Line UK LV= NFU Mutual Towergate Rosgosstrakh QBE Europe and a top three French insurer.

Ownership

Funds affiliated with Bay Partners own 10.9% of the company.

Company Background

Guidewire was founded in 2001 by CEO Marcus Ryu Product Strategy Director Kenneth Branson and four others who are no longer with the company. Its ClaimCenter product launched in 2003 PolicyCenter in 2004 and BillingCenter in 2006.

Guidewire filed a $100 million initial public offering in September 2011 and began trading on the NYSE in 2012.

EXECUTIVES

Chairman, Craig A. Conway, age 58
VP Worldwide Sales, Peter A. Espinosa, age 52
VP Marketing, Brian Desmond
Chief Executive Officer, Marcus S. Ryu, age 39
Chief Financial Officer, Karen Blasing, age 56
Vice President Product Development, Jeremy Henrickson, age 37
VP Professional Services, Alexander C. Naddaff, age 57
Director of Product Strategy; Director, Kenneth W. Branson, age 40
SVP Operations and Corporate Development, Priscilla Hung
CTO, Ben Brantley
Vice President Product Management, Dan Gordon
VP and General Counsel, Bob Donohue
Media Relations, Diana Stott
Vice President General Counsel Secretary, Winston King
Vice President Professional Services, Alex Naddaff
SVP Worldwide Sales, Scott Roza
Director, Neal Dempsey, age 61
Director, Steven M. Krausz, age 58
President CEO and Director, Marcus S. Ryu, age 38
Director, Craig Ramsey, age 66
Director of Product Strategy; Director, Kenneth W. Branson, age 40

Director, Clifton Thomas Weatherford, age 65
Auditors: KPMGLLP

LOCATIONS

HQ: Guidewire Software Inc
1001 E. Hillsdale Blvd., Suite 800, Foster City, CA 94404
Phone: 650 357-9100
Web: www.guidewire.com

2012 Sales

	% of total
US	55
Canada	15
Australia	8
UK	7
Other	15
Total	**100**

PRODUCTS/OPERATIONS

2012 Sales

	$ mil.	% of total
Services	105	45
Licenses	97	42
Maintenance	29	13
Total	**232**	**100**

COMPETITORS

Accenture	Oracle
Applied Systems	Pegasystems
CCC Information	SAP
Camilion	Sapiens
Computer Sciences	StoneRiver
Corp.	SunGard Financial
Cover-All	Systems
Duck Creek	Tata Consultancy
Ebix	Vertafore

HISTORICAL FINANCIALS

Company Type: Public

Income Statement

FYE: July 31

	REVENUE ($ mil.)	NET INCOME ($ mil.)	NET PROFIT MARGIN	EMPLOYEES
07/13	300.6	15.3	5.1%	1,149
07/12	232.0	15.2	6.6%	837
07/11	172.4	35.5	20.6%	684
07/10	144.6	15.5	10.7%	0
07/09	84.7	(10.9)	—	0
Annual Growth	**37.2%**	**—**	**—**	**—**

2013 Year-End Financials

Debt ratio: —
Return on equity: 7.4%
Cash ($ mil.): 79
Current ratio: 2.81
Long-term debt ($ mil.): —

No. of shares (mil.): 57
Dividends
Yield: —
Payout: —
Market value ($ mil.): 2,534

	STOCK PRICE ($) FY Close	P/E High/Low		PER SHARE ($) Earnings	Dividends	Book Value
07/13	43.76	168	91	0.25	0.00	3.94
07/12	25.66	122	59	0.25	0.00	3.41
Annual Growth	**70.5%**	**—**	**—**	**(0.0%)**	**—**	**15.7%**

Gulfport Energy Corp.

Gulfport Energy is an oil and gas exploration and production company. In the US its main producing properties are located along the Louisiana Gulf Coast and in the Permian Basin in West Texas. It also holds and is expanding acreage positions in the Niobrara Formation in western Colorado and the Utica Shale in eastern Ohio. Additionally Gulfport Energy holds a sizeable acreage position in the Alberta oil sands in Canada through its interest in Grizzly Oil Sands ULC and it has interests in entities that operate in the Phu Horm gas field in northern Thailand.

EXECUTIVES

Chairman, Mike Liddell, age 59, $261,373 total compensation
Chief Executive Officer; Director, James D. (Jim) Palm, age 68, $225,000 total compensation
Chief Financial Officer; Vice President; Secretary, Michael G. (Mike) Moore, age 56, $300,000 total compensation
Vice President Geological & Geophysical, Stuart Maier
Director Investor Relations, Paul Heerwagen
Vice President Reservoir Engineering, Steve Baldwin
Director, David L. Houston, age 60
CEO and Director, James D. (Jim) Palm, age 68
Director, Scott E. Streller, age 45
Director, Donald (Don) Dillingham, age 50
Independent Director, Craig Groeschel
Auditors: GrantThorntonLLP

LOCATIONS

HQ: Gulfport Energy Corporation
14313 N. May Ave. Ste. 100, Oklahoma City OK 73134
Phone: 405-848-8807 **Fax:** 405-848-8816
Web: www.gulfportenergy.com

PRODUCTS/OPERATIONS

2008 Sales

	$ mil.	% of total
Oil & condensate	131	93
Gas	6	5
Natural gas liquids	3	2
Other	(0.4)	-
Total	**141**	**100**

COMPETITORS

Abraxas Petroleum	Exxon Mobil
Apache	

HISTORICAL FINANCIALS

Company Type: Public

Income Statement

FYE: December 31

	REVENUE ($ mil.)	NET INCOME ($ mil.)	NET PROFIT MARGIN	EMPLOYEES
12/12	248.9	68.3	27.5%	128
12/11	229.2	108.4	47.3%	50
12/10	126.9	47.3	37.3%	45
12/09	85.2	23.6	27.7%	40
12/08	141.2	(184.5)	—	37
Annual Growth	**15.2%**	**—**	**—**	**36.4%**

2012 Year-End Financials

Debt ratio: 18.9%
Return on equity: 7.7%
Cash ($ mil.): 167
Current ratio: 1.90
Long-term debt ($ mil.): 298

No. of shares (mil.): 67
Dividends
  Yield: —
  Payout: —
Market value ($ mil.): 2,581

	STOCK PRICE ($) FY Close	P/E High/Low		PER SHARE ($) Earnings	Dividends	Book Value
12/12	38.22	32	13	1.21	0.00	16.68
12/11	29.45	17	9	2.20	0.00	11.37
12/10	21.68	21	8	1.07	0.00	4.73
12/09	11.45	21	3	0.55	0.00	2.93
12/08	3.95	—	—	(4.33)	0.00	2.68
Annual Growth	76.4%	—	—	—	—	58.0%

Haemonetics Corp.

Haemonetics helps health care providers keep track of blood. The company develops and produces automated blood collection systems that collect and process whole blood taking only the components (such as plasma or red blood cells) needed and returning the remainder to the donors. Typically these systems sold under the Cymbal or MCS brands are bought and used by plasma centers and blood banks. Haemonetics also makes hospital systems that collect and re-infuse a patient's own blood during surgery; these surgical blood salvage systems are sold under the cardioPAT and Cell Saver brand names. Additionally the company sells information management software and provides consulting services to blood banks and hospitals.

Geographic Reach

Haemonetics products are sold in about 100 countries primarily in the Americas Europe Asia and the Middle East with sales in the US market accounting for half of annual revenues. The company has manufacturing facilities in the US Italy Mexico Scotland and Switzerland and is supplied by third party manufacturers in Japan and Thailand.

Operations

More than 80% of the company's revenues come from the sale of single-use disposable products that work with its specialized blood collection and processing systems. The balance of revenues comes from sales and maintenance of its systems and software products and consulting services. It also rents equipment to some customers.

Haemonetics products are divided into four segments: Plasma blood center hospital and software solutions. The blood center segment (which makes blood collection and processing devices and related consumables) is the largest operating division and accounts for 40% of sales while the plasma segment (collection devices and consumables) accounts for about 30%. The hospital segment which includes blood salvage and blood-demand diagnostic equipment and consumables accounts for 15% of sales while IT platforms and consulting services provided by the software solutions segment account for 10%.

Sales and Marketing

Haemonetics markets its products and services worldwide through a direct sales force and distributors. It has direct sales forces in the primary markets of the US Europe and Japan though it also maintains a direct sales presence in Canada and China. It uses distributors to sell its products in South America the Middle East and other markets.

The company's customers include plasma-derived pharmaceutical manufacturers blood collection organizations and hospitals. Its largest customers each accounting for about 10% of sales are the Japanese Red Cross Society and plasma firm Grifols.

Financial Performance

Haemonetics reported a 23% increase in revenues in fiscal 2013 which was attributed to completed acquisitions higher sales of plasma disposables and surgical disposables and adoption of new diagnostic products as well as significant growth in emerging markets such as China. The company has experienced revenue growth over the last five years due to organic and acquisitive expansion.

Net income has declined in recent years however including a 43% drop in fiscal 2013 due to increased R&D sales general and administrative costs (including acquisition and integration costs) as well as asset write-downs and other expenses.

Strategy

Haemonetics is working to expand its product offerings to provide a comprehensive array of blood management solutions. It also aims to expand its geographic reach especially in high-growth regions of the world. The company spent some $45 million on R&D efforts in fiscal 2013 towards the development of new offerings including a next-generation orthopedic surgery blood system and an automated whole blood collection system; it also grows through acquisitions.

Mergers and Acquisitions

Collecting and banking blood is easier when hospitals and banks have good software to manage the process. To meet that need Haemonetics has built up its information management systems and services. Its subsidiary Haemonetics Software Solutions grew from the 2009 additions of Altivation Software and Neoteric Technology and in 2010 the company paid $60 million in cash to purchase Global Med Technologies a health information technology firm.

Once it got its IT purchases squared away Haemonetics put its attention back on actual blood processing hardware. The company spent some $535 million to acquire blood collection and processing product lines and manufacturing facilities from Pall Corporation in 2012. In 2013 it also bought up the assets of Minnesota-based Hemerus Medical a developer of innovative whole blood collection processing and storage equipment in a deal worth some $27 million.

HISTORY

Allan Latham founded Haemonetics in 1971. Its first product was a blood processing machine sold to blood banks and hospitals. The company went public in 1979. Early in the 1980s the company introduced the Cell Saver automated blood-salvage system. The product debuted at a time when the possibility of contracting HIV from blood transfusions had become a serious health concern and by 1988 sales topped $90 million. The company was bought in 1983 and was passed around between several owners including Baxter International before going public again in 1991.

In 1996 the company formed key relationships with blood bank customers through which Haemonetics performed such management services as component collection distribution and donor recruitment; the move allowed the company to become more vertically integrated. The following year it acquired Santa Barbara California-based Tri-

Counties Blood Bank which gave Haemonetics access to a distribution network of 24000 annual units of red blood cells. A restructuring charge and discontinuation of some operations drained the company's bottom line in 1998.

The company's venture into blood bank operation was short-lived; by 1999 it exited that line when results didn't live up to expectations. The next year Haemonetics expanded its product line with its purchase of Transfusion Technologies. New devices included the Chairside Separator System which separates donated blood into one unit of red blood cells and one unit of plasma.

In 2006 Haemonetics began broadening its product line to include software and consulting solutions offering blood banks and hospitals ways to improve efficiencies and manage their blood supply as well as providing equipment.

EXECUTIVES

Vice President - Human Resources, Joseph J. Forish

Chairman, Richard J. (Rich) Meelia, age 64

VP and General Manager Global Plasma Services, Stephen C. Swenson, $276,660 total compensation

President Global Markets, Mikael Gordon, age 57, $385,443 total compensation

President Japan, Keiko Hattori, age 60

VP Corporate Affairs, Alicia R. (Lisa) Lopez, $393,220 total compensation

Chief Financial Officer; Vice President, Christopher J. (Chris) Lindop, age 55, $420,251 total compensation

President - Global Plasma, Peter M. Allen, age 54, $398,559 total compensation

President; Chief Executive Officer; Director, Brian Concannon, age 55, $546,197 total compensation

President Chief Medical Officer, Mark Popovsky

President Asia/Pacific, Remi Corlin

Vice President - Worldwide Quality & Regulatory Affairs, Warren G. Nighan, age 44

VP and General Counsel, James (Jim) O'Shaughnessy

Vice President - Finance, Susan M. Hanlon

VP and General Manager Software Solutions Arryx and Haemoscope, Janet (Jan) Conneely

VP Research and Development, Jonathan White, age 54

President; North America, Michael (Mike) Kelly, age 49

Media Contact, Bryanne Salmon

VP Global Manufacturing, Phillip Brancazio

Vice President; Chief Legal Officer, Sandra Jesse

Vice President - Global Manufacturing, David Helsel

Director, Paul M. Black, age 54

Director, Pedro P. Granadillo, age 66

Director, Lawrence C. (Larry) Best, age 63

Director, Ronald G. (Ron) Gelbman, age 65

Director, Susan Bartlett Foote, age 66

Director, Mark W. Kroll, age 61

President; Chief Executive Officer; Director, Brian Concannon, age 55

Director, Ronald L. Merriman, age 68

Independent Director, Susan Foote

Auditors: Ernst&YoungLLP

LOCATIONS

HQ: Haemonetics Corporation
400 Wood Rd., Braintree MA 02184-9114
Phone: 781-848-7100   **Fax:** 781-356-3558
Web: www.haemonetics.com

2013 Sales

North America
US   454   50

Other North America	6	1
Europe	224	25
Asia		
Japan	120	14
Total	**892**	**100**

PRODUCTS/OPERATIONS

2013 Sales
Disposables	757	85
Equipment & other	64	7

Selected Products
Blood and Plasma Center products
  ACP (red blood cell collection and processing system)
  Cymbal (automated red blood cell collection system)
  MCS (automated platelet collection system)
  PCS (plasma collection system)
  SEBRA Sealers
Hospital products
  cardioPAT (heart surgery blood salvage system)
  Cell Saver (autologous blood recovery system)
  OrthoPAT (orthopedic blood salvage system)
  SmartSuction Harmony
  TEG 5000 (diagnostics)

COMPETITORS

Baxter International	Sunquest Information
CaridianBCT	Systems
Fresenius	Surgical Innovations
Mediware	Terumo Medical
Medtronic	Corporation
Sorin	

HISTORICAL FINANCIALS
Company Type: Public

Income Statement
FYE: March 30

	REVENUE ($ mil.)	NET INCOME ($ mil.)	NET PROFIT MARGIN	EMPLOYEES
03/13	891.9	38.8	4.3%	3,563
03/12*	727.8	66.8	9.2%	2,337
04/11	676.6	79.9	11.8%	2,201
04/10	645.4	58.3	9.0%	227
03/09	597.8	59.3	9.9%	2,016
Annual Growth	**10.5%**	**(10.1%)**	**—**	**15.3%**

*Fiscal year change

2013 Year-End Financials
Debt ratio: 32.8%	No. of shares (mil.): 51
Return on equity: 5.1%	Dividends
Cash ($ mil.): 179	Yield: —
Current ratio: 3.31	Payout: —
Long-term debt ($ mil.): 456	Market value ($ mil.): 2,126

	STOCK PRICE ($) FY Close	P/E High/Low		PER SHARE ($) Earnings	Dividends	Book Value
03/13	41.66	109	52	0.74	0.00	15.07
03/12*	69.68	53	42	1.30	0.00	14.48
04/11	66.57	42	32	1.56	0.00	13.37
04/10	56.48	52	43	1.12	0.00	11.66
03/09	54.76	56	42	1.14	0.00	10.54
Annual Growth	**(6.6%)**	**—**	**—**	**(10.1%)**	**—**	**9.4%**

*Fiscal year change

Hain Celestial Group Inc

The Hain Celestial Group serves up guiltless eating and grooming. The company manufactures and distributes natural and organic food snacks beverages and personal care and cleaning products in North America and Europe. Its vast pantry of "better-for-you" brands includes Celestial Seasonings (specialty teas) Terra and Garden of Eatin' (snacks) and Earth's Best (organic baby food). Hain's products are mainstays in natural foods stores and are increasingly available in mainstream supermarkets; club mass-market and drug stores; and grocery wholesalers. Fast-growing Hain is also a supplier of TenderCare disposable diapers; its J?SON Natural Products makes grooming products.

HISTORY

Irwin Simon a former marketer at Slim-Fast and Haagen-Dazs founded Kineret Acquisition Corp. in 1993 to acquire Kineret Food a maker of kosher foods. Before closing the deal in late 1993 Simon acquired the product line of Pizsoy (soy-based pizza) and two small companies: California Slim (dietary foods) and Barricini Foods (frozen desserts and organic bread). He took the company public that year. In 1994 Kineret quadrupled its size by adding Hain Pure Food (natural foods and cooking oils); the company changed its name later that year to The Hain Food Group to take advantage of the well-known Hain label.

Hain expanded in 1995 with its purchase of diabetic foods maker Estee Corp. Sales dropped during fiscal 1997 in part because of decreasing demand for rice cakes which had accounted for nearly three-quarters of Hain Pure Food's sales. To invigorate its stable of brands in 1997 Hain bought Boston Better Snacks (chips and popcorn); a Weight Watchers line and Alba Foods (dietary drinks) from Heinz; and Westbrae Natural (including Westsoy nondairy drinks). The company added more brands in 1998 when it bought four business lines from Shansby Group: Arrowhead Mills (grains) DeBoles Nutritional Foods (pasta) Terra Chips and Garden of Eatin' (snack foods). It then added Quaker Oats' Nile Spice (soups and meal cups) to the mix.

The company added Natural Nutrition Group a natural and organic foods maker in 1999. Hain enriched its alliance with Heinz when the giant bought nearly 20% of Hain in exchange for access to the rapidly growing natural foods market. In 2000 Hain bought leading specialty tea-maker Celestial Seasonings for about $330 million and subsequently changed the company name to The Hain Celestial Group.

In 2001 Hain Celestial bought Netherlands-based chip maker Fruit Chips (Gaston's fruit vegetable and potato chips) and later changed its name to Terra Chips to reflect the expansion of the Terra Chips brand in Europe. It followed that purchase with the acquisition of Yves Veggie Cuisine a Canadian maker of soy protein meat and cheese alternatives. Also that year the company formed a joint venture with Grupo Siro of Spain to market snack foods in southern Europe and it acquired Belgian natural and organic foods marketer Lima.

The company expanded into the Asia/Pacific region in 2002 by agreeing to distribute and sell some of its products (including its Yves Veggie Cuisine line) though Japanese food manufacturer and distributor Shin-shin. That year Hain agreed to supply veggie burgers to all Canadian McDonald's restaurants. It also formed a joint venture with pasta maker Barilla to manufacture market and distribute Terra brand products in Europe. That June Hain discontinued its supplements business and terminated its licensing agreement with Weight Watchers.

Later in 2002 Hain purchased Imagine Foods for $52 million in cash and stock. The acquisition added such well-known milk-substitute brands as Rice Dream Power Dream and Soy Dream as well as Imagine's frozen dessert and organic soup and broth business to the Hain stable.

The company created a soy-based patty called the McVeggie Burger for McDonald's in 2003. Hain's subsidiary Yves Veggie Cuisine manufactures the patties for and supplies them to McDonald's. Later that year Hain acquired Acirca maker of Walnut Acres brand foods. It also introduced a line of low-carbohydrate food called Carb Fit. Also in 2003 the company announced a joint venture with Cargill to develop healthy functional foods and beverages using Cargill's isoflavones inulin and chondroitin products.

In 2004 Hain bought Natumi AG a German maker of non-dairy beverages and desserts. Later that year it acquired frozen food brands Ethnic Gourmet and Rosetto from Heinz. The company also announced a relationship with Sesame Workshop to promote children's healthy eating habits. Later that year Hain began making a soy burger called the McVeggie Burger for McDonald's Manhattan New York locations.

And perhaps in its biggest move in 2004 Hain expanded into a new but complementary natural product market with the acquisition of J?SON Natural Products a maker of health and body care products. At the same time Hain introduced a selection of its own body care products called Earth's Best for babies and children. In 2005 Hain purchased another personal care company Zia Natural Skincare. Also on Hain's shopping list was Pennsylvania-based College Hill Poultry a joint venture with Pegasus Capital. Not forgetting its food lineup in 2005 Hain acquired Spectrum Organic Products. In addition Hain sold its Kineret and Kosherific frozen food brands to Kedem Food Products International for an undisclosed amount.

In 2006 the company introduced its Estee brand –a product line of Low-G (glycemic) nutrition bars. It also acquired personal care product company Para Laboratories whose brands include Batherapy Footherapy and Queen Helene. That year it acquired Spectrum Organic Products as well as a 51% interest in organic chicken producer Hain Pure Protein.

Expanding its European operations in 2006 Hain acquired the England-based fresh prepared foods business of H. J. Heinz as well as Heinz's frozen meat-free business (including the Linda McCartney brand) both located in England. It also bought the 100-year-old UK firm Haldane Foods (including its meat-free and non-dairy beverages businesses) from Archer Daniels Midland. The Haldane acquisition brought the Realeat (frozen foods and dry mixes) Granose and WhiteWave's non-dairy beverages brands to the Hain roster.

The company also acquired Avalon Natural Products that year from private equity firm North Castle Partners for $120 million. The deal added such organic personal care brands as Avalon Organic Botanicals and Alba Botanica to Hain's portfolio.

Hain Pure Protein (HPP) a joint venture between Hain Celestial and private equity firm Pegasus Capital Advisors acquired Plainville Turkey Farm in 2007. The enterprise renamed Plainville Farms joined FreeBird organic chicken producer also owned by Hain Pure Protein. In 2008 HPP acquired the turkey operations (New Oxford Foods) of Pilgrim's Pride. New Oxford's operations were switched to antibiotic-free and joined Plainville and FreeBird in furthering Hain's strategy of offering organic branded food products.

In 2009 HPP introduced a line of kosher chicken and turkey products under the Kosher Valley name which is available at Whole Foods and specialty retailers. The brand serves two customer bases: those of the Jewish faith and those preferring more healthful proteins. In mid-2010 Hain Pure Protein sold the Kosher Valley brand to Empire Kosher Poultry an established Pennsylvania-based processor. In exchange Hain Pure Protein received shares in Empire.

EXECUTIVES

SVP Finance and Chief Accounting Officer, Michael J. Speiller, age 58, $300,000 total compensation
Chairman President and CEO, Irwin D. Simon, age 55, $1,400,000 total compensation
SVP Special Projects, Benjamin Brecher
SVP Global Technical Services and Chief Sustainability Officer, Ellen B. Deutsch, $160,000 total compensation
EVP and CFO, Stephen J. (Steve) Smith, age 51
EVP and CFO, Ira J. Lamel, age 65, $540,000 total compensation
CEO Hain Celestial Europe, Philippe Woitrin
EVP; CEO Hain Celestial US, John Carroll, age 54, $525,000 total compensation
SVP Corporate Relations, Mary Celeste Anthes, age 53, $250,000 total compensation
President Celestial Seasonings and Chief Sales Officer Grocery Snacks and Personal Care, Peter J. Burns, age 52
President Hain Celestial Personal Care and Chief Supply Chain Officer Grocery Snacks and Personal Care, James R. (Jim) Meiers
CEO Hain Daniels Group, Rob Burnett
President Hain Celestial Canada, Beena G. Goldenberg
VP Information Technology, Michael E. Calderon
Vice President Treasurer, Pasquale Conte
EVP General Counsel and Chief Compliance Officer, Denise M. Faltischek, age 40
President Hain Celestial Club Division, Jason Cohen
Senior Vice President General Counsel, Denise ????ltischek
Executive Vice President Chief Financial Officer, Ira ??mel
Director, Richard C. Berke, age 68
Director, Barry J. Alperin, age 73
Director, Jack Futterman, age 80
Director, Marina Hahn, age 56
Director, Roger Meltzer, age 63
Director, Lawrence S. (Larry) Zilvay, age 61
Director, Lewis D. Schiliro, age 64
Director, Brett Icahn, age 33
Director, David S. Schechter, age 37
Independent Director, Lawrence Zilavy
Independent Director, Scott ONeil
Auditors: Ernst&YoungLLP

LOCATIONS

HQ: The Hain Celestial Group Inc.
58 S. Service Rd., Melville NY 11747
Phone: 631-730-2200   **Fax:** 631-730-2550
Web: www.hain-celestial.com

2013 Sales

	$ mil.	% of total
US	1,095	63
UK	420	24
Rest of world	218	13
Total	**1,734**	**100**

PRODUCTS/OPERATIONS

2013 Sales

	$ mil.	% of total
Grocery	1,286	74
Snacks	220	13
Personal care	117	7
Tea	110	6
Total	**1,734**	**100**

Selected Subsidiaries

Arrowhead Mills Inc.
Celestial Seasonings Inc.
Daily Bread Ltd. (UK)
Ella's Kitchen Group Ltd. (UK)
Health Valley Company
Histon Sweet Spread Ltd. (UK)
Jason Natural Products
Lima S.A.R.L. (France)
Spectrum Organic Products LLC
Terra Chisp B.V. (Netherlands)
Zia Cosmetics Inc.

Selected Brands and Products

Fresh and Frozen Foods
Daily Bread (fresh prepared foods UK only)
  Ethnic Gourmet (frozen meals)
  Linda McCartney (frozen vegetarian meals)
  Rice Dream (frozen desserts)
  Rosetto (frozen Italian foods)
  Soy Dream (frozen desserts)
Milk-free Beverages
  BluePrint (raw juice)
  Natumi (non-dairy beverages and desserts Europe only)
  Rice Dream (rice-based non-dairy milk and ice cream)
  Soy Dream (soy-based non-dairy milk and ice cream)
Natural Foods
  Arrowhead Mills (natural and organic whole grain products)
  Bearitos (canned chilies and sauce mixes)
  Breadshop (cereal)
  Casbah (prepared vegetarian mixes and side dishes)
  Danival (organic fruits vegetables and deli products)
  DeBoles (dried pasta)
  Earth's Best (organic baby and toddler food licensed)
  Europe's Best (frozen fruits and vegetables)
  FreeBird (organic chicken)
  GG UniqueFiber (whole grain crackers)
  Hain Pure Foods (condiments cookies cooking oils rice cakes sea salt snacks and soups)
  Health Valley (fat-free soups cereals and baked products)
  Hollywood (edible oils US only)
  Imagine Foods (soups and broths)
  Little Bear (organic snacks)
  MaraNatha (nut butters)
  Mountain Sun (juice)
  Nile Spice (soups and meal cups)
  Plainville Farms (antibiotic-free chicken and turkey)
  Spectrum (edible oil vinegar condiments and butter substitutes)
  SunSpire (nut butters)
  Walnut Acres (juice pasta sauce salsa and soup)
  Westbrae Natural (canned vegetables)
  Westsoy (soy-based beverages)
  Yves (soy protein meat alternatives)
Snack Foods
  Boston's (popcorn)
  Garden of Eatin' (snack foods)
  Harry's Premium Snacks
  Terra Chips (gourmet vegetable chips)

Specialties
  ALBA (dry milk mixes and shakes)
  Celestial Seasonings (teas)
  Estee (sugar-free products)
  Hollywood (carrot juice condiments and cooking oils)
  Mountain Sun (juice)
  TenderCare (disposable diapers and baby wipes)
  Tushies (disposable diapers and baby wipes)
Natural Body Care and Home Care
  Alba Botanica (personal care products)
  Avalon Organics (Personal care products)
  J?SON (shampoo soap and shaving products)
  Orjene Organics (beauty and personal care products)
  Queen Helene (body care products)
  Zia Natural Skincare (therapeutic skin care products)

COMPETITORS

Amy's Kitchen	Johnson & Johnson
Annie's Inc.	Kellogg
Armanino Foods	Kerry Group
Associated British Foods	Kimberly-Clark
Beech-Nut	Kiss My Face
Boca Foods	Kraft Foods Group Inc.
Burt's Bees	Mondelez International
Butterball	Monterey Gourmet Foods
Campbell Soup	Nature's Path
Cargill	Nestle
Clif Bar	Newman's Own
Colgate-Palmolive	Northern Foods
ConAgra	PepsiCo
Danone	Pilgrim's Pride
Dean Foods	Procter & Gamble
Dr. Bronner's	R.C. Bigelow
Eden Foods	Sara Lee
Empire Kosher Poultry	Small Planet Foods
Estee Lauder	Smucker
Frito-Lay	Spectrum Foods
Galaxy Nutritional Foods	Stash Tea
General Mills	Stonyfield Farm
Gerber Products	Tofutti Brands
Hormel	Tom's of Maine
Inventure foods	TreeHouse
Jennie-O	Tyson Foods
	Unilever
	Vita Food Products

HISTORICAL FINANCIALS

Company Type: Public

Income Statement

FYE: June 30

	REVENUE ($ mil.)	NET INCOME ($ mil.)	NET PROFIT MARGIN	EMPLOYEES
06/13	1,734.6	114.6	6.6%	3,665
06/12	1,378.2	79.2	5.7%	3,720
06/11	1,130.2	54.9	4.9%	2,031
06/10	917.3	28.6	3.1%	2,059
06/09	1,135.3	(24.7)	—	2,022
Annual Growth	**11.2%**	—		**16.0%**

2013 Year-End Financials

Debt ratio: 29.4%
Return on equity: 10.5%
Cash ($ mil.): 41
Current ratio: 2.10
Long-term debt ($ mil.): 653
No. of shares (mil.): 47
Dividends
  Yield: —
  Payout: —
Market value ($ mil.): 3,100

	STOCK PRICE ($) FY Close	P/E High/Low		PER SHARE ($) Earnings	Dividends	Book Value
06/13	65.01	29	21	2.41	0.00	25.19
06/12	55.04	32	15	1.73	0.00	21.46
06/11	33.36	28	15	1.23	0.00	19.74
06/10	20.17	33	21	0.69	0.00	17.99
06/09	15.61	—	—	(0.61)	0.00	17.23
Annual Growth	**42.9%**	—	—	—	—	**10.0%**

Hallador Energy Co

Hallador Energy puts most of its energy into selling coal from its Carlisle Mine in Indiana to three utilities in the Midwest and one in Florida. Hallador has recoverable coal reserves of 43.5 million tons (34.2 million tons proven and 9.3 million tons probable). In addition to the Carlisle Mine it get coals from a mine in Clay County Indiana and has two inactive mines in Illinois. The company is exploring the possibility of other contracts with a number of coal purchasers (primarily utilities and distribution cooperatives). Additionally Hallador has a 45% stake in Savoy Energy L.P. an oil and gas company with operations in Michigan and a 50% interest in Sunrise Energy LLC a private oil and gas exploration and production company with assets in Indiana.

Sales and Marketing

Hallador sells coal in the Midwest to Duke Energy Hoosier Energy and Indianapolis Power & Light. It also sells coal to JEA in Florida.

Financial Performance

In 2012 the company's revenues declined by 10% due to a price decrease and unfavorable weather conditions crimping demand. Hallador's net income decreased by 34% due to lower net sales and higher operating costs.

Strategy

Expanding its geographic coverage in 2011 the company sold 300000 tons of coal to JEA its first such sale to a Florida-based customer. It sold 18500 tons to JEA in 2012.

Ownership

Some 70% of the company is held by officers directors and their affiliates. Chairman David Hardie holds a 12% stake in Hallador.

Company Background

Hallador was founded in 1949. In 1997 investment company Yorktown Energy Partners II and affiliates invested $5 million in Hallador.

Despite its Harry Potter-like name Hallador Petroleum could find no magic in oil and natural gas exploration and production –just a lot of hard and dirty work. It therefore decided to focus on its coal operations. The company acquired control of Sunrise Coal co-developer of the Carlisle Mine in 2008.

Hallador in Spanish means "finder" or "discoverer" or "one who leads the way."

EXECUTIVES

Chairman, David Hardie, age 63
Chief Executive Officer, Victor P. Stabio, age 66, $180,000 total compensation
CFO Sunrise Coal, Larry Martin, age 48, $102,000 total compensation
Chief Financial Officer; Chief Accounting Officer, William A. (Andy) Bishop, age 60
President and appointed to our board, Brent Bilsland
Director, Sheldon B. Lubar, age 84
Director, Bryan H. Lawrence, age 71
CEO and Director, Victor P. Stabio, age 65
Independent Director, John Heuvelen
Auditors: EhrhardtKeefeSteiner&HottmanPC

LOCATIONS

HQ: Hallador Energy Company
1660 Lincoln St. Ste. 2700, Denver CO 80264-2701
Phone: 303-839-5504   **Fax:** 303-832-3013
Web: www.halladorenergy.com

PRODUCTS/OPERATIONS

2012 Sales

	$ mil.	% of total
Coal sales	131.4	93
Other income	4	3

COMPETITORS

Alpha Natural Resources
Anadarko Petroleum
Arch Coal
CONSOL Energy
Chesapeake Energy
Noble Energy
Peabody Energy
Pioneer Natural Resources
SandRidge Energy

HISTORICAL FINANCIALS

Company Type: Public

Income Statement

FYE: December 31

	REVENUE ($ mil.)	NET INCOME ($ mil.)	NET PROFIT MARGIN	EMPLOYEES
12/12	141.3	23.8	16.8%	330
12/11	157.3	35.8	22.8%	333
12/10	129.2	22.3	17.3%	332
12/09	116.3	20.1	17.4%	300
12/08	70.2	8.9	12.7%	6
Annual Growth	19.1%	27.9%	—	172.3%

2012 Year-End Financials

Debt ratio: 4.9%
Return on equity: 14.7%
Cash ($ mil.): 21
Current ratio: 3.16
Long-term debt ($ mil.): 11
No. of shares (mil.): 28
Dividends
  Yield: 9.6%
  Payout: 83.3%
Market value ($ mil.): 236

	STOCK PRICE ($) FY Close	P/E High/Low		PER SHARE ($) Earnings	Dividends	Book Value
12/12	8.26	13	8	0.83	0.80	5.68
12/11	9.93	9	6	1.25	0.12	5.69
12/10	10.49	16	9	0.78	0.10	4.54
12/09	7.85	11	4	0.83	0.00	3.91
12/08	3.00	12	5	0.46	0.00	3.25
Annual Growth	28.8%			— — 15.9%		— 15.0%

Hancock Holding Co.

Hancock Holding holds its own as a Gulf Coast financial force. It is the holding company of Mississippi-based Hancock Bank and Louisiana-based Whitney Bank. Together the banks have about 300 branches throughout the Gulf South from Florida to Texas. The community-oriented banks offer traditional products and services such as deposit accounts trust services and consumer and business lending. Hancock Holding also has subsidiaries or business units that offer insurance discount brokerage services mutual funds and consumer financing. In 2011 the company acquired regional rival Whitney Holding for some $1.5 billion.

The combination of Hancock and Whitney brought together two of the largest (and oldest) financial companies in the Gulf region. Following the merger bank branches in Louisiana and Texas operate under the Whitney Bank name while branches in Mississippi Alabama and Florida have the Hancock Bank brand. Hancock Holding was required to divest nearly 10 locations acquired in the deal in Louisiana and Mississippi to satisfy antitrust concerns.

Hancock Holding reported net income of $76.8 million on revenues of nearly $800 million. The Whitney acquisition boosted both of those numbers. The company also benefitted from fewer provisions for loan losses and charged-off loans.

The company's market area has faced plenty of challenges in recent years. Devastating hurricanes the recession and a major oil spill have plagued Gulf Coast communities. However Hancock Holding has continued to grow across its market and enter new ones.

It is looking to increase its international profile. The company which operates in major Gulf of Mexico port cities sees opportunity to be more involved in trade work as the Panama Canal is expanded. The canal expansion (expected to be completed in 2014) will increase trade between Central and South America and North America.

EXECUTIVES

President; Chief Executive Officer; Director, Carl J. Chaney, age 52, $425,769 total compensation
Executive Vice President; Chief Credit Officer, Sam B. Kendricks, age 53
Chairman, James B. Estabrook Jr., age 69
Chief Executive Officer; Chief Operating Officer; Director, John M. Hairston, age 49, $425,769 total compensation
Executive Vice President; Chief Retail Banking Officer, Richard T. Hill, $249,231 total compensation
Executive Vice President; Chief Wealth Management Officer, Clifton J. Saik, $277,269 total compensation
VP Investor Relations, Paul D. Guichet
SVP and Internal Auditor, Alfreda A. Horne
Executive Vice President; General Counsel; Corporate Secretary, Joy Lambert Phillips
Director; Chairman Hancock Bank of Louisiana, John H. Pace, age 83
Executive Vice President; Chief Commercial Banking Officer, Edward G. Francis
Executive Vice President; Chief Risk Officer, D. Shane Loper
VP and Manager Corporate Communications, R. Paul Maxwell
SVP and Treasurer, Gerry Dugal
Chief Financial Officer; Executive Vice President, Michael M. Achary, $249,231 total compensation
SVP and Director Marketing, Robert A. Seals
SVP and Director Compliance, Sandra A. Wilbourn
Affairs Manager P.O. Bo, Lea Stone
President of Whitney Bank, Joseph Exnicios
Chief Wholesale Credit Approval Officer, Suzanne Thomas
Executive Vice President; Chief Credit Officer, Samuel Kendricks
Chief Accounting Officer, Stephen Barker
President; Chief Executive Officer; Director, Carl J. Chaney, age 52
Director, Robert W. Roseberry, age 63
Director, Frank E. Bertucci, age 57
Director, James H. Horne, age 61
Chief Executive Officer; Chief Operating Officer; Director, John M. Hairston, age 49
Director, Anthony J. Topazi, age 63
Director, Alton G. Bankston, age 72
Director, Don P. Descant, age 65
Director; Chairman Hancock Bank of Louisiana, John H. Pace, age 83
Director, Christine L. Pickering, age 52
Director, Randy W. Hanna, age 54
Director, Jerry L. Levens, age 56
Director, Thomas H. Olinde, age 57

LOCATIONS

HQ: Hancock Holding Co.
One Hancock Plaza, P.O. Box 4019, Gulfport, MS 39501
Phone: 228 868-4000
Web: www.hancockbank.com

2011 Sales

	$ mil.	% of total
Whitney	476	60
Hancock	272	34
Other	50	6
Total	**798**	**100**

PRODUCTS/OPERATIONS

2011 Sales

	$ mil.	% of total
Interest		
Loans including fees	499	63
Securities	90	11
Other	2	.
Noninterest		
Service charges on deposit accounts	55	7
Bank card fees	28	4
Trust fees	23	3
Accretion of indemnification asset	16	2
Insurance commissions and fees	16	2
Investment & annuity fees	15	2
ATM fees	14	2
Other	36	4
Total	**798**	**100**

Subsidiaries
Berwick LLC
Community First Inc.
Dudley Ventures Hancock Fund LLC
Gulf South Technology Center LLC
The Gulfport Building Inc.
Hancock Bank
Hancock Bank of Alabama
Hancock Bank Securities Corporation II
Hancock Community Investment Corporatio
Hancock Enterprise Investment Fund LLC
Hancock Insurance Agency
Hancock Insurance Agency of Alabama
Hancock Insurance Agency of Florida
Hancock Investment Services of Alabama Inc.
Hancock Investment Services of Florida Inc.
Hancock Investment Services of Louisiana Inc.
Hancock Investment Services of Mississippi Inc.
Hancock Investment Services Inc.
Harrison Finance Company
Harrison Loan Company
HBSC LLC
HMC LLC
Invest-Sure Inc.
J Everett Eaves Inc.
Lighthouse Services Corporatio
Peoples First Transportation Inc.
Town Properties Inc.
Whitney Bank

COMPETITORS

BancorpSouth	MidSouth Bancorp
Capital One	Regions Financial
First Horizon	Renasant
First NBC Bank	Trustmark
IBERIABANK	

HISTORICAL FINANCIALS

Company Type: Public

Income Statement

FYE: December 31

	ASSETS ($ mil.)	NET INCOME ($ mil.)	INCOME AS % OF ASSETS	EMPLOYEES
12/12	19,464.4	151.7	0.8%	4,235
12/11	19,774.1	76.7	0.4%	4,745
12/10	8,138.3	52.2	0.6%	2,271
12/09	8,697.0	74.7	0.9%	5,837
12/08	7,167.2	65.3	0.9%	1,952
Annual Growth	**28.4%**	**23.4%**	**—**	**21.4%**

2012 Year-End Financials

Return on assets: 0.7%
Return on equity: 6.2%
Long-term debt ($ mil.): —
No. of shares (mil.): 84
Sales ($ mil): 1,016

Dividends
  Yield: 3.0%
  Payout: 54.8%
Market value ($ mil.): 2,692

	STOCK PRICE ($) FY Close	P/E High/Low		PER SHARE ($) Earnings	Dividends	Book Value
12/12	31.73	21	16	1.75	0.96	28.91
12/11	31.97	31	22	1.15	0.96	27.95
12/10	34.86	32	19	1.40	0.96	23.22
12/09	43.81	20	10	2.26	0.96	22.74
12/08	45.46	28	17	2.05	0.96	19.18
Annual Growth	**(8.6%)**	**—**	**—**	**(3.9%)**	**(0.0%)**	**10.8%**

Hanger Inc

Hanger gets people back to reaching walking and running. It is one of the leading US operators of orthotic and prosthetic (O&P) patient care centers with some 700 facilities nationwide. The company's Southern Prosthetic Supply procures and distributes standard and customized braces and prosthetic devices to affiliated and independent O&P centers. Its therapeutic solutions units Accelerated Care Plus (ACP) and Innovative Neurotronics (IN) respectively provide rehabilitation supplies to care centers and make neuromuscular stimulation products for patients with a loss of mobility. The company also manages O&P networks and care programs for health insurers through subsidiary Linkia.

In addition to its O&P patient care centers which provide device fitting and adjustment services for orthopedic braces and limb prosthetics Hanger has distribution custom-fabrication and corporate facilities across the US. The patient care segment accounts for more than 80% of revenues with about 40% of those sales coming from Medicare Medicaid and other government program reimbursement. The remaining patient care revenues come from private pay customers which include private insurance companies HMO and PPO plans workers' compensation programs and individuals.

Hanger has grown by acquiring small and midsized O&P patient care service companies as well as opening satellite patient-care centers. The company acquired more than 240 care centers between 1997 and 2012. It continuously looks for opportunities to expand product and service offerings and patient volumes at its existing centers as well through such strategic measures as process enhancement programs technology improvements marketing initiatives vendor consolidation and new payer contracts.

While O&P patient care services remains the company's focus Hanger is looking to broaden its other offerings. It is strengthening the operations of its Southern Prosthetic Supply division by developing additional delivery channels conducting targeted sales efforts and expanding its product offerings. In addition Hanger is working to increase the customer base for its Linkia network management offerings which aim to assist managed care companies with reducing costs and monitoring service quality levels. It is also looking to add new high-tech neuromuscular product to its IN division through licensing opportunities and product development programs.

In 2010 the company entered the nursing home rehabilitation services market by acquiring ACP for $155 million. ACP provides clinical rehab products services to about 4000 sub-acute and long-term skilled nursing facilities in the US. The purchase broadened Hanger's customer base while expanding its operations into an adjacent therapeutic care market. Following the transaction Hanger created a new therapeutic solutions segment to hold the ACP and IN divisions.

To explore its footing in additional markets Hanger has launched a new CARES pilot program to help hospitals manage their O&P needs in the emergency room setting. Another pilot program Dosteon helps physicians manage postoperative O&P needs for their patients.

Hanger has managed to increase net sales and profits in recent years thanks to its growth initiatives. In 2011 Hanger reported a 12% revenue increase to some $918 million; the firm also more than doubled its net income levels to some $55 million. The 2011 results were attributed to its organic growth and acquisition initiatives in the patient care segment its marketing and product expansion efforts in the distribution segment and the growth of the new therapeutics solutions segment from the purchase of ACP.

Lured by financial incentives Hanger moved its corporate headquarters from Bethesda Maryland to Austin Texas in 2010. As part of a larger branding effort in 2012 the company shortened its name from Hanger Orthopedic Group to simply Hanger Inc.

EXECUTIVES

Chairman, Ivan R. Sabel, age 67, $605,000 total compensation
Chief Financial Officer; Executive Vice President; Secretary, George E. McHenry, age 60, $313,250 total compensation
President and COO Southern Prosthetic Supply, Kenneth W. Wilson
EVP; President and COO Hanger Prosthetics and Orthotics and HPO, Richmond L. (Rick) Taylor, age 64, $390,600 total compensation
VP and CIO, Walt Meffert Jr., age 47
Vice Chairman, Thomas F. Kirk, age 67, $605,000 total compensation
VP Finance and Chief Accounting Officer, Thomas C. Hofmeister, age 46
President; Chief Executive Officer; Director, Vinit K. Asar, age 46
President of Linkia; LLC, Rebecca Hast
VP Prosthetics, Kevin Carroll
Press Contact, Jennifer Bittner
VP and General Counsel, Thomas E. Hartman
VP and Chief Human Resources Officer, Drew Morton
Vice President; Treasurer, Russell Allen
Vice President Hanger UEPP, Troy Farnsworth

Vice President - Human Resources, Andrew Morton
Director, Patricia B. Shrader, age 63
Director, Isaac Kaufman, age 66
Director, Stephen E. Hare, age 59
Director, Peter J. Neff, age 74
Director, Thomas P. Cooper, age 69
Director, Eric A. Green, age 51
Vice Chairman, Thomas F. Kirk, age 67
Director, Cynthia L. Feldmann, age 60
Director, Bennett Rosenthal, age 48
CEO and Director, Vinit K. Asar, age 45
Auditors: PricewaterhouseCoopersLLP

LOCATIONS

HQ: Hanger Inc.
10910 Domain Dr. Ste. 300, Austin TX 78758
Phone: 512-777-3800   **Fax:** 920-751-5395
Web: www.plexus.com

PRODUCTS/OPERATIONS

2011 Sales

Patient care	753	82
Distribution	100	11
Therapeutic solutions	64	7
Total	918	100

Selected Subsidiaries

Accelerated Care Plus Corp.
Dosteon Solutions LLC
Hanger Europe N.V. (60% Belgium)
Hanger Clinic. (patient care services)
Innovative Neurotronics Inc.
Linkia LLC
OPNET Inc.
Southern Prosthetic Supply Inc.

COMPETITORS

AmSurg	Otto Bock HealthCare
BREG	PC Group
BSN Medical	Patterson Companies
Buffalo Supply	Physiotherapy
DJO Global	Associates
DePuy	RehabCare
Deroyal Industries	Symbion
HCA	The Orthotic Group
HealthSouth	U.S. Physical Therapy
Newsplint	

HISTORICAL FINANCIALS

Company Type: Public

Income Statement

FYE: December 31

	REVENUE ($ mil.)	NET INCOME ($ mil.)	NET PROFIT MARGIN	EMPLOYEES
12/12	985.5	63.6	6.5%	4,700
12/11	918.5	55.0	6.0%	4,420
12/10	817.3	21.4	2.6%	4,273
12/09	760.0	36.0	4.7%	3,636
12/08	703.1	26.7	3.8%	3,211
Annual Growth	8.8%	24.2%	—	10.0%

2012 Year-End Financials

Debt ratio: 42.0%	No. of shares (mil.): 35
Return on equity: 13.6%	Dividends
Cash ($ mil.): 19	Yield: —
Current ratio: 3.35	Payout: —
Long-term debt ($ mil.): 509	Market value ($ mil.): 971

	STOCK PRICE ($) FY Close	P/E High/Low		PER SHARE ($) Earnings	Dividends	Book Value
12/12	27.36	16	10	1.83	0.00	14.18
12/11	18.69	17	9	1.61	0.00	12.28
12/10	21.19	33	20	0.65	0.00	10.65
12/09	13.83	14	10	1.13	0.00	9.62
12/08	14.51	24	11	0.78	0.00	8.24
Annual Growth	17.2%	—	—	23.8%	—	14.5%

Hatteras Financial Corp

Hatteras Financial hopes for smooth sailing on the sometimes tumultuous seas of mortgage investing. The company is a real estate investment trust (REIT) that invests in adjustable-rate and hybrid adjustable-rate single-family residential mortgages guaranteed by a US government agency or a government-backed company such as Ginnie Mae Fannie Mae or Freddie Mac. Hatteras Financial's investment portfolio valued at some $7 billion consists mostly of hybrid adjustable-rate loans with terms of three to five years. Hatteras Financial is externally managed by Atlantic Capital Advisors.

The manager is responsible for Hatteras Financial's day-to-day operations including buying and selling investments financing risk management and advisory services. It also oversees another mortgage REIT ACM Financial Trust. The two REITs and Atlantic Capital all share CEO Michael Hough and other top executives.

Though the mortgage market has been battered analysts have likened Hatteras' strategy of only buying government-backed loans to one of investing in bonds since the government would cover any defaults. The REIT prefers to invest in mortgage securities backed by Fannie Mae which pays principal and interest sooner than Freddie Mac.

EXECUTIVES

Chairman and CEO, Michael R. Hough, age 52
President COO and Director, Benjamin M. (Ben) Hough, age 48
EVP and Co-Chief Investment Officer, William H. Gibbs Jr., age 53
CFO Secretary and Treasurer, Kenneth A. Steele, age 49
EVP and Co-Chief Investment Officer, Frederick J. Boos II, age 59
President COO and Director, Benjamin M. (Ben) Hough, age 48
Director, David W. Berson, age 58
Director, Jeffrey D. Miller, age 42
Director, Ira G. Kawaller, age 63
Director, Thomas D. Wren, age 61
Auditors: Ernst&YoungLLP

LOCATIONS

HQ: Hatteras Financial Corp.
110 Oakwood Dr. Ste. 340, Winston-Salem NC 27103
Phone: 336-760-9331   **Fax:** -10101
Web: www.globespanmedia.com

COMPETITORS

AG Mortgage Investment Trust	Anworth Mortgage Asset Capstead Mortgage

ARMOUR Residential REIT
Annaly Capital Management

Redwood Trust
Walter Investment Management

HISTORICAL FINANCIALS

Company Type: Public

Income Statement

FYE: December 31

	REVENUE ($ mil.)	NET INCOME ($ mil.)	NET PROFIT MARGIN	EMPLOYEES
12/12	506.3	349.2	69.0%	0
12/11	426.1	284.3	66.7%	0
12/10	265.0	169.5	64.0%	0
12/09	283.1	174.4	61.6%	0
12/08	198.3	79.1	39.9%	0
Annual Growth	26.4%	44.9%	—	—

2012 Year-End Financials

Debt ratio: —	No. of shares (mil.): 98
Return on equity: 13.5%	Dividends
Cash ($ mil.): 168	Yield: 13.3%
Current ratio: 0.03	Payout: 92.9%
Long-term debt ($ mil.): —	Market value ($ mil.): 2,452

	STOCK PRICE ($) FY Close	P/E High/Low		PER SHARE ($) Earnings	Dividends	Book Value
12/12	24.81	8	7	3.67	3.30	31.09
12/11	26.37	8	6	3.97	3.90	27.08
12/10	30.27	7	6	4.30	4.40	24.84
12/09	27.96	7	5	4.82	4.50	25.74
12/08	26.60	8	5	3.48	2.80	20.35
Annual Growth	(1.7%)	—	—	1.3%	4.2%	11.2%

Hawaiian Holdings Inc

Luaus leis and laying in the sun —Hawaiian Holdings knows how to get you there. The company's main subsidiary Hawaiian Airlines transports passengers and cargo between Honolulu and about a dozen major cities in the western US. Transpacific routes account for most of the carrier's revenue. Hawaiian Airlines also serves four of the six main Hawaiian Islands and destinations in the South Pacific such as American Samoa Australia the Philippines and Tahiti. It operates a fleet of about 35 aircraft (most are Boeing 717s for flights between the Hawaiian Islands and Boeing 767s for transpacific flights). In addition to its scheduled passenger and cargo operations Hawaiian Airlines provides charter services.

Operations

To supplement its own inter-island offerings Hawaiian Airlines serves other destinations within Hawaii via a code-sharing deal with Island Air. In addition Hawaiian Airlines maintains code-sharing arrangements with carriers such as American Airlines Continental Airlines Delta Air Lines United and US Airways. Code-sharing allows airlines to extend their networks by selling tickets on other carriers' flights.

Sales and Marketing

Hawaiian Airlines uses various distribution channels including its website (mostly for North America and regional island routes) and travel agencies and wholesale distributors for international flights.

Financial Performance

Hawaiian Airlines has enjoyed three straight years of steady growth. Revenues spiked 19% from $1.65 billion in 2011 to reach a historical milestone of $1.96 billion in 2012. After suffering a net loss of nearly $3 million in 2011 the airline posted $53 million in net income for 2012.

The growth in 2012 was driven by an increase in passenger revenue due to an uptick in capacity across its network. The positive net income was due to the absence of a $70 million litigation charge it incurred in 2011 related to the purchase of aircraft.

Strategy

Hawaiian Airlines is counting on continued growth in its transpacific and South Pacific operations through expanded service to Tahiti Australia Japan and the Philippines. It has instituted a code-sharing agreement with Korean Air Lines and now offers nonstop flights to that country. Hawaiian Airlines is currently the only airline to offer nonstop service from Honolulu to Pago Pago and American Samoa. To support its expansion plans the company has ordered a dozen wide-body and extra-wide-body aircraft from Airbus for delivery between 2012 and 2020.

In mid-2013 the airline announced plans to launch a non-stop service between Honolulu and Beijing beginning in April 2014. This flight will represent the airlines' tenth international destination and will make China one of Hawaiian Airlines' most important visitor destinations.

HISTORY

In 1929 former Navy pilot Stanley Kennedy general manager of the Inter-Island Steam Navigation Company persuaded the Inter-Island board to fund a passenger line linking Honolulu (Oahu) with the other Hawaiian Islands. The new airline which started out with amphibian aircraft began inter-island airmail service in 1934.

The company became Hawaiian Airlines in 1941. TWA bought control in 1944 but sold out four years later after the new Trans-Pacific Airlines (later Aloha Airlines) ended Hawaiian's 17-year monopoly in Hawaii in 1946. The two competed intensely for the same routes. Investor John Magoon bought control of Hawaiian in 1964. The rival airlines agreed to merge in 1970 but negotiations failed a year later.

Airline deregulation in 1978 gave Hawaiian access to new markets. It adopted the name HAL in 1982 and by 1985 had added service to the US West Coast (where it was hammered by United and Continental) and to the South Pacific. HAL built the $8.5 million West Maui Airport in 1987. Rising costs forced Magoon to sell 47% of HAL to an investor group that included Magoon's friend former baseball commissioner Peter Ueberroth. The group led by Jet America Airlines founder Thomas Talbot bought control of HAL in 1989 and Talbot took over as chairman and CEO.

Rival Aloha surpassed HAL at home capturing 61% of the interisland market in 1991. HAL had also gained a nickname "Hawaiian Always Late" from complaining passengers. To raise $20 million HAL sold Northwest a 25% stake (which Northwest later disposed of) along with some international routes. HAL's president John Ueberroth (Peter's brother) replaced Talbot as chairman. In 1992 as HAL was narrowing its losses Hurricane Iniki cost it some $7 million in sales. HAL filed for bankruptcy in 1993 and Ueberroth resigned.

Airline veteran Bruce Nobles became CEO that year. He guided HAL through reorganization and in 1994 the slimmed-down airline took the name Hawaiian Airlines once again.

John Adams of Smith Management formed a partnership to invest in the airline in 1996 and was subsequently named Hawaiian's chairman. Before CEO Nobles made way for Paul Casey in 1997 he won a union wage concession and an agreement from American to defer aircraft lease payments. In 1998 Hawaiian partnered with American in a code-sharing deal and launched another in 1999 this time with Continental. Also in 1999 Hawaiian began negotiations with the pilots union and in 2000 the airline requested a federal mediator to assist in the negotiations.

The airline came to an agreement with the pilots in 2001 and reached another agreement with the union representing its flight attendants later that year. Also in late 2001 Hawaiian and Aloha Airlines both suffering from the industry downturn that followed the September 11 terrorist attacks agreed to merge and form a new company Aloha Holdings but the plans were abandoned in 2002 because of heavy opposition to the merger by employees and shareholders of Hawaiian. The company formed a holding company later that year called Hawaiian Holdings.

As the effects of September 11 on the air travel market lingered Hawaiian Airlines filed for Chapter 11 bankruptcy protection in March 2003. (Hawaiian Holdings was not included in the filing.) During the carrier's reorganization San Diego-based investment firm Ranch Capital's RC Aviation bought Adams' stake in Hawaiian Holdings. (RC Aviation dissolved in 2008 and distributed the shares among the investors in the group.)

Hawaiian Airlines completed its reorganization and emerged from bankruptcy in June 2005. The carrier established its dominance in Hawaii once again when Aloha Airlines filed for bankruptcy and liquidated its inventory in March 2008.

EXECUTIVES

SVP Sales and Marketing Hawaiian Airlines, Glenn G. Taniguchi, age 70, $250,000 total compensation
VP Customer Services Hawaiian Airlines, Blaine J. Miyasato
Senior Vice President - Human Resources of Hawaiian, Barbara D. Falvey, age 54, $280,000 total compensation
SVP Operations Hawaiian Airlines, Charles R. Nardello
Chairman, Lawrence Hershfield
President CEO and Director, Mark B. Dunkerley, age 49, $583,182 total compensation
Director, Samson Poomaihealani, age 71
VP Public Affairs Hawaiian Airlines, John R. (Keoni) Wagner, age 46
VP Finance Hawaiian Airlines, Karen A. Berry
VP Inflight Services Hawaiian Airlines, Louis D. Saint-Cyr
Executive Vice President and Chief Commercial Officer of Hawaiian, Peter R. Ingram, age 46, $330,000 total compensation
VP Sales and Marketing Hawaiian Airlines, Richard J. (Rick) Peterson
VP Corporate Audit Hawaiian Airlines, Donald A. E. Sealey
VP Flight Operations Hawaiian Airlines, Kenneth E. Rewick
Secretary; Senior Vice President; General Counsel and Corporate Secretary of Hawaiian, Hoyt H. Zia, age 59
SVP Corporate Communications and Public Affairs, Alan L. Hoffman
VP and Controller Hawaiian Airlines, Brian T. Stewart

Vice President Marketing, Avi A. Mannis
Vice President Controller, Shannon L. Okinaka
Vice President Strategic Procurement, Tom E. Wessner
Vice President Planning & Revenue Management, Andrew Watterson
Vice President Financial Planning & Analysis, Christian Forbes
Chief Financial Officer; Executive Vice President; Treasurer, Scott Topping
Senior Vice President and Chief Information Officer, Ron Anderson-Lehman
Vice President Maintenance & Engineering, Lorrin Sardinha
Senior Director, Susan Donofrio
Director, Donald J. (Don) Carty Jr., age 65
Director, Bert T. Kobayashi Jr., age 73
President CEO and Director, Mark B. Dunkerley, age 49
Director, Samson Poomaihealani, age 71
Director, Gregory S. Anderson, age 56
Director, Randall L. Jenson, age 44
Director, William S. Swelbar, age 54
Director, L. Todd Budge, age 52
Director, Crystal K. Rose, age 55
Director, Brian E. Boyer
Independent Director, Richard Zwern
Auditors: Ernst&YoungLLP

LOCATIONS

HQ: Hawaiian Holdings Inc.
3375 Koapaka St. Ste. G-350, Honolulu HI 96819
Phone: 808-835-3700   **Fax:** 808-835-3690
Web: www.hawaiianair.com

PRODUCTS/OPERATIONS

2012 Sales

Passenger	1,767	90
Total	**1,962**	**100**

Selected Transpacific Destinations

Las Vegas
Los Angeles
Oakland CA
Phoenix
Portland OR
Sacramento CA
San Diego
San Francisco
San Jose CA
Seattle

COMPETITORS

ACE Aviation	Hawaii Island Air
ANA Holdings	Japan Airlines
Air Canada	Mesa Air
Alaska Air	Qantas
American Airlines	US Airways
Group	United Continental
Delta Air Lines	

HISTORICAL FINANCIALS

Company Type: Public

Income Statement

FYE: December 31

	REVENUE ($ mil.)	NET INCOME ($ mil.)	NET PROFIT MARGIN	EMPLOYEES
12/12	1,962.3	53.2	2.7%	4,906
12/11	1,650.4	(2.6)	—	4,314
12/10	1,310.0	110.2	8.4%	4,023
12/09	1,183.3	116.7	9.9%	3,844
12/08	1,210.8	28.5	2.4%	3,707
Annual Growth	**12.8%**	**16.8%**	**—**	**7.3%**

2012 Year-End Financials

Debt ratio: 35.4%
Return on equity: 21.6%
Cash ($ mil.): 405
Current ratio: 0.87
Long-term debt ($ mil.): 553

No. of shares (mil.): 51
Dividends
  Yield: —
  Payout: —
Market value ($ mil.): 338

	STOCK PRICE ($) FY Close	P/E High/Low		PER SHARE ($) Earnings	Dividends	Book Value
12/12	6.57	7	5	1.01	0.00	5.22
12/11	5.80	—	—	(0.05)	0.00	4.39
12/10	7.84	4	2	2.10	0.00	5.53
12/09	7.00	4	1	2.22	0.00	3.42
12/08	6.38	18	6	0.57	0.00	1.03
Annual Growth	0.7%	—	—	15.4%	—	49.9%

HCP, Inc.

Old age isn't for sissies but as far as HCP is concerned it is for making money. HCP is a self-administered real estate investment trust (REIT) that invests in develops and manages real estate that it leases to health care facilities. Its real estate portfolio consists of senior living and skilled nursing facilities hospitals medical office buildings and biotech and pharmaceutical laboratories. HCP has interests in more than 1000 properties in 40-plus states and Mexico though nearly half of its holdings are located in California and Texas. The REIT which has $21.4 billion in assets under management invests in properties through direct ownership mortgage loans and joint ventures.

Ownership
The Vanguard Group and its affiliates own more than 11% interest in the company.

Geographic Reach
Based in California HCP operates across more than 40 states and Mexico.

Operations
The company operates its business through five segments: senior housing post-acute/skilled nursing life science medical office and hospital.

HCP which maintains offices in both Nashville and San Francisco generates 44% of its revenue from properties located in California (22%) Texas (12%) and Florida (10%).

HCP's five investment products include properties under lease debt investments developments and redevelopments investment management and investments in senior housing operations. Besides its investments in properties under lease and debt investments HCP at the beginning of 2013 had an aggregate investment of $540 million in assets under development including redevelopment and land held for future development primarily in its life science and medical office segments.

Financial Performance
HCP has logged sales growth during the past five years mostly from organic growth.

Resident fees and services and income from direct financing lease revenues helped HCP post 10% revenue increases in 2012 as compared to 2011. These gains were offset however by rising rental and related revenues and tenant recoveries revenue. Both senior housing and post-acute/skilled nursing accounted for most of the revenue boost.

HCP's net income jumped by 54% during the same reporting period due to rising revenue and lower costs and expenses as well as a boost in equity income from unconsolidated joint ventures and a gain on the sales of real estate.

Sales and Marketing
Major tenants include Brookdale Senior Living Emeritus Corporation HCR ManorCare HCA Amgen Genetech and Sunrise Senior Living.

Strategy
HCP has built its business by leasing healthcare properties under long-term leases with fixed and/or inflation indexed escalators. Most of the company's rents and other earned income from leases are received under triple-net leases or leases that provide for substantial recovery of operating expenses. Some of its medical office and life science leases however are structured as gross or modified gross leases.The company regularly invests in its business. In 2012 it invested $270 million. These deals included the purchase of a medical office building for $13 million; a life science facility for $8 million; a senior housing facility for $4 million; a parcel of land adjacent to one of its hospitals for $3 million; and funding of development and other capital projects of $242 million primarily in its life science senior housing and medical office segments.Mergers and Acquisitions

The REIT's usual strategy is to grow by acquisitions –often major ones –rather than through development.

HCP in 2012 bought eight on-campus medical office buildings for $80 million from Scottsdale Healthcare as well as 12 medical office buildings from The Boyer Company valued at $188 million primarily located on the campuses of HCA Iasis Healthcare and Community Health Systems. HCP also acquired 129 senior housing communities for $1.7 billion from a joint venture between Emeritus and the Blackstone JV. Located in 29 states the portfolio encompasses 10077 units representing a diversified care mix of 61% assisted living 25% independent living 13% memory care and 1% skilled nursing. As part of this acquisition HCP entered into triple-net master leases with Emeritus the nation's largest assisted living and memory care operator who will continue to operate the communities.Previously HCP bought 334 post-acute skilled nursing and assisted living facilities of HCR Manor-Care in 2011 for $6 billion. As part of the purchase HCP entered into a long-term triple-net master lease under which HCR ManorCare will continue to operate the facilities.

In 2011 HCP acquired most of HCR Manor Care's property assets including more than 300 facilities for some $6.1 billion; the deal made the health care provider HCP's largest tenant and helped boost its revenue and earnings for that year. Previous large acquisitions included its 2007 buy of the Slough Estates USA portfolio of British real estate giant SEGRO for $2.9 billion and the $5.3 billion cash-and-stock acquisition of CNL Retirement Properties from CNL Financial (which added its portfolio of Sunrise Senior Living properties) in 2006.

EXECUTIVES

EVP, Edward J. (Ed) Henning, age 60, $350,000 total compensation
Chairman, Michael D. McKee
President and CEO, Lauralee E. Martin
Chairman President and CEO, James F. (Jay) Flaherty III, age 55, $600,000 total compensation
EVP Acquisitions and Valuations, Thomas D. (Tom) Kirby
EVP and Chief Investment Officer, Paul F. Gallagher, $350,000 total compensation
EVP Medical Office Properties, Thomas M. (Tom) Klaritch, $350,000 total compensation
VP Asset Management, S. Paul Brown
EVP Post-Acute and Hospitals, Susan M. Tate
VP and Treasurer, Matthew A. Brill
VP Tax, Michael A. Congdon
VP Risk Management, Patrick J. Strangle
SVP Associate General Counsel and Assistant Corporate Secretary, Brian J. Maas
EVP and CFO, Timothy M. (Tim) Schoen
VP and Corporate Controller, Jose M. Castro
VP and Controller, Reid L. Babin
EVP Life Science Estates, Jonathan M. Bergschneider
VP Medical Office Properties, James A. Croy
VP Financial Planning and Analysis, John Lu
VP Medical Office Properties, George M. McIlwain
SVP Acquisitions and Valuations, Darrin L. Smith
VP Acquisitions and Valuations, John D. Stasinos
SVP Life Science Estates, Randall W. Rohner
SVP and Chief Accounting Officer, Scott A. Anderson, age 50
Assistant Corporate Secretary, Eric J. Stambol
VP Accounting, Michelle L. Wood
VP Medical Office Properties, Angela Playle
VP Legal, Jeana H. Park
VP Accounting, Kimberley P. Myers
VP Medical Office Properties, Kelly J. Manion
VP Asset Management, Michael S. Julian
VP Medical Office Properties, Thomas W. Hulme
VP Accounting, Susan B. Cullen
VP Medical Office Properties, Andrew Cressman
SVP Tax, Timothy A. Hall
SVP Medical Office Properties, Glenn T. Preston
VP Accounting, Jeannine N. Bonesteele
VP Information Technology, Darren J. Bordeaux
EVP General Counsel and Secretary, James W. (Jim) Mercer
EVP Senior Housing, Kendall K. Young
Director, Joseph P. Sullivan, age 70
Director, Kenneth B. (Ken) Roath, age 77
Director, Michael D. McKee, age 67
Director, Lauralee E. Martin, age 62
Director, David B. Henry, age 64
Director, Christine N. Garvey, age 65
Director, Richard M. Rosenberg, age 81
Director, Peter L. Rhein, age 71
Auditors: Deloitte&ToucheLLP

LOCATIONS

HQ: HCP Inc.
3760 Kilroy Airport Way Ste. 300, Long Beach CA 90806
Phone: 562-733-5100   **Fax:** 562-733-5200
Web: www.hcpi.com

PRODUCTS/OPERATIONS

2012 Properties

Senior housing facilities	441	
Post-acute/skilled nursing facilities	268	
Medical offices	207	
Life sciences	109	
Hospitals	17	
Total	**0**	**1,086**

Selected Subsidiaries

HCP Atrium MOB LLC (95.30%)
HCP DR California LLC
HCP CTE L.P. (99.9%)
HCP Pleasant LLC
HCP DR MCD LLC (69.34%)
HCP MCD TRS LLC
HCP EGP Inc.
HCP ETE L.P. (99.9%)
HCP Life Science REIT Inc. (99.99%)

COMPETITORS

Cousins Properties	Omega Healthcare
Extendicare	Investors
Health Care REIT	Sabra Health Care
Healthcare Realty	Senior Housing
Trust	Properties
LTC Properties	Ventas
National Health	
Investors	

HISTORICAL FINANCIALS

Company Type: Public

Income Statement

FYE: December 31

	REVENUE ($ mil.)	NET INCOME ($ mil.)	NET PROFIT MARGIN	EMPLOYEES
12/13	2,099.8	970.8	46.2%	154
12/12	1,900.7	832.5	43.8%	149
12/11	1,725.3	538.8	31.2%	147
12/10	1,255.1	330.7	26.3%	148
12/09	1,157.0	146.1	12.6%	142
Annual Growth	16.1%	60.5%	—	2.0%

2013 Year-End Financials

Debt ratio: 43.1%
Return on equity: 9.1%
Cash ($ mil.): 300
Current ratio: 0.88
Long-term debt ($ mil.): 8,661

No. of shares (mil.): 456
Dividends
  Yield: 5.7%
  Payout: 103.4%
Market value ($ mil.): 16,597

	STOCK PRICE ($) FY Close	P/E High/Low	PER SHARE ($) Earnings	Dividends	Book Value
12/13	36.32	26 17	2.13	2.10	23.47
12/12	45.16	25 20	1.90	2.00	23.28
12/11	41.43	32 22	1.29	1.92	22.11
12/10	36.79	38 27	1.00	1.86	21.45
12/09	30.54	82 40	0.40	1.84	19.69
Annual Growth	4.4%	— —	51.9%	3.4%	4.5%

Health Care REIT Inc.

Health Care REIT is a real estate investment trust (REIT) that invests in senior living and health care facilities primarily skilled nursing and assisted-living facilities designed for older people needing help with everyday living. The trust also has investments in independent living facilities hospitals medical office buildings and specialty care facilities. Its $21-billion portfolio includes more than 1200 properties leased to health care operators in some 45 US states the UK and Canada. Additionally the company develops new build-to-suit properties through its HCN Development Services Group subsidiary. It also invests in mortgage loans and provides construction financing for its existing properties.

Geographic Reach

Based in Ohio Health Care REIT operates nationwide as well as in the UK and Canada. Three states —California Texas and New Jersey —accounted for 27% of the firm's 2012 revenue.

In 2012 Health Care REIT expanded into Canada through a partnership with Chartwell Seniors Housing REIT. The partnership acquired more than 40 senior housing and care communities in Canadian markets for $925 million.

Sales and Marketing

The company's customers include property lessee Genesis HealthCare (15% of sales) and property management partners Benchmark Senior Living and Merrill Gardens (together with more than 10% of sales) as well as Belmont Village.

Operations

Health Care REIT operates its business through three segments: seniors housing triple-net seniors housing operating and medical facilities.

The company generates about 80% of its revenue from senior housing such as independent living facilities continuing care retirement communities assisted living facilities Alzheimer's/dementia facilities and skilled nursing/post-acute facilities. Half of the 80% comes from properties leased to third-party operators (such as Genesis HealthCare) under triple-net master leases and the other half is from properties jointly owned and operated with partners the likes of Benchmark Senior Living and Merrill Gardens.

Health Care REIT's third segment which accounts for about 20% of sales includes medical facilities such as physician offices ambulatory surgery centers diagnostic facilities outpatient services and labs.

Financial Performance

Health Care REIT has nearly tripled its revenue during the past three years due to significant acquisitions. The company's revenue rose 28% in 2012 vs. 2011 due to a boost from both its seniors housing triple-net and medical facilities segments. Its joint venture seniors housing operating segment posted the year's most impressive gains however. The segment accounted for 37% of Health Care REIT's 2012 revenue up significantly from 32% in 2011 helped by the company's early 2013 purchase of Sunrise Senior Living. The firm's net income also jumped by 37% during the same reporting period thanks to revenue increases offset by rising expenses from higher interest expenses property operating expenses and general and administrative costs.

Strategy

The company grows primarily through acquisitions and development. It targets the full spectrum of seniors housing and health care real estate diversifying through property type and customer and geographic location.To its benefit Health Care REIT boasts partnerships with several companies including Benchmark Senior Living Brandywine Senior Living Brookdale Senior Living Capital Senior Living Forest City-University Park at MIT NuHealth Signature Healthcare and Virtua Health System.Mergers and Acquisitions

After rival health care REITs Ventas and Nationwide Health Properties merged in 2011 Health Care REIT arranged to buy the real estate assets of facilities operator Genesis HealthCare. The $2.4 billion deal added some 150 properties to Health Care REIT's portfolio.

In 2013 the company acquired Sunrise Senior Living in a deal worth some $3.4 billion. The transaction included almost 60 properties in the US and Canada and interests in nearly 70 additional ones with options to acquire most of them outright.

In 2013 Health Care REIT also acquired a 75% stake in Ontario-based Revera a provider of seniors' accommodation care and services. It serves 47 high-quality seniors housing and care communities comprising 5000 units located in major Canadian metropolitan markets.

These and similar deals speak to the expected boom in senior housing needs as the nation's median age continues to rise.

Company Ownership

Mutual fund manager The Vanguard Group holds a more than 11% stake in Health Care REIT.

LOCATIONS

HQ: Health Care REIT Inc.
1 SeaGate Ste. 1500, Toledo OH 43603
Phone: 419-247-2800   Fax: 419-247-2826
Web: www.hcreit.com

2012 Revenue

	% of total
California	9
New	9
Texas	9
Florida	7
Pennsylvania	5
Remaining	61
Total	**100**

PRODUCTS/OPERATIONS

2012 Revenue

	$ mil.	% of total
Rental income	1,080	59
Resident fees & services	697	38
Interest income	39	2
Other income	5	1
Total	**1,822**	**100**

2012 Revenue

	$ mil.	% of total
Seniors housing triple-net	719	39
Seniors housing operating	703	39
Medical facilities	397	22
Non-segment/corporate	0	—
Total	**1,822**	**100**

2012 Property Types

	No.
Seniors housing	573
Medical	246
Seniors housing	154
Total	**973**

Selected Segments
Seniors housing triple-net
Seniors housing operating
Medical facilities

COMPETITORS

Cousins Properties	Omega Healthcare
HCP	Investors
Healthcare Realty	Sabra Health Care
Trust	Senior Housing
LTC Properties	Properties
National Health	Ventas
Investors	

HISTORICAL FINANCIALS

Company Type: Public

Income Statement
FYE: December 31

	REVENUE ($ mil.)	NET INCOME ($ mil.)	NET PROFIT MARGIN	EMPLOYEES
12/12	1,822.1	294.8	16.2%	366
12/11	1,421.1	212.7	15.0%	308
12/10	680.5	128.8	18.9%	263
12/09	568.9	192.9	33.9%	217
12/08	551.2	288.1	52.3%	203
Annual Growth	**34.8%**	**0.6%**	**—**	**15.9%**

2012 Year-End Financials

Debt ratio: 43.6%
Return on equity: 3.3%
Cash ($ mil.): 1,033
Current ratio: —
Long-term debt ($ mil.): 8,531

No. of shares (mil.): 260
Dividends
  Yield: 4.8%
  Payout: 302.0%
Market value ($ mil.): 15,958

	STOCK PRICE ($) FY Close	P/E High/Low		PER SHARE ($) Earnings	Dividends	Book Value
12/12	61.29	63	53	0.98	2.96	39.54
12/11	54.53	61	46	0.90	2.84	37.06
12/10	47.64	62	48	0.83	2.74	31.29
12/09	44.32	31	18	1.49	2.72	30.77
12/08	42.20	19	11	2.81	2.70	30.67
Annual Growth	**9.8%**			**—(23.2%)**	**2.3%**	**6.6%**

Healthcare Services Group, Inc.

Healthcare Services Group gets swept up in its work every day. The company provides housekeeping laundry and linen food and maintenance services to hospitals nursing homes rehabilitation centers and retirement facilities. It tidies up around 3000 long-term care facilities in Canada and almost every state in the US. Housekeeping and laundry and linen services are the company's top revenue generators. The company's dietary division prepares food for residents and monitors nutritional needs in more than 600 facilities. Healthcare Services Group was established in 1977.

Geographic Reach
The company operates in 48 states and Canada.

Operations
The company's operations are divided in two segments: Housekeeping and Dietary.

Housekeeping consists of the managing of the client's housekeeping department which is principally responsible for the cleaning disinfecting and sanitizing of patient rooms and common areas of a client's facility as well as the laundering and processing of the personal clothing belonging to the facility's patients. Dietary consists of managing the client's dietary department which is principally responsible for food purchasing meal preparation and providing dietitian consulting professional services which includes the development of a menu that meets the patient's dietary needs.

Dietary services represented 32% of consolidated revenues in fiscal 2012 while Housekeeping services represented about 68%.

Sales and Marketing
The company markets its services primarily through referrals and in-person solicitation of target facilities. They also utilize direct mail campaigns and participate in industry trade shows health care trade associations and healthcare support service seminars.

Financial Performance
The company has seen its revenues and net income steadily increase year over year for a long time.

Healthcare Services Group revenues increased 21% and net income increased 16% in fiscal 2012 compared with 2011. Net cash inflow increased by $31 billion in 2012 compared with the prior year.

The increase in revenues was attributed to the increase in revenue from the company's reportable segments. Housekeeping revenues increased 13% driven by an increase in revenues attributable to service agreements entered into with new clients. Dietary segment revenues increased 45% primarily as a result of providing this service to a greater number of existing Housekeeping clients.

Mergers and Acquisitions
In 2013 Healthcare Services Group agreed with Platinum Health Services to acquire substantially all of its operating assets for approximately $380 million. Platinum is a privately-held provider of professional housekeeping laundry and maintenance services to long-term and post-acute care facilities.

EXECUTIVES

Chief Compliance Officer, Richard W. Hudson, age 65, $440,492 total compensation
VP Southeast Division, Brian M. Waters, $212,863 total compensation
President and Director, Thomas A. Cook, age 67, $252,750 total compensation
Division VP and Director, Joseph F. McCartney, age 58, $102,597 total compensation
Director Human Resources, Nicholas R. (Nick) Marino
Chairman of the Board; Chief Executive Officer, Daniel P. McCartney, age 61, $1,005,108 total compensation
VP Western Division, John D. Kelly
Executive Vice President; Director, Michael E. McBryan
Executive Vice President, Bryan D. McCartney, $155,966 total compensation
VP Mid-Atlantic Division, James P. O'Toole
VP Northeast Division, Kevin McCartney
VP Western Division, David Smigel
President; Chief Operating Officer; Director, Theodore Wahl, age 40, $190,249 total compensation
VP Midwest Division, David Hurlock
VP Southeast Division, Nicholas Rucker
VP Midwest Division, James Schreck
VP Mid-Atlantic Division, Robert Scutta
Chief Financial Officer; Secretary, John Shea
Chief Compliance Officer; Corporate Counsel, Jason Bundick
President and Director, Thomas A. Cook, age 67
Division VP and Director, Joseph F. McCartney, age 58
Director, Robert L. Frome, age 75
Director, Robert J. Moss, age 75
Director, John M. Briggs, age 62
SVP and Director, Michael E. McBryan
Director, Dino D. Ottaviano, age 65
EVP COO and Director, Theodore Wahl, age 38
Independent Director, Diane Casey
Auditors: GrantThorntonLLP

LOCATIONS

HQ: Healthcare Services Group, Inc.
  3220 Tillman Drive, Suite 300, Bensalem, PA 19020
Phone: 215 639-4274
Web: www.hcsgcorp.com

PRODUCTS/OPERATIONS

2012 Sales

	% of total
Housekeeping services	68
Dietary services	32
Total	**100**

COMPETITORS

ABM Industries	Ecolab
ARAMARK	G&K Services
Alsco	Sodexo USA
Angelica Corporation	SureQuest Systems
Crothall Healthcare	UGL Services UNICCO
Cygnet Foods	

HISTORICAL FINANCIALS

Company Type: Public

Income Statement
FYE: December 31

	REVENUE ($ mil.)	NET INCOME ($ mil.)	NET PROFIT MARGIN	EMPLOYEES
12/12	1,077.4	44.2	4.1%	7,000
12/11	889.0	38.1	4.3%	6,850
12/10	773.9	34.4	4.5%	5,400
12/09	692.7	30.3	4.4%	4,900
12/08	602.7	26.6	4.4%	4,500
Annual Growth	**15.6%**	**13.5%**	**—**	**11.7%**

2012 Year-End Financials

Debt ratio: —
Return on equity: 19.7%
Cash ($ mil.): 68
Current ratio: 3.96
Long-term debt ($ mil.): —

No. of shares (mil.): 68
Dividends
  Yield: 2.8%
  Payout: 100.3%
Market value ($ mil.): 1,581

STOCK PRICE ($) FY Close	P/E High/Low	PER SHARE ($) Earnings	Dividends	Book Value
12/12 23.23	37 27	0.65	0.65	3.37
12/11 17.69	33 22	0.56	0.63	3.26
12/10 16.27	48 30	0.51	0.60	3.22
12/09 21.46	47 30	0.46	0.49	3.19
12/08 15.93	60 31	0.40	0.39	3.11
Annual Growth 9.9%	— —	12.9%	14.0%	2.1%

Healthstream Inc

HealthStream replenishes the well of knowledge for medical workers. The company supplies Internet-based learning and research content to health care organizations throughout the US to meet their training certification and development needs. HealthStream's core learning product is HealthStream Learning Center (HLC) which offers educational and training courseware to more than 2.5 million subscribers (representing some 2600 hospitals) via a software-as-a-service (SaaS) model. The company's research offerings include quality and satisfaction surveys data analysis and other research-based management tools; the Patient Insights survey generates most of the research business' revenues.

Geographic Reach

HealthStream serves customers in all US states from its corporate headquarters in Nashville and its satellite office in Laurel Maryland.

Sales and Marketing

HealthStream generates sales from subscription fees based on the number of users and type of content provided. Clients include US health care organizations –primarily acute care hospitals such as HCA Tenet and LifePoint —and pharmaceutical and medical device companies.

HealthStream markets its products primarily through direct sales teams consultants and account relationship managers. Its marketing programs include catalogs trade shows online promotions telemarketing campaigns public relations direct mail and advertising.

Financial Analysis

HealthStream's revenues have climbed steadily over the last decade. For instance in 2011 the company reported a 25% sales increase to some $82 million due to growth in both the learning and research segments. The learning division saw a 29% increase in sales due to its growing subscriber base and expanded courseware offerings (including the new SimVentures program) while research revenues rose 16% from increased patient survey volumes. HealthStream's revenue growth also prompted 67% increase in profits to some $6.9 million that year.

Strategy

While many of its competitors are offering course material in a range of formats (print online instructor-led) HealthStream focuses on its Internet-based offerings. In order to remain competitive HealthStream tailors its HLC course delivery methods to provide clients with access to the specific educational resources they need. While HealthStream is focused on adding subscribers to the HLC platform it also aims to have existing subscribers order additional courses and new software applications. To take advantage of the increasing use of simu-

lation technology to educate students and medical professionals HealthStream partnered with Laerdal Medical to form a joint venture called SimVentures in 2011. The venture sells patient simulation scenarios through a simulation management platform called SimCenter.

HealthStream's Research division only brings in about 30% of its income but it could start seeing more demand since the government is increasingly tying reimbursements to improved patient safety and performance results. The company's research services are meant to complement its learning segment. Its HealthStream Improvement Center is an online system designed to help hospital leaders accelerate the execution of the improvement plans they come up with thanks to the research services. Plans are generally based on results from patient employee physician and community surveys.

Mergers and Acquisitions

In 2012 the company added competency management products when it acquired Decision Critical a private firm that provides software-as-a-service (SaaS) solutions that allow hospitals to manage and develop their workforce. The purchase expanded HealthStream's talent management offerings through the addition of the Critical Portfolio SaaS platform; it also adds other learning management and skill evaluation tools.

Ownership

CEO Robert Frist owns around 23% of HealthStream.

EXECUTIVES

EVP, Alfred E. Newman, $204,170 total compensation
Chairman President and CEO, Robert A. Frist Jr., $205,000 total compensation
SVP and CFO, Gerard M. (Gerry) Hayden Jr., $124,359 total compensation
SVP and COO, J. Edward Pearson, $209,167 total compensation
SVP and CTO, Jeffrey S. Doster, $128,077 total compensation
SVP General Counsel Secretary and Compliance Officer, Kevin O'Hara, age 43, $183,332 total compensation
Assistant VP Communications Research and Investor Relations, Mollie Condra
SVP, Michael J. Sousa
Senior Vice President General Counsel, Kevin OHara
Director, Thompson S. Dent, age 63
Director, Dale W. Polley, age 63
Director, Linda E. Rebrovick, age 57
Director, William W. Stead, age 64
Director, Jeffrey L. McLaren, age 46
Director, Michael D. Shmerling, age 57
Director, Frank Gordon, age 50
Director, C. Martin Harris, age 56
Director, Ronald (Ron) Hinds, age 62
Director, Deborah Taylor Tate
Independent Director, Deborah Tate
Auditors: Ernst&YoungLLP

LOCATIONS

HQ: HealthStream Inc.
209 10th Ave. South Ste. 450, Nashville TN 37203
Phone: 615-301-3100   **Fax:** 615-301-3200
Web: www.healthstream.com

PRODUCTS/OPERATIONS

2011 Sales

Learning	58	71
Total	**82**	**100**

Selected Products

Learning
  HealthStream Connect
  HealthStream Express
  HealthStream Improvement Center
  HealthStream Learning Center (HLC)
  SimVentures
Research
  Community Insights
  Employee Insights
  Insights Online
  Patient Insights
  Physician Insights

COMPETITORS

AMA	NRC
Cengage Learning	Press Ganey
Cornerstone OnDemand	Reed Elsevier Group
EBSCO	Saba Software
Foresight Group	SuccessFactors
Gallup	SumTotal
Kenexa	Taleo
Medscape llc	

HISTORICAL FINANCIALS

Company Type: Public

Income Statement

FYE: December 31

	REVENUE ($ mil.)	NET INCOME ($ mil.)	NET PROFIT MARGIN	EMPLOYEES
12/12	103.7	7.6	7.4%	587
12/11	82.0	6.9	8.5%	504
12/10	65.7	4.1	6.3%	432
12/09	57.4	13.9	24.3%	397
12/08	51.6	2.8	5.5%	400
Annual Growth	19.1%	27.9%	—	10.1%

2012 Year-End Financials

Debt ratio: —	No. of shares (mil.): 26
Return on equity: 6.0%	Dividends
Cash ($ mil.): 41	Yield: —
Current ratio: 3.38	Payout: —
Long-term debt ($ mil.): —	Market value ($ mil.): 638

	STOCK PRICE ($) FY Close	P/E High/Low	PER SHARE ($) Earnings	Dividends	Book Value
12/12	24.31	105 57	0.28	0.00	5.04
12/11	18.45	61 22	0.29	0.00	4.67
12/10	8.04	38 18	0.18	0.00	2.60
12/09	3.95	8 3	0.64	0.00	2.40
12/08	2.33	27 15	0.13	0.00	1.72
Annual Growth	79.7%	— —	21.1%	—	30.8%

Healthways Inc

For health insurers healthy plan members are cheap plan members; that's where Healthways comes in. The health services company provides disease management and wellness programs to managed care companies self-insured employers governments and hospitals with the ultimate goals of improving members' health and lowering health care costs. Its disease management programs help members manage chronic illnesses like diabetes and emphysema making sure they keep up with treatment plans and maintain healthy behaviors. Healthways' wellness offerings including its SilverSneakers program for seniors encourage fitness and other positive lifestyle choices.

Geographic Reach

Healthways operates in all 50 US states as well as Washington DC and Puerto Rico through about a dozen service centers. Additionally it administers health improvement programs and services in Brazil France and Australia and is seeking to grow its overseas operations especially in Asia Africa and Europe.

Operations

The company provides services to some 40 million people around the globe. In its core market in North America Healthworks relies primarily on contracts with health plans for the majority of its income which typically last three to five years. It also contracts with governments employers pharmacy benefit managers and hospitals. The company provides analytical and data management tools to allow clients to access and evaluate their members' health information; therefore it must invest heavily in its IT resources including outsourcing agreements with the likes of HP Enterprise Services.

Healthways attracts customers by using convenience as a marketing point offering a myriad of ways for members to take part in its programs including via phone mobile devices mail online through face-to-face interactions and by visiting care centers. In addition to its wellness and disease management programs the company helps clients identify at-risk members (those who may soon need medical attention) and provides access to a contracted network of fitness centers and alternative medicine providers.

Financial Analysis

Though the company has grown its services over the years due to the demand for consumer engagement in the health insurance industry Healthways' bottom line is vulnerable to shifts in customer contract levels. For instance the firm took a hit when its biggest customer health insurer CIGNA (accounting for more than 15% of sales) announced plans to wind down its contract during 2012. As a result Healthways took a $182 impairment charge in 2011 causing net income to fall into the red that year. Overall revenues also dropped by about 4% to $689 million in 2011 due to other contract losses during the year (somewhat offset by new contract gains) as well as due to increased program reimbursements the previous year from the Centers for Medicare and Medicaid Services (CMS).

Strategy

Since healthy people require expensive medical services less often Healthways' strategy consists of finding new ways to control health care costs by improving members' well-being. For instance it pursues partnerships with other health care companies such as pharmacy benefits managers or medical providers which often open up new distribution channels for its products and allow it to create new products and services for niche clients. For instance through a partnership with Johns Hopkins Medicine Healthways launched a weight management program based on clinical research conducted at the Johns Hopkins hospitals. The company is also adding custom programs for targeted markets such as its Senior Care Management (SCM) program which identifies and manages the care of high-risk Medicare Advantage members; the SCM program can be integrated with the SilverSneakers fitness program.

In 2012 Healthways formed a joint venture with consumer research firm Gallup to develop a new portolio of well-being assessment tools. The venture will provide products that give care providers patients employers and other customers access to predictive health monitoring tools.

Healthways also occasionally pursues acquisitions as a means of growth. For instance in 2011 it acquired Navvis a provider of change management and consulting services for health care systems in a $29 million deal. The purchase allowed Healthways to enhance its involvement in cost-control initiatives at the provider level by offering clinical integration leadership training and partnering strategy services to medical systems working to adapt to health reform measures. In 2012 acquired Philadelphia based Ascentia Health Care Solutions to bring on its health management technology. Ascentia's products are developed by and for physicians and helps to measure quality of care instead of just volume of care. Also known as Physician-Directed Population Health (PDPH) capabilities such products are increasingly in demand.

HISTORY

In 1981 Thomas Cigarran and Henry Herr (alumni of a company that later became part of HCA) joined with venture capitalist Martin Koldyke to found American Healthcorp to buy hospitals. The company diversified entering the diabetes market in 1984 and arthritis care in 1987.

With profitability lagging the company sold its hospitals to focus on niche care. In the same spirit it de-emphasized arthritis care in 1990. The company went public in 1991.

After a brief foray into obesity treatment the company in 1994 invested in AmSurg a manager of ambulatory surgery centers. (AmSurg was spun off in 1997.)

By the late 1990s the company increasingly targeted HMOs. It signed its first contract with Principal Health Care (1996 ended in 1998 after Coventry Health Care bought the HMO). Contracts with such HMOs as John Deere Health Care and Health Options of Blue Cross & Blue Shield of Florida followed in 1998.

To standardize income the company in 1998 converted all of its contracts from shared savings arrangements (in which the company's earnings were based on the payers' savings) to fee-based arrangements. In 1999 American Healthcorp began offering a cardiac health management program to its hospital and HMO clients; that year it changed its name to American Healthways to reflect its expanded product line.

American Healthways in 2000 signed a deal with Agilent Technologies to offer that company's home heart monitoring systems to American Healthways' patients. It also launched MYHEALTHWAYS a Web-based application which offers disease-prevention plans to health plan members.

In 2001 American Healthways launched Comprehensive Care Enhancement Programs under which all health plan members are screened and provided with any needed health care programs.

The company acquired Company StatusOne Health Systems in 2003 to expand its health management service offerings for high-risk populations. American Healthways changed its name to Healthways in early 2006.

In late 2006 the firm acquired preventive health services provider AXIA Health Management for more than $450 million. The acquisition added a host of wellness services such as fitness and nutrition programs to Healthways' service offering. Among them were the SilverSneakers program as well as an online smoking cessation support group called QuitNet.

Healthways set up shop overseas at the beginning of 2008 with a contract to provide disease management and wellness services to members of German health insurer Deutsche Angestellten Krankenkasse. That year it also entered the Brazil market via a partnership with Brazilian health services company Fleury. In 2009 the company established a presence in Australia when it entered into a wellness contract with insurer Hospitals Contribution Fund.

EXECUTIVES

VP, Robert E. Stone, age 65, $353,430 total compensation

Chairman, John W. Ballantine, age 66

EVP, Mary D. Hunter, age 66

President CEO and Director, Ben R. Leedle Jr., age 51, $685,000 total compensation

VP and CFO, Alfred Lumsdaine, age 46

VP and Chief Science Officer, James E. (Jim) Pope, age 58, $404,400 total compensation

EVP Operations Services, Robert L. Chaput, age 61

Vice President Employer Market, Christopher (Chris) Cigarran

Media Relations, Todd Hasting

Media Relations, Melissa Wyllie

VP Innovations and Chief Wellness Officer, John Harris

President Healthways International, Peter Choueiri

VP and COO, Thomas F. Cox

CEO Navvis Healthways, Mike Farris

VP Human Resources, Jeff Klem

Director of Operations, William Geller

Founder of Pro-Change Behavior Systems, James O. Prochaska

IR Contact Officer, Chip Wochomurka

VP-Health Plan Market, Clay Richards

Senior Vice President General Counsel, Mary S. Flipse

President Chief Executive Officer, Owen Kratz

Chairman Emeritus, Thomas G. (Tom) Cigarran, age 70

Director, Alison Taunton-Rigby, age 67

Director, C. Warren Neel, age 73

Director, William D. (Bill) Novelli

President CEO and Director, Ben R. Leedle Jr., age 51

Director, William C. O'Neil Jr., age 77

Independent Director, Jay Crispin (Cris) Bisgard, age 71

Director, L. Ben Lytle, age 65

Director, Mary Jane England, age 73

Director, John A. Wickens, age 55

Independent Director, William ONeil

Auditors: Ernst&YoungLLP

LOCATIONS

HQ: Healthways Inc.
701 Cool Springs Blvd., Franklin TN 37067
Phone: 615-614-4929   **Fax:** 402-240-4707
Web: www.conagrafoods.com

PRODUCTS/OPERATIONS

Selected Products and Services

Disease management programs
  Asthma
  Back pain
  Cancer
  Chronic kidney disease/end-stage renal disease (CKD/ESRD)
  Chronic obstructive pulmonary disease (COPD)
  Coronary artery disease
  Depression
  Diabetes
  Heart failure

Hepatitis C
Obesity
Osteoporosis
Gallup-Healthways Well-Being Index (collection and
  measurement of national health)
Prime Fitness (fitness program for adults under 65 years
  of age)
QuitNet (smoking cessation program)
SilverSneakers (fitness program for older adults)
WholeHealth (alternative and complementary medicine
  and therapy program)

COMPETITORS

APS Healthcare	Express Scripts
Accordant Health	Fresenius Medical Care
Services Inc.	Health Advocate
Accredo Health	Health Dialog
ActiveHealth	Humana
Management	Magellan Health
Aetna	Omnicare
Alere	OptumHealth
CIGNA	SHPS
Catalyst Health	Wal-Mart
Solutions	Walgreen
Comprehensive Care	iMetrikus

HISTORICAL FINANCIALS

Company Type: Public

Income Statement

FYE: December 31

	REVENUE ($ mil.)	NET INCOME ($ mil.)	NET PROFIT MARGIN	EMPLOYEES
12/12	677.1	8.0	1.2%	2,400
12/11	688.7	(157.6)	—	2,400
12/10	720.3	47.3	6.6%	2,800
12/09	717.4	10.3	1.4%	3,000
12/08	244.7	0.7	0.3%	0
Annual Growth	29.0%	81.8%	—	—

2012 Year-End Financials

Debt ratio: 38.8%	No. of shares (mil.): 33
Return on equity: 2.9%	Dividends
Cash ($ mil.): 1	Yield: —
Current ratio: 1.11	Payout: —
Long-term debt ($ mil.): 278	Market value ($ mil.): 363

	STOCK PRICE ($) FY Close	P/E High/Low		PER SHARE ($) Earnings	Dividends	Book Value
12/12	10.70	49	26	0.24	0.00	8.22
12/11	6.86	—	—	(4.68)	0.00	7.98
12/10	11.16	14	7	1.36	0.00	12.66
12/09	18.34	60	24	0.30	0.00	11.14
12/08	11.48	3467	296	0.02	0.00	10.61
Annual Growth	(1.7%)	—	—	86.1%	—	(6.2%)

Hecla Mining Co.

Not all that glitters at Hecla Mining is gold —in
fact the majority of it is silver. Hecla explores for
and mines gold silver lead and zinc. In 2012 the
mining and natural resource exploration company
produced some 6.4 million ounces of silver and
about 55500 ounces of gold; silver accounted for
more than half of the company's sales that year.
Hecla operates mines in the US (Alaska and Idaho)
and has interests in mines in Colorado Nevada
and in Mexico. The company sells to metals buyers around the world primarily to zinc producers
in Asia.

Geographic Reach

Hecla has operating mines in Alaska and Idaho
exploration and pre-development properties in four
world-class silver mining districts in the US and
Mexico and an exploration office and investments
in early-stage silver exploration projects in Canada.
It operates the Greens Creek mine in Alaska and
Lucky Friday mine (Idaho) and owns land in the
Silver Valley (northern Idaho) San Juan Silver in
Creede (Colorado) and San Sebastian (Durango
Mexico). The company also owns the Monte Cristo
exploration project in Nevada.In 2012 Korea ac-
counted for 37% of Hecla's revenues; Japan and
China 22% each.

Operations

The company is organized around its two operating mines —Greens Creek and Lucky Friday.

Sales and Marketing

In 2012 Korea Zinc accounted for 37% of
Hecla's revenues; Trafigura 22% MS Zinc 12%
and Teck Metals 10%.

Financial Performance

Helcla's revenues dropped by 33% in 2012 primarily due to 100% decrease in the Lucky Friday
segment revenues as the result of the suspension
of production at the Lucky Friday mine during
2012. Lower average prices for silver zinc and lead
(partially offset by higher gold prices) led the
Greens Creek segment revenues to decreased by
6% that year. Net income plummeted by 90% in
2012 because of lower sales and Lucky Friday
suspension-related costs (including an increase in
costs for maintenance of surface facilities and mine
workings and refurbishing the Luck Friday mill in
preparation for a return to production).

Strategy

The company's strategy is to expand its operations through investing in its four current exploration projects expanding its reserves operating
efficiently and seeking opportunities to acquire
new mining properties.

The rising price of metals had Hecla looking at
reopening three mines in 2011 that had been
closed in previous years: the Star Mine in Idaho's
Silver Valley the San Juan silver mine in Colorado
and the Hugh Zone at the company's San Sebastian project in Mexico. The mines had been closed
in the early 2000s as silver prices dropped below
$10 but by mid-2011 they had risen to around $40.
In late 2011 Hecla acquired the remaining 30%
stake in the San Juan Silver mine in one of Colorado's largest silver-producing districts.

Mergers and Acquisitions

In 2013 Hecla agreed to buy fellow miner Aurizon Mines for C$796 million (US$771 million).
Hecla and Aurizon together create a unique precious metals company with three long-life high-
grade low-cost mines in some of the best mining
area in the world. The move came after the company made an unsolicited 2012 bid for U.S. Silver
which already agreed to be acquired by RX Gold
& Silver. Hecla's offer C$110.7 million (US$108.6
million US) represented a 28% premium over the
RX offer. However the bid was rejected.

In 2012 it agreed to buy stakes in Canamex Resources a Canadian-based resource exploration
company focused on the exploration of two gold
properties the Bruner gold project located in Nye
County Nevada and the Aranka North gold project located in Guyana. That year it also agreed to
acquire stakes in the Dolly Varden Silver Corporation.

EXECUTIVES

President; Chief Executive Officer; Director,
Phillips S. Baker Jr., age 53, $426,250 total
compensation
Chairman of the Board; Lead Independent Director, Theodore (Ted) Crumley, age 68
Chief Financial Officer; Senior Vice President,
James A. (Jim) Sabala, age 58, $214,308 total
compensation
Vice President - Exploration, Dean W. A. McDonald,
age 55, $187,583 total compensation
Vice President - Corporate Development, Don
Poirier, age 54
VP Investor Relations, Melanie Hennessey
Vice President; General Counsel, David C. Sienko
Vice President General Manager, Ed Sutich
Vice President - Technical Services, John Jordan
Vice President - Operations, Lawrence Radford
Vice President - Investor Relations, Mike
Westerlund
President CEO and Director, Phillips S. Baker Jr.,
age 53
Director, Theodore (Ted) Crumley, age 68
Director, Charles B. (Chuck) Stanley, age 54
Director, David J. Christensen, age 50
Director, Terry V. Rogers, age 66
Director, Anthony P. Taylor, age 71
Director, John H. Bowles, age 67
Director, George R. Nethercutt Jr., age 69
Auditors: BDOSeidmanLLP

LOCATIONS

HQ: Hecla Mining Company
6500 N. Mineral Dr. Ste. 200, Coeur d' Alene ID 83815
Phone: 208-769-4100   **Fax:** 208-769-7612
Web: www.hecla-mining.com

2012 Sales

Asia		
China	72	22
Japan	70	22
Canada	34	11
US	25	8
Total	**321**	**100**

PRODUCTS/OPERATIONS

2012 Sales

Lucky Friday	0	25
Total	**321**	**100**

Selected Properties

Greens Creek mine (silver Alaska)
Lucky Friday mine (silver and lead Idaho)
San Sebastian mine (silver Mexico)

Selected Mergers and Acquisitions

2013
Aurizon Mines (pending —$771 million; Canada silver
  mine)

COMPETITORS

Agnico-Eagle	Newmont Mining
Barrick Gold	Pan American Silver
Coeur mining	Pe?oles
Golden Minerals	Silverado Gold Mines
Company	Sunshine Silver Mines

Company Type: Public

Income Statement
FYE: December 31

	REVENUE ($ mil.)	NET INCOME ($ mil.)	NET PROFIT MARGIN	EMPLOYEES
12/12	321.1	14.9	4.7%	735
12/11	477.6	151.1	31.6%	735
12/10	418.8	48.9	11.7%	686
12/09	312.5	67.8	21.7%	656
12/08	192.6	(66.5)	—	742
Annual Growth	13.6%	—	—	(0.2%)

2012 Year-End Financials

Debt ratio: 1.2%	No. of shares (mil.): 284
Return on equity: 1.3%	Dividends
Cash ($ mil.): 190	Yield: 1.0%
Current ratio: 2.98	Payout: 120.0%
Long-term debt ($ mil.): 11	Market value ($ mil.): 1,658

	STOCK PRICE ($) FY Close	P/E High/Low		PER SHARE ($) Earnings	Dividends	Book Value
12/12	5.83	137	75	0.05	0.06	4.00
12/11	5.23	21	9	0.51	0.02	4.00
12/10	11.26	81	32	0.13	0.00	3.72
12/09	6.18	31	5	0.23	0.00	3.63
12/08	2.80	—	—	(0.57)	0.00	3.60
Annual Growth	20.1%	—	—	—	—	2.7%

Heico Corp.

Here's a HEICO haiku: HEICO companies/ Providing for jet engines/ In flight or on land. Its Flight Support Group consisting of HEICO Aerospace and its subsidiaries makes FAA-approved replacement parts for jet engines that can be substituted for original parts including airfoils bearings and fuel pump gears. Flight Support also repairs overhauls and distributes jet engine parts as well as avionics and instruments for commercial air carriers. HEICO's second segment Electronic Technologies Group makes a variety of electronic equipment for the aerospace/defense electronic medical and telecommunications industries. The company has facilities in the US Canada India Singapore and the UK.

Operations

HEICO's Flight Support Group competes with industry leading OEMs and to a lesser extent with smaller independent parts distributors. Historically the three main jet engine OEMs General Electric Pratt & Whitney and Rolls Royce have been the source of substantially all jet engine replacement parts for their own jet engines. HEICO is seeking to capture some of that market by adding new products at a rate of 400 manufacturer-approved parts (also called PMAs) per year.

Strategy

The company uses acquisitions to build out a diverse product and service portfolio in order to reduce exposure to cyclical swings in any single market. Its current set of offerings have broad-range applications in aircraft missiles ships surveillance systems computer and networking devices telecom equipment surgical equipment CT scanners and X-ray systems.

In mid-2013 HEICO announced it was acquiring Reinhold Industries a leading producer of components in the solid rocket propulsion industry. Reinhold will be folded into HEICO's Flight Support Group.

HISTORY

Founded in 1957 as Heinicke Instruments to make laboratory products the company moved into jet engine parts in 1974 with the acquisition of Jet Avion. The company changed its name to HEICO (a shortened version of its previous name) in 1985. After a faulty combustion chamber erupted in flames that year the FAA ordered all combustion chambers on US jets to be inspected and if necessary replaced. HEICO's sales skyrocketed but descended back to earth after airlines found they had overstocked.

By the early 1990s defense cutbacks and declining aircraft orders reduced business and HEICO began to diversify. In 1991 it formed MediTek to acquire medical imaging facilities but then sold the company to U.S. Diagnostic for $24 million five years later. Lufthansa Technik AG the service subsidiary of Deutsche Lufthansa paid HEICO $26 million for a 20% stake in HEICO's flight support operations in 1997.

HEICO acquired jet engine parts companies McClain International and Rogers-Dierks in 1998. The next year the company added Radiant Power (back-up power supplies and battery packs for aerospace applications) Turbine Kinetics and Aero-Kinetics (replacement parts for aircraft engines) Santa Barbara Infrared (infrared and ground support equipment) and Thermal Structures (insulation products).

HEICO sold its Trilectron Industries ground support equipment subsidiary to Illinois Tool Works in 2000 in a deal worth about $64 million. The following year the company formed a joint venture with AMR (parent of American Airlines) to accelerate development of FAA-approved replacement parts. Also in 2001 HEICO bought Inertial Airline Services Avitech Engineering Corp. and Aviation Facilities Inc. In 2003 HEICO acquired Niacc Technology an aircraft component repair and overhaul company.

The company added to its aerospace electronics operations with the acquisition of Connectronics a maker of high-voltage wire and interconnection devices in 2004.

In 2005 HEICO moved to expand its flight support business by buying a 51% stake in Seal Dynamics a designer and distributor of hydraulic pneumatic mechanical and electromechanical components for the commercial regional and general aviation markets.

HEICO's Flight Support Group acquired Arger Enterprises a subsidiary of Melrose PLC in 2006. Arger made and distributed aircraft parts mainly for the commercial aviation market. That year HEICO bought a controlling stake in Prime Air Parts which dealt in spare parts for aircraft.

In 2007 HEICO's Electronic Technologies Group acquired EMD Technologies a maker of high-voltage energy generators used in medical industrial imaging and baggage scanning systems.

A few years of careful acquisitions complemented by organic growth contributed to record sales and profits for HEICO in fiscal 2007. The company's Flight Support Group led the charge with a 38% increase in sales; Electronic Technologies was no slouch with an 8% increase.

In 2009 the Electronic Technologies Group acquired VPT a maker of DC-DC power converters and other electronics which complemented HEICO's customer base in electronics and telecommunications and to a lesser extent in the industrial and medical sectors.

Later that year Electronic Technologies bought the Seacom division of Dukane Corp. a maker of acoustic beacons. Officially known as an Underwater Locator Beacon (ULB) pingers are attached to flight data and cockpit voice recorders as well as marine voyage recorders and are required to be installed on aircraft by the FAA and European Aviation Safety Agency.

In 2011 HEICO acquired France-based 3D Plus a leading designer and manufacturer of three-dimensional microelectronic and stacked memory products which are used primarily in satellites. The acquisition expanded HEICO's presence in the space products business as well as the medical sector. Earlier in the year HEICO's Flight Support Group enhanced its parts and repair operations and competitive position by acquiring an 80% interest in Blue Aerospace. Since 2002 Blue Aerospace has supplied military aircraft parts and support services for the C-130 P-3 and F-16 aircraft largely to foreign military allies of the US. It also manages aircraft parts repair. The deal is expected to boost earnings within the year.

Later in the year HEICO through its Electronics Technologies group acquired Chicago-based Switchcraft. Switchcraft founded in 1946 is the manufacturer of electronic connectors for use in harsh environments as well as cables jacks and plugs patch panels and other products requiring high performance and reliability. The terms of the deal were not disclosed but adds a product line and customer base not presently served by HEICO.

EXECUTIVES

Vice President - Corporate Development, William S. Harlow, age 65, $200,000 total compensation
Co-President and Director; President and CEO HEICO Electronic Technologies, Victor H. Mendelson, age 45, $500,000 total compensation
Co-President and Director; President and CEO HEICO Aerospace Holdings, Eric A. Mendelson, age 48, $500,000 total compensation
Senior Executive Vice President, Thomas S. Irwin, age 67, $500,000 total compensation
Chairman of the Board; Chief Executive Officer, Laurans A. Mendelson, age 75, $960,000 total compensation
VP Sales, Buddy Padilla
VP Marketing, Paul Belisle
Chief Financial Officer; Executive Vice President; Treasurer, Carlos Macau
Director, Wolfgang Mayrhuber, age 66
Co-President and Director; President and CEO HEICO Electronic Technologies, Victor H. Mendelson, age 45
Co-President and Director; President and CEO HEICO Aerospace Holdings, Eric A. Mendelson, age 48
Director, Mitchell I. (Mitch) Quain, age 60
Director, Samuel L. Higginbottom, age 92
Director, Alan Schriesheim, age 83
Director, Frank J. Schwitter, age 80
Director, Mark H. Hildebrandt, age 56
Independent Director, Adolfo Henriques
Auditors: Deloitte&ToucheLLP

LOCATIONS

HQ: HEICO Corporation
3000 Taft St., Hollywood FL 33021
Phone: 954-987-4000   **Fax:** 954-987-8228
Web: www.heico.com

2010 Sales

	$ mil.	% of total
US	423	69
Other countries	193	31
Total	**617**	**100**

PRODUCTS/OPERATIONS

2010 Sales

	$ mil.	% of total
Flight Support Group	412	67
Electronic Technologies Group	205	33
Adjustments	(1.0)	-
Total	**617**	**100**

Selected Products

Flight Support Group
  Cockpit/avionics parts
  Electro-mechanical components
  Engine parts
  Fuselage/interior parts
  Wing parts
Electronic Technologies Group
  Aircraft power supplies and batteries
  Circuit board shielding
  Electro-optical infrared simulation and test equipment
  Electro-optical laser products
  High-voltage interconnect and cable assembly devices
  Medical power supplies and power generators

COMPETITORS

AAR Corp.	Kellstrom Industries
ATI Ladish	LMI Aerospace
BBA Aviation	Pratt & Whitney
Barnes Group	Rolls-Royce
CIC International	SAFRAN
Doncasters	SIFCO
EMS Technologies	TIMCO Aviation
GE Aviation	Triumph Group
Goodrich Corp.	Wyman-Gordon
Honeywell Aerospace	

HISTORICAL FINANCIALS

Company Type: Public

Income Statement

FYE: October 31

	REVENUE ($ mil.)	NET INCOME ($ mil.)	NET PROFIT MARGIN	EMPLOYEES
10/13	1,008.7	102.4	10.2%	3,500
10/12	897.3	85.1	9.5%	3,100
10/11	764.8	72.8	9.5%	2,500
10/10	617.0	54.9	8.9%	2,300
10/09	538.3	44.6	8.3%	2,100
Annual Growth	**17.0%**	**23.1%**	**—**	**13.6%**

2013 Year-End Financials

Debt ratio: 24.6%
Return on equity: 16.7%
Cash ($ mil.): 15
Current ratio: 2.74
Long-term debt ($ mil.): 376

No. of shares (mil.): 66
Dividends
  Yield: 4.2%
  Payout: 157.6%
Market value ($ mil.): 3,556

	STOCK PRICE ($) FY Close	P/E High/Low	PER SHARE ($) Earnings	Dividends	Book Value
10/13	53.58	45 25	1.53	2.27	9.14
10/12	38.63	47 26	1.28	0.11	9.33
10/11	57.02	57 37	1.09	0.09	8.05
10/10	49.78	65 41	0.83	0.06	7.28
10/09	38.03	62 31	0.68	0.05	7.18
Annual Growth	**8.9%**	**— —**	**22.7%**	**160.7%**	**6.2%**

Heritage Financial Group Inc.

Established in the 1950s as a credit union to serve its hometown Marine base HeritageBank of the South has remained always faithful to its local customers. The flagship subsidiary of Heritage Financial Group operates some 20 branches that provide traditional deposit and loan products and services to individuals and small to midsized businesses in southwestern Georgia and Ocala Florida. Consumer loans and residential mortgages each account for about a quarter of the company's loan portfolio. The bank also offers investment and insurance products and services. Mutual holding company Heritage MHC owns more than 70% of Heritage Financial which acquired the failed Citizens Bank of Effingham in 2011.

EXECUTIVES

Vice Chairman and Secretary, Joseph C. Burger Jr., age 76
Chairman, Antone D. Lehr, age 72
President; Chief Executive Officer; Director, O. Leonard (Len) Dorminey, age 60, $285,533 total compensation
Director; President Albany Region HeritageBank of the South, Carol W. Slappey, age 57, $175,538 total compensation
Executive Vice President Chief Credit Officer, O. Mitchell Smith, age 59, $135,018 total compensation
Executive Vice President Chief Financial Officer, T. Heath Fountain, age 38
SVP and Principal, Patrick Watson
President, Gary Johnson
Executive Vice President; Chief Banking Officer, David Durland
Chief Accounting Officer, Robert Krimmel
Vice Chairman and Secretary, Joseph C. Burger Jr., age 76
President CEO and Director; CEO HeritageBank of the South, O. Leonard (Len) Dorminey, age 60
Director; President Albany Region HeritageBank of the South, Carol W. Slappey, age 57
Auditors: Mauldin&JenkinsLLC

LOCATIONS

HQ: Heritage Financial Group
  721 North Westover Blvd., Albany GA 31707
Phone: 229-420-0000   **Fax:** 229-878-2054
Web: www.eheritagebank.com

PRODUCTS/OPERATIONS

2007 Sales

	$ mil.	% of total
Interest		
Loans including fees	22	63
Securities	5	15
Other	0	2
Noninterest		
Service charges on deposit accounts	3	11
Other service charges commissions & fees	1	3
Brokerage fees	0	3
Other	1	3
Total	**35**	**100**

COMPETITORS

BB&T	Regions Financial
Bank of America	SunTrust
Citigroup	Synovus

First Horizon

HISTORICAL FINANCIALS

Company Type: Public

Income Statement

FYE: December 31

	REVENUE ($ mil.)	NET INCOME ($ mil.)	NET PROFIT MARGIN	EMPLOYEES
12/12	68.4	6.7	9.9%	321
12/11	56.9	3.8	6.7%	327
12/10	40.9	1.4	3.4%	217
12/09	31.1	(1.6)	—	194
12/08	31.7	(0.2)	—	0
Annual Growth	**21.1%**	**—**	**—**	**—**

2012 Year-End Financials

Debt ratio: 8.4%
Return on equity: 5.5%
Cash ($ mil.): 43
Current ratio: 0.31
Long-term debt ($ mil.): 93

No. of shares (mil.): 8
Dividends
  Yield: 2.6%
  Payout: 50.7%
Market value ($ mil.): 113

	STOCK PRICE ($) FY Close	P/E High/Low	PER SHARE ($) Earnings	Dividends	Book Value
12/12	13.79	16 13	0.85	0.36	14.76
12/11	11.80	29 21	0.47	0.12	14.25
12/10	12.42	74 60	0.17	0.36	13.70
Annual Growth	**5.4%**	**— —**	**123.6%**	**(0.0%)**	**3.8%**

Hersha Hospitality Trust

Hersha Hospitality Trust's fortune is in hotels not chocolate. The self-advised real estate investment trust (REIT) invests in hotel properties primarily midscale upscale and extended stay properties in metropolitan markets. It owns or co-owns about 70 hotels containing more than 9600 rooms most of them in Boston New York and Washington DC as well as in Miami and Los Angeles. The properties are operated under such brand names as Marriott International Hilton Hotels Starwood Hotels and Hyatt. Hersha Hospitality Trust owns a minority stake in Hersha Hospitality Management which manages the REIT's properties. Starwood Capital Group owns the remainder of Hersha Hospitality Management

Hersha Hospitality Trust leases its wholly owned hotels to subsidiary 44 New England Management Company. In the past the company has provided on a limited basis financing for hotel property development loans though it stopped pursuing new investments during the economic downturn. It maintains first right of purchase or refusal on these newly developed properties. Hersha Hospitality doesn't expect to make any new property joint ventures development loans or land leases.

The hotel REIT sector along with Hersha is recovering from the economic downturn which drove down demand in 2008 and 2009. The lack of demand sent hotel occupancy rates and revenues down. By 2010 the economy began to improve and profits and revenues rebounded at Hersha. However the sector remained volatile. While revenues remained steady in 2011 the company reported a

25% drop in net income. The net loss in 2011 was attributed mainly to impairment charges recorded on its noncore properties.

Hersha Hospitality has repositioned itself to accommodate the unstable and fluid market. It raised capital and revamped its portfolio to focus on urban high-demand gateway markets such as New York and Washington DC. In 2010 and 2011 Hersha Hospitality acquired 12 properties (many at discount prices). The company also acquired its first hotels in Los Angeles and Miami.

Hersha also is disposing of properties in less-appealing markets. Towards that end the REIT sold a portfolio of 18 noncore properties to Starwood Capital Group for about $155 million in 2012. (It will use the proceeds to repay debt among other purposes.)

In addition to acquisitions in urban areas the REIT is focused on property renovations designed to boost occupancy rates and enhance hotel value. In 2011 the company undertook a $26 million renovation project at several of its hotels.

EXECUTIVES

Independent Trustee, Kiran P. Patel, age 63
Chairman, Hasu P. Shah, age 67, $150,000 total compensation
CFO, Ashish R. Parikh, age 42, $275,000 total compensation
President and COO, Neil H. Shah, age 38, $400,000 total compensation
Treasurer and Corporate Secretary, David L. Desfor, age 50
CEO and Trustee, Jay H. Shah, age 43, $425,000 total compensation
Chief Accounting Officer, Michael R. Gillespie, age 38, $192,500 total compensation
VP Acquisitions and Development, Robert C. Hazard III
VP Asset Management, William J. Walsh
Independent Trustee, Daniel Elsztain
Vice President of Finance and Sustainability, Bennett Thomas
Independent Trustee, Kiran P. Patel, age 63
CEO and Trustee, Jay H. Shah, age 43
Auditors: KPMGLLP

LOCATIONS

HQ: Hersha Hospitality Trust
44 Hersha Dr., Harrisburg PA 17102
Phone: 717-236-4400   **Fax:** 717-774-7383
Web: www.hersha.com

PRODUCTS/OPERATIONS

2011 Sales

	$ mil.	% of total
Hotel operating revenues	282	99
Interest from development loans	3	1
Other	0	-
Total	**286**	**100**

COMPETITORS

Ashford Hospitality Trust	Innkeepers USA
DiamondRock Hospitality	LaSalle Hotel Properties
FelCor	Shaner Hotel Group
Hospitality Properties Trust	Strategic Hotels
Host Hotels & Resorts	Sunstone Hotel Investors
	Supertel Hospitality

HISTORICAL FINANCIALS

Company Type: Public

Income Statement

FYE: December 31

	REVENUE ($ mil.)	NET INCOME ($ mil.)	NET PROFIT MARGIN	EMPLOYEES
12/12	358.2	22.2	6.2%	46
12/11	286.4	(26.9)	—	36
12/10	282.7	(17.2)	—	28
12/09	220.4	(58.4)	—	24
12/08	264.7	(8.8)	—	24
Annual Growth	**7.8%**	**—**	**—**	**17.7%**

2012 Year-End Financials

Debt ratio: 46.4%
Return on equity: 2.8%
Cash ($ mil.): 69
Current ratio: 1.66
Long-term debt ($ mil.): 792

No. of shares (mil.): 198
Dividends
Yield: 4.8%
Payout: 2,400.0%
Market value ($ mil.): 993

	STOCK PRICE ($) FY Close	P/E High/Low	PER SHARE ($) Earnings	Dividends	Book Value
12/12	5.00	145 107	0.04	0.24	4.18
12/11	4.88	— —	(0.21)	0.23	4.30
12/10	6.60	— —	(0.16)	0.20	4.04
12/09	3.14	— —	(1.08)	0.33	5.24
12/08	3.00	— —	(0.31)	0.72	7.25
Annual Growth	**13.6%**	**— —**	**—**	**(24.0%)**	**(12.9%)**

Hexcel Corp.

The first footprints on the moon didn't come from Neil Armstrong but from Hexcel a maker of composite materials. Back then Hexcel made the footpads on the Apollo 11 lunar module; today the company makes advanced structural materials used in everything from aircraft components to wind turbine blades. Its composite materials include structural adhesives and honeycomb panels used in products like satellites auto parts golf clubs and even window blinds. Commercial aerospace companies account for nearly 60% of Hexcel's sales; governmental space and defense sales and industrial sales account for the rest. Markets for Hexcel industrial products include wind energy recreational equipment and transportation.

Geographic Reach

Hexcel operates domestic manufacturing facilities in Alabama Arizona Colorado Pennsylvania Texas Washington. International locations reside in Belgium China Colorado France Germany Spain and the UK. It also holds an interest in a manufacturing joint venture in Malaysia that makes composite structures for the company's Commercial Aerospace segment.

The US represents 50% of its total sales while France and Spain account for 18% and 10% respectively.

Operations

The company's advanced composites are divided into two main segments: Composite Materials (78% of total sales) and Engineered Products (22%). Composite Materials include carbon fiber resins specialty reinforcements prepegs (resins impregnated with fibers) and other fiber-reinforced materials and honeycomb core products.

Engineered Products include lightweight high-strength composite structures molded components and specialty machined honeycomb products. The end markets for Hexcel's products make up its three main sales segments: Commercial Aerospace (60% of total sales) Space and Defense (23%) and Industrial (17%).

Sales and Marketing

Hexcel gets about 30% of its total sales from contracts from Boeing and related contractors (25% for its Commercial Aerospace segment and 5% for its Space and Defense segment). European Aeronautic Defence and Space Company (EADS) including its Airbus division and subcontractors account for another quarter of the company's total sales. The Space and Defense segment has worked on a number of military projects including Blackhawk helicopters the F/A-18 Hornet the F-35 Joint Strike Fighter and the EADS A400M military transport.

Financial Performance

Hexcel has enjoyed three straight years of growth. From 2011 to 2012 its net revenues increased by 13% to reach $1.58 billion and its profits surged by 21% to reach $164 million. Both of these totals were record highs for the company.

The growth was due to higher sales and volumes in all its segments but especially in its Commercial Aerospace unit. This unit was helped by new aircraft programs and increased build rates. In 2012 sales for Airbus and Boeing programs increased by 16%. Total sales for Space and Defense surged by 12% while Industrial increased by 11%. Within the Industrial segment wind energy sales jumped by 30% for 2012.

Hexcel attributes the 2012 profit growth to the strong performance of its segments coupled with a tight control on costs over the last few years.

Strategy

Hexcel has cut down on spending but it continues to add production capacity in key areas and to develop new products. It seeks new opportunities for both its Composite Materials and Engineered Products segments to compensate for weakened demand from defense markets. Among trends it hopes to capitalize on is the use by helicopter manufacturers of new rotor blades based on composite materials for better lift and durability. Hexcel also focuses on growth markets where it believes it can achieve a competitive advantage over the long term.

The company's strategy has succeeded with demand for Hexcel composites —used to build both Airbus and Boeing aircraft —soaring. Production rates for the super jumbo A380 of Airbus and the ramp up of Boeing's new B787 and B747-8 jets have helped grow Hexcel's sales each year for the last four years. The company's involvement in major product development with both Boeing and Airbus have driven its sales increases. Hexcel has been a major parts supplier for Boeing's 787 Dreamliner and 747-8 Series as well as the Airbus A360 and A380 —all aircraft that have a large amount of advanced composite parts.

HISTORY

Hexcel was founded in 1946 and incorporated in California in 1948. The company's businesses formerly included polymer technology for medical devices chemicals electromagnetic materials and a European resins unit. These were all sold as part of Hexcel's restructuring following Chapter 11 bankruptcy in 1993.

In 1996 Hexcel purchased the composite divisions of specialty chemicals maker Hercules and Swiss drugmaker Ciba-Geigy; it then combined the operations with similar businesses of Arizona's Fiberite in 1997 thus positioning itself for leadership in the manufacture of preimpregnated reinforcing materials and honeycomb products used to make aircraft wings flaps and elevators.

In 1998 Hexcel bought Clark-Schwebel's glass fiber business to broaden its printed circuit board offerings to the electronics and telecommunications industries and reduce its reliance on the aerospace industry. To establish a presence in Asia the company formed China-based BHA Aero Composite Parts a joint venture with Boeing and Aviation Industries of China and Asian Composite Manufacturing a Malaysian joint venture with Boeing Sime Darby Berhad and Malaysia Helicopter Services.

The US Department of Justice began an antitrust investigation of Hexcel in 1999 as the market leader in the production and sale of carbon fiber and preimpregnated materials (ongoing in 2002). Hexcel sold its aircraft interiors unit to Britax International for $117 million in 2000. The same year Ciba Specialty Chemicals sold the bulk of its 49% stake in Hexcel to a Goldman Sachs investor group.

In another effort to decrease its reliance on the aerospace market in 2001 the company announced production of an energy-absorbing honeycomb made of spun-bond nylon and polyester for the automotive market. Responding to the downturn in the aerospace market after September 11 Hexcel began a restructuring plan that cut fixed overhead costs capital spending and about 25% of its workforce.

In 2008 investment group OSS Capital initiated a proxy fight to place three new independent directors on Hexcel's Board. OSS said that it believed Hexcel's management hadn't done enough to improve its margins and lagged behind competitors like Cytec and Toray Industries. In the end the company-backed slate of directors won out.

EXECUTIVES

Chairman and CEO, David E. Berges, age 63, $905,013 total compensation
SVP General Counsel and Secretary, Ira J. Krakower, age 73, $341,219 total compensation
Manager Investor Relations, Michael W. Bacal
SVP Human Resources, Robert G. Hennemuth, age 57, $320,436 total compensation
Treasurer, Michael J. MacIntyre, age 51
President, Nick L. Stanage, age 55, $72,019 total compensation
VP Corporate Controller and Chief Accounting Officer, Kimberly A. Hendricks, age 49
SVP and CFO, Wayne C. Pensky, age 58, $368,550 total compensation
VP Operations, Andrea Domenichini, age 64
VP Sales and Marketing Americas, Mike Canario
Manager Sales Carbon Fiber, Tom Haulik
Director, W. Kim Foster, age 64
Director, Jeffrey C. (Jeff) Campbell, age 52
Director, David L. Pugh, age 64
Director, Thomas A. Gendron, age 52
Director, Lynn Brubaker, age 56
Director, David C. Hill, age 66
Director, Jeffrey A. (Jeff) Graves, age 52
Director, Sandra L. (Sandy) Derickson, age 61
Director, Joel S. Beckman, age 57
Director, Jeffrey C. Campbell, age 52
Director, David C. Hurley, age 70
Auditors: PricewaterhouseCoopersLLP

LOCATIONS

HQ: Hexcel Corporation
281 Tresser Blvd. 2 Stamford Plaza 16th Fl., Stamford CT 06901
Phone: 203-969-0666   **Fax:** 203-358-3977
Web: www.hexcel.com

2012 Sales

US	801	51
Spain	150	10
Austria	105	7
Total	**1,578**	**100**

PRODUCTS/OPERATIONS

2012 Sales

Composite Materials	1,230	78
Total	**1,578**	**100**

2012 Sales

	% of total
Commercial	60
Space &	23
Industrial	17
Total	**100**

Selected Products

Carbon fibers
Composite structures
Honeycomb
Honeycomb composite panels
Honeycomb parts
Preimpregnated materials (prepegs)
Structural adhesives

COMPETITORS

3M	PRC-DeSoto
Alcoa	Park Electrochemical
BP	SGL CARBON
Baltek	Teijin
Cytec	Toho Tenax
Dow Corning	Toray Industries
Honeywell International	Zoltek

HISTORICAL FINANCIALS

Company Type: Public

Income Statement

FYE: December 31

	REVENUE ($ mil.)	NET INCOME ($ mil.)	NET PROFIT MARGIN	EMPLOYEES
12/13	1,678.2	187.9	11.2%	5,274
12/12	1,578.2	164.3	10.4%	4,973
12/11	1,392.4	135.5	9.7%	4,508
12/10	1,173.6	77.4	6.6%	4,043
12/09	1,108.3	56.3	5.1%	3,734
Annual Growth	**10.9%**	**35.2%**	**—**	**9.0%**

2013 Year-End Financials

Debt ratio: 16.0%	No. of shares (mil.): 98
Return on equity: 17.4%	Dividends
Cash ($ mil.): 65	Yield: —
Current ratio: 2.44	Payout: —
Long-term debt ($ mil.): 292	Market value ($ mil.): 4,420

	STOCK PRICE ($) FY Close	P/E High/Low	PER SHARE ($) Earnings	Dividends	Book Value
12/13	44.69	24 14	1.84	0.00	11.73
12/12	26.96	17 14	1.61	0.00	9.95
12/11	24.21	19 13	1.35	0.00	8.12
12/10	18.09	24 13	0.77	0.00	6.78
12/09	12.98	23 8	0.57	0.00	5.96
Annual Growth	**36.2%**	**— —**	**34.0%**	**—**	**18.5%**

HFF Inc

Don't huff and puff —HFF will help you finance that high-rise. The company's Holliday Fenoglio Fowler subsidiary is a large commercial real estate capital intermediary. The firm provides capital markets services including structured financing commercial loan servicing investment sales loan sales and debt placement. Real estate investment banking subsidiary HFF Securities provides advisory services seeks private and joint venture equity capital places private listings and provides institutional marketing for property investments. Unlike most commercial property brokerage firms HFF does not provide leasing or property management services. The company operates about 20 offices throughout the US.

The company has seen its revenues rebound after they plummeted during the global financial downturn. Frozen credit markets reduced liquidity which severely impacted commercial real estate activity. In 2008 HFF advised on less than half the previous year's total. Activity slowed down further in 2009 when transaction values once again fell by more than half. As a result HFF's revenues declined. The company made cuts to operating expenses including cutting staff in efforts to boost cash flow. Signaling a modest recovery in the commercial property markets HFF advised on some $19.5 billion in real estate transactions in 2010 — still lower than pre-recession levels.

The company continues to seek to improve its market share by penetrating national and regional markets. The company's biggest capital services market is Texas accounting for about 20% of total revenues. Other key markets include Florida Massachusetts and the DC area. HFF hopes to grow by opening additional offices in key US markets; it opened an office in Austin Texas in 2011. The company is also eyeing operations in foreign markets. However the recession has put the brakes on much of HFF's plans to expand.

EXECUTIVES

Vice Chairman, Mark D. Gibson, age 54
Executive Managing Director Washington D.C., Stephen C. Conley
Vice Chairman, John P. Fowler, age 67
Executive Managing Director, Gerard Sansosti
Vice Chairman, Mark D. Gibson, age 54
Auditors: Ernst&YoungLLP

LOCATIONS

HQ: HFF Inc.
One Oxford Centre 301 Grant St. Ste. 600, Pittsburgh PA 15219
Phone: 412-281-8714   **Fax:** 412-281-2792
Web: www.hfflp.com

PRODUCTS/OPERATIONS

2010 Sales

	$ mil.	% of total
Capital markets services	136	97
Interest on mortgage notes receivable	2	2
Other	1	1
Total	**140**	**100**

COMPETITORS

Arbor Commercial	Eastdil Secured
BGC Partners	Jones Lang LaSalle
Boston Capital	NorthMarq Capital

CBRE Group
Capmark
Cushman &
Wakefield

Trammell Crow Company

HISTORICAL FINANCIALS
Company Type: Public

Income Statement
FYE: December 31

	REVENUE ($ mil.)	NET INCOME ($ mil.)	NET PROFIT MARGIN	EMPLOYEES
12/12	284.9	43.8	15.4%	574
12/11	254.6	40.0	15.7%	498
12/10	139.9	10.8	7.8%	427
12/09	77.4	(0.7)	—	376
12/08	131.6	0.2	0.2%	433
Annual Growth	21.3%	272.0%	—	7.3%

2012 Year-End Financials

Debt ratio: 44.4%
Return on equity: 35.3%
Cash ($ mil.): 126
Current ratio: 1.24
Long-term debt ($ mil.): 0

No. of shares (mil.): 37
Dividends
  Yield: 10.2%
  Payout: 128.8%
Market value ($ mil.): 552

	STOCK PRICE ($) FY Close	P/E High/Low		PER SHARE ($) Earnings	Dividends	Book Value
12/12	14.90	14	9	1.18	1.52	3.27
12/11	10.33	15	7	1.11	0.00	3.52
12/10	9.66	25	15	0.40	0.00	2.45
12/09	6.25	—	—	(0.05)	0.00	2.36
12/08	2.45	774	190	0.01	0.00	2.38
Annual Growth	57.0%			—229.6%	—	8.2%

hhgregg Inc

hhgregg has evolved from black-and-white to digital. The appliance and electronics retailer began as a small storefront selling washing machines refrigerators and black-and-white TVs. Today the fast-growing company sells name-brand products at more than 225 stores in about 20 mostly southern states and online. Its offerings include TV and video products (LED TVs Blu-ray disc players) home and car audio gear (CD players home theater systems) appliances (refrigerators washers and dryers) computers gaming consoles digital cameras GPS navigators and mattresses. Founded in 1955 hhgregg has been growing aggressively amid tough economic conditions and a bleak outlook for consumer electronics retailers.

Geographic Reach
hhgregg operates stores in Alabama Delaware Florida Georgia Illinois Indiana Kentucky Louisiana Maryland Mississippi Missouri New Jersey North Carolina Ohio. Pennsylvania South Carolina Tennessee Virginia West Virginia and Wisconsin. Florida with 35 stores is the retailer's largest market.

Operations
In addition to its fast-growing chain of retail stores hhgregg is working to expand its online operation. The appliances and electronics retailer offers shoppers the option of buying online and then picking up their purchase in the store or home delivery for online orders.

Financial Performance

The company's sales dipped 1% in fiscal 2013 (ended March) versus the prior year while net income declined 69% over the same period. The decline in sales was due to a 9% drop in same-store sales (sales at stores open for more than 1 year) partially offset by the addition of 20 new stores. The steep decline in net income was attributed to the receipt of $40 million of life insurance proceeds in fiscal 2012 (the executive chairman of the board passed away in January 2012) the decline in same-store sales and an increase in general expenses as well as higher advertising expenses as a percentage of net sales.

The modest decline in fiscal 2013 sales reversed three years of gains for the retail chain

Strategy
Sensing opportunity hhgregg adopted an accelerated growth strategy in the aftermath of the demise its rival Circuit City in 2009. Indeed over the past four years the chain has added about 120 stores many in new markets. The retail chain looks to new locations to fuel sales and income growth. But while sales have nearly doubled over the past five years a closer look at hhgregg's performance reveals that sales at stores open more than one year (a key indicator of a retailer's overall health) have been posting declines. Like market leader Best Buy hhgregg appears to be suffering from "showrooming" when shoppers view a product in its stores and then order it online for less from Amazon.com. The fickle US economy and stubborn high unemployment have reduced demand for big ticket items especially TVs and appliances. (Video and appliances account for more than 75% of hhgregg's sales.)

In response to declining same-store sales which are largely due to the poor performance of the video category hhgregg has set three key initiative for fiscal 2014: evolving its sales mix expanding its customer base and enhancing its service offerings. To make up for the drop in TV sales the company is looking to sell more appliances as the housing market in the US improves.

Ownership
The investment firm Freeman Spogli & Co. owns 43% of the company's shares.

EXECUTIVES
CIO, Trent E. Taylor, age 56
Chairman, Michael L. Smith, age 64
President CEO and Director, Dennis L. May, age 46, $400,000 total compensation
Chief Administrative Officer, Michael D. (Mike) Stout, age 59, $260,000 total compensation
SVP Appliance Merchandising, Jeffrey J. McClintic, age 57, $178,130 total compensation
General Merchandising Officer, Michael G. Larimer, age 59, $260,000 total compensation
Director Finance and Investor Relations, Andy Giesler
CFO, Jeremy J. Aguilar, age 38, $265,000 total compensation
Chief Human Resources Officer, Charles B. Young, age 49
EVP COO and Director, Gregg W. Throgmartin, age 35, $275,000 total compensation
Director, Darell E. (Gene) Zink Jr., age 66
Director, Lawrence P. Castellani, age 67
Director, Peter M. Starrett, age 65
Director, John M. Roth, age 54
Director, Charles P. Rullman, age 65
President CEO and Director, Dennis L. May, age 46
Director, Catherine A. (Cathy) Langham, age 56
Director, Kathleen (Kathy) Tierney, age 69
Director, Benjamin D. Geiger, age 38

EVP COO and Director, Gregg W. Throgmartin, age 35
Auditors: KPMGLLP

LOCATIONS
HQ: hhgregg Inc.
  4151 E. 96th St., Indianapolis IN 46240
Phone: 317-848-8710   **Fax:** 317-848-8723
Web: www.hhgregg.com

2013 Stores

	No.
Florida	35
Ohio	28
Illinois	19
Indiana	19
Pennsylvania	19
North	17
Georgia	16
Virginia	15
Maryland	11
Tennessee	11
South	7
Kentucky	6
Alabama	6
Wisconsin	5
Delaware	3
Louisiana	3
Missouri	3
New	3
Mississippi	1
West	1
Total	**228**

PRODUCTS/OPERATIONS

2013 Sales

	% of total
Appliances	42
Video	36
Computing & mobile	11
Other	11
Total	**100**

COMPETITORS

Amazon.com	Kmart
Best Buy	Lowe's
BrandsMart USA	RadioShack
Costco Wholesale	Sears
Fry's Electronics	Target Corporation
Home Depot	Wal-Mart
J. C. Penney Company	

HISTORICAL FINANCIALS
Company Type: Public

Income Statement
FYE: March 31

	REVENUE ($ mil.)	NET INCOME ($ mil.)	NET PROFIT MARGIN	EMPLOYEES
03/13	2,474.7	25.3	1.0%	6,300
03/12	2,493.3	81.3	3.3%	6,700
03/11	2,077.6	48.2	2.3%	5,600
03/10	1,534.2	39.2	2.6%	4,900
03/09	1,396.6	36.5	2.6%	3,500
Annual Growth	15.4%	(8.7%)	—	15.8%

2013 Year-End Financials

Debt ratio: —
Return on equity: 7.1%
Cash ($ mil.): 48
Current ratio: 1.75
Long-term debt ($ mil.): —

No. of shares (mil.): 31
Dividends
  Yield: —
  Payout: —
Market value ($ mil.): 348

STOCK PRICE ($) FY Close	P/E High/Low		PER SHARE ($) Earnings	Dividends	Book Value
03/13	11.05	16 8	0.74	0.00	11.02
03/12	11.38	8 4	2.14	0.00	9.89
03/11	13.39	25 11	1.19	0.00	7.97
03/10	25.24	25 12	1.03	0.00	6.58
03/09	14.15	13 3	1.10	0.00	3.82
Annual Growth	(6.0%)	— —	(9.4%)	—	30.3%

HI-Tech Pharmacal Co., Inc.

Hi-Tech Pharmacal combines imitation with innovation making and distributing dozens of liquid and semi-solid prescription over-the-counter (OTC) and vitamin products. The company primarily produces generic forms of prescription drugs including versions of allergy medicine Flonase (from GlaxoSmithKline). Hi-Tech's ECR Pharmaceuticals business makes branded over-the-counter products including Bupap analgesic tablets and Zolpimist insomnia spray. Its Health Care Products division markets OTC products including nutritional products and devices for people with diabetes and the Zostrix line of pain and arthritis medications. Hi-Tech Pharmacal is being acquired by drugmaker Akorn.

Change in Company Type

Akorn agreed to purchase Hi-Tech Pharmacal for some $640 million in 2013. Through the purchase Akorn will grow its development pipeline and diversify its retail and OTC pharmaceutical offerings.

Operations

Hi-Tech's expertise is with difficult-to-manufacture liquid and semi-solid dosage products including ophthalmic and inhaled pharmaceuticals. It provides contract manufacturing services to other drug firms needing this specialty. The company's products are marketed across the US through large retailers and wholesale distributors.

Sales from its generic drugs and contract manufacturing bring in more than 80% of Hi-Tech's revenue. Its generic product line focuses on oral solutions and suspensions creams and ointments and nasal sprays. The company maintains a steady pipeline of new products seeking approval. In 2011 it launched generic versions of Pfizer's Neurontin and Vistakon's Quixin among others.

ECR manufactures branded specialty prescription drugs (allergy headache and dermatitis) and promotes them through an in-house force of sales representatives active in the mid-Atlantic and southern US. Most of ECR's products are made by contract manufacturers.

The firm's Health Care Products division which handles its branded OTC business targets diabetic patients with such products as DiabetiSweet (sugar substitute) and DiabetiDerm (moisturizing lotion).

Strategy

An FDA crack-down on unapproved products in 2011 bit deep into the ECR product line. Along with other manufacturers Hi-Tech Pharmacal had presumed the products —which had been on the market for over six decades —did not require new drug applications. However the FDA got extra par-

ticular and yanked over 500 drugs off shelves including ECR's antihistamine Lodrane which had accounted for 85% of its sales. The company discontinued the line of antihistamines in 2012.

The ECR division relaunched Zolpamist and DexPak in 2013 while divesting its Hylase and Orbivan offerings. The division announced its intention to focus its operations on Bupap Tussicaps Zolpimist and DexPak.

Mergers and Acquisitions

To offset losses in the ECR division Hi-Tech Pharmacal refilled ECR's offerings in 2011 with the $3.6 million purchase of a portfolio of pain medications from private drugmaker Atley Pharmaceuticals. It further added to the ECR line by acquiring marketing and distribution rights for OTC cough medicine TussiCaps from Covidien's Mallinckrodt unit. It also purchased the Cormax line of skin products from Watson Laboratories in 2012.

Hi-Tech Pharmacal added to the Health Care Products division with the 2010 purchase of the Mag-Ox line of magnesium supplements from Blaine Pharmaceuticals.

Ownership

CEO David Seltzer and his brother director Reuben Seltzer own more than 20% of the firm their grandfather and father founded.

HISTORY

Reuben Seltzer started Hi-Tech Pharmacal's predecessor Success Chemical around 1930 in the back of his brother's drugstore in Brooklyn New York. His son Bernard joined the company in the late 1940s and continued the business after his father died. The firm was acquired in 1967 by drug wholesaler Ketchum & Co. and adopted the name Ketchum Labs.

Seltzer and an associate bought the liquid and ointment division from Ketchum in 1981 and started the new company as Hi-Tech Pharmacal to make generic drugs. It went public in 1992 and started its Health Care Products division the next year to market hemorrhoid pads cough remedies and skin creams. In 1994 the company purchased Dr. Rose Inc. a maker of generic over-the-counter and prescription suppositories creams and lotions.

Hi-Tech Pharmacal's 1995 product introductions included generic equivalents of constipation medications developed by what is now Sanofi-Aventis. In 1996 the company began marketing DiabetiSweet sugar substitute for diabetics and other people on special diets. That year the company opened a facility for making sterile ophthalmic and ear medication products. In 1996 and 1997 Hi-Tech Pharmacal won FDA approval for six new products including a generic substitute for hair-growth stimulant Rogaine. The next year it added a painkiller and pediatric antibiotic to its roster.

In 2000 Hi-Tech Pharmacal signed a co-marketing agreement with Diabetic.com a website that targets the needs of individuals with diabetes. The company also launched its Kosher Care brand of products (cough allergy and pain treatments) aimed at the kosher consumer market. The following year the firm further bolstered its Internet presence with its acquisition of diabetic support site SweetThoughts.com.

In 2007 the company acquired Midlothian Laboratories gaining specialization in cough and cold medicines and prescription vitamins. It only held Midlothian a short while before selling the business in 2011 to focus on its other generic product lines.

To enter the branded drug game the company purchased privately held ECR Pharmaceuticals for

$5.1 million in 2009. A price hike in 2010 helped boost the division's sales.

EXECUTIVES

President - Health Care Products Division, Gary M. April, age 56, $218,000 total compensation
Chairman President CEO Secretary and Treasurer, David S. Seltzer, age 53, $442,000 total compensation
Chief Financial Officer; Vice President, William Peters, age 45, $251,000 total compensation
VP Pharmaceutical Operations ECR Pharmaceuticals, Davis Caskey, age 65, $27,000 total compensation
Executive Vice President; Chief Scientific Officer, Kamel Egbaria
Investor Relations Officer, Anne Siebert
Director, Anthony J. Puglisi, age 65
Chairman President CEO Secretary and Treasurer, David S. Seltzer, age 53
Director, Bruce W. Simpson, age 72
Director, Reuben Seltzer, age 56
Director, Martin M. Goldwyn, age 61
Director, Yashar Hirshaut, age 76
Director, Jack Van Hulst, age 73
Independent Director, Jack Hulst

LOCATIONS

HQ: Hi-Tech Pharmacal Co. Inc.
369 Bayview Ave., Amityville NY 11701
Phone: 631-789-8228   Fax: 631-789-8429
Web: www.hitechpharm.com

PRODUCTS/OPERATIONS

2011 Sales

	$ mil.	% of total
Hi-Tech Generics	157	83
ECR Pharmaceuticals	19	10
Health Care Products	13	7
Total	**190**	**100**

COMPETITORS

Actavis Inc.	Perrigo
Bayer HealthCare	Pfizer
Caraco Pharmaceutical	Ranbaxy Laboratories
Forest Labs	Roche Holding
GlaxoSmithKline	Sandoz International
Johnson & Johnson	GmbH
Merck	Taro
Mylan	Teva Pharmaceuticals
Par Pharmaceutical	USA
Companies	

HISTORICAL FINANCIALS

Company Type: Public

Income Statement

FYE: April 30

	REVENUE ($ mil.)	NET INCOME ($ mil.)	NET PROFIT MARGIN	EMPLOYEES
04/13	232.3	16.2	7.0%	448
04/12	230.0	48.3	21.0%	428
04/11	190.8	41.4	21.7%	408
04/10	163.6	31.1	19.0%	391
04/09	108.6	9.8	9.0%	375
Annual Growth	20.9%	13.4%	—	4.5%

2013 Year-End Financials

Debt ratio: 0.4%
Return on equity: 6.7%
Cash ($ mil.): 100
Current ratio: 5.00
Long-term debt ($ mil.): 0

No. of shares (mil.): 13
Dividends
  Yield: 4.5%
  Payout: 126.0%
Market value ($ mil.): 449

STOCK PRICE ($) FY Close	P/E High/Low		PER SHARE ($) Earnings	Dividends	Book Value
04/13	33.06	31 23	1.19	1.50	18.07
04/12	32.59	11 7	3.59	0.00	18.12
04/11	27.66	8 5	3.19	0.00	14.25
04/10	24.33	11 3	2.50	0.00	10.73
04/09	7.55	14 4	0.84	0.00	7.62
Annual Growth 44.7%	— —		9.1%	—	24.1%

Hibbett Sports Inc

Small-town sports fans are the bread and butter for Hibbett Sports. The company sells sports equipment athletic apparel and footwear in small to midsized markets in about 25 states mainly in the South and Midwest. Its flagship Hibbett Sports chain is composed of more than 810 locations and stores are primarily found in malls and strip centers anchored by a Wal-Mart. Hibbett also operates a single Sports & Co. superstore a larger format featuring in-store putting greens basketball hoops and appearances by athletes. On a smaller scale it runs about 20 mall-based Sports Additions shoe shops most of which are situated near Hibbett Sports stores. The company also operates an e-commerce site.

Hibbett whose roots reach back to 1945 sticks to communities of about 25000 to 75000 people —towns where it can top local retailers without drawing much attention from large-market chains such as The Sports Authority. Apparently its strategy is working. Hibbett in fiscal 2012 (ends January) saw its sales increase by about 10% vs. the prior year with net income up about 27% over the same period. The addition of about 35 new stores and a nearly 7% increase in sales at existing stores contributed to the gain. Indeed Hibbett has been a relatively strong performer over the past four years despite the recent recession. Between fiscal 2008 and 2012 sales grew by about 40% to $732 million.

While the economic downturn didn't hurt sales much it did slow the chain's expansion as Hibbett found it more difficult to secure new commercial leases. To compensate the company focused on expanding high performing stores with good results. Going forward Hibbett expects to pick up the pace of new store openings with about 60 new locations slated to open in fiscal 2013. Ultimately Hibbett expects to grow to more than 1300 stores within its existing markets.

The company customizes merchandise to communities' local sports teams and events such as university championships. The company's Hibbett Team Sales subsidiary sells sports equipment apparel and footwear to school athletic programs primarily in Alabama.

T. Rowe Price Associates and Neuberger Berman Group each own about a 10% stake in Hibbett Sports.

HISTORY

Rufus Hibbett a high school coach and educator in Florence Alabama founded single-store Dixie Supply which sold athletic marine and small aircraft equipment in 1945. Rufus' boys Ike and George got involved in the business and in 1952 the company took the name Hibbett & Sons and began to focus on team sports sales. It changed its name and emphasis again in the mid-1960s when as Hibbett Sporting Goods it became primarily a retailer.

The Anderson family owners of the Alabama-based retailer now known as Books-A-Million bought Hibbett in 1980 and continued its gradual expansion. With just over 10 stores Hibbett promoted company veteran Mickey Newsome to president two years later.

Starting in 1993 the chain began opening about 10 new stores each year. Hibbett opened its first Sports & Co. store in 1995. That year the Anderson family sold control of the company to Saunders Karp & Megrue Partners which took it public in 1996. Also in 1996 the chain doubled its store-opening pace.

Hibbett opened 33 stores in fiscal 1998 and 53 stores in fiscal 1999. Newsome was appointed CEO in 1999. By 2000 the company had weathered a shake-out of sporting goods retailers and expanded its store base more than 270% over five years opening 50 stores in fiscal 2000. The company opened more than 60 stores the following year.

In March 2004 chairman John Megrue Jr. retired and Newsome was given the position. Overall the company added 53 Hibbett Sports stores and a single Sports Additions store in 2004.

In August 2005 Brian Priddy joined Hibbett from Bombay Company as president. Newsome retained the titles of chairman and CEO.

In early 2007 the company created its holding company Hibbett Sports to separate itself from its existing operating entity. Priddy resigned in 2007 to pursue other interests. That fiscal year the company opened 64 stores.

In fiscal 2008 it opened 75 retail stores bringing its total count to 688. The following year it added 60 retail stores which boosted its network to 748 locations.

In fiscal 2009 the company opened about 20 stores.

EXECUTIVES

Senior Vice President - Operations, Cathy E. Pryor, $270,000 total compensation
Executive Chairman, Michael J. (Mickey) Newsome, age 74, $541,000 total compensation
President; Chief Executive Officer, Jeffry O. Rosenthal, age 55, $325,000 total compensation
SVP Merchandising, Rebecca A. (Becky) Jones, $265,000 total compensation
VP and General Counsel, David M. Benck
VP and CIO, Terry Mayfield
VP Apparel and Licensed, Chuck Mallet
VP Human Resources, Victoria (Vicky) Moore
Chief Financial Officer; Senior Vice President, Scott Bowman
Senior Vice President & Principal, Tripp Sullivan
Director, Jane F. Aggers, age 64
Director, Terrance G. (Terry) Finley
Director, Alton E. (Al) Yother, age 60
Director, Ralph T. Parks, age 67
Director, Thomas A. Saunders III, age 75
Director, Carl Kirkland, age 72
Director, Albert C. Johnson, age 68
Auditors: KPMGLLP

LOCATIONS

HQ: Hibbett Sports Inc.
451 Industrial Ln., Birmingham AL 35211
Phone: 205-942-4292   **Fax:** 205-912-7290
Web: www.hibbett.com

2012 Locations

	No.
Georgia	89
Alabama	83
Texas	83
Mississippi	60
Tennessee	56
North	47
Kentucky	43
Louisiana	43
Arkansas	41
Oklahoma	40
Florida	39
South	32
Missouri	26
Kansas	21
Indiana	20
Illinois	19
Ohio	19
Virginia	17
New	11
West	10
Iowa	8
Wisconsin	7
Arizona	6
Nebraska	6
Colorado	5
South	1
Total	**832**

PRODUCTS/OPERATIONS

2012 Stores

	No.
Hibbett	812
Sports	19
Sports &	1
Total	**832**

COMPETITORS

Academy Sports	REI
Dick's Sporting Goods	Sears
Finish Line	Sports Authority
Foot Locker	Target Corporation
J. C. Penney	Wal-Mart
Kmart	shoebuy.com

HISTORICAL FINANCIALS

Company Type: Public

Income Statement

FYE: February 2

	REVENUE ($ mil.)	NET INCOME ($ mil.)	NET PROFIT MARGIN	EMPLOYEES
02/13*	818.7	72.5	8.9%	7,400
01/12	732.6	59.0	8.1%	6,700
01/11	664.9	46.4	7.0%	6,050
01/10	593.4	32.5	5.5%	5,900
01/09	564.1	29.4	5.2%	5,500
Annual Growth	9.8%	25.3%	—	7.7%

*Fiscal year change

2013 Year-End Financials

Debt ratio: 0.7%	No. of shares (mil.): 25
Return on equity: 32.2%	Dividends
Cash ($ mil.): 76	Yield: —
Current ratio: 2.71	Payout: —
Long-term debt ($ mil.): 2	Market value ($ mil.): 1,374

	STOCK PRICE ($) FY Close	P/E High/Low		PER SHARE ($) Earnings	Dividends	Book Value
02/13*	53.22	23 17		2.72	0.00	9.26
01/12	48.95	23 14		2.15	0.00	7.72
01/11	32.48	24 13		1.60	0.00	7.17
01/10	21.22	21 12		1.12	0.00	6.11
01/09	13.61	24 11		1.02	0.00	4.78
Annual Growth 40.6%		— —		27.8%	—	17.9%

*Fiscal year change

Higher One Holdings Inc.

The higher ambition at Higher One Holdings is to facilitate higher education payments. The company provides payment processing and disbursement services to colleges and universities and their students. Designed to make financial transactions in higher education settings more efficient the company's suite of offerings includes OneDisburse which more than 500 US schools use to electronically distribute financial aid and other funds to students. For students it offers the OneAccount banking service a deposit account and debit card. The company also provides online billing and payment services to make tuition payments convenient. Higher One Holdings went public in June 2010 after several years of steady growth.

The company raised some $171 million in the offering which it used to pay down debts and other obligations. By taking itself public Higher One expects to further expand its market position as a service provider in the higher education industry targeting schools whose in-house disbursement and payment systems may be outdated or inefficient. It has also been pursuing cross-selling opportunities presented by its 2009 acquisition of CASHNet a provider of cashiering and payment services for higher education.

Since its 2000 inception the company has experienced overall growth in revenue cash flow and net income. The majority of its revenues comes from ATM intechange and other service fees charged through its OneAccount service for students. Other revenues are generated from convenience fees charged to parents and students who make online tuition payments and annual subscription fees charged to schools. Recent federal legislation has passed limiting bank overdraft and related fees which translates to lower fee-per-account revenues. However Higher One has continued to land new schools expanding the number of accounts it services so those revenues are still growing.

Higher One sells itself as a "one-stop shop" of technology and payment services to keep a leg up on such competitors as Nelnet Sallie Mae and TouchNet which offer similar payment software and services. In addition to serving student banking needs it addresses the needs of its educational institution clients by helping them to streamline administrative processes reduce paper and other expenses and remain compliant with federal regulations governing financial aid transactions. Higher One's strategic attention to customer service and brand development has helped it grow a diverse base of clients.

The company partners with banks to provide depository and other services for its OneAccounts. Previously it worked solely with The Bancorp Bank but in 2012 Higher One established new agreements with savings bank Urban Trust Bank and Wright Express Financial Services (an industrial banking subsidiary of Wright Express Corporation) to provide the same functions. The company plans to secure more bank partners in its shift away from using a single provider.

Private equity firm Lightyear Capital invested in Higher One in 2008 and helped take the company public. It owns 26% of the company and has board representation through director Stewart Gross.

EXECUTIVES

President CEO and Director, Dean Hatton, age 52
Director, F. Patrick McFadden Jr., age 75
Chairman and CFO, Mark Volchek, age 35
COO and Director, Miles Lasater, age 35
Chief Service Officer, Casey McGuane, age 38
Chief Sales Officer, Robert (Rob) Reach, age 56
President CEO and Director, Dean Hatton, age 52
Director, Charles E. (Chuck) Moran, age 59
Director, Paul A. Biddelman, age 67
Director, Stewart K. P. Gross, age 53
Director, F. Patrick McFadden Jr., age 75
COO and Director, Miles Lasater, age 35
Director, David Cromwell, age 68
Independent Director, Robert Hartheimer
Auditors: PricewaterhouseCoopersLLP

LOCATIONS

HQ: Higher One Holdings Inc.
115 Munson Street, New Haven, CT 06511
Phone: 203 776-7776
Web: www.higherone.com

PRODUCTS/OPERATIONS

2011 Sales

	$ mil.	% of total
Account revenue	142	79
Payment transaction revenue	18	10
Higher education institution revenue	16	9
Other	3	2
Total	**181**	**100**

COMPETITORS

American Student Assistance	Mohela
Bank of America	Nelnet
CampusLogic	PNC Financial
First Marblehead	Sallie Mae
Great Lakes Higher Education	U.S. Bancorp
	Wells Fargo

HISTORICAL FINANCIALS

Company Type: Public

Income Statement

FYE: December 31

	REVENUE ($ mil.)	NET INCOME ($ mil.)	NET PROFIT MARGIN	EMPLOYEES
12/12	197.7	36.8	18.6%	880
12/11	176.3	31.8	18.1%	700
12/10	144.9	25.0	17.3%	450
12/09	75.5	14.2	18.8%	380
12/08	44.0	6.3	14.5%	0
Annual Growth	**45.6%**	**55.1%**	—	—

2012 Year-End Financials

Debt ratio: 41.9%
Return on equity: 40.5%
Cash ($ mil.): 13
Current ratio: 1.10
Long-term debt ($ mil.): 80

No. of shares (mil.): 46
Dividends
  Yield: —
  Payout: —
Market value ($ mil.): 492

	STOCK PRICE ($) FY Close	P/E High/Low		PER SHARE ($) Earnings	Dividends	Book Value
12/12	10.54	27	13	0.65	0.00	1.24
12/11	18.44	36	24	0.54	0.00	2.18
12/10	20.23	46	24	0.44	0.00	1.49
Annual Growth	**(27.8%)**	—	—	**21.5%**	—	**(8.8%)**

Hillenbrand Inc

Hillenbrand knows a thing or two about life and death. Through its largest subsidiary BatesvilleHillenbrand is a top supplier to the death care industry providing nearly half the caskets used in the US. Batesville makes a variety of caskets in materials ranging from wood to stainless steel. Increasingly it also produces urns and other cremation products to satisfy increasing demand for lower-cost cremation. The company's Process Equipment Group (PEG) designs and makes equipment and systems used by industrial manufacturers. The PEG includes subsidiaries K-Tron Rotex and Coperion and was formed by a trio of acquisitions made in the past several years. Hillenbrand was spun off from Hillenbrand Industries.

Geographic Reach

Historically a US-centric business Hillenbrand has worked to lessen its reliance on US customers by extending its reach abroad. To this end the company has concentrated on developing its presence in Switzerland and Canada. In fiscal 2012 (ended September) the US accounted for 83% of Hillenbrand's sales (versus 93% in 2009) while Switzerland and Canada accounted for 8% and 5% respectively. Batesville makes most of its caskets in the US but also operates production facilities in Mexico.

Operations

Hillenbrand has two primary businesses. The largest Batesville accounting for about 60% of Hillenbrand's sales is an established company founded in 1884 that sells its burial products through a direct sales force to more than 12000 licensed funeral homes in the US Puerto Rico Canada Mexico the UK and Australia. Batesville manufactures both metal and solid and veneer hardwood caskets cremation urns and burial vaults. It also makes caskets suitable for "green" burials.

The company's Process Equipment Group (PEG) was formed by the purchases of Coperion Rotex and K-Tron. It accounts for about 40% of sales. New Jersey-based K-Tron produces feeders crushers conveying systems and other equipment used in the industrial manufacturing processes. Under the Rotex brand the PEG designs makes sells and services dry material separation machines that sort particles based on their size. Rotex brand equipment is used in a variety of industries including frac sand potash urea phosphates plastics and food processing.

Sales and Marketing

Batesville branded burial and cremation caskets and other funeral supplies are marketed by a direct sales force to licensed funeral professionals. The PEG also sells its material handling equipment through independent sales representatives.

Financial Performance

Hillenbrand's sales topped $983 million in fiscal 2012 (ended September) an increase of 11% versus the prior year. Net income declined by 1% over the same period. Driving the double-digit increase was the PEG which posted a 53% increase in annual sales due primarily to the Rotex acquisition in 2011. Batesville's sales declined 5% over the same period. 2012 marked the third year of increasing sales for the company. The small decline in net income was attributed to increased operating expenses and the amortization expense related to the Rotex purchase.

Strategy

Hillenbrand has moved to diversify its revenue stream in recent years as consumer preferences are shifting and as the total number of deaths in North America where most of Batesville's products are sold has been flat. More consumers are choosing cremation and other alternatives to traditional burials. Cremations as a percentage of total deaths now represent more than one-third in the US and more than one-half in Canada.

Mergers and Acquisitions

Aiming to build a "family of companies" revolving around manufacturing distribution and customer service Hillenbrand acquired Stuttgart Germany-based Coperion Capital GmbH for $545 million in December 2012. The purchase expanded the company's global footprint bolstered its PEG and leveraged replacement parts and service capabilities. It's anticipated that the group with Coperion under its umbrella will generate more than $1 billion in revenue and represent two-thirds of Hillenbrand's overall sales in fiscal 2013.

Previously the firm expanded its manufacturing equipment division through the purchase of ROTEX Global from Windjammer Capital Investors for $240 million in cash in September 2011. ROTEX makes machines (along with replacement parts and accessories) that separate dry materials for various industrial applications a complementary addition to Hillenbrand's existing equipment line. Although its products are sold throughout the US and abroad ROTEX boasts a significant customer base in Europe and Asia — two regions in which Hillenbrand has been looking to strengthen its presence.

In 2010 the company acquired New Jersey-based K-Tron International which produces feeders crushers conveying systems and other equipment used in the industrial manufacturing processes. The $435-million purchase gave Hillenbrand access to a much more diverse customer base that comprises chemical food pharmaceutical and plastics companies.

EXECUTIVES

Chairperson, F. Joseph (Joe) Loughrey, age 63
President Coperion K-Tron, Kevin C. Bowen, age 62
Chairman, Ray J. Hillenbrand, age 78
President CEO and Director, Kenneth A. (Ken) Camp, age 67, $669,315 total compensation
President Chief Executive Officer and Director, Joseph A. (Joe) Raver, age 48, $411,589 total compensation
President Batesville Services, Kimberly K. Dennis, age 45
Vice President Enterprise Information Systems, Darryl M. Maslar
Senior Vice President and Chief Financial Officer, Cynthia L. (Cindy) Lucchese, age 53, $309,271 total compensation
SVP General Counsel and Secretary, John R. Zerkle, age 59, $282,726 total compensation
SVP and Chief Administrative Officer, P. Douglas (Doug) Wilson, age 61, $257,726 total compensation
VP and Treasurer, Theodore S. (Ted) Haddad, age 49
VP Business Development and Strategy, Hinesh Patel, age 45
VP Lean Business, Jan M. Santerre
VP Controller and Chief Accounting Officer, Elizabeth E. Dreyer
President Rotex, Anthony S. Casablanca
Vice President Corporate Strategy, Diane R. Bohman
Senior Vice President Corporate Development, Scott P. George
Executive Vice President, Helen W. Cornell

Vice President Human Resources and Administration, Philip C. Waddell
Vice President Marketing, Michael L. DiBease
Vice President General Counsel, Richard S. Barnett
Vice President General Manager Vaults, Troy J. Turner
Vice President General Manager Options?, Jason L. Burlage
Senior Vice President President Batesville, Kimberly K. Ryan
President Coperion, Thomas Kehl
President TerraSource Global, Mark L. Kohler
Director, Mark C. DeLuzio, age 56
Director, Edward B. (Ed) Cloues II, age 65
Director, William J. Cernugel, age 70
Director, F. Joseph (Joe) Loughrey, age 63
Director, Neil S. Novich, age 58
President CEO and Director, Kenneth A. (Ken) Camp, age 67
Director, Stuart A. Taylor II, age 52
Director, W. August Hillenbrand, age 72
Director, James A. Henderson, age 78
Director, Thomas H. Johnson, age 62
Independent Director, Eduardo Menasce
Auditors: PricewaterhouseCoopersLLP

LOCATIONS

HQ: Hillenbrand Inc.
1 Batesville Blvd., Batesville IN 47006
Phone: 812-934-7000   **Fax:** 812-934-7613
Web: www.hillenbrandinc.com

2012 Sales

	$ mil.	% of total
US	817	83
Switzerland	76	8
Canada	46	5
Other foreign business units	43	4
Total	**983**	**100**

PRODUCTS/OPERATIONS

2012 Sales

	$ mil.	% of total
Batesville caskets	606	62
Other	376	38
Total	**983**	**100**

Selected Subsidiaries

Batesville (Batesville Indiana)
Coperion (Germany)
K-Tron International (Pitman New Jersey)
Rotex Global (Cincinnati Ohio)

COMPETITORS

Aurora Casket	Matthews International
Badger Meter	Stewart Enterprises
Costco Wholesale	Wal-Mart
Goliath Casket	Wilbert
Heat and Control	York Group
Key Technology	

HISTORICAL FINANCIALS

Company Type: Public

Income Statement

FYE: September 30

	REVENUE ($ mil.)	NET INCOME ($ mil.)	NET PROFIT MARGIN	EMPLOYEES
09/13	1,553.4	63.4	4.1%	6,000
09/12	983.2	104.8	10.7%	3,900
09/11	883.4	106.1	12.0%	4,200
09/10	749.2	92.3	12.3%	3,850
09/09	649.1	102.3	15.8%	3,250
Annual Growth	**24.4%**	**(11.3%)**	**—**	**16.6%**

2013 Year-End Financials

Debt ratio: 33.1%	No. of shares (mil.): 62
Return on equity: 11.8%	Dividends
Cash ($ mil.): 42	Yield: 2.8%
Current ratio: 1.37	Payout: 75.0%
Long-term debt ($ mil.): 654	Market value ($ mil.): 1,722

	STOCK PRICE ($) FY Close	P/E High/Low		PER SHARE ($) Earnings	Dividends	Book Value
09/13	27.37	28	18	1.01	0.78	9.03
09/12	18.19	14	10	1.68	0.77	8.09
09/11	18.40	14	10	1.71	0.76	7.09
09/10	21.51	17	12	1.49	0.75	5.97
09/09	20.37	13	8	1.66	0.74	4.91
Annual Growth	**7.7%**	—	—	**(11.7%)**	**1.3%**	**16.5%**

Hittite Microwave Corp

And lo the Hittites did rise up out of their land (the Commonwealth of Massachusetts) and they did conquer Babylon...well semiconductors in any case. Hittite Microwave designs and develops microwave millimeter-wave and radio-frequency integrated circuits (RFICs) for aerospace broadband cellular and military applications. In addition to standard amplifiers frequency multipliers mixers modulators switches and other components the company provides custom RFICs. It gets more than half of its sales from customers in international locations. Boeing (more than 15% of sales) is Hittite Microwave's top customer.

As a fabless semiconductor company Hittite Microwave contracts out the production of its chips. Its principal foundry contractors are Cobham Cree Global Communication Semiconductors (GCS) IBM Microelectronics Jazz Semiconductor Northrop Grumman Taiwan Semiconductor Manufacturing Telefunken Semiconductor TriQuint Semiconductor United Monolithic Semiconductors (UMS) and WIN Semiconductors. Hittite Microwave also competes with some of those companies with its microwave and RFICs. Some of these companies (such as TriQuint and UMS) as well as customers such as NEC are also competitors.

Part of its strategy to preserve its own competitive niche is to concentrate on delivering high-performance rather than high-volume addressing technically challenging needs rather than offering commodity RFICs. Even with its standard products which serve a variety of basic needs Hittite Microwave aims for a unique combination of form factor functionality and performance to set itself apart in the marketplace.

In the notoriously cyclical semiconductor industry Hittite Microwave had a pleasing sales run from 2003 to 2008 growing from around $40 million to more than $180 million before the global recession knocked it back a step. It came back swinging though with 50% growth in 2010 and kept punching in 2011 as it scored an 8% gain. The increase came mainly from the breadth of product offerings and improved market acceptance for its test and measurement products as well as from fulfillment on a military order for microwave subsystems announced back in 2009. Hittite Microwave relies on a small number of customers for much of its sales the 10 largest bringing in nearly 45%.

In early 2011 Hittite Microwave acquired Norway-based Arctic Silicon Devices a developer of mixed-signal integrated circuit technology for about $12 million. The purchase gave the company new IC design and integration capabilities as well as an analog-to-digital converter product line used in test and measurement and communications infrastructure applications.

EXECUTIVES

Chief Executive Officer, Rick D. Hess, age 59
Chairman President and CEO, Stephen G. Daly, age 47, $284,242 total compensation
Chief Financial Officer; Vice President; Treasurer, William W. Boecke, age 61, $221,692 total compensation
CTO, Michael J. Koechlin, age 53, $202,500 total compensation
VP, Norman G. Hildreth Jr., age 49, $221,693 total compensation
Manager MarCom (Marketing Communications), Beth McGreevy
VP Operations, Brian J. Jablonski, age 53, $201,541 total compensation
VP, Michael Olson, age 52, $189,616 total compensation
Vice President of Hybrid Manufacturing, Everett N. Cole III
Vice President of Global Operations, William D. Hannabach
VP Sales, Thomas D. H. Hwang
Vice President, Antonio Visconti
Vice President, Gorkem Guven
Demer IR Counsel, Peter DeNardo
Vice President - Sales, Dong Hwang
Managing Director Hittite Microwave International Limited, Jason M. Lynch
Director, Franklin A. (Frank) Weigold, age 74
Director, Brian P. McAloon, age 62
Director, Ernest L. (Ernie) Godshalk, age 68
Director, Cosmo S. (Cos) Trapani, age 74
Director, Rick D. Hess, age 59
Director, Adrienne M. Markham, age 62
Auditors: PricewaterhouseCoopersLLP

LOCATIONS

HQ: Hittite Microwave Corporation
20 Alpha Rd., Chelmsford MA 01824-4123
Phone: 978-250-3343   **Fax:** 978-250-3373
Web: www.hittite.com

2010 Sales

	$ mil.	% of total
International	144	55
US	119	45
Total	**264**	**100**

PRODUCTS/OPERATIONS

Selected Products
Amplifiers
Attenuators
Frequency dividers and detectors
Frequency multipliers
Mixers and converters
Modulators
Oscillators
Sensors
Switches

Selected Customer Groups and Applications
Automotive
  Collision avoidance
  Telematics & GPS
Broadband
  Cable TV & modems
  Direct broadcast satellite

Fixed & mobile wireless networks
Cellular infrastructure
  3G & 4G base stations and repeaters
  E911 & GPS
Fiber optic
  Communications infrastructure
  Network data communications
  Test equipment
Microwave & millimeterwave communications
  Commercial very small aperature terminal (VSAT)
  Point-to-point & -to-multi-point radio systems
  Short range LANs
Military
  Radar guidance electronic countermeasure
  Sensing & detection
Space
  Command control & communications
  Communication & imaging payloads
Test & measurement
  Homeland security
  Medical & industrial imaging

COMPETITORS

ANADIGICS
Aeroflex Control Components
Analog Devices
Avago Technologies
Cobham
L-3 Communications
Linear Technology
Merrimac Industries
NEC
Peregrine Semiconductor

Powerwave Technologies
RF Micro Devices
RF Monolithics
Rohde & Schwarz
Skyworks
Sumitomo Electric Device Innovations
Tektronix
TriQuint

HISTORICAL FINANCIALS
Company Type: Public

Income Statement
FYE: December 31

	REVENUE ($ mil.)	NET INCOME ($ mil.)	NET PROFIT MARGIN	EMPLOYEES
12/12	264.4	68.5	25.9%	486
12/11	264.1	84.6	32.1%	469
12/10	244.2	77.0	31.5%	402
12/09	162.9	46.1	28.3%	349
12/08	180.2	53.8	29.9%	332
Annual Growth	**10.1%**	**6.2%**	**—**	**10.0%**

2012 Year-End Financials

Debt ratio: —
Return on equity: 13.4%
Cash ($ mil.): 269
Current ratio: 24.58
Long-term debt ($ mil.): —

No. of shares (mil.): 31
Dividends
  Yield: —
  Payout: —
Market value ($ mil.): 1,959

	STOCK PRICE ($) FY Close	P/E High/Low		PER SHARE ($) Earnings	Dividends	Book Value
12/12	62.06	28	21	2.22	0.00	17.46
12/11	49.38	24	16	2.77	0.00	14.93
12/10	61.04	24	14	2.56	0.00	12.02
12/09	40.77	26	15	1.55	0.00	9.08
12/08	29.46	27	14	1.74	0.00	7.82
Annual Growth	**20.5%**	**—**	**—**	**6.3%**	**—**	**22.2%**

HMS Holdings Corp

HMS Holdings makes sure health benefits providers are paying only as much as they have to. Through its Health Management Systems subsidiary the company specializes in helping providers determine participant eligibility coordinate benefits and identify and recover claims that were paid in error or should have been paid by another party. It serves state Medicaid agencies and Children's Health Insurance Programs in some 40 states as well as federal agencies including Centers for Medicare & Medicaid Services and Veterans Health Administration. The company also provides services to commercial insurers employer groups and pharmacy benefits managers.

Sales and Marketing

The largest customers of HMS include the New Jersey Department of Human Services and the New York State Office of the Medicaid Inspector General each of which account for about 7% of annual revenues.

Financial Analysis

HMS's revenue charts have a nice slant upwards through the years due in part to acquisitive and organic growth measures that have widened its customer base and its service offerings. In 2011 the company reported a 20% increase in revenues (to some $364 million) and a 19% rise in net income (to $48 million) primarily due to broader services provided to existing customers.

Strategy

HMS regularly seeks to add new government and private clients to its customer base as well as to provide a wider breadth of services to existing clients. Towards that end the company has added new service offerings to its lineup over the years partly through acquisitions of niche providers in areas such as dependent eligibility audits and employer sponsored benefits.

HMS has benefitted in recent years from US government agencies placing increasing pressure on medical providers to cut health care costs and drive out process inefficiencies. It first received a boost from federal mandates under the 2006 Deficit Reduction Act and then again with the Patient Protection and Affordable Care Act in 2010.

Mergers and Acquisitions

In late 2011 HMS acquired HealthDataInsights for some $400 million to expand its recovery audit contractor services for government and commercial health plans. The previous year the company built up its employer-sponsored benefits division with the 2010 acquisition of Chapman Kelly which provides dependent eligibility audits and claims audits to large self-insured employers and expanded its fraud detection services through the purchase of Allied Management Group's Special Investigation Unit.

EXECUTIVES

Chairman, Robert M. Holster, age 67, $467,692 total compensation
President; Chief Executive Officer; Director, William C. (Bill) Lucia, age 55, $406,923 total compensation
Chief Operations Officer, Sean Curtin
EVP Corporate Development, Christina Dragonetti
Vice President Chief Financial Officer Chief Administrative Officer, Walter D. Hosp, age 55, $337,500 total compensation
Senior Vice President; Chief Counsel; Corporate Secretary, Edith Marshall
EVP Government Markets, Maria Perrin
Chief Compliance Officer, Alexandra Holt
Chief Security Officer, Scott Pettigrew
Executive Vice President; President of HDI, Andrea Benko
Vice President Chief Information Officer, Cynthia Nustad
Executive Vice President Commercial Markets, Ronald Singh
Senior Vice President - Human Resources, Tracy South

Senior Vice President; Chief Corporate Counsel; Corporate Secretary, Jzaneen Lalani
Senior Vice President Managing Director, Michele Carpenter
Executive Vice President of Operations, Semone Wagner
Director, Michael A. Stocker, age 71
Director, James T. Kelly, age 66
Director, Richard H. Stowe, age 70
Director, William F. Miller III, age 64
Director, Ellen A. Rudnick, age 62
Director, Bart M. Schwartz
President; Chief Executive Officer; Director, William C. (Bill) Lucia, age 55
Director, William S. Mosakowski, age 59
Auditors: KPMGLLP

LOCATIONS

HQ: HMS Holdings Corp.
401 Park Ave. South, New York NY 10016
Phone: 212-857-5000   Fax: 212-857-5973
Web: www.hms.com

PRODUCTS/OPERATIONS

Selected Services

Coordination of Benefits
Customer Service Operations
Eligibility and Enrollment
Healthstone Data Analytics
Pharmacy Services
Program Integrity

COMPETITORS

Accretive Health	HP Enterprise Services
ActiveHealth	MAXIMUS
Management	Magellan Medicaid
Affiliated Computer	Administration
Services	McKesson
Allscripts	MedAssets
Argus	NHXS
Catamaran	OptumnInsight
CorVel	PRGX
Emdeon	Quality Systems
Expert Global	athenahealth
Solutions	

HISTORICAL FINANCIALS

Company Type: Public

Income Statement

FYE: December 31

	REVENUE ($ mil.)	NET INCOME ($ mil.)	NET PROFIT MARGIN	EMPLOYEES
12/12	473.7	50.5	10.7%	2,702
12/11	363.8	47.7	13.1%	2,249
12/10	302.8	40.0	13.2%	1,736
12/09	229.2	30.0	13.1%	1,306
12/08	184.5	21.3	11.6%	922
Annual Growth	26.6%	24.0%	—	30.8%

2012 Year-End Financials

Debt ratio: 35.9%
Return on equity: 11.8%
Cash ($ mil.): 135
Current ratio: 3.04
Long-term debt ($ mil.): 297
No. of shares (mil.): 86
Dividends
 Yield: —
 Payout: —
Market value ($ mil.): 2,254

	STOCK PRICE ($) FY Close	P/E High/Low	PER SHARE ($) Earnings	Dividends	Book Value
12/12	25.92	62 35	0.57	0.00	5.32
12/11	31.98	150 40	0.55	0.00	4.57
12/10	64.77	136 89	0.47	0.00	3.69
12/09	48.69	130 76	0.36	0.00	2.96
12/08	31.52	126 65	0.27	0.00	2.33
Annual Growth	(4.8%)	— —	20.9%	—	22.9%

Holly Energy Partners LP

Holly Energy Partners is having a jolly good time piping petroleum products and crude oil from refineries. It operates petroleum product and crude gathering pipelines (in New Mexico Oklahoma Texas and Utah) distribution terminals (in Arizona Idaho New Mexico Oklahoma Texas Utah and Washington) and refinery tankage in New Mexico and Utah. It operates 1330 miles of refined petroleum pipelines (340 miles leased) 960 miles of crude oil trunk lines 10 refined product terminals one jet fuel terminal and two truck-loading facilities. It also has three 65-mile pipelines that ship feedstocks and crude oil. HollyFrontier holds a 41% stake in Holly Energy Partners.

Holly Energy Partners' strategy is to make acquisitions that complement its existing portfolio both in tandem with HollyFrontier and independently.

Holly Energy Partners is integral to HollyFrontier's business growth by developing and extending that company's assets. In 2009 it picked up the Roadrunner pipeline a 65-mile pipeline connecting HollyFrontier's refining facilities in Lovington New Mexico to the terminus of a Centurion pipeline linking West Texas and Cushing Oklahoma. In 2010 it acquired petroleum storage tanks at HollyFrontier's Tulsa refinery (2 million barrels of capacity) and other assets from HollyFrontier for $93 million.

Building the largest refinery complex in the area in 2009 HollyFrontier acquired refineries and related assets in Tulsa from Sunoco and Sinclair. In 2011 HollyFrontier's acquisition of Frontier Oil (with refineries in Kansas and Wyoming) boosted its total refining capacity to 443.000 barrels per day.

Building its portfolio in 2011 Holly Energy Partners acquired pipeline tankage loading rack and crude receiving assets from HollyFrontier's El Dorado and Cheyenne refineries for $340 million. In 2012 it also acquired HollyFrontier's 75% stake in UNEV Pipeline for $315 million. The UNEV refined products pipeline runs from Woods Cross Utah to Las Vegas Nevada.

Increased pipeline shipments and higher operating margins (thanks to the 2011 asset expansion and higher oil prices) helped to lift Holly Energy Partners' revenues and net income in 2011 by 17% and 32 % respectively.

EXECUTIVES

VP Pipeline Operations, James G. Townsend, age 59, $203,940 total compensation

---

President Holly Energy Partners and Holly Logistic Services, David G. Blair, age 54, $269,100 total compensation
Chairman of the Board Chief Executive Officer, Matthew P. (Matt) Clifton, age 61
President DQ Holdings, Charles M. Darling IV, age 65
Vice President; Controller, Scott C. Surplus
President, Bruce R. Shaw, age 46
VP Investor Relations Holly Energy Partners and Holly Corporation, M. Neale Hickerson, age 61
VP and Treasurer, Stephen D. Wise
Senior Vice President General Counsel Secretary, Denise C. McWatters
Senior Vice President of Operations, Mark Cunningham
Executive Vice President Chief Financial Officer, Douglas Aron
Director, Jerry W. Pinkerton, age 72
Director, Charles M. Darling IV, age 64
Director, William P. Stengel, age 65
Director, P. Dean Ridenour, age 71
Auditors: Ernst&YoungLLP

LOCATIONS

HQ: Holly Energy Partners L.P.
2828 N. Harwood Ste. 1300, Dallas TX 75201
Phone: 214-871-3555   Fax: 214-871-3560
Web: www.hollyenergy.com

PRODUCTS/OPERATIONS

2011 Sales

	$ mil.	% of total
Pipelines		
Refined products	86	40
Crude oil	46	22
Intermediates	21	10
Terminals & truck loading racks	58	28
Total	213	100

COMPETITORS

ExxonMobil Pipeline	Shell Pipeline
Magellan Midstream	Wolverine Pipe Line
NuStar Energy	Company

HISTORICAL FINANCIALS

Company Type: Public

Income Statement

FYE: December 31

	REVENUE ($ mil.)	NET INCOME ($ mil.)	NET PROFIT MARGIN	EMPLOYEES
12/12	292.5	91.1	31.1%	232
12/11	213.5	78.0	36.5%	216
12/10	182.1	58.8	32.3%	148
12/09	146.5	66.0	45.0%	140
12/08	118.0	25.3	21.5%	121
Annual Growth	25.5%	37.7%	—	17.7%

2012 Year-End Financials

Debt ratio: 62.0%
Return on equity: —
Cash ($ mil.): 5
Current ratio: 1.33
Long-term debt ($ mil.): 864
No. of shares (mil.): 56
Dividends
 Yield: 5.5%
 Payout: 129.5%
Market value ($ mil.): 3,735

STOCK PRICE ($) FY Close	P/E High/Low	PER SHARE ($) Earnings	Dividends	Book Value
12/12	65.78	57 41	1.29	1.81	6.21
12/11	53.78	45 35	1.34	1.72	6.02
12/10	50.91	50 37	1.06	1.64	2.48
12/09	39.84	26 13	1.59	1.56	4.39
12/08	21.35	69 25	0.67	1.48	(0.06)
Annual Growth	32.5%	— —	17.8%	5.1%	

Home Bancorp Inc

Making its home in Cajun Country Home Bancorp is the holding company for Home Bank a community bank which offers deposit and loan services to consumers and small to midsized businesses in southern Louisiana. Through about two dozen branches the bank offers standard savings and checking accounts as well as lending services such as mortgages consumer loans and credit cards. Home Bank serves the areas of Greater Lafayette Baton Rouge Greater New Orleans and Northshore (of Lake Pontchartrain). It has expanded its reach via acquisitions.

EXECUTIVES

Chief Operations Officers and Executive Vice President of the Bank, Scott T. Sutton, age 60
President; Chief Executive Officer; Director, John W. Bordelon, age 57, $215,000 total compensation
Executive Vice President; Chief Lending Officer of the Bank, Darren E. Guidry, age 50, $137,000 total compensation
Chief Financial Officer & Executive Vice President of the Bank, Joseph B. Zanco, age 43, $99,018 total compensation
Director and Secretary, Henry William Busch Jr., age 72, $30,300 total compensation
President CEO and Director Home Bancorp and Home Bank, John W. Bordelon, age 57
Director, Michael P. Maraist, age 65
Director, Paul J. Blanchet III, age 58
Director, Richard J. Bourgeois, age 66
Director and Secretary, Henry William Busch Jr., age 72
Director, John A. Hendry, age 63
Director, Marc W. Judice, age 66
Auditors: PorterKeadleMooreLLP

LOCATIONS

HQ: Home Bancorp Inc
503 Kaliste Saloom Road, Lafayette, LA 70508
Phone: 337 237-1960   **Fax:** 337 264-9280
Web: www.home24bank.com

COMPETITORS

Capital One
IBERIABANK
JPMorgan Chase
Louisiana Bancorp
MidSouth Bancorp
Regions Financial
Teche Holding

HISTORICAL FINANCIALS
Company Type: Public

Income Statement
FYE: December 31

	ASSETS ($ mil.)	NET INCOME ($ mil.)	INCOME AS % OF ASSETS	EMPLOYEES
12/12	962.9	9.1	1.0%	0
12/11	963.7	5.1	0.5%	0
12/10	700.4	4.6	0.7%	0
12/09	524.6	4.6	0.9%	0
12/08	528.4	2.7	0.5%	0
Annual Growth	16.2%	35.6%	—	—

2012 Year-End Financials

Return on assets: 0.9%
Return on equity: 6.6%
Long-term debt ($ mil.): —
No. of shares (mil.): 7
Sales ($ mil): 53
Dividends
  Yield: —
  Payout: —
Market value ($ mil.): 136

STOCK PRICE ($) FY Close	P/E High/Low	PER SHARE ($) Earnings	Dividends	Book Value
12/12	18.25	14 12	1.28	0.00	19.03
12/11	15.50	22 18	0.71	0.00	17.30
12/10	13.82	23 19	0.62	0.00	16.18
12/09	12.19	22 16	0.58	0.00	15.13
12/08	9.75	9 7	1.32	0.00	14.22
Annual Growth	17.0%	— —	(0.8%)	—	7.6%

HomeAway, Inc.

There's no place like a home away from home for fun or functionality. HomeAway boasts more than 500000 paid listings for vacation rental properties across 145 countries worldwide and helps property owners rent out their shack condo or chateau. Its HomeAway.com website is free to travelers who are typically affluent and is searchable by destination. Its listings include information on weekly rates availability and amenities as well as photographs descriptions and contact information. HomeAway also maintains 30 other travel-related websites. Founded in 2005 as WVR Group the company changed its name in 2006 to HomeAway launched its flagship website that year and went public in mid-2011.

Raising $216 million through its initial public offering HomeAway plans to use the proceeds to not only pay off investors but to continue its strategy of buying businesses expanding into new global markets adding more product lines and increasing the functionality and relevance of its websites. The company has grown organically and by acquiring several US-centric vacation rental websites. It logged a year-over-year growth rate of nearly 40% in 2010 despite the global economy recovering from a downturn.

The renter's resource also has reached outside the US to develop its business abroad. In 2012 HomeAway announced it's purchasing a minority stake in Tujia.com an online vacation rental service in China that caters to upscale travelers there. As part of the deal HomeAway is funding the effort with Ctrip.com International and venture capital firms Lightspeed China Partners and CDH Investments. In 2010 the company purchased Brazilian-based website AlugueTemporada.com.br. To further extend its geographic presence the com-

pany acquired Spanish-based Top Rural S.L. (known as Toprural) which provides accommodations in Southern Europe through its website in 2012. Toprural offers more than 11600 paid listing and close to 30000 free listings across rural France Spain Italy and Portugal.

To better cater to property management professionals the firm has been adding software providers to its portfolio. In late 2010 it acquired industry-leading developers Escapia and Instant Software which together represent about 1700 property managers in the US. HomeAway hopes that by bolstering its software operations it will simplify property-management duties and drive traffic to listings through partner platforms.

Property listings accounted for about 91% of the company's 2010 revenue. HomeAway charges fees to property owners to market their properties through online listings. Property managers vacation rental sellers and buyers and relatively larger landlords (owners of between one and five vacation rentals) enlist the help of HomeAway to help them peddle their properties. The more listings the more cash in HomeAway's pocket. To this end the company offers a variety of listing packages and services including online payments for one-time smaller clients to customers with multiple listings.

HomeAway also generates a growing percentage of its revenue from advertising. In 2006 the company's "other revenue" which includes money generated through online advertising accounted for 2% of its sales. HomeAway's other revenue in 2010 reached 9% of its overall sales thanks to a 142% increase in online advertising revenue as more companies returned to the medium. The company also attributes the boost in non-listing sales to changes it has made to its websites to cater to advertisers revenue from its software acquisitions money received from the sale of gift cards and royalties from the sale of travel insurance among other items.

With property owners and managers paying for online marketing HomeAway looks to attract tech-savvy travelers who regularly book vacation rentals. Its websites also showcase temporary housing for those who are having a home remodeled and need another place to hang their hat. Compared to the average leisure traveler the firm cites that vacation rental bookers spend more and travel more frequently and for longer periods of time. To make it easier for customers to find properties while traveling HomeAway in 2010 launched an iPhone application.

EXECUTIVES

Chief Strategy and Development Officer and Director, Carl G. Shepherd, age 61
CFO, Lynn Atchison, age 53
President CEO and Director, Brian H. Sharples, age 52
CTO, Ross A. Buhrdorf, age 48
VP North America, Alexis de Belloy
Director Global Public Relations, Eileen Buesing
VP Hosting Operations and Technology, Steve Davis
President Europe, Petra Friedmann
VP Partner Channels, Martin Slagter
VP Customer Experience, Jeffrey (Jeff) Mosler
COO, Brent Bellm, age 41
Chief Product Officer, Thomas (Tom) Hale, age 44
Owner, Noe St
Owner, Charlotte Amalie
Owner, Diane Lees
Owner, Deborah Davidson
Chief Product Officer, Tom Hale

Chief Strategy and Development Officer and Director, Carl G. Shepherd, age 61
Director, Kenneth P. (Ken) DeAngelis, age 60
President CEO and Director, Brian H. Sharples, age 52
Director, Todd C. Chaffee, age 53
Director, Philip S. Siegel, age 48
Director, Jeffrey D. (Jeff) Brody, age 53
Director, Christopher P. (Woody) Marshall, age 45
Director, John H. Moragne, age 56
Director, Robert Solomon, age 46
Independent Director, Charles Baker
Independent Director, Simon Breakwell
Independent Director, Susan Wojcicki
Auditors: PricewaterhouseCoopersLLP

LOCATIONS

HQ: HomeAway Inc.
1011 W. 5th St. Ste. 300, Austin TX 78703
Phone: 512-493-0382   **Fax:** -12198
Web: www.gafisa.com.br

2010 Sales

	$ mil.	% of total
US	104	62
France	27	16
UK	23	14
Other international	12	8
Total	**167**	**100**

PRODUCTS/OPERATIONS

2010 Sales

	$ mil.	% of total
Listings	152	91
Other	15	9
Total	**167**	**100**

Company Trademarks
Abritel.fr
Aluguetemporada BedandBrea
Clearstay
CyberRentals.com
Entech
Escapia
FeWo-Direkt
First Resorts
Holiday-Rentals
HomeAway
Homelidays
InstantSoftware
OwnersDirect
PropertyPlus
Rezovation
V12
VacationRentals.com
Villanao.fr
VRBO
Webervations

Selected Websites

Abritel.fr (France)
AlugueTemporada.com.br (Brazil)
BedandBreakfast.com
HomeAway.co.uk (UK)
HomeAway.com (US)
HomeAway.de (Germany)
HomeAway.es (Spain)
HomeAwayRealEstate.com
Homelidays.com (France)
OwnersDirect.co.uk (UK)
VacationRentals.com (US)
VRBO.com (US)

COMPETITORS

Century 21 Real Estate	Orbitz Worldwide
Coldwell Banker	Prudential
Expedia	RE/MAX
Fairfax Media	Telecom Italia
Google	Teletext
Hotels.com	Travelocity
Hotwire Inc.	Wyndham Worldwide

Internet Brands	Yahoo!
Interval Leisure Group	craigslist
Kayak Software	eBay
MSN	priceline.com

HISTORICAL FINANCIALS

Company Type: Public

Income Statement

FYE: December 31

	REVENUE ($ mil.)	NET INCOME ($ mil.)	NET PROFIT MARGIN	EMPLOYEES
12/12	280.4	14.9	5.3%	1,228
12/11	230.2	6.1	2.7%	935
12/10	167.8	16.9	10.1%	842
12/09	120.2	7.6	6.4%	0
12/08	82.3	(5.6)	—	0
Annual Growth	**35.9%**			

2012 Year-End Financials

Debt ratio: —
Return on equity: 3.1%
Cash ($ mil.): 189
Current ratio: 1.69
Long-term debt ($ mil.): —

No. of shares (mil.): 83
Dividends
Yield: —
Payout: —
Market value ($ mil.): 1,836

	STOCK PRICE ($) FY Close	P/E High/Low	PER SHARE ($) Earnings	Dividends	Book Value
12/12	22.00	151 110	0.18	0.00	6.20
12/11	23.25	— —	(0.31)	0.00	5.47
Annual Growth	**(5.4%)**	**— —**	**—**	**—**	**13.4%**

Homefed Corp.

HomeFed won't provide you with room and board but it can help you get a home. The company earns its keep by investing in and developing residential real estate in California. Through subsidiaries HomeFed is developing a master-planned community in San Diego County called San Elijo Hills which is expected to contain approximately 3500 residences. The company is responsible for design engineering infrastructure and finishing individual lots. HomeFed also owns a portion of another community under development Otay Ranch as well as some 1500 acres of a grape vineyard in California.

Leucadia from which the company acquired the San Elijo Hills and Otay Ranch projects controls about 30% of HomeFed. Jospeh Steinberg president of Leucadia and chairman of HomeFed owns almost 10%. Ian Cumming who is chairman of Leucadia and a director of HomeFed holds more than 7%.

EXECUTIVES

President and Director, Paul J. Borden, age 60, $255,742 total compensation
Chairman, Joseph S. Steinberg, age 65
Secretary, Corinne A. Maki
VP, Curt R. Noland, age 52, $165,500 total compensation
VP Treasurer and Controller, Erin N. Ruhe, age 43, $133,900 total compensation
President and Director, Paul J. Borden, age 60
Director, Ian M. Cumming, age 69
Director, Patrick D. Bienvenue, age 54
Director, Timothy M. Considine, age 68

Director, Michael A. Lobatz, age 60
Auditors: PricewaterhouseCoopersLLP

LOCATIONS

HQ: HomeFed Corporation
1903 Wright Place Ste. 220, Carlsbad CA 92008
Phone: 760-918-8200   **Fax:** 760-918-8210

PRODUCTS/OPERATIONS

2007 Sales

	$ mil.	% of total
Sales of real estate	22	95
Co-op marketing & advertising fees	0	3
Options on real estate properties	0	2
Total	**23**	**100**

COMPETITORS

Brookfield Homes	Newhall Land
Corky McMillin	Tejon Ranch
Irvine Company	

HISTORICAL FINANCIALS

Company Type: Public

Income Statement

FYE: December 31

	REVENUE ($ mil.)	NET INCOME ($ mil.)	NET PROFIT MARGIN	EMPLOYEES
12/12	35.6	6.0	16.9%	14
12/11	34.1	4.4	13.2%	13
12/10	35.9	3.5	9.8%	13
12/09	14.8	2.8	18.9%	13
12/08	10.4	(9.9)	—	13
Annual Growth	**36.0%**	**—**		**1.9%**

2012 Year-End Financials

Debt ratio: —
Return on equity: 3.6%
Cash ($ mil.): 22
Current ratio: 3.56
Long-term debt ($ mil.): —

No. of shares (mil.): 7
Dividends
Yield: —
Payout: —
Market value ($ mil.): 209

	STOCK PRICE ($) FY Close	P/E High/Low	PER SHARE ($) Earnings	Dividends	Book Value
12/12	26.50	38 24	0.76	0.00	21.37
12/11	19.40	53 32	0.57	0.00	20.01
12/10	21.80	73 45	0.45	0.00	19.42
12/09	24.50	71 36	0.36	0.00	18.95
12/08	16.50	— —	(1.21)	0.00	18.58
Annual Growth	**12.6%**	**— —**	**—**	**—**	**3.6%**

Hudson Technologies Inc

Hudson Technologies defends the ozone. Using proprietary reclamation technology to remove moisture and impurities from refrigeration systems it recovers and reclaims chlorofluorocarbons (CFCs) used in commercial air-conditioning and refrigeration systems. The company sells both reclaimed and new refrigerants and also buys used refrigerants for reclamation and sale. In addition Hudson Technologies offers on-site decontamination services as well as services designed to improve the efficiency of customers' refrigeration systems. Customers include commercial and industrial enterprises and government entities along with refrigerant contractors distributors and wholesalers and makers of refrigeration equipment.

To expand its presence both in the US and overseas Hudson Technologies formed an alliance with BOC Group a UK-based producer of industrial and specialty gases that has since been acquired by and integrated into Linde.

EXECUTIVES

VP Sales and Marketing, Charles F. Harkins Jr., age 51, $164,019 total compensation
Director Engineering, Joseph Longo
VP Legal and Regulatory and Secretary, Stephen P. Mandracchia, age 53, $129,879 total compensation
President COO and Director, Brian F. Coleman, age 51, $175,377 total compensation
Chairman and CEO, Kevin J. Zugibe, age 49, $198,021 total compensation
CFO, James R. Buscemi, age 60, $113,091 total compensation
Director Energy Assets and Optimization, Riyaz Papar
Account Manager All, Marla Waggoner
Vice President - Marketing, Greg Heilbrunn
President COO and Director, Brian F. Coleman, age 51
Director, Vincent P. Abbatecola, age 67
Director, Dominic J. Monetta, age 72
Director, Otto C. Morch, age 80
Auditors: BDOSeidmanLLP

LOCATIONS

HQ: Hudson Technologies Inc
1 Blue Hill Plaza, P.O. Box 1541, Pearl River, NY 10965
Phone: 845 735-6000
Web: www.hudsontech.com

PRODUCTS/OPERATIONS

2007 Sales

	$ mil.	% of total
Refrigerant & reclamation sales	23	85
RefrigerantSide Services	3	15
Total	**26**	**100**

COMPETITORS

Airgas	Hatco
C. C. Dickson	Kyzen

HISTORICAL FINANCIALS

Company Type: Public

Income Statement

FYE: December 31

	REVENUE ($ mil.)	NET INCOME ($ mil.)	NET PROFIT MARGIN	EMPLOYEES
12/12	56.4	12.8	22.7%	94
12/11	44.3	1.0	2.3%	88
12/10	37.2	0.7	1.9%	79
12/09	24.1	(2.5)	—	75
12/08	33.1	6.6	20.1%	80
Annual Growth	**14.2%**	**17.7%**	**—**	**4.1%**

2012 Year-End Financials

Debt ratio: 30.8%	No. of shares (mil.): 24
Return on equity: 49.3%	Dividends
Cash ($ mil.): 3	Yield: —
Current ratio: 2.40	Payout: —
Long-term debt ($ mil.): 4	Market value ($ mil.): 88

	STOCK PRICE ($) FY Close	P/E High/Low		PER SHARE ($) Earnings	Dividends	Book Value
12/12	3.64	8	3	0.49	0.00	1.36
12/11	1.45	56	26	0.04	0.00	0.80
12/10	1.64	96	47	0.03	0.00	0.76
12/09	1.46	—	—	(0.12)	0.00	0.57
12/08	1.35	9	2	0.33	0.00	0.65
Annual Growth	**28.1%**	**—**	**—**	**10.4%**	**—**	**20.0%**

Hurco Companies, Inc.

When it comes to improving automation and productivity Hurco happily helps. The company designs and makes computerized metal cutting and forming machine tools such as vertical machining (mills) and turning (lathes) centers as well as the software that automates the machinery. Its machines are manufactured and assembled by Taiwan subsidiary Hurco Manufacturing using components produced by neighboring contract suppliers. Hurco markets its five-axis machines through its TM/TMM TMX and VMX series and other specialty product lines. It sells to customers in the aerospace/military automotive computers/electronics energy medical equipment and transportation industries spanning about 50 countries.

Hurco subsidiaries are located in Canada China France Germany India Italy Poland Singapore South Africa the UK and the US. Its manufacturing and distribution facilities reside in the Netherlands Taiwan China and the US.

After taking a major hit during the recession Hurco has managed to increase its revenue and finally get out of the red. From 2011 to 2012 revenues jumped 70% from $106 million to $180 million. Due to previous cost-cutting initiatives the company posted positive net income of $11 million after suffering net losses the previous two years. It was helped by an increased overall demand for its machine tools as global manufacturing rebounded. The company derives about 60% of its revenues from Europe. Around 10% of its sales come from the Asia/Pacific region due largely to its expansion into the markets of China and India where entry-level lower-priced machines are popular.

Going forward the company is buoyed by its cash reserves of more than $45 million a very small debt load ($865 thousand) and expertise in software development marketed under the Win-MAX brand. Hurco continues to invest in research and development enabling introduction of new products touting productivity features.

EXECUTIVES

Director Human Resources, Judy Summers
Chairman of the Board; Chief Executive Officer, Michael Doar, age 58, $349,039 total compensation
Chief Accounting Officer Controller and Assistant Secretary, Sonja K. McClelland, age 42, $121,000 total compensation
Chief Financial Officer; Vice President; Treasurer; Secretary, John G. Oblazney, age 45, $172,192 total compensation
Manager Media Relations, Maggie Smith
Executive Vice President - Worldwide Sales and Service, John P. Donlon
President, Gregory Volovic

Director, Robert W. Cruickshank, age 68
Director, Richard T. Niner, age 72
Director, Charles E. (Charlie) Rentschler, age 72
Director, Stephen H. Cooper, age 72
Director, Michael P. Mazza, age 49
Director, Janaki Sivanesan, age 42
Director, Philip James, age 70
Auditors: Ernst&YoungLLP

LOCATIONS

HQ: Hurco Companies Inc.
1 Technology Way, Indianapolis IN 46268-0180
Phone: 317-293-5309   **Fax:** 317-328-2811
Web: www.hurco.com

2011 Sales

	$ mil.	% of total
Europe		
UK	22	12
Italy	5	3
North America	47	26
Other regions	3	2

PRODUCTS/OPERATIONS

2011 Sales

	$ mil.	% of total
Computerized machine tools	156	87
Service fees	5	3
Total	**180**	**100**

Selected Products

Computerized machine tools
  5-axis vertical machining centers
  Autobend/back gauges
  Controls
  Machining centers (vertical and horizontal)
  Metal-forming systems
  Milling machines
  Rotary tables
  Turning centers
Other
  Control upgrades
  Hardware accessories
  Replacement parts
  Retrofit systems for metal-cutting and metal-forming machine applications
  Software

COMPETITORS

DMG Mori Seiki	Mazak
Doosan Corp	Nicolas Correa
FANUC	Okuma
Genesis Worldwide	Siemens AG
Gleason Corp.	TRUMPF
Haas Automation	Thermwood
Hardinge	Toyoda Machinery USA
IMTA	
MAG Giddings & Lewis	

HISTORICAL FINANCIALS

Company Type: Public

Income Statement

FYE: October 31

	REVENUE ($ mil.)	NET INCOME ($ mil.)	NET PROFIT MARGIN	EMPLOYEES
10/13	192.8	8.1	4.2%	625
10/12	203.1	15.6	7.7%	560
10/11	180.4	11.1	6.2%	520
10/10	105.8	(5.7)	—	440
10/09	91.0	(2.3)	—	390
Annual Growth	**20.6%**	**—**	**—**	**12.5%**

2013 Year-End Financials

Debt ratio: 1.7%
Return on equity: 5.5%
Cash ($ mil.): 42
Current ratio: 3.32
Long-term debt ($ mil.): —

No. of shares (mil.): 6
Dividends
 Yield: 0.4%
 Payout: 6.3%
Market value ($ mil.): 158

	STOCK PRICE ($) FY Close	P/E High/Low		PER SHARE ($) Earnings	Dividends	Book Value
10/13	24.49	25	17	1.25	0.10	23.43
10/12	22.98	12	8	2.40	0.00	22.30
10/11	26.12	20	11	1.71	0.00	19.60
10/10	18.40	—	—	(0.89)	0.00	17.81
10/09	15.90	—	—	(0.36)	0.00	18.69
Annual Growth	11.4%	—	—	—	—	5.8%

Hyster-Yale Materials Handling, Inc.

Hyster-Yale Materials Handling isn't scared of a little heavy lifting. A leading lift truck manufacturer the company designs manufactures and sells a variety of forklifts and other lift truck products through its NACCO Materials Handling subsidiary. Its trucks are sold under the Hyster Yale and UTILEV brands and include everything from hand-controlled pallet lifts to heavy-duty container handlers. The company which operates facilities in North America Europe and Asia was spun off from NACCO Industries in 2012 and restructured as an independently operated public company. Hyster and Yale branded products originally made and sold in Japan have been sold worldwide since the early 1970s.

Geographic Reach

Based in Ohio Hyster-Yale Materials operates a dozen manufacturing and assembly facilities worldwide as well as five plants in the Americas three in Europe and four in the Asia/Pacific region. It also enjoys a global reach through joint venture operations.

Operations

Hyster-Yale Materials operates its business through three reportable segments: the Americas Europe and Asia/Pacific. The Americas comprises the US Canada Mexico Brazil Latin America and its corporate headquarters. The company's Europe segment consists of Europe the Middle East and Africa. Its Asia/Pacific business includes operations in the Asia/Pacific region including China.

Sales and Marketing

The company logged $9 million in advertising expenses in 2012 down slightly from $10.3 million in 2011.

Hyster-Yale Materials distributes lift trucks and aftermarket parts primarily through two channels: independent dealers and a national accounts program. Its dealers which are located in 169 countries are generally independently-owned and -operated. The company operates a national accounts program for both Hyster and Yale that focuses on large customers with centralized purchasing and geographically dispersed operations in multi-dealer territories.

Financial Performance

Revenues decreased 3% in fiscal 2012 as compared to 2011 due primarily to a decline in unit volume in Europe and to the impact of unfavorable foreign currency movements as the euro and Brazilian real weakened against the US dollar. Net income for Hyster-Yale Materials meanwhile rose 19% during the same reporting period. The company points to the favorable effect of lower income tax expense in 2012 as compared to 2011 for the gains.

Looking ahead Hyster-Yale Materials anticipates the overall global market to grow moderately driven primarily by increased volumes in the Americas principally as a result of moderate growth in Brazil and Latin America and moderate growth in the Asia/Pacific and Middle East and Africa markets.

Strategy

The company is banking on a new range of UTILEV-branded lift trucks first introduced into global markets during 2012 to lift its sales. In mid-2011 Hyster-Yale Materials rolled out into certain Latin American markets a new range of UTILEV-branded lift trucks which meet the needs of lower-intensity users. This series of internal combustion engine utility lift trucks is expected to continue to gain market position in 2013.

Company Ownership

J.C. Butler Jr. and Claiborne R. Rankin both own about a 10% stake in Hyster-Yale Materials. Alfred M. Rankin Jr. holds another 12% stake.

EXECUTIVES

SVP Marketing and Consulting, Lauren E. Miller, age 59

VP and CFO, Kenneth C. Schilling, age 54

VP General Counsel and Secretary, Charles A. Bittenbender, age 63

Chairman President and CEO, Alfred M. Rankin Jr., age 71

President and CEO NACCO Materials Handling Group, Michael P. Brogan, age 63

Deputy General Counsel and Assistant Secretary Hyster-Yale Materials Handling Inc. and NACCO Materials Handling Group, Suzanne S. Taylor, age 50

Associate General Counsel and Assistant Secretary Hyster-Yale Materials Handling Inc. and NACCO Materials Handling Group, Mary D. Maloney, age 51

Controller Hyster-Yale Materials Handling Inc. and NACCO Materials Handling Group, Jennifer M. Langer, age 39

Vice President Treasurer Hyster-Yale Materials Handling Inc. and NACCO Materials Handling Group, Brian K. Frentzko

Director, Eugene (Gene) Wong, age 79
Director, Dennis W. LaBarre, age 70
Director, John F. (Jack) Turben, age 78
Director, Richard de J. Osborne, age 79
Director, Britton T. Taplin, age 57
Director, David F. Taplin, age 64
Director, Michael E. Shannon, age 76
Director, Gen. John P. Jumper, age 68
Auditors: Ernst&YoungLLP

LOCATIONS

HQ: Hyster-Yale Materials Handling Inc.
5875 Landerbrook Dr., Cleveland OH 44124
Phone: 440-449-9600   **Fax:** 904-357-1105
Web: www.fisglobal.com

2012 Sales

	% of total
Americas	63
Europe	27
Asia/Pacific	10
Total	**100**

PRODUCTS/OPERATIONS

Selected Brands

Hyster
Yale
UTILEV

COMPETITORS

Crown Equipment
Jungheinrich
Komatsu
Linde Lift Truck

MCFA
Toyota Material
Handling

HISTORICAL FINANCIALS

Company Type: Public

Income Statement

FYE: December 31

	REVENUE ($ mil.)	NET INCOME ($ mil.)	NET PROFIT MARGIN	EMPLOYEES
12/12	2,469.1	98.0	4.0%	5,400
12/11	2,540.8	82.6	3.3%	5,300
12/10	1,801.9	32.4	1.8%	5,000
12/94	1,178.8	15.5	1.3%	0
12/93	908.1	(8.4)	—	0
Annual Growth	**28.4%**	—	—	—

2012 Year-End Financials

Debt ratio: 13.3%
Return on equity: 30.6%
Cash ($ mil.): 151
Current ratio: 1.64
Long-term debt ($ mil.): 106

No. of shares (mil.): 16
Dividends
 Yield: 4.6%
 Payout: 38.5%
Market value ($ mil.): 817

	STOCK PRICE ($) FY Close	P/E High/Low		PER SHARE ($) Earnings	Dividends	Book Value
12/12	48.80	8	7	5.83	2.25	20.40
Annual Growth	—	—	—	—	—	—

IBERIABANK Corp

IBERIABANK Corp. serves up financial services with a Cajun flare. Through its flagship bank subsidiary also called IBERIABANK the holding company operates some 185 branches in Louisiana and five other southern states. It also has about 20 title insurance offices in Louisiana and Arkansas in addition to some 60 mortgage loan offices in a dozen states. Offering deposit products such as checking and savings accounts CDs and IRAs the bank uses funds gathered mainly to make loans. Commercial real estate and business loans make up nearly three-quarters of the company's loan portfolio which also includes consumer loans and residential mortgages. Founded in 1887 IBERIABANK Corp. has $12.5 billion in assets.

Geographic Reach

Beyond Louisiana IBERIABANK has branches in Alabama Arkansas Florida Tennessee and Texas.

Operations

IBERIABANK has eight wholly-owned nonbank subsidiaries including brokerage unit Iberia Financial Services IBERIABANK Insurance Services Acadiana Holdings IBERIABANK Mortgage Company Little Rock Arkansas-based Lenders Title Company and several investment funds.

Financial Analysis

IBERIABANK's 2011 revenue increased 4% vs. 2010 while profits climbed 10% over the same period. The revenue gain was attributed to an increase in both interest and dividend income. The bank's 2011 results were driven by both organic growth and acquisitions.

Strategy

Acquisitions have been a big part of IBERIABANK's growth strategy since 2003. Most recently in 2012 IBERIABANK struck an agreement to buy Florida Gulf Bank. In 2011 the bank completed three acquisitions: OMNI Bank with 14 offices in New Orleans and Baton Rouge Louisiana; Cameron State Bank with 22 offices in Lake Charles Louisiana; and the assets of Florida Trust Company a subsidiary of the failed Bank of Florida Corporation. (Between 2003 and 2010 the bank completed 13 acquisitions with combined total assets of more than $6 billion.) All of the acquisition activity has expanded the company's assets and branch network helped it enter new markets such as Florida and Texas and strengthen its presence in existing ones.

EXECUTIVES

President; Chief Executive Officer; Director, Daryl G. Byrd, age 58, $467,010 total compensation
Senior Executive Vice President - Mergers & Acquisitions & Investor Relations, John R. Davis, age 52, $287,308 total compensation
EVP Corporate Secretary and Director Corporate Operations, George J. Becker III, age 72, $177,308 total compensation
Market President New Iberia and Community Markets, Taylor F. Barras
Chairman, William H. Fenstermaker, age 64
Vice Chairman, E. Stewart Shea III, age 61
Vice Chairman and Managing Director Brokerage Trust and Wealth Management, Jefferson G. (Jeff) Parker, age 60
EVP and Director Communications, Beth Ardoin
Chief Financial Officer; Senior Executive Vice President, Anthony J. Restel, age 43, $199,231 total compensation
Market President New Orleans, Karl E. Hoefer
Market President Baton Rouge, J. Keith Short
Market President Lafayette, Pete M. Yuan
President, Paul E. Hutcheson Jr.
EVP and President Mobile Alabama, Lawrence G. (Russ) Ford Jr.
Vice Chairman; Chief Operating Officer, Michael J. (Mike) Brown, age 56
Executive Vice President and Regional President; Florida, James B. Gburek
President Chief Executive Officer, Chuck M. Quick Jr.
President Mortgage Market Alabama and Georgia IBERIABANK, Barry Carroll
EVP; President Birmingham Alabama IBERIABANK, Gregory A. King
Executive Vice President, H. Gregg Strader, age 55
Executive Vice President and Director - Retail and Small Business, Robert Kottler
Senior Vice President; Chief Accounting Officer; Controller, Michael Price
Executive Vice President; Chief Credit Officer, Spurgeon Mackie
Executive Vice President; Director - Organizational Development, Barry Berthelot
Chief Risk Officer, Randolph Bryan
Executive Vice President, Robert B. Worley
President CEO and Director; President and CEO IBERIABANK, Daryl G. Byrd, age 58
Director, John N. Casbon, age 64
Director, Elaine D. Abell, age 70

Director, Harry V. Barton Jr., age 58
Vice Chairman, E. Stewart Shea III, age 61
Director, Ernest P. Breaux Jr., age 68
Director, O. Miles Pollard Jr., age 75
Director, David H. Welch, age 64
Independent Director, John Koerner
Auditors: Ernst&YoungLLP

LOCATIONS

HQ: IBERIABANK Corp
200 West Congress Street, Lafayette, LA 70501
Phone: 337 521-4003
Web: www.iberiabank.com

PRODUCTS/OPERATIONS

2011 Sales

	$ mil.	% of total
Interest		
Loans including fees	436	79
Securities	50	9
Other	3	1
Adjustments (70.1) (13)		
Noninterest		
Gain on sale of loans net	44	8
Service charges on deposit accounts	25	5
Title revenue	18	3
ATM/debit card fees	11	2
Broker commissions	10	2
Net gain on sale of investments	3	1
Income from bank owned life insurance	3	-
Gain on sale of assets	0	-
Other	15	3
Adjustments	(1.7)	-
Total	**552**	**100**

Selected Mergers and Acquisitions

2012
Florida Gulf Bancorp Inc. (Fort Myers Florida; commercial banking)
2011
OMNI BANCSHARES Inc. (Metairie Louisiana; commercial banking)
Cameron Bancshares Inc. (Lake Charles Louisiana; commercial banking)
Florida Trust Company (Naples Florida; commercial banking)

Selected Subsidiaries

IB Aircraft Holdings LLC
IBERIA Asset Management Inc.
IBERIA Capital Partners LLC
IBERIABANK
  Acadiana Holdings LLC
  CB Florida RRE Holdings LLC
  Finesco LLC
  Iberia Financial Services LLC
  IBERIABANK Insurance Services LLC
  Jefferson Insurance Corporation
Lenders Title Company
  American Abstract and Title Company Inc.
  Asset Exchange Inc.
  United Title & Abstract LLC
  United Title of Louisiana Inc.

COMPETITORS

Bank of America	JPMorgan Chase
Bank of the Ozarks	Louisiana Bancorp
Capital One	MidSouth Bancorp
First NBC Bank	Regions Financial
Hancock Holding	Teche Holding
Home Bank	

HISTORICAL FINANCIALS

Company Type: Public

Income Statement

FYE: December 31

	ASSETS ($ mil.)	NET INCOME ($ mil.)	INCOME AS % OF ASSETS	EMPLOYEES
12/12	13,129.6	76.4	0.6%	2,758
12/11	11,757.9	53.5	0.5%	2,645
12/10	10,026.7	48.8	0.5%	2,193
12/09	9,700.4	151.2	1.6%	1,685
12/08	5,583.2	39.9	0.7%	1,356
Annual Growth	23.8%	17.6%	—	19.4%

2012 Year-End Financials

Return on assets: 0.6%
Return on equity: 5.0%
Long-term debt ($ mil.): —
No. of shares (mil.): 29
Sales ($ mil): 621

Dividends
  Yield: 2.7%
  Payout: 52.5%
Market value ($ mil.): 1,449

	STOCK PRICE ($) FY Close	P/E High/Low		PER SHARE ($) Earnings	Dividends	Book Value
12/12	49.12	21	17	2.59	1.36	51.88
12/11	49.30	32	23	1.87	1.36	50.48
12/10	59.13	33	26	1.88	1.36	48.50
12/09	53.81	7	5	8.03	1.36	45.99
12/08	48.00	20	13	3.04	1.36	46.17
Annual Growth	0.6%	—	—	(3.9%)	(0.0%)	3.0%

ICF International Inc

Consultant ICF International sees opportunity — and most of its business —in government spending. The firm advises government entities and businesses on issues related to health human services and social programs as well as defense and homeland security energy and climate change and the environment. The company groups its consulting and information technology services into three main categories: advice implementation and evaluation and improvement. ICF International has more than 60 offices in Asia Canada Europe and South America. Almost 75% of its total revenue comes from government clients.

Geographic Reach

ICF International has more than 60 offices in Beijing; Brussels; Hong Kong; London; New Delhi India; Ottawa Canada; Rio de Janeiro; and the US.

Sales and Marketing

ICF International collects 73% of its revenue from government clients. Three government customers accounted for about 35% of the company's total revenues in 2012: the Department of Health and Human Services (19%) the Department of Defense (9%) and the Department of State (6%).

Financial Performance

For four straight years ICF International has enjoyed steady growth. From 2011 to 2012 revenue increased by 12% and its profits jumped by 9%. The growth was attributed to the acquisitions of Ironworks and GHK which increased revenue by $89.6 million compared to the prior year accounting for about 93% of the revenue growth.

ICF International in 2012 was also helped by a 29% increase in revenue from its commercial clients and a 6% rise from government clients. Growth was achieved from each of its main markets: health social programs and consumer/financial surged by 20%; energy environment and infrastructure increased about 6%; and public safety and defense climbed by 2%.

Strategy

ICF International hopes to grow by selling more services to existing clients and by moving into markets related to education social and criminal justice and veterans' affairs programs. In addition it will pursue higher-margin projects in areas related to air transportation climate change and energy efficiency for commercial as well as government clients. It anticipates the growth rate of its revenue from commercial clients will continue to exceed the revenue growth rate from its government client.

Working to achieve these goals ICF has been looking to acquisitions. Right out of the gate in early 2012 it purchased Ironworks Consulting a Web development firm that offers customer management technology spanning the Internet and mobile and social media platforms. The deal worth around $100 million not only enhanced ICF's expertise in the all important digital sector but it extended the reach of its commercial business fortified its expertise in the energy sector and opened the door to the commercial health market.

Also in 2012 ICF picked up GHK a London-based multi-disciplinary consultancy serving government and commercial clients on environment employment health education and training transportation social policy business and economic development and international development issues. ICF previously extended its expertise in the North American energy sector in early 2011 when it obtained Marbek Resource Consultants an energy and environmental consulting firm based in Canada.

EXECUTIVES

senior Vice President for ICF International NASDAQ:ICFI, Andy Robinson
Chairman and CEO, Sudhakar Kesavan, age 58, $480,002 total compensation
President and COO, John Wasson, age 53, $400,005 total compensation
SVP, Douglas (Doug) Beck
EVP, Ellen Glover, age 57, $307,104 total compensation
CIO, John M. George
VP Emergency Management Homeland Security and Program Management, John P. Paczkowski
Director Global Recruiting, Irvin Towson
EVP, Gerald (Jerry) Croan, age 63, $265,527 total compensation
Executive Vice President, Donald Zimmerman
senior Vice President and homeland and national security expert, Michael Byrne
Executive Vice President, Sergio Ostria
EVP, Isabel Reiff, age 63
Executive Vice President, Philip Mihlmester
SVP Human Resources, Candice Mendenhall
EVP, Jeanne Townend
Managing Director New Delhi, Nitin Zamre
Senior Vice President + ICF Intl, Sandra Murray, age 57
VP, Donald McMaster
VP, Janet D'Ignazio
SVP, Frank J. Abramcheck
SVP, Barbara Rudin
Executive Vice President Chief Financial Officer, James C. Morgan, age 48
Senior Director of Public Affairs, Steve Anderson
Vice President, Carlos VTlez
Vice President, Carol Freeman
Marketing Director ICF International, Carolyn Wixson
Senior Vice President, Matthew Perry

Senior Vice President, Robert Toth
Director, Edward H. (Ed) Bersoff, age 70
Director, Ernest J. Moniz, age 69
Director, Srikant M. Datar, age 59
Director, Peter M. Schulte, age 55
Independent Director, Eileen Auen
Auditors: GrantThorntonLLP

LOCATIONS

HQ: ICF International Inc.
9300 Lee Hwy., Fairfax VA 22031
Phone: 703-934-3000   **Fax:** 703-934-3740
Web: www.icfi.com

2012 Sales

	% of total
US	92
Other	8
Total	**100**

PRODUCTS/OPERATIONS

Selected Mergers and Acquisitions
2012
  Ironworks Consulting L.L.C. ($100 million; interactive web development firm)
  GHK Holdings Limited ($30 million; London; consultancy)
2011
  Marbek Resource Consultants Ltd (Canada; energy and environmental consulting firm)

Selected Services
Economic policy and regulatory analysis
Human capital strategies
Information technology
Management consulting
Market assessment
Program management
Regulatory support
Scientific and risk assessment
Strategic communications
Training and education

COMPETITORS

AECOM	Navigant Consulting
Abt Associates	Northrop Grumman
Booz Allen	PA Consulting
CACI International	Research Triangle
CRA International	Institute
Deloitte LLP	SAIC
IHS	SRA International
L-3 Communications	Sapient
Lockheed Martin	Westat

HISTORICAL FINANCIALS
Company Type: Public

Income Statement
FYE: December 31

	REVENUE ($ mil.)	NET INCOME ($ mil.)	NET PROFIT MARGIN	EMPLOYEES
12/12	937.1	38.0	4.1%	4,500
12/11	840.7	34.8	4.1%	4,000
12/10	764.7	27.1	3.6%	3,700
12/09	674.4	22.3	3.3%	3,500
12/08	697.4	28.7	4.1%	3,600
Annual Growth	**7.7%**	**7.3%**	**—**	**5.7%**

2012 Year-End Financials

Debt ratio: 14.7%		No. of shares (mil.): 19
Return on equity: 9.2%		Dividends
Cash ($ mil.): 14		Yield: —
Current ratio: 1.62		Payout: —
Long-term debt ($ mil.): 105		Market value ($ mil.): 458

	STOCK PRICE ($) FY Close	P/E High/Low		PER SHARE ($) Earnings	Dividends	Book Value
12/12	23.44	15	9	1.91	0.00	21.92
12/11	24.78	15	10	1.75	0.00	19.86
12/10	25.72	20	15	1.38	0.00	18.03
12/09	26.80	21	15	1.40	0.00	16.47
12/08	24.57	14	8	1.88	0.00	13.43
Annual Growth	**(1.2%)**	—	—	**0.4%**	**—**	**13.0%**

ICG Group, Inc.

B2B or not B2B? That is the question for ICG Group Inc. (formerly Internet Capital Group). The company invests in companies in the business-to-business (B2B) market working with its holdings to develop strategy. ICG owns stakes in about a dozen companies involved in technology-enabled business process outsourcing cloud-based software Internet marketing and software as a service (SaaS). Its core holdings include international trade facilitator FreeBorders and Procurian (formerly ICG Commerce) which offers procurement outsourcing services. ICG closely works with its core companies and often helps them with day-to-day management.

Geographic Reach

The firm's operations have locations in Connecticut Florida Georgia Illinois Minnesota New York Pennsylvania Texas and Washington DC. Administrative offices reside in Brazil China the Czech Republic Europe India Israel and the UK.

Operations

ICG has been working to build Procurian for more than a decade. Over the years it has increased its ownership in Procurian from 64% to 85%. It owns a 53% interest in SeaPass Solutions a provider of Web-based software and services serving the property and casualty industry. ICG also owns a significant stake in WhiteFence which allows consumers to compare utilities providers.

Sales and Marketing

In 2012 Zurich Insurance Company a customer of Procurian generated 17% of ICG's consolidated revenue.

Financial Performance

ICG has enjoyed four straight years of unprecedented growth. Revenues jumped by 19% from $141 million in 2011 to reach $167 million in 2012 a historic milestone for the firm. Profits however were down by 17% from $28 million in 2011 to $23 million in 2012 due to an increase operating expenses. (Note: the company restated its financials for 2011 due to discontinued operations.)

The growth for 2012 was mainly driven by a 16% surge in revenue from Procurian. The previous acquisition of MSDSonline also contributed around $8 million to the growth in revenue for the year.

Strategy

In 2013 ICG sold data management software company Investor Force to investment tools maker MSCI Inc. a deal valued at $23.5 million in cash. It also sold 49%-owned Channel Intelligence which helps consumers to connect online with manufacturer retailers and publishers to Google for $125 million in cash.

In 2011 the company sold business process management software maker Metastorm to Open

Text Corporation. The sale yielded more than $50 million for ICG. At the end of 2011 ICG sold scheduling software and services company StarCite to The Active Network for $25 million. It used the proceeds from such transactions towards other software and services investments.

ICG plans to make more acquisitions and seek bolt-on acquisitions for its portfolio companies. Demand in for business outsourcing and software as a service has increased as companies look to cut costs by automating or improving processes. ICG expanded its presence in the government and compliance sector in 2012 with the $48 million acquisition of MSDSonline which offers cloud-based solutions for environmental and health and safety clients.

Ownership
FMR LLC owns 12% of ICG.

HISTORY

Armed with a model for business-to-business (B2B) e-commerce Safeguard Scientifics veterans Walter Buckley and Ken Fox formed Internet Capital Group (ICG) in 1996. Funded by Safeguard Scientifics Comcast and Compaq (now Hewlett-Packard) the firm invested in 1997 in Water Online a municipal wastewater site (now VerticalNet) and some 15 other startups.

The next year fueled by a second round of funding ICG realized the savings of vertical portals when it took stakes in chemicals paper and plastics exchanges. It also hit it big when it sold two companies MatchLogic (online advertising) and WiseWire (online directory-building software).

In 1999 ICG posted its first profit when VerticalNet went public. The firm went public itself that year. In 2000 it began using those funds for more buys including stakes in RightWorks (52% procurement software) eCredit.com (30% online financing) and DNI Holdings (electronic over-the-counter derivatives trading system).

In 2000 ICG launched an e-procurement venture with Accenture (formerly Andersen Consulting). The downturn in Internet stocks took its toll on the firm's holdings: It shut down one firm and merged two others in late 2000 and sold its stakes in e-chemicals and RightWorks in 2001.

Following that strategy Logistics.com an ICG partner company sold substantial assets to Manhattan Associates for $20 million in 2002. ICG expected to see net proceeds of about $12 million come their way after repaying some debt costs and liabilities.

Safeguard Scientifics sold its stake in ICG in 2003.

ICG sold its stake in financial services provider Creditex in 2008 to IntercontinentalExchange for some $35 million and divested its interest in online marketing firm Vcommerce the following year. In 2010 ICG acquired an 89% stake in GovDelivery for $20 million. The acquired firm provides digital subscription management software that enables government organizations to provide citizens with information through email mobile text alerts and other channels.

The company changed its name to ICG Group Inc. in 2011.

EXECUTIVES

Managing Director, Kamal Advani, age 53
President, Douglas A. (Doug) Alexander, age 52, $450,000 total compensation
Chairman of the Board; Chief Executive Officer, Walter W. Buckley III, age 54, $450,000 total compensation
Managing Director, Darren Sandberg
VP Treasury and Tax, Philip A. (Phil) Rooney
Managing Director General Counsel and Secretary, Suzanne L. Niemeyer
Chief Financial Officer, R. Kirk Morgan, age 47, $275,000 total compensation
VP Investor Relations and Corporate Communications, Karen Greene
VP, Matthew J. Safaii
Managing Director, Paul Slaats
Managing Director, John Loftus
Director, David J. Berkman, age 52
Director, Philip J. Ringo, age 71
Director, Thomas P. Gerrity, age 71
Director, Warren V. (Pete) Musser, age 85
Director, Peter K. Miller, age 51
Director, Michael J. Hagan, age 50
Director, Thomas A. (Tad) Decker, age 68
Director, David K. Downes, age 74
Independent Director, David Adelman
Auditors: KPMGLLP

LOCATIONS

HQ: ICG Group Inc.
690 Lee Rd. Ste. 310, Wayne PA 19087
Phone: 610-727-6900   **Fax:** 610-727-6901
Web: www.internetcapital.com

COMPETITORS

Accel Partners	Kleiner Perkins
Alloy Ventures	Matrix Partners
American Capital	Menlo Ventures
Benchmark Capital	ModusLink
Capital Southwest	Rand Capital
Hummer Winblad	SOFTBANK
IVP	Safeguard Scientifics
Idealab	Sevin Rosen

HISTORICAL FINANCIALS

Company Type: Public

Income Statement

FYE: December 31

	REVENUE ($ mil.)	NET INCOME ($ mil.)	NET PROFIT MARGIN	EMPLOYEES
12/12	166.5	22.9	13.8%	1,125
12/11	140.5	27.5	19.6%	829
12/10	115.7	46.5	40.3%	747
12/09	90.2	15.5	17.2%	27
12/08	71.1	(22.9)	—	23
Annual Growth 23.7%		—	—	164.5%

2012 Year-End Financials

Debt ratio: 7.4%	No. of shares (mil.): 37
Return on equity: 8.9%	Dividends
Cash ($ mil.): 45	Yield: —
Current ratio: 2.59	Payout: —
Long-term debt ($ mil.): 27	Market value ($ mil.): 434

	STOCK PRICE ($) FY Close	P/E High/Low		PER SHARE ($) Earnings	Dividends	Book Value
12/12	11.43	18	13	0.63	0.00	7.01
12/11	7.72	19	10	0.74	0.00	6.57
12/10	14.25	11	5	1.26	0.00	6.05
12/09	6.65	20	8	0.42	0.00	7.72
12/08	5.45	—	—	(0.60)	0.00	6.73
Annual Growth 20.3%		—	—	—	—	1.0%

Iconix Brand Group Inc

Once a shoemaker Iconix Brand Group has stepped it up as a licensing and brand management company. Its company-owned consumer and home brands are licensed to third parties that make and sell apparel footwear and a variety of other fashion and home products. Consumer brands in the Iconix stable include Badgley Mischka Danskin Ocean Pacific Mossimo London Fog Mudd and Rocawear; among the company's home brands are Cannon Fieldcrest and Waverly. The firm diversified through its high-profile purchase of the Peanuts cartoon brand from E. W. Scripps in 2010. Along with licensing the brands Iconix markets and promotes them through its in-house advertising and public relations services.

Iconix uses acquisitions to broaden its revenue stream and stretch its brand portfolio. The company owns about 20 brands and hopes to one day own a collection of 25-30 brands. To that end it acquired the Umbro football brand from shoe giant NIKE for $225 million in 2012.

In late 2011 Iconix acquired The Sharper Image brand from Sharper Image Acquisition LLC for about $66 million in cash. It projects the deal will add between $12 million and $13 million in annual royalty revenue. The Sharper Image brand name also blankets a wide variety of categories in the consumer electronics sector including audio and video electronics personal home products kitchen and bath accessories and travel gear among others.

Iconix previously made industry news in 2010 when it acquired a majority stake in United Media Licensing the owner of Charles M. Schulz's world-famous Peanuts brand and its cast of characters including Charlie Brown and Snoopy. Iconix and the Schulz family teamed up to buy the business for $175 million. (Iconix owns 80% of the company and the Schulz family owns the rest.) In addition the deal included properties such as disgruntled office worker Dilbert and children's book heroine Fancy Nancy. The deal was a strong play by Iconix to expand its business beyond fashion brands. Iconix also hopes the worldwide Peanuts presence will open up new international markets for its existing fashion business. (E. W. Scripps' United Media Syndicate subsidiary continues to syndicate the Peanuts comic strip.)

In May 2013 Iconix purchased the remaining 49% of urban fashion firm Marc Ecko Enterprises that it didn't already own for $45 million. The company had taken a controlling interest in the brand in 2009. The firm manages such brands as Ecko Unlimited Marc Ecko the Rhino logo and Zoo York.

Collectively the acquisitions of the Peanuts and Ecko assets generated around $90 million in additional revenue for the company in 2010. Iconix also enjoyed a 31% increase in net income ($75 million to almost $99 million) from 2009 to 2010.

As another means for growth Iconix expects to grow through its licensing agreements with Wal-Mart to sell Ocean Pacific Danskin Now and Starter apparel and accessories. The company also is looking to international markets to boost revenues as the US economy weakens; it has joint ventures in China Europe and Latin America to advance its brands.

Iconix formerly a footwear company known as Candie's Inc. changed its name in 2005 to reflect a shift in focus from manufacturing to brand management. The company continues to keep a toe in the footwear business with the Candie's brand and through its subsidiary Bright Star which oversees the design and arranges for the manufacturing and distribution of men's shoes sold under private labels primarily by Wal-Mart.

EXECUTIVES

Chairman President and CEO, Neil Cole, age 56, $1,000,000 total compensation

Chief Creative Officer Ecko.Complex, Marc Ecko, age 41

Chief Marketing Officer, Dari Marder

EVP and CFO, Warren Clamen, age 49, $356,806 total compensation

EVP and General Counsel, Andrew Tarshis, age 47, $356,806 total compensation

COO, Yehuda Shmidman, $262,121 total compensation

Chief Merchandising Officer, Lanie List

EVP and Head Strategic Development, David Blumberg, age 54, $400,000 total compensation

IR Contact Officer, Jaime Sheinheit

Executive Vice President General Counsel, Jason Schaefer

President of the Mens Division, Seth Horowitz

Director, F. Peter Cuneo, age 68

Director, Barry Emanuel, age 71

Director, James A. (Jim) Marcum, age 53

Director, Drew Cohen, age 44

Director, Mark Friedman, age 49

Director, Laurence N. Charney, age 66

Auditors: BDOSeidmanLLP

LOCATIONS

HQ: Iconix Brand Group Inc.
1450 Broadway 4th Fl., New York NY 10018
Phone: 212-730-0030   **Fax:** 212-391-2057
Web: iconixbrand.com

2011 Sales

	$ mil.	% of total
US	302	82
Total	**369**	**100**

PRODUCTS/OPERATIONS

2011 Sales

	$ mil.	% of total
Wholesale license	203	55
Direct-to-retail license	139	38
Entertainment & other (commissions sales of trademarks etc.)	26	7

Selected Brands

Consumer
Badgley Mischka
Bongo
Buffalo David Bitton (51%)
Candie's
Danskin
Dilbert
Fancy Nancy
Joe Boxer
London Fog
Material Girl
Mossimo
Mudd
Ocean Pacific
Peanuts
Rampage
Rocawear
Starter
Home
Cannon
Charisma
Fieldcrest
Royal Velvet

COMPETITORS

Ann Taylor
Billabong
Calvin Klein
Cherokee Inc.
Collective Licensing
Diesel SpA
Fifth & Pacific
Guess?
H&M
Hanesbrands
J. C. Penney
Jaclyn
Jones Group
Jordache Enterprises
Kellwood

L Brands
L' Oreal
Levi Strauss
NIKE
Pacific Sunwear
Pentland Group
Quiksilver
R. Griggs
Ralph Lauren
The Gap
VF Corporation
Vera Wang
Williamson-Dickie Manufacturing

HISTORICAL FINANCIALS

Company Type: Public

Income Statement

FYE: December 31

	REVENUE ($ mil.)	NET INCOME ($ mil.)	NET PROFIT MARGIN	EMPLOYEES
12/12	353.8	109.4	30.9%	148
12/11	369.8	126.1	34.1%	129
12/10	332.5	98.8	29.7%	133
12/09	232.0	75.1	32.4%	66
12/08	216.7	70.1	32.4%	82
Annual Growth	**13.0%**	**11.8%**	**—**	**15.9%**

2012 Year-End Financials

Debt ratio: 36.7%	No. of shares (mil.): 66
Return on equity: 9.1%	Dividends
Cash ($ mil.): 255	Yield: —
Current ratio: 3.64	Payout: —
Long-term debt ($ mil.): 859	Market value ($ mil.): 1,487

	STOCK PRICE ($) FY Close	P/E High/Low		PER SHARE ($) Earnings	Dividends	Book Value
12/12	22.32	14	9	1.52	0.00	17.81
12/11	16.29	15	8	1.67	0.00	16.36
12/10	19.31	15	9	1.32	0.00	14.29
12/09	12.67	16	6	1.10	0.00	12.71
12/08	9.78	19	5	1.15	0.00	10.55
Annual Growth	**22.9%**	**—**	**—**	**7.2%**	**—**	**14.0%**

ICU Medical, Inc.

ICU Medical sees the future of infection prevention. The company's devices protect health care workers and patients from the spread of diseases such as HIV and hepatitis. Its primary products are intravenous (IV) connection devices called Clave needleless connectors that reduce the risk of needle sticks and disconnections. The firm also makes custom IV sets many of which use Clave connectors and other ICU products for third parties. Additionally ICU Medical makes critical care equipment such as angiography kits and heart monitors. ICU Medical sells its products to other equipment makers and distributors throughout the US and internationally.

Operations

ICU Medical develops makes and sells innovative medical devices used in vascular therapy oncology and critical care applications. Its products improve patient outcomes by helping prevent bloodstream infections and protecting healthcare workers from

exposure to infectious diseases or hazardous drugs. The company's products include custom IV systems closed delivery systems for hazardous drugs needlefree IV connectors catheters and cardiac monitoring systems.

Geographic Reach

The company sells is products to more than 50 countries around the world. Its administrative office are in San Clemente California Vrable Slovakia Roncanova Italy. and Ludenscheid Germany. Customers in Europe are served by facilities in Slovakia and Germany. Customers elsewhere are served from facilities in the US and Mexico. ICU Medical has sought to save on manufacturing costs by moving more of its US production to Mexico where it operates a plant with about 1100 workers in Ensenada.

Sales & Marketing

On the sales side the company is increasingly directing its marketing efforts toward securing long-term contracts with large buying organizations. ICU Medical is reacting to an increasingly consolidated health care provider marketplace because the providers have more buying power as they get larger. Long-term contracts help the company lock in prices even as the market changes around them.

Financial Analysis

The company's 7% increase in revenues in 2011 was due to growth in domestic and international product sales. US revenues grew because of increased CLAVE product sales due to the conversion of products sold for needlefree connectors and increased market share through in marketing relationship with medical device maker Hospira. International sales increased thanks to a jump in Infusion therapy sales primarily from a $3.5 million increase in custom infusion set sales and a $0.9 million increase in CLAVE product sales.

The company's 49% increase in net income in 2011 was due to a gain in sale of assets of its Orbit diabetes infusion set product line and growth in other income primarily due to higher interest income earned because of higher invested balances and higher interest rates in 2011 and a small gain on disposal of assets in 2011 versus a loss on disposal of assets in 2010.

Strategy

ICU Medical has a long-standing relationship with Hospira. Way back in 2005 ICU Medical purchased Hospira's Salt Lake City manufacturing plant which produces catheters angiography kits and cardiac monitors among other devices. At that time the two entered a 20 year agreement under which ICU Medical will manufacture the products and Hospira will purchase them. Then in 2009 ICU Medical purchased the commercial rights and physical assets from Hospira's critical care product line giving ICU Medical complete control of manufacturing and marketing rights of the critical care line.

Through yet another agreement with Hospira ICU Medical makes and co-promotes custom IV systems under the name SetSource. That agreement is set to last through 2014. All told sales to Hospira account for more than 40% of ICU Medical's yearly income.

Aside from bringing home the bacon ICU Medical's dealings with Hospira provide ICU Medical access to the IV set market in the US in which Hospira has a significant share. The company expects Hospira will be important to growth its CLAVE line (which accounted for 36% of sales in 2011) custom infusion sets and its other products worldwide.

Outside of its dealings with Hospira ICU Medical's growth strategy hinges upon its ability to continue to develop and introduce new products to its customers particularly in the face of upcoming patent expirations on some of its products. Much like pharmaceutical companies medical device manufacturers enjoy a certain amount of market exclusivity on their patented products but once those patents expire competitors are free to introduce their own versions of the devices.

It's getting itself ready for patent expirations by diversifying its product line internally developing products and systems and by acquiring product lines. These products include the TEGO for use in dialysis the Orbit 90 diabetes set and a line of oncology products including the Spiros male luer connector device the Genie vial access device custom IV sets and ancillary products specifically designed for chemotherapy.

Ownership

In 2012 CEO George Lopez owned 16.3% of ICU Medical and River Road Asset Management LLC 10.7%.

EXECUTIVES

Director Human Resources, James J. (Jim) Reitz
VP Sales, Richard A. (Richie) Costello, age 49, $280,000 total compensation
Chairman President and CEO, George A. Lopez, age 65, $544,000 total compensation
VP Operations, Steven C. (Steve) Riggs, age 54, $280,000 total compensation
CEO, Vivek Jain, age 53
VP Product Development, Alison D. Burcar, age 40, $195,000 total compensation
VP International Sales, Greg Pratt
CFO Secretary and Treasurer, Scott E. Lamb, age 50, $275,000 total compensation
Central Region Manager Hospital Sales, Randy Clark
Director National Accounts, Mark Jorgensen
National Manager Western Canada, Neil Perrett
Product Specialist Eastern Canada, Don McDonald
President Europe, Gabriele Giovanelli
European Product Specialist Northern Europe, Andre Schepers
European Product Specialist Spain and Portugal, Roberto Zambrano
Manager International Sales South East Asia and India, Jason Kuan
Senior Marketing Manager and International Marketing Manager IV Systems Global Latin America and Mexico, Michelle Olivo
Manager International Marketing Southeast Asia Middle East India and Africa, Mike Sweeney
Manager Sales and Marketing Asia Pacific, Russell Nicholson
Director Oncology Systems Sales, Rob Houde
Director Renal Systems Sales Louisiana Arkansas Texas Oklahoma Kansas Mississippi Nebraska North Dakota and South Dakota, Greg Walpole
Manager Oncology Systems Sales, Mike Lester
Controller, Kevin McGrody
Director Media Relations, James McCusker
Eastern Region Manager Alternate Site Sales, Dave Bolesta
Central Region Manager Alternate Site Sales, Dan Marten
Western Region Manager Hospital Sales, Gary Soileau
Director Critical Care Systems, Rob Kraal
Sales Manager Critical Care Systems, Andrew Wickersham
Product Manager Oncology Systems, Tim Shannon
Senior Product Specialist Renal Systems Ohio Michigan Wisconsin Minnesota Iowa Illinois Kentucky Indiana and Missouri, Bill Grimes
Manager Animal Health, Scott St. Germain
European Product Specialist UK and Ireland, David Chantry

European Product Specialist Italy, Mirco Bordoni
Manager Sales Northern Asia, Masayoshi Iwata
International Product Specialist Brazil, Valter J. Loio
Manager International Sales Mexico, Xalixia Larrea
Eastern Region Manager Hospital Sales, Bruce Dragish
Southern Region Manager Alternate Site Sales, Tim Lefort
Western US Sales Manager Critical Care Systems, Mike Schoonover
Critical Care Product Manager, Tage Grant
Senior Critical Care Device Specialist, Glen Hill
Senior Product Specialist Renal Systems Colorado Wyoming Montana Idaho Utah Arizona California Nevada Oregon Washington Hawaii Alaska and New Mexico, Billy Huard
Product Specialist Renal Systems Maine Vermont New Hampshire Massachusetts New York Pennsylvania Connecticut Rhode Island New Jersey Deleware Maryland District of Columbia Virginia and West Virginia, Jim Wickersham
Product Specialist Renal Systems Tennessee North Carolina South Carolina Georgia Alabama and Florida, J D Shuff
Vice President of Marketing, Tom McCall
Director, Jack W. Brown, age 73
Director, John J. Connors, age 73
Director, Michael T. Kovalchik III, age 67
Director, Richard H. Sherman, age 66
Director, Robert S. Swinney, age 67
Director, Joseph R. Saucedo, age 69
Auditors: Deloitte&ToucheLLP

LOCATIONS

HQ: ICU Medical, Inc.
    951 Calle Amanecer, San Clemente, CA 92673
Phone: 949 366-2183   **Fax:** 949 366-8368
Web: www.icumed.com

2011 Sales

	% of total
US	76
Other	24
Total	**100**

PRODUCTS/OPERATIONS

2011 Sales

	% of total
Infusion Therapy	
CLAVE	36
Custom infusion	25
Other infusion	5
Critical	20
Oncology	8
Other	
TEGO	3
Other	3
Total	**100**

COMPETITORS

B. Braun Melsungen
Baxter International
Becton Dickinson
Cardinal Health
Covidien

Edwards Lifesciences
Fresenius
Merit Medical Systems
Navilyst Medical

HISTORICAL FINANCIALS
Company Type: Public

Income Statement   FYE: December 31

	REVENUE ($ mil.)	NET INCOME ($ mil.)	NET PROFIT MARGIN	EMPLOYEES
12/12	316.8	41.2	13.0%	2,239
12/11	302.2	44.6	14.8%	2,128
12/10	284.5	30.9	10.9%	2,437
12/09	231.5	26.5	11.5%	1,936
12/08	204.7	24.3	11.9%	1,911
Annual Growth	**11.5%**	**14.2%**	**—**	**4.0%**

2012 Year-End Financials

Debt ratio: —	No. of shares (mil.): 14
Return on equity: 11.5%	Dividends
Cash ($ mil.): 226	Yield: —
Current ratio: 11.18	Payout: —
Long-term debt ($ mil.): —	Market value ($ mil.): 881

	STOCK PRICE ($) FY Close	P/E High/Low		PER SHARE ($) Earnings	Dividends	Book Value
12/12	60.93	22	15	2.80	0.00	27.03
12/11	45.00	14	11	3.15	0.00	23.11
12/10	36.50	17	14	2.23	0.00	20.08
12/09	36.44	24	15	1.77	0.00	18.61
12/08	33.14	22	13	1.67	0.00	17.18
Annual Growth	**16.4%**		**—**	**— 13.8%**	**—**	**12.0%**

IDEX Corporation

The idea at IDEX is to dispense with inefficiencies and pump up profits. The company organized into three business segments that consist of various operating units is a diversified manufacturer of pumps and other engineered products geared at different niche markets around the world. Its largest segment Fluid & Metering Technologies makes pumps flow meters and injectors used to handle or monitor water chemicals and fuels. Its Health & Science Technologies segment produces fluidics and pumps used in medical devices analytical instrumentation and photonics. The Fire & Safety/Diversified Products segment manufactures firefighting pumps and rescue tools including the branded Hurst Jaws of Life.

Geographic Reach

IDEX has production facilities in China and India that support multiple business units. Personnel in various locations in Europe Asia South America and the Middle East provide sales and marketing support to IDEX business units in those regions. The US accounts for nearly 50% of sales; Europe 25%.

Operations

The Fluid & Metering Technologies segment is made up of such business units as Banjo (special-purpose severe-duty pumps valves and fittings); Energy & Fuels (including Liquid Controls); Chemical Food & Process Diaphragm & Dosing Pump Technology; and Water Services & Technology. This segment serves a range of markets including agriculture chemical processing food and beverage industrial infrastructure (fossil and alternative fuels) plastics pulp and paper transportation and water and wastewater.

The Health & Science Technologies segment consists of IDEX Health & Science; IDEX Optics

& Photonics; Containment; Gast; Micropump; and Materials Process Technologies (including Microfluidics and Quadro Engineering). Meanwhile the Fire & Safety/Diversified Products segment is comprised of the Fire Suppression Rescue Band-It and Dispensing Equipment units.

Financial Performance

IDEX saw its revenues reach record-setting highs in 2012 spiking 6% to nearly $2 billion. Although IDEX is seeing year-over-year sales increases its net income nosedived 81% from a high of $194 million in 2011 to $38 million in fiscal 2012 impacted by a significant drop in Health & Science Technologies' operating income. That segment recorded an operating loss of $62.8 million in 2012 compared to operating income of $106 million in 2011 primarily due to impairment and restructuring charges.

Strategy

IDEX's strategy is to grow through organic investments and acquisitions. In 2013 it bought FTL Seals Technology a maker of rotary seals specialty bearings and other custom products for the oil and gas mining power generation and marine markets. The deal fortified IDEX's Precision Polymer Engineering subsidiary within its Health & Science Technologies segment.

The company also boosted its Health & Science Technologies' optics and photonics capabilities by acquiring Colorado-based Precision Photonics Corporation (PPC) for $20.6 million in 2012 and purchasing New Mexico-based CVI Melles Griot (CVI MG) for about $395 million in mid-2011. PPC makes optical components and coatings for applications for such markets as scientific research aerospace and telecommunications. CVI makes lasers and light sources and other electro-optical and opto-mechanical components and assemblies.

Earlier in 2011 IDEX bought out Colorado-based Advanced Thin Films for $34.5 million. Advanced Thin Films added optics design technology as well as an impressive list of customers to the Health & Science Technologies segment. Boosting its Fluid & Metering Technologies segment IDEX in spring 2011 acquired Microfluidics in a $18.5 million cash deal that added pharmaceutical and chemical equipment for making micro particles.

Ownership

T. Rowe Price Associates is IDEX's largest shareholder with about a 10% stake.

HISTORY

IDEX is the successor of Houdaille (pronounced "WHO-dye") Industries which took its name from Maurice Houdaille the French inventor of recoilless artillery used in World War I. After that war a US firm bought the name and the rights to Houdaille's patented rotary shock absorber. By the 1930s Houdaille was the #1 maker of shock absorbers in the US. During WWII it was involved in building the atomic bomb. With the trend toward in-house manufacture by the auto giants in the 1950s the company diversified into industrial and construction products pumps and machine tools. Facing difficult economic conditions Phil Reilly (Houdaille's then CEO-nominee) and investors Kohlberg Kravis Roberts took the company private in 1979 in the first leveraged buyout of any company worth more than $100 million.

In 1987 IDEX (an acronym for "innovation diversity and excellence") was formed to buy back six units Houdaille had sold to the British TI Group earlier that year. In 1989 IDEX went public. Following the IPO the company pursued an aggressive acquisition strategy. Purchases included Corken (1991) Devjo's Pump Group (now Viking Pump 1992) and Hale Products (1994).

The company acquired Micropump (small magnetically driven pumps) for $33 million in 1995. The following year it paid $135 million for Fluid Management a top maker of color-formulation equipment for paints coatings inks and dyes.

In 1998 IDEX acquired Gast Manufacturing which makes vacuum pumps air motors and compressors for about $118 million. The following year it gained a foothold in Italy when it paid $62 million for FAST (refinishing and color-formulation equipment). In 2000 IDEX acquired Trebor International maker of high purity fluid handling products for the microelectronics industry.

In 2001 IDEX acquired displacement flow meter and process control systems maker Liquid Controls LLC. Acquisitions in 2003 included Sponsler Co. (turbine meters) and Classic Engineering (industrial pumps). In early 2004 Idex acquired Manfred Vetter a Germany-based rescue equipment (pneumatic lifting and sealing bags) manufacturer as well as Systec a vacuum degassing product manufacturer. Later in the year IDEX purchased Scivex a pump and valve manufacturer that serves medical companies.

In 2006 it acquired Banjo Corporation which makes specialized pumps and related hardware for handling fluids in agricultural and industrial applications. The following year the company expanded its sanitary control operations with the purchase of Quadro Engineering which provides particle handling products to the pharmaceutical laboratory market. Quadro operates as a unit of IDEX's FMT segment. That same year it picked up Isolation Technologies which makes analytical chemistry instruments. IDEX paid about $30 million for the company.

Acquisitions in 2008 (Richter Integrated Environmental Technology Group and iPEK) gave IDEX additional water distribution and sewer management products and services as well as wastewater infrastructure inspection capabilities. These deals followed IDEX's move to pick up ADS a provider of metering technology and flow monitoring services. Later in the year IDEX's HST segment snagged Semrock a supplier of optical filters was acquired. The deal widened IDEX's access to health and life science OEMs specializing in biotechnology and analytical instrumentation.

In 2010 IDEX purchased Seals Ltd. (now called PPE) a manufacturer of advanced sealing systems for about $54 million. The company now operating within the HST segment opened the door to new markets including clean room food processing and pharmaceutical research.

EXECUTIVES

VP General Counsel and Secretary, Frank J. Notaro, age 49

VP and Group Executive Process Technology, John L. McMurray, age 61, $305,100 total compensation

VP Human Resources, Harold Morgan, age 55

VP Mergers Acquisitions and Treasurer, Daniel J. Salliotte, age 46

VP and CFO, Heath A. Mitts, age 41

VP and Chief Accounting Officer, Michael J. Yates, age 47

VP Tax and International Finance, Gerald F. (Jerry) Carter

Chairman and CEO, Andrew K. Silvernail, age 41

Chief Compliance Officer, Garin L. Bergman, age 39

VP Continuous Improvement, Mark H. Kohler, age 54

VP Supply Chain and Procurement, Rob Stoppek, age 41

VP; Group Executive Fluid & Metering Technologies and IDEX Asia, Brett Finley, age 42

CIO, James MacLennan, age 49

VP Diversified Technologies, Eric D. Ashleman

Chief Human Resources Officer, Jeffrey Bucklew

Director, Michael T. Tokarz

Director, Frank S. Hermance, age 63

Director, William M. (Bill) Cook, age 60

Director, Bradley J. (Brad) Bell, age 61

Director, Gregory F. Milzcik, age 54

Director, Livingston L. (Tony) Satterthwaite, age 53

Director, Ernest J. (Ernie) Mrozek, age 60

Director, Ruby R. Chandy, age 52

Auditors: Deloitte&ToucheLLP

LOCATIONS

HQ: IDEX Corporation
1925 W. Field Ct. Ste. 200, Lake Forest IL 60045-4824
Phone: 847-498-7070   Fax: 314-863-5306
Web: www.furniturebrands.com

2012 Sales

US	963	49
Other countries	511	26

PRODUCTS/OPERATIONS

2012 Sales

	$ mil.	% of total
Fluid & Metering Technologies	833	43
Health & Science Technologies	695	35
Fire & Safety/Diversified Products	437	22
Adjustments	(11.3)	-
Total	**1,954**	**100**

Selected Mergers and Acquisitions

FY2013
FTL Seals Technology Ltd. (England; rotary seals maker)

FY2012
Matcon Group Limited ($45.8 million; UK; material processing equipment for high value powders)
ERC ($18 million; Japan; manufacturer of gas liquid separations and detection solutions)
Precision Photonics Corporation ($20.6 million; Colorado; optical components maker)

FY2011
CVI Melles Griot ($394.7 million; New Mexico; electro-optical and opto-mechanical components and assemblies
Microfluidics International ($18.5 million; pharmaceutical and chemical equipment for making micro particles)
Advanced Thin Films ($34.5 million; Colorado; optic design technology)

FY2010
Seals Ltd. ($54 million; maker of advanced sealing systems)
The Fitzpatrick Company ($20 million; size reduction roll compaction and drying systems)
OBL (Italy; pumps and dispensing equipment)

Selected Business Units Products and Brands

Fire & Safety/Diversified Products
BAND-IT (stainless-steel bands buckles and clamping systems)
Hale-Fire Suppression and Hale-Hydraulic Equipment (fire pumps and rescue tool systems)
HURST Jaws of Life/LUKAS/Dinglee/Vetter (hydraulic rescue tools re-railing equipment lifting and position devices)
Fluid & Metering Technologies
ADS (metering and flow monitoring equipment)
Air operated double diaphragm pumps (air-operated and motor-driven double diaphragm pumps)
Banjo (severe-duty pumps valves fittings and systems)
iPEK (remote-controlled infrastructure inspection equipment)
Liquid controls (flow meters and electronic controls)
Pulsafeeder (rotary pumps metering pumps peristaltic pumps electronic controls and dispensing equipment)

Richter (corrosion-resistant lined pumps valves and
  controls)
Viking Pump (gear pumps strainers and reducers and
  controls)
Health & Science Technologies
Gast Manufacturing (air motors blowers compressors
  vacuum generators and vacuum pumps)
HST Core (valves fitting injectors medical tubing
  assemblies optical filters filter sensors nano-fluidic
  components and engineered plastics)
Micropump (rotary gear piston and centrifugal pumps)
Seals Ltd. (seals for analytical instrumentation clean
  room environments food processing hazardous
  applications and pharmaceutical research)

Selected Markets

Agriculture
Analytical instrumentation
Chemical processing
Clinical diagnostics
Custom precision dispensing
Fire and rescue
Fuels and energy
Medical
Sanitary
Semiconductor
Water

COMPETITORS

American Cast Iron	Panduit
Pipe	Parker-Hannifin
Dionex	Pentair
Dover Corp.	Robbins & Myers
Dresser Inc.	Roper Industries
Flowserve	Thermo Fisher
Gardner Denver	Scientific
Gorman-Rupp	Tuthill
Graco	United Technologies
Graham Corp.	Weir Group
ITT Corp.	Wilden Pump &
Illinois Tool Works	Engineering
Oilgear	

HISTORICAL FINANCIALS

Company Type: Public

Income Statement

FYE: December 31

	REVENUE ($ mil.)	NET INCOME ($ mil.)	NET PROFIT MARGIN	EMPLOYEES
12/12	1,954.2	37.6	1.9%	6,717
12/11	1,838.4	193.8	10.5%	6,814
12/10	1,513.0	157.1	10.4%	5,966
12/09	1,329.6	113.3	8.5%	5,300
12/08	1,489.4	131.3	8.8%	5,813
Annual Growth	7.0%	(26.8%)	—	3.7%

2012 Year-End Financials

Debt ratio: 28.2%	No. of shares (mil.): 82
Return on equity: 2.5%	Dividends
Cash ($ mil.): 318	Yield: 1.6%
Current ratio: 3.03	Payout: 31.5%
Long-term debt ($ mil.): 779	Market value ($ mil.): 3,849

	STOCK PRICE ($) FY Close	P/E High/Low		PER SHARE ($) Earnings	Dividends	Book Value
12/12	46.53	103	80	0.45	0.77	17.71
12/11	37.11	20	13	2.32	0.66	18.18
12/10	39.12	21	14	1.90	0.57	16.76
12/09	31.15	23	12	1.40	0.48	15.66
12/08	24.15	25	11	1.60	0.48	14.54
Annual Growth	17.8%	—	—(27.2%)	12.5%		5.1%

iGate Corp

iGate is open to all things IT. The company provides business process outsourcing (BPO) and offshore development services including software development and maintenance outsourcing. In addition to IT-related services iGate handles such tasks as mortgage and claims processing and call center operations. The company targets midsized and large corporations in the banking financial services and insurance industries. Its more than 300 active customers include General Electric IBM Royal Bank of Canada and TEKsystems. The majority of iGate's operations are in India but the company earns most of its sales from customers in North America.

Operations

iGate separates itself from the pack by offering both IT and business services in what it calls the iTOPS (integrated technology and operations) model. Other companies including rival Infosys manage their IT and business operations separately which iGate claims can lead to competing interests and redundancy. The company specializes in BPO applications by Oracle (PeopleSoft and Siebel) and SAP.

Geographic Reach

While headquartered in the US most of its employees are based in India which has lower wages than the US and Europe for skilled technical professionals. iGate maintains more than 3 million sq. ft. of office space in India compared to its 12000-sq.-ft. corporate headquarters in the US.

iGate also has offices in Australia Canada China Japan Malaysia Mauritius Mexico Singapore South Africa Switzerland the UAE and the UK.

Sales and Marketing

The company's customer base fell to about 300 in 2012 down from 380 in 2011 as iGate ended relationships with some of its smaller clients in order to focus on larger accounts. Its top two customers General Electric and the Royal Bank of Canada together account for about a quarter of overall sales.

Financial Performance

iGate became a billion-dollar company in 2012 after acquiring India-based Patni. In 2013 overall sales grew 7% to $1.15 billion while profits climbed 35% to $129 million.

Mergers and Acquisitions

In 2011 iGate bought a majority stake in Patni Computer in a transaction valued at around $1 billion. Patni Computer the sixth- largest Indian software exporter was considered a pioneer of the outsourcing industry in India. By 2012 iGate acquired the remainder of Patni which has since been absorbed into iGate.

HISTORY

Sunil Wadhwani and Ashok Trivedi Indian emigrants who met at a party in the late 1970s formed Mastech in 1986. Started in Carnegie Mellon graduate Wadhwani's home the company offered systems integration and networked computer software development consultants to IT departments. Demand blossomed with the increased pace of technological change that left in-house IT departments struggling and sales leapt from $200000 in 1987 to $50 million by 1993.

Mastech fed its expansion by making overseas recruiting a top priority. The company attracted a broad base of technical talent interested in traveling the US on different jobs rather than working

full-time at a single company. In the mid-1990s Mastech established an offshore software development facility in India to take advantage of that country's lower employment costs and its large pool of qualified job candidates.

The company opened offices in Canada and Singapore in 1995 and went public a year later. It continued growth in 1999 through acquisitions buying UK financial services firm Direct Resources among others.

In 2000 Mastech restructured as a holding company changing its name to iGate Capital and forming independent e-commerce consulting-focused units. Also that year it formed a venture fund to invest in e-services companies. The restructuring helped cause losses for 2000. In response iGate stopped funding the investment arm in 2001 and shuttered or sold its interests in several operating companies.

In 2002 it further divested and changed its name to iGate Corporation. It formed iGATE Clinical Research International (formerly iGATE Clinical Management) in 2003 through the acquisition of 90% of Pennsylvania clinical trial manager PCRN a group created by the University of Pittsburgh Medical Center. iGate also acquired DiagnoSearch a clinical research outsourcer based in India in 2003.

The company sold its recruiting and placement firm jobcurry in 2007.

EXECUTIVES

Co-Chairman, Ashok Trivedi, age 63, $250,000 total compensation
Co-Chairman, Sunil Wadhwani, age 60, $250,000 total compensation
President CEO and Director, Phaneesh Murthy, age 49, $500,000 total compensation
Interim President; Chief Executive Officer, Gerhard Watzinger, age 52
VP Legal and Corporate Secretary, Mukund Srinath
VP and Regional Manager Canada, Jason A. Trussell, age 40, $159,245 total compensation
Chief Financial Officer, Sujit Sircar, age 45, $54,672 total compensation
SVP and Head iTOPS Delivery, Anil Bajpai
Corporate Communication and Media Relations, Prabhanjan (PD) Deshpande
Chief Delivery Officer, Sean S. Narayanan, age 44
Manager Investor Relations, Araceli Roiz
Chief Sales Officer, Robert W. Massie
SVP iTOPS and Consulting Solutions, David A. Kruzner
VP and Delivery Head - Healthcare Insurance Media & Entertainment, Vish Viswanathan
Chief Accounting Officer, Prashanth Idgunji
Sr. Vice President CSO, John Robertson
Vice President St, David Flood
Vice President Infrastructure Management Solutions, Vikram Watave
Executive VP CIO, Dennis Callahan
Head Information Management, Jakob JSggli
Director Marketing, Jeremy Mackinlay
Vice President Public Sector at iGATE, Timothy Coffin
Global Head - Alliances & Head - Sales; North America, Sanjay Tugnait
Executive Vice President; Head of PES Management, Satish Joshi
Executive Vice President; Head of Sales for EMEA; Asia & Australia, Derek Kemp
Executive Vice President; Co-Head of Consulting & Solutions, Vijay Khare
Vice-President, Steve Jolley
Director, W. Roy Dunbar, age 52
Director, Martin G. (Marty) McGuinn, age 69
Co-Chairman, Sunil Wadhwani, age 60

President CEO and Director, Phaneesh Murthy, age 49
Director, J. Gordon Garrett, age 72
Director, Joseph J. (Joe) Murin, age 63
Director, Salim Nathoo, age 42
Director, Goran Lindahl, age 69
Independent Director, Naomi Seligman
Auditors: Ernst&Young

LOCATIONS

HQ: iGate Corporation
6528 Kaiser Dr., Fremont CA 94555
Phone: 510-896-3000   **Fax:** 510-896-3010
Web: www.igatecorp.com

2012 Sales

	% of total
North	81
Europe	13
Asia-Pacific	6
Total	**100**

PRODUCTS/OPERATIONS

Selected Services

Application Development
Application Management
BI and DW
Business Process Management
CIS and BPO
Customized Learning Solutions
Embedded Systems
Engineering Services
Enterprise Application Solutions
Enterprise Integration
Enterprise Mobility
Infrastructure Management
IT Consulting
IT Governance
IT Services
Open Source Software Services
User Experience Management
Verification and Validation
Web Technology Solutions

COMPETITORS

ADP	Getronics
Accenture	HCL Technologies
Affiliated Computer Services	HP Enterprise Group
	HP Enterprise Services
Boston Consulting	Hexaware Technologies
CGI Group	IBM Global Services
Capgemini	Infosys
Cognizant Tech Solutions	Logica
	MindTree
Computer Enterprises	Satyam
Computer Sciences Corp.	Tata Consultancy
	Tech Mahindra
Deloitte Consulting	Wipro Technologies
Genpact	

HISTORICAL FINANCIALS

Company Type: Public

Income Statement

FYE: December 31

	REVENUE ($ mil.)	NET INCOME ($ mil.)	NET PROFIT MARGIN	EMPLOYEES
12/12	1,073.9	95.8	8.9%	27,616
12/11	779.6	51.4	6.6%	26,889
12/10	280.6	51.7	18.4%	8,338
12/09	193.1	28.5	14.8%	6,910
12/08	218.8	30.9	14.1%	6,658
Annual Growth	**48.8%**	**32.7%**	**—**	**42.7%**

2012 Year-End Financials

Debt ratio: 61.0%	No. of shares (mil.): 57
Return on equity: 21.1%	Dividends
Cash ($ mil.): 95	Yield: —
Current ratio: 3.12	Payout: —
Long-term debt ($ mil.): 1,033	Market value ($ mil.): 907

	STOCK PRICE ($) FY Close	P/E High/Low		PER SHARE ($) Earnings	Dividends	Book Value
12/12	15.77	22	17	0.85	0.00	8.31
12/11	15.73	51	24	0.38	0.00	7.51
12/10	19.71	27	10	0.90	0.26	4.41
12/09	10.00	19	4	0.51	0.11	3.47
12/08	6.51	21	8	0.56	0.00	2.70
Annual Growth	**24.8%**	**—**	**—**	**11.0%**	**—**	**32.5%**

IHS Inc

IHS Inc. (Information Handling Services Inc.) handles the hottest commodity around: information. A publisher of technical documents for clients in industries such as energy defense aerospace electronics and automotive the company distributes its data in several electronic formats (Internet intranet extranet CD-ROM). Products such as collections of technical specifications and standards regulations parts data and design guides are sold through its four areas of information: Energy Product Lifecycle Security and Environment. The company also offers economic-focused information and analysis through its IHS Global Insight subsidiary. IHS primarily earns revenue through subscription sales.

The company specializes in delivering information to engineers designers technical professionals senior managers compliance officers marketing executives and strategic planners at both small and large businesses as well as goverment agencies. Topics range from detailed technical specifications to industry trends and geopolitical analysis.

IHS's Energy segment is focused on information related to all aspects of oil and gas exploration development production and transportation while its Product Lifecycle segment provides information on all areas of a product's development including conception research production maintenance and disposal. The Security segment focuses on topics such as defense aerospace and weapon systems and the Environment segment provides data to help customers comply with environmental regulations and related issues.

Subscription sales account for more than 75% of business. In 2011 the company achieved higher revenues compared to the previous year due to an increase in subscription sales. (It also reported a dip in net income due to pension-related costs without which net income would have increased.) Much of this increase in subscription sales is due to its acquisition activity a key component of the company's growth strategy. IHS has completed more than 40 purchases since its IPO in 2005. The acquisitions reflect the firm's growth strategy of selecting information-intensive companies in industries in which it already has a significant presence such as energy defense manufacturing and technology.

In 2012 the company made a string of strategic acquisitions to enhance its capabilities in technol-ogy media and telecommunications electronic components and energy. That year it acquired GlobalSpec provider of a searchable online database of supplier catalogs for engineers from Warburg Pincus for $135 million. IHS also purchased Displaybank a provider of market research and consulting for the display industry; the Computer Assisted Product Selection electronic components database and tools business; and the digital oil and gas pipeline and infrastructure information business from Hild Technology Services. The combined purchase price of those three acquisitions was approximately $45 million.

IHS made its largest acquisition to date in 2011 when it purchased Seismic Micro-Technology a provider of geoscience software for $500 million in cash. The deal enabled IHS to provide information browsing and analysis tools for the oil and gas industry. Prior key acquisitions gave the company subsidiaries such as IHS Jane's (a provider of information and analysis on global defense and security) and IHS Global Insight (economic-focused research). And in 2011 the company formed IHS Chemical in part from assets it acquired from Access Intelligence (business-to-business periodicals in the energy and chemical sectors including Chemical Week and The Energy Daily).

All total IHS operates in some 180 countries; nearly 50% of its sales are conducted outside of the US. The company's sales teams are organized to support three geographic segments: Americas; Europe Middle East and Africa; and the Asia/Pacific region.

The Thyssen-Bornemisza family controls about 25% of IHS.

HISTORY

IHS Group traces its roots to Rogers Publishing a company formed by Thomas Rogers in the 1940s to publish engineering magazine "Design News." In the 1950s Rogers Publishing branched into automated information retrieval systems choosing microfilm as a publishing medium for reference information.

In 1959 Richard O'Brien an executive with Rogers Publishing developed a product catalog database for aerospace engineers. The flagship product Vendor Specs Microfilm File (VSMF) was indexed to locate information quickly and was produced on microfilm to conserve space that was generally occupied by libraries of hardcopy documents. When Cahners Publishing bought Rogers in 1961 the technical services division which included catalog operations was spun off as a separate company and named Information Handling Services (IHS).

An extended series of acquisitions helped to shape the company and bring it to the forefront of technical publishing. By the 1980s global giant TBG had become Information Handling Services' parent company and established the foundation for further growth. IHS Group was formed in 1989 as the holding company for new subsidiaries as the company expanded into other markets including regulatory information and entered the international arena through a series of acquisitions.

Among the company's 1990s acquisitions were Beilstein Informationssysteme (Germany 1994) Global Info Center Hong Kong (1994) Media Library (Japan 1995) and Petroconsultants (Switzerland 1996). The company branched into cyberspace in 1997 with the debut of its first Web-based products. Focusing on Web-based and electronic products IHS Group ceased production of microfilm products the following year.

As IHS Group expanded into energy information. it acquired Petroleum Information/Dwights PI (ERICO) IEDS MAI Consultants and QC Data Petroleum Services Division and its AccuMap Enerdata Division forming IHS Energy in 1998 as a separate division of IHS Group to streamline energy information operations and services.

In 2000 IHS Group formed a joint venture with standards and quality service organization British Standards Institution (BSI) to distribute BSI's content. Additional acquisitions included the 2004 purchase of USA Information Systems and Intermat the 2004 purchase of Cambridge Energy Research Associates (CERA) and the 2005 acquisition of American Technical Publishers.

IHS underwent a reorganization in 2005 which included 100 job cuts and two office closings in its Engineering segment; also that year the company filed an initial public offering and began using the name IHS Inc. In 2006 IHS further reduced its headcount by 40 and sold certain IHS Energy assets.

Also in 2006 the company bought geoPLUS Corporation (software used by oil and gas companies to analyze data from oil and gas wells); Construction Research Communications Limited (products relating to the construction industry ranging from environmental issues to fire safety); and Canadian Hydrodynamics Ltd (drillstem test information for the Western Canadian Sedimentary Basin).

Purchases in 2007 included Jane's Information Group a provider of information and analysis on global defense and security (now IHS Jane's) and John S. Herold Inc. a research firm specializing in the oil and gas sector (now IHS Herold). Also in 2007 it acquired EnvironMax a provider of environmental management information systems; and McCloskey Group a coal research firm.

In 2008 the company added economic-focused research offerings to its portfolio with the purchase of consulting firm Global Insight which became IHS Global Insight after the deal closed. IHS paid about $165 million in cash and stock for Global Insight. In 2009 IHS acquired Environmental Support Solutions (ESS) for approximately $59 million. ESS provides software to help companies comply with environmental health and safety regulations.

Acquisitions in 2010 included Atrion International (hazardous materials document management) and Syntex Management Systems (operational risk management software and services) for a combined purchase price of about $80 million. IHS bought those two companies in order to beef up its Environment practice. Later in 2010 IHS acquired iSuppli for approximately $94 million. The iSuppli deal included Screen Digest Limited a digital media and technology research company. iSuppli and Screen Digest boosts IHS's technology value chain research and advisory services.

Also in 2010 the company added a few key business-to-business periodicals to its holdings with the acquisition of the energy and chemical portfolio of information publisher Access Intelligence for approximately $79 million. Included in the deal were key brands such as Chemical Week and The Energy Daily. In 2011 IHS made its largest acquisition yet when it obtained Seismic Micro-Technology for $500 million.

EXECUTIVES

Senior Vice President and Chief Sustainability, Jane Okun Bomba, age 50

SVP and Chief Accounting Officer, Heather Matzke-Hamlin, age 45

Chairman and CEO, Jerre L. Stead, age 70, $750,000 total compensation

Senior Vice President Vice President, Jonathan Gear

EVP Global Finance, Richard G. (Rich) Walker, age 49

SVP Secretary and General Counsel, Stephen (Steve) Green, age 61, $272,058 total compensation

SVP and Chief Human Resources Officer, Jeffrey (Jeff) Sisson, age 56

SVP CFO and CIO, Todd Hyatt

President and COO, Scott Key, age 54, $408,173 total compensation

EVP; Chairman CERA, Daniel Yergin, age 66, $511,538 total compensation

VP Investor Relations, Andy Schulz

Executive Vice President Legal & Corporate Secretary Stephen, Stephen Green

Executive Vice President - Information and Insight Operations and Research and Analysis, Arshad Matin

Senior Vice President - Global Sales, Brian Sweeney

Senior Vice President; Chief Marketing Officer, Stephanie Buscemi

Executive Vice President Products and Operations Anurag, Anurag Gupta

Chief Compliance Officer; Anti-Money Laundering Officer, Brian Kindelan

Executive Vice President Vice President, Sean Menke

Director, Brian H. Hall, age 65
Director, C. Michael Armstrong, age 74
Director, Michael S. Klein, age 49
Director, Ruann F. Ernst, age 66
Director, Balakrishnan S. (Bala) Iyer, age 57
Director, Richard W. (Rich) Roedel, age 63
Director, Roger Holtback
Director, Christoph V. Grolman, age 54
Director, Steven A. Denning, age 63
Auditors: Ernst&YoungLLP

LOCATIONS

HQ: IHS Inc.
15 Inverness Way East, Englewood CO 80112-5776
Phone: 303-790-0600   **Fax:** 303-754-3940
Web: www.ihs.com

2011 Sales

	$ mil.	% of total
Americas	798	60
Europe Middle East & Africa	384	29
Asia/Pacific	142	11
Total	**1,325**	**100**

PRODUCTS/OPERATIONS

2011 Sales

	$ mil.	% of total
Energy	571	43
Product Lifecycle	436	33
Security	119	9
Environmental	98	7
Macroeconomic Forecasting & other	99	7
Total	**1,075**	**100**

2011 Sales

	$ mil.	% of total
Subscription	1,020	77
Transaction	90	7
Consulting	63	5
Other	151	11
Total	**1,325**	**100**

Selected Information Offerings

Energy
  Exploration analysis
  Oil and gas well data
Production data
Reservoir data
Product Lifecycle
  Catalog information
  Electronic components parts information
  Government parts information
  Regulatory data
  Specifications and standards
Security
  Defense forecasting
  Ports and terminals data
  Public safety handbooks and guides
  Terrorism and insurgency monitoring
Environment
  Climate change greenhouse gas and sustainability information
  Hazardous materials compliance

Selected Acquisitions

Canadian Hydrodynamics Ltd (2006 drillstem test information for the Western Canadian Sedimentary Basin $3.5 million)
CDS (2005 electronic component parts data $33 million)
CERA (2004 research service $31 million)
Chemical Market Associates (2011 chemical information and analysis $73 million)
Construction Research Communications Limited (2006 construction industry data $5.8 million)
Documental Solutions (2008 market intelligence and analysis tools for the defense and aerospace industry $22.2 million)
Dolphin Software (2008 chemical data information and software $23.7 million)
Emerging Energy Research (2010 advisory for technological and regulatory trends in emerging energy $18 million)
Environmental Support Solutions (2009; environmental health and safety and crisis management software; $59 million)
geoPLUS Corporation (2006 software used by oil and gas companies to analyze data $42.1 million)
Global Insight (2008; global economic information analysis and consulting; $165 million)
Intermat (2004 decision support $5 million)
International Petrodata Limited (2004 geological information provider $16 million)
iSuppli (2010 technology value chain research and advisory services $94 million)
McCloskey Group (2007 coal research firm $28 million)
ODS-Petrodata (2011 information and market intelligence to the offshore energy industry $75 million)
Seismic Micro-Technology (2011 geoscience software $500 million)
USA Information Systems (2004 decision support $20 million)

COMPETITORS

Advanstar	John Wiley
Bureau of National Affairs	MSDSonline
	McGraw Hill Financial
Crain Communications	Nielsen Holdings
Divestco	Pearson plc
GlobalSpec	Penton Media
Hearst Corporation	Reed Elsevier Group
Informa	Thomson Reuters
International Data Group	Wolters Kluwer
	ubm

HISTORICAL FINANCIALS

Company Type: Public

Income Statement

FYE: November 30

	REVENUE ($ mil.)	NET INCOME ($ mil.)	NET PROFIT MARGIN	EMPLOYEES
11/13	1,840.6	131.7	7.2%	8,000
11/12	1,529.8	158.1	10.3%	6,000
11/11	1,325.6	135.4	10.2%	5,500
11/10	1,075.4	141.3	13.1%	4,400
11/09	967.3	134.9	14.0%	4,100
Annual Growth	17.4%	(0.6%)	—	18.2%

2013 Year-End Financials

Debt ratio: 40.5%
Return on equity: 7.5%
Cash ($ mil.): 258
Current ratio: 0.71
Long-term debt ($ mil.): 1,779

No. of shares (mil.): 67
Dividends
  Yield: —
  Payout: —
Market value ($ mil.): 7,711

	STOCK PRICE ($) FY Close	P/E High/Low	PER SHARE ($) Earnings	Dividends	Book Value
11/13	114.43	59 45	1.95	0.00	28.30
11/12	92.14	49 34	2.37	0.00	24.16
11/11	88.38	43 33	2.06	0.00	21.26
11/10	72.32	34 22	2.18	0.00	18.31
11/09	50.28	25 16	2.11	0.00	16.02
Annual Growth 22.8%		— —	(2.0%)	—	15.3%

II-VI Inc.

II-VI sees the world through amber-colored lenses. The company (pronounced "two-six") makes lenses mirrors prisms and other optical components and materials. It also produces selenium and tellurium metals and silicon carbide substrates. II-VI's clients —drawn from the aerospace health care industrial military and telecom equipment sectors —use these components in lasers and other systems used in precision manufacturing communications networks military targeting and navigation systems and other applications. The company has manufacturing operations throughout the US as well as in Asia and Germany. Customers have included Caterpillar Volkswagen Raytheon and the US government.

Geographic Reach

The US is II-VI's largest market accounting for 45% of its total sales. China is next representing more than 20% of annual sale while Germany represents about 10%. The company has production facilities in nine US states including its home state of Pennsylvania and half a dozen foreign countries such as China and Vietnam.

Operations

Vertically integrated II-VI operates four primary business segments. The largest is infrared optics which accounts for more than a third of its sales. II-VI Infrared manufactures optical and opto-electronic components for industrial laser and thermal imaging systems and subsidiary HIGHYAG Lasertechnologie GmbH ((YAG stands for yttrium aluminum garnet) manufactures fiber-delivered beam delivery systems and processing tools for industrial lasers.

The near-infrared optics business (nearly 30% of sales) Photop Technologies manufactures crystal materials optics microchip lasers and opto-electronic modules for use in optical communication networks and other diverse consumer and commercial applications. Photop Aegis makes tunable optical devices required for high speed optical networks that provide the bandwidth expansion necessary for increasing Internet traffic.

II-VI's military & materials business (20% of sales) LightWorks Optical Systems manufactures infrared products for military applications precision optical systems and components for defense aerospace industrial and life science applications. Lastly the advanced products group the Wide Bandgap Materials unit manufactures and markets single crystal silicon carbide substrates for use in the

solid-state lighting wireless infrastructure RF electronics and power switching industries; Marlow Industries Inc. (Marlow) designs and manufactures thermoelectric cooling and power generation solutions for use in defense space photonics telecommunications medical consumer and industrial markets.

Financial Performance

The company reported sales of about $558 million in fiscal 2013 (ended June) a 4% increase versus the prior year. Net income declined by 16% over the same period. Driving the revenue gain in fiscal 2013 was a 28% jump in sales by the company's Advance Products Group buoyed by the acquisition of M Cubed Technologies in November 2012. The infrared optics business posted a modest 1% increase in sales while near-infrared optics saw sales climb 11%. The Military & Materials business saw its sales fall 12% on lower product demand and pricing for both tellurium and selenium at Pacific Rare Specialty Metals & Chemicals (PRM) which more than offset the additional revenue resulting from the purchase of LightWorks Optics in December 2012.

On a geographic basis sales in the US (II-VI's largest market) increased 23% in fiscal 2013 compared to the prior year while international sales declined 1% over the same period. Germany and the UK both posted double-digit annual sales increases while sales in China were flat and declined in most other foreign markets.

Strategy

Research and development is vital to the company's success. Indeed II-VI aims to invest between 5% and 7% of its revenues each year in R&D. Its recent focus has been in silicon carbide substrates chemical vapor deposition (CVD) synthetic diamond materials photonics and thermoelectric materials and devices. II-VI uses a mix of internal and external funding for most areas but devotes only internal funds to CVD diamond and photonics.

II-VI's Pacific Rare Specialty Metals & Chemicals (PRM) subsidiary in 2013 discontinued its tellurium line and downsized its selenium production line to focus on providing selenium metal to the company's Infrared Optics business while distancing the business from volatile metal index price fluctuations.

The company uses acquisitions to build its business around core strengths in engineered materials and components.

Mergers and Acquisitions

In September 2013 the company acquired the Switzerland-based semiconductor laser business of Oclaro Inc. for $115 million. II-VI will operate the newly acquired business as II-VI Laser Enterprise GmbH.

In 2012 it bought Connecticut-based M Cubed Technologies for about $71 million and California-based LightWorks Optics for about half that amount. M Cubed manufactures advanced ceramic materials and precision motion control products and LightWorks supplies advanced optical systems used in defense aerospace and commercial operations. The prior year brought the acquisition of Massachusetts-based Aegis Lightwave for $52 million. Aegis' tunable optical devices are used to expand bandwidth in high speed optical networks and will contribute to II-VI's near-infrared optics business.

In early 2010 the company purchased China-based crystal materials and optical components maker Photop Technologies in a deal valued at about $83 million. The acquisition reinforced II-VI's focus on materials and components for the optical communications and display markets strengthened its photonics portfolio and expanded

its presence in China. In a move to expand its product line late that year the company acquired Max Levy Autograph a manufacturer of microfine conductive mesh patterns for optical mechanical and ceramic components used in electronic circuitry target calibration and the suppression of electromagnetic interference.

Ownership

Columbia Wanger Asset Management owns about 12% of II-VI's shares.

HISTORY

Electrical engineer Carl Johnson who had worked at Bell Labs (now part of Alcatel-Lucent) among other companies founded II-VI in 1971 to produce infrared optical materials for the emerging laser market. These materials —including cadmium zinc telluride zinc selenide and zinc sulfide —gave the company its name; they are from the "two-six" family of materials. (Cadmium and zinc are from column two on the periodic table; tellurium and selenium are from column six.)

By the 1980s II-VI was the leading maker of optical components for carbon dioxide lasers. The company went public in 1987 and the next year added a factory in Singapore.

Decreased military spending during the early 1990s stifled II-VI's growth. To compensate the company invested: it acquired eV Products in 1992 (divested in 2009) and Sandoz Chemicals' Virgo Optics Division (now VLOC) in 1994. The company opened a factory in China in 1996.

In 1999 II-VI formed a new division Electronic & Photonic Materials to develop uses for silicon carbide and sapphire materials. That year II-VI acquired 15% of rival Laser Power.

II-VI completed its acquisition of Laser Power in 2001. That year it also purchased Silicon Carbide (SiC) Group from Litton Systems (now part of Northrop Grumman). In 2003 II-VI consolidated Laser Power's operations into other branches of the company.

In 2004 the company bought Dallas-based Marlow Industries for around $31 million in cash. Marlow became an operating unit of II-VI's Compound Semiconductor Group.

In 2005 the company set plans to establish a silicon carbide semiconductor substrate manufacturing facility in Mississippi in cooperation with Mississippi State University and SemiSouth Laboratories. II-VI also made an equity investment in SemiSouth.

Also that year the company acquired the 25% equity interest in II-VI Deutschland GmbH it didn't already own buying the minority equity stake from L.O.T.-Oriel Laser Optik GmbH & Co. KG.

Carl Johnson chairman and CEO of II-VI since 1985 gave up the CEO's post in 2007 while remaining executive chairman. Francis Kramer the company's president and COO since 1985 succeeded Johnson as CEO retaining the president's title.

Also in 2007 II-VI acquired Pacific Rare Specialty Metals & Chemicals adding a long-term supply of selenium and tellurium raw materials essential to the company's operations. The following year II-VI sold its 36% stake in 5NPlus for about $30 million. 5NPlus was a supplier of high-purity antimony cadmium selenium tellurium and zinc — all materials that went into II-VI products.

The company's 2008 purchase of HIGHYAG Lasertechnologie brought expertise in high-power lasers for welding drilling and cutting. In 2009 II-VI sold eV Products (X-ray and gamma-ray sensors for nuclear radiation detection) to Endicott Interconnect Technologies. Also that year it entered into a joint venture with Beijing Supower Science and Technology Developing Co. in mid-2009; II-VI holds a minority share in the venture which makes diamond and laser cutting machines.

EXECUTIVES

VP Military and Materials Businesses, James Martinelli, age 55, $194,000 total compensation
President and CEO, Francis J. Kramer, age 64, $433,000 total compensation
Chairman, Carl J. Johnson, age 71, $212,000 total compensation
CFO and Treasurer, Craig A. Creaturo, age 43, $227,125 total compensation
EVP, Vincent D. (Chuck) Mattera Jr., age 57, $208,500 total compensation
Secretary, Robert D. German
Director, Marc Y. E. Pelaez, age 67
Director, Joseph J. (Joe) Corasanti, age 49
President CEO and Director, Francis J. Kramer, age 63
Director, Wendy F. DiCicco, age 46
Director, Peter W. Sognefest, age 72
Director, Thomas E. Mistler, age 71
Independent Director, Howard Xia
Auditors: Ernst&YoungLLP

LOCATIONS

HQ: II-VI Incorporated
375 Saxonburg Blvd., Saxonburg PA 16056-9499
Phone: 724-352-4455   **Fax:** 724-352-5284
Web: www.ii-vi.com

2013 Sales

	$ mil.	% of total
US	251	45
Asia/Pacific		
China	123	22
Vietnam	29	5
Philippines	24	4
Japan	29	5
Singapore	6	1
Europe		
Germany	59	11
Switzerland	10	2
Italy	7	1
UK	6	2
Belgium	5	1
Australia	3	1
Total	**558**	**100**

Selected Production Operations

US
  California
  Connecticut
  Delaware
  Florida
  Massachusetts
  Mississippi
  New Jersey
  Pennsylvania
  Texas
International
  Australia
  China
  Germany
  Philippines
  Singapore
  Vietnam

PRODUCTS/OPERATIONS

2013 Sales

	$ mil.	% of total
Infrared Optics	203	36
Near-Infrared Optics	154	28
Military & Materials	104	19
Advanced Products Group	95	17
Total	**558**	**100**

Selected Business Segments

dvanced Materials Development Center (AMDC)
AOFR
Aegis Lightwave
HIGHYAG Lasertechnologie
LightWorks Optical Systems
M Cubed
Marlow Industries
Max Levy Autograph
Photop Technologies
Pacific Rare Specialty Metals & Chemicals (PRM)
Wide Bandgap Materials Group

Selected Products

Beam expanders
Beam splitters
Detectors
Etalons
Infrared and near-infrared optics
Laser crystals
  Clear yttrium aluminum garnet (YAG) laser crystals
  Custom crystals and fluorides
  Machined and polished laser rods
  Monolithic crystal assemblies (MCA)
  Neodymium doped YAG
  Non-linear crystals
  Oxide laser crystal products
  Ruby laser crystals
Laser gain materials
Lenses
Military infrared optics
Mirrors
Modulators
One micron laser
Optical assemblies
Optical coatings
Output windows
Partial reflectors
Phase retarders
Polarization devices
Prisms
Rhombs
Selenium metal (material processing and refinement)
Silicon carbide substrates (SiC)
Solid-state laser optics and optical cavities
Substrates
Tellurium metal (material processing and refinement)
Thermo-electric coolers
Wave plates

COMPETITORS

AXSUN Technologies
CVI Laser
Coherent Inc.
CoorsTek
Cree
Cymer
DRS Technologies
Dow Corning
Ferrotec
Goodrich Corp.
Jenoptik
Komatsu
Laird Technologies
LightPath
Newport Corp.
Nippon Steel & Sumitomo Metal Corporation
Northrop Grumman
Oplink Communications
Orbotech
ROFIN-SINAR
Raytheon
Saint-Gobain
Spectra-Physics
Sumitomo Electric
Umicore
Zygo

HISTORICAL FINANCIALS

Company Type: Public

Income Statement

FYE: June 30

	REVENUE ($ mil.)	NET INCOME ($ mil.)	NET PROFIT MARGIN	EMPLOYEES
06/13	558.4	50.8	9.1%	6,185
06/12	534.6	60.3	11.3%	6,030
06/11	502.8	82.6	16.4%	6,195
06/10	345.0	38.5	11.2%	6,869
06/09	292.2	36.7	12.6%	1,913
Annual Growth	**17.6%**	**8.4%**	**—**	**34.1%**

2013 Year-End Financials

Debt ratio: 13.2%
Return on equity: 8.2%
Cash ($ mil.): 185
Current ratio: 4.88
Long-term debt ($ mil.): 114

No. of shares (mil.): 62
Dividends
  Yield: —
  Payout: —
Market value ($ mil.): 1,012

	STOCK PRICE ($) FY Close	P/E High/Low	PER SHARE ($) Earnings	Dividends	Book Value
06/13	16.26	25 18	0.80	0.00	10.22
06/12	16.67	29 17	0.94	0.00	9.39
06/11	25.60	44 19	1.30	0.00	8.33
06/10	29.63	59 30	0.63	0.00	6.64
06/09	22.23	76 24	0.61	0.00	5.46
Annual Growth	**(7.5%)**	**— —**	**7.0%**	**—**	**17.0%**

Illumina Inc

Illumina elucidates the human genome. The firm makes tools used by life sciences and drug researchers to isolate and analyze genes. Its systems include the machinery and the software used to sequence pieces of DNA and RNA and the means to put them through large-scale testing of genetic variation and biological function. Its proprietary BeadArray technology uses microscopic glass beads which can carry samples through the genotyping process. The tests allow medical researchers to determine what genetic combinations are associated with various diseases enabling faster diagnosis better drugs and individualized treatment. Customers include pharma and biotech companies research centers and academic institutions.

Operations

Though Illumina's expensive analysis systems are its primary focus sales of such systems account for only about one-third of revenues while the related consumables (chemical reagents flow cells and BeadChip microarrays) account for more than half of annual sales. Products are marketed directly and through independent distributors to life science researchers in medical forensics agriculture and animal health industries around the globe.

For customers who choose not to buy its systems and consumables Illumina offers outsourced life science research services such as genome sequencing and genotyping array services. Customers for such services which account for less than 10% of sales include schools agricultural and energy biotech research firms and drug development companies. In addition the company has a consumer genomics unit (launched in 2009) to meet the growing demand for personal genome sequencing through physician intermediaries. And while most of the company's revenues come from providing life sciences equipment and services Illumina has also established a small business in the field of molecular diagnostics which uses genetic biomarkers to diagnose clinical health conditions.

Geographic Reach

Illumina gets about half of its annual revenues from sales in the US market. Other key regions include Europe (25% of sales) and Asia/Pacific (20%). The company has increased revenues across all geographic markets in recent years with sales in the Asia/Pacific region in the lead.

Financial Analysis

Illumina has steadily augmented its life sciences product lines and has experienced rapidly climbing revenues in recent years as a result. The company reported a 17% increase in sales in 2011 to some $1.1 billion due to increased instrument sales (due to new product launches) and consumable sales (driven by a higher base of installed equipment) as well as a rise in its sequencing services segment. However profits dropped by about 30% to some $87 million that year due to increased operating expenses from sales and marketing efforts R&D programs and headquarters relocation efforts. To help reduce those expenses as well as to better insulate itself against economic uncertainties Illumina announced a restructuring effort towards the end of 2011 that resulted in an 8% workforce reduction by mid-2012 as well as the consolidation of some facilities.

Strategy

Through acquisitions and internal development efforts Illumina is adding a full line of genetic analysis technologies including DNA sequencing (determining the order of DNA codes) and gene expression analysis (studying when genes switch on or off) to its existing expertise in genotyping (identifying the gene's nucleotide base or code) making it a one-stop-shop for genetic researchers.

Illumina is conducting internal R&D programs as part of its efforts to make its systems faster and more affordable. One new product the HiSeq 2000 instrument (based on technology gained through the 2007 acquisition of Solexa) allows for the sequencing of whole human genomes. The system was first launched in 2010 and was upgraded to lower the cost of whole genome analysis (to less than $5000 in consumable costs) in 2011. As competition in the genome field intensified in 2012 the company further introduced a next-generation version —the HiSeq 2500 —that allows sequencing in a one-day timeframe. Other new products include the HiScanSQ system (used to compare genotyping and gene expression tests) in 2010 and the MiSeq machine (personal sequencing for small-scale research) in 2011. Sales of these new systems and related consumable microarrays contributed strongly to sales growth during 2010 and 2011.

Outside of the life sciences segment Illumina is working hard to expand its operations in the high-growth business of molecular diagnostics through both acquisitions and R&D efforts. To that end the company received FDA approval in 2010 for its BeadXpress Multiplex analysis system (based on the VeraCode technology acquired in 2006) and it is developing molecular diagnostic tests for conditions such as heart disease viral infections and cancers for use with the new system. It is also exploring use of its iScan genotyping instrument to detect chromosomal abnormalities indicating mental and developmental disabilities and it formed a partnership with Siemens in 2011 to conduct infectious disease testing and monitoring.

Mergers and Acquisitions

Acquisitions that have enhanced Illumina's offerings include the 2010 purchase of Helexis in a deal worth up to $105 million. The acquisition added the Eco Real Time PCR (polymerase chain reaction) genetic analysis system to the company's lineup of sequencing applications. Illumina followed that with Epicentre Biotechnologies in early 2011 adding the Nextera line of nucleic acid sample preparation reagents and enzymes used in sequencing and microarrays. In 2012 Illumina also purchased UK-based BlueGnome to expand its reproductive health screening offerings.

In 2012 Illumina's board of directors rejected two hostile takeover bids from Swiss drugmaker Roche one for $5.7 billion and the second for $6.7 billion. After shareholders further rejected Roche's attempt to elect members to Illumina's board Roche —which is looking to expand in the life science research and molecular diagnostics industries —stated that it would not extend or raise its offer.

EXECUTIVES

Chairman of the Board, William H. Rastetter
President & Chief Executive Officer; Director, Jay T. Flatley, age 61, $749,162 total compensation
Senior Vice President & Chief Commercial Officer, Tristan B. Orpin, age 47, $380,123 total compensation
Senior Vice President & General Manager Genomic Solutions, Christian O. Henry, age 45, $390,203 total compensation
VP and Chief Scientist, David Bentley
SVP General Counsel and Secretary, Christian G. (Chris) Cabou, age 65, $366,677 total compensation
VP Business Development, Jorge Velarde
Senior Director Investor Relations, Peter J. Fromen
Senior Vice President & General Manager Diagnostics, Gregory F. (Greg) Heath, age 55, $398,865 total compensation
SVP and CTO, Mostafa Ronaghi, age 44
Senior Manager Product Marketing, Tanya Boyaniwsky
VP-Global Supply Chain, Elizabeth Brady
Senior Manager Public Relations, Wilson Grabill
Senior Vice President & Chief Financial Officer, Marc Stapley, age 43
Chief Medical Officer; Vice President, Daniel Grosu
Senior Director - Investor Relations, Rebecca Chambers
VP-Quality & Regulatory Affairs, Melina Cimler
Chief Accounting Officer; Vice President - Finance, Michel Bouchard
Senior Vice President and General Manager Molecular Biology & PCR, Mark L. Lewis, age 60
Senior Vice President Human Resources, Paul L. Bianchi
Director, Karin Eastham, age 64
Director, A. Blaine Bowman, age 67
Director, Daniel M. (Dan) Bradbury, age 51
Director, Roy A. Whitfield, age 59
President & Chief Executive Officer; Director, Jay T. Flatley, age 61
Director, David R. Walt, age 61
Director, Paul C. Grint, age 55
Director, Gerald (Gerry) Moller
Independent Director, Gerald Moller
Auditors: Ernst&YoungLLP

LOCATIONS

HQ: Illumina Inc.
5200 Ilumina Way, San Diego CA 92122
Phone: 858-202-4500   **Fax:** 858-202-4766
Web: www.illumina.com

2011 Sales

	$ mil.	% of total
US	528	50
Europe		
UK	67	6
Other Europe	210	20
Asia/Pacific	197	19
Other regions	51	5
Total	**1,055**	**100**

PRODUCTS/OPERATIONS

2011 Sales

	$ mil.	% of total
Products	987	94
Total	**1,055**	**100**

Selected Products

BeadXpress Reader (VeraCode molecular diagnostics development genotyping and screening)
Eco Real-Time PCR System (molecular diagnostics development profiling and genotyping)
Genome Analyzer IIx (gene sequencing and genotyping system)
GoldenGate Assay Method (high-throughput genotyping system)
GoldenGate Universal-32 Sample BeadChip (genotyping arrays)
HiScanSQ (gene sequencing genotyping)
HiSeq 2000 and HiSeq 1000 (high-throughput gene sequencing genotyping and whole-genome sequencing systems)
Infinium HD Whole Genome BeadChips (microarrays)
iScan System (high-resolution imaging for BeadArray genotyping assays)
iSelect Genotyping BeadChips (custom genotyping arrays)
MiSeq (small scale gene sequencing and genotyping)
Paired-End Genomic DNA Sample Prep Kit (library preparation kit)

COMPETITORS

Affymetrix	Life Technologies
Agilent Technologies	Corporation
Beckman Coulter	Luminex
Complete Genomics	Pacific Biosciences
Fluidigm	QIAGEN
GE Healthcare Medical	Roche Diagnostics
Diagnostics	Sequenom
Helicos	

HISTORICAL FINANCIALS

Company Type: Public

Income Statement

FYE: December 30

	REVENUE ($ mil.)	NET INCOME ($ mil.)	NET PROFIT MARGIN	EMPLOYEES
12/12*	1,148.5	151.2	13.2%	2,400
01/12	1,055.5	86.6	8.2%	2,200
01/11	902.7	124.8	13.8%	2,100
01/10	666.3	72.2	10.8%	1,781
12/08	573.2	50.4	8.8%	1,536
Annual Growth	19.0%	31.6%	—	11.8%

*Fiscal year change

2012 Year-End Financials

Debt ratio: 32.8%	No. of shares (mil.): 123
Return on equity: 12.6%	Dividends
Cash ($ mil.): 433	Yield: —
Current ratio: 5.87	Payout: —
Long-term debt ($ mil.): 805	Market value ($ mil.): 6,786

	STOCK PRICE ($) FY Close	P/E High/Low		PER SHARE ($) Earnings	Dividends	Book Value
12/12*	54.75	46 25		1.13	0.00	10.64
01/12	30.48	111 37		0.62	0.00	8.81
01/11	63.34	65 30		0.87	0.00	9.46
01/10	30.68	74 40		0.53	0.00	7.23
12/08	25.36	219 46		0.38	0.00	7.01
Annual Growth	21.2%	—	— 31.3%		—	11.0%

*Fiscal year change

Impax Laboratories Inc

Impax Laboratories is betting that its pharmaceuticals will make a positive impact on the world's health. The company makes specialty generic pharmaceuticals which it markets through its Global Pharmaceuticals division and through marketing alliances with other pharmaceutical firms. It concentrates on controlled-release versions of various generic versions of branded and niche pharmaceuticals that require difficult-to-obtain raw materials or specialized expertise. Additionally the company's branded pharmaceuticals business (Impax Pharmaceuticals) is developing and improving upon previously approved drugs that target Parkinson's disease multiple sclerosis and other central nervous system disorders.

Operations

Impax earns the majority (more than 75%) of its revenue through its Global division which produces dosage variations of about 40 generic compounds including fenofibrate (generic Lofibra for high cholesterol) midodrine HCl (generic ProAmatine) and generic Adderall XR (for attention-deficit hyperactivity disorder or ADHD). Several of those compounds are sold through licensing or collaboration partnerships with companies including Teva Shire and Tolmar. Revenues for the unit fluctuate from year to year due to competitive conditions (how many additional generic versions of a product are on the market) and shifts in consumer demand for certain medications.

Its smaller Impax Pharmaceuticals division invests heavily in R&D costs and has historically brought in few earnings though the unit produces some revenues through development partnership income. However in 2012 the division grew rapidly to account for more than 20% of sales as it launched its first commercial branded product orally disintegrating and nasal spray versions of migraine drug Zomig (licensed from AstraZeneca).

Sales and Marketing

Impax's Global Pharmaceuticals division sells its generic products to wholesalers chain drug stores and mail order pharmacies. Impax also works through strategic alliances that include co-promotion licensing third-party marketing or manufacturing and supply agreements with other generic and branded pharmaceutical manufacturers.

Financial Performance

Impax has reported increasing revenues from 2008 to 2010 due to increased generic drug sales from products including its generic ADHD and cholesterol-lowering drugs; that trend was reversed in 2011 due to lower tamsulosin sales. Growth resumed in 2012 as overall revenue increased 13% to $582 million due to increased revenues from the Impax Pharmaceuticals division which was somewhat offset by a decline in generic drug sales (lower sales of Adderall XR authorized generics due to additional competitive products reaching the market offset by increased fenofibrate sales).

Net income in 2012 decreased to $56 million due to higher general administrative and sales expenses. The company also reported a decrease in profits in 2011 following three years of growth.

Strategy

To expand the operations of its main Global Pharmaceuticals division Impax works to develop new generic versions of drugs that have lost (or are about to lose) patent protection with a focus on controlled-release and specialty products. It also develops medicines that come in alternative-dosage forms such as nasal sprays inhalers ointments injectables and patches. The company's generic development programs are conducted both independently and through research or licensing partnerships with other drugmakers. Impax seeks to gain first-to-file and first-to market status with its new products and in some cases Impax enters agreements with branded pharmaceutical firms to make authorized generic versions of off-patent drugs.

The Impax Pharmaceuticals division has products in clinical stages of development including treatments for multiple sclerosis and Parkinson's disease. The division also focuses its development efforts on other central nervous system disorders such as Alzheimer's disease depression epilepsy and migraines. The company hopes to build its portfolio of branded products through internal development acquisitions and licensing agreements with the ultimate goal of selling some products commercially.

EXECUTIVES

Senior Vice President; General Counsel; Corporate Secretary, Mark Schlossberg
President CEO and Director, Larry Hsu, age 64, $585,144 total compensation
Chairman, Robert L. (Bob) Burr, age 62
President Impax Pharmaceuticals, Michael J. Nestor, age 60, $459,038 total compensation
President - Global Pharmaceuticals Division, Carole S. Ben-Maimon, age 54
Senior Director Investor Relations and Corporate Communications, Mark Donohue
Senior Vice President Finance and Chief Financial Officer, Bryan Reasons, age 46
Director, Allen Y. Chao, age 67
President CEO and Director, Larry Hsu, age 64
Director, Nigel Ten Fleming, age 59
Director, Michael Markbreiter, age 51
Director, Leslie Z. Benet, age 75
Director, Peter R. Terreri, age 55
Auditors: KPMGLLP

LOCATIONS

HQ: Impax Laboratories Inc.
30831 Huntwood Ave., Hayward CA 94544
Phone: 510-476-2000   **Fax:** 510-471-3200
Web: www.impaxlabs.com

Selected generic drugs

Acarbose Precose Antidiabetic
Bethanechol Chloride USP Urecholine Urinary tract stimulant
Bupropion HCl ER Wellbutrin SR Antidepressants
Bupropion HCl XL Wellbutrin XL Antidepressants
Carbidopa / Levodopa ER Sinemet CR Antiparksonian
Chloroquine Phosphate USP Aralen Antimalarials
Colestipol HCl for Oral Suspension USP Colestid Lipid-lowering agents
Colestipol HCl Tablet Colestid Lipid-lowering agents
Dantrolene Sodium Dantrium Skeletal muscle relaxants
Demeclocycline HCl USP Declomycin Antibactrerials
Digoxin USP Lanoxin Antiarrhythmics inotropics
Dipyridamole USP Persantine Vasodialators
Doxycycline Monohydrate Adoxa Antibiotic
Fenofibrate Capsules (Micronized) Lofibra Lipid-lowering agents
Fenofibrate Tablets Lofibra Lipid-lowering agents
Flavoxate HCl Urispas Antidepressants
Fludrocortisone Acetate USP Florinef Hormones
Galantamine HBr ER Razadyne ER Parasympathomimetic (Cholinergic Agents)
Gemfibrozil Lopid Antilipemic / Fibric Acid Derivatives
METHITEST CIII (Methyltestosterone USP) Android Hormones
Midodrine HCl ProAmatine Vasopressors Tablet
Minocycline HCl ER Solodyn Antibactrerials
Minocycline HCl USP Minocin Antibactrerials
Mixed Amphetamine Salts ER (CII) Adderall XR CNS Stimulants
Nadolol / Bendroflumethiazide USP Corzide Antihypertensive / Beta Blockers
Orphenadrine Citrate ER Norflex Skeletal muscle relaxants
Pilocarpine HCl Salagen Parasympathomimetic (Cholinergic Agents)
Primidone USP Mysoline Anticonvulsants
Promethazine HCl USP Phenergan Antihistamines
Pyridostigmine Bromide USP Mestinon Antimyasthenics
Rimantadine HCl Flumadine Antivirals
Tamsulosin HCl Flomax Alpha1-Adrenergic-Receptor Antagonists
Terbutaline Sulfate USP

PRODUCTS/OPERATIONS

2012 Sales

	$ mil.	% of total
Global division	448	77
Impax division	133	23
Total	**581**	**100**

COMPETITORS

Actavis	Sandoz International
Actavis Inc.	GmbH
Caraco Pharmaceutical	SkyePharma
Forest Labs	Synovics
K-V Pharmaceutical	Teva
Mylan	URL Pharma
Par Pharmaceutical	Valeant
Companies	Pharmaceuticals
Ranbaxy Laboratories	

HISTORICAL FINANCIALS

Company Type: Public

Income Statement
FYE: December 31

	REVENUE ($ mil.)	NET INCOME ($ mil.)	NET PROFIT MARGIN	EMPLOYEES
12/12	581.6	55.8	9.6%	1,125
12/11	512.9	65.5	12.8%	1,002
12/10	879.5	250.4	28.5%	918
12/09	358.4	50.0	14.0%	801
12/08	210.0	18.7	8.9%	768
Annual Growth	**29.0%**	**31.5%**	**—**	**10.0%**

2012 Year-End Financials

Debt ratio: —	No. of shares (mil.): 68
Return on equity: 8.6%	Dividends
Cash ($ mil.): 142	Yield: —
Current ratio: 3.75	Payout: —
Long-term debt ($ mil.): —	Market value ($ mil.): 1,399

	STOCK PRICE ($) FY Close	P/E High/Low		PER SHARE ($) Earnings	Dividends	Book Value
12/12	20.49	32	22	0.82	0.00	10.12
12/11	20.17	28	15	0.97	0.00	9.07
12/10	20.11	5	3	3.82	0.00	7.88
12/09	13.61	17	3	0.82	0.00	3.58
12/08	8.89	35	27	0.31	0.00	2.66
Annual Growth	**23.2%**	**—**	**—**	**27.5%**	**—**	**39.7%**

Infinity Property & Casualty Corp

Infinity Property and Casualty does have its limits but it goes farther than most to cover high-risk drivers. The insurer primarily provides personal nonstandard auto policies —Infinity is a leading writer of policies for high-risk drivers in the US. The company also offers standard and preferred personal auto commercial small fleet and classic collector auto insurance. Licensed in all 50 states the company currently focuses its business on targeted urban areas of a handful of states. Personal non-standard auto insurance accounts for more than 90% of its premiums; California accounts for about half of that business. Infinity distributes its products through more than 12900 independent agents.

Infinity has its sights set on expanding its business in the urban areas of large states (specifically California Florida Texas Georgia Pennsylvania Arizona Nevada and Illinois). The company has increased advertising spending and agency incentives including commissions to stimulate growth in these areas. It is however also happily maintaining its presence in less densely populated states with plenty of bad drivers such as Colorado Alabama South Carolina Tennessee and Connecticut.

Infinity is pursuing a strategy for growth that it hopes will help it to overcome the soft insurance market of the past several years and deliver shareholder value. It is depending on meeting customers' lifestyle and budget needs by providing flexible product offerings and pricing options. For example the company offers products with buy-up/buydown options and introduced its new DriverClub service with free membership for roadside assistance. The company is also committed to building relations with its agents and brokers by investing in agency productivity lead generation and training.

Factors that contributed to strong premium growth (11%) for Infinity in fiscal 2011 included improvements in agency incentives the addition of policies with broader coverage into its business mix decreases in rates in some states and competitor rate increases in some states. As a result revenues for the year increased by about 10%. Net income however decreased by 54%. The decline in net earnings was mainly due to unfavorable development related to accident year 2010 resulting from increases in severities on personal injury protection in Florida.

By the end of fiscal 2011 Infinity had repurchased $403 million or about 46% of the shares issued since its 2003 IPO. The company had also increased dividends by 309% for a total compound annual return to shareholders (dividends and capital appreciation) of 16% for that same time period.

Before its IPO Infinity was owned by property/casualty giant American Financial Group (AFG). AFG transferred the personal insurance business of its property/casualty subsidiary Great American Financial Resources to Infinity but that business is now in runoff with no new policies being written.

EXECUTIVES

Chairman of the Board; President; Chief Executive Officer, James R. Gober, age 61, $558,800 total compensation

Chief Financial Officer; Executive Vice President; Treasurer; Director, Roger Smith, age 52, $304,800 total compensation

Executive Vice President; General Counsel; Assistant Secretary; Director, Samuel J. Simon, age 56, $406,400 total compensation

Senior Vice President - Product Management, Scott C. Pitrone, age 50, $220,000 total compensation

Senior Vice President - Business Development, Glen N. Godwin, age 55, $237,806 total compensation

Director, Harold E. Layman, age 66

Director, Drayton Nabers Jr., age 72

Director, W. Stancil (Stan) Starnes, age 64

Director, Gregory C. Thomas, age 64

EVP CFO Treasurer and Director, Roger Smith, age 52

EVP Secretary General Counsel and Director, Samuel J. Simon, age 56

Director, Jorge G. Castro, age 55

Director, Samuel J. Weinhoff, age 62

Director, Maria Teresa A. Canida, age 59

Auditors: Ernst&YoungLLP

LOCATIONS

HQ: Infinity Property and Casualty Corporation
3700 Colonnade Pkwy., Birmingham AL 35243
Phone: 205-870-4000   **Fax:** 205-803-8231
Web: www.ipacc.com

PRODUCTS/OPERATIONS

2011 Revenues

Earned premiums	1,019	95
Realized investment gains	8	1
Gain on sale of subsidiaries	4	-
Total	**1,072**	**100**

2011 Gross Written Premiums

Personal automobile	93
Classic collector and other	1

COMPETITORS

Affirmative Insurance	Kingsway America
Direct General	Permanent General
First Acceptance Corporation	Progressive Corporation
GMAC Insurance	Safe Auto
Hagerty Insurance	

HISTORICAL FINANCIALS

Company Type: Public

Income Statement

FYE: December 31

	REVENUE ($ mil.)	NET INCOME ($ mil.)	NET PROFIT MARGIN	EMPLOYEES
12/12	1,249.6	24.3	1.9%	2,200
12/11	1,072.6	42.0	3.9%	2,100
12/10	961.2	91.5	9.5%	1,900
12/09	883.4	70.5	8.0%	1,780
12/08	930.9	19.2	2.1%	1,860
Annual Growth	7.6%	6.0%	—	4.3%

2012 Year-End Financials

Debt ratio: 11.9%	No. of shares (mil.): 11
Return on equity: 3.6%	Dividends
Cash ($ mil.): 165	Yield: 1.5%
Current ratio: 4.62	Payout: 32.3%
Long-term debt ($ mil.): 275	Market value ($ mil.): 676

	STOCK PRICE ($) FY Close	P/E High/Low		PER SHARE ($) Earnings	Dividends	Book Value
12/12	58.24	30	24	2.04	0.90	56.55
12/11	56.74	18	13	3.39	0.72	56.59
12/10	61.80	9	5	6.95	0.56	53.03
12/09	40.64	9	6	5.09	0.48	45.80
12/08	46.73	38	28	1.23	0.44	37.14
Annual Growth	5.7%	—	—	13.5%	19.6%	11.1%

Informatica Corp.

Big data is a big opportunity for Informatica. The company provides enterprise data integration software that enables companies to access integrate and consolidate their data across a variety of systems and users. Its PowerCenter platform consolidates codes and moves large data warehouses and its PowerExchange software enables access to bulk or changed data. Other products include Master Data Management (MDM) and the Informatica B2B Data Exchange as well as Fast Clone (data replication) Data Explorer (data quality) and a range of software-as-a-service (SaaS) offerings which integrate data from other business applications into a single hosted platform.

Geographic Reach

Informatica has offices in about 45 countries. North America is its largest market accounting for about two-thirds of sales. Customers in Europe account for about a quarter of sales.

Sales and Marketing

The company's products are sold directly in 20 countries and also through systems integrators resellers and distributors and strategic partners in 80 other countries. Informatica targets chief information officers and other departmental heads in marketing sales service finance human resources manufacturing distribution and procurement as well as other IT professionals focused on data integration. Altogether it counts more than 5000 corporate customers.

Financial Performance

Informatica's sales continued along a decade-long upward trajectory in 2013. Overall revenues increased 17% in 2013 to $948 million. Software revenues were up 18% license revenues were up 14% and subscription revenues were up 60%. The company cited continuing strong demand for its data integration applications data warehousing offerings and compliance program. It attributed increased sales of services to a growing customer base that is opting for more consulting and training as well as requiring more maintenance. Profits fell 7% to $86 million.

Strategy

Informatica continues to shift its focus from data warehousing to a broader enterprise data integration platform which encompasses data migration consolidation management and synchronization capabilities. The company has targeted the financial services industry by tailoring versions of its software for customers in banking and insurance. It also develops tools specifically for the retail health care and telecommunications industries among others.

Mergers and Acquisitions

The company supplements its organic growth with acquisitions. In 2012 it bought DataScout Solutions Group Limited and TierData combined for $12 million. It also bought a 98% stake in Germany-based Heiler Software AG for $82.1 million. Heiler Software AG provides enterprise product information management and master data management that allows retailers distributors and manufacturers to manage product information across channels and data sources.

EXECUTIVES

Chairman President and CEO, Sohaib Abbasi, age 56, $585,000 total compensation

EVP Global Customer Support CFO Chief Administration Officer and Secretary, Earl E. Fry, age 55, $350,000 total compensation

EVP; President Worldwide Field Operations, Paul J. Hoffman, age 62, $350,000 total compensation

CEO 29West, Mark G. Mahowald, age 53

EVP and Chief Product Officer, Girish Pancha, age 49, $330,000 total compensation

EVP and CTO, James Markarian, age 46

Senior Vice President Chief Information Officer, Tony Young

Chief Marketing Officer and SVP Education and Enablement, Chris Boorman

Vice President - Investor Relations, Stephanie Wakefield

Executive Vice President and General Manager Data Quality Product Division, Ivan Chong, age 46

Executive Vice President and Chief Product Officer, Anil S. Chakravarthy

Senior Vice President Global Customer Support, Ansa Sekharan

EVP Worldwide Field Operations, John McGee

Senior Vice President Global Human Resources, Jo Stoner

EVP and Chief Marketing Officer, Margaret Breya

Senior Vice President of Marketing Services bei HP war Breya noch vor kurzem f??r die Optimierung der Marketing-Investitionen des weltweit gr??? ten IT-Unternehmens verantwortlich, Bereich Technologiemanagement

Director, Godfrey R. Sullivan, age 59

Director, Mark S. Garrett, age 55

Director, Charles J. Robel, age 63

Director, Geoffrey W. (Geoff) Squire, age 66

Director, David W. (Dave) Pidwell, age 64

Director, Mark A. Bertelsen, age 68

Director, A. Brooke Seawell, age 65

Director, Gerald D. (Jerry) Held, age 65

Auditors: Ernst&YoungLLP

LOCATIONS

HQ: Informatica Corporation
100 Cardinal Way, Redwood City CA 94063
Phone: 650-385-5000   **Fax:** 650-385-5500
Web: www.informatica.com

2012 Sales

	$ mil.	% of total
North America	524	65
Europe	202	25
Other regions	84	10
Total	**811**	**100**

Selected Products

Informatica PowerCenter
 Standard Edition
 Real Time Edition
 Advanced Edition
 Big Data Edition
 Data Virtualization Edition
Informatica PowerExchange
Informatica Data Services
Informatica Data Quality
 Informatica Data Explorer
 AddressDoctor
Informatica Master Data Management (MDM)

Informatica Cloud MDM
Informatica Identity Resolution
Informatica B2B Data Exchange
 Informatica B2B Data Transformation
 Informatica HParser
Informatica Application Information Lifecycle
 Management (ILM)
 Informatica Data Archive
 Informatica Data Subset
 Informatica Persistent Data Masking
 Informatica Dynamic Data Masking
 ILM Nearline
Informatica Data Replication
 Informatica Fast Clone
Informatica Complex Event Processing (CEP)
 Informatica RulePoint
 Informatica Proactive Monitoring
Informatica Ultra Messaging
 Informatica Ultra Messaging Streaming Edition
 Informatica Ultra Messaging Queuing Edition
Informatica Cloud Data Integration
 Informatica Cloud Integration Applications
 Informatica Cloud Connectors

PRODUCTS/OPERATIONS

2012 Sales

	$ mil.	% of total
Service		
Maintenance	360	44
Consulting education & other	129	16
License	320	40
Total	**811**	**100**

Selected Acquisitions

FY2012
 DataScout Solutions Group Limited
 Heiler Software AG ($82 million)
 TierData Inc.
FY2011
 ActiveBase Ltd.
 WisdomForce Technologies Inc.
FY2010
 Siperian Inc. ($171 million)

COMPETITORS

Embarcadero	Oracle
Technologies	SAP
IBM	SAS Institute
MicroStrategy	Sybase
Microsoft	Trillium

HISTORICAL FINANCIALS

Company Type: Public

Income Statement

FYE: December 31

	REVENUE ($ mil.)	NET INCOME ($ mil.)	NET PROFIT MARGIN	EMPLOYEES
12/12	811.5	93.1	11.5%	2,814
12/11	783.7	117.5	15.0%	2,554
12/10	650.0	86.3	13.3%	2,126
12/09	500.6	64.2	12.8%	1,755
12/08	455.7	55.9	12.3%	1,611
Annual Growth	**15.5%**	**13.6%**	**—**	**15.0%**

2012 Year-End Financials

Debt ratio: —
Return on equity: 8.8%
Cash ($ mil.): 190
Current ratio: 2.05
Long-term debt ($ mil.): —
No. of shares (mil.): 107
Dividends
 Yield: —
 Payout: —
Market value ($ mil.): 3,253

	STOCK PRICE ($) FY Close	P/E High/Low	PER SHARE ($) Earnings	Dividends	Book Value
12/12	30.32	63 29	0.83	0.00	10.28
12/11	36.93	54 32	1.05	0.00	9.28
12/10	44.03	49 25	0.83	0.00	6.83
12/09	25.88	37 16	0.66	0.00	5.36
12/08	13.73	30 17	0.58	0.00	4.11
Annual Growth	**21.9%**	**— —**	**9.4%**	**—**	**25.8%**

InnerWorkings Inc

InnerWorkings has inserted itself into the nuts and bolts of the corporate printing world. The company procures manages and delivers printed products (brochures catalogs and other promotional materials) to companies in the advertising consumer products publishing and retail industries. InnerWorkings' proprietary software application and database PPM4 matches customers' jobs with printing companies' equipment and capacity. The InnerWorkings system submits a job to multiple printers who then bid for the business. Approximately 9000 suppliers participate in the company's network which includes includes printers graphic designers paper mills and merchants digital imaging companies and binders.

Most of InnerWorkings' business comes from enterprise customers for whom the company handles print jobs on a recurring basis. The company also takes work from customers on a transactional basis one order at a time. It hopes to grow by converting transactional customers to enterprise customers. So far it is on track with this strategy; in 2011 nearly 75% of revenues came from enterprise clients up from 71% in 2010 and 66% in 2009. Clients have included corporation such as Rent-A Center Payless and Advance Auto Parts.

The company reported 2011 revenues of $633.8 million up from $482.2 million in 2010. The growth was the result of new accounts as well as from expansion into Latin America through the 2011 acquisition of CPRO and into Europe through the 2011 acquisition of Productions Graphics. Net income also grew —the company posted profits of $16.4 million in 2011 vs. $11.2 million in 2010. It owes the increase to revenue growth combined with a decrease in selling general and administrative expenses. Such expenses include commissions paid to our account executives and employee compensation costs as well as facilities travel and entertainment expenses.

InnerWorkings bought Chilean printer CPRO in order to expand its reach into Central and South America. CPRO caters to more than 12 countries throughout Latin America. It also acquired Productions Graphics a leading international print management firm headquartered in Paris. Production Graphics also has offices in European countries such as Hungary Germany Spain and Italy.

Co-founders Richard Heise and Eric Lefkofsky together control about 20% of the company.

EXECUTIVES

Chairman, Jack M. Greenberg, age 69
SVP and General Counsel, Todd Andrews
Vice Chairman, Steven E. (Steve) Zuccarini, age 55, $550,000 total compensation

President CEO and Director, Eric D. Belcher, age 43, $500,000 total compensation
CFO and Secretary, Joseph M. Busky, age 44, $350,000 total compensation
SVP Enterprise Sales, Robert (Rob) Hart
President New York Operations, David Freundlich
VP Sales, Michael (Mike) Holewinski
Senior Vice President Global Strategy, Seth M. Kessler
Chief Operating Officer, John Eisel
President Southern Region, Richard L. Doss
President EMEA, Christophe Delaune
Sr. Vice President Enterprise Operations, Patrick McCusker
Senior Vice President Business Technology Chicago, Rob Burkart
Sr. Vice President Business Technology, Rob Burkhart
Sr. Vice President Global Sourcing, Ryan Cox
Director, John R. Walter, age 65
Director, Peter J. Barris, age 60
Director, Linda S. Wolf, age 64
Director, Eric P. Lefkofsky, age 43
Vice Chairman, Steven E. (Steve) Zuccarini, age 55
President CEO and Director, Eric D. Belcher, age 43
Director, Sharyar Baradaran, age 44
Director, Charles K. (Charlie) Bobrinskoy, age 52
Independent Director, David Fisher
Independent Director, Patrick Gallagher
Auditors: Ernst&YoungLLP

LOCATIONS

HQ: InnerWorkings Inc.
600 W. Chicago Ave. Ste. 850, Chicago IL 60610
Phone: 312-642-3700   **Fax:** 312-642-3704
Web: www.inwk.com

2011 Sales

	% of total
US	85
International	15
Total	**100**

PRODUCTS/OPERATIONS

2011 Sales

	% of total
Enterprise	74
Transactional	26
Total	**100**

Selected Products

Books
Brochures
Catalogs
CDs/DVDs
Direct mail pieces
Envelopes
Labels
Packaging
Stationery

Selected Suppliers

Digital imaging companies
Finishing and engraving firms
Fulfillment and distribution centers
Graphic designers
Paper mills and merchants
Printers
Specialty binders

COMPETITORS

Cirqit	R.R. Donnelley
Consolidated Graphics	Standard Register
NewlineNoosh	Williams Lea
Quad/Graphics	WorkflowOne

HISTORICAL FINANCIALS

Company Type: Public

Income Statement

FYE: December 31

	REVENUE ($ mil.)	NET INCOME ($ mil.)	NET PROFIT MARGIN	EMPLOYEES
12/12	797.7	19.1	2.4%	1,379
12/11	633.8	16.3	2.6%	1,034
12/10	482.2	11.2	2.3%	743
12/09	400.4	6.3	1.6%	667
12/08	419.0	15.9	3.8%	761
Annual Growth	**17.5%**	**4.6%**	**—**	**16.0%**

2012 Year-End Financials

Debt ratio: 12.4%
Return on equity: 9.4%
Cash ($ mil.): 17
Current ratio: 1.53
Long-term debt ($ mil.): 65

No. of shares (mil.): 50
Dividends
  Yield: —
  Payout: —
Market value ($ mil.): 692

	STOCK PRICE ($) FY Close	P/E High/Low	PER SHARE ($) Earnings	Dividends	Book Value
12/12	13.78	38 25	0.37	0.00	4.44
12/11	9.31	28 18	0.34	0.00	3.86
12/10	6.55	30 21	0.24	0.00	3.48
12/09	5.90	49 14	0.13	0.00	3.22
12/08	6.55	51 14	0.32	0.00	2.95
Annual Growth	**20.4%**	**— —**	**3.7%**	**—**	**10.8%**

Insteel Industries, Inc.

Insteel Industries is part of many concrete victories. The company manufactures steel welded wire reinforcement (WWR) used primarily in concrete construction materials such as pipe (pipe mesh building mesh engineered structural mesh and precast manholes) driveways and slabs. Its prestressed concrete (PC) strand products are the spine for concrete structures from bridges to parking garages. Insteel's customers include concrete pipe and precast and prestressed producers distributors and rebar fabricators. Insteel Industries operates about 10 manufacturing facilities in the US the company's core market. A majority of its sales come from manufacturers of non-residential concrete construction products.

The economic recession's impact on the construction market coupled with the crisis in credit markets has continued to hurt demand for Insteel products. Funding for infrastructure projects promised by the American Recovery and Reinvestment Act has been equally disappointing; state and local budgets already operating at a deficit were largely limited to pavement resurfacing and repair work which does not use wire reinforcement.

Insteel's own manufacturing budget took a hit from higher prices for hot-rolled steelwire rod a necessary raw material for its products. The industry's competitive pricing prevented the company from passing all of the increase onto customers. Nonetheless despite a modest decline in sales attributable to weak selling prices Insteel managed to return to profitability in 2010 following a $22 million loss in 2009 (compared to a $43 million profit the year before). Earnings were buoyed by both lower general expenses (since 2008 Insteel has reduced headcount by almost 20%) and a gain on the sale of real estate related to its discontin-

ued industrial wire business. One driver of the 2009 loss was reportedly an impairment charge taken on the real estate.

Insteel in late 2010 also capitalized on a recession bargain by acquiring Ivy Steel & Wire a division of Oldcastle (the US arm of CRH) for approximately $51 million. Ivy is the second largest US maker of WWR and wire products for concrete construction materials. The deal expanded Insteel's operations with five facilities in Arizona Florida Missouri Pennsylvania and Texas. Although the company signaled its intention to close facilities in Texas and Delaware Insteel maintains its lead in US production of PC strand and WWR. It is the only producer in the US to make both products (and one of only two national producers of WWR).

Moving forward the company has had success in fighting back against one of its biggest challenges —PC strand imports from foreign competitors which erode Insteel's shipments and pricing. The US government's 30% "Buy American" requirement for public infrastructure projects leaves 70% of the materials used in such projects subject to competition from abroad. In 2010 Insteel together with a coalition of domestic producers won a favorable ruling from the US Department of Commerce against Chinese imports sold at a less than fair value (a practice called "dumping".) As a result Chinese producers were assessed anti-dumping duties and restricted in participating in the US market. Insteel was successful in a similar action against a wave of other foreign producers in 2003.

HISTORY

Howard Woltz Sr. bought a premixed concrete and concrete-block plant and formed Exposaic Industries Inc. in 1953. Son Howard Woltz Jr. took over as chairman and president in 1958 adding welded-wire production equipment to the plant in 1975 during a shortage of wire reinforcing for its precast-concrete operations. Exposaic diversified again into industrial wire products in 1981 and went public in 1985.

The company sold its precast concrete unit in 1988 and changed its name to Insteel Industries. The next year it formed a joint venture with EVG (Austria) to make Insteel 3-D Panels (used in building construction) in Mexico.

Earnings fluctuated during the 1990s as Insteel tinkered with product lines and facilities under Howard Woltz III who became CEO in 1991. Waning sales in its industrial wire and bulk nail segments caused it to seek increased market share in higher margin businesses —PC strand (used to strengthen concrete) collated fasteners and tire bead wire. Insteel reorganized and consolidated its wire products subsidiaries in 1993. The company then opened a PC-strand facility in 1994. It bought the rest of the Insteel 3-D Panel joint venture in 1995 only to sell it to management two years later.

Insteel added welding wire and tire bead wire but start-up costs and slow sales of the new lines contributed to losses in fiscal 1997 and 1998. The company sold its agricultural fencing product line in 1998 and in 1999 agreed to buy the Florida Wire and Cable unit (prestressed concrete strand) of GS Industries for $68.5 million. The deal closed in 2000. The following year Insteel sold its galvanized strand business to Bekaert Corporation for approximately $9 million. In 2002 the company sold its South Carolina industrial wire unit to Leggett & Platt for approximately $10.2 million.

EXECUTIVES

VP Administration and Secretary, James F. (Jim)
Petelle, age 60, $156,154 total compensation
VP CFO and Treasurer, Michael C. Gazmarian, age
51, $250,000 total compensation
Director Human Resources, Deborah Van Etten
Chairman President and CEO, Howard O. (H. O.)
Woltz III, age 54, $430,000 total compensation
Senior Vice President, Louis E. Hannen, age 74
Executive Vice President, Charles B. Newsome, age
75
VP and General Manager Insteel Wire Products,
Richard T. Wagner, age 51, $220,000 total
compensation
Purchasing, Patty Carpenter
Quality Assurance and Shipping Manager, David
Goings
Plant Manager, Larry Blood
CTO, Lyle Bullington
**Chief Accounting Officer and Corporate
Controller,** Scott R. Jafroodi
**VP and General Manager Concrete and
Reinforcing Materials Business Unit,** Richard
Wagner
Materails Director, Robert Welch
Natational Sales Manager, Dick Wells
Chief Financial Officer; Executive Vice President,
David Berger
**Executive Vice President; Chief Human
Resources & Communication Officer,** Harold
Somerdyk
Chairman of the Board; Chief Executive Officer,
Michael Connors
Lead Independent Director, Robert Weissman
Director, Howard O. Woltz Jr., age 85
Director, Gary L. Pechota, age 61
Director, W. Allen Rogers II, age 64
Director, William J. Shields, age 78
Director, C. Richard Vaughn, age 71
Director, Louis E. Hannen, age 72
Director, Charles B. Newsome, age 73
Independent Director, Donald Waite
Independent Director, Gerald Hobbs
Independent Director, Guillermo Marmol
Independent Director, Neil Budnick
Independent Director, Duncan Gage
Auditors: GrantThorntonLLP

LOCATIONS

HQ: Insteel Industries Inc.
1373 Boggs Dr., Mt. Airy NC 27030
Phone: 336-786-2141   **Fax:** 336-786-2144
Web: www.insteel.com

2010 Sales

	$ mil.	% of total
US	205	97
Total	211	100

PRODUCTS/OPERATIONS

2010 Sales

	$ mil.	% of total
Welded wire reinforcement	109	52
Prestressed concrete strand	102	48
Total	211	100

2010 Sales

	% of total
Manufacturers of products	
Nonresidential	63
Residential	7
Distributors & rebar	30
Total	100

Selected Products

Prestressed concrete (PC) strand (seven-wire strand used
to strengthen concrete)
Welded wire reinforcement (used to reinforce concrete
structures)
Concrete pipe reinforcement
Engineered structural mesh
Standard welded wire reinforcement

Selected Subsidiaries

Insteel Wire Products Company
Intercontinental Metals Corporation (an inactive
subsidiary)

COMPETITORS

Dayton Superior	Oklahoma Steel and
Gerdau Ameristeel	Wire
Keystone Consolidated	Petron Pacific
MMI Products	SteelFab
MNP Corp.	Sumitomo Electric
Nucor	U.S. Concrete

HISTORICAL FINANCIALS

Company Type: Public

Income Statement

FYE: September 28

	REVENUE ($ mil.)	NET INCOME ($ mil.)	NET PROFIT MARGIN	EMPLOYEES
09/13	363.9	11.7	3.2%	687
09/12*	363.3	1.8	0.5%	682
10/11	336.9	(0.3)	—	725
10/10	211.5	0.4	0.2%	421
10/09	230.2	(22.0)	—	438
Annual Growth	12.1%	—		11.9%

*Fiscal year change

2013 Year-End Financials

Debt ratio: —
Return on equity: 7.5%
Cash ($ mil.): 15
Current ratio: 3.24
Long-term debt ($ mil.): —

No. of shares (mil.): 18
Dividends
Yield: 0.0%
Payout: 57.8%
Market value ($ mil.): 291

	STOCK PRICE ($) FY Close	P/E High/Low		PER SHARE ($) Earnings	Dividends	Book Value
09/13	16.00	30	16	0.64	0.37	8.86
09/12*	11.73	137	91	0.10	0.12	8.44
10/11	10.07	—	—	(0.02)	0.12	8.43
10/10	8.93	451	260	0.03	0.12	7.98
10/09	11.64	—	—	(1.27)	0.12	8.08
Annual Growth	8.3%	—	—	—	32.5%	2.3%

*Fiscal year change

Integrated Silicon Solution, Inc.

Fabless semiconductor company Integrated Silicon Solution Inc. (ISSI) has the right acronyms for the manufacturing process. ISSI primarily makes SRAMs (static random-access memory) chips and DRAMs (dynamic RAM) chips which account for most of its sales. Its chips are used in cars computers consumer electronics cell phones and telecommunications networking devices. ISSI sells its chips to dozens of top electronics manufacturers such as Cisco Garmin Nokia Siemens Networks

Sony and TRW Automotive either directly or through distributors and contract manufacturers. The company spun off its other chip business as Giantec Semiconductor in 2010. Asia accounts for about two-thirds of sales.

China-based Giantec Semiconductor was responsible for ISSI's ASSP (application-specific standard products) business specifically EEPROM and SmartCards –two kinds of non-volatile memory chips that retain their information and instructions even when the computer is turned off. ISSI continues to own an equity share in Giantec which otherwise operates in the Chinese market as an independent entity. Shanghai Pudong Science and Technology and Super Solution Limited both made investments in the company.

Like its competitors ISSI was hit hard by the global economic recession beginning in 2008. Sales dropped slightly that year but the company recorded a net loss for the first time. In 2009 total revenue dropped by more than one third as the price of semiconductors dropped and the company shifted its ASSP business into Giantec. Net sales rose 64% in 2010 mainly because of an increase in unit shipments and the average selling prices for some DRAM products and more unit shipments of SRAM and ASSP products.

Year-over-year net sales then rose 7% in 2011 mainly as a result once again of more unit shipments and higher average selling prices for some DRAM products as well as a better product mix of SRAM products. ASSP sales were lower because of the spinoff of Giantec. The company recorded net income in both 2011 and 2010.

ISSI is targeting specific memory market segments rather than commodity memory markets; establishing long-term supplying relationships with customers; continuing to develop new high-performance products; and selling deeper into industry leaders that are existing customers.

In 2011 the company acquired China-based Si En Integration Holdings for about $20 million in cash. The deal supported its effort to diversify products lines and tap new markets for its memory products. A fabless chip maker Si En Integration specialized in analog and mixed signal devices including power amplifiers for cell phones GPS devices and MP3 players; LED drivers for cell phones digital cameras and laptops; industrial voltage converters; and temperature sensors for a variety of applications.

The following year ISSI bought Chingis Technology Corporation for about $33 million. The acquisition bolsters ISSI's specialty memory product line adding non-volatile NOR flash memory to meet customer demand particularly from clients in the automotive and industrial sectors.

ISSI outsources all of its manufacturing to factories in Asia. Its principal silicon foundries (contract semiconductor manufacturers) are GLOBAL-FOUNDRIES) Nanya Technology Powerchip Semiconductor Semiconductor Manufacturing International Corp. (SMIC) and Taiwan Semiconductor Manufacturing Co. (TSMC).

While ISSI is a fabless semiconductor company one of its competitive advantages is a process development team that works with the company's silicon foundries in chip manufacturing rather than solely relying on foundry personnel to decide how the chips will be fabricated. On the customer side ISSI deploys low-cost engineering development teams close to customers in the Asia/Pacific region through its subsidiaries in China Taiwan and South Korea.

HISTORY

Integrated Silicon Solution Inc. (ISSI) was co-founded in 1988 by veteran electrical engineers Jimmy Lee (chairman) and Kong-Yeu Han. It shipped its first static random-access memory (SRAM) chips in 1990 its first nonvolatile memories in 1992 and its first flash memories in 1994. The company went public in 1995. That year sales jumped more than 100% thanks to a booming business in SRAMs.

In 1996 ISSI received a license for certain flash memory technologies from Intel which was then the leader in that market. However the company's income plummeted that year hurt by lowered SRAM prices and a write-off for inventory. Also in 1996 ISSI made its first foray into manufacturing when it teamed up with Taiwan Semiconductor Manufacturing (TSMC) Altera and Analog Devices to form WaferTech.

ISSI added DRAM and microcontroller products to its line in 1997. That year the company bought flash memory R&D company Nexcom Technology. ISSI moved to cut expenses in 1998 by forming subsidiary NexFlash Technologies (flash memories; ISSI retained 32%) and by partially spinning off ISSI-Taiwan to private investors. In 2000 the company sold its interest in WaferTech to joint venture partner TSMC.

In 2001 ISSI-Taiwan (renamed Integrated Circuit Solution Inc. or ICSI) was spun off as a public company in Taiwan; ISSI kept a 39% stake (later reduced to 29%). Also that year Winbond Electronics bought a major stake in NexFlash reducing ISSI's share of NexFlash to 14%.

In late 2004 ISSI acquired a majority stake in Signia Technologies a Taiwan-based maker of radio-frequency chipsets used in consumer electronic devices. Two years later the company sold its assets in Bluetooth wireless communications and most of its shares in Signia.

In early 2005 ISSI set plans to buy the majority stake in ICSI for about $69 million in cash. It ended the year owning 83% of the Taiwanese company. Also that year Winbond acquired all of NexFlash.

ISSI bought another 15% of ICSI in 2006. The company transferred a number of job functions to Taiwan from the US as a result lowering its cost structure. ISSI also decided to exit the flash controller business that year selling the product technology and assets while continuing to supply flash controllers to one customer on an exclusive basis.

Under the threat of a proxy fight in 2006 ISSI's board capitulated to activist investor Bryant Riley to avoid a costly battle. The board agreed to increase its size from seven to nine members on a temporary basis and the two extra board seats were taken by Riley and Melvin Keating who was installed as CEO of Alliance Semiconductor after Riley led a successful proxy challenge to its board. After witnessing Alliance's dismantling by Riley and his fellow dissident shareholders the ISSI directors apparently had little stomach for a similar fate to befall their company. Keating and Riley agreed to resign from the ISSI board in late 2007 upon the company's completion of a stock buyback totaling 10 million shares of common stock. The buyback was completed in early 2008 with ISSI repurchasing about 27% of its common shares outstanding for $70 million. Keating and Riley then left the board.

ISSI wound up acquiring Alliance Semi's synchronous SRAM product line in the auctioning of Alliance's assets.

In 2007 the SEC brought civil charges against ISSI and its former CFO Gary Fischer for fraudulently backdating stock option grants and concealing millions of dollars in compensation expenses. The company and Fischer settled the charges without admitting or denying guilt. Fischer agreed to repay $414830 in ill-gotten gains and to pay a civil penalty of $125000 and consented to an order prohibiting him from serving as an officer or director of a publicly held company for five years. ISSI got off fairly lightly agreeing to a permanent injunction against violating federal securities laws on books and records fraud internal controls and reporting. The SEC cited the company's cooperation with the securities regulator's staff in the investigation.

EXECUTIVES

Chairman, Jimmy S. M. Lee, age 57, $90,326 total compensation

VP Finance and Administration and CFO, John M. Cobb, age 55, $201,938 total compensation

SVP Worldwide Sales, Sanjiv Asthana

President CEO and Director, Scott D. Howarth, age 51, $248,722 total compensation

Vice Chairman, Kong Yeu Han, age 57, $220,661 total compensation

EVP and General Manager ISSI-Taiwan and SRAM/DRAM Business, Chang-Chaio (James) Han, age 59, $250,000 total compensation

VP Quality and Reliability Assurance, Shou-kong Fan

Vice President of Worldwide Sales, Sanjiv AsthanaSr

Director, W. Keith McDonald Sr., age 64

Director, Bruce A. Wooley, age 69

President CEO and Director, Scott D. Howarth, age 51

Vice Chairman, Kong Yeu Han, age 57

Director, Paul Chien, age 60

Director, Stephen Pletcher, age 71

Director, John Zimmerman, age 64

Independent Director, Jonathan Khazam

Auditors: GrantThorntonLLP

LOCATIONS

HQ: Integrated Silicon Solution Inc.
1940 Zanker Rd., San Jose CA 95112-4216
Phone: 408-969-6600 **Fax:** 408-969-7800
Web: www.issi.com

2011 Sales

	$ mil.	% of total
Asia/Pacific		
Hong Kong	74	28
Taiwan	28	11
Japan	23	9
China	10	4
Other countries	37	14
Europe	53	19
US	40	15
Other regions	1	-
Total	**270**	**100**

COMPETITORS

Atmel
Cypress Semiconductor
Elpida Memory
Freescale Semiconductor
GSI Technology
Integrated Device Technology
Microchip Technology
Micron Technology
Mosel Vitelic
Oki Semiconductor
Ramtron International
SK Hynix
STMicroelectronics
Samsung Electronics
Silicon Motion
Sony
Toshiba Semiconductor & Storage Products
Winbond Electronics

HISTORICAL FINANCIALS

Company Type: Public

Income Statement

FYE: September 30

	REVENUE ($ mil.)	NET INCOME ($ mil.)	NET PROFIT MARGIN	EMPLOYEES
09/13	307.5	17.5	5.7%	590
09/12	265.9	(2.7)	—	552
09/11	270.5	55.9	20.7%	469
09/10	252.4	42.2	16.7%	452
09/09	154.2	(5.0)	—	445
Annual Growth	**18.8%**	**—**	**—**	**7.3%**

2013 Year-End Financials

Debt ratio: 1.3%	No. of shares (mil.): 29
Return on equity: 6.7%	Dividends
Cash ($ mil.): 120	Yield: —
Current ratio: 4.15	Payout: —
Long-term debt ($ mil.): 4	Market value ($ mil.): 316

	STOCK PRICE ($) FY Close	P/E High/Low		Earnings	Dividends	Book Value
09/13	10.89	19	13	0.59	0.00	9.65
09/12	9.26	—	—	(0.10)	0.00	8.80
09/11	7.81	6	3	1.98	0.00	8.79
09/10	8.61	8	2	1.56	0.00	6.57
09/09	3.76	—	—	(0.20)	0.00	4.89
Annual Growth	**30.5%**	**—**	**—**	**—**	**—**	**18.5%**

Inter Parfums, Inc.

Would a perfumer by any other name smell as sweet? Inter Parfums certainly hopes not. Most of the fragrance developer and manufacturer's revenue is generated by sales of its prestige fragrance brands including Karl Jimmy Choo Lanvin Montblanc Repetto S.T. Dupont Van Cleef & Arpels Paul Smith and (for now) Burberry. It also sells moderately priced perfumes personal care products and cosmetics for specialty retailers such as The Gap bebe stores Brooks Brothers and Anthropologie. The company owns Lanvin Perfumes and upscale men's skin care firm Nickel. Customers include specialty and department stores mass merchandisers and drugstore chains. Its fragrances are sold in more than 120 countries.

Inter Parfums' European subsidiary publicly-held Paris-based Inter Parfums S.A. makes and markets the company's prestige fragrance lines (90% of 2011 net sales). The European arm has distribution operations in Germany Italy and the UK. The fragrance maker's three wholly-owned subsidiaries in the US are Jean Philippe Fragrances Inter Parfums USA and Nickel USA. The company's largest market is Europe (about 40% of 2011 sales) followed by the US with about 22%. Asia with its seemingly insatiable thirst for luxury brands is a fast-growing market for Inter Parfums accounting for about 15% of sales in 2011. To strengthen its position in prestige fragrance and boost its European unit Inter Parfums in late 2012 inked a noteworthy 20-year licensing agreement with international haute couture fashion house

Karl Lagerfeld BV. The worldwide and exclusive agreement to create produce and distribute perfumes under the Karl Lagerfeld brand replaces a previous agreement held with Coty that was terminated by mutual consent.

Inter Parfums saw its 2011 net sales jump 34% vs. 2010 to a record $615 million. Sales by its European arm increased 36% to $552 million while sales at its US-based operations grew by 13%. Net income grew by more than 21% over the same period. Growth in Europe was fueled by the launch of a new Burberry fragrance Burberry Body which ranks as the largest fragrance launch in Inter Parfums' history. Indeed Burberry product sales in 2011 increased 26% to more than $307 million compared with about $245 million in 2010. Jimmy Choo and Montblanc brand fragrances also gained sales momentum in 2011.

Inter Parfums' strategy is to continue to expand its portfolio of high-profile prestige brands. Prestige scents have grown to account for 90% of 2011 sales up from 76% in 2003. To that end the fragrance maker in late 2011 signed a 13-year licensing agreement with France's Repetto a maker of dance and dance-inspired shoes and accessories. The first fragrance from the new partnership is due in 2013. Given the importance of the Burberry license to Inter Parfums' overall business the two companies were exploring ways to increase the brand's potential. Under consideration was the establishment of a new operating structure for the Burberry fragrance and beauty business. Potentially detrimental to the Inter Parfums business Burberry opted to buy out the unexpired portion of the license for E181 million (or $220 million) on December 31 2012. Burberry has been the company's largest brand encompassing eight fragrance families and accounting for 50% of total sales in 2011 (down from 57% in 2009).

Since Inter Parfums' entry into the specialty retail market via an exclusive agreement with Gap Inc. (signed in mid-2005) to design and manufacture personal care products under the Gap and Banana Republic brands the company inked similar deals with retailers New York & Company and Brooks Brothers in 2007 and bebe stores in 2008. Newer retail partners include Anthropologie Betsy Johnson Lane Bryant and Nine West. The company's mass-market business includes several proprietary fragrance brands (including Jean Philippe Paris) a license for Jordache fragrances low-priced cosmetics (Aziza) and health and beauty aids.

Founders Jean Madar (CEO) and Philippe Benacin (vice chairman and president and CEO of Inter Parfums S.A.) own 24% and 23% of the company's stock respectively.

HISTORY

Jean Madar and Philippe Benacin founded Jean Philippe Fragrances in 1985 to make knockoff fragrances in the US and took it public three years later. Jean Philippe bought fragrance and cosmetics rights from Jordache Enterprises in 1990. The next year it bought Inter Parfums S.A. a French affiliate Madar and Benacin founded in 1983. Jean Philippe took that subsidiary public in 1995.

The company aggressively expanded its markets and product line. In 1994 Inter Parfums S.A. acquired trademarks for a variety of fragrances from Parfums Molyneux and Parfums Weil and Jean Philippe bought the worldwide trademark for Intimate and Chaz from Revlon. From Chesebrough-Pond's Jean Philippe acquired rights that year to Cutex nail enamel and lipsticks (later relinquished) and Aziza eye makeup which brought it

greater access to mass-merchandise channels such as Wal-Mart.

A year later Jean Philippe launched Romantic Illusions a collection of eight perfumes packed in cartons designed to look like romance novels. Sales declined in 1996-97 partly due to increased US competition economic turmoil in Russia and lagging sales in Brazil. (The company closed its Brazilian subsidiary in 1998.) Also in 1998 Jean Philippe developed a line of medium-priced fragrances (not knockoffs).

The following year Jean Philippe decided to take the name of its primary sales vehicle subsidiary Inter Parfums S.A. adding an Americanized "Inc." to the end. France's LVMH which bottles Christian Dior and Givenchy perfumes upped its stake in Inter Parfums to 20%.

Inter Parfums launched its Paul Smith line of fragrances in 2000 and announced plans for a new line of bath products under the Burberry name. Two years later the company purchased certain mass-market fragrances and inventories of bankrupt and now-defunct rival Tristar Corporation and also signed a license agreement with Diane Von Furstenberg to market her fragrance and beauty products.

In April 2004 Inter Parfums acquired a 68% interest in Nickel S.A. a men's skin care company with 1700 outlets in Western Europe and the US as well as men's spas in Paris and New York. The acquisition cost Inter Parfums approximately $8.3 million in cash.

Inter Parfums signed an exclusive worldwide licensing deal in 2006 with sports manufacturer and retailer Quiksilver for a namesake and Roxy line of personal care products. As part of the deal Inter Parfums developed and distributed Roxy fragrance sun care skin care and related items and Quiksilver sun care and other products. The two parties agreed to early termination of the agreement in mid-2010 (about six-and-a-half years earlier than originally scheduled).

The company replaced LVMH's YSL Beaute as the licensing contractor for Van Cleef & Arpels in 2006. Inter Parfums inked the deal to add a jewelry brand to its portfolio.

In December 2011 Inter Parfums signed a 13-year license agreement with Repetto known for its dance and dance-inspired shoes and accessories.

EXECUTIVES

Chief Financial Officer; Executive Vice President; Director, Russell Greenberg, age 57, $435,000 total compensation
Vice Chairman and President; President and CEO Inter Parfums S.A., Philippe Benacin, age 54, $348,492 total compensation
Chairman and CEO; Director General Inter Parfums S.A., Jean Madar, age 53, $380,000 total compensation
Director; EVP CFO and Director of Finance Inter Parfums S.A., Philippe Santi, age 52, $348,492 total compensation
Director Luxury and Fashion division Inter Parfums S.A., Frederic Garcia-Pelayo, age 54, $348,492 total compensation
Controller and Secretary, Michelle Habert
VP Distribution and Warehousing, Alex Canavan
VP Retail Sales, Michel Bes
President of Inter Parfums USA; LLC, Henry B. (Andy) Clarke, age 52
Director Operations Inter Parfums S.A., Axel Marot, age 39
Director Parfums Burberry, Hugues de La Chevasnerie, age 44
Sales Administration, Jennifer Giachino

EVP CFO and Director, Russell Greenberg, age 56
Vice Chairman and President; President and CEO Inter Parfums S.A., Philippe Benacin, age 54
Director, Patrick Choel, age 68
Director; EVP CFO and Director of Finance Inter Parfums S.A., Philippe Santi, age 52
Director, Francois Heilbronn, age 53
Director, Jean Levy, age 80
Director, Robert Bensoussan-Torres, age 56
Director, Serge Rosinoer, age 82
Independent Director, Patrick Choel
Independent Director, Robert Torres
Auditors: MazarsLLP

LOCATIONS

HQ: Inter Parfums Inc.
551 5th Ave. Ste. 1500, New York NY 10176
Phone: 212-983-2640 **Fax:** 212-983-4197
Web: www.interparfumsinc.com

2011 Sales

	$ mil.	% of total
Europe	246	40
North America	150	24
Asia	95	15
Central & South America	61	10
Middle East	57	9
Other	6	2
Total	**615**	**100**

PRODUCTS/OPERATIONS

2011 Sales

	% of total
Prestige	90
Specialty retail & mass-market fragrance & fragrance-related	10
Total	**100**

Selected Brand Name and Licensed Fragrances and Cosmetics

Anna Sui
Boucheron
Burberry
Jimmy Choo
Karl Lagerfeld
Lane Bryant
Lanvin
Montblanc
Nickel
Paul Smith
Pierre Balmain
Repetto
S.T. Dupont
Van Cleef & Arpels

COMPETITORS

Abercrombie & Fitch	Elizabeth Arden Inc
Adolfo Dominguez	Estee Lauder
Ales	L Brands
American Eagle Outfitters	L' Oreal
Avon	LVMH
Body Shop	Mary Kay
Borghese	Parlux Fragrances
Bulgari	Procter & Gamble
Chanel	Revlon
Clarins	Richemont
Coty Inc.	Shiseido
Dana Classic Fragrances	Unilever
	Victoria' s Secret Stores
	Wella AG

HISTORICAL FINANCIALS

Company Type: Public

Income Statement

FYE: December 31

	REVENUE ($ mil.)	NET INCOME ($ mil.)	NET PROFIT MARGIN	EMPLOYEES
12/12	654.1	131.1	20.0%	312
12/11	615.2	32.3	5.3%	283
12/10	460.4	26.5	5.8%	271
12/09	409.4	22.3	5.5%	256
12/08	446.1	23.7	5.3%	245
Annual Growth	10.0%	53.3%	—	6.2%

2012 Year-End Financials

Debt ratio: 3.6%
Return on equity: 41.2%
Cash ($ mil.): 307
Current ratio: 2.43
Long-term debt ($ mil.): —

No. of shares (mil.): 30
Dividends
  Yield: 1.6%
  Payout: 7.5%
Market value ($ mil.): 597

	STOCK PRICE ($) FY Close	P/E High/Low		PER SHARE ($) Earnings	Dividends	Book Value
12/12	19.46	5	4	4.26	0.32	12.43
12/11	15.56	23	13	1.05	0.32	8.27
12/10	18.85	22	13	0.87	0.26	7.72
12/09	12.17	18	5	0.74	0.13	7.58
12/08	7.68	37	7	0.77	0.13	6.77
Annual Growth	26.2%	—	—	53.4%	24.7%	16.4%

IntercontinentalExchange Group Inc.

If there were money to be made in ice futures IntercontinentalExchange (ICE) would probably trade that as well. The firm is a leading provider of online marketplaces and clearing services for global commodity trading primarily of electricity natural gas crude oil refined petroleum products precious metals and weather and emission credits. It manages a handful of global OTC markets and regulated futures exchanges. The firm owns the ICE Futures Europe a leading European energy futures and options platform. ICE Data provides real-time daily and historical market data reports. ICE serves clients in more than 120 countries globally.

ICE is based in Atlanta and has offices in Calgary; Chicago; Houston; London; New York; San Francisco; Singapore; Stamford Connecticut; Washington DC; and Winnipeg. The company makes some 80% of its profits from transaction and clearing fees for both exchange and over-the-counter (OTC) products.

Over the past four years the company has reported a major spike in revenues driven by the recovering global economy and higher commodity prices. In 2011 revenues grew 15% to $1.3 billion while net income rose 28% to $509.7 million. The company's global OTC segment has been leading its growth as have strong performances of its ICE Brent Crude and ICE Gas Oil futures contracts and an increase in credit default swaps clearing revenues.

ICE has grown rapidly through a series of acquisitions and portfolio diversifications. In 2010 it acquired Climate Exchange a leader in the development of traded emissions markets. Expanding its options market portfolio in 2011 the company acquired broker/dealer Ballista which offers an electronic options platform for the execution of large and complex multi-leg options transactions. Also that year it bought 12% of Brazilian clearinghouse operator Cetip SA for $514 million. In 2012 ICE bought WhenTech a provider of options technology including valuation analytics and risk management.

The company has also added to its OTC contracts offerings through the recently formed ICE Clear Europe. In 2011 alone it launched more than 250 new contracts for oil natural gas power emissions and refined petroleum products. ICE that year also launched new futures contracts including currency futures contracts and coal and natural gas option contracts. In Canada in early 2012 the company began trading new futures contracts on wheat and barley.

In a major move in 2011 ICE and NASDAQ OMX Group teamed up to make a joint $11.3 billion bid for NYSE Euronext. As part of the deal ICE would buy NYSE Euronext's derivatives businesses while NASDAQ OMX would keep the remaining businesses including the US-based business and NYSE Euronext stock exchanges in Amsterdam Brussels Lisbon New York and Paris. However the bid which countered Deutsche Borse's earlier offer to acquire NYSE EURONEXT was initially rejected prompting the two partners to reaffirm their bid. The companies subsequently dropped the bid following discussions with the Antitrust Division of the US Department of Justice

EXECUTIVES

Chairman and CEO, Jeffrey C. (Jeff) Sprecher, age 58, $780,000 total compensation
SVP and CTO, Edwin D. Marcial, age 45, $406,000 total compensation
SVP and Chief Strategic Officer, David S. Goone, age 52, $488,000 total compensation
President and COO, Charles A. (Chuck) Vice, age 49, $530,000 total compensation
VP Investor Relations and Corporate Communications, Kelly L. Loeffler
President and COO ICE Futures Canada, E. Bradley (Brad) Vannan
President ICE; CEO NYSE, Duncan L. Niederauer, age 53
President and COO ICE Futures Europe, David J. Peniket, age 47
SVP General Counsel and Secretary, Johnathan H. Short, age 47
Senior Vice President - Financial Markets, Thomas W. (Tom) Farley, age 37
SVP and CFO, Scott A. Hill, age 45, $414,000 total compensation
President and COO ICE Clear U.S., Thomas J. (Tom) Hammond
President and COO ICE Clear Europe, Paul Swann
COO ICE Futures U.S., Benjamin R. (Ben) Jackson
VP Operations, Mark P. Wassersug
CEO Euronext, Dominique Cerutti, age 52
President ICE Clear Credit, Christopher S. (Chris) Edmonds
Director, Charles R. Crisp, age 66
Director, Frederic V. (Fred) Salerno, age 70
Director, Judith A. (Judy) Sprieser, age 59
Director, Vincent S. Tese, age 70
Director, Jean-Marc Forneri, age 53
Director, Sir Robert Reid, age 78
Director, Fred W. Hatfield, age 58
Director, Terrence F. Martell, age 67
Director, Sir Callum McCarthy, age 69
Independent Director, Judd Gregg
Auditors: Ernst&YoungLLP

LOCATIONS

HQ: IntercontinentalExchange Inc.
  2100 RiverEdge Pkwy. Ste. 500, Atlanta GA 30328
Phone: 770-857-4700   **Fax:** 770-857-4755
Web: www.theice.com

2011 Sales

	$ mil.	% of total
US	682	51
Other countries	644	49
Total	**1,327**	**100**

PRODUCTS/OPERATIONS

2011 Sales

	$ mil.	% of total
Net transaction & clearing fees	1,176	89
Other	26	2

2011 Sales by Segment

	$ mil.	% of total
Global OTC	636	48
Futures	615	46
Market Data	76	6
Total	**1,327**	**100**

Founding Partners
BP p.l.c.
Deutsche Bank AG
The Goldman Sachs Group Inc.
Morgan Stanley Dean Witter & Co.
Royal Dutch Shell plc
Societe Generale

Total	**0**	**0**

COMPETITORS

APX	GFI Group
BGC Partners	ICAP
Bloomberg L.P.	NYMEX Holdings
CHOICE! Energy	NYSE Euronext
CME	Reuters
Enporion	Unitil

HISTORICAL FINANCIALS

Company Type: Public

Income Statement

FYE: December 31

	REVENUE ($ mil.)	NET INCOME ($ mil.)	NET PROFIT MARGIN	EMPLOYEES
12/13	1,674.0	254.0	15.2%	4,232
12/12	1,362.9	551.5	40.5%	1,077
12/11	1,327.4	509.6	38.4%	1,013
12/10	1,149.9	398.3	34.6%	933
12/09	994.7	315.9	31.8%	826
Annual Growth	13.9%	(5.3%)	—	50.4%

2013 Year-End Financials

Debt ratio: 7.8%
Return on equity: 3.1%
Cash ($ mil.): 961
Current ratio: 1.00
Long-term debt ($ mil.): 3,923

No. of shares (mil.): 115
Dividends
  Yield: 0.2%
  Payout: 8.5%
Market value ($ mil.): 25,866

	STOCK PRICE ($) FY Close	P/E High/Low		PER SHARE ($) Earnings	Dividends	Book Value
12/13	224.92	70	38	3.21	0.65	109.42
12/12	123.81	19	15	7.52	0.00	50.27
12/11	120.55	19	15	6.90	0.00	43.10
12/10	119.15	23	17	5.35	0.00	37.89
12/09	112.30	28	12	4.27	0.00	32.65
Annual Growth	19.0%	—	—	(6.9%)	—	35.3%

Interdigital Inc (PA)

InterDigital is more than just interested in wireless digital telecommunications. The company develops and licenses circuitry designs software and other technology using CDMA (code-division multiple access) and other wireless communications standards. Altogether it holds a patent portfolio of about 1500 US patents and 8800 foreign ones. InterDigital licenses its technology patents to companies that make smartphones tablets notebook computers and wireless personal digital assistants as well as wireless infrastructure equipment such as base stations and components dongles and modules for wireless devices. Top customers include Acer Apple HTC and other makers of chips software and telecom equipment.

Operations

In 2012 InterDigital formed a joint venture with Sony Corporation of America. Convida Wireless is a research organization devoted to developing wireless machine-to-machine (M2M) technology. The deal also includes a three-year patent license to Sony for its 3G and 4G products.

Also that year it established a business unit InterDigital Solutions dedicated to monetizing its market-ready technologies and research capabilities.

Geographic Reach

InterDigital operates from four research and development offices in the US and one in Canada.

Sales and Marketing

Historically the company generates most of its revenues from Asia where the world's electronics are manufactured. However after selling 1700 patents to Intel in 2012 the US accounted for the majority of revenues that year.

Financial Performance

InterDigital generates revenues primarily from royalties for patent license agreements and by licensing technology solutions and providing related development support. However its big patent sale to Intel in 2012 resulted in an extra $384 million in sales. That year the company earned $663 million a 271% increase from 2011. Profits also shot up 200% to $271 million.

Strategy

As a patent licensing firm InterDigital must continually expand its pool of licensing customers to continue its growth and the company has a limited number of licensees contributing most of its revenues. InterDigital must also spend money on developing patentable technologies and it has had to litigate to defend the patents it holds for years at a time in some cases.

Some 1400 patents were issued to the company in 2012 and it has about 9000 patent applications pending around the world.

In 2012 InterDigital recognized revenue from more than half of all 3G mobile devices sold around the world. It is working to secure licensing agreements for 4G phones.

The company has built its suite of technology and patent offerings through internal development joint development projects with other companies and acquisitions (although it hasn't made an acquisition in years.)

HISTORY

InterDigital was founded in 1972 as International Mobile Machines Corporation by Sherwin Seligsohn who was its chairman until 1990. It began to develop technologies that held the potential to revolutionize radiotelephone communications but as a small company unable to usher in the digital age on its own the company patented its inventions. It went public in 1981 which allowed it to expand into product development.

The company expanded its technology portfolio by acquiring the assets of Tantivy Communications a designer of CDMA-based and other wireless gear in 2003 for $11.5 million.

Interdigital worked with Nokia at the turn of the century to develop Internet access technology for mobile phones. A legal dispute between the two companies over the amount of royalties Nokia owed was resolved in InterDigital's favor in 2005 when a US District Court judge upheld an international tribunal's verdict ordering Nokia to pay additional royalties to InterDigital. In 2006 Nokia agreed to pay $253 million in one lump sum to InterDigital and the companies agreed to end their litigation against each other. Nokia and InterDigital immediately terminated their original license agreement and began negotiating a new pact.

Those talks apparently came to naught as InterDigital in 2007 filed a complaint against Nokia with the US International Trade Commission (ITC) alleging that Nokia's handsets infringe on patents held by InterDigital. The company sought to ban sales in the US of the Nokia N75 model and any other handsets that infringe on InterDigital patents. InterDigital separately filed a patent infringement lawsuit against Nokia in US District Court in Delaware. Nokia said it would vigorously defend against both actions.

LG Electronics signed a five-year patent licensing agreement with InterDigital in 2006. The pact calls for the Korean manufacturer of consumer electronics and home appliances to pay InterDigital a total of $285 million in the first three years of the agreement in annual installments of $95 million. Even more checks should be coming from the Korean peninsula: An international arbitration tribunal awarded InterDigital $134 million in past royalties plus interest from Samsung Electronics. The amount of royalties is tied to the company's patent licensing agreement with Nokia.

In 2007 the company shortened its name from InterDigital Communications Corporation to InterDigital Inc. The change was made in connection with a reorganization that saw the company shift from a pure R&D and licensing venture to one selling application-specific integrated circuits (ASICs) and making strategic investments in addition to wireless communications research and technology licensing.

In 2008 InterDigital and Nokia entered into settlement talks on the patent issues after a US District Court ruling went against InterDigital and the company was ordered to enter arbitration with Nokia. InterDigital appealed the court ruling but also said it made "substantial progress" in privately resolving the dispute with Nokia.

Unable to reach a patent licensing agreement with Samsung Electronics InterDigital filed a complaint against the giant Korean manufacturer with the US International Trade Commission. It also filed a lawsuit in US District Court in Delaware alleging patent infringement by Samsung's Blackjack mobile phone and other models. The $134 million award against Samsung was upheld by the US District Court for the Southern District of New York in 2007.

In late 2008 InterDigital reported reaching terms of a possible settlement with Samsung including a royalty-bearing license for Samsung that would be in effect through 2012. The companies in early 2009 signed a licensing agreement that calls for the Korean giant to pay $400 million in royalties to InterDigital.

In 2009 InterDigital ceased product development of its SlimChip High Speed Packet Access (HSPA) technology and offered the HSPA intellectual property for licensing resulting in the layoff of about 100 employees a reduction in force of around 26%. The move marked a shift away from a strategy of developing silicon products initiated two years earlier due to the cost of designing and fabricating products. This returned the company to technology development and licensing for cellular and non-cellular wireless protocols. In 2010 it signed its first license agreement for the SlimChip 2G and 3G modem technology to Inventec Appliances a Chinese mobile chipset manufacturer and subsidiary of Taiwanese contract manufacturer Inventec.

InterDigital was approached by Google in 2011 about a possible sale as the Internet giant sought to expand its patent portfolio.

	$ mil.	% of total
US		61
Korea		18
Canada		6
Taiwan		6
Japan		6
China		1
Germany		1
Other		1
Total		**100**

PRODUCTS/OPERATIONS

2012 Sales

	% of total
Patent	58
Fixed-fee	20
Per-unit	17
Past sales	4
Technology solutions	1
Total	**100**

COMPETITORS

Alcatel-Lucent	LSI Corp.
Broadcom	Marvell Technology
Conexant Systems	Nokia
Freescale	QUALCOMM
Semiconductor	ST-Ericsson
IBM Microelectronics	Sonics
Infineon Technologies	Texas Instruments
Intel	Xora

HISTORICAL FINANCIALS

Company Type: Public

Income Statement

FYE: December 31

	REVENUE ($ mil.)	NET INCOME ($ mil.)	NET PROFIT MARGIN	EMPLOYEES
12/12	663.0	271.8	41.0%	290
12/11	301.7	89.4	29.7%	330
12/10	394.5	153.6	38.9%	300
12/09	297.4	87.2	29.3%	299
12/08	228.4	26.2	11.5%	379
Annual Growth	30.5%	79.5%	—	(6.5%)

2012 Year-End Financials

Debt ratio: 18.9%	No. of shares (mil.): 41
Return on equity: 54.7%	Dividends
Cash ($ mil.): 349	Yield: 4.6%
Current ratio: 4.71	Payout: 29.1%
Long-term debt ($ mil.): 200	Market value ($ mil.): 1,687

	STOCK PRICE ($) FY Close	P/E High/Low		PER SHARE ($) Earnings	Dividends	Book Value
12/12	41.09	7	4	6.26	1.90	12.64
12/11	43.57	38	18	1.94	0.50	10.36
12/10	41.64	12	7	3.43	0.00	7.84
12/09	26.56	17	9	1.95	0.00	3.92
12/08	27.50	48	29	0.57	0.00	2.02
Annual Growth	10.6%	—	—	82.0%	—	58.1%

Intrepid Potash Inc

Hungry plants turn to Intrepid Potash for their food supply. The mining company produces two potassium-containing minerals potash and langbeinite that are essential ingredients in plant and crop fertilizer. Intrepid culls these minerals from five mines in New Mexico and Utah where it also operates production facilities. The company has the capacity to annually produce about 870000 tons of potash and 200000 tons of langbeinite and sells its products primarily in the US to the agricultural industrial and feed markets. It markets langbeinite under the brand Trio. Intrepid Potash is the largest producer of muriate of potash (potassium chloride) in the US the second-largest consuming country of potash.

Intrepid Potash and Russia's Uralkali are the only two publicly traded potash-only companies in the world. Intrepid sells its potash as a fertilizer for the agricultural market as an ingredient in drilling and fracturing fluids for the oil and gas market and as a nutrient for the animal feed market. The agricultural market accounts for more than 80% of the company's potash sales. The company's langbeinite is also sold as a fertilizer in the agricultural market and as a nutrient in the animal feed market.

The company operates three potash production facilities in the Carlsbad New Mexico area and two in Utah which it refers to as its Moab and Wendover facilities. Its Carlsbad assets use underground mining supported by surface processing to recover the potash. Its Utah facilities use solar mining techniques to recover potash. From langbeinite ore it produces sulfate of potash magnesium giving it the added benefits of sulfate and magnesium in providing a multi-nutrient product.

About 90% of its revenues come from its production and sales of potash. The agricultural market primarily uses the granular-sized potash and Trio while the industrial and animal feed markets use standard and fine sizes of the product. The company's sales focus on the agricultural areas and feed manufacturers of the central and western US and the oil and gas drilling areas of the Rocky Mountains and greater Permian Basin region. Trio is sold in the agricultural market as a fertilizer and the animal feed market as a nutrient. Intrepid also markets internationally through an agreement with PCS Sales.

In fiscal 2011 the company generated sales of $443 million a 24% increase from the previous year. The increase resulted from the increase in production of potash by 86000 tons as well as a 30% jump in the average net realized sales price for potash that year. Driven by higher average sales prices for both potash and Trio Intrepid's net income for 2011 also increased reaching $109.4 million over the $45.3 million posted the prior year.

The company's strategy focuses on maximizing margins by trying to reduce per ton operating costs and production downtime. Intrepid's mines are strategically located near its largest customers which allows it to realize higher average net sales than many of its competitors who depend on exports.

Intrepid also has been expanding its operating facilities to increase production. In 2011 and 2012 it expanded its mining capacity at its East and West sites in Carlsbad and expanded the cavern network of its Moab facility in 2011. In addition the company has been adding granulation capacity which will enhance its sales opportunities for both potash and Trio. Also slated to increase production is Intrepid's HB mine near Carlsbad which had been idled but is being converted to a solar mine using the same solar evaporation and solution mining technology as the Moab mine in Utah. Intrepid's Langbeinite Recovery Improvement Project included the company's construction of a dense media separation plant in 2011 to improve langbeinite recoveries and reduce process water consumption. The project also includes the new granulation plant.

Chairman Robert Jornayvaz and Vice Chairman Hugh Harvey Jr. together control about 28% of Intrepid Potash.

HISTORY

Intrepid Potash went public in 2008 at which time it acquired all the assets and four main subsidiaries from former parent Intrepid Mining.

The company intends to boost its production of langbeinite by constructing a new plant which is expected to be completed by the end of 2011 at a cost of between $85 million and $95 million. The new plant will allow the company to granulate its standard-sized langbeinite product giving it marketing flexibility by making a granular-sized product available for sale.

Demand for potash improved in 2010 resulting in higher prices and sales volumes which had decreased in late 2008 because of economic uncertainty. The rebound in agricultural demand began in late 2009 and continued throughout 2010. Intrepid's net sales of potash increased $56.3 million (24%) in 2010 over the previous year as production volumes of potash and Trio reached a combined 886000 tons up from 696000 tons in 2009. However despite the hike in sales and increased production to meet demand the company experienced a lower net income in 2010 over 2009. Intrepid was selling more product than in 2009 but at lower prices and higher costs because of the slump in business conditions beginning in 2008. By the end of 2010 however potash prices began rising.

EXECUTIVES

President Chief Financial Officer, David W. (Dave) Honeyfield, age 46, $236,250 total compensation
Chairman, Robert P. Jornayvaz III, age 54, $487,500 total compensation
Vice Chairman, Hugh E. Harvey Jr., $487,500 total compensation
Executive Vice President of Human Resources and Risk Management, James N. Whyte, age 54, $225,845 total compensation
Executive Vice President General Counsel Secretary, Martin D. Litt, age 48
Senior Vice President of Operations, John G. Mansanti, age 58
Vice President Chief Accounting Officer, Brian D. Frantz, age 50
Vice President of Business Development & Research, Kenneth G. Taylor
Senior Vice President - Sales and Marketing, Kelvin G. Feist
Vice President - Taxation, Matthew Adams
Director - Investor Relations, William Kent
Vice President of Investor Relations, Gary A. Kohn
Director, Terry Considine, age 65
Director, J. Landis (Lanny) Martin, age 68
Director, Barth E. Whitham, age 56
Vice Chairman, Hugh E. Harvey Jr.
Director, Chris A. Elliott
Auditors: KPMGLLP

LOCATIONS

HQ: Intrepid Potash Inc.
700 17th St. Ste. 1700, Denver CO 80202
Phone: 303-296-3006   **Fax:** 303-298-7502
Web: www.intrepidpotash.com

2011 Sales

	% of total
US	95
Mexico & Latin	3
Canada &	2
Total	**100**

PRODUCTS/OPERATIONS

2011 Sales

	$ mil.	% of total
Potash	392	89
Langbeinite (Trio)	50	11
Total	**442**	**100**

COMPETITORS

AMCOL	Israel Chemicals
Agrium	K+S
American Vanguard	Mosaic Company
Arab Potash	Potash Corp
CF Industries	SQM

HISTORICAL FINANCIALS

Company Type: Public

Income Statement

FYE: December 31

	REVENUE ($ mil.)	NET INCOME ($ mil.)	NET PROFIT MARGIN	EMPLOYEES
12/12	451.3	87.4	19.4%	935
12/11	442.9	109.4	24.7%	871
12/10	359.3	45.2	12.6%	803
12/09	301.8	55.3	18.3%	778
12/08	305.9	98.1	32.1%	776
Annual Growth	**10.2%**	**(2.9%)**	**—**	**4.8%**

2012 Year-End Financials

Debt ratio: —	No. of shares (mil.): 75
Return on equity: 9.8%	Dividends
Cash ($ mil.): 33	Yield: 3.5%
Current ratio: 2.41	Payout: 63.0%
Long-term debt ($ mil.): —	Market value ($ mil.): 1,603

	STOCK PRICE ($) FY Close	P/E High/Low	PER SHARE ($) Earnings	Dividends	Book Value
12/12	21.29	23 16	1.16	0.75	12.03
12/11	22.63	27 14	1.45	0.00	11.58
12/10	37.29	61 33	0.60	0.00	10.09
12/09	29.17	45 20	0.74	0.00	9.45
12/08	20.77	56 11	1.31	0.00	8.71
Annual Growth	**0.6%**	**— —**	**(3.0%)**	**—**	**8.4%**

Intuitive Surgical Inc

Intuitive Surgical gives an artistic flair to advanced surgical equipment. Employing haptics (the science of computer-aided touch sensitivity) the firm developed the da Vinci Surgical System a combination of software hardware and optics that allows doctors to perform robotically aided surgery from a remote console. The da Vinci system reproduces the doctor's hand movements in real time during minimally invasive surgery performed by tiny electromechanical arms and instruments. The company manufactures its systems and relies upon contract manufacturers to supply the instruments and accessories used with the systems.

Geographic Reach

Intuitive Surgical sells its products in North America Asia and Europe.

Operations

The da Vinci system's oldest applications —use gynecological and urological procedures —still account for more than 90% of da Vinci-assisted surgeries. (About 450000 procedures are performed each year.) Over time the company has widened the system's applications to include cardiothoracic transoral (head and neck) and general surgical procedures.

Along with reducing trauma to the patient related to large incisions Intuitive Surgical promotes its minimally invasive robotic systems as a means of increasing a surgeon's precision intuitive control range of motion and vision during procedures.

Initial sales of the da Vinci systems make up about 45% of revenues while follow-up sales of instruments and accessories account for another 40% of sales. Intuitive Surgical also maintains relationships with (and earns additional revenues from) customers by providing system support and physician training services.

Sales and Marketing

Intuitive Surgical sells its products through a direct sales force in the US Korea and most European countries. It uses independent distributors in other global markets.

Hospitals can take several routes to obtain the big-ticket da Vinci systems. Some can plunk down the $1 million plus in cash while others work with third-party leasing companies to spread the payments out over time. Once the system is in place a hospital must continue to purchase replacement instruments and accessories from the company.

Financial Performance

The leading maker of surgical robots Intuitive Surgical has seen strong growth in recent years as demand for less traumatic minimally invasive surgical procedures has increased. Revenues increased 24% in 2012 to nearly $2.2 billion due to increased product sales in the US and abroad (attributed to new system sales and higher procedure volumes) as well as higher service revenues. Net income grew 33% to $657 million due to higher revenues interest income and other income.

Strategy

Part of Intuitive Surgical's growth strategy is to introduce next generation versions of the original da Vinci system. Newer models build on the robot's core technology adding enhancements that include increased visual acuity and ease of use. The da Vinci Single-Site instruments and accessories were introduced in 2011 to allow the systems to work through a single incision reducing trauma to the patient. In 2012 the company also received FDA approval for its EndoWrist One vessel sealing instrument (also for use with da Vinci systems).

The company is also expanding its organization as use of the da Vinci system increases. Intuitive Surgical is growing its direct sales organization as well as its manufacturing and R&D workforces. It also occasionally forms strategic alliances with other medical device firms in areas including product development training and marketing

Mergers and Acquisitions

Intuitive Surgical grows through occasional acquisitions as well. In 2012 it expanded its direct sales operations by purchasing its Korean distributor for an undisclosed price.

EXECUTIVES

Chairman, Lonnie M. Smith, age 69, $508,700 total compensation

President CEO and Director, Gary S. Guthart, age 47, $430,000 total compensation

SVP and General Counsel, Mark J. Meltzer, age 64, $328,750 total compensation

EVP Worldwide Sales and Marketing, Jerome J. (Jerry) McNamara, age 55, $341,250 total compensation

VP Strategy, Aleks Cukic

SVP Product Operations, Augusto V. Castello

SVP and CFO, Marshall L. Mohr, age 57, $340,000 total compensation

SVP Customer Support Group, Colin Morales

SVP Product Development, Salvatore J. (Sal) Brogna

SVP Sales - Americas/Australia, Jim Alecxih

VP Marketing and Business Development, Frank P. Grillo

SVP Scientific Affairs, David J. (Dave) Rosa

VP Human Resources, Nancy L. Hill

Sales Manager, Joan Comes

Director, D. Keith Grossman, age 53

President CEO and Director, Gary S. Guthart, age 47

Director, Eric H. Halvorson, age 64

Director, Alan J. Levy, age 75

Director, Floyd D. Loop, age 76

Director, Mark J. Rubash, age 56

Director, Robert W. Duggan, age 69

Director, George Stalk Jr., age 63

Independent Director, Amal Johnson

Independent Director, Craig Barratt

Auditors: Ernst&YoungLLP

LOCATIONS

HQ: Intuitive Surgical Inc.
1266 Kifer Rd. Bldg. 101, Sunnyvale CA 94086-5304
Phone: 408-523-2100   **Fax:** 408-523-1390
Web: www.intuitivesurgical.com

2012 Sales

US	1,726	79
Total	**2,178**	**100**

PRODUCTS/OPERATIONS

2012 Sales

	$ mil.	% of total
Products	1,836	84
Services	342	16
Total	**2,178**	**100**

COMPETITORS

Accuray	Medtronic
Bard	Medtronic Sofamor
Boston Scientific	Danek
Curexo Technology	Stereotaxis
Freehand 2010	Toshiba
Hansen Medical	

HISTORICAL FINANCIALS

Company Type: Public

Income Statement

FYE: December 31

	REVENUE ($ mil.)	NET INCOME ($ mil.)	NET PROFIT MARGIN	EMPLOYEES
12/13	2,265.1	671.0	29.6%	2,792
12/12	2,178.8	656.6	30.1%	2,362
12/11	1,757.3	495.1	28.2%	1,924
12/10	1,413.0	381.8	27.0%	1,660
12/09	1,052.1	232.6	22.1%	1,263
Annual Growth	**21.1%**	**30.3%**	**—**	**21.9%**

2013 Year-End Financials

Debt ratio: —
Return on equity: 18.9%
Cash ($ mil.): 782
Current ratio: 5.07
Long-term debt ($ mil.): —

No. of shares (mil.): 38
Dividends
  Yield: —
  Payout: —
Market value ($ mil.): 14,672

	STOCK PRICE ($) FY Close	P/E High/Low		PER SHARE ($) Earnings	Dividends	Book Value
12/13	384.08	34	21	16.73	0.00	91.66
12/12	490.37	36	27	15.98	0.00	89.06
12/11	463.01	37	20	12.32	0.00	67.32
12/10	257.75	40	25	9.47	0.00	52.38
12/09	303.43	51	14	5.93	0.00	39.93
Annual Growth	6.1%	—	—	29.6%	—	23.1%

Inventure Foods Inc.

It's always an adventure in taste at Inventure Foods (formerly The Inventure Group). The company makes potato and other snack chips pretzels and more under Bob's Texas Style Braids Poore Brothers Boulder Canyon Natural Foods and Tato Skins brands to name a few. Inventure Foods also makes salted snacks branded with the T.G.I. Friday's (29% of sales) and BURGER KING names and manufactures private label snacks for several grocery chains and natural food stores in the US. The firm also distributes its own and other companies' snack food products. Its Rader Farms business grows and processes berries in Washington State. Warehouse club operator Costco accounts for about a quarter of the company's sales.

Americans were in a snacking mood in 2010 as Inventure Foods' total sales rose more than 10% vs. 2009 boosted by sales gains from the launch of Jamba Juice-brand smoothie make-at-home kits several new snack products under the Boulder Canyon brandand Rader Farms frozen berry snack packs. The new snack and berry products capitalize on consumers' growing taste for healthy fruit-based products and diversify Inventure's core business as a salty snack-food manufacturer.

The 2010 sales gain was the fourth consecutive annual revenue increase for the business which has grown through acquisitions organically through new product introductions and partnerships such as its licensing agreement with Jamba (expires in 2014). The Jamba-brand smoothies that are sold in supermarkets and contain raspberries and blueberries grown by Rader Farms. The firm is also growing its distribution network to get its products into more stores and new markets.

The $20.9-million purchase of Rader Farms (in 2007) launched Inventure's effort to move beyond its core business as a salty snack-food manufacturer. Rader grows processes freezes and markets raspberries blueberries rhubarb and berry blends. It also purchases marionberries cherries cranberries and strawberries from fruit growers for processing and sale. It sells its products to wholesale customers under the Radar Farms and private-label brands.

Director Larry Polhill owns about 23% of Inventure Foods through Capital Foods LLC. Investment firm Heartland Advisors owns about 16% of the snack maker's shares.

HISTORY

The Company was formed in 1995 as a holding company to acquire a potato chip manufacturing and distribution business which had been founded by Donald and James Poore in 1986.

In 1996 the company went public.

In 1998 it acquired Bob's Style Potato Chips.

A Bluffton Indiana facility - the location where T.G.I. Friday's snack foods are produced - was acquired in 1999 and the Boulder Canyon brand was purchased in 2000.

In 2005 the company proposed changing its name from Poore Brothers Inc. to The Inventure Group Inc. in order to reflect its array of holdings which includes many well-known national snack brands. The change was approved by the shareholders in 2006.

In May 2007 Inventure acquired Rader Farms Inc. a farm and berry processing facility in Lynden Washington.

In May 2010 the company changed its name from The Inventure Group to Inventure Foods to better reflect its changing strategy in recent years.

EXECUTIVES

Chief Executive Officer; Director, Terry McDaniel, age 56, $385,619 total compensation
Chairman and Director, Larry R. Polhill, age 61
SVP Marketing, Steve Sklar, $224,826 total compensation
Chief Financial Officer, Steve Weinberger, age 61, $256,867 total compensation
Senior Vice President - Sales & Marketing, Rick Suchenski, age 54
Director, Itzhak Reichman, age 56
Director, Mark S. Howells, age 59
Director, Macon Bryce Edmonson, age 58
Chief Executive Officer; Director, Terry McDaniel, age 56
Chairman and Director, Larry R. Polhill, age 61
Director, Ashton D. Asensio, age 68
Auditors: MossAdamsLLP

LOCATIONS

HQ: Inventure Foods Inc.
  5415 East High Street, Suite #350, Phoenix, AZ 85054
Phone: 623 932-6200
Web: www.inventurefoods.com

PRODUCTS/OPERATIONS

2010 Sales

	$ mil.	% of total
Branded snack & berry products		81
Private-label products		16
Distribution		3
Total		**100**

2010 Sales

	$ mil.	% of total
Snack products	85	64
Berry products	48	36
Total	**134**	**100**

Selected Brands

Bob's Texas Style
Boulder Canyon Natural Foods
Braids
BURGER KING (licensed)
Jamba All Natural Smoothies
Knots
O' Boisies
Pizzarias
Poore Brothers
Rader Farms
T.G.I. Friday's (licensed)
Tato Skins

Selected Subsidiaries

BN Foods Inc.
Boulder Natural Foods Inc.
La Cometa Properties Inc.
Poore Brothers Bluffton LLC
Rader Farms Inc.
Tejas PB Distributing Inc.

COMPETITORS

American Pop Corn
Auntie Anne's
Beer Nuts
Bridgford Foods
C.J. Vitner
Campbell Soup
ConAgra
Diamond Foods
Dole Food
Encore Software
Frito-Lay
General Mills
Global Trading
Goya
Graceland Fruit
Grupo Bimbo
Hain Celestial
Herr Foods
Idaho Fresh-Pak
J & J Snack Foods

Kellogg U.S. Snacks
King Nut Companies
Legacy Bakehouse
Mondelez International
Monster Beverage
Mrs. Fields
Nestle
Pepperidge Farm
Pretzels Inc.
Procter & Gamble
Ralcorp
Shoreline Fruit
Silver Lake Cookie
Snappy Popcorn
Snyder's-Lance
SunOpta
Texoma Peanut
Weaver Popcorn Company
Wetzel's Pretzels
Wise Foods

HISTORICAL FINANCIALS

Company Type: Public

Income Statement

FYE: December 29

	REVENUE ($ mil.)	NET INCOME ($ mil.)	NET PROFIT MARGIN	EMPLOYEES
12/12	185.1	7.4	4.0%	497
12/11	162.2	2.8	1.7%	448
12/10	133.9	4.4	3.3%	389
12/09	121.0	3.7	3.1%	372
12/08	113.0	2.3	2.1%	374
Annual Growth	13.1%	33.2%	—	7.4%

2012 Year-End Financials

Debt ratio: 19.4%
Return on equity: 16.1%
Cash ($ mil.): 0
Current ratio: 2.13
Long-term debt ($ mil.): 17

No. of shares (mil.): 19
Dividends
  Yield: —
  Payout: —
Market value ($ mil.): 121

	STOCK PRICE ($) FY Close	P/E High/Low		PER SHARE ($) Earnings	Dividends	Book Value
12/12	6.31	19	9	0.38	0.00	2.66
12/11	3.74	30	21	0.15	0.00	2.28
12/10	4.32	18	9	0.24	0.00	2.10
12/09	2.32	14	6	0.21	0.00	1.84
12/08	1.60	17	9	0.13	0.00	1.59
Annual Growth	40.9%	—	—	30.8%	—	13.7%

Investors Bancorp Inc

Investors Bancorp is the holding company for Investors Savings Bank which serves New Jersey and New York from more than 85 branch offices. Founded in 1926 the bank offers such standard deposit products as savings and checking accounts CDs money market accounts and IRAs. Over the past few years Investors Savings Bank has increasingly focused on commercial lending; its residential mortgages have gone from more than 90% to around 60% of the bank's total loan portfolio. Other offerings include commercial mortgages multifamily loans and construction loans.

Investors Bancorp has been growing through acquisitions and by opening new branches. In 2012 it announced plans to acquire Marathon Banking Corporation (a subsidiary of Greece-based Piraeus Bank) for $135 million. The deal will add 13 branches in the New York metro area —more than doubling its branches in New York. The deal also will mark Investors Bancorp's entry into Manhattan and Staten Island.

In 2011 Investors acquired Brooklyn Federal Bancorp a deal that added five branches in Brooklyn and Long Island New York. The company has focused on expanding its geographic footprint since it entered New York in 2010 through its purchase of Millennium Bank which had 17 branches in New Jersey New York and Massachusetts. (It sold the four Massachusetts locations to Rhode Island-based Domestic Bank after the deal closed.)

The company's growth has helped it improve income and grow deposits. Sales grew by 10% in 2011 pushing that figure to half a billion. Net income also improved that year by more than 27%. Investors Bancorp's level of nonperforming loans has remained low as it sticks to conservative lending standards. The company's funding costs also have been low thanks to favorable interest rates.

Mutual holding company Investors Bancorp MHC owns a majority of Investors Bancorp's stock.

EXECUTIVES

Independent Director, Doreen R. Byrnes, age 64
Chairman, Robert M. Cashill, age 70, $960,000 total compensation
Senior Executive Vice President Chief Operating Officer, Domenick A. Cama, age 57, $437,500 total compensation
President Chief Executive Officer, Kevin Cummings, age 58, $703,766 total compensation
Executive Vice President Chief Lending Officer, Richard S. Spengler, age 51, $245,004 total compensation
Senior Vice President Chief Financial Officer, Thomas F. Splaine Jr., age 48, $191,002 total compensation
SVP; Summit Market Manager, William V. Cosgrove
Executive Vice President Director of Retail Banking, Paul Kalamaras
Independent Director, Doreen R. Byrnes, age 64
Director, James H. Ward III, age 64
SEVP COO and Director, Domenick A. Cama, age 56
Director, Brian D. Dittenhafer, age 71
Director, Vincent D. Manahan III, age 75
Director, Stephen J. Szabatin, age 76
President Chief Executive Officer, Kevin Cummings, age 58
Auditors: KPMGLLP

LOCATIONS

HQ: Investors Bancorp Inc.
101 JFK Pkwy., Short Hills NJ 07078-2716
Phone: 973-924-5100 **Fax:** 973-924-5192
Web: www.isbnj.com

PRODUCTS/OPERATIONS

2011 Sales

	$ mil.	% of total
Interest		
Loans receivable and held-for-sale	434	87

Mortgage-backed securities	29	6
Municipal bonds & other debt	5	1
Other	4	1
Noninterest		
Fees & service charges	12	2
Gain on sales of mortgage loans	9	2
Income on bank owned life insurance	3	1
Other	1	–
Total	**500**	**100**

COMPETITORS

24.1	M&T Bank
Bank of America	New York Community
Bank of New York	Bancorp
Mellon	OceanFirst Financial
Center Bancorp	PNC Financial
Citigroup	Susquehanna Bancshares
Fulton Financial	

HISTORICAL FINANCIALS

Company Type: Public

Income Statement

FYE: December 31

	ASSETS ($ mil.)	NET INCOME ($ mil.)	INCOME AS % OF ASSETS	EMPLOYEES
12/12	12,722.5	88.7	0.7%	1,219
12/11	10,701.5	78.8	0.7%	982
12/10	9,602.1	62.0	0.6%	892
12/09*	8,357.8	22.5	0.3%	731
06/09	8,136.4	(64.9)	—	705
Annual Growth	**11.8%**	**—**	**—**	**14.7%**

*Fiscal year change

2012 Year-End Financials

Return on assets: 0.7%
Return on equity: 8.7%
Long-term debt ($ mil.): —
No. of shares (mil.): 111
Sales ($ mil): 540
Dividends
Yield: 0.2%
Payout: 6.1%
Market value ($ mil.): 1,990

	STOCK PRICE ($) FY Close	P/E High/Low	Earnings	Dividends	Book Value
12/12	17.78	23 16	0.82	0.05	9.53
12/11	13.48	21 17	0.73	0.00	8.72
12/10	13.12	25 19	0.56	0.00	7.99
12/09*	10.94	64 33	0.21	0.00	7.43
06/09	9.20	— —	(0.62)	0.00	7.14
Annual Growth	**17.9%**	**— —**	**—**	**—**	**7.5%**

*Fiscal year change

Investors Title Co.

Investors Title insures you in case your land is well not completely yours. It's the holding company for Investors Title Insurance and Northeast Investors Title Insurance which underwrite land title insurance and sell reinsurance to other title companies. (Title insurance protects those who invest in real property against loss resulting from defective titles.) Investors Title Insurance serves customers from about 30 offices in North Carolina South Carolina Michigan and Nebraska and through branches or agents in 20 additional states. Northeast Investors Title operates through an agency office in New York. Founder and CEO J. Allen Fine and his family own more than 20% of Investors Title.

While the company does business throughout the eastern and midwestern US North Carolina accounts for 50% of its title insurance premiums.

Investors Title also provides tax-deferred exchange services through its Investors Title Exchange and Investors Title Accommodation subsidiaries. Its Investors Capital Management Company subsidiary offers investment advisory and management services.

EXECUTIVES

Co-President and COO, W. Morris Fine, $252,487 total compensation
Co-President Principal Financial Officer and Treasurer, James A. Fine Jr., $254,393 total compensation
Chairman and CEO, J. Allen Fine, $302,027 total compensation
Senior Vice President, Kim Dean
SVP and Senior Title Attorney, David A. Bennington
EVP National Marketing, George A. Snead
Lead Independent Director, Richard Hutson
VP Information Technology, John Ferrie
SVP Agency and Branch Operations, Joanna Biliouris
VP and Manager ITEC ITAC and Trust, Jane Crewse
EVP Secretary and Director, W. Morris Fine, age 46
President CFO Chief Accounting Officer Treasurer and Director, James A. Fine Jr., age 50
Director, David L. Francis, age 80
Director, H. Joe King Jr., age 80
Director, James R. Morton, age 75
Director, R. Horace Johnson, age 68
Director, James H. Speed Jr., age 59
Auditors: DixonHughesGoodmanLLP

LOCATIONS

HQ: Investors Title Company
121 N. Columbia St., Chapel Hill NC 27514
Phone: 919-968-2200 **Fax:** 919-968-2235
Web: www.invtitle.com

PRODUCTS/OPERATIONS

2007 Revenues

	$ mil.	% of total
Net premiums written	70	83
Investment income	5	6
Exchange services	4	5
Net realized gain on sale of investments	0	1
Other	4	5
Total	**84**	**100**

Selected Subsidiaries

Investors Title Accommodation Corporation
Investors Title Exchange Corporation
Investors Title Insurance Company
Investors Title Management Services Inc.
Northeast Investors Title Insurance Company

COMPETITORS

Fidelity National	Ticor Title Co.
Financial	Title Resource Group
First American	United General Title
Old Republic	Insurance
Stewart Information	
Services	

HISTORICAL FINANCIALS

Company Type: Public

Income Statement

FYE: December 31

	ASSETS ($ mil.)	NET INCOME ($ mil.)	INCOME AS % OF ASSETS	EMPLOYEES
12/12	171.9	11.1	6.5%	212
12/11	157.9	6.9	4.4%	199
12/10	153.4	6.3	4.2%	196
12/09	146.4	4.8	3.3%	216
12/08	139.8	(1.1)	—	239
Annual Growth	5.3%	—	—	(3.0%)

2012 Year-End Financials

Return on assets: 6.7%
Return on equity: 10.0%
Long-term debt ($ mil.): —
No. of shares (mil.): 2
Sales ($ mil): 115

Dividends
Yield: 0.4%
Payout: 5.5%
Market value ($ mil.): 123

	STOCK PRICE ($) FY Close	P/E High/Low		PER SHARE ($) Earnings	Dividends	Book Value
12/12	60.00	13	7	5.24	0.29	56.10
12/11	35.77	13	9	3.20	0.28	50.54
12/10	30.50	13	10	2.78	0.28	45.53
12/09	30.90	18	9	2.11	0.28	42.56
12/08	37.35	—	—	(0.50)	0.28	39.18
Annual Growth	12.6%	—	—	—	0.9%	9.4%

IPC The Hospitalist Co, Inc.

IPC The Hospitalist Company (IPC) is on the leading edge of a growing US trend toward hospitalist specialization. The staffing firm provides some 1200 hospitalists to more than 365 hospitals and 550 other inpatient facilities in about 25 states. Hospitalists are health care providers (physicians nurses and physicians assistants) who oversee all of a patient's treatment from the beginning to the end of their stay. They answer questions and coordinate treatment programs to improve the quality of care and reduce the length of a patient's hospital stay. In addition to providing staff IPC offers training data management billing and risk management services for its medical professionals and clients.

Operations

In addition to its staff of affiliated hospitalists IPC also utilizes another 630 physician and non-physician providers as needed; the doctors are contracted through more than 200 independent physician groups. Altogether the company's hospitalists have handled about 12 million patient encounters between 2009 and 2011. Private-pay patients make up only 5% of the company's revenue; the remainder is attributed to Medicare (45%) Medicaid (5%) and other third-party payers (45%).

Financial Analysis

As IPC has expanded its operations the company has seen steadily rising revenues over the last decade and profits have also increased each year since 2008. IPC reported a 26% increase in revenues to some $457 million in 2011 as well as net income growth of 21% to about $29 million.

Growth in 2011 was attributed to increased numbers of patient encounters in new and existing markets.

Strategy

In addition to its main growth strategy of acquiring existing practice groups in new markets IPC strives to offer its services to new institutions in areas where it already operates. In 2011 for example IPC partnered with Northeast Hospital Corporation to provide services to two of its hospitals in Massachusetts and in 2012 it signed contracts to provide hospitalist services to four Methodist Healthcare System hospitals in San Antonio. The company also sees room for growth by recruiting and training additional hospitalists. Targeted regions for expansion include New England the Northwest the Southwest and the Southeast. IPC is also looking to expand into specialist areas such as behavioral health.

Mergers and Acquisitions

IPC made acquisitions in 2011 of about 15 additional practices adding approximately 240000 annual patient encounters. These included practices in new areas of operation such as Idaho Washington State Southern California and Orlando Florida. Other acquisitions expanded operations in established practice areas in Arizona Florida Michigan and Nevada. The company continued its practice of buying up small regional hospitalist groups in 2012 expanding its operations in the greater St. Louis area southern Florida northwestern Ohio southern Texas Massachusetts and Rhode Island.

Also in 2012 IPC entered a new service market behavioral health through the acquisition of Asana Integrated Medical Group which provides coordination of mental health services through a team of psychologists psychiatrists and nurse practitioners in Arizona and California.

Company Background

IPC completed an IPO in 2008 using funds to help pay off debt and acquire smaller regional hospitalist practice groups.

EXECUTIVES

Chairman CEO and Chief Medical Officer, Adam D. Singer, age 53, $543,000 total compensation
President COO and Director, R. Jeffrey Taylor, age 64, $345,000 total compensation
Chief Administrative Officer, Devra G. Shapiro, age 66, $328,000 total compensation
EVP and Chief Development Officer, Richard G. Russell, age 53, $274,000 total compensation
Chief Financial Officer, Richard H. (Rick) Kline III
Vice President of Medical Affairs, Felix Aguirre
VP Information Systems, Mark C. Citron
VP Financial Analysis and Revenue Controls, Jamie S. Glazer
VP Technology, Patrick Holmes
VP Marketing and Development, Todd Kislak
VP Physician Staffing, Timothy Lary
Vice President Health Services, Kathleen Loya
VP Corporate Development, Marcie Matthews
Vice President of Legal Affairs, Perri Melnick
SVP Finance and Chief Accounting Officer, Fernando J. Sarria
Vice President Central Business Office, Fred Torres
Chief Medical Officer, Kerry Weiner
Vice President Corporate Development, Cary Rosoff
Vice President of Corporate Development, John Fretz
Vice President of IT Operations, Roie Edery
Senior Vice President of Operations, Glenn Appelbaum
Director, C. Thomas Smith, age 75

Director, Thomas P. Cooper, age 69
Director, Mark J. Brooks, age 47
Director, Chuck Timpe, age 66
Director, Woodrin (Woody) Grossman, age 68
President COO and Director, R. Jeffrey Taylor, age 64
Director, Franscesco Federico, age 63
Auditors: Ernst&YoungLLP

LOCATIONS

HQ: IPC The Hospitalist Company Inc.
4605 Lankershim Blvd. Ste. 617, North Hollywood CA 91602
Phone: 888-447-2362 **Fax:** 818-766-3999
Web: www.hospitalist.com

PRODUCTS/OPERATIONS

2011 Employees

	No.	% of total
Clinical		
Employed physicians	972	48
Nurse practitioners & phycician assistants	229	11
Independent contracted physicians	216	11
Non-clinical employees	613	30
Total	**2,030**	**100**

Selected Acquisitions

2012
GLT Medical Services Ltd. (GLT; Toledo Ohio)
Inpatient Clinical Solutions Inc. (ICS; Coral Springs Florida)
Midwest Acute Care Consultants (MACC; St. Louis)
Nexis Healthcare Inc. (Taunton Massachusetts)
Omni Medical Diagnostics PC (Fall River Massachusetts)
Park Medical Associates LLC (North Smithfield Rhode Island)
Valley Hospital Doctors PLLC (VHD; McAllen Texas)
2011
Coast To Coast Physicians Alliance (Orlando Florida)
Hospitalist Specialists (Idaho and Washington State)
Inland Hospitalist Medical Group (Riverside California)
Mid-Michigan Hospitalist Group (Grand Blanc Michigan)
North Florida Acute Care Specialists (Jacksonville Florida)
2010
Hospital Internists of Bristol (Connecticut)

Selected Administrative and Professional Services

Billing and collections
Compliance
Financial reporting
Information management system
Recruiting
Regional management
Risk management
Training
Transition management

COMPETITORS

Cogent HMG
EmCare
Envision Healthcare
Hospital Physician Partners

MEDNAX
Schumacher Group
Sheridan Healthcare
Team Health

HISTORICAL FINANCIALS

Company Type: Public

Income Statement

FYE: December 31

	REVENUE ($ mil.)	NET INCOME ($ mil.)	NET PROFIT MARGIN	EMPLOYEES
12/12	523.4	32.5	6.2%	2,381
12/11	457.4	29.2	6.4%	2,030
12/10	363.4	24.2	6.7%	1,792
12/09	310.5	18.6	6.0%	1,451
12/08	251.1	13.5	5.4%	1,028
Annual Growth	20.2%	24.5%	—	23.4%

2012 Year-End Financials

Debt ratio: 5.1%
Return on equity: 13.8%
Cash ($ mil.): 16
Current ratio: 1.67
Long-term debt ($ mil.): 20

No. of shares (mil.): 16
Dividends
  Yield: —
  Payout: —
Market value ($ mil.): 663

	STOCK PRICE ($) FY Close	P/E High/Low	PER SHARE ($) Earnings	Dividends	Book Value
12/12	39.71	24 16	1.92	0.00	15.36
12/11	45.72	29 20	1.74	0.00	12.91
12/10	39.01	27 15	1.46	0.00	10.71
12/09	33.25	29 13	1.14	0.00	8.98
12/08	16.83	32 15	0.87	0.00	7.65
Annual Growth	23.9%	— —	21.9%	—	19.0%

IPG Photonics Corp

IPG Photonics has a laser focus. The company makes fiber lasers and amplifiers and diode lasers which are primarily used in materials processing applications (nearly 90% of sales) such as welding cutting marking and engraving. Its fiber lasers also have applications in medicine and in telecommunications networks from enabling data signal transmission to surgical cosmetic urological and dental procedures. The company's customers have included BAE SYSTEMS Mitsubishi Heavy Industries and Nippon Steel. Deriving more than 80% of its sales outside North America IPG Photonics operates sales offices in about a dozen countries in Asia and Europe.

Operations

The vertically integrated manufacturer design and makes most of the components used in its finished products from semiconductor diodes to optical fiber preforms finished fiber lasers and amplifiers. It also manufactures other products used in its lasers including optical delivery cables fiber couplers beam switches optical heads and chillers. By not outsourcing its manufacturing to third-party companies IPG Photonics is able to better control its proprietary processes and technologies as well as the supply of its materials.

Geographic Reach

The company conducts R&D in the same city as its headquarters as well as in New Hampshire and overseas in the German city of Burbach (near Frankfurt) and in Fryazino Russia (outside Moscow).

It has four manufacturing facilities for lasers amplifiers and components one in each of its R&D cities and the fourth one in Cerro Maggiore Italy outside Milan. Manufacturing facilities for optical components are in India and China.

Sales and Marketing

IPG Photonics primarily uses a direct sales force. It has a diverse customer base - its five-largest customers only account for about 15% of sales. In 2012 it shipped more than 25000 units to some 1900 customers worldwide.

It has sales offices at each of its manufacturing facilities as well as in Michigan and California in the US. International sales offices are located in China France India Spain Singapore Turkey and the UK.

Financial Performance

Overall sales were up 19% in 2012 to $562 million. Its core business materials processing applications sold more high-power and medium-power lasers used in cutting and welding applications and pulsed lasers used in marking and engraving applications. The advanced applications segment which makes and sells high-power high-brightness lasers saw sales shoot up 66%. The company has relatively low operating expenses and profits were up 23% in 2012 to $145 million.

Mergers and Acquisitions

Increasing demand has led IPG to pursue operational expansion in Russia Germany and the US. In 2012 the company paid $55.4 million to acquire the 22.5% of Russia-based subsidiary NTO IRE-Polus that it did not already own to extend its control over R&D sales and manufacturing infrastructure in the country.

Also in 2012 IPG bought privately held J.P. Sercel Associates (JPSA) a New Hampshire-based supplier of UV excimer and diode-pumped solid-state industrial laser micromachining systems used in high-volume biomedical industrial automation LED microelectromechanical systems (MEMS) microfluidics thin-film solar panel and semiconductor manufacturing applications. The purchase expands IPG's custom laser system offerings to include fine processing precision cutting drilling and micromachining of ceramics glass and semiconductors. The company further enhanced its UV laser development with the purchase the following year of California-based Mobius Photonics.

Strategy

IPG remains focused on fiber lasers as an alternative to conventional lasers such as gas or crystal. Its strategy is to exploit the advantages that fiber lasers offer such as superiority in electrical efficiency beam quality and control maintenance costs longevity flexibility and usability. Traditional laser technologies have advantages that make them more suitable for some applications but fiber lasers continue to gain ground. Crystal lasers generate higher peak power pulses fiber lasers don't achieve the deep ultraviolet light needed for some semiconductor applications and carbon dioxide lasers are better for non-metallic applications such has plastics. Fiber lasers however have made improvements in power output that has opened them up to new markets and IPG believes the technology can reach additional nascent applications such as natural resource extraction.

HISTORY

IPG Photonics raised about $100 million in private equity funding with its investors including Apax Partners Merrill Lynch TA Associates and Winston Partners. The company filed for an IPO in 2000 and withdrew the registration statement six months later. It filed for another IPO in 2006 and completed the offering by the end of the year.

The company used proceeds of its public offering to repurchase warrants pay off debts and for general corporate purposes including working capital expansion of manufacturing facilities purchases

of equipment and expansion of applications development and services.

In 2007 IPG Photonics acquired its Chinese distributor HM Laser and established a subsidiary IPG China with an office in Beijing. China is one of IPG's principal markets along with Germany Japan Russia and the US.

The company stepped forward with its purchase of laser material manufacturer Photonics Innovations (PII) in January 2010. The acquisition expanded IPG's products and services portfolio for optical and laser materials fabrication tunable laser design and optical and sensing systems. Transaction details were not divulged.

EXECUTIVES

Chief Executive Officer Chairman of the Board, Valentin P. Gapontsev, age 75, $375,000 total compensation

Director; Managing Director IPG Laser, Eugene Shcherbakov, age 65, $357,967 total compensation

Chief Financial Officer Vice President, Timothy P. V. Mammen, age 44, $279,814 total compensation

VP Operations, Dennis P. Leonard Jr.

Director; Acting General Manager NTO IRE-Polus, Igor Samartsev, age 51

VP General Counsel and Secretary, Angelo P. Lopresti, age 50, $279,814 total compensation

VP Telecommunications Products, George H. BuAbbud, age 58, $240,000 total compensation

VP Industrial Markets, William S. (Bill) Shiner, age 71

VP Components, Alexander (Alex) Ovtchinnikov, age 52, $248,723 total compensation

General Manager West Coast Operations, Tony Hoult

Regional Sales Manager Midwest, Shawn Murphy

Senior Vice President U.S. Operations, Felix Stukalin

Director, Henry E. Gauthier, age 73

Director, William S. Hurley, age 69

Director, William F. Krupke, age 77

Director, Michael C. Child, age 59

Director; Managing Director IPG Laser, Eugene Shcherbakov, age 65

Director; Acting General Manager NTO IRE-Polus, Igor Samartsev, age 50

Director, Robert A. Blair, age 67

Independent Director, Michael Kampfe

Auditors: Deloitte&ToucheLLP

LOCATIONS

HQ: IPG Photonics Corporation
50 Old Webster Rd., Oxford MA 01540
Phone: 508-373-1100   **Fax:** 508-373-1103
Web: www.ipgphotonics.com

2012 Sales

	$ mil.	% of total
Asia-Pacific	251	45
Europe	200	36
US	108	19
Other	1	-
Total	**562**	**100**

PRODUCTS/OPERATIONS

2012 Sales by Market

	$ mil.	% of total
Materials processing	492	87
Advanced applications	43	8
Communications	21	4
Medical	5	1
Total	**562**	**100**

Selected Products

Broadband light sources
Continuous wave lasers
Diode laser systems
Diode-pumped solid-state laser systems
Erbium lasers
Fiber amplifiers
Fiber lasers
Fiber-coupled direct diode laser systems
Pulsed fiber lasers
Raman pump lasers
Thulium lasers
UV excimer laser systems
Ytterbium lasers

COMPETITORS

Cisco Systems	Mitsubishi Materials
Coherent Inc.	Newport Corp.
EMCORE	Oclaro
FANUC	Presstek
Furukawa Electric	ROFIN-SINAR
GSI Group	Swatch
Huawei Technologies	TRUMPF
JDS Uniphase	

HISTORICAL FINANCIALS

Company Type: Public

Income Statement

FYE: December 31

	REVENUE ($ mil.)	NET INCOME ($ mil.)	NET PROFIT MARGIN	EMPLOYEES
12/12	562.5	145.0	25.8%	2,400
12/11	474.4	117.7	24.8%	2,137
12/10	299.2	53.9	18.0%	1,760
12/09	185.8	5.4	2.9%	1,430
12/08	229.0	36.6	16.0%	1,420
Annual Growth	25.2%	41.0%	—	14.0%

2012 Year-End Financials

Debt ratio: 2.0%
Return on equity: 24.3%
Cash ($ mil.): 384
Current ratio: 5.30
Long-term debt ($ mil.): 14

No. of shares (mil.): 51
Dividends
  Yield: 0.9%
  Payout: 23.1%
Market value ($ mil.): 3,423

	STOCK PRICE ($) FY Close	P/E High/Low	PER SHARE ($) Earnings	Dividends	Book Value
12/12	66.65	23 12	2.81	0.65	14.47
12/11	33.87	31 12	2.41	0.00	9.31
12/10	31.62	28 12	1.13	0.00	6.74
12/09	16.73	145 57	0.12	0.00	5.57
12/08	13.18	27 14	0.79	0.00	5.30
Annual Growth	50.0%	— —	37.3%	—	28.6%

iRobot Corp

Fans of The Jetsons appreciate iRobot. The company makes robots for all sorts of applications — from defense and security to industrial use and home appliances. Its Roomba FloorVac and Scooba are the first of their kind to automatically clean floors. The company's defense and security robots perform tasks such as battlefield reconnaissance and bomb disposal. iRobot has sold more than 4500 robots to military and civil defense forces including PackBots to the US Army. The firm has offices in the US and Hong Kong and sells its home products worldwide through retailers.

iRobot was founded in 1990 by robot engineers from the Massachusetts Institute of Technology.

Geographic Reach

Massachusetts-based iRobot has offices in the US and Hong Kong. Sales to customers outside the US accounted for about 57% of the company's revenue in 2012 (up from 42% in 2011).

Operations

iRobot operates two primary business segments. Home Robots account for more than 80% of sales while Defense & Security Robots represent the remainder. In 2012 the company sent four robots to Japan to explore reactor buildings at the Fukushima Daiichi nuclear plant.

Sales and Marketing

The US federal government accounted for about 15% of the company's total revenue in 2012 down from 36% and 38% in 2011 and 2010 respectively. Boeing as a subcontractor for the government is another significant customer contributing 4.5% of 2012 sales. Sales to Japan's Sales on Demand Corp. and a network of affiliated European distributors accounted for about 30% of home robot sales in 2012.

Financial Performance

iRobot's sales declined by 6% in 2012 compared with 2011 while net income fell 57% over the same period. The decrease was caused by a 57% decline in sales of defense and security robots as the wars in Iraq and Afghanistan wound down and demand for the company's PackBot and small unmanned ground vehicle (SUGV) robots wanes. Away from the battlefield sales of home robots jumped 28% to nearly $357 million in 2012 due to more items shipped and a 7% increase in average selling price.

The decline in sales and profits in 2012 reversed two years of significant sales gains for the company and three consecutive years of increasing profitability.

Strategy

Amid falling sales of its tactical military robots the company is focusing on its home care robots. In 2012 iRobot reorganized into three newly formed business units focused on home robots military robots and emerging technologies in a bid to advance its long-term strategy to be the technology leader in remote presence and automated home maintenance. With its foothold in the robotic appliances niche iRobot has boosted its consumer business by developing new products such as the new Roomba 700 series built on popular brand names. It has introduced several products including the Roomba for Pets Roomba Discovery for Pets and the Dirt Dog Workshop Robot which is designed to keep work spaces free of sawdust small nails and debris. To keep its product pipeline full iRobot invested $37.2 million in research and development in 2012 up from $36.5 million and $24.8 million in 2011 and 2010 respectively.

Mergers and Acquisitions

iRobot acquired privately-held Evolution Robotics the maker of Mint brand automatic floor cleaning robots for $74 million in October 2012. The purchase expanded iRobot's technology leadership through a combination of intellectual property engineering talent and new products that broadened its robot offering.

EXECUTIVES

Chief Financial Officer; Executive Vice President; Principal Accounting Officer; Treasurer, John J. Leahy, age 54, $356,743 total compensation
SVP Human Resources, Russell J. (Russ) Campanello, age 57
Investor Relations, Elise P. Caffrey

Chairman and CEO, Colin M. Angle, age 45, $386,053 total compensation
EVP and Chief Legal Counsel, Glen D. Weinstein, age 42, $290,353 total compensation
Chief Strategy Officer, Joseph W. (Joe) Dyer, age 67, $331,250 total compensation
COO, Jeffrey A. (Jeff) Beck, age 50, $250,000 total compensation
EVP and CFO, Alison Dean, age 48, $228,654 total compensation
SVP Information Technology and CIO, Jay Leader
CTO, Tom Wagner
Senior Vice President & General Manager - Defense & Security Business Unit, Frank Wilson
Chief Technology Officer, Paolo Pirjanian
Senior Vice President and General Manager - Home Robots, Christian Cerda
Director, George C. McNamee, age 66
Director, Andrea Geisser, age 70
Director, Paul L. Sagan, age 54
Director, Ronald Chwang, age 65
Director, Helen Greiner, age 45
Director, Rodney A. Brooks, age 59
Director, Peter T. Meekin, age 64
Director, Paul J. Kern, age 67
Director, Jacques S. Gansler, age 78
Independent Director, Deborah Ellinger
Independent Director, Gail Deegan
Auditors: PricewaterhouseCoopersLLP

LOCATIONS

HQ: iRobot Corporation
8 Crosby Dr., Bedford MA 01730
Phone: 781-430-3000   **Fax:** 781-430-3001
Web: www.irobot.com

PRODUCTS/OPERATIONS

2012 Sales

	$ mil.	% of total
Product	418	96
Contract	17	4
Total	**436**	**100**

2012 Sales

	$ mil.	% of total
Home robots	356	82
Defense & security	79	18
Total	**436**	**100**

COMPETITORS

AM General	General Dynamics
Allen-Vanguard Corporation	LG Electronics
BAE SYSTEMS	Lockheed Martin
BISSELL	QinetiQ
Electrolux	REMOTEC UK
GE Appliances & Lighting	Samsung Electronics

HISTORICAL FINANCIALS

Company Type: Public

Income Statement

FYE: December 29

	REVENUE ($ mil.)	NET INCOME ($ mil.)	NET PROFIT MARGIN	EMPLOYEES
12/12	436.2	17.3	4.0%	534
12/11*	465.5	40.1	8.6%	619
01/11	400.9	25.5	6.4%	657
01/10	298.6	3.3	1.1%	538
12/08	307.6	0.7	0.2%	479
Annual Growth	9.1%	118.7%	—	2.8%

*Fiscal year change

2012 Year-End Financials

Debt ratio: —   No. of shares (mil.): 27
Return on equity: 6.6%   Dividends
Cash ($ mil.): 126   Yield: —
Current ratio: 3.08   Payout: —
Long-term debt ($ mil.): —   Market value ($ mil.): 516

	STOCK PRICE ($) FY Close	P/E High/Low		PER SHARE ($) Earnings	Dividends	Book Value
12/12	18.59	61	26	0.61	0.00	9.93
12/11*	29.85	26	15	1.44	0.00	8.93
01/11	24.88	25	15	0.96	0.00	6.77
01/10	17.60	136	55	0.13	0.00	5.31
12/08	9.29	747	241	0.03	0.00	4.82
Annual Growth	**18.9%**			—	—112.3%	— 19.8%

*Fiscal year change

ITC Holdings Corp

ITC Holdings (ITC) owns and operates 15000 circuit miles of power transmission lines. Through its subsidiaries ITC Transmission Michigan Electric Transmission Company (METC) ITC Great Plains and ITC Midwest ITC operates regulated high-voltage transmission systems in Michigan's Lower Peninsula and portions of Illinois Iowa Kansas Minnesota Missouri and Oklahoma serving a combined peak load of more than 26000 MW. ITC is a member of the Midwest ISO (MISO) a regional transmission organization. The company also operates as ITC Grid Development which invests in transmission infrastructure development.

Geographic Reach

ITC's regulated operating subsidiaries' transmission facilities are located in Michigan's Lower Peninsula and portions of Illinois Iowa Kansas Minnesota Missouri and Oklahoma.

Operations

Through subsidiaries ITC Transmission Michigan Electric Transmission Company (METC) ITC Great Plains and ITC Midwest ITC operates regulated high-voltage transmission systems incuding 15000 miles of.

Sales and Marketing

Detroit Edison Consumers Energy and Interstate Power and Light accounted for 26.7% 25.6%. and 27.0% respectively of ITC's total operating revenues in 2012.

Financial Performance

ITC's 2012 revenues increased by 10% (to $831 million) reflecting growth across all of its segments. Network revenues grew by 5% due due to a higher rate base partially offset by a short term ITC Transmission rate freeze revenue deferral. Regional cost sharing revenues increased by 40% thanks to additional capital projects that were placed into service. Point-to-point revenues grew by 10% thanks to an increase in the number of point-to-point reservations. Scheduling control and dispatch revenues jumped by 30% as the result of a change in MISO's revenue distribution methodology (implemented by MISO in 2012 to better align billing rates with projected expenses).The company's net income increased by 9% in 2012 thanks to higher revenues and lower operational and maintenance expenses.

ITC has seen a steady growth in revenues and net income since 2008.

Strategy

ITC's strategy is to operate maintain and invest in transmission infrastructure while pursuing development projects to improve overall grid reliability.

ITC is working on building a robust regional power infrastructure using both renewable and traditional power resources. Through its Green Power Express unit ITC is looking to integrate wind and other renewable sources into ITC's future energy mix as the company strives to meet state and federal demands for power generators to use cleaner energy. It is developing a network of 765 kV transmission facilities that will move up to 12000 MW of renewable energy (primarily wind-powered) to major load centers in the Midwest.

The company has a capital investment plan aimed at investing $1.7 billion from 2012 through 2016 to construct its portions of various development projects in the South Central and North Central regions of the US.

In a major move to grow its business in 2012 the company agreed to acquire the electric transmission business of Entergy to create a leading transmission enterprise with more than 30000 miles of lines.

EXECUTIVES

Chairman President and CEO, Joseph L. Welch, age 65, $737,827 total compensation
EVP CFO and Treasurer, Cameron M. Bready, age 41, $217,692 total compensation
EVP and Chief Business Officer, Linda H. Blair, age 44, $345,323 total compensation
Senior Vice President; General Counsel, Daniel J. Oginsky, age 40, $255,208 total compensation
EVP and COO, Jon E. Jipping, age 48, $345,323 total compensation
VP Information Technology and Facilities and CIO, Denis Y. DesRosiers
VP Operations, Elizabeth A. Howell
VP; President ITC Michigan, Gregory (Greg) Ioanidis
Vice President General Counsel, Wendy A. McIntyre
VP Federal Affairs, Nina Plaushin
VP and General Counsel Utility Operations, Christine Mason Soneral
VP Planning, Thomas W. (Tom) Vitez
VP ITC Grid Development, Terry S. Harvill
Media Contact, Louise Beller
VP; President ITC Midwest, Doug Collins
Vice President Regulatory and External Affairs, Simon S. Whitelocke
VP Human Resources, Christine (Chris) Kujawa
Vice President Engineering, Brian Slocum
Vice President Controller, Fred G. Stibor
Vice President - Finance; Treasurer, Rejji Hayes
VP Information Technology and CIO, Ron Hinsley
Director, Edward G. Jepsen, age 70
Director, Lee C. Stewart, age 65
Director, Gordon B. Stewart III, age 61
Director, William J. Museler, age 73
Director, Hazel O'Leary, age 76
Director, Richard D. McLellan, age 70
Independent Director, Christopher Franklin
Independent Director, Hazel OLeary
Independent Director, J. Watts
Independent Director, Michael Rounds
Independent Director, Thomas Stephens
Auditors: Deloitte&ToucheLLP

LOCATIONS

HQ: ITC Holdings Corp.
27175 Energy Way, Novi MI 48377
Phone: 248-946-3000   **Fax:** 262-754-0318
Web: www.loducabros.com

PRODUCTS/OPERATIONS

2012 Sales

Network revenues	669	80
Point-to-point	17	2
Other	6	1

COMPETITORS

DTE Electric	SEMCO ENERGY
Indiana Michigan Power	We Energies
Integrys Energy Group	Wolverine Power Supply
Lansing Board of Water and Light	Xcel Energy
Midland Cogeneration Venture	

HISTORICAL FINANCIALS

Company Type: Public

Income Statement

FYE: December 31

	REVENUE ($ mil.)	NET INCOME ($ mil.)	NET PROFIT MARGIN	EMPLOYEES
12/12	830.5	187.8	22.6%	503
12/11	757.4	171.6	22.7%	452
12/10	696.8	145.6	20.9%	433
12/09	621.0	130.9	21.1%	413
12/08	617.8	109.2	17.7%	392
Annual Growth	**7.7%**	**14.5%**	—	**6.4%**

2012 Year-End Financials

Debt ratio: 56.5%   No. of shares (mil.): 52
Return on equity: 14.0%   Dividends
Cash ($ mil.): 26   Yield: 1.9%
Current ratio: 0.20   Payout: 40.5%
Long-term debt ($ mil.): 2,495   Market value ($ mil.): 4,018

	STOCK PRICE ($) FY Close	P/E High/Low		PER SHARE ($) Earnings	Dividends	Book Value
12/12	76.91	22	18	3.60	1.46	27.08
12/11	75.88	23	18	3.31	1.38	24.53
12/10	61.98	22	17	2.84	1.31	22.03
12/09	52.09	20	12	2.58	1.25	20.20
12/08	43.68	26	16	2.19	1.19	18.71
Annual Growth	**15.2%**			**13.2%**	**5.2%**	**9.7%**

Ixia

Ixia nixes network glitches. The company designs network validation testing hardware and software that provides visibility into traffic performance and also addresses the network applications. Hardware consists of optical and electrical interface cards and the chassis to hold them. Its software tests the functionality of video voice conformance and security across ethernet wi-fi and 3G/LTE equipment and networks. Ixia primarily serves network equipment manufacturers (Cisco) service providers (AT&T) corporate customers (Bloomberg) the federal government (US Army) and its contractors (General Dynamics). Geographically sales are about evenly divided between the US and international customers.

Geographic Reach

Headquartered in the US Ixia has international offices in Australia Canada China France Germany India Ireland Japan South Korea Sweden the UAE and the UK.

It outsources the manufacturing of its hardware to third-party contract and assembly companies in Malaysia.

Sales and Marketing

For the most part Ixia uses a direct sales force except in certain foreign markets where it relies on distributors partners and other resellers.

Cisco is its largest customer accounting for about 10% of overall sales.

Financial Performance

Overall sales increased 34% in 2012 to $413 million a record in revenues for the company. The growth was mostly inorganic that is due to recent acquisitions. But Ixia did sell another $36.7 million in hardware spearheaded by its 10 Gigabit 40/100 Gigabit Ethernet cards and IxVeriwave products. It also enjoyed another $21 million in revenue for services such as customer support and maintenance-related warranty contracts. In addition the company took in $45 million in profits for an 11% profit margin.

Strategy

Ixia's goal of being a leader in network test and visibility capabilities involves expanding its product base through acquisitions and internal research and development. R&D is a big focus; the company spends about 25% of annual revenue on it and also operates Ixia Labs a technology development incubator.

Mergers and Acquisitions

Ixia frequently adds to its product portfolio through acquisitions. In late 2013 it bought Net Optics a provider of network visibility hardware and software for $190 million in cash. The year before it network optimization systems provider Anue Systems for $145 million to strengthen its capabilities in validating wirelessly-delivered next-generation networks and applications. Later that year it bought network security testing company BreakingPoint Systems for $160 million rounding out its network test and visibility product offerings. In 2011 Ixia paid more than $15 million for VeriWave a performance testing company for wireless LAN and Wi-Fi enabled smart devices.

HISTORY

Chairman Errol Ginsberg founded Ixia in 1997 "in rather humble digs above a Mexican restaurant" in Calabasas California about an hour north of Los Angeles. The company went public in 2000 in a $57.5 million IPO but sales failed to top $100 million for three more years.

In 2003 Ixia acquired G3 Nova Technology a developer of VoIP test tools for enterprise call centers communications networks and network devices for about $12 million in cash and stock. Two years later it bought Communication Machinery Corp. (CMC) a developer of Wi-Fi network testing tools for $4 million in cash.

In 2006 Ixia acquired the video telephony test products of Dilithium Networks for around $5 million in cash. With the acquisition the company introduced a product based on the Dilithium Network Analyzer (DNA). The IxMobile Video Telephony test tools are focused on mobile wireless conformance interoperability capacity and performance testing.

Atul Bhatnagar who came from Nortel succeeded Ginsberg as CEO in 2007.

The company made two acquisitions in 2009 that helped it reach record revenues in 2010. Ixia purchased the assets of Agilent Technologies' N2X Data Networks product line for about $44 million in cash. The purchase brought an intuitive and powerful user interface as well as a customer base to open further markets in the Middle East and Asia/Pacific regions. Earlier in 2009 Ixia bought Catapult Communications for about $105 million in cash. The company sees Catapult's 3G and 4G wireless networking test products as complementary to its Internet protocol performance test systems and service verification platforms.

EXECUTIVES

Senior Vice President - Corporate Affairs; General Counsel; Corporate Secretary, Ronald W. (Ron) Buckly, age 61, $259,088 total compensation
Chairman and Chief Innovation Officer, Errol Ginsberg, age 58, $363,708 total compensation
Chief Financial Officer, Thomas B. (Tom) Miller, age 58, $262,500 total compensation
Senior Vice President and General Manager Product Development, Andy Fruhling
President CEO and Director, Victor (Vic) Alston, age 41, $275,000 total compensation
VP Global Customer Delight, Walker H. Colston II, age 52, $251,152 total compensation
SVP Worldwide Sales, Alan Grahame, age 61, $275,000 total compensation
VP Operations, Raymond de Graaf, age 47
VP Human Resources, Christopher L. (Chris) Williams, age 52
VP Marketing, Jim Smith
Vice President - Operations, Raymond Graaf
Chief Product Officer, Dennis Cox
Senior Vice President Marketing, Jim Doherty
Senior Vice President & General Manager Network Visibility Solutions, Alex Pepe
Director, Gail E. Hamilton, age 63
Director, Jon F. Rager, age 73
Director, Jonathan Fram, age 56
President CEO and Director, Victor (Vic) Alston, age 41
Director, Laurent Asscher, age 43
Auditors: PricewaterhouseCoopersLLP

LOCATIONS

HQ: Ixia
26601 W. Agoura Rd., Calabasas CA 91302
Phone: 818-871-1800 **Fax:** 818-871-1805
Web: www.ixiacom.com

2012 Sales

	$ mil.	% of total
US	198	48
International	215	52
Total	**413**	**100**

PRODUCTS/OPERATIONS

2012 Sales

	$ mil.	% of total
Products	330	80
Services	83	20
Total	**413**	**100**

COMPETITORS

Aeroflex	Fluke Networks
Agilent Technologies	JDS Uniphase
Anritsu	RADCOM
Azimuth Systems	Rohde & Schwarz
Digital Lightwave	Spirent
EADS North America	Sunrise Telecom
Test and Services	Tektronix
EXFO	Tollgrade
Emrise	Communications

HISTORICAL FINANCIALS

Company Type: Public

Income Statement

FYE: December 31

	REVENUE ($ mil.)	NET INCOME ($ mil.)	NET PROFIT MARGIN	EMPLOYEES
12/12	413.4	45.4	11.0%	1,710
12/11	308.3	23.7	7.7%	1,300
12/10	276.8	11.2	4.0%	1,100
12/09	177.9	(44.2)	—	1,073
12/08	175.8	(15.9)	—	769
Annual Growth	**23.8%**	**—**	**—**	**22.1%**

2012 Year-End Financials

Debt ratio: 24.4%	No. of shares (mil.): 74
Return on equity: 11.4%	Dividends
Cash ($ mil.): 47	Yield: —
Current ratio: 2.74	Payout: —
Long-term debt ($ mil.): 200	Market value ($ mil.): 1,259

	STOCK PRICE ($) FY Close	P/E High/Low		PER SHARE ($) Earnings	Dividends	Book Value
12/12	16.98	27	16	0.59	0.00	6.04
12/11	10.51	56	21	0.33	0.00	4.90
12/10	16.78	107	41	0.17	0.00	4.31
12/09	7.45	—	—	(0.70)	0.00	3.75
12/08	5.78	—	—	(0.24)	0.00	4.31
Annual Growth	**30.9%**	**—**	**—**	**—**	**—**	**8.8%**

J&J Snack Foods Corp.

J & J Snack Foods boasts freezers full of goodies. The company offers an assortment of brands including SUPERPRETZEL soft pretzels ICEE frozen drinks Whole Fruit juice treats Tio Pepe's churros and Funnel Cake Factory funnel cakes. J & J also sells snacks made under license such as Cinnabon's CinnaPretzels and Mrs. GoodCookie pastries as well as Minute Maid's frozen lemonade and juice bars. Besides serving foodservice operators and retail food outlets J & J caters to consumers directly too through BAVARIAN PRETZEL BAKERY shops in the mid-Atlantic region of the US. Adding to its offerings J & J acquired the Patio Hand Fulls Villa Taliano and other frozen snack brands from ConAgra Foods in 2011.

Geographic Reach

North American snacks company J & J boasts warehouses and distribution centers in more than 40 states Mexico and Canada. The company operates manufacturing facilities in New Jersey Pennsylvania Texas Georgia Missouri Florida Ohio and California. Through its purchase of ConAgra's frozen foods business J & J picked up production facilities in (Holly Ridge) North Carolina and (Weston) Oregon.

Operations

J & J estimates that its products are sold in up to 90% of US supermarkets.

The company operates through three business segments: Food Service Retail Supermarkets and Frozen Beverages. Food Service include soft pretzels frozen juice treats and desserts churros dough-enrobed handheld products and baked goods. Through its Retail Supermarkets segment J & J sells soft pretzel products - including SUPERPRETZEL frozen juice treats and desserts such as Luigi's Real Italian Ice Minute Maid Juice Bars and

Soft Frozen Lemonade Whole Fruit frozen fruit bars and sorbet ICEE Squeeze-Up Tubes and Patio burritos. Within its Frozen Beverages unit J & J sells its products to the food service industry primarily under the names ICEE Slush Puppie Parrot Ice and Arctic Blast throughout the US Mexico and Canada. It provides repair and maintenance service to customers for their owned equipment.

Mergers and Acquisitions

By regularly buying other companies J & J has expanded its existing business and extended the reach of its retail footprint.

Spying an uptick in consumer interest in specialty foods J & J in 2012 acquired Kim & Scott's Gourmet Pretzels. The maker of frozen ready-to-bake pretzels has a shelf presence in Whole Foods and Sam's Club and sales of about $8 million to $10 million. To bolster growth Kim & Scott is testing potential demand for its products in new venues including selling pretzels and sandwiches through Cold Stone Creamery ice-cream stores.

Buying ConAgra's frozen snack brands in 2011 broadened J & J's own range of consumer-facing products —with burritos stuffed sandwiches pizza pockets and more —and added to its list of private-label customers.

The deals build upon two purchases J & J completed in 2010: California Churros and Parrot Ice. California Churros makes frozen churros and supplies supermarkets delis schools and other food-service operators. Parrot Ice a frozen beverage brand sold mainly in convenience stores was acquired out of bankruptcy and added to J & J's ICEE operations.

Financial Performance

Net sales for J & J rose 12% in fiscal 2012 as compared to 2011 thanks to its acquisitions of ConAgra's frozen handheld business in mid-2011 and Kim & Scott's gourmet Pretzels in mid-2012. The company logged a 12% increase across its Food Service segment driven by a 14% rise in sales of soft pretzels from restaurant chains warehouse club stores and its own customer base. Net income during the same reporting period dropped however due to lower gross profits from higher packaging costs and lower gross profit margins of handheld sales.

Sales and Marketing

Through its warehouses and distribution centers in more than 40 states Mexico and Canada the company is able to service customers directly. Food Service customers include snack bars and food stands in chain department and discount stores; malls and shopping centers; casual dining restaurants; fast food outlets; stadiums and sports arenas; leisure and theme parks; convenience stores; movie theatres; warehouse club stores; and schools colleges and other institutions. Its Retail Supermarket sales channel peddles frozen and prepackaged products that are purchased by consumers for home consumption.

Company Ownership

The company's long-term future is guided by chairman president and CEO Gerald Shreiber who owns more than 20% of J & J.

HISTORY

Shreiber bought bankrupt J & J Soft Pretzel then making about $400000 a year in sales for $72100 in 1971. Sales more than quadrupled by 1975 and Shreiber began buying other regional pretzel makers (Framptom Soft Pretzel of St. Louis and Pretzel Man of Los Angeles 1978). J & J began producing new snacks in the 1980s including churros (fried pastries) in 1981 and Super Juice fruit bars in 1984.

The company went public in 1986 and the next year acquired a 38% interest in ICEE-USA. (It bought the remaining interest in 1988 and international marketing rights in 1995.) J & J further expanded in the 1990s with purchases such as Bavarian Soft Pretzels and the Funnel Cake Factory in fiscal 1994 and Pretzel Gourmet (five soft pretzel stores) and Mazzone Enterprises (Italian ices and frozen desserts) in 1996 and 1997.

In 1997 a jury ruled against J & J in a same-sex harassment suit awarding a former employee $4.2 million in damages (later settled for less). That year the company bought Mama Tish's International Foods (including licensing to make Snapple Ice frozen treats) and Pretzels Inc. (Texas Twist soft pretzels). J & J gained national ICEE distribution when it acquired the controlling interest in National ICEE that same year. The next year it cut a marketing deal for ICEE with beverage giant The Coca-Cola Company.

Sales of the company's key soft pretzel lines fell in 1998. J & J closed underperforming Bavarian Pretzel Bakery and Pretzel Gourmet stores that year and it introduced products such as frozen ready-to-bake cookie dough (Mrs. GoodCookie) and soft pretzel hot dog buns.

In 1999 J & J formed an alliance with Coca-Cola's The Minute Maid Company to market Minute Maid and Hi-C frozen drinks. In 2000 the company had to recall about 300000 boxes of Minute Maid juice bars due to a packaging defect. J & J acquired New Jersey-based Uptown Bakeries the primary supplier of fresh bakery products to the Wawa convenience store chain (about 550 stores primarily in the Northeast) in 2001.

In 2004 J & J acquired the bakery assets of bankrupt Country Home Bakers whose brands include Country Home Readi-Bake and various private labels. In 2005 the company acquired Snackworks LLC (dba Bavarian Brothers) a manufacturer of soft pretzels under the Seriously Twisted! Bavarian Brothers and CinnaPretzel brand names.

Expanding its presence into the frozen drinks market J & J acquired ICEE of Hawaii a distributor of frozen drinks throughout the Hawaiian islands as well as the SLUSH PUPPIE brand from Dr Pepper/Seven Up (now the bottling operations of Dr Pepper Snapple Group) in 2006.

During 2007 J & J acquired the assets of Hom/Ade Foods which manufactures and distributes biscuits and dumplings under the Mary B's label and store brands; Radar a maker of Daddy Ray's brand fig and fruit bars; and the Whole Fruit and Fruit-A-Freeze frozen fruit bar brands. It also bought the assets of an ICEE distributor in Kansas.

Amid the economic downturn in the US the company ceased acquisitions until 2010. That year it purchased the assets of California Churros a manufacturer of frozen churros and Parrot Ice a supplier of frozen beverages.

EXECUTIVES

VP-Sls, Steven J. Taylor
President The ICEE Company, Daniel (Dan) Fachner, age 53, $316,137 total compensation
SVP CFO Secretary Treasurer and Director, Dennis G. Moore, age 58, $336,271 total compensation
SVP and COO, Robert M. Radano, age 65, $318,777 total compensation
Chairman President and CEO, Gerald B. Shreiber, age 72, $700,000 total compensation
VP-Sls, Robert J. Pape, age 55
VP-Ops, Thomas Weber
VP-Distributor Sls, Cliff Best

SVP and Assistant to the President, Gerard (Jerry) Law
SVP CFO Secretary Treasurer and Director, Dennis G. Moore, age 58
Director, Sidney R. (Sid) Brown
Director, Leonard M. Lodish, age 70
Director, Peter G. Stanley, age 71
Auditors: GrantThorntonLLP

LOCATIONS

HQ: J & J Snack Foods Corp.
6000 Central Hwy., Pennsauken NJ 08109
Phone: 856-665-9533   **Fax:** 856-663-8002
Web: www.jjsnack.com

PRODUCTS/OPERATIONS

2012 Sales

	$ mil.	% of total
Food Service	521	63
Frozen Beverages	199	24
Retail Supermarket	109	13
Total	**830**	**100**

Selected Sales Channels

Snack bars and food stands in chain department discount and convenience stores
Retail supermarkets
Malls and shopping centers
Fast food outlets
Stadiums and sports arenas
Leisure and theme parks
Movie theatres
Schools colleges and other institutions
Healthcare foodservice locations
Mergers and Acquisitions
FY2012
  Kim & Scott's Gourmet Pretzels
FY2001
  ConAgra's snack foods brands
FY2010
  California Churros
  Parrot Ice (pairs with ICEE operations)

Selected Products and Brands

Bakery
  Camden Creek Bakery
  Country Home
  Daddy Ray's
  Mary B's
  Mrs. GoodCookie
  Pretzel Cookie
  Readi-Bake
Churros
  California Churros
  L.A. Churros
  Tio Pepe's
Frozen Beverages
  Arctic Blast
  California Natural
  ICEE
  Java Freeze
  Slush Puppie
  Parrot Ice
  Whole Fruit
Frozen Handheld
  Hand Fulls
  Holly Ridge Bakery
  Patio
  Top Picks
  Villa Taliano
Frozen Juice Treats and Desserts
  Barq's (licensed from Barq's Inc.)
  Fruit-A-Freeze
  ICEE
  Luigi's
  Minute Maid (licensed from The Minute Maid Company)
  Whole Fruit
Soft Pretzels
  Cinnapretzel (licensed from Cinnabon Inc.)
  Dutch Twist
  Gourmet Twists

Hot Knots
Kim & Scott's Gourmet Pretzels
Mr. Twister
Pretzel Fillers
Pretzelfils
Sandwich Twist
Seriously Twisted!
Soft Pretzel Bites
Soft Pretzel Buns
SoftStix
SUPERPRETZEL
Texas Twist
Other
  Funnel Cake Factory

COMPETITORS

American Dairy Queen	Kellogg U.S. Snacks
Auntie Anne's	McKee Foods
Cinnabon	Mister Twister
Dawn Food Products	Pretzels
Dippin Dots	Mondelez International
Dreyer's	Mrs. Fields
Flowers Foods	Nestle USA
Frito-Lay	Otis Spunkmeyer
General Mills	Planet Smoothie
Golden Enterprises	Ruiz Foods Inc.
Goya	Sara Lee
Hanover Foods	Snyder's-Lance
Hostess Brands	Sorbee International
Jamba	Unilever NV
Jel Sert	Wetzel's Pretzels

HISTORICAL FINANCIALS

Company Type: Public

Income Statement

FYE: September 28

	REVENUE ($ mil.)	NET INCOME ($ mil.)	NET PROFIT MARGIN	EMPLOYEES
09/13	867.6	64.3	7.4%	3,400
09/12	830.8	54.1	6.5%	3,200
09/11	744.0	55.0	7.4%	3,100
09/10	696.7	48.4	6.9%	2,700
09/09	653.0	41.3	6.3%	2,700
Annual Growth	7.4%	11.7%	—	5.9%

2013 Year-End Financials

Debt ratio: 0.0%
Return on equity: 13.0%
Cash ($ mil.): 97
Current ratio: 3.18
Long-term debt ($ mil.): 0

No. of shares (mil.): 18
Dividends
  Yield: 0.0%
  Payout: 18.7%
Market value ($ mil.): 1,509

	STOCK PRICE ($) FY Close	P/E High/Low		PER SHARE ($) Earnings	Dividends	Book Value
09/13	80.79	25	16	3.41	0.64	27.66
09/12	57.33	21	16	2.86	0.52	25.32
09/11	47.59	18	14	2.93	0.47	23.09
09/10	41.75	18	14	2.59	0.43	20.58
09/09	42.83	20	12	2.21	0.39	18.51
Annual Growth	17.2%	—	—	11.5%	13.2%	10.6%

j2 Global Inc

Checked your messages lately? j2 Global provides Web-based communications and other cloud services that allow customers to retrieve e-mail faxes and voicemail from a single phone line. Clients receive a private phone number that can handle unlimited incoming messages. The company operates primarily under the eFax eVoice FuseMail CampaignerCRM KeepItSafe and Onebox brands and claims more than 11 million phone numbers for customers located in nearly 50 countries. In 2012 the company expanded to digital media when it bought Ziff Davis the online publisher of PCMag.com and Toolbox.com among others. j2 Global generates more than 60% of its revenues in the US.

Geographic Reach

Outside the US the company has customers in Canada (20% of sales) and Ireland (10%). It also has offices there as well as in Hong Kong and Japan.

Financial Performance

j2 Global is profitable and revenues increase every year. In 2012 sales grew 12% to $371 million and profits increased 6% to $121 million. Its growth is primarily due to acquisitions.

Mergers and Acquisitions

Acquisitions are a large part of the company's growth strategy. It has bought more than 40 companies since 2000. In 2013 it bought Backup Connect BV an online backup provider based in The Netherlands. With this acquisition j2 now has customer bases and prospects serviced by local sales support and online backup infrastructures in Ireland New Zealand The Netherlands the US and the UK. Also that year it bought MetroFax a US provider of Internet faxing services.

Its most substantial acquisition however has been the 2012 purchase of online publisher Ziff Davis for $167 million. Ziff Davis publishes technology gaming and lifestyle content through its digital properties. Titles include PCMag.com IGN.com AskMen.com Toolbox.com and others. It also operates BuyerBase a digital ad targeting platform and Ziff Davis B2B which offers research to enterprise buyers and leads to IT vendors. j2 Global expects the new digital media division to add $60 million in sales every year.

Other 2012 acquisitions include Australia-Based Zintel Communications UK-based Zimo Communications and US-based Landslide Technologies and Offsite Backup Solutions.

HISTORY

What did rap music East Berlin and the dot-com crowds have in common? The answer was Jaye Muller. Born in the former East Germany Muller moved to Paris at 17 to pursue a rap music career. During a 1994 UK concert tour he became frustrated at missing too many faxes and phone messages. Conveniently enough Muller had attended tech school and invented a virtual fax machine. He moved to New York to work on music but it was the siren song of a universal inbox that haunted him. Finding software programmers in Australia to help develop a system he launched the company in 1995 as JFAX Communications.

JFAX began offering voice and fax messages via e-mail in 1996 in Atlanta London and New York. The service soon caught on and by the end of the year the company had phone numbers available in 15 cities. Muller snagged professional talent hiring Motorola's Hemi Zucker as COO.

In 1997 the company introduced its outbound faxing service and Muller brought in big investors including Richard Ressler who left his job at IT firm MAI Systems to become CEO. Shifting coasts JFAX left New York for Los Angeles. The company penned a deal with QUALCOMM to offer JFAX through its Eudora e-mail client and closed out the year serving 45 cities.

JFAX came of age in 1998 when it embarked on a three-year marketing agreement with America Online (now AOL) which promoted JFAX as its exclusive unified messaging service while e-mail provider Critical Path Internet portal Yahoo! and ISP Prodigy Communications became strategic partners. Anxious to get back to his music at least part time Muller hired former AT&T executive Gary Hickox as president.

The company went public in 1999 and changed its name to JFAX.COM and it launched free service in hopes of attracting customers that would upgrade to fee-based plans.

In 2000 JFAX.COM acquired Internet-based messaging provider SureTalk.Com for $9 million. SureTalk's Steven Hamerslag became president (Hickox left the company) and CEO (Ressler became chairman). Later the company changed its name again this time to j2 Global Communications and expanded by purchasing rival message services provider eFax.com. When Hamerslag resigned at year's end the board replaced him with a management team made up of the company's top executives.

The next year j2 Global was granted a US patent for its core technology. Also in 2001 the company announced an expansion of its network into Argentina Chile Colombia and Mexico.

Expansion remained a big part of j2 Global Communications' scheme. The company increased its customer base with the acquisitions of rival messaging services providers SureTalk.com and eFax.com and in 2004 it acquired British Columbia-based outsourced e-mail and messaging services provider The Electric Mail Company. That year the company also acquired the unified communications assets branded Onebox from Call Sciences.

Its expansion plans in Europe got a boost with the company's acquisition in 2005 of UK-based messaging services provider Puma United Communications. In 2007 j2 Global acquired messaging services firm YAC (as in "you're always connected") Limited. The company specialized in hosted messaging and communications services such as inbound call management fax to e-mail virtual numbers audio conferencing and personal numbers. j2 Global also bought the RapidFax business of EasyLink Services International.

In 2008 j2 Global bought San Diego-based Phone People Holdings Corporation (toll-free calling services); UK-based Mediaburst (digital faxing products and services); the assets of MailWise a provider of hosted e-mail security services; and the fax and voice messaging assets of Mijanda which offers digital fax and voice messaging applications. The company made just one acquisition in 2009 buying the Internet fax technology business of CallWave.

J2 Global bought seven companies in 2010 including the voice assets of UK-based Realty Telecom LTD the email assets of Quexion and the fax assets of Comodo Communications which does business as TrustFax. It also acquired the messaging and communications business of Australia-based mBox in a move to build its Asia/Pacific client base particularly in Australia New Zealand and Singapore where mBox is most active. Additionally it purchased Miami-based Internet fax messaging specialist Venali for $17 million (following the dismissal of a patent dispute between j2 and Venali by the courts) online data backup specialist KeepItSafe and UK-based Alban Telecom.

j2 Global ended 2010 with the purchase of Canada-based Protus IP Solutions a provider of hosted Internet fax (MyFax) e-mail marketing (Campaigner) and voice communications (My1Voice) services for the enterprise market. j2 paid about $213 million for the company which boosted its number of paid subscribers to around 1.9 million.

EXECUTIVES

VP Engineering, Vincent P. (Vince) Niedzielski
VP Human Resources, Patty Brunton
EVP Corporate Strategy, Zohar Loshitzer, age 55
CEO, Nehemia (Hemi) Zucker, age 56, $459,000 total compensation
Chairman, Richard S. Ressler, age 55, $144,000 total compensation
CFO, Kathleen M. (Kathy) Griggs, age 59, $270,000 total compensation
President, R. Scott Turicchi, age 50, $375,000 total compensation
VP Products, Michael W. Harris, age 50
VP General Counsel and Secretary, Jeffrey D. (Jeff) Adelman, age 46, $270,000 total compensation
Vice President Marketing, Mike Pugh
VP Corporate Development, Ken Truesdale
VP Network Operations, Alan Alters
Vice President International, Tim McLean
VP and General Manager Europe, Paul Kinsella
Manager of Operations, Warner Bros
Vice President General Counsel Secretary, Jeff Adelman
Vice President Engineering, Vince Niedzielski
Chief Accounting Officer, Steve Dunn
Director, William B. (Brian) Kretzmer, age 58
Director, Douglas Y. Bech, age 68
Director, Robert J. Cresci, age 69
Director, John F. Rieley, age 70
Director, Michael P. Schulhof, age 71
Director, Stephen Ross, age 64
Auditors: SingerLewakLLP

LOCATIONS

HQ: j2 Global Inc.
6922 Hollywood Blvd. Ste. 500, Hollywood CA 90028
Phone: 323-860-9200   **Fax:** -140
Web: www.edap-tms.com

2012 Sales

	% of total
US	63
Canada	21
Ireland	11
Other	5
Total	**100**

PRODUCTS/OPERATIONS

2012 Sales

	$ mil.	% of total
Business cloud		97
Digital media		3
Total		**100**

Mergers & Acquisitio

2013
Backup Connect (The Netherlands online data backup)
MetroFax (US Internet faxing)

2012
Landslide Technologies (US CRM for small and midsized businesses
Offsite Backup Solutions (US online data backup)
Zimo Communications (UK voice services)
Zintel Communications (Australia voice services)
Ziff Davis (US online publisher)

2011
Data Haven (Ireland online data backup)
C Infinity (Ireland online data backup)
Offsite Backup Solutions (US online data backup)

COMPETITORS

CommTouch Software	Notify Technology
Deltathree	Open Text
EasyLink	Satellink
FuzeBox	

HISTORICAL FINANCIALS

Company Type: Public

Income Statement

FYE: December 31

	REVENUE ($ mil.)	NET INCOME ($ mil.)	NET PROFIT MARGIN	EMPLOYEES
12/12	371.4	121.5	32.7%	680
12/11	330.1	114.7	34.8%	600
12/10	255.3	83.0	32.5%	600
12/09	245.5	66.8	27.2%	400
12/08	241.5	72.5	30.0%	400
Annual Growth	11.4%	13.8%	—	14.2%

2012 Year-End Financials

Debt ratio: 24.6%
Return on equity: 21.1%
Cash ($ mil.): 218
Current ratio: 4.78
Long-term debt ($ mil.): 245

No. of shares (mil.): 45
Dividends
 Yield: 2.8%
 Payout: 33.7%
Market value ($ mil.): 1,380

	STOCK PRICE ($) FY Close	P/E High/Low		PER SHARE ($) Earnings	Dividends	Book Value
12/12	30.60	13	9	2.61	0.87	13.19
12/11	28.14	13	10	2.43	0.41	11.87
12/10	28.95	16	10	1.81	0.00	9.59
12/09	20.35	16	11	1.48	0.00	7.60
12/08	20.04	17	8	1.58	0.00	5.73
Annual Growth	11.2%		— —	13.4%	—	23.2%

Jack Henry & Associates, Inc.

Jack Henry & Associates (JHA) provides integrated in-house and outsourced software systems for data processing to some 12000 banks credit unions and other financial services companies. Products include core processing systems electronic funds transfer (EFT) systems automated teller machine networking products digital check and document imaging systems Internet banking tools and customer relationship management (CRM) software. The company's three primary brands include Jack Henry Banking Symitar and ProfitStars. JHA also provides electronic bill payment services through iPay Technologies. It primarily serves small and midsized institutions in the US.

Financial Analysis JHA has enjoyed steady revenue and net income growth over the past decade. In fiscal 2012 (ended June 30) it reported revenue of $1 billion up 6% from 2011. Net income was up 13% to $155 million. The company saw growth in all areas (support and service hardware license) with support and service sales particularly boosted by demand for electronic payment services. JHA's bottom line has been helped by its focus on cost control and its reduced interest cost due to continued long-term debt repayment.

Strategy JHA uses a combination of alliances internal product development and acquisitions to expand its offerings for its core bank and credit union markets. The company has an alliance with IBM where it sells IBM hardware and equipment resells maintenance on IBM hardware products and designs IBM-compatible software. Other hardware by Dell Digital Check Lenovo RDM and Unisys are bought by JHA at a discount and resold to customers. Hardware sales accounted for 6% of revenue in 2012.

Mergers and Acquisitions Since embarking on its acquisition strategy in 2004 the company has purchased some 20 companies including - in 2010 —iPay Technologies one of the largest independent electronic bill pay providers in the US and a long-time partner. The $301 million deal increased the company's transaction-based and recurring revenue streams and expanded its product line and its presence in the growing electronic payments industry. Other acquisitions that year include PEMCO Technology (payment processing for credit unions) and Goldleaf Financial (integrated technology and payment processing).

HISTORY

John W. "Jack" Henry managed the computer system of a small bank in Monett Missouri until 1977 when the bank was purchased and he lost his job. That year he founded Jack Henry & Associates with partners Jerry Hall and Kendall Kinnear. Boosted by a contract with IBM by 1985 — when it went public —JHA was one of the US's fastest-growing companies.

JHA made two significant missteps over the next two years. It acquired a securities brokerage that lost nearly $1 million and it signed a contract with Unisys that required it to distance itself from IBM. (JHA has since formed a remarketing agreement with IBM.) Consequently the company developed a system that broadened JHA's market to larger banks. The company bounced back in 1989 after returning to its core business of small banks.

In the 1990s JHA used purchases of similar companies to expand its services to small banks facing increasing pressure from acquisitive nationwide banking chains. In 1993 it bought BankVision which was developing a global version of JHA's large bank system under a partnership agreement. In 1994 Michael Henry Jack's son and an employee of JHA since he graduated from high school in 1979 was named CEO.

In 1999 JHA expanded its customer base by almost 50% with the purchase of BancTec's community banking business. The next year it acquired BancData Solutions a provider of core data processing and item capture for Southern California banks. Responding to customer demand for alternative hardware products in 2001 JHA expanded its offerings beyond IBM products to include Unisys reader/sorter hardware. In early 2002 it purchased Transcend Systems Group a provider of customer relationship management (CRM) software for community financial institutions; and Credit Union Solutions a provider of data processing systems for small credit unions.

By 2004 the company began a buying spree. It bought Banc Insurance Services Optinfo SERsynergy TWS Systems and Verinex Technologies and the next year it snatched up Profitstar Stratika Symitar and Tangent Analytics.

Mr. Henry passed away in April 2007 at age 71. A book about the founders and the company's history "You Don't Know Jack ... or Jerry" was published in 2008.

Over the years JHA has actively pursued acquisitions of companies that provide complementary products and services to its own core customer base. It has bought five companies (including iPay) since 2007 beginning with AudioTel and Gladiator Technology Services. In 2009 it acquired Goldleaf Financial Solutions (now doing business as ProfitStars) for about $67 million; and PEMCO

Technology Services (a subsidiary of PEMCO Insurance) for $61 million.

EXECUTIVES

President, Tony L. Wormington, age 51, $408,484 total compensation
CFO and Treasurer, Kevin D. Williams, age 54, $368,225 total compensation
Chairman and CEO, John F. (Jack) Prim, age 58, $495,733 total compensation
Vice Chairman, Matthew C. (Matt) Flanigan, age 51
General Manager E-Services, Terry McMullen
VP and CTO, Mark S. Forbis, age 50, $238,333 total compensation
President of ProfitStars R, David (Dave) Foss
Vice Chairman and EVP, Jerry D. Hall, age 69
Director, James J. (Jim) Ellis, age 78
CEO and Director, John F. (Jack) Prim, age 57
Vice Chairman, Matthew C. (Matt) Flanigan, age 51
Director, Craig R. Curry, age 51
Director, Wesley A. Brown, age 59
Director, Marla K. Shepherd, age 64
Independent Director, Jacqueline Fiegel
Independent Director, Thomas Wimsett
Independent Director, Tom Wilson
Auditors: Deloitte&ToucheLLP

LOCATIONS

HQ: Jack Henry & Associates Inc.
663 W. Hwy. 60, Monett MO 65708-8215
Phone: 417-235-6652   **Fax:** 417-235-4281
Web: www.jackhenry.com

PRODUCTS/OPERATIONS

2012 Sales

	$ mil.	% of total
Support & service	909	89
Hardware	63	6
Licensing	55	5
Total	**1,027**	**100**

Selected Products and Services

Asset management (Biodentify Centurion Disaster Recovery Fraud Detective)
Banking software suite (CIF 20/20 Core Director Silverlake)
Business banking (Mutual Fund Sweep Remote Deposit Capture NetTeller)
Business intelligence (ARGOKeys eEMS Stratika Synapsys)
Credit union software suite (Cruise Episys)
Electronic funds transfer (ATM Manager Pro ImageCenter ATM PassPort.atm)
Internet banking (DirectLine eStatements NetTeller OFX)
Item and document imaging (4|sight Check 21 ImageCenter Check)
Professional services (FormSmart Intellix Matrix Network Services)
Retail delivery (InTouch Voice Response OnTarget Vertex Teller Automation System)

COMPETITORS

ACI Worldwide
BancTec
Fidelity National Information Services
Financial Fusion
First Data
Fiserv
Harland Financial Solutions
Intuit Financial Services
Misys
Open Solutions
Oracle Financial Services Software
SunGard Financial Systems
Total System Services
US Dataworks

HISTORICAL FINANCIALS

Company Type: Public

Income Statement

FYE: June 30

	REVENUE ($ mil.)	NET INCOME ($ mil.)	NET PROFIT MARGIN	EMPLOYEES
06/13	1,129.3	176.6	15.6%	5,139
06/12	1,027.1	154.9	15.1%	4,872
06/11	966.9	137.4	14.2%	4,667
06/10	836.5	117.8	14.1%	4,528
06/09	745.5	103.1	13.8%	3,808
Annual Growth	10.9%	14.4%	—	7.8%

2013 Year-End Financials

Debt ratio: 0.9%
Return on equity: 17.1%
Cash ($ mil.): 127
Current ratio: 1.09
Long-term debt ($ mil.): 7

No. of shares (mil.): 85
Dividends
Yield: 0.0%
Payout: 27.4%
Market value ($ mil.): 4,017

	STOCK PRICE ($) FY Close	P/E High/Low	PER SHARE ($) Earnings	Dividends	Book Value
06/13	47.13	23 17	2.04	0.56	12.58
06/12	34.52	20 14	1.78	0.44	11.43
06/11	30.01	21 15	1.59	0.40	10.19
06/10	23.88	19 14	1.38	0.36	8.79
06/09	20.75	20 12	1.22	0.32	7.49
Annual Growth	22.8%	— —	13.7%	15.0%	13.8%

Jos. A. Bank Clothiers, Inc.

When casual Fridays put a wrinkle in the starched selling philosophy of Jos. A. Bank Clothiers the company dressed down. Although it is still best known for making tailored clothing for the professional man including suits sport coats dress shirts and pants it has added casual wear suitable for those dress-down Fridays and weekends. It also launched the David Leadbetter line of golf wear. The company sells its Jos. A. Bank clothes and a few shoe brands through its catalogs website and some 625 company-owned or franchised stores in 40-plus states and the District of Columbia. For corporate customers it offers a credit card that provides users with discounts. Most of its stores house a tailoring shop.

Strategy

Jos. A. Bank has dropped its bid to acquire its larger rival Men's Wearhouse for $48 per share in cash. Men's Wearhouse rejected the unsolicited offer saying it undervalued the company and then turned the tables on Bank on its would-be acquirer and bid to acquire it. After Bank tightened its poison pill requirements in early 2014 to prevent a hostile takeover Men's Wearhouse upped its offer to $1.6 billion. (Men's Wearhouse has twice as many stores as Jos. A Bank and two-and-a-half times its annual sales.) Still hot on the acquisition trail Bank in February 2014 agreed to buy the Eddie Bauer brand (owned by the private equity firm Golden Gate Capital) in a deal valued at $825 million including cash and debt. (Bank will pay $564 million in cash and issue about 4.7 million new shares of its stock to fund the acquisition.)

Bank says the deal is an opportunity for growth and expansion. Eddie Bauer operates about 370 stores and an online and catalog business.

Fast-growing Jos. A. Bank has added more than 400 stores over the past nine years topping the 600-store mark in 2013.

Financial Performance

The growing store base and increasing same-store sales (up 7% in fiscal 2011) have resulted in healthy sales and profit growth. Fiscal 2011 sales increased by about 11% vs. the prior year while net income was up more than 20% over the same period. (Indeed 2011 marked the 10th consecutive year of increasing sales and profits for the retailer.) The chain saw strong sales increases in dress shirts other tailored clothing (particularly sportcoats blazers and dress pants) sportswear and suits. In 2011 Jos. A. Bank began taking online orders from international customers giving a boost to its growing e-commerce business.

The retailer covers all the bases with its "Three Levels of Luxury" strategy which includes the Jos. A. Bank Executive collection the more luxurious Signature collection and the exclusive Signature Gold collection. (The higher-end lines feature superfine qualities of wool and other materials.) Together the Signature and Signature Gold collections accounted for more than 25% of total merchandise sales in 2011.

The chain has sought growth through nontraditional means. It began offering tuxedo rentals in about half of its stores in 2010 and now offers rentals at all of its locations. While Jos. A Bank already sells formalwear it believes it can tap into an additional revenue stream by offering the rental option. It competes with the likes of Men's Wearhouse and Tux and other formal wear chains.

Ownership

Investment firm FMR LLC owns nearly 15% of the company's shares while Royce & Associates owns about 11%.

EXECUTIVES

EVP CFO Principal Financial and Accounting Officer, David E. Ullman, age 55, $450,000 total compensation
Chairman, Robert N. Wildrick, age 69, $944,191 total compensation
EVP Human Resources Real Estate and Loss Prevention, Robert B. Hensley, age 60, $475,000 total compensation
President CEO and Director, R. Neal Black, age 58, $750,000 total compensation
EVP Store and Catalog Operations, Gary M. Merry, age 51, $355,000 total compensation
EVP Merchandising and Chief Merchandising Officer, James W. (Jim) Thorne, age 53, $350,000 total compensation
Director, James H. Ferstl, age 70
President CEO and Director, R. Neal Black, age 58
Director, Gary S. Gladstein, age 67
Director, Andrew A. Giordano, age 80
Director, William E. Herron, age 68
Director, Sidney H. Ritman, age 80
Director, Henry Homes III, age 65
Auditors: Deloitte&Touche

LOCATIONS

HQ: Jos. A. Bank Clothiers Inc.
500 Hanover Pike, Hampstead MD 21074
Phone: 410-239-2700   **Fax:** 410-239-5700
Web: www.josbank.com

2011 Stores

	No.
Alabama	13

Arizona	5
Arkansas	4
California	31
Colorado	9
Connecticut	14
Delaware	1
Florida	35
Georgia	22
Idaho	1
Illinois	29
Indiana	9
Iowa	3
Kansas	3
Kentucky	5
Louisiana	6
Maryland	21
Massachusetts	16
Michigan	13
Minnesota	7
Mississippi	3
Missouri	8
Nebraska	2
Nevada	3
New	2
New	29
New	1
New	21
North	21
Ohio	22
Oklahoma	4
Pennsylvania	27
Rhode	2
South	11
South	1
Tennessee	12
Texas	48
Utah	2
Virginia	25
Washington	3
District of	5
West	1
Wisconsin	6
Total	**506**

PRODUCTS/OPERATIONS

2011 Sales

	$ mil.	% of total
Stores	754	88
Direct marketing	85	10
Other	18	2
Total	**858**	**100**

Selected Merchandise

Clothing accessories
Dress and casual shirts
Formal wear
Mufflers
Overcoats
Pajamas
Polos
Shoes
Shorts
Sport coats
Suits
Sweaters
Ties
Trousers
Underwear
Vests

COMPETITORS

Allen-Edmonds	Macy's
Astor & Black	Men's Wearhouse
Brooks Brothers	Nordstrom
Dillard's	PVH
Lands' End	Ralph Lauren

HISTORICAL FINANCIALS

Company Type: Public

Income Statement

FYE: February 2

	REVENUE ($ mil.)	NET INCOME ($ mil.)	NET PROFIT MARGIN	EMPLOYEES
02/13*	1,049.3	79.7	7.6%	6,342
01/12	979.8	97.4	9.9%	5,883
01/11	858.1	85.8	10.0%	4,998
01/10	770.3	71.1	9.2%	4,318
01/09	546.3	43.2	7.9%	4,040
Annual Growth	**17.7%**	**16.5%**	**—**	**11.9%**

*Fiscal year change

2013 Year-End Financials

Debt ratio: —
Return on equity: 12.5%
Cash ($ mil.): 71
Current ratio: 4.36
Long-term debt ($ mil.): —

No. of shares (mil.): 27
Dividends
Yield: —
Payout: —
Market value ($ mil.): 1,144

	STOCK PRICE ($) FY Close	P/E High/Low		PER SHARE ($) Earnings	Dividends	Book Value
02/13*	40.93	19	14	2.84	0.00	23.87
01/12	48.06	16	12	3.49	0.00	21.02
01/11	41.95	21	12	3.08	0.00	17.47
01/10	41.91	19	8	2.56	0.00	14.29
01/09	27.46	25	10	1.57	0.00	11.73
Annual Growth	**10.5%**	**—**	**—**	**15.9%**	**—**	**19.4%**

*Fiscal year change

K12 Inc

K12 isn't a missing element from the periodic table but it could help kids learn the periodic table. The company offers online educational programs to students in kindergarten through 12th grade through "virtual schools." It also offers online curriculum to public and private schools. It provides course material and product sales directly to parents and individualized supplemental programs offered through schools. K12 also manages and sells its products and services to blended schools (public schools that combine online and face-to-face instruction) and provides services to US school districts and to international partners.

Geographic Reach

K12 serves students from 85 countries around the world. K12 operates overseas through the K12 International Academy a private school that enables K12 to deliver its learning system to students in other countries. In 2010 the company opened offices in Singapore and Switzerland. In 2012 it was distributing its products and services to more than 1000 school partners.

Operations

The company operates in three segments: Managed Public Schools (virtual and blended); Institutional Business (school district partnerships focused on curriculum development and teacher training); and International and Private Pay Business (three online and one brick and mortar private school and international distribution partnerships).

K12's Managed Public School segment (its largest revenue generator) develops online programs that adhere to the policies of public entities such as public school districts independent non-profit charter school boards and state education agencies. It offers the same coursework and curriculum as most school districts' "brick and mortar" campuses. However since virtual schools don't have the requirement of a physical classroom they can accommodate a large dispersed student population. They also allow for more capital resources to be directed toward teaching curriculum and technology rather than keeping up a physical infrastructure. Students who attend virtual public schools receive assignments complete lessons and obtain instruction from certified teachers with whom they interact online telephonically in virtual classroom environments and at times face-to-face.

K12 also has a contract with the Delaware Department of Education to manage the Moyer Charter School. The agreement (reached in 2010) representes K12's first foray into bricks-and-mortar school management. Through the agreement K12 is authorized to serve up to 460 students in grades 6-12. K12 intends to expand its work with school districts and has established a dedicated sales team to further that effort. The services it provides to districts include teacher training programs administrator support and a student account management system.

Financial Analysis

In FY 2012 the company saw an increase in revenues due to sales growth in its Managed Public Schools Institutional Business and International and Private Pay Business segments. Managed Public Schools revenues saw organic growth of $116.7 million and acquired growth of $25.4 million; Institutional Business revenues grew as the result of the full year effect of acquired businesses such as American Education Corporation (AEC); and International and Private Pay revenues grew through the IS Berne acquisition. Revenues for the Managed Public Schools grew 31% year-over-year while total average enrollment growth for Managed Public Schools students grew by 41%.

Net income increased in FY 2012 due to a drop in interest expenses —$1 million as compared to net interest expense of $1.2 million for the prior fiscal year primarily due to lower interest rates on capital leases and equipment financing arrangements.

Business Strategy

K12's growth strategy consists of leveraging the investments it has made in curriculum online learning and school management to serve adjacent markets and to diversify its risk profile. It plans to increase enrollment in its public school programs and expand into additional US states and cities while increasing its institutional and international footprint.

In 2011 the company acquired IS Berne a traditional private school located in Berne Switzerland serving students in grades Pre-K through 12. That year K12 agreed to acquire the online high school business of Kaplan. The unit targets adults without high school diplomas and high school students who are looking to augment their brick-and-mortar education.

K12 started out offering programs for children in kindergarten through second grade. It gradually expanded and now offers instruction all the way up to a self-paced high school program. The company made a greater investment in its middle and high school products with its 2010 acquisition of KC Distance Learning (KCDL). The purchase brought in three brands targeting both public and private schools: Aventa Learning The Keystone School and iQ Academies. Also that year K12 formed a 60-40 joint venture with Middlebury College to create online foreign language classes.

In late 2010 K12 acquired AEC a provider of research-based core curriculum instructional software for kindergarten through adult learners. The acquisition added to K12's portfolio of instructional and curriculum offerings and assessment tools.

Ownership

In 2012 the Learning Group LLC held 19% of the company Jon Q. Reynolds 11%.

Company Background

CEO Ron Packard founded K12 in 2000.

EXECUTIVES

EVP General Counsel Secretary, Howard D. Polsky, age 61

CEO and Director, Ronald J. (Ron) Packard, age 49, $475,000 total compensation

Chairman CEO, Craig R. Barrett, age 74

EVP and CFO, Harry T. Hawks, age 59

Chairman, Nathaniel A. (Nate) Davis, age 59

EVP and CFO, James Rhyu

Senior Vice President - Human Resources, Howard Allentoff, age 51

Executive Vice President and Chief Marketing & Enrollment Officer, Chuck Sullivan, age 55

EVP and Chief Marketing Officer, Celia Stokes, age 49, $300,300 total compensation

Executive Vice President - Operations, John Olsen

EVP Worldwide Business Development, Bruce J. Davis, age 50, $309,000 total compensation

EVP School Services, George B. (Chip) Hughes Jr., age 54, $300,248 total compensation

Senior Vice President of Public Affairs, Bryan W. Flood, age 46

Senior Vice President of School Development, Peter G. Stewart, age 43

EVP Product Development, Maria A. Szalay, age 46

SVP Systems and Technology, Ray Williams, age 50

Senior Vice President of Content and Curriculum, John Holdren

VP Public Relations, Jeff Kwitowski

Senior Vice President of School Development, Peter Stew

President and COO, Timothy L. Murray

Finance Manager, Tammy Quesenberry

Vice President Western Region, James Konantz

Vice President - Investor Relations, Christina Parker

Chief Academic Officer, Margaret Jorgensen

SVP and CIO, James Donley

EVP School Management and Services, Allison Cleveland

Senior Vice President Human Resources at K12 Inc, Valerie Maddy

CEO and Director, Ronald J. (Ron) Packard, age 49

Director, Craig R. Barrett, age 73

Director, Guillermo Bron, age 61

Director, Steven B. (Steve) Fink, age 62

Director, Mary Hatwood Futrell, age 73

Director, Thomas J. Wilford, age 70

Independent Director, John Engler

Independent Director, Jon Reynolds

Auditors: BDOUSALLP

LOCATIONS

HQ: K12 Inc.
2300 Corporate Park Dr., Herndon VA 20171
Phone: 703-483-7000   **Fax:** 703-483-7330
Web: www.k12.com

PRODUCTS/OPERATIONS

Selected Students Served/Services

Advanced and Enrichable Learners
Athletes and Performers

Credit Recovery (for missed classes make-up credits)
Expat Foreign Service Overseas
Homebound
Homeschoolers
Military Families
Reading Program
Struggling Students
Summer School
Supplemental Education
World Languages

COMPETITORS

Apollo Education	ITT Educational
Capella Education	Kaplan
DeVry Education Group	McGraw Hill Financial
Edison Learning	Nobel Learning
Edmentum	Communities
Florida Virtual School	Pearson plc
Houghton Mifflin	Rosetta Stone
Harcourt	

HISTORICAL FINANCIALS

Company Type: Public

Income Statement

FYE: June 30

	REVENUE ($ mil.)	NET INCOME ($ mil.)	NET PROFIT MARGIN	EMPLOYEES
06/13	848.2	28.1	3.3%	3,500
06/12	708.4	17.5	2.5%	3,300
06/11	522.4	12.7	2.4%	2,500
06/10	384.4	21.5	5.6%	1,065
06/09	315.5	12.3	3.9%	993
Annual Growth	28.0%	22.9%	—	37.0%

2013 Year-End Financials

Debt ratio: 4.9%
Return on equity: 5.6%
Cash ($ mil.): 181
Current ratio: 4.19
Long-term debt ($ mil.): 16

No. of shares (mil.): 40
Dividends
 Yield: —
 Payout: —
Market value ($ mil.): 1,056

	STOCK PRICE ($) FY Close	P/E High/Low	PER SHARE ($) Earnings	Dividends	Book Value
06/13	26.27	42 22	0.72	0.00	13.19
06/12	23.30	80 38	0.45	0.00	12.99
06/11	33.14	106 58	0.37	0.00	12.49
06/10	22.18	36 22	0.71	0.00	7.29
06/09	21.55	67 29	0.42	0.00	6.22
Annual Growth	5.1%	— —	14.4%	—	20.7%

Kansas City Southern

Kansas City Southern (KCS) rides the rails of a 6300-mile network that stretches from Missouri to Mexico. The company's Kansas City Southern Railway (KCSR) owns and operates about 3500 miles of track in the midwestern and southern US. KCS offers rail freight service in Mexico through Kansas City Southern de Mexico (KCSM formerly TFM) which maintains more than 3100 miles of track and serves three major ports. Another KCS unit Texas Mexican Railway connects the KCSR and KCSM systems. The KCS railroads transport such freight as industrial and consumer products agricultural and mineral products and chemical and petroleum products.

HISTORY

Arthur Edward Stilwell founded the Kansas City Southern Railway (KCSR) in 1887 to transport commodities for local meatpackers and granaries. By 1891 Stilwell had expanded the line southward to Fort Smith Arkansas. Two years later he extended the line to the Gulf of Mexico to give the heartland's agricultural producers an outlet to the sea. Stilwell decided to route his lines to Lake Sabine Texas seven miles inland from the Gulf and relatively protected from hurricanes. He built a port on the lake and then dredged a canal to the Gulf. Subsequently named Port Arthur the site became the second-largest grain port after New York.

In the 1920s and 1930s Leonore Loree Stilwell's successor guided the company through the Depression and beyond with sound financial management. In 1939 KCSR bought the Louisiana and Arkansas Railways to extend its lines to New Orleans and Dallas. That year General Motors chose the railroad to test its first passenger-service diesel-electric locomotive.

Kansas businessmen wrested control of the company from its eastern owners in 1944 and appointed William Deramus as president. With a new leader and operating strategy in place the railroad focused on expanding its business into territories that were experiencing a post-WWII industrial boom.

In the 1950s KCSR developed a computerized data-processing system for its businesses. During the mid-1950s Deramus and his son William Deramus III (then president of the Chicago Great Western and Katy Railway) were heavily involved in building the Mid-America Pipeline (MAPCO) along their railroads' rights-of-way though KCSR's interest ended by the early 1980s.

In 1961 William Deramus III joined his father in senior management at the company. Kansas City Southern Industries (KCSI) was incorporated as a holding company for the purpose of diversification in the face of growing competition from airlines and the trucking industry. As the company's data-processing and information management needs increased KCSI capitalized on its early data-processing experience by forming DST Systems.

Growth during the 1980s resulted from an increase in coal transport and additional freight traffic. In 1983 KCSI bought a majority stake in Janus Capital a Denver-based mutual funds company. By the late 1980s the company's transportation and financial management divisions were prospering because of higher coal volume and the growth of the mutual funds industry.

KCSI increased its mutual funds holdings by buying Berger and Associates in 1992. In 1997 the company formed Kansas City Southern Lines a holding company for its transportation segments to streamline its corporate structure and refocus on its core businesses.

The next year KCSI created FAM Holding Company to house its financial asset management subsidiaries including Janus Capital Berger Associates and DST Systems and it expanded its financial operations with the acquisition of 80% of UK-based Nelson Money Managers. Also in 1998 with partner Mi-Jack Products (a maker of intermodal equipment) KCSI was awarded the Panama Canal railroad concession by the government of Panama.

The company's founder returned in spirit in 1999 when KSCI announced plans to spin off its financial services businesses to shareholders as a new company Stilwell Financial. Although executives at Janus then one of the hottest US mutual fund managers lobbied for their company to be spun off separately Janus was part of Stilwell when

Stilwell began trading in 2000. (Janus and Stilwell were combined in 2003 to form Janus Capital Group.)

KCSI completed reconstruction of the Panama Canal Railway in 2001 and reopened the railroad for freight and passenger transport.

Two years after the Stilwell spinoff KCSI shortened its name to Kansas City Southern (KCS) to reflect its renewed focus on transportation. Also in 2002 KCS increased its stake in Grupo TFM when shares held by the Mexican government were put up for sale.

In 2003 KCS agreed to acquire the stake in Grupo TFM held by Grupo TMM but the deal ran into a roadblock the next year when it was rejected by TMM shareholders. The companies continued to negotiate however and a new agreement was announced in December 2004. KCS completed its purchase of Grupo TMM's stake in Grupo TFM in April 2005.

Later in 2005 the settlement of a tax dispute that involved KCS TFM Grupo TFM Grupo TMM and the Mexican government resulted in KCS receiving the 20% stake in TFM held by the government and thus gaining full ownership of the railroad. In return KCS and Grupo TMM gave up their claim to a tax refund the companies had been seeking. In a separate deal KCS took over TFM's Mexrail unit (owner of Texas Mexican Railway).

In December 2005 KCS changed TFM's name to Kansas City Southern de Mexico (KCSM).

After suffering declines in revenues and net income during the Great Recession KCS saw its revenues in 2010 jump more than 20% compare to the previous year. Overall revenue per carload increased just over 15% in the period with coal and automobile improving the most at 36% and 34% respectively.

EXECUTIVES

EVP Administration and Corporate Affairs, Warren K. Erdman, age 55

Chairman, Michael R. (Mike) Haverty, age 69, $763,330 total compensation

VP Investor Relations, William (Bill) Galligan

Assistant VP Corporate Communications and Community Affairs, C. Doniele Kane

Assistant VP Sales and Marketing Transload, Rich Weigel

Director Security Mexico, James (Jim) Kniestedt

Assistant VP Claims and Litigation, Jack E. Hamer

Director Sports Operations, Jacobo Jacome

VP Sales and Marketing Carload Business Unit U.S., Owen M. Zidar

SVP and Chief Legal Officer, W. James (Jim) Wochner, age 65, $254,567 total compensation

VP Sales and Marketing Agriculture and Minerals, Michael R. Bilovesky

SVP and CIO, Michael J. (Mike) Naatz

Associate General Counsel and Corporate Secretary, Brian P. Banks

EVP and Assistant to the Chairman, Larry M. Lawrence, age 49

President and Executive Representative KCSM, Jose G. Zozaya Delano, age 59, $329,279 total compensation

First VP Operations Mexico, William H. (Bill) Nolen

SVP Sales and Marketing and Asset Management, David Eaton

Assistant VP Facilities and Heritage Operations, Douglas A. (Doug) Banks

VP Administration Kansas City Southern Railway, Gene M. Goode

Assistant VP International Internal Audit and Financial Compliance, T. Nicholas (Nick) Nocita

EVP Sales and Marketing, Patrick J. (Pat) Ottensmeyer, age 56, $381,498 total compensation

Director Revenue and Disbursements Accounting, Julio Quintero

Associate General Counsel, David C. Reeves

Assistant VP Real Estate and Industrial Development, Glen Ebeling

Director Engineering Mexico, Cesar Polack

General Manager Midwest Division, Kevin McIntosh

Assistant VP Police and Special Services, Al Rawls

VP International Taxes, James D. Byrd

Assistant VP Internal Reporting and Control, Scott L. Mylin

VP Capital Investment Accounting, Edward E. (Ed) Scott

EVP and COO, David R. (Dave) Ebbrecht

Associate General Counsel, Kayden B. Howard

Assistant Treasurer, Rodrigo Flores

VP Information Technology and Telecommunications, Carl Harrison

Assistant VP Marketing Intermodal and Automotive, Thomas (Tom) Naso

VP Yield Management, Timothy M. (Tim) Befort

Associate General Counsel, Leonard L. Wagner

SVP Human Resources, John E. Derry, age 45

General Manager Southeast Division, Claude N. Friesland

VP Transportation KCSR Network, Mark A. Redd

EVP and CFO, Michael W. (Mike) Upchurch, age 52, $321,600 total compensation

SVP Intermodal and Automotive, Brian Bowers, age 60

Assistant VP Revenue Accounting, Rito Arredondo

Assistant VP Financial Reporting and Compliance, Suzie Grafton

Associate General Counsel and Assistant Secretary, Adam Godderz

Assistant VP Legal, Edgar Aguileta

Assistant VP Legal Mexico, Alejandro Lopez

VP Network Planning and Customer Service Mexico, Jorge de Leon

VP and Chief Mechanical Officer, John Foster

SVP Operations KCSM, Oscar Del Cueto

Assistant VP Government Accounts, Maricio Guizar

Assistant VP Sales and Marketing, Steve Milligan

VP Intermodal and Automotive Operations, D. Morris Godwin

President CEO and Director, David L. Starling, age 63, $502,500 total compensation

VP Business Solutions, Jorge Marquez

Assistant VP Sales and Marketing Carload Business Unit in U.S., Steve Evans

Assistant VP Datacenter and Telecommunications, Danny Hall

Asstant Chief Engineer Signal and Administration US, Buck Jones

Assistant VP Sales and Marketing Coal Business Unit, Darin Selby

Assistant VP Operations Process Management, Rick Stones

Assistant VP Business Solutions and Delivery, Thomas A (Tom) Govreau

SVP and Chief Engineer, John S. Jacobsen

Assistant VP Intermodal Sales and Marketing, Brett C. Jensen

VP Purchasing, Michael (Mike) Walczak

Director System Operations, Edgar Diaz

Assistant VP IT Process Control and Security, Pedro Garduza

General Manager Locomotive Operations, Mitch Whitmire

VP Agra Industrial, Antonio Amerigo

Assistant VP Sales Operations and Administration, Gil A. Niesen

SVP and Chief Accounting Officer, Mary K. Stadler, age 53

Assistant VP Business Solutions, Kelly Platt

Assistant VP Intermodal Operations Mexico, Carlos Rojas

Head Corporate Affairs, Edgar Guillaumin

SVP Intermodal and Automotive, Brian Borrows

VP Finance and Treasurer, Michael W. Kline

President and Executive Representative of Kansas City Southern de M??xico; S.A. de C.V., Jose Delano

Director, Robert J. Druten, age 66

Director, Thomas A. (Tom) McDonnell, age 68

Director, Terrence P. (Terry) Dunn

Director, Rodney E. Slater, age 58

Director, Antonio O. Garza Jr., age 53

Director, Henry Davis, age 72

President CEO and Director, David L. Starling, age 63

Director, Lu M. Cordova, age 57

Independent Director, Henry Signoret

Independent Director, Lu Cordova

Auditors: KPMGLLP

LOCATIONS

HQ: Kansas City Southern
427 W. 12th St., Kansas City MO 64105
Phone: 816-983-1303   **Fax:** 816-983-1108
Web: www.kcsi.com

2012 Sales

	$ mil.	% of total
US	1,216	54
Total	**2,238**	**100**

PRODUCTS/OPERATIONS

2012 Sales

	$ mil.	% of total
Carload revenues		
Chemical & petroleum	410	18
Agriculture & minerals	400	18
Energy	312	14
Automotive	174	8
Total	**2,238**	**100**

COMPETITORS

American Commercial Lines	Grupo Carso
Burlington Northern Santa Fe	Grupo Mexico
	Ingram Industries
CSX	J.B. Hunt
Canadian National Railway	Kirby Corporation
	Norfolk Southern
Canadian Pacific Railway	Schneider National
	Union Pacific
Crowley Maritime	Werner Enterprises

HISTORICAL FINANCIALS

Company Type: Public

Income Statement

FYE: December 31

	REVENUE ($ mil.)	NET INCOME ($ mil.)	NET PROFIT MARGIN	EMPLOYEES
12/13	2,369.3	351.4	14.8%	6,260
12/12	2,238.6	377.3	16.9%	6,110
12/11	2,098.3	330.3	15.7%	6,140
12/10	1,814.8	180.2	9.9%	6,100
12/09	1,480.2	68.0	4.6%	6,100
Annual Growth	**12.5%**	**50.8%**	**—**	**0.6%**

2013 Year-End Financials

Debt ratio: 29.4%	No. of shares (mil.): 110
Return on equity: 10.8%	Dividends
Cash ($ mil.): 429	Yield: 0.6%
Current ratio: 1.29	Payout: 28.7%
Long-term debt ($ mil.): 1,856	Market value ($ mil.): 13,650

| | STOCK PRICE ($) | P/E | PER SHARE ($) | | |
	FY Close	High/Low	Earnings	Dividends	Book Value
12/13	123.83	39 26	3.18	0.86	30.58
12/12	83.48	24 18	3.43	0.78	28.12
12/11	68.01	23 15	3.00	0.00	25.15
12/10	47.86	30 18	1.67	0.00	23.68
12/09	33.29	56 21	0.61	0.00	21.40
Annual Growth	38.9%	— —	51.1%	—	9.3%

KapStone Paper & Packaging Corp

Rock paper sissors? KapStone Paper and Packaging has the upper hand in the game of unbleached kraft. The company manufactures largely linerboard a type of paperboard that is converted into laminated tier sheets and wrapping material. It also produces kraft paper (industry-speak for strong wrapping paper) for multiwall bags; saturating kraft (sold under the Durasorb brand) to produce mainly high pressure laminates for furniture construction materials and electronics; and unbleached folding carton board (Kraftpak) which is converted into packaging for consumer goods. KapStone counts 500-plus customers including Graphic Packaging Exopack and other major converters. The US represents about 60% of sales.

Established in 2005 KapStone has evolved through a series of mergers acquisitions and other investments in the paper packaging and forest products industry. As of 2010 it is more than one-third of the way toward its goal of becoming a $2 billion revenue company by 2015.

In line with this strategy KapStone announced in 2011 an agreement to acquire the stock of U.S. Corrugated Inc. (USC) for $330 million in cash. USC operates a 240000-ton recycled containerboard paper mill in South Carolina and 20 converting facilities in the eastern and midwestern US six of which will be disposed of by USC prior to the closing. The operations to be acquired from USC generated $423 million in net sales in 2010 and the deal is expected to increase KapStone's profitability.

Previous acquisitions have also helped to fuel KapStone's earnings. It acquired MeadWestvaco's North Charleston Kraft Division in 2008 for approximately $485 million. That deal added saturating kraft and unbleached kraft board to KapStone's offerings and significantly expanded its customer base outside of the US. It also gained a cogeneration facility chip mills and a lumber mill.

In 2007 KapStone pocketed the Kraft Papers Business of International Paper Company (IP) for $155 million. The business included an unbleached kraft paper manufacturing facility in North Carolina and Ride Rite Converting an inflatable dunnage bag manufacturer. The latter business was sold to Illinois Tool Works for $36 million in 2009 to help KapStone trim its debt and concentrate on its kraft operations. In early 2011 the company parlayed an early settlement with IP; it managed to pay IP the remaining purchase price for the papers business at a reduced amount.

The company has benefited recently from higher mill operating rates coupled with price increases in linerboard and kraft paper driven by market demand from the recovering economy. Unbleached kraft sales have maintained a four-year positive trajectory increasing by nearly 25% in 2010 over 2009. Nonetheless year-over-year earnings in 2010 declined by almost 20% due in large part to expiring alternate fuel mixture tax credits inflated input and freight costs and fatter paychecks and employee benefits. Cash generated from operations dwindled too in 2010 diminished by capital expenditures for equipment upgrades and IT projects and financing activities.

The kraft paper maker has also taken advantage of tax credits associated with the use of black liquor a biofuel that is a by-product of the wood pulping process to power its production facilities. As a result it appreciably reduced its debt in 2009 and 2010 and effective tax rate in 2010 which helped position the company closer to its goals.

EXECUTIVES

President Secretary Director, Matthew S. (Matt) Kaplan, age 56, $420,000 total compensation
Chairman of the Board Chief Executive Officer, Roger W. Stone, age 78, $420,000 total compensation
Chief Financial Officer; Vice President, Andrea K. Tarbox, age 62, $275,000 total compensation
Manager Public Affairs and Communications Kapstone Charleston, Larry Cobb
VP and General Manager KapStone Charleston Kraft, Bruce Hoffman
Director, David P. Storch, age 60
President Secretary Director, Matthew S. (Matt) Kaplan, age 56
Director, Brian R. Gamache, age 54
Director, Matthew H. (Matt) Paull, age 62
Director, Ronald J. (Ron) Gidwitz, age 69
Director, Jonathan R. Furer, age 56
Director, John M. Chapman, age 53
Auditors: Ernst&YoungLLP

LOCATIONS

HQ: KapStone Paper & Packaging Corp
1101 Skokie Blvd., Suite 300, Northbrook, IL 60062
Phone: 847 239-8800
Web: www.kapstonepaper.com

2010 Sales

	$ mil.	% of total
US	482	62
Other countries	300	38
Total	782	100

PRODUCTS/OPERATIONS

2010 Sales

	$ mil.	% of total
Unbleached kraft	782	100
Other - -		
Total	782	100

2010 Sales

	% of total
Linerboard	51
Kraft	21
Saturating kraft product	21
Unbleached folding carton board	7
Total	100

COMPETITORS

Canfor	International Paper
Caraustar	Longview Fibre
Georgia-Pacific	Rock-Tenn
Graphic Packaging Holding	Temple-Inland
	West Fraser Timber

HISTORICAL FINANCIALS

Company Type: Public

Income Statement

FYE: December 31

	REVENUE ($ mil.)	NET INCOME ($ mil.)	NET PROFIT MARGIN	EMPLOYEES
12/12	1,216.6	62.5	5.1%	2,760
12/11	906.1	123.9	13.7%	2,715
12/10	782.6	65.0	8.3%	1,600
12/09	632.4	80.2	12.7%	1,600
12/08	524.5	19.6	3.7%	1,750
Annual Growth	23.4%	33.5%	—	12.1%

2012 Year-End Financials

Debt ratio: 31.6%
Return on equity: 11.7%
Cash ($ mil.): 16
Current ratio: 1.35
Long-term debt ($ mil.): 294
No. of shares (mil.): 94
Dividends
  Yield: 18.0%
  Payout: 305.3%
Market value ($ mil.): 2,106

| | STOCK PRICE ($) | P/E | PER SHARE ($) | | |
	FY Close	High/Low	Earnings	Dividends	Book Value
12/12	22.19	34 23	0.66	2.00	5.46
12/11	15.74	13 9	1.31	0.00	5.88
12/10	15.30	22 11	0.69	0.00	4.54
12/09	9.83	9 1	1.15	0.00	3.84
12/08	2.38	22 6	0.29	0.00	3.19
Annual Growth	74.7%	— —	23.1%	—	14.4%

Key Tronic Corp.

Contract electronics manufacturing is key for Key Tronic. The company which does business as KeyTronicEMS to highlight its focus on electronics manufacturing services provides printed circuit board assembly tooling and prototyping box build (completely built) systems and plastic injection molding. In addition Key Tronic offers such services as product design engineering materials management and in-house testing. The company also makes customized and standard keyboards for PCs terminals and workstations. Customers located in the US account for more than two-thirds of Key Tronic's sales.

The percentage of international sales has grown from 10% in 2009 to about 30% in 2011. Customers in Canada represent more than half of foreign sales while those in Australia make up another quarter. Key Tronic also has significant sales to customers in Switzerland the UK and New Zealand. Though the company maintains facilities in the US most of its manufacturing takes place in Mexico and China.

Overall year-over-year sales for 2011 were up 27% driven by new programs for both new and long-term customers with production ramping up throughout the year. Key Tronic absorbed the costs associated with bringing the programs into production and dealt with worldwide component shortages affecting its margins. Production processes and supply chains had improved by the fourth quarter and Key Tronic reported another year of solid profits though net income was 34% lower than 2010.

A majority of Key Tronic's sales are to the communications consumer device and printer industries; its top five customers account for more than 60% of sales. During 2011 the company expanded its customer base to 30 EMS customers (from 20 the prior year). It continues to diversify into new industries including industrial processing equipment medical devices military equipment educational displays and consumer products. Key Tronic won contracts to produce solar power controllers fire safety devices energy monitors and electronic whiteboards late in fiscal 2011.

To move beyond its single-product emphasis — keyboards once accounted for almost all of sales — and overcome years of spotty profitability Key Tronic rapidly expanded its contract manufacturing service offerings. As price erosion in the keyboard market made that segment less profitable the company continued its manufacturing push increasing the range of electronic products it can manufacture.

HISTORY

Lewis Zirkle who had worked for more than 20 years at General Electric in various engineering and manufacturing positions founded Key Tronic in 1969. In 1975 Key Tronic became the first independent supplier to develop and market keyboards for heavy-duty office use. By 1981 the company was a leader in manufacturing ergonomic keyboards. It went public two years later. In 1987 Key Tronic developed a membrane switch technology that integrated switching points into a custom-designed structure.

Hard times hit in 1991 and 1992 as overseas competition and a failed attempt to produce a computer notebook contributed to losses. Turnaround artist Stanley Hiller stepped in as CEO in 1992. Key Tronic acquired Honeywell's keyboard operations in 1993 and the following year it moved much of its production to Honeywell's former plant in Mexico to reduce expenses.

In 1995 more efficient operations and new products pushed Key Tronic's sales above the $200 million mark for the first time; net income also hit a 10-year high. Former Honeywell manager Jack Oehlke replaced Hiller as CEO in 1997 the year Key Tronic launched a fingerprint scanning line that let a user's fingerprints function as a password. In 1998 the company intensified a push into contract manufacturing. To reduce costs Key Tronic cut about 200 jobs at its Washington plant and moved those operations to its facility in Mexico. It also closed its manufacturing plant in Taiwan. After a profitable fiscal 1997 a decline in keyboard sales caused a loss for fiscal 1998.

In 2000 Key Tronic agreed to manufacture circuits for glucose-monitoring devices made by Cygnus and make point-of-sale printers for Axiohm Transaction Solutions (now TPG IPB). During the first half of 2001 the company began doing business as KeyTronicEMS as part of a company-wide transition to firmly plant itself in the electronics manufacturing services (EMS) industry. Later that year the company was ordered to pay $16.5 million in damages when a jury found that it had misappropriated trade secrets and breached a confidentiality agreement with F&G Scrolling Mouse in 1993.

Key Tronic returned to profitability in fiscal 2003 although profits were typical of the razor-thin margins in the EMS industry. Lewis Zirkle who retired from Key Tronic in 1993 died in 2005 at the age of 90.

Keyboards continued to dwindle as a business in the early 21st century from one-quarter of sales in 2001 to about 4% in fiscal 2006 and around 3% in fiscal 2007 and fiscal 2008.

After closing its Las Cruces New Mexico plant in 2005 Key Tronic sold the facility in 2007 to Ade-

vco Corp. for about $4 million including nearly $3 million in cash. Jack Oehlke retired as president and CEO in 2009. EVP/GM Craig Gates succeeded him.

EXECUTIVES

Executive Vice President - Worldwide Operations, Douglas G. (Doug) Burkhardt, age 54
EVP Administration CFO and Treasurer, Ronald F. (Ron) Klawitter, age 61, $264,819 total compensation
President; Chief Executive Officer; Director, Craig D. Gates, age 54, $290,230 total compensation
Chairman, Dale F. Pilz, age 87
VP Engineering and Quality, Lawrence (Larry) Bostwick, age 60
VP Finance and Controller, Brett R. Larsen, age 39
Vice President - Program Management, Duane Mackleit
Vice President - Materials, Frank Crispigna
Investor Relations Officer, Michael Newman
President CEO and Director, Craig D. Gates, age 54
Director, Jack W. Oehlke, age 65
Director, Yacov A. Shamash, age 64
Director, Patrick Sweeney, age 78
Director, James R. (Jim) Bean, age 63
Auditors: BDOSeidmanLLP

LOCATIONS

HQ: Key Tronic Corporation
4424 N. Sullivan Rd. Lower Level, Spokane WA 99216
Phone: 509-928-8000   **Fax:** 509-927-5383
Web: www.keytronic.com

2011 Sales

	$ mil.	% of total
US	172	68
Other countries	81	32
Total	**253**	**100**

PRODUCTS/OPERATIONS

2011 Sales

	$ mil.	% of total
Electronics manufacturing services	249	98
Keyboard products	3	2
Total	**253**	**100**

2011 Sales by Industry

	% of total
Communication	22
Consumer	20
Transaction	18
Gaming	16
Computer &	13
Industrial	6
Commercial	5
Total	**100**
Services	
Circuit assembly	
Contract design manufactur	
Custom molding tooling	
Engineering services	
Logistics	
Materials management	
Product design	
Prototyping	
Products	
Computer keyboards	

COMPETITORS

APEM	Jabil
Am-Mex	Mitsumi Electric
Applied Technical Services	Plexus
Celestica	Sanmina
DDi Corp.	Sparton
Flextronics	Suntron
Hon Hai	ZF Electronics

HISTORICAL FINANCIALS

Company Type: Public

Income Statement
FYE: June 29

	REVENUE ($ mil.)	NET INCOME ($ mil.)	NET PROFIT MARGIN	EMPLOYEES
06/13	361.0	12.5	3.5%	2,584
06/12*	346.4	11.6	3.4%	2,700
07/11	253.8	5.7	2.3%	1,997
07/10	199.6	8.6	4.4%	2,036
06/09	184.9	1.0	0.6%	1,963
Annual Growth	18.2%	85.5%	—	7.1%

*Fiscal year change

2013 Year-End Financials

Debt ratio: —
Return on equity: 14.6%
Cash ($ mil.): 10
Current ratio: 2.95
Long-term debt ($ mil.): —

No. of shares (mil.): 10
Dividends
  Yield: —
  Payout: —
Market value ($ mil.): 109

	STOCK PRICE ($) FY Close	P/E High/Low		PER SHARE ($) Earnings	Dividends	Book Value
06/13	10.35	10	6	1.15	0.00	8.97
06/12*	8.24	12	3	1.10	0.00	7.50
07/11	4.52	12	8	0.55	0.00	6.54
07/10	4.88	8	2	0.85	0.00	5.79
06/09	1.65	35	8	0.11	0.00	5.08
Annual Growth	58.3%	—	—	79.8%	—	15.3%

*Fiscal year change

Kilroy Realty Corp

Kilroy is still here especially if you're referring to the West Coast. A self-administered real estate investment trust (REIT) Kilroy Realty owns manages and develops Class A office space mostly in suburban Southern California's Orange County San Diego and Los Angeles but it has since expanded to the San Francisco Bay and greater Seattle area to woo technology companies as tenants. Its portfolio includes about 115 office properties encompassing more than 13 million square feet of leasable space. A majority of Kilroy Realty's 500-plus tenants are involved in technology media financial services and real estate.

Geographic Reach
Besides 10 office buildings in Washington all of the REIT's property is located in California.

Sales and Marketing
Its 15 largest tenants accounted for 34% of the REIT's base rental revenue in 2012; these include DIRECTV Intuit and Bridgepoint Education. Its properties are 92% occupied.

Financial Performance
Overall sales grew 10% to $405 million in 2012. Profits jumped more than 300% to $270 million after the trust recorded gains on properties it sold.

As a REIT Kilroy Realty is exempt from paying federal income tax as long as it distributes quarterly dividends to shareholders.

Strategy
Kilroy Realty has moved away from owning industrial properties in order to focus on office buildings which generally earn more in rental income. In late 2012 it sold its entire portfolio of 44 industrial properties in California to two unnamed buy-

ers for $355 million. The industrial properties totaled almost 4 million-sq.-ft. of space.

At the same time the trust boosted its portfolio of office buildings in San Francisco and Seattle home to many of the nation's wealthy tech companies. In 2012 it paid $330 million for three properties totaling 837000 square feet in Seattle $162 million for a 374000-sq.-ft. office park in Silicon Valley and it paid $52 million for a building in downtown San Francisco that it will spend another $200 million redeveloping into a 27-story glass office tower for new tenant salesforce.com. In addition the trust is spending $315 million to develop a 587000-sq.-ft. office complex for LinkedIn in Sunnyvale California.

Not missing a beat in 2013 the trust boosted its Bay Area construction pipeline to more than 1.8 million square feet with new developments in Redwood City and downtown San Francisco (most of the space is pre-leased).

In addition Kilroy Realty has approximately 110 acres of undeveloped land in San Diego with the capacity for more than 2 million sq. ft. of rentable office space.

EXECUTIVES

Chief Financial Officer; Executive Vice President; Secretary, Tyler H. Rose, age 53, $365,000 total compensation

Chief Operating Officer; Executive Vice President, Jeffrey C. Hawken, age 55, $575,000 total compensation

Chairman of the Board President & Chief Executive Officer, John B. Kilroy Jr., age 65, $1,050,000 total compensation

Senior Vice President Asset Management, John T. Fucci

Senior Vice President San Diego, Steven R. Scott, age 57, $365,000 total compensation

Executive Vice President Development and Construction Services, Justin W. Smart

Senior Vice President Chief Accounting Officer Controller, Heidi R. Roth

VP and Treasurer, Michelle Ngo

Executive Vice President Chief Investment Officer, Eli Khouri

Executive Vice President, David Simon

Senior Vice President Development and Construction Services, Justin W. Sm

VP-Pacific Northwest Reg, Mike Shields

Vice President Communications, Susan Moss

Executive Vice President; Chief Investment Officer, Marcum Khouri

President CEO and Director, John B. Kilroy Jr., age 63

Director, William P. Dickey, age 71

Director, Dale F. Kinsella, age 65

Director, Scott S. Ingraham, age 59

Auditors: Deloitte&ToucheLLP

LOCATIONS

HQ: Kilroy Realty Corporation
12200 W. Olympic Blvd. Ste. 200, Los Angeles CA 90064
Phone: 310-481-8400   **Fax:** 310-481-6580
Web: www.kilroyrealty.com

PRODUCTS/OPERATIONS

2012 Sales

	% of total
Rental	91
Tenant	8
Other	1
Total	**100**

COMPETITORS

BioMed Realty	MPG Office Trust
Brandywine Realty	Majestic Realty
CommonWealth REIT	PS Business Parks
Digital Realty	Prologis
Douglas Emmett	Shorenstein
Equity Office	The Koll Company
Hudson Pacific	Trammell Crow Company
Irvine Company	

HISTORICAL FINANCIALS

Company Type: Public

Income Statement

FYE: December 31

	REVENUE ($ mil.)	NET INCOME ($ mil.)	NET PROFIT MARGIN	EMPLOYEES
12/12	404.9	270.9	66.9%	201
12/11	367.1	66.0	18.0%	169
12/10	301.9	19.7	6.5%	141
12/09	279.4	36.9	13.2%	132
12/08	289.9	44.1	15.2%	134
Annual Growth	8.7%	57.4%	—	10.7%

2012 Year-End Financials

Debt ratio: 44.2%	No. of shares (mil.): 74
Return on equity: 15.1%	Dividends
Cash ($ mil.): 16	Yield: 2.9%
Current ratio: 2.16	Payout: 54.6%
Long-term debt ($ mil.): 2,040	Market value ($ mil.): 3,549

	STOCK PRICE ($) FY Close	P/E High/Low	PER SHARE ($) Earnings	Dividends	Book Value
12/12	47.37	14 11	2.56	1.40	29.22
12/11	38.07	48 34	0.87	1.40	23.25
12/10	36.47	525382	0.07	1.40	22.16
12/09	30.67	63 29	0.53	1.63	21.52
12/08	33.46	52 21	1.06	2.32	22.05
Annual Growth	9.1%	— —	24.7%	(11.9%)	7.3%

Kirby Corp.

Where Kirby hauls cargo the only curbs are riverbanks –the company is the largest inland tank barge operator in the US. Its fleet operated by subsidiary Kirby Inland Marine consists of over 840 barges and about 250 inland towboats with a transportation capacity of 16.7 million barrels. The vessels are used to transport liquid bulk cargo: petrochemicals crude and refined petroleum products and agricultural chemicals. Its Marine Transportation segment (inland/offshore operations) is joined by its Engine Systems segment which is a leading provider of diesel engine services and parts for marine rail and power generation customers.

Geographic Reach

Kirby provides marine transportation of refined petroleum products petrochemicals and black oil products in the coastal regions of the US. The coastal operations consist of the Atlantic New York Pacific and Hawaii Divisions.

Operations

The Marine segment represents 67% of its total sales and manages its core tank barge transportation services for the inland and coastal markets. Kirby Engine Systems (33%) offers services throughout the US and in parts of the Caribbean and the Pacific Rim. This division provides over-

haul and repair of diesel engines and reduction gears line boring and block welding for its customers; it also sells and distributes parts for diesel engines as well as fuel lubrication and engine control systems to the nuclear industry.

Financial Performance

Kirby has enjoyed unprecedented growth over the years. Revenues jumped 14% from $1.85 billion in 2011 to $2.11 billion in 2012. Profits also climbed 14% from $183 million in 2011 to $209 million in 2012. Both these totals for 2012 represented historic milestones for the company.

The growth was driven by an 18% jump in Marine transportation revenue for 2012 reflecting its expansion into the coastal transportation business from several acquisitions made in 2011 and 2012. It was also helped by a 7% spike in Engine Systems revenue for 2012.

Strategy

Both segments have expanded via acquisitions and capital investments. In late 2012 Kirby acquired Allied Transportation in a transaction valued at $116 million. Kirby gained Allied's fleet of 13 offshore barges and seven tugboats serving petrochemical companies (some of which were current Kirby customers). The deal bolstered Kirby's hold in the petrochemical market. Kirby also in 2012 purchased Penn Maritime a coastal transportation provider with 18 coastal double hull tank barges and 16 tugboats for $300 million.

Buoying its Marine Transportation business in 2011 Kirby scooped up K-Sea Transportation Partners in a deal valued at approximately $604 million. K-Sea specialized in transporting gasoline and other fuel-related products with a particular presence on the East and West coasts —a geographic market that further diversified Kirby's business. Kirby has benefited from strong demand for petrochemicals which accounts for a large portion of the company's transportation revenue. In addition to its primary inland tank barge operations Kirby maintains a fleet of four offshore dry cargo barges and seven offshore tugboats which are operated by Kirby Ocean Transport.

The company signed another deal earlier in 2011 to bulk up its Marine Transportation business with the acquisition of Enterprise Marine Services bunker fuel transportation operations for a reported $53.2 million. Included in the deal were 21 tank barges and 15 towboats (used to deliver engine fuel to cruise ships) and container vessels and freighters at ports in South Florida Alabama and Kirby's home port of Houston.

HISTORY

Kirby Petroleum entered the marine transportation business in 1968 with the purchase of Dixie Carriers an inland barge business started in 1948 by the family of George Peterkin. In 1969 Kirby Exploration was set up as a subsidiary of Kirby Petroleum to operate Dixie Carriers. Kirby Petroleum went public in 1976 and in 1982 it entered the diesel-repair business by acquiring Marine Systems.

In 1988 Kirby exited the oil and gas industries to focus on marine transportation. Kirby Exploration was renamed Kirby Corporation in 1990. Because of overbuilding in the 1970s Kirby was able to snap up several shipping companies at bargain prices (including Brent Towing in 1989 and Sabine Towing in 1992); its fleet expanded from 71 vessels in 1988 to more than 400 by 1993. The next year the company created Rail Systems a diesel locomotive repair service and bought Dow Chemical's marine assets.

In 1995 J. H. Pyne was promoted to CEO replacing longtime leader Peterkin who became chairman. A company restructuring hurt sales the following year. Flooding on the Mississippi River disrupted barge traffic and slowed Kirby's performance in 1997.

To raise cash and focus on the inland market Kirby sold its offshore tanker and harbor service operations in 1998 to Hvide Marine (subsequently renamed Seabulk International) for $38.6 million. It exited the insurance market with the sale of its 45% stake in Universal Insurance Company a Puerto Rican property and insurance firm. Kirby also sold its remaining offshore tug and tank barge units.

In 1999 the company gained 256 inland tank barges and 104 tow boats when it bought rival Hollywood Marine in a $325 million deal. Hollywood's Berdon Lawrence took over as Kirby's chairman.

That year and into 2000 the company's diesel engine services unit faced difficulties as a result of depressed Gulf Coast drilling and offshore supply vessel markets. In 2001 with the oil market rebounding Kirby leased 94 inland tank barges from a subsidiary of Dow Chemical vessels that Dow had acquired as part of its merger with Union Carbide. Kirby bought the former Union Carbide barges for $23 million in December 2002.

In 2003 Kirby acquired 45 double-hull inland tank barges and seven inland towboats from SeaRiver Maritime an affiliate of Exxon Mobil for about $32 million. The next year Kirby bought a one-third interest in Osprey Line a provider of barge transportation of cargo containers along the Gulf Coast and on the Mississippi River. It bought another one-third stake in Osprey in January 2006.

In 2005 the company bought 10 inland tank barges configured for carrying black oil products from rival American Commercial Lines. The next year Kirby expanded its diesel engine services business by acquiring Houma Louisiana-based Global Power Holding owner of Global Power Systems. Kirby paid about $100 million for Global Power which posted sales of $63 million in 2005.

In 2008 Kirby acquired the assets of Lake Charles Diesel a high-speed diesel engine service provider for over $3.6 million in cash. Lake Charles Diesel brought with it the marine dealerships it operated for Cummins Detroit Diesel Volvo as well as Caterpillar engines (in Louisiana).

EXECUTIVES

VP Engine Systems Inc., John A. Manno
President Kirby Engine Systems, Dorman L. Strahan, age 57, $248,800 total compensation
Chairman and Chief Executive Officer, Joseph H. (Joe) Pyne, age 65, $680,000 total compensation
President Kirby Inland Marine, William G. (Bill) Ivey
EVP Marketing Kirby Inland Marine, Mel R. Jodeit
Chairman Emeritus, George A. Peterkin Jr., age 85
VP Kirby Ocean Transport Company, William M. (Bill) Withers
President Kirby Offshore Marine LLC, James F. (Jim) Farley
President Marine Transportation Group, Gregory R. (Greg) Binion, age 48, $248,800 total compensation
Executive Vice President and Chief Financial Officer, David W. Grzebinski, age 52
VP Osprey Line, Charles J. Duet
VP and CIO, David R. Mosley, age 51
President Osprey Line, John T. Hallmark
EVP Engine Services, David D. Whisenhunt
President United Holdings LLC, Bill F. Moore Jr.
President United Engines, Garth C. Bates

Chairman and Chief Executive Officer, Joseph H. (Joe) Pyne, age 65
Director, C. Sean Day, age 62
Chairman Emeritus, George A. Peterkin Jr., age 84
Director, Bob G. Gower, age 74
Director, William M. Lamont Jr., age 63
Director, David L. (Dave) Lemmon, age 69
Director, Monte Miller, age 68
Director, James R. Clark, age 61
Director, Richard R. Stewart, age 62
Independent Director, Richard Alario
Auditors: KPMGLLP

LOCATIONS

HQ: Kirby Corporation
55 Waugh Dr. Ste. 1000, Houston TX 77007
Phone: 713-435-1000   **Fax:** 713-435-1146
Web: www.kirbycorp.com

PRODUCTS/OPERATIONS

2012 Sales

Marine transportation	1,408	67
Total	**2,112**	**100**

COMPETITORS

Adams Resources	Ingram Industries
American Commercial Lines	International Shipholding
Burlington Northern Santa Fe	Kansas City Southern
CSX	Kenan Advantage Group
Canadian National Railway	Norfolk Southern
Crowley Maritime	Quality Distribution
Cummins	SEACOR
Illinois Auto Electric	Trimac
	Union Pacific

HISTORICAL FINANCIALS

Company Type: Public

Income Statement

FYE: December 31

	REVENUE ($ mil.)	NET INCOME ($ mil.)	NET PROFIT MARGIN	EMPLOYEES
12/12	2,112.6	209.4	9.9%	1,275
12/11	1,850.4	183.0	9.9%	4,100
12/10	1,109.5	116.2	10.5%	2,520
12/09	1,082.1	125.9	11.6%	2,675
12/08	1,360.1	157.1	11.6%	3,100
Annual Growth	**11.6%**	**7.4%**	**—**	**(19.9%)**

2012 Year-End Financials

Debt ratio: 31.0%	No. of shares (mil.): 56
Return on equity: 13.3%	Dividends
Cash ($ mil.): 11	Yield: —
Current ratio: 1.68	Payout: —
Long-term debt ($ mil.): 1,070	Market value ($ mil.): 3,502

	STOCK PRICE ($) FY Close	P/E High/Low		PER SHARE ($) Earnings	Dividends	Book Value
12/12	61.89	19	12	3.73	0.00	29.95
12/11	65.84	20	13	3.33	0.00	25.88
12/10	44.05	21	15	2.15	0.00	21.59
12/09	34.83	17	9	2.34	0.00	19.55
12/08	27.36	20	7	2.91	0.00	16.64
Annual Growth	**22.6%**	**—**	**—**	**6.4%**	**—**	**15.8%**

KKR Financial Holdings LLC

KKR Financial Holdings is a specialty finance company that invests in a variety of financial products primarily below-investment-grade corporate debt as well as public and private equity. Its portfolio which weighs in at more than $8 billion includes syndicated bank loans mezzanine loans high-yield corporate bonds asset-backed securities commercial real estate and debt and equity securities. KKR Financial Holdings is externally managed by KKR Financial Advisors; both firms are affiliates of private equity and leveraged buyout giant KKR & Co.

KKR Financial Holdings was formerly a real estate investment trust (REIT) with significant investments in residential mortgages and related securities. During the mortgage meltdown that began in 2007 the company restructured dropped its REIT status and stopped investing in residential mortgages. After reporting more than $1 billion in losses in 2008 (mainly due to losses from investments and impaired securities) the company tweaked its investment focus to include mezzanine financing natural resources commercial real estate and distressed situations as other investors shied away from these activities in the wake of the credit crisis. The strategy paid off as KKR Financial cut its losses significantly in 2009 and returned to profitability in 2010.

William Sonneborn formerly president of The TCW Group was named CEO of KKR Financial in 2008. He succeeded Saturnino Fanlo who resigned. Sonneborn was also tapped to head KKR's newly created asset management division (which includes KKR Financial).

EXECUTIVES

Chairman, Paul M. Hazen, age 71
President CEO and Director, William C. (Bill) Sonneborn, age 43
COO and CFO, Michael R. (Mike) McFerran, age 41
General Counsel; Secretary of the Manager, Nicole J. Macarchuk
Vice President Corporate Marketing and Communications, Jenny Farrelly
Chief Administrative Officer, Todd A. Fisher
Director, Deborah H. McAneny, age 54
Director, Willy R. Strothotte, age 68
President CEO and Director, William C. (Bill) Sonneborn, age 43
Director, Scott C. Nuttall, age 40
Director, Ross J. Kari, age 54
Director, R. Glenn Hubbard, age 54
Director, Ely L. Licht, age 65
Director, Scott A. Ryles, age 54
Director, Tracy L. Collins, age 49
Director, Vincent P. Finigan, age 66
Independent Director, Robert Edwards
Auditors: Deloitte&ToucheLLP

LOCATIONS

HQ: KKR Financial Holdings LLC
555 California St. 50th Fl., San Francisco CA 94104
Phone: 415-315-3620   **Fax:** 415-391-3077
Web: ir.kkr.com/kfn_ir/kfn_overview.cfm

PRODUCTS/OPERATIONS

2010 Sales

	$ mil.	% of total
Interest		
Loans	397	60
Securities	104	16
Other	3	-
Noninterest		
Net gains on investments	109	16
Net gain on restructuring & extinguishment of debt	40	6
Other	10	2
Adjustments	(16.8)	-
Total	**648**	**100**

COMPETITORS

Arlington Asset Investment	Prospect Capital
Capital Trust	Resource America
Opus Investment Management	iStar Financial Inc

HISTORICAL FINANCIALS

Company Type: Public

Income Statement

FYE: December 31

	ASSETS ($ mil.)	NET INCOME ($ mil.)	INCOME AS % OF ASSETS	EMPLOYEES
12/12	8,358.8	348.2	4.2%	0
12/11	8,647.2	318.0	3.7%	0
12/10	8,418.4	371.0	4.4%	0
12/09	10,300.0	76.9	0.7%	0
12/08	12,515.0	(1,075.0)	—	0
Annual Growth	**(9.6%)**	**—**	**—**	**—**

2012 Year-End Financials

Return on assets: 4.0%	Dividends
Return on equity: 19.7%	Yield: 8.1%
Long-term debt ($ mil.): —	Payout: 45.0%
No. of shares (mil.): 178	Market value ($ mil.): 1,884
Sales ($ mil): 696	

	STOCK PRICE ($) FY Close	P/E High/Low		PER SHARE ($) Earnings	Dividends	Book Value
12/12	10.56	6	4	1.87	0.86	10.31
12/11	8.73	6	4	1.75	0.67	9.41
12/10	9.30	4	2	2.33	0.43	9.24
12/09	5.80	12	1	0.50	0.05	7.37
12/08	1.58	—	—	(7.68)	1.30	4.40
Annual Growth	**60.8%**	**—**	**—**	**—**	**(9.8%)**	**23.7%**

KMG Chemicals, Inc.

KMG Chemicals protects wood and helps make chips though it has nothing to do with wood chips. Its electronic chemicals are used in the manufacture of semiconductors. KMG's largest customer is silicon chip kingpin Intel which regularly accounts for about 10% of total sales. Its wood preservatives are pentachlorophenol (penta) sodium penta and creosote. KMG sells penta and creosote in the US primarily to the railroad construction and utility industries. Sodium penta is sold in Latin America. Creosote customer Stella-Jones accounted for 10% or more of total sales in 2011 and 2012. To focus on its core businesses in 2012 the company agreed

to sell its animal health business to Bayer Health-Care.

Operations

KMG produces and distributes specialty chemicals worldwide. It is a US market leader in producing and supplying high-purity process chemicals (an integral part of the semiconductor manufacturing process) and wood treating chemicals used to extend the useful life of the country's wood-based infrastructure.

KGM's wood preserving chemicals pentachlorophenol or penta and creosote are sold to industrial customers who use these preservatives primarily to extend the useful life of utility poles and railroad ties. The company is the sole distributor of penta for wood treatment purposes in the US and the principal supplier of creosote in the US to wood treaters who do not produce their own creosote.

Financial Analysis

KMG's revenues increased by 7% in fiscal year 2012 thanks to a 5% rise in net sales from electronic chemicals segment which came from greater volume and price increases (to recover higher raw material costs) and a 9% jump in net sales of wood treating chemicals segment due to higher sales in both wood treating chemical product lines and price increases.

The company reported a net income increase of 42% in FY 2012 thanks to a 7% decrease in distribution expenses due to efficiency improvements in its electronic chemicals segment supply chain costs derived from the integration of the General Chemical Performance Products (acquired in 2010) and a pre-tax gain of $90000 on the sale of its animal health business.

Strategy

The company's strategy is to grow by discovering and exploiting opportunities that other companies overlook. It focuses on customer satisfaction operational efficiencies and optimizing its assets. It also seeks targeted acquisitions that mesh with and enhance existing business segments and to effectively integrate acquisitions into ongoing operations while divesting non-core businesses.

In 2013 KMG Chemicals agreed to acquire the Ultra Pure Chemicals subsidiaries of OM Group in the US the UK Singapore and France for $60 million.

In 2012 the company agreed to sell its animal health business to Bayer Healthcare including brands such as Patriot cattle ear tag and Rabon and Permectrin insecticides. Because KMG has grown significantly in the last five years in its electronic chemicals and wood-treating chemicals units the company decided its animal health business no longer fit within its strategic objectives.

KMG acquired the electronic chemicals unit of General Chemical Performance Products in 2010 for $27 million. The unit manufactures wet process chemicals used primarily to clean and etch silicon wafers in the production of semiconductors. The deal not only increased KGM's electronic chemicals business but also expanding its reach into Asia markets.

Ownership

Chairman David Hatcher owned 23% of KMG in 2012.

EXECUTIVES

VP Sales KMB-Bernuth, Thomas H. (Tom) Mitchell, age 69, $143,287 total compensation
VP and CFO, John V. Sobchak, age 52, $193,345 total compensation
Vice President; General Counsel; Secretary, Roger C. Jackson, age 61, $178,590 total compensation

Chairman, Christopher T. (Chris) Fraser, age 54
President and CEO, J. Neal Butler, age 60, $339,454 total compensation
VP Operations, Ernest C. (Ernie) Kremling II, age 48, $210,684 total compensation
Investor Relations Manager, Eric Glover
Vice President Electronic Chemicals, Andrew Lau
Director, Stephen A. (Steve) Thorington, age 57
Director, Fred C. Leonard III, age 67
Director, Gerald G. (Jerry) Ermentrout, age 64
Director, Karen A. Twitchell
Director, George W. Gilman, age 70
Director, Richard L. Urbanowski, age 76
Director, Christopher T. (Chris) Fraser, age 54
President CEO COO and Director, J. Neal Butler, age 60
Independent Director, John Hunter
Auditors: UHYLLP

LOCATIONS

HQ: KMG Chemicals Inc.
9555 W. Sam Houston Pkwy. South Ste. 600, Houston TX 77099
Phone: 713-600-3800   **Fax:** 713-600-3850
Web: www.kmgchemicals.com

2012 Sales

	$ mil.	% of total
US	229	84
Other countries	43	16
Total	**272**	**100**

PRODUCTS/OPERATIONS

2012 Sales

	$ mil.	% of total
Electronic chemicals	159	59
Wood treating	113	41
Other	0	-
Total	**272**	**100**

Selected Products

Creosote (wood preservative)
Hydrochloric acid (for use in the steel and oil well service industries)
Monosodium and disodium methanearsonic acids (MSMA herbicide)
Pentachlorophenol (aka "penta" wood preservative)
Sodium pentachlorophenol (aka "sodium penta" wood preservative)
Tetrachlorvinphos (insecticide)

COMPETITORS

American Vanguard	Merichem
Arch Chemicals	Monsanto Company
Cytec	Osmose
Innospec	Perstorp
Koppers Holdings	Rasa Industries

HISTORICAL FINANCIALS

Company Type: Public

Income Statement

FYE: July 31

	REVENUE ($ mil.)	NET INCOME ($ mil.)	NET PROFIT MARGIN	EMPLOYEES
07/13	263.3	9.3	3.6%	740
07/12	272.7	13.8	5.1%	331
07/11	266.3	9.7	3.7%	336
07/10	208.6	15.3	7.3%	318
07/09	190.7	10.2	5.4%	272
Annual Growth	**8.4%**	**(2.2%)**	**—**	**28.4%**

Debt ratio: 32.4%
Return on equity: 8.3%
Cash ($ mil.): 13
Current ratio: 2.59
Long-term debt ($ mil.): 85

No. of shares (mil.): 11
Dividends
 Yield: 0.5%
 Payout: 11.0%
Market value ($ mil.): 260

	STOCK PRICE ($) FY Close	P/E High/Low		PER SHARE ($) Earnings	Dividends	Book Value
07/13	22.58	29	20	0.81	0.12	10.18
07/12	17.88	16	10	1.20	0.11	9.36
07/11	16.76	24	15	0.85	0.09	8.53
07/10	15.17	15	5	1.34	0.08	7.55
07/09	7.32	13	2	0.91	0.08	6.39
Annual Growth	32.5%	—	—	(2.9%)	10.7%	12.3%

Kronos Worldwide Inc

Kronos Worldwide produces pigments that impart whiteness brightness and opacity to everything from plastics paper and coatings to inks food and cosmetics. Controlled by Valhi Kronos is a leading manufacturer of a commercially used base white inorganic pigment known as titanium dioxide (TiO2). TiO2 is designed based on specific end-use applications. Kronos makes and sell some 40 different TiO2 grades; the company and its distributors and agents also provide technical services for its products in some 100 countries mainly in Europe and North America.

Geographic Reach

Kronos Worldwide has produced and marketed TiO2 in Europe and North America its primary markets for more than 90 years.

Operations

At its six plants in Europe and North America Kronos produced 469000 metric tons of TiO2 in 2012 down from 550000 metric tons of the pigment in 2011. Its plants are located in Germany Belgium Norway Canada and the US (through a joint venture plant in Lake Charles Louisiana).

Kronos' core TiO2 business is complemented by three other businesses. It owns and operates two ilemite mines with long reserve lives in Norway. Ilemite is used as a feedstock by some TiO2 plants. The ilemite produced by Kronos is sold to third parties some of whom are competitors. A second business focuses on manufacturing and selling iron-based chemicals used in the treatment of municipal wastewater and in the manufacture of iron pigments cement and agricultural products. A third complementary business manufactures and sells itanium oxychloride and titanyl sulfate TiO2 byproducts that are used to formulate pearlescent pigments among other applications.

Sales and Marketing

A majority of its core TiO2 pigment products are sold through Kronos' direct sales force operating from six sales offices in Europe and one in North America. Sales agents and distributors are authorized to sell Kronos brand products in specific geographic regions. TiO2 products represented 90% of the company's revenue in fiscal 2012.

Kronos has a diverse customer base of paint plastics decorative laminate and paper manufacturers worldwide. Only one customer BEHR Process generates more than 10% of its sales.

Financial Performance

Kronos' sales increased 2% in fiscal 2012 primarily due to a 10% increase in average TiO2 selling prices. Its slight 2012 sales increase builds upon a more dramatic 35% sales increase in 2011

over 2010. Meanwhile net income was down 32% in 2012 following a 146% increase in 2011 over 2010. Recent global economic weakness is causing TiO2 producers to pull back on inventory as industrywide sales and production volumes decrease. Other factors that impacted 2012 results were higher costs for raw materials such as feedstock ore and petroleum coke.

Strategy

Overall industry demand is expected to be higher in 2013 than in 2012 as a result of improving economic conditions. Kronos is therefore operating its facilities to align production levels and inventories to current and anticipated near-term customer demand levels. Concurrently the company is trying to keep its manufacturing costs as low as possible while dealing with a significant amount of debt. One advantage Kronos has is that it competes in an industry that has high barrier to entry and is dominated by just a few namely itself Dupont Millennium Inorganic Chemicals (also known as Cristal) Huntsman and Tronox. It typically competes based on price product quality and service.

Ownership

Valhi and its subsidiary NL Industries own 50% and 30% of Kronos Worldwide respectively.

Company Background

Kronos and its predecessors have been producing TiO2 since 1916. In 2003 NL Industries spun off Kronos to its shareholders.

EXECUTIVES

Vice Chairman of the Board; Chief Executive Officer, Steven L. (Steve) Watson, age 62, $693,000 total compensation

Chief Financial Officer; Executive Vice President, Gregory M. (Greg) Swalwell, age 56, $272,400 total compensation

VP and Tax Director, Kelly D. Luttmer, age 49

Executive Vice President; Chief Administrative Officer; General Counsel, Robert D. Graham, age 57

VP and Controller, Tim C. Hafer, age 52

Vice President - Strategic Business Development, Brian Christian

Vice President - Investor Relations, Janet Keckeisen

President - Manufacturing and Technology, Klemens Schluter

Director, Glenn R. Simmons, age 85

Director, Keith R. Coogan, age 60

Director, George E. Poston, age 78

Director, Cecil H. Moore Jr., age 73

Auditors: PricewaterhouseCoopersLLP

LOCATIONS

HQ: Kronos Worldwide Inc.
 5430 LBJ Fwy. Ste. 1700, Dallas TX 75240-2697
Phone: 972-233-1700 **Fax:** 972-448-1445
Web: www.kronostio2.com

2012 Sales by Origin

US	1,042	36
Germany	977	33
Canada	339	12
Norway	284	10
Belgium	272	9
Total	**1,976**	**100**

2012 Sales by Destination

	$ mil.	% of total
Europe	1,011	51
North America	652	33
Other regions	312	16
Total	**1,976**	**100**

COMPETITORS

DuPont	Kemira
DuPont Performance Coatings	National Titanium Dioxide Company
Huntsman Corp	TOR Minerals
Huntsman International	Tronox
Imerys Pigments	Tronox Limited

HISTORICAL FINANCIALS
Company Type: Public

Income Statement
FYE: December 31

	REVENUE ($ mil.)	NET INCOME ($ mil.)	NET PROFIT MARGIN	EMPLOYEES
12/12	1,976.3	218.5	11.1%	2,555
12/11	1,943.3	321.0	16.5%	2,470
12/10	1,449.7	130.6	9.0%	2,440
12/09	1,142.0	(34.7)	—	2,440
12/08	1,316.9	9.0	0.7%	2,450
Annual Growth	10.7%	122.0%		1.1%

2012 Year-End Financials

Debt ratio: 19.7%
Return on equity: 21.9%
Cash ($ mil.): 282
Current ratio: 3.73
Long-term debt ($ mil.): 378

No. of shares (mil.): 115
Dividends
 Yield: 3.0%
 Payout: 21.5%
Market value ($ mil.): 2,260

	STOCK PRICE ($) FY Close	P/E High/Low		PER SHARE ($) Earnings	Dividends	Book Value
12/12	19.50	13	7	1.89	0.60	9.16
12/11	18.04	23	5	2.77	1.08	7.97
12/10	42.49	35	10	1.30	0.13	6.57
12/09	16.25	—	—	(0.36)	0.50	3.19
12/08	11.65	349	89	0.09	0.50	3.24
Annual Growth	13.7%	—	—	114.1%	4.7%	29.6%

L&L Energy Inc

You'll excuse L & L Energy (formerly L & L International) if it's a bit jet lagged. Incorporated in Nevada with headquarters in Seattle the company mines coal in China. Granted a license by the government to extract a set amount of coal in exchange for up-front fees L & L owns mines in China's Yunnan and Guizhou provinces. The company currently extracts more than 630000 tons of coal per year from the mines. It also processes coal to produce coke used in steel production medium coal used for heating and coal slurries used as a lower quality fuel. L & L is swapping a stake in a coking mine with Singapore-based Union Energy to acquire a 50% stake in the LuoZhou coal mine.

On the heels of the Chinese government's mandate for coal industry consolidation L & L Energy plans to expand its existing coal mines and purchase smaller operations that fail to meet the government's mandated production minimums. Inland China has begun to develop at a more rapid rate leading to an increased demand for energy which is 70% coal fueled in that country.

As part of its plan to focus on inland coal operations in 2009 L & L sold its 80% share in LEK air compressor operations back to the company for about $4.2 million. The following year it sold its 93% interest in Hon Shen Coal to Guangxi Liuzhou Lifu Machinery for $6 million. It had purchased the coal washing facility in late 2009 for $3.8 million. Also in 2010 the company purchased its Ping Yi mine Hong Xing Coal Washing and Zone Lin Coking.

President and CEO Dickson Lee holds about a quarter of the company's stock.

EXECUTIVES

Vice Chairman, Norman Y. (Norm) Mineta, age 81
VP Corporate Infrastructure, Edmund C. Moy
Chairman and CEO, Dickson V. Lee, age 64, $174,503 total compensation
EVP US Operations, Clayton Fong, $75,000 total compensation
CEO of a Hong Kong listed energy company, James Schaeffer
Controller, Keith So
Senior Sales Director, Zhi Xie
Director, Ian Robinson, age 73
Vice Chairman, Norman Y. (Norm) Mineta, age 81
Director, Shirley Kiang, age 61
Director, Dennis Bracy, age 63
Director, Joseph J. Borich, age 68
Independent Director, Jingcai Yang
Independent Director, Syd Peng
Auditors: Kabani&CompanyInc.

LOCATIONS

HQ: L & L Energy Inc.
130 Andover Park East Ste. 200, Seattle WA 98188
Phone: 206-264-8065   **Fax:** 206-264-7971
Web: www.lnlinternational.com

PRODUCTS/OPERATIONS

2010 Sales

	$ mil.	% of total
Mining	64	59
Washing	18	17
Wholesale	13	12
Coking	13	12
Total	**109**	**100**

COMPETITORS

Anglo American	Rio Tinto plc
BHP Billiton	Shenhua
BHP Billiton Plc	Yanzhou Coal
China Coal Energy	

HISTORICAL FINANCIALS

Company Type: Public

Income Statement

FYE: April 30

	REVENUE ($ mil.)	NET INCOME ($ mil.)	NET PROFIT MARGIN	EMPLOYEES
04/13	198.9	38.3	19.3%	1,364
04/12	143.5	14.2	9.9%	1,330
04/11	223.8	36.7	16.4%	1,600
04/10	109.2	32.9	30.1%	1,400
04/09	40.9	9.9	24.3%	1,200
Annual Growth	48.5%	40.1%	—	3.3%

2013 Year-End Financials

Debt ratio: 1.7%	No. of shares (mil.): 38
Return on equity: 19.8%	Dividends
Cash ($ mil.): 9	Yield: —
Current ratio: 1.66	Payout: —
Long-term debt ($ mil.): 0	Market value ($ mil.): 147

STOCK PRICE ($) FY Close	P/E High/Low		PER SHARE ($) Earnings	Dividends	Book Value
04/13 3.87	4	1	0.98	0.00	5.61
04/12 2.25	17	5	0.42	0.00	4.70
04/11 6.95	11	4	1.21	0.00	4.40
04/10 10.80	11	1	1.28	0.00	2.76
04/09 1.80	5	1	0.46	0.00	1.06
Annual Growth 21.1%	—	—	20.8%	—	51.8%

Landec Corp.

Landec's products don't turn into pumpkins at midnight but the changes are nearly as sudden and much more practical. The company has developed a technology that allows polymers to change physical characteristics when exposed to temperature changes. Its BreatheWay permeable membrane packaging allows oxygen and carbon dioxide to enter and escape from sealed fresh-cut produce packages to keep produce fresh. It's used primarily by subsidiary Apio which grows and packages fresh vegetables. Landec's Lifecore Biomedical subsidiary is a leading supplier of premium hyaluronan-based biomaterials for the ophthalmic and orthopedic markets. Landec has licensing deals with Air Products and Chemicals and Monsanto.

Financial Analysis

Landec's revenues increased by 15% in fiscal year 2012 due to a 19% increase in Apio's value-added revenues thanks to an 11% increase in unit volume sales to existing customers resulting primarily from expanded product offerings $9.1 million of revenues from GreenLine (acquired in 2012) and a larger percentage of Apio's value-added revenues being generated from sales to club stores rather than retail grocery chains. Other factors included a 16% increase in Apio Export due to 11% increase in export unit volume sales due to a greater volume of fruit and vegetables being available to export and due to more favorable pricing for export products in fiscal year 2012.

Apio Packaging's revenues decreased by 32% due to lower sales of BreatheWay membranes to Chiquita for packaged avocados as a result of Chiquita placing large initial orders of membranes during the first half of fiscal year 2011.

The hyaluronic acid-based (HA) biomaterials segment revenue grew by 5% in fiscal year 2012 due to an increase in sales to existing customers. Technology licensing revenue decreased by 39% due to the termination of the Monsanto Agreement in fiscal year 2012.

Net income increased by 207% in fiscal year 2012 thanks to an increase in other income of $5.8 million in the fair market value of the Windset investment (made in 2010) and increase in dividend income due to the receipt of a full year of dividends from the $15 million preferred stock investment in Windset. (Windset is a Canada-based company that packages greenhouse grown cucumbers peppers and tomatoes.)

Strategy

In 2012 the company agreed to sell its seed coating business Landec Ag to INCOTEC Holding North America for $600000. It also agreed to partner with INCOTEC Coating and Seed Technology Companies which will give it access to global markets for its polymer technology used in seed treatment. Landec also signed a seven-year technology licensing and polymer supply agreement with INCOTEC Field Crops North America to license its polymer seed coating technology for corn sold under the label Pollinator Plus. It also signed a five-year agreement with INCOTEC Holdings to partner on the development of new polymer and unique coatings for seed treatment. The agreements allow Landec to focus on its food products and biomedical materials businesses.

Through Apio a food subsidiary Landec acquired Ohio-based GreenLine Foods in 2012 which processes fresh-cut green beans in North America. The acquisition combined GreenLine's green beans brand with the Apio Eat Smart brand to cover about 80% of market presence in North American retail grocery stores.

Moving into the healthcare materials market in 2010 Landec acquired Lifecore Biomedical from Warburg Pincus in a $40 million cash and debt deal. Lifecore is a supplier of hyaluronic acid-based biomaterials for the medical and veterinary markets. Hyaluronan biopolymers are used in many therapeutic treatments including cataract surgery degenerative joint disease spinal defect filling and medical device coatings.

Ownership

Wynnefield Capital owns 10% of the company; Security Investors 9%.

Company Background

In 1999 Landec bought its largest customer Apio.

EXECUTIVES

Chairman President and CEO, Gary T. Steele, age 65, $375,000 total compensation
CFO, Gregory S. (Greg) Skinner, age 53, $265,000 total compensation
VP Corporate Technology, Steven P. Bitler, age 56, $190,000 total compensation
CEO Apio, Ronald (Ron) Midyett, age 48, $275,000 total compensation
Chief Commercial Officer, Molly A. Hemmeter
Chief Scientific Officer, Damian A. Hajduk
CEO Lifecore Biomedical, Dennis J. Allingham
Director, R. Dean Hollis, age 52
Director, Steven D. Goldby, age 72
Chairman Apio; Director, Nicholas (Nick) Tompkins, age 58
Director, Frederick (Fred) Frank, age 79
Director, Richard S. Schneider, age 71
Director, Stephen E. Halprin, age 75
Director, Duke K. Bristow, age 56
Director, Robert Tobin, age 74
Auditors: Ernst&YoungLLP

LOCATIONS

HQ: Landec Corporation
3603 Haven Ave., Menlo Park CA 94025
Phone: 650-306-1650   **Fax:** 650-368-9818
Web: www.landec.com

PRODUCTS/OPERATIONS

2011 Sales

	$ mil.	% of total
Apio		
Value-added	205	65
Export	71	22
Packaging	2	1
HA	34	11
Technology licensing	4	1
Total	**317**	**100**

HISTORICAL FINANCIALS

Company Type: Public

Income Statement

FYE: May 26

	REVENUE ($ mil.)	NET INCOME ($ mil.)	NET PROFIT MARGIN	EMPLOYEES
05/13	441.7	22.8	5.2%	526
05/12	317.5	13.1	4.1%	532
05/11	276.7	4.2	1.5%	255
05/10	238.2	4.4	1.9%	229
05/09	235.9	7.7	3.3%	110
Annual Growth	17.0%	31.1%	—	47.9%

2013 Year-End Financials

Debt ratio: 15.2%
Return on equity: 13.9%
Cash ($ mil.): 13
Current ratio: 1.69
Long-term debt ($ mil.): 34

No. of shares (mil.): 26
Dividends
  Yield: —
  Payout: —
Market value ($ mil.): 366

	STOCK PRICE ($) FY Close	P/E High/Low		PER SHARE ($) Earnings	Dividends	Book Value
05/13	13.88	17	8	0.85	0.00	6.77
05/12	7.07	14	10	0.49	0.00	5.84
05/11	5.83	47	36	0.15	0.00	5.15
05/10	6.19	50	38	0.15	0.00	4.94
05/09	6.78	33	13	0.29	0.00	4.76
Annual Growth	19.6%	—	—	30.8%	—	9.2%

Legacy Reserves LP

Legacy Reserves has its sights set on creating its very own prosperous legacy. The independent oil and gas company explores for oil and gas deposits in the Permian Basin of West Texas and southeast New Mexico and exploits those resources. In Legacy Reserves has proved reserves of 37.1 million barrels of oil equivalent (72% oil and natural gas liquids; 84% proved developed). In 2011 the company acquired a 126-well Permian Basin natural gas property for $66.1 million. Legacy Reserves was formed in 2005 to own and operate the oil and natural gas properties that it acquired from the Moriah Group the Brothers Group and MBN Properties.

In 2009 the company received a proposal from investment firm Apollo Management VII LP to acquire control of Legacy Reserves but turned downed the offer after failing to reach an agreement on terms.

Depressed oil demand and low commodity prices saw a slump in Legacy Reserve's sales in 2009.

The company has pursued a strategy of growth through acquisitions. It made eight property acquisitions in 2009 and 15 in 2008 including Pantwist LLC from Cano Petroleum for about $43 million. It also paid St. Mary Land & Exploration about $130 million for working interests in 13 oil fields in Wyoming.

In 2010 the company acquired a number of West Texas oil and gas assets for $9.2 million. It also bought several Permian Basin oil and natural gas properties with proved reserves of 5.8 million barrels of oil equivalent from Concho Resources for $103 million.

In 2011 it further expanded its Permian Basin assets acquiring natural gas properties in Eddy and Chaves Counties New Mexico for $66 million. In 2012 the company bought Permian Basin oil and natural gas properties from Concho Resources for $520 million in cash.

EXECUTIVES

Chairman President and CEO, Cary D. Brown, age 47, $325,000 total compensation
EVP Business Development and Land and Director, Kyle A. McGraw, age 54, $235,000 total compensation
EVP and COO, Paul T. Horne, age 51, $250,000 total compensation
VP Chief Accounting Officer and Controller, William M. Morris, age 60, $220,000 total compensation
Manager Business Development, Danny Boone
VP Finance and Treasurer, James R. Lawrence
Chief Financial Officer; Executive Vice President of Legacy Reserves GP; LLC, James (Dan) Westcott
Vice President General Counsel Secretary, Dan G. LeRoy
Chief Accounting Officer Controller, Micah C. Foster
Director, William D. (Bill) Sullivan, age 56
Director, Kyle D. Vann, age 65
Director, William R. (Bill) Granberry, age 71
EVP Business Development and Land and Director, Kyle A. McGraw, age 54
Director, Dale A. Brown, age 70
Director, G. Larry Lawrence, age 61
Auditors: BDOSeidmanLLP

LOCATIONS

HQ: Legacy Reserves LP
  303 W. Wall, Suite 1800, Midland, TX 79701
Phone: 432 689-5200
Web: www.legacylp.com

PRODUCTS/OPERATIONS

2009 Sales

	$ mil.	% of total
Oil	103	75
Gas	22	16
Natural gas liquids	11	9
Total	137	100

COMPETITORS

Carrizo Oil & Gas
Clayton Williams
  Energy
Eden Energy
Ellora

Frontier Oilfield
  Services
Glen Rose Petroleum
Occidental Permian

HISTORICAL FINANCIALS

Company Type: Public

Income Statement

FYE: December 31

	REVENUE ($ mil.)	NET INCOME ($ mil.)	NET PROFIT MARGIN	EMPLOYEES
12/12	346.4	68.6	19.8%	206
12/11	336.8	72.0	21.4%	163
12/10	216.3	10.8	5.0%	140
12/09	137.2	(92.8)	—	95
12/08	215.4	158.2	73.4%	98
Annual Growth	12.6%	(18.8%)	—	20.4%

2012 Year-End Financials

Debt ratio: 45.9%
Return on equity: —
Cash ($ mil.): 3
Current ratio: 0.85
Long-term debt ($ mil.): 775

No. of shares (mil.): 57
Dividends
  Yield: 9.3%
  Payout: 159.2%
Market value ($ mil.): 1,358

	STOCK PRICE ($) FY Close	P/E High/Low		PER SHARE ($) Earnings	Dividends	Book Value
12/12	23.80	21	16	1.40	2.23	11.75
12/11	28.24	21	14	1.63	2.14	10.22
12/10	28.72	105	68	0.27	2.08	9.00
12/09	19.67	—	—	(2.89)	2.08	7.99
12/08	9.31	5	1	5.17	1.98	12.26
Annual Growth	26.4%	—	—	(27.9%)	3.0%	(1.1%)

LHC Group Inc

The injured and ailing in need of a little TLC need look no further than LHC. LHC Group administers post-acute health care services through home nursing agencies hospices and long-term acute care hospitals (LTAC). The company operates through two segments: home-based services and facility-based services in rural areas in about 25 US states. LHC's home health nursing agencies provide care to Medicare beneficiaries offering such services as private duty nursing physical therapy and medically-oriented social services. Its hospices provide palliative care for terminal patients while its LTACs serve patients who no longer need intensive care but still require complex care in a hospital setting.

Operations

LHC also operates a handful of rehabilitation disease management and other specialty health facilities. Its Telehealth Services segment delivers medical care remotely via telephone Web-based applications and e-mail. The use of telehealth expands access to care to more patients and rural locations as well as provides for better monitoring of patients with chronic health problems.

The company gets the majority of its revenue from its home-based health services located primarily in the Southeast and Midwest regions of the country. Medicare payments account for the bulk of its service income. Given that such a significant portion of the company's revenue is derived from federal payments LHC is vulnerable to changes in reimbursement levels to Medicare.

LHC also partners with not-for-profit hospitals because such joint ventures tend to provide a more attractive return on investment for the company. It has such agreements with Baptist Health System (Alabama) West Tennessee Healthcare Southeast

Alabama Medical Center East Alabama Medical Center Three Rivers Community Hospital (Oregon) Woods Memorial Hospital (Tennessee) the continuing care arm of CHRISTUS Health (northeast Texas) Texas Health Resources and Methodist Health System (Texas). In total it has more than 100 joint venture locations in close to 20 states across its home nursing hospice and LTAC agencies although most are in collaboration with hospitals.

Financial Analysis

The company saw flat revenues in 2011 due to an increase in the number of people covered an increase in admissions and the additions of 2010 acquisitions offset by the effect of a government rule for 2011 that reduced home health Medicare rates by 5.2%.

LHC's net income dropped by 127% in 2011 due to a payment made to the US government pursuant to a settlement agreement involving Medicare reimbursement for home health services for 2006 to 2008 and an increase in the provision for bad debts due to the rise in commercial receivables.

Strategy

The Patient Protection and Affordable Care Act first enacted in 2010 calls for a number of changes to the way Medicare is paid out and LHC may have to adjust its compliance reporting measures as a result. Unlike its Medicare funded activities demand for services is an area that LHC is not expected to have problems with. Home health care long-term care and nursing services are expected to see a surge in demand with the aging US population.

The company pursues a strategy of expanding into new markets through organic development or acquisitions as well as by forming new partnerships.

Mergers and Acquisitions

In 2013 LHC expanded through the purchases of the home health businesses of Addus HomeCare adding about 20 agencies and two hospices in five states and AseraCare adding four agencies in four states. In 2012 in partnership with Texas Health Resources and Methodist Health System it acquired Huguley Home Health Agency from Huguley Memorial Medical Center in Burleson Texas. In 2011 it bought hospice locations in Alabama and Louisiana and entered into a home health joint venture in Kentucky.

Ownership

Chairman and CEO Keith Myers who cofounded LHC Group in 1994 owns nearly 13% of the company.

EXECUTIVES

Chief Financial Officer; Executive Vice President, Peter J. (Pete) Roman, age 62, $200,000 total compensation

Chairman and CEO, Keith G. Myers, age 53, $339,900 total compensation

Special Advisor CEO and Director, John L. Indest, age 61, $309,000 total compensation

SVP Corporate Development, Daryl J. Doise, age 55, $231,750 total compensation

VP Government Affairs, Harold Taylor

VP-Info Sys Ops, Morris Sanford

Jr. Senior Vice President Treasurer, Albert Simien Jr.

President and COO, Donald D. (Don) Stelly, age 44, $240,000 total compensation

SVP Senior Counsel Director Corporate Compliance and Director Regulatory and Government Affairs, Richard A. MacMillan, age 60

Senior Vice President Home Care Operations, Angie Begnaud

Executive Vice President Chief Administrative Officer, Marcus Macip

VP Investor Relations, Eric C. Elliott

Executive Vice President; General Counsel; Corporate Secretary, Peter C. November, age 43

Senior Vice President Chief Information Officer, Rajesh (Raj) Shetye

Senior Vice President Clinical Services, Barbara Goodman

VP-Clinical Leadership Trng, Melanie Kuehn

Senior Vice President Chief Compliance Officer, Josh Proffitt

VP-Ops, Ammy Lee

VP-Home Based Svcs, Chris Stagg

Compliance Officer, Josh Profitt

Senior Vice President Clinical Program Development, Cathy S. Newhouse

Senior Vice President Chief Development Officer, Don Adam

Senior Vice President of Finance, Jeffrey M. Kreger

Senior Vice President Chief Compliance Officer, JoAnne Little

Director, Monica Azare, age 46

Special Advisor CEO and Director, John L. Indest, age 61

Director, Ronald T. Nixon, age 57

Director, Ted W. Hoyt, age 58

Director, George A. Lewis, age 76

Director, John B. Breaux, age 68

Director, W. J. (Billy) Tauzin, age 69

Director, Dan S. Wilford, age 72

Director, Kenneth Thorpe

Independent Director, Kenneth Thorp

Auditors: KPMGLLP

LOCATIONS

HQ: LHC Group Inc.
420 W. Pinhook Rd. Ste. A, Lafayette LA 70503
Phone: 337-233-1307 **Fax:** 337-235-8037
Web: www.lhcgroup.com

2011 Selected Locations

State	No.
Louisiana	50
Alabama	33
Tennessee	33
Kentucky	30
Mississippi	28
Arkansas	21
West Virginia	18
Washington	12
Missouri	10
Idaho	10
Maryland	9
Texas	9
Georgia	7
Florida	5
Oregon	5
Virginia	4
Ohio	3
North Carolina	2
Oklahoma	1
Total	0 290

PRODUCTS/OPERATIONS

2011 Sales

	$ mil.	% of total
Home-based services	557	88
Total	**633**	**100**

COMPETITORS

Almost Family	HCR ManorCare
Amedisys	Health First
American HomePatient	Home Instead
Apria Healthcare	Kindred Healthcare

Consulate Health Care	NHC
Critical Homecare	National Home Health
Solutions	Odyssey HealthCare
Ensign Group	Personal-Touch Home
Gentiva	Care
Girling Health Care	RehabCare
Guardian Home Care	Trinity HomeCare
Holdings	VITAS Healthcare

HISTORICAL FINANCIALS

Company Type: Public

Income Statement FYE: December 31

	REVENUE ($ mil.)	NET INCOME ($ mil.)	NET PROFIT MARGIN	EMPLOYEES
12/12	637.5	27.4	4.3%	7,903
12/11	633.8	(13.2)	—	7,571
12/10	635.0	48.7	7.7%	7,973
12/09	531.9	43.8	8.2%	6,998
12/08	383.3	30.2	7.9%	5,376
Annual Growth	**13.6%**	**(2.4%)**	**—**	**10.1%**

2012 Year-End Financials

Debt ratio: 5.0%	No. of shares (mil.): 16
Return on equity: 10.2%	Dividends
Cash ($ mil.): 9	Yield: —
Current ratio: 2.19	Payout: —
Long-term debt ($ mil.): 19	Market value ($ mil.): 361

	STOCK PRICE ($) FY Close	P/E High/Low		PER SHARE ($) Earnings	Dividends	Book Value
12/12	21.30	14	8	1.53	0.00	15.84
12/11	12.83	—	—	(0.73)	0.00	14.41
12/10	30.00	14	7	2.68	0.00	15.06
12/09	33.61	15	7	2.43	0.00	12.29
12/08	36.00	21	9	1.69	0.00	9.88
Annual Growth	**(12.3%)**	**—**	**—**	**(2.5%)**	**—**	**12.5%**

Liberator Medical Holdings, Inc.

Miscellaneous retail stores nec nsk

EXECUTIVES

Coo, Mr John Leger

LOCATIONS

HQ: Liberator Medical Holdings, Inc.
2979 SE Gran Park Way, Stuart, FL 34997
Phone: 772 287-2414
Web: www.liberatormedical.com

HISTORICAL FINANCIALS

Company Type: Public

Income Statement FYE: September 30

	REVENUE ($ mil.)	NET INCOME ($ mil.)	NET PROFIT MARGIN	EMPLOYEES
09/13	69.1	7.0	10.2%	297
09/12	60.9	2.5	4.1%	326
09/11	52.7	0.2	0.5%	307
09/10	40.9	2.6	6.4%	214
09/09	25.8	2.2	8.6%	139
Annual Growth	**27.9%**	**33.6%**	**—**	**20.9%**

2013 Year-End Financials

Debt ratio: 3.0%
Return on equity: 24.9%
Cash ($ mil.): 12
Current ratio: 2.71
Long-term debt ($ mil.): 1

No. of shares (mil.): 52
Dividends
  Yield: 3.9%
  Payout: 66.6%
Market value ($ mil.): 107

	STOCK PRICE ($) FY Close	P/E High/Low		PER SHARE ($) Earnings	Dividends	Book Value
09/13	2.04	17	4	0.14	0.08	0.57
09/12	0.79	24	14	0.05	0.00	0.56
09/11	0.85	154	77	0.01	0.00	0.50
09/10	1.26	35	16	0.05	0.00	0.41
09/09	1.45	21	5	0.06	0.00	0.11
Annual Growth	8.9%	—	—	23.6%	—	52.4%

Life-Time Fitness Inc

Life Time Fitness wants to help you keep your New Year's resolutions. The company operates more than 100 exercise and recreation centers. Life Time Fitness facilities offer swimming pools basketball and racquet courts child care centers spas dining services and climbing walls in addition to some 400 pieces of exercise equipment. Most facilities are open 24 hours a day seven days a week and average around 100000 sq. ft. in size. They target a membership of about 7500 to 11000 and are designed to serve as an all-in-one sports and athletic club professional fitness facility family recreation center and spa and resort.

Geographic Reach

Life Time Fitness operates in 28 major markets in 22 states including Illinois Indiana Michigan Texas and Virginia. The chain also has a few facilities in Ontario Canada.

Operations

The company's revenue comes primarily from membership dues sales of in-center products programming services and enrollment fees. Life Time Fitness generated about 65% of its revenue from membership dues in fiscal 2012.

Life Time Fitness has more than 1.5 million members; monthly fees range from $50 to $250 depending on available amenities and access levels.

Financial Performance

The company's revenue increased by about 11% and profits increase by 20% in fiscal 2012 compared to fiscal 2011. It reported around $1.1 billion in revenue for 2012 after brining in about roughly $1 billion the previous year. The growth was attributed to increases in membership dues and in-center revenue.

Strategy

The company's three-pronged strategy includes opening new centers growing membership at its existing centers and increasing its in-center products and services revenue. In-center offerings include sessions with personal trainers spa services member activities and wellness programs nutritional products and food and beverage sales from its LifeCafes.

Ownership

Founder chairman and CEO Bahram Akradi owns about 5% of Life Time Fitness.

EXECUTIVES

Chairman President and CEO, Bahram Akradi, age 51, $750,000 total compensation
EVP and CFO, Michael R. (Mike) Robinson, age 53, $335,000 total compensation
Senior Director Corporate Communications, Jason Thunstrom
EVP Real Estate and Development, Mark L. Zaebst, age 53, $268,000 total compensation
EVP Club Operations, Jeffrey G. (Jeff) Zwiefel, age 50
EVP, Eric J. Buss, age 46, $268,000 total compensation
VP Finance, Kenneth E. (Ken) Cooper
VP Life Time University, Jess Elmquist
Editor in Chief Experience Life, Pilar Gerasimo
VP and Corporate Controller, John Hugo
VP Corporate Business, John Reilly
VP Fitness and Nutrition Services, Mark Thom
Executive Chef LifeCafe, David Fhima
EVP Real Estate and Development, Tami Kozikowski
Director, Jack W. Eugster, age 67
Director, Martha A. (Marti) Morfitt, age 55
Director, Giles H. Bateman, age 68
Director, Joseph S. (Joe) Vassalluzzo, age 65
Director, Guy C. Jackson, age 71
Director, John K. Lloyd, age 67
Director, John B. Richards, age 64
Auditors: Deloitte&ToucheLLP

LOCATIONS

HQ: Life Time Fitness Inc.
  2902 Corporate Place, Chanhassen MN 55317
Phone: 952-947-0000   **Fax:** 952-947-9137
Web: www.lifetimefitness.com

Selected Locations

Arizona
Colorado
Florida
Georgia
Illinois
Kansas
Maryland
Michigan
Minnesota
Missouri
Nebraska
New Jersey
North Carolina
Ohio
Tennessee
Texas
Utah
Virginia

PRODUCTS/OPERATIONS

2012 Sales

	$ mil.	% of total
Membership dues	727	65
Enrollment fees	15	3
Total	**1,126**	**100**

Selected Amenities

Basketball courts
Cardiovascular training
Child care center
Free weights
Lap pool
Racquetball courts
Rock climbing
Saunas
Spa

Selected Services

Activities and events
  Cycling
  Pilates
  Swimming lessons

Yoga
Locker and towel services
Massage therapy
Metabolic testing
Nutrition coaching
Personal training

COMPETITORS

24 Hour Fitness
Bally Total Fitness
Equinox Holdings
Gold's Gym
LA Fitness
Lifestyle Family Fitness
The Sports Club
Town Sports International Holdings
Wellbridge
World Gym
YMCA

HISTORICAL FINANCIALS

Company Type: Public

Income Statement

FYE: December 31

	REVENUE ($ mil.)	NET INCOME ($ mil.)	NET PROFIT MARGIN	EMPLOYEES
12/12	1,126.9	111.5	9.9%	21,700
12/11	1,013.6	92.6	9.1%	20,000
12/10	912.8	80.6	8.8%	19,000
12/09	837.0	72.3	8.6%	17,400
12/08	769.6	71.8	9.3%	16,700
Annual Growth	10.0%	11.6%	—	6.8%

2012 Year-End Financials

Debt ratio: 34.0%
Return on equity: 10.9%
Cash ($ mil.): 16
Current ratio: 0.60
Long-term debt ($ mil.): 691

No. of shares (mil.): 43
Dividends
  Yield: —
  Payout: —
Market value ($ mil.): 2,123

	STOCK PRICE ($) FY Close	P/E High/Low		PER SHARE ($) Earnings	Dividends	Book Value
12/12	49.21	19	15	2.66	0.00	24.87
12/11	46.75	21	15	2.26	0.00	22.57
12/10	40.99	21	11	2.00	0.00	20.05
12/09	24.93	17	4	1.82	0.00	17.81
12/08	12.95	27	5	1.83	0.00	16.48
Annual Growth	39.6%	—	—	9.8%	—	10.8%

Lindsay Corp

Liquid resources are big assets at Lindsay Corp. The company designs and manufactures irrigation systems primarily for farmers. The Zimmatic brand irrigation system a self-propelled center-pivot and lateral-move lineup is designed to use water energy and labor more efficiently than traditional flood or surface irrigation equipment. Touting better-to-bumper crop yields a dealer network sells to farmers in key markets worldwide. (The US represents more than 60% of sales.) Lindsay offers chemical injection systems water pumping stations (via subsidiary Watertronics) as well as replacement parts. An infrastructure division supplies movable barriers for traffic control and crash cushions for road safety.

Geographic Reach

With most of its operations residing in the US Lindsay has production and sales operations in Brazil China France Italy as well as distribution and sales operations in Australia New Zealand and South Africa.

Operations

Lindsay operates through two primary segments. Its largest irrigation is responsible for making its irrigation systems and water pumping stations. It also offers repair services and replacement parts. The company's infrastructure segment makes road safety equipment such as movable barriers for traffic control and crash cushions for road safety.

Financial Performance

Due to favorable economic conditions within key US agriculture markets Lindsay has seen historic growth over the years. From 2011 to 2012 its total sales increased by 15% leveling out at $551 million. During that same time period its net income increased by 18% to $43 million. Both totals were the highest posted in the company's recent history.

The surge in revenue is attributed to healthy growth in the irrigation markets. For 2012 irrigation equipment revenues increased by 28% and international revenues for this segment jumped by 19% (mostly in the Middle East Latin America China Canada and Africa). In addition overall revenues in the US grew by 15%.

The bad news for Lindsay was that revenues for its infrastructure products segment declined by 30% from 2011 to 2012.

Strategy

Lindsay looks to drive growth through acquisitions. In 2011 it obtained IRZ Consulting an irrigation consulting and design firm that caters to large growers to help them design water delivery systems. IRZ helps its clients with soil moisture monitoring and energy usage monitoring to save on costs. Around that same time period Lindsay snapped up ez-Wireless a company that provides wireless communications solutions to power advanced applications such as sensor networks video surveillance and telemetry. It purchased Digitec an electronics R&D and manufacturing company specializing in irrigation products in 2010.

Simultaneously Lindsay invests in its own product portfolio. It spends around $3 million to more than $4 million a year in research and development of irrigation products. Its irrigation systems are made to work in harsh environments such as on steep grades. Among its recent introductions Lindsay launched a pivot control for smartphones. The application allows farmers to control and monitor their irrigation pivots whenever and wherever they are. Benefits include optimized growing conditions and lower labor costs. R&D expenses related to its roadway infrastructure products are also considerable averaging more than $3 million annually.

Ownership

Neuberger Berman Management LLC owns 10% of Lindsay Corporation.

HISTORY

Lindsay Manufacturing was founded in 1955 as a farm equipment repair firm. In 1969 the company introduced its first Zimmatic-brand center-pivot irrigation system. Diversified agricultural firm DEKALB bought Lindsay in 1974. Gary Parker was appointed Lindsay's CEO in 1984 and in 1988 DEKALB spun off the company.

Lindsay's export revenues grew to a peak of $48 million (44% of total revenues) in 1992. The company began losing market share in Saudi Arabia (its major non-US market) when the Saudi government put an end to farm subsidies in 1994. That year investment firm Bass Management Trust led by Perry Sid and Lee Bass bought an initial 7% stake in the firm. In 1995 exports slumped to only 10% of total revenues.

Bass Management Trust increased its stake in Lindsay to about 18% in 1997 then upped it to 27% the following year. With the Asian financial crisis hurting foreign sales and US farmers unable to afford equipment outlays Lindsay's revenues dropped 25% in fiscal 1999. That year Bass Management Trust decreased its stake in the company to 15%.

Parker retired in 2000. He was replaced by Richard Parod who had been the VP of Toro's Irrigation Division. Also that year Lindsay acquired Colorado-based irrigation systems maker Oasis Enterprises.

Lindsay acquired a facility in La Chappelle d'Aligne France in 2001 in order to establish a European location for the manufacture of its irrigation products. As part of its continuing global expansion Lindsay established Lindsay Manufacturing Africa to promote local manufacturing inventory and support for the long term in 2002.

In 2003 the company introduced its Growth Smart Micro Climate Station which enables farmers to monitor precise evapotranspiration readings and graphic modeling to predict potentially damaging situations in the fields.

The company changed its name from Lindsay Manufacturing to Lindsay Corporation late in 2006.

Lindsay Corporation entered a new market segment in 2006 when it acquired Barrier Systems Inc. of California for $35 million in cash. Barrier Systems was a maker of specialty roadway barriers and crash cushion products used to increase highway safety and reduce traffic congestion.

Later in 2006 Lindsay complemented its new infrastructure segment with the purchase of Italy's Snoline S.P.A. a maker of road marking and other roadway safety equipment.

In 2007 Lindsay further augmented its infrastructure division with the purchase of certain assets of Traffic Maintenance Attenuators Inc. and Albert W. Unrath Inc. (or U-Mad). U-Mad designed truck- and trailer-mounted crash attenuators that improved motorist safety and protected workers in roadway work zones. In 2008 Lindsay obtained Watertronics a maker of water pumping stations and controls used with irrigation systems in the golf landscaping and municipal markets. Lindsay's Infrastructure division in 2009 expanded its safety offerings swallowing up the business of GE Transportation Systems Global Signaling.

Lindsay enjoyed an 80% increase in year-over-year earnings in 2010. The result marked a rebound; earnings took a 65% hit in 2009 from 2008 largely attributed to flagging capital investments in farm equipment coupled with weak commodity prices as well as delayed or reduced public infrastructure activity. Lindsay responded by cutting 25% of its workforce in 2009 but with improving revenues increased headcount by more than 15% in 2010.

EXECUTIVES

President CEO and Director, Richard W. (Rick) Parod, age 60, $474,359 total compensation
Chairman, Michael N. Christodolou, age 52
President Agricultural Irrigation, David B. Downing, age 58, $284,096 total compensation
President Technology Business, Douglas A. (Doug) Taylor, age 50
President Infrastructure, Barry A. Ruffalo, age 43, $252,404 total compensation
Vice President - Corporate Development & Treasurer, Mark A. Roth, age 39
Chief Accounting Officer, Lori L. Zarkowski, age 38
Vice President General Counsel Secretary, Eric R. Arneson, age 39
CFO, James C. Raabe
President Infrastructure Business, Steven S. Cotariu
Vice President - Human Resources, Reuben Srinivasan
Director, Michael D. Walter, age 63
Director, Michael C. Nahl, age 69
Director, J. David McIntosh, age 69
Director, W. Thomas (Jag) Jagodinski, age 56
Director, Howard G. Buffett, age 58
Director, William F. Welsh II, age 71
President CEO and Director, Richard W. (Rick) Parod, age 59
Auditors: KPMGLLP

LOCATIONS

HQ: Lindsay Corporation
2222 N. 111th St., Omaha NE 68164
Phone: 402-829-6800   **Fax:** 402-829-6834
Web: www.lindsaymanufacturing.com

2012 Sales

US	354	64
Total	**551**	**100**

PRODUCTS/OPERATIONS

2012 Sales

Irrigation	475	86
Total	**551**	**100**

Selected Products

Infrastructure
   Crash cushions
   Large diameter steel tubing
   Movable barriers for traffic lane management
   Preformed reflective pavement tapes
   Railroad signals and structures
   Specialty barriers
Irrigation
   Aerators
   Center-pivot irrigation systems
   Chemical injection systems
   Fertilizer injectors
   Filters and screens
   Hose reel irrigation systems
   Irrigation controls
   Lateral-move irrigation systems
   Pond controls
   Pump systems
      Custom-built
      Horizontal centrifugal
      Self-contained enclosed
      Submerged sled
      Vertical centrifugal
      Vertical turbine
   Remote monitoring and control systems

Selected Mergers and Acquisitions

FY2011
   IRZ Consulting (Irrigation consulting and design firm)
   ez-Wireless (Wireless communications solutions)
FY2010
   Digitec (electronics R&D and manufacturing company specializing in irrigation products)

COMPETITORS

AK Steel Holding Corporation	Rain Bird Corporation
Habasit America	Toro Company
Quanex Building Products	Valmont Industries

HISTORICAL FINANCIALS

Company Type: Public

Income Statement

FYE: August 31

	REVENUE ($ mil.)	NET INCOME ($ mil.)	NET PROFIT MARGIN	EMPLOYEES
08/13	690.8	70.5	10.2%	1,262
08/12	551.2	43.2	7.9%	1,082
08/11	478.8	36.8	7.7%	999
08/10	358.4	24.8	6.9%	891
08/09	336.2	13.8	4.1%	766
Annual Growth	19.7%	50.3%	—	13.3%

2013 Year-End Financials

Debt ratio: —	No. of shares (mil.): 12
Return on equity: 20.4%	Dividends
Cash ($ mil.): 151	Yield: 0.0%
Current ratio: 3.61	Payout: 8.6%
Long-term debt ($ mil.): —	Market value ($ mil.): 979

	STOCK PRICE ($) FY Close	P/E High/Low	PER SHARE ($) Earnings	Dividends	Book Value
08/13	76.02	17 12	5.47	0.48	29.57
08/12	65.36	22 15	3.38	0.39	24.43
08/11	62.20	27 13	2.90	0.35	21.75
08/10	36.87	23 16	1.98	0.33	18.39
08/09	41.51	76 20	1.11	0.31	16.79
Annual Growth	16.3%	— —	49.0%	11.7%	15.2%

Linear Technology Corp.

Linear Technology's high performance linear integrated circuits (ICs) create a connection from the analog world to the digital one. Its chips convert temperature pressure sound speed and other information into a digital form that can be read by digital devices. Linear Technology also makes linear devices that control power and regulate voltage in electronic systems. The company's products are used in a myriad of equipment from PCs to radar systems satellites and industrial instrumentation. It caters largely to communications and industrial markets as well as to the computer consumer goods aerospace and automotive markets. Customers outside the US account for more than 70% of sales.

Geographic Reach The US is Linear Technology's largest single market representing nearly 30% of sales. Asian customers account for more than half of sales with Japanese customers specifically generating 16%. European customers contribute the remaining 20%. The company saw declines across all geographic markets in fiscal 2012. Sales and Marketing Linear Technology markets its products through its own domestic and international sales teams as well as through third-party sales representatives in South America and India and electronics distributors. It has about 20 sales offices in the US and another 30 in Europe Asia and the Asia-Pacific region. The company's primary domestic distributor Arrow Electronics accounts for more than 10% of sales.

Financial Analysis The company reported revenue of $1.3 billion in fiscal 2012 (ended June)

which is down nearly 15% from the prior year record of $1.5 billion. Economic conditions resulted in Linear Technology customers reducing their inventories which led to the decline in sales. Positive growth in the automotive market which the company has been targeting was not enough to offset weakness in most other markets (industrial consumer computer and aerospace among them). Net income was also down that year falling more than 30% to $398 million on the lower revenue.

Strategy The breadth of Linear Technology's product lineup and customer base keeps the company from being too dependent on any one customer or any particular type of end use. The company has worked to avoid competition from Asian rivals —which tend to focus on high-volume low-margin chips —by offering semiconductor design and verification software lines as well as IC manufacturing software products to the high-end of the global electronics market.

Mergers and Acquisitions Linear Technology acquired California-based Dust Networks in 2011 to extend the functionality of its wireless sensor networking product line and raise its profile in new market niches. Dust specialized in low-power radio systems and software for such purposes industrial instrumentation power management and energy harvesting; its clients included such top industrial manufacturers as GE and Emerson.

Ownership Investment management firms Capital Research Global Investors and Capital World Investors own about 10% and 9% of the company respectively.

HISTORY

In 1981 Robert Swanson (chairman) persuaded five of his fellow employees at National Semiconductor to join him in a new venture. (It soon had to defend itself in a series of lawsuits filed by National Semiconductor over trade secrets and patent infringement.) Linear Technology benefited from an analog integrated circuit (IC) shortage in the mid-1980s and used profits to develop proprietary products for laptop computers and data processing equipment. The company went public in 1986.

Linear Technology spent much of the 1990s expanding its design and production facilities adding factories or design centers in Singapore (1994) Malaysia (1995) and Colorado and Washington (1997).

Despite a slump that bedeviled the chip industry Linear Technology enjoyed record sales in fiscal 1998 during which it introduced 100 new products. Because of this rapid growth the company reorganized in 1999 and again expanded its facilities. Company veteran Clive Davies became president and Swanson remained CEO.

Davies retired in 2003 and another company veteran David Bell succeeded him as president. Company COO Lothar Maier succeeded Swanson as CEO early in 2005 (Swanson remained executive chairman).

Linear Technology opened its first European design center in early 2006 launching a facility in Munich Germany.

Like many other Silicon Valley companies that generously gave out stock options to employees executives and directors Linear Technology reviewed its past stock-option granting practices. The Internal Revenue Service the SEC and the US Department of Justice all initiated informal inquiries into the company's history of granting stock options. Linear Technology denied that it used backdating a shady if generally legal practice in timing the issuing and sales of stock options in

granting its options and concluded its review without finding any apparent fraud or misconduct nor any need to restate its financial results from 1995 through 2006.

In late 2007 the SEC informed the company that it had concluded its investigation into Linear Technology's stock-option grants and didn't take any enforcement action.

EXECUTIVES

CEO and Director, Lothar Maier, age 58, $428,366 total compensation
VP Quality and Reliability, Paul Chantalat, age 62
VP Finance CFO and Secretary, Paul Coghlan, age 68, $367,961 total compensation
VP Engineering and CTO, Robert C. Dobkin, age 69, $339,836 total compensation
Chairman, Robert H. (Bob) Swanson Jr., age 75, $375,553 total compensation
VP International Sales, David A. Quarles, age 47
VP North American Sales, Richard Nickson, age 63
Vice President and Chief Operating Officer, Alexander R. (Alex) McCann, age 47
VP and General Manager Mixed Signal Products, Robert Reay, age 52
Director Marketing Communications, John Hamburger
Manager Media Relations, Doug Dickinson
VP and General Manager D Power Products, Donald E. (Don) Paulus, age 56, $251,966 total compensation
VP and General Manager Signal Conditioning Products, Erik M. Soule, age 49
VP and General Manager S Power Products, Steve Pietkiewicz, age 53
CEO and Director, Lothar Maier, age 58
Director, Thomas S. Volpe, age 61
Director, David S. Lee, age 75
Director, Richard M. (Dick) Moley, age 73
Director, Arthur C. Agnos, age 74
Director, John J. Gordon, age 66
Auditors: Ernst&YoungLLP

LOCATIONS

HQ: Linear Technology Corporation
1630 McCarthy Blvd., Milpitas CA 95035-7417
Phone: 408-432-1900   **Fax:** 408-434-0507
Web: www.linear.com

2012 Sales

	$ mil.	% of total
US	366	29
Europe	243	19
Japan	204	16
Other regions	452	36
Total	**1,266**	**100**

PRODUCTS/OPERATIONS

Selected Products

Amplifiers
Analog-to-digital and digital-to-analog converters
Battery monitors
Buffers
Comparators
Data converters
DC/DC power systems
Drivers
Filters
Hot swap circuits
Interface circuits
LED driver controllers
Line drivers
Line receivers
Lithium ion battery chargers
Monolithic filters
Motor controllers
Operational amplifiers

Power management devices
Power over Ethernet controllers
Radio-frequency (RF) circuits
Signal chain modules
Thermoelectric coolers
Timing devices
Transceivers
Voltage regulators
Voltage references

COMPETITORS

Allegro MicroSystems	Maxim Integrated
Analog Devices	Products
Analogic	Micrel
Cirrus Logic	Microchip Technology
Fairchild	Microsemi
Semiconductor	O2Micro
Freescale	ON Semiconductor
Semiconductor	ROHM
Hittite Microwave	STMicroelectronics
IXYS	Semtech
International	Siliconix
Rectifier	Texas Instruments
Intersil	Zetex
Marvell Technology	

HISTORICAL FINANCIALS

Company Type: Public

Income Statement

FYE: June 30

	REVENUE ($ mil.)	NET INCOME ($ mil.)	NET PROFIT MARGIN	EMPLOYEES
06/13*	1,282.2	406.9	31.7%	4,306
07/12	1,266.6	398.1	31.4%	4,365
07/11	1,483.9	580.7	39.1%	4,505
06/10	1,169.9	361.3	30.9%	4,191
06/09	968.5	313.5	32.4%	3,821
Annual Growth	7.3%	6.7%	—	3.0%

*Fiscal year change

2013 Year-End Financials

Debt ratio: 39.3%
Return on equity: 47.4%
Cash ($ mil.): 126
Current ratio: 1.75
Long-term debt ($ mil.): —
No. of shares (mil.): 233
Dividends
 Yield: 0.0%
 Payout: 59.6%
Market value ($ mil.): 8,585

	STOCK PRICE ($) FY Close	P/E High/Low		PER SHARE ($) Earnings	Dividends	Book Value
06/13*	36.84	22	17	1.71	1.02	4.21
07/12	31.33	20	15	1.70	0.98	3.20
07/11	33.43	14	11	2.50	0.94	2.22
06/10	28.92	20	14	1.58	0.90	0.17
06/09	23.51	24	13	1.41	0.86	(1.20)
Annual Growth	11.9%	—	—	4.9%	4.4%	—

*Fiscal year change

LinkedIn Corp

Feeling a bit disconnected to the business world? LinkedIn wants to help. The firm operates an online professional network designed to help members find jobs connect with other professionals and locate business opportunities. The site has grown to reach more than 160 million users in some 200 countries since its launch in 2003. LinkedIn is free to join; it offers a paid premium membership with additional tools and sells advertising. It addition-

ally earns revenue through its job listing service which allows companies to post job openings and search for candidates on LinkedIn. Former CEO and current chairman Reid Hoffman co-founded the company which filed to go public in 2011.

LinkedIn's public offering is significant in that as the precursor to Facebook's IPO it was the first major social networking company to file an IPO and was initially the biggest US Internet IPO since Google. Through the offering LinkedIn raised more than $352 million. That figure was at the high end of underwriters' expectations and valued LinkedIn at about $4.25 billion. The company is using the proceeds for more investment increasing its product development efforts and expanding its sales organization in the US and internationally.

The IPO came during a period of rapid growth via the addition of new users. Total members have jumped from about 55 million in 2009 to its current figure of some 160 million. While this increase in membership caused revenue growth over the last four consecutive fiscal years reaching revenues of more than $522 million in 2011 the company warned that it expects its growth rate to decline. It made only $11.9 million in 2011 down from about $15.4 million in 2010. The drop was due to higher income taxes and higher expenses (such as sales and marketing product development and general and administrative) associated with growing the business.

Continued growth efforts include acquisitions such as the 2012 purchase of SlideShare for some $119 million. SlideShare is an application that allows users to share slide show presentations and LinkedIn made the deal to strengthen its professional content offerings. In addition the company has launched its Talent Pipeline offering a new recruiter product. Mobile is another area of focus; in 2011 about 15% of member visits came from mobile and mobile page views were up more than 300% year-over-year.

LinkedIn is also ramping up its international expansion activities having experienced growth in India Brazil and China. About 60% of its member base comes from outside the US and its service is available in languages such as French German Italian Portuguese and Spanish. A reflection of its global focus LinkedIn recently opened international offices in London Mumbai and Sydney. These operations add to its presence in Canada Ireland and the Netherlands.

Hoffman and his wife Michelle Yee control more than 40% of LinkedIn's total votes.

EXECUTIVES

SVP Operations, David Henke, age 56
Chief Financial Officer; Senior Vice President, Steven J. (Steve) Sordello, age 44
VP Marketing, Nick Besbeas
Chief Executive Officer; Director, Jeffrey (Jeff) Weiner, age 43
Chairman, Reid Hoffman, age 46
VP General Counsel and Secretary, Erika Rottenberg, age 51
SVP Products and User Experience, Dipchand (Deep) Nishar, age 45
VP Talent, Steve Cadigan
SVP Global Sales, Michael (Mike) Gamson, age 39
VP Corporate Development, Sara Clemens
SVP Engineering and Operations, Kevin Scott
VP Corporate Communications, Shannon Stubo
Founder, Molly Garh
Vice President Legal, Alyssa Dawson
Vice President General Counsel, Gabrielle Walker
Vice President of Creative, Gary Irwin
Vice President Associate General., Larry Denny

Owner Director, Mark Leonard
Founder, Zach Web
Founder, Mae OMalley
Corporate Senior Vice President AECOM, Randy Castro
Executive Vice President Chief Technology Officer at Cox Communications, Kevin T. Hart
President AT&T Federal, Kay Kapoor
Vice President ATK Spacecraft Systems & Services, Jim Armor
Director, Michael J. (Mike) Moritz, age 59
Director, Leslie J. Kilgore, age 48
Director, A. George (Skip) Battle, age 70
Director, David L. M. Sze, age 47
Director, Stanley J. (Stan) Meresman, age 66
CEO and Director, Jeffrey (Jeff) Weiner, age 42
Auditors: Deloitte&ToucheLLP

LOCATIONS

HQ: LinkedIn Corporation
2029 Stierlin Ct., Mountain View CA 94043
Phone: 650-687-3600   **Fax:** 650-687-0505
Web: www.linkedin.com

2011 Sales

	$ mil.	% of total
US	353	68
International	168	32
Total	**522**	**100**

International Locations
Australia
Canada
India
Ireland
The Netherland
The UK

PRODUCTS/OPERATIONS

2011 Sales

	$ mil.	% of total
Hiring solutions	260	50
Marketing solutions	155	30
Premium subscriptions	105	20
Total	**522**	**100**

Selected Offerings

Premium Subscriptions
 Enhanced search results
 Enhanced communication capability
 Improved organizational functionality
 Priority customer support
Marketing Solutions
 Display ads
 Text ads
Hiring Solutions
 View candidates based on select criteria
  Industry
  Job function
  Geography
  Education

COMPETITORS

CareerBuilder	Socialtext
Classroom Connect	Spoke Software
Facebook	TheSquare
Gather Inc.	Tribe Networks
Harris Connect	Twitter
Jigsaw Data	Vault.com
Monster Worldwide	ZoomInfo
Plaxo	

HISTORICAL FINANCIALS

Company Type: Public

Income Statement

FYE: December 31

	REVENUE ($ mil.)	NET INCOME ($ mil.)	NET PROFIT MARGIN	EMPLOYEES
12/12	972.3	21.6	2.2%	3,458
12/11	522.1	11.9	2.3%	2,116
12/10	243.1	15.3	6.3%	1,288
12/09	120.1	(3.9)	—	0
12/08	78.7	(4.5)	—	0
Annual Growth	87.4%	—	—	—

2012 Year-End Financials

Debt ratio: —	No. of shares (mil.): 108
Return on equity: 2.8%	Dividends
Cash ($ mil.): 270	Yield: —
Current ratio: 2.45	Payout: —
Long-term debt ($ mil.): —	Market value ($ mil.): 12,475

	STOCK PRICE ($) FY Close	P/E High/Low	PER SHARE ($) Earnings	Dividends	Book Value
12/12	114.82	587 294	0.19	0.00	8.36
12/11	63.01	733 394	0.11	0.00	6.16
Annual Growth	82.2%	— —	72.7%	—	35.8%

Liquidity Services Inc

Hey bidder bidder. Take a swing at Liquidity Services (LSI). The online auction firm provides manufacturers retailers corporations and governments with an electronic marketplace to dispose of liquidate and track goods in the reverse supply chain. More than one million professional buyers are registered on the firm's online marketplaces through which they can bid for wholesale surplus and salvage items like retail customer returns overstock products and end-of-life goods. LSI founded in 1999 also offers valuation appraisal inventory marketing sale and logistical management of assets; warehousing and inspection of inventory; and transaction support such as collections and dispute mediation.

Geographic Reach

Liquidity Services (LSI) operates in more than 25 countries around the world. The company is growing by expanding into new markets and geographic areas.

Operations

LSI's online auction marketplaces include liquidation.com govliquidation.com and govdeals.com. Subsidiary Government Liquidation provides a marketplace for US military surplus assets. One of the company's largest sellers is the US Department of Defense which sells scrap and surplus assets. The government's surplus contract with LSI accounts for some 30% of the company's yearly revenues. Liquidity Services Limited (liquibiz.com) manages the sale and disposal of surplus assets in Europe. Clients there include corporations and government agencies such as the Ministry of Defence in the UK. The company's goWholesale.com portal connects advertisers with buyers seeking products for sale and business services.

LSI operates about 10 warehouses which house surplus products and act as distribution centers once items are sold.

Sales and Marketing

LSI utilizes a direct sales and marketing force to acquire and manage its seller and buyer accounts. The company currently has about 160 sales and more than 55 marketing personnel. Its sales activities are focused primarily on acquiring new sellers and improving the value to existing sellers. Its marketing activities are focused primarily on acquiring new buyers and increasing existing buyer participation.

Products sold on LSI's sites are organized within more than 500 categories and are sold by the truckload pallet or individual package. Most of the products fall within categories such as consumer electronics apparel scientific equipment aerospace parts and equipment technology hardware specialty equipment store fixtures and general merchandise.

Financial Performance

The company has enjoyed a dramatic upward trend in revenue during recent fiscal years. After claiming about $286.8 million in fiscal 2010 LSI brought in around $327.4 million in fiscal 2011. Fiscal year 2012 was even better as LSI reported more than $475 million in revenue.

The nearly 45% increase in revenue during 2012 compared to 2011 was attributed to increases in LSI's commercial business as a result of its acquisitions in 2011 and early 2012 along with several new programs for large retailers and manufacturers.

Mergers and Acquisitions

LSI enhanced its ability to deliver large retailers and OEMs across Canada and the US through its acquisition of National Electronics Service Association (NESA) for $18.3 million in 2012.

In early 2012 LSI expanded through the acquisition of GoIndustry-DoveBid a provider of surplus asset management auction and valuation services for $31 million. The deal added big names to its client roster (including Pfizer and Honeywell) and added some 458000 professional buyers and 1000 annual online sales events to its holdings.

In late 2011 LSI swallowed up Jacobs Trading Co. for $140 million in cash and stock. The purchase enhanced LSI's ability to resell retail merchandise and it expanded its relationship with important companies like Wal-Mart.

EXECUTIVES

Chairman and CEO, William P. (Bill) Angrick III, age 46, $303,188 total compensation

EVP and President Capital Assets Group, Thomas B. Burton, age 54, $267,750 total compensation

EVP and President Retail Supply Chain Group, G. Gayce (Cayce) Roy III, age 48

EVP EMEA & APAC, Holger Schwarz, age 47

CFO and Treasurer, James M. (Jim) Rallo, age 48, $267,120 total compensation

VP Marketing Strategy and Communications, Ben Hanna

CIO, Leoncio (Leo) Casusol

Auditors: Ernst&YoungLLP

LOCATIONS

HQ: Liquidity Services Inc.
1920 L St. NW 6th Fl., Washington DC 20036
Phone: 202-467-6868   **Fax:** 202-467-5475
Web: www.liquidityservicesinc.com

PRODUCTS/OPERATIONS

Selected Mergers and Acquisitions
FY2012

National Electronics Service Association ($18.3 million; Toronto Canada; distribution and logistics service)
GoIndustry-DoveBid ($31 million; Owings Mills MD; provider of surplus asset management auction and valuation services)
FY2011
Jacobs Trading Co. ($140 million; Des Moines IA; merchandise reseller)

Selected Subsidiaries
DOD Surplus LLC
GovDeals Inc.
Government Liquidation.com LLC
Liquidity Services Limited
Surplus Acquisition Venture LLC

COMPETITORS

Argent Trading	Overstock.com
Buxbaum Group	Taylor & Martin
ICON International	Group
ITEX	eBay
International Monetary Systems	

HISTORICAL FINANCIALS

Company Type: Public

Income Statement

FYE: September 30

	REVENUE ($ mil.)	NET INCOME ($ mil.)	NET PROFIT MARGIN	EMPLOYEES
09/13	505.8	41.1	8.1%	1,302
09/12	475.3	48.3	10.2%	965
09/11	327.3	8.5	2.6%	694
09/10	286.7	12.0	4.2%	704
09/09	236.2	5.7	2.4%	698
Annual Growth	21.0%	63.7%	—	16.9%

2013 Year-End Financials

Debt ratio: —	No. of shares (mil.): 31
Return on equity: 14.5%	Dividends
Cash ($ mil.): 95	Yield: —
Current ratio: 1.93	Payout: —
Long-term debt ($ mil.): —	Market value ($ mil.): 1,066

	STOCK PRICE ($) FY Close	P/E High/Low	PER SHARE ($) Earnings	Dividends	Book Value
09/13	33.50	38 22	1.26	0.00	9.90
09/12	50.21	42 18	1.47	0.00	8.03
09/11	32.07	112 41	0.29	0.00	5.56
09/10	16.01	37 18	0.44	0.00	4.18
09/09	10.32	56 22	0.21	0.00	3.77
Annual Growth	34.2%	— —	56.5%	—	27.3%

LivePerson Inc

LivePerson wants to inject some life into your customer service. The company provides hosted software applications that help companies communicate with customers. Primarily serving retailers and other companies with an online presence LivePerson's software enhances communications through multiple channels including text-based chat e-mail and customer self-service tools. Clients install an icon on their websites that when clicked opens a dialogue window with a customer service representative. As part of its service LivePerson keeps transcripts of customer interactions and offers the option of conducting user exit surveys.

Customers in the US make up more than three-quarters of sales.

Revenues related to business customers account for nearly 90% of sales. While monthly services fees make up the majority of sales to businesses the company also gets revenues from related professional and call center services. In its consumer business LivePerson generates sales from online transactions between experts and users accounting for 11% of sales down from 13% in 2010. Its consumer business is an online marketplace where consumers pay a fee to chat live with experts who provide information in categories such as personal coaching computers health education shopping spirituality and religion finance legal services and the like.

Overall sales were up about 21% in 2011 over 2010 driven by a 24% increase in business sales. The company credits a balance of new client acquisitions and expanded services provided to existing clients for growth across all of its product lines. In its consumer business a 2% increase in sales for the year was primarily due to higher rates charged by experts offset in part by a decrease in minutes. After reporting a loss in 2008 LivePerson returned to profitability the following year and net income has increased steadily since then. In 2011 the company's net income was 30% higher than 2010.

LivePerson's strategy includes focusing on key industry sectors: financial services retail telecomm travel and hospitality. It is also looking to expand its reach in the small and midsized business (SMB) market. The company has identified new markets that are adjacent to its target industries including health care insurance and energy and utilities. In addition to developing its own applications which can be accessed across multiple platforms LivePerson is working with some 25 partners that provide tools and applications that expand its reach to social media and mobile channels as well as provide complementary services.

LivePerson is also expanding internationally. The company has invested in direct sales and services in order to expand its customer base in the UK and Western Europe adding several enterprise customers in the financial services and telecomm markets in the regions. LivePerson is also looking at growth opportunities in the Asia/Pacific region specifically Australia New Zealand the Philippines and Singapore. The company has added direct sales and service personnel in Australia and is looking for partners to support sales and marketing in the other countries.

LivePerson is selective in its use of acquisitions for growth. In 2010 it bought Israeli start-up NuConomy for about $3 million. NuConomy's software monitors a website's traffic targeting the user behaviors that companies should act on in real-time. LivePerson bought the company primarily for its Web analytics intellectual property. It acquired the assets of another Israeli company Amadesa in 2012. Amadesa developed website testing and relevance targeting software designed to improve online conversions sales and customer interactions. Furthering its operations in the Asia-Pacific region LivePerson in late 2012 agreed to acquire Australian contact center services provider ENGAGE.

LivePerson claims more than 8500 customers including Cisco Systems HP Microsoft Orbitz Snapfish Verizon and Walt Disney.

Chairman and CEO Robert LoCascio owns around 9% of LivePerson.

EXECUTIVES

Chairman of the Board Chief Executive Officer, Robert P. LoCascio, age 44, $325,000 total compensation
EVP and GM Technology Operations - Israel, Eli Campo, age 47, $244,156 total compensation
Senior Vice President; Corporate Controller, Michael I. Kovach, age 44
SVP Business Affairs and General Counsel, Monica L. Greenberg, age 44, $255,000 total compensation
EVP, Peter Phillips
VP Platform Technologies and Ecosystem, Mark Trang
CFO, Daniel Murphy, age 46
Executive Vice President - Global Sales and Markets, Erica Schultz
Director, Kevin C. Lavan, age 60
Director, Steven Berns, age 47
Director, William G. Wesemann
Independent Director, David Vaskevitch
Independent Director, Peter Block
Auditors: BDOSeidmanLLP

LOCATIONS

HQ: LivePerson Inc.
462 7th Ave. 3rd Fl., New York NY 10018
Phone: 212-609-4200 **Fax:** 212-609-4201
Web: www.liveperson.com

2011 Sales

	$ mil.	% of total
US	101	76
UK	18	14
Other countries	13	10
Total	**133**	**100**

PRODUCTS/OPERATIONS

2011 Sales

	$ mil.	% of total
Hosted services - Business	112	84
Hosted services - Consumer	14	11
Professional services	6	5
Total	**133**	**100**

Selected Software

LivePerson Contact Center
LivePerson Enterprise for Sales
LivePerson Enterprise for Service
LivePerson for Online Sales
LivePerson Premiere (for midsized businesses)
LivePerson Pro (for small businesses)

COMPETITORS

About.com	RightNow Technologies
Adobe Systems	SAP
Google	Talisma
KANA	Yahoo!
Microsoft	eGain
Oracle	salesforce.com

HISTORICAL FINANCIALS

Company Type: Public

Income Statement

FYE: December 31

	REVENUE ($ mil.)	NET INCOME ($ mil.)	NET PROFIT MARGIN	EMPLOYEES
12/12	157.4	6.3	4.0%	748
12/11	133.0	12.0	9.0%	524
12/10	109.8	9.2	8.4%	481
12/09	87.4	7.7	8.9%	416
12/08	74.6	(23.8)	—	349
Annual Growth	**20.5%**	**—**	**—**	**21.0%**

2012 Year-End Financials

Debt ratio: —	No. of shares (mil.): 55
Return on equity: 4.1%	Dividends
Cash ($ mil.): 103	Yield: —
Current ratio: 3.83	Payout: —
Long-term debt ($ mil.): —	Market value ($ mil.): 735

	STOCK PRICE ($) FY Close	P/E High/Low		PER SHARE ($) Earnings	Dividends	Book Value
12/12	13.14	177 108		0.11	0.00	3.04
12/11	12.55	64 40		0.22	0.00	2.55
12/10	11.30	65 33		0.18	0.00	2.02
12/09	6.97	45 11		0.16	0.00	1.64
12/08	1.82	— —		(0.50)	0.00	1.34
Annual Growth	**63.9%**	**—** **—**		**—**	**—**	**22.7%**

LTC Properties, Inc.

Specializing in TLC LTC Properties sees real estate as a healthy investment. The self-administered real estate investment trust (REIT) primarily invests in health care and long-term care facilities. Its portfolio includes about 90 assisted living centers (homes for elderly residents not requiring constant supervision) more than 100 skilled nursing facilities (which provide rehabilitative and restorative nursing care) a dozen other health care properties (such as independent living or memory care) and even a couple of schools. It owns properties in more than 25 states. Top tenants include Brookdale Senior Living Extendicare and Prestige Care.

Operations

The REIT also invests in mortgage loans secured by long-term health care properties and participates in joint ventures that invest in health care properties and loans.

Geographic Reach

LTC's properties are located in 26 states. Texas Ohio Colorado and Florida are its largest markets.

Financial Performance

As a REIT the company is exempt from paying federal income tax as long as it distributes quarterly dividends to shareholders.

The trust makes money from rent and interest earned on outstanding loans. Rental income accounts for almost 95% of revenue; interest income contributes the other 5%.

EXECUTIVES

Senior Vice President Marketing and Strategic Planning, T. Andrew Stokes, age 58, $163,200 total compensation
Executive Chairman, Andre C. Dimitriadis, age 72, $240,000 total compensation
President CEO and Director, Wendy L. Simpson, age 63, $408,012 total compensation
Executive Vice President Chief Financial Officer Secretary, Pamela (Pam) Shelley-Kessler, $193,800 total compensation
VP and Chief Investment Officer, Clint B. Malin, $163,200 total compensation
VP and Director Tax, Peter G. Lyew, $133,000 total compensation
VP Controller and Treasurer, Caroline Wong
Vice President Controller Treasurer, Caroline Chikhale
Vice President Investment and Asset Management, Mark Hemingway

Executive Vice President Chief Financial Officer, Pam Kessler

President CEO and Director, Wendy L. Simpson, age 63

Director, Timothy J. Triche, age 68

Director, Boyd W. Hendrickson, age 69

Director, Edmund C. King, age 79

Director, Devra G. Shapiro, age 66

Auditors: Ernst&YoungLLP

LOCATIONS

HQ: LTC Properties Inc.
31365 Oak Crest Dr. Ste. 200, Westlake Village CA 91361

Phone: 805-981-8655   **Fax:** 805-981-8663

Web: www.ltcproperties.com

2012 Properties

	No.
Texas	41
Ohio	19
Colorado	13
Florida	13
Washington	9
Iowa	8
Kansas	8
Arizona	7
New	7
Oklahoma	6
North	5
Alabama	4
Idaho	4
Nebraska	4
Oregon	4
California	4
Georgia	3
Indiana	3
Pennsylvania	3
South	5
Virginia	4
New	5
Tennessee	2
Total	**184**

PRODUCTS/OPERATIONS

2012 Sales

	$ mil.	% of total
Rental income	87	93
Interest income from mortgage loans	5	6
Interest & other income	0	1
Total	**94**	**100**

COMPETITORS

Aviv REIT	NorthStar Healthcare
Chartwell Seniors	Investors
Housing	Omega Healthcare
HCP	Investors
Health Care REIT	Sabra Health Care
Healthcare Realty	Senior Housing
Trust	Properties
Legacy Healthcare	Tiptree
NHC	Ventas
National Health	
Investors	

HISTORICAL FINANCIALS

Company Type: Public

Income Statement

FYE: December 31

	REVENUE ($ mil.)	NET INCOME ($ mil.)	NET PROFIT MARGIN	EMPLOYEES
12/12	94.0	51.2	54.5%	18
12/11	85.1	49.2	57.8%	17
12/10	74.3	45.8	61.7%	13
12/09	69.8	44.0	63.0%	13
12/08	69.3	42.9	62.0%	13
Annual Growth	**7.9%**	**4.5%**	**—**	**8.5%**

2012 Year-End Financials

Debt ratio: 38.4%
Return on equity: 11.0%
Cash ($ mil.): 7
Current ratio: 0.29
Long-term debt ($ mil.): 188

No. of shares (mil.): 30
Dividends
  Yield: 5.0%
  Payout: 114.0%
Market value ($ mil.): 1,075

	STOCK PRICE ($) FY Close	P/E High/Low	PER SHARE ($) Earnings	Dividends	Book Value
12/12	35.19	24 19	1.57	1.79	15.16
12/11	30.86	23 16	1.36	1.68	15.38
12/10	28.08	24 19	1.21	1.58	17.29
12/09	26.75	22 13	1.27	1.56	19.40
12/08	20.28	25 12	1.24	1.56	19.79
Annual Growth	**14.8%**	**— —**	**6.1%**	**3.5%**	**(6.4%)**

lululemon athletica inc

lululemon athletica designs and sells yoga-inspired apparel under the lululemon athletica and ivivva athletica brands to the limber and athletically hip. It operates some 250 company-owned stores primarily located in North America. The rest are in Australia and New Zealand where lululemon operates through a joint venture. While it specializes in making women's clothing for yoga dance and running the company also offers men's apparel. Third-party mostly Taiwanese vendors make its clothing which is distributed from facilities in Canada the US and Australia. The fast-growing company was founded in 1998 by Chairman Dennis "Chip" Wilson.

Geographic Reach

Vancouver Canada-based lululemon athletica rings up about 60% of its sales in the US with stores in some 35 states and the District of Columbia. California is the company's largest market home to nearly 20% of its US stores. Canada accounts for about a third of the company's sales with other countries (including Australia and New Zealand) bringing in the rest.

Operations

Lululemon's growing network of company-owned stores accounts for 80% of its sales. Online sales account for nearly 15% of the total while wholesale sales (to select yoga studios health clubs and fitness centers) brings in the rest. The company's chain of eight ivivva athletica stores specialize in dance-inspired apparel for girls.

Sales and Marketing

Lululemon's target customer is an sophisticated educated physically-active woman who can afford to spend upwards of $80 on a pair of yoga pants.

Financial Performance

Lululemon's sales have soared along with the growing popularity of yoga and its growing brand awareness —from about $40 million in fiscal 2004 to more than $1.3 billion in fiscal 2013 (ended January) —despite an economic downturn that conspired against the company. The apparel retailer logged its most recent revenue leap from about $1 billion in fiscal 2012 to $1.37 billion in fiscal 2013 and increase of 37%. Growth drivers included a 33% sales gain at its corporate-owned stores due to more than 35 new store openings and a 16% gain in same-store sales. Online sales increased 86% year over year while wholesale sales fell.

Strategy

Fiscal 2014 proved to be a tough year for lululemon during which quality control problems (too-shear pants) in its core yoga pant line plagued the company and lead to changes in the management and organization of the product organization the resignation of its CEO and the pending departure of its founder and chairman in June 2014. The company's new CEO is the former president of TOMS Shoes. Nevertheless the company continued to grow its store network and online business in the US and abroad. Beyond North America lululemon is looking to the Asia/Pacific region and eventually Europe for expansion. (The company has a showroom in Hong Kong.)

Granted most of lululemon's sales are to women but the retailer is working to attract men as well as more males are participating in yoga to stay fit. It's enticing men by marketing the "technical rigor" of its products. Aging Baby Boomers looking to adopt a lifestyle focused on longevity is another gain for lululemon. The apparel maker also concentrates on developing its ivivva dance-inspired line targeted to dancers and gymnasts age 6 to 12 years. Part of this strategy includes adding company-owned stores under the ivivva banner.

EXECUTIVES

Chairman, Michael Casey, age 67

CFO, John E. Currie, age 57, $332,780 total compensation

CEO and Director, Christine M. Day, age 51, $492,250 total compensation

Chief Executive Officer; Director, Laurent Potdevin

EVP and Chief Product Officer, Sheree Waterson, age 57, $192,235 total compensation

Chairman, Dennis J. (Chip) Wilson, age 57, $241,822 total compensation

SVP Global eCommerce, Chris Ladd

Executive Vice President Retail Operations North America, Delaney Schweitzer

CIO, Kathryn Henry

Director, R. Brad Martin, age 61

Director, Thomas G. (Tom) Stemberg, age 64

Director, Michael Casey, age 67

Director, Martha A. (Marti) Morfitt, age 55

Director, RoAnn Costin, age 60

CEO and Director, Christine M. Day, age 51

Chief Executive Officer; Director, Laurent Potdevin

Chairman, Dennis J. (Chip) Wilson, age 57

Director, Rhoda M. Pitcher, age 58

Director, Emily White

Auditors: PricewaterhouseCoopersLLP

LOCATIONS

HQ: lululemon athletica inc.
2285 Clark Dr., Vancouver British Columbia V5N 3G9 Canada

Phone: 604-732-6124   **Fax:** 604-874-6164

Web: www.lululemon.com

Lumber Liquidators Holdings Inc

2013 Stores

	No.
US	135
Canada	51
Australia	23
New	2
Total	**211**

2013 Sales

	$ mil.	% of total
US	839	61
Canada	461	34
Outside North America	68	5
Total	**1,370**	**100**

PRODUCTS/OPERATIONS

2013 Sales

	$ mil.	% of total
Corporate-owned stores	1,090	80
Direct to consumer	197	14
Other	82	6
Total	**1,370**	**100**

COMPETITORS

Capezio	NIKE
Fifth & Pacific	The Gap
Finish Line	Triumph Apparel
Gildan Activewear	Under Armour
Jacques Moret	adidas
Jockey International	bebe stores
Lucy Activewear	

HISTORICAL FINANCIALS

Company Type: Public

Income Statement

FYE: February 3

	REVENUE ($ mil.)	NET INCOME ($ mil.)	NET PROFIT MARGIN	EMPLOYEES
02/13*	1,370.3	270.5	19.7%	6,383
01/12	1,000.8	184.0	18.4%	5,807
01/11	711.7	121.8	17.1%	4,572
01/10	452.9	58.2	12.9%	3,219
02/09	353.4	39.3	11.1%	2,861
Annual Growth	**40.3%**	**61.9%**	**—**	**22.2%**

*Fiscal year change

2013 Year-End Financials

Debt ratio: —	No. of shares (mil.): 144
Return on equity: 35.7%	Dividends
Cash ($ mil.): 590	Yield: —
Current ratio: 5.90	Payout: —
Long-term debt ($ mil.): —	Market value ($ mil.): 9,801

	STOCK PRICE ($) FY Close	P/E High/Low		PER SHARE ($) Earnings	Dividends	Book Value
02/13*	67.86	43	28	1.85	0.00	6.14
01/12	64.12	94	34	1.27	0.00	4.19
01/11	68.61	85	31	0.85	0.00	2.74
01/10	28.24	78	11	0.41	0.00	1.65
02/09	6.80	129	22	0.28	0.00	1.11
Annual Growth	**77.7%**	—	—	**61.0%**	—	**53.5%**

*Fiscal year change

Customers can find their floors at Lumber Liquidators Holdings. Known for its low prices Lumber Liquidators is one of the nation's largest retailers of hardwood flooring. It sells more than 25 domestic and exotic species of hardwoods from more than 300 Lumber Liquidators stores in about 45 states and Canada online by catalog and from its Virginia call center. The company also offers antique and reclaimed boards laminate flooring moldings and installation products. Its brands include Bellawood Builder's Pride Schon Morning Star and Virginia Mill Works. Homeowners represent about 90% of Lumber Liquidators' customer base. The company was founded in 1994 by chairman Tom Sullivan.

Geographic Reach

Virginia-based Lumber Liquidators operates more than 300 stores in 46 US states and nine retail stores in Ontario Canada. The company's largest markets are California Texas Florida New York and Pennsylvania which combined are home to about a third of its stores.

Sales and Marketing

The flooring company makes use of celebrity endorsements and product placement opportunities to tout its brands. Lumber Liquidators has a long-standing relationship with home improvement celebrities Bob Vila and Ty Pennington Vila in particular has been associated specifically with the company's Bellawood brand for several years. It also uses targeted television advertising on cable networks such as Discovery Channel HGTV TLC and DIY Network.

Financial Performance

Lumber Liquidators sales increased 19% in 2012 versus 2011 to about $813 million. Net income rose 79% over the same period to $47 million. The double-digit increases in sales and profits were driven by higher sales at existing Lumber Liquidator stores (up 11% year over year) and the addition of 25 new locations in 2012. Higher average retail price per unit sold has also contributed to sales gains. Also customers' preferences for premium flooring products has increased particularly within certain product categories including laminates engineered hardwood bamboo cork and resilient. Indeed Lumber Liquidators has enjoyed about a decade of steadily increasing sales despite the deep recession and crisis in the housing market.

Strategy

Lumber Liquidators markets itself as a supplier of premium hardwoods and flooring products with a cost-effective retail format. Typically situated in low-rent commercial and industrial districts its stores average about 6500 sq. ft. They allot up to 1000 sq. ft. for the showroom area which spotlights flooring samples on racks and as part of the showroom floor. The warehouse area takes up the remaining space stocking a combination of high-volume products with the most popular items at that particular location.

The company has rapidly expanded its retail footprint in recent years. In 2012 the fast-growing chain added 25 stores. It plans to continue adding 40 to 50 locations annually in new and existing markets for the next several years as part of its growth strategy. It is also remodeling select older stores. During 2011 Lumber Liquidators extended its network north of the US border opening its first Canadian locations in Ontario.

Because of its size Lumber Liquidators believes it can obtain better prices from its suppliers which helps to keep costs under control and ensures a competitive edge. The company purchases its products from about 90 vendors (mostly mills and trading companies) in the US and abroad however the Sequoia Floorings trading company handles more than a third of Lumber Liquidators' purchases. About 40% of Lumber Liquidators' products come from North America and some 45% are sourced from the Asia/Pacific region.

The company has been investing in its infrastructure to support continued expansion in recent years including refining its product selection improving logistics and providing training to store managers. In 2010 it launched an integrated software system that offers enhancements for its existing point-of-sale merchandising store operations and inventory control systems. (Lumber Liquidators said it faced decreased productivity while the integrated system was rolled out however and could not adequately serve customers during the second half of the year.)

Ownership

The investment firms T. Rowe Price and FMR LLC each own about 12% of the company's shares while BlackRock holds about 11%.

EXECUTIVES

CEO and Director, Jeffrey W. (Jeff) Griffiths, age 62, $524,904 total compensation
Chief Marketing Officer of Lumber Liquidators, Marco Q. Pescara, age 48, $156,351 total compensation
Chairman, Thomas D. (Tom) Sullivan, age 53, $314,942 total compensation
VP Store Operations, Tyler C. Greenan, age 44, $230,000 total compensation
SVP Store Operations, Robert W. Morrison, age 57, $297,358 total compensation
Secretary and General Corporate Counsel, E. Livingston B. (Livy) Haskell, age 40
Chief Financial Officer, Daniel E. Terrell, age 48, $234,423 total compensation
SVP Human Resources, E. Jean Matherne, age 58
Regional Manager, John Coffey
Regional Manager, Shane Jones
Regional Manager, Abe Diaz
Regional Manager, Mike Halford
President; Chief Executive Officer; Director, Robert M. Lynch, age 47
Chief Merchandising Officer, William K. Schlegel
IR Contact Officer, Ashleigh McDermott
Senior Vice President - Supply Chain, Carl Daniels
Director, Martin F. Roper, age 50
Director, Macon F. Brock Jr., age 70
CEO and Director, Jeffrey W. (Jeff) Griffiths, age 62
Director, Peter B. Robinson, age 64
Director, Douglas T. (Doug) Moore, age 56
Director, John M. Presley, age 52
Independent Director, Jimmie Wade
Auditors: Ernst&YoungLLP

LOCATIONS

HQ: Lumber Liquidators Holdings Inc
3000 John Deere Road, Toano, VA 23168
Phone: 757 259-4280
Web: www.lumberliquidators.com

2012 Stores

	No.
US	
California	27
Texas	22

Florida	19
New	15
Pennsylvania	13
Illinois	11
Virginia	11
North	10
Ohio	10
Georgia	9
Michigan	8
New	8
Massachusetts	7
Washington	7
Colorado	6
Indiana	6
Tennessee	6
Alabama	5
Arizona	5
Connecticut	5
Louisiana	5
Maryland	5
Minnesota	5
Missouri	5
Other	52
Canada	9
Total	**291**

PRODUCTS/OPERATIONS

2012 Sales

	% of total
Hardwood (solid &	47
Laminates	22
Moldings &	16
Bamboo cork and	14
Other	1
Total	**100**

COMPETITORS

CCA Global	Lowe' s
Floor and Decor	MasterTile
Outlets	Menard
Home Depot	Sears

HISTORICAL FINANCIALS

Company Type: Public

Income Statement

FYE: December 31

	REVENUE ($ mil.)	NET INCOME ($ mil.)	NET PROFIT MARGIN	EMPLOYEES
12/12	813.3	47.0	5.8%	1,420
12/11	681.5	26.2	3.9%	1,302
12/10	620.2	26.2	4.2%	1,191
12/09	544.5	26.9	4.9%	934
12/08	482.1	22.1	4.6%	788
Annual Growth	14.0%	20.7%	—	15.9%

2012 Year-End Financials

Debt ratio: —
Return on equity: 20.8%
Cash ($ mil.): 64
Current ratio: 2.85
Long-term debt ($ mil.): —

No. of shares (mil.): 27
Dividends
Yield: —
Payout: —
Market value ($ mil.): 1,438

	STOCK PRICE ($) FY Close	P/E High/Low		PER SHARE ($) Earnings	Dividends	Book Value
12/12	52.83	34	10	1.68	0.00	8.62
12/11	17.66	30	15	0.93	0.00	7.71
12/10	24.91	33	21	0.93	0.00	6.57
12/09	26.80	28	7	0.97	0.00	5.45
12/08	10.56	20	7	0.82	0.00	4.27
Annual Growth	49.6%	—	—	19.6%	—	19.2%

Luminex Corp

William Blake could "see a world in a grain of sand" and Luminex Corporation can reveal 100s of secrets in a drop of fluid. Its xMAP (Multi-Analyte Profiling) technology allows simultaneous analysis of up to 500 bioassays or tests from a single drop of fluid. xMAP consists of instruments software and disposable microspheres (microscopic polystyrene beads on which tests are performed). Luminex's systems are used by clinical and research laboratories and are distributed through strategic partnerships with other life sciences firms. Luminex also develops testing assays and disposable testing supplies for the clinical diagnostics market.

Geographic Reach

More than 80% of Luminex's sales are made in the US. It also sells to customers in other countries in North America Europe and the Asia/Pacific region. Luminex has facilities in Australia Canada China Japan the Netherlands and the US.

Operations

The company's TSP (technology and strategic partners) segment accounts for 60% of annual revenues and makes Luminex's instrumentation systems used by clinical labs as well as the research labs of pharmaceutical biotech diagnostic medical and life science entities. The division primarily sells systems through licensing or distribution relationships with more than 55 strategic partners. The partners distribute Luminex systems (or their own systems that incorporate the xMAP technology) to end users or use Luminex systems to perform testing services for their customers. About 40 partners have commercialized their own reagent-based tests using the xMAP technology. Altogether the strategic partners have sold some 9700 Luminex instrumentation sets to laboratories around the world.

Luminex earns royalties from the sales of xMAP-based assays and services developed by partners. In addition the TSP segment sells of the disposable microspheres and fluids used with the systems and it earns fees through maintenance services through contracts with laboratories.

Sales from the ARP (assays and related products) segment have grown in recent years accounting for 40% of revenues in 2012 as the firm works to increase direct sales of testing assays in core fields including human genetics infectious disease and personalized medicine testing.

Sales and Marketing

About 55% of the company's TSP segment revenues in 2012 were generated by its top three strategic partner customers: Thermo Fisher Scientific Bio-Rad Laboratories and EMD Millipore. The ARP segment also has three customers that account for a majority (more than 70%) of sales: LabCorp Thermo Fisher Scientific and Abbott Laboratories. Luminex shifted its ARP distribution model to focus on direct sales in 2013 (as opposed to sales through distribution partners) and as a result it expects to see less customer concentration in the ARP segment in future years.

Advertising expenses including trade show and convention activities were some $2.4 million in 2012 down from $3.1 million in 2011.

Financial Performance

Revenues increased 10% to some $202.6 million in 2012 due to 44% growth in the ARP segment on higher assay sales primarily in the infectious disease category. Growth in the ARP segment was offset by declined sales of systems and consumables in the TSP segment. Net income fell 14% due to higher R&D sales administrative and general expenses including costs related to recent acquisitions.

Strategy

The technology-based company has implemented a strategy to transform itself into a market-driven customer-focused company. To achieve this goal Luminex is focusing on key markets including life sciences research molecular infectious disease genetic disease pharmacogenetic testing bio-defense testing and immunodiagnostics. In addition it aims to develop next-generation systems to bring efficient portable testing solutions to market as well as market-leading assays in the human molecular diagnostic testing market. It is also working to develop strategic partnerships in its key markets and to pursue acquisitions that could hasten its goals.

To increase product demand and build on direct end-user relationships in the ARP segment the company assumed responsibility from major distributors of proprietary molecular diagnostic products in 2013.

Mergers and Acquisitions

Luminex has made careful acquisitions to build up its product and geographic range. For example to further its goal of delivering a market leading molecular diagnostics system the company in 2012 paid some $50 million (along with potential milestone and performance payments) to acquire GenturaDx a private molecular diagnostics firm that is developing an automated real-time testing system that extracts and analyzes molecular samples using patented single-use cartridges. Luminex hopes to integrate its MultiCode-RTx chemistry with GenturaDx's instrument to make better and faster molecular testing tools available to health providers throughout the world.

Ownership

New Orleans-based investment advisor St. Denis J. Villere & Company is Luminex's largest stockholder owning about 11% of the company.

Company Background

Luminex takes its name from the special laser beams that each microsphere passes through during the bioassay screening process. The lasers excite dyes inside and on the surface of the microspheres and the resulting fluorescence is measured in real time and analyzed by the system's software.

EXECUTIVES

Chairman, G. Walter Loewenbaum II, age 68

VP Global Marketing, Timothy R. (Tim) Dehne, age 45

VP Quality Assurance and Regulatory Affairs, Oliver H. Meek, age 61, $187,917 total compensation

Chief Financial Officer Senior Vice President Finance and Treasurer, Harriss T. Currie, age 52, $280,234 total compensation

President and Chief Executive Officer; Director, Patrick J. Balthrop Sr., age 57, $483,750 total compensation

Senior Vice President Research and Development, Jeremy Bridge-Cook, age 44, $310,375 total compensation

VP General Counsel and Corporate Secretary, David S. Reiter, age 46, $266,951 total compensation

VP Immunodiagnostics, Gregory J. Gosch, age 50, $219,364 total compensation

Senior Vice President Corporate Development and Global Marketing, Russell W. Bradley, age 50, $215,710 total compensation

Vice President Manufacturing and Quality Surveillance, Steve Back

VP Partner and Operations Development, Andrew D. Ewing

Senior Vice President Operations, Michael F. Pintek, age 44, $157,500 total compensation

Vice President Luminex Molecular Diagnostics, Nancy Krunic

Vice President Biodefense, Amy L. Altman

VP Luminex Life Sciences, Thomas J. Copa

Vice President Systems Research and Development, Charles J. Collins

Vice President Product Development & Manufacturing, Scott C. Johnson

Senior Vice President - Assay Group, Jeremy Cook

Vice President Human Resources, Nancy Capezzuti

Vice President Accounting, Kendel B. Martin

Vice President Manufacturing and Quality Surveillance, Steven Back

Director, Kevin M. McNamara, age 57

Director, Fred C. Goad Jr., age 72

Director, Edward A. Ogunro, age 60

Director, Jim D. Kever, age 60

Director, Robert J. Cresci, age 69

Director, Thomas W. (Tom) Erickson, age 62

President CEO and Director, Patrick J. Balthrop Sr., age 56

Director, Jay B. Johnston, age 70

Director, Gerard Vaillant, age 70

Auditors: Ernst&YoungLLP

LOCATIONS

HQ: Luminex Corporation
12212 Technology Blvd., Austin TX 78727
Phone: 512-219-8020   **Fax:** 512-219-5195
Web: www.luminexcorp.com

2012 Sales

	$ mil.	% of total
US	167	83
Asia	10	5
Australia	1	-
Total	**202**	**100**

PRODUCTS/OPERATIONS

2012 Revenues

	$ mil.	% of total
TSP segment	121	60
ARP segment	81	40
Total	**202**	**100**

2012 Revenues

	$ mil.	% of total
Assay revenue	75	37
Royalty revenue	31	15
Service revenue	8	4
Total	**202**	**100**

Selected Products

Assay Development Tools
Calibration and Control Microspheres
Clinical Diagnostic Assays
FLEXMAP 3D
Life Science Research Assays
Luminex LX 100/200 (LX Systems)
MagPlex Microspheres
MicroPlex Microspheres
SeroMAP Microspheres
xPONENT
xTAG Microspheres

Selected Acquisitions

2012
  GenturaDx ($50 million molecular diagnostics testing system)
2011
  EraGen Biosciences (renamed Luminex Madison; $34 million; diagnostic assay technologies based on its proprietary MultiCode platform and marketed diagnostic products for such conditions as herpes simplex virus and organ transplant infections)
2010

Bizpac (dry sample preparation newborn screening forensics and molecular diagnostics; Australia)

COMPETITORS

Abbott Labs	Illumina
Affymetrix	Johnson & Johnson
Beckman Coulter	Life Technologies
Becton Dickinson	Corporation
Celera	Orchid Cellmark
Cepheid	QIAGEN
GE Healthcare	Roche Diagnostics
Gen-Probe	Sequenom
GenMark	Siemens Healthcare
Hologic	

HISTORICAL FINANCIALS

Company Type: Public

Income Statement

FYE: December 31

	REVENUE ($ mil.)	NET INCOME ($ mil.)	NET PROFIT MARGIN	EMPLOYEES
12/12	202.5	12.4	6.1%	687
12/11	184.3	14.4	7.9%	614
12/10	141.5	5.2	3.7%	525
12/09	120.6	17.7	14.7%	437
12/08	104.4	3.0	2.9%	384
Annual Growth	**18.0%**	**41.9%**	**—**	**15.7%**

2012 Year-End Financials

Debt ratio: 0.9%	No. of shares (mil.): 40
Return on equity: 4.8%	Dividends
Cash ($ mil.): 42	Yield: —
Current ratio: 4.71	Payout: —
Long-term debt ($ mil.): 1	Market value ($ mil.): 686

	STOCK PRICE ($) FY Close	P/E High/Low		PER SHARE ($) Earnings	Dividends	Book Value
12/12	16.80	85	54	0.30	0.00	6.36
12/11	21.23	70	48	0.34	0.00	6.12
12/10	18.28	152	104	0.12	0.00	5.69
12/09	14.93	50	30	0.43	0.00	5.37
12/08	21.36	330	171	0.08	0.00	4.82
Annual Growth	**(5.8%)**	**—**	**—**	**39.2%**	**—**	**7.2%**

Lumos Networks Corp.

Lumos Networks hopes your every telephone conversation is illuminating. The company spun off from wireless operator NTELOS in 2011 comprises NTELOS' wireline business. Lumos Networks provides data voice and IP service to carrier business government and residential customers over a 5800-mile fiber network in the Mid-Atlantic region (Virginia West Virginia and portions of Kentucky Maryland Ohio and Pennsylvania). Its network allows it to offer bundled cable Internet and phone service. It also operates as a rural local-exchange carrier (RLEC) in the rural Virginia cities of Waynesboro and Covington and portions of Alleghany Augusta and Botetourt counties.

NTELOS made the tax-free spinoff to focus on its growing wireless operations. Its shareholders received one share of Lumos Networks for every two shares of NTELOS stock held. (Known as a 1-for-2 reverse stock split halving the amount of shares doubles the stock's value.) Lumos Networks used the proceeds from the spinoff to repay NTELOS. Private investment firm Quadrangle Capital Partners owns 27% of Lumos Networks' stock and has two seats on its board of directors. Quadrangle Capital Partners also maintains the same stake in NTELOS.

NTELOS separated the two businesses to allow each to manage its operations and capital investments pursue growth strategies and enhance stockholder value. While NTELOS caters to individuals with cell phone plans Lumos Networks' customers are mostly regional enterprise business government and carrier customers. (In fact Verizon accounted for 12% of sales in 2010.) Wireless and wireline operations also have very different regulatory requirements at both the state and federal level.

Lumos Networks is made up of two divisions as a competitive local-exchange carrier (CLEC) and a rural local-exchange carrier (RLEC) business. Its CLEC offers the most growth potential and accounts for about 60% of the company's sales. Wireless carriers such as Verizon use its network for wholesale carrier transport services but the business counts some 23000 enterprise customers. Lumos Networks has grown its fiber network to 5800 miles through acquisitions beginning in late 2009 with Allegheny Energy's 2200-mile network for $27 million. A year later it bought the FiberNet business of One Communications Corp. for $163 million in cash. The FiberNet acquisition expanded its footprint to Kentucky Maryland Ohio and Pennsylvania and brought 30000 business customers. The CLEC division's revenues grew some 25% in 2010 from the two acquisitions.

Its RLEC division doesn't face any competition in the rural Virginia areas that it operates but it doesn't offer a lot of growth. Lumos Networks had 50000 customers in 2011 but continues to lose a few thousand customers every year as people switch to wireless-only plans or move their landline to digital phone services from a competing cable provider. The RLEC division accounts for about 40% of overall sales.

EXECUTIVES

President and Director, Michael B. Moneymaker, age 55

Chairman, Robert E. Guth

SVP Legal and Regulatory Affairs and Secretary, Mary McDermott, age 58

Chief Financial Officer; Executive Vice President; Treasurer, Harold L. (Hal) Covert, age 66

SVP Wireline Sales and Customer Care, David J. Keller, age 47

SVP Finance and Corporate Controller, Kenneth R. Boward, age 51

VP Operations, Diego B. Anderson, age 45

VP Human Resources, Joseph A. Leigh, age 56

Chief Executive Officer, Timothy G. Biltz

Director, Michael K. Robinson, age 56

Director, Steven G. (Steve) Felsher, age 64

President and Director, Michael B. Moneymaker, age 55

Director, Jerry E. Vaughn, age 69

Director, Julia B. North, age 66

Director, Michael Huber, age 44

Auditors: KPMGLLP

LOCATIONS

HQ: Lumos Networks Corp.
1 Lumos Plaza, Waynesboro VA 22980
Phone: 540-946-2000   **Fax:** -1637
Web: www.gazit-globe.com

COMPETITORS

AT&T
CenturyLink
Comcast
EarthLink
Frontier
Communications

Shenandoah
Telecommunications
Verizon
Windstream

HISTORICAL FINANCIALS

Company Type: Public

Income Statement

FYE: December 31

	REVENUE ($ mil.)	NET INCOME ($ mil.)	NET PROFIT MARGIN	EMPLOYEES
12/12	206.8	16.3	7.9%	602
12/11	207.4	(43.9)	—	524
12/10	145.9	20.8	14.3%	0
12/09	130.6	23.3	17.9%	0
Annual Growth	16.6%	(11.2%)	—	—

2012 Year-End Financials

Debt ratio: 60.8%
Return on equity: 27.9%
Cash ($ mil.): 0
Current ratio: 0.68
Long-term debt ($ mil.): 304

No. of shares (mil.): 21
Dividends
Yield: 5.5%
Payout: 73.6%
Market value ($ mil.): 215

	STOCK PRICE ($) FY Close	P/E High/Low		PER SHARE ($) Earnings	Dividends	Book Value
12/12	10.02	23	10	0.76	0.56	2.98
12/11	15.34	—	—	(2.11)	0.14	2.47
12/10	0.00	—	—	(0.00)	0.00	(0.00)
Annual Growth	—			—	—	—

M.D.C. Holdings, Inc.

Being king of the mountain isn't enough for M.D.C. Holdings (MDC). Operating through its Richmond American Homes subsidiary and several other units the company is one of the largest homebuilders in Colorado and is active in about a dozen other states in the West and mid-Atlantic. MDC annually builds about 3000 single-family detached homes that range in price from $170000 to $450000. The company also constructs a limited number of luxury homes. Subsidiary Home-American Mortgage provides loans to buyers of MDC's homes. MDC also has subsidiaries that offer homeowners and title insurance.

Operations

As with many of its fellow homebuilders the MDC has been hampered by the housing bust and mortgage meltdown which has led to higher unemployment and lower consumer confidence and as a result fewer orders for new homes (and more cancelled orders). In response the company is limiting new construction of unsold homes and lowered prices on some of its existing homes to stimulate sales.

Financial Performance

MDC's revenue and homebuilding volume decreased each year from 2007 to 2009. In 2010 the federal homebuyer tax credit helped to stem the decline but MDC slipped back into the red as the cost of home sales increased. Its losses continued to mount in 2011 as home sales dipped again and

the company recorded charges related to abandoned projects and the extinguishment of debt.

Strategy

To help rein in expenses MDC has also reduced headcount and reorganized some back-office functions like accounting sales and marketing to simplify its processes. The company is not turning its back on growth though. In 2011 it acquired almost all of the assets of homebuilder SDC Homes marking its entry to the Seattle market.

Company Ownership

Chairman Larry Mizel who founded the company in 1972 owns approximately 16% of the company's stock; president and COO David Mandarich owns about 8%. Institutional investors hold more than a third.

EXECUTIVES

Senior Vice President; General Counsel, Michael Touff, age 68, $353,279 total compensation
President Chief Operating Officer, David D. Mandarich, age 65, $830,000 total compensation
Chairman Chief Executive Officer, Larry A. Mizel, age 70, $1,000,000 total compensation
Senior Vice President Treasurer, John J. Heaney
SVP CFO and Principal Accounting Officer, John M. Stephens, age 44
Secretary and Corporate Counsel, Joseph H. Fretz
Senior Vice President, Liesel W. Cooper
VP Internal Audit, Shelley Casagrande
VP Finance and Business Development, Robert N. (Bob) Martin
VP - Finance and Business Development, Bob Martin
Vice President of Information Technology, Kelly Taga
Director, Steven J. Borick, age 59
President COO and Director, David D. Mandarich, age 65
Director, David E. Blackford, age 64
Director, Herbert T. Buchwald, age 82
Director, William B. Kemper, age 75
Director, David Siegel, age 56
Director, Michael A. Berman, age 62
Independent Director, Raymond Baker
Auditors: Ernst&YoungLLP

LOCATIONS

HQ: M.D.C. Holdings Inc.
4350 S. Monaco St. Ste. 500, Denver CO 80237
Phone: 303-773-1100   **Fax:** 720-977-4307
Web: www.richmondamerican.com

2011 Sales

	$ mil.	% of total
Home sales		
Mountain (Colorado & Utah)	317	37
West (Arizona California & Nevada)	267	31
East (Delaware Valley Maryland & Virginia)	182	21
Other	46	6
Other	39	5
Intercompany adjustments	(9.6)	-
Total	**844**	**100**

Selected Markets

Arizona
California
Colorado
Delaware
Florida
Maryland
Nevada
New Jersey
Pennsylvania
Utah
Virginia

PRODUCTS/OPERATIONS

2011 Sales

	$ mil.	% of total
Home sales	805.2	96
Land sales	11.9	1
Other	27	3
Total	**844**	**100**

Selected Subsidiaries

Allegiant Insurance Company Inc. A Risk Retention Group
American Home Insurance Agency Inc.
American Home Title and Escrow Company
HomeAmerican Mortgage Corporation
Richmond American Construction Inc.
Richmond American Homes Corporation
StarAmerican Insurance Ltd.

COMPETITORS

Beazer Homes
D.R. Horton
Hovnanian Enterprises
J.F. Shea
KB Home
Lennar
M/I Homes

Meritage Homes
NVR
PulteGroup
Ryan Building
Standard Pacific
The Ryland Group
Toll Brothers

HISTORICAL FINANCIALS

Company Type: Public

Income Statement

FYE: December 31

	REVENUE ($ mil.)	NET INCOME ($ mil.)	NET PROFIT MARGIN	EMPLOYEES
12/13	1,680.4	314.3	18.7%	1,111
12/12	1,203.0	62.7	5.2%	920
12/11	844.1	(98.3)	—	854
12/10	958.6	(64.7)	—	1,119
12/09	898.3	24.6	2.7%	1,089
Annual Growth	16.9%	88.9%		0.5%

2013 Year-End Financials

Debt ratio: 2.4%
Return on equity: 30.0%
Cash ($ mil.): 199
Current ratio: 1.61
Long-term debt ($ mil.): —

No. of shares (mil.): 48
Dividends
Yield: —
Payout: —
Market value ($ mil.): 1,573

	STOCK PRICE ($) FY Close	P/E High/Low		PER SHARE ($) Earnings	Dividends	Book Value
12/13	32.24	7	4	6.34	0.00	24.87
12/12	36.76	31	14	1.28	2.00	18.09
12/11	17.63	—	—	(2.12)	1.00	18.11
12/10	28.77	—	—	(1.40)	1.00	20.87
12/09	31.04	74	45	0.52	1.00	22.82
Annual Growth	1.0%	—	—	86.9%	—	2.2%

M/A-Com Technology Solutions Holdings Inc.

M/A-COM has many components for all your semiconductor needs. The holding company makes analog semiconductors used in wireless and wireline applications across the radio-frequency (RF) microwave and millimeter wave spectrum. Its portfolio encompasses some 2700 standard and custom integrated circuits modules and subsystems across 38 product lines. M/A-COM's chips are used in such products as automotive navigation systems point-to-point radios radars CATV set-top boxes MRI systems and unmanned aerial vehicles. Cisco Motorola Solutions Ford Motor Nokia and Samsung are among its top customers. More than half of sales come from customers in the US. M/A-COM went public in 2012.

The company plans to use the proceeds from the IPO to pay off preferred stock shareholders including chairman John Ocampo and Summit Partners. The remainder will be used to acquire or invest in complementary technologies companies and products. At the end of 2011 M/A-COM had more than 150 products in development across three target markets: networks (cable television cellular backhaul cellular infrastructure fiber optics); aerospace and defense (military communications and public safety products); and other markets (automotive industrial medical mobile and scientific).

M/A-COM uses a fab-lite manufacturing model which involves using both company-owned fabrication facilities (fabs) and third-party foundries to meet production needs. Fab-lite is used by many chip makers to maintain control over quality and proprietary processes while having access to additional production capacity when needed to meet increased demand. The fab-lite model also reduces the amount of capital investment required to maintain and upgrade semiconductor fabs. M/A-COM produces gallium arsenide (GaAs) and silicon semiconductors at its facility in Massachusetts which also serves to meet the internal domestic facility requirement to be a strategic supplier under aerospace and defense contracts. The company also has design and component manufacturing facilities in California China Ireland and Australia.

Overall sales in 2011 were up 19% over 2010. The higher sales were due in part to a 34% increase in networks revenues as telecommunications operators upgraded broadband and cellular networks to support expanding mobile Internet and data service bandwidth. Growth in its multi-market product lines were up 17% on recovery in the automotive industry and growth in the smartphone market. After two years of profits M/A-COM reported a net loss for 2011 primarily due to changes in the value of its Class B convertible preferred stock. (Without that expense the company would have had a nice profit on the books for the year.)

The company arose out of the former M/A-COM Inc. which was bought by Tyco Electronics (now TE Connectivity) and renamed Tyco Electronics Wireless Systems. TE Connectivity sold M/A-COM's RF components and microwave subsystems assets to Cobham for $425 million in 2008 and its wireless assets to Harris for $675 million in 2009. Cobham then sold M/A-COM Technology Solutions Inc. (M/A-COM Tech) the company's commercial business to a private equity firm GaAs Labs for $90 million in 2009. (M/A-COM Tech traces its roots back to 1950 when it was founded as Microwave Associates.) GaAs Labs was founded by John Ocampo who established M/A-COM Technology Solutions Holdings Inc. and made M/A-Com Tech its primary operating subsidiary.

Ocampo sold another of GaAs Labs' majority-owned companies Mimix Broadband to M/A-COM Tech in 2010. Mimix supplies high-performance gallium arsenide (GaAs) semiconductors from DC to 50 GHz for RF microwave and millimeter-wave applications. The Mimix acquisition more than doubled M/A-COM's revenues for 2010. In April 2011 it bought California-based Optomai Inc. a fabless company that develops high-performance

chips and modules for next-generation 40 Gbps and 100 Gbps fiber optic networks. It also divested its laser diode and ferrite business lines.

Chairman John Ocampo through family trusts and ownership of GaAs Labs controls about 57% of M/A-COM Technology Solutions Holdings.

EXECUTIVES

Chairman, John Ocampo, age 54
President and CEO, John R. Croteau, age 52
CFO, Conrad Gagnon, age 59
COO, Robert Donahue
VP Engineering, Michael Murphy, age 51
VP and General Manager Market-Facing Businesses, Suja Ramnath
VP Operations, Robert Dennehy
VP Sales, Jack Kennedy
Director Global Distribution, James (Jim) Dempsey
Senior Director Asia Pacific Sales, Vincent Pelliccia
Director Aerospace and Defense, Glen Fields
Corporate Controller, Michael Dys
Auditors: Deloitte&ToucheLLP

LOCATIONS

HQ: M/A-COM Technology Solutions Holdings Inc.
100 Chelmsford St., Lowell MA 01851
Phone: 978-656-2500   **Fax:** 212-931-1299
Web: www.worldnow.com

2011 Sales

	$ mil.	% of total
US	166	54
International	144	46
Total	**310**	**100**

PRODUCTS/OPERATIONS

2011 Sales

	$ mil.	% of total
Aerospace & defense	94	31
Networks	94	30
Multi-market	122	39
Total	**310**	**100**

Selected Products

Active splitter
Amplifier
Attenuator
Automotive module
Balun
Bias networks
Capacitor
Component
Coupler
Diode
Down converter IC
Filter
Frequency multiplier
Hybrid voltage controlled oscillator
Integrated receiver IC
Integrated transmitter IC
Logic driver circuit
Mixer
Modulator/demodulator
Multi-function integrated circuit
Multi-function module
Optical limiting amplifier
Optical modulator driver
Phase shifter
Power combiner
Power detector
Power divider
Power hybrid pallet
Power hybrid transistor
Switch
Switch limiter
Synthesizer
Transceiver
Transformer
Transimpedance amplifier

Upconverter IC
Variable gain amplifier
Voltage controlled oscillator

COMPETITORS

Aeroflex	Maxim Integrated
Analog Devices	Products
Analogic	Microsemi
Avago Technologies	NXP Semiconductors
Broadcom	ON Semiconductor
Fairchild	RF Micro Devices
Semiconductor	STMicroelectronics
Freescale	Skyworks
Semiconductor	Texas Instruments
Hittite Microwave	TriQuint
Infineon Technologies	

HISTORICAL FINANCIALS

Company Type: Public

Income Statement

FYE: September 27

	REVENUE ($ mil.)	NET INCOME ($ mil.)	NET PROFIT MARGIN	EMPLOYEES
09/13	318.7	27.3	8.6%	675
09/12	302.2	(1.0)	—	669
09/11*	310.3	(1.0)	—	667
10/10	260.3	6.8	2.6%	0
10/09	102.7	4.1	4.1%	0
Annual Growth	32.7%	60.0%	—	—

*Fiscal year change

2013 Year-End Financials

Debt ratio: —	No. of shares (mil.): 46
Return on equity: 12.5%	Dividends
Cash ($ mil.): 110	Yield: —
Current ratio: 4.85	Payout: —
Long-term debt ($ mil.): —	Market value ($ mil.): 800

	STOCK PRICE ($) FY Close	P/E High/Low		PER SHARE ($) Earnings	Dividends	Book Value
09/13	17.21	29	18	0.58	0.00	5.10
09/12	12.70	—	—	(0.15)	0.00	4.38
Annual Growth	35.5%	—	—	—	—	16.4%

Madden (Steven) Ltd.

Steven Madden elevates chunky heels to new heights. It operates through five business segments: wholesale footwear wholesale accessories retail first cost and licensing. Its wholesale business boasts seven divisions such as Madden Girl Steven Steve Madden Men's and Stevies as well as its Daisy Fuentes Betsey Johnson and Olsenboye accessories business through licenses. Its retail operations include about 120 Steve Madden Steven and Report stores along with several websites. Its First Cost segment designs and sources private-label footwear such as Candie's for mass merchants. Steven Madden shoes are sold in the US and Canada through its own shops and such stores as Nordstrom and Dillard's.

Geographic Reach

New York-based Steven Madden rings up 92% of its sales in the US. The company's shoes and accessories are also sold in Asia Europe the Middle East Mexico Australia South Africa South America and India through special distribution arrangements. More than 120 Steven Madden-owned stores are located across the US with noteworthy penetration in New York California and Florida.

Operations

The company's wholesale operation accounts for 85% of its revenue with footwear contributing 65% of that. Subsidiary Steven Madden Retail owns and operates about 120 stores including about 90 Steve Madden full price stores a dozen Steve Madden outlet stores a pair of Steven stores a single Report shop and Superga store and thee e-commerce sites. The retail business accounted for 15% of sales in 2012. The company's First Cost business earns commissions as a buying agent for footwear products under private labels and licensed brands such as Candies for many large mass merchants shoe chains and other retailers.

Sales and Marketing

Steven Madden looks to department stores specialty stores and independent boutiques for the majority of its revenue. The company's sells its footwear and accessories through 15 department store chains throughout North America. Major accounts include Macy's Nordstrom Bloomingdale's Dillard's and Lord & Taylor. Major specialty store accounts include DSW Famous Footwear and Journeys.

To promote itself as a leading designer of fashion footwear for style-conscious young women and men the company's marketing activities include placements in lifestyle and fashion magazines personal appearances by founder and design chief Steve Madden and in-store promotions. The company's website and social media forums including Facebook and Twitter are other sales and marketing tools.

Financial Performance

Steven Madden's sales jumped 24% in 2012 versus 2011 to $.123 billion after rising more than 50% in the previous annual comparison. Indeed 2012 marked the fourth consecutive year of rapidly rising sales and profits for the firm with growth accelerating in 2011 and 2012. The strong sales performance in 2012 was broadly supported by double-digit growth across all of the company's business segments. Gains by the wholesale business have been the primary sales driver in recent years. Net income increased 23% in 2012 versus 2011 to nearly $120 million driven by rising sales.

Strategy

Steven Madden's recent success is a result of its focus on its wholesale operation. The company is also gaining a foothold in areas beyond shoes and it continues to invest in its accessories business. (The footwear maker's accessories business has eclipsed its men's business.) While small compared to the wholesale business retail is an important avenue for growth at Steve Madden. The company has added more than 30 stores over the past two years and is looking to enter new markets.

Mergers and Acquisitions

In February 2012 the company acquired its licensee Steve Madden Canada (SMC) for about $29 million. Privately-held SMC markets Steven Madden products in Canada on a wholesale basis and well as in Steve Madden-branded retail stores.

Looking to increase its private-label footprint Steven Madden bought Topline Corp. for $55 million in May 2011. Topline which rang up sales of about $189 million in 2010 sells private-label and branded footwear (Report Report Signature R2 by Report) primarily to specialty retailers and department stores. Also in May Steven Madden acquired the Cejon group of design and marketing companies for about $30 million. The purchase included Cejon Inc. Cejon Accessories and New East De-

signs. The companies design scarves wraps winter accessories and other items and expanded Steven Madden's accessories business beyond handbags and belts.

EXECUTIVES

COO, Awadhesh K. Sinha, age 67, $540,000 total compensation
CFO Chief Accounting Officer and Secretary, Arvind Dharia, age 63, $479,573 total compensation
Creative and Design Chief, Steven (Steve) Madden, $525,808 total compensation
Brand Director, Robert (Rob) Schmertz, age 49, $600,000 total compensation
EVP Wholesale, Amelia Newton Varela, age 42, $400,000 total compensation
Chairman and CEO, Edward R. (Ed) Rosenfeld, age 38, $400,000 total compensation
Director, Peter Migliorini, age 64
Director, John L. Madden, age 66
Director, Richard P. (Dick) Randall, age 75
Director, Thomas H. Schwartz, age 65
Director, Ravi Sachdev, age 36

LOCATIONS

HQ: Steven Madden Ltd.
52-16 Barnett Ave., Long Island City NY 11104
Phone: 718-446-1800   **Fax:** 718-446-5599
Web: www.stevemadden.com

2012 Sales

	$ mil.	% of total
Domestic	1,133	92
International	94	8
Total	**1,227**	**100**

PRODUCTS/OPERATIONS

2012 Sales

	$ mil.	% of total
Wholesale		
Footwear	794	65
Accessories	241	20
Retail	191	15
Total	**1,227**	**100**

Selected Segments

Wholesale Footwear
  Betsey Johnson shoes
  Big Buddha Shoes
  Elizabeth and James (licensed)
  l.e.i. (licensed)
  Madden
  Madden Girl
  Olsenboye (licensed)
  Report
  Steve Madden Men' s
  Steve Madden Women' s
  Steven
  Stevies
  Superga (licensed)
Wholesale Accessories
  Betsey Johnson
  Betseyville
  Big Buddha
  Cejon
  Daisy Fuentes (licensed)
  Olsenboye (licensed)
  Steve Madden
  Steven by Steve Madden
Steve Madden Retail
  Steve Madden retail stores
  Steven retail stores
  www.stevemadden.com
First Cost
  Buying agent for footwear products under private
    labels
Licensing
  Betsey Johnson trademark
  Betseyville trademark

Steve Madden trademark
  Steven by Steve Madden trademark
Licensed Products
  Belts
  Hair accessories
  Handbags
  Hosiery
  Jewelry
  Outerwear
  Socks
  Sportswear
  Sunglasses

COMPETITORS

Bakers Footwear	Kenneth Cole
Brown Shoe	NIKE
Diesel SpA	Nine West
Donna Karan	R. Griggs
Guess?	Reebok
Iconix Brand Group	Skechers U.S.A.
Jimlar	

HISTORICAL FINANCIALS

Company Type: Public

Income Statement

FYE: December 31

	REVENUE ($ mil.)	NET INCOME ($ mil.)	NET PROFIT MARGIN	EMPLOYEES
12/12	1,227.0	119.6	9.7%	2,650
12/11	968.5	97.3	10.0%	2,370
12/10	635.4	75.7	11.9%	1,440
12/09	503.5	50.1	10.0%	1,370
12/08	457.0	27.9	6.1%	1,510
Annual Growth	**28.0%**	**43.8%**	**—**	**15.1%**

2012 Year-End Financials

Debt ratio: —
Return on equity: 21.6%
Cash ($ mil.): 168
Current ratio: 3.28
Long-term debt ($ mil.): —

No. of shares (mil.): 69
Dividends
  Yield: —
  Payout: —
Market value ($ mil.): 2,925

	STOCK PRICE ($) FY Close	P/E High/Low	PER SHARE ($) Earnings	Dividends	Book Value
12/12	42.27	24 17	1.81	0.00	9.06
12/11	34.50	37 18	1.50	0.00	7.36
12/10	41.72	48 25	1.19	0.00	5.67
12/09	41.24	52 16	0.81	0.00	4.34
12/08	21.32	63 31	0.45	0.00	3.42
Annual Growth	**18.7%**	**— —**	**41.8%**	**—**	**27.6%**

Magellan Midstream Partners LP

Having circumnavigated the world of midstream energy assets Magellan Midstream Partners is looking to discover even more profits. The energy infrastructure enterprise has ammonia and petroleum products storage transportation and distribution assets. Magellan Midstream Partners' portfolio includes 27 inland terminals and 1100 miles of ammonia pipeline 9600 miles of refined petroleum pipeline and 49 distribution terminals (with a combined usable storage capacity of 37 million barrels) in the US Midwest. The partnership also owns seven marine terminal facilities on the US East and Gulf coasts.

Geographic Reach

The company's petroleum products pipelines provide transportation storage and distribution services for liquefied petroleum gases and refined petroleum products in 14 US states extending from refineries on the Gulf Coast across Texas and through the Midwest to Colorado North Dakota Minnesota Wisconsin and Illinois. The company's major refineries are in Kansas Minnesota Oklahoma Texas and Wisconsin. Magellan Midstream Partners' ammonia pipeline and storage system delivers ammonia from Texas and Oklahoma to the Midwest primarily for use as fertilizer by the agricultural industry.

Sales and Marketing

The company ships petroleum products for a range of customers including oil companies wholesalers retailers railroads regional farm cooperatives and airlines. End markets for Magellan Midstream Partners' refined products deliveries retail gasoline stations truck stops farm cooperatives railroad fueling depots and airports (both military and commercial).In 2012 the company's petroleum pipeline system had 60 transportation customers primarily independent refining companies integrated oil companies and farm cooperatives. Its top 10 shippers in 2012 accounted for 46% of total revenues.

Operations

Magellan Midstream Partners manages a portfolio of ammonia petroleum products storage transportation and distribution assets. It owns the longest refined petroleum products pipeline system in the US with access to more than 40% of the country' refining capacity and can store over 80 million barrels of petroleum products (including gasoline diesel fuel and crude oil).

Financial Performance

Magellan Midstream Partners' revenues grew by 1% in 2012 primarily due to a 9% rise in transportation and terminals revenues. This increase was due to higher petroleum pipeline system sales and a rise in petroleum terminals revenues as a result of leasing tanks that came on line in 2011 (including new crude oil storage tanks in Cushing Oklahoma) and higher rates at the company's marine terminals. Other factors included stronger ammonia pipeline system sales thanks to a rate increase and higher product sales volumes. Also affiliate management fee revenues increased by 153% in 2012.Net income grew by 5% in 2012 as higher net sales outpaced an increase in operating expenses.With the exception of a revenue slump in 2009 (the result of the global recession dampening both demand and prices) the company saw an upward trend in revenues between 2008 to 2012.

Strategy

Magellan Midstream Partners has grown through acquisitions and has spent more than $2 billion in buying complementary assets since going public in 2001. It focuses on growth through organic growth projects joint ventures and acquisitions that expand or upgrade its existing facilities.

Expanding its existing refined products distribution system and moving into new markets in 2013 the company bought 800 miles of refined petroleum products pipeline in the Rockies and New Mexico from Plains All American Pipeline for $190 million.In 2012 it formed joint venture BridgeTex Pipeline Company LLC with an affiliate of Occidental Petroleum. BridgeTex was formed to build and operate the BridgeTex pipeline a 400-mile pipeline that will move 300000 barrels per day of Permian Basin crude oil from Colorado City Texas to an East Houston Texas terminal. The project also in-

cludes a 50-mile pipeline between East Houston and Texas City and 2.6 million barrels of crude oil storage. Magellan Midstream Partners expects to spend a $600 million in connection with its 50% stake in BridgeTex.Further growing its infrastructure assets in 2011 the company bough the remaining 50% stake it did not own in a Southlake Texas terminal a 38-mile petroleum products pipeline segment connected to its petroleum pipeline system at Reagan Texas petroleum products storage tanks in Riverside Missouri and a private investment group's interest in Magellan Crude Oil LLC (for $40.5 million). That year Magellan Midstream Partners also teamed up with Copano Energy forming a joint venture to deliver Eagle Ford Shale condensate to Corpus Christi Texas. The Double Eagle Pipeline JV will build 140 miles of new pipeline to connect an existing 50-mile pipeline segment owned by Copano enabling delivery of condensate to Magellan's terminal in Corpus Christi.

Boosting its oil storage assets in 2011 the company bought the remaining stake it did not own in a joint venture to build a 4.25 million barrels oil storage terminal in Cushing. The project has a price tag of about $110 million including the price of the acquisition. To better serve Gulf Coast refineries that year the company announced plans to reverse the flow and purpose of its Longhorn Houston-El Paso pipeline (formerly a petroleum products carrier) to deliver oil from West Texas fields.

EXECUTIVES

Chairman President and CEO, Michael N. (Mike) Mears, age 50, $351,831 total compensation
SVP and CFO, John D. Chandler, age 44, $319,846 total compensation
SVP Business Development, Brett C. Riley, age 44
Investor Analyst and Financial Media Contact, Paula Farrell
SVP Human Resources and Administration, Lisa J. Korner, age 52
SVP General Counsel Compliance and Ethics Officer and Assistant Secretary, Douglas J. May, age 43
SVP Operations and Technical Services, Larry J. Davied
Director, Walter R. Arnheim, age 68
Director, Robert G. (Bob) Croyle, age 70
Director, James C. Kempner, age 74
Director, Barry R. Pearl, age 63
Director, Patrick C. Eilers, age 47
Director, James R. Montague, age 66
Auditors: Ernst&YoungLLP

LOCATIONS

HQ: Magellan Midstream Partners L.P.
1 Williams Center, Tulsa OK 74172
Phone: 918-574-7000   **Fax:** 918-573-6714
Web: www.magellanlp.com

PRODUCTS/OPERATIONS

2012 Sales

	$ mil.	% of total
Transportation & terminals	970	55
Products	799	45
Affiliate management fees	2	-
Total	**1,772**	**100**

COMPETITORS

Dynegy	Sunoco Logistics
El Paso Corporation	TransMontaigne

Enterprise Products	Transammonia
Gateway Energy	
Kinder Morgan Energy Partners	

HISTORICAL FINANCIALS
Company Type: Public

Income Statement
FYE: December 31

	REVENUE ($ mil.)	NET INCOME ($ mil.)	NET PROFIT MARGIN	EMPLOYEES
12/12	1,772.0	435.6	24.6%	1,339
12/11	1,748.6	413.5	23.7%	1,297
12/10	1,557.4	311.5	20.0%	1,271
12/09	1,014.1	226.4	22.3%	1,217
12/08	1,212.7	346.6	28.6%	1,204
Annual Growth	**9.9%**	**5.9%**	**—**	**2.7%**

2012 Year-End Financials

Debt ratio: 54.1%	No. of shares (mil.): 226
Return on equity: —	Dividends
Cash ($ mil.): 328	Yield: 4.1%
Current ratio: 1.78	Payout: 206.2%
Long-term debt ($ mil.): 2,393	Market value ($ mil.): 9,770

	STOCK PRICE ($) FY Close	P/E High/Low	PER SHARE ($) Earnings	Dividends	Book Value
12/12	43.19	47 21	1.92	1.78	6.70
12/11	68.88	38 29	1.83	1.56	6.49
12/10	56.50	40 29	1.43	1.45	6.47
12/09	43.33	39 23	1.11	1.42	5.61
12/08	30.21	43 21	1.03	1.36	4.53
Annual Growth	**9.3%**	**— —**	**16.7%**	**7.0%**	**10.3%**

Manitex International Inc

Manitex International makes products that are uplifting —literally. One of the largest manufacturers of lifting equipment in North America Manitex makes and sells boom trucks and sign cranes used in industrial jobs as well as energy exploration construction and commercial building. Through Liftking the company makes rough terrain forklifts heavy handling transports and military specialty vehicles. The Manitex family includes Badger Equipment (cranes and material handling) and Load King (trailers). A Crane & Machinery unit distributes Manitex Terex and Fuchs equipment.

Geographic Reach

Headquartered at Bridgeview Illinois the company has six main operating plants in North America and Italy. It has operations throughout the Americas Autralia and the EMEA regions including Russia Korea Switzerland and other countries. The US accounts for nearly 55% of the company's total revenue; Canada contributes nearly 25%.

Operations

The company divides its operations across two segments: lifting equipment (92% of sales) and equipment distribution (8%). Sales for boom trucks contributed 44% of its total revenue in 2012 while part sales and container handling equipment represented 16% and 12% respectively.

Sales and Marketing

Manitex sells its products through a network of about 50 full service dealers in Canada Mexico South America the US and the Middle East. It uses direct sales to sell its Sign Cranes. The company's exported military products are sold through Canadian Commercial Corporation to various foreign countries (outside of Canada). Major customers include Cropac Equipment (about 11% of its total revenue) the US Department of Defense and other government agencies (both domestic and foreign).

Financial Performance

Manitex has enjoyed unprecedented growth over the last few years. Revenues surged 44% from $142 million in 2011 to $205 million in 2012. Profits more than doubled from $2.8 million to $8.1 million. Both these totals represented historic milestones for the company.

The growth for 2012 was attributed to a 45% spike in lifting equipment sales and a 43% rise in equipment distribution sales. The company saw explosive growth in both Canada (80%) and the US (52%). Sales in both Germany and Venezuela skyrocketed by more than 100% during 2012.

The surge in profits for 2012 was attributed to the higher revenue and the favorable impact of non-recurring expenses related to legal settlements of two product liability cases.

Mergers and Acquisitions

Manitex grows through the use of acquisitions. In 2013 it bought Indiana-based Sabre Manufacturing a manufacturer of specialized tanks for liquid storage and containment services for a purchase price of $14 million. The acquisition expanded its specialized product portfolio in its target markets.

EXECUTIVES

Chief Financial Officer, David H. Gransee, age 61, $167,417 total compensation

President COO, Andrew M. Rooke, age 55, $230,198 total compensation

Chairman of our Board of Directors and our Chief Executive Officer, David J. Langevin, age 62, $263,667 total compensation

Regional Vice President, Peter L. Seltzberg

President - Manufacturing Operations, Lubomir Litchev

Director, Stephen J. Tober, age 48

Director, Marvin B. Rosenberg, age 72

Director, Robert S. Gigliotti, age 64

Director, Ronald M. Clark, age 64

Auditors: UHYLLP

LOCATIONS

HQ: Manitex International Inc.
9725 Industrial Dr., Bridgeview IL 60455
Phone: 708-430-7500   **Fax:** 708-430-1227
Web: www.manitexinternational.com

2012 Sales

	$ mil.	% of total
US	114	56
Canada	55	27
Italy	11	6
Other Countries	23	11
Total	**205**	**100**

PRODUCTS/OPERATIONS

2012 Sales

	$ mil.	% of total
Lifting equipment	188	92
Equipment distribution	16	8
Total	**205**	**100**

2012 Sales

	% of total
Boom	44
Part sales	16
Container handling equipment	12
Specialized trainers	8
Military forklifts	6
Rough terrain forklifts	6
Rough terrain & truck cranes	4
Used construction equipment	4
Total	**100**

Selected Products

Boom trucks
Container handling equipment (ports and inter-modal customers)
Empty container handlers
Equipment distribution segment (infrastructure development and commercial construction)
Forklifts
Fuchs material handlers
Hydroscopic Truck Mounted Excavators
Lattice Boom Cranes
Lift Trucks
Lifting equipment segment
Manitex boom trucks and sky cranes
Military forklifts (national militaries)
Mission oriented vehicles and specialized carriers (utility ship building steel mill industries)
Reach stackers
Repair and replacement parts
Repair parts
Rough terrain cranes
Rough terrain forklifts
Sign cranes
Specialized tanks
Straddle carriers
Terex rough terrain and truck cranes
Trailers (low-bed heavy-haul bottom-dump and platform trailers and hauling systems)
Used Equipment
Wheeled Excavators

COMPETITORS

Altec Industries	Manitowoc Crane Group
CNH Global	Terex
Linamar Corp.	Trail King Industries
MANITOU BF	

HISTORICAL FINANCIALS

Company Type: Public

Income Statement

FYE: December 31

	REVENUE ($ mil.)	NET INCOME ($ mil.)	NET PROFIT MARGIN	EMPLOYEES
12/12	205.2	8.0	3.9%	386
12/11	142.2	2.7	2.0%	344
12/10	95.8	2.1	2.2%	229
12/09	55.8	3.6	6.5%	172
12/08	106.3	2.2	2.1%	190
Annual Growth	**17.9%**	**38.5%**	**—**	**19.4%**

2012 Year-End Financials

Debt ratio: 32.4%
Return on equity: 15.1%
Cash ($ mil.): 1
Current ratio: 2.42
Long-term debt ($ mil.): 41
No. of shares (mil.): 12
Dividends
  Yield: —
  Payout: —
Market value ($ mil.): 88

	STOCK PRICE ($) FY Close	P/E High/Low		PER SHARE ($) Earnings	Dividends	Book Value
12/12	7.14	15	6	0.68	0.00	4.85
12/11	4.24	27	14	0.24	0.00	4.01
12/10	3.85	20	9	0.19	0.00	3.80
12/09	1.92	9	1	0.33	0.00	3.62
12/08	1.02	28	4	0.21	0.00	3.31
Annual Growth	**62.7%**	—	—	**34.1%**	—	**10.1%**

MarketAxess Holdings Inc.

A little creative spelling never got in the way of a good bond trade. MarketAxess offers an electronic multi-dealer platform for institutional traders buying and selling US corporate high-yield and emerging market bonds as well as Eurobonds. Participating broker-dealers include some of the world's largest such as BNP Paribas Citigroup Deutsche Bank Goldman Sachs and Merrill Lynch. In all MarketAxess serves more than 800 investment firms mutual funds insurance companies pension funds and other institutional investors. The company also provides real-time corporate bond price information through its Corporate BondTicker service.

Geographic Reach

The company is focused on countries it classifies as emerging markets such as Argentina Brazil Colombia Mexico Peru the Philippines Russia Turkey and Venezuela.

In late 2010 MarketAxess began offering services to institutions based in the Asia/Pacific region. The company is targeting sovereign wealth funds pension funds asset managers and central banks in the region.

Operations

The majority of the company's revenues come from monthly distribution fees and commissions for transactions executed on its platform between institutional investor and broker-dealer clients.

Financial Performance

MarketAxess has enjoyed an upward trend in revenue during recent fiscal years. The company's revenue increased to about $198.2 million in fiscal 2012 up from the roughly $181.1 million the company brought in during fiscal 2011 and the $146.2 million it claimed in revenue for fiscal 2010. The spikes came from increases in commission revenue and increased revenue from technology products and services.

Strategy

MarketAxess is focusing on technology investments to expand its connectivity offerings for electronic transactions. In 2012 the company expanded its suite of electronic trading protocols to help investors and broker-dealers more effectively source liquidity in the credit markets.

Mergers and Acquisitions

In 2012 MarketAxess expanded its capacity when it acquired Xtrakter Limited a leading provider of regulatory transaction reporting financial market data and trade matching services to the European securities markets.

EXECUTIVES

Chairman and CEO, Richard M. (Rick) McVey, age 54, $400,000 total compensation

CFO, Antonio L. (Tony) DeLise, age 51

Head Human Resources, Cordelia Boise, age 46

General Counsel and Corporate Secretary, Charles R. Hood, age 62

CIO, Nicholas Themelis, age 50, $200,000 total compensation

Chief Credit and Risk Officer, James N.B. (Jim) Rucker

Head of Marketing and Communications, Florencia Panizza

Head of US Sales, Kevin McPherson

Head Europe and Asia, Robert H. Urtheil

Director, Carlos M. Hernandez, age 52
Director, David G. Gomach, age 55
Director, Roger Burkhardt, age 50
President and Director, T. Kelley Millet, age 52
Director, Ronald M. (Ron) Hersch, age 66
Director, Jerome S. Markowitz, age 72
Director, Nicolas S. Rohatyn, age 51
Director, John Steinhardt, age 60
Director, Stephen P. (Steve) Casper, age 64
Director, Robert W. Trudeau, age 43
Director, Sharon Brown-Hruska
Independent Director, James Sullivan
Independent Director, Sharon Hruska
Independent Director, Steven Begleiter
Auditors: PricewaterhouseCoopersLLP

LOCATIONS

HQ: MarketAxess Holdings Inc.
299 Park Ave. 10th Fl., New York NY 10171
Phone: 212-813-6000   Fax: 212-813-6390
Web: www.marketaxess.com

PRODUCTS/OPERATIONS

Selected Mergers and Acquisitions
FY2012
Xtrakter Limited (undisclosed price; London UK;
provider of regulatory transaction reporting)

COMPETITORS

BGC Partners	Interactive Brokers
BondsOnline	
Cantor Fitzgerald	TRADEBOOK
GFI Group	Tradeweb
ICAP	Weeden

HISTORICAL FINANCIALS

Company Type: Public

Income Statement
FYE: December 31

	REVENUE ($ mil.)	NET INCOME ($ mil.)	NET PROFIT MARGIN	EMPLOYEES
12/12	198.2	60.0	30.3%	240
12/11	181.1	47.7	26.3%	232
12/10	146.2	31.4	21.5%	229
12/09	114.4	16.1	14.1%	212
12/08	93.0	7.9	8.5%	185
Annual Growth	20.8%	66.1%	—	6.7%

2012 Year-End Financials

Debt ratio: —	No. of shares (mil.): 37
Return on equity: 21.5%	Dividends
Cash ($ mil.): 128	Yield: 4.9%
Current ratio: 4.31	Payout: 109.4%
Long-term debt ($ mil.): —	Market value ($ mil.): 1,320

	STOCK PRICE ($) FY Close	P/E High/Low	PER SHARE ($) Earnings	Dividends	Book Value
12/12	35.30	23 16	1.59	1.74	6.49
12/11	30.11	24 15	1.20	0.36	8.06
12/10	20.81	24 14	0.80	0.28	7.85
12/09	13.90	31 14	0.42	0.07	7.18
12/08	8.16	56 19	0.22	0.00	6.67
Annual Growth	44.2%	— —	64.0%	—	(0.7%)

Masimo Corp.

As important as the blood running through your veins is the oxygen it carries. Masimo knows that and makes tools that monitor arterial blood-oxygen saturation levels and pulse rates in patients. The company's product range which is based on Signal Extraction Technology (SET) offers pulse oximeters in both handheld and stand-alone (bedside) form. Product benefits include the provision of real-time information and elimination of signal interference such as patient movements. In addition to general product sales Masimo licenses SET-based products to dozens of medical equipment manufacturers including CareFusion Covidien Medtronic and Welch Allyn.

Geographic Reach

While the Americas account for about three-fourths of its product sales Masimo is working to grow its operations in Africa Asia Australia Europe and the Middle East. It has operations in about 25 countries.

Sales and Marketing

The company markets its products globally through direct sales representatives and distributors. Customers include hospitals alternative care entities OEMs and wholesalers. Two distributors Owens & Minor and Cardinal Health each account for more than 10% of annual sales.

Advertising costs for fiscal 2012 was about $9.5 million compared to $5.6 million in 2011. Masimo is expanding marketing programs to build consumer brand awareness through means including print and digital advertising trade show participation and direct mail campaigns. It also distributes publications and sponsors seminars to educate medical professionals about its products.

In 2012 the company entered partnerships with several group purchasing organizations (GPOs) to facilitate increased direct sales of pulse oximetry products to hospitals.

Financial Performance

Masimo increased revenues in 2012 by 12% to $493 million due to higher product sales especially of consumable items (related to its rising number of installed equipment locations) and increased sales of new Rainbow SET products. It also experienced growth from acquisitions increased marketing efforts and through partnerships with OEMs and GPOs. Increased product sales were offset by lower royalties (caused by a decrease in the royalty rate of its partnership with Covidien).

Net income decreased 2% to $62 million in 2012 due to higher costs for goods sold and increased operating expenses (related to increased staffing levels in the administrative and research divisions) and non-operating expenses (from currency exchange recognitions).

Masimo has reported steadily rising revenues over the last five years from organic growth measures. However net income has declined over the past three years due to the increased costs of a growing business.

Strategy

Expansion is key to Masimo's strategy for growth. Its research and development efforts (with expenses of around $40 to $50 million per year) focus on novel products as well as improvements to existing products. Product enhancements have included a new monitoring capability that can detect methemoglobin (a form of hemoglobin that can cause a lack of oxygen in the blood) and the addition of total hemoglobin (oxygen in red blood cells) measurement. It is expanding the applica-

tions of its Rainbow SET products which measure multiple blood components at once; it is also adding products that reduce the invasiveness of testing and that provide remote monitoring and alarm capabilities.

To branch out beyond its traditionally targeted emergency and critical care setting markets Masimo is promoting existing products (and adding new products) to meet the general treatment needs of hospitals and non-hospital environments. For example its company is promoting its SET technology as ideal for use by home care agencies post-acute care hospitals and sleep diagnostic centers. It is also introducing new handheld products that allow for fast and simple measurement of perimeters in a variety of care settings. The company expects moves such as these to greatly expand its presence in non-critical care markets.

Masimo also expands by entering new OEM licensing agreements (such as a long-term agreement for the use of its Rainbow SET products in GE Healthcare's patient monitors in 2012); by widening agreements with wholesale distributors; and by making occasional acquisitions.

Mergers and Acquisitions

To bring manufacturing of some key components in-house Masimo acquired Spire Semiconductor for $7 million in early 2012. Masimo had been one of Spire's largest customers and having the LED manufacturer under its wing promises to speed development of new products.

Also in 2012 Masimo acquired Phasein AB which manufactures and sells ultra-compact capnography and gas analyzers for some $30 million. The added products complement the company's existing portfolio of OEM solutions.

Ownership

Chairman and CEO Joe Kiani who founded Masimo in 1989 holds roughly 10% of the company's stock. The company went public in 2007 and used proceeds from the IPO towards capital and equipment expenses and product development efforts.

EXECUTIVES

Chief Executive Officer Chairman of the Board, Joe E. Kiani, age 48, $688,647 total compensation
EVP Regulatory Affairs and CIO, Yongsam Lee, age 48, $307,955 total compensation
President Worldwide OEM Business and Corporate Development, Rick Fishel, age 54, $308,607 total compensation
COO, Anthony (Tony) Allan, age 48
Executive Vice President Marketing & Clinical Development, Paul R. Jansen, age 42
Executive Vice President Engineering, Anand Sampath, age 46
Executive Vice President Chief Medical Officer, Michael O'Reilly, age 60, $267,292 total compensation
President Worldwide Sales and Marketing and Clinical Research, Jon Coleman, age 49, $270,964 total compensation
EVP Acute Care Sales, Stephen Paul, age 42
Manager Public Relations, Dana Banks
Executive Vice President Chief Medical Officer, Michael OReilly
Executive Vice President Chief Financial Officer, Mark Raad
Investor Relations Officer, Sheree Aronson
Executive Vice President General Counsel, Tom McClenahan
Director, Sanford (Sandy) Fitch, age 72
President and CEO, Joe E. Kiani, age 47
Director, Jack W. Lasersohn, age 59
Director, Robert Coleman, age 67

Director, Edward L. Cahill, age 59
Director, Steven Barker, age 68
Auditors: GrantThorntonLLP

LOCATIONS

HQ: Masimo Corporation
40 Parker, Irvine CA 92618
Phone: 949-297-7000   **Fax:** 949-297-7499
Web: www.masimo.com

2012 Product Sales

	% of total
The	73
Europe Middle East & Africa	15
Asia &	12
Total	**100**

PRODUCTS/OPERATIONS

2012 Sales

Product	464	94
Royalty	28	6

Selected Products

Capnography and Multigas Monitoring
Patient SafetyNet Remote Monitoring
Rainbow Acoustic Monitoring
Rainbow Pulse CO-Oximetry
SedLine Brain Function Monitoring
Signal Extraction Pulse Oximetry

Selected OEM Customers

3F Medical Co. Ltd (China)
Atom Medical Corporation
Biolight Meditech Co. Ltd. (China)
Bitmos GmbH (Germany)
BMEYE (The Netherlands)
CareFusion
CAS Medical Systems Inc.
Comen Medical Instruments Co. Ltd. (China)
Corpuls
Digicare
Drager Medical AG & Co. KG (Germany)
Excel-Tech Ltd (XLTEK a Canadian division of Natus
   Medical Incorporated)
Fritz Stephan GmbH (Germany)
Fukuda Denshi Co. LTD. (Japan)
GE Healthcare
GETEMED Medizin- und Informationstechnik AG
   (Germany)
Imagenes y Medicina S.A. de C.V. (Mexico)
Impact Instrumentation Inc.
International Biomedical
IRadimed Corporation
Ivy Biomedical Systems Inc.
Medtronic Inc.
Mennen Medical Corp. (Israel)
Mindray
Newtech Inc. (China)
Nihon Kohden
Norwood Scientific
Oridion Capnography Inc.
Osypka Medical Inc.
Philips Healthcare/Respironics Inc. (The Netherlands
   and US)
Phoenix Medical Systems Pvt. Ltd. (India)
Physio-Control
Pooyandegan Rah Saadat Co. Ltd. (Iran)
Radiometer Medical ApS (Denmark)
RDECON
Schiller AG (Switzerland)
ShenZhen HeXin ZONDAN Medical Equipment CO. LTD
   (China)
Spacelabs Healthcare
Toitu Co. Ltd. (Japan)
Welch Allyn Inc.
ZOLL Medical Corporation

Selected Acquisitions

2012
Phasein AB ($30 million Sweden ultra-compact
   capnography and gas analyzer manufacturing)
Spire Semiconductor ($7 million New Hampshire LED
   manufacturing)

2010
SEDLine (brain function monitoring equipment for
   hospital patients under anesthesia and sedation)

COMPETITORS

Bio-logic	Mindray
CAS Medical	Philips Healthcare
Covidien	Siemens Healthcare
Criticare	Thoratec Corp
GE Healthcare	
Instrumentation	
Laboratory Company	

HISTORICAL FINANCIALS

Company Type: Public

Income Statement

FYE: December 29

	REVENUE ($ mil.)	NET INCOME ($ mil.)	NET PROFIT MARGIN	EMPLOYEES
12/12	493.2	62.2	12.6%	2,866
12/11*	438.9	63.7	14.5%	2,548
01/11	405.4	73.5	18.1%	2,397
01/10	349.1	53.2	15.2%	2,199
01/09	307.0	31.9	10.4%	1,739
Annual Growth	**12.6%**	**18.2%**	**—**	**13.3%**

*Fiscal year change

2012 Year-End Financials

Debt ratio: 0.0%
Return on equity: 22.7%
Cash ($ mil.): 71
Current ratio: 2.45
Long-term debt ($ mil.): 0

No. of shares (mil.): 57
Dividends
Yield: 0.0%
Payout: 93.4%
Market value ($ mil.): 1,179

	STOCK PRICE ($) FY Close	P/E High/Low		PER SHARE ($) Earnings	Dividends	Book Value
12/12	20.58	23	17	1.07	1.00	4.77
12/11*	18.69	33	17	1.05	0.00	4.75
01/11	29.07	26	17	1.21	2.75	3.83
01/10	30.42	34	24	0.88	0.00	5.00
01/09	29.70	74	39	0.53	0.00	3.83
Annual Growth	**(8.8%)**	**—**	**—**	**19.2%**	**—**	**5.6%**

*Fiscal year change

Materion Corp

Materion (formerly Brush Engineered Materials) provides advanced engineered materials and services worldwide. It sells products to a number of markets including consumer electronics aerospace and defense industrial components telecommunications infrastructure automotive electronics and medical and appliance. It manufactures a variety of precious and specialty metal products including frame lid assemblies and clad and plated metal systems. Other products include precision optics and thin film coatings; inorganic chemicals and powders; specialty coatings; beryllium (which it mines in Utah) beryllium composites and beryllium alloys.

Geographic Reach

Materion serves customers in 50 countries. It has manufacturing plants in the US (Arizona California Connecticut Massachusetts New York Ohio Pennsylvania Rhode Island Utah and Wisconsin) and in China Ireland the Philippines Singapore Taiwan and the UK.

In 2012 the US accounted for 69% of Materion's sales.

Operations

The company operates in four segments: Advanced Material Technologies; Beryllium and Composites; Performance Alloys; and Technical Materials.

Each of Materion's divisions serves specialized markets but its Advanced Materials Technologies group is the company's primary breadwinner accounting for two-thirds of annual sales. The Advanced Materials Technologies group manufactures precious non-precious and specialty metal products such as clad and precious metal preforms high temperature brazing materials ultrafine wire optics performance coatings and electronic packages.

Other groups have a different mission. For example the Beryllium and Composites group is focused on the defense industry. The company extracts beryllium from its bertrandite mine in Utah where it also produces beryllium hydroxide at its milling facilities. In addition to using the beryllium hydroxide as a raw material for its strip and bulk products it sells the material to NGK INSULATORS.

Performance Alloys makes high precision strip and bulk products from copper and nickel-based alloys while Technical Materials makes clad inlay and overlay metals precious and base metal electroplated systems and other related items.

Sales and Marketing

Materion has service and distribution centers in Germany Japan Singapore the UK and the US. The company sells its products both directly and through independent sales representatives throughout the world.

It serves customers in range of industries including aerospace automotive electronics consumer electronics defense energy industrial components medical and telecommunications infrastructure. In 2012 Materion's major customer NGK INSULATORS which is accounted for 4% of the Performance Alloys segment's total sales.

Financial Performance

Materion's revenues dropped by 17% in 2012 due to lower metal commodity prices an increase in the use of customer-supplied metal and the loss of a non-strategic product line. Advanced Material Technologies' revenues slumped by 19% due to lower revenues. Performance Alloys' sales were down by 13% as the result of weaker demand for strip products from consumer electronics and appliance customers. Net income decreased by 38% in 2012 primarily due lower revenues and higher selling general and administrative expenses and higher research and development expenses stemming from its acquisition of Aerospace Metal Composites and EIS Optics.

Strategy

Materion's key strategy for growth has been to pursue niche acquisitions primarily for its advanced material business.

Mergers and Acquisitions

In 2012 the company acquired UK-based Aerospace Metal Composites (AMC). AMC makes a product line that fits in with Materion's beryllium metal-based product lines (including AlBeMet) and is derived from powder metals. AMC also produces reinforced metal matrix composites made mainly from aluminum and it sells to the aerospace and defense automotive and precision machinery markets.

In keeping with Materion's overall strategy for growth subsidiary Materion Advanced Materials Technologies and Services acquired EIS Optics in 2011 to bolster its precision thin film optical filters and coatings operations. The acquisition also widens Materion's footprint in Asia and gives it access to the fast-growing Chinese market where EIS Optics operates a manufacturing site in Shanghai. The buy complements a number of recent acquisitions Materion has made to bolster its precision thin film optical filters and coatings operations.

Ownership

Heartland Advisors Inc. owns 9.3% of Materion.

Company Background

The company was founded in 1931. The company consolidated all divisions under the Materion name in 2011.

EXECUTIVES

Vice President Treasurer Secretary, Michael C. Hasychak

Senior Vice President Chief Financial Officer, John D. Grampa, age 65, $339,900 total compensation

Vice President Controller, James P. Marrotte

Senior Vice President Administration, Daniel A. Skoch, age 63, $324,450 total compensation

Assistant Treasurer and Assistant Secretary, Gary W. Schiavoni

VP Corporate Communications, Patrick S. Carpenter

Chairman of the Board President Chief Executive Officer, Richard J. (Dick) Hipple, age 61, $674,650 total compensation

President Beryllium Products, Michael D. Anderson, age 60

President Performance Alloys, W. Glenn Maxwell, age 53

Vice President General Counsel, Gregory R. Chemnitz

President Brush International; Sales Marketing and Technical Services Alloy Products, Richard L. Trate

Director, William B. Lawrence, age 69

Director, Joseph P. Keithley, age 65

Director, William P. Madar, age 72

Director, Craig S. Shular, age 60

Director, Vinod M. Khilnani, age 60

Director, William R. (Bill) Robertson, age 72

Director, John Sherwin Jr., age 75

Director, Albert C. Bersticker, age 77

Director, N. Mohan Reddy, age 60

Director, William G. (Jerry) Pryor, age 72

Independent Director, Darlene Solomon

Independent Director, Geoffrey Wild

Auditors: Ernst&YoungLLP

LOCATIONS

HQ: Materion Corporation
6070 Parkland Blvd., Mayfield Heights OH 44124
Phone: 216-486-4200   **Fax:** 216-383-4091
Web: www.materion.com

2012 Sales

US	882	69
Total	**1,273**	**100**

Archive This Chart
Archive This Chart

PRODUCTS/OPERATIONS

2012 Sales

Advanced Material Technologies	847	66
Technical Materials	72	6
Other	0	

Selected Mergers and Acquisitions

2012
Aerospace Metal Composites (UK; beryllium metal-based products and reinforced metal matrix composites)

2011
EIS Optics (precision thin film optical filters and coatings)

COMPETITORS

Aeroflex	Kyocera
American Technical Ceramics	NGK INSULATORS
Anaren	Olin
BASF Catalysts	Praxair
Carpenter Technology	Sumitomo Metal Industries
Heraeus Holding	Vesuvius
Honeywell International	

HISTORICAL FINANCIALS

Company Type: Public

Income Statement

FYE: December 31

	REVENUE ($ mil.)	NET INCOME ($ mil.)	NET PROFIT MARGIN	EMPLOYEES
12/12	1,273.0	24.6	1.9%	2,833
12/11	1,526.7	39.9	2.6%	3,015
12/10	1,302.3	46.4	3.6%	2,484
12/09	715.1	(12.3)	—	2,196
12/08	909.7	18.3	2.0%	2,235
Annual Growth	**8.8%**	**7.7%**	**—**	**6.1%**

2012 Year-End Financials

Debt ratio: 11.5%
Return on equity: 5.9%
Cash ($ mil.): 16
Current ratio: 2.69
Long-term debt ($ mil.): 44
No. of shares (mil.): 20
Dividends
  Yield: 0.8%
  Payout: 18.9%
Market value ($ mil.): 527

	STOCK PRICE ($) FY Close	P/E High/Low		PER SHARE ($) Earnings	Dividends	Book Value
12/12	25.78	27	16	1.19	0.23	20.30
12/11	24.28	23	10	1.93	0.00	19.99
12/10	38.64	17	7	2.25	0.00	18.92
12/09	18.54	—	—	(0.61)	0.00	16.80
12/08	12.72	42	9	0.89	0.00	17.14
Annual Growth	**19.3%**	**—**	**—**	**7.5%**	**—**	**4.3%**

Matrix Service Co.

Matrix Service Company makes sure that oil and water don't mix. The company provides a variety of construction repair and maintenance services mainly to the petroleum and power industries. Its Storage Solutions business which accounts for about 45% of sales specializes in above-ground storage tanks to hold oil gas and specialty materials. It also designs and builds plants refineries and other installations. Through its Oil Gas & Chemical segment Matrix provides preventive routine and emergency repair services focusing on turnarounds outages and shutdowns when time is of the essence. Founded in 1984 the firm has around a dozen locations in the US and Canada.

Geographic Reach

Tulsa Oklahoma-based Matrix Service Company generates about 90% of its revenue in the US. The firm is licensed to operates in all 50 US states and four Canadian provinces.

Operations

Matrix's other operations include its Electrical Infrastructure segment which builds and repairs substations and power generation facilities while its Industrial segment provides services for the mining and minerals sector as well as other industrial and manufacturing markets.

Sales and Marketing

The specialty contractor services about 500 customers including petroleum companies refiners pipeline operators and oil and gas marketing firms. Enbridge is its single largest client accounting for about 11% of sales of fiscal 2013 (ended June) sales.

Financial Performance

After a whopping 70% decline in revenue between fiscal 2007 and 2010 Matrix's sales are on the road to recovery. In fiscal 2013 (ended June) sales increased 21% versus the prior year to $892.6 million. Net income increased by 40% over the same period to $24 million. (2013 marked the third consecutive year of rising sales and profits for the firm.) The double-digit increase in annual sales was broadly supported across all four of the firm's operating segments with Industrial (the firm's smallest unit) up 172% while Oil Gas & Chemical posted a 33% year over year gain followed by Electrical Infrastructure up 27%. The Electrical Infrastructure business got a boost from increased demand for high voltage work primarily related to storm restoration services and higher transmission and distribution work in the Northeastern US. Still the $892 million in fiscal 2013 revenue was below 2007's nearly $940 million. Cash flow from operations was up sharply.

Strategy

The company hopes that environmental regulations will lead customers to seek out Matrix's services to help them meet compliance standards. One of the largest above-ground storage tank builders in North America Matrix also expects that business to grow over the long term as infrastructure ages and demand for storage capacity increases.

In an effort to diversify Matrix has been focused on expanding its customer base and geographic presence. The company is making inroads in the alternative energy sector by adding products and services related to wind farms geothermal projects and solar panel installation.

Mergers and Acquisitions

In December 2013 Matrix acquired Kvaerner North American Construction a provider of capital construction and maintenance services to power generation integrated iron and steel and industrial process facilities in North America for about $80.3 million in cash. Post sale the business was renamed Matrix North American Construction. In January 2013 the company acquired Pelichem Industrial Cleaning Services LLC a privately-owned industrial cleaning business based in Louisiana. The Pelichem purchase expanded Matrix's industrial cleaning business and extended its geographic reach along the Gulf Coast.

HISTORY

Doyl West and William Lee both former officers with Tank Service founded Matrix in 1984 in Oklahoma. After buying Petrotank Equipment in 1989 they reincorporated as Matrix Environmental Co. which became Matrix Service Co. in 1990. Matrix grew rapidly through acquisitions including Midwest Industrial Contractors (1990) San Luis Tank Piping Construction (1991) and Brown Steel Contractors (1994). Its innovations included a "tank jacking" process to elevate and support water tanks during renovation and a safety nozzle that revolutionized the cleaning and desludging of crude oil tanks.

In 1993 Matrix's sales dropped from increased competition but rebounded in late 1994 as US petroleum companies rescheduled work they had postponed while the EPA finalized rules for the Clean Air Act.

To broaden its reach Matrix acquired General Service Corp. in 1997. That year ITEQ which provides liquid and gas storage systems and services agreed to buy Matrix but the deal was called off in early 1998 amid perceived integration problems. Founders West (who had served as CEO) and Lee (who had been CFO) retired in 1998. Longtime executive Martin Rinehart took over as CEO that year but left in 1999 during the company's second year of losses. Bradley Vetal (formerly COO of Matrix's industrial services unit) succeeded him.

Matrix recovered after disposing of its troubled municipal water services subsidiaries: It sold one Brown Steel Contractors to Caldwell Tanks in 1999 and closed the other San Luis Tank Piping in 2000. Once it disposed of its municipal water services Matrix was able to focus on aboveground storage tank (AST) operations and grow its construction services operations in 2001.

The next year Matrix experienced a healthy hike in sales with the growth in new tank construction (many of the industry's tanks were 20 years old or older) and an increase in the company's services to power plants.

To strengthen its presence in the mid-Atlantic region the company in 2003 acquired Pennsylvania-based Hake Group an industrial contractor for the power generation petroleum chemical and manufacturing industries.

Vetal resigned as CEO in 2005; director Michael Hall stepped in as interim CEO (Michael Bradley ultimately took over the position) and director Ed Hendrix was elected chairman. That year two employees who worked at subsidiary Matrix Service Industrial Contractors lost their lives after being exposed to nitrogen fumes while working at a Valero Energy Corporation refinery in Delaware City Delaware.

The company also expanded its capabilities when it purchased oilfield construction equipment and cryogenic tank technology use from Chicago Bridge & Iron Co. in 2008. The deal which helped grow the company's liquefied natural gas business also included $20 million in contract work.

In 2009 Matrix enhanced its electrical and instrumentation capabilities with the acquisition of S.M. Electric Company in New Jersey. The addition helps Matrix grow its business in the Mid-Atlantic and southern New England.

Michael Bradley resigned as CEO and president in 2010 along with CFO and VP Thomas Long. Both men left the firm to join the same midstream petroleum business that they had worked for before Matrix. The following year John Hewitt of Aker Solutions was named CEO of Matrix Service Company.

EXECUTIVES

Chairman, Michael J. Hall, age 69, $258,166 total compensation
Vice President Midwestern Operations, Bradley J. Rinehart, age 50, $205,000 total compensation
Vice President Accounting and Administration, Albert D. Fosbenner, age 58
President Matrix Service Inc., James P. (Jim) Ryan, age 59, $303,300 total compensation
Vice President - Human Resources, Nancy E. Austin, age 46
President and CEO, John R. Hewitt

CFO, Kevin S. Cavanah, age 49, $163,167 total compensation
VP Fabrication Engineering and Procurement, Lansing G. Smith, age 60
President Matrix SME, Matthew J. Petrizzo, age 51, $265,000 total compensation
COO, Joseph F. Montalbano, age 64, $350,000 total compensation
VP Western Operations Matrix Service Inc., William R. Sullivan, age 47
Vice President Business Development, Kevin A. Durkin, age 51
VP Gulf Coast Operations Matrix Service Inc., Robert A. Long, age 69
Vice President; Treasurer, Jason W. Turner
Vice President Midwestern Operations, Bradley J. Rineh
IR Officer, Carter Peters
Vice President - Environmental; Health and Safety, Jack Frost
Vice President Construction Services, Alan Updyke
Director, Thomas E. (Tom) Maxwell, age 67
Director, I. Edgar (Ed) Hendrix, age 68
Director, Paul K. Lackey, age 70
Director, David J. Tippeconnic, age 73
Auditors: Deloitte&ToucheLLP

LOCATIONS

HQ: Matrix Service Co.
5100 East Skelly Drive, Suite 700, Tulsa, OK 74135
Phone: 918 838-8822   **Fax:** 918 838-8810
Web: www.matrixservice.com

2013 Sales

	$ mil.	% of total
US	814	91
International	77	9
Total	**892**	**100**

PRODUCTS/OPERATIONS

2013 Sales By Segment

	$ mil.	% of total
Storage solutions	393	44
Oil gas & chemical	273	31
Electrical infrastructure	171	19
Industrial	54	6
Total	**892**	**100**

COMPETITORS

Arizona Instrument
Brown and Caldwell
Chart Industries
Chicago Bridge & Iron
Denali
ENGlobal
Halliburton
OP-TECH Environmental
Shaw Group
Veolia Environmental Services North America
ZCL Composites

HISTORICAL FINANCIALS

Company Type: Public

Income Statement

FYE: June 30

	REVENUE ($ mil.)	NET INCOME ($ mil.)	NET PROFIT MARGIN	EMPLOYEES
06/13	892.5	24.0	2.7%	3,587
06/12	739.0	17.1	2.3%	2,692
06/11	627.0	18.9	3.0%	2,623
06/10	550.8	4.8	0.9%	2,477
06/09	45.8	0.9	2.2%	0
Annual Growth	**110.1%**	**121.7%**	**—**	**—**

Debt ratio: —	No. of shares (mil.): 26
Return on equity: 10.6%	Dividends
Cash ($ mil.): 63	Yield: —
Current ratio: 1.80	Payout: —
Long-term debt ($ mil.): —	Market value ($ mil.): 407

	STOCK PRICE ($) FY Close	P/E High/Low		PER SHARE ($) Earnings	Dividends	Book Value
06/13	15.58	19	11	0.91	0.00	9.12
06/12	11.33	23	12	0.65	0.00	8.20
06/11	13.38	20	12	0.71	0.00	7.54
06/10	9.31	65	45	0.18	0.00	6.74
06/09	11.48	663	128	0.04	0.00	(0.00)
Annual Growth	**7.9%**	**—**	**—**	**118.4%**	**—**	**—**

Mattress Firm Holding Corp

Mattress Firm Holding is soft on comfort. The bedding retailer owns and operates or franchises about 1000 stores primarily under the Mattress Firm name in 26 states. It sells conventional (Simmons) and specialty (Tempur Sealy) mattresses which together account for most of its sales in addition to other brands. The company also sells bed frames and bedding accessories. From its humble beginnings in 1986 when three friends pooled their resources to purchase a downtrodden spot in a Houston strip center the chain has grown into the top US bedding retailer. After raising about $105 million in an initial public offering in late 2011 the company bought Mattress Giant in 2012.

The acquisition valued at about $47 million gave Mattress Firm an additional 180 stores in seven markets across Texas and Florida where the company has already built a strong foundation. The move made Mattress Firm the nation's largest specialty bedding retailer. As part of the transaction the retailer plans to rebrand the Mattress Giant stores under the Mattress Firm banner and replace products sold across the Mattress Giant chain with its own items.

Mattress Firm was put on firm footing during the past year by going public allowing its primary investor to cash out. The company which initially sought to raise about $115 million was taken public in November 2011 by its owner J.W. Childs Associates (JWC). (Most of the proceeds from the offering were used to repay more than $84 million in debt and fees to JWC.) The IPO came as the industry benefitted from economic improvements and pent-up demand for mattresses and related bedding products in the aftermath of the deep recession and housing crisis. In fiscal 2011 Mattress Firm's sales jumped 14% vs. the previous year and it returned to profitability (after losing more than $4 million in 2010).

Besides being big in Texas Florida Georgia and North Carolina Mattress Firm continues to extend its reach across the country and enters new markets through franchising the latest being Tulsa Oklahoma; Johnson City Tennessee; and Tyler Texas. To set itself apart the multi-brand mattress seller offers the Mattress Firm Red Carpet Delivery Service which includes a three-hour delivery window and recently introduced its proprietary YuMe mattress. The temperature-controlled mattress uses ambient air to heat and cool the mattress surface.

EXECUTIVES

Chairman, William E. Watts, age 60
Chief Financial Officer; Executive Vice President, James R. (Jim) Black, age 54
President; Chief Executive Officer; Director, R. Stephen (Steve) Stagner, age 44
Executive Vice President - Marketing and Merchandising, Karrie D. Forbes, age 37
Executive Vice President - Sales and Operations, Kenneth E. (Ken) Murphy III, age 37
Vice President - Field Operations, George W. McGill, age 54
Franchise Development, Harry Roberts
Franchise Development, Charlie Roberts
Manager Franchising, Jason Goodman
Director Merchandising, Kim Vanek
National Recruiting Manager, Abby Ludens
Vice President Human Resources, Christine Brinkley, age 44
Chief Strategy Officer, Steven G. (Steve) Fendrich, age 51
Vice President - Real Estate and Construction, Bruce Levy, age 55
Executive Vice President of Retail Concept Development, Craig McAndrews, age 44
Chief Strategy Officer, Stephen Fendrich
Senior Vice President of Finance, Alex Weiss
Director, John W. Childs, age 71
Director, Adam L. Suttin, age 45
Director, David A. Fiorentino, age 37
President CEO and Director, R. Stephen (Steve) Stagner, age 44
Director, Frederick C. Tinsey III, age 61
Auditors: GrantThorntonLLP

LOCATIONS

HQ: Mattress Firm Holding Corp.
5815 Gulf Fwy., Houston TX 77023
Phone: 713-923-1090   **Fax:** 713-923-1096
Web: www.mattressfirm.com

2011 Stores

	No.
Texas	204
Florida	94
Georgia	49
North	47
Arizona	31
Ohio	30
Tennessee	29
Missouri	27
Nevada	20
Colorado	19
Indiana	19
South	18
Wisconsin	18
New	14
Oklahoma	14
Alabama	11
Kansas	10
Louisiana	9
Mississippi	5
New	5
Illinois	4
Kentucky	3
Virginia	2
Iowa	1
Total	**683**

PRODUCTS/OPERATIONS

2011 Stores

	No.
Company owned	592
Franchised	88
Total	**680**

Selected Brands

Hampton & Rhodes
Sealy Posturpedic
Simmons Beautyrest
Sleep to Live
Stearns & Foster
Tempur-Pedic
YuMe

COMPETITORS

1800Mattress.com	Macy's
Costco Wholesale	Rooms To Go
Dillard's	Sears
Gallery Furniture	Sleepy's
Havertys	The RoomStore
J. C. Penney Company	Wal-Mart

HISTORICAL FINANCIALS
Company Type: Public

Income Statement
FYE: January 29

	REVENUE ($ mil.)	NET INCOME ($ mil.)	NET PROFIT MARGIN	EMPLOYEES
01/13	1,012.7	39.8	3.9%	3,340
01/12*	708.6	34.3	4.8%	2,230
02/11	497.3	0.3	0.1%	2,040
02/10	434.3	(4.6)	—	0
02/09	435.3	(124.8)	—	0
Annual Growth	**23.5%**	—	—	—

*Fiscal year change

2013 Year-End Financials

Debt ratio: 34.9%
Return on equity: 16.2%
Cash ($ mil.): 14
Current ratio: 0.86
Long-term debt ($ mil.): 219

No. of shares (mil.): 33
Dividends
  Yield: —
  Payout: —
Market value ($ mil.): 938

	STOCK PRICE ($) FY Close	P/E High/Low	PER SHARE ($) Earnings	Dividends	Book Value
01/13	27.75	39 19	1.18	0.00	7.92
01/12*	33.03	23 15	1.40	0.00	6.64
Annual Growth	**(16.0%)**	—	**(15.7%)**	—	**19.2%**

*Fiscal year change

Maxim Integrated Products, Inc.

Maxim's maxim? Invent! Maxim Integrated Products makes analog and mixed-signal integrated circuits (ICs); more than 80% of which were invented by the company. Maxim's chips —which include amplifiers data converters transceivers and switching ICs —translate physical data such as temperature pressure and sound into signals for electronic processing. The company serves four major end-markets: industrial communications consumer and computing. Its ICs are used in products such as appliances telecommunications and networking gear automobiles medical devices instruments and utility meters. Some 75% of sales come from customers located in Asia mostly in China.

HISTORY

Jack Gifford a former UCLA baseball star who began his career at Fairchild Semiconductor and later headed the Intersil subsidiary (later divested) of General Electric founded Maxim in 1983. Gifford focused on analog chips which were less vulnerable to Japanese competition than digital integrated circuits (ICs) had a longer product life and cost less to make. Maxim went public in 1988.

From the beginning Maxim emphasized research and development: Gifford's 1983 business plan set the ambitious goal of developing at least 15 new products each quarter. The company developed 479 new products between 1993 and 1996.

In 1994 Maxim bought Tektronix's IC business and the two companies formed the Maxtek joint venture a maker of multichip modules and hybrid circuits. For the rest of the decade Maxim focused on expanding and modernizing its manufacturing. It opened offices in Hong Kong South Korea and Singapore in 1996 and added factories in the Philippines and California in 1997.

Maxim released 250 new products in fiscal 1998 including breakthrough chips for portable computers flat-panel displays and paging. Maxim sold its half of Maxtek to Tektronix in 2000. That year it also introduced a record 383 products and broke ground for a testing facility in Thailand.

In 2001 Maxim acquired specialty IC maker Dallas Semiconductor for about $2.5 billion. It also continued its "product proliferation" strategy as it topped itself once again by introducing 500 new products. Fiscal 2001 also saw the company expand its facilities in California Thailand and the Philippines.

Maxim bought a Texas chip fabrication plant from Philips Semiconductors (now NXP) in 2003.

In 2005 Maxim reorganized into two main product groups —Portable Computing and Instrumentation Electronics with 10 business units and Multimedia Automotive and Telecommunications Electronics with seven business units. The company retained finance manufacturing and planning as central corporate functions.

For health reasons Jack Gifford retired as CEO at the end of 2006 and also left the board of directors. He remained with the company on a part-time basis as a strategic advisor focusing on business direction and product planning. Tunc Doluca a group president and 22-year veteran of Maxim was named president and CEO effective at the beginning of 2007. Director Kipling Hagopian a member of the board since 1997 was elected interim chairman to succeed Gifford.

Gifford's sudden departure came while the company was still investigating its past practices in granting stock options a subject that came to dominate his last year with Maxim. Although he stepped down at the age of 65 many Silicon Valley observers were surprised to see Gifford go when he did as many other founder CEOs kept running their companies well into their 70s. A shareholder derivative lawsuit challenging Maxim's practices in stock-option grants was filed in May 2006. While the company publicly dismissed the complaint as without merit the SEC soon after opened an informal inquiry on the subject and a month later Maxim received a subpoena from federal prosecutors for corporate records on stock options. The company's board also initiated a review of stock-option granting practices with help from outside independent legal counsel. Maxim delayed releasing its 10-K annual report for fiscal 2006 as a result of the investigations.

The board's special committee wrapped up its review in 2007 concluding that there were instances from 2000 to 2006 where the recorded price of certain stock-option grants did not reflect the fair market value of the shares on the actual measurement dates. As a result Jack Gifford retired from his part-time advisory position and CFO Carl Jasper resigned from the company.

Near the end of 2007 Maxim reached a settlement with the SEC on options backdating agreeing to a permanent injunction against violations of federal securities laws and anti-fraud statutes. The SEC didn't assess any fines penalties or money damages against the company under the settlement. The regulators brought civil charges against Gifford and Jasper for their roles in backdating options.

Gifford settled his case with the SEC agreeing to return more than $650000 in bonuses and to pay a penalty of $150000. Jasper contested the charges however.

Maxim also implemented a number of corporate reforms such as new corporate governance guidelines formal procedures for the granting of stock options and other equity awards and a more comprehensive insider trading policy.

In 2007 Maxim bought a wafer fab in Irving Texas from competitor Atmel for about $38 million in cash. The 200mm wafer fab is idle while Maxim waits for market demand to recover. Later that year looking to boost its storage product offerings Maxim bought the Storage Products division of Vitesse Semiconductor for about $63 million in cash. The acquired business included serial attached storage ICs and related software and firmware.

The company also discontinued development of certain stand-alone high-speed high-resolution analog-to-digital converters. While Maxim concluded there was a limited market for these parts it cut the converters in part to avoid an intellectual property dispute with rival Analog Devices over the devices. Jettisoning the products helped the company settle the case with ADI rather than going to trial.

In 2008 the company settled the shareholder derivative lawsuit over the misdated stock options for $28.5 million in cash to be paid to Maxim —$21 million from liability insurers $6 million from Gifford and $1.5 million from three directors. The plaintiffs received up to $15 million for legal fees and up to $500000 for other expenses. Gifford cancelled vested and unexercised options for about 3.1 million shares of common stock.

Gifford died in 2009 at the age of 67.

In 2009 Maxim acquired two product lines from ZiLOG. The company purchased ZiLOG's Wireless Control business in concert with Universal Electronics. Maxim received the hardware portion of the business microcontrollers and related intellectual property and it combined those products with its ultra-low-power infrared microcontroller family. On its own Maxim bought ZiLOG's Secure Transaction product line with its Zatara line of 32-bit MCUs used in consumer payment terminals. The acquisition dovetailed with Maxim's earlier purchase of a French firm Innova Card in providing chips for the financial transaction terminal market.

Later that year Maxim spun out its radio-frequency (RF) division —consisting of designs intellectual property and an engineering team —to Intelleflex in exchange for equity ownership in that company and an agreement to partner on future product marketing.

EXECUTIVES

Chief Technology Officer Technology Development and Innovation Group, Pirooz Parvarandeh, age 53, $360,000 total compensation
President and Chief Executive Officer; Director, Tunc Doluca, age 55, $500,000 total compensation
Chairman, B. Kipling (Kip) Hagopian, age 71

Senior Vice President of Manufacturing Operations, Vivek Jain, age 53, $330,000 total compensation
SVP and CFO, Bruce E. Kiddoo, age 53, $350,000 total compensation
SVP Communications and Automotive Solutions Group, Matthew J. (Matt) Murphy, age 40
SVP Industrial and Medical Solutions Group, Christopher J. (Chris) Neil, age 47
SVP Mobility Group, Chae Lee
Vice President Worldwide Sales and Marketing, Walter L. Sangalli
Director, Joseph R. (Joe) Bronson, age 64
President CEO and Director, Tunc Doluca, age 54
Director, William D. (Bill) Watkins, age 59
Director, Robert E. (Bob) Grady, age 54
Director, James R. Bergman, age 70
Director, A. R. Frank Wazzan, age 76
Auditors: Deloitte&ToucheLLP

LOCATIONS

HQ: Maxim Integrated Products Inc.
120 San Gabriel Dr., Sunnyvale CA 94086
Phone: 408-601-1000   **Fax:** 858-503-3301
Web: www.maxwell.com

2013 Sales

	$ mil.	% of total
Asia		
China	996	41
Korea	235	10
Vietnam	235	10
Rest of Asia	329	13
Europe	295	12
US	283	12
Rest of World	66	3
Total	**2,441**	**100**

PRODUCTS/OPERATIONS

Selected Markets

Communications
  Basestations
  Network & datacom
  Telecom
Computing
  Computer peripherals
  Data storage
  Financial terminals
  Notebook computers
  Server & desktop computers
Consumer
  Digital cameras
  Handheld computers
  Home entertainment & appliances
  Mobile phones
Industrial
  Automatic test equipment
  Automotive
  Control & automation
  Electronic instrumentation
  Medical
  Military & aerospace
  Security
  Utility & other meters

Selected Products

Amplifiers and comparators
  Audio amplifiers
  Operational amplifiers
Analog switches and multiplexers
Data converters sample-and-hold devices and voltage references
Digital potentiometers
Fiber and communications devices
  Circuits for fiber and cable data transmission
  Framers
  Transceivers
Filters
High-frequency application-specific integrated circuits (ASICs)
Hot-swap and power switching circuits

Interface and interconnect devices
LED lighting and LCD display devices
Memories
  Electrically erasable programmable read-only memories (EEPROMs)
  Erasable programmable read-only memories (EPROMs)
  Non-volatile static random-access memories (SRAMs)
  Non-volatile timekeeping RAMs
Microcontrollers
Microprocessor supervisors and non-volatile RAM controllers
Multiplexers
Optoelectronic devices
Power supplies and battery management devices
  DC-to-DC power supplies
  Low-dropout linear regulators
  Power metal oxide semiconductor field-effect transistor (MOSFET) drivers
Protection and isolation circuits
Sensors sensor conditioners and thermal management devices
Storage products
Timing devices
  Counters and timers
  Oscillators and waveform generators
  Real-time clocks (RTCs)
Wireless and radio-frequency (RF) products
  Amplifiers
  Receivers
  Transmitters and transceivers
Video amplifiers processors and switches
Voltage monitors

Selected Acquisitions

2011
  Calvatec (Scotland; analog and mixed signal technology for consumer electronics and communications products)
  SensorDynamics ($130 million; Austria: automotive sensor technology for microelectromechanical (MEMS) systems)
2010
  Teridian Semiconductor ($315 million; chip designs for the energy measurement and " smart meter" market)
  Phyworks ($73 million; chips for high-speed optical networks and other broadband communications)

COMPETITORS

Advanced Analogic Technologies	Mindspeed
	Mitsubishi Corp.
Altera	Mitsui
Analog Devices	Monolithic Power
Applied Micro Circuits	Systems
Atmel	NXP Semiconductors
Broadcom	O2Micro
Conexant Systems	ON Semiconductor
Exar	PMC-Sierra
Fairchild	QUALCOMM
Semiconductor	RF Micro Devices
Freescale	ROHM
Semiconductor	Ricoh Company
Fujitsu Semiconductor	STMicroelectronics
America	Seiko
Infineon Technologies	Semtech
Intel	Silicon Labs
International	Siliconix
Rectifier	Skyworks
Intersil	Texas Instruments
Linear Technology	Vishay Intertechnology
Marvell Technology	Vitesse Semiconductor
Micrel	Volterra Semiconductor
Microchip Technology	

HISTORICAL FINANCIALS
Company Type: Public

Income Statement
FYE: June 29

	REVENUE ($ mil.)	NET INCOME ($ mil.)	NET PROFIT MARGIN	EMPLOYEES
06/13	2,441.4	454.9	18.6%	9,019
06/12	2,403.5	386.7	16.1%	9,065
06/11	2,472.3	489.0	19.8%	9,370
06/10	1,997.6	125.1	6.3%	9,200
06/09	1,646.0	10.4	0.6%	8,765
Annual Growth	10.4%	156.8%	—	0.7%

2013 Year-End Financials

Debt ratio: 12.8%	No. of shares (mil.): 287
Return on equity: 18.0%	Dividends
Cash ($ mil.): 1,174	Yield: 0.0%
Current ratio: 4.79	Payout: 63.1%
Long-term debt ($ mil.): 503	Market value ($ mil.): 7,990

	STOCK PRICE ($) FY Close	P/E High/Low	PER SHARE ($) Earnings	Dividends	Book Value
06/13	27.78	21 15	1.52	0.96	8.72
06/12	25.64	23 16	1.29	0.88	8.67
06/11	24.10	17 10	1.61	0.84	8.49
06/10	17.41	52 37	0.40	0.80	7.82
06/09	16.12	740358	0.03	0.80	8.48
Annual Growth	14.6%	—	—166.8%	4.7%	0.7%

MAXIMUS Inc.

Efforts by government agencies to maximize efficiency mean money for MAXIMUS. The company gets about two-thirds of its sales from its health services segment which offers outsourced program management and administrative services mainly to government agencies responsible for health and human services programs. Its human services segment provides administrative and consulting support to welfare-to-work programs child support enforcement and higher education and K-12 special education schools. MAXIMUS conducts consulting and programs management services for government-sponsored programs such as Medicaid Medicare the Children's Health Insurance Program (CHIP) and Welfare-to-Work.

Geographic Reach

Operating through more than 220 offices MAXIMUS gets more than 70% of its revenue from the US where the company has drawn clients from all 50 states. It also has won contracts in Australia Canada Israel Saudi Arabia and the UK.

Operations

The company operates through two segments: Health Services and Human Services. The Health Services Segment generated 64% of total revenue in fiscal 2012 while the Human Services segment accounted for the other 36%.

Financial Performance

MAXIMUS has enjoyed an upward trend in revenue over the course of recent fiscal years. The company reported $1.05 billion in revenue for fiscal 2012 up from the $929.6 million it claimed for fiscal 2011. MAXIMUS brought in $831.7 million back in fiscal 2010.

Strategy

The company hopes to continue to benefit from the trend toward outsourcing of administrative functions by government agencies. However MAXIMUS faces the risk of losing business when economic downturns lead to spending cuts by state and local governments.

In fiscal 2012 more than 60% of the company's total revenue came from state and local government agencies whose programs received significant federal funding.

HISTORY

David Mastran who worked for the Department of Health Education and Welfare during the Nixon administration founded MAXIMUS in 1975. The company's name comes from its goal of maximizing US government efficiency.

Most of MAXIMUS' growth has come in the past decade. In 1989 it won a contract to help California welfare recipients get job training and education and in 1995 it helped Nebraska find $50 million in federal funds. However it has not been easy sailing. In 1994 Mississippi froze a child-support collection contract with MAXIMUS when costs nearly doubled the state's expectations. MAXIMUS was disqualified from bidding on a West Virginia contract in 1995 after a state employee was convicted of bribery (MAXIMUS was not charged).

In 1996 California chose MAXIMUS to create a benefits information program for Medi-Cal applicants and beneficiaries. But late that year the federal government eliminated a Social Security Administration program that had been a major income source for MAXIMUS (55% in 1996).

MAXIMUS went public in 1997. Also that year the company added some 2500 new clients to its roster with four acquisitions which included government services providers David M. Griffith & Associates and Spectrum Consulting.

In 1999 MAXIMUS moved to bolster its human services and fleet management software capabilities respectively with acquisitions of Public Systems and Control Software. The company also landed large contracts to manage Medicaid enrollment for the state of Massachusetts child support enforcement for Maryland and Wisconsin's nationally recognized welfare-to-work program.

In 2000 MAXIMUS made acquisitions across the board in such areas as Web-enabled information systems child support collection services and infrastructure management systems. MAXIMUS only made one acquisition in 2001 preferring to integrate its previous purchases into a new business structure.

The company branched out internationally in 2004 when it signed a 10-year agreement with the Ministry of Health Services in British Columbia Canada.

Mastran retired in 2004 and company veteran Lynn Davenport replaced him as CEO. Davenport was dismissed in April 2006 however because of "conduct towards a female MAXIMUS employee" the company said. Richard Montoni a former EVP and CFO of the company was named president and CEO.

To concentrate on its core operations MAXIMUS discontinued its student loan collections business and sold its corrections services business in 2006. The next year MAXIMUS engaged advisers to help evaluate a wide range of options –including a sale of the company –in an effort to improve shareholder value. After the review the company's board decided in November 2007 to sharpen its focus on its core health and human services-related operations and to buy back up to $150 million worth of stock.

EXECUTIVES

President CEO & Director, Richard A. (Rich) Montoni, age 62, $700,000 total compensation
Chief Human Capital, Mark S. Andrekovich, age 52, $389,000 total compensation
Chairman, Peter B. Pond, age 68
Health Services President & General Manager, Bruce L. Caswell, age 47, $431,000 total compensation
CFO, David N. Walker, age 55, $410,000 total compensation
President Human Services, Akbar Piloti, age 56
President CEO and Director, Richard A. (Rich) Montoni, age 61
Director, James R. Thompson Jr., age 76
Independent Director, John J. Haley, age 64
Director, Russell A. Beliveau, age 65
Director, Raymond B. Ruddy, age 70
Director, Paul R. Lederer, age 74
Director, Marilyn R. Seymann, age 71
Director, Wellington E. Webb, age 72
Auditors: Ernst&YoungLLP

LOCATIONS

HQ: MAXIMUS Inc.
11419 Sunset Hills Rd., Reston VA 20190
Phone: 703-251-8500   **Fax:** 703-251-8240
Web: www.maximus.com

COMPETITORS

Accenture	Deloitte Consulting
Affiliated Computer Services	Goodwill Industries
	HP Enterprise Services
Bain & Company	IBM
Booz Allen	McKinsey & Company
Boston Consulting	Oracle
CACI International	SAP
Catholic Charities USA	Unisys
Computer Sciences Corp.	United Way
	Xerox

HISTORICAL FINANCIALS
Company Type: Public

Income Statement
FYE: September 30

	REVENUE ($ mil.)	NET INCOME ($ mil.)	NET PROFIT MARGIN	EMPLOYEES
09/13	1,331.2	116.7	8.8%	12,000
09/12	1,050.1	76.1	7.2%	8,657
09/11	929.6	81.1	8.7%	7,102
09/10	831.7	70.4	8.5%	6,834
09/09	717.3	46.5	6.5%	6,594
Annual Growth	16.7%	25.8%	—	16.1%

2013 Year-End Financials

Debt ratio: 0.1%	No. of shares (mil.): 68
Return on equity: 23.8%	Dividends
Cash ($ mil.): 125	Yield: 0.4%
Current ratio: 1.87	Payout: 24.0%
Long-term debt ($ mil.): 1	Market value ($ mil.): 3,086

	STOCK PRICE ($) FY Close	P/E High/Low	PER SHARE ($) Earnings	Dividends	Book Value
09/13	45.04	47 21	1.67	0.18	7.73
09/12	59.72	53 30	1.10	0.18	6.64
09/11	34.90	72 27	1.14	0.15	5.54
09/10	61.58	64 44	0.98	0.12	4.93
09/09	46.60	72 40	0.65	0.12	4.22
Annual Growth	(0.8%)	—	— 26.6%	11.9%	16.3%

Maxwell Technologies, Inc.

Maxwell Technologies is more than capable of making products that store energy and deliver power you might even say ultracapable. The company makes ultracapacitors postage stamp-sized cells that are able to provide quick bursts of energy to meet power demands then recharge by capturing excess power that would otherwise be lost. Its ultracapacitors are used to provide additional power for hybrid cars electric trains and semi-trucks as well as in energy grid solid-state memory and other applications that need fast reliable power. Maxwell also makes high-voltage capacitors that protect power grid systems and radiation-shielded microelectronics for satellites and spacecraft.

Founded in 1965 Maxwell is not a new company but the market for ultracapacitors is. The transportation industry is using ultracapacitors in braking systems starters and power steering systems for hybrid and electric vehicles as well as to provide reliable starting power for large trucks in cold weather and to open aircraft doors during power failures.

Maxwell's ultracapacitors are used in wind turbine blade-pitch systems to regulate voltage to the power grid. In data centers the products provide the energy between power failures and the initiation of backup power systems such as diesel generators and fuel cells. In another application the company announced that ShinMaywa Industries a Japanese maker of special purpose trucks designed Maxwell's ultracapacitors into the all-electric loading mechanism for garbage trucks to reduce noise and emissions during loading and unloading.

Customers outside the US account for more than 80% of sales. Nearly half of its sales come from China and Germany. Maxwell has significant operations in Switzerland and the US (in San Diego); it is opening another larger US production facility in Arizona. The company also has sales offices in China Germany and the UK. In addition to direct sales Maxwell sells through distributors that include Digi-Key TTI (and its Mouser Electronics unit) Tecate Group RUTRONIK and Bainacap.

Ultracapacitors are Maxwell's largest segment accounting for 62% of 2011 sales. Sales of the products have seen five years of year-over-year growth in the 50% range. High-voltage capacitors which are used to protect electric utility infrastructure systems from voltage spikes and are sold to power plant systems integrators make up another 27%. Radiation-shielded microelectronic products —including single-board computers and memory and power components —account for the remaining 11% of revenues.

Overall sales for Maxwell Technologies increased 29% to $157 million in 2011 driven by a 42% increase in sales of ultracapacitors and an 18% increase in sales of high-voltage capacitors. The company benefited from strong demand in markets for hybrid and electric automotive systems electric transit vehicles and backup power applications for computing systems. Revenues related to microelectronic products were flat for the year. Though the company has a history of losses it recorded a profit of $849000 in 2011.

Maxwell continues to seek opportunities in China its largest market where it has a contract manufacturing arrangements with Belton Technology Group and Tianjin Lishen Battery. Maxwell collaborates with Chinese companies to expand its presence in that burgeoning market supplying ultracapacitor electrode materials to Shanghai Sanjui Electric Equipment and Yeong-Long Technologies. In China the company must carefully guard its intellectual property rights since some contract manufacturers will illegally copy a company's product and then sell it for less in export markets.

EXECUTIVES

President Communications and Investor Relations, Michael W. (Mike) Sund
SVP Sales and Marketing, Van M. Andrews
Chairman, Mark Rossi, age 56
SVP CFO Treasurer and Secretary, Kevin S. Royal, age 48
SVP and COO, John J. Warwick
VP Advanced Power Energy Development and CTO, Michael A. (Mike) Everett
VP; General Manager Microelectronics Products, Larry Longden
VP Marketing and Engineering, Chris Humphrey
VP Business Development Market Intelligence and Strategic Planning, Michael J. Liedtke, age 52
President; Chief Executive Officer; Director, David J. Schramm, age 63, $423,800 total compensation
VP Operations, Everett E. (Earl) Wiggins III
VP High Tension; General Manager Maxwell SA, Sacha Jenny, age 44
VP Ultracapacitor Engineering, Jeremy Cowperthwaite
Vice President of Human Resources, Shannon Kehle
Vice President Controller, Sabrina Randolph
Director, Robert L. Guyett, age 76
Director, Jean Lavigne, age 75
Director, Yon Y. Jorden, age 58
Director, Jose L. Cortes, age 48
Director, Roger L. Howsmon, age 68
President; Chief Executive Officer; Director, David J. Schramm, age 63
Director, Burkhard Goeschel, age 66
Auditors: McGladreyLLP

LOCATIONS

HQ: Maxwell Technologies Inc.
9244 Balboa Ave., San Diego CA 92123
Phone: 858-503-3300   **Fax:** 858-503-3301
Web: www.maxwell.com

2011 Sales

	$ mil.	% of total
China	43	28
Germany	32	21
US	30	19
Other countries	50	32
Total	**157**	**100**

PRODUCTS/OPERATIONS

2011 Sales

	$ mil.	% of total
Ultracapacitors	97	62
High-voltage capacitors	42	27
Microelectronic products	18	11
Total	**157**	**100**

COMPETITORS

Analog Devices	Panasonic Corp
BAE SYSTEMS	SION Power
EPCOS	Siemens AG
Honeywell	Silicon Valley Analog
International	Spectrum Control
KEMET	Teledyne Technologies
Lockheed Martin	Vishay Intertechnology
Murata Manufacturing	W.L. Gore
PMC Global	

HISTORICAL FINANCIALS

Company Type: Public

Income Statement

FYE: December 31

	REVENUE ($ mil.)	NET INCOME ($ mil.)	NET PROFIT MARGIN	EMPLOYEES
12/12	159.2	7.1	4.5%	408
12/11	157.3	0.8	0.5%	435
12/10	121.8	(6.0)	—	368
12/09	101.3	(22.9)	—	361
12/08	82.2	(14.8)	—	346
Annual Growth	**18.0%**	**—**	**—**	**4.2%**

2012 Year-End Financials

Debt ratio: 5.4%	No. of shares (mil.): 29
Return on equity: 6.2%	Dividends
Cash ($ mil.): 28	Yield: —
Current ratio: 2.18	Payout: —
Long-term debt ($ mil.): 0	Market value ($ mil.): 242

	STOCK PRICE ($) FY Close	P/E High/Low	PER SHARE ($) Earnings	Dividends	Book Value
12/12	8.30	84 24	0.25	0.00	4.28
12/11	16.24	707463	0.03	0.00	3.67
12/10	18.89	— —	(0.23)	0.00	3.24
12/09	17.84	— —	(0.94)	0.00	2.96
12/08	5.07	— —	(0.71)	0.00	2.81
Annual Growth	**13.1%**	**— —**	**— —**	**—**	**11.1%**

McRae Industries, Inc.

McRae Industries has interests ranging from bar codes to boots. The company's footwear segment consisting of subsidiaries McRae Footwear and Dan Post Boot Co. makes combat boots for the US and foreign militaries Western boots and work boots. Dan Post Boot markets and distributes boot brands Laredo Dingo John Deere and Dan Post. A third subsidiary Compsee makes bar code readers printers and optical data-collection equipment. Compsee also licenses and sells computer software worldwide. McRae Industries makes most of its money from the Western and work boot segment. The McRae family controls more than 50% of the company's voting power.

EXECUTIVES

Director Human Resources, Kay Martin
President Treasurer and Director, D. Gary McRae, $204,903 total compensation
VP Finance Controller and Director, Marvin G. Kiser Sr., age 58, $114,060 total compensation
VP Product Development Dan Post Boot Co., Dave Mitchell
VP Marketing Compsee, Billy Graham
Auditors: GrantThorntonLLP

LOCATIONS

HQ: McRae Industries Inc.
400 N. Main St., Mt. Gilead NC 27306
Phone: 910-439-6147   **Fax:** 910-439-9596
Web: www.mcraeindustries.com

HISTORICAL FINANCIALS

Company Type: Public

Income Statement

FYE: August 3

	REVENUE ($ mil.)	NET INCOME ($ mil.)	NET PROFIT MARGIN	EMPLOYEES
08/13*	97.0	7.5	7.7%	0
07/12	75.6	4.8	6.4%	0
07/11	74.7	3.8	5.1%	0
07/10	62.5	2.9	4.7%	0
08/09	62.2	(0.5)	—	0
Annual Growth 11.8%		—	—	—

*Fiscal year change

2013 Year-End Financials

Debt ratio: —	No. of shares (mil.): 2
Return on equity: 13.8%	Dividends
Cash ($ mil.): 10	Yield: 0.0%
Current ratio: 6.97	Payout: 22.6%
Long-term debt ($ mil.): —	Market value ($ mil.): 60

	STOCK PRICE ($) FY Close	P/E High/Low		PER SHARE ($) Earnings	Dividends	Book Value
08/13*	24.50	5	3	3.79	0.86	23.07
07/12	14.80	6	5	2.27	0.36	20.82
07/11	13.63	7	6	1.84	0.36	19.06
07/10	13.25	8	4	1.47	0.36	17.78
08/09	10.25	—	—	(0.11)	0.36	16.79
Annual Growth 24.3%		—	—	—	24.3%	8.3%

*Fiscal year change

Meadowbrook Insurance Group Inc

Meadowbrook Insurance puts its clients' liabilities and risks out to pasture. Through subsidiaries including Star Insurance Savers P&C Williamsburg National Ameritrust ProCentury and Century Surety the company writes a variety of specialty commercial property/casualty insurance policies including workers' compensation commercial auto and multi-peril liability policies. With coverage tailored to fit small to midsized businesses customers include self-insured companies trade groups and associations. Meadowbrook also offers brokering risk management consulting and insurance management services including claims handling and administrative services.

Geographic Reach

Meadowbrook's income is diversified geographically with California accounting for the largest portion of its premium income (roughly one-third). The next-largest markets are Florida and Texas which together account for more than 15% of Meadowbrook's premiums. The company has offices in 17 states.

Of its different segments Meadowbrook's workers' compensation line of business is focused in California and New England while other commercial liability lines are clustered in the Southeast (including Texas) and California. The company's fee-for-service business is focused in New England the Midwest and the Southeast regions while its brokerage units are located in California Florida Massachusetts and Michigan.

Operations

Meadowbrook's subsidiaries derive revenue from a balance of underwriting premiums fee-for-service revenue (for risk management services) and agency commissions.

The company's products are divided into four categories. Its admitted and standard market programs cover specialty and standard commercial lines including workers' compensation and niche education agricultural and food service policies. Two segments —the excess and surplus lines division and the non-admitted programs division — cover commercial risks not eligible for standard coverage including bars hotels energy contractors and professional liabilities. Meanwhile the specialty market programs segment provides unique underwriting services in fields including excess workers' compensation and marine coverage.

Sales and Marketing

Meadowbrook primarily markets its products through a network of independent agents across the US. The company also has about 1000 associates at 30 locations scattered across the US that provide policy underwriting and administration services. Its brokerage locations sell products from Meadowbrook's subsidiaries and other insurance companies. Its largest producer in 2012 was Midwest General Insurance Agency an affiliated broker accounting for 13% of gross written premiums.

The company serves small to midsized businesses including agricultural technology manufacturing contracting retail and professional service entities. It also serves noncommercial organizations including associations and trade groups.

Financial Performance

The company's selective growth strategy and conservative investment policy seem to be paying off. The company's total revenue has increased each year for several years as have its gross and net written premiums. In 2012 Meadowbrook reported a 19% increase in revenues to $997 million due to increased premiums and commission revenues as well as from net gains on bond sales.

However net income fell 73% to about $12 million in 2012 following a decline of 27% in 2011. The company has experienced decreased profits due to loss adjustments from catastrophic weather events including Super Storm Sandy as well as from policy acquisition and underwriting expenses newly launched sales initiatives and certain restructuring measures. Due to the cyclical nature of the insurance industry Meadowbrook counts on years of lower loss and higher underwriting demand to balance out its profits.

Strategy

Meadowbrook's corporate strategy emphasizes spreading risk across all of its operations. In addition to maintaining a diversified revenue base the company's business units operate in localized service territories allowing for targeted growth efforts in their respective regions. It expands into new territories or lines of business through organic measures as well as through occasional acquisitions. At the same time the company occasionally reduces its activities in unprofitable segments.

Meadowbrook's diversification strategy helps the firm insulate itself extreme vulnerability to catastrophic events (such as earthquakes or terrorist attacks) or intense competitive conditions in any one market. To enhance operations in existing territories the company seeks to retain talented insurance professionals and maintain quality agent relationships.

Company Background

Meadowbrook was founded in 1955.

EXECUTIVES

President and CEO, Robert S. Cubbin, age 55, $650,000 total compensation
Vice President Chief Financial Officer, Karen M. Spaun, age 48, $315,000 total compensation
Chairman, Merton J. Segal, age 84, $385,000 total compensation
Senior Vice President; General Counsel; Secretary, Michael G. Costello, age 52, $315,000 total compensation
President Meadowbrook Insurance Agencies, Kenn R. Allen, age 64, $206,000 total compensation
Vice President Chief Actuary, Stephen A. Belden, age 57, $275,000 total compensation
SVP Business Operations and CIO, R. Christopher Spring, age 59, $210,500 total compensation
Vice President Business Development, Archie S. McIntyre, age 47
VP Corporate Communications, Carol Ziecik
SVP Insurance Operations, Joseph E. Mattingly, age 53
Senior Vice President - Field Operations, James M. Mahoney, age 62, $225,000 total compensation
Vice President Business Development, James P. LeRoy
EVP and President Century Insurance, Christopher J. Timm, age 56
IR Contact, John P. Shallcross
President CEO and Director, Robert S. Cubbin, age 55
Director, Joseph S. Dresner, age 86
Director, Florine Mark, age 80
Director, David K. Page, age 79
Director, Bruce E. Thal, age 81
Director, Herbert Tyner, age 82
Director, Robert W. Sturgis, age 71
Director, Hugh W. Greenberg, age 82
Director, Robert H. Naftaly, age 75
Director, Robert F. Fix, age 66
Director, Jeffrey A. Maffett, age 65
Auditors: Ernst&YoungLLP

LOCATIONS

HQ: Meadowbrook Insurance Group Inc.
26255 American Dr., Southfield MI 48034-6112
Phone: 248-358-1100   **Fax:** 248-358-1614
Web: www.meadowbrookinsgrp.com

2012 Premiums

	% of total
California	33
Florida	9
Texas	6
New	4
Michigan	4
New	4
Illinois	3
Missouri	2
Pennsylvania	2
Louisiana	2
Other	31
Total	**100**

PRODUCTS/OPERATIONS

2012 Revenues

	$ mil.	% of total
Net earned premiums	854	86
Net realized gains	55	5
Net investment income	53	5
Commissions	15	2
Management administrative fees	11	1
Claims fees	6	1
Total	**996**	**100**

2012 Net Written Premiums

Workers' compensation	43
Commercial auto liability	10
Commercial multi-peril liability	7
Excess workers' compensation	7
Other liability	17
Total	**0** **100**

Selected Operations

Insurance
  Ameritrust Insurance Corp.
  Century Surety Company
  ProCentury
  Savers Property & Casualty Insurance Company
  Star Insurance Company
  Williamsburg National Insurance Company
Retail Agencies
  Commercial Carriers Insurance
  Insurance & Benefits Consultants
  Meadowbrook Insurance Agency
Wholesale Agencies
  Interline Insurance Agency
  Meadowbrook TPA Associates
  Preferred Comp
  US Specialty Underwriters

COMPETITORS

AIG
Alliant
American Financial Group
Delphi Financial Group
Markel
Sedgwick Claims Management Services
Specialty Underwriters' Alliance
Travelers Companies
W. R. Berkley
XL Group plc

HISTORICAL FINANCIALS

Company Type: Public

Income Statement

FYE: December 31

	ASSETS ($ mil.)	NET INCOME ($ mil.)	INCOME AS % OF ASSETS	EMPLOYEES
12/12	2,713.2	11.7	0.4%	1,032
12/11	2,381.2	43.6	1.8%	1,054
12/10	2,177.6	59.7	2.7%	967
12/09	1,989.8	52.6	2.6%	918
12/08	1,813.9	27.4	1.5%	921
Annual Growth	**10.6%**	**(19.1%)**	**—**	**2.9%**

2012 Year-End Financials

Return on assets: 0.4%
Return on equity: 2.0%
Long-term debt ($ mil.): —
No. of shares (mil.): 49
Sales ($ mil): 996

Dividends
  Yield: 2.9%
  Payout: 73.9%
Market value ($ mil.): 288

	STOCK PRICE ($) FY Close	P/E High/Low	PER SHARE ($) Earnings	Dividends	Book Value
12/12	5.78	52 23	0.23	0.17	11.22
12/11	10.68	13 10	0.83	0.17	11.60
12/10	10.25	9 5	1.10	0.13	10.28
12/09	7.40	9 6	0.92	0.09	9.06
12/08	6.44	16 7	0.61	0.08	7.64
Annual Growth	**(2.7%)**	**— —**	**(21.6%)**	**20.7%**	**10.1%**

Measurement Specialties, Inc.

Sensing the pressure? Measurement Specialties would rather do that for you. The company's industrial product line includes sensors that measure such properties as fluid level and properties gas concentration and flow rate humidity torque pressure vibrations and more. Its sensors are used in aerospace consumer appliance environmental water monitoring industrial medical military test and measurement transportation and vehicle applications. The company's biggest customer Sensata Technologies (about 15% of sales) serves the automotive market. US customers account for one-thirds of sales; those in China make up nearly a quarter.

Operations

Measurement Specialties has 14 primary manufacturing facilities spread across Ireland Scotland France Germany Switzerland China and the US.

Sales and Marketing

Measurement Specialties sells its products through regional sales managers distributors and outside sales representatives mainly in North America Asia/Pacific and western Europe.

Financial Analysis

Although profits took a dive along with revenues in 2009 and 2010 against the headwind of the global recession it still managed to stay profitable continuing a streak going back to 2004. Revenues in fiscal 2012 (ended March) continued the climb back up topping the 10-year high achieved in 2011 by nearly 15%. Acquisitions were a big factor but broader product adoptions drove organic growth to a tidy 6% from almost all product lines particularly humidity position and vibration and orders from its top customer. Only optical piezo and temperature products lagged. As manufacturers toil to bring their customers "smart" products Measurement Specialties expects demand for sensors to remain strong.

Strategy

Measurement Specialties uses acquisitions to add technologies expand product lines and grow geographically. The company has spent a combined $250 million snapping up 18 businesses since 2004. With the company's strategy of using customer proximity to maintain strong service levels for its global customers and attain economies of scale acquisitions come from all around the world and usually correspond to the amount of revenue a region brings in. While China is the exception to that rule (the #2 region for Measurement Specialties but producing only one purchase in the above-noted period) third-ranked region

France and Europe in general has been a hotspot for strategic buys behind only the US.

Mergers and Acquisitions

In 2013 it acquired the sensors business of API Technologies for about $51 million.

EXECUTIVES

Vice President - Finance; Treasurer, Jeffrey C. Kostelni, age 46
Chairman, Morton L. (Mort) Topfer, age 76
President CEO and Director, Frank D. Guidone, age 48, $439,892 total compensation
CFO and Secretary, Mark Thomson, age 46, $228,200 total compensation
Executive Vice President, Glen MacGibbon, age 52, $201,688 total compensation
EVP, Jean-Francois Allier, age 60, $204,675 total compensation
Chief Operating Officer, Steven (Steve) Smith, age 65, $196,385 total compensation
VP Technology, Mitch Thompson, age 58
Director Global Integration, Erik Wikstrom
Director Global Sourcing, Vicente Piedrahita
Director, John D. Arnold, age 59
Director, Satish Rishi, age 54
President CEO and Director, Frank D. Guidone, age 48
Director, R. Barry Uber, age 69
Director, Kenneth E. Thompson, age 54
Auditors: KPMGLLP

LOCATIONS

HQ: Measurement Specialties, Inc.
  1000 Lucas Way, Hampton, VA 23666
Phone: 757 766-1500
Web: www.meas-spec.com

2012 Sales

	$ mil.	% of total
US	109	35
China	74	24
France	55	18
Ireland	28	9
Germany	19	6
Switzerland	18	6
Scotland	6	2
Total	**313**	**100**

PRODUCTS/OPERATIONS

Selected Products

Sensors
  Displacement
  Fluid monitoring
  Force load cells
  Humidity
  Microstructures
  Piezoelectric film custom & traffic
  Pressure components sensors & transducers
  Rotary position transducers
  Temperature thermistors
  Tilt & angle
  Torque & force
  Vibration accelerometers
Test & Measurement
  Aircraft flight
  Automotive design & test
  Motorsport
  Safety

Selected Mergers & Acquisitions

2012
  Resistance Temperature Detector Company Inc. and parent Cambridge Technologies Inc. ($17.3 million; temperature sensors and probes)
  Cosense ($12 million; ultrasonic sensors and switches used in semiconductor medical aerospace and industrial applications)
2011

Celesco Transducer Products ($35 million; US; linear and rotary measurement transducers for construction equipment medical equipment and automotive applications)
Eureka Environmental ($2 million; US; multi-parameter instruments used in water analysis)
Gentech International (#7 million ($11 million); Scotland; position sensors used largely for tank liquid level measurement)
2010
Esterline Technologies' pressure systems unit ($25 million; US; pressure sensing instrumentation)

Selected Subsidiaries

Encoder Devices LLC
Entran Devices Inc.
IC Sensors
Schaevitz Sensors
Humirel SA (France)
MWS Sensorik GmbH (Germany)
Jingliang Electronics (Shenzhen) Co. Ltd. (China)
Measurement Limited (Hong Kong)

COMPETITORS

Agilent Technologies	Murata Manufacturing
Apogee Technology	Rice Lake Weighing
Avery Weigh-Tronix	Systems
Bonso Electronics	Schneider Electric
CTS Valpey	Siemens AG
Crane Co.	SpaceAge Control
Danaher	TE Connectivity
GE	Taylor Precision
Honeywell	Products
International	Timex
Mettler-Toledo	WIKA
Motorola Solutions	

HISTORICAL FINANCIALS

Company Type: Public

Income Statement

FYE: March 31

	REVENUE ($ mil.)	NET INCOME ($ mil.)	NET PROFIT MARGIN	EMPLOYEES
03/13	346.9	34.1	9.9%	3,154
03/12	313.2	27.7	8.8%	3,235
03/11	274.7	28.1	10.3%	2,923
03/10	209.6	5.9	2.8%	2,520
03/09	203.9	5.2	2.6%	2,184
Annual Growth	14.2%	59.5%	—	9.6%

2013 Year-End Financials

Debt ratio: 22.0%
Return on equity: 13.0%
Cash ($ mil.): 36
Current ratio: 3.11
Long-term debt ($ mil.): 98
No. of shares (mil.): 15
Dividends
Yield: —
Payout: —
Market value ($ mil.): 619

	STOCK PRICE ($) FY Close	P/E High/Low	PER SHARE ($) Earnings	Dividends	Book Value
03/13	39.77	18 13	2.12	0.00	18.02
03/12	33.70	21 13	1.74	0.00	15.89
03/11	34.02	17 6	1.84	0.00	13.95
03/10	14.71	39 9	0.40	0.00	11.49
03/09	4.09	56 7	0.36	0.00	10.86
Annual Growth	76.6%	— —	55.8%	—	13.5%

Medical Properties Trust Inc

Hospitals trust Medical Properties to provide the leases under which their facilities operate. The self-administers real estate investment trust owns about 50 health care facilities including acute-care physical rehabilitation and regional and community hospitals in more than 20 states. Almost half are in California and Texas; California alone represents approximately 45% of the REIT's annual revenue. It leases the facilities to some 15 hospital operators under long-term triple-net leases where the tenant bears most of the operating costs. Prime Healtcare Services and Vibra Healthcare are the REIT's largest clients; together they account for more than half of its revenue.

Medical Properties Trust also offers financing to hospital operators including long-term interest-only mortgage loans and capital for acquisitions expansions or new development.

In a move that significantly broaded its holdings and geographic reach the REIT acquired 20 health care facilities from rival HCP for about $360 million in 2008.

EXECUTIVES

EVP CFO and Director, R. Steven Hamner, age 56, $347,000 total compensation
Chairman President and CEO, Edward K. Aldag Jr., age 49, $510,000 total compensation
Vice Chairman, William G. McKenzie, age 54, $107,846 total compensation
EVP COO Treasurer and Secretary, Emmett E. McLean, age 57, $345,000 total compensation
Director Finance, Charles Lambert
Chief Financial Officer Corporate Secretary, John Sheffield
Director, Sherry A. Kellett, age 68
EVP CFO and Director, R. Steven Hamner, age 56
Vice Chairman, William G. McKenzie, age 54
Director, G. Steven (Steve) Dawson, age 55
Director, Robert E. Holmes, age 71
Director, L. Glenn Orr Jr., age 72
Auditors: KPMGLLP

LOCATIONS

HQ: Medical Properties Trust Inc.
1000 Urban Center Dr. Ste. 501, Birmingham AL 35242
Phone: 205-969-3755 **Fax:** 205-969-3756
Web: www.medicalpropertiestrust.com

2009 Sales

$ mil % of total	$ mil.	% of total
California	57	44
Texas	17	14
Indiana	7	6
Utah	6	5
Massachusetts	6	5
Idaho	5	4
South Carolina	3	3
Missouri	3	3
Oregon	3	3
Louisiana	3	2
Florida	2	2
West Virginia	1	1
Kansas	1	1
Arkansas	1	1
Michigan	1	1
Colorado	1	1
Connecticut	1	1
Virginia	1	1
Pennsylvania	0	1
Arizona	0	-
Rhode Island	0	-
Total	**129**	**100**

PRODUCTS/OPERATIONS

2009 Sales

	$ mil.	% of total
Rent billed	92	71
Interest & fee income	29	23
Straight-line rent	8	6
Total	**117**	**100**

2009 Sales by Property Type

$ mil % of total

	$ mil.	% of total
General acute care hospitals	90	70
Long-term acute care hospitals	25	19
Rehabilitation hospitals	10	8
Wellness centers	2	2
Medical office buildings	1	1
Total	**129**	**100**

COMPETITORS

Extendicare	Omega Healthcare
HCP	Investors
Health Care REIT	Universal Health
Healthcare Realty	Realty
Trust	Ventas
LTC Properties	
National Health	
Investors	

HISTORICAL FINANCIALS

Company Type: Public

Income Statement

FYE: December 31

	REVENUE ($ mil.)	NET INCOME ($ mil.)	NET PROFIT MARGIN	EMPLOYEES
12/12	201.4	89.9	44.6%	33
12/11	143.3	26.5	18.5%	29
12/10	121.8	22.9	18.8%	29
12/09	129.7	36.3	28.0%	29
12/08	117.5	34.4	29.3%	25
Annual Growth	14.4%	27.1%	—	7.2%

2012 Year-End Financials

Debt ratio: 47.0%
Return on equity: 9.5%
Cash ($ mil.): 37
Current ratio: 1.37
Long-term debt ($ mil.): 1,025
No. of shares (mil.): 136
Dividends
Yield: 6.6%
Payout: 142.8%
Market value ($ mil.): 1,631

	STOCK PRICE ($) FY Close	P/E High/Low	PER SHARE ($) Earnings	Dividends	Book Value
12/12	11.96	18 13	0.67	0.80	7.70
12/11	9.87	54 36	0.23	0.80	7.48
12/10	10.83	52 39	0.22	0.80	8.16
12/09	10.00	23 6	0.45	0.80	8.53
12/08	6.31	23 7	0.55	1.01	9.51
Annual Growth	17.3%	— —	5.1%	(5.7%)	(5.1%)

Medicines Co (The)

The Medicines Company will meet you at the hospital. The drug developer focuses on treatments used in acute care settings including the ER the surgical suite and the cardiac catheterization lab.

Its marketed products are Angiomax an anticoagulant used during coronary angioplasties and Cleviprex an IV drug used to control blood pressure spikes. It also sells Argatroban Recothrom Thrombin and Brilinta. The Medicines Company has other compounds in various stages of development including cangrelor an anti-platelet agent with possible use during cardiac catheterization and antibiotic oritavancin.

Geographic Reach

The US accounts for more than 90% of The Medicine Company's annual revenues. Its products are sold in more than 25 countries.

Operations

A majority of the company's income (98%) comes from sales of Angiomax in the US; the drug is also available internationally and is known in some regions as Angiox. The company depends on third parties (including Lonza) for manufacturing of its drugs. Sales of Cleviprex and other products accounted for about 2% of annual revenues in 2012. It also sells acute care generics.

Sales and Marketing

Angiomax Cleviprex and Argatroban are sold in US through sole-source distributor ICS (Integrated Commercialization Solutions); ICS markets and sells the products to hospitals and wholesalers. For Angiomax its sales force targets hospitals with cardiac catheterization laboratories that perform 200 or more coronary angioplasties annually.

In Europe Angiomax is sold as Angiox through an inside sales force consisting of 30 representatives; the company also directly sells Angiomax in Australia and New Zealand. In other international markets Angiomax/Angiox is sold through distributors including Sunovion in Canada and Grupo Ferrer Internacional in Greece Portugal Spain and some Central and South American countries.

Financial Performance

The Medicines Company reported increased revenues over the past five years as its product offerings have grown including a 15% increase to $558.6 million in 2012. The rise in earnings was driven by a price increase on Angiomax in the US as well as increased global Angiomax sales and higher sales of Cleviprex and Argatroban. Net income fell 60% to $51 million in 2012 however due to income tax provisions and higher operating expenses.

Strategy

The company has been working to expand the number of approved indications for Angiomax as well as to expand the drug into new markets. The Medicines Company is also moving Cleviprex into new markets. Development candidates include products aiming to reduce blood loss during surgery and to reduce the risk of coronary events in patients who have heart problems including angina and coronary thrombosis.

Without a drug discovery operation of its own The Medicines Company licenses or acquires clinical-stage compounds from others and shepherds them through clinical trials and (hopefully) onto the market. It licensed Angiomax for example from Biogen Idec and Cleviprex and another compound from AstraZeneca. It is on the lookout for additional candidates (or approved drugs) that would fit easily into its portfolio of products aimed at the hospital market. In 2012 it licensed Recothrom marketing rights from Bristol-Myers Squibb.

The company implemented a workforce reduction program to reduce costs and increase efficiencies. The program reduced The Medicines Company's workforce by some 12%.

Mergers and Acquisitions

The company has made selected acquisitions of development candidates over the years to expand its pipeline in fields including cardiovascular care. It also occasionally purchases small stakes in drug technology firms. In 2013 it purchased Incline Therapeutics for $185 million to add a pain management candidate. The Medicines Company acquired ProFibrix for biologic surgery candidates that year.

EXECUTIVES

Chairman of the Board; Chief Executive Officer, Clive A. Meanwell, age 55, $588,640 total compensation
President; Chief Financial Officer; Director, Glenn P. Sblendorio, age 57, $434,534 total compensation
Executive Director Corporate Affairs, Michael Mitchell
Senior Vice President, Stephanie Plent, age 51
Senior Vice President; General Counsel, Paul M. Antinori, age 59, $381,150 total compensation
Chief Accounting Officer; Vice President, William B. (Bill) O'Connor, age 54, $284,762 total compensation
Chief Accounting Officer; Vice President, William Connor
Chief Accounting Officer; Vice President, William OConnor
Director, William W. Crouse III, age 70
Director, Robert J. (Bob) Hugin, age 58
Director, Armin M. Kessler, age 75
Director, Robert G. Savage, age 59
Director, Elizabeth H. S. Wyatt, age 65
Director, Melvin K. (Mel) Spigelman, age 64
Director, Hiroaki Shigeta, age 69
Independent Director, John Kelly
Auditors: Ernst&YoungLLP

LOCATIONS

HQ: The Medicines Company
8 Sylvan Way, Parsippany NJ 07054
Phone: 973-290-6000 **Fax:** 973-656-9898
Web: www.themedicinescompany.com

2012 Sales

	$ mil.	% of total
US	512	92
Europe	38	7
Other	8	1
Total	**558**	**100**

PRODUCTS/OPERATIONS

2012 Sales

	$ mil.	% of total
Angiomax	548	98
Cleviprex/Argatroban	10	2
Total	**558**	**100**

COMPETITORS

Baxter International	Medicure
Bayer HealthCare	Merck
Pharmaceuticals Inc.	Mitsubishi Chemical
Bristol-Myers Squibb	Pfizer
Eisai	Sandoz International
Eli Lilly	GmbH
GlaxoSmithKline	Sanofi
Janssen Biotech	

HISTORICAL FINANCIALS

Company Type: Public

Income Statement

FYE: December 31

	REVENUE ($ mil.)	NET INCOME ($ mil.)	NET PROFIT MARGIN	EMPLOYEES
12/12	558.5	51.2	9.2%	538
12/11	484.7	127.8	26.4%	421
12/10	437.6	104.6	23.9%	420
12/09	404.2	(76.2)	—	462
12/08	348.1	(8.5)	—	453
Annual Growth	**12.5%**	**—**	**—**	**4.4%**

2012 Year-End Financials

Debt ratio: 23.2%
Return on equity: 9.3%
Cash ($ mil.): 519
Current ratio: 5.59
Long-term debt ($ mil.): 226

No. of shares (mil.): 53
Dividends
  Yield: —
  Payout: —
Market value ($ mil.): 1,293

	STOCK PRICE ($) FY Close	P/E High/Low		PER SHARE ($)		
				Earnings	Dividends	Book Value
12/12	23.97	28	19	0.93	0.00	10.87
12/11	18.64	8	5	2.35	0.00	9.42
12/10	14.13	8	4	1.97	0.00	6.69
12/09	8.34	—	—	(1.46)	0.00	4.55
12/08	14.73	—	—	(0.16)	0.00	5.70
Annual Growth	**12.9%**	**—**	**—**	**—**	**—**	**17.5%**

Medidata Solutions, Inc.

Medidata Solutions has electronic remedies to help clinical trials run smoothly. Founded in 1999 the company offers cloud-based applications that help biotechnology pharmaceutical and other life sciences companies conduct clinical trials and related research. Its products include hosted software for administering and managing clinical trials electronic data capture applications study management applications and patient diaries. The company also offers a variety of professional services such as consulting implementation integration and maintenance. Medidata operates in more than 115 countries but most of its sales come from the US.

Geographic Reach

Metidata does most of its business in the US which accounted for 67% of the company's sales in 2012. Japan is the company's second-largest geographic market accounting for 14% of sales during the same period. Other key markets include the UK and Switzerland.

Sales and Marketing The company markets its products primarily through a direct sales force across North America Europe and Asia; however it does leverage relationships with contract research organizations such as PAREXEL and Quintiles Transnational to make its software the foundation for outsourced services they provide. Medidata's top five customers including Johnson & Johnson Roche and AstraZeneca account for more than 30% of sales.

Financial Analysis Medidata continued its strong upward revenue trajectory in 2012 with sales increasing 18% year-over-year. The application services segment (its core business) was up 18% with revenue from new customers (including those brought in via the 2011 Clinical Force acquisition) driving that growth. Higher revenues from the professional services segment also contributed to the overall revenue increase. Higher operating expenses particularly research and development and sales and marketing costs drove the company's profits down 54% in 2012 from 2011 levels.

Strategy Expanding its customer base is a key element of Medidata's strategy. It has grown from less than 100 customers in 2008 to some 350 by the end of 2012. Among the segments the company is targeting are midsized companies non-US geographies the medical device industry and academic research centers and government organizations. Medidata is also focused on expanding its product line including through acquisitions.

Mergers and Acquisitions In 2011 the company acquired UK-based Clinical Force which added clinical trial management software to its offerings for $7 million.

Ownership Investment management firm Brown Capital Management owns about 14% of Medidata.

EXECUTIVES

EVP Customer Operations, Steven I. (Steve) Hirschfeld, age 51, $240,000 total compensation
VP Global CRO Partnerships, Graham Bunn
CFO, Cory Douglas, age 47
Chairman and CEO, Tarek Sherif, age 51, $360,000 total compensation
SVP Sales Operations and Knowledge Management, Joseph A. (Joe) Tyers
VP Global Quality Assurance, Frances (Fran) Nolan
VP Operations Trial Planning, Lori Shields
SVP Facilities and People Services, Arden Schneider
EVP Product and Marketing, Lineene N. Krasnow, age 62, $235,000 total compensation
VP Sales Global, Alan Mateo
VP and Head Europe Middle East Africa and Australia, Steven (Steve) Heath
SVP Services, Vik Shah
VP New Products, Richard J. Piazza, age 55
SVP Regulatory Compliance, Earl Hulihan
Senior Vice President Research & Development, Andrew Newbigging
Executive Vice President General Counsel, Michael I. Otner
Senior Director Global Quality Assurance EMEA, Tony Hewer
VP Global Information Security and Privacy and Corporate Security and Privacy Officer, Glenn Watt
VP Corporate Strategy, Shih-Yin Ho
VP Development Trial Planning, Peter Abramowitsch
VP Information Services Trial Planning, David Gemzik
Investor Contact, Hulus Alpay
Executive Vice President Strategy & Corporate Development, Bryan Spielman
Senior Product Director Medidata Solutions Worldwide, Steve Young
Executive Vice President Human Resources, Eileen Schloss
President, Glen Vries
Senior Vice President Chief Data Officer, Adindu Uzoma
Senior Vice President Professional Services, Daniel Shannon
Vice President of data operations Lori Shields, Kelly Willenberg

Director, George W. McCulloch, age 36
Director, Robert B. Taylor, age 66
Director, Carlos Dominguez, age 55
Director, Neil M. Kurtz, age 62
Independent Director, Lee Shapiro
Auditors: Deloitte&ToucheLLP

LOCATIONS

HQ: Medidata Solutions Inc.
79 5th Ave. 8th Fl., New York NY 10003
Phone: 212-918-1800 **Fax:** 212-918-1818
Web: www.mdsol.com

2011 Sales

	$ mil.	% of total
US	118	64
Japan	25	14
UK	11	6
Switzerland	10	6
Other countries	19	10
Total	**184**	**100**

PRODUCTS/OPERATIONS

2012 Sales

	$ mil.	% of total
Application services	171	79
Professional services	46	21
Total	**218**	**100**

Selected Customers

Pharmaceutical
 Abbott Laboratories
 Astellas Pharma
 AstraZeneca
 Baxter International
 Bayer HealthCare
 Daiichi Sankyo
 F. HoffmannLa Roche
 Johnson & Johnson
 H. Lundbeck
 Orion Corporation
 Pfizer
 Roche Holding
 Shionogi & Co.
 Takeda Pharmaceutical
Biotechnology
 Amgen
 Array BioPharma
 Elan Pharmaceuticals
 Genzyme Corporation
 Gilead Sciences
 Infinity Pharmaceuticals
 Seattle Genetics
Medical Devices and Diagnostics
 bioMerieux
 Boston Scientific
 DePuy International
 Edwards Lifesciences
Contract Research Organizations
 CMIC
 EPS
 ICON Clinical Research
 INC Research
 Kendle International
 PRA International
 Quintiles Transnational
 Sumisho Computer Systems
Institutions
 Ludwig Institute for Cancer Research
 Northwestern University

COMPETITORS

Aptuit	MedNet Solutions
BioClinica	Merge Healthcare
DATATRAK International	Microsoft
DRS Data &	OmniComm
Research	Oracle
DrugLogic	Patni Life Sciences
Liquent	Perceptive Informatics
M2S	eResearchTechnology

HISTORICAL FINANCIALS

Company Type: Public

Income Statement

FYE: December 31

	REVENUE ($ mil.)	NET INCOME ($ mil.)	NET PROFIT MARGIN	EMPLOYEES
12/12	218.3	18.0	8.3%	796
12/11	184.4	39.4	21.4%	690
12/10	166.4	22.8	13.7%	598
12/09	140.4	5.1	3.7%	574
12/08	105.7	(18.2)	—	671
Annual Growth	**19.9%**	**—**	**—**	**4.4%**

2012 Year-End Financials

Debt ratio: 0.0%
Return on equity: 14.6%
Cash ($ mil.): 122
Current ratio: 2.46
Long-term debt ($ mil.): 0
No. of shares (mil.): 52
Dividends
 Yield: —
 Payout: —
Market value ($ mil.): 2,040

	STOCK PRICE ($) FY Close	P/E High/Low	PER SHARE ($) Earnings	Dividends	Book Value
12/12	39.18	117 51	0.36	0.00	2.73
12/11	21.75	32 17	0.80	0.00	2.09
12/10	23.88	49 28	0.48	0.00	1.06
12/09	15.62	116 90	0.13	0.00	0.44
Annual Growth	**35.9%**	**— —**	**41.6%**	**—**	**83.5%**

Medifast Inc

Medifast seeks to help people slim down and shape up... fast. The company develops and markets health and diet products under the Medifast brand name. The products which are manufactured by subsidiary Jason Pharmaceuticals include food and beverages (meal replacement shakes bars) as well as disease management products for diabetics. Medifast operates through three channels: The Medifast Direct segment is the direct-to-consumer part of the business through which consumers order Medifast products online; Take Shape for Life is Medifast's personal coaching division composed of independent contractor health coaches; and its Weight Control Centers are Medifast's bricks-and-mortar walk-in clinics.

Operations

Medifast's largest sales channel is its personal coaching division Take Shape for Life which accounts for more than 60% of sales. For customers who want more supervision Medifast operates a chain of bricks-and mortar weight control centers (MWCC). The fast-growing MWCC division accounted for about 13% of Medifast's 2011 sales (up from 10% in 2009). Currently the company has about 80 company-owned weight loss centers in about half a dozen states including Florida New Jersey and Texas. Franchisees operate another 30 weight loss centers in six other states including Arizona and California. New MWCC markets include Miami and southern Virginia.

Sales and Marketing

Medifast uses multiple marketing strategies to reach its target audiences. It runs ads in national and regional magazines on television radio and the Web. It also uses direct mail and social media channels. Advertising costs (excluding direct-response advertising) totaled $27 million in 2011 compared with $23 million and $17.4 million in 2010 and 2009 respectively. Direct response advertising in 2011 totaled $26 million.

Financial Analysis

Medifast's sales and profits are growing in tandem with the rise in obesity rates and the diabetic population. Indeed its sales have increased 255% since 2007 while profits and cash flow also climbed steeply. Most recently sales rose nearly 16% in 2011 vs. 2010 while net income fell by more the 5% over the same period. The drop in net income —the company's first decline in four year —was attributed to costs associated with hiring and the opening of new Medifast Weight Control Centers over the course of the year. Both the Medifast and Weight Control Center & Wholesale businesses posted sales gains. The Take Shape for Life personal coaching business saw its sales rise by 12% while increased advertising for Medifast Direct Response drove sales up 14%. The addition of about 30 new company-owned weight control centers in 2011 also contributed to the annual increase in sales.

Strategy

While the ranks of the overweight are growing the company is also working to tailor its products to the rapidly growing population of diabetics. It maintains an in-house call center and support staff with registered dieticians on hand to assist customers.

Medifast's promotion and distribution model has changed over time. When it was founded in 1993 the company primarily sold its products through doctor's offices. Customers received supervision from their family physician who in turn received commissions on any products sold. However as physicians had increasingly less time to spend with patients the method grew less effective. While some doctors still stock an inventory and resell the company's products most of Medifast's sales are made through the its website thus reducing the complexity of its product distribution. Even its Take Shape For Life coaches simply direct customers to the website or call centers and receive commissions for orders placed there. New doctors who wish to promote the products are signed on as coaches.

In 2012 the company moved into international territory by partnering with Productos Medix S.A. de C.V. a leader in pharmaceutical obesity products in Mexico to exclusively distribute its Medifast meal replacement products and programs through physicians and Weight Control Centers in Mexico under its Medifast brand.

EXECUTIVES

EVP Human Resources, Jeanne M. Uphouse, age 53
Chairman and CEO, Michael C. MacDonald, age 60
EVP and General Counsel, Jason L. Groves, age 42
President, Guy H. Johnson
President of Strategy, Sylvia B. Rowe
Research Manager, Christopher D. Coleman
EVP and Chief Marketing Officer, Brian Kagen
Interim Chief Financial Officer, Edward Powers
President and COO, Margaret Sheetz
VP-Mktg, Jaime Elwood
CFO, Timothy Robinson
EVP Information Technology, Donald Gould
EVP Company Strategy International and Business Development, Brian Lloyd
EVP Take Shape for Life, Jeannette Mills
EVP Supply Chain, Guy Sheetz
EVP Medifast Weight Control Centers, Dominick Vietri
Director, John P. McDaniel, age 70
Director, Rev Donald F. (Don) Reilly, age 65

Director, Michael C. MacDonald, age 60
Director, Barry B. Bondroff, age 64
CEO and Director, Michael S. McDevitt, age 34
Director, Charles P. Connolly Jr., age 64
Director, George J. Lavin Jr., age 84
President COO and Director, Margaret MacDonald-Sheetz, age 35
Director, Jeannette M. Mills, age 46
Director, Sister Catherine T. Maguire, age 62
Director, Jerry D. Reece, age 73
Director, Harvey C. (Barney) Barnum Jr., age 72
Director, Jason L. Groves, age 42
Auditors: BagellJosephsLevine&CompanyLLC

LOCATIONS

HQ: Medifast Inc.
 11445 Cronhill Dr., Owings Mills MD 21117
Phone: 410-581-8042   **Fax:** 410-581-8070
Web: www.medifast.net

PRODUCTS/OPERATIONS

2012 Sales

Medifast	87
Weight control centers and wholesale	13

Selected Subsidiaries

Jason Enterprises Inc.
Jason Pharmaceuticals Inc.
Jason Properties LLC
Seven Crondall LLC.
Take Shape For Life Inc.

COMPETITORS

Atkins Nutritionals	Reliv' International
Bazi	Slim-Fast
Herbalife Ltd.	USANA Health Sciences
Jenny Craig	Weight Watchers
NBTY	International
Nu Skin	eDiets.com
Nutrisystem	

HISTORICAL FINANCIALS
Company Type: Public

Income Statement
FYE: December 31

	REVENUE ($ mil.)	NET INCOME ($ mil.)	NET PROFIT MARGIN	EMPLOYEES
12/12	356.7	15.8	4.5%	947
12/11	298.1	18.5	6.2%	860
12/10	257.5	19.6	7.6%	507
12/09	165.6	11.9	7.2%	365
12/08	105.4	5.4	5.2%	290
Annual Growth	**35.6%**	**30.7%**	**—**	**34.4%**

2012 Year-End Financials

Debt ratio: 3.3%	No. of shares (mil.): 13
Return on equity: 19.2%	Dividends
Cash ($ mil.): 39	Yield: —
Current ratio: 3.08	Payout: —
Long-term debt ($ mil.): 3	Market value ($ mil.): 363

	STOCK PRICE ($) FY Close	P/E High/Low		PER SHARE ($) Earnings	Dividends	Book Value
12/12	26.39	28	13	1.16	0.00	6.59
12/11	13.72	22	10	1.31	0.00	5.22
12/10	28.88	26	12	1.35	0.00	4.78
12/09	30.58	40	5	0.81	0.00	3.30
12/08	5.52	22	9	0.38	0.00	2.67
Annual Growth	**47.9%**	**—**	**—**	**32.2%**	**—**	**25.4%**

Mednax, Inc.

MEDNAX is a multi-specialty medical group with a national focus. Through its Pediatrix Medical Group American Anesthesiology and Mednax Services units the holding company operates a medical network comprised of more than 2000 affiliated physicians specialty practitioners and subspecialists who focus on women's and children's health. It provides neonatal obstetric and pediatric care primarily in hospitals; it also operates a growing number of anesthesia practices. In addition MEDNAX conducts clinical research and offers practice administration services to physician members and hospital customers in the areas of billing compliance managed care contracting recruiting risk management and staffing.

Operations

Pediatrix Medical Group's affiliated physicians include about 1000 doctors who provide neonatal care for premature or ill newborns primarily in hospital-based neonatal intensive care units; other specialize in fields including pediatric cardiology (120 physicians) and pediatric intensive care (100 doctors). Altogether neonatal and pediatric subspecialty services account for about 60% of annual patient service revenues. The company's maternal-fetal unit (10% of sales) employs some 200 physicians specializing in the care of pregnant women (including general obstetrics and pregnancy complications). The Pediatrix unit also conducts multi-center clinical trials and research studies and it provides educational opportunities to its physicians.

The American Anesthesiology division —accounting for about a quarter of patient service revenues —includes some 625 affiliates who provide medication and pain management services at hospitals (including birthing wings) physician practices and outpatient health and surgery centers.

Geographic Reach

The company operates in about 35 states and Puerto Rico. MEDNAX's five largest markets are Texas (with more than 20% of patient service revenues) North Carolina Florida Georgia and California.

Sales and Marketing

Some two-thirds of the company's net patient service revenue comes from managed care reimbursements from contracted services provided to hospitals. Another significant portion is received from government-sponsored plans principally state Medicaid programs.

Financial Performance

The company's revenues and profits have continued to climb alongside its business expansion efforts over the last five years. Acquisitive growth as well as higher income from existing practices (from patient volume and reimbursement contract increases) led to a 14% increase in revenues (to $1.8 billion) and an 11% increase in net income (to $241 million) during 2012.

Strategy

Today the company's business strategy is to become a leading provider of physician services by acquiring smaller physician practice groups across the US and continuing to develop administrative expertise. MEDNAX added 16 physician groups during 2012 through transactions totaling more than $450 million in value. Purchases included anesthesiology maternal-fetal neonatal and pediatric specialty practices.

The company also works to retain and strengthen existing physician practice relations and win new contracts by offering services and management information systems that improve operational efficiencies. In addition MEDNAX has established a Patient Safety Organization tasked with improving the quality and safety of care by collecting and analyzing data related to patients.

Company Background

Hoping to reproduce its pediatric business model for its anesthesiology business MEDNAX expanded its acquisitions beyond maternal-fetal newborn and pediatric care to include anesthesiology practices in 2007. To reflect its broadening operations the company —formerly named Pediatrix Medical Group —undertook a name and business structure change in late 2008 with MEDNAX established as a holding company.

EXECUTIVES

President American Anesthesiology, Karl B. Wagner, age 47, $500,000 total compensation
CEO and Director, Roger J. Medel, age 67, $950,000 total compensation
Regional President Central Region, Robert J. Balcom
President and COO, Joseph M. Calabro, age 52, $600,000 total compensation
Regional President Mountain Region, Eric H. Kurzweil
Regional President Caribbean Region, Carlos A. Perez
Chairman, Cesar L. Alvarez, age 66
SVP and CIO, Robert C. Bryant
President Pediatrix Division, Michael D. Stanley
COO Pediatrix Division, David A. Clark, age 46
Regional President Pacific Region, Gary A. Twiggs
Regional President Atlantic Region, Alan Oliver
Regional President South Central Region, James Q. Swift
SVP General Counsel and Secretary, Thomas W. Hawkins, age 51, $425,000 total compensation
VP Communications and Investor Relations, David Parker
SVP Research Education and Development, Alan R. Spitzer
SVP Operations Anesthesia Services, William C. Hawk
CFO and Treasurer, Vivian Lopez-Blanco, age 55
SVP Business Development, Steve C. Collins
Senior Vice President General Counsel Secretary, Dominic J. Andreano
Senior Vice President American Anesthesiology, Eric W. Mason
Regional President American Anesthesiology, Harris Thompson
Director, Enrique J. Sosa, age 72
Director, Paul G. Gabos, age 48
CEO and Director, Roger J. Medel, age 66
Director, Donna E. Shalala, age 72
Director, Waldemar A. Carlo, age 60
Director, Michael B. Fernandez, age 60
Director, Roger K. Freeman, age 77
Director, Manuel Kadre, age 47
Director, Pascal J. Goldschmidt, age 59
Director, Dany Garcia, age 44
Auditors: PricewaterhouseCoopersLLP

LOCATIONS

HQ: MEDNAX Inc.
1301 Concord Terrace, Sunrise FL 33323
Phone: 954-384-0175   **Fax:** 954-838-9961
Web: www.mednax.com

Selected Locations
Alaska
Arizona
Arkansas
California
Colorado
Florida
Georgia
Idaho
Indiana
Illinois
Iowa
Kansas
Kentucky
Louisiana
Maryland
Michigan
Missouri
Montana
Nevada
New Jersey
New Mexico
New York
North Carolina
Ohio
Oklahoma
Oregon
Pennsylvania
South Carolina
Tennessee
Texas
Utah
Virginia
Washington
West Virginia
Puerto Rico

PRODUCTS/OPERATIONS

2012 Net Patient Service Revenue

	% of total
Neonatal & other pediatric	56
Anesthesia	27
Maternal-fetal	12
Pediatric	5
Total	**100**

2012 Payer Mix

	% of total
Contracted managed	69
Government	24
Other third	6
Private-pay	1
Total	**100**

Selected Physician Specialties
Anesthesia care (inpatient pain relief care before during and after surgery)
Anesthesia subspecialty care (obstetrical critical care cardiac and pediatric anesthesia subspecialties)
Maternal-fetal care (inpatient and outpatient clinical care of high-risk expectant mothers and fetuses)
Neonatal care (clinical care of premature newborns or babies with complications)
Pain management (acute and chronic pain management services; postoperative acute pain management; outpatient chronic pain services at clinics and medical offices)
Pediatric cardiology care (inpatient and outpatient care of fetuses infants children and adolescents with congenital heart defects or acquired heart diseases; through affiliations care of adults with congenital heart defects)
Other pediatric subspecialty care (inpatient care for critically ill or injured children and adolescents)

COMPETITORS

ApolloMD	IPC The Hospitalist
CEP America	Company
Cogent HMG	Orion HealthCorp
EmCare	Physician Staffing
Hospital Physician	Sheridan Healthcare
Partners	Team Health

HISTORICAL FINANCIALS
Company Type: Public

Income Statement

	REVENUE ($ mil.)	NET INCOME ($ mil.)	NET PROFIT MARGIN	EMPLOYEES
			FYE: December 31	
12/13	2,154.0	280.5	13.0%	8,800
12/12	1,816.6	240.9	13.3%	7,900
12/11	1,588.2	218.0	13.7%	6,967
12/10	1,401.5	202.6	14.5%	6,270
12/09	1,288.2	175.8	13.6%	4,150
Annual Growth	**13.7%**	**12.4%**	**—**	**20.7%**

2013 Year-End Financials

Debt ratio: 0.8%	No. of shares (mil.): 101
Return on equity: 12.8%	Dividends
Cash ($ mil.): 31	Yield: —
Current ratio: 1.25	Payout: —
Long-term debt ($ mil.): 27	Market value ($ mil.): 5,402

	STOCK PRICE ($) FY Close	P/E High/Low		PER SHARE ($)		
				Earnings	Dividends	Book Value
12/13	53.38	40	19	2.78	0.00	23.15
12/12	79.52	33	24	2.43	0.00	20.35
12/11	72.01	33	26	2.24	0.00	17.69
12/10	67.29	31	21	2.13	0.00	15.10
12/09	60.11	32	13	1.89	0.00	12.67
Annual Growth	**(2.9%)**	**—**	**—**	**10.1%**	**—**	**16.3%**

Mentor Graphics Corp

Mentor Graphics knows that everyone sometimes needs a helping hand even engineers. The company is a leading global developer of electronic design automation (EDA) software and systems used by engineers to design simulate and test electronic components such as integrated circuits (IC's) wire harness systems and printed circuit boards (PCBs). Products include PADS (PCB design) Nucleus (operating system) and Calibre (IC design). Its software is used to design components for such products as computers and wireless handsets. Clients come from such industries as aerospace IT and telecommunications. Mentor Graphics gets more than half of its revenues from Europe and the Asia/Pacific region particularly Japan.

In fiscal 2012 Mentor Graphic's revenue crested the $1 billion dollar mark for the first time. Sales of software and related systems which account for more than 60% of sales enjoyed a jump of 12% for the year compared with 2011 thanks mainly to large contract renewals as well as an increase in smaller sales. Sales of services and technical support also grew 9% on strong demand. The company's top ten clients accounted for 45% of its business in 2012.

Despite higher operating expenses in 2012 particularly in the areas of sales marketing and research and development Mentor Graphics enjoyed profit growth of about 300% for the year by keeping other costs down.

Mentor Graphics sees the development of new EDA applications as key to maintaining market share and like many competitors in the market the company is aggressive on the acquisition front buying smaller companies for both the technology they've developed and for their engineering staff and expertise.

In 2012 Mentor Graphics acquired Dutch-owned UK-based Flowmaster Group a developer of system design software used by engineers to simulate computational fluid dynamics. Flowmaster's applications aid in the design of complex fluid flow network systems such as water-cooled electronic racks automotive vehicle thermal management and aerospace fuel systems. The deal complemented Mentor Graphic's existing mechanical analysis products such as its Flomerics application.

In 2010 the company purchased Valor Computerized Systems an Israel-based provider of productivity improvement software for printed circuit board manufacturers and distributors. Also that year it acquired the Virtual Garage product line from Freescale. Virtual Garage is used in designing automotive electrical and electronic systems and Mentor Graphics saw it as complementary technology to its CHS software for electrical systems design and wire harness engineering.

The company additionally bought California-based software developer CodeSourcery in 2010 to strengthen its open source systems development holdings. CodeSourcery specialized in tools designed to help embedded software developers create open source applications for use in consumer electronics such as cell phones.

HISTORY

Mentor Graphics was founded in 1981 by a group from instrument maker Tektronix to market desktop computers to design engineers. Throughout the 1980s the company was a leader in electronic design automation (EDA) software but the early 1990s found it in trouble. Revenues fell because of delays in upgrade releases and a worldwide recession.

In 1992 Mentor Graphics began phasing out hardware sales further disrupting operations. Texas Instruments veteran Walden Rhines became CEO in 1993. That year the company acquired CheckLogic a maker of testing software for integrated circuit (IC) design. By 1994 cost-cutting and product line restructuring returned Mentor to profitability.

The company bought ANACAD which developed design software for analog and mixed-signal ICs and Model Technology a very-high-density logic simulation tool firm in 1994. It acquired 14 more companies in 1995 and 1996 including embedded software tool developer Microtec Research (1996) which moved Mentor into the market for software development tools.

In 1997 a federal court rejected Mentor Graphics's appeal of a 1996 International Trade Commission ruling that the company had infringed on patents by rival Quickturn Design Systems and Mentor Graphics was prohibited from selling its SimExpress emulation products in the US. This sparked Mentor Graphics's harsh feud with Quickturn that would include a number of rejected buyout offers and a proxy fight. It lost its last hostile bid for Quickturn to a higher offer from EDA rival Cadence Design Systems.

Mentor Graphics in 1998 acquired CLK Computer-Aided Design and OPC Technology (optical proximity correction software). In 1999 the company bought Intergraph's EDA subsidiary VeriBest. The next year it acquired Germany-based Descon Informationssysteme a privately held maker of product data management software.

In 2002 the company bought Accelerated Technology for $23.4 million IKOS Systems for $103 million and Innoveda for $155.8 million.

Mentor Graphics bought mechanical analysis tools developer Flomerics in 2008. In 2009 the

company purchased LogicVision for $13 million. The deal added built-in-self-test (BIST) technologies that strengthened the company's silicon test offerings enabling it to offer a comprehensive product for customers looking to test digital logic and memory designs.

EXECUTIVES

SVP World Trade, L. Don Maulsby, age 61, $383,790 total compensation

VP and General Manager Systems Design, Henry (Henry) Potts, age 66, $405,373 total compensation

VP General Counsel and Secretary, Dean M. Freed, age 54, $179,572 total compensation

President, Gregory K. (Greg) Hinckley, age 64, $539,111 total compensation

Chairman and CEO, Walden C. (Wally) Rhines, age 66, $659,551 total compensation

VP and General Manager Deep Submicron Division, Robert Hum, age 60, $319,725 total compensation

VP Corporate Marketing, Brian Derrick, age 49, $278,882 total compensation

VP Europe, Hanns Windele

VP and General Manager Design-to-Silicon, Joseph D. (Joe) Sawicki, age 52, $345,000 total compensation

VP Global Accounts, Don Cantow

Director Public and Investor Relations, Ryerson (Ry) Schwark

VP and General Manager Mentor Emulation, Eric Selosse

VP New Ventures; General Manager System-Level Engineering, Serge Leef

VP and General Manager Design and Synthesis Division, Simon Bloch

VP Sales Americas, Marc A. Corbacho

VP and Chief Human Resources Officer, Michael H. (Mike) Vishny, age 49

Senior Public Relations Manager, Suzanne Graham

General Manager Mentor Graphics Embedded Software Division, Glenn Perry

Vice President PacRim, Danny Perng

Senior Public Relations Manager, Sonia Harrison

VP and General Manager Design Verification Technology, John Lenyo

VP Worldwide Consulting, Paul Hofstadler

Product Marketing Communications ESL Functional Verification Deep Submicron, Carole Thurman

Product Marketing Communications PCB FPGA Embedded S/W Mechanical Analysis, Larry Toda

Product Marketing Communications Automotive and Aerospace Tools, James Price

VP and CIO, Ananthan Thandri

Regional Business Manager Americas Valor Division, Dan Weitzman

VP Corporate Development and Investor Relations, Joseph (Joe) Reinhart

Product Marketing Communications Design-to-Silicon, Gene Forte

Manager Public Relations, Kim Coxe

Media Relations, Ry Schwark

Director Embedded Tools Embedded Software Division, Mark Mitchell

Media Relations, Carole Dunn

Director Marketing Emulation Division, Jim Kenney

Director Marketing Embedded Software Division, Shay Benchorin

General Manager Mechanical Analysis Division, Erich Buergel

General Manager Place and Route Group, Pravin Madhani

Corporate Controller and Chief Accounting Officer, Richard Trebing

VP Global Distribution Channel, Rick Bosshardt

Director of Marketing, Jake Alamat

Senior Vice President - World Trade, Don Maulsby

Vice President - Corporate Development and Investor Relations, Joe Reinhart

President and Director, Gregory K. (Greg) Hinckley, age 65

Director, James R. (Jim) Fiebiger, age 70

Director, Fontaine K. Richardson, age 71

Director, Marsha B. Congdon, age 66

Director, Kevin C. McDonough, age 63

Director, Sir Peter L. Bonfield, age 68

Director, Patrick (Pat) McManus, age 73

Independent Director, David Schechter

Auditors: KPMGLLP

LOCATIONS

HQ: Mentor Graphics Corporation
8005 SW Boeckman Rd., Wilsonville OR 97070-7777
Phone: 503-685-7000   **Fax:** 503-685-1204
Web: www.mentor.com

2012 Sales

	$ mil.	% of total
North America		
US	397	39
Other countries	18	3
Europe	247	24
Pacific Rim		
Japan	116	11
Other countries	234	23
Total	**1,014**	**100**

PRODUCTS/OPERATIONS

2012 Sales

	$ mil.	% of total
System & software	631	62
Service & support	383	38
Total	**1,014**	**100**

Selected Products

Embedded software development
  Compilers
  Debugger
  Real-time operating system
Integrated circuit (IC) design and verification
  Analog/mixed signal
  Custom design
  Design-for-test
  Field-programmable gate array/application-specific IC design
  Formal verification
  High-capacity circuit simulation
  Interconnect modeling
  Physical optimization
  Physical verification & manufacturability
  Resolution enhancement technologies
  Static timing
  Synthesis
Printed circuit board design and analysis
  Design tools
  Digital high-speed
  Integration interfaces and viewers
  Layout
  Library management
  Radio-frequency/mixed-signal
  Simulation and analysis
System-level design and verification
  Accelerated system verification
  Cabling design and analysis
  Design creation
  Digital simulation
  Hardware emulation and simulation
  Intellectual property
  Process management
  System-on-a-chip
  Web-based development system

COMPETITORS

ANSYS	Interra Systems
AXIOM Design	Intrinsix

Altium
Ansoft
Atrenta
Autodesk
Blue Ridge Numerics
Cadence Design
CollabNet
Green Hills Software

Magma Design
PDF Solutions
QNX Software Systems
Silvaco
Synopsys
Wind River Systems
Zuken

HISTORICAL FINANCIALS
Company Type: Public

Income Statement
FYE: January 31

	REVENUE ($ mil.)	NET INCOME ($ mil.)	NET PROFIT MARGIN	EMPLOYEES
01/13	1,088.7	138.7	12.7%	5,029
01/12	1,014.6	83.8	8.3%	4,800
01/11	914.7	28.5	3.1%	4,700
01/10	802.7	(21.8)	—	4,400
01/09	789.1	(88.8)	—	4,500
Annual Growth	8.4%	—	—	2.8%

2013 Year-End Financials

Debt ratio: 12.8%
Return on equity: 14.5%
Cash ($ mil.): 223
Current ratio: 1.71
Long-term debt ($ mil.): 218

No. of shares (mil.): 112
Dividends
Yield: —
Payout: —
Market value ($ mil.): 1,934

	STOCK PRICE ($) FY Close	P/E High/Low		PER SHARE ($) Earnings	Dividends	Book Value
01/13	17.13	14	11	1.17	0.00	9.15
01/12	13.87	21	12	0.74	0.00	7.92
01/11	12.74	47	29	0.26	0.00	6.98
01/10	8.02	—	—	(0.23)	0.00	6.37
01/09	4.66	—	—	(0.97)	0.00	6.10
Annual Growth	38.5%	—	—	—	—	10.7%

MercadoLibre Inc

Mercadolibre greases the wheels of commerce in Latin America. Its online trading service enables individuals and businesses to electronically arrange the sale and purchase of items in more than 2000 categories. In addition to its auction and classified listing services Mercadolibre offers an online payment service (MercadoPago) to further facilitate electronic transactions. The company serves some 550 million users in about a dozen countries in Latin America; the majority of its sales come from Brazil. Sales come from listing fees fees based on the value of goods sold and ancillary services. Online auction giant eBay owns about 18% of Mercadolibre.

Geographic Reach
Mercadolibre's reporting segments include its operations in Brazil Argentina Mexico Venezuela and other countries (Chile Colombia Costa Rica Dominican Republic Ecuador Panama Peru Portugal and Uruguay).

Financial Performance
The company's annual revenue has been trending upward year-over-year. In fiscal 2012 it claimed revenue of $373.6 million up from the $298.9 million it brought in during fiscal 2011 and the $216.7 million the company reported for revenue during fiscal 2010.

EXECUTIVES

Executive Vice President Chief Operating Officer, Hernan Kazah, age 42, $206,840 total compensation
Executive Vice President; Chief Operating Officer, Stelleo Tolda, age 45, $209,650 total compensation
VP and Chief Accounting Officer, Marcelo Melamud, age 42, $83,646 total compensation
Investor Relations, Pedro Arnt
Media Relations, Lorena Diaz Quijano
SVP Payments, Osvaldo Gimenez, age 42, $153,215 total compensation
Senior Vice President; Chief Technology Officer, Daniel Rabinovich
Chairman of the Board; President; Chief Executive Officer, Marcos Galperin
Independent Director, Michael Spence, age 69
Independent Director, Veronica Allende Serra, age 43
Independent Director, Emiliano Calemzuk, age 39
Independent Director, Mario Vazquez
Independent Director, Susan Segal
Auditors: PriceWaterhouse&Co.SRL

LOCATIONS

HQ: MercadoLibre Inc
  Arias 3751, 7th Floor, Buenos Aires C1430CRG
Phone: (54) 11 4640 8000
Web: www.mercadolibre.com

COMPETITORS

Amazon.com
Google
PayPal
Yahoo!
eBay

HISTORICAL FINANCIALS
Company Type: Public

Income Statement
FYE: December 31

	REVENUE ($ mil.)	NET INCOME ($ mil.)	NET PROFIT MARGIN	EMPLOYEES
12/12	373.6	101.2	27.1%	1,892
12/11	298.9	76.7	25.7%	1,633
12/10	216.7	56.0	25.9%	1,567
12/09	172.8	33.2	19.2%	1,466
12/08	137.0	18.8	13.7%	1,295
Annual Growth	28.5%	52.3%	—	9.9%

2012 Year-End Financials

Debt ratio: —
Return on equity: 39.6%
Cash ($ mil.): 101
Current ratio: 1.62
Long-term debt ($ mil.): —

No. of shares (mil.): 44
Dividends
Yield: 0.5%
Payout: 18.9%
Market value ($ mil.): 3,468

	STOCK PRICE ($) FY Close	P/E High/Low		PER SHARE ($) Earnings	Dividends	Book Value
12/12	78.55	45	28	2.30	0.44	6.56
12/11	79.54	55	29	1.73	0.32	4.97
12/10	66.65	59	29	1.27	0.00	3.89
12/09	51.87	73	17	0.75	0.00	2.59
12/08	16.41	172	19	0.42	0.00	2.12
Annual Growth	47.9%	—	—	53.0%	—	32.7%

Meridian Interstate Bancorp Inc

Contrary to its name Meridian Interstate Bancorp pretty much keeps it to a single state. It is the holding company of East Boston Savings Bank which provides standard deposit and lending services to individuals and businesses in the greater Boston area. The bank writes single-family commercial and multifamily mortgages as well as construction and business loans and consumer loans. East Boston Savings operates about 20 branches in eastern Massachusetts. Mutual holding company Meridian Financial Services owns 55% of Meridian Interstate Bancorp.

As part of its growth strategy the bank intends to bolster its commercial real estate and business loans as well as its construction loans. Currently residential mortgages represent the company's largest loan segment.

The bank also intends to grow through the opening of de novo branches and pursuing branch acquisitions. In 2010 East Boston Savings Bank acquired Mt. Washington Cooperative Bank in a stock swap. Mt. Washington had six branches in central and suburban Boston giving East Boston Savings some 20 full service branch offices in the metropolitan area.

Meridian Interstate owns a 40% stake in Hampshire First Bank a New Hampshire-chartered bank established in 2006.

EXECUTIVES

Chief Financial Officer, Mark L. Abbate, age 58
Senior Vice President Consumer & Business Banking, Keith D. Armstrong
Chairman and CEO, Richard J. Gavegnano, age 65, $311,400 total compensation
EVP and Director, Philip F. Freehan, age 61, $239,757 total compensation
Senior Vice President Operations, Paula M. Cotter
VP Deposit Operations, Lynne Brown
Human Resources Officer, Anne Lyon
Marketing Director, Lisa M. Kornachuk
Executive Vice President Corporate Banking, Frank Romano
Senior Vice President Chief Information Officer, John A. Carroll
Executive Vice President Lending, John Migliozzi
President Chief Operating Officer, Deborah J. Jackson
Senior Vice President Human Resources, Eric M. Heath
Vice President Residential Loan Officer, Peter Hughes
EVP and Director, Philip F. Freehan, age 61
Director, Vincent D. Basile, age 72
Director, James P. Del Rossi, age 75
Director, James G. Sartori, age 68
Director, Paul T. Sullivan, age 66
Director, Marilyn A. Censullo, age 55
Director, Edward L. Lynch, age 71
Director, Gregory F. Natalucci, age 66
Director, Anna R. DiMaria, age 66
Director, Richard F. Fernandez, age 70
Director, Domenic A. Gambardella, age 66
Auditors: Wolf&CompanyP.C.

Merit Medical Systems, Inc.

When it comes to medical devices this company believes its merits speak for themselves. Merit Medical Systems makes disposable medical products used during interventional and diagnostic cardiology radiology gastroenterology and pulmonary procedures. The company's products include catheters guide wires needles and tubing used in heart stent procedures pacemaker placement and angioplasties as well as products for endoscopy dialysis and other procedures. Merit Medical sells its products as stand-alone items or in custom-made kits to hospitals and other health care providers as well as to custom packagers and equipment makers worldwide.

Geographic Reach

Though the US accounts for more than 60% of sales the company is focused on growth in over-seas markets. It experienced a 37% increase in international sales during 2012.

Headquartered in South Jordan Utah Merit Medical has a major manufacturing and distribution center in Ireland. It also has manufacturing centers in Texas and Virginia in the US as well as in the Netherlands and France.

Operations

The company's largest operating segment —accounting for more than 95% of sales —is its cardiovascular division which makes cardiology and radiology devices for the diagnosis of arterial and vascular disease among other conditions. Offerings include stand-alone devices custom procedure trays and kits inflation devices and catheters. It also includes embolotherapy products which use bioengineered microspheres to create targeted vascular occlusion (the blockage of blood vessels) and drug delivery.

Merit Medical's much smaller endoscopy segment makes devices for gastroenterology and pulmonary treatments including minimally-invasive treatment of throat and biliary constriction from malignant tumors. The endoscopy operations are conducted through Merit Medical's Endotek subsidiary.

The company also conducts selected manufacturing of custom medical kits and components for third parties through its OEM division.

Sales and Marketing

Marketing and sales efforts in the US and abroad are conducted through a direct sales force of about 200 representatives as well as through independent distributors and manufacturers. Products are marketed to hospital and clinic-based medical professionals in fields including cardiology radiology gastroenterology pulmonary medicine vascular surgery pain management and thoracic surgery.

Financial Performance

Continuing on its growth trajectory over the last five years Merit Medical's revenues grew by 10% in 2012 thanks to increased sales from its cardiovascular and endoscopy segments. The increase in sales of guidewires hemostasis valves catheters and custom kits and trays attributed to growth in the Cardiovascular segment and a rise in sales of the EndoMAXX esophageal stent helped to grow revenue in the Endoscopy segment.

Net income has fluctuated however as Merit Medical has worked to balance costs with earnings. The company's net income decreased by 14% due to higher operating expenses primarily from the expansion of its sales and marketing force as well as higher R&D costs. In 2011 jumped by 85% in 2011 due to increased sales volumes higher gross margins and a lower effective income tax rates.

Strategy

Though a sizable part of Merit Medical's strategy is growth by acquisition the company also invests about 5% of its annual income in research and development efforts. In 2012 the company got FDA clearance to market the Merit Laureate hydrophilic guide wire as well as its 30-60um QuadraSphere Microspheres and its ONE Snare endovascular system. Also in 2012 the company made several investments to expand its international sales and distribution network especially in emerging markets such as Brazil India and Russia.

Mergers and Acquisitions

In 2012 Merit Medical acquired Ostial Solutions LLC a privately-held company based in Kalamazoo Michigan which makes a tool that improves the accuracy of stent placement. Also that year it purchased catheter-based vascular access device maker Thomas Medical Products for some $167 million and peritoneal dialysis catheter manufacturer Medigroup for $4 million.

Ownership

Investors in Merit Medical include Edgepoint Investment Group and Blackrock each of which hold a 10% stake.

EXECUTIVES

CFO Secretary Treasurer and Director, Kent W. Stanger, age 58, $251,296 total compensation
Chairman President and CEO, Fred P. Lampropoulos, age 63, $555,185 total compensation
IR Officer; Vice President - Corporate Communications, Anne-Marie Wright
Chief Legal Officer, Rashelle Perry, age 47, $196,296 total compensation
Chief Accounting Officer, Gregory L. Barnett, age 51
EVP Sales and Marketing, Martin R. (Marty) Stephens, age 59, $350,000 total compensation
President Merit Endotek, Darla R. Gill
President Merit Technology Group, Joseph (Joe) Wright
COO, Arlin D. Nelson, age 72, $217,871 total compensation
Chief Information Officer, Joe Pierce
EVP Global OEM and Europe the Middle East and Africa, Justin Lampropoulos
Chief Information Officer, Joseph Pierce
CFO Secretary Treasurer and Director, Kent W. Stanger, age 58
Director, Rex C. Bean, age 83
Director, Richard W. Edelman, age 72
Director, James J. (Jim) Ellis, age 78
Director, Michael E. Stillabower, age 69
Director, Franklin J. Miller, age 72
Independent Director, Nolan Karras
Independent Director, Scott Anderson
Auditors: Deloitte&ToucheLLP

LOCATIONS

HQ: Merit Medical Systems Inc.
1600 W. Merit Pkwy., South Jordan UT 84095
Phone: 801-253-1600 **Fax:** 801-253-1687
Web: www.merit.com

2012 Sales

US	248	63
Total	**394**	**100**

PRODUCTS/OPERATIONS

2012 Sales

	$ mil.	% of total
Cardiovascular	378	96
Endoscopy	15	4
Total	**394**	**100**

Selected Products

Backstop (waste handling system)
BasixCOMPAK (inflation devices)
Blue Diamond (inflation devices)
Captiva Blood Containment Device (safety and waste management)
DialEase (sheath introducers)
En Snare (retrieval device)
Fountain (thrombolytic infusion catheters)
Inqwire (diagnostic guide wire)
Intellisystem (inflation devices)
Majestik (angiography needles)
Medallion (specialty syringes)
Merit Disposal Depot (waste handling system)
Meritrans (disposable blood pressure transducer)
Monarch (inflation devices)
Prelude (sheath introducers)
ProGuide (chronic dialysis catheter)
Smart Tip (coronary control syringes)

HISTORICAL FINANCIALS

Company Type: Public

Income Statement

FYE: December 31

	REVENUE ($ mil.)	NET INCOME ($ mil.)	NET PROFIT MARGIN	EMPLOYEES
12/12	394.2	19.7	5.0%	2,760
12/11	359.4	23.0	6.4%	2,400
12/10	296.7	12.4	4.2%	2,178
12/09	257.4	22.5	8.8%	1,875
12/08	227.1	20.7	9.1%	1,654
Annual Growth	14.8%	(1.2%)	—	13.7%

2012 Year-End Financials

Debt ratio: 33.6%
Return on equity: 5.3%
Cash ($ mil.): 9
Current ratio: 2.22
Long-term debt ($ mil.): 227

No. of shares (mil.): 42
Dividends
 Yield: —
 Payout: —
Market value ($ mil.): 591

	STOCK PRICE ($) FY Close	P/E High/Low	PER SHARE ($) Earnings	Dividends	Book Value
12/12	13.90	32 25	0.46	0.00	8.98
12/11	13.38	41 21	0.58	0.00	8.50
12/10	15.83	56 40	0.34	0.00	6.64
12/09	19.24	31 15	0.63	0.00	6.21
12/08	17.93	35 21	0.58	0.00	5.53
Annual Growth	(6.2%)	— —	(5.8%)	—	12.9%

Mesa Laboratories, Inc.

Mesa Laboratories is reaching a plateau in the field of measurements. The company makes niche-market electronic measurement testing and recording instruments for medical food processing electronics and aerospace applications. Mesa's products include sensors that record temperature humidity and pressure levels; flow meters for water treatment polymerization and chemical processing applications; and sonic concentration analyzers. The company also makes kidney hemodialysis treatment products including metering equipment and machines that clean dialyzers (or filters) for reuse. It also provides repair recalibration and certification services.

Operations

The company is organized into two segments - biological indicators and instruments - each accounting for about half of sales. Biological indicators sold under the Mesa and Apex brands are used by dental offices hospitals and manufacturers of medical devices and pharmaceuticals for quality control testing in sterilization processes. The instruments division includes the DataTrace (data loggers) Bios Torqo (bottle cap test systems) and Nusonics (ultrasonic fluid measurement systems) brands.

A third division continuous monitoring was created in 2013 through the acquisition of two businesses. Continuous monitoring systems provide temperature control to laboratories that require stable environments such as hospitals blood banks pharmacies and medical device manufacturers.

Geographic Reach

Mesa Laboratories has manufacturing plants in Lakewood Colorado; Butler New Jersey; Bozeman Montana; and Omaha Nebraska. The new continuous monitoring division operates from Marlton New Jersey; and Emeryville California.

Sales and Marketing

The company uses a direct sales force as well as distributors for international sales. Customers in the US account for about 60% of revenue.

Financial Performance

Overall sales grew 17% in fiscal 2013 (year-end March) to $46 million. Both product segments - biological indicators and instruments - enjoyed increased sales from both organic (new customers) and inorganic (acquisitions) growth. Profits grew 6% to $8 million. While the company has always been small (less than $50 million in sales) it also keeps low operating expenses and thus has always been profitable.

Mergers and Acquisitions

Inorganic growth is a key strategy of Mesa Laboratories. In November 2013 it bought two companies to create the continuous monitoring systems segment which is expected to add about $10 million a year to its top line. The company paid almost $22 million for New Jersey-based Amega Scientific Corporation and California-based TempSys Inc. Continuous monitoring systems provide temperature control to laboratories that require stable environments such as hospitals blood banks pharmacies and medical device manufacturers.

Earlier that year it bought the SureTorque line of bottle cap torque testing instruments from ST Acquisitions LLC for $2 million. SureTorque instruments can be configured for a variety of industries including pharmaceutical biotechnology and food and beverage.

In 2012 Mesa bought the flow calibrator business of Bios International for more than $15 million. Bios flow calibration instrumentation is used in applications such as industrial hygiene and process control environmental monitoring and meteorology in sectors such as automotive biotech food processing semiconductors and more. The purchase followed Mesa's acquisition strategy of finding successful products in regulated industries.

HISTORY

In 2009 president John Sullivan took the reins as CEO replacing Luke Schmieder who had been CEO since founding the company in 1982. Still chairman of the board Schmieder owns about 9% of Mesa Laboratories.

EXECUTIVES

Chairman, Luke R. Schmieder, age 71, $85,221 total compensation
President; Chief Executive Officer; Treasurer; Director, John J. Sullivan, age 61, $181,000 total compensation
VP Sales and Marketing, Glenn E. Adriance, age 59, $103,334 total compensation
Chief Financial Officer; Executive Vice President; Corporate Secretary, John Sakys
Director, David M. Kelly, age 71
Director, Evan C. Guillemin, age 46
Director, H. Stuart Campbell, age 84
Director, Michael T. Brooks, age 65

President CEO and Director, John J. Sullivan, age 60
Director, Robert V. Dwyer, age 73
Auditors: EhrhardtKeefeSteiner&HottmanPC

LOCATIONS

HQ: Mesa Laboratories Inc.
 12100 W. 6th Ave., Lakewood CO 80228
Phone: 303-987-8000 **Fax:** 303-987-8989
Web: www.mesalabs.com

2013 Sales

	$ mil.	% of total
US	28	62
Other countries	17	38
Total	46	100

PRODUCTS/OPERATIONS

2013 Sales

	$ mil.	% of total
Product	35	76
Other	11	24
Total	46	100

2013 Sales

	$ mil.	% of total
Instruments	25	53
Biological indicators	21	47
Total	46	100

Selected Products

Biological and chemical indicators (Raven Biological Laboratories)
Electronic thermal sensors
 DATATRACE
 DATATRACE Micropack Tracers
 ELOGG
 Flatpack Tracers
 FRB Tracers
Hemodialysis products (Automata)
 Database management software (Reuse Data Management System)
 Dialyzer reprocessors (ECHO MM-1000)
 Meters (Western Meters)
Sonic fluid measurement products (NuSonics)
 Sonic concentration analyzers
 Sonic flowmeters

HISTORICAL FINANCIALS

Company Type: Public

Income Statement

FYE: March 31

	REVENUE ($ mil.)	NET INCOME ($ mil.)	NET PROFIT MARGIN	EMPLOYEES
03/13	46.4	8.4	18.2%	215
03/12	39.6	7.9	20.0%	186
03/11	32.8	6.1	18.8%	177
03/10	21.9	4.7	21.7%	112
03/09	21.5	4.7	22.2%	111
Annual Growth	21.2%	15.2%	—	18.0%

2013 Year-End Financials

Debt ratio: 6.0%	No. of shares (mil.): 3	
Return on equity: 17.4%	Dividends	
Cash ($ mil.): 4	Yield: 0.0%	
Current ratio: 4.17	Payout: 22.9%	
Long-term debt ($ mil.): 4	Market value ($ mil.): 179	

	STOCK PRICE ($) FY Close	P/E High/Low	PER SHARE ($) Earnings	Dividends	Book Value
03/13	52.78	22 17	2.35	0.54	15.57
03/12	49.32	24 12	2.29	0.50	13.22
03/11	28.80	16 11	1.86	0.46	11.20
03/10	25.96	19 11	1.45	0.42	9.74
03/09	16.00	16 10	1.48	0.40	8.67
Annual Growth	34.8%	— —	12.3%	7.8%	15.7%

Microchip Technology, Inc.

While bigger chip makers fight over your PC and mobile phone Microchip Technology has embedded itself in your car your copier and even your wallet. The semiconductor maker offers a variety of embedded devices including eight-bit microcontrollers (it's one of the top makers of them worldwide); specialty memory products such as electrically erasable programmable read-only memories (EEPROMs); and KEELOQ brand code-hopping devices used in keyless locks garage door openers and smart cards. Its chips are used by tens of thousands of customers in the automotive consumer industrial office automation and telecommunications markets. Microchip gets about 80% of sales from customers outside the US.

The percentage of Microchip Technology's sales attributable to Asia has increased as more customers have moved their manufacturing operations to the region generating more than half of the company's sales. Customers in China account for nearly a quarter of sales and those located in Taiwan make up another 15%. The company has production facilities in the US and Thailand and sales offices throughout the world. Sales operations in the Americas (the US Canada and Central and South America) and Europe support much of design for products shipped for Asia. In addition Microchip sources around 20% of its wafer needs from contract manufacturers or foundries.

Net sales decreased by about 7% to $1.38 billion in fiscal 2012 compared to 2011 primarily due to an 8% reduction in number of units sold and weakness in the semiconductor industry. Though Microchip Technology remained profitable net income was down 20% for the year. About $6.7 million of that decrease was due to lower capacity utilization; when production at its manufacturing facilities falls below normal operating capacity Microchip charges it directly to cost of sales.

By segment sales of microcontrollers which account for about two-thirds of Microchip's revenue dropped 8% in fiscal 2012 on weak economic conditions that affect sales to such end markets as automotive computing communications consumer and industrial control. Sales of memory products were down 19% for the year due to lower demand in the Serial EEPROM and Flash memory markets while sales of analog and interface products fell

4%. Unlike many chip makers Microchip doesn't experience significant fluctuations in average selling prices particularly in its microcontroller and analog and interface groups where a large proportion of products are considered proprietary. Though the company points to moderate pricing pressures average selling prices were flat for 2012 and didn't contribute to the lower sales.

Microchip's 2010 acquisition of Silicon Storage Technology (SST) contributed to higher sales of memory products in 2011 and an increase in global memory market share. The company acquired flash memory maker SST for around $275 million in cash. The deal added SST's flash technology more than 360 patents and more microcontrollers to Microchip's portfolio. As part of the transaction Microchip sold SST's NAND drives NAND controllers smart card integrated circuits and other products to Greenliant Systems a company formed by Bing Yeh the former chairman and CEO of SST.

Also in 2010 Microchip picked up ZeroG Wireless. The acquisition of Wi-Fi technology which is being used more in embedded applications was the crux of the purchase enhancing the company's product line with Wi-Fi capability and related software.

In 2012 Microchip bought Standard Microsystems Corporation (SMSC) in an equity transaction valued at around $939 million ($766 million net of SMSC's cash on hand and investments). SMSC's mixed-signal connectivity products for embedded applications will complement Microchip's embedded control products and further expand its reach in the automotive computing consumer industrial and wireless audio markets. Earlier that year Microchip bought Roving Networks a fabless developer of low-power embedded Wi-Fi transceivers and Bluetooth modules. The purchase improved its ability to target new markets for embedded components especially for such products as smartphone accessories.

HISTORY

Investment firm Sequoia Capital acquired a washed-up semiconductor subsidiary from General Instrument in 1989. Sequoia executive Steve Sanghi a veteran of Intel was tapped to head the operation Microchip Technology. Sanghi instituted a bare-bones operating budget and broadened the company's focus beyond low-cost memory products to include more profitable embedded microcontrollers. By 1992 Microchip turned a small profit.

In 1995 Microchip acquired the rights to KEELOQ secure data transmission products developed by South Africa's Nanoteq Ltd. The following year the company introduced its own line of secure data transmission products and its first flash memory microcontrollers. In 1997 Microchip unveiled the world's smallest erasable read-only memory to be used in devices such as keyless entries dimmers and thermostats. In 1998 Microchip settled litigation with ROHM whose Exel Microelectronics unit was an original KEELOQ licensee; ROHM surrendered its licensing rights to the technology.

Streamlining around its more cost-effective manufacturing operations Microchip in 1999 closed a wafer fabrication plant (or fab) and a test facility. In 2001 the company beefed up its analog product line by acquiring TelCom Semiconductor a maker of chips for wireless phones.

In 2002 Microchip paid $54 million in cash for privately held PowerSmart a Duracell spinoff that made embedded controllers and battery sensors.

Also that year the company acquired a large wafer fab in Oregon from Fujitsu for about $180 million in cash. Microchip launched a new e-commerce Web site in 2003.

CEO Steve Sanghi and former HR VP Michael Jones wrote a book about the company's early years and how Microchip survived and prospered. Published in 2006 by John Wiley & Sons Driving Excellence: How the Aggregate System Turned Microchip Technology from a Failing Company to a Market Leader recounted the hardscrabble measures taken in 1990 and following years to save the company from collapse leading to its successful IPO in 1993. The "aggregate system" referred to in the title was a collection of 10 corporate precepts including clear company values and having employees share in the company's prosperity.

Also in 2006 Microchip created a Medical Products Group targeting the $100 billion medical devices market especially those devices used by consumers.

In 2008 Microchip made an unsolicited takeover offer for competitor Atmel a supplier of microcontrollers and other chips. The company privately approached Atmel about a potential merger before going public with a cash offer to buy the company valued at around $2.3 billion.

Microchip made the bid in concert with ON Semiconductor which wanted to buy Atmel's automotive nonvolatile memory and radio-frequency (RF) product lines if Microchip succeeded in acquiring Atmel. Microchip also planned to divest Atmel's application-specific integrated circuit business which provides customized chips to customers to a third party.

Atmel's board of directors rejected the Microchip/ON Semi bid. Microchip then said it intended to nominate a slate of directors at Atmel's next annual meeting. The company reported that it received clearance from US antitrust regulators on acquiring Atmel.

In late 2008 however ON Semi reported it was dropping out of the bid citing "the unforeseen deterioration in the semiconductor market since we announced our proposal as well as the unprecedented weakness in the financial markets." Microchip withdrew its proposal as a result while later nominating a dissident slate of nominees for Atmel's annual meeting. The company dropped the proxy battle in 2009 citing deteriorating conditions in Atmel's business the semiconductor industry in general and the global economy.

In 2009 the company purchased R&E International. R&E developed integrated circuits used in security and life safety equipment (smoke and carbon monoxide detectors). Also that year Microchip acquired Australia-based HI-TECH Software. The purchase added development tools for embedded systems and extended the company's market share in the compiler technology sector.

EXECUTIVES

VP Analog and Interface Products Division, Richard J. Simoncic, age 49, $163,184 total compensation

VP Business Development and Investor Relations, Gordon W. Parnell, age 63, $207,816 total compensation

VP Fab Operations, David S. Lambert, age 61, $208,334 total compensation

VP Worldwide Sales and Applications, Mitchell R. Little, age 61, $240,290 total compensation

Chairman President and CEO, Steve Sanghi, age 57, $505,762 total compensation

VP Americas Sales, Thomas J. Grune, age 48

EVP and COO, Ganesh Moorthy, age 53, $242,483
total compensation
VP Fab 2 Operations, Michael A. Finley
Investor Relations, Deborah L. Wussler
**VP Security Microcontroller and Technology
Division,** Stephen V. (Steve) Drehobl, age 51
VP Memory Products Division, Randall L. (Randy)
Drwinga
VP Analog and Interface Marketing, Bryan J.
Liddiard
VP High-Performance Microcontroller Division,
Sumit K. Mitra
VP Information Services, Robert H. Owen
VP Vertical Markets Group, Dan L. Termer
VP Pacific Rim Finance, William Yang
**VP Advanced Microcontroller Architecture
Division,** Mitchel Obolsky
VP Development Tools Group, Derek P. Carlson
VP and CFO, J. Eric Bjornholt, age 42, $165,476 total
compensation
**VP Global Sales Support and Electronic
Manufacturing Systems,** Paul R. Breault
VP European Sales, Gary P. Marsh
VP Worldwide Applications Engineering, Ken N.
Pye
VP Human Resources, Lauren A. Carr
VP Asia Sales, Joseph R. Krawczyk
VP Pacific Rim Manufacturing Operations,
Mathew B. Bunker
VP RF Division, P. Daniel Chow
VP Licensing, Mark W. Reiten
Vice President Europe Finance, Nawaz Sharif
VP SuperFLASH Design, Ian Yue
Vice President Computing Products Group, Ian F.
Harris
**Vice President General Counsel Corporate
Secretary,** Kimberly Herk
Vice President Wireless Products Division,
Stephen T. Caldwell
Vice President India Development Center,
Sudarshan Iyengar
Director, Albert J. Hugo-Martinez, age 67
Director, Matthew W. Chapman, age 62
Director, Wade F. Meyercord, age 72
Director, L. B. Day, age 68
Auditors: Ernst&YoungLLP

LOCATIONS

HQ: Microchip Technology Incorporated
  2355 W. Chandler Blvd., Chandler AZ 85224-6199
Phone: 480-792-7200   **Fax:** 480-899-9210
Web: www.microchip.com

2012 Sales

	$ mil.	% of total
Asia	772	56
Europe	319	23
Americas	290	21
Total	**1,383**	**100**

PRODUCTS/OPERATIONS

2012 Sales

	$ mil.	% of total
Microcontrollers	928	67
Memory products	179	13
Analog & interface products	171	13
Technology licensing	87	6
Other	17	1
Total	**1,383**	**100**

Selected Products

Analog and Interface Integrated Circuits (ICs)
  Interface devices
    Controllers
    Infrared codecs
  Linear devices
    Audio amplifiers

Comparators
Operational amplifiers
Mixed-signal devices
  Analog-to-digital (A/D) and digital-to-analog (D/A)
    converters
  Digital potentiometers
Power management devices
  DC-to-DC converters
  Linear regulators
  Power MOSFET drivers
  Switching regulators
  System supervisors
  Voltage detectors
  Voltage references
Thermal management devices
  Brushless DC fan controllers
  Temperature sensors
KEELOQ Security Devices
  Decoders
  Encoders
  Transcoders
Memory Chips
  Serial and parallel erasable programmable read-only
    memories (EPROMs)
  Serial electrically erasable programmable read-only
    memories (EEPROMs)
Microcontrollers
  Eight-bit microcontrollers (PICmicro and rfPIC lines)
  Mixed-signal controllers
Radio-frequency identification (RFID) ICs

COMPETITORS

Altera	Maxim Integrated
Analog Devices	Products
Atmel	Mitsubishi Electric
Cypress Semiconductor	ON Semiconductor
Dialog Semiconductor	Oki Semiconductor
Echelon Corporation	ROHM
Fairchild	RadiSys
Semiconductor	Ramtron International
Freescale	Renesas Electronics
Semiconductor	STMicroelectronics
Fujitsu Semiconductor	Silicon Labs
Intel	Texas Instruments
Intersil	Winbond Electronics
Linear Technology	ZiLOG
Macronix International	

HISTORICAL FINANCIALS

Company Type: Public

Income Statement

FYE: March 31

	REVENUE ($ mil.)	NET INCOME ($ mil.)	NET PROFIT MARGIN	EMPLOYEES
03/13	1,581.6	127.3	8.1%	8,003
03/12	1,383.1	336.7	24.3%	6,923
03/11	1,487.2	418.9	28.2%	6,970
03/10	947.7	217.0	22.9%	5,418
03/09	903.3	248.8	27.5%	4,895
Annual Growth	**15.0%**	**(15.4%)**	**—**	**13.1%**

2013 Year-End Financials

Debt ratio: 25.5%
Return on equity: 6.4%
Cash ($ mil.): 528
Current ratio: 6.55
Long-term debt ($ mil.): 983

No. of shares (mil.): 196
Dividends
  Yield: 0.0%
  Payout: 226.7%
Market value ($ mil.): 7,224

	STOCK PRICE ($) FY Close	P/E High/Low		PER SHARE ($) Earnings	Dividends	Book Value
03/13	36.77	57	45	0.62	1.41	9.84
03/12	37.20	23	17	1.65	1.39	10.31
03/11	38.01	17	12	2.15	1.72	9.56
03/10	28.16	25	17	1.16	1.36	8.27
03/09	21.19	28	12	1.33	1.35	5.42
Annual Growth	**14.8%**	**—**	**—**	**(17.4%)**	**1.1%**	**16.1%**

MicroFinancial, Inc.

MicroFinancial thinks big when it comes to leasing small-ticket commercial items to small and midsized businesses. Through subsidiary Time-Payment MicroFinancial leases items that are generally valued between $500 and $15000. Although the "microticket" leaser provides financing for a variety of office and commercial equipment the majority of the contracts in its portfolio are for point-of-sale authorization systems for debit and credit cards. It doesn't lease and rent equipment directly but through a network of independent dealers across the US. Internet-based TimePaymentDirect processes applications and approves credit; Insta-Lease provides the same services via telephone fax and e-mail.

Until 2002 the company operated primarily through subsidiary Leasecomm. That unit ran into legal difficulties over its business practices and lost its credit facility. MicroFinancial resumed lease-financing originations in 2004 primarily under the TimePayment subsidiary.

Chairman Peter Bleyleben and directors Brian Boyle and Torrence Harder each own more than 10% of MicroFinancial.

EXECUTIVES

VP Human Resources, Stephen J. Constantino, age
  54, $134,898 total compensation
**President; Chief Executive Officer; Secretary;
  Treasurer; Clerk; Director,** Richard F. Latour, age
  60, $301,273 total compensation
Chairman, Peter R. Bleyleben, age 61, $130,000 total
  compensation
Chief Financial Officer; Vice President, James R.
  Jackson Jr., age 52, $210,230 total compensation
VP Legal and Vendor Lessee Relations, Steven J.
  LaCreta, age 54, $137,560 total compensation
VP Sales TimePayment, Mark Sullivan
Vice President - Sales, Vartan Hagopian
Director, John W. Everets, age 65
Director, Frederick E. (Fritz) von Mering, age 59
**President CEO Secretary Treasurer Clerk and
  Director,** Richard F. Latour, age 59
Director, Brian E. Boyle, age 66
Director, Alan J. Zakon, age 78
Director, Torrence C. Harder, age 70
Auditors: VitaleCaturano&CompanyPC

LOCATIONS

HQ: MicroFinancial Incorporated
  10M Commerce Way, Woburn MA 01801
Phone: 781-994-4800   **Fax:** 781-994-4710
Web: www.microfinancial.com

PRODUCTS/OPERATIONS

2009 Sales

	$ mil.	% of total
Financing leases	29	64
Loss & damage waiver fees	4	9
Service contracts	0	1
Service fees & other	3	7

COMPETITORS

CIT Group	Electro Rent
CalFirst	Fiserv
ECHO Inc.	

HISTORICAL FINANCIALS

Company Type: Public

Income Statement

FYE: December 31

	REVENUE ($ mil.)	NET INCOME ($ mil.)	NET PROFIT MARGIN	EMPLOYEES
12/12	59.3	9.3	15.8%	152
12/11	54.6	8.9	16.4%	135
12/10	50.9	5.3	10.4%	118
12/09	46.1	4.1	8.9%	111
12/08	39.5	5.9	15.1%	103
Annual Growth	10.7%	12.0%	—	10.2%

2012 Year-End Financials

Debt ratio: 41.4%
Return on equity: 11.8%
Cash ($ mil.): 3
Current ratio: 0.33
Long-term debt ($ mil.): 70

No. of shares (mil.): 14
Dividends
  Yield: 3.3%
  Payout: 37.5%
Market value ($ mil.): 105

	STOCK PRICE ($) FY Close	P/E High/Low		PER SHARE ($) Earnings	Dividends	Book Value
12/12	7.28	15	9	0.64	0.24	5.69
12/11	5.82	10	6	0.62	0.21	5.31
12/10	4.03	13	8	0.37	0.20	4.88
12/09	3.10	13	6	0.29	0.20	4.71
12/08	2.02	15	4	0.42	0.20	4.58
Annual Growth	37.8%	—	—	11.1%	4.7%	5.6%

Micros Systems, Inc.

MICROS' systems don't fold sheets bus tables or stock shelves but they do keep hotels restaurants and retail stores in order. MICROS Systems supplies point-of-sale terminals central reservation systems inventory and loss prevention systems and other hardware and software for the hospitality and retail industries. Customers include Hyatt Hotels InterContinental Hotels and Marriott International as well as IHOP Starbucks Wendy's Belk and The Jones Group. Additionally MICROS products are used in related settings such as casinos cruise ships sports arenas airport concourses and theme parks. The company generates more than half of its sales outside the US and Canada.

Operations MICROS outsources manufacturing of its computer hardware to Venture Group of Singapore a contract electronics manufacturer that is a wholly owned subsidiary of Venture Corporation.

Financial Analysis In fiscal 2012 (ended June 30) MICROS reported double-digit growth in both revenue and net income. Its revenue rose 10% to $1.1 billion while net income rose 16% to $167 million. An improving global economy and higher service revenues from an expanded customer base were key factors in the uptick.

Mergers and Acquisitions MICROS has used acquisitions to expand its product line and geographic presence. In 2012 the company acquired Torex Retail Holdings which operates mainly in the UK and Europe (but also in the US) to further its strategy of international expansion. Other acquisitions include TIG Global an interactive marketing firm for the hospitality and travel industries and Fry a provider of e-commerce design and development and managed services. Fry which became part of MICROS-Retail was acquired for its e-commerce expertise and technology for retail Web

sites; MICROS has extended Fry's technology to industries other than retail.

HISTORY

MICROS Systems was founded in 1977 as an offshoot of IDEAS a computer consulting firm founded by MICROS director Louis Brown. IDEAS consulted for MKD a cash register company whose VP Bernie Silverman suggested that IDEAS could use PC technology in making its own point-of-sale terminals. Brown ran with the idea. In 1981 MICROS went public and five years later Westinghouse Electric bought 19% of the company (that stake reached 62% before Westinghouse —later CBS Corporation —sold it off in 1995).

With Westinghouse's deep pockets behind it MICROS landed national restaurant clients such as Burger King T.G.I. Friday's and Wendy's. In 1993 it bought into Fidelio Software a maker of systems for processing reservations and providing sales and accounting information at hotels and resorts. Two years later MICROS enhanced its market share by acquiring the rest of Fidelio whose hotel clients included Hyatt Marriott and Radisson.

The hospitality industry's need for greater cost and inventory control spurred MICROS to grow and diversify into areas such as casinos and cruise ships. In 1998 MICROS streamlined operations by moving away from hardware manufacturing and toward higher-commodity software closing a German office and outsourcing hardware production.

In 1999 MICROS bought its largest North American distributor Hayman Systems and OPUS 2 Revenue Technologies a provider of yield management software for the hospitality industry. The following year the company installed its largest ever front-office system for the 2000 Summer Olympic Games in Sydney.

In 2001 MICROS acquired Germany-based point-of-sale systems maker Indatec. The company launched myfidelio.net a portal for the hotel industry in 2002. In 2003 MICROS acquired store management software maker Datavantage for approximately $52 million in cash and stock.

The company acquired wireless paging specialist JTECH Communications in 2005. JTECH made pagers that soundlessly alert restaurant patrons usually with flashing LEDs that their table is finally available or their takeout order is ready.

In 2006 MICROS purchased the assets of TangentPOS a provider of point-of-sale systems for foodservice and retail operators; TangentPOS had 200 installations across North America. In 2007 MICROS acquired the hospitality and retail subsidiaries of RedSky IT a UK-based developer of lifecycle management and supply chain software.

EXECUTIVES

Executive Vice President Strategic Initiatives and General Counsel, Thomas L. Patz, age 53, $715,000 total compensation

EVP Latin American Region, Bernard Jammet, age 55, $410,700 total compensation

Chairman, A.L. (Tom) Giannopoulos, age 73, $2,000,000 total compensation

President CEO and Director, Peter A. Altabef, age 53

EVP and CFO, Cynthia A. Russo, age 43, $265,314 total compensation

Executive Vice President North America Restaurants, Ed Chapel

Executive Vice President of Investor Relations and Business Development, Peter J. Rogers Jr., age 58

EVP Asia Pacific Region, Stefan M. Piringer, age 47

Executive Vice President Europe-Africa-Middle East Region, Kaweh Niroomand, age 59

Executive Vice President North America Operations, Jennifer M. (Jenny) Kurdle, age 46, $400,000 total compensation

Executive Vice President MICROS eCommerce U.S., John E. Gularson, age 43

VP-Bus Svcs, Jim Borkowski

Chief Information Security Officer, James T. Walsh

SVP Hotels Leisure and Entertainment, Daniel J. Bell

SVP Restaurants, Jeffrey A. Pinc

Vice President Leisure and Entertainment, Don DeMarinis

Vice President West Major Account Restaurants, Dan Harley

Vice President MICROS-Retail John E. Gularson, Jeremy Grunzweig

Director, Louis M. (Lou) Brown Jr., age 69

President CEO and Director, Peter A. Altabef, age 53

Director, Dwight S. Taylor, age 67

Director, John G. Puente, age 82

Director, F. Suzanne Jenniches, age 65

Director, B. Gary Dando, age 70

Auditors: PricewaterhouseCoopersLLP

LOCATIONS

HQ: MICROS Systems Inc.
7031 Columbia Gateway Dr., Columbia MD 21046-2289
Phone: 443-285-6000   Fax: 443-285-0650
Web: www.micros.com

2012 Sales

	$ mil.	% of total
US/Canada	521	47
International	586	53
Total	1,107	100

PRODUCTS/OPERATIONS

2012 Sales

	$ mil.	% of total
Services	727	66
Hardware	238	21
Software	142	13
Total	1,107	100

Selected Product Types

Hotel Systems (OPERA Fidelio)
  Central reservation
  Customer information
  Internet-based hotel reservations
  Property management
  Revenue management
Restaurant Systems
  Point-of-sale (POS) hardware and software systems (Simphony mymicros.net MICROS 9700 HMS MICROS 3700 POS MICROS e7 POS)
Retail Systems
  POS software (Store 21 Tradewind Xstore)
  Inventory and order managment (CWDirect Cross Channel CWLocate CWCollaborate)

COMPETITORS

Agilysys	Oracle
Amadeus IT	PAR Technology
CAM Commerce Solutions	Panasonic Corp
CASIO COMPUTER	Pegasus Solutions
Dell	SAP
Demandware	Sabre Holdings
Epicor Software	ScanSource
Equinox Payments	Sharp Corp.
GSI Commerce	Torex Retail
Hewlett-Packard	TravelCLICK
IBM	Travelport
Ingenico	VeriFone

JDA Software
NCR
Newmarket
International

Wincor Nixdorf

HISTORICAL FINANCIALS
Company Type: Public

Income Statement
FYE: June 30

	REVENUE ($ mil.)	NET INCOME ($ mil.)	NET PROFIT MARGIN	EMPLOYEES
06/13	1,268.0	171.4	13.5%	6,506
06/12	1,107.5	166.9	15.1%	6,383
06/11	1,007.8	144.0	14.3%	4,953
06/10	914.3	114.3	12.5%	4,646
06/09	911.8	99.3	10.9%	4,757
Annual Growth	8.6%	14.6%		8.1%

2013 Year-End Financials

Debt ratio: 0.1%	No. of shares (mil.): 76
Return on equity: 15.5%	Dividends
Cash ($ mil.): 486	Yield: —
Current ratio: 2.35	Payout: —
Long-term debt ($ mil.): —	Market value ($ mil.): 3,311

	STOCK PRICE ($) FY Close	P/E High/Low	PER SHARE ($) Earnings	Dividends	Book Value
06/13	43.15	25 18	2.12	0.00	14.53
06/12	51.20	28 19	2.03	0.00	13.61
06/11	49.71	30 19	1.74	0.00	12.58
06/10	31.87	26 16	1.41	0.00	9.79
06/09	25.32	28 11	1.21	0.00	9.01
Annual Growth	14.3%	— —	15.1%	—	12.7%

Microsemi Corp.

Microsemi is on a power trip. The company makes power management semiconductors that regulate and condition electricity to make it more usable by electrical and electronic systems. Its products include discrete components such as diodes and rectifiers along with integrated circuits such as amplifiers and voltage regulators. Microsemi also makes devices for pacemakers GPS products LCD TVs and wireless networks. The company's high-reliability semiconductors go into jet engines missile systems oilfield equipment and satellites. Top customers have included big names like Boeing Dell Honeywell Medtronic Boston Scientific and Lockheed Martin. More than 40% of sales come from outside the US.

HISTORY

Microsemiconductor Corporation started in 1960 as a maker of power conditioning equipment. Early acquisitions included two lines of semiconductors from Globe Union. Philip Frey joined the company as CEO and president in 1971. It went public in 1981 and changed its name to Microsemi in 1982.

Throughout the mid-1980s and early 1990s military business accounted for up to 75% of sales. By means of acquisitions Microsemi consolidated its clout as a military contractor and diversified its customer base. In 1992 it bought a semiconductor manufacturing division of Unitrode —a pur-

chase that also increased its presence in Europe and Asia. Other acquisitions included units from Raytheon (1995) SGS-Thomson (now STMicroelectronics) and National Semiconductor (1996) PPC Products (1997) and BKC Semiconductors and Semicon (1998).

Microsemi sold its low-growth contract circuit board assembly operations in 1998. It formed a development pact with Advanced Power Technology (APT) that year to expand in the medical market. In 1999 Microsemi acquired SymmetriCom's Linfinity Microelectronics subsidiary (power management products for consumer electronics) and Narda Microwave's semiconductor operations.

In 2000 former Linfinity president James Peterson replaced Frey as CEO (Frey remained chairman until 2002). The following year saw Microsemi acquire Compensated Devices and New England Semiconductor both makers of electronic components primarily for aerospace customers.

In 2002 Microsemi launched a restructuring effort that included closing plants and relocating operations. The company also sold its Carlsbad design center to AMI Semiconductor as well as its India-based Semcon Electronics subsidiary.

Nick Yocca who had served as the company's chairman since 2002 retired from the board in 2004. Dennis Leibel succeeded him as chairman. Later that year Microsemi sued rival Monolithic Power Systems alleging patent infringement involving certain products. (The litigation was settled in 2006.) Also that year the company licensed packaging technology from Diodes Inc.

Microsemi initiated further consolidation in 2005 planning to shutter its wafer fab in Broomfield Colorado and its plant in Ennis Ireland. Work done in those two facilities was to be reassigned to other Microsemi facilities.

The company later reversed its plant-closing moves due to customer demand. The reprieve for the Broomfield fab was temporary lasting into 2009 while increased demand for high-reliability defense and commercial air/satellite products kept the Ennis plant open.

In 2006 Microsemi acquired Advanced Power Technology (APT) for about $130 million in cash and stock. APT became a wholly owned subsidiary of Microsemi functioning as the company's Power Products Group.

In 2007 the company acquired PowerDsine for about $245 million in cash and stock. PowerDsine specialized in chips for transmitting electrical power over Ethernet local-area networks. The Israeli-American firm complemented Microsemi's analog and mixed-signal semiconductor design expertise.

In 2008 the company acquired the assets of Microwave Device Technology Corporation (MDT) for nearly $9 million. The purchase added microwave diodes made of gallium arsenide to Microsemi's portfolio of silicon-based microwave semiconductors as well as added sensor devices for intrusion alarms motion and speed detectors and other products.

In 2009 Microsemi acquired the defense electronics and security business of Endwave strengthening its existing RF operations. Earlier that year it bought the Space Level Power Products business of Spectrum Microwave Inc. a wholly owned subsidiary of Spectrum Control. The acquisition complements the company's offerings in radiation-hardened and radiation-tolerant transistors for the military/aerospace market as well as Microsemi's DC-DC power management devices.

In 2009 the company also bought Electro Module and subsidiary Babcock Inc. adding power supplies flat-panel displays and relays to its power

management division. In its last purchase of the year Microsemi bought Nexsem which makes high-voltage DC-DC power conversion devices for LCD TV notebook netbook and set-top box applications.

In 2009 the company announced it would lay off about 300 employees (an 18% reduction in workforce) and that it would close its Scottsdale Arizona facility as part of consolidation efforts.

In 2010 the company acquired Actel a maker of field programmable gate arrays (FPGAs) in a transaction valued at around $430 million. Actel became Microsemi's SoC Division. Earlier the same year the company swallowed up White Electronic Designs (semiconductor design assembly and test integration for military/aerospace applications) for about $163 million in cash.

In a deal that bolstered its US Defense Department (DoD) business Microsemi bought the Arxan Defense Systems subsidiary of Arxan Technologies in 2010. Arxan Defense Systems made the EnforcIT software and firmware platform that defense contractors use to protect their systems against piracy reverse engineering tampering and other threats.

EXECUTIVES

Executive Vice President Chief Financial Officer Secretary and Treasurer, John W. Hohener, age 59, $300,000 total compensation
Chairman of the Board and Chief Executive Officer, James J. (Jim) Peterson, age 58, $600,000 total compensation
SVP Human Resources, John M. Holtrust, age 62, $259,500 total compensation
EVP and COO, Ralph Brandi, age 67, $399,640 total compensation
Corporate Communications Manager, Cliff Silver
Senior Vice President Distribution Sales, Michael G. (Mike) Sivetts III
Chairman, Dennis R. Leibel, age 68
President and Chief Operating Officer, Paul Pickle
VP Hi-Rel Sales, John Costello
EVP and Chief Strategy Officer, Steven G. Litchfield, age 44, $290,640 total compensation
VP Corporate Development, Robert C. Adams
EVP Worldwide Marketing, Russell Garcia, age 52
SVP Worldwide Sales, Frederick C. (Rick) Goerner, age 64
VP Legal, David Goren
Director, Matthew E. (Matt) Massengill, age 52
Director, Paul F. Folino, age 67
Director, William E. (Bill) Bendush, age 63
Director, William L. Healey, age 67
President CEO and Director, James J. (Jim) Peterson, age 57
Director, Thomas R. Anderson, age 68
Auditors: PricewaterhouseCoopersLLP

LOCATIONS

HQ: Microsemi Corporation
1 Enterprise, Aliso Viejo CA 92656
Phone: 949-380-6100   **Fax:** 949-215-4996
Web: www.microsemi.com

2012 Sales

US	565	56
Europe	290	29

PRODUCTS/OPERATIONS

2012 Sales by Market

Communications	312	31
Security & defense	286	28
Aerospace	212	21
Total	**1,012**	**100**

Selected Products

Application-specific standard products (ASSPs)
 Audio amplification integrated circuits (ICs)
 Backlight inverters
 Small computer standard interface (SCSI) terminators
Discrete components
 Automatic surge protectors
 Computer switching diodes
 Low-leakage and high-voltage diodes
 Silicon rectifiers
 Transient suppressor diodes
 Transistors
 Zener diodes
EnforcIT software and firmware platform for securing
 defense-related projects
Standard linear ICs (SLICs)
 Low-dropout regulators (LDOs)
 Pulse width modulators (PWMs)

COMPETITORS

ANADIGICS	Monolithic Power
Aeroflex	Systems
Altera	NXP Semiconductors
Analog Devices	O2Micro
Conexant Systems	ON Semiconductor
Diodes	RF Micro Devices
Fairchild	Sanken Electric
Semiconductor	Semtech
Freescale	Shindengen Electric
Semiconductor	Manufacturing
IXYS	Silicon Labs
Integrated Device	Skyworks
Technology	Supertex
International	Texas Instruments
Rectifier	TriQuint
Linear Technology	Vishay Intertechnology
M/A-COM	Vitesse Semiconductor
Maxim Integrated	Volterra Semiconductor
Products	Xilinx
Micrel	

HISTORICAL FINANCIALS

Company Type: Public

Income Statement

FYE: September 29

	REVENUE ($ mil.)	NET INCOME ($ mil.)	NET PROFIT MARGIN	EMPLOYEES
09/13	975.9	43.6	4.5%	3,100
09/12*	1,012.5	(29.6)	—	2,200
10/11	835.8	54.4	6.5%	2,700
10/10	518.2	59.0	11.4%	2,250
09/09	452.9	(26.8)	—	2,200
Annual Growth	21.2%	—	—	9.0%

*Fiscal year change

2013 Year-End Financials

Debt ratio: 35.4%
Return on equity: 4.4%
Cash ($ mil.): 256
Current ratio: 4.67
Long-term debt ($ mil.): 678

No. of shares (mil.): 93
Dividends
 Yield: —
 Payout: —
Market value ($ mil.): 2,245

	STOCK PRICE ($) FY Close	P/E High/Low		PER SHARE ($) Earnings	Dividends	Book Value
09/13	23.92	54	36	0.48	0.00	11.00
09/12*	20.07	—	—	(0.35)	0.00	10.28
10/11	15.98	38	23	0.63	0.00	10.26
10/10	17.11	25	18	0.72	0.00	9.21
09/09	15.41	—	—	(0.34)	0.00	8.31
Annual Growth	11.6%	—	—	—	—	7.3%

*Fiscal year change

MicroStrategy Inc.

MicroStrategy knows you need the details to make a good plan. The company's business intelligence software addresses functions such as building reports and dashboards managing mobile applications and capitalizing on social media. Specific analytics modules include human resources management Web traffic analysis and sales and distribution. Its Angel.com unit provides cloud-based customer experience management software. It sells to many of the world's largest companies such as Aetna and eBay as well as midsized companies and government agencies such as NASA and the US Army. MicroStrategy also offers consulting and support services. Founded in 1989 MicroStrategy has operations in about 25 countries.

Geographic Reach

North America is the Virginia-based company's largest market accounting for 60% of its revenue. Europe the Middle East and Africa accounts for about 30%.

Sales and Marketing

Marketing its products worldwide MicroStrategy targets a variety of user types. In addition to large and medium-sized enterprises and government customers the company also targets advertising agencies and systems integrators that cater to those clients as well targeting independent software vendors that want to incorporate MicroStrategy's tools. The company primarily uses a direct sales force but it also distributes through indirect channel partners that include value-added resellers system integrators and OEMs.

Financial Performance

The company's revenue increased 6% in 2012 versus 2011 to $595 million driven by a 16% jump in sales by its Angel.com subsidiary. Also revenue from product support and other services grew 9% year over year on an increase in the number of product support contracts and an overall increase in renewal pricing on existing support contracts. While MicroStrategy has added more than $200 million in revenue since 2009 the rate of increase slowed in 2012.

Net income grew 15% to $21 million in 2012 versus 2011 primarily due to the increase in sales. The increase in profitability in 2012 followed two years of steep decline as the firm invested heavily in research and development sales and marketing and consulting capabilities during 2011. While it continued to invest in R&D in 2012 the rate of increase of expenses related to such investments was lower in 2012 compared with 2011. Investments in R&D and related expenses are expected to be higher in 2013.

Strategy

Areas of investment focus for the company include software technologies designed to help clients capitalize on four technology trends: Big Data; Mobile applications; Cloud-based services: and Social Networking. Recent entries include mobile and cloud-based platforms. The company's MicroStrategy 9 is the software platform that contains its core products. Mobile apps based on MicroStrategy 9 include integrated mapping with Google Maps integration with on-device sensors such as bar-code readers and mobile alerts. Besides mobile Microstrategy sees three other disruptive trends that it will focus on: big data the cloud and social media. The company's Microstrategy Wisdom for example analyzes Facebook data.

MicroStrategy has faced increasing competition from large enterprise software companies such as Oracle SAP and IBM as those companies acquire smaller business intelligence software makers in deals similar to IBM's purchase of SPSS. Despite the competitive relationship with these companies MicroStrategy also works through partnerships with them and many others including Leidos Symantec and Adobe.

MicroStrategy serves such industries as communications (BSkyB Cox Communications) consumer goods (Chiquita Danone) financial services (ABN AMRO Credit Agricole) healthcare (Bayer HealthCare Novation) insurance (Pacific Life GEICO) manufacturing (Michelin Philips Electronics) retail (Starbucks Guess?) technology (eBay McAfee) and the government (US Postal Service US Department of Homeland Security).

Ownership

Chairman and CEO Michael Saylor control the company through ownership of 64% of the company's voting shares and an 18% stake in the common stock.

EXECUTIVES

EVP Law and General Counsel, Jonathan F. Klein, age 47, $400,000 total compensation
EVP Strategic Development, Eduardo S. Sanchez, age 57, $250,000 total compensation
Vice Chairman EVP and COO, Sanju K. Bansal, age 48, $325,000 total compensation
Chairman President and CEO, Michael J. Saylor, age 49, $875,000 total compensation
Manager Customer Marketing, Claudia Cahill
EVP Worldwide Sales and Operations, Donald W. (Don) Hunt, age 58
Director Public Relations, Wende Cover
EVP Human Resources, Vincent M. Gabriele
Senior Executive Vice President; Chief Technology Officer, Peng Xiao
EVP Finance CFO and Treasurer, Douglas K. Thede, age 44
EVP Worldwide Professional Services, Bob Watts, age 45
Executive Vice President CIO, Michael Relich
Senior Director of Marketing, Richard Krueger
Senior Director of Marketing, Roland Fiege
Senior Vice President CIO, Thomas H. Murphy
VP of Information Strategy, Guillermo Ramas
Vice President and CMO, Joe Dupriest
President Chief Research Officer, Howard Dresner
Vice Chairman EVP and COO, Sanju K. Bansal, age 48
Director, Carl J. (Rick) Rickertsen, age 54
Director, Matthew W. (Matt) Calkins, age 41
Director, Jarrod M. Patten, age 42
Director, Robert H. Epstein, age 61
Director, David W. LaRue, age 63
Director, Thomas P. Spahr, age 49
Auditors: GrantThorntonLLP

LOCATIONS

HQ: MicroStrategy Inc.
 1850 Towers Crescent Plaza, Tysons Corner, VA 22182
Phone: 703 848-8600   **Fax:** 703 848-8610
Web: www.microstrategy.com

2012 Sales

	$ mil.	% of total
US & Canada	355	60
Europe the Middle East& Africa	177	30
Other regions	61	10
Total	**594**	**100**

PRODUCTS/OPERATIONS

2012 Sales

	$ mil.	% of total
Product support &other services	418	70
Product licenses	147	25
Angel.com	28	5
Total	**594**	**100**

Selected Products

MicroStrategy 9
  Command Manager
  Desktop
  Distribution Services
  Intelligence Server
  Office
  Report Services
  SDK
  Transaction Services
MicroStrategy Cloud
MicroStrategy Mobile
MicroStrategy Social
  Emma
  Usher
  Wisdom

COMPETITORS

Actuate	Oracle
IBM	QlikTech
Infor Global	SAP
Informatica	SAS Institute
Information Builders	TIBCO Software
JasperSoft	Tableau Software
Microsoft	Teradata

HISTORICAL FINANCIALS

Company Type: Public

Income Statement
FYE: December 31

	REVENUE ($ mil.)	NET INCOME ($ mil.)	NET PROFIT MARGIN	EMPLOYEES
12/12	594.6	20.5	3.5%	3,221
12/11	562.1	17.9	3.2%	3,088
12/10	454.5	43.7	9.6%	2,597
12/09	377.7	74.8	19.8%	1,816
12/08	360.3	41.8	11.6%	1,915
Annual Growth	13.3%	(16.3%)	—	13.9%

2012 Year-End Financials

Debt ratio: —	No. of shares (mil.): 11
Return on equity: 11.1%	Dividends
Cash ($ mil.): 224	Yield: —
Current ratio: 1.63	Payout: —
Long-term debt ($ mil.): —	Market value ($ mil.): 1,054

	STOCK PRICE ($) FY Close	P/E High/Low	PER SHARE ($) Earnings	Dividends	Book Value
12/12	93.38	84 46	1.84	0.00	17.75
12/11	108.32	105 51	1.62	0.00	15.67
12/10	85.47	27 18	3.72	0.00	14.02
12/09	94.02	15 5	6.09	0.00	17.93
12/08	37.13	27 9	3.40	0.00	11.61
Annual Growth	25.9%	— —(14.2%)	—	11.2%	

Mid-America Apartment Communities Inc

For Mid-America Apartment Communities the Sunbelt is where it's at. Operating as MAA the firm is a self-administered self-managed real estate investment trust (REIT) that focuses solely on buying multifamily residences. MAA owns or has interests in approximately 49500 apartment units in some 160 suburban communities primarily located in the Southeast and south-central US. Its largest markets are California Florida Tennessee and Texas where about 75% of its portfolio is located. The REIT's properties comprise some 49 million sq. ft. of rentable space. MAA which has an average property occupancy rate of 95% targets large and midsized markets. MAA has agreed to buy Colonial Properties.

Change in Company Type

MAA has offered to buy its smaller rival Colonial Properties Trust for about $2.1 billion in stock to create a Sunbelt-focused multifamily REIT with approximately 85000 apartments across 285 properties. Upon completion of the deal which has been approved by the boards of both companies and is expected to close in the third quarter of 2013 the combined company will retain the MAA name and be headquartered in Memphis.

Strategy

Rather than developing new properties MAA prefers to buy and upgrade existing complexes increasing curb appeal to attract middle-income residents. Although MAA generally considers property management and maintenance its focus and strength it does invest in new properties with joint venture partners from time to time and anticipates that that will be a growing part of its strategy.

The REIT has grown through acquisitions and development over the years. Although acquisition activity slowed a bit during the recession the company's purchasing has picked up speed as the country recovers from the economic downturn. Limited supply of new apartment communities being built and a decline in home ownership will drive up the demand for established apartment properties. Since the beginning of 2009 the REIT has invested in about two dozen new communities in its target markets; it acquired about a dozen new properties in 2011 alone. MAA also develops new properties but on a very limited scale. Occasionally the company sells properties that no longer fit in with its strategy; it sold two communities in 2011.

Multifamily investors have been leading the way in the slowly recovering property markets and MAA in particular has had strongly growing sales for at least a decade. Net income for the company rose 64% in 2011 largely due to an increase in revenues (which grew 11% to $499 million) and a gain on the sale of discontinued operations of about $12.8 million. The REIT's revenues grew as a result of the property acquisitions and rent increases at its existing holdings.

EXECUTIVES

Chairman President and CEO, H. Eric Bolton Jr., age 56, $404,134 total compensation

EVP and Director Property Management Operations, Thomas L. (Tom) Grimes Jr., $168,928 total compensation
SVP and Director of Corporate Support, James Maclin
SVP and Director of Physical Assets, Kevin Perkins
EVP and CFO, Albert M. (Al) Campbell III, age 46, $158,223 total compensation
VP Director External Reporting and Corporate Secretary, Leslie B. C. Wolfgang
SVP and Controller, Rick Barton
SVP South Regions Operations, Diane Chastain
SVP North Region Operations, Kim Banks
SVP West Region Operations, Cynthia Cloud McMillion
SVP East Region Operations, Jackie Melnick
SVP Management Information Systems, Shelton Barron
VP Marketing, Melintha Ogle
VP and Director of Risk Management, Doug Clark
VP Central Region Operations, Beth Brock
VP Coastal Region Operations, Robert Donnelly
Director, Alan B. Graf Jr., age 57
Director, D. Ralph Horn, age 72
Director, Simon R. C. Wadsworth, age 65
Director, William B. (Bill) Sansom, age 71
Director, John S. Grinalds, age 76
Director, W. Reid Sanders, age 64
Director, Philip W. Norwood
Auditors: Ernst&YoungLLP

LOCATIONS

HQ: Mid-America Apartment Communities Inc.
6584 Poplar Ave. Ste. 300, Memphis TN 38138
Phone: 901-682-6600   **Fax:** 404-601-6106
Web: www.jamesoninns.com

2010 Wholly-Owned Properties

	No.
Texas	33
Georgia	26
Florida	25
Tennessee	22
South	14
Kentucky	7
North	7
Mississippi	6
Alabama	4
Arkansas	3
Arizona	3
Ohio	1
Virginia	1
Total	**152**

PRODUCTS/OPERATIONS

2011 Sales

	$ mil.	% of total
Rental income	410	92
Other property income	37	8
Management fees	1	—
Total	**449**	**100**

COMPETITORS

AMLI Residential	Colonial Properties
Apartment Investment and Management	Equity Residential
	Milestone Management
Berkshire Income Realty	Post Properties
	Southern Management
Camden Property	UDR

HISTORICAL FINANCIALS

Company Type: Public

Income Statement

FYE: December 31

	REVENUE ($ mil.)	NET INCOME ($ mil.)	NET PROFIT MARGIN	EMPLOYEES
12/12	497.1	105.2	21.2%	1,446
12/11	448.9	48.8	10.9%	1,466
12/10	402.2	29.7	7.4%	1,389
12/09	378.5	37.2	9.8%	1,282
12/08	369.8	30.2	8.2%	1,245
Annual Growth	7.7%	36.6%	—	3.8%

2012 Year-End Financials

Debt ratio: 60.8%
Return on equity: 12.7%
Cash ($ mil.): 9
Current ratio: 0.88
Long-term debt ($ mil.): 1,673

No. of shares (mil.): 42
Dividends
Yield: 4.0%
Payout: 103.1%
Market value ($ mil.): 2,740

	STOCK PRICE ($) FY Close	P/E High/Low	PER SHARE ($) Earnings	Dividends	Book Value
12/12	64.75	27 23	2.56	2.64	21.71
12/11	62.55	55 42	1.31	2.51	18.54
12/10	63.49	113 80	0.56	2.46	14.98
12/09	48.28	58 27	0.85	2.46	14.89
12/08	37.16	92 37	0.64	2.46	14.67
Annual Growth	14.9%	— —	41.4%	1.8%	10.3%

Mid-Con Energy Partners LP

Mid-Con Energy Partners is a Delaware limited partnership that owns operates and develops producing oil and natural gas properties in North America. With a focus on the Mid-Continent region of the US in particular Oklahoma and Colorado the company's operations primarily consist of enhancing the development of mature producing oil properties through an oil recovery method called waterflooding. It has total estimated proved reserves of about 8 million barrels of oil equivalent a majority of which is oil. Managed by Mid-Con Energy GP Mid-Con Energy Partners was formed in July 2011 and went public in December 2011.

Following its $97 million offering Mid-Con Energy I and Mid-Con Energy II were merged into Mid-Con Energy Partners' wholly-owned subsidiary Mid-Con Energy Properties which holds the title to its parent's properties. A portion of the net proceeds from its IPO was used to pay the cash portion of the consideration in the merger.

Mid-Con Energy Partners filed its IPO on the strength of an asset portfolio that largely consists of properties that have relatively predictable production profiles modest capital requirements and good growth potential for waterflood development. More than 90% of its properties are already being waterflooded and have been producing since 1982 or earlier. Mid-Con Energy Partners' management team has actively operated most of its properties since 2005.

The company's primary business strategy is to generate stable cash flow by continuing to exploit its proved reserves to maximize production. It also

plans to pursue acquisitions of onshore properties with long-lived reserves low production decline rates and low-risk development potential as well as properties within mature oil fields with opportunities for incremental improvements in oil recovery. In addition the company will seek to reduce the impact of commodity price volatility on its cash flow through a commodity hedging strategy.

EXECUTIVES

Executive Chairman, S. Craig George, age 61
CEO and Director, Charles R. (Randy) Olmstead, age 65
President CFO and Director, Jeffrey R. Olmstead, age 36
VP and Chief Accounting Officer, David A. Culbertson, age 48
VP and Chief Engineer, Robbin W. Jones, age 54
Director, Peter A. Leidel, age 57
CEO and Director, Charles R. (Randy) Olmstead, age 65
President CFO and Director, Jeffrey R. Olmstead, age 36
Director, Cameron O. Smith, age 63
Director, Robert W. Berry, age 89
Director, Peter Adamson III, age 72
Auditors: GrantThorntonLLP

LOCATIONS

HQ: Mid-Con Energy Partners LP
2501 North Harwood Street, Suite 2410, Dallas, TX 75201
Phone: 972 479-5980
Web: www.midconenergypartners.com

COMPETITORS

Abraxas Petroleum
Chaparral Energy
Chesapeake Energy

Denbury Resources
EXCO Resources

HISTORICAL FINANCIALS

Company Type: Public

Income Statement

FYE: December 31

	REVENUE ($ mil.)	NET INCOME ($ mil.)	NET PROFIT MARGIN	EMPLOYEES
12/12	67.2	29.8	44.4%	0
12/11	39.3	18.9	48.3%	0
12/10	17.4	1.0	6.2%	0
12/09	5.9	(9.1)	—	0
Annual Growth	124.1%	—	—	—

2012 Year-End Financials

Debt ratio: 49.1%
Return on equity: —
Cash ($ mil.): 1
Current ratio: 2.13
Long-term debt ($ mil.): 78

No. of shares (mil.): 18
Dividends
Yield: 7.9%
Payout: 92.1%
Market value ($ mil.): 355

	STOCK PRICE ($) FY Close	P/E High/Low	PER SHARE ($) Earnings	Dividends	Book Value
12/12	18.70	15 11	1.62	1.49	3.80
12/11	18.35	18 17	1.05	0.00	2.46
12/10	0.00	— —	0.06	0.00	2.44
Annual Growth	—	—	419.6%	—	24.8%

Middleby Corp.

Middleby Corp. has been cashing in on cooks for more than a century. Founded in 1888 the company makes a slew of commercial and institutional foodservice equipment for restaurants retailers and hotels worldwide. Middleby operates through two segments: Commercial Foodservice Equipment and Food Processing Equipment. The largest Foodservice makes machines for most types of cooking and warming activities. Products are sold under some two dozen blue chip brands —Anets Blodgett Southbend and TurboChef among them. The Food Processing arm makes cooking mixing slicing and packaging machines for global food processing giants notably precooked meat.

Geographic Reach

Middleby operates nearly 20 manufacturing facilities in the US and 12 internationally throughout the Americas Europe Asia and the Middle East. About 70% of its revenues come from the US and Canada. Europe and the Middle East account for 15%.

Operations

The company's mainstay Commercial Foodservice Equipment segment offers ovens ranges broilers fryers toasters coffee and tea brewers and other cooking equipment; it generates around 75% of total sales each year. Its Food Processing Equipment group (25% of sales) offers a slate of labor-saving products from batch ovens to mixing and slicing machines packaging and food safety equipment. The group's manufacturing facilities often neighbor major food processors.

Sales and Marketing

Middleby's Commercial Foodservice Equipment products are sold in 100 countries through a combination of sales and marketing personnel and an extensive network of independent dealers distributors consultants sales representatives and agents. International sales are primarily made through a network of independent local country stocking and servicing distributors and dealers and directly to major chains hotels and other large end-users.

For its Food Processing Equipment segment Middleby employs regional sales managers each with responsibility for a group of customers and a particular region. Internationally it has sales and distribution offices in Australia Brazil Denmark France Italy Germany and Mexico along with global sales managers supported by a network of independent sales representatives.

Financial Performance

Middleby has enjoyed unprecedented growth over the last three years. Revenues rose by 21% from $856 million in 2011 to more than $1 billion in 2012. Profits also surged by 26% from $95 million in 2011 to $121 million in 2012. (Both these totals represented historic milestones for the company.)

Sales from its Food Processing Equipment segment soared by almost 90% for 2012 and Latin America sales shot up by more than 50%. The company attributes its sizable growth to incremental sales generated from acquisitions as well as the proliferation of chain restaurants in developing regions coupled with a slow recovery by major chains at home. The uptick in sales also reflects growing demand by retailers and restaurants for processed foods.

Strategy

Acquisitions have added to Middleby's revenue stream and strengthened its competitive position as a one-stop-shop for such giants as Cracker Barrel McDonald's Olive Garden and Panda Express. In 2013 it bought Spooner Vicars Bakery Systems a UK-based maker of baking machinery used in the cookie and cracker sector. The year before it purchased Nieco Corporation a maker of automatic broilers for $24 million. It also scooped up Viking Range Corporation a manufacturer of residential cooking ranges ovens and kitchen appliances for $380 million during 2012.

The company in 2011 obtained Denmark-based Danfotech a supplier of processing equipment (meat tenderizers presses and defrosting systems) for the meat industry. In a larger move Middleby purchased cooking equipment rival Lincat Group for almost $95 million. The acquisition not only expanded Middleby's international presence with brand names Lincat IMC and Brittania but secured manufacturing capacity in the UK.

EXECUTIVES

Chairman of the Board; President; Chief Executive Officer, Selim A. Bassoul, age 56, $1,000,000 total compensation

Chief Financial Officer; Vice President, Timothy J. (Tim) Fitzgerald, age 43, $400,000 total compensation

President Pitco Frialator, Paul Angrick, age 55

EVP Food Processing Group, Magdy Albert, age 61, $200,000 total compensation

Division President, Nestor Ibrahim, age 59, $150,000 total compensation

Director Investor and Public Relations, Darcy Bretz

President Middleby Cooking Systems Group, Mark A. Sieron, age 64, $200,000 total compensation

Treasurer, Martin M. Lindsay, age 48, $140,000 total compensation

Chief Operating Officer - Commercial Foodservice Equipment Group, David Brewer, age 56, $400,000 total compensation

President of Jade Range, Ray Williams, age 49

President Blodgett Oven Company, Gary Mick, age 50, $200,000 total compensation

VP Supply Chain; President Huono A/S Middleby Philippines Giga Grandi Cuicine and Frifri, Ousama Sidani, age 55

General Manager Middleby Worldwide, Douglas Dunn

President Southbend, John Perruccio

Regional Sales Manager India, Abhishek Azad

Regional Controller, Agustin Zufia

Sales Manager Spain and Portugal, Ana Alana

V.P. Latin American Operations, John Richardson

Sales Manager Western & Central Europe, Sebas Fernandez

Service Director, Jesus Guerrero

Sales Manager UAE Bahrain, Muhammad Qureshi

Sales Manager Saudi Arabia and Lebanon, Nabil Baba

Sales Manager Eastern Europe, Tarek Sarkis

Sales Manager, Martin Durante

Regional Vice President, Jerry Koo

Regional Sales Manager Hong Kong, Dennis Lam

Lead Independent Director, Gordon Brien

Sales Manager Belgium and Netherlands, Henk Roessink

Controller, Michele Oliveira

Lead Independent Director, Gordon OBrien

Director, John R. Miller III, age 72

Director, Philip G. Putnam, age 72

Director, Sabin C. Streeter, age 71

Director, Gordon J. O'Brien, age 48

Director, Robert B. Lamb, age 71

Director, Ryan Levenson, age 37

Auditors: Deloitte&ToucheLLP

LOCATIONS

HQ: The Middleby Corporation
1400 Toastmaster Dr., Elgin IL 60120
Phone: 847-741-3300   **Fax:** 847-741-0015
Web: www.middleby.com

2012 Sales

US & Canada	711	68
Asia	91	9
Total	**1,038**	**100**

PRODUCTS/OPERATIONS

2012 Sales

Commercial foodservice	786	76
Total	**1,038**	**100**

Selected Mergers and Acquisitions

FY2013
  Spooner Vicars Bakery Systems ($10 million; baking systems)
FY2012
  Turkington USA LLC ($10 million; maker of baked ovens)
  Stewart Systems Global LLC ($28 million; automated proofing and oven baking systems)
  Nieco Corporation ($24 million; manufacturer of automatic broilers)
  Viking Range Corporation ($280 million; cooking ranges ovens and kitchen appliances)
FY2011
  Lincat Group PLC ($82 million; ranges ovens and counterline equipment)

Selected Products and Brands

Commercial Foodservice Equipment Group
  Anets (griddles fryers dough rollers)
  Blodgett (convection and combi-ovens)
  Bloomfield (coffee and tea brewers beverage dispensing equipment)
  Carter-Hoffmann (heated cabinets rethermalizing and foodservice equipment)
  CookTek (induction cooking and warming systems)
  CTX (conveyor oven equipment)
  Doyon (baking ovens)
  Frifri (fryers and frying systems)
  GIGA Grandi Cucine (ranges steam cooking equipment and ovens)
  Holman (high-speed conveyor toasting equipment)
  Houno (combi-ovens and baking ovens)
  Jade (specialty cooking equipment)
  Lang (gas and electric solutions for commercial and marine applications)
  MagiKitch' n (charbroiling products)
  Middleby Marshall (conveyor oven equipment)
  Nu-Vu (on-premise baking equipment)
  Pito Frialator (fryers)
  Perfect Fry (fryers)
  Southbend (heavy-duty gas-fired equipment)
  Star (equipment for fast food and concessions)
  Toastmaster (conveyor toasters hot food servers griddles)
  TurboChef (rapid-cook ovens)
  Wells (countertop and drop-in warmers)
Food Processing Equipment Group
  Alkar (batch and belt ovens conveyor cooking systems)
  Cozzini (food processing equipment for grinding slicing emulsification mixing & blending)
  MP Equipment (breading battering mixing forming and slicing machines)
  RapidPak (packaging and food safety equipment)

COMPETITORS

AGA Rangemaster	Heat and Control
Ali SpA	Hobart Corp.
Alto-Shaam	Illinois Tool Works
Bally Refrigerated Boxes	Ingersoll-Rand
Cleveland Range	Krack
Dover Corp.	Lincoln Foodservice
Electrolux	Manitowoc Foodservice
Franke Group	Standex
Frymaster	Strategic Equipment and Supply
Gold Medal Products	Vulcan-Hart

HISTORICAL FINANCIALS

Company Type: Public

Income Statement

FYE: December 29

	REVENUE ($ mil.)	NET INCOME ($ mil.)	NET PROFIT MARGIN	EMPLOYEES
12/12	1,038.1	120.7	11.6%	3,140
12/11*	855.9	95.4	11.2%	2,150
01/11	719.1	72.8	10.1%	2,060
01/10	646.6	61.1	9.5%	1,902
01/09	651.8	63.9	9.8%	1,779
Annual Growth	**12.3%**	**17.2%**	**—**	**15.3%**

*Fiscal year change

2012 Year-End Financials

Debt ratio: 20.9%
Return on equity: 20.8%
Cash ($ mil.): 34
Current ratio: 1.70
Long-term debt ($ mil.): 258

No. of shares (mil.): 18
Dividends
  Yield: —
  Payout: —
Market value ($ mil.): 2,359

	STOCK PRICE ($) FY Close	P/E High/Low		PER SHARE ($) Earnings	Dividends	Book Value
12/12	125.47	20	14	6.49	0.00	34.57
12/11*	94.04	18	13	5.15	0.00	27.39
01/11	84.42	21	10	3.97	0.00	23.02
01/10	49.02	16	6	3.29	0.00	18.47
01/09	28.61	19	6	3.75	0.00	13.41
Annual Growth	**44.7%**	**—**	**—**	**14.7%**	**—**	**26.7%**

*Fiscal year change

Mistras Group, Inc.

Mistras could be all that stands between you and a massive oil refinery explosion nuclear facility meltdown or big bridge collapse. The engineering services company conducts non-destructive testing on critical equipment and processes used by petroleum aerospace infrastructure power generation and chemical manufacturing companies worldwide. It checks plant infrastructure for defects and problems without interrupting production; inspections take place during facility design build maintenance and operation phases. Mistras works from about 75 offices in 15 nations to serve clients that include Alcan Honeywell Bechtel BP Dow Chemical Airbus and federal and state governments.

Mistras helps its customers beyond just avoiding catastrophic events. The company help clients comply with government safety standards minimize repair costs extend the useful life of assets and increase productivity.

In addition to its on-site testing services the company also offers testing equipment instruments and software through its Software and Products division. Testing services include mechanical integrity and visual testing along with digital radiography ground penetrating radar and infrared and ultrasonic sensor testing. Mistras' software offerings include databases and enterprise software to store and analyze testing data planning software and on-line monitoring systems.

In the past Mistras has grown through acquisitions. More recently though the company has grown organically. The company also wants to delve into newer markets seeing opportunities in alternative energy and public infrastructure. The company hopes to expand its services into such emerging markets as India and China. Mistras also wants to expand its services to existing clients which includes providing multinational companies services in many of the countries they operate.

Asset heavy companies make up the bulk of Mistras' clients. Customers coming from the oil gas and chemical industries have historically comprised more than 50% of the company's international revenues stemming primarily from contracts with major oil refineries in Brazil and Russia. Smaller pieces of the revenue pie come from testing other safety-critical industrial sites infrastructure manufacturing facilities research centers and universities.

Chairman president and CEO Sotirios Vahaviolos owns about 45% of the company.

EXECUTIVES

EVP CFO and Treasurer, Jonathan H. (Jon) Wolk, age 47
EVP CFO and Treasurer, Francis T. (Frank) Joyce, age 60
EVP General Counsel and Secretary, Michael C. Keefe, age 56
Chairman President and CEO, Sotirios J. Vahaviolos, age 67, $285,000 total compensation
Group EVP Services and Director, Michael J. Lange, age 53, $163,577 total compensation
Executive Vice President Products and Systems, Mark F. Carlos, age 62, $130,000 total compensation
Executive Vice President - International, Phillip T. Cole, age 60, $175,088 total compensation
President Chief Operating Officer, Dennis M. Bertolotti
Vice President Power Generation Technical Services, Jim Keener
Executive Vice President Marketing and Sales, Ralph L. Genesi
Director, James J. Forese, age 77
Director, Ellen T. Ruff, age 66
Director, Richard H. Glanton, age 66
Director, Daniel M. Dickinson, age 51
Group EVP Services and Director, Michael J. Lange, age 53
Director, Manuel N. Stamatakis, age 66
Auditors: PricewaterhouseCoopersLLP

LOCATIONS

HQ: Mistras Group, Inc.
195 Clarksville Road, Princeton Junction, NJ 08550
Phone: 609 716-4000
Web: www.mistrasgroup.com

2011 Sales

US	277	82
Europe	25	7
Asia-Pacific	10	4

COMPETITORS

GE Inspection Technologies	Siemens AG
	Team
Lloyd's Register	The Carlyle Group
SGS	

HISTORICAL FINANCIALS

Company Type: Public

Income Statement

FYE: May 31

	REVENUE ($ mil.)	NET INCOME ($ mil.)	NET PROFIT MARGIN	EMPLOYEES
05/13	529.2	11.6	2.2%	4,400
05/12	436.8	21.3	4.9%	3,500
05/11	338.5	16.4	4.9%	2,700
05/10	272.1	10.4	3.8%	2,300
05/09	209.1	5.4	2.6%	2,000
Annual Growth	26.1%	20.8%	—	21.8%

2013 Year-End Financials

Debt ratio: 20.7%	No. of shares (mil.): 28
Return on equity: 5.7%	Dividends
Cash ($ mil.): 7	Yield: —
Current ratio: 1.93	Payout: —
Long-term debt ($ mil.): 63	Market value ($ mil.): 603

	STOCK PRICE ($) FY Close	P/E High/Low	PER SHARE ($) Earnings	Dividends	Book Value
05/13	21.38	66 45	0.40	0.00	7.45
05/12	22.54	34 19	0.74	0.00	6.89
05/11	17.41	30 15	0.61	0.00	6.04
05/10	11.94	19 13	0.43	0.00	4.89
Annual Growth	21.4%	— —	(2.4%)	—	15.1%

Mitcham Industries, Inc.

Here's a shocker: Mitcham Industries has few rivals that can match 'em when it comes to the leasing and sales of seismic equipment to the global seismic industry. The company's equipment offerings include channel boxes geophones earth vibrators various cables and other peripheral equipment. Through short-term leasing (three to nine months) from Mitcham Industries oil and gas companies can improve their chances of drilling a productive well and reduce equipment costs. Most of its leases are located in North America. The company also manufactures marine seismic equipment under the Seamap brand. In fiscal 2008 CGGVeritas (renamed CGG) accounted for 21% of Mitcham Industries' consolidated revenues.

Mitcham Industries' seismic surveys used to identify and define potential reservoirs of oil and gas involve generating an acoustic wave into the earth using compressed air explosives or vibrators. Geophones then capture the reflected energy and channel boxes convert the signals from analog to digital data which is later interpreted.

In an effort to anticipate the need for seismic surveys and create new business Mitcham Industries formed Drilling Services Inc. (DSI) in 2002. Mitcham sold the newly formed subsidiary in 2003 to WBW Enterprises of Texas in an effort to focus on its core operating units. The company acquired Seamap International a provider of products and services to the seismic hydrographic and offshore industries in 2005.

Although the company's business has traditionally been concentrated in North America its leasing activities have been on the rise in Latin Amer-

ica. Mitcham Industries also operates in Asia and Europe and it has an exclusive marketing agreement with Sercel one of the top seismic equipment makers. The company has expanded its operations to Southeast Asia by acquiring Seismic Asia Pacific an oceanographic seismic and hydrographic equipment provider based in Brisbane Australia.

In 2008 Seismic Asia Pacific secured a $4.5 million contract to provide equipment to the Royal Australian Navy.

HISTORY

Mitcham Industries was founded in 1987 by geophysical industry veteran Billy Mitcham Jr. a former Halliburton employee. The firm's strategy included growing and diversifying its lease pool of seismic equipment expanding its international presence and developing alliances with major seismic equipment manufacturers. In 1994 the company entered into an agreement with leading equipment maker Input/Output (I/O): Mitcham Industries bought I/O equipment and in turn I/O referred rental inquiries.

The company went public in 1995. The next year Mitcham Industries penned another agreement with Sercel (a subsidiary of France's Compagnie Generale de Geophysique S.A.) and became the manufacturer's exclusive worldwide leasing agent. Because Sercel was a major player in Canada the deal immediately pumped up Mitcham Industries' sales in that country.

After the oil industry downturn in 1998 the company decided it only had room for one major marketing partner: In 1999 it terminated the agreement with I/O and renewed its deal with Sercel. Mitcham Industries launched a stock buyback in 2000.

A year later the company settled a 1998 lawsuit brought by shareholders (who claimed that Mitcham had made misleading statements about its finances) for about $2.7 million.

In 2002 Mitcham formed subsidiary Drilling Services (DSI) to provide front-end services (permitting surveying shot hole drilling and other activities) for its customers. It later sold the operating assets of DSI to WBW Enterprises and returned its focus to its core operating units.

In 2003 the company moved in to the Southeast Asia market by acquiring Australian-based Seismic Asia Pacific an equipment supplier to Southeast Asia. In 2004 the company decided to separate the roles of its chairman president and CEO positions. Billy Mitcham stepped down as chairman retaining his role as president and CEO for the company. Director Peter Blum replaced Mitcham as chairman.

To complement its marine rental and sales business in 2005 Mitcham purchased Seamap International Holdings and its three subsidiaries in Texas the UK and Singapore for $6.5 million. The units produce proprietary products for the seismic hydrographic and offshore industries.

EXECUTIVES

President; Chief Executive Officer; Director, Billy F. Mitcham Jr., age 65, $387,267 total compensation
Chief Financial Officer; Executive Vice President - Finance; Director, Robert P. (Rob) Capps, age 59, $204,100 total compensation
Chairman, Peter H. Blum, age 56
EVP Business Development, Paul G. (Guy) Rogers, age 63, $204,100 total compensation
Executive Vice President - Marine Systems, Guy Malden, age 61, $204,100 total compensation

Information Technology and Web Site, Craig Middleton
Assistant Controller, Cheryl Wilson
Accounting Corporate Controller, Jesse Shockley
Investor Relations Officer, Jack Lascar
Vice President EAME, Brad Coram
Vice President South America, Gustavo Solorzano
President CEO and Director, Billy F. Mitcham Jr., age 65
EVP Finance CFO and Director, Robert P. (Rob) Capps, age 59
Director, R. Dean Lewis, age 70
Director, John F. Schwalbe, age 69
Director, Robert J. Albers, age 72

LOCATIONS

HQ: Mitcham Industries Inc.
  8141 SH 75 South, Huntsville TX 77342
Phone: 936-291-2277   Fax: 936-295-1922
Web: www.mitchamindustries.com

2008 Sales

	$ mil.	% of total
UK/Europe	27	37
North America		
US	13	18
Canada	6	9
Eurasia	10	14
Asia/Australia	9	12
South America	4	5
Other regions	4	5
Total	**76**	**100**

PRODUCTS/OPERATIONS

2008 Sales

	$ mil.	% of total
Equipment leasing	34	45
Equipment sales		
Seamap equipment sales	24	32
Lease pool equipment sales	3	5
Other equipment sales	13	18
Total	**76**	**100**

Selected Products

Boats
Buoys
CDP cables
CDP systems
Drills
Energy sources
Geophones
GPR
Heli Bags
Hydrophones
MarshPhones
Plotters
Radio systems
Refraction systems
Seismographs
Shooting systems
Streamers
Tape trasports
Telemetry cables
Telemetry systems
Test equipment
Vehicles
Vibrators
Vibrator electronics

COMPETITORS

Ashtead Group	Halliburton
Baker Hughes	ION Geophysical
CGG	Petroleum Geo-Services
Dawson Geophysical	Schlumberger
Geospace Technologies Corporation	Seitel

HISTORICAL FINANCIALS

Company Type: Public

Income Statement
FYE: January 31

	REVENUE ($ mil.)	NET INCOME ($ mil.)	NET PROFIT MARGIN	EMPLOYEES
01/13	104.6	17.0	16.3%	184
01/12	112.8	24.3	21.6%	169
01/11	71.3	4.7	6.6%	125
01/10	55.1	0.5	0.9%	116
01/09	66.8	9.0	13.6%	129
Annual Growth	**11.9%**	**17.1%**	**—**	**9.3%**

2013 Year-End Financials

Debt ratio: 2.3%
Return on equity: 10.2%
Cash ($ mil.): 15
Current ratio: 6.11
Long-term debt ($ mil.): 4

No. of shares (mil.): 12
Dividends
  Yield: —
  Payout: —
Market value ($ mil.): 190

	STOCK PRICE ($) FY Close	P/E High/Low		PER SHARE ($) Earnings	Dividends	Book Value
01/13	14.82	19	9	1.29	0.00	13.73
01/12	21.97	12	5	2.02	0.00	12.31
01/11	11.02	25	12	0.46	0.00	9.52
01/10	7.40	160	48	0.05	0.00	8.66
01/09	3.62	23	3	0.89	0.00	7.87
Annual Growth	**42.2%**	**—**	**—**	**9.7%**	**—**	**14.9%**

Monarch Financial Holdings Inc

Money rules at Monarch Financial Holdings. The holding company serves the South Hampton Roads area of southeastern Virginia through Monarch Bank Monarch Mortgage Monarch Capital Monarch Investment and OBXBank. With nearly a dozen branches Monarch Bank offers standard services including savings and checking accounts IRAs and CDS. Bank subsidiary Monarch Mortgage formed in 2007 has about a dozen offices. Other divisions sell insurance title and investment products. Single-family mortgages make up the largest portion of the company's loan portfolio which also includes commercial construction and land development loans. Monarch Bank division OBX Bank operates in North Carolina's Outer Banks area.

Strategy

Monarch Mortgage in 2013 entered into a marketing agreement to provide mortgage banking services to clients of Rose & Womble Realty Company with offices in Hampton Roads Virginia and North Carolina. The two firms are planning to form a joint venture to support a long-term mortgage partnership.

EXECUTIVES

EVP and Senior Operations Officer, Barbara N. Lane, age 63
EVP COO CFO Secretary and Director; CEO Monarch Bank, Brad E. Schwartz, age 50, $200,000 total compensation
Vice Chairman, Lawton H. Baker, age 69, $6,400 total compensation
Chairman, Jeffrey F. Benson, age 51, $9,800 total compensation
SVP and Chief Accounting Officer; SVP and CFO Monarch Bank, Lynette P. Harris
SVP Monarch Bank, R. Craig Baker
SVP and Chief Credit Officer, Andrew N. Lock, age 49
President Monarch Bank and Director, E. Neal Crawford, age 50, $128,000 total compensation
EVP and COO Monarch Mortgage, William T. Morrison, age 50
Market President; Virginia Beach of Monarch Bank, Steve Layden
Executive Vice President; Chief Information Officer, Denys Diaz
EVP COO CFO Secretary and Director; CEO Monarch Bank, Brad E. Schwartz, age 50
Vice Chairman, Lawton H. Baker, age 69
Director, Taylor B. Grissom, age 47
Director, Robert M. Oman, age 58
Director, Elizabeth T. Patterson, age 64
President Monarch Bank and Director, E. Neal Crawford, age 50
Director, Joe P. Covington Jr., age 62
Director, Dwight C. Schaubach, age 70
Director, Virginia Sancilio (Ginny) Cross
Auditors: Goodman&CompanyL.L.P.

LOCATIONS

HQ: Monarch Financial Holdings Inc.
  1101 Executive Blvd., Chesapeake VA 23320
Phone: 757-389-5159   Fax: 757-222-2101
Web: www.monarchbank.com

COMPETITORS

BB&T	Hampton Roads
Bank of America	Bankshares
Commonwealth	SunTrust
Bankshares	

HISTORICAL FINANCIALS

Company Type: Public

Income Statement
FYE: December 31

	ASSETS ($ mil.)	NET INCOME ($ mil.)	INCOME AS % OF ASSETS	EMPLOYEES
12/12	1,215.5	12.8	1.1%	663
12/11	908.4	7.1	0.8%	579
12/10	825.5	5.9	0.7%	527
12/09	689.5	4.8	0.7%	432
12/08	597.2	1.1	0.2%	295
Annual Growth	**19.4%**	**83.4%**	**—**	**22.4%**

2012 Year-End Financials

Return on assets: 1.2%
Return on equity: 15.6%
Long-term debt ($ mil.): —
No. of shares (mil.): 8
Sales ($ mil): 136

Dividends
  Yield: 1.9%
  Payout: 12.6%
Market value ($ mil.): 70

	STOCK PRICE ($) FY Close	P/E High/Low		PER SHARE ($) Earnings	Dividends	Book Value
12/12	8.22	7	5	1.25	0.16	10.21
12/11	7.69	11	8	0.70	0.13	10.59
12/10	7.80	14	10	0.63	0.12	9.99
12/09	6.10	16	8	0.55	0.00	9.65
12/08	6.75	64	36	0.18	0.00	8.69
Annual Growth	**5.0%**	**—**	**—**	**63.5%**	**—**	**4.1%**

Monmouth Real Estate Investment Corp

Monmouth specializes in mammoth industrial properties particularly warehouses and distribution centers. The real estate investment trust (REIT) owns about 80 industrial buildings and a single New Jersey shopping center comprising some 10.7 million sq. ft. in more than 25 states mostly in the East and Midwest. Most are net-leased (in which tenants pay insurance taxes and maintenance costs) under long-term leases. The REIT's two largest tenants FedEx and Milwaukee Electric Tool together account for half of its revenue. The firm also invests in REIT securities. Founded in 1968 Monmouth is one of the oldest public equity REITs in the nation.

Geographic Reach

New Jersey-based Monmouth's properties are located in 27 states including Arizona Connecticut Florida Illinois Michigan New Jersey New York Ohio Pennsylvania Tennessee Texas and Wisconsin.

Sales and Marketing

FedEx is the REIT's single largest customer accounting for 44% of its leasable space.

Financial Performance

The industrial REIT's revenue increased 5% in fiscal 2013 (ended September) versus the prior year to $66.3 million due to an increase in rental and reimbursement revenues generated by its larger portfolio of properties. Net income grew 15% over the same period to $21 million. The firm's revenue and profits have increased steadily over the past four years as its portfolio increased in size.

Strategy

The REIT specializes in net-leased industrial properties subject to long-term leases primarily to investment grade tenants. It derives its income primarily from real estate rental operations. Monmouth owns all of its properties with the exception of two in New Jersey in which it holds a majority interest.

In 2013 the REIT acquired five industrial properties totaling approximately 1.1 million square feet with net-leased terms ranging from 10 to 20 years of which about 237000 square feet (or 21%) is leased to FedEx Ground Package System. The REIT paid about $73.9 million for the five sites which are located in Kansas Kentucky Oklahoma Pennsylvania and Texas. The firm intends to continue increasing its real estate investments in fiscal 2014 through acquisitions and the expansion of select properties.

EXECUTIVES

Treasurer, Anna T. Chew, age 54, $73,400 total compensation

President and CEO, Eugene W. Landy, age 80, $225,000 total compensation

CFO, Kevin S. Miller, age 43

Chairman and COO, Michael P. Landy, age 52, $181,500 total compensation

Auditors: ReznickGroupP.C.

LOCATIONS

HQ: Monmouth Real Estate Investment Corporation
Juniper Business Plaza 3499 Rte. 9 North Ste. 3-C,
Freehold NJ 07728
Phone: 732-577-9996   **Fax:** 732-577-9981
Web: www.mreic.com

2013 Locations

	No.
Alabama	1
Arizona	1
Colorado	2
Connecticut	1
Florida	9
Georgia	3
Illinois	7
Iowa	1
Kansas	2
Maryland	1
Michigan	3
Minnesota	2
Mississippi	4
Missouri	4
Nebraska	1
New	4
New	3
North	3
Ohio	5
Oklahoma	1
Pennsylvania	1
South	3
Tennessee	4
Texas	7
Virginia	5
Wisconsin	2
Total	**80**

PRODUCTS/OPERATIONS

2013 Sales

	$ mil.	% of total
Income		
Rental	46	70
Reimbursement	7	12
Lease termination	0	1
Other		
Interest & dividends	3	6
Gain on securities	7	11
Total	**66**	**100**

COMPETITORS

Brandywine Realty	Mack-Cali
CenterPoint Properties	One Liberty Properties
First Industrial Realty	PS Business Parks
First Potomac Realty	Prologis

HISTORICAL FINANCIALS

Company Type: Public

Income Statement

FYE: September 30

	REVENUE ($ mil.)	NET INCOME ($ mil.)	NET PROFIT MARGIN	EMPLOYEES
09/13	55.3	21.4	38.7%	14
09/12	53.7	18.6	34.8%	11
09/11	48.1	15.4	32.0%	10
09/10	45.2	11.0	24.3%	9
09/09	41.3	1.6	4.0%	9
Annual Growth	**7.6%**	**89.7%**	**—**	**11.7%**

2013 Year-End Financials

Debt ratio: 44.1%
Return on equity: 6.5%
Cash ($ mil.): 12
Current ratio: 3.46
Long-term debt ($ mil.): 272
No. of shares (mil.): 44
Dividends
  Yield: 6.6%
  Payout: 142.8%
Market value ($ mil.): 404

	STOCK PRICE ($) FY Close	P/E High/Low	PER SHARE ($) Earnings	Dividends	Book Value
09/13	9.07	23 17	0.50	0.60	7.55
09/12	11.19	25 16	0.47	0.60	7.76
09/11	7.93	20 17	0.44	0.60	6.38
09/10	7.82	23 18	0.37	0.60	6.27
09/09	6.96	— —	(0.00)	0.60	6.26
Annual Growth	**6.8%**	**— —**	**—**	**(0.0%)**	**4.8%**

Monolithic Power Systems Inc

Monolithic Power Systems (MPS) doesn't make enormous electrical equipment but rather tiny silicon chips. The fabless semiconductor company offers analog and mixed-signal microchips —especially DC-to-DC converters for powering flat-panel TVs wireless communications equipment notebook computers set-top boxes and other consumer electronic devices. MPS outsources production of its chips to three China-based silicon foundries. The company's products are incorporated into electronic gear from tech heavyweights such as Dell Hewlett-Packard Samsung Electronics and Sony. The company was founded in 1997.

Monolithic Power Systems (MPS) earns 85% of its sales from DC-to-DC power management chips. It focuses on the market for high performance analog and mixed-signal integrated circuits (ICs) that have a longer product life cycle can be sold to various market segments and have technology that is difficult to replicate. MPS uses its own proprietary process technology to manufacture its designs at its contracted foundries. Its second-largest product line is LCD backlight inverter ICs which account for about 13% of sales. These chips are used to light monitors and screens in personal computers PDAs LCD and plasma TVs and GPS devices. Audio amplifier chips make up the remainder less than 10% of sales.

MPS generates the majority of its sales outside the US; more than half of sales come from China. In fact the Asia/Pacific region accounts for around 90% of direct and indirect sales. Since most of its customers are located in Asia along with the foundries that produce its chips MPS maintains sales offices in China Japan Singapore South Korea Taiwan as well as the US. It sells through marketing representatives in Europe. In addition the company has R&D offices in the US and China.

Sales for MPS in 2011 were $196.5 million a 10% decrease over the prior year. The company points to lower sales across all of its product lines. Particularly damaging was the loss of several Korean converter customers after reduced production capacity led to product shortages in 2010 leading those customers to look for other suppliers. While converter sales fell just over 9% sales of audio chips were down nearly 40% in 2011 (47% in 2010) on changes in product mix and lighting control products were 7% lower on reduced demand. Profits for MPS were down 55% on lower gross margins.

MPS plans to introduce new products within its existing products such as high-current high-voltage small form-factor switching voltage regulators as well as expand its newer products in battery chargers voltage references and low-dropout (LDO) regulators.

Despite its name Monolithic Power Systems is a smaller player on the chip market. With revenues under $200 million it's nowhere near the size of analog giants such as Analog Devices and industry leader Texas Instruments.

EXECUTIVES

CFO, Meera Rao, age 51
President CEO and Director, Michael R. Hsing, age 52, $400,000 total compensation
Chief Design Engineer and Director, James C. (Jim) Moyer, age 69, $175,385 total compensation
President Asia Operations, Deming Xiao, age 49, $280,000 total compensation
VP General Counsel and Secretary, Saria Tseng, age 39, $180,000 total compensation
SVP Worldwide Sales and Tactical Marketing, Maurice Sciammas, age 52, $297,615 total compensation
SVP Engineering, Paul Ueunten, age 57, $276,662 total compensation
Marketing Communications, Jae H. Park
Director, Douglas M. (Doug) McBurnie, age 69
Director, Umesh Padval, age 54
Director, Victor K. Lee, age 55
Director, Kuo Wei (Herbert) Chang, age 50
President CEO and Director, Michael R. Hsing, age 52
Chief Design Engineer and Director, James C. (Jim) Moyer, age 69
Director, Karen A. Smith-Bogart, age 55
Director, Jeff Zhou, age 56
Director, Karen A. Smith, age 54
Independent Director, Karen Bogart
Auditors: Deloitte&ToucheLLP

LOCATIONS

HQ: Monolithic Power Systems Inc.
6409 Guadalupe Mines Rd., San Jose CA 95120
Phone: 408-826-0600   **Fax:** 408-826-0601
Web: www.monolithicpower.com

2011 Sales

	$ mil.	% of total
China	113	58
Taiwan	23	12
Europe	14	7
South Korea	14	7
Japan	10	6
US	4	2
Other regions	15	8
Total	**196**	**100**

PRODUCTS/OPERATIONS

2011 Sales

	$ mil.	% of total
DC-to-DC converters	165	85
LCD backlight inverters	26	13
Audio amplifiers	4	2
Total	**196**	**100**

Selected Products

AC/DC Offline
  Bridge rectifier
  Controllers and regulators
  Synchronous rectifiers
Audio amplifiers
Backlighting solutions
  EL drivers
  White LED drivers (inductors and charge pumps)
Automotive
Battery chargers
  Cradle chargers
  Linear chargers

Protection
  Switching chargers
Full-bridge and half-bridge power drivers
Isolated and transformer-based power supplies
Lighting and illumination
Low dropout (LDO) linear regulators
Motor drivers
  Brushless DC motor drivers
  Stepper DC motor drivers
Photo-flash chargers and drivers
Power Over Ethernet powered device (PD) solutions
  PD controllers
  PD identity
Precision analog
  Analog switches
  High-side current sense amplifiers
  Operational amplifiers
  Voltage reference
Supervisory circuits and voltage supervisors
Switching power supply regulators
  DC-DC (step-down)
    Controller
    Intelli-Phase (monolithic driver + MOSFET)
    Non-synchronous switcher
    Synchronous switcher
  DC-DC (step-up)
    Controller
    Energy storage and release management
    LNB power supply
    Non-synchronous switcher
    Synchronous switcher
USB and current-limit load switches

COMPETITORS

Analog Devices	Microsemi
BCD Semiconductor	O2Micro
Fairchild	ON Semiconductor
Semiconductor	Power Integrations
International	ROHM
Rectifier	Richtek Technology
Intersil	Corp.
Linear Technology	STMicroelectronics
Maxim Integrated	Semtech
Products	Texas Instruments
Micrel	Volterra Semiconductor
Microchip Technology	iWatt

HISTORICAL FINANCIALS

Company Type: Public

Income Statement

FYE: December 31

	REVENUE ($ mil.)	NET INCOME ($ mil.)	NET PROFIT MARGIN	EMPLOYEES
12/12	213.8	15.7	7.4%	993
12/11	196.5	13.3	6.8%	922
12/10	218.8	29.5	13.5%	889
12/09	165.0	19.6	11.9%	692
12/08	160.5	24.2	15.1%	579
Annual Growth	7.4%	(10.2%)	—	14.4%

2012 Year-End Financials

Debt ratio: —
Return on equity: 6.2%
Cash ($ mil.): 75
Current ratio: 9.13
Long-term debt ($ mil.): —

No. of shares (mil.): 35
Dividends
  Yield: 4.4%
  Payout: 232.5%
Market value ($ mil.): 795

	STOCK PRICE ($) FY Close	P/E High/Low	PER SHARE ($) Earnings	Dividends	Book Value
12/12	22.28	50 33	0.43	1.00	7.24
12/11	15.07	44 25	0.38	0.00	7.18
12/10	16.52	30 18	0.78	0.00	7.04
12/09	23.97	44 19	0.54	0.00	6.06
12/08	12.61	39 11	0.67	0.00	4.89
Annual Growth	15.3%	— —	(10.5%)	—	10.3%

Monotype Imaging Holdings Inc

Monotype Imaging may be the one to thank if you're reading this whether it's on a portable electronic device or a printed page. With most sales going to device manufacturers (OEMs) the company's text imaging software is integrated into applications and embedded in electronics ranging from mobile phones to laser printers automotive displays and digital cameras. Its applications manage compression scaling color and layout. Providing customers access to thousands of typefaces OEM sales are complemented by about a quarter of revenue coming from licenses to creative professionals mostly commercial clients. Customers have included Nokia Sony and Microsoft. The US accounts for nearly half of sales.

Geographic recognition of revenue does not necessarily reflect the destination of the company's products as sales are attached to the subsidiary receiving the revenue. Sales by a US subsidiary to Korea-based customers for example are classified as US sales. The company's products are sold from offices in Germany Hong Kong Japan the UK and the US. Sales from Asia generally go to Asian customers while the other subsidiaries cover many different countries including the US.

Sales from overseas subsidiaries may account for more than half of sales but the US has grown as a percentage of revenue having been just a third of the total in 2009. The company does however expect international to continue to be a major percentage of revenue. Since Asia is an underpenetrated region for Monotype Imaging it is a particularly attractive growth opportunity specifically in Chinese Japanese and Korean language markets for laser printers digital copiers and other devices.

Sales to its core customers OEMs grew 15% for 2011 thanks to its customers shipping more units —such as e-readers smartphones and automotive displays —that rely on the company's products. Within this customer set consumer electronic device manufacturers represent the most revenue but it also serves independent software vendors that have multilingual text needs and typeface functionality. Its smaller segment creative professionals grew even more climbing nearly 20%. Demand for Web related products did improve from those clients but the larger contributor was non-Web revenue from enterprise customers.

Although no customer accounts for more than 10% of sales Monotype Imaging's top ten clients account for about half of revenue. The company serves many of its target industries' leaders including four of the top five e-book reader makers eight of the top 10 laser printer manufacturers and twelve of the top fifteen phone makers.

At the center of Monotype Imaging's growth strategy is a focus on serving high growth consumer electronic devices such as smartphones tablets navigation devices and consumer appliances to name a few. It will however also stay focused on the slower-growth laser printer market where it holds a leadership position and sees a demand for customized driver applications such as language interpretation. The company also continues to value its creative professionals and consumer users. It has several Websites including fonts.com and linotype.com.

In 2012 the company furthered its aspirations for both of its primary customer groups when it acquired major competitor Bitstream for $50 million. With that purchase Monotype Imaging gained the 62000 fonts on MyFonts.com font capabilities such as an identification service and font rendering and layout technologies fonts for embedded and mobile settings and 10 patents as well as 40 engineers and type designers at a facility in India.

In 2009 Monotype Imaging saw a chance to build on its strategy of expanding its offerings for OEM customers acquiring Planetweb for about $2 million. PlanetWeb provided user interface developer tools for consumer electronics manufacturers.

Monotype Imaging was formed when a group of investors including TA Associates acquired Agfa Monotype (then a subsidiary of Agfa) in 2004. The company does business as International Typeface Corporation or ITC in the US; Monotype Hong Kong and Monotype Japan in Asia; and Monotype UK and Linotype in Europe.

EXECUTIVES

Vice President Corporate Development, Daniel T. (Dan) Gerron, age 47
Chairman, Robert M. Givens, age 69
Chief Executive Officer President, Douglas J. (Doug) Shaw, age 58, $270,000 total compensation
Executive Vice President, John L. Seguin, age 59, $240,625 total compensation
VP and General Manager Creative Professional, David R. DeWitt, age 55
Vice President General Counsel Secretary, Janet M. Dunlap, age 48, $216,269 total compensation
VP New Type Technology, Geoffrey W. Greve, age 55
VP Engineering and Development, Steven R. Martin, age 50
VP and General Manager Enterprise Solutions; Managing Director Monotype UK, John H. McCallum, age 57
VP and General Manager OEM Sales, David L. McCarthy, age 55, $192,400 total compensation
Vice President - Human Resources, Patricia J. Money, age 56
VP and Chief Technologist, Jack P. Murphy, age 64
Managing Director Linotype GmbH, Frank Wildenberg, age 46
VP and General Manager E-Commerce, Christopher J. Roberts, age 47
Senior Vice President Chief Financial Officer Treasurer Secretary, Scott Landers, age 42, $124,038 total compensation
Director Words and Letters, Allan Haley
Managing Director, Ricky Chun
President Founder, William Garth
Vice President; General Manager - Display Imaging, Ira Mirochnick
Vice President - Corporate Marketing, Lisa Landa
Senior Vice President of Engineering, Steve Martin
President of the Lanston Monotype Machine Company, Harvey Best
Vice President Product Management, Tim McManus
Director, Peter J. Simone, age 65
Director, Pamela F. Lenehan, age 60
Director, Roger J. Heinen Jr., age 62
Director, Robert (Bob) Lentz Sr.
Chief Executive Officer President, Douglas J. (Doug) Shaw, age 57
Director, A. Bruce Johnston, age 51
Independent Director, Timothy Yeaton
Auditors: Ernst&YoungLLP

LOCATIONS

HQ: Monotype Imaging Holdings Inc.
500 Unicorn Park Dr., Woburn MA 01801
Phone: 781-970-6000   **Fax:** 781-970-6001
Web: www.monotypeimaging.com

2011 Sales

	$ mil.	% of total
US	56	46
Asia	44	36
Germany	17	14
UK	5	4
Total	**123**	**100**

PRODUCTS/OPERATIONS

2011 Sales

	$ mil.	% of total
OEM	91	74
Creative Professional	31	26
Total	**123**	**100**

Selected Customers

E-book readers
  Amazon
  Kobo
Digital TVs and set-top-boxes
  Sharp
  Toshiba
  TTE Technology
Mobile phones
  Motorola
  Nokia
  RIM
  Sony
  ZTE
Other
  Activision
  Gannett Company
  Google
  Microsoft
  Nintendo
  Ubisoft
  UBS
  TiVo
  Whirlpool

COMPETITORS

Adobe Systems	Extensis
Bitstream	Xara

HISTORICAL FINANCIALS

Company Type: Public

Income Statement

FYE: December 31

	REVENUE ($ mil.)	NET INCOME ($ mil.)	NET PROFIT MARGIN	EMPLOYEES
12/12	149.8	28.9	19.3%	335
12/11	123.2	22.6	18.4%	272
12/10	106.6	18.3	17.2%	251
12/09	94.0	13.4	14.3%	239
12/08	110.8	15.3	13.9%	238
Annual Growth	**7.8%**	**17.1%**	**—**	**8.9%**

2012 Year-End Financials

Debt ratio: 6.9%	No. of shares (mil.): 37
Return on equity: 13.3%	Dividends
Cash ($ mil.): 39	Yield: 0.5%
Current ratio: 1.36	Payout: 10.5%
Long-term debt ($ mil.): 12	Market value ($ mil.): 595

	STOCK PRICE ($) FY Close	P/E High/Low		PER SHARE ($) Earnings	Dividends	Book Value
12/12	15.98	22	16	0.76	0.08	6.32
12/11	15.59	27	16	0.61	0.00	5.47
12/10	11.10	22	14	0.51	0.00	4.66
12/09	9.03	24	5	0.38	0.00	4.06
12/08	5.80	36	9	0.44	0.00	3.51
Annual Growth	**28.8%**	—	—	**14.6%**	—	**15.8%**

Monro Muffler Brake, Inc.

If you can't stop point your car toward Monro Muffler Brake and coast on in. The company provides a full range of brake tire exhaust system suspension and steering and alignment services at more than 800 automotive repair shops. Its operations span nearly 20 states in the Northeast and Midwest and include Monro Muffler Brake & Service Mr. Tire Tread Quarters Autotire Car Care Center and Tire Warehouse. Along with under-car work the company offers air conditioning maintenance state inspections and scheduled maintenance services including fleet maintenance. Tire replacements and service account for more than 35% of sales. Monro Muffler Brake services more than 4.4 million vehicles annually.

Geographic Reach

Monro Muffler Brake operates company stores in 19 states including New York Pennsylvania Ohio Massachusetts New Jersey the Carolinas and Illinois.

Operations

Monro Muffler Brake operates about 535 service stores which specialize in repairing and replacing worn out auto parts as well as some 265 tire stores which sell install and align tires. In addition to Monro Muffler Brake's 800-plus company owned stores there are three franchised locations and 14 dealer-operated stores providing automotive under-car repair and tire services.

Sales and Marketing

Monro Muffler Brake advertises through direct mail coupon inserts and in-store promotional signage and displays. It also advertises through radio yellow pages newspapers service reminders and digital marketing. It cross markets its services promoting the Monro Muffler Brake & Service brand in its Tire Warehouse stores. During fiscal 2012 (ends March) the company launched mobile apps on the iPhone and Android platforms that allow customers to manage and maintain their vehicle maintenance records make appointments locate stores and search for promotions/coupons and tires.

Financial Performance

Monro Muffler Brake's $686.5 million in fiscal 2012 (ends March) sales was an all-time high for the fast-growing company. Indeed 2012 marked the fifth consecutive year of increasing sales and fourth year of steadily increasing profits. The company's sales climbed 8% in 2012 vs. the prior year while net income rose by 19% over the same period. Sales got a boost from the addition of new stores several acquisitions and rising comparable sales at existing shops (up 2%). Monro has widened its margins by controlling spending on operations amid increased sales.

Strategy

The company whose roots reach back to 1957 has seen its revenues steadily climb over the years as its footprint expanded. The business continues to grow through both acquisitions and organic growth. Unlike many of its competitors Monro owns almost all of its stores believing it can better manage repair shops and train employees through more centralized control. Independent dealers operate only about 15 locations. It also operates nearly 35 full-service Monro stores onsite at BJ's Wholesale Clubs.

In recent years Monro's sales have also been helped by the economic downturn which has resulted in tightened credit markets and decreased consumer spending prompting Americans to drive and maintain their vehicles instead of trade them in for new models.

Mergers and Acquisitions

With earnings on a roll Monro in fiscal 2012 spent approximately $50 million to buy 18 retail tire and automotive repair stores in North Carolina from Colony Tire Corp. as well as 20 other tire and repair stores in Virginia from Kramer Tire Co. The Kramer purchase included two heavy-truck tire and truck repair stores two wholesale operations and a retread facility in Virginia. The acquired stores operate primarily under the Tread Quarters name. In 2011 the firm purchased Vespia Tire Centers which operated two dozen locations throughout New Jersey and Pennsylvania. During 2010 Monro acquired Import Export Tire a five-store tire chain in Pittsburgh and three Courthouse Tire auto repair and tire shops in Fredericksburg Virginia.

Ownership

T. Rowe Price owns about 12% of Monro Muffler Brakes' shares.

HISTORY

Charles August founded Monro Muffler Brake in 1957 as a franchise of Midas Muffler (later Midas Inc.). August hoped to expand his services under the Midas name but was refused so in 1966 he broke with Midas and began his own full line of undercar services. The company name was derived from Monroe County New York where it is headquartered; August decided to drop the "e" to save money on his sign. Monro Muffler Brake had 59 shops by 1984 when an investor group led by Peter Solomon and Donald Glickman purchased a controlling interest. In 1987 despite Solomon's objections August retired and was replaced by Jack Gallagher a 20-year veteran of the automotive industry. The firm went public in 1991.

Gallagher stepped down in March 1995. New CEO Lawrence Day wasted little time in expanding Monro Muffler Brake's customer base. In July 1995 the company acquired Durham North Carolina-based Muffler Xpress establishing Monro Muffler Brake in the Carolinas. The company also opened its first store in Maine that year.

In 1997 Monro Muffler Brake agreed to sell Bridgestone/Firestone tires in its stores and entered a joint venture with Q-Lube (a subsidiary of Pennzoil-Quaker State which was acquired by Royal Dutch Shell in 2002) to develop co-branded stores offering fast oil changes and undercar services. (The company abandoned the concept the following year.)

Monro Muffler Brake bought about 205 repair shops mostly in the Northeast in 1998 from Speedy Muffler King for $52 million. Store expansions hurt earnings that year and Day stepped down. Robert Gross was named president and CEO later in 1998. Monro Muffler Brake began opening shops in BJ's Wholesale Club outlets in 1999. In 2000 the company which previously had carried only Firestone tires announced it would sign with another tire supplier in order to assuage customers alarmed by the Firestone recall.

Monro Muffler Brake purchased Kimmel Automotive Inc. in 2002 and 10 Frasier Tire Service stores in 2003.

In March 2004 Monro Muffler Brake acquired more than 35 Mr. Tire locations in Maryland and Virginia from Atlantic Automotive. The next year Monro Muffler Brake added Donald B. Rice Tire

and Henderson Holdings gaining a total of 15 tire and auto repair shops. The company also opened additional shops inside BJ's Wholesale Clubs.

In November 2005 Monro acquired a minority stake in Strauss Discount Auto and an option to take full ownership but the company said it would not exercise the option after Strauss filed for bankruptcy protection in August 2006. (Monro wrote-off its $2.8 million investment in Strauss in fiscal 2008.)

In 2006 the company bought key operations of bankrupt ProCare Automotive Service Solutions. The $15 million deal gave Monro an additional 75 stores in Ohio and Pennsylvania. Monro went on to acquire Valley Forge Tire & Auto Centers and Craven Tire & Auto in mid-2007 adding about 20 locations and expanding Monro's tire business to Philadelphia and Northern Virginia.

Peter Solomon stepped down as chairman in August 2007. He was succeeded by Robert Gross.

In early 2008 the firm acquired seven retail tire and automotive repair stores in Buffalo New York from the Broad Elm Group. In 2009 the company acquired privately owned Tire Warehouse Central with 40-plus locations throughout New England; Midwest Tire & Auto Repair a small chain in northwest Indiana; and Autotire Car Care Centers of St. Louis from American Tire Distributors.

EXECUTIVES

VP-Mdsg, David M. (Dave) Baier
Chief Financial Officer; Executive Vice President - Finance; Treasurer; Secretary, Catherine D'Amico, age 57, $230,000 total compensation
Divisional VP Western Operations, Christopher R. Hoornbeck, age 62, $168,100 total compensation
Divisional VP Southern Operations, Craig L. Hoyle, age 59, $145,000 total compensation
Executive Vice President - Store Operations, Joseph Tomarchio Jr., age 57, $380,000 total compensation
President; Chief Executive Officer, John W. Van Heel, age 47, $308,000 total compensation
VP-Sys Dev, Jarret J. Lobb
President; Chief Executive Officer, John Heel
Director, Robert E. (Rob) Mellor, age 69
Director, Frederick M. Danziger, age 73
Director, Elizabeth A. Wolszon, age 59
Director, Peter J. Solomon, age 75
Director, Donald Glickman, age 79
Director, Richard A. Berenson, age 77
Independent Director, James Wilen
Auditors: PricewaterhouseCoopersLLP

LOCATIONS

HQ: Monro Muffler Brake Inc.
200 Holleder Pkwy., Rochester NY 14615
Phone: 585-647-6400   **Fax:** 585-647-0945
Web: www.monro.com

Selected Operating Locations

Connecticut
Delaware
Illinois
Indiana
Maine
Maryland
Massachusetts
Missouri
New Hampshire
New Jersey
New York
North Carolina
Ohio
Pennsylvania
Rhode Island
South Carolina
Vermont
Virginia
West Virginia

PRODUCTS/OPERATIONS

2012 Sales

	% of total
Tires	39
Maintenance	28
Brakes	18
Steering	10
Exhaust	5
Total	**100**

2012 Company-owned Stores

	No.
Service (including	536
Tire	267
Total	**803**

COMPETITORS

AAMCO	Midas
Bridgestone Retail	Pep Boys
Operations	Precision Auto
Discount Tire	Sears
Goodyear Tire &	TBC
Rubber	TCI Tire Centers
Jiffy Lube	Valvoline
Meineke	Wal-Mart

HISTORICAL FINANCIALS

Company Type: Public

Income Statement

FYE: March 30

	REVENUE ($ mil.)	NET INCOME ($ mil.)	NET PROFIT MARGIN	EMPLOYEES
03/13	732.0	42.5	5.8%	5,850
03/12	686.5	54.6	8.0%	5,113
03/11	636.6	45.8	7.2%	5,005
03/10	564.6	33.1	5.9%	4,926
03/09	476.1	24.0	5.1%	4,277
Annual Growth	**11.4%**	**15.3%**	**—**	**8.1%**

2013 Year-End Financials

Debt ratio: 26.9%
Return on equity: 12.3%
Cash ($ mil.): 1
Current ratio: 1.22
Long-term debt ($ mil.): 186
No. of shares (mil.): 31
Dividends
  Yield: 0.0%
  Payout: 30.3%
Market value ($ mil.): 1,241

	STOCK PRICE ($) FY Close	P/E High/Low	PER SHARE ($) Earnings	Dividends	Book Value
03/13	39.71	31 23	1.32	0.40	11.68
03/12	41.49	27 17	1.69	0.35	10.60
03/11	31.78	35 20	1.44	0.33	9.20
03/10	35.99	33 21	1.07	0.18	7.77
03/09	26.01	33 18	0.80	0.16	6.67
Annual Growth	**11.2%**	**— —**	**13.3%**	**25.7%**	**15.0%**

Monster Beverage Corp

Monster Beverage certainly has the energy to reach beyond the blue sky. Along with its Blue Sky beverages the company serves up a variety of "alternative" sodas juices and teas. Its most popular and now namesake brand Monster is the #2 energy drink behind Red Bull and has spawned the

Java Monster coffee drink. Other products include fruit juice smoothies and dry juice mixes. The company sells most of its products in the US and Canada through a distribution network but also directly to retailers such as grocery chains and wholesale clubs. With the addition of their Brandon Limited Partnership chairman and CEO Rodney Sacks and vice chairman and president Hilton Schlosberg own about 30% of the company.

Company Ownership

Company executives Sacks and Schlosberg have since adjusted their beneficial ownership in the drinks maker. In January 2012 as part of a two-for-one stock split of its common stock the company changed its ticker symbol from HANS to MNST and its company name from Hansen Natural Corporation to Monster Beverage Corporation. The move doubled the number of outstanding shares of common stock to about 174 million shares and placed the beverage company's already popular Monster brand name at the center of its focus.

Operations

California-based Monster Beverage is organized into two separate business segments. The company's Direct Store Delivery (DSD) segment generates 95% of 2012 revenues up from 90% in 2008. Because Monster is the top brand in this segment the company works aggressively to pique the interest of trendy consumers in the niche market by regularly rolling out new products. In recent years the beverage maker has been focused on launching new products as extensions of the Monster brand. Monster Beverage's other business segment Warehouse comprises juice-based beverages and sodas. The business has stalled in recent years bringing in 5% of 2012 sales as compared to 10% in 2008 as customers have bypassed pricier sodas and functional drinks for more mainstream options.

Sales and Marketing

A multi-channel marketer Monster Beverage serves a variety of customers. Customers include full service distributors (63% of 2012 sales); those outside the US (22%); club stores drug chains and mass merchants (9%); retail grocery specialty chains and wholesalers (4%); and other (2%).

Looking to increase brand awareness and spur sales Monster Beverage spent more on advertising and promotional activities in 2012 shelling out $165 million in 2012 as compared to $149 million in 2011.

Financial Performance

Monster Beverage has posted sales increases during the past five years recording its highest sales in 2012 due to successes across its primary DSD segment mainly due to sales boosts among the Monster Energy brand. The drinks maker logged net sales increases of 21% in 2012 as compared to 2011. Net sales for the DSD segment increased 22%. Indeed the Monster Energy brand energy drinks accounted for 97% of the overall increase in net sales for the DSD segment. Monster Energy posted increased sales by volume as a result of rising domestic and international consumer demand as well as the company's expansion into new international markets.

Net income for the same reporting period rose 19% attributable to rising gross profit as the result of increased gross sales of the Monster Energy brand energy drinks.

Strategy

The "alternative beverage" industry has grown increasingly crowded as it includes bottled water and juices from beverage giants such as Coca-Cola and PepsiCo. To compete Monster Beverage's product line includes "functional" drinks made by

adding Echinacea ginseng guarana and other supplements to the beverages. The company also benefits from consumers who thrive on caffeine consumption whether it's Boomers needing more energy to retain their youthful pace or Gen Y's use of the drink to stay awake to study and party.

Like Big Red Monster Beverage does not make its own products. It outsources the manufacturing and packaging to third-party bottlers and contract packers. Instead the company purchases the concentrates juices flavors supplements and other ingredients along with packaging materials (cans bottles aseptic boxes aseptic pouches caps labels) and has them delivered to the bottlers and co-packers.

Monster Beverage also relies on distributors such as Anheuser-Busch to sell the Monster Energy Lost Energy Rumba Samba and Tango brands in markets determined by the company. Monster Beverage also has agreements with The Coca-Cola Company and Coca-Cola Enterprises for distribution of its products in selected parts of the US and Canada. Its agreement with Jumex calls for distribution in Mexico. Although most of Monster Beverage's sales are generated in the US it continues to expand its international footprint; its products are now available in some 70 countries worldwide.

EXECUTIVES

Assistant Secretary and Director, Benjamin M. Polk, age 62

President Monster Beverage Company, Mark J. Hall, age 57, $340,000 total compensation

Vice Chairman COO CFO President and Secretary, Hilton H. Schlosberg, age 60, $385,000 total compensation

Chairman and CEO, Rodney C. Sacks, age 63, $385,000 total compensation

VP Finance, Thomas J. Kelly, age 58, $195,000 total compensation

Assistant Secretary and Director, Benjamin M. Polk, age 62

Vice Chairman COO CFO President and Secretary, Hilton H. Schlosberg, age 60

Director, Sydney Selati, age 74

Director, Norman C. Epstein, age 72

Director, Harold C. Taber Jr., age 74

Director, Mark S. Vidergauz, age 59

Auditors: Deloitte&ToucheLLP

LOCATIONS

HQ: Monster Beverage Corporation
550 Monica Circle Ste. 201, Corona CA 92880
Phone: 951-739-6200   **Fax:** 951-739-6220
Web: monsterbevcorp.com

2012 Sales

	% of total
US	75
Other	25
Total	**100**

PRODUCTS/OPERATIONS

2012 Sales

	$ mil.	% of total
Energy drinks	1,906	92
Non-carbonated beverages	110	5
Carbonated beverages	31	2
Other	13	1
Total	**2,060**	**100**

2012 Sales

	$ mil.	% of total
DSD	1,966	95

Warehouse	94	5
Total	**2,060**	**100**

2012 Sales

	% of total
Full service	63
Outside the	22
Club stores drug chains & mass	9
Retail grocery specialty chains &	4
Other	2
Total	**100**

Selected Products and Brands

Bottled water
  Blue Sky Seltzer Water
  Hansen's Junior Organic Water
  Vidration
Energy drinks
  Blue Sky
  Diet Red Energy
  Hansen Energy
  Java Monster
  Lost Energy
  Monster Energy
  Monster Hitman Energy Shooter
  Nitrous Monster Energy
  X-Presso Monster
Energy juices
  Rumba
  Samba
  Tango
Juice products and smoothies
  Hansen
Juices for children
  Juice Blast
Soda
  Blue Sky
  Hansen's Diet
  Hansen's Natural
Tea
  Hansen's Iced Tea
  Peace Tea

COMPETITORS

5-hour ENERGY	Mott's
Bazi	Naked Juice
Campbell Soup	National Beverage
Caribou Coffee	National Grape
Celsius Holdings	Cooperative
Chiquita Brands	Nestle
Cinnabon	Ocean Spray
Clearly Canadian	Odwalla
Coca-Cola	PepsiCo
Cott	Red Bull
Del Monte Foods	Reed's
Dole Food	Smucker
Dr Pepper Snapple	South Beach Beverage
Group	Starbucks
Energy Brands	Sunny Delight
Gatorade	Suntory Holdings
Godiva Chocolatier	Tree Top
Goya	Tropicana
Hornell Brewing	Unilever
IZZE	Welch's
Impulse Energy USA	Wet Planet Beverages
Jones Soda	illy
Mondelez International	

HISTORICAL FINANCIALS

Company Type: Public

Income Statement

FYE: December 31

	REVENUE ($ mil.)	NET INCOME ($ mil.)	NET PROFIT MARGIN	EMPLOYEES
12/12	2,060.7	340.0	16.5%	2,180
12/11	1,703.2	286.2	16.8%	1,900
12/10	1,303.9	212.0	16.3%	1,497
12/09	1,143.3	208.7	18.3%	1,430
12/08	1,033.7	108.0	10.5%	1,270
Annual Growth	**18.8%**	**33.2%**	**—**	**14.5%**

Debt ratio: —
Return on equity: 41.7%
Cash ($ mil.): 222
Current ratio: 2.89
Long-term debt ($ mil.): —

No. of shares (mil.): 165
Dividends
Yield: —
Payout: —
Market value ($ mil.): 8,760

	STOCK PRICE ($) FY Close	P/E High/Low	PER SHARE ($) Earnings	Dividends	Book Value
12/12	52.84	56 21	1.86	0.00	3.89
12/11	92.14	60 32	1.53	0.00	5.62
12/10	52.28	45 31	1.14	0.00	4.65
12/09	38.40	38 24	1.11	0.00	3.32
12/08	33.53	77 36	0.56	0.00	2.42
Annual Growth	12.0%	— —	35.3%	—	12.6%

MSC Industrial Direct Co., Inc.

Many a small thing has been made large by MSC Industrial Direct's business; the company stands as one the largest US direct suppliers of industrial products. It distributes fasteners and measuring instruments cutting tools and plumbing supplies to customers in metalworking and maintenance repair and overhaul (MRO) businesses. MSC Industrial stocks approximately 900000 products from 3000 suppliers. The company sells —mainly to small and mid-size firms — through its master catalog (which runs to several thousand pages) promotional mailings and brochures as well as via telemarketing and the Internet.

Geographic Reach

MSC operates primarily in the US through a network of five customer fulfillment centers and nearly 105 branch offices. MSC's customer fulfillment centers reside in Harrisburg Pennsylvania; Atlanta Georgia; Elkhart Indiana; Reno Nevada; and Wednesbury UK.

Sales and Marketing

To sell its products MSC uses master catalogs promotional catalogs and brochures and it is shifting its strategy to include search engine marketing email marketing and online advertising. It uses its own database of over 3 million contacts together with external mailing lists to target offline and online investments. It employs 1150 in-bound sales and 1095 field sales representatives who work out of the branches and generate a significant portion of the company's sales.

Financial Performance

MSC has enjoyed significant growth over the last three years. From 2011 to 2012 its revenues jumped by 17% reaching a historic total of $2.4 billion. Profits also spiked by 18% to reach another milestone of $259 million. The growth was due to increase sales volumes including the impact of the extra week and the impact of previous acquisitions (American Tool Supply and its affiliate American Specialty Grinding).

Strategy

MSC has shifted its product mix and customer base by pursuing non-manufacturing large accounts such as government projects. Mega buyers these accounts also command volume discounts and purchase more lower-margin products. (Re-

sponding the company has added to the number of MSC proprietary brands offered in its catalog.)

Mergers and Acquisitions

MSC extends its geographic presence and increases its revenues through strategic acquisitions. In 2013 it acquired Barnes Distribution North America (BDNA) the North American distribution business of Barnes Group for some $550 million. The purchase added fastener supply operations as well as vendor inventory solutions and a leading field sales force. The significant deal also gave MSC access to BDNA's 31000 customers with a major presence in the government manufacturing transportation and natural resources sectors.

In 2011 it acquired American Tool Supply and its affiliate American Specialty Grinding adding metalworking supply operations and locations in Massachusetts New Hampshire Connecticut and North Carolina.

In late 2010 MSC swallowed up the assets of California-based Rutland Tool & Supply a subsidiary of Lawson Products that markets and distributes a myriad metalworking tools and MRO supplies. The $11 million acquisition fueled sales and profits by strengthening MSC's customer base on the West Coast.

Ownership

Chairman Mitchell Jacobson owns about 16% of MSC Industrial.

HISTORY

Sidney Jacobson and his brother founded Sid Tool Co. in a Manhattan storefront in 1941. In the late 1950s the company bought Manhattan Supply Co. which became its distribution arm. Fresh out of law school son Mitchell Jacobson joined the company's ranks in 1976; he took over from his father as president and CEO in 1982. In 1990 with profits declining Mitchell reorganized the enterprise following Japanese management techniques to retrain and empower employees. The company restructured in 1995 forming MSC as a holding company for Sid Tool and went public that year.

MSC expanded its business geographically through acquisitions. In 1996 it bought DTC Tool (Florida) wholesaler Swiss Precision Instruments (California) and distributors Cut-Rite Tool (Florida) and Brooks Precision Supplies (Massachusetts). MSC also broadened its distribution by opening a center in Elkhart Indiana. In 1997 MSC bought Cleveland-based Discount Tool and Supply.

Continuing to buy complementary lines MSC acquired distributors in Delaware Mississippi Tennessee and Wisconsin in 1998. The company ventured into the Southwest the next year opening a distribution center in Reno Nevada. MSC also added plumbing equipment pumps and pneumatics equipment and process instrumentation to its product line. Acquisitions that year included Direct Line (New York) and Corbin Corporation (Ohio).

EXECUTIVES

Executive Vice Chairman, David Sandler, age 56, $740,000 total compensation

Chairman, Mitchell Jacobson, age 62, $975,000 total compensation

EVP Sales, Thomas (Tom) Cox, age 52, $317,818 total compensation

EVP and CFO, Jeffrey (Jeff) Kaczka, age 53

SVP and CIO, Charles Bonomo, age 48

EVP Global Supply Chain Operations, Douglas (Doug) Jones, age 49, $308,000 total compensation

EVP Human Resources, Eileen McGuire, age 48, $263,310 total compensation

President CEO and Director, Erik Gershwind, age 42

Executive Vice Chairman, David Sandler, age 56

Director, Louise K. Goeser, age 59

Director, Roger Fradin, age 59

Director, Denis Kelly, age 63

Director, Philip Peller, age 73

President CEO and Director, Erik Gershwind, age 42

Director, Jonathan L.S. Byrnes, age 63

Auditors: Ernst&YoungLLP

LOCATIONS

HQ: MSC Industrial Direct Co. Inc.
75 Maxess Rd., Melville NY 11747-3151
Phone: 516-812-2000   **Fax:** 516-349-1301
Web: www.mscdirect.com

2010 Sales

	$ mil.	% of total
US	1,654	98
UK	37	2
Total	**1,692**	**100**

PRODUCTS/OPERATIONS

Selected Mergers and Acquisitions

FY2011
American Tool Supply Inc. (Massachusetts; metalworking supplies)
American Specialty Grinding Co. Inc. (Massachusetts; metalworking supplies)

FY2010
Rutland Tool & supply ($11 million; California; metalworking tools)

Selected Products

Abrasives and files
  Grinding wheels
  Sand blasters
  Sanding belts and accessories
  Tumblers
Carbide inserts and indexable tooling
  Cut-off and grooving blades
  Indexable boring bars
  Indexable cutting tools
  Indexable inserts
Drills reamers and counterbores
  Burs
  Counterbores
  Countersinks and deburring equipment
  Drills
  Reamers
Electrical HVAC and plumbing products
  Electrical supplies
  Fans
  Fuses
  HVAC equipment
  Lamps/light bulbs
  Light fixtures
  Plumbing products
  Transformers
Endmills saws cutters tool bits and band saws
  Band saw blades
  Broaches
  Carbide blanks
  Cutters
  Double end mills
  Saws
  Single end mills
  Tool bits
Flat stock drill rod and raw materials
  Drill rod
  Flat stock
  Metal
  Plastic
  Raw materials
  Wirecloth
Hand/power tools and hardware
  Air/power tools
  Files
  Hand tools
  Hardware

Machinery accessories knurls Digital Readouts (DRO)
  Electrical Discharge Machining (EDM) products and
  books
  Collets
  Knurls and holders
  Machine tool accessories
  Machinery publications
  Rotary tool holders
  Software
  Vises
Material-handling storage packaging shipping and
  janitorial products
  Chain
  Cable
  Rope and hardware
  Janitorial products
  Material-handling equipment
  Material-storage equipment
  Office equipment
  Packaging and shipping
  Pressure washers
Measuring instruments
  Bench centers
  DROs
  Levels
  Measuring instruments
  Rules
Paints adhesives labeling fluids and lubes
  Coolant systems
  Lubricants and industrial chemicals
  Marking and labeling devices
  Metalworking fluids
  Paints sundries and adhesives
  Parts cleaners
Pneumatics hydraulics and power transmission
  Bearings
  Belts
  Cylinders
  Hydraulics
  Linear motion
  Pneumatics
  Power transmission
Pumps hose and tubing process equipment and pumps
  Hose
  Tube and fittings
  Process instrumentation
  Pumps
Safety communication soldering and welding products
  Batteries
  Communications equipment
  Flashlight products
  Gloves
  Matting
  Safety products
  Spill containment products
  Welding equipment
Taps dies and other threading equipment
  Dies
  Solid threading
  Boring and grooving tools
  Taps
Tooling components and fasteners
  Components
  Fasteners
  Handwheels
  Industrial magnets
  Knobs
  Levers and handles
  Threaded rod and studs

COMPETITORS

Align Aerospace
Alleghany Corporation
Applied Industrial
  Technologies
C. C. Dickson
Communications Supply
DXP Enterprises
DoALL
Etna Supply
Famous Distribution
Fastenal
Hagemeyer North
  America
Hajoca Corporation

Kaman Industrial
  Technologies
L. S. Starrett
McMaster-Carr
Park-Ohio Holdings
Precision Industries
Production Tool Supply
Redlon & Johnson
Simpson Manufacturing
Strategic Distribution
Turtle & Hughes
W.W. Grainger
WinWholesale
Wolseley

Hillman Companies
Horizon Solutions
Industrial
  Distribution Group

Wurth Group

HISTORICAL FINANCIALS

Company Type: Public

Income Statement

FYE: August 31

	REVENUE ($ mil.)	NET INCOME ($ mil.)	NET PROFIT MARGIN	EMPLOYEES
08/13*	2,457.6	238.0	9.7%	6,257
09/12	2,355.9	259.0	11.0%	4,982
08/11	2,021.7	218.7	10.8%	4,644
08/10	1,692.0	150.3	8.9%	4,304
08/09	1,489.5	125.1	8.4%	4,193
Annual Growth	13.3%	17.4%	—	10.5%

*Fiscal year change

2013 Year-End Financials

Debt ratio: 13.1%
Return on equity: 18.5%
Cash ($ mil.): 55
Current ratio: 4.18
Long-term debt ($ mil.): 241

No. of shares (mil.): 63
Dividends
Yield: 0.0%
Payout: 32.0%
Market value ($ mil.): 4,821

	STOCK PRICE ($) FY Close	P/E High/Low		PER SHARE ($) Earnings	Dividends	Book Value
08/13*	76.00	23	18	3.75	1.20	21.92
09/12	69.30	20	14	4.09	1.00	18.90
08/11	58.99	22	13	3.43	1.88	15.81
08/10	46.09	24	16	2.37	0.82	14.33
08/09	39.97	26	14	2.00	0.80	12.86
Annual Growth 17.4%		—	—	17.0%	10.7%	14.3%

*Fiscal year change

MSCI Inc

You ask your asset manager how your portfolio is doing but who does he ask? Probably MSCI. The company formerly Morgan Stanley Capital International manages more than 145000 daily equity fixed income and hedge fund indices for use by large asset management firms. MSCI is organized through two business segments. Its Performance and Risk business provides equity indices portfolio risk and performance analytics credit analytics and environmental social and governance (ESG) products under brands such as MSCI RiskMetrics and Barra. Its Governance business provides corporate governance and specialized financial research and analysis. MSCI has about 7500 clients across more than 80 countries.

Geographic Reach

Nearly half of the company's revenues come from outside the Americas. MSCI has more than 38 offices in 22 countries worldwide including headquarters in New York and offices in San Francisco Chicago and S?o Paulo Brazil. As part of its global expansion efforts in the last few years MSCI has opened international offices in Budapest Dubai Monterrey Mumbai and Shanghai.

Operations

The company's indices act as benchmarks that measure the performance of global funds. Institutional investors use the indices as research tools and as the basis for their various investment vehi-

cles. MSCI's Performance and Risk segment is by far its largest accounting for 87% of the company's revenue in 2012 while the company's Governance segment brought in the remaining 13%. MSCI makes the majority of its revenues (more than 75%) from annual recurring subscriptions to its products.

Strategy

The company has consistently achieved revenue growth and positive earnings by continually expanding its relationships with investment institutions and regularly developing and enhancing its products. It has also made key acquisitions in order to complement or expand its client base and offerings.

Mergers and Acquisitions

In early 2013 the company acquired Investor Force Holdings a provider of asset performance reporting for $23.5 million in cash. The previous year 2012 the company acquired IPD Group a global real estate information business for approximately $125 million. The purchase expanded its portfolio of investment tools for the equities fixed income hedge fund energy and commodities markets.

MSCI made a significant purchase in 2010 with the acquisition of rival RiskMetrics Group through a cash and stock transaction valued at approximately $1.5 billion. The deal united two risk management market leaders. The purchase enhanced MSCI's ability to provide investment decision support tools and widened its geographical reach. It also strengthened its customer base adding RiskMetrics' 3500 clients including several of the largest asset managers mutual funds and hedge funds.

Company Background

MSCI was formerly owned by financial services powerhouse Morgan Stanley which began spinning off the business in 2007. MSCI became an independent stand-alone public company 2009. Morgan Staley maintains an 8% share in the firm.

EXECUTIVES

Chairman of the Board; President; Chief Executive Officer, Henry A. Fernandez, age 55, $250,000 total compensation
Chief Operating Officer, David C. Brierwood, $339,603 total compensation
Head of Client Coverage and Marketing, C.D. Baer Pettit, $284,915 total compensation
President, Gary Retelny, $185,000 total compensation
Investor Relations, Lisa Monaco
Chief Financial Officer, Robert Qutub
Director, Patrick J. (Pat) Tierney, age 67
President CEO and Director, Henry A. Fernandez, age 54
Director, Linda H. Riefler, age 53
Director, Scott M. Sipprelle, age 50
Director, Benjamin F. duPont, age 49
Director, Rodolphe M. Vallee, age 52
Director, Alice W. Handy, age 63
Director, George W. Siguler, age 65
Director, Catherine R. Kinney, age 61
Auditors: Deloitte&ToucheLLP

LOCATIONS

HQ: MSCI Inc.
One Chase Manhattan Plaza 44th Fl., New York NY 10005
Phone: 212-804-3900   **Fax:** 212-804-2919
Web: www.msci.com

2012 Sales

	$ mil.	% of total
Americas	517	55

Europe Middle East & Africa	308	32
Asia & Australia	124	13
Total	**950**	**100**

PRODUCTS/OPERATIONS

2012 Sales

	$ mil.	% of total
Index and ESG	441	47
Risk management analytics	260	27
Portfolio management analytics	116	12
Governance	123	13
Energy & commodity analytics	9	1
Total	**950**	**100**

Selected Offerings

Barra (equity and multi-asset class portfolio analytics product)
CFRA (forensic accounting risk research legal/regulatory risk assessment due-diligence and educational services)
FEA (entergy and commodity asset valuation analytics)
ISS (governance research and outsourced proxy voting and reporting services)
MSCI Indices (flagship global equity indices)
RiskMetrics (risk and wealth management products)

COMPETITORS

Algorithmics	Liquid Holdings
Deutsche Borse	Nomura Securities
Dow Jones	Russell
FTSE Group	S&P
FactSet	

HISTORICAL FINANCIALS

Company Type: Public

Income Statement

FYE: December 31

	REVENUE ($ mil.)	NET INCOME ($ mil.)	NET PROFIT MARGIN	EMPLOYEES
12/12	950.1	184.2	19.4%	2,759
12/11	900.9	173.4	19.3%	2,429
12/10*	72.5	13.8	19.1%	0
11/10	662.9	92.1	13.9%	2,077
11/09	442.9	81.8	18.5%	974
Annual Growth	21.0%	22.5%	—	29.7%

*Fiscal year change

2012 Year-End Financials

Debt ratio: 28.3%	No. of shares (mil.): 120
Return on equity: 13.4%	Dividends
Cash ($ mil.): 183	Yield: —
Current ratio: 1.01	Payout: —
Long-term debt ($ mil.): 811	Market value ($ mil.): 3,722

	STOCK PRICE ($) FY Close	P/E High/Low		PER SHARE ($) Earnings	Dividends	Book Value
12/12	30.99	25	17	1.48	0.00	11.87
12/11	32.93	28	20	1.41	0.00	10.77
12/10*	38.96	364	248	0.11	0.00	9.22
11/10	34.06	46	33	0.81	0.00	9.04
11/09	30.47	41	16	0.80	0.00	4.84
Annual Growth	0.4%	—	—	16.6%	—	25.1%

*Fiscal year change

MTS Systems Corp.

In this world nothing is certain but death and taxes —and those things tested by MTS Systems. The company produces testing systems that simulate repeated or harsh conditions to determine mechanical behavior of materials products and structures. Its systems are used worldwide in infrastructure markets from inspecting steel to locomotive rail testing. MTS caters to auto makers with road simulators. In aerospace MTS tests aircraft fatigue. Services include maintenance and training. MTS also supplies industrial sensors (Temposonics) to increase machine efficiency and safety. About three-quarters of the company's customers operate outside the US.

Geographic Reach

MTS has operations in Africa the Asia/Pacific Central and South America Europe and North America. Asia generated 37% of its overall sales in 2012 while Europe accounted for 31%; the US for 26%.

Operations

MTS's test segment primarily comprises products for the testing of ground vehicles (accounting for 50% of the segment's revenue) and products for testing materials in industries that include power generation aerospace vehicles and bio-medicine (30% of the segment's revenue). Structure-testing products for aerospace wind energy structural engineering petroleum and other industries account for the remainder of the test segment's revenue.

The company's sensors which automate machinery to increase safety and productivity are used in such industries as the manufacturing of plastic injection molding machines steel mills fluid power oil and gas and alternative energy.

Sales and Marketing

The test segment has sales staff in the US and China and sales and service subsidiaries in Canada China France Germany Italy Japan South Korea Sweden the UK. Sold through a direct sales force and independent distributors MTS's sensors are engineered and assembled in North Carolina Germany and Japan.

Financial Performance

Behind both a high backlog and new orders within its test segment revenue was up about 16% in fiscal 2012 compared with 2011. The company's test segment which accounts for 82% of sales surged by about 21%. Sales for the sensors segment however decreased by 3% in 2012. MTS' net income increased by 1% due to the higher revenue levels and a decrease in interest expenses.

Ownership

Mutual fund manager Mairs and Power owns roughly 12% of MTS.

HISTORY

MTS Systems a spinoff of Research Incorporated was started in 1966 to make software so automakers could replicate test track conditions in the laboratory. MTS's first products measured auto body endurance. Donald Sullivan who became president in 1982 and CEO in 1987 pulled the company through a market slump in the early 1990s by steering it into the factory automation business. The move was initiated by the 1992 acquisition of small startup Custom Servo Motors a maker of compact powerful motors used to control fabrication and packaging motions in factory applications. Sullivan was named chairman in 1994 replacing company co-founder George Butzow.

To feed revenue momentum the company made some of its systems compatible with Microsoft's Windows NT environments and it tailored tools to specific customers. In 1996 the Japanese government bought a $23 million seismic simulator in the wake of the 1995 Hanshin earthquake. The company moved into the aerospace products market in 1997 creating titanium-based component subsidiary AeroMet. (MTS shut down AeroMet in late 2005 saying the unit could not achieve a sustainable business model.)

Sullivan stepped down as CEO in 1998 and was replaced by longtime Honeywell executive Sidney (Chip) Emery. MTS in 1999 bought engine design testing specialist DSP Technology. A drop in profits for the fiscal year partly the result of the purchase prompted MTS to restructure and lay off nearly 10% of its workforce.

In 2000 the company won a $37 million contract from the US Army to design manufacture and install an advanced roadway simulator. The next year MTS sold its electronic assembly operations to PEMSTAR and expanded its line of software products for the auto industry.

MTS sold its automation division in 2003 to Parker Hannifin.

The company signed an agreement with National Instruments in 2004 to cooperate on research and development of a low-cost framework for noise and vibration testing.

In 2005 MTS sold its Powertrain Technology (engine testing) division to A&D Co. Ltd. of Japan.

Chip Emery left the CEO's post in early 2008 and was succeeded by president/COO Laura Hamilton. Emery remained chairman until the end of fiscal 2008.

In mid 2008 the company sold off its Nano Instruments business to Agilent Technologies. The deal marked MTS's exit from supplying nanoindentation systems and related equipment used in verifying structural integrity of semiconductor devices and coatings and thin films.

In late 2008 the company widened its pipeline to China. MTS acquired the assets of SANS Group a Chinese supplier of materials testing systems for nearly $44 million. The Shenzhen-based firm makes electromechanical and static-hydraulic testing machines among other products. The deal builds upon MTS' move to establish a wholly foreign-owned enterprise in Shanghai in 2007. A sales office was first opened in China in 1985.

EXECUTIVES

SVP and CFO, Susan E. (Sue) Knight, age 58, $331,250 total compensation
President and CEO, Jeffrey A. (Jeff) Graves, age 52
Senior Vice President Sensors, William E. Bachrach, age 53
SVP Sensors Division, Joachim Hellwig, age 63, $306,806 total compensation
Chairman, David J. (Dave) Anderson, age 65
SVP Test, Arthur (Rich) Baker
SVP General Counsel and Chief Compliance Officer, Steven G. Mahon
VP and Chief Human Resources Officer, Kristin E. Trecker
Senior Vice President and Chief Information Officer, Mark D. Losee
Director, Emily M. Liggett, age 57
Director, Gail P. Steinel, age 56
Director, Barb J. Samardzich, age 54
Director, Jean-Lou A. Chameau, age 59
Director, Brendan C. Hegarty, age 70

Director, William V. (Bill) Murray, age 52
Auditors: KPMGLLP

LOCATIONS

HQ: MTS Systems Corp.
  14000 Technology Drive, Eden Prairie, MN 55344
Phone: 952 937-4000
Web: www.mts.com

2012 Sales

	$ mil.	% of total
Asia		
Europe		
Other European countries	114	21
Other	30	6

PRODUCTS/OPERATIONS

2012 Sales

	$ mil.	% of total
Test	442	82
Total	**542**	**100**

COMPETITORS

ACS Motion Control	Mechanical Technology
AMETEK	Moog
Aero Systems	OYO
Engineering	Pepperl+Fuchs
GE	PerkinElmer
HORIBA	Pure Technologies
Illinois Tool Works	Schmitt Industries
Instron	Tech/Ops Sevcon
JT3	

HISTORICAL FINANCIALS

Company Type: Public

Income Statement

FYE: September 28

	REVENUE ($ mil.)	NET INCOME ($ mil.)	NET PROFIT MARGIN	EMPLOYEES
09/13	569.4	57.8	10.2%	2,299
09/12*	542.2	51.5	9.5%	2,147
10/11	467.3	50.9	10.9%	2,003
10/10	374.0	18.5	5.0%	1,948
10/09	408.8	17.3	4.3%	2,015
Annual Growth	8.6%	35.0%	—	3.4%

*Fiscal year change

2013 Year-End Financials

Debt ratio: 7.7%
Return on equity: 23.9%
Cash ($ mil.): 48
Current ratio: 1.89
Long-term debt ($ mil.): —

No. of shares (mil.): 15
Dividends
  Yield: 0.0%
  Payout: 32.9%
Market value ($ mil.): 981

	STOCK PRICE ($) FY Close	P/E High/Low		PER SHARE ($) Earnings	Dividends	Book Value
09/13	63.65	18	12	3.64	1.20	16.65
09/12*	53.55	17	9	3.21	1.05	14.50
10/11	30.64	15	9	3.24	0.85	13.49
10/10	31.50	28	9	1.14	0.60	10.88
10/09	28.13	38	19	1.03	0.60	12.31
Annual Growth	22.6%	—	—	37.1%	18.9%	7.8%

*Fiscal year change

Multi-Color Corp.

Multi-Color Corporation's labels aren't just black and white and red all over. The company produces printed labels for product makers in markets such as home and personal care wine and spirit food and beverage and specialty consumer goods. Multi-Color serves customers in North and South America Europe the Asia/Pacific region and South Africa. The company prints and affixes heat transfer re-sealable shrink wrap pressure sensitive and other label types to glass and plastic containers. Multi-Color also offers gravure printing and injection in-mold labels. Over the years the company has counted Procter & Gamble and Miller Brewing among its biggest customers. Multi-Color traces its roots to 1916.

The company has been working to alleviate its dependency on a concentrated set of customers. Major consumer product and beverage manufacturers Procter & Gamble and Miller Lite collectively accounted for 28% of the company's total sales in fiscal year 2011 down from 38% in 2010 45% in 2011 and 50% in 2008. Multi-Color attributes the decline to the addition of international customers and products it gained through prior acquisitions such as Collotype (a maker of pressure-sensitive labels for wine and spirits that has operations in Australia South Africa and California); Guidotti CentroStampa (a European wine spirit and olive oil label printer based in Italy); and Monroe Etiquette (a French wine label specialist based in Montagny France).

In fiscal year 2011 the company reported an increase in revenues and net income. Positive earnings were primarily due to the acquisitions of Guidotti CentroStampa and Monroe Etiquette. The remaining gains were due to growth in sales volume a favorable foreign exchange rate and the increase of operating efficiencies through cutting costs.

Multi-Color continued its international expansion strategy in 2011. That year it purchased La Cromografica an Italian wine label specialist in Florence Italy. Later that year it entered the growing Latin American wine and spirit markets when it acquired 70% of two label operations one in Santiago Chile and the other in Mendoza Argentina It acquired rival LabelCorp Holdings doing business as York Label Group for about $356 million to expand in North America and Chile. It also entered the Chinese market establishing operations in the major southern city of Guangzhou in 2011.

EXECUTIVES

Chairman, Lorrence T. Kellar, age 73
VP Human Resources, Lesha K. Spahr
VP and Treasurer, Mary T. Fetch
VP Operations Controller North America Consumer Products, Steven T. Walker
VP Information Technology, Gregory L. Myers
President and CEO, Nigel A. Vinecombe, age 47, $188,856 total compensation
President Consumer Products Group North America, Floyd E. Needham, age 42
President Consumer Products Asia Pacific, Brenton K. Barrett
VP CFO and Chief Accounting Officer, Sharon E. Birkett, age 45
President Wine and Spirits Group North America, David G. Buse
President Republic of South Africa, Rian Moore
President Wine and Spirits Asia Pacific, Vadis A. Rodato

Senior Director Global Purchasing and Procurement, Daren Hudson
Director, Robert R. (Bob) Buck, age 62
Director, Charles B. Connolly, age 54
Director, Roger A. Keller, age 66
Director, Thomas M. Mohr, age 58
Independent Director, Simon Roberts
Auditors: GrantThorntonLLP

LOCATIONS

HQ: Multi-Color Corporation
  4053 Clough Woods Dr., Batavia OH 45103-2586
Phone: 513-381-1480   **Fax:** 513-381-2813
Web: www.multicolorcorp.com

2011 Sales

US	212	63
Italy	38	11
South Africa	14	4

PRODUCTS/OPERATIONS

Selected Products and Services

Labels
  Heat transfer
  In-mold
  Neck bands
  Peel-away
  Pressure sensitive
  Re-sealable
  Shrink sleeve

COMPETITORS

Convergent Label	Jordan Industries
Technology	Outlook Group
Fort Dearborn	WS Packaging Group
H. S. Crocker	

HISTORICAL FINANCIALS

Company Type: Public

Income Statement

FYE: March 31

	REVENUE ($ mil.)	NET INCOME ($ mil.)	NET PROFIT MARGIN	EMPLOYEES
03/13	659.8	30.3	4.6%	2,800
03/12	510.2	19.7	3.9%	2,749
03/11	338.2	18.4	5.4%	1,430
03/10	276.8	14.2	5.2%	1,186
03/09	289.7	11.3	3.9%	1,252
Annual Growth	22.8%	28.0%	—	22.3%

2013 Year-End Financials

Debt ratio: 47.9%
Return on equity: 11.4%
Cash ($ mil.): 15
Current ratio: 1.56
Long-term debt ($ mil.): 378

No. of shares (mil.): 16
Dividends
  Yield: 0.0%
  Payout: 10.7%
Market value ($ mil.): 417

	STOCK PRICE ($) FY Close	P/E High/Low		PER SHARE ($) Earnings	Dividends	Book Value
03/13	25.79	14	10	1.86	0.20	17.02
03/12	22.51	21	14	1.32	0.20	15.68
03/11	20.21	14	7	1.40	0.20	14.40
03/10	11.98	15	9	1.16	0.20	11.86
03/09	12.23	28	11	0.92	0.20	8.35
Annual Growth	20.5%	—	—	19.2%	(0.0%)	19.5%

Multimedia Games Holding Company, Inc.

You might say this company's games help casinos hit the jackpot. Multimedia Games is a leading manufacturer of slot machines and other gaming systems used by both commercial casinos and by establishments in the Native American gaming industry. It makes both video reel and mechanical reel games as well as multi-terminal games that allow gamblers to compete for jackpots. In addition to its proprietary gaming machines Multimedia Games licenses games from third parties such as WMS Industries and Aristocrat Technologies. The company also makes casino management systems that monitor gaming machine performance and tracking player activity as well as video lottery terminals and charitable gaming systems.

Like other gaming machine manufacturers Multimedia Games plays an obviously important role in the casino gambling business. It focuses on making machines that are enticing enough to attract attention on the crowded casino floor and also entertaining enough to keep players engaged for several rounds of action. The company's games compete against similar products from such manufacturers as Bally Technologies International Game Technology and Video Gaming Technologies.

Multimedia Games has more than 13000 gaming units in operation. The company generates the lion's share of its revenue from participation agreements (also known as revenue share agreements) through which it receives ongoing fees and royalties paid by gaming operators generally a percentage of wagers accepted by its machines. The company also makes money from sales of gaming equipment as well as from supplying the gaming system for about 12500 video lottery terminals at racetracks in the State of New York. More than 40% of its total revenues come from the Chickasaw Nation a Native American tribe in Oklahoma. In 2010 the company's profits increased primarily due to receiving an income tax benefit that year.

Going forward the company is focusing on increasing the sale of player terminals and game content systems and services. It is doing so by developing new products. In 2010 it introduced its Maximum Lockdown and Side Action series of games. Multimedia Games is also working to expand its footprint into new jurisdictions by pursuing new licenses in states such as Nevada Florida Indiana Michigan and New York.

Patrick Ramsey was promoted from COO to CEO in 2010 to replace Anthony Sanfilippo who left to become chief casino operator of Pinnacle Entertainment. Sanfilippo had joined Multimedia Games from casino giant Harrah's Entertainment (now called Caesars Entertainment) in 2008.

HISTORY

The Indian Gaming Regulatory Act in 1988 gave entrepreneurs opportunities to bring reservation-based gaming to players around the country. In 1991 Gordon Graves founder of Datatrol —which had launched the first online lottery system in the US - set up TV Bingo Network which went public in 1993. The next year the company acquired American Gaming & Entertainment which operated bingo games via closed-circuit television and changed its name to Multimedia Games.

In 1995 it introduced MegaMania which lets bingo hall patrons play games against each other through linked electronic terminals for average jackpots of $20000. But casino competition lowered the odds of growth so Multimedia turned to the potential of at-home play creating a Web site that let patrons play bingo cards by proxy.

MegaMania began attracting attention from federal agencies which noticed its resemblance to the Las Vegas-style casino electronic games forbidden in Indian bingo halls. A federal investigation concluded in 1997 that Multimedia's games were permitted under the Gaming Regulatory Act. Unsatisfied the FBI and a US attorney's office conducted a raid on Multimedia's headquarters on New Year's Eve of 1998. Later that year a district court affirmed the legal gaming status of MegaMania; an appellate court later upheld the decision. Also in 1998 Multimedia moved its headquarters from Tulsa Oklahoma to Austin Texas.

In 1999 the company struck a licensing deal with WMS Gaming and sold 70% of its ownership of Gamebay.com an online sweepstakes site launched in October. The same year the company agreed to pay Network Gaming International more than $3 million to settle a breach of contract lawsuit. In 2000 it introduced the first WMS machines into Washington State tribal casinos through its licensing agreement. In 2001 Multimedia Games signed a licensing agreement with Alliance Gaming giving the company permission to distribute Bally gaming products.

In 2002 Multimedia Games filed suit against the National Indian Gaming Commission (NIGC) claiming its CountDown Bingo and Two Step Bingo games are "Class II" games and may therefore be legally conducted on Indian lands without government interference. The NIGC had issued violation notices to facilities operating the games arguing they were "Class III" and therefore subject to state and local government regulations. Later in the year the case was dismissed on the grounds that the court did not have proper jurisdiction to consider the case and that game vendors are not entitled to contest the classification of their games.

Graves stepped down as CEO in 2003 and Clifton Lind was promoted to the top position. That same year Multimedia Games entered the charitable bingo market with the installation of several bingo stations in Alabama. The company purchased in 2005 most of the assets of Sigma Game a maker of mechanical slot and video gaming machines.

Multimedia Games moved into Mexico's bingo market in 2006 when it agreed to provide electronic bingo to Grupo Televisa subsidiary Apuestas Internacionales an operator of bingo halls and sports books.

Lind stepped down as CEO in 2008 and was replaced by Anthony Sanfilippo who previously served with casino giant Harrah's Entertainment (now Caesars Entertainment). Sanfilippo left the company in 2010 to become head of casino operator Pinnacle Entertainment. Former COO Patrick Ramsey was named CEO.

EXECUTIVES

SVP and CFO, Adam D. Chibib, age 44, $152,885 total compensation
SVP Sales, Mickey D. (Mick) Roemer, age 58
VP Legal Affairs and Operations, James A. Bannerot, age 65, $183,750 total compensation
VP Accounting, Shannon C. Brooks
President CEO and Director, Patrick J. Ramsey, age 37, $300,000 total compensation
Director Compliance, Dallas Burnett

VP Sales Casino Gaming, Randi Ingram, age 47
Chairman, Stephen J. (Steve) Greathouse, age 60
SVP General Counsel and Secretary, Uri L. Clinton, $250,000 total compensation
VP Technology, Joaquin Aviles
Senior VP Sales, Ken Lynchard
Senior Vice President; Chief Compliance Officer; General Counsel; Corporate Secretary, Jerome Smith
Senior Vice President - Sales, Mick Roemer
Senior Vice President; Chief Compliance Officer; General Counsel; Corporate Secretary, Todd McTavish
Director, Timothy S. (Tim) Stanley, age 45
Director, Neil E. Jenkins, age 61
Director, Michael J. (Mike) Maples Sr., age 68
Director, Anthony M. Sanfilippo, age 52
Director, Robert D. (Rob) Repass, age 50
President CEO and Director, Patrick J. Ramsey, age 37
Director, Justin A. Orlando, age 40
Auditors: BDOUSALLP

LOCATIONS

HQ: Multimedia Games Inc.
206 Wild Basin Rd. Bldg. B. Ste. 400, Austin TX 78746
Phone: 512-334-7500 **Fax:** 512-334-7695
Web: www.multimediagames.com

PRODUCTS/OPERATIONS

2010 Sales

	$ mil.	% of total
Gaming Operations		
Participation revenue	85	72
Lottery	7	7
Gaming Equipment and System Sales		
Player terminal and equipment sales	18	15
Systems and Licensing	5	4
Other	1	2
Total	**117**	**100**

Selected Casino Systems

TournEvent (allows slot tournament play)
Cash and Cage (for small to mid-size casinos)
Slot management

COMPETITORS

Aristocrat Technologies	Konami Gaming
Bally Technologies	Scientific Games
GTECH	Video Gaming Technologies
GameTech	WMS Industries
International Game Technology	

HISTORICAL FINANCIALS

Company Type: Public

Income Statement

FYE: September 30

	REVENUE ($ mil.)	NET INCOME ($ mil.)	NET PROFIT MARGIN	EMPLOYEES
09/13	189.3	34.9	18.4%	528
09/12	156.1	28.1	18.0%	471
09/11	127.8	5.6	4.4%	410
09/10	117.9	2.6	2.2%	397
09/09	127.1	(44.7)	—	412
Annual Growth	**10.5%**	**—**	**—**	**6.4%**

2013 Year-End Financials

Debt ratio: 10.5%
Return on equity: 19.2%
Cash ($ mil.): 102
Current ratio: 4.70
Long-term debt ($ mil.): 25
No. of shares (mil.): 29
Dividends
  Yield: —
  Payout: —
Market value ($ mil.): 1,015

	STOCK PRICE ($) FY Close	P/E High/Low		PER SHARE ($) Earnings	Dividends	Book Value
09/13	34.55	32	11	1.14	0.00	7.11
09/12	15.73	16	4	0.96	0.00	5.50
09/11	4.04	30	17	0.20	0.00	4.32
09/10	3.70	64	35	0.09	0.00	4.15
09/09	5.12	—	—	(1.67)	0.00	3.95
Annual Growth	61.2%	—	—	—		15.8%

	STOCK PRICE ($) FY Close	P/E High/Low		PER SHARE ($) Earnings	Dividends	Book Value
12/12	23.76	12	6	3.55	3.55	(0.00)
12/11	39.64	13	10	3.45	3.45	(0.00)
12/10	39.87	14	7	2.76	2.76	(0.00)
12/09	20.20	13	5	1.56	1.56	(0.00)
12/08	7.85	16	4	1.81	1.81	(0.00)
Annual Growth	31.9%	—	—	18.4%	18.4%	

MV Oil Trust

Call it what you will black gold Texas tea or the black blood of the earth MV Oil Trust is wringing out the value from each drop and distributing it to shareholders. MV Oil Trust receives royalty interests from the mature oil and gas properties of MV Partners located in Kansas and Colorado. The properties have proved reserves of 9.5 million barrels of oil from 922 net wells. The trust receives royalties based on the amount of oil (and gas) produced and sold and then distributes virtually all of the proceeds to shareholders on a regular basis. MV Partners a private company engaged in the exploration production gathering aggregation and sale of oil and natural gas has the rights to 80% of net proceeds.

MV Partners has an agreement by which Vess Oil and Murfin Drilling operate the underlying properties on behalf of MV Partners for which MV Partners is designated as the operator.

The trust has 43 882 net acres of undeveloped acreage.

Auditors: GrantThorntonLLP

LOCATIONS

HQ: MV Oil Trust
Global Corporate Trust 919 Congress, Austin TX 78701
Phone: 307-777-7852   **Fax:** 307-777-5466
Web: legisweb.state.wy.us

COMPETITORS

Cross Timbers Royalty Trust	Mesa Royalty Trust
Hugoton Royalty Trust	Panhandle Oil and Gas
LL&E Royalty Trust	Sabine Royalty Trust
	San Juan Basin

HISTORICAL FINANCIALS

Company Type: Public

Income Statement

FYE: December 31

	REVENUE ($ mil.)	NET INCOME ($ mil.)	NET PROFIT MARGIN	EMPLOYEES
12/12	41.5	40.8	98.3%	0
12/11	40.5	39.6	97.8%	0
12/10	32.5	31.6	97.4%	0
12/09	18.7	17.9	95.6%	0
12/08	21.5	20.7	96.3%	0
Annual Growth	17.8%	18.4%	—	—

2012 Year-End Financials

Debt ratio: —	No. of shares (mil.): 11
Return on equity: 128.7%	Dividends
Cash ($ mil.): 0	Yield: 14.9%
Current ratio: —	Payout: 95.1%
Long-term debt ($ mil.): —	Market value ($ mil.): 273

MWI Veterinary Supply Inc

While MWI could stand for Mastiff Weimaraner and Irish Setter MWI Veterinary Supply is actually named after founder and veterinarian Millard Wallace Ickes. The veterinary products distributor supplies drugs diagnostics equipment and other medical supplies for companion animals and livestock. It serves veterinary practices from about a dozen distribution centers across the US and in the UK. The firm offers 40000 products from more than 700 vendors. In addition to medical supplies and equipment MWI distributes pet food and nutritional products. The company in business since 1976 offers customers online ordering tools to manage inventory consultation for equipment and pet cremation services.

Geographic Reach

About 85% of MWI's sales come from the US market. The company operates about a dozen facilities in the US and one in the UK.

Operations

About 95% of MWI's product sales are from the sale of pharmaceuticals and supplies to veterinary practices; the rest come from commissions and sales to parties other than veterinary practices. Pharmaceuticals account for 40% of its product sales and typically include anesthetics analgesics antibiotics opthalmics and hormones. Vaccines are MWI's second biggest earner bringing in about 15% of product revenues and are mostly composed of small animal equine and production animal biologicals. Its parasiticides (10%) are used to get rid of fleas ticks flies mosquitoes and internal parasites.

The company also makes veterinary pet food and nutritional products that include premium pet foods livestock feed ingredients dietary supplements vitamins and specialty treats. MWI's other products range from diagnostic testing supplies to capital equipment. The firm also offers services including e-commerce support procurement and order fulfillment.

The company does not manufacture the vast majority of its products instead it relies on suppliers that include Pfizer Merck and Merial. Products from its ten largest vendors account for about 70% of its sales. Pfizer is MWI's single biggest supplier providing products that account for about 20% of MWI's sales.

Sales and Marketing

MWI publishes product catalogs and monthly magazines which are often used by customers as reference tools for ordering. While a robust sales force and roster of printed materials are vital to its marketing strategy online ordering is becoming a significant sales channel.

MWI has 300 field sales and 170 telesales representatives serving its clients. Its largest customers include Medical Management International (known as Banfield the nation's largest private veterinary practice with about 750 vet hospitals) and Feeders' Advantage a buying group formed by feedlot operators.

Financial Performance

MWI reported a 33% increase in revenues to nearly $2.1 billion in 2012 due to product sales growth in the US and the UK largely from acquisitions new product launches and growth of its e-commerce platform and sales team. The company has experienced rising sales levels over the past five years. Net income also rose by 26% to $42.6 million in 2012 as a result of the revenue growth.

Strategy

MWI has widened its geographic presence by expanding or constructing new distribution centers. Areas targeted for growth include the Northeastern Midwestern and Southeastern regions of the US.

The company also captures new customers by offering improved technology systems (its e-commerce platform for example) and by increasing the numbers of sales and customer service representatives available to its potential and existing clients. Acquisitions also enhance the firm's technology offerings.

Mergers and Acquisitions

MWI grows in part by acquiring regional suppliers. Since the market for animal health products distribution is highly fragmented there are plenty of national regional and local distributors that make attractive candidates for MWI to purchase.

For instance in 2013 the company acquired IVESCO Holdings for some $67.5 million to expand its protein-based production animal offerings as well as other complementary animal health product lines. IVESCO operates as a division of MWI following the acquisition.

Previous acquisitions include the 2011 purchase of Micro Beef Technologies a distributor of production animal health products for some $60 million. The acquisition helped to expand MWI'S distribution network and management systems products; it also added computerized management systems for the production animal market.

Though the company makes the majority of its sales in the US it is also pursuing acquisitions in the UK.

Ownership

MWI became an independent company in 2002 when venture capital firm Bruckmann Rosser Sherrill & Co. bought the firm from Agri Beef Co. Bruckmann Rosser Sherrill & Co. gradually sold off its shares in MWI while Agri Beef retains a small minority (about 4%) stake of the publicly traded company. The majority shareholder in MWI is investment manager Neuberger Berman with about 12%.

EXECUTIVES

President and CEO, James F. (Jim) Cleary Jr., age 50, $325,000 total compensation

SVP Finance and Administration and CFO, Mary Patricia B. Thompson, age 50, $180,000 total compensation

VP Sales, Jeffrey J. Danielson, age 53, $151,720 total compensation

VP Marketing, John R. Ryan, age 44

Chairman, John F. McNamara, age 78

VP Operations, Bryan P. Mooney, age 45

VP and General Manager Specialty Resource Group, John J. Francis, age 60, $148,320 total compensation
Sales Rocky Mountain Region, Steve Fitzjames
Sales Southwest Region, Jeff Hicks
Sales Southeast Region, Bob Weinschenk
Sales Great Lakes Region, Terry Walsh
Sales Gulf States Region, Dianne Gallagher
VP and CIO, Alden J Sutherland, age 50
Vice President - Inventory Management, Kevin Price
Director, Bruce C. Bruckmann, age 59
Director, Keith E. Alessi, age 58
Director, Robert N. Rebholtz Jr., age 49
President CEO and Director, James F. (Jim) Cleary Jr., age 49
Director, A. Craig Olson, age 61
Director, William J. Robison, age 77
Auditors: Deloitte&ToucheLLP

LOCATIONS

HQ: MWI Veterinary Supply Inc
3041 W. Pasadena Dr., Boise, ID 83705
Phone: 208 955-8930
Web: www.mwivet.com

2012 Sales by Region

	$ mil.	% of total
US	1,776	86
UK	298	14
Total	**2,075**	**100**

PRODUCTS/OPERATIONS

2012 Sales

Product sales	1,996	96
Commissions	17	1

2012 Product Sales

Pharmaceuticals	38
Parasiticide	12
Micro feed ingredients	8
Diagnostic	6
Capital equipment	2
Total	**0**	**100**

Selected Products

Analgesics
Anesthesia machines
Anesthetics
Antibiotics
Bandages
Cages
Dental machines
Dietary supplements
Feline leukemia diagnostics
Grooming materials
Heartworm diagnostics
Hormones
Lyme diagnostics
Ophthalmics
Parasiticides
Parvovirus diagnostics
Premium pet foods
Specialty treats
Surgical monitors
Syringes
X-ray machines
Vaccines
Vitamins

Selected Acquisitions

2013
IVESCO Holdings ($67.5 million protein-based animal production products and health products)
2012
Precision Containers Inc. (dba PCI Animal Health $17 million northeastern US distributor of animal health products)
2011
Micro Beef Technologies ($60 million distributor of production animal health products)

Nelson Laboratories Limited Partnership ($7 million distributor of animal health products)
2010
Centaur Services (UK supplier of animal health products)

COMPETITORS

A.C. Graham Animal Health International	IVESCO Lambriar Animal Health Merck Animal Health
Central Garden & Pet	Patterson Companies PetMed
Darby Dental	TW Medical
FarmVet	The Harvard Drug Group
Henry Schein	

HISTORICAL FINANCIALS

Company Type: Public

Income Statement

FYE: September 30

	REVENUE ($ mil.)	NET INCOME ($ mil.)	NET PROFIT MARGIN	EMPLOYEES
09/13	2,347.4	62.8	2.7%	1,732
09/12	2,075.1	53.4	2.6%	1,629
09/11	1,565.3	42.5	2.7%	1,273
09/10	1,229.3	33.4	2.7%	1,179
09/09	941.3	24.9	2.6%	887
Annual Growth	25.7%	26.0%	—	18.2%

2013 Year-End Financials

Debt ratio: 2.3%	No. of shares (mil.): 12
Return on equity: 16.0%	Dividends
Cash ($ mil.): 0	Yield: —
Current ratio: 1.76	Payout: —
Long-term debt ($ mil.): 0	Market value ($ mil.): 1,919

	STOCK PRICE ($) FY Close	P/E High/Low	Earnings	Dividends	Book Value
09/13	149.36	31 21	4.95	0.00	33.18
09/12	106.68	26 14	4.23	0.00	28.09
09/11	68.82	26 16	3.40	0.00	23.21
09/10	57.72	21 13	2.70	0.00	19.81
09/09	39.95	20 10	2.02	0.00	17.05
Annual Growth	39.1%	— —	25.1%	—	18.1%

MYR Group Inc

MYR Group's work can be electrifying. The specialty contractor builds and maintains electric delivery infrastructure systems for utilities and commercial clients. MYR Group constructs transmission and distribution lines for the oil and gas power and telecommunications industries. The company also installs and maintains electrical wiring in commercial and industrial facilities and traffic and rail systems. The group operates nationwide through subsidiaries including The L.E. Myers Co. Harlan Electric Hawkeye Construction Sturgeon Electric MYR Transmission Services and Great Southwestern Construction. MYR's transmission and distribution segment accounts for more than three-fourths of the group's revenues.

Strategy

MYR Group looks to grow organically or through strategic acquisitions and joint ventures. It aims to improve its competitive position in existing markets while also expanding into new ge-

ographic markets. The company has also dog-eared funds to invest in additional properties and equipment to support its strategy. To this end MYR Group in 2013 gained district operations located in Anchorage and Fairbanks Alaska when its Sturgeon Electric Company subsidiary acquired the equipment and transferred personnel from an existing operation of NORCON a unit of CH2M HILL.

The Transmission & Distribution segment counts some 125 cooperatives electric utilities and municipalities as customers. The business stands to benefit from a continued emphasis on improving and upgrading the country's power supply and the increasing market for alternative energy. As wind and solar farm developments grow there is an increasing demand to link the farms to large power grids. MYR Group works on numerous wind farm projects each year. The company expects increased activity in that sector.

The company's Commercial & Industrial segment has a regional focus in Colorado and Arizona.

MYR Group maintains one of the largest fleets of vehicles in the US (some 5000 units) that can be mobilized for transmission and distribution work around the country. Because of this asset MYR Group often is called to restore power in the aftermath of hurricanes floods ice storms and other natural disasters. This is a relatively small part of the company's business though.

The group's strategy to take advantage of the growing need for infrastructure work includes seeking out possible acquisition targets or joint venture partners as well as expanding into new markets. It will also add to its fleet as it deems beneficial and has been spending tens of millions of dollars on new specialty equipment and tooling.

Operations

The company's Transmission & Distribution customers generated 83% of MYR Group's revenue in 2012 up from 80% in 2011 and 75% in 2010. Its Commercial & Industrial segment brought in 17% 20% and 25% of revenue in 2012 2011 and 2010 respectively.

Completed projects include the Cross Texas Transmission 345kV Transmission Line Project Spearville to Axtell 345kV Transmission Line (also known as the KETA Project) the Meadowbrook to Loudoun 500kV Transmission Line and Carson Substation to Suffolk Substation 500kV Transmission Lines.

Sales and Marketing

Transmission & Distribution customers include electric utilities private developers cooperatives and municipalities. Its Commercial & Industrial segment provides electrical contracting services to property owners and general contractors in the Western US.

Its top 10 customers account for nearly 60% of its revenues in fiscal 2012. Cross Texas Transmission its largest customer contributed 15% of its sales.

MYR Group has logged between $400000 and $500000 each year since 2010 on selling general and administrative expenses.

Financial Performance

Thanks to a few $10-million transmission projects MYR Group in fiscal 2012 logged 28% increases in revenue vs. 2011. Both small (less than $3 million in contract value) and medium-sized (between $3 million and $10 million) transmission projects as well as the same size commercial and industrial projects boosted revenue during the reporting period.

Net income meanwhile rose by 87% in 2012 vs. 2011 due to increasing revenue offset in part by rising costs; selling general and administrative expenses; and income tax expenses.

Company Background

MYR was founded in 1891 by Lewis Edward Myers who briefly worked as a salesman with Thomas Edison.

EXECUTIVES

President Chief Executive Officer, William A. (Bill) Koertner, age 63, $500,000 total compensation

Vice President Large Projects, John A. Fluss, age 61, $237,238 total compensation

Senior Vice President, William H. Green, age 69, $297,708 total compensation

Vice President Chief Legal Officer, Gerald B. Engen Jr., age 62, $254,904 total compensation

Chief Operating Officer; Senior Vice President, Richard S. Swartz Jr., age 49, $232,500 total compensation

VP CFO and Treasurer, Marco A. Martinez, age 46, $243,750 total compensation

Vice President Chief Financial Officer Treasurer, Paul J. Evans

Chief Accounting Officer; Vice President, Gregory Wolf

Director, Larry F. Altenbaumer, age 64

Director, Gary R. Johnson, age 66

Director, Jack L. Alexander, age 66

Director, William D. (Bill) Patterson, age 58

Director, Henry W. Fayne, age 66

Director, Betty R. Johnson, age 54

Director, Maurice E. Moore

Auditors: Ernst&YoungLLP

LOCATIONS

HQ: MYR Group Inc.
3 Continental Towers 1701 W. Golf Rd. Ste. 1012, Rolling Meadows IL 60008-4270
Phone: 847-290-1891   **Fax:** 847-290-1892
Web: www.myrgroup.com

PRODUCTS/OPERATIONS

2012 Sales by Segment
$ in mil. % of total

Transmission & Distribution	828	83
Commercial & Industrial	170	17
Total	**999**	**100**

Selected Services

Electrical
  Commercial/Industrial
  Construction
  Design-build services
  Directional boring
  Emergency storm response
  Fiber optics
  Foundations & caissons
  Gas distribution
  Highway lighting
  Overhead distribution
  PCS/Cellular towers
  Preconstruction services
  Substation
  Telecommunications
  Traffic signals
  Transmission
  Underground distribution
Mechanical
  Boiler construction and maintenance
  Erection of piping systems
  General contracting
  In-house fabrication
  Instrumentation
  Maintenance
  Preconstruction services
  Retrofit to existing systems

Selected Subsidiaries

ComTel Technology Inc.
Great Southwestern Construction Inc.
Harlan Electric Company
Hawkeye Construction Inc.
Meyers International Inc.
MYR Transmission Services Inc.
MYRpower Inc.
The L.E. Myers Co.
Sturgeon Electric Company Inc.

COMPETITORS

Austin Industries	MDU Resources
Cupertino Electric	MasTec
Dycom	Mass Electric
EEI	Pike Electric
EMCOR	Corporation
Goldfield	Quanta Services
Henkels & McCoy	Siemens AG
Integrated Electrical	Vario Construction
Services	Company
Kelso-Burnett	

HISTORICAL FINANCIALS
Company Type: Public

Income Statement
FYE: December 31

	REVENUE ($ mil.)	NET INCOME ($ mil.)	NET PROFIT MARGIN	EMPLOYEES
12/12	998.9	34.2	3.4%	3,300
12/11	780.3	18.3	2.3%	3,000
12/10	597.0	16.1	2.7%	2,800
12/09	631.1	17.2	2.7%	3,000
12/08	616.1	23.6	3.8%	2,900
Annual Growth	**12.8%**	**9.7%**	**—**	**3.3%**

2012 Year-End Financials

Debt ratio: —	No. of shares (mil.): 20
Return on equity: 14.5%	Dividends
Cash ($ mil.): 19	Yield: —
Current ratio: 1.47	Payout: —
Long-term debt ($ mil.): —	Market value ($ mil.): 462

	STOCK PRICE ($) FY Close	P/E High/Low		PER SHARE ($) Earnings	Dividends	Book Value
12/12	22.25	14	9	1.60	0.00	12.28
12/11	19.14	29	17	0.87	0.00	10.57
12/10	21.00	27	16	0.78	0.00	9.63
12/09	18.07	26	11	0.83	0.00	8.79
12/08	10.00	14	5	1.14	0.00	7.88
Annual Growth	**22.1%**	**—**	**—**	**8.8%**	**—**	**11.7%**

Myriad Genetics, Inc.

There are a myriad of diseases out there and Myriad Genetics is working to detect which ones you might develop based on your genes. The company develops and sells molecular diagnostic tests in three main areas: predictive medicine (to assess a patient's risk for developing disease) personalized medicine (to identify likelihood of drug response to therapies) and prognostic medicine (to assess risk of disease progression or recurrence). Its biggest revenue maker BRACAnalysis helps determine risk for breast or ovarian cancer. Myriad Genetics markets its products in the US through its own sales force and uses collaborations to sell them elsewhere.

Operations

The company operates in three segments: research molecular diagnostics and companion diagnostics. The research segment is focused on the discovery of genes related to major common diseases and includes corporate services such as finance human resources legal and information technology. The molecular diagnostics segment provides testing that is designed to assess an individual's risk for developing disease later in life identify a patient's likelihood of responding to drug therapy and guide a patient's dosing to ensure optimal treatment or assess a patient's risk of disease progression and disease recurrence. The companion diagnostics segment provides testing products and services to the pharmaceutical biotechnology and medical research industries.

Myriad Genetics' primary line of molecular diagnostic testing products includes BRACAnalysis COLARIS and MELARIS. The company markets these to physicians engaged in preventive rather than reactive treatments. These tests are designed to assess whether a patient's genetic makeup makes the patient more likely to develop certain cancers such as breast colorectal and skin. Myriad is ramping up its sales marketing and education efforts aimed at OB/Gyn doctors in the US a market that targets women.

The company's personalized medicine line of products gauges a patient's response to certain drugs and dosages which then helps physicians tailor treatments to the individual. The THERAGUIDE 5-FU product shows oncologists whether a cancer patient through a small blood sample is likely to have adverse reactions to a common chemotherapy.

A third set of tests includes prognostic medicine diagnostics that assess disease progression or recurrence rates. Its PROLARIS product helps physicians predict the aggressiveness of prostate cancer in men.

Geographic Reach

Based in the US the company serves major markets in Asia Europe and Latin America. In the US Myriad Genetics operates from offices and labs in Austin Texas; Salt Lake City; and Lake Placid New York. In Europe it has sales offices in Munich Paris Madrid and Milan laboratory operations in Munich and an international headquarters in Zurich.

Financial Analysis

Myriad Genetics reported a 23% increase in revenues in 2011 thanks to increased molecular diagnostic testing volume (18% of revenue growth) thanks to increased demand for its BRACAnalysis COLARIS & COLARIS AP and other products and higher companion diagnostic service revenues (5% of growth) thanks to the acquisition of the Rules-Based Medicine company.

The 11% increase in net income in 2011 was primarily due to higher revenues offset by higher research and development expenses.

Strategy

In order to develop the next generation of molecular diagnostic products Myriad Genetics continues to develop its own proprietary technologies including bioinformatics and robotics to better understand genes and proteins and their role in human disease. It also seeks to license or acquire biomarkers or genes from third-party organizations to augment its own in-house product development programs. For instance in 2012 Myriad Genetics obtained an exclusive worldwide license (excepting co-exclusivity in Germany) to commercially test the RAD51C gene for hereditary breast and ovarian cancer risk. That year it also signed a deal with Cephalon to conduct BRCA1 and BRCA2 mutation testing on patients to be enrolled in a Phase I/II clinical study.

In 2011 the company moved to expand its offerings by acquiring Austin Texas-based diagnostics firm Rules-Based Medicine for some $80 million. The purchase added biomarker products that aid in the diagnoses of neurological disorders and inflammatory and infectious diseases as well as companion diagnostic offerings and additional products under development. Renamed Myriad RBM it operates as an R&D subsidiary in Austin.

In 2010 a federal court revoked two of Myriad Genetics' patents related to the BRACAnalysis test on the premise that isolated DNA strains are not patentable since they are products of nature. The ruling could affect future research projects and have a lasting impact on the entire biopharmaceutical development market.

Ownership

In 2012 Royce and Associates LLC owned 12.4% of the company.

Company Background

Myriad Genetics spun off its drug development operations in mid-2009. The spin-off of its drug development arm Myriad Pharmaceuticals into a separate publicly traded company (called Myrexis) has allowed Myriad Genetics to dedicate substantial focus on molecular diagnostics. Previously the company had used revenue from its profitable diagnostics business to fund its drug development efforts. But with the company reaching profitability overall for the first time in 2008 it revisited the dual business structure and decided to split itself into two.

EXECUTIVES

President CEO and Director, Peter D. Meldrum, age 66, $800,552 total compensation
Vice Chairman, Walter Gilbert
EVP General Counsel and Secretary, Richard M. Marsh, age 55
Chairman, John T. Henderson, age 69
EVP International Operations, Gary A. King, age 57
Chief Scientific Officer, Jerry S. Lanchbury, age 54
President Myriad Genetic Laboratories, Mark C. Capone, age 51, $361,512 total compensation
CFO and Treasurer, James S. (Jim) Evans, age 50, $375,552 total compensation
CIO, Robert G. Harrison, age 47
EVP Corporate Communications, Ronald Rogers
Director Investor Relations, Suzanne Barton
President Myriad RBM, T. Craig Benson
EVP Human Resources, Jayne B. Hart
Director Investor Relations, Rebecca Chambers
Vice-President Quality Assurance and Regulatory Compliance, Margaret Sandefur
Vice President of Corporate Development, Samuel T. LaBrie
Director, Lawrence C. (Larry) Best, age 63
President CEO and Director, Peter D. Meldrum, age 66
Vice Chairman, Walter Gilbert
Director, Linda S. Wilson, age 76
Director, Dennis H. Langer, age 61
Director, Heiner Dreismann, age 60
Director, S. Louise Phanstiel
Auditors: Ernst&YoungLLP

LOCATIONS

HQ: Myriad Genetics Inc.
320 Wakara Way, Salt Lake City UT 84108
Phone: 801-584-3600   **Fax:** 801-584-3640
Web: www.myriad.com

PRODUCTS/OPERATIONS

2012 Sales

	$ mil.	% of total
Molecular Diagnostics	472	95
Companion Diagnostics	23	5
Total	**496**	**100**

2012 Molecular Diagnostics Sales

	$ mil.	% of total
BRACAnalysis	405	86
COLARIS & COLARIS AP	43	9
Other	23	5
Total	**472**	**100**

Selected Molecular Diagnostic Tests

BRACAnalysis (breast and ovarian cancer predictive test)
COLARIS (colorectal and uterine cancer predictive test)
COLARIS AP (colon cancer predictive test)
MELARIS (melanoma predictive test)
OnDose (chemotherapy dosing level personalized diagnostic test)
PREZEON (cancer drug responsivity personalized diagnostic test)
PROLARIS (prostate cancer prognostic test)
THERAGUIDE 5-FU (chemotherapy toxicity personalized diagnostic test)

Selected Companion Diagnostic Services

Multi-Analyte Profile (MAP): library contains more than 550 individual human and rodent immunoassays for use in MAP testing
Multiplexed Immunoassay Kits: enable customers to leverage Myriad's technology services with their in-house capabilities
TruCulture: a self-contained whole blood culture that can be deployed worldwide to clinical sites for acquiring cell culture data without specialized facilities or trainingp>d

COMPETITORS

Abbott Labs	Illumina
Abviva	Innogenetics
Beckman Coulter	Interleukin Genetics
Becton Dickinson	NeoGenomics
Bio-Rad Labs	Oncolab
Celera	Pathwork Diagnostics
Clarient	QIAGEN
CombiMatrix	Roche Diagnostics
DiagnoCure	Sequenom
Epigenomics	Siemens Healthcare
EraGen Biosciences	Diagnostics
Foundation Medicine	Third Wave
Genzyme	Technologies
Hologic	Transgenomic

HISTORICAL FINANCIALS

Company Type: Public

Income Statement

FYE: June 30

	REVENUE ($ mil.)	NET INCOME ($ mil.)	NET PROFIT MARGIN	EMPLOYEES
06/13	613.1	147.1	24.0%	1,325
06/12	496.0	112.1	22.6%	1,169
06/11	402.0	100.7	25.0%	1,057
06/10	362.6	152.3	42.0%	870
06/09	326.5	84.6	25.9%	869
Annual Growth	**17.1%**	**14.8%**	**—**	**11.1%**

2013 Year-End Financials

Debt ratio: —
Return on equity: 21.5%
Cash ($ mil.): 104
Current ratio: 7.50
Long-term debt ($ mil.): —
No. of shares (mil.): 80
Dividends
Yield: —
Payout: —
Market value ($ mil.): 2,165

	STOCK PRICE ($) FY Close	P/E High/Low	PER SHARE ($) Earnings	Dividends	Book Value
06/13	26.87	19 13	1.77	0.00	9.04
06/12	23.77	20 13	1.30	0.00	7.70
06/11	22.71	23 13	1.10	0.00	6.57
06/10	14.95	23 10	1.54	0.00	5.93
06/09	35.65	98 34	0.86	0.00	4.53
Annual Growth	**(6.8%)**	**— —**	**19.8%**	**—**	**18.9%**

Nathan's Famous, Inc.

Patrons of this restaurateur are in the dog house. Nathan's Famous is a leading franchisor of quick-service restaurants with a chain of about 265 Nathan's outlets known for all-beef frankfurters served with a variety of toppings. The eateries located in about 25 states and a half dozen other countries also serve hamburgers crinkle-cut fries and breakfast sandwiches. More than 50 Nathan's units also feature fish and chips under the Arthur Treacher's brand. In addition to restaurants the company sells Nathan's branded products through vending machines Subway units at Wal-Mart stores and Auntie Anne's pretzel shops. Specialty Foods Group makes Nathan's hot dogs for retail sale under a licensing deal.

While its restaurant chain still forms the core identity of Nathan's the company has been focused on expanding the sale of branded products through third-party foodservice operators. It branded products segment accounts for more than 50% of sales. Meanwhile Nathan's has launched a limited-menu concept designed to allow other quick-service restaurants such as Brusters Real Ice Cream shops to offer its branded hot dogs.

With its flagship store still operating in Coney Island New York Nathan's is the official "non-kosher" hot dog of both the New York Yankees and the New York Mets. The company also holds a competitive eating contest held at Coney Island every July Fourth. Joey Chestnut a competitive eater from California won his fifth consecutive title in 2011 out-eating the competition by consuming 62 dogs in 10 minutes.

Nathan's has been expanding internationally in recent years. The company opened two locations in Beijing China during fiscal 2011. Fiscal 2012 plans call for two more Beijing locations to open along with Nathan's first franchised location in Canada.

Nathan's sold Kenny Rogers Roasters a quick service chain specializing in rotisserie chicken to an affiliate of Malaysia's Berjaya Corporation in 2008. The company disposed of its Miami Subs sandwich chain the previous year selling the business to an investment group for $3.2 million. Nathan's had acquired both the chicken outlets and the sandwich business in 1999.

Howard Lorber who owns about 15% of the company stepped away from his duties as CEO in 2007 while remaining with the company as chairman. Eric Gatoff Nathan's corporate counsel and a board member was named as the company's new CEO.

HISTORY

Ida Handwerker and her husband Nathan opened the first Nathan's Famous food stand in Coney Island in 1916. Ida's special blend of herbs and spices helped popularize the hot dogs and Nathan's went on to become a Coney Island institution. In 1957 the Handwerker family opened a second restaurant and by 1969 the year Nathan's went public the company operated four stores.

In 1987 investment group Equicor bought Nathan's. The next three years the company suffered through multiple changes in leadership and posted a record loss in 1990. A turnaround led by Wayne Norbitz who took over as president in 1989 helped restore the company's stability.

Nathan's went public again in 1993. Also that year Howard Lorber (who came on board as part of Equicor) was named CEO. Two years later the company opened its first outlets inside Home Depot stores. In 1996 Nathan's implemented a co-branding strategy and by the following year it participated in nearly 60 co-branded operations.

In 1998 the company introduced a new product line (chicken strips creamed spinach salads) available in grocery stores and the next year it acquired the Miami Subs sandwich shop chain (sold in 2007) and the Kenny Rogers Roasters chain of rotisserie chicken outlets (disposed of in 2008). Later in 1999 the company's traditional Fourth of July hot dog eating contest was marred by controversy when a videotape showed the winner biting into his wiener before the gun went off.

The following year Nathan's Famous became the official hotdog of the New York Yankees. The 16 new restaurants opened by the company during 2001 included locations in Israel and Egypt. Hard economic times led the company to close several stores in 2002 and Home Depot later terminated its agreements to sell Nathan's Famous in its stores. In 2003 locations in Israel and Brunei were closed and a new location in Japan was opened.

Nathan's Famous acquired the Arthur Treacher's brand and franchising system from TruFoods in 2006. The following year Eric Gatoff was named CEO; Lorber remained as chairman.

Nathan's sold Kenny Rogers Roasters to an affiliate of Malaysia's Berjaya Corporation in 2008. The company disposed of its Miami Subs sandwich chain the previous year selling the business for $3.2 million.

The company expanded into China in 2011 and plans to open locations in Canada during 2012.

EXECUTIVES

Executive Vice President; Director, Donald L. (Don) Perlyn, age 71, $210,000 total compensation

VP Development Architecture and Construction, Donald P. (Don) Schedler, age 60, $140,000 total compensation

Chief Financial Officer; Vice President - Finance; Secretary, Ronald G. DeVos, age 58, $162,750 total compensation

President; Chief Operating Officer; Director, Wayne Norbitz, age 65, $288,750 total compensation

Chairman, Howard M. Lorber, age 64, $400,000 total compensation

VP Franchise Operations, Randy K. Watts, age 57

Chief Executive Officer; Director, Eric Gatoff, age 44, $225,000 total compensation

Director, Attilio F. Petrocelli, age 69

EVP and Director, Donald L. (Don) Perlyn, age 70

President COO and Director, Wayne Norbitz, age 65

Director, Robert J. Eide, age 60

Director, Brian S. Genson, age 64

Director, Barry Leistner, age 62
Director, Charles Raich, age 70
CEO and Director, Eric Gatoff, age 44
Auditors: GrantThorntonLLP

LOCATIONS

HQ: Nathan's Famous, Inc.
One Jericho Plaza, Second Floor - Wing A, Jericho, NY 11753
Phone: 516 338-8500
Web: www.nathansfamous.com

2011 Locations

US	
New Jersey	39
Florida	20
Ohio	11
Massachusetts	8
Connecticut	5
California	4
North Carolina	4
Alabama	3
Arkansas	1
Delaware	1
Maryland	1
Mississippi	1
Rhode Island	1
Texas	1
International	
Dominican Republic	3
China	2
Afghanistan	1
United Arab Emirates	1

COMPETITORS

AFC Enterprises	Jack in the Box
Burger King	Kahala
CKE Restaurants	McDonald's
Captain D's	Potbelly Sandwich Shop
Chick-fil-A	Quiznos
Church's Chicken	Sbarro
Dairy Queen	Subway
Galardi Group	Wendy's
Golden Krust	YUM!
HDOS Enterprises	

HISTORICAL FINANCIALS

Company Type: Public

Income Statement

FYE: March 31

	REVENUE ($ mil.)	NET INCOME ($ mil.)	NET PROFIT MARGIN	EMPLOYEES
03/13	71.5	7.4	10.4%	161
03/12	66.2	6.1	9.3%	219
03/11	57.2	2.2	3.9%	219
03/10	50.8	5.5	10.9%	215
03/09	49.2	7.4	15.2%	216
Annual Growth	9.8%	(0.0%)	—	(7.1%)

2013 Year-End Financials

Debt ratio: —	No. of shares (mil.): 4
Return on equity: 23.3%	Dividends
Cash ($ mil.): 13	Yield: —
Current ratio: 3.04	Payout: —
Long-term debt ($ mil.): —	Market value ($ mil.): 185

	STOCK PRICE ($) FY Close	P/E High/Low		PER SHARE ($) Earnings	Dividends	Book Value
03/13	42.25	25	12	1.63	0.00	7.80
03/12	21.01	17	14	1.22	0.00	6.61
03/11	17.10	47	36	0.40	0.00	7.49
03/10	15.25	16	12	0.97	0.00	7.92
03/09	12.99	13	9	1.21	0.00	7.46
Annual Growth	34.3%	—	—	7.7%	—	1.1%

National Health Investors, Inc.

National Health Investors has a financial investment in the nation's health. The real estate investment trust (REIT) owns or makes mortgage investments in health care properties primarily long-term care facilities. With about 120 facilities in some 17 states holdings also include residences for people with developmental disabilities assisted-living complexes medical office buildings retirement centers and an acute care hospital. About one-third of National Health Investors' properties are leased to its largest tenant National HealthCare Corporation; half are leased to regional health care providers. A majority of the REIT's facilities are located in Florida Texas and Tennessee.

Strategy

National Health Investors (NHI) typically takes a purchase-leaseback approach in which it acquires properties and leases them back to their previous operators. It provides mortgage and construction loans to operators who agree to lease the property once built. In 2012 the company teamed with Bickford Senior Living to build up to eight new assisted living and memory care centers; once completed the facilities will be leased to Bickford. Also in 2012 NHI acquired a 181-unit senior living campus in Loma Linda California for $12 million from Chancellor Health Care (CHC) thereby establishing a presence in Southern California. CHC will lease and continue to operate the facility.

More recently NHI in April 2013 acquired a pair of skilled nursing facilities in Canton and Corinth Texas for $26.3 million. The purchase added a total of 254 beds to the REIT's portfolio.

NHI in late 2013 has also agreed to buy 25 independent-living properties which boast 2841 units from Holiday Acquisition Holdings for $491 million.

Ownership

Chairman and CEO Andy Adams owns about 10% of National Health Investors. He previously made three management buyout offers to acquire the REIT all of which were rejected in 2007. The company subsequently announced that it was taking the possible sale of the company off the table.

EXECUTIVES

Chairman, W. Andrew (Andy) Adams, age 67
Chief Credit Officer, Kristin S. Gaines
SVP Investments, Kevin Pascoe
Chief Accounting Officer, Roger R. Hopkins, age 51, $200,000 total compensation
President and CEO, Justin Hutchens, age 39
Director, Robert A. (Rob) McCabe Jr., age 62
Director, Robert T. Webb, age 68
Director, Ted H. Welch, age 79
Auditors: BDOSeidmanLLP

LOCATIONS

HQ: National Health Investors Inc.
750-B South Church St., Murfreesboro TN 37130
Phone: 615-890-9100 **Fax:** 615-890-0123
Web: www.nhinvestors.com

COMPETITORS

Cousins Properties	Omega Healthcare
HCP	Investors
Health Care REIT	Senior Housing

Healthcare Realty Trust
LTC Properties
Medical Properties Trust

Properties
Ventas

HISTORICAL FINANCIALS

Company Type: Public

Income Statement

FYE: December 31

	REVENUE ($ mil.)	NET INCOME ($ mil.)	NET PROFIT MARGIN	EMPLOYEES
12/12	96.9	90.9	93.8%	10
12/11	82.7	81.1	98.1%	0
12/10	78.4	69.4	88.6%	0
12/09	64.2	64.2	100.0%	0
12/08	63.0	57.5	91.3%	0
Annual Growth	11.4%	12.1%	—	—

2012 Year-End Financials

Debt ratio: 28.7%
Return on equity: 20.1%
Cash ($ mil.): 9
Current ratio: 0.65
Long-term debt ($ mil.): 203

No. of shares (mil.): 27
Dividends
  Yield: 4.6%
  Payout: 80.9%
Market value ($ mil.): 1,575

	STOCK PRICE ($) FY Close	P/E High/Low		PER SHARE ($) Earnings	Dividends	Book Value
12/12	56.53	18	13	3.26	2.64	16.41
12/11	43.98	17	13	2.92	2.72	15.98
12/10	45.02	19	13	2.50	2.36	15.98
12/09	36.99	16	9	2.32	2.30	15.73
12/08	27.43	17	9	2.07	2.42	15.58
Annual Growth	19.8%	—	—	12.0%	2.2%	1.3%

National Instruments Corp.

National Instruments (NI) knows you like to take tests. The company's instrumentation hardware and graphical software convert standard PCs into industrial automation and test and measurement systems. These "virtual instruments" can observe measure and control electrical signals and physical attributes such as voltage and pressure. The company also offers programming environments (LabVIEW and Measurement Studio) for creating customizable graphical interfaces controlling instruments and capturing and analyzing data. In addition NI provides test management software for running automated factory test systems. Customers outside the Americas account for around 60% of sales.

Geographic Reach

NI has offices in more than 40 countries. Its manufacturing plants are located in the US (Texas) as well as in Hungary and Malaysia.

Customers located in North and South America account for 40% of sales. Asia accounts for another 35% of sales while customers in Europe round out the remaining 25%.

Sales and Marketing

NI relies on a direct sales force to   il hardware and software to its customer base of 35000 companies. Less than 10% of sales are made through alternative channels such as distributors original equipment manufacturers (OEMs) value-added resellers (VARs) system integrators and consultants.

The company targets the automotive aerospace computer and electronics automated test equipment consumer electronics education government and defense medical research energy pharmaceutical semiconductor and telecommunications industries among others.

Throughout its history NI has relied on relentless promotion and publicity to get its name out in front of engineers and researchers. It advertises heavily in trade publications from Reed Business Information US CMP MediaPenton Media and other publishers while unleashing barrages of product press releases on trade editors on an almost daily basis.

The company also promotes itself through technical seminars and conferences presented around the world and over the Internet. Its biggest event is the annual NIWeek conference staged each summer at the Austin Convention Center near NI's headquarters. Held every year since 1995 NIWeek attracts thousands of attendees from all over the world.

Financial Performance

Sales were up 12% in 2012 to a record $1.14 billion. (NI hit the $1 billion mark for the first time in 2011.) The company enjoyed robust sales in both product and software maintenance around the world. Large orders (valued at more than $100000) were also on the rise - in 2012 NI sold $59 million in graphical system design application products to one customer. That year the company also took in $90 million in profits.

Mergers and Acquisitions

NI is not heavily acquisitive but it did buy two companies in 2011 beginning with development partner Phase Matrix for $40 million. Phase Matrix makes radio-frequency (RF) and microwave test and measurement instruments subsystems and components. The acquisition drove growth in RF and microwave test instrumentation by adding high-frequency technology and manufacturing capabilities. Phase Matrix will operate as a subsidiary of NI and continue to sell products directly to customers and OEMs.

A couple months later it bought AWR Corporation a developer of software used to design RF and high-frequency components and systems for the aerospace and defense communications test equipment and semiconductor industries. NI paid around $66 million for the company which strengthened its LabVIEW software and RF testing hardware platforms.

HISTORY

In the 1970s James Truchard working at the University of Texas Applied Research Laboratory was frustrated by the lack of connectivity between the lab's computers and testing equipment. Truchard who as a kid built homemade radios founded National Instruments in 1976 with fellow lab employees Jeffrey Kodosky and William Nowlin. The trio raised $13000 which included part of Truchard's teacher retirement fund savings and set up camp in a room behind Truchard's garage.

Using Hewlett-Packard's technology for collecting test and measurement data from its own machines the trio created the general-purpose interface bus (GPIB) a device that links computers to scientific instruments. The devices eliminated the practice of using paper pencils and rulers to track instruments. The colleagues' vigor kept the company small but busy. Truchard designed hardware and wrote press releases. Kodosky developed programs and handled customer support.

National Instruments thrived as PCs became popular. LabVIEW introduced in 1986 used graphics to simulate the dials of an engineering instrument's control panel. Users worked the controls simply by moving the mouse. The company expanded internationally in 1987 opening an office in Tokyo. It suffered a loss for 1989 after expanding into Europe.

In 1990 NASA used one of the company's programs to trace fuel system leaks affecting Space Shuttle launches. National Instruments went public in 1995 and intensified product development. It also began acquiring small businesses to expand its technology base buying industrial automation specialist Georgetown Systems (1996) and motion control equipment maker nuLogic (1997).

In 1998 National Instruments bought two German makers of data acquisition tools DATALOG and DASYtec. The next year the company and computer maker Dell joined forces to market a scientific measuring and testing workstation. National Instruments also launched an online store then followed that in 2000 with the NI Developer Zone a resource for information on automation and measurement systems.

In 2001 NI established a subsidiary in Russia. The following year it opened a manufacturing facility in Hungary. The company acquired Hyperception a provider of graphical development tools for digital signal processing in 2003.

NI expanded its product offerings with its 2005 purchases of data acquisition instrumentation makers Measurement Computing and IOtech. In 2007 chairman president and CEO James Truchard was elected to the National Academy of Engineering. The following year the company purchased microLEX Systems A/S a Danish instrumentation firm for about $18 million in cash.

EXECUTIVES

VP Sales and Marketing Americas, John M. Graff, age 46, $252,500 total compensation
VP General Counsel and Secretary, David G. Hugley, age 48
SVP Sales, Peter (Pete) Zogas Jr., age 51, $235,250 total compensation
VP Worldwide Human Resources, Mark A. Finger, age 54
EVP COO CFO and Treasurer, Alexander M. (Alex) Davern, age 46, $310,000 total compensation
Chairman President and CEO, James J. Truchard, age 69, $200,000 total compensation
VP Product Marketing Core Platforms, Raymond C. (Ray) Almgren, age 46, $242,500 total compensation
Vice President Corporate Marketing and eBusiness, John Pasquarette
SVP Research and Development, Phillip D. (Phil) Hester
VP Life Sciences, John Hanks
VP Manufacturing, Robert R. (Rob) Porterfield, age 45
VP Research and Development Application and System Software, Jon Bellin
VP Research and Development Data Acquisition and Distributed I/O, Kevin Schultz
VP Global Information Technology, Arleene Porterfield
VP Global Energy Segment, Owen Golden
VP Sales and Marketing Europe, Francis Griffiths
VP Sales and Marketing Asia Pacific, Victor Mieres
VP Systems and Applications Engineering, Tony Vento
VP Finance, John Roiko

VP Research and Development Core PXI and Distributed Control, Robert Canik

VP Quality and Continuous Improvement, Andrew Krupp

VP Research and Development NI Penang, Scott Rust

SVP Marketing, Eric Starkloff

Investor Relations, Veronica Garza

VP Product Marketing Core DAQ and Instrument Control, Ajit Gokhale

Vice President Application and Embedded Software R&D, David Fuller

Vice President Mobile Device Test, David Loadman

Vice President RF R&D, Jin Bains

Vice President Semiconductor Test, Ron Wolfe

Vice President Scientific Research and Lead User Program, Stefano Concezzi

Director, John M. Berra, age 65

Director, Jeffrey L. Kodosky, age 63

Director, Charles J. Roesslein, age 64

Director, Donald M. Carlton, age 75

Director, John K. Medica, age 54

Director, Duy-Loan T. Le, age 50

Auditors: Ernst&YoungLLP

LOCATIONS

HQ: National Instruments Corporation
11500 N. MoPac Expwy., Austin TX 78759-3504
Phone: 512-338-9119   Fax: 512-683-5759
Web: www.ni.com

2012 Sales

	% of total
Americas	40
Asia/Pacific	34
Europe	26
Total	**100**

PRODUCTS/OPERATIONS

2012 Sales

	% of total
Product	92
Software	8
Total	**100**

Selected Products

Measurement and Automation Software
  LabVIEW
  Measurement Studio
  LabWindows/CVI
  Switch Executive
  TestStand
  VI Logger
Measurement Hardware
  Counters and timers
  Data acquisition (DAQ) hardware
  Digital input and output devices
  Digital multimeters
  Dynamic signal acquisition devices
  Dynamic signal analyzers
  High-speed digitizers
  Radio-frequency measurement devices
  Signal sources

COMPETITORS

Advantest	Teradyne
Agilent Technologies	Thermo Fisher
MathWorks	Scientific
Tektronix	Wolfram Research

HISTORICAL FINANCIALS

Company Type: Public

Income Statement

FYE: December 31

	REVENUE ($ mil.)	NET INCOME ($ mil.)	NET PROFIT MARGIN	EMPLOYEES
12/12	1,143.6	90.1	7.9%	6,869
12/11	1,024.1	94.0	9.2%	6,235
12/10	873.2	109.1	12.5%	5,280
12/09	676.5	17.0	2.5%	5,120
12/08	820.5	84.8	10.3%	5,157
Annual Growth	**8.7%**	**1.5%**	**—**	**7.4%**

2012 Year-End Financials

Debt ratio: —
Return on equity: 10.0%
Cash ($ mil.): 162
Current ratio: 3.13
Long-term debt ($ mil.): —

No. of shares (mil.): 122
Dividends
  Yield: 2.1%
  Payout: 72.7%
Market value ($ mil.): 3,171

	STOCK PRICE ($) FY Close	P/E High/Low	PER SHARE ($) Earnings	Dividends	Book Value
12/12	25.81	39 32	0.73	0.56	7.64
12/11	25.95	61 27	0.78	0.40	7.06
12/10	37.64	41 30	0.92	0.35	6.31
12/09	29.45	203 109	0.15	0.32	5.64
12/08	24.36	49 29	0.71	0.29	5.74
Annual Growth	**1.5%**	**— —**	**0.6%**	**17.5%**	**7.4%**

National Interstate Corp

National Interstate stands behind you when you get on the bus! The specialty property/casualty insurer concentrates on the transportation market. One of the nation's largest insurers of truck and passenger transportation fleets the company also provides insurance to moving companies and personal lines of coverage for recreational vehicles. Additionally National Interstate offers general commercial insurance for small businesses in Alaska and Hawaii. The company distributes its products throughout the US. American Financial Group spun off National Interstate in 2005 but continues to control the company through a 52% stake held by its Great American Insurance Company.

National Interstate distributes its more than 35 product lines through affiliated agencies independent agents and brokers and agents' online initiatives. Its largest markets are California (with about 15% of gross premiums written) and Texas (with less than 10%). Other significant markets include New York Florida Pennsylvania North Carolina New Jersey Massachusetts and Missouri.

National Interstate insures charter bus companies school bus fleets limousine companies and public transportation operations as well as other passenger transportation and cargo truck fleets. In 2011 the company entered the ambulance insurance market by partnering with McNeil & Company. Together National Interstate and McNeil provide insurance coverage and claims services for emergency and non-emergency medical transportation operators through the Ambulance Services Insurance Program. McNeil administers the program and also provides risk management and loss control services.

National Interstate offers services to its commercial transportation customers under two models: alternative risk transfer and traditional coverage. Under the alternative risk transfer model (which accounts for the majority of the company's commercial transportation policies) the company provides underwriting and other services for captive insurance programs that are owned or rented by its customers; in such an arrangement the client participates in assuming risks and sharing in underwriting profits.

National Interstate operates primarily through five subsidiaries: Hudson Indemnity (reinsurance) National Interstate Insurance Company National Interstate Insurance Company of Hawaii Triumphe Casualty and Vanliner Insurance Company. It bought Vanliner Insurance Company for $128 million in 2010 to complement its existing transportation insurance offerings. Vanliner was previously a subsidiary of UniGroup.

National Interstate's strategic plans for growth include organic growth through the development of new products expansion into new product lines and expansion of its insurance distribution network. Additionally the company explores opportunities to acquire other companies or selected books of business.

In fiscal 2011 National Interstate achieved revenue of $468.5 million representing a 15% increase over 2010. Contributing to its growth were increases in gross premiums written and earned premiums income from investments (which were concentrated in commercial and residential mortgage-backed securities and municipal bonds) and realized gains on its investments. Although the company's net income from operations increased by 12% its total net income for 2011 dropped by nearly 10% due to the after-tax impact from the operating results of Vanliner's guaranteed runoff business.

Founder and chairman Alan Spachman controls 7.5% of the company.

EXECUTIVES

Chief Financial Officer; Vice President; Treasurer, Julie A. McGraw, age 49, $190,424 total compensation

EVP and COO, Tony Mercurio

Chairman, Alan R. Spachman, age 65, $330,000 total compensation

President; Chief Executive Officer; Director, David W. Michelson, age 55, $350,000 total compensation

SVP, Terry E. Phillips, age 63, $220,194 total compensation

VP and Chief Investment Officer, Gary N. Monda, age 56, $172,424 total compensation

VP General Counsel and Secretary, Arthur J. Gonzales, age 53

Director, Keith A. Jensen, age 62

President CEO and Director, David W. Michelson, age 55

Director, Theodore H. Elliott Jr., age 77

Director, Gary J. Gruber, age 57

Director, Donald D. Larson, age 61

Director, Joel Schiavone, age 76

Director, Joseph E. (Jeff) Consolino, age 46

Director, Vito C. Peraino

Auditors: Ernst&YoungLLP

LOCATIONS

HQ: National Interstate Corporation
3250 Interstate Dr., Richfield OH 44286-9000
Phone: 330-659-8900 **Fax:** 330-659-8901
Web: www.nationalinterstate.com

PRODUCTS/OPERATIONS

2011 Revenues

	$ mil.	% of total
Premiums earned		
Alternative risk transfer	204	44
Transportation	151	32
Specialty personal lines	53	11
Hawaii & Alaska	14	3
Other	6	1
Net investment income	30	7
Net realized gains on investments	4	1
Other	3	1
Total	**468**	**100**

2011 Premiums Earned

	% of total
Alternative risk	48
Transportation	35
Specialty personal	12
Hawaii &	3
Other	2
Total	**100**

COMPETITORS

American Modern
  Insurance
Canal Insurance
Dongbu
First Insurance
  Company of Hawaii
GMAC Insurance
Great West Casualty
Island Insurance

Lancer Insurance
McM Corporation
Progressive
  Corporation
RLI
Sentry Insurance
Travelers Companies
Zurich American

HISTORICAL FINANCIALS

Company Type: Public

Income Statement

	ASSETS ($ mil.)	NET INCOME ($ mil.)	INCOME AS % OF ASSETS	EMPLOYEES
FYE: December 31				
12/12	1,570.2	34.2	2.2%	546
12/11	1,525.0	35.6	2.3%	532
12/10	1,488.6	39.5	2.7%	494
12/09	955.7	46.4	4.9%	351
12/08	990.8	10.6	1.1%	358
Annual Growth	**12.2%**	**33.9%**	**—**	**11.1%**

2012 Year-End Financials

Return on assets: 2.2%
Return on equity: 9.7%
Long-term debt ($ mil.): —
No. of shares (mil.): 19
Sales ($ mil): 502

Dividends
  Yield: 1.3%
  Payout: 137.1%
Market value ($ mil.): 565

	STOCK PRICE ($) FY Close	P/E High/Low	PER SHARE ($) Earnings	Dividends	Book Value
12/12	28.82	16 13	1.75	2.40	18.07
12/11	24.67	15 11	1.83	0.36	18.07
12/10	21.41	11 8	2.03	0.32	15.99
12/09	16.96	9 6	2.40	0.28	14.06
12/08	17.87	60 26	0.55	0.24	11.20
Annual Growth	**12.7%**	**— —**	**33.6%**	**77.8%**	**12.7%**

National Research Corp

The ultimate father figure National Research Corporation (NRC) is there to let you know when you're not measuring up. Founded in 1981 NRC offers performance measurement and analysis services to clients within the health care industry including hospitals HMOs home care hospice and regulatory groups. The company's performance tracking system uses individualized questionnaires to better determine an organization's satisfaction rating and the NRC Healthcare Market Guide provides industry statistics allowing clients to compare their services to those of competitors. Founder and CEO Michael Hays owns more than 65% of the company.

Striving to expand by investing in firms with common product lines and strategies in 2010 NRC purchased home care and hospice analytics specialist Outcome Concept Systems for an undisclosed sum.

Other recent acquisitions include Geriatric Health Systems a California-based health care survey research company (for $4 million) and TGI Group a provider of executive and physician staffing services catering to hospitals (for nearly $20 million). In late 2008 NRC acquired Wisconsin-based My InnerView a performance measurement company for the senior care industry.

EXECUTIVES

VP CFO Treasurer Secretary and Director, Patrick E. (Pat) Beans, age 53, $175,000 total compensation
President Governance Institute, Jona S. Raasch, age 52, $173,000 total compensation
President CEO and Director, Michael D. Hays, age 56, $127,400 total compensation
Chief Financial Officer Vice President Treasurer Secretary, Kevin Karas
President Chief Operating Officer, Susan Henricks
Vice President, Gregg Loughman
Vice President Operations, Cynthia A. Ballow
Director, Paul C. Schorr IV, age 74
Director, Gail L. Warden, age 72
VP CFO Treasurer Secretary and Director, Patrick E. (Pat) Beans, age 53
President CEO and Director, Michael D. Hays, age 56
Director, John N. Nunnelly, age 60
Director, JoAnn M. Martin, age 56
Auditors: KPMGLLP

LOCATIONS

HQ: National Research Corporation
1245 Q. St., Lincoln NE 68508
Phone: 402-475-2525 **Fax:** 402-475-9061
Web: www.nationalresearch.com

COMPETITORS

Abt Associates
Abt SRBI
Brand Pharm
Gallup
GfK
IMS Health
Ipsos
Kantar Group
MSI

Maritz Research
Nielsen Holdings
ORC
Press Ganey
ReGen Biologics
SDI Health
TNS Custom
Walker Information

HISTORICAL FINANCIALS

Company Type: Public

Income Statement

	REVENUE ($ mil.)	NET INCOME ($ mil.)	NET PROFIT MARGIN	EMPLOYEES
FYE: December 31				
12/12	86.4	15.0	17.4%	383
12/11	75.7	11.5	15.3%	376
12/10	63.4	8.5	13.4%	305
12/09	57.6	8.4	14.7%	302
12/08	51.0	7.4	14.6%	331
Annual Growth	**14.1%**	**19.3%**	**—**	**3.7%**

2012 Year-End Financials

Debt ratio: 12.7%
Return on equity: 26.7%
Cash ($ mil.): 8
Current ratio: 0.67
Long-term debt ($ mil.): 0

No. of shares (mil.): 6
Dividends
  Yield: —
  Payout: 117.0%
Market value ($ mil.): —

National Retail Properties Inc

For National Retail Properties good things come in big boxes. The self-administered real estate investment trust (REIT) acquires develops and manages freestanding retail properties in heavily traveled commercial and residential areas. Its portfolio includes about 1800 properties totaling more than 20 million sq. ft. of leasable space in nearly all 50 states concentrated in the Southeast the Midwest and Texas. National Retail Properties also invests in mortgages operates the retail businesses on some of its sites and develops properties with the intention of selling them for a profit. Convenience stores make up around 20% of its portfolio.

Operations

While some retail REITs own entire strip malls or shopping malls National Retail Properties keeps it simple with freestanding retail properties. The trust's retail tenants are made up of convenience store and gas stations such as Stripes (Susser Holdings) The Pantry and 7-Eleven. It also owns many buildings that house restaurants such as Applebee's Chili's Denny's and Logan's Roadhouse. Fast food tenants include Taco Bell and Wendys. Best Buy CarQuest and Pep Boys are also major tenants.

National Retail Properties typically signs triple-net leases with initial terms of 15 to 20 years in which tenants are responsible for expenses such as taxes utilities repairs and maintenance.

Financial Performance

Overall revenues increased 13% in 2012 to $350 million. That year the trust added another 400 properties to its portfolio. Profits also increased more than 50% to $142 million.

Strategy

National Retail Properties maintains a diverse portfolio in order to minimize risk. It often sells older properties and uses the proceeds to buy newer locations. For the past three years it's had an occupancy rate of at least 97%.

EXECUTIVES

EVP CFO Treasurer Assistant Secretary and Director, Kevin B. Habicht, age 53, $315,000 total compensation

Chairman of the Board; Chief Executive Officer, Craig Macnab, age 57, $506,000 total compensation

President; Chief Operating Officer, Julian E. (Jay) Whitehurst, age 55, $340,000 total compensation

Chief Investment Officer; Executive Vice President, Paul E. Bayer, age 61, $195,000 total compensation

Executive Vice President; General Counsel; Secretary, Christopher P. (Chris) Tessitore, age 45, $195,000 total compensation

VP Leasing, David Reif

VP-Comm, Chris Barry

EVP CFO Treasurer Assistant Secretary and Director, Kevin B. Habicht, age 53

Director, Donald (Don) DeFosset, age 64

Director, Richard B. Jennings, age 69

Director, Ted B. Lanier, age 78

Director, Robert C. Legler, age 69

Director, Robert Martinez, age 78

Director, David M. Fick, age 56

Independent Director, Edward Fritsch

Auditors: Ernst&YoungLLP

LOCATIONS

HQ: National Retail Properties Inc.
450 S. Orange Ave. Ste. 900, Orlando FL 32801
Phone: 407-265-7348   **Fax:** 407-650-3650
Web: www.nnnreit.com

2012 Properties

	No.
Texas	357
Florida	113
Pennsylvania	95
North	77
Georgia	77
Indiana	70
Illinois	60
Ohio	52
Virginia	52
California	40
Other	566
Total	**1,622**

COMPETITORS

Acadia Realty Trust	Glimcher Realty
Brixmor	Kimco Realty
DDR	One Liberty Properties
Federal Realty	Realty Income
Investment	Regency Centers

HISTORICAL FINANCIALS

Company Type: Public

Income Statement

FYE: December 31

	REVENUE ($ mil.)	NET INCOME ($ mil.)	NET PROFIT MARGIN	EMPLOYEES
12/12	331.7	142.0	42.8%	60
12/11	265.7	92.3	34.7%	59
12/10	229.0	73.0	31.9%	58
12/09	231.8	54.8	23.6%	57
12/08	226.5	123.0	54.3%	59
Annual Growth	**10.0%**	**3.6%**	**—**	**0.4%**

2012 Year-End Financials

Debt ratio: 39.7%
Return on equity: 6.5%
Cash ($ mil.): 2
Current ratio: 0.30
Long-term debt ($ mil.): 1,412

No. of shares (mil.): 111
Dividends
Yield: 5.0%
Payout: 147.1%
Market value ($ mil.): 3,481

	STOCK PRICE ($) FY Close	P/E High/Low		PER SHARE ($) Earnings	Dividends	Book Value
12/12	31.20	29	23	1.11	1.56	20.58
12/11	26.38	28	24	0.96	1.53	19.12
12/10	26.50	35	24	0.80	1.51	18.27
12/09	21.22	37	22	0.60	1.50	18.98
12/08	17.19	16	7	1.56	1.48	19.67
Annual Growth	**16.1%**	**—**	**—**	**(8.2%)**	**1.3%**	**1.1%**

National Western Life Insurance Co. (Austin, TX)

National Western Life Insurance sells life insurance and annuity products including individual universal whole and term plans. The company operates throughout the US except in New York and internationally in Central and South America the Caribbean Eastern Europe Asia and the Pacific Rim. Annuities sold by independent agents make up most of its US sales. Some two-thirds of its life insurance premiums come from outside the US where the company targets wealthy individuals. Investments mainly in fixed debt securities account for some 70% of revenues.

Operations The company has more than 60000 US life insurance policies and some 140000 annuity contracts representing $7 billion. Internationally it claims nearly 75000 life insurance policies. National Western also operates two nursing homes (in Nevada and Texas) which account for less than 5% of sales.

Financial Analysis National Western's revenue was flat in 2011 down less than 1% to $573 million. The company experienced growth in its life and annuity product segments but investment income (its largest revenue contributor) was hit by derivative losses. Net income fell in 2011 declining nearly 25% to $56 million because of increased amortization costs.

Ownership CEO Robert Moody a member of the powerful Moody family of Galveston Texas owns one-third of the company and effectively controls its board of directors.

EXECUTIVES

Senior Vice President; Secretary, James P. Payne, age 68

Chairman and CEO, Robert L. Moody Sr., age 77, $1,648,582 total compensation

SVP and Chief Investment Officer, Patricia L. Scheuer, age 61

SVP Mortgage Loan and Real Estate and Director, Charles D. Milos Jr., age 67, $249,130 total compensation

Senior Vice President; Chief Actuary, Paul D. Facey, age 61

President COO and Director, Ross R. Moody, age 50, $588,956 total compensation

SVP CFO and Treasurer, Brian M. Pribyl, age 54, $253,165 total compensation

SVP and Chief Marketing Officer, S. Christopher Johnson, age 44, $150,200 total compensation

Senior Vice President - International Marketing, Scott E Arendale, age 68, $158,878 total compensation

VP Controller and Assistant Treasurer, Thomas F. Kopetic, age 53

SVP Mortgage Loan and Real Estate and Director, Charles D. Milos Jr., age 67

President COO and Director, Ross R. Moody, age 50

Director, Frances A. Moody-Dahlberg, age 43

Director, Russell S. Moody, age 50

Director, E. Douglas McLeod, age 71

Director, Louis E. Pauls Jr., age 77

Director, E. J. (Jere) Pederson, age 65

Director, Stephen E. Glasgow, age 50

Auditors: KPMGLLP

LOCATIONS

HQ: National Western Life Insurance Company
850 E. Anderson Ln., Austin TX 78752-1602
Phone: 512-836-1010   **Fax:** 512-835-2729
Web: www.nationalwesternlife.com

PRODUCTS/OPERATIONS

2011 Revenues

	$ mil.	% of total
Investment income	391	68
Universal life & annuity contract revenues	132	23
Life & annuity premiums	18	3
Other income	25	5
Gains on investments	6	1
Total	**572**	**100**

COMPETITORS

Allstate	Lincoln Benefit Life
American Equity Life	Lincoln Life
American Fidelity	Old Mutual (US)
Assurance Company	Pan-American Life
Aviva	Presidential Life
BMI Financial Group	Sammons Financial
Citizens Inc.	Securian Financial
FBL Financial	

HISTORICAL FINANCIALS

Company Type: Public

Income Statement

FYE: December 31

	ASSETS ($ mil.)	NET INCOME ($ mil.)	INCOME AS % OF ASSETS	EMPLOYEES
12/12	10,263.8	92.5	0.9%	280
12/11	9,728.0	55.6	0.6%	278
12/10	8,773.9	72.9	0.8%	292
12/09	7,518.7	45.4	0.6%	294
12/08	6,786.4	33.6	0.5%	296
Annual Growth	**10.9%**	**28.8%**	**—**	**(1.4%)**

2012 Year-End Financials

Return on assets: 0.9%
Return on equity: 6.9%
Long-term debt ($ mil.): —
No. of shares (mil.): 3
Sales ($ mil): 664

Dividends
Yield: 0.2%
Payout: 1.7%
Market value ($ mil.): 573

	STOCK PRICE ($) FY Close	P/E High/Low		PER SHARE ($) Earnings	Dividends	Book Value
12/12	157.74	6	5	26.19	0.36	382.88
12/11	136.16	11	8	15.73	0.36	351.27
12/10	166.72	9	6	20.61	0.36	335.83
12/09	173.62	15	5	12.87	0.36	307.24
12/08	169.17	29	12	9.48	0.36	271.99
Annual Growth	**(1.7%)**	**—**	**—**	**28.9%**	**(0.0%)**	**8.9%**

Nationstar Mortgage Holdings Inc

Nationstar Mortgage helps turn home ownership into more than just a wish upon a star. The company services residential mortgage loans throughout the US. Its servicing portfolio comprises more than 1.8 million loans that total in excess of $300 billion in unpaid principal balances. Nationstar also originates loans primarily government- and agency-backed mortgages which it typically sells or securitizes within one month of origination. The company serves consumers directly through its Texas-based call center; it also offers its products through wholesalers. The firm has seen rapid growth as a result of its expanding servicing portfolio. Nationstar went public in 2012.

IPO

In March 2012 the company raised $247 million through the initial public offering which coincided with the economy's modest recovery. Nationstar plans to use the money to grow its mortgage servicing portfolio.

Financial Analysis

The company's revenues have grown significantly since 2009. In 2011 alone revenues climbed 20%. Nationstar also reported net income of $21 million that year compared to a loss of about $10 million the year before.

Strategy

Since its IPO Nationstar has embarked on a buying spree. In early 2013 the company acquired approximately $97 billion in residential mortgage serving rights and certain other assets from Bank of America. More recently it agreed to acquire the mortgage origination business of Greenlight Financial Services for up to $75 million. News of the pending purchase followed close on the heels of its acquisition of Equifax Settlement Solutuions in 2013. Shortly after its public offering it purchased the servicing assets of Aurora Loan Services a subsidiary of Aurora Bank for $268 million. The deal included $63 billion in residential mortgages. As part of the transaction affiliate Newcastle Investment paid $170 million to receive a portion of the servicing rights to the Aurora portfolio.

Nationstar sees opportunity in the weakened credit markets as it has been successful managing portfolios of higher-risk loans. Its high-touch approach an area in which the big banks tends to lack is well-suited to handling riskier loans. The firm has seen rapid growth as a result of its expanding servicing portfolio; it has added about a dozen new servicing clients in the past three years. Also by originating loans in-house Nationstar is further able to boost its servicing portfolio largely by offering borrowers refinancing options.

Ownership

Fortress Investment Group owns about 80% of Nationstar.

Company Background

Once a subsidiary of homebuilder Centex Nationstar Mortgage was acquired by Fortress Investment Group in 2006. At the time of the transaction which was valued at some $575 million Nationstar Mortgage (then named Centex Home Equity) was a subprime lender. Like many of its peers Nationstar Mortgage exited the subprime lending business in late 2007 thereby focusing on its servicing activities.

EXECUTIVES

EVP Portfolio Investments, Amar R. Patel
President and COO, Harold Lewis Jr.
CEO, Jay Bray
EVP and CFO, David C. Hisey
EVP Corporate Development and Investor Relations, Marshall Murphy
EVP Servicing, Robert L. Appel, age 51
EVP Capital Markets, Douglas Krueger, age 44
EVP and General Counsel, Anthony W. Villani
EVP and Chief Risk Officer, Ramesh Lakshminarayanan
Auditors: Ernst&YoungLLP

LOCATIONS

HQ: Nationstar Mortgage Holdings Inc.
 350 Highland Dr., Lewisville TX 75067
Phone: 469-549-2000   **Fax:** 952-853-1410
Web: www.nathcompanies.com/

PRODUCTS/OPERATIONS

2011 Sales

	$ mil.	% of total
Servicing fees	233	52
Gain on mortgages held for sale	109	25
Other fees	35	8
Interest income	66	15
Gain on interest rate swaps and caps	0	-
Fair value changes in ABS securitizations	(12.4)	-
Total	**432**	**100**

COMPETITORS

Aurora Loan Services	PHH Mortgage
Bank of America	Stonegate Mortgage
CitiMortgage	Synovus Mortgage
DHI Mortgage	UAMC
GMAC Mortgage	Wells Fargo Home
JPMorgan Chase	Mortgage

HISTORICAL FINANCIALS

Company Type: Public

Income Statement

FYE: December 31

	REVENUE ($ mil.)	NET INCOME ($ mil.)	NET PROFIT MARGIN	EMPLOYEES
12/12	984.3	205.2	20.9%	4,672
12/11	377.7	20.8	5.5%	2,599
12/10	261.4	(9.9)	—	0
12/09	78.8	(80.8)	—	0
Annual Growth	132.0%	—	—	—

2012 Year-End Financials

Debt ratio: 79.0%
Return on equity: 39.4%
Cash ($ mil.): 152
Current ratio: 5.68
Long-term debt ($ mil.): 5,633

No. of shares (mil.): 90
Dividends
 Yield: —
 Payout: —
Market value ($ mil.): 2,802

	STOCK PRICE ($) FY Close	P/E High/Low		Earnings	Dividends	Book Value
12/12	30.98	15	6	2.40	0.00	8.38
12/11	0.00	—	—	(0.00)	0.00	(0.00)
Annual Growth	—			—	—	—

Neogen Corp.

Bacteriophobes have a friend in Neogen a maker of products for the food safety and animal health markets. Its food safety testing products are used by the food industry to make sure our edibles are clean unspoiled and free of toxins pathogens and allergens. In core markets in the Americas and Europe Neogen reaches end users (including dairies meat processors and animal feed producers) through a direct sales force; it uses distributors elsewhere. On the animal health front Neogen produces drugs vaccines diagnostics and instruments for the veterinary market; it also makes rat poisons and disinfectants used in animal production plants and diagnostic products for research laboratories.

Geographic Reach

The firm's animal products are sold to distributors around the world as well as through farm supply retailers in North America. International sales of all of its products account for about 40% of Neogen's sales.

Operations

Some of the company's best-selling food-safety testing products include its Reveal and Alert tests used by meat poultry and seafood processors to detect food-borne bacteria. Others include its Veratox Agre-Screen and Reveal tests which are used by grain producers to detect mycotoxins (toxins produced by fungi).

When it comes to animals lead products include PanaKare a digestive aid; RenaKare a supplement for potassium deficiency in cats and dogs; and the NeogenVet brand including Vita-15 and Liver 7 which are used for the treatment and prevention of nutritional deficiencies in horses.

Financial Analysis

Neogen continued its growth trend by reporting a 7% increase in revenues to $184 million in 2012 due to strong product sales in both the food safety and animal safety segments. Net income declined more than 1% to some $22.5 million however due to increased sales marketing and administrative expenses.

Strategy

Though the company has primarily used acquisitions to achieve relatively rapid growth Neogen is also looking for organic growth over the longer term through new product introductions higher sales of existing products and international expansion efforts. Neogen has ongoing development projects for new diagnostic tests and other complementary products for both the food safety and animal safety markets. The company also sees its over-the-counter animal health products as being particularly ripe for growth and because of that it seeks to increase its line of rodenticides disinfectants instruments and horse care products.

Mergers and Acquisitions

During 2010 the company acquired GeneSeek which now operates as a subsidiary and an agricultural genetics laboratory that enhances Neogen's diagnostic test development operations. Neogen strengthened the unit in 2012 by acquiring the assets of the Igenity animal genomics business from Merial Limited. Igenity had previously operated as a lab partner with GeneSeek to identify cattle traits. The company also widened its equine antibiotic offerings through the acquisition of Macleod Pharmaceuticals later that year. In 2013 it purchased the assets of veterinary instruments firm SyrVet.

To enhance its aquaculture testing services in 2011 it acquired Scotland-based VeroMara from GlycoMar. Neogen will support the operations which provides seafood testing to the aquaculture industry through its European headquarters which are also based in Scotland.

EXECUTIVES

President; Chief Operating Officer; Director, Lon M. Bohannon, age 60, $215,000 total compensation

Chairman of the Board; Chief Executive Officer, James L. Herbert, age 73, $310,000 total compensation

Chief Financial Officer; Vice President, Steven J. (Steve) Quinlan, age 49

VP Food Safety Operations, Edward L. Bradley, age 53, $142,000 total compensation

VP Animal Safety Operations, Terri A. Morrical, age 48, $141,500 total compensation

VP Scientific Affairs, Joseph M. Madden, age 64

VP Research and Development, Mark A. Mozola, age 56

VP Manufacturing, Kenneth V. Kodilla, age 56

Senior Scientific Officer, Jennifer Rice

Director Industry Affairs and Hacco Operations, Keith Creagh

Head strip washer, Starter Kit

Vice President - Corporate Development, Jason Lilly

Vice President - Corporate Development, Jason W. Ph

Director, Thomas H. Reed, age 68

President COO and Director, Lon M. Bohannon, age 59

Director, A. Charles (Charlie) Fischer, age 71

Director, Robert M. Book, age 83

Director, G. Bruce Papesh, age 66

Director, Jack C. Parnell, age 78

Director, Clayton K. Yeutter, age 82

Independent Director, Richard Crowder

Independent Director, William Boehm

Auditors: Ernst&YoungLLP

LOCATIONS

HQ: Neogen Corporation
620 Lesher Place, Lansing MI 48912
Phone: 517-372-9200   **Fax:** 517-372-2006
Web: www.neogen.com

2012 Sales

	% of total
US	58
Other	42
Total	**100**

PRODUCTS/OPERATIONS

2012 Sales

	$ mil.	% of total
Animal safety	92	51
Total	**184**	**100**

2012 Sales

Food safety		
Natural toxins allergans drug residues	45	25
Bacterial and general sanitation	24	14
Dry culture media and other	20	11
Animal safety		
Veterinary instruments	37	20
Rodenticides and disinfectants	26	14
DNA testing	18	10
Vaccine	2	2
Total	**184**	**100**

Selected Products

Food safety
AccuClean (detects proteins and sugars)

AccuPoint (rapid sanitation test)
AgriScreen (detects mycotoxins)
Alert (detects food-borne bacteria food allergens)
Beta Star (detects antibiotics in milk)
BioKits (detects allergens in food; also used for species identification)
GeneQuence (detects food-borne bacteria)
Reveal (detects food-borne bacteria food allergens ruminant by-products)
Soleris (detects spoilage organisms)
Veratox (detects mycotoxins food allergens)
Animal safety
AgTek (Kane) products (apparel accessories etc.)
BioSentry (chemicals)
CyKill (rodent control)
Di-Kill (rodent control)
ElectroJac (automated semen collection)
Havoc (rodenticide)
Ideal (animal health products and instruments)
NeogenVet (animal health products)
Prozap (rodenticide)
Ramik (rodenticide)
Rodex (rodenticide)
Squire (animal health products)

COMPETITORS

American Animal Health	Merck
Bayer Animal Health	Merck Animal Health
Bioniche Life Sciences	Merial
Celldex Therapeutics	Novartis
Ecolab	Orchid Cellmark
Eurofins Scientific	Pfizer
Hartz Mountain	Phibro Animal Health
Heska	Silliker
IDEXX Labs	Strategic Diagnostics
Life Technologies Corporation	Virbac Corporation
	Warnex

HISTORICAL FINANCIALS

Company Type: Public

Income Statement

FYE: May 31

	REVENUE ($ mil.)	NET INCOME ($ mil.)	NET PROFIT MARGIN	EMPLOYEES
05/13	207.5	27.1	13.1%	781
05/12	184.0	22.5	12.2%	746
05/11	172.6	22.8	13.2%	654
05/10	140.5	17.5	12.5%	585
05/09	118.7	13.8	11.7%	515
Annual Growth	**15.0%**	**18.3%**	**—**	**11.0%**

2013 Year-End Financials

Debt ratio: —
Return on equity: 11.4%
Cash ($ mil.): 50
Current ratio: 9.51
Long-term debt ($ mil.): —

No. of shares (mil.): 36
Dividends
  Yield: —
  Payout: —
Market value ($ mil.): 1,965

	STOCK PRICE ($) FY Close	P/E High/Low	PER SHARE ($) Earnings	Dividends	Book Value
05/13	54.47	75 50	0.75	0.00	7.16
05/12	38.94	75 47	0.63	0.00	6.18
05/11	44.84	65 38	0.64	0.00	5.40
05/10	25.71	67 40	0.51	0.00	4.50
05/09	22.04	74 42	0.41	0.00	3.88
Annual Growth	**25.4%**	**— —**	**16.2%**	**—**	**16.5%**

Netgear, Inc.

NETGEAR keeps consumers and small businesses wired and wireless. The company designs a range of networking equipment –adapters hubs routers switches media servers and interfaces –for connecting PCs in home and small business settings to each other and the Internet. (Manufacturing is outsourced to contractors in Asia.) NETGEAR also supplies network-attached storage (NAS) systems VPN firewalls and digital media receivers. It sells through distributors including Ingram Micro and Tech Data and to retailers such as Best Buy Fry's Electronics and RadioShack. The company generates about half of its sales from international markets.

OperationsNETGEAR's products for homes include networking storage and digital media products that connect the Internet with computers and communication and entertainment devices such as smartphones and tablets. Known as its retail segment it accounts for 40% of sales. Broadband service providers which account for about 35% of sales look to NETGEAR for whole home networking products. The company serves the commercial market's networking storage and security needs with products that are less expensive than those traditionally used by large businesses. This segment makes up about 25% of sales.

Geographic Reach

The US is NETGEAR's largest market accounting for more than half of sales. The UK and the rest of the EMEA region contribute 35%. Customers in Asia account for about 10% of sales. Every region except the EMEA (outside the UK) experienced growth in 2012.

NETGEAR has a sales presence in 25 countries. Research and development facilities are located in China Taiwan and the US (in Atlanta Chicago and San Diego).

Sales and Marketing

NETGEAR's products are sold in some 45000 retail locations around the world and through about 39000 resellers.

It spent $19 million on advertising and promotional expenses in 2012.

Financial Performance

NETGEAR became a billion-dollar company in 2011 and overall revenue grew another 7% in 2012 to $1.2 billion. While sales of home wireless products rose in its retail segment sales of its powerline and home storage products decreased slightly. Broadband service providers however bought plenty of broadband gateway products primarily driven by demand for the Docsis 3.0 line of products.

Profits for 2012 decreased 5% to $86 million primarily due to increased spending on R&D and income taxes. NETGEAR upped its R&D spend by 25% in 2012 to add employees and invest in new software development projects.

StrategyCommitted to expanding internationally the company uses third-party manufacturing services contractors in China Taiwan and Vietnam to produce its equipment. Cameo Communications Delta Networks Hon Hai Precision and Pegatron are currently contracted as manufacturers and NETGEAR also outsources its warehousing and distribution logistics to APL Logistics Americas Kerry Logistics (in the Asia Pacific region) DSV Solutions and ModusLink (in EMEA) and Agility Logistics (in Australia and New Zealand).

NETGEAR has also been focusing product development on connectivity NAS with enhanced user interfaces security DOCSIS 3.0 gateways and 4G/LTE related repeaters and routers.Mergers and Acquisitions

In early 2013 it acquired the AirCard unit of Sierra Wireless for $138 million. AirCard provides mobile broadband service to any computer through a USB port and the deal helps NETGEAR expand into LTE access devices.

In 2012 it paid $24 million for AVAAK which makes wire-free video networking products. NET-GEAR believes the acquisition will bolster its retail business products and expand its presence into the smart home market. Also that year it paid $7 million for some intellectual property assets from Firetide to boost its wireless product offerings in its commercial segment and strengthen its market position in the campus wireless LAN market.

In 2011 NETGEAR bought the Customer Networking Solutions (CNS) division of Westell Technologies for about $34 million in cash. The division makes high-speed Internet networking products that allow telephone companies to offer voice data video and other streaming services over existing copper and fiber-optic wires. The acquisition expands NETGEAR's broadband networking product portfolio and its telecom provider customer base in the US.

HISTORY

Originally spun off from communications equipment giant Nortel Networks in 2000 NETGEAR bought out Nortel's remaining stake in 2002.

In 2008 NETGEAR acquired assets from security appliance developer CP Secure and hired engineers from the firm. The purchase of CP Secure's assets expanded its security offerings for small and midsized businesses.

EXECUTIVES

Chairman and CEO, Patrick C.S. Lo, age 56, $567,693 total compensation

Senior Vice President Advanced Engineering, Mark G. Merrill, age 58, $205,961 total compensation

SVP Operations and Support, Michael F. Falcon, age 56, $250,731 total compensation

VP and General Manager Home and Consumer Products, Vivek Pathela

SVP Engineering, Charles T. (Chuck) Olson, age 57, $254,711 total compensation

CFO, Christine M. Gorjanc, age 56, $302,769 total compensation

Vice President of Worldwide Sales, Michael A. Werdann, age 44, $208,154 total compensation

SVP; General Manager Retail Business Unit, David S. Soares, age 46, $264,336 total compensation

Chief Technology Officer, Jeff Capone

VP Legal and Corporate Development and Company Secretary, Andrew W. Kim, age 42

VP Human Resources, Tamesa Rogers

SVP; General Manager Commercial Business, Shane J. Buckley, age 45

SVP; General Manager Service Provider Business Unit, Michael P. Clegg, age 52

General Manager Vice President Commercial Business Unit, John McHugh

Director, Julie A. Shimer, age 60

Director, Linwood A. (Chip) Lacy Jr., age 67

Director, Prof George G. C. Parker, age 73

Director, Jocelyn E. Carter-Miller, age 55

Director, Ralph E. Faison, age 54

Director, Jef Graham, age 57

Director, Gregory J. Rossmann, age 51

Director, A. Timothy Godwin, age 63

Independent Director, Barbara Scherer

Auditors: PricewaterhouseCoopersLLP

LOCATIONS

HQ: NETGEAR Inc.
350 E. Plumeria Dr., San Jose CA 95134-1911
Phone: 408-907-8000 **Fax:** 408-907-8097
Web: www.netgear.com

2012 Sales

	$ mil.	% of total
North America		
US	661	53
Other	18	1
EMEA		
UK	184	14
Other	273	21
Asia-Pacific	134	11
Total	**1,271**	**100**

PRODUCTS/OPERATIONS

2012 Sales

	$ mil.	% of total
Retail	504	40
Service provider	459	36
Commercial	307	24
Total	**1,271**	**100**

Selected Products

Broadband access
  Gateways (routers with integrated modems wireless)
  Internet protocol (IP) telephony
  Routers
Ethernet networking
  Adapters
  Bridges
  Network interface cards (NICs)
  Peripheral servers
  Switches
  VPN firewalls
Network connectivity
  Media adapters
  Network-attached storage (NAS)
  Powerline adapters and bridges
  Wireless access points
  Wireless NICs and adapters

COMPETITORS

ARRIS	NetApp
Actiontec	Nokia Siemens Networks
Allied Telesis	Nortel Networks
Apple Inc.	Roku
Aruba Networks	SAFRAN
Barracuda Networks	SMC Corp.
Belkin	Seagate Technology
Buffalo Technology	SonicWALL
Cisco Systems	Technicolor
D-Link	WatchGuard
Dell	Technologies
Fortinet	Western Digital
Hewlett-Packard	ZTE
Huawei Technologies	ZyXEL Communications
Motorola Solutions	

HISTORICAL FINANCIALS

Company Type: Public

Income Statement

FYE: December 31

	REVENUE ($ mil.)	NET INCOME ($ mil.)	NET PROFIT MARGIN	EMPLOYEES
12/12	1,271.9	86.5	6.8%	850
12/11	1,181.0	91.3	7.7%	791
12/10	902.0	50.9	5.6%	654
12/09	686.6	9.3	1.4%	586
12/08	743.3	18.0	2.4%	579
Annual Growth	**14.4%**	**48.0%**	**—**	**10.1%**

2012 Year-End Financials

Debt ratio: —
Return on equity: 12.3%
Cash ($ mil.): 149
Current ratio: 3.31
Long-term debt ($ mil.): —
No. of shares (mil.): 38
Dividends
  Yield: —
  Payout: —
Market value ($ mil.): 1,512

	STOCK PRICE ($) FY Close	P/E High/Low	PER SHARE ($) Earnings	Dividends	Book Value
12/12	39.43	19 13	2.27	0.00	19.68
12/11	33.57	18 10	2.41	0.00	16.97
12/10	33.68	25 12	1.41	0.00	13.83
12/09	21.69	83 32	0.27	0.00	11.92
12/08	11.41	70 17	0.51	0.00	11.40
Annual Growth	**36.3%**	**— —**	**45.2%**	**—**	**14.6%**

NetSol Technologies Inc

NetSol Technologies is sold on the power of IT. The company provides information technology services and software for the banking financial services automotive leasing and financing and healthcare industries. NetSol's LeaseSoft software for asset-based lending organizations automates such tasks as credit valuation financial comparisons wholesale finance management and services tracking. NetSol also offers a hospital management information product. The company's services include assistance with SAP information security business intelligence project management maintenance and testing. NetSol Technologies was founded in 1997.

Revenue was down .63% in fiscal 2011 compared with 2010 mainly because of decreased demand behind the global recession but the company is optimistic about strong sales in 2012 of its next-generation NetSol Financial Suite for financing leasing and lending.

Other product-development efforts are focused on such trends as cloud computing resulting in the recent release for example of the smartOCI e-Procurement search engine for SAP which is being formed into a new unit with its own staff.

NetSol's has strategic alliances with such IT stalwarts as IBM Sun Microsystems GE and Intel.

NetsSol's customers include the financial services arms of a number of major automakers including Toyota Motor. Though headquartered in the US NetSol carries out the majority of its operations and development at its Lahore Pakistan location.

As 90% of its revenues were generated from business units outside North America in fiscal 2011 the company continues to seek out international opportunities for expansion particularly in such emerging markets as Latin America and Asia. Strategies for international development include partnerships with foreign companies that can act as agents for NetSol such as an agreement with Singapore Computer Systems for the marketing of the LeaseSoft product throughout Asia/Pacific and the establishment of subsidiaries in China and Thailand. The company is also developing business in the Middle East through a joint venture with Saudi Arabia's Atheeb conglomerate.

Besides the US and Pakistan NetSol Technologies has offices in Australia China Saudi Arabia Thailand and the UK as well as other countries as needed.

EXECUTIVES

President and Director; Chairman and CEO NetSol Technologies Limited; President Asia Pacific Region, Salim Ghauri, age 56, $175,000 total compensation

Chairman and CEO, Najeeb U. Ghauri, age 57, $272,265 total compensation

VP Partner Services, Mike Miller

CFO, Boo-Ali Siddiqui, age 37, $22,500 total compensation

EVP Information Technology and Operations Network Solutions Limited, Sajjad Kirmani

Corporate Counsel, Malea Farsai

Secretary; General Counsel, Patti L. W. McGlasson, age 48, $124,289 total compensation

SVP SAP Sales and Solutions, Shaz Khan

COO NetSol Technologies North America, Imran Haider

IR Contact Officer, Rob Whetstone

President and Director; Chairman and CEO NetSol Technologies Limited; President Asia Pacific Region, Salim Ghauri, age 56

Director; CEO NetSol Technologies Europe, Naeem Ghauri, age 53

Director, Eugen Beckert, age 65

Director, Mark Caton, age 63

Director, Shahid J. Burki, age 74

Director, Alexander Shakow, age 75

Auditors: Kabani&CompanyInc.

LOCATIONS

HQ: NetSol Technologies Inc.
23901 Calabasas Rd. Ste. 2072, Calabasas CA 91302
Phone: 818-222-9195   **Fax:** 818-222-9197
Web: www.netsoltek.com

2011 Sales

	$ mil.	% of total
Asia/Pacific	25	69
Europe	7	19
North America	4	12
Total	**36**	**100**

PRODUCTS/OPERATIONS

2011 Sales

	$ mil.	% of total
Services	17	49
License fees	11	31
Maintenance fees	7	20
Total	**36**	**100**

COMPETITORS

3i Infotech	KPMG L.L.P.
EDW	Satyam
HCL Technologies	Tata Consultancy
Infosys	Wipro Technologies
International Decision Systems	

HISTORICAL FINANCIALS

Company Type: Public

Income Statement

FYE: June 30

	REVENUE ($ mil.)	NET INCOME ($ mil.)	NET PROFIT MARGIN	EMPLOYEES
06/13	50.8	7.8	15.5%	1,119
06/12	39.7	2.4	6.2%	857
06/11	36.5	5.7	15.7%	879
06/10	36.7	1.3	3.8%	743
06/09	26.4	(8.0)	—	733
Annual Growth	**17.7%**	**—**	**—**	**11.2%**

2013 Year-End Financials

Debt ratio: 6.5%
Return on equity: 11.9%
Cash ($ mil.): 7
Current ratio: 3.54
Long-term debt ($ mil.): 1
No. of shares (mil.): 8
Dividends
  Yield: —
  Payout: —
Market value ($ mil.): 90

	STOCK PRICE ($) FY Close	P/E High	P/E Low	PER SHARE ($) Earnings	PER SHARE ($) Dividends	PER SHARE ($) Book Value
06/13	10.06	14	0	0.95	0.00	8.08
06/12	0.44	5	1	0.39	0.00	7.93
06/11	1.74	2	1	1.20	0.00	9.44
06/10	0.73	3	2	0.40	0.00	9.60
06/09	0.62	—	—	(3.00)	0.00	10.31
Annual Growth	**100.7%**	—	—	—	—	**(5.9%)**

NeuStar, Inc.

NeuStar shines as a key provider of registry and clearinghouse services used in telecommunications and Internet networks. The company manages the registry of North American area codes and telephone numbers and the database used by telecom carriers (Verizon AT&T) and cable companies (Comcast Cox Communications) to route phone calls. It is also a leading provider of operations support systems (OSS) clearinghouse services that provide ordering service provisioning billing and customer service functions. In addition NeuStar operates an Internet registry supporting domain addresses and provides a host of other registry domain name system and IP services. The company makes most of its sales in North America.

Operations NeuStar offers such services as database services (telephone number databases domain names short-codes and fixed IP addresses) analytics platforms used for Internet security caller ID web performance monitoring services and real-time information and analytics services.

Geographic Reach The company has a half-dozen locations in the US that support its three business segments - carrier services enterprise services and information services. An office in Costa Rica supports the information services segments and a small office in the UK supports the carrier and enterprise services segments.

Sales and Marketing In addition to major telecom and cable firms the company counts among its 14000 customers emerging telecom and VoIP service providers e-commerce companies information services providers media and advertising groups and domain name registrars such as Go Daddy.

Although no single customer accounts for more than 10% of sales NeuStar generates some 50% of revenue under contracts with North American Portability Management an industry group representing all US telecommunications services providers.

Financial Performance The company's revenue grew 34% in 2012 hitting $831 million as it saw double-digit growth in both of its traditional segments (carrier services and enterprise services) and the addition of a third segment information services that came about when NeuStar bought Targus Information in 2011. The information services segment contributed more than $158 million to NeuStar's top line in 2012.

Profits were down slightly (3%) to $156 million. In 2011 the company enjoyed a spike in profits after recording a one-time income tax benefit of more than $40 million after ceasing operations of its converged messaging services business.

Mergers and Acquisitions NeuStar uses periodic acquisitions to expand its business. In 2011 it bought Targus Information for about $650 million in cash. The Vienna Virginia-based company provided caller identification and other services that became the basis for a new operating segment - information services. NeuStar also paid $39 million in cash to buy the Numbering Solutions business of Evolving Systems that year to increase the number management and inventory capabilities of its carrier services business segment.

HISTORY

In 2006 the company bought UltraDNS a Reston Virginia-based provider of Domain Name System (DNS) and directory services in a cash deal valued at $61.8 million. It additionally purchased Followap a mobile instant messaging services provider for $139 million that year.

NeuStar acquired Webmetrics a provider of Web and network performance testing services in 2008 for $12.5 million in cash.

EXECUTIVES

President CEO and Director, Lisa A. Hook, age 54, $435,000 total compensation

Chairman, James G. Cullen, age 71

Senior VP Data Solutions, Steven J. (Steve) Edwards, age 54

Senior Director Corporate Communications, Susan Wade

Senior Vice President Chief Financial Officer, Paul S. Lalljie, age 40, $313,014 total compensation

SVP Human Resources, Christine C. Brennan, age 60

Investor Relations, Brandon Pugh

Senior VP Sales, Alexander L. (Alex) Berry, age 44

SVP and General Counsel, Scott B. Harris, age 60

Senior Vice President Infrastructure and Operations, Alex Tulchinsky, age 53

Senior VP Data Strategy, Dennis G. Ainge, age 50

SVP Strategy and Corporate Development, Julian Lighton

Chief Privacy Officer and Deputy General Counsel, Becky Burr

Chief Information Security Officer, Jonathan Coombes

Chairman of the Board, Alan Levy

Chief Financial Officer; Vice President - Finance; Secretary, Brian Dow

Vice President - Medical Affairs; Medical Director, Brian Kopell

Vice President - Product Development, Matthew Gani

Vice President of Legal, Scott Deutchman

Senior Vice President and Chief Technology Officer, Mark F. Bregman

Senior Vice President - Media and New Ventures, Ted Prince

Senior Vice President Carrier Services, Steve J. Edwards

Senior Vice President General Counsel, Len Kennedy

Senior Vice President Marketing, Sujata Gosalia

Chairman of the Board; Chief Executive Officer; President, Haim Katzman

Chief Administrative Officer, Mia Stark

Director, Paul A. Lacouture, age 62

Director, Michael J. Rowny, age 62

Director, Ross K. Ireland, age 64

Director, Hellene S. Runtagh, age 64
President CEO and Director, Lisa A. Hook, age 53
Director, Gareth C. C. Chang, age 70
Director, Joel P. Friedman, age 65
Director, Mark N. Greene
Auditors: Ernst&YoungLLP

LOCATIONS

HQ: NeuStar Inc.
21575 Ridgetop Circle, Sterling VA 20166
Phone: 571-434-5400   **Fax:** 847-437-4969
Web: www.lime-energy.com

2012 Sales

	$ mil.	% of total
North America	787	95
Europe & Middle East	27	3
Other Regions	16	2
Total	**831**	**100**

PRODUCTS/OPERATIONS

2012 Sales

	$ mil.	% of total
Carrier services	502	60
Enterprise services	170	21
Information services	158	19
Total	**831**	**100**

COMPETITORS

Accenture	Keynote Systems
Acxiom	NetCracker Technology
Akamai	Nielsen Holdings
Amdocs	Nokia
BSG Clearing Solutions	Oracle
Billing Services Group	PTGi International
CGI Group	Carrier Services
Computer Sciences	Register.com
Corp.	Sodalia North America
Evolving Systems	Synchronoss
F5 Networks	Syniverse
HP Enterprise Services	TNS Custom
Hewlett-Packard	Telcordia
IBM	Tucows
ICANN	VeriSign
Infoblox	XIUS-bcgi
Infogroup	

HISTORICAL FINANCIALS

Company Type: Public

Income Statement

FYE: December 31

	REVENUE ($ mil.)	NET INCOME ($ mil.)	NET PROFIT MARGIN	EMPLOYEES
12/12	831.3	156.0	18.8%	1,543
12/11	620.4	160.8	25.9%	1,488
12/10	526.8	106.2	20.2%	1,022
12/09	480.3	101.1	21.1%	896
12/08	488.8	4.2	0.9%	966
Annual Growth	**14.2%**	**145.5%**	**—**	**12.4%**

2012 Year-End Financials

Debt ratio: 38.4%
Return on equity: 27.0%
Cash ($ mil.): 340
Current ratio: 3.34
Long-term debt ($ mil.): 577

No. of shares (mil.): 66
Dividends
  Yield: —
  Payout: —
Market value ($ mil.): 2,775

	STOCK PRICE ($) FY Close	P/E High/Low		PER SHARE ($) Earnings	Dividends	Book Value
12/12	41.93	18	13	2.30	0.00	9.77
12/11	34.17	16	10	2.16	0.00	7.60
12/10	26.05	19	14	1.40	0.00	8.10
12/09	23.04	18	10	1.34	0.00	6.77
12/08	19.13	506	241	0.06	0.00	5.23
Annual Growth	**21.7%**	**—**		**—148.8%**	**—**	**16.9%**

New York Mortgage Trust Inc

New York Mortgage Trust is ready to invest in real estate now that the credit crisis has passed. A self-advised real estate investment trust (REIT) the company invests in real estate assets including high-quality adjustable rate residential mortgages and mortgage-backed securities. It primarily buys agency-rated securities which carry less risk but the REIT is also building up its non-agency assets (which bring higher returns). Its owned assets include non-agency mortgage-backed securities prime adjustable rate mortgage loans held in trusts commercial mortgage-backed securities and other commercial real estate-related investments. New York Mortgage Trust was formed in 2003.

Operations

New York Mortgage Trust has expertise in acquiring investing in financing and managing primarily mortgage-related assets (and to a lesser extent financial assets). Its portfolio includes credit sensitive assets and investments sourced from distressed markets in recent years that have created the potential for capital gains as well as more traditional types of mortgage-related investments that generate interest income. Its current portfolio includes distressed residential mortgage loans and prime adjustable rate mortgage (ARM) loans held in securitization trusts.

Financial Performance

After years of stagnation New York Mortgage Trust saw its revenues absolutely skyrocket by 560% from $23 million in 2011 to $147 million in 2012. Profits also shot up nearly 500% from $5 million in 2011 to $28 million in 2012.

The impressive growth for 2012 was due to a nearly 450% spike in interest income fueled by an increase in investment securities and revenue generated from multi-family loans held in securitization trusts and distressed residential mortgage loans held in securitization trusts.

Strategy

New York Mortgage Trust's strategy for growth involves building a residential portfolio that includes elements of both interest rate and credit risk by focusing its investments on credit residential assets and leveraged residential mortgage-backed securities. During 2012 it focused most of its investments in credit residential assets intent on expanding its portfolio of multi-family commercial mortgage-backed securities comprised of first loss fixed rate PO securities a first loss floating-rate security and certain IO securities issued by multi-family K-series securitizations sponsored by Freddie Mac.

EXECUTIVES

Chief Executive Officer President, Steven R. Mumma, age 54, $161,834 total compensation
VP and Secretary, Nathan R. Reese
Chief Financial Officer, Fredric S. Starker
Independent Chairman of the Board, Douglas Neal
Chief Executive Officer President, Steven R. Mumma, age 54
Director, David R. Bock, age 69
Director, Alan L. Hainey, age 67
Auditors: Deloitte&ToucheLLP

LOCATIONS

HQ: New York Mortgage Trust Inc.
52 Vanderbilt Ave. Ste. 403, New York NY 10017
Phone: 212-792-0107   **Fax:** 610-444-3010
Web: www.oakshire.com

PRODUCTS/OPERATIONS

2012 Sales

	$ mil.	% of total
Interest income	137	93
Other income	9	7
Total	**147**	**100**

Selected Subsidiaries and Operations

Hypotheca Capital LLC
New York Mortgage Funding LLC
New York Mortgage Ownership Corporation
New York Mortgage Securities Corporation
New York Mortgage Securitization Trust 2012-1
New York Mortgage Servicing Corporation
New York Mortgage Trust 2005-1
New York Mortgage Trust 2005-2
New York Mortgage Trust 2005-3
NYM Preferred Trust I
NYM Preferred Trust II
NYMT Commercial LLC
NYMT Residential 2012-RP1 LLC
NYMT Residential Tax LLC
NYMT Residential LLC
NYMT-Midway LLC
RB Commercial Mortgage LLC
RB Commercial Trust Series 2012-RS1

COMPETITORS

Annaly Capital Management	Institutional Financial Markets
Anworth Mortgage Asset	MFA Financial
CIFC	Newcastle Investment
Capstead Mortgage	Putnam Mortgage
Dynex Capital	Two Harbors
Impac Mortgage Holdings	iStar Financial Inc

HISTORICAL FINANCIALS

Company Type: Public

Income Statement

FYE: December 31

	REVENUE ($ mil.)	NET INCOME ($ mil.)	NET PROFIT MARGIN	EMPLOYEES
12/12	147.2	28.1	19.1%	4
12/11	22.2	4.8	21.9%	3
12/10	25.4	6.8	26.7%	3
12/09	34.2	11.6	34.1%	4
12/08	18.8	(24.1)	—	6
Annual Growth	**67.1%**	**—**	**—**	**(9.6%)**

2012 Year-End Financials

Debt ratio: 91.5%
Return on equity: 13.8%
Cash ($ mil.): 31
Current ratio: 0.03
Long-term debt ($ mil.): 5,663

No. of shares (mil.): 49
Dividends
  Yield: 16.7%
  Payout: 124.7%
Market value ($ mil.): 313

STOCK PRICE ($) FY Close	P/E High/Low		PER SHARE ($) Earnings	Dividends	Book Value
12/12 6.32	7	5	1.08	1.06	6.50
12/11 7.21	17	14	0.46	1.00	6.12
12/10 6.96	11	8	0.72	0.79	7.27
12/09 7.19	7	2	1.19	0.76	6.69
12/08 2.20	—	—	(2.91)	0.32	4.21
Annual Growth 30.2%	—	—	—	34.9%	11.4%

NewMarket Corp

Some people think petroleum is just fine the way it is; NewMarket thinks it needs a little something extra added to it. The company is a holding entity for two petroleum additive subsidiaries: Afton Chemical and Ethyl Corporation. Afton Chemical manufactures petroleum additives used to improve the performance of gasoline diesel and other fuels and as a lubricant in motor oil fluids and grease. Ethyl's main product is the antiknock additive tetraethyl lead though TEL has lost substantial ground in markets where unleaded gas is preferred. NewMarket also has a real estate unit.

Geographic Reach

The company has operations in Asia Australia Europe Latin America the Middle East and North America.

Operations

The company is engaged in two business segments: petroleum additives and real estate development. Its petroleum additives are used in lubricating oils and fuels to enhance their performance in machinery vehicles and other equipment. The petroleum additives market is an international marketplace with customers ranging from oil companies and refineries to OEMs and other specialty chemical companies.

Its Afton Chemical unit is among the world leaders in producing lubricant additives. The company joins with Infineum Lubrizol and Chevron Oronite to produce more than 80% of the world market.

Though its Ethyl Corporation subsidiary still markets its primary product tetraethyl lead in the US and abroad sales have dwindled to less than 1% of NewMarket's overall business. The company plans to eliminate the Ethyl segment at some point in the future as the global market for leaded gasoline is phased out.

The real estate development segment (NewMarket Development) represents the operations of Foundry Park I. In 2007 Foundry Park I entered into a Deed of Lease Agreement with MeadWestvaco under which it is leasing an office building which NewMarket built on three acres in Richmond Virginia. The lease expires in 2023 subject to certain extension options.

NewMarket Services provides various administrative services to NewMarket Afton Ethyl and NewMarket Development.

Financial Performance

Revenues increased by 3% in 2012 due to a 3.5% increase in petroleum additives net sales with increases in all regions except the Europe India Middle East and Africa region which was 5% lower in 2012. The rise in revenues resulted from higher selling prices offset by an unfavorable foreign exchange impact.

Net income increased by 16% in 2012 due to higher revenues a decrease in interest and financing expenses (resulting from both a lower average interest rate and lower average outstanding debt)

and a drop in Other Expense Net due to a gain of $2 million related to the sale of common stock that was received in September 2011 as part of the legal settlement with Innospec.

Except for a recession-related revenue slump in 2009 NewMarket saw an upward trend in revenue from 2008 to 2012. The slump in 2009 was due to lower total product shipments as well as a significant unfavorable foreign currency impact.

In 2010 Afton completed its acquisition of Polartech for $43 million. Polartech is a global company specializing in the supply of metalworking additives. The company acquired all physical assets of the Polartech business including its headquarters R&D and manufacturing facilities in the UK as well as manufacturing sites in India China and the US.

Ownership

Bruce C. Gottwald owns 10% of the company.

Company Background

NewMarket was founded in 1887 as the Albemarle Paper Manufacturing Company.

EXECUTIVES

Secretary, M. Rudolph West, age 58
President Afton Chemical Corporation, C. S. Warren Huang, age 62, $370,725 total compensation
Controller and Principal Accounting Officer, Wayne C. Drinkwater, age 65
Vice President and Chief Financial Officer (Principal Financial Officer), David A. Fiorenza, age 63, $285,558 total compensation
SVP Afton Chemical Corporation, Alexander McLean, age 55
President CEO and Director, Thomas E. (Teddy) Gottwald, age 52, $675,000 total compensation
Chairman, Bruce C. Gottwald, age 79
VP Corporate Resources, Bruce R. Hazelgrove III, age 52, $275,600 total compensation
VP and General Counsel, Steven M. Edmonds, age 60, $286,850 total compensation
President of Afton Chemical Corporation, Robert A. (Rob) Shama
President CEO and Director, Thomas E. (Teddy) Gottwald, age 51
Director, Charles B. Walker, age 74
Director, Patrick D. Hanley, age 68
Director, Phyllis L. Cothran, age 66
Director, James E. Rogers, age 66
Director, Mark M. Gambill, age 61
Auditors: PricewaterhouseCoopersLLP

LOCATIONS

HQ: NewMarket Corporation
330 S. 4th St., Richmond VA 23219-4350
Phone: 804-788-5000   **Fax:** 804-788-5688
Web: www.newmarket.com

2012 Sales

	$ mil.	% of total
US	811	36
Europe Middle East Africa & India	692	31
Asia/Pacific	440	20
Other regions	279	13
Total	**2,223**	**100**

PRODUCTS/OPERATIONS

2012 Sales

	$ mil.	% of total
Lubricant additives	1,750	79
Fuel additives	450	20
Real estate development & other	22	1
Total	**2,223**	**100**

COMPETITORS

BASF SE	Infineum
Balchem	Innospec
Chevron Oronite	Lubrizol
EPC United Kingdom	Methanex
Fuel Tech	SNPE

HISTORICAL FINANCIALS

Company Type: Public

Income Statement

FYE: December 31

	REVENUE ($ mil.)	NET INCOME ($ mil.)	NET PROFIT MARGIN	EMPLOYEES
12/12	2,223.3	239.5	10.8%	1,710
12/11	2,149.5	206.9	9.6%	1,625
12/10	1,797.3	177.1	9.9%	1,527
12/09	1,530.1	162.2	10.6%	1,308
12/08	1,617.4	73.2	4.5%	1,280
Annual Growth	8.3%	34.5%	—	7.5%

2012 Year-End Financials

Debt ratio: 34.1%
Return on equity: 50.2%
Cash ($ mil.): 89
Current ratio: 3.39
Long-term debt ($ mil.): 424

No. of shares (mil.): 13
Dividends
  Yield: 10.6%
  Payout: 170.1%
Market value ($ mil.): 3,518

STOCK PRICE ($) FY Close	P/E High/Low		PER SHARE ($) Earnings	Dividends	Book Value
12/12 262.20	16	10	17.85	28.00	29.98
12/11 198.11	13	8	15.09	2.39	41.00
12/10 123.37	11	7	12.09	1.57	35.03
12/09 114.77	11	3	10.65	1.08	30.12
12/08 34.91	19	5	4.75	0.80	19.15
Annual Growth 65.5%	—	—	39.2%	143.2%	11.8%

Nexstar Broadcasting Group Inc

Star light star bright Nexstar Broadcasting wishes for you to tune in tonight. The company is a leading television station operator with more than 70 stations serving 40 small and midsized markets. Nexstar has duopolies (two or more stations) in many of its markets. Its portfolio includes more than a dozen affiliates each of the FOX and NBC networks as well as stations affiliated with ABC CBS The CW and MyNetworkTV. More than 15 of its TV stations are operated through local service agreements with Mission Broadcasting which owns those broadcast licenses. Private investment firm ABRY Partners owns a majority share in the company and controls 88% of the voting power.

Geographic Reach

Nexstar operates in dozens of US states. Most of the company's television stations are located in the Northeast Midwest and Southwest.

Sales and Marketing

Nexstar spent about $2.1 million on advertising and marketing promotions during fiscal 2012.

Financial Performance

The company's revenues increased 24% in fiscal 2012 compared with 2011. Net cash inflow increased by $77 million in fiscal 2012 compared with 2011. The increase in annual revenue was primarily due to the acquisitions of WFRV and WEHT in 2011 the acquisitions of ten television stations and Inergize Digital Media from Newport and increases in political advertising and retransmission compensation during the year.

The company enjoyed a large spike in net income during fiscal 2012 that was attributed an income tax benefit of $131 million.

Strategy

Shared services agreements enable the Nexstar to provide sales news and other services to a second station in 66% of the markets where the company operates.

Mergers and Acquisitions

In 2013 Nexstar and Mission Broadcasting entered into definitive agreements to acquire privately-held Communications Corporation of America and White Knight Broadcasting the owners of nineteen television stations and seven associated digital sub-channels in ten markets for a total of $270 million. The planned acquisition of the CCA stations further broadens Nexstar's local television broadcasting platform with stations that are geographically complementary to Nexstar's operating base while also presenting significant financial and operating synergies with the company's existing portfolio. The acquisition will increase Nexstar's portfolio of stations that it owns operates programs or to which it provides sales and other services to 91 stations in 48 markets reaching approximately 14% of all U.S. television households.

With the recession behind it Nexstar is now poised to see its balance sheet emerge from the red by expanding and diversifying its group of television stations. In mid-2011 it acquired WFRV and WJMN the CBS affiliate stations serving the Green Bay Wisconsin and Marquette Michigan markets. Nexstar obtained the two stations from an affiliate of Liberty Media for around $20 million in an effort to increase its presence in midsized markets.

Striving to create a new revenue stream and expand the amount of content it offers in mid-2011 Nexstar bought GoLocal.Biz an Internet technology and marketing services firm that provides targeted online local business listings promotions and coupons embedded video contact information local advertiser web links and other related information to local consumers. Nexstar is combining GoLocal.Biz's platform with its own network of community portal websites.

EXECUTIVES

Chairman President and CEO, Perry A. Sook, age 55, $748,846 total compensation

VP Controller and Secretary, Shirley E. Green, age 53, $196,115 total compensation

VP and Director Engineering, Richard Stolpe, age 56

EVP and Co-COO, Timothy C. (Tim) Busch, age 50, $318,112 total compensation

Executive VP Chief Financial Officer, Brian Jones, age 53, $317,885 total compensation

Station Manager WTVO, Eileen Boucek

General Manager WCIA and WCFN, Russ Hamilton

Station Manager KOLR, Dean Wasson

General Manager KSFX, Mark Gordon

VP and General Manager WMBD; General Manager WYZZ, Coby Cooper

General Manager KSNF, John Hoffmann

Station Manager KODE, Shirley Morton

Station Manager WFXW, Lois Mathes

General Manager KSVI, Jerry Jones

Station Manager KHMT, Bill Burckhard

General Manager KQTV, Heather Shearin

General Manager and General Sales Manager WHAG, Hugh Breslin

General Manager WBRE, Louis J. Abitabilo

Station Manager WYOU, Gina Schreiber

VP General Manager and Director Sales WTAJ, Phil Dubrow

General Manager WTVW, Mike Smith

General Manager WJET and WROC, Louis A. Gattozzi

General Manager WFXV and WPNY, Steve Merren

Station Manager WUTR, Diane Siembab

General Manager and General Sales Manager WDHN, Janie Hinson

Sr. VP Station Operations, Richard E. (Rick) Rogala, age 52

SVP Station Operations, Blake Russell, age 42

General Manager KAMR, Mark McKay

Station Manager KCIT and KCPN, Amanda Bustamante

General Manager KARD KTAL and KTVE, Mark Cummings

General Manager KFDX, Julie Pruett

Station Manager KJTL and KJBO, Stephanie Reed

General Manager KLBK, Greg McAlister

General Manager KLST, Tom Stovall

VP and General Manager WFFT, Bill Ritchhart

Station Manager WLYH, Bob Patterson

General Manager WJET, Tim Dunst

General Manager KNWA and KFTA, Mike Vaughn

Mission Station Manager KAMC, George Damron

General Manager KTAB, Eric Thomas

Mission Station Manager KSAN, Sherri Scott

General Manager WTWO, Tim Sturgess

General Manager WQRF, Joe Denk

General Manager and General Sales Manager WLWC, Tina Castano

General Manager WCWJ, Marc Hefner

VP; General Manager WTVX-TV WTCN-CA WWHB-CA and Retro Television Network, Arika Zink

Chief Financial Officer; Executive Vice President, Thomas E. (Tom) Carter, age 55

SVP eMedia Sales and Operations, Marc Montoya, age 51

Director, I. Martin (Marty) Pompadur, age 78

Director, Royce R. Yudkoff, age 57

Director, Erik Brooks, age 46

Director, Jay M. Grossman, age 53

Director, Geoff Armstrong, age 55

Director, Michael Donovan, age 72

Director, Brent Stone, age 36

Director, Tomer Yosef-Or

Director, Lisbeth R. McNabb, age 52

Auditors: PricewaterhouseCoopersLLP

LOCATIONS

HQ: Nexstar Broadcasting Group Inc.
5215 N. O' Connor Blvd. Ste. 1400, Irving TX 75039
Phone: 972-373-8800   **Fax:** 972-373-8888
Web: www.nexstar.tv

PRODUCTS/OPERATIONS

2012 Sales

Local	50
Political	12
eMedia and other	2
Total	**100**

Selected Television Stations

KAMR (NBC; Amarillo TX)
KARD (FOX; Monroe LA)
KARK (NBC; Little Rock AR)
KBTV (NBC; Beaumont-Port Arthur TX)
KFDX (NBC; Wichita Falls TX)
KFTA (FOX; Ft. Smith-Fayetteville AR)
KLBK (CBS; Lubbock TX)

KLST (CBS; San Angelo TX)
KMID (ABC; Odessa-Midland TX)
KNWA (NBC; Ft. Smith-Fayetteville AR)
KQTV (ABC; St. Joseph MO)
KSFX (FOX; Springfield MO)
KSNF (NBC; Joplin MO)
KSVI (ABC; Billings MT)
KTAB (CBS; Abilene-Sweetwater TX)
KTAL (NBC; Shreveport LA)
WBRE (NBC; Wilkes Barre-Scranton PA)
WCFN (MyNetworkTV; Champaign-Springfield IL)
WCIA (CBS; Champaign-Springfield IL)
WDHN (ABC; Dothan AL)
WFFT (FOX; Ft. Wayne IN)
WFRV (CBS; Green Bay WI)
WFXV (FOX; Utica NY)
WHAG (NBC; Washington DC)
WJET (ABC; Erie PA)
WJMN (CBS; Marquette MI)
WLYH (CW; Harrisburg PA)
WMBD (CBS; Peoria-Bloomington IL)
WQRF (FOX; Rockford IL)
WROC (CBS; Rochester NY)
WTAJ (CBS; Johnstown-Altoona PA)
WTVW (FOX; Evansville IN)
WTWO (NBC; Terre Haute IN)

COMPETITORS

Allbritton Communications	Hearst Television
Barrington Broadcasting	LIN TV
Gannett	Local TV
Granite Broadcasting	Newport Television
Gray Television	Raycom Media
	Tribune Company

HISTORICAL FINANCIALS

Company Type: Public

Income Statement   FYE: December 31

	REVENUE ($ mil.)	NET INCOME ($ mil.)	NET PROFIT MARGIN	EMPLOYEES
12/12	378.6	182.4	48.2%	2,411
12/11	306.4	(11.8)	—	2,230
12/10	313.3	(1.8)	—	2,111
12/09	251.9	(12.6)	—	2,114
12/08	284.9	(78.0)	—	2,258
Annual Growth	7.4%	—		1.7%

2012 Year-End Financials

Debt ratio: 90.6%	No. of shares (mil.): 29
Return on equity: ***,***.*%	Dividends
Cash ($ mil.): 69	Yield: —
Current ratio: 2.82	Payout: —
Long-term debt ($ mil.): 855	Market value ($ mil.): 311

	STOCK PRICE ($) FY Close	P/E High/Low		Earnings	PER SHARE ($) Dividends	Book Value
12/12	10.59	2	1	5.94	0.00	0.10
12/11	7.84	—	—	(0.42)	0.00	(6.37)
12/10	5.99	—	—	(0.06)	0.00	(6.16)
12/09	4.05	—	—	(0.44)	0.00	(6.20)
12/08	0.51	—	—	(2.75)	0.00	(5.81)
Annual Growth	113.4%	—	—	—	—	—

NIC Inc.

So people can do business with government agencies NIC helps government agencies plug in to the Internet. The company is a leading provider of outsourced Web portal services for federal state and local governments. It designs implements and operates websites under contracts with more than 3500 government agencies. NIC generates much of its revenue from transaction fees for such services as online license renewals and for providing data on motor vehicle titles and business licenses to insurance companies lenders and other authorized organizations.

Geographic Reach

The company operates in about 30 states. NIC has offices in more than 40 of the top 50 major metropolitan areas in the US. It has international offices in Asia.

Operations

During fiscal 2012 Motor Vehicle Driver History Record retrieval service accounted for about 25% of NIC's total revenue. Motor Vehicle Registrations service accounted for about 10% of the company's revenue during fiscal 2012.

Sales and Marketing

The company has a national sales force and a marketing department dedicated to its outsourced portal businesses. NIC's largest client LexisNexis Risk Solutions (formerly ChoicePoint) accounted for about 26% of its total revenue during fiscal 2012.

Financial Performance

NIC's revenue has been steady and trending upwards over the course of recent fiscal years. Its revenue increased by 17% in fiscal 2012 ($211.1 million) compared to fiscal 2011 ($180.9 million). The spike was powered by double digit growth in the company's portal revenues which increased by 17% in fiscal 2012 compared to the previous fiscal period. NIC's software and services revenues increased by 11% in 2012 compared to fiscal 2011 largely because of higher revenues from its contract with the FMCSA.

NIC's net profit increased from $22.94 million in fiscal 2011 to $26.34 million in fiscal 2012.

Strategy

To grow NIC is striving to renew its existing contracts which typically run for three- to five-year terms and to win new portal contracts. In addition the company has been developing new applications for government websites from which it can generate transaction fees especially outside the realm of motor vehicle records.

EXECUTIVES

Chairman of the Board; Chief Executive Officer, Harry H. Herington, age 53, $315,000 total compensation

Executive Vice President; Chief Administrative Officer; General Counsel; Secretary, William F. (Brad) Bradley Jr., age 58, $240,167 total compensation

Chief Financial Officer, Stephen M. (Steve) Kovzan, age 44, $227,917 total compensation

Vice President of Sales, Elizabeth Proudfit

Chief Operating Officer, Robert Knapp, age 45

Senior Vice President - Business Development, Ron Thornburgh

Director, Alexander C. (Sandy) Kemper, age 47

Director, William M. (Bill) Lyons, age 58

Director, Daniel J. (Dan) Evans, age 88

Director, Ross C. Hartley, age 65

Director, Pete Wilson

Director, Art N. Burtscher, age 62

Independent Director, Brad Henry

Auditors: PricewaterhouseCoopersLLP

LOCATIONS

HQ: NIC Inc.
25501 W. Valley Pkwy. Ste. 300, Olathe KS 66061
Phone: 877-234-3468   **Fax:** 913-498-3472
Web: www.nicusa.com

PRODUCTS/OPERATIONS

2012 Sales

Outsourced portals	199	94
Total	**211**	**100**

COMPETITORS

Accenture	Link2Gov
Affiliated Computer Services	MAXIMUS
	Manatron
Agency.com	Microsoft
CGI Group	Official Payments
Computer Sciences Corp.	Official Payments Holdings
HP Enterprise Services	Oracle
IBM Global Services	Tyler Technologies
Idea Integration	USTI
Leidos	Unisys

HISTORICAL FINANCIALS

Company Type: Public

Income Statement

FYE: December 31

	REVENUE ($ mil.)	NET INCOME ($ mil.)	NET PROFIT MARGIN	EMPLOYEES
12/12	211.1	26.3	12.5%	714
12/11	180.9	22.9	12.7%	653
12/10	161.5	18.3	11.4%	596
12/09	132.8	13.9	10.5%	606
12/08	100.5	11.9	11.9%	473
Annual Growth	**20.4%**	**21.9%**	**—**	**10.8%**

2012 Year-End Financials

Debt ratio: —
Return on equity: 36.4%
Cash ($ mil.): 62
Current ratio: 2.04
Long-term debt ($ mil.): —

No. of shares (mil.): 64
Dividends
  Yield: 3.0%
  Payout: 142.8%
Market value ($ mil.): 1,056

	STOCK PRICE ($) FY Close	P/E High/Low		PER SHARE ($) Earnings	Dividends	Book Value
12/12	16.34	41	26	0.40	0.50	1.22
12/11	13.31	41	27	0.35	0.25	1.01
12/10	9.71	35	23	0.28	0.55	0.84
12/09	9.14	43	19	0.22	0.30	1.05
12/08	4.60	46	19	0.19	0.25	1.07
Annual Growth	**37.3%**	—	—	**20.5%**	**18.9%**	**3.3%**

Nordson Corp.

When it comes to adhesion coating and spraying Nordson dispenses with admirable stick-to-itiveness. Its adhesive dispensing systems are used on a range of packaging paperboard and nonwoven products. A line of sealant systems bond and seal plastic metal and wood products. Nordson's spray systems apply powder paints and coatings to appliances and auto parts. The company also produces inspection systems for high-tech manufacturing. Nordson sells to the appliance automotive medical solar energy and semiconductor markets among others. About 75% of sales come from outside the US.

Adhesive dispensing systems 50% of revenue are used to decrease consumption create more production efficiency and to make products stronger and more durable as well optimize their brand presence and appearance. The segment's products are divided between four families: nonwovens (equipment for such products as diapers feminine hygiene products surgical gowns shoe covers and face masks); packaging (systems for food packages wrappers and beverage containers); product assembly (for building and construction materials electronics bags sacks books and envelopes); web coating & extruding (for continuous-roll goods such as carpet labels tapes textiles wraps).

Advanced technology systems 36% of revenue serves the electronics medical and high-tech markets with technologies that help accomplish surface preparation (contact lenses electronics medical instruments printed circuit boards); dispensing materials on surfaces (piezoelectric and motionless two-component mixing dispensing systems for cell phones liquid crystal displays micro hard drives among other products); bond testing and X-ray inspection (for the semiconductor and printed circuit board industries' manufacturing related to desktop computers digital music players mobile phones and other products).

Industrial coating systems 14% of revenue provides equipment for applying coatings paint finishes sealants and for curing and drying applied material. The segment is divided between automotive (powertrain components body assembly final trim); container coating (beverage containers and food cans); liquid finishing (automotive components construction metal shelving drums); and powder coating (agriculture and construction equipment appliances automotive components metal shelving). Its curing and drying systems are used for electronics containers and durable goods.

The company has production facilities in seven US states and in Belgium China Germany India the Netherlands and the UK.

Nordson's revenue rose 18% in 2011 compared with 2010 as a result mainly of larger volume and favorable currency exchange rates. By segment adhesive dispensing systems increased 16% thanks in part to strong sales in the Americas and in the consumer end markets. Advanced technology systems headed up about 19% in 2011 vs. 2010 to meet strong demand in all regions but especially in the US and from the consumer electronics market. In the same period revenue for the industrial coating systems surged 24% partly as a result of strong sales in all regions but particularly in Asia/Pacific and the Americas. Along with healthier sales the company has also enjoyed a positive trend for net income. After weathering a net loss of more than $160 million in 2009 Nordson posted a net income of more than $168 million in 2010 and one of more than $222.3 million in 2011.

Nordson's strategy includes expanding its international footprint which already covers more than 30 countries through direct operations. The company focuses on its existing products nurturing them along with engineering and research and development while also seeking growth markets through such methods as the acquisition of companies active in the multinational market. A more specific strategy is the restructuring of adhesive dispensing systems' operations in Georgia which includes expanding a facility in Duluth and building a new plant to replace an old one in Swainsboro where operations in Norcross and Dawsonville are being transferred. The former Swainsboro plant and the Norcross and Dawsonville facilities are being sold.

Meanwhile Nordson has expanded both its offerings and network of direct operations through a series of acquisitions. In mid-2012 it acquired Wisconsin-based EDI Holdings (which stands for Extrusion Die Industries) a provider of slot coating and flat polymer extrusion dies serving plastic processors and web converters for around $200 million from private equity investment firm Bertram Capital. With overseas operations in Germany and China EDI will be integrated into Nordson's adhesive dispensing systems segment. Also in mid-2012 Nordson acquired Pennsylvania-based Xaloy Superior Holdings which makes melt delivery components for injection and extrusion machinery used in plastic processing. With overseas operations in Germany and Thailand Xaloy will also be integrated into Nordson's adhesive dispensing systems segment.

In 2011 Nordson paid $250 million for Colorado-based Value Plastics which manufactures plastic molded single-use fluid connection components used primarily in flow control applications. The acquisition helped Nordson build its medical and life sciences business. Also in 2011 the company acquired Constructiewerkhuizen G. Verbruggen a Belgium-based manufacturer of flexible packaging including bags wraps and pouches. It now operates as a part of the adhesive dispensing systems division.

HISTORY

Nordson was founded in 1909 as the U.S. Automatic Company a maker of low-cost screw machine parts for the auto industry. After the company went bankrupt in 1929 Walter Nord bought the company and reorganized it in 1935 as U.S. Automatic Corp. Following WWII Walter and sons Eric and Evan developed high-pressure paint-spraying equipment. In 1954 Evan formed the Nordson Division to make airless spray equipment; the division moved into thermoplastic adhesion in the 1960s. The division absorbed the parent company in 1966. In 1979 Nordson went public. Eric who became president and chairman brought in 20-year Standard Oil veteran William Madar as CEO in 1986. During Madar's tenure Nordson's sales quadrupled to $600 million annually.

Nordson grew by expanding its business geographically and by developing technology to open new industrial markets. In 1995 the company bought Walcom Benelux a Dutch maker of liquid adhesive-dispensing systems and it introduced the Versa-Spray II powder spray system which automatically adjusts electrostatic output to improve coating uniformity and operating efficiency. Nordson opened a subsidiary in India in 1996 and in 1997 Madar replaced Eric (who retired) as chairman. Edward Campbell the company's president and COO succeeded Madar as CEO that year.

In 1998 Nordson purchased competitor J&M Laboratories' parent company BDL Holdings. Nordson continued to focus on new technology by acquiring Advanced Plasma Systems and March Instruments (both made gas plasma systems used to clean components) as well as Horizon Lamps (ultraviolet lamps) in 1999. That year under its "Action 2000" plan Nordson began trimming its workforce. Late the next year Nordson agreed to acquire EFD Inc. a privately held maker of low-pressure industrial dispensing valves and components. The EFD deal was completed in mid-2001.

To expand the efficiencies of its high-tech technologies Nordson launched a companywide life sciences venture in 2002 to develop products for the pharmaceuticals and medical and genetic research industries and for manufacturers of medical instruments and medical supplies.

Edward Campbell who had joined the board in 1996 became chairman in March 2004 while remaining CEO. Eric Nord retired in November 2004 and was named to the honorary position of chairman emeritus.

Also in 2004 Nordson expanded its international operations through the acquisition of German-based dispensing systems manufacturer W. Puffe Technologie. In 2005 the company planned to buy Germany-based hhs Leimauftrags-Systeme GmbH a provider of cold glue and hot-melt adhesive dispensing technologies from the Baumer Group but the companies mutually terminated the agreement in July.

In 2006 Nordson acquired Dage Holdings a UK-based manufacturer of inspection and testing equipment for printed circuit boards and semiconductors. The purchase price was #117 million (about $228 million). Dage's equipment tests the integrity of electronic connections in semiconductor packages and electronics assemblies a feature that grows more critical as electronics products continue to shrink in size. Dage employed more than 200 people and had sales of about $59 million for the 12 months ended October 31 2006.

In late 2006 Nordson sold its Fiber Systems Group which had come to the company through the acquisition of J&M Laboratories eight years earlier to the Neumag unit of Saurer a Swiss manufacturer of textile machinery and transmission systems. Nordson acquired the Fiber Systems business as part of its purchase of J&M Laboratories in 1998. The group manufactures systems used in the production of non-woven fibers. Neumag/Saurer paid nearly $6 million in cash for Fiber Systems. Nordson divested the business because it was not meeting financial performance objectives.

Eric Nord died in mid-2008 at the age of 90. Among other accomplishments he received 25 US patents.

Reaching into South Africa Nordson obtained MLT Systems along with its MLT Application Systems subsidiary in mid-2008. A familiar face MLT had been supplying Nordson products to South African markets since 1989.

In 2010 Nordson sold subsidiary Nordson UV Ltd. a supplier of graphic arts and lamps product lines (part of its advanced technology systems) to Baldwin Technology. The deal freed up Nordson's resources for use in markets more material to its bottom line.

Also in 2010 Nordson purchased Micromedics a St. Paul Minnesota-based company specialized in dispensing biomaterials for wound care and similar medical procedures. Earlier in the year Nordson acquired GLT a German distributor of the Nordson EFD (electron fusion devices) line since 1977. In 2011 GLT was rebranded as Nordson EFD Deutschland.

EXECUTIVES

Chairman, Joseph P. Keithley, age 63
Chairman Chief Executive Officer, Edward P. (Ed) Campbell, age 63
Treasurer, Raymond L. Cushing
Chief Tax and Risk Officer, Beverly J. Coen
VP General Counsel and Secretary, Robert E. Veillette, age 59
General Manager Micromedics, Lise W. Duran, age 56

President CEO and Director, Michael F. Hilton, age 57
VP Human Resources and CIO, Shelly M. Peet, age 46
Director Supply Chain Management, John C. Dillon
SVP Advanced Technology Systems, John J. Keane, age 50, $301,153 total compensation
VP Global Continuous Improvement, James E. (Jim) DeVries
President Nordson EFD, Jeffrey A. (Jeff) Pembroke
VP Industrial Coating Systems, Douglas (Doug) Bloomfield, age 52
SVP Adhesive Dispensing Systems, Peter G. Lambert, age 51, $222,923 total compensation
VP and CFO, Gregory A. Thaxton, age 50, $254,269 total compensation
VP Pacific South Division, Gregory P. (Greg) Merk, age 40
President Nordson MARCH, Peter F. Bierhuis
President Nordson ASYMTEK, John Byers
VP Southern and Western Regions, Patrice Boyer
VP Finishing Europe, Andre P.M. de Veer
VP Adhesive Dispensing Europe, Axel Wenz
President Nordson K.K., Shigeru Kobayashi
Group VP Asia Pacific Group, Bradley C. Davis
Chief Executive Nordson DAGE, Steven Kew
Director Corporate Communications and Investor Relations, James R. (Jim) Jaye
Managing Director Nordson Korea, Hyun Seop (Steve) Shin
Global Controller, Viktor Yenibehar
President Nordson YESTECH, Donald Miller
Director Internal Audit, Indrani Egleston
Director Corporate DevelopmentMr, Anne Pombier
Director of Human Resources, Elizabeth Cabral
Director of Finance & Administration, David Guiot
Vice President General Counsel of Nordson Corporation, Robert Bob
Director of Marketing, Srini Subramanian
Vice President General Manager, Ken Forden
Vice President, Doug Bloomfield
President of Nordson DAGE, Phil Vere
President of Nordson, James Getty
Director, Benedict P. (Dick) Rosen, age 75
Director, Randolph W. (Randy) Carson, age 60
Director, Mary G. Puma, age 54
Director, William P. Madar, age 72
Director, Victor L. (Vic) Richey Jr., age 54
Director, Michael J. (Mike) Merriman Jr., age 55
Director, Lee C. Banks, age 48
Director, David W. Ignat, age 70
Director, William L. Robinson, age 70
President CEO and Director, Michael F. Hilton, age 57
Auditors: Ernst&YoungLLP

LOCATIONS

HQ: Nordson Corporation
28601 Clemens Rd., Westlake OH 44145
Phone: 440-892-1580   **Fax:** 440-892-9507
Web: www.nordson.com

2011 Sales

	$ mil.	% of total
Asia/Pacific		
Japan	111	9
Other Asia/Pacific	317	26
Americas		
US	312	25
Other Americas	102	8
Europe	390	32
Total	**1,233**	**100**

PRODUCTS/OPERATIONS

2011 Sales

	$ mil.	% of total
Adhesive dispensing systems	611	50
Advanced technology systems	438	36
Industrial coating systems	182	14
Total	**1,233**	**100**

Selected Products

Adhesive Dispensing Systems
Nonwovens (equipment for applying adhesives lotions liquids and fibers to disposable products)
Packaging (automated adhesive dispensing systems used in the food and beverage and packaged goods industries)
Product assembly (adhesive and sealant dispensing systems for bonding or sealing plastic metal and wood products)
Web coating & extruding (laminating and coating systems used to manufacture continuous-roll goods in the nonwovens textile paper and flexible-packaging industries)

Advanced Technology Systems
Bond testing & inspection systems (bond testing and automated optical and x-ray inspection systems used in the semiconductor and printed circuit board industries)
Dispensing systems (controlled manual and automated systems for applying materials in customer processes typically requiring extreme precision and material conservation)
Surface preparation (automated gas plasma treatment systems used to clean and condition surfaces for the semiconductor medical and printed circuit board industries)

Industrial Coatings Systems
Automated & manual dispensing systems
Automotive (used to apply materials in the automotive heavy truck and recreational vehicle manufacturing industries)
Container coating (automated and manual dispensing and curing systems used to coat and cure containers)
Liquid finishing (used to apply liquid paints and coatings to consumer and industrial products)
Powder coating (used to apply powder paints and coatings to a variety of metal plastic and wood products)
Curing & drying systems (ultraviolet equipment used primarily in curing and drying operations for specialty coatings semiconductor materials and paints)

Selected Divisions

Adhesive Dispensing Systems
Industrial Coating Systems
Nordson ASYMTEK
Nordson DAGE
Nordson EFD
Nordson MARCH
Nordson MICROMEDICS
Nordson YESTECH
UV Curing
Value Plastics

COMPETITORS

3M	Graco
BASF SE	Illinois Tool Works
Brady Corporation	PPG Industries
Cohesant	Paper Converting
Curran Group	Machine
Durr	Sono-Tek
EMS-CHEMIE	Spraying Systems
EXEL Industries	W. R. Grace

HISTORICAL FINANCIALS

Company Type: Public

Income Statement

FYE: October 31

	REVENUE ($ mil.)	NET INCOME ($ mil.)	NET PROFIT MARGIN	EMPLOYEES
10/13	1,542.9	221.8	14.4%	5,801
10/12	1,409.5	224.8	16.0%	5,361
10/11	1,233.1	222.3	18.0%	4,094
10/10	1,041.5	168.0	16.1%	3,680
10/09	819.1	(160.0)	—	3,681
Annual Growth	**17.2%**	**—**	**—**	**12.0%**

2013 Year-End Financials

Debt ratio: 32.7%
Return on equity: 28.4%
Cash ($ mil.): 42
Current ratio: 2.55
Long-term debt ($ mil.): 648

No. of shares (mil.): 64
Dividends
 Yield: 0.8%
 Payout: 17.8%
Market value ($ mil.): 4,629

	STOCK PRICE ($) FY Close	P/E High/Low	Earnings	Dividends	Book Value
10/13	72.09	22 17	3.42	0.63	13.83
10/12	59.03	18 11	3.45	0.53	10.42
10/11	46.37	36 11	3.25	0.44	8.71
10/10	78.02	32 21	2.46	0.39	7.44
10/09	52.77	— —	(2.39)	0.37	5.49
Annual Growth	**8.1%**	**— —**	**—**	**14.3%**	**26.0%**

Northern Oil & Gas Inc (NV)

It wouldn't be crude to say that living up north is a gas for this company. Northern Oil and Gas explores for and produces oil and natural gas on properties in the northern US. The company keeps overhead and risk down by purchasing minority or non-operating interests in producing oil and gas projects. With leaseholds on more than 151000 acres in the Bakken and Three Forks oil and gas fields in North Dakota and Montana the company has developed 15% of its property. That development has yielded proved and probable reserves of nearly 16 million barrels of oil equivalent (BOE) almost all of it crude. Northern Oil and Gas was formed in 2007.

In 2010 the company drilled 170 exploratory wells and had a 100% success rate increasing its proved reserves by nearly 160%. It also acquired nearly 57000 acres across a handful of properties. Northern Oil and Gas looks for projects that are in the early stages of drilling or are about to start drilling.

EXECUTIVES

Chairman of the Board; Chief Executive Officer, Michael L. Reger, age 36
President and Director, Ryan R. Gilbertson, age 36
COO General Counsel and Secretary, James R. Sankovitz, age 37
VP Business Development, Erik Nerhus
Land Manager, Kruise Kemp
CFO, Thomas Stoelk
Director, Lisa G. Meier, age 41
President and Director, Ryan R. Gilbertson, age 36

Director, Robert Grabb, age 60
Director, Jack E. King, age 60
Director, Loren J. O?Toole, age 81
Independent Director, Delos Jamison
Independent Director, Loren OToole
Independent Director, Richard Weber
Auditors: MantylaMcReynoldsLLC

LOCATIONS

HQ: Northern Oil and Gas Inc.
 315 Manitoba Ave. Ste. 200, Wayzata MN 55391
Phone: 952-476-9800   **Fax:** 952-476-9801
Web: www.northernoil.com

COMPETITORS

Adams Resources	EOG
American Oil & Gas	Exxon Mobil
Anadarko Petroleum	Hunt Consolidated
Apache	Jones Energy
BP	Key Energy
Cabot Oil & Gas	National Fuel Gas
Chesapeake Energy	Noble Energy
Chevron	Pioneer Natural
Cimarex	Resources
ConocoPhillips	Royal Dutch Shell
Devon Energy	

HISTORICAL FINANCIALS

Company Type: Public

Income Statement

FYE: December 31

	REVENUE ($ mil.)	NET INCOME ($ mil.)	NET PROFIT MARGIN	EMPLOYEES
12/12	311.5	72.2	23.2%	19
12/11	149.3	40.6	27.2%	19
12/10	44.5	6.9	15.5%	11
12/09	14.2	2.8	19.7%	8
12/08	4.3	2.3	54.6%	5
Annual Growth	**191.4%**	**135.3%**	**—**	**39.6%**

2012 Year-End Financials

Debt ratio: 35.6%
Return on equity: 13.3%
Cash ($ mil.): 13
Current ratio: 0.94
Long-term debt ($ mil.): 424

No. of shares (mil.): 63
Dividends
 Yield: —
 Payout: —
Market value ($ mil.): 1,069

	STOCK PRICE ($) FY Close	P/E High/Low	Earnings	Dividends	Book Value
12/12	16.82	23 12	1.15	0.00	9.23
12/11	23.98	50 20	0.65	0.00	7.84
12/10	27.21	199 78	0.14	0.00	7.01
12/09	11.84	155 27	0.08	0.00	2.81
12/08	2.60	227 31	0.07	0.00	1.45
Annual Growth	**59.5%**	**— —**	**—101.3%**	**—**	**58.8%**

NU Skin Enterprises, Inc.

Multi-level marketer Nu Skin Enterprises keeps itself busy exfoliating and polishing. It offers 200-plus personal care products including cleansers toners and anti-aging skin care products through a global network of 950000 independent distributors sales reps and preferred customers. It also sells cosmetics fragrances hair care items and mouthwash. Nu Skin has its foot in the door in 50-plus global markets including cherished China. Its Pharmanex unit sells LifePak nutritional supplements. Its Big Planet subsidiary offers personal and small-business technology and communications products as well as Internet and long-distance services. Nu Skin was founded in 1984 by its former chairman Blake Roney.

Geographic Reach

Geographically diverse Nu Skin rings up almost 90% of its sales outside the US. Japan is the company's largest market accounting for more than 20% of sales. Greater China (including Taiwan and Hong Kong) is an important growth market for Nu Skin accounting for about 25% of sales.

Operations

The company operates through two primary business segments: Nu Skin (55% of sales) its proprietary brand of anti-aging personal care products including the ageLOC line of skin care and nutritional items; and Pharmanex distributor of the LifePak brand and other nutritional supplements.

Sales and Marketing

Nu Skin relies on person-to-person marketing — rather than traditional media advertising or direct marketing campaigns —to sell its personal care and other products. Its cadre of nearly 950000 active distributors and consumers purchase products directly from the company and resell them. However Nu Skin employs a different business model in China where it has an employed sales force and contractual sales promoters to sells products in stores.

Financial Performance

In 2012 Nu Skin posted record sales of nearly $2.2 billion a 24% increase versus 2011. Net income was up 45% over the same period. Sales of Pharmanex brand products rose 28% outperforming the Nu Skin line (up a robust 22%). The company credited the strong sales performance to sustained interest in its products including ageLOC anti-aging potions and growth of its independent distributor force particularly in emerging markets such as China South Asia and Korea. Sales in Greater China an emerging and important market for the company rose 67% in 2012 compared with 2011 while sales in the South Asia/Pacific region climbed 40%. The company credited the recent global launch of its ageLOC anti-aging line of products for much of the growth. Indeed Nu Skin's sales profits and cash flow from operations have posted steady gains with revenue growth accelerating in recent years.

Strategy

Nu Skin is betting on rapid growth in the global anti-aging market as Baby Boomers in the US and skin-obsessed women in Asia fuel demand for its products. Since entering China in 2003 the company has expanded to more than 50 cities in 15 provinces. Indeed the company has big plans for the Chinese market including tripling the number of stores and sale support centers there by 2017. To meet increasing demand in China the company is expanding its manufacturing capacity there.

To fuel sales growth the company is developing new ageLOC anti-aging supplements including a weight management system slated to launch in the second half of 2013. Nu Skin's stream of super-class age-fighters is fed by a scientific collaboration with Wisconsin-based LifeGen Technologies a research company specializing in the genetic sources of aging. Nu Skin acquired LifeGen for $11.7 million in 2011. The deal aims to further strengthen Nu Skin's share of the global anti-aging market as well as its mighty but modest staff of in-house scientists which have helped to keep the company on the forefront of skin care research. The firm has increased its spending on R&D in recent years from about $9.6 million in 2008 to $14.9 million in 2012.

Mergers and Acquisitions

Nu Skin's acquisition of NOX Technologies in late 2012 gave the company a deeper understanding of the aging process through its arNOX age-related protein. Buying the Malvern Pennsylvania-based biotechnology and biodiagnostic company for $12.5 million brought onboard technology and patents including those previously licensed and utilized in connection with Nu Skin's anti-aging research efforts.

Nu Skin in 2011 invested in its Utah headquarters by acquiring the building and a distribution center from founding stockholders for some $33 million. The move is part of the beauty company's development project in Provo.

Ownership

Royce & Associates owns more than 12% of the company shares.

HISTORY

Brigham Young University graduate Blake Roney and his sister Nedra came up with the idea for Nu Skin in 1984 while pondering the amount of fillers in personal care products. They compiled a list of beneficial ingredients came up with $5000 (from friend and present SVP Sandra Tillotson) and found a manufacturer to make their product —and Nu Skin International was born. Roney was dead-set against incurring debt so he decided to use multilevel marketing to push the products. Such marketing systems are often accused of being illegal pyramid schemes and Nu Skin has drawn the attention of many attorneys general across the US.

Nevertheless the company expanded rapidly and soon entered other countries including Canada (1990) Taiwan (1992) and Australia and Japan (1993). Nu Skin introduced Interior Design Nutritionals in 1992 and a line of plaque-fighting oral care products in 1993. Expansion continued as the company entered several European countries during 1996.

Roney formed Nu Skin Asia Pacific as a public company in 1995 and 1996 while maintaining Nu Skin International as a privately held affiliate. In 1996 the company introduced its Epoch line of products containing ingredients used by indigenous cultures around the world. The following year supermodel Christie Brinkley signed on as Nu Skin spokeswoman and in 1998 Nu Skin Asia Pacific acquired its parent —excluding its North American operations —for about $250 million plus up to $100 million more in performance-based payments. Nu Skin Asia Pacific was renamed Nu Skin Enterprises.

Nu Skin Enterprises bought the assets of Nu Skin USA in March 1999 in a continuing effort to simplify the Nu Skin organization and gain worldwide ownership and marketing rights. In August 1999 it bought technology and communications products maker Big Planet and later organized its personal care nutritional and technological products into three separate divisions.

Nu Skin expanded Pharmanex into the emergency food supply market through its 2002 acquisition of First Harvest International and began selling Vitameals a dehydrated food product. It also established a humanitarian initiative (Nourish the Children) through which Vitameals can be distributed to malnourished children worldwide.

Nu Skin opened more than 100 retail outlets in China in January 2003.

The company increased revenue in 2005 with year-over-year growth in certain markets including Korea Taiwan Europe and the US as well as with its expansion into Indonesia.

Nu Skin exited Brazil in 2007 after nearly 10 years of unprofitability in that market. Ensuring it's one step ahead of rivals Amway and Avon Nu Skin shed jobs at its US corporate office in 2008 and shuttered about 70 of its 115 retail stores in China shifting focus to open a handful of stores in Beijing Guangzhou and Shanghai soon thereafter.

The company celebrated its 25th anniversary in 2009.

In April 2011 Nu Skin won approval to begin direct sales in the provinces of Zhejiang Guizhou Sichuan and Shandong and in the city of Tianjin —adding to existing approvals in Beijing Shanghai and Guangdong.

EXECUTIVES

VP Community Relations, Gary B. Garrett

President Americas Region, Scott E. Schwerdt, age 55

EVP Product Development and Chief Scientific Officer, Joseph Y. (Joe) Chang, age 60, $500,000 total compensation

Founder Vice President, Sandra N. (Sandie) Tillotson, age 56, $400,000 total compensation

President CEO and Director, M. Truman Hunt, age 54, $776,849 total compensation

Chairman, Steven J. Lund, age 59, $750,000 total compensation

CIO, Mark L. Adams, age 61

President Greater China Region, Andrew Fan, age 49

CFO, Ritch N. Wood, age 47, $371,154 total compensation

VP Corporate Finance, Chris Nielson

VP Corporate Administrative Services, Charles H. (Charlie) Allen

President North America, Brett Nelson, age 49

VP Global Opportunity Marketing, Elizabeth Thibaudeau

VP Global Sales Development and Global Distributor Programs, Antonia Chang

President Global Sales and Operations, Daniel R. (Dan) Chard, age 48, $371,154 total compensation

President Nu Skin Taiwan, Charlene Chiang

President North Asia Region and Korea, Luke B. Yoo

President Hong Kong and Macau, Angela Lau

President Europe Middle East and Africa, Mikael Linder

President Southeast Asia and Pacific Region, Melisa T. Quijano

VP Finance Asia and the Pacific; COO Nu Skin China, Owen Messick

VP Special Events and Distributor Recognition, Jodi Durrant

VP Distributor Success Nu Skin China, Patrick Yeung

Director Investor Relations, Scott Pond

VP Global Sales and Operations Beijing Office Greater China, Keynes (Chaodong) Li

VP Regional Marketing Americas Europe and South Pacific, Greg Darlington

VP Global Research and Development Pharmanex, Mark Bartlett

VP Global Product Marketing, Kevin Fuller

VP Human Resources, David Daines

VP Global Research and Development Nu Skin, Helen E. Knaggs

President Japan, Ryan Napierski

VP Global Supply Chain, Jeff Henderson

VP Sales and Operations Pacific Region, Mike Colvin
VP and General Counsel, Tyler Whitehead
Vice President of Sales, Matt Hall
Vice President Visit to Nu Skin, Marie Claire
Founder of Nu Skin Enterprises, Sandie Tilltoson
General Counsel; Secretary, Matthew Dorny
SVP and Director, Sandra N. (Sandie) Tillotson, age 55
President CEO and Director, M. Truman Hunt, age 54
Vice Chairman, Steven J. Lund, age 58
Director, Nevin N. Andersen, age 72
Director, Daniel W. (Dan) Campbell, age 58
Director, E. J. (Jake) Garn, age 81
Director, Andrew D. Lipman, age 61
Director, Patricia A. Negron, age 45
Director, David D. Ussery, age 77
Director, Thomas R. Pisano, age 68
Independent Director, Neil Offen
Independent Director, Patricia Negron
Auditors: PricewaterhouseCoopersLLP

LOCATIONS

HQ: Nu Skin Enterprises Inc.
75 W. Center St., Provo UT 84601
Phone: 801-345-1000   Fax: 800-487-8000
Web: www.nuskinenterprises.com

2012 Sales

	$ mil.	% of total
North Asia		
Japan	497	23
South Korea	297	14
Greater China		
China	264	12
Hong Kong	169	8
Taiwan	136	6
Americas	288	13
South Asia/Pacific	330	15
Europe the MiddleEast & Africa	185	9
Total	2,169	100

PRODUCTS/OPERATIONS

2012 Sales

	$ mil.	% of total
Nu Skin	1,178	55
Pharmanex	983	45
Other	7	.
Total	2,169	100

Selected Products

Nu Skin
  Body care products (Galvanic Spa Nu Skin)
  Cosmetics (Nu Colour)
  Facial care products (ageLOC Galvanic Spa)
  Hair care products (Epoch Nutriol)
  Oral care products (AP-24)
Pharmanex
  Botanical and herbal products (Tegreen BioGinkgo)
  Emergency nutritional supply (Vitameal)
  Multivitamin/mineral supplement (LifePak)
  Sports nutrition (OverDrive)
  Weight management (My Victory)
Big Planet
  Educational and training products
  E-commerce products
  Internet access products
  Long-distance and voice-messaging services
  Pagers
  Prepaid calling cards

COMPETITORS

AMS Health Sciences	Mannatech
Alticor	Mary Kay
Amazon.com	Melaleuca
Amway	Merle Norman
Avon	Microsoft
Bath & Body Works	Murad Inc.
BeautiControl	Nature's Sunshine
Beiersdorf	Oriflame Cosmetics SA
Body Shop	Procter & Gamble
Buy.com	Revlon
CCA Industries	Schiff Nutrition
Clarins	International
Comcast	Shaklee
EarthLink	Shiseido
Estee Lauder	Sprint Communications
Forever Living	Sunrider
ForeverGreen Worldwide	The Stephan Co.
GNC	Time Warner Cable
Herbalife Ltd.	Tom's of Maine
Kodak Imaging Network	Unilever
L'Oreal	

HISTORICAL FINANCIALS

Company Type: Public

Income Statement

FYE: December 31

	REVENUE ($ mil.)	NET INCOME ($ mil.)	NET PROFIT MARGIN	EMPLOYEES
12/12	2,169.6	221.6	10.2%	3,733
12/11	1,743.9	153.3	8.8%	5,980
12/10	1,537.2	136.0	8.9%	5,054
12/09	1,331.0	89.8	6.7%	8,900
12/08	1,247.6	65.3	5.2%	9,185
Annual Growth	14.8%	35.7%	—	(20.2%)

2012 Year-End Financials

Debt ratio: 16.8%
Return on equity: 37.9%
Cash ($ mil.): 320
Current ratio: 1.87
Long-term debt ($ mil.): 154

No. of shares (mil.): 58
Dividends
  Yield: 2.1%
  Payout: 25.2%
Market value ($ mil.): 2,164

	STOCK PRICE ($) FY Close	P/E High/Low		Earnings	Dividends	Book Value
12/12	37.05	17	9	3.52	0.80	10.11
12/11	48.57	21	11	2.38	0.59	9.22
12/10	30.26	15	11	2.11	0.50	7.59
12/09	26.87	20	6	1.40	0.46	5.98
12/08	10.43	19	9	1.02	0.44	4.99
Annual Growth	37.3%	—	—	36.3%	16.1%	19.3%

Oiltanking Partners LP

What do Germany and Houston have in common? Not much besides Oiltanking Partners. The limited partnership formed in March 2011 by Oiltanking Holding Americas a subsidiary of Oiltanking GmbH the world's second-largest independent storage provider for crude oil liquid chemicals and gases. (Oiltanking GmbH is in turn owned by private German conglomerate Marquard & Bahls). Oiltanking Partners owns and operates pipeline terminals with about 135 tanks in Houston and Beaumont that have a storage capacity of about 18 million barrels. Customers include oil and companies marketers and distributors. Oiltanking Partners raised $215 million in its 2011 initial public offering.

Oiltanking GmbH spun off its Texas assets as Oiltanking Partners to combine two of its Gulf Coast businesses Oiltanking Houston L.P. and Oiltanking Beaumont Partners L.P. (Oiltanking GmbH retained two other Texas assets in Port

Neches and Texas City). Oiltanking GmbH intends for Oiltanking Partners to be its growth vehicle in the US to acquire own and operate terminals oil storage and pipeline assets. In the short term it expects to expand storage capacity at its Houston and Beaumont terminals and it the long term the company has its eye on operations outside the Gulf Coast. Before it can do that Oiltanking Partners needs to pay off some debt and the company plans to use the proceeds from its IPO to repay its former parent and replenish working capital.

The company is banking its expansion plans to take advantage of pipeline construction by a number of oil & gas firms operating in Houston's Ship Channel. Enbridge Enterprise Products Partners Magellan Midstream and TransCanada have all announced plans to expand their pipeline operations and while these companies have their own terminal storage operations Oiltanking Partners intends to be ready to offer additional storage capacity. It has options to buy land and build the necessary pipeline connections for another 7 million barrels of crude storage capacity. It also owns 24 acres located about six miles from the terminal and is allowed to build pipeline connections to link the two and is permitted to locate more storage tanks on 63 acres also nearby the terminal.

EXECUTIVES

President and CEO, Anne-Marie Ainsworth, age 56
CFO, Kenneth F. Owen, age 39
VP Marketing and Sales, Robert J. (Bo) McCall, age 48
VP Corporate Affairs and Strategic Planning, Jan P. Vogel, age 43
VP Operations, Kevin L. Campbell, age 48
VP General Counsel and Secretary, Brian C. Brantley
Senior Vice President IR Counsel, Lisa Elliott
Auditors: BDOUSALLP

LOCATIONS

HQ: Oiltanking Partners LP
  333 Clay Street, Suite 2400, Houston, TX 77002
Phone: 281 457-7900
Web: www.oiltankingpartners.com

COMPETITORS

Buckeye Partners	Magellan Midstream
Cheniere Energy	Martin Midstream
Partners	Partners
DCP Midstream Partners	TransCanada
Enbridge Energy	Williams Partners
Enterprise Products	
Kinder Morgan Energy	
Partners	

HISTORICAL FINANCIALS

Company Type: Public

Income Statement

FYE: December 31

	REVENUE ($ mil.)	NET INCOME ($ mil.)	NET PROFIT MARGIN	EMPLOYEES
12/12	135.5	62.6	46.2%	0
12/11	117.3	62.4	53.2%	0
12/10	116.4	37.8	32.5%	0
12/09	100.8	25.1	24.9%	0
Annual Growth	10.3%	35.6%	—	—

2012 Year-End Financials

Debt ratio: 31.8%
Return on equity: —
Cash ($ mil.): 7
Current ratio: 1.46
Long-term debt ($ mil.): 146

No. of shares (mil.): 38
Dividends
Yield: 3.7%
Payout: 95.6%
Market value ($ mil.): 1,473

	STOCK PRICE ($) FY Close	P/E High/Low		PER SHARE ($) Earnings	Dividends	Book Value
12/12	37.86	26	17	1.57	1.43	7.35
12/11	27.92	48	37	0.60	0.27	7.19
12/10	0.00	—	—	(0.00)	0.00	(0.00)
Annual Growth	—	—	—	—	—	—

Old Dominion Freight Line, Inc.

Old Dominion Freight Line still makes its stand in Dixie but the trucking company serves the rest of the US as well. Less-than-truckload (LTL) shipments (freight from multiple shippers consolidated into a single truckload) accounts for the bulk of the company's revenues. Old Dominion operates a fleet of more than 6070 tractors and more than 24000 trailers from about 220 service centers. In addition to its core LTL services the company offers its customers a broad range of logistics services including ground and air transportation supply chain consulting container delivery and warehousing and household moving.

Geographic Reach

The company directly serves the 48 contiguous states of the continental US and Hawaii and offers service elsewhere in North America as well as Central America South America and Asia.

Along with its standard LTL offerings Old Dominion provides expedited delivery and logistics services including warehousing and distribution. Old Dominion also offers drayage services such as direct point-to-point delivery and unloading from about 10 cities including Atlanta Chicago Dallas Los Angeles Memphis and Salt Lake City.

Though it operates throughout the US Old Dominion is a multiregional carrier rather than a national one. The company divides its US territory into six regions: Southeast Gulf Coast Northeast Midwest Central and West. It provides next-day and second-day service within regions.

Financial Performance

Old Dominion's revenues grew by 12% in 2012 thanks to increases in tonnage and pricing.

Net income increased by 21% in 2012 as the result of higher revenues partially offset by an increase in operating expenses. Depreciation and amortization expenses grew as the result of higher capital expenditures including a major spend on purchasing tractors and trailers. n Salaries wages and benefits also as the company hired more workers to keep pace with the increase in shipments.

Strategy

The company grows through both acquisitions and internal growth. Old Dominion hopes to continue growing by gaining more customers in its current operating territory and by building out its network of service centers. The company added nearly 35 service centers between 2007 and 2012. It also expands by adding new services such as consumer household moving services added to the menu in 2012. More generally another strategy is focused on maintaining a fair price. The company did raise rates slightly in 2011 but it did not make the significant increases that were typical of the industry.

Ownership

Members of the founding Congdon family own a significant minority stake in Old Dominion.

Company Background

Old Dominion was founded in 1934 by Earl Congdon.

Once a regional trucker the company has expanded beyond the southeastern US particularly since the mid-1990s.

EXECUTIVES

VP Equipment and Maintenance, J. Edward Richardson
VP Southern Region, Hugh N. Morris Jr.
VP Transportation, Buddy S. McBride
VP Northeast Region, Mark M. Madden
SVP Pricing and Strategic Development, Richard F. (Rick) Keeler
VP Field Services, Terry L. Hutchins
SVP Sales, Kevin M. Freeman
VP and Controller, John P. Booker III
SVP General Counsel and Secretary, Joel B. McCarty Jr., age 75, $138,860 total compensation
SVP and Vice Chairman, John R. Congdon, age 80, $315,860 total compensation
President and CEO, David S. Congdon, $509,595 total compensation
VP Safety and Personnel, Brian J. Stoddard
SVP Finance and CFO, J. Wes Frye, $304,265 total compensation
Chairman, Earl E. Congdon, $509,595 total compensation
VP Human Resources, Kenneth M. (Ken) Ludwig, age 58
VP Gulf Coast Region, Gerry L. Broadwell
VP Midwest Region, Michael A. (Mike) Wood
SVP Marketing Pricing and Strategic Development, Cecel E. (Chip) Overbey Jr.
VP Western Region, Robert H. (Bob) Foote
VP Information Services and Technology, Kenneth D. (Ken) Erdner
VP Old Dominion Global, Gregory B. Plemmons
VP Pacific Northwest Region, Charles W. (Chuck) Powell
VP Midsouth Region, Lemuel B. Clayton
VP Corporate Services and Collections, David N. Heaton
Senior Vice President - Operations, David J. Bates
EVP and COO, Gregory C. (Greg) Gantt, $278,250 total compensation
Director Marketing, David Carter
VP and Assistant General Counsel, William T. Cranfill
VP Pricing, Todd A. Polen
VP Supply Chain Services, Michael J. Venegoni
VP Information Systems and Technology, Chris Young
SVP and Vice Chairman, John R. Congdon, age 80
President CEO and Director, David S. Congdon, age 56
Director, Robert G. Culp III, age 66
Director, J. Paul Breitbach, age 75
Director, Leo H. Suggs, age 73
Director, John R. Congdon Jr., age 56
Director, John D. Kasarda, age 67
Director, D. Michael Wray, age 52
Auditors: Ernst&YoungLLP

LOCATIONS

HQ: Old Dominion Freight Line Inc.
500 Old Dominion Way, Thomasville NC 27360
Phone: 336-889-5000 **Fax:** 336-822-5229
Web: www.odfl.com

PRODUCTS/OPERATIONS

Domestic LTL Service
Continental US Coverage
Direct Points
Household Services
OD Domestic
Regional/Super-Regional Locations
Security Divider Service
Transit
OD Expedited Service
Expedited Transit Times
Expo Services
OD Expedited
Security Divider Service
Speed Service
Speed Service Air
Speed Service On Demand
Time-sensitive delivery
White Glove Service
Truckload and Special Services
LTL/Truckload
Global Services
Global Assembly and Distributi
Nationwide Container Drayage
Pacific Promise
Worldwide LCL and FCL Service

COMPETITORS

AAA Cooper Transportation
Arkansas Best
Averitt Express
Central Freight Lines
Con-way Freight
Estes Express
FedEx Freight
J.B. Hunt
Saia
Schneider National
Southeastern Freight Lines
Swift Transportation
UPS Freight
Vitran
YRC Worldwide

HISTORICAL FINANCIALS

Company Type: Public

Income Statement

FYE: December 31

	REVENUE ($ mil.)	NET INCOME ($ mil.)	NET PROFIT MARGIN	EMPLOYEES
12/12	2,110.4	169.4	8.0%	13,016
12/11	1,882.5	139.4	7.4%	12,022
12/10	1,481.0	75.6	5.1%	11,179
12/09	1,245.0	34.8	2.8%	9,608
12/08	1,537.7	68.6	4.5%	10,864
Annual Growth	8.2%	25.3%	—	4.6%

2012 Year-End Financials

Debt ratio: 14.0%
Return on equity: 17.9%
Cash ($ mil.): 12
Current ratio: 1.22
Long-term debt ($ mil.): 201

No. of shares (mil.): 86
Dividends
Yield: —
Payout: —
Market value ($ mil.): 2,954

	STOCK PRICE ($) FY Close	P/E High/Low		PER SHARE ($) Earnings	Dividends	Book Value
12/12	34.28	25	15	1.97	0.00	11.91
12/11	40.53	25	17	1.63	0.00	9.94
12/10	31.99	45	26	0.90	0.00	7.97
12/09	30.70	91	46	0.42	0.00	7.07
12/08	28.46	47	23	0.82	0.00	6.65
Annual Growth	4.8%	—	—	24.6%	—	15.7%

Old Line Bancshares Inc

Old Line Bancshares is the holding company for Old Line Bank serving consumers businesses and wealthy individuals in the Old Line State and in the Washington DC area. With more than 20 branch offices and total assets in excess of $1.1 billion the bank offers standard retail products including deposit accounts CDs and credit cards. It uses funds from deposits to write business and consumer loans; commercial real estate loans make up about half of its portfolio. The bank also offers luxury boat financing. The company also owns 50% of real estate firm Pointer Ridge Office Investment. Old Line acquired Maryland Bankcorp in 2011 and WSB Holdings the parent company of The Washington Savings Bank in 2013.

Mergers and Acquisitions

Old Line Bancshares is pursuing growth via acquisitions. It $54.7-million purchase of WSB Holdings closed in May 2013. Previously Old Line acquired Maryland Bankcorp in 2011 in a move that doubled its branch network and asset portfolio.

EXECUTIVES

Senior Vice President Buy, Joseph E. Burnett, age 67, $164,100 total compensation
President and CEO Old Line Bancshares and Old Line Bank, James W. Cornelsen, age 58, $237,600 total compensation
EVP CFO and Secretary; EVP CFO Chief Credit Officer, and Secretary Old Line Bank, Christine M. (Chris) Rush, age 57, $156,600 total compensation
Chairman Old Line Bancshares and Old Line Bank, Craig E. Clark, age 71
Vice Chairman Old Line Bancshares and Old Line Bank, Frank Lucente Jr., age 71
Vice Chairman Old Line Bancshares and Old Line Bank, Frank Lucente Jr., age 71
Independent Director, Andre Gingles
Independent Director, Frank Taylor
Auditors: Rowles&CompanyLLP

LOCATIONS

HQ: Old Line Bancshares Inc.
1525 Pointer Ridge Place, Bowie MD 20716
Phone: 301-430-2500   **Fax:** 301-932-5458
Web: www.oldlinebank.com

COMPETITORS

BB&T	M&T Bank
Bank of America	PNC Financial
First Mariner Bancorp	Tri-County Financial

HISTORICAL FINANCIALS

Company Type: Public

Income Statement

FYE: December 31

	ASSETS ($ mil.)	NET INCOME ($ mil.)	INCOME AS % OF ASSETS	EMPLOYEES
12/12	861.8	7.5	0.9%	182
12/11	811.0	5.3	0.7%	177
12/10	401.9	1.5	0.4%	81
12/09	357.2	2.0	0.6%	83
12/08	317.7	1.7	0.6%	67
Annual Growth	28.3%	43.9%	—	28.4%

2012 Year-End Financials

Return on assets: 0.9%	Dividends
Return on equity: 10.5%	Yield: 1.4%
Long-term debt ($ mil.): —	Payout: 14.6%
No. of shares (mil.): 6	Market value ($ mil.): 77
Sales ($ mil): 42	

	STOCK PRICE ($) FY Close	P/E High/Low		PER SHARE ($) Earnings	Dividends	Book Value
12/12	11.29	11	7	1.09	0.16	10.94
12/11	8.10	11	8	0.86	0.13	9.98
12/10	8.06	23	16	0.38	0.12	9.52
12/09	6.59	18	11	0.40	0.12	9.31
12/08	6.07	20	14	0.44	0.12	10.79
Annual Growth	16.8%	—	—	25.5%	7.5%	0.3%

Omega Healthcare Investors, Inc.

Omega Healthcare Investors can put an end to the burdens of real-estate management. The self-administered real estate investment trust (REIT) invests in health care facilities throughout the US. It owns some 300 properties primarily long-term care facilities in about 30 states. The REIT specializes in sales/leaseback transactions in which it purchases properties owned by health care providers and leases them back to those companies (thereby freeing the health care companies from the responsibilities of real estate management). Sun Healthcare CommuniCare Health Services and Advocat are Omega Healthcare's largest tenants.

The company boosted its portfolio when it bought more than than 140 long-term care facilities from CapitalSource for approximately $565 million in cash stock and debt. The three-step deal closed in 2010.

EXECUTIVES

Chairman, Bernard J. (Bernie) Korman, age 81
Chief Executive Officer; Director, C. Taylor Pickett, age 51, $549,500 total compensation
Chief Operating Officer, Daniel J. Booth, age 49, $338,500 total compensation
SVP Operations, R. Lee Crabill Jr., age 59, $262,500 total compensation
Chief Financial Officer, Robert O. Stephenson, age 49, $272,000 total compensation
Chief Accounting Officer, Michael D. Ritz, age 44, $181,500 total compensation
Senior Vice President - Operations, Lee Crabill
Director, Stephen D. Plavin, age 53
Director, Edward Lowenthal, age 69
CEO and Director, C. Taylor Pickett, age 51
Director, Thomas F. Franke, age 83
Director, Harold J. Kloosterman, age 71
Auditors: Ernst&YoungLLP

LOCATIONS

HQ: Omega Healthcare Investors Inc.
9690 Deereco Rd. Ste. 100, Timonium MD 21093
Phone: 410-427-1700   **Fax:** 410-427-8800
Web: www.omegahealthcare.com

2009 Properties

	No.
Ohio	48
Florida	38
Texas	27
Pennsylvania	25
Louisiana	14
Tennessee	13
Arkansas	11
California	11
Alabama	10
Kentucky	10
West	10
Colorado	9
Maryland	7
Massachusetts	7
Indiana	6
Connecticut	5
North	5
Arizona	4
Georgia	4
Idaho	4
Illinois	4
Rhode	4
Nevada	3
New	3
Iowa	2
Mississippi	2
Missouri	2
Vermont	2
Washington	2
Alaska	1
New	1
Wisconsin	1
Total	**295**

PRODUCTS/OPERATIONS

2009 Sales

	$ mil.	% of total
Rental income	164	83
Nursing home income of owned & operated assets	18	9
Mortgage interest	11	6
Other	2	2
Total	**197**	**100**

COMPETITORS

G&L Realty Properties	LTC Properties
HCP	National Health Investors
Health Care REIT	Senior Housing
Healthcare Realty Trust	Properties
	Ventas

HISTORICAL FINANCIALS

Company Type: Public

Income Statement

FYE: December 31

	REVENUE ($ mil.)	NET INCOME ($ mil.)	NET PROFIT MARGIN	EMPLOYEES
12/12	350.4	120.7	34.4%	25
12/11	292.2	52.6	18.0%	24
12/10	258.3	58.4	22.6%	24
12/09	197.4	82.1	41.6%	19
12/08	193.7	78.1	40.3%	19
Annual Growth	16.0%	11.5%	—	7.1%

2012 Year-End Financials

Debt ratio: 61.2%	No. of shares (mil.): 112
Return on equity: 12.7%	Dividends
Cash ($ mil.): 1	Yield: 7.0%
Current ratio: —	Payout: 150.8%
Long-term debt ($ mil.): 1,824	Market value ($ mil.): 2,681

STOCK PRICE ($) FY Close	P/E High/Low	PER SHARE ($) Earnings	Dividends	Book Value
12/12 23.85	22 17	1.12	1.69	9.00
12/11 19.35	53 31	0.46	1.55	8.50
12/10 22.44	46 34	0.52	1.37	10.12
12/09 19.45	23 14	0.87	1.20	9.80
12/08 15.97	21 11	0.94	1.19	9.57
Annual Growth 10.5%	— —	4.5%	9.2%	(1.5%)

OmniVision Technologies Inc

OmniVision Technologies gets the big picture with a single chip. The fabless semiconductor company designs semiconductor image sensors (CameraChips) that capture and convert images for cameras mobile phones notebooks webcams surveillance equipment and medical imaging systems among other applications. Its CameraCubeChip device combines the company's image sensors with wafer-level optics for a complete camera module. OmniVision outsources manufacturing chores to silicon foundries (contract semiconductor manufacturers) primarily Taiwan Semiconductor Manufacturing Company (TSMC). Most sales are from Asia predominantly China.

Geographic Reach Asia is OmniVision's largest market with China accounting for nearly 60% of sales; South Korea Malaysia and Japan together contribute nearly 30%. The US only accounted for 7% of sales in fiscal 2012 but that was up nearly 300% from the prior year. The company attributes the rise in US sales to a temporary change in purchasing preference for one customer that it does not expect to continue.

Sales and Marketing Manufacturers and value-added resellers account about three-fourths of OmniVision's sales while distributors make up the rest. Components manufacturer LG Innotek contributes about 15% of sales and distributor World Peace International (part of WPG Holdings) accounts for more than 10%.

Financial Performance After a banner year in fiscal 2011 in which revenue grew nearly 60% the company reported revenue for fiscal 2012 (ended April) of $898 million down about 6%. The decline was primarily the result of weakness in low-resolution sensors as competition intensified to serve the entry-level mobile phone and notebook markets.

Net income was also down that year falling nearly 50% to $66 million. In addition to lower sales net income was impacted by substantial growth in research and development expenses related to new product development and amortization of the patent portfolio OmniVision acquired in 2011.

Strategy OmniVision depends on sales to customers in many markets (automotive entertainment mobile phone notebook) that are particularly vulnerable to periods of economic turmoil. In addition much of OmniVision's business is in mobile phones a highly competitive market with a handful of leading manufacturers. The company must continually develop and introduce new products for the market to remain competitive with its industry rivals. OmniVision is looking to expand in the medical and surveillance markets which are less tied to consumer buying patterns. The company is making image sensors used in disposable medical ventilation tubes. Its automotive sensors are being used in driver assistance applications including lane departure warning systems and 360 degree viewers features that are growing in popularity on new cars. Mergers and Acquisitions In a move that showcases the company's commitment to new product growth in early 2011 it bought 850 patents related to sensor imaging from Eastman Kodak for $65 million in cash in 2011. The deal doubled the size of the company's intellectual property holdings. Also that year OmniVision moved to take more control of its CameraCube technology by reclaiming the CameraCubeChip production operations from VisEra its manufacturing joint venture with TSMC.

EXECUTIVES

Chairman President and CEO, Shaw Hong, age 76, $494,167 total compensation
VP-Quality & Reliability, John T. Yue, age 66, $228,333 total compensation
SVP Global Management and General Counsel, Y. Vicky Chou, age 50, $311,667 total compensation
VP Finance and CFO, Anson H. Chan, age 44, $262,513 total compensation
COO, Henry Yang
CTO, Howard E. Rhodes
Senior Vice President - Worldwide Sales and Sales Operations, Ray Cisneros
VP Operations, Eugene Liaw
Vice President - System Technologies, John Li
Vice President - Worldwide Marketing and Business Development, Hasan Gadjali
Vice President of Product & Manufacture Engineering, Cooper Wu
Vice President - Quality and Reliability, Zille Hasnain
Senior Vice President - Global Management; General Counsel, Vicky Chou
Director, William Wen-Liang Hsu, age 55
COO and Director, Xinping (James) He, age 49
Director, Joseph Jeng, age 64
Director, Dwight Steffensen, age 69
VP Engineering and Director, Henry Yang
Auditors: PricewaterhouseCoopersLLP

LOCATIONS

HQ: OmniVision Technologies Inc.
4275 Burton Dr., Santa Clara CA 95054
Phone: 408-542-3000 **Fax:** 408-542-3001
Web: www.ovt.com

2012 Sales

	$ mil.	% of total
China	520	58
South Korea	147	16
US	61	7
Malaysia	50	6
Japan	46	5
Other countries	71	8
Total	**897**	**100**

PRODUCTS/OPERATIONS

2012 Sales

	% of total
OEMs and value-added	78
Distributors	22
Total	**100**

Selected Products

CameraCube (combines image sensors chip scale packaging and wafer-level optics)
Single-chip image sensors (CameraChip OmniPixel)
Software drivers (for Linux Mac and Windows operating systems)

COMPETITORS

Aptina
Avago Technologies
Canon
Eastman Kodak
FUJIFILM
Foveon
Freescale Semiconductor
Melexis
Mitsubishi Electric
NXP Semiconductors
Panasonic Corp
Pixelplus
Pixim
SANYO Semiconductor
SK Hynix
STMicroelectronics
Samsung Electronics
Sharp Corp.
Sony
Teledyne DALSA
Tessera
Texas Instruments
Toshiba Semiconductor & Storage Products

HISTORICAL FINANCIALS

Company Type: Public

Income Statement

FYE: April 30

	REVENUE ($ mil.)	NET INCOME ($ mil.)	NET PROFIT MARGIN	EMPLOYEES
04/13	1,407.9	42.9	3.0%	2,057
04/12	897.7	65.8	7.3%	1,796
04/11	956.4	124.4	13.0%	1,465
04/10	602.9	6.7	1.1%	1,450
04/09	507.3	(37.3)	—	1,328
Annual Growth	29.1%	—		11.6%

2013 Year-End Financials

Debt ratio: 3.2%
Return on equity: 5.3%
Cash ($ mil.): 190
Current ratio: 3.29
Long-term debt ($ mil.): 35
No. of shares (mil.): 53
Dividends
 Yield: —
 Payout: —
Market value ($ mil.): 724

	STOCK PRICE ($) FY Close	P/E High/Low	PER SHARE ($) Earnings	Dividends	Book Value
04/13	13.41	23 15	0.80	0.00	15.66
04/12	18.42	31 9	1.13	0.00	14.53
04/11	33.59	16 7	2.11	0.00	12.96
04/10	17.56	149 64	0.13	0.00	10.25
04/09	9.51	— —	(0.74)	0.00	9.77
Annual Growth	9.0%	— —	—	—	12.5%

Omnova Solutions Inc

OMNOVA Solutions is not quite omnipresent but it does manufacture and sell performance chemicals and decorative surfaces around the world. It is an innovator of emulsion polymers in dry powder and latex forms specialty chemicals and also decorative and functional surfaces for a variety of commercial industrial and residential end uses. The performance chemicals segment produces emulsion polymers and specialty chemicals to makers of paper carpet and textiles. The decorative products segment makes vinyl- and paper-based wall coverings coated fabrics laminates and films.

Sales and Marketing

Major performance chemical customers include Sherwin Williams RPM Rhodia PPG PGI Freudenburg Hyosung Shurtape Xerox and Fiberweb. Decorative products customers include Armstrong CGT BYD Ashley Furniture Patrick Industries Herculite and Masco.

Geographic Reach

The company serves the global marketplace from 10 chemical production facilities in Europe Asia and North America. It has strategically located manufacturing plants in China France India Thailand and the US.

Financial Performance

OMNOVA's revenues increased by 54% in 2011 driven by net sales from the ELIOKEM acquisition and performance chemicals' stronger net sales because of higher selling prices and foreign currency translation effects partially offset by lower decorative products' net sales decreased primarily due to weaker volumes.

Net income dropped by 103% in 2011 due to an increase in interest expense due to higher borrowing levels and higher interest rates for the company's refinancing activities in 2010 to facilitate the ELIOKEM acquisition. Other factors included a decrease in gross profit margin due to raw material price inflation the impact of performance chemicals index pricing (in which raw material costs were passed on to the customer) contractual time lags new plant start-up costs and changes in the product mix.

The company has made significant inroads into Asian markets in the past few years. OMNOVA acquired full ownership of existing joint ventures in Singapore and in Thailand —both in OMNOVA's decorative products segment —to provide increased access to the region's emerging economies. As a result by 2011 sales to Asia jumped to 16% of OMNOVA's total sales; prior to 2008 Asian business added up to less than 1%.

Strategy

To focus on its higher value operations OMNOVA has been divesting its commercial wallcovering businesses. In late 2011 it sold some of its North American wallcovering operations to J. Josephon and in 2012 sold its UK-based Muraspec wallcovering business to a2e Venture Catalysts. The divestments which have netted the company about $10 million for the North American business and $6.2 million for the UK business allow OMNOVA to focus on its global performance chemicals unit and the coated fabrics laminates and performance films operations within its decorative products unit.

The company acquired specialty chemicals manufacturer ELIOKEM International from AXA Private Equity in 2011 for $300 million. The deal creates a larger more diverse company by adding manufacturing capabilities in Europe and Asia to OMNOVA's production facilities in the US. France-based ELIOKEM is now part of OMNOVA's performance chemicals business. As part of the ELOKEM integration in 2012 OMNOVA expanded manufacturing capability for its Pliotec water-based acrylic coating resins to include three locations in the US.

In 2010 OMNOVA acquired Dow Chemical's hollow sphere plastic pigment or HPP product line.

At the same time the company terminated its RohmNova joint venture with partner Rohm and Haas which was acquired by Dow. The JV in place since 2002 made and marketed coated paper and paperboard. The acquired HPP business serve the same markets.

Ownership

FMR LLC owns 15% of the company.

EXECUTIVES

Senior Vice President and Chief Financial Officer, Michael E. Hicks, age 55, $301,154 total compensation

Chairman Chief Executive Officer and President, Kevin M. McMullen, age 53, $657,523 total compensation

President - Engineered Surfaces, David (Dave) Maynard

Senior Vice President and Chief Information Officer, Douglas E. Wenger, age 57, $229,600 total compensation

Senior Vice President; President - Performance Chemicals, James J. Hohman, age 65, $274,046 total compensation

Vice President - Global Sourcing and Logistics, Jay T. Austin

Senior Vice President; Chief Human Resources Officer, Michael A Quinn

Director, William R. Seelbach, age 65

Director, Larry B. Porcellato, age 54

Director, David J. D'Antoni, age 67

Director, Robert A. (Bob) Stefanko, age 71

Director, Michael J. (Mike) Merriman Jr., age 57

Director, Steven W. Percy, age 67

Director, Allan R. Rothwell, age 65

Independent Director, David DAntoni

Auditors: Ernst&YoungLLP

LOCATIONS

HQ: OMNOVA Solutions Inc.
175 Ghent Rd., Fairlawn OH 44333-3300
Phone: 330-869-4200   **Fax:** 412-454-5555
Web: www.moai.com

2011 Sales

US		
Export	11	1
Asia	198	16

PRODUCTS/OPERATIONS

2011 Sales

Performance Chemicals

Paper & Carpet Chemicals	399	33
Coated Fabrics	147	12

Selected Products

Performance Chemicals
Adhesives
Binders
Coatings
Latex
Lubricants
Pigments
Resins
Saturants
Decorative Products
Coated fabrics
Decorative laminates
Graphic arts and industrial films
Wallcoverings

COMPETITORS

Air Products	Dai Nippon Printing
BASF SE	Dow Chemical
Celanese	Lubrizol
Chiyoda Corp.	RJF International

HISTORICAL FINANCIALS

Company Type: Public

Income Statement

FYE: November 30

	REVENUE ($ mil.)	NET INCOME ($ mil.)	NET PROFIT MARGIN	EMPLOYEES
11/13	1,018.1	19.6	1.9%	2,300
11/12	1,125.5	27.6	2.5%	2,390
11/11	1,201.1	(2.8)	—	2,300
11/10	846.2	107.9	12.8%	2,430
11/09	696.4	26.2	3.8%	2,320
Annual Growth	10.0%	(7.0%)	—	(0.2%)

2013 Year-End Financials

Debt ratio: 52.4%
Return on equity: 12.7%
Cash ($ mil.): 164
Current ratio: 3.17
Long-term debt ($ mil.): 444

No. of shares (mil.): 47
Dividends
  Yield: —
  Payout: —
Market value ($ mil.): 413

	STOCK PRICE ($) FY Close	P/E High/Low		PER SHARE ($) Earnings	Dividends	Book Value
11/13	8.76	21	15	0.42	0.00	3.77
11/12	7.42	14	7	0.60	0.00	2.78
11/11	4.35	—	—	(0.06)	0.00	2.66
11/10	8.78	4	2	2.40	0.00	2.74
11/09	6.62	13	1	0.61	0.00	0.34
Annual Growth	7.3%	—	—	(8.9%)	—	82.5%

On Assignment, Inc.

Attention scientists: Tired of unreliable assistants? Try On Assignment. The specialist staffing agency places scientists and other professionals from lab assistants to nurses with clients in need of temporary help. The firm operates through several divisions: Apex (IT and engineering staffing for temporary temp-to-hire and permanent placements); Healthcare (nurse travel clinical lab diagnostic and imaging staffing services); Life Sciences (scientists chemists technicians); Oxford (engineering and specialized high-end IT consultants); and Physician (short- and long-term physician staffing). On Assignment provides staff to more than 6500 clients and was founded in 1985.

Geographic Reach

The company operates from about 130 branch offices in nearly 35 states and seven foreign countries including Belgium Canada China Ireland the Netherlands Spain and the UK. The US accounts for nearly 95% of its total sales.

Operations

On Assignment has changed its operating structure due to milestone acquisitions it has made over the last few years. Its chief operating segments include Apex (41% of total sales) Oxford (28%) Life Sciences (13%) Healthcare (10%) and Physician (8%).

Financial Performance

The company has enjoyed unprecedented growth over the last two years primarily due to acquisitions. Its revenues doubled from $598 million in 2011 to $1.2 billion in 2012. Profits also climbed 76% from $24 million in 2011 to nearly $43 million in 2012. Both these totals for 2012 represented historic milestones for the company.

Its 2012 purchase of Apex Systems was the main driver of growth in addition to 22% year-over-year growth from its other business segments. Its Oxford segment revenues jumped 30% due to an increase in the average number of contract professionals on assignment and a rise in the average bill rate and in conversion and permanent placement revenue.

Healthcare segment revenues in 2012 were up by 27% due to improved conditions within the healthcare sector resulting in a higher number of contract professionals on assignment and open orders and average bill rates. The 27% increase in Physician segment revenue was attributable to the inclusion of a full year's operating results from HCP an acquisition it made in 2011 and a nearly $8 million increase in its legacy physician business. Its Life Sciences segment revenues were also up by 5% during 2012.

Strategy

On Assignment's business strategy involves steady growth through targeted acquisitions. Since its founding it has purchased more than a dozen companies. In 2012 the company made its most meaningful acquisition to date with the purchase of Apex Systems the sixth largest staffing firm and one of the fastest growing IT staffing firms in the US for $600 million. The deal represented efforts to fortify its most lucrative segment the IT and engineering industry. The company sees the sector growing by 12% over the years while other industries shrink or remain stable.

On Assignment in 2011 obtained Valesta a provider of clinical research specialized staffing services with headquarters in Belgium and additional offices in Spain and The Netherlands. It also improved its Physician segment that year with the $19 million purchase of HealthCare Partners (HCP) a physician staffing firm based in Atlanta.

In early 2013 On Assignment sold its Nurse Travel business to focus on its five core business segments. It believes the nurse staffing market is a relatively small sector and is contracting at a much quicker pace than other specialized staffing spheres.

HISTORY

Chemists Bruce Culver and Raf Dahlquist concocted the company in 1985. Lab Support (its original name) got off to a good start but the founders were scientists not business strategists; by 1989 the company was losing steam. The firm's venture investors took over installing new management under Tom Buelter who had developed Kelly Services' home care division. He refocused operations to temporary scientific services and turned the company around. It went public in 1992 as On Assignment.

In 1994 On Assignment bought 1st Choice Personnel and Sklar Resource Group which specialized in temporary placement of financial professionals. The next year it started its Advanced Science Professionals unit to place temps in highly skilled scientific positions. With the 1996 purchase of Minneapolis-based EnviroStaff On Assignment also began providing temporary workers in environmental fields. On Assignment crossed the border and started operations in Canada in 1997. In 1999 it established Clinical Lab Staff as its fourth division. Also by 1999 the company had opened the first three of several planned European offices in the UK.

In 2001 Buelter relinquished the CEO position to Joe Peterson. (Buelter resigned as chairman early the following year.) Also in 2002 the company acquired Health Personnel Options Corporation a provider of temporary travel nurses and other health care professionals. The end of 2003

saw the appointment of Peter Dameris as the president and CEO of On Assignment.

In 2007 On Assignment reached new levels of growth with the key acquisitions of IT and engineering staffing provider Oxford Global Resources and physician staffing firm VISTA Staffing Solutions.

As with most players in the staffing sector On Assignment felt the painful effects of the global recession in 2008 and 2009 as it was hurt by high unemployment rates and shrinking demand for its staffing services.

As the economy began to pick up in 2010 On Assignment bought The Cambridge Group Ltd. a staffing services firm placing physicians clinical and scientific personnel and IT professionals. Also that year the company acquired Sharpstream a firm with expertise in search services for executive to middle managers residing in the life sciences sector. The deal added offices in the US the UK and Shanghai.

Continuing its string of acquisitions in 2011 On Assignment obtained Valesta a provider of clinical research specialized staffing services with headquarters in Belgium and additional offices in Spain and The Netherlands. The company next acquired Apex Systems the sixth largest staffing firm and one of the fastest growing IT staffing firms in the US in 2012.

EXECUTIVES

President Apex, Randolph C. (Rand) Blazer, age 63
Chief Financial Officer and Executive Vice President, Edward L. Pierce, age 57
Senior Vice President Chief Administrative Officer and Treasurer, James L. Brill, age 61, $293,760 total compensation
Chairman, Jeremy M. Jones, age 71
President CEO and Director, Peter T. Dameris, age 53, $635,250 total compensation
SVP Shared Services and CIO, Michael C. Payne, $216,000 total compensation
President Life Sciences and Allied Divisions, Emmett B. McGrath, age 51, $316,200 total compensation
Chief Operating Officer; President Oxford Global Resources, Michael J. McGowan, age 60, $345,000 total compensation
Vice President - Finance; Corporate Controller, Christina Gibson
VP Recruiting, Carol McNamara
VP-HR, Angela Kolarek
VP-Support Svcs, Karen Keppel
VP and General Counsel, Tarini Ramaprakash
President On Assignment Nurse Travel and EVP President On Assignment Nurse Travel and VISTA Physician International, Kathryn Hoffman-Abby
President VISTA Staffing Solutions, Christian Rutherford
Finance Administrator, Debbie Tiberi
Chief Financial Officer and Executive Vice President, Edward L. Pierce, age 57
Director, William E. (Bill) Brock, age 83
Director, Jonathan S. Holman, age 68
President CEO and Director, Peter T. Dameris, age 53
Independent Director, Marty Kittrell
Auditors: Deloitte&ToucheLLP

LOCATIONS

HQ: On Assignment Inc.
  26745 Malibu Hills Rd., Calabasas CA 91301
Phone: 818-878-7900   **Fax:** 818-871-3001
Web: www.thecheesecakefactory.com

2012 Sales

US	1,161	94
Total	**1,239**	**100**

PRODUCTS/OPERATIONS

2012 Sales

Apex	508	41
Oxford	345	28
Healthcare	120	10
Total	**1,239**	**100**

Selected Divisions and Operating Units

Apex (IT staffing)
On Assignment Allied Travel
On Assignment Clinical Research
On Assignment Engineering
On Assignment Healthcare Staffing
On Assignment Health Information Management
On Assignment Lab Support
Oxford Global Resources (IT and engineering staffing)
VISTA Staffing Solutions (physician staffing)

COMPETITORS

AMN Healthcare	Insight Global
ATC Healthcare	Kelly Services
Accenture	Kforce
Adecco	ManpowerGroup
Aerotek	Medical Staffing
Allegis Group	Network
CHG Healthcare	Professional Staff
Cross Country	RehabCare
Healthcare	Robert Half
Day & Zimmermann	TEKsystems
IBM	The Everhart Group

HISTORICAL FINANCIALS

Company Type: Public

Income Statement

FYE: December 31

	REVENUE ($ mil.)	NET INCOME ($ mil.)	NET PROFIT MARGIN	EMPLOYEES
12/12	1,239.7	42.6	3.4%	34,530
12/11	597.2	24.3	4.1%	15,511
12/10	438.0	(9.9)	—	12,530
12/09	416.6	4.7	1.1%	13,815
12/08	618.0	18.9	3.1%	17,373
Annual Growth	19.0%	22.5%	—	18.7%

2012 Year-End Financials

Debt ratio: 38.8%
Return on equity: 10.9%
Cash ($ mil.): 27
Current ratio: 2.47
Long-term debt ($ mil.): 416

No. of shares (mil.): 52
Dividends
  Yield: —
  Payout: —
Market value ($ mil.): 1,074

	STOCK PRICE ($) FY Close	P/E High/Low		Earnings	Dividends	Book Value
12/12	20.28	23	12	0.89	0.00	10.06
12/11	11.18	18	10	0.64	0.00	6.67
12/10	8.15	—	—	(0.27)	0.00	6.03
12/09	7.15	57	11	0.13	0.00	6.25
12/08	5.67	18	8	0.53	0.00	6.12
Annual Growth	37.5%			— 13.8%	—	— 13.2%

OpenTable Inc.

Even if your favorite restaurant is closed for the day you can still try to reserve a table through OpenTable. The firm provides online reservations at about 27000 upscale restaurants around the world. The service is free to diners but OpenTable charges participating restaurants an installation and monthly license fee for its Electronic Reservation Book (ERB) a computerized reservation system. It also provides training and support for ERB and charges a fee for tables booked through Connect a Web-based solution for reservations with less functionality than ERB. Since its founding in 1998 OpenTable has seated more than 200 million diners.

Geographic Reach

OpenTable operates in the US Canada and Mexico as well as Germany Japan and the UK.

Operations

The company's operations are divided in to two geographic segments: North America and International. The North America segment is comprised of operations in the US Canada and Mexico while the International segment is comprised of all non-North America operations which includes operations in select countries in Europe and Asia. North America is the largest market accounting for approximately 85% of revenues.

Sales and Marketing

Restaurants pay between $200-$300 per month for an OpenTable subscription; they pay $2.50 for each reservation made through Connect and $1 per diner booked directly through OpenTable.com.

The company markets its service through a direct sales force and sales representatives. OpenTable also benefits from word-of-mouth referrals and natural-search traffic to its websites and mobile apps. The company runs a point-based loyalty program to encourage repeat usage.

OpenTable itself spent about $3 million on advertising and promotional activities during fiscal 2012.

Financial Performance

The company's revenues increased 16% and its net income increased 11% in fiscal 2012 compared with 2011. Net cash inflow increased by $63 million in 2012 compared with the prior year.

Strategy

The company began the mobile app push in 2008 when it launched the product allowing users to book reservations from their mobile phones including Apple's iPhone. OpenTable also expanded its offerings when it began providing restaurant lists based on user reviews. Other growth strategies include adding more restaurants to its North American Network which includes the US Mexico and Canada as well as plans for international expansion.

Mergers and Acquisitions

In 2012 OpenTable acquired San Francisco-based Treat Technologies for $4 million in cash. Treat Technologies is a provider of the Treatful-branded online gift card solutions for restaurants. OpenTable will integrate Treatful's online gift card business for local restaurants into its existing technology and services.

EXECUTIVES

SVP Engineering, Charles (Charlie) McCullough, age 62, $235,000 total compensation
President OpenTable Japan KK, Masao Tejima

Senior Vice President Business Development, Douglas Boake
Chief Executive Officer, Matthew (Matt) Roberts, age 45, $225,000 total compensation
SVP Operations, Joel Brown, age 52, $225,000 total compensation
Managing Director, Michael Xenakis
Senior Vice President Sales, Michael Dodson, age 55, $175,000 total compensation
SVP and Managing Director Europe, David Pritchard
Chief Financial Officer, Duncan Robertson, age 46
Senior Vice President Marketing, Ann Shepherd
Vice President Industry Relations, Chris Wood
Vice President Consumer Product Management, Jocelyn Mangan
Senior Vice President General Counsel, John Orta
Chief Technology Officer, Joseph Essas
Senior Vice President - Engineering, Charlie McCullough
Vice President Restaurant Products, Elizabeth Casey
Vice President International Development, Catherine Porter
Vice President Customer Experience, Karen Barker
Vice President People & Culture, Natasha Kehimkar
Director, Paul S. Pressler, age 56
Director, A. George (Skip) Battle, age 70
Director, Danny Meyer, age 55
President CEO and Director, Matthew (Matt) Roberts, age 43
Director, Michelle A. Peluso, age 42
Director, J. William (Bill) Gurley, age 45
Director, Adam R. Dell, age 42
Director, Thomas H. Layton, age 51
Auditors: Deloitte&ToucheLLP

LOCATIONS

HQ: OpenTable Inc.
799 Market St. 4th Fl., San Francisco CA 94103
Phone: 415-344-4200   **Fax:** 415-267-0944
Web: www.opentable.com

2012 Sales

North America	139	86
Total	**161**	**100**

PRODUCTS/OPERATIONS

2012 Sales

Reservations	91	56
Installation & other	14	9

Selected Offerings

Connect
ERB
Mobile applications
OpenTable website
Spotlight

COMPETITORS

CityGrid Media	SavvyDiner.com
Groupon	Time Out Group
LivingSocial	Yelp
Restaurant.com	Zagat

HISTORICAL FINANCIALS

Company Type: Public

Income Statement

FYE: December 31

	REVENUE ($ mil.)	NET INCOME ($ mil.)	NET PROFIT MARGIN	EMPLOYEES
12/12	161.6	23.9	14.8%	580
12/11	139.5	21.5	15.4%	558
12/10	98.9	14.0	14.2%	493
12/09	68.6	5.0	7.4%	198
12/08	55.8	(1.0)	—	304
Annual Growth	**30.4%**	—		**17.5%**

2012 Year-End Financials

Debt ratio: —	No. of shares (mil.): 22
Return on equity: 17.1%	Dividends
Cash ($ mil.): 102	Yield: —
Current ratio: 2.96	Payout: —
Long-term debt ($ mil.): —	Market value ($ mil.): 1,117

	STOCK PRICE ($) FY Close	P/E High/Low		PER SHARE ($) Earnings	Dividends	Book Value
12/12	48.80	49	32	1.03	0.00	7.33
12/11	39.13	126	35	0.88	0.00	4.85
12/10	70.48	119	40	0.58	0.00	4.38
12/09	25.46	121	88	0.22	0.00	3.27
Annual Growth	**24.2%**	—	—	**67.3%**	—	**30.9%**

ORBCOMM Inc

ORBCOMM uses its fleet of 26 low-Earth-orbit (LEO) satellites to help businesses keep an eye on their earthbound assets. The system's two-way data transmission capabilities enable users to track vehicles and mobile equipment monitor fixed assets such as utility meters and pipelines and communicate with mobile and remote workers around the globe. It also provides machine-to-machine (M2M) communications and telematics services. Key clients include heavy equipment makers Caterpillar (about 20% of sales) Komatsu (10% of sales) and Hitachi (10% of sales). The company also serves government customers with Automatic Identification System (AIS) data services for marine vessel tracking.

Geographic Reach

Headquartered in New Jersey the company's network control center is located in Dulles Virginia. While it has international offices in Argentina Australia Japan Malaysia and South Africa ORBCOMM gets more than 80% of sales from customers in the US.

Sales and Marketing

For its satellite-based data and terrestrial-based cellular communications services ORBCOMM markets to end users directly and indirectly through resellers such I.D. Systems inthinc Technology Solutions and American Innovations.

The company counts some 759000 billable subscribers in 2012 up from 648000 in 2011.

Financial Performance

Overall sales grew 40% to $64.5 million in 2012 due to both organic and inorganic growth.

It was also the first year ORBCOMM turned a profit recording $8.7 million in net revenue. Previously ORBCOMM has lost money every year since its inception citing the high cost associated with maintaining a satellite network particularly in the areas of satellite launch and construction.

Strategy

ORBCOMM teamed up with satellite heavyweight Inmarsat in 2013 to collaborate on product development and distribution capabilities for the growing satellite M2M market.

The company hopes to increase sales and move closer to profitability by expanding its reseller network and pushing into new territories.

Mergers and Acquisitions

The company has grown through several acquisitions. In 2013 alone it bought three divisions of other companies beginning with the GlobalTrak division of System Planning Corporation. GlobalTrak is an information services company that provides intelligence to improve logistics and security processes to military international government and commercial customers. Next it bought MobileNet one of its longtime resellers which allows ORBCOMM to offer MobileNet's fleet management products directly to OEMs dealers and fleet owners.

Also that year it bought Comtech's Sensor Enabled Notification System (SENS) business which includes satellite hardware network technology and web platforms. SENS provides one-way satellite products and services to more than 20000 subscribers worldwide.

As a result of acquisitions in 2011 and in 2012 ORBCOMM expanded its products and services in the cold chain telematics business that allows customers to monitor manage and remotely control refrigerated assets. In 2012 it bought PAR Logistics Management Systems which offers monitoring technology for transportation and distribution companies from PAR Technology for about $6 million.

In 2011 it bought the GPS tracking business of holding company Alanco for $18.5 million in cash and stock. Known as StarTrak Information Technologies the business provides subscription-based GPS tracking data services for the refrigerated transport industry in North America. StarTrak operates as a subsidiary of ORBCOMM.

EXECUTIVES

Chairman, Jerome B. Eisenberg, age 73, $256,500 total compensation
Executive Vice President Technology and Operations, John J. Stolte Jr., age 54, $236,250 total compensation
Executive Vice President Chief Financial Officer, Robert G. Costantini, age 54, $283,500 total compensation
CEO and Director, Marc J. Eisenberg, age 47, $356,437 total compensation
Executive Vice President General Counsel, Christian G. Le Brun, age 45, $201,300 total compensation
EVP Sales and Marketing, Brian Bell
Executive Vice President General Counsel, Christian Brun
Director, Didier J. Delepine, age 65
Director, John E. Major, age 67
Director, Gary H. Ritondaro, age 67
Director, Hans E.W. Hoffmann, age 78
CEO and Director, Marc J. Eisenberg, age 47
Director, Marco Fuchs, age 51
Director, Timothy Kelleher, age 51
Director, Lt. Gen. John R. (Bob) Wood, age 63
Auditors: Deloitte&ToucheLLP

LOCATIONS

HQ: ORBCOMM Inc.
2115 Linwood Ave. Ste. 100, Fort Lee NJ 07024
Phone: 703-433-6300   **Fax:** 703-433-6400
Web: www.orbcomm.com

2012 Sales

	% of total
US	82
Japan	15
Other	3
Total	**100**

PRODUCTS/OPERATIONS

2012 Sales

	% of total
Services	76
Products	24
Total	**100**

COMPETITORS

Globalstar	QUALCOMM
Inmarsat	TerreStar
Iridium	

HISTORICAL FINANCIALS

Company Type: Public

Income Statement

FYE: December 31

	REVENUE ($ mil.)	NET INCOME ($ mil.)	NET PROFIT MARGIN	EMPLOYEES
12/12	64.5	8.7	13.6%	162
12/11	46.3	(0.0)	—	136
12/10	36.6	(5.1)	—	99
12/09	27.5	(3.4)	—	101
12/08	30.0	(4.5)	—	108
Annual Growth	**21.0%**	**—**	**—**	**10.7%**

2012 Year-End Financials

Debt ratio: 2.3%
Return on equity: 4.9%
Cash ($ mil.): 34
Current ratio: 4.76
Long-term debt ($ mil.): 4
No. of shares (mil.): 46
Dividends
Yield: —
Payout: —
Market value ($ mil.): 183

	STOCK PRICE ($) FY Close	P/E High/Low	PER SHARE ($) Earnings	Dividends	Book Value
12/12	3.92	21 15	0.18	0.00	3.91
12/11	2.99	— —	(0.00)	0.00	3.75
12/10	2.59	— —	(0.12)	0.00	3.72
12/09	2.70	— —	(0.08)	0.00	3.75
12/08	2.16	— —	(0.11)	0.00	3.84
Annual Growth	**16.1%**	**— —**	**—**	**—**	**0.4%**

Oritani Financial Corp (DE)

Oritani Financial could give an oratory on local banking in New Jersey. The holding company owns Oritani Bank which offers retail and commercial deposit and loan banking services from about 25 locations in several Garden State counties. Oritani Financial specializes in multi-family and commercial real estate lending which make up more than half of its loan portfolio. Oritani Financial also writes one- to four-family and second mortgages as well as equity and construction loans. It invests in real property through its Hampshire Financial Oritani LLC and Ormon divisions; Oritani Asset is a real estate investment trust (REIT). Century-old Oritani Bank has more than $2 billion in assets.

Geographic Reach

Oritani Bank has 25 full-service branches in Bergen Essex Hudson and Passaic counties in New Jersey.

Financial Performance

The bank's 2012 (ends June) revenue increased 4% vs. the prior year and net income grew by 11% over the same period. The revenue increase was due to a 4% jump in interest income. partially offset by a nearly 1% drop in non-interest income. Fiscal 2012 marked Oritani Bank's eighth consecutive year of increasing revenue although growth has slowed somewhat. The increase in net income in 2012 was primarily due to a higher net interest spread and a larger asset base.

Strategy

Oritani Bank is expanding its branch network. It recently opened new branches in Ramsey Upper Montclair and Clifton New Jersey.

EXECUTIVES

EVP COO and Director, Michael A. DeBernardi, age 59, $263,846 total compensation
Chairman President and CEO, Kevin J. Lynch, age 67, $550,750 total compensation
SVP Retail Banking, Anthony V. Bilotta Jr., age 53
SVP and Secretary, Philip M. Wyks, age 59, $191,181 total compensation
Chief Financial Officer; Executive Vice President, John M. Fields Jr., age 50, $211,077 total compensation
Executive Vice President; Chief Lending Officer, Thomas Guinan, age 49, $211,077 total compensation
VP and Chief Residential Loan Officer, Paul M. Cordero, age 58
SVP and Human Resources Officer, Anne Mooradian, age 52
VP Commercial Lending, Leonard Carlucci, age 49, $140,352 total compensation
SVP and Chief Compliance Officer, Rosanne P. Buscemi, age 61
VP and Principal Accounting Officer, Ann Marie Jetton, age 47
VP and CIO, Paul C. Skinner, age 51
VP Commercial Lending, Daniel Schapira
VP Commercial Lending, Matthew Carcich
VP Commercial Lending, Joe Laquidara
VP Commercial Lending, David Garcia
Commercial Lender, David May
Commercial Lender, Christopher Carola
SVP Chief Credit Officer, Louis A. Manderino
Administrative Assistant, Eralba Manno
Vice President, Bing Luh
Vice President, John Pagano
Administrative Assistant, Joanne Roszkowski
Administrative Assistant, Kamille Shyroky
Vice President, Richard Bianchi
Vice President, Christopher Canlas
EVP COO and Director, Michael A. DeBernardi, age 59
Director, James J. Doyle Jr., age 63
Director, Nicholas Antonaccio, age 66
Director, Robert S. Hekemian Jr., age 53
Director, John J. Skelly Jr., age 73
Auditors: KPMGLLP

LOCATIONS

HQ: Oritani Financial Corp.
370 Pascack Rd., Washington Township NJ 07676
Phone: 201-664-5400 **Fax:** -3975
Web: www.cpu.edu.ph

PRODUCTS/OPERATIONS

2012 Sales

	$ mil.	% of total
Interest		
Mortgage loans	108	85
Interest on securities available for sale	11	9
Interest on securities held & dividends	2	2
Federal funds sold & short-term investments	0	
Noninterest		
Bank-owned life insurance	1	1
Real estate operations	1	1
Service charges	1	1
Other	1	1
Total	**127**	**100**

COMPETITORS

1st Colonial Bancorp	Sun Bancorp (NJ)
Hudson City Bancorp	Valley National
OceanFirst Financial	Bancorp
Provident Financial	
Services	

HISTORICAL FINANCIALS

Company Type: Public

Income Statement
FYE: June 30

	REVENUE ($ mil.)	NET INCOME ($ mil.)	NET PROFIT MARGIN	EMPLOYEES
06/13	133.0	39.5	29.7%	212
06/12	127.3	31.6	24.8%	217
06/11	122.8	28.5	23.2%	206
06/10	110.8	8.3	7.5%	207
06/09	91.2	5.5	6.1%	202
Annual Growth	**9.9%**	**63.4%**	**—**	**1.2%**

2013 Year-End Financials

Debt ratio: 29.4%
Return on equity: 7.6%
Cash ($ mil.): 12
Current ratio: 0.30
Long-term debt ($ mil.): 833

No. of shares (mil.): 45
Dividends
  Yield: 0.0%
  Payout: 111.4%
Market value ($ mil.): 712

	STOCK PRICE ($) FY Close	P/E High/Low	PER SHARE ($) Earnings	Dividends	Book Value
06/13	15.68	17 15	0.92	1.03	11.43
06/12	14.39	21 16	0.71	0.50	11.30
06/11	12.79	24 17	0.54	0.38	11.63
06/10	10.00	69 68	0.15	0.00	11.45
Annual Growth	**16.2%**	**— —**	**83.0%**	**—**	**(0.1%)**

OSI Systems, Inc. (DE)

OSI Systems is keeping a close scan on transportation security and health care worldwide. The company's security division manufactures specialized inspection equipment under the Rapiscan Systems name used to screen everything from baggage and people to cargo and vehicles at airports ports and borders. Its Spacelabs Healthcare subsidiary makes patient monitoring cardiac monitor-

ing and clinical networking systems primarily for hospitals. A third division makes optoelectronic devices (OSI Optoelectronics) for aerospace/defense electronics industrial automation security medical diagnostics and other applications. That division also offers contract electronics manufacturing services (OSI Electronics).

Geographic Reach

The company maintains manufacturing research and development and sales operations in North America Europe Asia and Australia.

Operations

Security is OSI Systems' largest segment accounting for almost half of annual revenues. Offering a broad range of screening technologies Rapiscan Systems has built a solid reputation for its inspection systems having been installed in such security-tight locations as Buckingham Palace the Kremlin the Vatican and high-profile events such as the Olympic Games and the World Cup.

Meanwhile its health care division is focused on designing products that make critical patient information more readily accessible both within and outside of a hospital. Its optoelectronic products and manufacturing services are geared at OEM customers in need of specialized electronic components. They also serve OSI Systems' own security and health care divisions.

Sales and Marketing

There products are sold by direct sales and marketing representatives and by a network of independent distributors. Major customers within its security segment include the Transportation Security Administration the Bureau of Prisons and various international airports around the globe. Health care and optoelectronic customers include Eisenhower Medical Center and Honeywell respectively.

Financial Analysis

OSI Systems' revenues increased 21% to some $793 million due to increased sales in all of its operating segments primarily from new security contracts and a larger base of installed equipment in the health care and optoelectronics segments. Net income also increased by 36% to $46 million that year.

Strategy

In the security division OSI Systems depends on the growing needs of the international government security markets. It expands in this segment by forming new supply contracts with government agencies; for instance it entered new contracts with the US Army (for vehicle inspection and personal screening products) and the Mexican customs authority (for cargo and vehicle screening equipment) during 2011 and 2012.

OSI Systems believes demand for patient monitoring systems and other health solutions will continue to grow in the US market (and other developing countries) due to an aging population as well as in developing nations where health care infrastructures are being built and expanded. As such its research programs focus on new products such as the 2011 launch of the elance critical care monitor.

EXECUTIVES

EVP and Director OSI Systems; President Rapiscan Systems, Ajay Mehra, age 52, $380,000 total compensation
Chairman and CEO, Deepak Chopra, age 62, $1,000,000 total compensation
EVP and CFO, Alan I. Edrick, age 45, $355,000 total compensation
EVP General Counsel and Secretary, Victor S. Sze, $330,000 total compensation

President Spacelabs Healthcare, Nicholas Ong, age 49
President Optoelectronics Division, Manoocher Mansouri, $250,000 total compensation
VP Business Development, Ajay Vashishat
EVP OSI Systems and President, Ajay Merhra
Director, Meyer Luskin, age 88
EVP and Director OSI Systems; President Rapiscan Systems, Ajay Mehra, age 52
Director, Steven C. (Steve) Good, age 71
Director, David T. Feinberg, age 51
Director, William F. Ballhaus Jr.
Auditors: MossAdamsLLP

LOCATIONS

HQ: OSI Systems Inc.
12525 Chadron Ave., Hawthorne CA 90250
Phone: 310-978-0516 **Fax:** 650-238-2312
Web: www.futureus.com

2012 Sales

	$ mil.	% of total
North America	552	66
Europe	153	18
Asia	132	16
Adjustments	(45.2)	
Total	**793**	**100**

PRODUCTS/OPERATIONS

2012 Sales

	$ mil.	% of total
Security	391	47
Healthcare	235	28
Optoelectronics & manufacturing	210	25
Adjustments	(45.2)	-
Total	**793**	**100**

Selected Products

Rapiscan Systems (Security segment)
  Gamma ray screeners (for detecting weapons explosives drugs & other hidden contraband)
  Metal detectors (for screening people)
  Neutron scanners (for detecting elemental ingredients in inspected objects)
  Passive millimeter wave scanners (for detecting concealed objects against wave energy emitted by the human body)
  Real-time tomography screeners (for detecting liquid explosives)
  X-ray screeners (for detecting weapons explosives drugs & other hidden contraband)
Spacelabs Healthcare (Healthcare segment)
  ARKON anesthesia delivery systems
  Blease anesthesia ventilators
  CardioDirect Stress Testing System
  CardioExpress ECG machines (cardiac monitors)
  XPREZZON patient monitors
  Sentinel Cardiology Data Management
  Vaporizers
OSI Optoelectronics (Optoelectronics segment)
  Blood pressure cuffs (medical devices and instrumentation)
  Bone densitometers (for measuring bone density in individuals with osteoporosis)
  Filters lenses mirrors prisms (passive components for copiers printers microscopes telescopes and other detection/vision equipment)
  Fluid delivery unifusors (medical devices and instrumentation)
  Laser-based remote sensing devices (for detecting vehicles in toll and traffic management systems)
  Oximetry sensors and accessories (medical devices and instrumentation)
  Photodetectors (active component for use in copiers laser printers microscopes telescopes and other detection and vision equipment)

COMPETITORS

American Science and Engineering	L-3 Communications Leidos

Analogic
Benchmark Electronics
CTS Corp.
Cardiac Science
  Corporation
Celestica
Criticare
Dragerwerk
GE Healthcare
Hamamatsu Photonics
Jabil

Maquet
Mindray
Optek Technology
Orthometrix
PerkinElmer
Philips Healthcare
Plexus
Ranger Security
  Detectors
Smiths Detection

HISTORICAL FINANCIALS

Company Type: Public

Income Statement

FYE: June 30

	REVENUE ($ mil.)	NET INCOME ($ mil.)	NET PROFIT MARGIN	EMPLOYEES
06/13	802.0	44.1	5.5%	5,200
06/12	792.9	45.5	5.7%	3,900
06/11	656.1	33.4	5.1%	3,700
06/10	595.1	23.5	4.0%	3,183
06/09	590.3	11.1	1.9%	3,151
Annual Growth	8.0%	41.0%	—	13.3%

2013 Year-End Financials

Debt ratio: 7.7%
Return on equity: 9.6%
Cash ($ mil.): 34
Current ratio: 1.87
Long-term debt ($ mil.): 10

No. of shares (mil.): 19
Dividends
  Yield: —
  Payout: —
Market value ($ mil.): 1,283

	STOCK PRICE ($) FY Close	P/E High/Low		PER SHARE ($) Earnings	Dividends	Book Value
06/13	64.42	37	23	2.15	0.00	24.03
06/12	63.34	29	14	2.24	0.00	21.90
06/11	43.00	24	14	1.71	0.00	19.73
06/10	27.77	24	12	1.28	0.00	17.12
06/09	20.85	40	16	0.63	0.00	15.85
Annual Growth	32.6%	—	—	35.9%	—	11.0%

Outerwall Inc

Outerwall (formerly Coinstar) takes its name from the previously underutilized "fourth wall" area between the cash registers and the front door in retail stores. The company began as an operator of coin-counting machines but underwent a major transformation when it acquired Redbox. Since then the DVD kiosk business which generates more than 85% of Outerwall's sales has eclipsed coin-counting. Redbox operates some 43700 DVD rental kiosks located at supermarkets big-box retailers drug and convenience stores and restaurants across North America. The fast-growing company changed its name to Outerwall in 2013 to reflect its evolution from coin-counting to an operator of various automated retail businesses.

Geographic Reach

While the US accounts for 98% of Outerwall's sales its retail kiosks are also found inside and outside stores in Canada Puerto Rico the UK and Ireland.

Operations

Beyond DVD rentals and coin-counting machines Outerwall's other automated retail concepts (house by its New Ventures segment) include Rubi coffee kiosks (launched in 2012) that feature Seat-

tle's Best Coffee beverages; Redbox Tickets also launched in 2012 that offer tickets to live events and attractions in the Philadelphia market; and refurbished electronics and photo self-service concepts.

Sales and Marketing

Walgreen and Wal-Mart Stores each account for about 16% of Outerwall's sales while grocery giant Kroger represents about 11% of sales.

Financial Performance

Outerwall's sales topped $2 billion in 2012 a 19% increase compared with 2011. Net income rose 45% over the same period. The growth driver is clearly Redbox which posted a 22% increase in annual sales primarily due to $167.5 million from new kiosk installations and increasing sales at existing DVD rental machines. The company's Coinstar coin-counting business posted a modest 3% increase in revenue in 2012 versus 2011 as a result of a larger kiosk base and higher than average coin-to-voucher transactions. The New Ventures segment which includes automated retail concepts such as Rubi coffee kiosks and ecoATM kiosks saw revenue increase 80% on kiosk growth.

Indeed since acquiring Redbox in 2008 the company's sales have more than doubled from about $1.1 billion in 2009 to $2.2 billion in 2012.

Strategy

Since its purchase of Redbox in 2008 the company rapidly evolved from a one-product business —offering just coin-counting services —to one that offers a variety of products and services. Indeed its tiny New Ventures segment is a laboratory of sorts for the development and application of new automated retail concepts. It has grown primarily through acquisitions and is said to be exploring the sale of beauty products. Still its acquisitions have not been nearly as successful as Redbox which now accounts for more than 85% of the company's total revenue.

Focusing on its top-earning divisions the company has been exiting less profitable enterprises amid tough economic conditions worldwide. In mid-2011 Coinstar sold its money-transfer business which served the US and Latin America to California-based financial serves firm Sigue. The deal valued at about $40 million strengthens Sigue's coverage as it provides money-transfer services in more than 135 countries and allows Coinstar to concentrate on its automated retail strategy (i.e. coin counting and video rental). Indeed Coinstar also sold off some 900 DVDXpress kiosks (400 of which were active) in 2010 as well as DVD discs that were in the kiosks as it had deemed the business as unprofitable.

Ownership

Goldman Sachs Asset Management owns about 10% of Outerwall's shares.

EXECUTIVES

CEO and Director, Paul D. Davis, age 56, $555,000 total compensation
President and COO, Gregg A. Kaplan, age 43, $411,717 total compensation
Chairman, Nelson C. Chan, age 51
Chairman, Deborah L. Bevier, age 61
Chief Legal Officer General Counsel and Corporate Secretary, Donald R. (Don) Rench, age 46, $265,360 total compensation
President Redbox, Mark Horak
CEO, J. Scott Di Valerio, age 51
President Redbox, Anne Saunders
President Coinstar, Michael J. (Mike) Skinner, age 59
President ecoATM, Maria D. Stipp
CTO, Carole McCluskey
CFO, Galen Smith

Chief Strategy Sales and Services Officer, James Pinckney
President Coinstar, James Gaherity
Director, Robert D. Sznewajs, age 65
CEO and Director, Paul D. Davis, age 55
Director, Nelson C. Chan, age 50
Director, Ronald B. Woodard, age 67
Director, David M. Eskenazy, age 50
Director, Daniel W. (Dan) O'Connor, age 54
Director, Arik Ahitov, age 36
Auditors: KPMGLLP

LOCATIONS

HQ: Outerwall Inc
  1800 114th Avenue SE, Bellevue, WA 98004
Phone: 425 943-8000
Web: www.outerwall.com

2012 Sales

	$ mil.	% of total
US	2,157	98
All other	44	2
Total	**2,202**	**100**

PRODUCTS/OPERATIONS

2012 Sales

	$ mil.	% of total
Redbox	1,908	87
Coin	290	13
New ventures	2	-
Total	**2,202**	**100**

COMPETITORS

Amazon.com
Blockbuster
Cash Technologies
Cummins-Allison
GameFly

Global Payment
  Technologies
Hulu
Netflix
Safeway

HISTORICAL FINANCIALS

Company Type: Public

Income Statement

FYE: December 31

	REVENUE ($ mil.)	NET INCOME ($ mil.)	NET PROFIT MARGIN	EMPLOYEES
12/13	2,306.6	174.7	7.6%	2,900
12/12	2,202.0	150.2	6.8%	2,927
12/11	1,845.3	103.8	5.6%	2,676
12/10	1,436.4	51.0	3.6%	2,585
12/09	1,144.7	53.6	4.7%	2,600
Annual Growth	19.1%	34.4%	—	2.8%

2013 Year-End Financials

Debt ratio: 40.3%
Return on equity: 32.7%
Cash ($ mil.): 371
Current ratio: 1.12
Long-term debt ($ mil.): 661

No. of shares (mil.): 26
Dividends
  Yield: —
  Payout: —
Market value ($ mil.): 1,759

	STOCK PRICE ($) FY Close	P/E High/Low		PER SHARE ($) Earnings	Dividends	Book Value
12/13	67.27	11	7	6.16	0.00	19.83
12/12	52.01	14	8	4.67	0.00	19.18
12/11	45.64	17	11	3.26	0.00	17.20
12/10	56.44	41	16	1.57	0.00	13.93
12/09	27.78	21	11	1.76	0.00	13.27
Annual Growth	24.7%	—	—	36.8%	—	10.6%

Overstock.com Inc. (DE)

Overstock.com allows you to shop a Persian bazaar of clothes housewares music books and more. The online discount retailer hawks brand-name merchandise including furniture electronics jewelry travel and insurance. Most of its inventory comes from manufacturers stuck with overproduction older models or some color that wasn't as popular as the designer had envisioned. The company's products portfolio includes brands Bissell Hewlett-Packard Movado and Steve Madden among others. In addition to its main website Overstock.com manages an online auction site and provides car and real estate listings. The retailer's Club O loyalty program offers discounts to members on selected items and shipping.

Operations

The online discount retailer has two operating segments: Direct and Fulfillment. The direct business (16% of sales) sells merchandise to individual consumers and businesses. The larger Fulfillment partner business (84% of sales) sells merchandise for other retailers and manufacturers from the Overstock.com website. The company acts as a host for some 2000 third parties who supply about 242000 products.

Geographic Reach

While Overstock.com has no operations outside the US it began selling products to customers in more than 100 countries outside the country from its website in mid-2008.

Financial Analysis

Overstock.com's sales dipped by about 3% in 2011 vs. 2010 and the company was unprofitable. (Indeed Overstock.com has failed to turn a profit in eight of the last 10 years.) While revenue from its larger fulfillment partner business segment inched up by about 1% the direct business saw sales decline 22%. The company blamed the double-digit drop in direct sales on a transition of some of its clothing and shoes category to a fulfillment partner model. The poor financial performance in 2011 followed a banner year in 2010 when Overstock.com's revenue jumped 24% vs. 2009 driven by pricing and marketing efforts that lured new customers to its website and helped to boost the average order size.

Strategy

Over the years Overstock.com has evolved from an online seller of discount merchandise to an operator of multiple websites that list cars and real estate for sale host online auctions and provides other specialized services. In 2010 the firm launched Eziba.com a private sale website where members shop for exclusive deals on home decor furniture jewelry and more. In 2009 its O.biz website began offering bulk and business related items. After selling its travel subsidiary at a loss to Castles Travel in 2009 –following the downturn in the travel industry —Overstock.com in 2011 is once again offering vacations.

Given Overstock.com's failure to turn a profit in eight of the past 10 years an ongoing investigation by the Securities and Exchange Commission following the discovery that the company violated various accounting rules and losses related to failed litigation by the company Overstock.com's shares have been battered.

Ownership

Chairman and CEO Patrick Byrne who started the company with former president Jason Lindsey owns about 29% of Overstock.com through his control of High Plains Investments LLC and personal holdings. In addition Fairfax Financial Holdings owns about 14% of the company as does Francis Chou a Canadian fund manager. (Byrne is on a temporary leave of absence for medical reasons.)

EXECUTIVES

Chairman and CEO, Patrick M. Byrne, age 50
Vice Chairman, Jonathan E. Johnson III, age 47, $248,958 total compensation
Co-President and Board Member, Stormy D. Simon, age 44, $200,000 total compensation
SVP Human Capital Management, Stephen P. Tryon, age 51, $200,000 total compensation
SVP Technology, Samuel J. (Sam) Peterson, $201,033 total compensation
IR Contact Officer, Kevin Moon
SVP Finance and Risk Management, Stephen J. (Steve) Chesnut, age 53, $190,256 total compensation
SVP Analytics Analytics Marketing and Merchandising, Geoffrey R. (Geoff) Atkinson
Senior Vice President - Marketing, Timothy Dilworth
Senior Vice President - Technology, Bhargav Shah
Co-President, David Nielsen
SVP Finance and Risk Management, Robert Hughes
SVP Marketing, Saum Noursalehi
Director, John J. (Jack) Byrne, age 80
Director, Allison H. Abraham, age 50
Director, Barclay F. (Clay) Corbus, age 46
Vice Chairman, Jonathan E. Johnson III, age 47
Co-President and Board Member, Stormy D. Simon, age 44
Director, Joseph J. Tabacco Jr., age 64
Director, Samuel A. (Sam) Mitchell, age 70
Auditors: KPMGLLP

LOCATIONS

HQ: Overstock.com Inc. (DE)
6350 South 3000 East, Salt Lake City, UT 84121
Phone: 801 947-3100
Web: www.overstock.com

PRODUCTS/OPERATIONS

2011 Sales

	% of total
Home &	58
Jewelry watches clothing &	20
Books music movies games electronics &	10
Other	12
Total	**100**

2011 Sales

	$ mil.	% of total
Fulfillment partner	890	84
Direct	163	16
Total	**1,054**	**100**

Selected Suppliers
Anne Klein
Bissell
Blue Ridge Home Fashions
Broyhill
Canon
Charles David
Drexel Heritage
Dyson
Fuji
Hewlett-Packard
Hoover
Hunter Fan
Joseph Abboud
JVC
Kodak
Movado
Novica
Panasonic
Philips
Random House
RCA
Samsonite
Seiko
Simon & Schuster
Sony
Steve Madden
Thomasville
Toshiba
Wenger

Selected Products
At Home
Bedding
Books
Clothing and shoes
Electronics
Furniture
Jewelry
Sports
Watches
Worldstock

COMPETITORS

Amazon.com	OnlineAuction
American Express	Orbitz Worldwide
Barnes & Noble	Ross Stores
Best Buy	Sears Holdings
Bidz.com	Sierra Trading Post
Blue Nile Inc.	TJX Companies
Bluefly	Target Corporation
Buy.com	Travelocity
Costco Wholesale	Wal-Mart
Expedia	craigslist
J. C. Penney	eBay
Kohl's	priceline.com
Liberty Interactive	

HISTORICAL FINANCIALS

Company Type: Public

Income Statement

FYE: December 31

	REVENUE ($ mil.)	NET INCOME ($ mil.)	NET PROFIT MARGIN	EMPLOYEES
12/12	1,099.2	14.6	1.3%	1,300
12/11	1,054.2	(19.4)	—	1,300
12/10	1,089.8	13.8	1.3%	1,500
12/09	876.7	7.7	0.9%	1,300
12/08	834.3	(12.6)	—	1,036
Annual Growth	**7.1%**	**—**	**—**	**5.8%**

2012 Year-End Financials

Debt ratio: —
Return on equity: 66.2%
Cash ($ mil.): 95
Current ratio: 1.05
Long-term debt ($ mil.): —
No. of shares (mil.): 23
Dividends
  Yield: —
  Payout: —
Market value ($ mil.): 336

	STOCK PRICE ($) FY Close	P/E High/Low		PER SHARE ($) Earnings	Dividends	Book Value
12/12	14.31	25	8	0.62	0.00	1.32
12/11	7.84	—	—	(0.84)	0.00	0.57
12/10	16.48	40	19	0.59	0.00	1.36
12/09	13.56	52	20	0.33	0.00	0.51
12/08	10.78	—	—	(0.55)	0.00	(0.13)
Annual Growth	**7.3%**	—	—	—	—	—

Pacific Premier Bancorp Inc

Pacific Premier Bancorp is the holding company of Pacific Premier Bank which has about 10 branches serving Southern California's Los Angeles Orange Riverside and San Bernardino counties. The bank offers standard deposit products and services including checking and savings accounts and cash management services. Multi-family residential mortgages account for about half of the company's loan portfolio. It also writes business and consumer loans such as Small Business Administration loans commercial and industrial loans and single-family residential mortgages.

After a stint during the 1990s in which the bank focused on subprime mortgages and nearly went under Pacific Premier reorganized as a commercial bank in 2007.

The company expanded into Riverside County in 2011 when it acquired the banking operations of the failed Canyon National Bank after that institution was seized by regulators. The transaction which included loss-sharing agreements with the FDIC brought in three branch locations. The following year Pacific Premier acquired the deposits and assets of the failed single-branch Palm Desert National Bank.

Los Angeles-based Security Pacific Bancorp owns some 25% of Pacific Premier Bancorp.

EXECUTIVES

President CEO and Director Pacific Premier Bancorp and Pacific Premier Bank, Steven R. (Steve) Gardner, age 52, $373,558 total compensation
EVP CFO and Treasurer; EVP and CFO Pacific Premier Bank, Kent J. Smith, age 51
EVP and Chief Banking Officer Pacific Premier Bank, Edward (Eddie) Wilcox, age 46, $215,000 total compensation
Chairman, Jeff C. Jones, age 58
Executive Vice President; Chief Credit Officer, Michael S. Karr
President CEO and Director Pacific Premier Bancorp and Pacific Premier Bank, Steven R. (Steve) Gardner, age 52
Director, John D. Goddard, age 74
Director, Michael L. McKennon, age 52
Director, Jeff C. Jones, age 57
Director, David L. Hardin, age 58
Independent Director, Joseph Garrett
Auditors: VavrinekTrineDay&Co.LLP

LOCATIONS

HQ: Pacific Premier Bancorp Inc.
1600 Sunflower Ave. 2nd Fl., Costa Mesa CA 92626
Phone: 714-431-4000 **Fax:** 714-433-3000
Web: www.ppbi.net

PRODUCTS/OPERATIONS

2007 Sales

	$ mil.	% of total
Interest		
Loans	45	81
Other	4	7
Noninterest		
Net gain on sale of loans	3	7
Loan servicing fee income	1	2
Other	1	3
Total	**55**	**100**

COMPETITORS

Bank of America	JPMorgan Chase
Citibank	U.S. Bancorp
City National	Zions Bancorporation
Comerica	

HISTORICAL FINANCIALS

Company Type: Public

Income Statement

FYE: December 31

	ASSETS ($ mil.)	NET INCOME ($ mil.)	INCOME AS % OF ASSETS	EMPLOYEES
12/12	1,173.7	15.7	1.3%	183
12/11	961.1	10.5	1.1%	149
12/10	826.8	4.2	0.5%	105
12/09	807.3	(0.4)	—	91
12/08	739.9	0.7	0.1%	94
Annual Growth	**12.2%**	**117.3%**	**—**	**18.1%**

2012 Year-End Financials

Return on assets: 1.4%
Return on equity: 14.2%
Long-term debt ($ mil.): —
No. of shares (mil.): 13
Sales ($ mil): 65

Dividends
  Yield: —
  Payout: —
Market value ($ mil.): 140

	STOCK PRICE ($) FY Close	P/E High/Low		PER SHARE ($) Earnings	Dividends	Book Value
12/12	10.24	8	4	1.44	0.00	9.85
12/11	6.34	7	5	0.99	0.00	8.39
12/10	6.48	15	8	0.38	0.00	7.83
12/09	3.38	—	—	(0.08)	0.00	7.33
12/08	4.00	61	24	0.11	0.00	11.74
Annual Growth	**26.5%**	—	—	**90.2%**	**—**	**(4.3%)**

Pain Therapeutics Inc

Pain Therapeutics is providing opiates for the masses. The development-stage company is working on abuse-resistant painkillers including Remoxy a version of the frequently abused Oxycontin. Pain Therapeutics is developing Remoxy and other painkiller candidates in partnership with Pfizer which holds all of the commercialization rights to the drugs. In addition to its chronic pain candidates Pain Therapeutics has development programs in oncology and hematology underway. Because many of its drug candidates already contain FDA-approved components the firm hopes for a faster approval process on its lead candidates.

All of Pain Therapeutics' revenue comes from its collaboration with Pfizer which reimburses the company for development expenses. Pfizer took over the collaboration when it acquired former partner King Pharmaceuticals in 2011. Pain Therapeutics' originally licensed rights to the drug from drug delivery firm DURECT.

It has begun clinical work with a monoclonal antibody developed by the Albert Einstein College of Medicine that targets metastatic melanoma. It has also licensed a genetic treatment for hemophilia from Poetic Genetics; the treatment is undergoing preclinical testing.

Founder and CEO Remi Barbier owns about 18% of the company.

EXECUTIVES

Chairman of the Board; President; Chief Executive Officer, Remi Barbier, age 53, $566,250 total compensation
Secretary and Director, Michael J. O'Donnell, age 54
COO Chief Medical Officer and Director, Nadav Friedmann, age 70, $438,542 total compensation
Chief Financial Officer; Vice President, Peter S. Roddy, age 53, $293,125 total compensation
Chief Scientific Officer, Grant L. Schoenhard, age 68, $328,125 total compensation
SVP Technical Operations, Michael Zamloot
SVP Technology, George (Ben) Thornton
Secretary; Independent Director, Michael Donnell
Director, Patrick J. (Pat) Scannon, age 65
Secretary and Director, Michael J. O'Donnell, age 54
Director, Sanford R. (Sandy) Robertson, age 81
COO Chief Medical Officer and Director, Nadav Friedmann, age 70
Director, Robert Z. Gussin, age 75
Auditors: Ernst&YoungLLP

LOCATIONS

HQ: Pain Therapeutics Inc
7801 N. Capital of Texas Highway, Suite 260, Austin, TX 78731
Phone: 512 501-2444
Web: www.paintrials.com

COMPETITORS

Abbott Labs	Endo
Actavis Inc.	Forest Labs
Acura Pharmaceuticals	Purdue Pharma
Adolor	Roxane Laboratories
Akela	Teva
Cephalon	Titan Pharmaceuticals

HISTORICAL FINANCIALS

Company Type: Public

Income Statement

FYE: December 31

	REVENUE ($ mil.)	NET INCOME ($ mil.)	NET PROFIT MARGIN	EMPLOYEES
12/13	41.1	31.5	76.7%	8
12/12	10.8	(3.4)	—	8
12/11	11.4	(2.6)	—	10
12/10	16.8	(12.0)	—	18
12/09	20.5	(3.4)	—	27
Annual Growth	**18.9%**	**—**	**—**	**(26.2%)**

2013 Year-End Financials

Debt ratio: —
Return on equity: 102.6%
Cash ($ mil.): 48
Current ratio: 27.82
Long-term debt ($ mil.): —

No. of shares (mil.): 45
Dividends
  Yield: —
  Payout: —
Market value ($ mil.): 221

	STOCK PRICE ($) FY Close	P/E High/Low		PER SHARE ($) Earnings	Dividends	Book Value
12/13	4.86	8	3	0.70	0.00	1.06
12/12	2.71	—	—	(0.08)	0.75	0.29
12/11	3.80	—	—	(0.06)	0.00	0.99
12/10	6.75	—	—	(0.28)	2.00	0.77
12/09	5.36	—	—	(0.08)	0.00	2.56
Annual Growth	**(2.4%)**	—	—	—	—	**(19.7%)**

Panera Bread Co.

Panera Bread is ready for an epochal change in American eating habits. The company is a leader in the quick-casual restaurant business with more than 1650 bakery-cafes in about 45 states and Canada. Its locations which operate under the banners Panera Bread Saint Louis Bread Co. and Paradise Bakery & Cafe offer made-to-order sandwiches using a variety of artisan breads including Asiago cheese bread focaccia and its classic sourdough bread. The chain's menu also features soups salads and gourmet coffees. In addition Panera sells its bread bagels and pastries to go. More than 800 of its locations are company-operated while the rest are run by franchisees.

Geographic Reach

Panera operates in 44 states in the US Washington D.C. and Ontario Canada. In 2010 Panera moved its corporate headquarters to spacious offices in a building previously occupied by Anheuser-Busch in St. Louis.

Operations

The company's three business segments consist of the Bakery-Cafe Operations segment the Franchise Operations segment and the Fresh Dough and Other Product Operations segment that provides fresh food supplies to company-owned and franchise-operated bakery-cafes through a contract manufacturing arrangement.

Sales and Marketing

Panera sells its products directly to customers and also acts as its own distributor by supplying most of its company-owned and franchised locations with fresh product. The company was a pioneer in the quick-casual dining segment which offers quick counter service but boasts higher-quality ingredients.

The chain built significant brand loyalty by targeting suburban markets with its menu of European-inspired sandwich creations. It competes with other national fast-casual chains such as California Pizza Kitchen Chipotle Mexican Grill and Einstein Bros. Bagels (operated by Einstein Noah Restaurant Group) as well as #1 coffee house chain Starbucks.

Financial Performance

Panera's revenue has been trending up in recent fiscal years. Revenue increased by 17% and profits rose by 28% in fiscal 2012 compared to fiscal 2011. The revenue increase was primarily the result of the company opening more than 100 new locations during 2012.

Strategy

Like many other dining operators Panera (which is Latin for "time for bread") relies on a mix of corporate-run locations and franchising to expand and operate its restaurant chain. The company-owned stores give the chain a significant footprint from which to control the consistency of food and service quality.

Panera's franchising efforts allow the company to expand into new markets without the expense of construction and operation. Local franchisees pay the company royalties and other fees in order to use the Panera brand and other intellectual property.

In 2012 about 51% of the company's bakery-cafes were operated by franchisees (843 franchise-operated bakery-cafes out of a total of 1652 bakery-cafes system-wide). Panera's growth strategy includes selectively opening bakery-cafes in Canada and urban areas.

Panera opened its first Manhattan location in 2012 hoping to build upon the success the company has had in urban markets like Washington D.C. Boston and Chicago. Plans call for two more Manhattan locations to be open by early 2013.

Ownership

Chairman Ron Shaich co-founded the business under the name Au Bon Pain a brand now owned by Boston-based ABP Corporation. He controls more than 10% of Panera's voting stock. T. Rowe Price Associates Inc. owns 12% of the company.

HISTORY

Panera Bread traces its roots to a restaurant opened in Boston by French commercial oven manufacturer Pavailler. Au Bon Pain opened in 1976 was intended as a showcase for Pavailler's ovens. The scent of hot croissants (and money) caught the attention of Louis Kane who bought the business in 1978 and began expanding in Boston. Ron Shaich (pronounced "shake") joined Kane in 1981 and together they formed Au Bon Pain Co. Inc. The chain grew rapidly until the early 1990s saturating the high-traffic areas in eastern US cities. After its IPO in 1991 Au Bon Pain began making acquisitions including Saint Louis Bread in 1993.

Saint Louis Bread was founded in 1987 when Ken Rosenthal spurred into the restaurant business by his brother opened his first cafe in Kirkwood Missouri. Based on sourdough bakeries in San Francisco the concept eventually spread to five stores by 1990 and nearly 20 units two years later. In 1993 the company made "Inc." magazine's list of the 500 fastest-growing companies. At the end of that year Au Bon Pain paid $24 million for the company franchising its new units outside of the St. Louis area as Panera Bread. Rosenthal stayed on with Au Bon Pain as chairman of its new chain before leaving to become a major franchisee.

By 1995 the company was facing new competition from coffee and bagel shops. Flat sales and sharp price increases for butter hurt the chain's bottom line. By 1997 the company had added bagels to its menu and was considering extensive renovations. It ultimately decided the chain had peaked in the US and it limited expansion to countries with dense urban areas and emerging middle classes such as Brazil and Indonesia.

During 1998 Au Bon Pain's Panera Bread unit perked up with new stores and growing sales. But that success was offset by the company's namesake chain where sales continued to struggle. The company eventually sold the Au Bon Pain chain in 1999 to investment firm Bruckmann Rosser Sherrill and Co. for $73 million. (Bruckmann Rosser later sold the chain to UK-based Compass Group which ran the eateries through its subsidiary ABP Corporation until it sold a majority stake to a management group.) Shaich remained with the company which was renamed Panera Bread as chairman and CEO. Panera Bread later moved its headquarters back to the St. Louis area.

In 2001 president and COO Rich Postle resigned to run a joint venture with Panera Bread to build and manage 40 bakery-cafes in the northern Virginia and central Pennsylvania regions.

The company introduced its new upscale takeout program Via Panera in 2004. With Via Panera the company simplified the to-go ordering process while upgrading its customization particularly for larger orders. Panera Bread also released its first cookbook that year The Panera Bread Cookbook: Breadmaking Essentials and Recipes from America's Favorite Bakery-Cafe.

In 2007 the company acquired a 51% stake in Paradise Bakery & Cafe the operator of a small bakery-cafe chain in the Southwest for about $20 million. (Panera acquired the remaining stake for about $22 million two years later.)

EXECUTIVES

EVP and COO, John M. Maguire, age 46, $400,000 total compensation
SVP Chief Franchise Officer, Michael J. (Mike) Kupstas, age 55, $350,000 total compensation
EVP and Chief Concept and Innovation Officer, Scott G. Davis, age 49, $290,961 total compensation
Vice Chairman, William W. (Bill) Moreton, age 53, $297,220 total compensation
Chairman and CEO, Ronald M. (Ron) Shaich, age 59, $600,000 total compensation
EVP Technology and Transformation, Blaine E. Hurst, age 55
SVP Chief Development Officer, Michael J. Nolan, age 52, $259,231 total compensation
EVP and COO, Charles J. (Chuck) Chapman III, age 50
SVP and CIO, Thomas C. (Tom) Kish, age 47
SVP and Chief Supply Chain Officer, Mark A. Borland, age 60, $310,200 total compensation
EVP and Chief Marketing Officer, Michael Simon, age 53
SVP and Chief People Officer, Elizabeth M. Dunlap, age 50
EVP and Chief Development Officer, Mark Wesley
Director Product Development, John Taylor
SVP Chief Company and Joint Venture Operations Officer, William H. (Hank) Simpson, age 49
Chief Accounting Officer and Assistant Controller, Mark D. Wooldridge, age 37
VP and Controller, Amy L. Kuzdowicz, age 42
SVP Chief Legal Officer General Counsel and Secretary, Scott G. Blair, age 54
Interim CFO, Thomas Patrick Kelly, age 54
SVP Chief Company & JV Operations Officer, Irene Cook
EVP and CFO, Roger C. Matthews Jr.
President and Co-CEO, William W. (Bill) Moreton, age 52
Director, Fred K. Foulkes, age 70
Director, Domenic Colasacco, age 63
Director, Larry J. Franklin, age 63
Director Emeritus, George E. Kane
EVP and Director, Charles J. (Chuck) Chapman III, age 49
Director, Thomas E. Lynch, age 52
Auditors: PricewaterhouseCoopersLLP

LOCATIONS

HQ: Panera Bread Company
3630 S. Geyer Rd. Ste. 100, St. Louis MO 63127
Phone: 314-984-1000 **Fax:** 314-909-3300
Web: www.panerabread.com

PRODUCTS/OPERATIONS

2012 Sales

Restaurants	1,879	88
Franchising	102	5

COMPETITORS

ABP Corporation	Einstein Noah
Boston Market	Restaurant Group
Bruegger's	Fresh Enterprises
CBC Restaurant	Potbelly Sandwich Shop
California Pizza	Qdoba Restaurants
Kitchen	Quiznos
Caribou Coffee	Starbucks
Chipotle	Subway

HISTORICAL FINANCIALS

Company Type: Public

Income Statement

FYE: December 25

	REVENUE ($ mil.)	NET INCOME ($ mil.)	NET PROFIT MARGIN	EMPLOYEES
12/12	2,130.0	173.4	8.1%	36,300
12/11	1,822.0	135.9	7.5%	32,600
12/10	1,542.4	111.8	7.3%	25,600
12/09	1,353.4	86.0	6.4%	25,300
12/08	1,298.8	67.4	5.2%	21,800
Annual Growth	13.2%	26.6%	—	13.6%

2012 Year-End Financials

Debt ratio: —
Return on equity: 23.5%
Cash ($ mil.): 297
Current ratio: 1.73
Long-term debt ($ mil.): —

No. of shares (mil.): 29
Dividends
  Yield: —
  Payout: —
Market value ($ mil.): 4,686

	STOCK PRICE ($) FY Close	P/E High/Low	PER SHARE ($) Earnings	Dividends	Book Value
12/12	158.34	29 23	5.89	0.00	27.77
12/11	141.01	31 21	4.55	0.00	22.09
12/10	102.11	29 18	3.62	0.00	19.59
12/09	68.63	24 15	2.78	0.00	18.90
12/08	50.22	26 14	2.22	0.00	16.07
Annual Growth	33.3%	— —	27.6%	—	14.7%

Panhandle Oil & Gas Inc

You won't find this Panhandle on a street corner but you will find it pocketing the oil and gas royalties from more than 6100 gross producing oil and gas wells. Panhandle Oil and Gas (formerly Panhandle Royalty) owns mineral interests both working and royalty in oil- and gas-producing properties in 10 states. The company does not operate any of its own wells but instead maintains them through partnerships with other oil and gas companies. Its major properties are located primarily in Oklahoma (44% of its net land holdings in fiscal 2013 of 255300 acres). In fiscal 2013 Panhandle Oil and Gas reported proved reserves of 151.8 billion cu. ft. of natural gas equivalent.

Geographic Reach

The company's primary assets are in Arkansas New Mexico North Dakota Oklahoma and Texas. Most of its oil NGL and natural gas production comes from wells in Arkansas and Oklahoma.

Financial Performance

In fiscal 2013 Panhandle Oil and Gas' revenues rose by 30% due to higher oil and natural gas sales volumes and prices partially offset by lower lease bonuses received.

Net income increased by 89% thanks to higher net sales and lower operating costs.

Strategy

Rather than operating any of the wells in which it has an interest the company relies on companies with more assets and experience to operate the wells during the drilling and production phases. It either elects to participate in drilling operations with these larger companies or to lease or farmout its mineral or leasehold acreage while retaining a royalty interest. This strategy allows Panhandle Oil and Gas to compete effectively in drilling operations while maintaining low overhead costs.

HISTORY

In 1926 Panhandle Cooperative Royalty was formed by ranchers and farmers in Range Oklahoma (located in that state's panhandle). At the time Oklahoma was a homesteader state in which hopeful landowners after cultivating a parcel of 160 acres would receive full title (including mineral rights) to the land. The cooperative got started by offering each prospective member one share for the undivided mineral rights to 40 acres. Royalties from any mineral production were divided 75% to the property owner and 25% to the cooperative. Earnings remaining at year-end were split among the shareholders. Because landowners with imminent drilling prospects were uninterested in joining the cooperative Panhandle often found itself striking deals in then-unexplored areas such as the Anadarko Basin.

In 1979 a period of rapidly rising oil prices Panhandle realized that as a cooperative its inability to retain any earnings severely limited its expansion potential. The cooperative was merged into the Panhandle Royalty Company and went public that year. In 1988 the company acquired New Mexico Osage Royalty Company itself a cooperative. In 1995 Panhandle acquired a half interest in more than 65000 acres from PetroCorp Inc.

Panhandle was primarily a passive owner until 1991 when it got a new CEO geologist H. W. Peace. The firm plans to continue expanding through acquisitions and to increase its participation in drilling projects. Peace retired in 2006. Company veteran Michael Coffman took over as CEO in 2007.

EXECUTIVES

President CEO, Michael C. Coffman, age 60, $216,250 total compensation
Lead Independent Director, Robert O. Lorenz, age 66
VP Land, Ben Spriestersbach, age 62, $119,775 total compensation
VP CFO and Secretary, Lonnie J. Lowry, age 61, $139,875 total compensation
Controller Chief Accounting Officer and Director Internal Audit, Robb P. Winfield
SVP and COO, Paul F. Blanchard Jr.
Executive Vice President of Marketing and Midstream, Darryl Smette
Independent Director, Duke R. Ligon, age 71
President CEO, Michael C. Coffman, age 60
Independent Director, Robert A. Reece, age 69
Independent Director, Bruce M. Bell, age 72
Independent Director, Grant Swartzwelder
Auditors: Ernst&YoungLLP

LOCATIONS

HQ: Panhandle Oil and Gas Inc.
5400 N. Grand Blvd. Ste. 300 Grand Centre Bldg., Oklahoma City OK 73112
Phone: 405-948-1560 **Fax:** 405-948-2038
Web: www.panhandleoilandgas.com

PRODUCTS/OPERATIONS

2013 Sales

Oil & gas	60	96
Income from partnerships	0	1

COMPETITORS

Abraxas Petroleum	Gastar Exploration
Anadarko Petroleum	Hugoton Royalty Trust
Bill Barrett	Matador Resources
Brigham Exploration	Range Resources
Cabot Oil & Gas	SM Energy
Crimson Exploration	Sabine Royalty Trust
Cross Timbers Royalty Trust	Warren Resources

HISTORICAL FINANCIALS

Company Type: Public

Income Statement

FYE: September 30

	REVENUE ($ mil.)	NET INCOME ($ mil.)	NET PROFIT MARGIN	EMPLOYEES
09/13	62.8	13.9	22.2%	21
09/12	48.5	7.3	15.2%	20
09/11	44.9	8.4	18.9%	19
09/10	51.9	11.4	22.0%	18
09/09	39.9	(2.4)	—	17
Annual Growth	12.0%	—	—	5.4%

2013 Year-End Financials

Debt ratio: 5.5%
Return on equity: 15.5%
Cash ($ mil.): 2
Current ratio: 1.73
Long-term debt ($ mil.): 8

No. of shares (mil.): 8
Dividends
  Yield: 0.9%
  Payout: 27.7%
Market value ($ mil.): 233

	STOCK PRICE ($) FY Close	P/E High/Low	PER SHARE ($) Earnings	Dividends	Book Value
09/13	28.28	20 15	1.67	0.28	11.62
09/12	30.67	41 27	0.88	0.28	10.16
09/11	28.37	36 24	1.01	0.28	9.54
09/10	24.69	22 14	1.36	0.28	8.85
09/09	21.36	— —	(0.29)	0.28	7.71
Annual Growth	7.3%	— —	—	(0.0%)	10.8%

PAREXEL International Corp.

PAREXEL International excels in pharmaceutical development services. A top contract research organization (CRO) the firm counts among its clients some of the world's largest drug biotech and medical device firms. Its Clinical Research Services segment provides clinical trial and data management study design patient recruitment biostatistical analysis clinical pharmacology and industry training and publishing. PAREXEL Consulting and Medical Communications Services handles the non-clinical aspects of drug development regulatory affairs and new product launches. Its Perceptive Informatics unit offers information technology systems and services that help manage clinical trials.

The company has some 70 facilities in more than 50 countries in Europe the Asia/Pacific region North America South America and Africa. More than half of its sales are generated outside the US partly because of its core client base of large multinational corporations. PAREXEL's sales force directs custom marketing efforts towards niche market segments to match the appropriate services with each customer's needs. Its overall goal is to help clients reduce costs and risks related to product development and commercialization.

The company's largest segment Clinical Research Services (CRS) accounts for two-thirds of sales. Its core development business covers all phases of drug and device development from discovery research through clinical trials and post-marketing studies. The division has benefited from the market trend of increased R&D outsourcing by pharmaceutical and biotech drug companies. The company seeks to widen its service offerings geographic presence and client base both through internal initiatives and via acquisitions. In late 2012 it purchased Liquent for about $72 million which added regulatory software and technology.

The firm has also built up its other divisions to lessen the blow it might suffer if it were to lose a big CRS client. In 2008 PAREXEL paid $190 million for UK firm ClinPhone to boost its clinical information technology offerings. ClinPhone's trial management technologies including phone and Internet response systems were then integrated into Perceptive Informatics.

While the company's revenues have grown steadily over time in 2011 its cash flow dropped sharply due to the expense of implementing a new accounting and billing system. That same year the company launched a restructuring of its Early Phase clinical development services within CRS to improve efficiencies. However that move also added to the dip in the company's cash flow.

HISTORY

Founders Josef von Rickenbach a health care and international products specialist and Anne Sayigh a chemist and regulatory affairs specialist started PAREXEL in 1982 to provide regulatory consulting services to pharmaceutical firms. Its name referred to 16th-century Swiss physician Theophrastus Bombastus von Hohenheim –better known as Paracelsus the father of empirical chemistry.

In 1988 PAREXEL bought Consulting Statisticians and moved into the biostatistics and data management market. The next year it went international with the purchase of the biostatistics and data management division of McDonnell Douglas Information Systems. In 1991 PAREXEL augmented its European operations with the acquisition of German contract researcher AFB Arzneimittelforschung –a move that paid off in rising sales.

PAREXEL went public in 1995. In the following two years it bought six health consulting firms including State and Federal Associates and medical marketing firm Rescon with the intention of boosting its ability to get its clients' products on the market. The company continued its acquisition spree in 1998; this time European marketing and research companies were on the shopping list. Competitor Covance was set to buy PAREXEL in 1999 then called off the deal when investors balked.

The company announced in 2000 that it would lay off more than 400 workers after Novartis cancelled a major contract. That year the company formed new alliances with such companies as NeuroRecovery Research Phenome Sciences and Prevention Concepts. PAREXEL also bought a full-service clinical pharmacology unit in the UK from GlaxoWellcome (now GlaxoSmithKline) as well as a majority stake in FARMOVS a clinical pharmacology research business and laboratory in South Africa.

In 2001 the company formed Perceptive Informatics a subsidiary focused on developing Internet-based information management systems. To strengthen its clinical trial management services PAREXEL bought software developer FW Pharma Systems in 2003. In 2006 it purchased US-based

Behavioral and Medical Research LLC for $69 million to expand its research services.

EXECUTIVES

SVP and CFO, James F. Winschel Jr., age 63, $365,000 total compensation
Chairman and CEO, Josef H. von Rickenbach, age 58, $650,000 total compensation
SVP and Chief Administrative Officer, Ulf I. Schneider, age 55, $376,695 total compensation
Corporate Vice President - Investor Relations, Jill L. Baker
COO and President, Mark A. Goldberg, age 53, $450,000 total compensation
President Perceptive Informatics, Xavier Flinois
Senior Vice President - Clinical Research Services, Joseph C. (Joe) Avellone, age 63
President Perceptive Informatics, Steven J. Kent, age 50
President - PACE and PAREXEL Consulting and Medical Communication Services, Kurt A. Brykman, age 55, $350,000 total compensation
SVP General Counsel and Secretary, Douglas A. Batt, age 47, $307,000 total compensation
SVP Clinical Research Services, Gadi Saarony
VP Start-up and Accelerated Recruitment Team, Lars-Olof Eriksson
SVP Clinical Research Services, Anita Cooper, age 54
VP Project Management and Regulatory Affairs Asia Pacific, Karen Chu
VP Early Phase, Samira Moran
VP PAREXEL Consulting, Paul Bridges
Senior Director Product Strategy Perceptive Informatics, William (Bill) Byrom
Principal Consultant Reimbursement and Market Access PAREXEL Consulting, Saurabh Aggarwal
Senior Portfolio Director Peri-Approval Clinical Excellence, Gary Coward
VP and Worldwide Head Early Phase, Sy Pretorius
VP Project Management Clinical Research Services, Niki Harrop
VP Technical Strategic Compliance Services PARAXEL Consulting, Edwin Rivera-Martinez
Director Strategic Research PAREXEL Consulting, Mark Mathieu
Chairman of the Board; Chief Executive Officer, Josef Rickenbach
VP-Clinical Ops, Diego Glancszpigel
VP-Corp, Dieter Russmann
VP-Client Rels, Marcia Lund
Senior Vice President Clinical Research Services, Joe Avellone
CFO, Ingo Bank
Director, Patrick J. (Pat) Fortune, age 66
Director, Richard L. Love, age 70
Director, Ellen M. Zane, age 62
Director, A. Dana Callow Jr., age 61
Director, Christopher J. (Chris) Lindop, age 55
Director, Eduard E. Holdener, age 68
Auditors: Ernst&YoungLLP

LOCATIONS

HQ: PAREXEL International Corporation
195 West St., Waltham MA 02451
Phone: 781-487-9900   **Fax:** -1221
Web: www.derigo.com

2011 Service Revenue

Europe Middle East & Africa	46
Asia/Pacific	14

PRODUCTS/OPERATIONS

2011 Sales

	$ mil.	% of total
Service revenue		
Perceptive Informatics	159	11
Reimbursement revenue	210	15

COMPETITORS

Albany Molecular Research
BioClinica
Charles River Laboratories
Covance
DATATRAK International
ICON
Life Sciences Research
PRA International
PharmaNet Development Group
Pharmaceutical Product Development
Quintiles Transnational
ReSearch Pharmaceutical Services
WuXi PharmaTech
eResearchTechnology

HISTORICAL FINANCIALS

Company Type: Public

Income Statement

FYE: June 30

	REVENUE ($ mil.)	NET INCOME ($ mil.)	NET PROFIT MARGIN	EMPLOYEES
06/13	1,995.9	95.9	4.8%	14,700
06/12	1,618.2	63.1	3.9%	12,695
06/11	1,422.4	48.7	3.4%	10,550
06/10	1,335.8	41.5	3.1%	9,720
06/09	1,246.8	39.3	3.2%	9,275
Annual Growth	12.5%	25.0%	—	12.2%

2013 Year-End Financials

Debt ratio: 24.9%
Return on equity: 16.7%
Cash ($ mil.): 144
Current ratio: 1.60
Long-term debt ($ mil.): 424

No. of shares (mil.): 56
Dividends
  Yield: —
  Payout: —
Market value ($ mil.): 2,589

	STOCK PRICE ($) FY Close	P/E High/Low	Earnings	Dividends	Book Value
06/13	45.97	30 16	1.61	0.00	9.57
06/12	28.23	27 15	1.05	0.00	10.14
06/11	23.56	33 21	0.81	0.00	9.59
06/10	21.68	35 16	0.71	0.00	7.52
06/09	14.38	53 10	0.68	0.00	7.18
Annual Growth	33.7%	— —	24.0%	—	7.5%

Patrick Industries, Inc.

A recreational vehicle is just an empty motor home until Patrick Industries adds the finishing interior touches. The company makes and distributes a range of building materials and prefinished products primarily for the manufactured home (MH) and RV industries. Patrick Industries manufactures decorative paper and vinyl panels moldings countertops doors and cabinet and slotwall components. In addition to these the firm distributes roofing siding flooring drywall ceiling and wall panels household electronics electrical and plumbing supplies and adhesives. Founded in 1959 the company operates about two dozen production facilities distribution centers and warehouses in a dozen states.

Operations

Patrick Industries operates seven manufacturing plants where it makes furniture shelving wall counter and cabinet products mouldings interior passage doors and slotwall panels and components among other products. Its manufacturing segment contributes about three-quarters of its annual revenue. The company also distributes prefinished wall and ceiling panels drywall and drywall finishing products. electronics. wiring electrical and plumbing products shower doors fireplaces and other miscellaneous products from five distribution facilities nationwide. Distribution accounts for about 25% of sales.

Sales and Marketing

Patrick Industries counts most of the major manufactured housing (MH) and RV manufacturers among its clientele but it also serves customers in the marine casegoods home furniture and the commercial furnishings and fixtures industries. The company has about 600 active customers of which five account for nearly two-thirds of its sales in 2012. The RV industry represented approximately 69% of the company's sales in 2012 while manufactured housing accounted for 19%. The industrial market represented the rest.

Financial Performance

The company's sales and profits have rebounded since the global economic downturn cut sales by more than a third. In 2012 Patrick's sales jumped 42% compared with 2011 to a record $437.4 million. Net income surged 232% over the same period to $28.1 million. Indeed 2012 marked the third consecutive year of rising sales and profits for the company. Increased wholesale shipments to the RV industry and contributions from recent acquisitions bolstered sales.

Strategy

The company took a beating as a result of the global economic downturn that began in late 2007. In response it disposed of non-core businesses streamlined administrative and support functions and reduced inventory levels. Now with the economy improving and RV business back on track Patrick Industries is looking to complement its existing product lines and has been expanding its operations through acquisitions.

Mergers and Acquisitions

In October 2012 the company bought Middlebury Hardwood Products a maker and distributor of hardwood cabinet doors as well as Indiana-based Creative Wood Designs which manufactures hardwood furniture including tables chairs and dinettes for the RV industry for $5.7 million. The purchase came on the heels of the July acquisition of another Indiana firm Gustafson Lighting a maker of lighting products ceiling fans and accessories also for RVs. It also acquired Oregon-based Decor Mfg. LLC which makes laminated and wrapped products specifically for the recreational vehicle market for about $4.4 million. Previously Patrick Industries purchased A.I.A. Countertops a fabricator of DuPont and Corian countertops backsplashes tables and more for about $5.7 million in 2011.

EXECUTIVES

EVP Finance CFO Secretary Treasurer and Director, Andy L. Nemeth, age 44, $212,659 total compensation

Chairman, Paul E. Hassler, age 66, $326,045 total compensation

President; Chief Executive Officer; Director, Todd M. Cleveland, age 45, $260,730 total compensation

Vice President - Human Resources, Courtney Blosser

Vice President - Sales; South and West, James Ritchey

Executive Vice President - Sales and Operations, Jeffrey Rodino

VP of Sales & Operations, Jeffrey Jeff

Director, Keith V. Kankel, age 70

Director, Walter E. Wells, age 74

Director, Terrence D. Brennan, age 74

Director, Larry D. Renbarger, age 74

EVP Finance CFO Secretary Treasurer and Director, Andy L. Nemeth, age 44

President; Chief Executive Officer; Director, Todd M. Cleveland, age 45

Director, Joseph M. (Joe) Cerulli, age 54

Independent Director, John Forbes

Auditors: Ernst&YoungLLP

LOCATIONS

HQ: Patrick Industries Inc.
107 W. Franklin St., Elkhart IN 46516
Phone: 574-294-7511   **Fax:** 574-522-5213
Web: www.patrickind.com

PRODUCTS/OPERATIONS

2012 Sales

	$ mil.	% of total
Manufacturing	331	76
Distribution	106	24
Total	**437**	**100**

2012 Sales by Customer Type

	% of total
RV	69
Manufactured	19
Industrial	12
Total	**100**

COMPETITORS

Decorator Industries	Lowe's
Drew Industries	Quanex Building
Flexsteel	Products
HD Supply	Saint-Gobain
LaSalle Bristol	

HISTORICAL FINANCIALS

Company Type: Public

Income Statement

FYE: December 31

	REVENUE ($ mil.)	NET INCOME ($ mil.)	NET PROFIT MARGIN	EMPLOYEES
12/12	437.3	28.1	6.4%	1,678
12/11	307.8	8.4	2.8%	900
12/10	278.2	1.2	0.4%	668
12/09	212.5	(4.5)	—	580
12/08	325.1	(71.5)	—	924
Annual Growth	**7.7%**	**—**	**—**	**16.1%**

2012 Year-End Financials

Debt ratio: 34.6%
Return on equity: 62.0%
Cash ($ mil.): 0
Current ratio: 2.53
Long-term debt ($ mil.): 49

No. of shares (mil.): 10
Dividends
  Yield: —
  Payout: —
Market value ($ mil.): 169

	STOCK PRICE ($) FY Close	P/E High/Low		PER SHARE ($) Earnings	Dividends	Book Value
12/12	15.56	8	2	2.64	0.00	5.66
12/11	4.10	5	2	0.83	0.00	2.89
12/10	1.90	28	13	0.12	0.00	1.95
12/09	2.43	—	—	(0.49)	0.00	1.78
12/08	0.64	—	—	(8.93)	0.00	2.30
Annual Growth	**122.1%**			**—**	**—**	**25.2%**

Peapack-Gladstone Financial Corp.

Peapack-Gladstone Financial hopes its customers are happy as peas in a pod. The company is the parent of Peapack-Gladstone Bank which operates more than 20 branches serving New Jersey's Hunterdon Morris Somerset and Union counties. Founded in 1921 the bank serves area individuals and small businesses by providing such traditional services as checking savings and money market accounts; CDs; IRAs; and credit cards. It offers trust and investment management services through its PGB Trust and Investments unit. Mortgages secured by residential properties represent about half of the company's loan portfolio. The bank also originates commercial real estate construction consumer and business loans

PGB Trust and Investments which accounts for some 15% of the company's revenues has approximately $2 billion in assets under administration. It has benefitted from the lagging economy and volatile markets as it saw an increase in customers seeking financial assistance. The unit saw 8% growth in fee income in 2011.

Peapack-Gladstone's overall profits grew some 59% that year from $7.7 million in 2010 to $12.2 million. In addition to increases in trust fee income the company reported a lower provision for loan losses as the quality of its loan portfolio improved. It has also been selling investment securities to raise capital. These gains were slightly offset by a decrease in interest income primarily due to low interest rates.

EXECUTIVES

EVP and CFO Peapack-Gladstone Financial and Peapack-Gladstone Bank, Jeffrey J. Carfora, age 55
President and CEO, Douglas L. Kennedy, age 55
Chairman, Frank A. Kissel, age 62, $350,000 total compensation
President COO and Director; President and COO Peapack-Gladstone Bank, Robert M. Rogers, age 54, $225,000 total compensation
President Trust and Investments, Craig C. Spengeman, age 57, $250,000 total compensation
SVP Retail Lending, Michael J. Giacobello
SEVP COO and General Counsel, Finn M.W. Casperson Jr., age 43
SVP and Branch Administrator, Robert A. Buckley
VP-Corp Trainer, Doreen A. Macchiarola
EVP Commercial Banking, Vincent A. Spero
VP Peapack-Gladstone Bank, Karen M. Ferraro
VP Peapack-Gladstone Bank, Stephen S. Miller
VP-Loan & Admin, Christopher P. Pocquat
VP-Small Bus Banking, Scott Searle

VP Peapack-Gladstone Bank, Susan K. Smith
VP Peapack-Gladstone Bank, James S. Stadtmueller
VP Peapack-Gladstone Bank, Jesse D. Williams
VP Peapack-Gladstone Bank, Randall J. Williams
VP Peapack-Gladstone Bank, Frank C. Waldron
VP Peapack-Gladstone Bank, Marc R. Magliaro
First VP and Director Business Development
 PGB Trust and Investments, John M. Bonk
VP and Trust Officer PGB Trust and Investments,
 John Tarver
General Counsel, Finn Caspersen
VP-HR, Rohinton Madon
SVP and Chief Risk Officer, Karen A. Rockoff
President COO and Director; President and COO
 Peapack-Gladstone Bank, Robert M. Rogers, age 54
EVP and Director; President PBG Trust and
 Investments Peapack-Gladstone Bank, Craig C.
 Spengeman, age 57
Director, F. Duffield (Duff) Meyercord, age 66
Director, Anthony J. Consi II, age 67
Director, Pamela Hill, age 74
Director, John D. Kissel, age 59
Director, James R. Lamb, age 70
Director, Edward A. Merton, age 72
Director, John R. Mulcahy, age 74
Director, Philip W. Smith III, age 56
Auditors: CroweHorwathLLP

LOCATIONS

HQ: Peapack-Gladstone Financial Corporation
 500 Hills Dr, Bedminster NJ 07921
Phone: 908-234-0700   Fax: 908-234-0795
Web: www.pgbank.com

PRODUCTS/OPERATIONS

2011 Sales

	$ mil.	% of total
Interest		
Loans including fees	46	64
Securities	9	13
Other	0	-
Noninterest		
Trust fees	10	15
Service charges & fees	2	4
Other	3	4
Total	**72**	**100**

COMPETITORS

Bank of America	PNC Financial
Hudson City Bancorp	TD Bank USA
JPMorgan Chase	Valley National
MSB Financial	Bancorp

HISTORICAL FINANCIALS

Company Type: Public

Income Statement

FYE: December 31

	ASSETS ($ mil.)	NET INCOME ($ mil.)	INCOME AS % OF ASSETS	EMPLOYEES
12/12	1,667.8	9.7	0.6%	292
12/11	1,600.3	12.1	0.8%	295
12/10	1,505.4	7.6	0.5%	284
12/09	1,512.3	7.1	0.5%	281
12/08	1,385.4	(22.0)	—	278
Annual Growth	**4.7%**	**—**	**—**	**1.2%**

2012 Year-End Financials

Return on assets: 0.5%
Return on equity: 7.8%
Long-term debt ($ mil.): —
No. of shares (mil.): 8
Sales ($ mil): 77

Dividends
 Yield: 1.4%
 Payout: 19.0%
Market value ($ mil.): 126

	STOCK PRICE ($) FY Close	P/E High/Low	PER SHARE ($) Earnings	Dividends	Book Value
12/12	14.08	16 10	1.05	0.20	13.69
12/11	10.75	11 8	1.25	0.20	13.92
12/10	13.05	23 16	0.68	0.20	13.39
12/09	12.68	42 17	0.64	0.40	13.70
12/08	26.64	— —	(2.53)	0.61	9.64
Annual Growth	**(14.7%)**	**— —**	**—**	**(24.3%)**	**9.2%**

Pegasystems Inc.

Pegasystems helps companies soar through business changes without being tied down by their old processes. The company provides rules-driven business process management software PegaRules Process Commander designed to help large companies in the financial services insurance and health care industries update their operations and systems to reflect changes in business goals and strategies. Established in 1983 Pegasystems offers tools for analyzing and simulating processes integrating enterprise applications and portals managing content integration and managing processes for customer service claims resolution and transaction processing.

Geographic Reach

Pegasystems is stationed in Massachusetts and has offices in Australia Canada India the UK the US and other countries. The US accounts for nearly 55% of its total revenue; the UK generates 19% and the rest of Europe 15%.

Sales and Marketing

Financial services and health care companies are Pegasystems' primary markets but the company also sells to clients in the manufacturing government travel and hospitality retail consumer packaged goods and telecommunications industries.

Pegasystems sells its products through its direct sales force as well as through distributors resellers and trade shows (including its PegaWorld user conference).

Financial Performance

In 2012 Pegasystems' cash flow and net income again turned up to match its continuously improving revenue. Overall revenues grew about 11% from $417 million in 2011 to reach $472 million in 2012 a historic milestone for the company.

It attributed the growth for 2012 to an 18% surge in license revenue. Maintenance revenue also spiked by 14% in 2012 due to the value of the installed base of its software coupled with higher renewal rates. Professional services revenue also jumped 2% due to higher consulting services revenue.

Profits skyrocketed 116% from $10 million in 2011 to $23 million in 2012 even as the company paid more in operational costs and expanding its headcount by 16%. Its bottom line was unencumbered by acquisitions and was helped by favorable foreign currency translations for 2012.

Strategy

To extend its geographic reach and attract additional customers Pegasystems enters partnerships with major IT services and software providers. Its list of strategic partners includes Accenture Capgemini Cognizant Infosys Mahindra Tata Consultancy Services Virtusa and Wipro.

In 2013 it signed a new partner in Anantara Solutions in an effort to enhance its software offerings and expand its reach further into the UK and mainland Europe. Anantara is developing testing automation framework for Pega-based applications that should speed up the testing process and shorten its window for bringing new Pegasystems products to market.

Ownership

Founder and CEO Alan Trefler owns more than 53% of Pegasystems.

EXECUTIVES

SVP Human Capital, Jeff Yanagi
Chairman and CEO, Alan Trefler, age 57, $288,000
 total compensation
Vice Chairman, Richard H. (Rick) Jones, age 61,
 $187,500 total compensation
Chief Marketing Officer, Grant E. Johnson
Chief Financial Officer VP, Craig A. Dynes, age 57,
 $288,000 total compensation
SVP Engineering and Product Development,
 Michael R. (Mike) Pyle, age 58, $255,000 total
 compensation
SVP Global Services, Douglas I. (Doug) Kra, age 50,
 $260,000 total compensation
VP General Counsel and Secretary, Shawn S. Hoyt,
 $199,583 total compensation
SVP Corporate Development, Max Mayer, $255,000
 total compensation
VP Finance and Chief Accounting Officer,
 Efstathios A. (Stathis) Kouninis, age 51
senior Vice President Global Sales, Edward L.
 Hughes, age 61
VP Industry Solutions, Willy Fox
Manager Public Relations and Communications
 Europe Middle East and Africa, Joanna Richardson
Senior Director Corporate Marketing, Russell
 Keziere
Director Corporate Communications, Brian
 Callahan
SVP Sales, Leon Trefler
Manager Public Relations, Frank Tutalo
Senior Vice President Business Unit Management
 at Pegasystems, Louis Blatt
Director, Craig A. Conway, age 58
Director, James P. O'Halloran, age 81
Vice Chairman, Richard H. (Rick) Jones, age 61
Director, Peter Gyenes, age 67
Director, William W. (Bill) Wyman, age 75
Independent Director, James OHalloran
Auditors: Deloitte&ToucheLLP

LOCATIONS

HQ: Pegasystems Inc.
 101 Main St., Cambridge MA 02142-1590
Phone: 617-374-9600   Fax: 617-374-9620
Web: www.pega.com

2012 Sales

	$ mil.	% of total
US	250	54
Europe		
UK	87	19
Other countries	69	15
Other regions	54	12
Total	**461**	**100**

PRODUCTS/OPERATIONS

2012 Sales

	$ mil.	% of total
Professional services	164	36
Software licenses	163	35
Maintenance	133	29
Total	**461**	**100**

Selected Software

PegaCloud
PegaCRM
Pega Decision Management
PegaRULES Process Commander
Solutions Frameworks

COMPETITORS

Appian	Progress Software
EMC	SAP
Fair Isaac	Software AG
Global 360	SunGard
Guidewire Software	TIBCO Software
IBM	TriZetto
Metastorm	Trintech
Microsoft Dynamics	salesforce.com
Oracle	

HISTORICAL FINANCIALS

Company Type: Public

Income Statement

FYE: December 31

	REVENUE ($ mil.)	NET INCOME ($ mil.)	NET PROFIT MARGIN	EMPLOYEES
12/12	461.7	21.8	4.7%	2,160
12/11	416.6	10.1	2.4%	1,858
12/10	336.6	(5.8)	—	1,509
12/09	264.0	32.2	12.2%	1,076
12/08	211.6	10.9	5.2%	825
Annual Growth	21.5%	18.8%	—	27.2%

2012 Year-End Financials

Debt ratio: —	No. of shares (mil.): 37
Return on equity: 9.8%	Dividends
Cash ($ mil.): 77	Yield: 0.6%
Current ratio: 1.80	Payout: 26.7%
Long-term debt ($ mil.): —	Market value ($ mil.): 861

	STOCK PRICE ($) FY Close	P/E High/Low	PER SHARE ($) Earnings	Dividends	Book Value
12/12	22.68	67 33	0.56	0.15	6.23
12/11	29.40	174 100	0.26	0.12	5.54
12/10	36.63	— —	(0.16)	0.12	5.25
12/09	34.00	40 13	0.85	0.12	5.57
12/08	12.36	50 30	0.29	0.12	4.83
Annual Growth	16.4%	— —	17.9%	5.7%	6.6%

Perficient Inc.

Perficient is proficient in helping its customers use technology to their advantage. The IT consultancy provides software development systems integration and technical support. It specializes in developing middleware applications used to integrate and modernize legacy computer hardware and software. Its expertise also encompasses content management systems ERP and CRM applications business process integration service oriented architectures business intelligence e-commerce and wireless communication. Perficient integrates and supports applications from vendors including IBM EMC Microsoft and Software AG. Customers have included Anheuser-Busch AT&T Mobility and Wachovia.

Geographic Reach

The company primarily serves customers in the US from about 20 locations. It has offshore software development facilities in China India and Macedonia.

Sales and Marketing

Perficient uses a direct sales force to target large enterprise customers that annually earn at least $500 million. Typically the company seeks to bill about $5 million for each account which it believes is below the target project range of most large systems integrators.

Financial Performance

Overall sales grew 25% in 2012 to $327 million primarily from acquisitions. (Perficient buys two or three companies every year.) The company makes most of its money by billing for services; less than 10% of sales come from licensing software and re-selling hardware which have lower profit margins. Expenses grew because of increased headcount and higher employee-related expenses. Still Perficient is also consistently profitable earning $16 million in profit for 2012.

Mergers and Acquisitions

Perficient has traditionally been an aggressive buyer of complementary businesses. It expanded its operations in the northeastern US –adding offices in Boston New York City and Washington DC –with the $19 million purchase of TriTek Solutions in 2013. Also that year it added salesforce.com consulting expertise to its portfolio with two companies - New Jersey-based CoreMatrix Systems and San Francisco-based Clear Task.

In 2012 it expanded in the Chicago Milwaukee and Boston markets with the $22 purchase of PointBridge Solutions. The acquisition solidified its position as a Microsoft systems integrator consultant. It also acquired Dallas-based Nascent Systems a business and technology consultancy focused on ERP applications from Oracle such as its E-Business Suite. Later that year it bought Atlanta-based Northridge Systems a consulting firm that provides collaboration services primarily using the Microsoft SharePoint platform for about $14 million. The purchase bolstered its Microsoft practice and extended its presence in the southeastern US.

In 2011 Perficient bought Charlotte North Carolina-based management consultancy Exervio to extend its expertise in program and project management in particular and to establish its presence in the state. Perficient also bought IT consultancy JCB Partners that year to build the part of its services business that focuses on IBM's Cognos suite of enterprise applications. The deal was part of an effort to boost its business intelligence and performance management capabilities.

EXECUTIVES

VP Field Operations Western Region, Don Kasica
President; Chief Executive Officer; Director, Jeffrey S. (Jeff) Davis, age 49, $285,000 total compensation
Chief Financial Officer; Treasurer; Secretary, Paul E. Martin, age 53, $225,000 total compensation
Chief Operating Officer, Kathryn J. (Kathy) Henely, age 48, $215,417 total compensation
VP Field Operations IBM Advanced Technology Services, John Jenkins
VP Field Operations Eastern Region, Chris Gianattasio
Marketing and Public Relations, Bill Davis
Vice President Industry Practices, David Hastoglis
General Manager China Global Services, Kevin Sheen
Vice President National and Emerging Technology Solutions, Jackie Thorn
General Manager Oracle Applications, Tim Robinson
Vice President IBM Business Process Management Systems, Hari Madamalla
General Manager Great Lakes, John Griffin
Vice President Oracle Applications, Emil Fernandez
Vice President Central Region, Ed Hoffman
General Manager IBM ATS, Joseph Klewicki
General Manager Dallas, Phil Leary
General Manager Enterprise Content Management, Ed Rawson
General Manager Houston and New Orleans, Jim Roberts
General Manager TIBCO EAI, Eric Roch
General Manager Microsoft West, Aaron Sloman
General Manager Detroit Philadelphia Toronto, Joel Stanesa
Vice President Microsoft, Mike Gersten
Director, Edward L. Glotzbach, age 63
Director, John S. Hamlin, age 47
Director, David S. Lundeen, age 51
President CEO and Director, Jeffrey S. (Jeff) Davis, age 48
Director, James R. Kackley, age 71
Director, Ralph C. Derrickson, age 55
Director, David D. May, age 49
Auditors: KPMGLLP

LOCATIONS

HQ: Perficient Inc.
520 Maryville Centre Dr. Ste. 400, St. Louis MO 63141
Phone: 314-529-3600   **Fax:** 314-529-3640
Web: www.perficient.com

PRODUCTS/OPERATIONS

2012 Sales

	% of total
Services	87
Software &	8
Reimbursable	5
Total	100

Mergers Acquisitio

2013
TriTek Solutions
Clear Task

2012
Nascent Systems
Northridge Systems
PointBridge Solutions

2011
Exervio
JCB Partners

2010
Kerdock Consulting
speakTECH

COMPETITORS

Accenture	Edgewater Technology
Avanade	HP Enterprise Services
CIBER	Hackett Group
Cognizant Tech Solutions	Infosys
Deloitte Consulting	Sapient
Deloitte LLP	Wipro

HISTORICAL FINANCIALS

Company Type: Public

Income Statement

FYE: December 31

	REVENUE ($ mil.)	NET INCOME ($ mil.)	NET PROFIT MARGIN	EMPLOYEES
12/12	327.1	16.1	4.9%	1,677
12/11	262.4	10.7	4.1%	1,484
12/10	214.9	6.4	3.0%	1,088
12/09	188.1	1.4	0.8%	1,015
12/08	231.4	10.0	4.3%	1,186
Annual Growth	9.0%	12.7%	—	9.0%

2012 Year-End Financials

Debt ratio: 1.0%
Return on equity: 7.4%
Cash ($ mil.): 5
Current ratio: 2.83
Long-term debt ($ mil.): 2

No. of shares (mil.): 30
Dividends
  Yield: —
  Payout: —
Market value ($ mil.): 363

	STOCK PRICE ($) FY Close	P/E High/Low	PER SHARE ($) Earnings	Dividends	Book Value
12/12	11.78	25 19	0.52	0.00	7.60
12/11	10.01	34 17	0.37	0.00	6.92
12/10	12.50	54 34	0.23	0.00	6.50
12/09	8.43	186 68	0.05	0.00	6.22
12/08	4.78	50 8	0.33	0.00	6.13
Annual Growth	25.3%	— —	12.0%	—	5.5%

PhotoMedex, Inc.

For PhotoMedex beauty is skin deep. The company manufactures and markets dermatological treatments for skin disorders such as acne psoriasis and vitiligo (loss of skin pigmentation). Other products include gels and creams intended to promote skin rejuvenation and hair growth. PhotoMedex also develops lasers and fiber-optic equipment for dermatological and surgical applications. Its FDA-approved XTRAC Excimer laser system is used for the treatment of psoriasis and eczema and its VTRAC lamp system is sold outside the US to treat the same ailments. Customers in the US and overseas include consumers dermatologists cosmetic surgeons and spas.

Operations

PhotoMedex breaks its operations into three categories: consumer (no!no! branded products) physician recurring (XTRAC lasers and NEOVA topical skin care) and professional (VTRAC Velocity and other light therapy equipment).

PhotoMedex conducts R&D at three facilities; along with developing new products its R&D activities are focused on expanding uses of the XTRAC system to include the treatment of inflammatory skin disorders; the development of complementary devices to improve XTRAC and other light-based systems' performance; and developing additional surgical products.

Geographic Reach

With headquarters in the US PhotoMedex exports to about 30 countries around the world. Key markets include Japan the UK Argentina and Australia.

Sales and Marketing

The company uses a direct sales force along with a global distribution and retail network to spread its products globally. The no!no! branded consumer products are available in about 55 countries.

Financial Analysis

PhotoMedex saw its revenues increase by nearly 70% in 2012 thanks to an 33% jump in consumer products revenues as a result of a growth in direct-to-consumer revenues due to successful marketing programs and an increase in retailers and home shopping channels sales thanks to successful marketing programs to the various home shopping channel customers in the UK and the US. It also saw an 48% increase in professional segment revenues.

The company saw a huge 300% increase in net income in 2012 as it offset an increase in selling and marketing expenses as the result of a rise in its direct-to-consumer advertising and selling activities and higher engineering and product development expenses related to pre-merged PhotoMedex products.

Strategy

The company seeks to expand by providing dermatologists professional aestheticians and consumers with the equipment and skin care products they need to treat psoriasis vitiligo acne and UV damage among other skin conditions.

Growing its portfolio of offerings in 2011 PhotoMedex merged with private dermatology firm Radiancy. Radiancy makes home-use and professional dermatology devices for hair removal skin rejuvenation and acne treatment under the no!no! and Radiancy brands. PhotoMedex acquired Radiancy in an all-stock transaction. Although the combined operations retained the PhotoMedex name and publicly traded status former Radiancy shareholders obtained about 75% of the combined company.

As a result of its merger with Radiancy PhotoMedex added a range of home-use devices under the no!no! brand for various indications including hair removal acne treatment and skin rejuvenation.

PhotoMedex is working hard to expand outside the US. Its primary distributor GlobalMed sells the company's laser- and light-based devices in all PhotoMedex's markets outside the US. The company has even reformulated some of its clinical skincare products removing certain preservatives to better comply with international regulations.

Ownership

CEO Dr. Dolev Rafaeli controls 10% of the company.

EXECUTIVES

President; Chief Financial Officer; Director, Dennis M. McGrath, age 57, $297,606 total compensation
CTO, Jeffrey L. Levatter
CEO and Director, Dolev Rafaeli
EVP and COO, Michael R. Stewart
Chairman, Lewis C. Pell
Vice Chairman, Yoav Ben Dror
President CFO and Director, Dennis M. McGrath, age 56
Director, James W. Sight, age 57
Director, Alan R. Novak, age 78
Director, Stephen P. Connelly, age 61
Director, David W. Anderson, age 60
Director, Leonard L. Mazur
Director, Paul J. Denby
CEO and Director, Dolev Rafaeli
Independent Director, Katsumi Oneda
Independent Director, Nahum Melumad
Vice Chairman, Yoav Ben Dror
Auditors: FahnKanne&Co.GrantThorntonIsrael

LOCATIONS

HQ: PhotoMedex Inc.
147 Keystone Dr., Montgomeryville PA 18936
Phone: 215-619-3600   Fax: 215-619-3208
Web: www.photomedex.com

2012 Sales

	$ mil.	% of total
North America	164	74
Asia/Pacific	28	13
Europe	25	12
South America	3	1
Total	**220**	**100**

PRODUCTS/OPERATIONS

2012 Sales

	$ mil.	% of total
Consumer	188	85
Physician Recurring	21	10
Professional	10	5
Total	**220**	**100**

COMPETITORS

Allergan Limited	Obagi Medical
Anacor	Osyris Medical
Boston Scientific	Palomar Medical
Candela Corporation	SkinMedica
Cutera	Solta Medical
Cynosure	Syneron
Hoffmann-La Roche	TRIA Beauty
Lumenis	Trimedyne
Murad Inc.	

HISTORICAL FINANCIALS

Company Type: Public

Income Statement

FYE: December 31

	REVENUE ($ mil.)	NET INCOME ($ mil.)	NET PROFIT MARGIN	EMPLOYEES
12/12	220.6	22.4	10.2%	177
12/11	132.0	(0.6)	—	183
12/10	34.8	(8.7)	—	144
12/09	32.6	(10.5)	—	131
12/08	34.7	(11.2)	—	171
Annual Growth	58.7%	—	—	0.9%

2012 Year-End Financials

Debt ratio: 0.2%
Return on equity: 16.0%
Cash ($ mil.): 44
Current ratio: 3.28
Long-term debt ($ mil.): —

No. of shares (mil.): 21
Dividends
  Yield: —
  Payout: —
Market value ($ mil.): 306

	STOCK PRICE ($) FY Close	P/E High/Low	PER SHARE ($) Earnings	Dividends	Book Value
12/12	14.53	17 10	1.08	0.00	7.95
12/11	12.90	— —	(0.06)	0.00	5.96
12/10	5.94	— —	(3.37)	0.00	6.57
12/09	0.95	— —	(6.42)	0.00	10.24
12/08	0.28	— —	(7.50)	0.00	19.78
Annual Growth	168.4%	— —	(20.4%)	—	—

Pike Corp

Pike Electric helps its customers stay current. The electrical services contractor (also known as Pike Energy Solutions) provides services for more than 200 public municipal and cooperative utility companies primarily in the eastern and southern US. Activities include the planning design engineering construction maintenance and repair of electric substations and transmission lines including renewable energy systems. Pike Electric owns a fleet of more than 4700 pieces of motorized equipment including trucks trailers cranes backhoes and generators. The company is active in some 40 states.

The company's top 10 customers generate more than half of its revenues annually; Duke Energy Carolinas alone accounts for about 20% of sales. Pike Electric has worked to broaden operations both geographically and in terms of services offered. The company hopes to capitalize not only the continually increasing demand for electricity in the US but also on the repair and maintenance of the nation's deteriorating electricity infrastructure.

In 2008 the company acquired Shaw Energy Delivery Services from the Shaw Group augmenting its capabilities for power lines and substations and expanding its operations in the West and Mid-Atlantic. The following year the company acquired the assets of Facilities Planning & Siting allowing it to offer a range of services for new projects including environmental economic and regulatory planning.

In 2010 Pike Electric bought Arizona-based Klondyke Construction expanding its presence in the western US and in the renewable energy market. Also that year the company secured contracts in Africa to construct or expand power lines in Tanzania.

Pike Electric further expanded its capabilities in the West with its 2011 acquisition of Pine Valley Power. The following year it paid $70 million for Synergetic Design Holdings whose subsidiary UC Synergetic provides electric utilities with services primarily around distribution powerline projects such as storm assessment and inspection. That purchase pumped up its position in the northeast and Midwest and its overall competitiveness as one of the largest utility infrastructure engineering and design companies in the US.

Because a portion of its revenues are related to the restoration of electrical service due to storms and severe weather Pike Electric's bottom line can literally change with the wind. Its storm restoration segment had record sales in 2005 and 2006 due to an increase in hurricane activity in the Gulf Coast and Florida. In 2009 Hurricanes Ike and Gustav and winter weather in the Midwest created another spike for the storm restoration unit. Due to the volatility of the demand for storm restoration the business's earnings can fluctuate from less than 10% to more than a quarter of the company's overall earnings.

Investment firm Lindsay Goldberg owns nearly 40% of Pike Electric and has board representation through managing partner Robert Lindsay.

EXECUTIVES

President Pike Energy Solutions, James R. (Jimmy) Hicks, age 67
Chairman President and CEO, J. Eric Pike, age 46, $728,745 total compensation
Operations Vice President FL, Neal Sanders

Operations Vice President GANorth FL, Phillip Combs
Operations Vice President TXOKAK, Bo Lankford
EVP and CFO, Anthony K. Slater, age 44, $409,160 total compensation
VP Risk Management General Counsel and Corporate Secretary, James R. (Jim) Fox, age 66, $346,262 total compensation
President Pike Electric LLC, James T. (Jim) Benfield, age 51, $359,436 total compensation
EVP Operations, Audie G. Simmons, age 58, $431,886 total compensation
Controller Chief Accounting Officer, Gary D. Waldman
Regional Vice President, Stan Marion
Operations Vice President NCSC, Donald B. (Don) Anderson
Vice President of Environmental, Ken Flechler
SVP Human Resources, Timothy (Tim) Harshbarger
Vice President of Information Technology, Michael D. Seymour
Vice President Project Management West, Brian R. Hay
Engineering Manager Region, David Rodriguez
Vice President Operations, Frank Hoffmann
SVP Engineering SCANA-PMO, Don Robertson
VP Engineering Northwest Region, George Culbertson
Chief Executive Officer, Peter J. Burlage
Program Director - Solar Energy, Ed M. Spooner
Operations Vice President ALMSFLLA, David Condrey
Senior Vice President, Frank Hopkins
Operations Vice President MDVANCSC, Gene Walden
VP Engineering West Region, Mansour Pourcyrous
Chief Information Officer, Mark Thomson
Vice President Project Management East, Mark Jennette
Program Director - Wind Energy, Stacey D. Nobles
President Chief Operating Officer, Tim Dove
Director, Charles E. Bayless, age 70
Director, Gen. Peter Pace, age 67
Director, Louis F. Terhar, age 64
Director, Robert D. Lindsay, age 58
Director, J. Russell Triedman, age 57
Director, James R. Helvey III, age 54
Independent Director, James Turner
Auditors: Ernst&YoungLLP

LOCATIONS

HQ: Pike Electric Corporation
100 Pike Way, Mt. Airy NC 27030
Phone: 336-789-2171   **Fax:** 336-719-4566
Web: www.pike.com

PRODUCTS/OPERATIONS

2011 Sales

	$ mil.	% of total
Core services	529	89
Storm restoration services	64	11
Total	**593**	**100**

COMPETITORS

APi Group	MasTec
EMCOR	Newtron Group
Forest Electric	Quanta Services
Integrated Electrical Services	Southern Telecom
	Team Fishel

HISTORICAL FINANCIALS

Company Type: Public

Income Statement

FYE: June 30

	REVENUE ($ mil.)	NET INCOME ($ mil.)	NET PROFIT MARGIN	EMPLOYEES
06/13	918.6	36.1	3.9%	5,700
06/12	685.1	10.8	1.6%	5,400
06/11	593.8	1.4	0.2%	4,600
06/10	504.0	(13.4)	—	4,500
06/09	613.4	31.5	5.1%	4,500
Annual Growth	**10.6%**	**3.5%**	**—**	**6.1%**

2013 Year-End Financials

Debt ratio: 35.4%	No. of shares (mil.): 31
Return on equity: 13.9%	Dividends
Cash ($ mil.): 2	Yield: 0.0%
Current ratio: 2.40	Payout: 96.1%
Long-term debt ($ mil.): 221	Market value ($ mil.): 390

	STOCK PRICE ($) FY Close	P/E High/Low		PER SHARE ($) Earnings	Dividends	Book Value
06/13	12.30	15	7	1.04	1.00	7.62
06/12	7.72	31	20	0.31	0.00	7.90
06/11	8.84	260	170	0.04	0.00	7.56
06/10	9.42	—	—	(0.41)	0.00	7.44
06/09	12.05	20	7	0.94	0.00	7.68
Annual Growth	**0.5%**	**—**	**—**	**2.6%**	**—**	**(0.2%)**

Pioneer Energy Services Corp

Pioneer Energy Services (formerly Pioneer Drilling) digs down deep to make money from beneath the land where Texas pioneers used to roam as well as in other locations. The company provides contract drilling services primarily to oil and gas companies in Texas and to a lesser degree in the Rockies and in Colombia. Pioneer Energy Services owns 64 land drilling rigs that can reach depths of 8000-18000 feet. In addition the company's Pioneer Production Services Division provides workover rig services wireline services and fishing and rental services to US-based oil and gas producers.

Operations

The company serves oil and gas companies through two business segments: Its Drilling Services Division provides contract land drilling services with its fleet of more than 60 drilling rigs. Its Production Services Division provides a range of exploration and production services including well services wireline coiled tubing and fishing and rental services.

Geographic Reach

It core services are heavily concentrated in the Bakken (North Dakota) and Eagle Ford (Texas) shale plays the Permian Basin (Texas and New Mexico) and along the Gulf Coast. In 2011 it was also operating eight drilling rigs in Colombia.

Financial Analysis

Strong demand from oil and gas drillers helped the company to report a 47% increase in revenues in 2011. Drilling Services sales increased by $121.7 million or 39% due to higher rig utilization rates (up to 73% in 2011 from 59% in 2010) and stronger drilling revenue rates (up 15%). Its Production Services revenues increased by $107 million or 61% primarily due to higher demand for wireline services well services and fishing and rental services. That year the company added 21 wireline units and 15 well service rigs to keep up with demand.

Net income grew from a net loss of $33.3 million in 2010 to a surplus of $11.2 million in 2011 as significantly higher revenues outstripped moderately higher costs. General and administrative expenses increased by $15.3 million (29%) in 2011 as compared to 2010 as a result of an increase in payroll and compensation related expenses and professional fees. Other operating expenses also increased due to $7.3 million tax expense for Pioneer Energy Services' Colombian operations. Depreciation and amortization expenses increased by $12 million.

Strategy

Since 2007 the company has transformed itself from a pure play US land contract driller to a diversified energy services provider with operations across the US and in Colombia. To reflect this broader profile in 2012 Pioneer Drilling changed its name to Pioneer Energy Services to reflect its wider range of services.

Pioneer Energy Services' long-term strategy is to maintain and leverage its position as top land drilling and production services company do more work for its existing customers while expanding its customer base in the areas in which it operates while looking to expand internationally through selective acquisitions. In the short term it is targeting high-return shale plays and lucrative oil and liquids conventional opportunities in the US.

M&A Activity

Growing its equipment portfolio in 2011 the company acquired Louisiana-based Go-Coil (which operates seven onshore coiled tubing units and three coiled tubing offshore units and related equipment) for $110 million. Go-Coil has facilities in Louisiana Oklahoma Pennsylvania and Texas.

That year Pioneer Energy Services also completed four other acquisitions of production services businesses for $6.5 million.

Major Customers

In 2011 the company's major customers in term of sales were: Ecopetrol (13.5%) Whiting Petroleum (10.6%) and Talisman Energy USA (3.6%).

Ownership

In 2012 BlackRock Inc. held 13.7% of Pioneer Energy Services.

EXECUTIVES

EVP and President Production Services, Joseph B. (Joe) Eustace, age 58, $209,828 total compensation
President CEO and Director, William S. (Stacy) Locke, age 57, $523,077 total compensation
SVP Marketing Drilling Services, Donald G. Lacombe, age 59, $205,962 total compensation
EVP and President Drilling Services, Franklin C. (Red) West, age 73, $388,269 total compensation
SVP Operations Drilling Services, J. Blaine David
EVP and CFO, Lorne E. Phillips, age 42
SVP and General Counsel, Carlos R. Pe?a, age 46
VP Global Human Resources, Scott Keenan
Director, John M. Rauh, age 62
President CEO and Director, William S. (Stacy) Locke, age 56
Director, C. John Thompson, age 59
Director, Scott D. Urban, age 58
Auditors: KPMGLLP

LOCATIONS

HQ: Pioneer Energy Services Corp.
1250 NE Loop 410 Ste. 1000, San Antonio TX 78209
Phone: 210-828-7689   **Fax:** 210-828-8228
Web: www.pioneeres.com

PRODUCTS/OPERATIONS

2011 Sales

	$ mil.	% of total
Drilling services	433	61
Production services	282	39
Total	**715**	**100**

COMPETITORS

Baker Hughes	Patterson-UTI Energy
Basic Energy	Precision Drilling
Halliburton	Rowan Companies
Helmerich & Payne	Schlumberger
Nabors Industries	Unit Corporation
National Oilwell Varco	Weatherford
Parker Drilling	International

HISTORICAL FINANCIALS
Company Type: Public

Income Statement
FYE: December 31

	REVENUE ($ mil.)	NET INCOME ($ mil.)	NET PROFIT MARGIN	EMPLOYEES
12/12	919.4	30.0	3.3%	3,750
12/11	715.9	11.1	1.6%	3,330
12/10	487.2	(33.2)	—	2,550
12/09	325.5	(23.2)	—	1,700
12/08	610.8	(62.7)	—	1,952
Annual Growth	**10.8%**	**—**		**17.7%**

2012 Year-End Financials

Debt ratio: 38.7%	No. of shares (mil.): 62
Return on equity: 5.6%	Dividends
Cash ($ mil.): 23	Yield: —
Current ratio: 1.40	Payout: —
Long-term debt ($ mil.): 518	Market value ($ mil.): 450

	STOCK PRICE ($) FY Close	P/E High/Low	PER SHARE ($) Earnings	Dividends	Book Value
12/12	7.26	21 12	0.48	0.00	8.83
12/11	9.68	93 34	0.19	0.00	8.26
12/10	8.81	— —	(0.62)	0.00	7.31
12/09	7.90	— —	(0.46)	0.00	7.79
12/08	5.57	— —	(1.26)	0.00	8.28
Annual Growth	**6.8%**	**— —**	**—**	**—**	**1.6%**

Piper Jaffray Companies

Piper Jaffray keeps the light on in the corner conference room. The investment banking firm specializes in supplying clients with mergers and acquisitions advice financing and industry research. Founded in 1895 it also offers equity and debt underwriting sales and trading. Piper Jaffray serves a variety of clients from corporations to government entities and not-for-profits. The company targets middle-market companies across many sectors such as consumer financial services health care technology and industrial among others. With some $11 billion in assets under management Piper Jaffray serves domestic and international clients throughout offices across the US and in two European cities.

Geographic Reach

Based in Minnesota Piper Jaffray operates through more than 40 principal offices in about two dozen US states and overseas in London and Zurich.

Operations

Piper Jaffray operates its business through two segments: Capital Markets (more than 80% of sales) and Asset Management (more than 10%).

Through its Capital Markets segment Piper Jaffray provides its clients with investment banking and institutional sales trading and research services for a variety of equity and fixed products. Additionally the segment comprises Piper Jaffray's alternative asset management funds and principal investments.

The company's Asset Management segment is focused on traditional asset management activities and their related services. It specifically markets its asset management business under the Advisory Research name.

Sales and Marketing

Piper Jaffray serves several sectors such as consumer financial services health care media telecommunications technology alternative energy business services and industrial. It spent 12% less on marketing and business development in 2012 ($19.9 million) as compared to $22.6 million in 2011.

The Capital Markets segment focuses on middle-market clients in business services clean technology and renewables consumer healthcare industrials technology media and communications. Within its Asset Management segment Piper Jaffray serves institutions and individuals providing traditional asset management services with both equity and Master Limited Partnership securities through proprietary distribution channels.

The company markets its primary investment banking and institutional securities businesses under the broader Piper Jaffray name.

Financial Performance

Revenue rose by 6% in 2012 to $518 million thanks to strong growth in the capital markets segment. Debt financing and advisory services sales boosted investment banking revenue while fixed income trading sales bolstered overall institutional brokerage revenues.

The asset management segment also grew although at a slower pace as the company reported increased management fees from its master limited partnership (MLP) offerings.

Strategy

In recent years Piper Jaffray has streamlined its European operations to focus on giving M&A advice and distributing US and Asian securities to institutional investors in Europe. Overseas it also divested its Hong Kong capital markets business.

The company has expanded its operations with new fixed income sales and trading offices in the US in North Carolina Ohio and Texas while also adding staff to its Asia business across the functions of investment banking sales and trading and research.

Mergers and Acquisitions

In an effort to expand its client base with companies valued at between $25 million and $500 million Piper Jaffray in 2013 acquired Edgeview Partners a Charlotte North Carolina-based middle-market advisory firm that specializes in mergers and acquisitions.

Giving it a leg up in all major US markets Piper Jaffray also bought Seattle-Northwest Securities Corporation. Purchasing the public finance firm expands the company's public finance franchise and fortifies its business of serving municipal and middle-market clients nationwide.

HISTORY

In 1913 Harry Piper and Palmer Jaffray founded a commercial paper brokerage that helped finance companies like Pillsbury and Archer-Daniels-Midland. It soon moved into public finance and underwriting. It gained a seat on the NYSE with its purchase of Hopwood & Co. which was hard hit by the 1929 crash. Piper Jaffray & Hopwood grew over the next 40 years going public in 1971. Three years later it became Piper Jaffray.

During the 1980s boom Piper Jaffray still managed by the Piper family expanded into asset management and mutual funds. It was relatively unscathed by the 1987 crash.

Real trouble hit in 1994 when a derivatives-heavy bond mutual fund foundered. Investors claiming they were uninformed of the risk brought a class-action suit against the firm which paid out more than $100 million in settlements beginning in 1995.

In 1997 Piper Jaffray began offering new classes of shares of its mutual funds to provide more fee options for investors. The SEC sued the company for fraud related to the 1994 mutual fund debacle in 1998.

That year U. S. Bancorp looking to expand its securities business bought the company and bundled its own investment operations into U. S. Bancorp Piper Jaffray. In 1999 the unit expanded with the purchase of investment banker Libra Investments. The firm also entered an alliance with Tel Aviv-based investment bank Nessuah Zannex to back technology and health care ventures in Israel.

Piper Jaffray traditionally has taken pride in its investment research yet it was one of several investment banks scrutinized for alleged conflicts-of-interest between research and I-banking operations. In 2003 the firm was fined $25 million and required to pay an additional $7.5 million to provide independent research for investors. As part of the settlement the company combined its research functions into a single group and implemented firewalls between its analysts and investment bankers. Losing money Piper Jaffray was spun off from U.S. Bancorp and returned to the publicly traded arena that same year.

Piper Jaffray sold its Private Client business which offered mutual funds securities and annuities to individual investors to UBS Financial Services in 2006. Piper Jaffray used proceeds from the sale of the unit which included some 90 branches mainly west of the Mississippi to expand its industry focus. It built its asset management business with the 2007 purchases of St. Louis-based Fiduciary Asset Management (FAMCO) which brought in some $6 billion of assets under management and Hong Kong-based Goldbond Capital.

EXECUTIVES

Chairman and CEO, Andrew S. Duff, age 55, $400,000 total compensation
Vice Chairman of Piper Jaffray & Co. and Managing Director Merchant Banking, Thomas P. (Tom) Schnettler, age 56, $300,000 total compensation
Managing Director and Global Co-Head Technology Media and Telecommunications Investment Banking, David Castagna

Managing Director Head Global Equities, Robert W. (Bob) Peterson, age 45, $225,000 total compensation
Global Co-Head Health Care Corporate Investment Banking, Stuart M. Duty, age 48
Global Head Technology Media & Telecommunications Corporate Investment Banking, Mark Leavitt
Managing Director Co-Head Public Finance and Fixed Income, R. Todd Firebaugh, age 50
Global Head Healthcare Corporate Investment Banking, Robert (Bob) DeSutter
Director Investor Relations, Jennifer A. Olson-Goude
Managing Director; Co-Head Investment Banking and Capital Markets, Chad R. Abraham
Managing Director Global Co-Head of Investment Banking and Capital Markets, R. Scott LaRue
Managing Director and Global Head Consumer Investment Banking, Murray Huneke
Managing Director Head of Fixed Income Sales Trading and Underwriting Head of Strategic Trading President of Piper Jaffray Investment Management, M. Brad Winges, age 45, $225,000 total compensation
Managing Director and Head Public Finance Services, Francis E. (Frank) Fairman, age 55, $205,000 total compensation
VP Municipal Derivatives and Reinvestment Products, Mark Kaplan
SVP Public Finance Investment Banking Real Estate and Housing, Patrick O'Leary
Managing Director Head of Asset Management, Brien M. O'Brien
Head Financial Institutions Corporate Investment Banking, Thomas (Tom) Chen
Managing Director and Global Head Clean Technology and Renewables Corporate Investment Banking, Chris McCabe
Senior Research Analyst Semiconductor and Enabling Tehnologies, Auguste (Gus) Richard
President and CEO Fiduciary Asset Management LLC (FAMCO), Wiley D. Angell
Managing Director Chief Financial Officer, Debbra L. Schoneman, age 44, $225,000 total compensation
CEO Piper Jaffray Asia, Alex P.M. Ko, age 54
Head and Managing Director Industrial Growth and Financial Sponsor Coverage Investment Banking, Larry Zimmerman
SVP Public Finance Investment Banking, Dustin Avey
SVP Public Finance Investment Banking, Matthew Challis
VP Public Finance Investment Banking, Helen Cregger
Managing Director Public Finance Investment Banking, Todd Goffoy
VP Public Finance Investment Banking, Gordon Hoven
VP Public Finance Investment Banking, Michael Lund
SVP Sacramento Public Finance Investment Banking, Dennis McGuire
VP Public Finance Investment Banking, John Peterson
Managing Director Public Finance Investment Banking Hospitality, Peter Phillippi
VP Public Finance Investment Banking, Greg Swartz
SVP Public Finance Investment Banking, Todd Van Deventer
SVP Public Finance Investment Banking, Mark Farrell
VP Public Finance Investment Banking, Matthew (Matt) Gillaspie
Head Asian Distribution, Michael Chan

Managing Director and Group Head Restructuring, Peter Schwab
Managing Director General Counsel and Secretary, John W. Geelan
Principal and Senior Research Analyst Solar and Clean Technologies, Ahmar Zaman
Managing Director Corporate Investment Banking, John Lonnquist
VP Corporate Investment Banking, Kevin Jakuc
SVP Public Finance Investment Banking, Jay Hromatka
VP Public Finance Investment Banking, Ivory Li
SVP Public Finance Investment Banking, Mark Piscatelli
Head Health Care Public Finance Investment Banking, Steven (Steve) Proeschel
Managing Director, Matthew Weaver
SVP Public Finance Investment Banking, Lisa Sexton
President Advisory Research Inc., Chris Crawshaw
Managing Director Global Head Human Capital and Assistant General Counsel, Christine Esckilsen
Managing Director and Head of Piper Jaffray Asia, Alex Ko Po Ming
Managing Director and Chief Information Officer of Piper Jaffray Companies; Chief Operating Officer of Piper Jaffray Investment Management, Shawn Quant
Managing Director Corporate Development, Thomas G. (Tom) Smith
SVP Public Finance Investment Banking, Eric Lunde
VP Public Finance Investment Banking, Craig Theis
Senior Vice President Fixed, Ben Armstrong
Head - Asset Management, Brien Brien
Vice President, Piper Jaffray
Vice President Public Finance Investment Banking, Sarkis Garabedian
Head - Asset Management, Brien OBrien
Managing Director and Head of Global Equities, Jeff Klinefelter
Director, Addison L. (Tad) Piper, age 66
Director, Jean M. Taylor, age 50
Director, Frank L. Sims, age 62
Director, Michael R. Francis, age 50
Vice Chairman and Managing Director Merchant Banking, Thomas P. (Tom) Schnettler, age 55
Director, B. Kristine (Kris) Johnson, age 61
Director, Michele Volpi, age 48
Director, Virginia Gambale, age 53
Director, Lisa K. Polsky, age 56
Independent Director, Hope Woodhouse
Auditors: Ernst&YoungLLP

LOCATIONS

HQ: Piper Jaffray Companies
800 Nicollet Mall, Suite 1000, Minneapolis, MN 55402
Phone: 612 303-6000
Web: www.piperjaffray.com

PRODUCTS/OPERATIONS

Selected Services
Investment Banking
  Services
    Mergers & Acquisitions
    Capital Markets
    Private Placements
    Restructuring
    Debt Advisory
    Corporate & Venture Services
Public Finance
  Government Expertise
    Local Municipalities
    States & State Agencies

2012 SALES

		No.
Investment banking	230.9	45
Institutional brokerage	172.0	33
Asset management	65.2	13
Interest	48.9	9
Other	1.2	—
Total	**518.2**	**100**

COMPETITORS

CIBC World Markets	JPMorgan Chase
Citigroup Global Markets	Jefferies Group
	Morgan Stanley
Cowen Group	Raymond James
Credit Suisse (USA)	Financial
Deutsche Banc Alex. Brown	Robert W. Baird & Co.
Goldman Sachs	Thomas Weisel Partners
Houlihan Lokey	UBS Financial Services

HISTORICAL FINANCIALS

Company Type: Public

Income Statement
FYE: December 31

	REVENUE ($ mil.)	NET INCOME ($ mil.)	NET PROFIT MARGIN	EMPLOYEES
12/12	488.9	41.2	8.4%	966
12/11	458.1	(102.0)	—	1,014
12/10	530.0	24.3	4.6%	1,053
12/09	468.7	30.3	6.5%	1,054
12/08	326.4	(182.9)	—	1,036
Annual Growth	10.6%	—	—	(1.7%)

2012 Year-End Financials

Debt ratio: 45.9%
Return on equity: 5.6%
Cash ($ mil.): 281
Current ratio: 1.41
Long-term debt ($ mil.): 125

No. of shares (mil.): 15
Dividends
Yield: —
Payout: —
Market value ($ mil.): 489

	STOCK PRICE ($) FY Close	P/E High/Low		PER SHARE ($) Earnings	Dividends	Book Value
12/12	32.13	14	9	2.26	0.00	48.20
12/11	20.20	—	—	(6.51)	0.00	45.61
12/10	35.01	42	22	1.23	0.00	55.51
12/09	50.61	37	12	1.55	0.00	49.80
12/08	39.76	—	—	(11.55)	0.00	47.69
Annual Growth	(5.2%)			—	—	0.3%

Plexus Corp.

Plexus isn't perplexed by even complex contract electronics manufacturing. The company develops and manufactures electronic products for companies in the telecommunications medical industrial and defense markets. Plexus provides product design assembly and testing of printed circuit boards (PCBs) test equipment and other electronic components. The company also offers prototyping materials procurement warehousing and distribution and other support services. Customers include networking equipment maker Juniper Networks (13% of sales) and General Electric. Plexus gets most of its sales from customers in the US and Malaysia.

Geographic Reach

Plexus operates more than a dozen manufacturing plants in China Malaysia Mexico Romania the UK and the US (in California and Wisconsin).

Sales and Marketing

Altogether Plexus has manufacturing contracts with about 140 customers. Juniper Networks which has been its largest customer for years ended its contract with Plexus in 2013. Between 50% and 60% of sales comes from Plexus' top 10 customers so losing just one can costly.

Financial Performance

Overall revenues fell slightly (3%) in fiscal 2013 (year-end September) after one of its customers in the industrial/commercial sector experienced a decrease in end-market demand and after the relationship with Juniper Networks was severed. Profits however were up 32% to $82 million thanks to a $17 million year-over-year valuation allowance adjustment.

Strategy

Plexus' sales and profits rely on demand from customers and end-users as well as the mix of products produced for its customers. The company's strategy is to focus on mid-to-low volume higher complexity turnkey programs focusing on flexibility technology quality and adhering to regulatory requirements. It also offers value-added services such as logistics management and repair services. In addition it segments its R&D with teams dedicated to each of its target sectors.

As a company dependent on technological know-how Plexus does invest in expanding and upgrading its plants. In 2013 it expanded its plant in Mexico by another 265000 square feet and built another 300000-sq.-ft. plant in Romania for $30 million. It also expanded its design and manufacturing operations in Scotland by 65000 square feet. In 2012 it began construction a new $50 million 410000-sq.-ft. manufacturing plant in Wisconsin.

Mergers and Acquisitions

In 2012 Plexus bought the Malaysian manufacturing operations of German computer manufacturer Kontron AG. Plexus paid $34 million for the inventory and equipment of Kontron Design Manufacturing Services which it moved to its own plant in Malaysia.

HISTORY

In the 1970s Peter Strandwitz needed a contract electronics manufacturer when his small electronics business suffered from a lack of engineering expertise. He founded Plexus in 1979 and marketed its services to electronics companies that could not efficiently operate their own manufacturing facilities. The company went public in 1986. Three years later it discontinued its faltering International Communications subsidiary which made pay phones to concentrate on its core business.

Plexus grew throughout the early 1990s and in 1994 doubled its manufacturing capabilities with a new facility in Neenah Wisconsin. In 1996 Plexus and Oneida Nation Electronics a company owned by the Native American Oneida tribe built an electronics fabrication plant in Green Bay Wisconsin. The next year Plexus acquired NEI Electronics and computer parts maker Tertronics.

In 1998 Plexus began building components for General Motors' test electric vehicles. The following year the company boosted its reach into the Pacific Northwest when it bought SeaMED a Seattle-area designer and manufacturer of electronic equipment for the medical industry.

In 2000 the company continued its acquisition binge purchasing manufacturing facilities in Mexico and the UK as well as US-based electronic manufacturing services providers Agility and e2E.

In 2001 COO John Nussbaum succeeded Strandwitz as CEO (Strandwitz remained chairman until the next year). Also in 2001 Plexus agreed to acquire most of the assets of contract manufacturer MCMS; the deal which closed early in 2002 expanded Plexus' reach into Asia thanks to MCMS's plants in Malaysia and China.

In 2002 COO Dean Foate succeeded Nussbaum as CEO (Nussbaum remained chairman).

Plexus lined up AuthenTec the developer of biometric chips as a customer in 2003 providing design engineering and integration services to the supplier of fingerprint sensors.

The company went through a corporate restructuring in 2004 closing a plant in the Seattle area. Plexus also mothballed facilities in New Hampshire and Oregon.

In 2006 Plexus expanded its manufacturing capacity in China and Malaysia.

Plexus decided in 2008 to close its facility in Ayer Massachusetts primarily transferring production to Neenah Wisconsin. The company expanded plants in Buffalo Grove Illinois and Fremont California during the year and leased about 106000 sq. ft. at an industrial park in Hangzhou China.

In response to the 2008-2009 global economic downturn Plexus restructured its North American operations including workforce reductions in the US and Mexico. The company closed its Ayer Massachusetts plant transferring production to other facilities. The company expanded its plants in China and Romania however as it looks to move production to regions with lower labor and materials costs in the future.

EXECUTIVES

President & Chief Executive Officer, Dean A. Foate, $745,673 total compensation
Senior Vice President General Counsel Corporate Compliance Officer and Secretary, Angelo M. Ninivaggi Jr., age 45, $228,827 total compensation
SVP and CFO, Ginger M. Jones, $339,529 total compensation
Executive Vice President Global Manufacturing Operations, Michael D. (Mike) Buseman, $303,654 total compensation
EVP Global Customer Services, Steven J. (Steve) Frisch, age 47
EVP and COO, Todd P. Kelsey, age 48
Regional President Asia Pacific, Yong Jin (Y. J.) Lim, $267,708 total compensation
President CEO and Director, Dean A. Foate, age 53
Director, Stephen P. Cortinovis, age 62
Director, Peter Kelly, age 54
Director, David J. Drury, age 63
Director, Charles M. Strother, age 71
Director, Michael V. Schrock, age 59
Director, Mary A. Winston, age 50
Director, Ralf R. Boer, age 64
Director, Philip R. (Phil) Martens, age 52
Auditors: PricewaterhouseCoopersLLP

LOCATIONS

HQ: Plexus Corp.
One Plexus Way, Neenah, WI 54956
Phone: 920 969-6000   **Fax:** 920 751-5395
Web: www.plexus.com

2013 Sales

	$ mil.	% of total
Americas		
US	1,004	43
Mexico	58	3
Asia/Pacifc		
Malaysia	877	38

China	268	11
Europe		
UK	81	3
Romania	38	2
Germany	2	-
Adjustments	(103.6)	-
Total	**2,228**	**100**

PRODUCTS/OPERATIONS

2013 Sales

	$ mil.	% of total
Networking/Communications	826	37
Healthcare/Life Sciences	563	25

Selected Services

Assembly
Design (printed circuit boards product housings)
Distribution
Logistics
Materials procurement
New product introduction
Product development and testing
Product manufacture and assembly
Prototyping
Support
Warehousing

COMPETITORS

Avnet	Nam Tai
Benchmark Electronics	Quanta Computer
CTS Corp.	SMTC Corp.
Celestica	SYNNEX
Cofidur	Sanmina
Ducommun LaBarge	Saturn Electronics
Technologies	Silicon Forest
Flextronics	Electronics
Hon Hai	Sparton
Jabil	Suntron
Key Tronic	TTM Technologies
Kimball International	Viasystems

HISTORICAL FINANCIALS

Company Type: Public

Income Statement

FYE: September 28

	REVENUE ($ mil.)	NET INCOME ($ mil.)	NET PROFIT MARGIN	EMPLOYEES
09/13	2,228.0	82.2	3.7%	9,200
09/12*	2,306.7	62.0	2.7%	9,600
10/11	2,231.2	89.2	4.0%	9,000
10/10	2,013.3	89.5	4.4%	8,700
10/09	1,616.6	46.3	2.9%	7,100
Annual Growth	**8.3%**	**15.4%**		**6.7%**

*Fiscal year change

2013 Year-End Financials

Debt ratio: 18.0%
Return on equity: 12.2%
Cash ($ mil.): 341
Current ratio: 2.29
Long-term debt ($ mil.): 257

No. of shares (mil.): 33
Dividends
  Yield: —
  Payout: —
Market value ($ mil.): 1,240

	STOCK PRICE ($) FY Close	P/E High/Low		PER SHARE ($) Earnings	Dividends	Book Value
09/13	36.90	15	9	2.36	0.00	20.81
09/12*	30.29	21	12	1.75	0.00	18.49
10/11	22.62	16	9	2.30	0.00	16.18
10/10	30.73	18	10	2.19	0.00	16.13
10/09	25.47	23	9	1.17	0.00	13.34
Annual Growth	**9.7%**			**19.2%**	**—**	**11.8%**

*Fiscal year change

Portfolio Recovery Associates Inc

When times are tough businesses find the going a little easier with Portfolio Recovery Associates (PRA). The firm collects on defaulted consumer debt. Its primary business is collections on behalf of clients (including banks credit unions consumer and auto finance companies and retail merchants) in the US and Scotland. PRA also buys charged-off and bankrupt consumer debt portfolios and then collects the debts on its own behalf. The company operates through its subsidiaries which specialize in location and skip tracing (PRA Location Services) class action claims monitoring (Claims Compensation Bureau or CCB) and government accounts receivable management (PRA Government Services).

The company's Core Asset Collection segment is its largest representing more than half of sales. It's followed by the Bankruptcy Services segment which accounts for about 30% of sales; and the Fee-for-Services segment which makes up the rest of PRA's business.

PRA has locations in Alabama California Kansas Nevada Tennessee Texas and Virginia. Its Mackenzie Hall unit operates in Scotland. The majority of PRA's purchased accounts come from Florida Texas and California.

PRA's earnings have risen despite (or perhaps because of) the weakened state of the economy after the recession. In general the company has had a nice run as of late: Sales grew nearly 33% from 2009 to 2010 and another 23% to $458.9 million from 2010 to 2011. Profits have also grown albeit not quite as consistently. The company attributes the growth to several long-term strategies such as strengthening operational efficiencies as well as expanding its internal legal collections business and bankruptcy business. Income recognized on finance receivables increased in 2011 and cash collections grew by about a third. This was offset by a decline in fee revenues which fell nearly 10% primarily because of a drop in automobile financing across the nation.

The company has focused on diversifying its business by expanding services through acquisitions of other companies and through the acquisition of debt portfolios. The company entered the UK market in early 2012 with its acquisition of Mackenzie Hall Holdings for some $51 million.

Another recent acquisition added to services in 2010. PRA acquired more than 60% of CCB which specializes in recovering and processing class action lawsuit claims and settlements. As part of the deal PRA has the right to buy the remaining stake in CCB. Other recent acquisitions have expanded the company's capabilities in the government sector and diversified its fee-based business.

EXECUTIVES

Chairman President and CEO, Steven D. (Steve) Fredrickson, age 54, $500,000 total compensation
EVP CFO Chief Administrative Officer Treasurer and Assistant Secretary, Kevin P. Stevenson, age 49, $300,000 total compensation
EVP General Counsel and Secretary, Judith S. (Judy) Scott, age 68, $245,000 total compensation
President Bankruptcy Services, Michael J. (Mike) Petit, $235,000 total compensation

SVP Core Asset Acquisitions, Chris Graves, $152,019 total compensation
EVP and COO Owned Portfolios, Neal Stern
EVP Strategy and Business Development, Peter K (Kent) McCammon, $220,000 total compensation
VP-Bankruptcy Underwriting, Luanne Ormsbee
VP-Utility Acq, Joel Lewis
VP Information Technology, Paul Carnes
SVP Human Resources, Michelle Link
President Business and Government Services, Steve Roberts
CEO Mackenzie Hall Holdings, Owen James
President Claims Compensation Bureau, Brad Heffler
SVP PRA Location Services, Andy Robinson
Executive Vice President; Chief Acquisitions Officer, Craig Grube
Vice President Corporate Communications, Rick Goulart
Chief Technical Officer; Member of the Executive Board, Peter Wiedemann
Chief Sales Officer; Member of the Executive Board, Reinhard Banasch
Director, Scott M. Tabakin, age 54
Director, Penelope W. (Penny) Kyle, age 65
Lead Director, David N. Roberts, age 51
Director, James M. Voss, age 70
Director, John H. Fain, age 64
Director, John F. Fuller, age 69
Auditors: KPMGLLP

LOCATIONS

HQ: Portfolio Recovery Associates Inc.
120 Corporate Blvd., Norfolk VA 23502
Phone: 757-519-9300   **Fax:** 757-518-0901
Web: www.portfoliorecovery.com

PRODUCTS/OPERATIONS

2011 Sales

	$ mil.	% of total
Finance receivables net	401	88
Fee income	57	12
Total	**458**	**100**

2011 Portfolio Composition

	% of total
Major credit	60
Consumer	20
Private-label credit	18
Auto	2
Total	**100**

COMPETITORS

Asset Acceptance Capital	FirstCity Financial
Asta Funding	GC Services
Encore Capital Group	Nationwide Recovery Systems
Expert Global Solutions	Rampart Capital
	iQor

HISTORICAL FINANCIALS

Company Type: Public

Income Statement

FYE: December 31

	REVENUE ($ mil.)	NET INCOME ($ mil.)	NET PROFIT MARGIN	EMPLOYEES
12/12	592.8	126.5	21.4%	3,200
12/11	458.9	100.7	22.0%	2,641
12/10	372.7	73.4	19.7%	2,473
12/09	281.0	44.3	15.8%	2,213
12/08	263.2	45.3	17.2%	2,032
Annual Growth	**22.5%**	**29.2%**	**—**	**12.0%**

2012 Year-End Financials

Debt ratio: 25.4%
Return on equity: 19.3%
Cash ($ mil.): 32
Current ratio: 0.20
Long-term debt ($ mil.): 327

No. of shares (mil.): 50
Dividends
  Yield: —
  Payout: —
Market value ($ mil.): 5,421

	STOCK PRICE ($) FY Close	P/E High/Low	PER SHARE ($) Earnings	Dividends	Book Value
12/12	106.86	43 24	2.46	0.00	13.97
12/11	67.52	46 30	1.95	0.00	11.58
12/10	75.20	53 29	1.45	0.00	9.58
12/09	44.85	53 21	0.96	0.00	7.21
12/08	33.84	51 26	0.99	0.00	6.19
Annual Growth	33.3%	— —	25.6%	—	22.6%

Preformed Line Products Co.

Masterful "preformances" are expected from Preformed Line Products by its audience in the energy and communications industries. The company designs and manufactures components and systems used by utility crews and others to construct repair and maintain overhead and underground networks for energy communications and broadband network companies. It provides formed wire products (for maintenance and repair of aging plant infrastructures) protective fiber-optic closures and splice cases solar hardware and data communication interconnect devices and enclosures for data communications networks. Chairman Robert Ruhlman and his family own almost 80% of the company.

Founded in 1947 Preformed Line Products (PLP) operates subsidiaries throughout the world including 17 sales and manufacturing facilities in 14 countries. In 2010 the company realigned its operations into four operating segments along geographic lines: PLP-USA The Americas EMEA (Europe Middle East & Africa) and Asia/Pacific. US operations adhere specifically to domestic energy and telecommunications products while the other three segments work across geographic regions.

The realignment came as a response to the global economic crisis allowing PLP to focus on its customers by investing in new product development activities specific to its regional markets. As a result the company realized more than a 30% increase in its 2010 sales compared to 2009 –a 40% rise for international business and 20% for the US –with all segments posting improvements. The Asia/Pacific region experienced an increase of almost 90% in its sales representing a lion's share of what was generated by the company's most recent acquisitions. Though PLP's net income dropped a little more than 1% it reports the $23 million bottom line is a record high amount for the company. PLP cites the growth in its energy and solar markets as integral to 2010's results while the company forecasts the distribution energy market will remain flat. The company is optimistic that its transmission and fiber optic products will see a greater demand in 2011.

PLP has been focusing its efforts on the energy and communications markets both of which have been undergoing consolidation. Internationally however the company continues to concentrate specifically on the energy markets especially in developing nations. In mid-2010 the company acquired New Zealand-based Electropar which designs manufactures and markets hardware for the global electrical utility industry. Electropar with subsidiaries in Australia expands PLP's presence in the Asia/Pacific market. In 2009 PLP picked up the Dulmison Business operations –crossing Australia Thailand Indonesia Malaysia China Mexico and the US –from TE Connectivity (formerly Tyco Electronics). The deal which includes Dulmison's competencies in designing manufacturing and marketing vibration control products and pole line hardware marks an upshift in PLP's portfolio and presence for targeting the global electrical utility industry.

While the energy market has been experiencing growth the communications business has been met with challenges especially with the global economic downturn. Many carriers refocused their operational funds on wireless communication projects which yield quicker returns. However PLP sees economic conditions improving especially as stimulus funds becoming more available. The company is using this positive trend for growth opportunities not only domestically but in emerging markets such as Central and South America.

PLP's other business segments also did well in 2010. Protective Closures the second largest segment produces copper closure offerings that protect fixed line communication networks. Other segments include Data Communication Cabinets (for the protection of electronic equipment) and Plastic Products (guy markers tree guards and fiber optic cable markers).

The company also makes products for the alternative energy market such as solar hardware systems and mounting hardware for different solar power applications. These products are included in the company's Other Products business segment. Since being added in 2008 this segment's sales more than doubled in two years.

The company pioneered the manufacture of helically (spiral) shaped armor rods to protect electrical conductors on overhead power lines. The helical technology gives the company a competitive advantage. Rather than traditional clamps that compress cable to the point of damage the spiral design of the company's products offer a gentler grip reducing the chance of fatigue or deterioration.

EXECUTIVES

Chairman of the Board; President; Chief Executive Officer, Robert G. Ruhlman, age 56, $650,000 total compensation
Chief Financial Officer; Vice President - Finance, Eric R. Graef, age 61, $300,000 total compensation
VP Marketing and Business Development, Dennis F. McKenna, age 46, $245,000 total compensation
VP Human Resources, J. Cecil Curlee Jr., age 56, $180,000 total compensation
Vice President - - International Operations, William H. Haag III, age 49, $250,000 total compensation
Vice President - Research and Engineering and Manufacturing, David C. Sunkle, age 54, $195,000 total compensation
General Counsel; Corporate Secretary, Caroline S. Vaccariello, age 46
Sales Manager Managing Director, Angel Guerrero
General Manager - Sales and Marketing, Michael Skinner

Business Development Manager - Solar, Teera Puxsupachat
Regional Sales Manager - Transmission, Montri Chomsin
Vice President - Human Resources, Cecil Curlee
Vice President??Sales and Global Communications Markets, John Hofstetter
Director, Glenn E. Corlett, age 69
Director, Michael E. Gibbons, age 60
Director, R. Steven (Steve) Kestner, age 58
Director, Randall M. Ruhlman, age 54
Director, Barbara P. Ruhlman, age 80
Director, Richard Gascoigne, age 63
Auditors: Ernst&YoungLLP

LOCATIONS

HQ: Preformed Line Products Company
660 Beta Dr., Mayfield Village OH 44143
Phone: 440-461-5200   **Fax:** 440-442-8816
Web: www.preformed.com

2010 Sales

	$ mil.	% of total
% mil. % of total		
Americas		
US	118	35
Other countries	79	23
Asia/Pacific	90	27
Europe Middle East & Africa (EMEA)	50	15
Total	**338**	**100**

PRODUCTS/OPERATIONS

2010 Sales

	% of total
Formed	65
Protective	17
Data communications	4
Plastic	3
Other	11
Total	**100**

Selected Products

Copper splice closures
Data communication cabinets
Fiber optic products (COYOTE brand)
Formed wire and related hardware products
High-speed cross-connect devices
Plastic products
Power transmission products (THERMOLIGN)
Protective closures (ARMADILLO stainless vault closures)
RAPTOR PROTECTOR (protects birds from power lines)

Selected Markets

Communication and cable
Data communication
Electric utilities and distribution
Electric utilities and transmission
Energy
Solar

COMPETITORS

3M	Maysteel
Corning Cable Systems	SWCC SHOWA
General Cable	Sumitomo Electric
Kyocera International	Tyco

HISTORICAL FINANCIALS

Company Type: Public

Income Statement

FYE: December 31

	REVENUE ($ mil.)	NET INCOME ($ mil.)	NET PROFIT MARGIN	EMPLOYEES
12/12	439.1	29.2	6.7%	2,901
12/11	424.4	30.9	7.3%	2,854
12/10	338.3	23.1	6.8%	2,617
12/09	257.2	23.3	9.1%	2,304
12/08	269.7	17.6	6.5%	1,858
Annual Growth	13.0%	13.5%	—	11.8%

2012 Year-End Financials

Debt ratio: 2.9%
Return on equity: 12.8%
Cash ($ mil.): 28
Current ratio: 3.33
Long-term debt ($ mil.): 9

No. of shares (mil.): 5
Dividends
Yield: 1.6%
Payout: 16.3%
Market value ($ mil.): 320

	STOCK PRICE ($) FY Close	P/E High/Low		PER SHARE ($) Earnings	Dividends	Book Value
12/12	59.42	13	9	5.45	1.00	44.83
12/11	59.66	13	7	5.78	0.80	39.91
12/10	58.53	14	6	4.33	0.80	37.21
12/09	43.80	11	6	4.35	0.80	32.58
12/08	46.04	20	10	3.30	0.80	26.09
Annual Growth	6.6%	—	—	13.4%	5.7%	14.5%

Premier Financial Bancorp, Inc.

Premier Financial Bancorp is the holding company for Citizens Deposit Bank and Premier Bank rural and small-town banks with locations across Kentucky Virginia Ohio Maryland West Virginia and the District of Columbia. Altogether the banks have about 40 branches that offer standard deposit trust and lending services. The firm entered the DC area with the 2009 purchase of Adams National Bank for some $11 million. In 2011 the company combined five of its banks including Adams National Bank to create Premier Bank. The following year it merged Farmers Deposit Bank and Ohio River Bank into Citizens Deposit Bank.

In April 2009 Premier Financial received approval for $24 million from the US Treasury from its Capital Purchase Program. Participation in the program was a condition of completing the merger with Adams National Bank. Investor Marshall Reynolds (chairman and CEO of Champion Industries) who specializes in troubled banks was the largest shareholder of both companies.

EXECUTIVES

Chairman of the Board, Marshall T. Reynolds, age 76
President CEO and Director, Robert W. Walker, age 66, $245,519 total compensation
SVP and CFO, Brien M. Chase, age 48, $110,435 total compensation
SVP; CEO First Central Bank, Dennis Klingensmith, age 59, $135,362 total compensation
VP Credit Administration, Scot A. Kelley, age 56
VP Human Resources, Katrina Whitt, age 38
Auditors: CroweHorwathLLP

LOCATIONS

HQ: Premier Financial Bancorp Inc.
2883 5th Ave., Huntington WV 25702
Phone: 304-525-1600   **Fax:** 304-525-9701

COMPETITORS

ASB Financial	Huntington Bancshares
BB&T	Ohio Valley Banc
Camco Financial	PNC Financial
City Holding	Porter Bancorp
Community Trust	S.Y. Bancorp
Farmers Capital Bank	United Bancorp
Fifth Third	United Bankshares

HISTORICAL FINANCIALS

Company Type: Public

Income Statement

FYE: December 31

	ASSETS ($ mil.)	NET INCOME ($ mil.)	INCOME AS % OF ASSETS	EMPLOYEES
12/12	1,120.7	10.3	0.9%	327
12/11	1,124.0	7.1	0.6%	364
12/10	1,183.2	9.1	0.8%	354
12/09	1,101.7	9.1	0.8%	369
12/08	724.4	7.5	1.0%	270
Annual Growth	11.5%	8.2%	—	4.9%

2012 Year-End Financials

Return on assets: 0.9%
Return on equity: 7.1%
Long-term debt ($ mil.): —
No. of shares (mil.): 7
Sales ($ mil): 59

Dividends
Yield: 2.0%
Payout: 17.7%
Market value ($ mil.): 86

	STOCK PRICE ($) FY Close	P/E High/Low		PER SHARE ($) Earnings	Dividends	Book Value
12/12	10.83	9	3	1.24	0.22	18.12
12/11	4.40	11	6	0.74	0.00	18.14
12/10	6.40	10	6	0.98	0.22	16.55
12/09	6.70	6	3	1.32	0.44	16.20
12/08	7.03	11	6	1.25	0.43	13.99
Annual Growth	11.4%	—	—	(0.2%)	(15.4%)	6.7%

Prestige Brands Holdings Inc

Prestige Brands is a lifesaver in the business of resuscitating offloaded consumer brands. The company acquires develops and markets over-the-counter (OTC) drugs and household cleaning products. Its portfolio includes Chloraseptic Clear Eyes Comet Compound W Dermoplast Doctor's Nightguard Little Remedies Murine New-Skin and many other big-name brands. Prestige Brands contracts out manufacturing of its products which are sold through mass merchandisers and retail stores primarily in North America. The company was formed in 1996 to acquire and revitalize leading but neglected consumer brands divested by major consumer companies such as Procter & Gamble.

Strategy

The company's strategy lies in acquiring new brands and developing effective marketing programs for its existing products. Acquisitions are

key to keeping its products portfolio fresh and it is constantly on the lookout for new additions to keep its two divisions competitive. Previously Prestige Brands had a third division of personal care items but the company sold its three shampoo brands (Prell Denorex Zincon) to personal care products company Ultimark in 2009 for about $9 million; in 2010 it sold off its Cutex line of nail care products to Arch Equity Partners.

When Prestige Brands is evaluating a product for acquisition it takes a number of factors into consideration including the period of time the product has been in existence the product's market position (typically about three-quarters of the company's sales come from brands with a #1 or #2 market position) its recent and projected sales growth and its potential for product extensions. Prestige Brands looks to acquire products that can be remarketed with additional enhancements such as its 2012 rollout of PediaCare 24 Hour Allergy Relief 2011 debut of Little Colds Honey Elixir and the introduction of liquid-centered Chloraseptic sore throat lozenges in 2010.

Mergers and Acquisitions

Prestige Brands paid $190 million in 2010 to acquire Blacksmith Brands which brought with it the well-known OTC denture-care brands Efferdent and Effergrip the PediaCare line of children's cold and cough remedies Luden's cough drops and NasalCrom allergy remedy. Prestige Brands also purchased the motion sickness treatment and blockbuster seller Dramamine in 2011 for $76 million from Johnson & Johnson's McNeil PPC unit (part of McNeil Consumer Healthcare). In 2012 Prestige Brands completed its largest asset acquisition to date spending $660 million to gain a portfolio of 17 North American OTC brands from GlaxoSmith Kline (GSK). The purchases added brands that included leading pain relief (BC Goody's and Ecotrin) gastrointestinal (Beano Fiber Choice Gaviscon Phazyme and Tagamet) sleep aid (Sominex) ear wax remover (Debrox) and oral rinse (Gly-Oxide) brands. Also in 2012 the company received an unsolicited acquisition proposal from Mexican health products firm Genomma Lab Internacional. The Prestige Brands board of directors rejected the proposal as inadequate and not in the best interest of the firm.

Geographic Reach

Nearly all of Prestige Brands' sales come from North America but the company is working to increase international sales by licensing some brands to large multinational companies in desirable international markets. It has one such agreement for Comet in Eastern Europe. It also sells Clear Eyes Chloraseptic and Murine internationally. Prestige Brands which in 2012 generated 3% of sales outside North America has already designed and developed product packaging for specific international markets and it is focused now on growing its distribution network to help increase its international penetration.

Financial Analysis

Prestige Brands posted 31% revenue gains in 2012 vs. 2011. The company points to healthy OTC Healthcare segment sales for the increase thanks to the positive impact of a full year of having Blacksmith and Dramamine in its portfolio and the acquisition of more than a dozen GlaxoSmith Kline's brands in 2012. Net revenue would have been even better but its Household Cleaning segment pulled down sales results due to softer sales of non-abrasive products. Paired with net revenue rises Prestige Brands saw net income increase by 27% in 2012 compared to 2011. The rise came from receipt of an $8 million settlement payment associated with a resolved legal matter during fiscal 2012. The settlement offset increased spending in general and administrative expenses depreciation and amortization expenses and net interest expense.

Operations

Instead of maintaining its own manufacturing facilities Prestige Brands contracts out product-making using third-party manufacturers and warehouse distribution partners to simplify its organizational structure.

Sales and Marketing

Prestige Brands generates revenue by leveraging several distribution channels to get its products on store shelves and in consumers' hands. Mass merchandisers represent the largest customer group it serves with a third of its 2012 sales coming from this retail channel. Drug stores (with 26%) and grocery stores (21%) also account for a huge percentage of sales. Other growing but smaller channels that Prestige Brands relies on include dollar stores (9%) club stores (2%) and other (8%). Uber worldwide retailer Wal-mart accounted for approximately 19% of the company's 2012 sales. Other notable customers include Walgreen CVS Target Dollar Tree Kmart Meijer Ahold and Kroger among others. Prestige Brands develops extensive marketing programs for new and existing products.

Company Background

Prestige Brands was pieced together in 1996 from the parts of defunct manufacturer Medtech Labs (shampoos nail care products) The Spic & Span Company and Prestige Brands International (Comet cleaners and Clear Eyes eye drops).

Ownership

FMR LLC owns about 15% of the company.

EXECUTIVES

Lead Director, Gary E. Costley, age 70
CFO, Ron Lombardi
President CEO and Director, Matthew M. (Matt) Mannelly, age 55, $299,667 total compensation
General Counsel VP Business Development and Secretary, Samuel C. (Sam) Cowley, age 50
SVP International, John F. Parkinson, age 60, $217,000 total compensation
SVP Science and Technology, Jean A. Boyko, age 54, $250,000 total compensation
EVP Sales and Marketing, Timothy J. Connors, age 46
VP Operations, Paul A. Hennessey, age 46
CFO, Ronald M. Lombardi, age 49
Auditors: PricewaterhouseCoopersLLP

LOCATIONS

HQ: Prestige Brands Holdings Inc.
660 White Plains Rd., Tarrytown NY 10591
Phone: 914-524-6810   **Fax:** 914-524-6815
Web: www.prestigebrands.com

2012 Sales

	% of total
US & Canada	97
Total	100

2012 Distribution Channels

	% of total
Mass	33
Drug	26
Food	21
Dollar	9
Club	2
Other	8
Total	100

PRODUCTS/OPERATIONS

2012 Sales

	$ mil.	% of total
Over-the-counter healthcare	345	78

2012 Sales

	$ mil.	% of total
Cough & Cold	116	34
Ear & Eye Care	74	22
Dermatologists	52	15
Oral Care	46	13
Gastrointestinal	29	9
Analgesics	18	5
Other OTC	6	2
Total	345	100

Selected Products

Over-the-counter
Clear Eyes
Chloraseptic
Clear Eyes
Compound W
Dermoplast
The Doctor's NightGuard
The Doctor's Brushpicks
Dramamine
Ecotrin
Efferdent
Effergrip
Fiber Choice
Little Remedies
Luden's
Murine
NasalCrom
New-Skin
PediaCare
Phazyme
Sominex
Tagamet
Wartner
Household cleaning
Comet
Chore Boy
Spic and Span

COMPETITORS

3M	Hi-Tech Pharmacal
Airborne Inc.	Inter Parfums
Bayer Consumer Care	Johnson & Johnson
Boulder Brands	Lifetime Brands
Chattem	McNeil Consumer
Church & Dwight	Healthcare
Clorox	Merck
Colgate-Palmolive	Mondelez International
Combe	Novartis Corporation
Coty Inc.	Pfizer
GlaxoSmithKline	Procter & Gamble
Hain Celestial	Reckitt Benckiser
Helen of Troy	USANA Health Sciences
HemCon Medical	Unilever
Technologies	Zep Inc.
Henkel Corp.	

HISTORICAL FINANCIALS

Company Type: Public

Income Statement

FYE: March 31

	REVENUE ($ mil.)	NET INCOME ($ mil.)	NET PROFIT MARGIN	EMPLOYEES
03/13	623.6	65.5	10.5%	117
03/12	441.0	37.2	8.4%	105
03/11	336.5	29.2	8.7%	100
03/10	302.0	32.1	10.6%	89
03/09	312.7	(186.7)	—	98
Annual Growth	18.8%	—	—	4.5%

2013 Year-End Financials

Debt ratio: 55.8%
Return on equity: 14.8%
Cash ($ mil.): 15
Current ratio: 1.70
Long-term debt ($ mil.): 970
No. of shares (mil.): 51
Dividends
  Yield: —
  Payout: —
Market value ($ mil.): 1,314

	STOCK PRICE ($) FY Close	P/E High/Low		PER SHARE ($) Earnings	Dividends	Book Value
03/13	25.69	20	10	1.27	0.00	9.35
03/12	17.48	24	11	0.73	0.00	8.01
03/11	11.50	22	12	0.58	0.00	7.22
03/10	9.00	14	8	0.64	0.00	6.58
03/09	5.18	—	—	(3.74)	0.00	5.90
Annual Growth	49.2%	—		—	—	12.2%

PriceSmart Inc

PriceSmart is wise in the ways of members-only club retailing. The retailer runs about 30 membership stores under the PriceSmart name in about a dozen countries and one US territory in Latin America and the Caribbean. It sells low-cost food pharmacy and basic consumer items. In each store nearly half of the merchandise comes from the US and the other half is sourced locally. In-store services include auto/tire centers banking and photo developing. PriceSmart stores are typically smaller than wholesale clubs in the US averaging about 50000-85000 sq. ft. and the membership fees average about $35. PriceSmart was founded in 1976 by father-and-son team Sol and Robert Price.

Geographic Reach

Latin America is PriceSmart's largest market accounting for about two-thirds of total sales. Costa Rica and Panama are major Latin American markets for the retail chain. The Caribbean including the Dominican Republic accounts for about a third of sales. The chain has one store in the U.S. Virgin Islands.

Sales and Marketing

PriceSmart subscribes to the belief that membership reinforces customer loyalty for both business and individual customers. The retailer promotes Business membership through its marketing programs and by offering products primarily targeted to small businesses such as restaurants hotels and convenience stores. Business members pay an annual membership fee of about $25 for a primary and secondary membership card and about $10 per additional add-on membership cards. In mid-2012 PriceSmart raised the annual membership fee by about $5 in most markets. The annual fee for a Diamond (individual) membership is now about $35 (for two cards).

Financial Analysis

PriceSmart's fiscal 2012 (ends August) sales increased nearly 20% vs. the prior year with net income up more than 9% over the same period. Indeed sales exceeded $2 billion in 2012 a record high for the company. It was the eighth consecutive year of climbing sales for PriceSmart as the popularity of US-style warehouse club shopping grows in popularity beyond America. The fiscal 2012 sales gain was driven by increasing sales at existing warehouse stores and the addition of one new warehouse club in Colombia. Sales from the company's stores in Latin America grew 24%.

Strategy

PriceSmart has been steadily acquiring property on which to build new stores for several years now. Most recently it has focused on buying land for expansion in and around Cali Colombia. The company believes Colombia has the potential for multiple PriceSmart warehouse clubs. Indeed in fiscal 2013 (ends August) two new warehouse clubs are slated to open in Colombia bringing the total there to four stores. Also a sixth warehouse club is slated to open in Costa Rica in 2013 and a third in Honduras the following year. In fiscal 2012 the chain invested more than $21 million in a number of warehouse clubs for expansion and improvements.

Ownership

Chairman and former CEO Robert Price individually and through The Price Group which he manages owns about 30% of PriceSmart's shares.

Company Background

Co-founder Sol Price died in December 2009 at the age of 93. The late Mr. Price was credited with pioneering the retail models –FedMart in 1954 and Price Club in 1976 –that were the inspiration for companies including Wal-Mart Sam's Club and Costco Wholesale. Indeed Wal-Mart founder Sam Walton admitted he "borrowed" many of his innovations.

HISTORY

Sol Price created the members-only warehouse retail concept in the mid-1950s when he started FedMart. In 1976 he and son Robert began Price Club. Facing pressure in the warehouse club niche Price Club and competitor Costco merged in 1993 forming Price/Costco. But their managements disagreed over direction and policy and the next year Price/Costco spun off Price Enterprises Inc. (PEI). PEI assets included commercial real estate and international development projects. Eventually Price/Costco resumed its maiden name Costco.

In mid-1997 PEI split into two companies Price Enterprises (a real estate investment trust now Price Legacy) and PriceSmart. PriceSmart was built from subsidiaries Price Quest Price Global Trading and Price Ventures. During a busy 1998 the company closed stores in Indonesia and Guam and opened locations in China and Panama. In addition it formed a joint venture (60% owned by PriceSmart) with Panamanian firm PSC to open nine new warehouse clubs in Central America and the Caribbean. That year the company's joint venture with PSC opened warehouses in Costa Rica the Dominican Republic El Salvador Guatemala and Honduras.

PriceSmart entered an agreement in fiscal 1999 with investors from Trinidad and Tobago to open two warehouses in Trinidad. (One opened a year later.) The company sold its domestic auto referral program in 1999 and its travel program in 2000. Also in 2000 the company announced a joint-venture with Philippine investors to open five to 10 stores in the Philippines. In 2001 the company received more than $30 million in loans to build 13 stores in Central America and the Caribbean. PriceSmart opened six stores in 2001 including two in the Philippines.

In 2002 PriceSmart opened four new warehouse stores in Trinidad Guam and two outlets in the Philippines. Also in 2002 the company opened three locations in Mexico and one in the Philippines.

In April 2003 president and CEO Gilbert A. Partida resigned from the company and its board of directors. Chairman Robert E. Price took on the additional role of interim president and CEO during the search for Partida's replacement. In 2003

the company opened three warehouse stores (one each in Jamaica Nicaragua and the Philippines) and closed four clubs.

In October 2004 Jose Luis Laparte became president of the company while chairman Robert E. Price remained interim CEO of PriceSmart. The company opened one new store in the Philippines and closed its warehouse club in Guam in 2004.

PriceSmart closed its Mexican operations and terminated its licensing agreement in China in 2005. In 2006 the retailer sold its interest in its PSMT Philippines subsidiary the operator of four warehouse clubs there.

In February 2008 PriceSmart agreed to pay $17.9 million to settle a lawsuit with PSC SA Tecnicard Inc. and Banco de la Produccion. Under the terms of the settlement PriceSmart will acquire PSC's 49% interest in PSMT Nicaragua (BVI) Inc. and become sole owner of the PriceSmart Nicaragua business. PriceSmart will also get land next to warehouse clubs in Nicaragua and Zapote and San Jose Costa Rica. PSC will sell its PriceSmart shares.

Founder Sol Price died in December 2009 at the age of 93. In July 2010 Jose Luis Laparte was promoted from president to CEO of the company succeeding Robert Price who remained chairman.

In August 2011 the chain opened its first store in Colombia located in Barranquilla.

EXECUTIVES

EVP Operations, John D. Hildebrandt, age 55
EVP and COO, William J. (Bill) Naylon, age 51, $283,733 total compensation
EVP and Chief Merchandising Officer, Thomas D. Martin, age 57, $195,833 total compensation
EVP Construction Management, Brud E. Drachman, age 58
EVP Secretary and General Counsel, Robert M. Gans, age 64, $276,944 total compensation
Chairman, Robert E. Price, age 71
SVP Latin America and Caribbean Legal Affairs, Ernesto Grijalva
EVP and CFO, John M. Heffner, $258,000 total compensation
SVP and Corporate Controller, Michael McCleary
President CEO and Director, Jose L. Laparte, age 47, $405,333 total compensation
SVP Merchandising, Jose Lopez
SVP Real Estate, Rodrigo Calvo
Director de Instalaciones y Mantenimiento, Nahum Ayestas
SVP Marketing and Member Services, Jose L. Marin
Director, Katherine L. Hensley, age 76
Director, Leon C. Janks, age 64
Director, Lawrence B. Krause, age 82
Director, Edgar A. Zurcher, age 62
Director, Keene Wolcott, age 80
President CEO and Director, Jose L. Laparte, age 47
Director, Gonzalo Barrutieta, age 47
Independent Director, Mitchell Lynn
Director, Sherry Bahrambeygui
Auditors: Ernst&YoungLLP

LOCATIONS

HQ: PriceSmart Inc.
9740 Scranton Rd., San Diego CA 92121-1745
Phone: 858-404-8800   **Fax:** 858-404-8848
Web: www.pricesmart.com

2012 Stores

	No.
Costa	5
Panama	4
Trinidad	4

Dominican	3
Guatemala	3
El	2
Honduras	2
Aruba	1
Barbados	1
Colombia	1
Jamaica	1
Nicaragua	1
U.S. Virgin	1
Total	**29**

2012 Sales

	% of total
Latin	65
Caribbean	34
US	1
Total	**100**

PRODUCTS/OPERATIONS

2012 Sales

	% of total
Food (dry &	53
Sundries	26
Hardlines	13
Softlines	6
Other	2
Total	**100**

COMPETITORS

Amazon.com	IGA
Carrefour	Wal-Mart
Falabella	

HISTORICAL FINANCIALS

Company Type: Public

Income Statement

FYE: August 31

	REVENUE ($ mil.)	NET INCOME ($ mil.)	NET PROFIT MARGIN	EMPLOYEES
08/13	2,299.8	84.2	3.7%	6,371
08/12	2,050.7	67.6	3.3%	5,752
08/11	1,714.2	61.7	3.6%	5,455
08/10	1,395.8	49.3	3.5%	4,728
08/09	1,251.6	42.3	3.4%	4,385
Annual Growth	**16.4%**	**18.8%**	**—**	**9.8%**

2013 Year-End Financials

Debt ratio: 8.8%	No. of shares (mil.): 30
Return on equity: 18.7%	Dividends
Cash ($ mil.): 121	Yield: 0.0%
Current ratio: 1.37	Payout: 21.5%
Long-term debt ($ mil.): 60	Market value ($ mil.): 2,599

	STOCK PRICE ($) FY Close	P/E High/Low		PER SHARE ($) Earnings	Dividends	Book Value
08/13	85.97	34	26	2.78	0.60	15.91
08/12	73.14	37	26	2.24	0.60	13.87
08/11	65.46	31	12	2.07	0.60	12.57
08/10	25.81	17	11	1.65	0.50	11.24
08/09	17.75	14	7	1.45	0.66	10.12
Annual Growth	**48.3%**	**—**	**—**	**17.7%**	**(2.4%)**	**12.0%**

Primoris Services Corp

Since the beginning of time or at least since the 20th century Primoris has played a part in the evolution of the utility and infrastructure landscape. Through subsidiaries the firm provides construction engineering and maintenance services such as replacing and repairing underground pipelines upgrading and maintaining industrial plants designing and building concrete structures and managing the construction of water and wastewater facilities. It also engineers industrial machinery used in oil refineries petrochemical plants and other facilities. The firm primarily operates in the US. Primoris' clients have included Duke Energy Chevron Sempra and Kinder Morgan as well as public sector entities.

Geographic Reach

Dallas-based Primoris Services rings up 99% of its revenue in the US although its nationwide operations extend to Canada. The firm has regional offices in Eastern and Western US the Pacific Northwest Florida and along the Gulf Coast into Texas.

Operations

Primoris operates through three primary subsidiaries: West Construction Services accounts for more than 50% of annual revenue; East Construction Services accounts for nearly 45%; Engineering including Onquest Inc. and Born Heaters Canada represents the rest. The Engineering segment specializes in the design and installation of high-performance furnaces heaters burner management systems and related combustion and process technologies for clients in the oil refining petrochemical and power generation industries.

Sales and Marketing

Primoris counts among its customers major public utilities petrochemical firms energy companies and municipalities. The Louisiana Department of Transportation accounted for 11% of the firm's 2012 revenue.

Financial Peformance

The specialty contractor and infrastructure firm's revenue increased 6% in 2012 versus 2011 to more than $1.5 billion. Net income dipped 3% over the same period to $56.8 million. 2012 marked the third consecutive year of steeply rising sales for Primoris after a decline in 2009 due to the drop off in construction activity especially in California and Florida during the deep recession. Acquisitions are driving the year-over-year increases in revenue.

Mergers and Acquisitions

2012 was an busy year on the acquisition front for Primoris. In November it acquired Q3 Contracting Inc. a privately-held Minnesota corporation that specializes in small diameter pipeline and gas distribution construction. In September the firm purchased assets of The Saxon Group based outside of Atlanta. Saxon is a full-service industrial construction firm with expertise in the industrial gas processing and power plant industries. As part of the $3.2 million deal The Saxon Group operates as Saxon Construction Inc. under the East Construction Services segment of Primoris and serves power and process customers located primarily in the Southeastern US. In May it acquired Silva Contracting Co. of Houston a provider of transportation infrastructure maintenance asphalt paving and material sales in the Gulf Coast region. In March Primoris acquired Sprint Pipeline Services in Pearland Texas (near Houston). Sprint is engaged in pipeline construction maintenance upgrade fabrication and specialty services primarily in the southeastern US.

Previous purchases include Texas-based Cravens Partners which it merged into JCG in 2011 and the assets of Texas-based transportation infrastructure maintenance firm the Silva Companies which now operates as part of JCG's East

Construction Services segment in 2012. Florida's James Construction Group (JCG) was purchased in 2009 and is one of the largest general contractors based in the Gulf Coast states engaging in highway industrial and environmental construction primarily in Louisiana Texas and Florida.

Strategy

Through acquisitions Primoris is able to deepen its presence in different markets and pick up niche industry operations. The firm is seeking more opportunities in the infrastructure and renewable energy sectors. It expects demand to rise as the need for electric power grows –a need that it could help deliver through solar power or other energy-efficient sources. To this end its Primoris Energy Services subsidiary in late 2012 acquired The Saxon Groupknown for its expertise in the industrial gas processing and power plant sectors.

With a focus on diversification Primoris is able to expand its service offerings and attract new clients. In 2009 the company created subsidiary Juniper Rock Corporation after buying the 88-acre Juniper Flats rock quarry in Southern California. The unit adds a new revenue source in the production and sale of aggregates and other construction materials.

In 2014 the firm announced it has secured new contracts worth about $200 million for construction work related to power pipeline and gas utility. Industrial highway infrastructure and water/wastewater are also part of the deal.

EXECUTIVES

Executive Vice President Chief Financial Officer, Peter J. Moerbeek, age 65
Senior Vice President - Finance and Accounting, Alfons Theeuwes, $257,506 total compensation
Senior Vice President; General Counsel, John M. Perisich
Executive Vice President Director of Construction Services, Michael D. (Mike) Killgore
Executive Vice President Corporate Development, John P. Schauerman, age 56, $245,833 total compensation
President ARB Structures, Mark A. Thurman
Chief Executive Officer President Chairman of the Board, Brian Pratt, age 61, $500,000 total compensation
President ARB Underground, Scott E. Summers, $300,000 total compensation
President ARB Industrial, Timothy R. Healy
President Cardinal Contractors, William J. McDevitt
SVP Government Contracting Services, R. Steve Lewis
President James Construction Group?East Construction Services, Danny L. Hester
President Chief Executive Officer, Randy Kessler
EVP CFO and Director, Peter J. Moerbeek, age 65
Director, Eric S. Rosenfeld, age 55
EVP Corporate Development and Director, John P. Schauerman, age 56
Director, Peter C. Brown, age 69
Director, Stephen C. Cook, age 63
Director, Thomas E. Tucker, age 70
Independent Director, Robert Tintsman
Auditors: MossAdamsLLP

LOCATIONS

HQ: Primoris Services Corporation
2100 McKinney Ave. Ste. 1500, Dallas TX 75201
Phone: 214-740-5600   **Fax:** 403-207-1629
Web: www.directcash.net

2012 Sales

	$ mil.	% of total
US	1,531	99

Other countries	11	1
Total	**1,542**	**100**

PRODUCTS/OPERATIONS

2012 Sales by Segment

	$ mil.	% of total
West Construction Services	832	54
East Construction Services	662	43
Engineering	46	6
Total	**1,541**	**100**

Selected Subsidiaries

ARB Inc.
Arb Chile Ltda
ARB Structures Inc.
Born Heaters Canada ULC
Cardinal Contractors Inc.
Cardinal Mechanical Inc.
Cravens Services Inc.
GML Coatings LLC
James Construction Group LLC
Juniper Rock Corporation
Onquest Inc.
Rockford Corporation
Stellaris LLC

COMPETITORS

AMEC	KBR
Balfour Beatty	MasTec
Infrastructure	Parsons Corporation
Bechtel	Peter Kiewit Sons'
Boh Bros Construction	Quanta Services
EMS USA	Skanska
FCI Constructors	Sterling Construction
Fluor	Willbros
Jacobs Engineering	

HISTORICAL FINANCIALS

Company Type: Public

Income Statement

FYE: December 31

	REVENUE ($ mil.)	NET INCOME ($ mil.)	NET PROFIT MARGIN	EMPLOYEES
12/12	1,541.7	56.7	3.7%	6,911
12/11	1,460.1	58.5	4.0%	4,058
12/10	941.7	33.6	3.6%	4,034
12/09	467.0	25.9	5.5%	2,648
12/08	609.0	36.4	6.0%	1,651
Annual Growth	**26.1%**	**11.7%**	**—**	**43.0%**

2012 Year-End Financials

Debt ratio: 16.6%	No. of shares (mil.): 51
Return on equity: 18.6%	Dividends
Cash ($ mil.): 157	Yield: 0.8%
Current ratio: 1.34	Payout: 10.9%
Long-term debt ($ mil.): 132	Market value ($ mil.): 773

	STOCK PRICE ($) FY Close	P/E High/Low		PER SHARE ($) Earnings	Dividends	Book Value
12/12	15.04	15	10	1.10	0.12	6.44
12/11	14.93	13	7	1.14	0.11	5.38
12/10	9.54	12	7	0.72	0.10	4.22
12/09	7.97	10	4	0.75	0.10	4.40
12/08	5.17	6	3	1.29	0.05	1.85
Annual Growth	**30.6%**	—	—	**(3.9%)**	**24.5%**	**36.6%**

PrivateBancorp, Inc.

It's your private banker a banker for money and any old teller won't do. PrivateBancorp is the holding company for The PrivateBank and Trust Co. which provides commercial and community banking business and real estate lending investments and money management services to middle-market companies commercial real estate professionals small business owners executives and wealthy individuals and their families. The bank has some 20 offices in the Chicago area and more than a dozen more than in the Atlanta Cleveland Denver Des Moines Detroit Milwaukee Minneapolis Kansas City St. Louis markets. The PrivateBank has restructured to become a leading middle market commercial bank.

Operations

PrivateBancorp's Lodestar Investment Counsel subsidiary provides trust and investment management services to families foundations and high-net-worth individuals with more than $500000 to invest. PrivateBancorp cross-sells its wealth management services to executives who have commercial banking relationships with the company.

Financial Analysis

The bank's sales decreased by nearly 4% in 2011 vs. 2010 while net income soared. Indeed after two unprofitable years (2008 and 2009) due largely to sour real estate loans the bank squeezed out a small profit in 2010 which ballooned to about $44 million in 2011. Net income growth benefited from the addition of $1.4 billion in new client relationships added in 2011 growth in the bank's higher-yielding commercial and industrial loan portfolio and improved asset quality among other factors. Meanwhile total deposits were $10.4 billion at the end of 2011 relatively flat compared to year end 2010.

Strategy

The strong return to profitability in 2011 affirmed PrivateBancorp's change in strategic direction. Formerly modeled after a traditional European private bank PrivateBancorp launched a strategic plan in late 2007 in response to Bank of America's acquisition of Chicago-based LaSalle Bank hoping to capitalize on area consumers and middle-market firms alienated by the sale. Former LaSalle Bank CEO Larry Richman was named president and CEO of PrivateBancorp and PrivateBank that year. PrivateBancorp also recruited several other LaSalle executives. The new management team's goal was to transform the organization into a leading middle market commercial bank. To that end over the next four years the bank added nearly 1000 client relationships and shifted the composition of its loan portfolio toward commercial and industrial loans.

As part of its effort to court midsized businesses PrivateBank has specialty banking groups devoted to the architecture construction and engineering health care and security alarm financing sectors. Targeting firms with $50 million to $2 billion in annual revenues the bank has expanded its fee-based activities such as treasury management and capital markets services. Since the shift in focus to commercial lending PrivateBancorp has more than doubled its assets and loan portfolio.

Ownership

Chicago-based investment firm GTCR Golder Rauner owns about 13.5% of PrivateBancorp.

EXECUTIVES

Chairman, James M. (Jim) Guyette
President Chief Executive Officer of PrivateBancorp, Larry D. Richman, age 60, $785,000 total compensation
Managing Director; Head Business Banking, Thomas (Tom) Doherty
Managing Director; Head Community Banking, Alan S. (Al) Adams
CEO Private Bank Georgia, Brian D. Schmitt, age 51
Executive Managing Director; President Commercial Real Estate, Karen B. Case, age 54, $56,435 total compensation
Executive Managing Director; President National Commercial Banking, Bruce R. Hague, age 58, $435,000 total compensation
Executive Managing Director; President Illinois Commercial and Specialty Banking, Bruce S. Lubin, age 59, $385,000 total compensation
Managing Director and CFO, Kevin M. Killips, age 57, $339,564 total compensation
Managing Director and Chief Credit Officer, Kevin J. Van Solkema, age 52, $246,333 total compensation
Managing Director and Chief Risk Officer, Leonard E. Wiatr
Managing Director; President Personal Client Services, C. Brant Ahrens, age 42
Director Communications, Amy K. Yuhn
Managing Director General Counsel and Corporate Secretary, Jennifer R. Evans, age 54
CTO, James (Chip) Bennett
Managing Director; Head Private Wealth Group, Kristine R. (Kris) Garrett
Managing Director; Head Mortgage Banking, Richard (Rick) Bechtel
Managing Director; Head Retail Banking, Tom Bugielski
Managing Director Chief Credit Officer, Kevin Solkema
IR Contact, Sarah Lewensohn
Director, Edward W. (Ed) Rabin Jr., age 66
Director, James C. Tyree, age 54
Director, Cheryl E. Mayberry McKissack, age 57
Director, William R. Rybak, age 62
Director, Robert F. Coleman, age 68
Director; Chairman PrivateBank and Trust, Norman R. (Norm) Bobins, age 70
Director, James B. (Jim) Nicholson, age 69
Director, Alejandro (Alex) Silva, age 65
Director, Collin E. Roche, age 42
President Chief Executive Officer of PrivateBancorp, Larry D. Richman, age 60
Auditors: Ernst&YoungLLP

LOCATIONS

HQ: PrivateBancorp Inc.
120 S. LaSalle St., Chicago IL 60603
Phone: 312-564-2000　　**Fax:** -10746
Web: www.infineum.com

PRODUCTS/OPERATIONS

2011 Sales

	$ mil.	% of total
Interest		
Loans including fees	413	72
Taxable securities	61	11
Other	6	1
Noninterest		
Loan and credit-related fees	22	4
Treasury management	19	3
Capital markets products	19	3
Trust and investments	17	3
Mortgage banking	6	1
Net securities gains	5	1
Other	6	1
Total	**579**	**100**

Selected Subsidiaries

The PrivateBank and Trust Company
　BBH Financial Advisors Inc.
　Lodestar Investment Counsel LLC
　PB Real Estate LLC
　PBTC & Company LLC
　PRIVATESTAR LLC
　TPB Title Agency LLC

COMPETITORS

Bank of America	Harris
CFS Bancorp	MB Financial
Citizens Republic	Northern Trust
Bancorp	Park Bancorp
First Midwest Bancorp	Wintrust Financial

HISTORICAL FINANCIALS

Company Type: Public

Income Statement
FYE: December 31

	ASSETS ($ mil.)	NET INCOME ($ mil.)	INCOME AS % OF ASSETS	EMPLOYEES
12/12	14,057.5	77.9	0.6%	1,105
12/11	12,416.8	44.3	0.4%	1,045
12/10	12,465.6	1.5	0.0%	1,060
12/09	12,059.4	(30.0)	—	1,040
12/08	10,040.7	(92.1)	—	773
Annual Growth	8.8%	—		9.3%

2012 Year-End Financials

Return on assets: 0.5%
Return on equity: 6.2%
Long-term debt ($ mil.): —
No. of shares (mil.): 77
Sales ($ mil): 598
Dividends
　Yield: 0.2%
　Payout: 5.5%
Market value ($ mil.): 1,181

	STOCK PRICE ($) FY Close	P/E High/Low	Earnings	Dividends	Book Value
12/12	15.32	20 13	0.88	0.04	15.65
12/11	10.98	38 16	0.43	0.04	18.07
12/10	14.38	— —	(0.17)	0.04	17.21
12/09	8.97	— —	(0.95)	0.04	17.31
12/08	32.46	— —	(3.13)	0.30	18.03
Annual Growth	(17.1%)	— —	—	(39.6%)	(3.5%)

Prospect Capital Corporation

Prospect Capital is a closed-end investment fund with holdings in the consumer food health care and manufacturing sectors among others. The company targets privately held middle-market firms with annual revenues of less than $500 million; it also considers thinly traded public companies or turnaround situtations. Prospect's portfolio includes interests in more than 80 companies mainly through senior loans and mezzanine debt. The company also makes equity and secured debt investments. Typically investing from $5 million to $75 million per transaction Prospect is a long-term investor that maintains regular contact with its portfolio company's management and participates in their board meetings.

Prospect has elected to be regulated as a business development company (BDC) a status which affords the firm certain tax benefits. Although it initially targeted on industrial and energy investments the company has broadened its focus in the past few years and minimized its holdings in the energy sector.

The company has been capitalizing on the tightened credit markets that have prevailed since the recession reared its head. The economic downturn has reduced competition and led larger rivals to pursue larger clients. Prospect's revenue and net income has increased each year since then. In fiscal 2012 the company's revenues grew 89% to $320.9 million while profits rose 61% to $190.9 million.

Fiscal 2012 proved an active year for Prospect which made nearly 40 new investments and about 20 follow-on investments. The company also sold five investments and wrote off its investment in Deb Shops (which went into bankruptcy). All said and done Prospect's investment portfolio grew by nearly half again that year.

EXECUTIVES

Chairman of the Board; Chief Executive Officer,
John F. Barry III, age 61
President; Chief Operating Officer; Director, M. Grier Eliasek, age 40
CFO Chief Compliance Officer Treasurer and Secretary, Brian H. Oswald, age 52
Executive Vice President Chief Credit Officer,
Brian Giovinazzi
Chairman President Chief Executive Officer,
Christopher Martin
Executive Vice President Chief Lending Officer,
Donald W. Blum
Senior Vice President Chief Accounting Officer,
Frank S. Muzio
Executive Vice President Chief Information Officer, Jack Novielli
Senior Vice President Chief Risk Officer, James A. Christy
Executive Vice President and Chief Wealth Management Officer, James D. Nesci
Executive Vice President General Counsel Corporate Secretary, John F. Kuntz
Senior Vice President and Investor Relations Officer, Leonard G. Gleason
Board Member, Andrew C. Cooper, age 52
President COO and Board Member, M. Grier Eliasek, age 40
Board Member, Eugene S. Stark, age 55
Board Member, William J. (Bill) Gremp
Auditors: BDOUSALLP

LOCATIONS

HQ: Prospect Capital Corporation
10 E. 40th St. 44th Fl., New York NY 10016
Phone: 212-448-0702   **Fax:** 212-448-9652
Web: www.prospectstreet.com

PRODUCTS/OPERATIONS

2012 Sales

	$ mil.	% of total
Interest	219	69
Dividends	64	20
Other	36	11
Total	**320**	**100**

Selected Investments

AIRMALL USA Inc. (property management)
Ajax Rolled Ring & Machine Inc. (manufacturing)
AWCNC (machinery)
Biotronic Neuronetwork (health care)
Borga Inc. (manufacturing)
Boxercraft (textiles and leather)

Clearwater Seafoods LP (food products)
Focus Products (consumer products)
H&M Oil & Gas LLC (oil and gas production)
Integrated Contract Services Inc. (contracting)
Iron Horse Coiled Tubing Inc. (productin services)
Manx Energy Inc. (oil and gas production)
NMMB (advertising media buying)
NRG Manufacturing Inc. (drilling rig components)
R-V Industries Inc. (metal fabrication)
Wind River (oil and gas production)

COMPETITORS

ACI Capital	NGPC
Apollo Investment	Stephens Group
First Reserve	TPG
GFI Energy Ventures	Venrock
Katalyst	

HISTORICAL FINANCIALS

Company Type: Public

Income Statement

FYE: June 30

	ASSETS ($ mil.)	NET INCOME ($ mil.)	INCOME AS % OF ASSETS	EMPLOYEES
06/13	4,448.2	324.9	7.3%	0
06/12	2,255.2	186.6	8.3%	0
06/11	1,549.3	94.2	6.1%	0
06/10	832.7	66.4	8.0%	0
06/09	667.0	59.1	8.9%	0
Annual Growth	**60.7%**	**53.1%**		

2013 Year-End Financials

Return on assets: 9.6%
Return on equity: 15.5%
Long-term debt ($ mil.): —
No. of shares (mil.): 247
Sales ($ mil): 576

Dividends
Yield: 0.1%
Payout: 81.4%
Market value ($ mil.): 2,677

	STOCK PRICE ($) FY Close	P/E High/Low		PER SHARE ($) Earnings	Dividends	Book Value
06/13	10.80	8	6	1.57	1.28	10.72
06/12	11.39	7	5	1.63	1.22	10.83
06/11	10.11	11	8	1.10	1.21	10.36
06/10	9.65	41	28	0.32	1.33	10.29
06/09	9.20	13	6	1.11	1.61	12.40
Annual Growth	**4.1%**	—	—	**9.1%**	**(5.6%)**	**(3.6%)**

Proto Labs Inc

Need a prototype pronto? Proto Labs can help with that. The industrial manufacturer creates custom parts in quick turnaround for prototype and short-run production. The company uses 3D CAD software to upload new parts designs and then its computer numerical control (CNC) process analyzes the design quotes a price and makes the parts. Proto Labs creates machined metal (Firstcut) and injection-molded plastic (Protomold) parts and can ship them the next business day. Its medical device electronics consumer products appliance and automotive manufacturing customers use the parts for prototyping market evaluation and functional testing. The company was established in 1999 and went public in 2012.

IPO

The company hoped to raise about $100 million in its IPO which it filed in July 2011 but ended up raising more than $70 million when it went pub-

lic in February 2012. It used the proceeds for general corporate purposes but mostly it beefed up its sales and marketing teams.

Operations

Proto Labs makes the majority of its revenue (more than 70%) from its Protomold segment which typically produces prototype quantities of 25-100 custom injection-molded plastic parts. It saves the designs and molds from these parts and benefits when the customer returns sometimes requesting up to 10000 additional parts for short-run production. The company's Firstcut segment (nearly 30%) specializes in designing and cutting plastic and metal blocks but in smaller quantities.

Geographic Reach

Proto Labs has manufacturing facilities in Japan the UK and the US; sales offices also reside in Italy. The US accounts for around 75% of its revenue each year.

Sales and Marketing

Proto Labs sells its products through an internal sales team in more than 50 countries. Customers include Avox Systems BOSS Products PHT Aerospace Micro Engineering IFM Efector OEM controls Lombard Medical and Gamesman Limited.

Financial Performance

Proto Labs has grown significantly since it was founded as revenues and profits continue to climb to unprecedented heights. From 2011 to 2012 Pro Labs revenues surged by 27% from $99 million to $126 million and its net income increased by 34% from $18 million to $24 million. (Both these totals represent historic milestones for the company.)

Protomold in 2012 saw an increase of 22% in net sales while Firstcut's revenue was bumped by almost 44%. It attributes about $21 million to sales from new customers acquired during 2012 and finished the year serving roughly 7750 customers.

Strategy

Its strategy includes increasing penetration within existing customer organization and in geographical markets it already operates (US Europe and Japan) moving into new geographic regions and expanding its parts range and manufacturing processes. Another important component of its strategy involves optimizing its 3D CAD and CNC technology in order to design parts faster and more efficiently.

Company Background

Proto Labs began as The Protomold Company (molded plastic parts) but added CNC metal part machining its Firstcut business in 2007. In 2009 both branches began operating under the Proto Labs banner. It all started when founder and computer geek Lawrence Lukis started a desktop printer design business and was astounded at the long turnaround (weeks) and cost (thousands) for prototype parts. He turned his computer skills to solving the problem and found a way to completely automate the entire process and produce a part in a day for prices starting at $1500.

EXECUTIVES

COO, Donald G. Krantz, age 58
CFO, John R. Judd, age 56
President CEO and Director, Bradley A. Cleveland, age 53
EVP Finance, William R. Langton, age 48
VP Sales and Customer Service, Jacqueline D. Schneider, age 48
Managing Director Proto Labs Limited, John B. Tumelty, age 42
Chairman and CTO, Lawrence J. Lukis, age 65
VP Marketing, William M. Dietrick, age 57
EVP, Mark R. Kubicek, age 55

Managing Director Proto Labs G.K., Thomas H.
Pang, age 53
Auditors: Ernst&YoungLLP

LOCATIONS

HQ: Proto Labs Inc.
5540 Pioneer Creek Dr., Maple Plain MN 55359
Phone: 763-479-3680   **Fax:** 763-479-2679
Web: www.protolabs.com

2012 Sales

	$ mil.	% of total
US	75	
Total	**0**	**100**

PRODUCTS/OPERATIONS

2012 Sales

	$ mil.	% of total
Protomold	90	72
Total	**126**	**100**

COMPETITORS

Ajax United Patterns and Molds	Deswell
	Richco
Anchor Mfg. Group	Total Plastics

HISTORICAL FINANCIALS

Company Type: Public

Income Statement   FYE: December 31

	REVENUE ($ mil.)	NET INCOME ($ mil.)	NET PROFIT MARGIN	EMPLOYEES
12/12	125.9	24.0	19.1%	622
12/11	98.9	17.9	18.2%	511
12/10	64.9	10.9	16.9%	0
12/09	43.8	4.2	9.6%	0
Annual Growth	42.2%	78.5%	—	—

2012 Year-End Financials

Debt ratio: 0.3%
Return on equity: 23.5%
Cash ($ mil.): 36
Current ratio: 7.81
Long-term debt ($ mil.): 0

No. of shares (mil.): 24
Dividends
Yield: —
Payout: —
Market value ($ mil.): 978

	STOCK PRICE ($) FY Close	P/E High/Low	PER SHARE ($) Earnings	PER SHARE ($) Dividends	PER SHARE ($) Book Value
12/12	39.42	38 26	0.98	0.00	6.32
12/11	0.00	— —	0.67	0.00	4.81
Annual Growth	—	— —	46.3%	—	31.4%

Providence Service Corp

When it comes to social services there's not much that isn't in this company's providence. Providence Service Corporation operates through two divisions: Social Services and Non-Emergency Transportation Services (NET) to provide behavioral health and counseling services as well as non-emergency transportation to people in home and community-based settings. Providence manages foster care systems provides correctional support such as probation supervision offers job training and provides substance abuse treatment. Its NET services are provided to people with disabilities hospital patients and Medicare and Medicaid members among others. Providence operates in about 40 states and British Columbia.

Geographic Reach

Just 2% of Providence Service Corp's. sales come from Canada where it operates foster care services through subsidiary British Columbia-based WCG International Consultants (acquired in 2007).

Operations

The majority of Providence's revenue comes from its NET services (more than 60%). NET's primary payers include state Medicaid programs local government agencies and hospital systems. Its clients range from senior citizens and individuals with limited mobility to people with limited means of transportation and people with disabilities that prevent them from using conventional methods of transportation. Most of the NET division's income comes from state payer contracts that are three-to-five years long with renewal options; only about 6% of the division's income is derived from fee-for-service contracts. Its biggest customers are the State of Virginia's Department of Medical Assistance Services (12%) and the State of New Jersey (11%).

Providence's government sponsored social services account for the remainder of the company's income. Its counselors social workers and behavioral health professionals work with some 61000 clients who are eligible for government assistance either because of their income level or because of emotional or educational problems. Some of its clients are also under court order to be seen by Providence's social workers (such as those on probation). Payers range from state and local government agencies to commercial insurers and HMOs. Unlike the NET division most of Social Services' contracts are fee-for-service arrangements which means they can be terminated at will by the payer making them less secure than the NET division's long-term contracts.

Financial Analysis

Providence Service Corp's. (PSC) 2011 sales increased 7% vs. 2010 driven by increased revenue from its Social Services and Non-Emergency Transportation Services (NET) businesses. New contracts in Michigan and Wisconsin in 2011 and expansion in New Jersey Arkansas and other regions helped bolster NET operations. Revenue from the Home and Community Based Services segment rose more than 7% aided by the acquisition of ReDCo Group a provider of home and community based services in Pennsylvania in mid-2011.

Net income fell 28% in 2011 vs. 2010 on higher operating expenses including steeper costs for NET services. Net income has been flat to down over the past two years after surging in 2009 following an unprofitable 2008. Meanwhile PSC's sales have surged nearly 400% over the past five years.

Strategy

Providence's primary form of growth has historically been through acquisitions. Most notably the 2007 acquisition of Charter LCI Corp. including its subsidiaries collectively referred to as LogistiCare transformed Providence and prompted it to form the NET division its main moneymaker. Between 2002 and 2008 the firm made about two dozen purchases of a range of businesses including tutoring behavioral health family services and correctional services.

Along with acquisitions Providence is focused on securing contracts such as those it has with Virginia and New Jersey to boost its income. To that end Providence tracks state legislation and funding trends to determine how they may impact its operations and targets states with favorable funding opportunities. It also establishes new contracts with commercial payers in regions in which it already has a presence by taking advantage of its existing networks in those areas.

Mergers and Acquisitions

PSC acquired Pennsylvania-based The ReDCo Group in June 2011 for $605000 and the repayment of about $8 million in ReDCo Group debt. The purchase added more than $20 million to home and community based services revenue in 2011.

Ownership

Ameriprise Financial and Coliseum Capital Management each own about 12% of the company's shares.

EXECUTIVES

CEO LogistiCare, Herman M. Schwarz
CEO, Warren S. Rustand
Chairman and CEO, Fletcher Jay McCusker, age 63, $575,000 total compensation
CFO Secretary and Treasurer, Michael N. Deitch, age 56, $300,000 total compensation
EVP Program Services, Mary J. Shea, $230,417 total compensation
CEO Providence Human Services, Craig A. Norris, $350,000 total compensation
EVP and General Counsel, Fred D. Furman, $300,000 total compensation
Director Organizational Development, Michelle Pitot
President Eastern Region, Michael Fidgeon
VP Clinical Services Eastern Region, Tasha Walsh
Chairman, Christopher S. Shackelton
Chief Strategy Officer, Leamon A. Crooms III, age 50
Human Resources Director, Karen Battle
Controller, Kevin Driscoll
Vice President Midwest Region, Chuck Boien
Vice President IES Program Operations, Brenda Motley-Aikens
CFO, Robert Wilson
Director, Warren S. Rustand, age 70
Director, Kristi L. Meints, age 58
Auditors: KPMGLLP

LOCATIONS

HQ: The Providence Service Corporation
64 East Broadway Boulevard, Tucson AZ 85701
Phone: 520-747-6600   **Fax:** 520-747-6605
Web: www.provcorp.com

2011 Sales

	$ mil.	% of total
US	920	98
Canada	22	2
Total	**943**	**100**

PRODUCTS/OPERATIONS

2011 Sales

	$ mil.	% of total
Non-emergency transportation services	581	62
Foster care services	34	4
Total	**943**	**100**

Selected Subsidiaries

A to Z In-Home Tutoring LLC
AlphaCare Resources Inc.
Camelot Care Centers Inc.

Children's Behavioral Health Inc.
Choices Group Inc.
College Community Services LLC
Dockside Services Inc.
Drawbridges Counseling Services LLC
Family Preservation Services Inc.
Health Trans Inc.
LogistiCare Inc.
Maple Star Nevada
Provado Insurance Service Inc.
Red Top Transportation Inc.

COMPETITORS

AMR	Res-Care
Acadian Ambulance	Rural/Metro
Service Inc.	Safe Ride Services
Devereux Foundation	Salvation Army
Hazelden	UBH
Mental Health Network	

HISTORICAL FINANCIALS

Company Type: Public

Income Statement

FYE: December 31

	REVENUE ($ mil.)	NET INCOME ($ mil.)	NET PROFIT MARGIN	EMPLOYEES
12/12	1,105.8	8.4	0.8%	8,400
12/11	942.9	16.9	1.8%	7,600
12/10	879.7	23.6	2.7%	7,000
12/09	801.0	21.1	2.6%	7,000
12/08	691.6	(155.6)	—	6,271
Annual Growth	**12.4%**	—	—	**7.6%**

2012 Year-End Financials

Debt ratio: 33.1%
Return on equity: 7.9%
Cash ($ mil.): 55
Current ratio: 1.33
Long-term debt ($ mil.): 116

No. of shares (mil.): 12
Dividends
　Yield: —
　Payout: —
Market value ($ mil.): 218

	STOCK PRICE ($) FY Close	P/E High/Low		PER SHARE ($) Earnings	Dividends	Book Value
12/12	16.99	26	15	0.64	0.00	8.69
12/11	13.76	14	7	1.27	0.00	7.85
12/10	16.07	10	6	1.78	0.00	6.31
12/09	15.80	10	1	1.60	0.00	4.29
12/08	1.45	—	—	(12.42)	0.00	2.38
Annual Growth	**85.0%**	—	—	—	—	**38.2%**

PTC Inc

PTC (formerly Parametric Technology Corporation) hopes to be a paradigmatic model of success. The company develops software used in computer-aided design manufacturing and mechanical engineering (CAD/CAM/CAE) applications. Its Creo product is used to create 3D computer models for aircraft engines car bodies mobile phones and toys. PTC also offers the Windchill software suite which enables collaborative content and process management —from design to supplier sourcing and production —over the Internet. The Mathcad application automates mathematical calculations for engineering purposes. PTC sells directly through resellers and via systems integrators including IBM Hewlett-Packard and Accenture.

Geographic Reach

PTC's customer base is focused on the most developed regions of the world with Europe (40% of sales) and the Americas (37%) accounting for the bulk of the company's sales; Japan and the Asia/Pacific region account for the rest.

Financial Performance

Despite significantly higher expenses in several parts of its businesss particularly in the areas of administration and sales PTC's profit more than tripled in 2011 over 2010. This was due to healthy revenue growth driven largely by sales of desktop products to large commercial clients. The desktop segment got a boost in 2011 following the release of a new version of the company's Creo application. Additionally sales of consulting services rose 23% and training revenue went up 15%. PTC makes more than 70% of its sales directly with more than 400 resellers handling the company's indirect sales.

Strategy

PTC is trying to broaden its reach into new markets by offering hardware and software development tools to a broader customer base and by branching into complementary products and services. It entered the service lifecycle management (SLM) game in 2005 with the purchase of Arbortext and subsequent acquisitions thereafter. In 2012 the company paid $220 million for SLM software developer Servigistics to solidify its market leadership in SLM. In 2011 PTC bought MKS for nearly C$295 million ($300 million). Also that year PTC acquired warranty management and service lifecycle management software developer 4CS Solutions that year to expand its lineup of applications for the product support and service organizations of equipment manufacturers. In early 2013 the company shortened its name from Parametric Technology Corporation to align it with popular usage.

Mergers and Acquisitions

PTC has made about 20 acquisitions since its founding in 1985 (more than 10 of those in the past decade) to round out its product line. Past purchases have included Arbortext Mathsoft CoCreate NC Graphics Logistics Business Systems Digital Human and ITEDO Software.

HISTORY

Geometry professor Samuel Geisberg fled the USSR in 1974 and worked for computer-aided design (CAD) software development firms Computervision and Applicon. At the urging of his brother Vladimir (who had emigrated in 1980 and started his own software firm) he founded Parametric Technology in 1985 to remedy flaws in mechanical design software.

With financial backing from Charles River Ventures and other investors Geisberg developed his CAD/CAM (computer-aided manufacturing) product. Charles River also brought in Steven Walske as CEO in 1986. The first Pro/ENGINEER product was shipped in 1988 and Parametric went public the next year building market strength by marketing to engineers and keeping prices at half those of competitors' products.

In 1994 Walske became chairman when Geisberg retired and took up the position of senior scientist. The next year Parametric purchased Evans & Sutherland Computer's conceptual design and rendering software business and model simulation firm Rasna which offered tools that let users simulate the operation of products in real-life settings. In 1996 Parametric acquired project modeling and management software from Greenshire License Company.

In 1998 Parametric acquired Computervision which brought in a strong base of automotive aerospace and shipbuilding customers and the company's first Internet product. That year Parametric also bought the automotive and aerospace engineering software operations of Control Data Systems and Web-based 3-D mechanical component parts catalog specialist InPart.

With sales for its legacy CAD/CAM products slowing Walske began pushing Web-based collaboration and business-to-business design through acquisitions. Parametric in 1999 bought UK-based data visualization tool specialist Division Group and auxilium a developer of Web-based software tools for integrating legacy product data. The company's Web-based collaborative software suite (Windchill) was introduced in late 1999. Walske turned over the CEO duties to president Richard Harrison in 2000 to focus on long-range strategies.

In 2002 Parametric sold its ICEM surface modeling operations to that division's management team. Also in 2002 Parametric sold its MEDUSA line of 2D CAD products to CAD Schroer a German reseller.

PTC in early 2004 acquired OHIO Design Automation a supplier of collaborative design software for about $12 million in cash. In 2005 it started offering service lifecycle management with the acquisition of Arbortext in 2005. In 2010 PTC acquired Planet Metrics a developer of environmental impact software.

EXECUTIVES

Executive Vice President Strategy, Barry F. Cohen, age 69, $415,000 total compensation
Chairman, C. Richard (Dick) Harrison, age 58, $600,000 total compensation
EVP Worldwide Sales and Distribution, Paul J. Cunningham, age 51, $415,000 total compensation
President and Chief Executive Officer; Director, James E. (Jim) Heppelmann, age 49, $521,650 total compensation
EVP Enterprise Segments, Brian Shepherd, age 46
SVP Global Partners and Education, John Stuart
Executive Vice President and Chief Financial Officer, Jeffrey D. (Jeff) Glidden, age 63
Corporate VP General Counsel and Secretary, Aaron C. von Staats, age 47
Executive Vice President CAD Segment, Michael (Mike) Campbell
EVP Application Lifecycle Management and Services Lifecycle Management, William (Bill) Berutti, age 42
Senior Divisional VP Worldwide Channel Sales, Robert Kocis
Executive Vice President Global Support, Anthony Paul (Tony) DiBona, age 58, $325,000 total compensation
Divisional VP and Chief Customer Officer, Mark Hodges
SVP Corporate Development, Iain Michel
VP Product Strategy Electronics, Chad Hawkinson
VP Marketing Strategy, Kathleen Mitford
Director Vertical Market Strategy PTC, Matthew McGovern
EVP Marketing, Robert C. Gremley, age 48
Director Product and Market Strategy, Sin Min Yap
Executive Vice President Global Services & Partners, Marc Diouane, age 44
Chief Compliance Officer, Martha Durcan, age 53
EVP Worldwide Sales, Robert (Bob) Ranaldi, age 43
CTO, Andrew Wertkin
Corporate Vice President; General Counsel; Secretary, Aaron Staats
Vice President Senior General Manager, Howard Heppelmann

Divisional Vice President ? PTC University, Matthew Cohen
Vice President - Investor Relations, Timothy Fox
Director, Paul A. Lacy, age 66
Director, Robert P. (Bob) Schechter, age 65
Director, Robert N. (Bob) Goldman, age 64
Director, Michael E. (Mike) Porter, age 65
Director, Donald K. (Don) Grierson, age 79
President and Chief Executive Officer; Director, James E. (Jim) Heppelmann, age 49
Independent Director, Renato Zambonini
Independent Director, Thomas Bogan
Auditors: PricewaterhouseCoopersLLP

LOCATIONS

HQ: PTC Inc.
140 Kendrick St., Needham MA 02494-2714
Phone: 781-370-5000   **Fax:** 781-370-6000
Web: www.ptc.com

2011 Sales

	$ mil.	% of total
Europe	466	40
Americas	429	37
Pacific Rim	148	13
Japan	123	10
Total	**1,166**	**100**

PRODUCTS/OPERATIONS

2011 Sales

	$ mil.	% of total
Software	875	75
Services	291	25
Total	**1,166**	**100**

2011 Sales

	$ mil.	% of total
Desktop	625	54
Enterprise	541	46
Total	**1,166**	**100**

Selected Software

2-D and 3-D visualization and virtual reality mockup (Division)
Collaborative product development (Windchill)
Entry-level product development (Pro/DESKTOP)
Product design automation and management (Pro/ENGINEER)
Simulation (Pro/MECHANICA)

COMPETITORS

ANSYS	Lectra
Ansoft	MSC Software
Auto-trol	MathWorks
Autodesk	Nemetschek North
Bentley Systems	America
Broadcaster	Oracle
Cimatron	SAP
CollabNet	SOGECLAIR
Dassault	Siemens PLM Software
Delcam	SofTech
Intergraph	Vero Software
Kubotek USA	

HISTORICAL FINANCIALS

Company Type: Public

Income Statement

FYE: September 30

	REVENUE ($ mil.)	NET INCOME ($ mil.)	NET PROFIT MARGIN	EMPLOYEES
09/13	1,293.5	143.7	11.1%	6,000
09/12	1,255.6	(35.4)	—	5,897
09/11	1,166.9	85.4	7.3%	6,122
09/10	1,010.0	24.3	2.4%	5,317
09/09	938.1	31.5	3.4%	5,165
Annual Growth	**8.4%**	**46.1%**	**—**	**3.8%**

2013 Year-End Financials

Debt ratio: 14.1%	No. of shares (mil.): 118
Return on equity: 16.6%	Dividends
Cash ($ mil.): 241	Yield: —
Current ratio: 1.29	Payout: —
Long-term debt ($ mil.): 243	Market value ($ mil.): 3,371

	STOCK PRICE ($) FY Close	P/E High/Low	PER SHARE ($) Earnings	Dividends	Book Value
09/13	28.46	24 16	1.19	0.00	7.82
09/12	21.77	— —	(0.30)	0.00	6.67
09/11	15.38	33 21	0.71	0.00	7.04
09/10	19.54	95 64	0.20	0.00	6.45
09/09	13.82	68 27	0.27	0.00	6.57
Annual Growth	**19.8%**	**— —**	**44.9%**	**—**	**4.5%**

Quality Systems, Inc.

Quality Systems can't help doctors' with the legibility of their signatures but it knows how to insure the integrity of their digital records. The company develops data management software for medical and dental practices and a variety of other health care businesses. Its NextGen subsidiary (75% of sales) makes electronic records and practice management software tailored for patient data scheduling billing and claims handling. Its practice management unit focuses on electronic claims submission remittance and payments services. The company's QSI Dental division makes practice management software for dentists. Its inpatient unit focuses on clinical and financial software for rural hospitals.

Expanding its inpatient services business in 2012 Quality Systems acquired The Poseidon Group which provides software and a Web-based system for managing emergency department documentation. The offerings will complement and be integrated into the NextGen Healthcare portfolio.

Quality Systems' NextGen medical practice software business represents three quarters of total sales. In 2010 the company expanded its product line with the acquisitions of Opus Healthcare Solutions and Sphere Health Systems. The Opus deal helped Quality Systems to target rural and community health care markets in keeping with a broader strategy of focusing on health care organizations and hospitals with 100 or fewer beds as works to diversify its market beyond products for larger institutions. The former Opus operations comprise the company's inpatient division.

The next year Quality Systems established an outsourcing operation in India known as QSIH to perform in-house application development and business processing services. Also in 2011 the acquired Texas-based CQI Solutions. The company provides software implementation and other IT services as well as the Care Tracker line of scheduling and surgical data management software for about 100 hospitals nationwide. That year Quality Systems also acquired ViaTrack Systems a specialist in electronic data interchange software that enables electronic claim services for health care providers.

The company acquired Ohio-based Matrix Management Solutions a reseller of NextGen Healthcare. Matrix Management provided revenue cycle management services healthcare IT software and training product implementation and technical

---

support to clients nationwide. The deal enabled Quality Systems to boost the profile of its NextGen practice management applications among hospitals and private physicians.

Quality Systems enjoyed increased revenue and profit for 2011 despite higher costs related to selling expenses which rose due to higher sales headcount and higher research and development costs. The company cited robust sales of recurring software maintenance service revenue as well as sales of tools for dental practices and small medical practice revenue cycle management as key drivers of growth.

While nearly all of Quality Systems' sales come from a traditional software licensing model the company has embraced the Software-as-a-Service (SaaS) delivery model which it offers as a way for smaller practices to quickly start using the select NextGen products. The company primarily makes sales directly with less than 10% of sales made through resellers.

Chairman Sheldon Razin and director Ahmed Hussein own 17% and 15% respectively of Quality Systems.

EXECUTIVES

EVP EDI and Dental, Donn E. Neufeld, age 56, $219,920 total compensation
President and CEO, Steven T. Plochocki, age 61, $296,875 total compensation
EVP General Counsel and Secretary, James J. (Jim) Sullivan, age 55
EVP and CFO, Paul A. Holt, age 47, $267,228 total compensation
Chairman, Sheldon Razin, age 75
President NextGen Healthcare Information Systems, Scott Decker
Chief Operating Officer; Executive Vice President, Daniel J. Morefield
Executive Vice President - NextGen Practice Solutions, Monte Sandler
EVP CTO, Steve Puckett
EVP General Counsel and Secretary, Jocelyn A Leavitt
Director, Patrick B. Cline, age 52
CEO and Director, Steven T. Plochocki, age 60
Director, Ahmed Hussein, age 72
Director, Russell Pflueger, age 49
Director, Craig A. Barbarosh
Director, Joseph I. (Joe) Davis, age 48
Director, George Bristol, age 63
Director, Murray Brennan, age 71
Independent Director, Maureen Spivack
Auditors: PricewaterhouseCoopersLLP

LOCATIONS

HQ: Quality Systems, Inc.
18111 Von Karman Avenue, Suite 700, Irvine, CA 92612
Phone: 949 255-2600
Web: www.qsii.com

PRODUCTS/OPERATIONS

2011 Sales

	$ mil.	% of total
NextGen	266	75
Practice solutions	49	14
QSI Dental	19	6
Inpatient solutions	17	5
Total	**353**	**100**

Selected Products

Clinical data management software
Dental charting software
Dental practice management systems

Internet-based consumer health portal
Medical records storage software
Medical practice management systems

COMPETITORS

Allscripts	GE Healthcare
CPSI	Global Med
CareCentric	MEDITECH
Cerner	McKesson
Epic Systems	QuadraMed

HISTORICAL FINANCIALS

Company Type: Public

Income Statement

FYE: March 31

	REVENUE ($ mil.)	NET INCOME ($ mil.)	NET PROFIT MARGIN	EMPLOYEES
03/13	460.2	42.7	9.3%	2,333
03/12	429.8	75.6	17.6%	1,938
03/11	353.3	61.6	17.4%	1,579
03/10	291.8	48.3	16.6%	1,502
03/09	245.5	46.1	18.8%	1,263
Annual Growth	17.0%	(1.9%)	—	16.6%

2013 Year-End Financials

Debt ratio: —	No. of shares (mil.): 59
Return on equity: 14.1%	Dividends
Cash ($ mil.): 106	Yield: 0.0%
Current ratio: 2.34	Payout: 97.2%
Long-term debt ($ mil.): —	Market value ($ mil.): 1,088

	STOCK PRICE ($) FY Close	P/E High/Low	PER SHARE ($) Earnings	Dividends	Book Value
03/13	18.27	61 22	0.72	0.70	5.16
03/12	43.73	78 26	1.28	0.70	4.99
03/11	83.34	78 51	1.06	0.63	3.87
03/10	61.44	81 52	0.84	0.60	3.26
03/09	45.25	58 33	0.81	0.58	2.73
Annual Growth	(20.3%)	— —	(2.9%)	5.0%	17.2%

Questcor Pharmaceuticals Inc

Questcor Pharmaceuticals is on a journey for better health for patients and some good profitability for itself to boot. The company makes and develops drugs for neurological conditions and kidney treatments. Most of its revenue comes from the sale of H.P. Acthar Gel (or Acthar). Acthar is approved for the treatment of nearly 20 indications but the company receives the majority of its income from sales related to three of those: multiple sclerosis nephrotic syndrome and infantile spasms (a rare form of pediatric epilepsy). Questcor also sells insomnia treatment Doral. The company's BioVectra subsidiary provides contract manufacturing to other pharma firms.

Operations

Questcor had some difficulties winning approval for Acthar as a treatment for infantile spasms although it is the most-often prescribed treatment for the rare condition (previously off-label). The FDA formerly rejected an application for approval prompting the company to rethink its strategy for the drug. For example Questcor expanded its sales force dedicated to the multiple sclerosis market which led to strong sales growth in that market. Now Acthar is approved for the treatment of infantile spasms in children under the age of two years.

Acthar is also approved help treat nephrotic syndrome (NS) a kidney disorder characterized by high levels of protein in the urine and low levels of protein in the blood that often leads to end-stage renal disease.

Geographic Reach

The company has its headquarters and a medical affairs office in California along with R&D facilities in Maryland.

Sales and Marketing

In the US Questco sells Acthar exclusively to CuraScript SD at a discount from its list price. CuraScript then resells Acthar (which is not a cheap drug) primarily to about a dozen specialty pharmacies including CuraScript Specialty Pharmacy or CuraScript SP and to children's hospitals. Questcor sells Doral to pharmaceutical wholesalers which resell the drug primarily to retail pharmacies and hospitals.

The company has an agreement with IDIS Limited for the exclusive marketing and distribution of Acthar in the UK.

Part of Questcor's end-user vial demand for Acthar is for patients covered under Medicaid Medicare and other government-related programs such as TRICARE and the Veterans Administration (VA). As required by Federal regulations Questcor provides rebates and discounts in connection with those programs. As a result of Medicaid rebates the company does not post any net sales with respect to Medicaid but it does generate net sales with respect to Medicare sales TRICARE sales and sales made to the VA. Of course all of that means that Questco is affected by changes to federal government payments of the drug.

Financial Performance

Questcor reported a 133% increase in revenue for 2012 attributed to increased demand for Acthar. Net income also jumped by 148% on the revenue uptick offset by increases in operating expenses. Cash flow however dropped $55 million as it used cash in financing activities.

Strategy

Questcor is exploring more uses for Acthar including collagen diseases such as treatment during an exacerbation or as maintenance therapy in selected cases of systemic lupus erythematosus (a long-term auto-immune disorder) and systemic dermatomyositis (a disorder that frequently affects the joints the esophagus the lungs and less commonly the heart).

The company is on the lookout for potential partners to help it develop its drugs as a collaborative partner including those related to product licensing and acquisition co-promotion and product development. In 2013 it purchased BioVectra manufacturer of the active pharmaceutical ingredient (API) for Acthar to ensure control over the drug's manufacturing process.

As part of its plan to expand its offerings Questcor acquired the rights to develop Synacthen and Synacthen Depot in the US from Novartis. Synacthen is being developed to treat autoimmune and inflammatory conditions.

Mergers and Acquisitions

In 2013 Questcor paid about $90 million for BioVectra which manufactures the key ingredient of Acthar.

EXECUTIVES

President and CEO, Don M. Bailey, $525,000 total compensation
Chairman, Virgil D. Thompson
EVP and CTO, David J. (Dave) Medeiros, $325,000 total compensation
COO, Stephen L. (Steve) Cartt, $350,000 total compensation
VP Strategic Marketing, James (Jiim) Knight
Chief Scientific Officer, David Young
Senior VP Corporate Strategic Development, Michael D. A. Aldridge, age 41
VP Contract Manufacturing, Timothy O'Neill
SVP Commercial Operations, Eldon Mayer
Vice President Regulatory Affairs, Sian E. Bigora
EVP CFO and General Counsel, Michael H. Mulroy
Chief Financial Officer; Member of the Management Board, Juergen Hermann
Vice President Chief Compliance Officer, Raymond Furey
Member of the Management Board; responsible for direct sales, Thomas Stoek
Vice President Contract Manufacturing, Timothy ONeill
Chairman of the Supervisory Board, Herbert Brenke
Vice President Medical Affairs, Gary S. Hogge
Member of the Management Board; Director of Sales, Arnold Stender
Vice President Neurology Sales, Darlene Romine
IR Contact Officer, Gregory Gin
Vice President Human Resources, Marilee Moy
Vice President Contract Manufacturing, Gregory F. Liposky
Director, Mitchell J. Blutt, age 56
President; Chief Executive Officer; Director, Don M. Bailey, age 67
Director, Louis E. (Lou) Silverman, age 54
Director, Stephen C. (Steve) Farrell, age 48
Director, Neal C. Bradsher, age 47
Director, Gregg A. Lapointe, age 53
Member of the Supervisory Board, David Ruberg
Chairman of the Supervisory Board, Herbert Brenke
Independent Director, Scott Whitcup
Auditors: OdenbergUllakkoMuranishi&Co.LLP

LOCATIONS

HQ: Questcor Pharmaceuticals Inc.
1300 North Kellogg Drive Suite D, Anaheim CA 92807
Phone: 714-786-4200   **Fax:** 714-789-4229
Web: www.questcor.com

COMPETITORS

Cephalon	Novartis
GlaxoSmithKline	Sanofi
H. Lundbeck	Somaxon
Lundbeck Inc.	Sunovion
Neurocrine Biosciences	

HISTORICAL FINANCIALS

Company Type: Public

Income Statement

FYE: December 31

	REVENUE ($ mil.)	NET INCOME ($ mil.)	NET PROFIT MARGIN	EMPLOYEES
12/12	509.2	197.6	38.8%	557
12/11	218.1	79.5	36.5%	206
12/10	115.1	35.0	30.5%	152
12/09	88.3	26.6	30.2%	77
12/08	95.2	40.5	42.6%	46
Annual Growth	52.1%	48.6%	—	86.5%

2012 Year-End Financials

Debt ratio: —	No. of shares (mil.): 58
Return on equity: 103.3%	Dividends
Cash ($ mil.): 155	Yield: 1.5%
Current ratio: 2.62	Payout: 15.2%
Long-term debt ($ mil.): —	Market value ($ mil.): 1,564

	STOCK PRICE ($) FY Close	P/E High/Low		PER SHARE ($) Earnings	Dividends	Book Value
12/12	26.72	18	5	3.14	0.40	2.76
12/11	41.58	36	10	1.21	0.00	3.45
12/10	14.73	28	8	0.54	0.00	1.92
12/09	4.75	23	9	0.40	0.00	1.26
12/08	9.31	18	7	0.49	0.00	1.03
Annual Growth	30.2%	—	—	59.1%	—	28.0%

Rackspace Hosting Inc

Rackspace Hosting is fanatically focused on hosting services but also has its head in the clouds. The company provides a range of Web hosting and managed network services for businesses. It offers traditional hosting services with dedicated servers but is expanding into cloud hosting which lets customers utilize pooled server resources on an on-demand basis. Its cloud computing services include public private and hybrid cloud hosting. Rackspace also provides hybrid hosting providing a combination of dedicated hosting and cloud computing. The company markets its services under the Fanatical Support brand. Founded in 1998 Rackspace has more than 200000 business customers in 120 countries.

Geographic Reach

Texas-based Rackspace Hosting rings up about three-quarters of its sales in the US. The company has data centers in Texas Virginia and Illinois as well as Australia Hong Kong and the UK.

Operations

Rackspace Hosting provides managed hosting and private and public cloud services. Public Cloud services accounts for nearly 25% of revenue while the company's dedicated cloud segment contributes the rest. The firm relies on more than 90000 serves at its data centers worldwide.

Financial Performance

Rackspace Hosting's sales and profits are growing in tandem with the increased popularity of cloud computing. In 2012 sales increased 28% versus 2011 to $1.3 billion. (Indeed the company has added a billion dollars in sales over the past five years.) The double-digit increase in annual sales was driven by a 61% jump in the company's public cloud sales while dedicated cloud sales increased 20% thanks to an increase in new customers and incremental sales to existing ones. International sales increased 30% while US sales rose 27% year over year.

Net income grew 38% in 2012 versus 2011 to $105.4 million on increased sales partially offset by increased costs and expenses related to additional headcount and employee-related expenses and equity awards granted in 2012.

Strategy

Cloud computing is the company's growth engine and Rackspace Hosting continues to make significant investments in the emerging technology. Rackspace has invested in internal development and acquisitions to build its cloud hosting

business. In 2010 the company launched several new products among them OpenStack (an open-source cloud platform) Cloud Servers for Windows (on-demand service for Windows users) and Rackconnect (integrates the Rackspace Cloud with dedicated hosting services). It has added a suite of combined dedicated and cloud computing services called Hybrid Hosting to its portfolio of products. The company is also actively pursuing customers in Europe Asia and Latin America for international expansion.

Partnerships are another avenue for growth. In 2013 Rackspace partnered will Magento a division of X.commerce an eBay company to work collabortively to serve both dedicated and open hybrid cloud customers with one of the fastest growing e-commerce platforms on the market. In 2012 Rackspace partnered with Hortonworks to focus on pursuing an OpenStack-based Hadoop solution for the public and private cloud.

Mergers and Acquisitions

In 2012 Rackspace acquired e-mail services company Mailgun looking to add functionality to its Rackspace Open Cloud platform. Mailgun let users integrate e-mail from within applications. Also that year the company acquired Share-Point911 a provider of consulting and training services for Microsoft's collaboration and document management software SharePoint. The purchase expands Rackspace's presence in Share-Point management market which it entered in 2008.

Previous purchases include San Francisco-based cloud data server management software startup Cloudkick in late 2010 to add tools for automating tasks for systems administrators. Previous purchases include cloud storage specialist Jungle Disk and cloud hosting service provider Slicehost.

Ownership

Chairman Graham Weston owns nearly 14% of Rackspace Hosting. The privately-owned investment manager Capital World Investors owns about 11% of the company.

EXECUTIVES

Chief Marketing Officer, Rick Jackson
Director, Michael S. (Sam) Gilliland, age 50
Chairman and CEO, Graham M. Weston, age 49
Managing Director and SVP International, David Kelly, age 48
CEO and Director, A. Lanham Napier, age 42, $351,955 total compensation
President Chief Strategy Officer and Director, Lew Moorman, age 42, $226,450 total compensation
VP-Sls, Pat Cathey
Chief Marketing Officer, Suaad H. Sait, age 45
CTO, John Engates
SVP Infrastructure Services, Klee Kleber, age 45, $160,864 total compensation
COO, Mark Roenigk, age 52, $20,192 total compensation
Director Marketing EMEA, Fabio Torlini
SVP General Counsel and Secretary, Alan Schoenbaum, age 55
SVP CFO and Treasurer, Karl Pichler, age 41
Director Software Development, Troy Toman, age 46
VP Sales and Marketing Cloud Division, Frederick Mendler
SVP and Co-General Manager Enterprise, Jim Lewandowski, age 52
Director Real Estate, Randy Smith
SVP Enterprise Fanatical Support, Wayne Roberts, age 50
VP Enterprise Strategy, Andy Schroepfer
CIO, Steve Mills, age 54

Managing Director International, William T. (Taylor) Rhodes, age 41
SVP Corporate Development, Pat Matthews, age 36
Director Product Cloud Applications, Kirk Averett
Media Contact, Rachel Ferry
SVP and General Manager Private Cloud, Jim Curry
Chief Accounting Officer, Joe Saporito, age 59
SVP and General Manager Americas, Odus (Boogie) Wittenburg
Chief Financial Officer, Jeffrey G. Winzeler
Chief Operating Officer, Steven C. Lagorio
VP of Technology Devel, Doug MacRae
Founder Chairman, Emmett R. DeMoss
SVP and General Manager Enterprise, Chris Cochran
Chairman of the Board; President; Chief Executive Officer, Guy Archbold
President, Taylor Rhodes
SVP Sales Americas, Todd Cione
Director, George J. Still Jr., age 55
Director, Michael S. (Sam) Gilliland, age 50
CEO and Director, A. Lanham Napier, age 42
President Chief Strategy Officer and Director, Lew Moorman, age 42
Director, Mark P. Mellin, age 52
Director, Palmer L. Moe, age 69
Director, Fred Reichheld, age 61
Director, S. James Bishkin, age 55
Auditors: KPMGLLP

LOCATIONS

HQ: Rackspace Hosting Inc.
5000 Walzem Rd., San Antonio TX 78218
Phone: 210-312-4000   **Fax:** 210-447-4300
Web: www.rackspace.com

2012 Sales

	$ mil.	% of total
US	973	74
Other countries	335	26
Total	**1,309**	**100**

PRODUCTS/OPERATIONS

2012 Sales

	$ mil.	% of total
Dedicated cloud	1,005	77
Public cloud	304	23
Total	**1,309**	**100**

COMPETITORS

AT&T	Microsoft
Amazon.com	NaviSite
BT	NetNation
Cable & Wireless	Communications
Computer Sciences	Red Hat
Corp.	SAVVIS
Critical Path	SoftLayer
CyrusOne	Terremark Worldwide
DuPont Fabros	USinternetworking
Equinix	Verio
Google	Verizon
HP Enterprise Services	XO Holdings
IBM	salesforce.com

HISTORICAL FINANCIALS

Company Type: Public

Income Statement

FYE: December 31

	REVENUE ($ mil.)	NET INCOME ($ mil.)	NET PROFIT MARGIN	EMPLOYEES
12/12	1,309.2	105.4	8.1%	4,852
12/11	1,025.0	76.4	7.5%	4,040
12/10	780.5	46.3	5.9%	3,262
12/09	628.9	30.2	4.8%	2,774
12/08	531.9	21.7	4.1%	2,611
Annual Growth	25.3%	48.5%	—	16.8%

2012 Year-End Financials

Debt ratio: 9.6%
Return on equity: 14.5%
Cash ($ mil.): 292
Current ratio: 1.66
Long-term debt ($ mil.): 62

No. of shares (mil.): 137
Dividends
  Yield: —
  Payout: —
Market value ($ mil.): 10,234

	STOCK PRICE ($) FY Close	P/E High/Low	PER SHARE ($) Earnings	Dividends	Book Value
12/12	74.27	94 53	0.75	0.00	6.12
12/11	43.01	78 50	0.55	0.00	4.54
12/10	31.41	86 42	0.35	0.00	3.46
12/09	20.85	92 18	0.24	0.00	2.82
12/08	5.38	59 24	0.19	0.00	2.30
Annual Growth	92.8%	— —	41.0%	—	27.7%

Raven Industries, Inc.

Quoth the Raven "Balloons (and more) ever-more!" Raven Industries' Aerostar division does sell high-altitude research balloons as well as parachutes and protective wear used by US agencies. Its Engineered Films Division makes reinforced plastic sheeting for various applications. The Applied Technology Division manufactures high-tech agricultural aids from global positioning system (GPS)-based steering devices and chemical spray equipment to field computers. The Electronic Systems Division offers electronic manufacturing services and supports the other divisions. Goodrich is a major customer.

The rugged sheeting made by the Engineered Films Division 34% of sales are applied for industrial energy construction geomembrane and agricultural uses. "Geomembrane" refers to containment liners used for environmental projects and water conservation. Products are marketed through independent distributors. Because the segment extrudes a large part of its products it needs a significant amount of capital expenditures to stay operational. Extrusion is a process that includes pushing material through a circular or slot die.

Besides GPS-based products and computers the Applied Technology Division also 34% of sales markets a software platform called Slingshot that offers Real Time Kinematic (RTK) corrections of GPS signals for more accurate steering. Served by a globally based staff the division markets its products to OEMs and through the aftermarket. The Electronic Systems Division 19% of sales makes such assemblies as avionics secure communication and environmental controls. Sales are made through competitive bids.

Besides balloons Aerostar 13% of sales also sells tethered aerostats which are similar to blimps used

for surveillance and aerial communication. Besides parachutes and protective gear the segment provides uniforms and also contracts to sew and seal products. Aerostar products are also marketed through competitive bids.

Net sales rose 21% in fiscal 2012 compared with 2011 a jump that was commensurate with upticks for all of the company's divisions. Thanks in part to more demand from a healthier agriculture market and international growth sales for Applied Technology Division increased 33%. The Engineered Films Division's sales were raised 26% on the back of high crude oil prices that caused more drilling and demand for pit liners. Electronic Systems headed up 9% thanks in part to demand for hand-held bed controls and secure communication electronics products. Aerostar gained 7% in 2012 compared with 2011. The slight uptick responded to demand for T-11 parachutes spare parts protective wear and tethered aerostats.

Operating income was up 26% in 2012 compared with year before. By division Engineered Films recorded a 10% uptick in operating income growth trailing sales growth mostly because of higher material costs. Operating income for Applied Technology soared 46% with higher sales and the better operating leverage that followed. A more favorable product mix as well as higher sales lifted Electronic Systems' operating income 14%. Higher sales and more efficient manufacturing boosted Aerostar's operating income by 22% in 2012 compared with 2011. Net income has been steadily rising from about $28.6 million in 2010 to more than $40.5 million in 2011 and then to more than $50.6 million in 2012.

Engineered Films touts its service in both extruding and converting films as a competitive advantage that provides more opportunity for customization to service its clients. One problem for Engineered Films is that no matter how well the economy may be operating adverse weather can limit construction and the division's sales of plastic sheeting as a result. Construction and energy are the segment's largest markets. While it can't predict the weather the company is optimistic about continued growth in oil and gas drilling that will increase demand for pit liners. Applied Technology has been innovating such improvements as Slingshot API though it too is subject to the same vagaries of the weather that challenge its agricultural clientele. The company is optimistic about the health of the agricultural economy in the immediate future however. Electronic Systems has struggled with lower avionics sales but division is expected to grow with demand for more support and service from its three sister divisions.

Raven's strategy for growth also includes acquisitions. In early 2012 Raven made a move to bolster the Aerostar division with the acquisition of Vista Research a provider of surveillance systems that use advanced algorithms to increase radar effectiveness. The company hopes to integrate Vista's technology with its marine navigation products and create better aerostat systems.

HISTORY

During 2009 Raven Industries purchased most the assets of Canadian-held Ranchview. Ranchview develops products that deliver real-time corrections to GPS equipment using cellular networks instead of radio systems. The same year Raven picked up a minority stake in SST Software a software development and information services provider for agricultural applications. The additions raised the efficiency and effectiveness of Raven's agricultural data transmission products.

EXECUTIVES

VP-Admin, Barbara K. (Barb) Ohme, age 65, $100,000 total compensation
Chief Financial Officer; Vice President, Thomas J. (Tom) Iacarella, age 59, $188,700 total compensation
Chairman, Thomas S. Everist, age 63
Chief Technology Officer, Mark L. West, age 59, $122,250 total compensation
President; Chief Executive Officer; Director, Daniel A. (Dan) Rykhus, age 48, $207,500 total compensation
Manager Marketing, Paul Welbig
Division VP and General Manager Electronic Systems Division, David R. Bair, age 56, $167,300 total compensation
Division VP and General Manager Engineered Films Division, James D. Groninger, age 53, $170,300 total compensation
Division VP and General Manager Applied Technology Division, Matthew T. (Matt) Burkhart, age 37
VP and General Manager Aerostar, Lon E. Stroschein
Division Vice President; General Manager - Engineered Films Division, Anthony Schmidt
Chief Information Officer, Brian Meyer
Vice President - Administration, Janet L. Matthiesen
Vice President - Corporate Development; General Counsel, Stephanie Sandlin
Director, Conrad J. Hoigaard, age 75
Director, Cynthia H. Milligan, age 67
Director, Anthony W. Bour, age 75
Director, David A. Christensen, age 78
Director, Mark E. Griffin, age 62
Director, Kevin T. Kirby, age 58
Independent Director, Marc Lebaron
Auditors: PricewaterhouseCoopersLLP

LOCATIONS

HQ: Raven Industries, Inc.
205 East 6th Street, P.O. Box 5107, Sioux Falls, SD 57117-5107
Phone: 605 336-2750
Web: www.ravenind.com

PRODUCTS/OPERATIONS

2012 Sales By Segment

	$ mil.	% of total
Engineered Films Division	133	34
Applied Technology Division	132	34
Electronic Systems Division	71	19
Aerostar Division	52	13
Adjustments	(8.7)	-
Total	**381**	**100**

2012 Sales By Product Group

	$ mil.	% of total
Agricultural precision control devices & accessories	131	34
Plastic films		
Pit lining & geomembrane films	80	21
Other plastic films	53	14
Electronic manufacturing services	63	17
Parachutes & protective gear	26	7
Tethered aerostats	17	5
Other	9	2
Total	**381**	**100**

Selected Products and Divisions

Aerostar
  Aerostats
  Parachutes
  Protective outerware
  Research balloons
Applied Technology
  Data collection
  GPS steering devices
  Planting and spraying controls
Electronic Systems

Electronics manufacturing services
Secure communication devices
Engineered Films plastic sheeting
  Agricultural
  Construction
  Geomembrane
  Energy
  Industrial

COMPETITORS

Astronautics	Graco
Cohesant	Sigma Plastics
Denali	Spartech
Emerson Electric	Williamson-Dickie
Flowserve	Manufacturing

HISTORICAL FINANCIALS
Company Type: Public

Income Statement
FYE: January 31

	REVENUE ($ mil.)	NET INCOME ($ mil.)	NET PROFIT MARGIN	EMPLOYEES
01/13	406.1	52.5	12.9%	1,379
01/12	381.5	50.5	13.3%	1,405
01/11	314.7	40.5	12.9%	1,112
01/10	237.7	28.5	12.0%	955
01/09	279.9	30.7	11.0%	1,020
Annual Growth	9.8%	14.3%	—	7.8%

2013 Year-End Financials

Debt ratio: —
Return on equity: 26.0%
Cash ($ mil.): 49
Current ratio: 4.74
Long-term debt ($ mil.): —

No. of shares (mil.): 36
Dividends
  Yield: 1.5%
  Payout: 29.1%
Market value ($ mil.): 978

	STOCK PRICE ($) FY Close	P/E High/Low	PER SHARE ($) Earnings	Dividends	Book Value
01/13	26.93	51 17	1.44	0.42	6.09
01/12	64.89	48 32	1.39	0.36	4.98
01/11	47.24	44 24	1.12	0.95	3.91
01/10	28.58	42 20	0.79	0.28	3.70
01/09	21.81	54 25	0.85	0.89	3.15
Annual Growth	5.4%	— —	14.1%	(17.0%)	17.9%

Realty Income Corp.

Retail real estate is a reality for Realty Income Corporation. The self-administered real estate investment trust (REIT) owns and manages primarily free-standing single-tenant properties which it leases to regional and national consumer retail and service chains. Realty Income owns more than 2600 properties containing some 27 million sq. ft. of leasable space in every state except Hawaii. Texas California Florida Minnesota Georgia Illinois and Virginia are its largest markets; combined they make up nearly half of the REIT's rental revenue. Realty Income is buying fellow REIT American Realty Capital Trust for nearly $3 billion. The deal will add more than 480 commercial properties to its portfolio.

Realty Income's occupancy rate has been above 96% every year since its 1969 founding. Top tenants include restaurants convenience stores theaters child care providers automotive care centers health and fitness facilities grocery stores and drug stores.

The REIT focuses on long-term sale-leaseback transactions in which the tenant is responsible for taxes and maintenance. It targets established middle-market retail chains with more than 50 operating locations in at least two geographic areas. Realty Income has traditionally grown through acquisitions and often sells properties with the intent to reinvest the proceeds in new real estate with the potential for higher returns. Subsidiary Crest Net owns properties which are held for sale rather than for long-term investment.

After slowing its acquisition activity in 2008 and 2009 due to economic conditions Realty Income resumed major dealmaking in 2010 when it bought 186 properties in several different transactions. It diversified into the winery business when it acquired nearly 1700 acres of vineyard property and almost 400000 sq. ft. of associated production retail and visitor center buildings of Sterling Vineyards and Beaulieu Vineyards. The company bought the real estate for some from $270 million in a sale-leaseback transaction with Diageo Chateau & Estate Wines now one of the REIT's largest tenants which will continue produce wine on and manage the properties.

In 2011 Realty Income invested some $1 billion to acquire more than 160 properties in 26 states also through several separate transactions. It represented the largest increase in new property investments in the company's history. The additions contributed to a 22% increase in rental income for the year and a corresponding rise in net income.

Institutional shareholders own more than 40% of Realty Income's stock.

EXECUTIVES

Vice President Corporate Communications and Investor Relations, Tere H. Miller
Executive Vice President; General Counsel; Secretary, Michael R. Pfeiffer, age 52, $275,000 total compensation
Vice Chairman of the Board; Chief Executive Officer, Thomas A. (Tom) Lewis, age 60, $350,000 total compensation
President; Chief Operating Officer, Gary M. Malino, age 55, $325,000 total compensation
Senior Vice President Controller, Gregory J. Fahey
SVP Research, Robert J. Israel, age 53
Senior Vice President; Assistant General Counsel and Assistant Secretary, Laura S. King, age 51
Vice President Director of Acquisitions, Cary J. Wenthur
Vice President Information Technology, Theresa M. Casey
Chairman, Donald R. Cameron, age 73
Chief Financial Officer; Executive Vice President; Treasurer, Paul M. Meurer, age 47, $300,000 total compensation
Vice President Portfolio Management, Dawn Nguyen
SVP and Head Acquisitions, Michael K. Press, age 39
Associate Vice President Portfolio Management, Kristin K. Ferrell
VP Portfolio Management, Elizabeth Cate
Associate Vice President Director of Investment Property Sales, Jenette O'Brien
Executive Vice President - Portfolio Management, Richard G. Collins, age 64, $220,000 total compensation
Associate VP and Senior Legal Counsel, Steve Burchett
Associate Vice President Director of Research, Scott Kohnen
Vice President Director of Acquisitions, Joel Tomlinson
Associate Vice President Controller, Jill Cossaboom
Associate Vice President Director of Sales, Jenette OBrien
Associate Vice President Senior Legal Counsel, Elizabeth Bonacci
Vice President Strategic Initiatives, Benjamin Fox
Associate Vice President Human Resources and Operations, Teresa Glenn
Senior Vice President - Acquisitions, Sumit Roy
Associate Vice President Property Management, Pat Rea
Associate Vice President Manager Finance and Accounting Department, Sean Nugent
Associate Vice President Senior Legal Counsel, Ann Nguyen
Director, Michael D. McKee
Chairman, Donald R. Cameron, age 73
Director, Kathleen R. Allen, age 67
Director, Ronald L. Merriman, age 68
Director, Gregory T. (Greg) McLaughlin, age 53
Director, Priya C. Huskins, age 41
Independent Director, Larry Chapman
Auditors: KPMGLLP

LOCATIONS

HQ: Realty Income Corporation
600 LaTerraza Blvd., Escondido CA 92025
Phone: 760-741-2111   **Fax:** 760-741-2235
Web: www.realtyincome.com

PRODUCTS/OPERATIONS

2011 Sales

	$ mil.	% of total
Rents by property type		
Convenience stores	77	18
Casual dining restaurants	45	11
Theaters	36	9
Quick service restaurants	27	6
Health & fitness	26	6
Beverages	23	6
Automotive tire services	23	6
Child care	22	5
Drug stores	15	4
Automotive service	15	4
Transportation services	7	2
Grocery stores	6	2
Other	90	21
Other	1	-
Total	**421**	**100**

COMPETITORS

Acadia Realty Trust	National Retail
Capital Automotive	Properties
DDR	One Liberty Properties
EPR Properties	Regency Centers
Federal Realty	Simon Property Group
Investment	Weingarten Realty
Kimco Realty	

HISTORICAL FINANCIALS
Company Type: Public

Income Statement
FYE: December 31

	REVENUE ($ mil.)	NET INCOME ($ mil.)	NET PROFIT MARGIN	EMPLOYEES
12/12	475.5	159.1	33.5%	97
12/11	421.0	157.0	37.3%	83
12/10	345.0	130.7	37.9%	79
12/09	327.5	131.1	40.0%	72
12/08	330.2	131.8	39.9%	69
Annual Growth	9.5%	4.8%	—	8.9%

2012 Year-End Financials

Debt ratio: 52.9%
Return on equity: 6.8%
Cash ($ mil.): 5
Current ratio: 0.22
Long-term debt ($ mil.): 2,883

No. of shares (mil.): 133
Dividends
  Yield: 4.4%
  Payout: 206.7%
Market value ($ mil.): 5,366

	STOCK PRICE ($) FY Close	P/E High/Low	PER SHARE ($) Earnings	Dividends	Book Value
12/12	40.21	50 40	0.86	1.78	18.08
12/11	34.96	34 27	1.05	1.74	16.93
12/10	34.20	35 25	1.01	1.72	15.64
12/09	25.91	27 15	1.03	1.71	14.27
12/08	23.15	29 15	1.06	1.67	14.92
Annual Growth	14.8%	— —	(5.1%)	1.6%	4.9%

Red Hat Inc

Red Hat doffs its cap to businesses that embrace open-source computing tools. The company dominates the market for Linux the open-source computer operating system (OS) that is the chief rival to Microsoft's Windows operating system. In addition to its Red Hat Enterprise Linux OS the company's product line includes database content and collaboration management applications; server and embedded operating systems; and software development tools. Red Hat also provides consulting custom application development support and training services. The company's business model is a mix of providing free open-source software paired with subscription-based support training and integration services.

Operations

Red Hat's JBoss unit specializes in open-source middleware software including application servers and messaging systems which are used to develop and deploy applications throughout an enterprise that are accessible via the Internet intranets extranets and virtual private networks.

Financial Analysis

Red Hat's revenue continued its upward march in 2012 cresting the $1 billion mark on growth of about 25% while net income rose 36% compared with 2010. Both subscription and training and services revenue rose by about one quarter for the year on strong global demand.

Strategy

Although Red Hat originally offered support for consumer-oriented Linux products the company shifted its focus entirely to the more lucrative business of supporting and servicing Linux technologies in enterprise environments. While Linux has failed to gain much traction against Microsoft's Windows operating system in the consumer space open-source platforms have been much more successful in corporate deployments especially for back-end tasks such as managing data center operations including virtualization server and data management and enterprise application integration.

With interest in open-source technologies growing in the Asia/Pacific region in 2012 Red Hat expanded two engineering centers in India. Located in Pune and Bangalore the company's software engineering teams in India work with local universities research organizations and agencies to develop standards for and support the adoption of open source in the region.

Mergers and Acquisitions

Red Hat acquired Massachusetts-based open-source integration and messaging provider FuseSource from Progress Software for an undisclosed sum in 2012 to enhance its ability to deliver application integration products to commercial customers. Later that year it agreed to purchase ManageIQ for some $104 million to enhance its hybrid cloud management services.

In 2011 Red Hat expanded into the storage market with the purchase of California-based Gluster for more than $136 million in cash. Gluster's open-source file system enables cloud-based storage of big data. Customers such as Brightcove and Pandora Media have used the GlusterFS open-source system to store large amounts of unstructured data (pictures audio video etc.) and minimize their investment in conventional hardware-based storage systems.

HISTORY

Finnish graduate student Linus Torvalds created the Linux operating system in 1991 as a hobby. When Torvalds released its programming code free over the Internet for anyone to revise Linux quickly attracted a core base of devoted programmers –including Marc Ewing. A programmer for IBM by day Ewing developed improvements to Linux in his spare bedroom. Soon he began selling the improved operating system as Red Hat — named after a red and white Cornell lacrosse cap Ewing's grandfather had given him.

In 1994 Ewing was contacted by Robert Young who after selling typewriters and running a computer leasing company had started a UNIX newsletter. But Young saw better profit margins in catalog sales. Young's ACC Corp. bought the rights to Ewing's creation and the two went into business together. ACC Corp. was renamed Red Hat Software Inc.

The company compiled Linux's most significant improvements and distributed them on a CD-ROM and through the budding Internet. Their revenues actually came from manuals and technical support sold to new users and businesses who were challenged by the software's ever-changing source code.

By 1997 Linux –and Red Hat's package –were known only among the most militant programmers who sought alternatives to Microsoft's Windows. Hundreds of developers had continually doctored Linux online to create an operating system known for its speed and reliability.

Red Hat exploded in popularity in 1998 after Intel and Netscape both made minor investments in the company. In 1999 Compaq IBM Novell Oracle and SAP invested in Red Hat. The company went public later that year.

In 2000 Red Hat used its soaring stock as currency to acquire embedded programming specialist Cygnus Solutions for $674 million and Hell's Kitchen Systems (HKS) a maker of payment processing software. President Matthew Szulik replaced Young as CEO and Ewing stepped down as CTO.

Red Hat expanded its software products in 2001 to include database applications and an e-commerce software suite designed for midsized businesses. The following year Szulik assumed the additional role of chairman.

In late 2003 Red Hat acquired Sistina Software a supplier of data storage infrastructure software for Linux operating systems for about $31 million in stock.

The company established a government business unit in 2005; Red Hat's US government customers have included the Department of Energy and the Federal Aviation Administration. In 2006 it acquired open-source middleware developer JBoss for about $350 million adding middleware applications to its product line.

Red Hat expanded its middleware offerings in 2007 through the acquisition of MetaMatrix. Jim Whitehurst took over as president and CEO that year. In 2008 the company purchased Qumranet an Israel-based virtualization software provider for $107 million.

In mid-2010 director Hugh Shelton a retired general replaced Szulik as chairman.

The company bought data services deployment and management software developer Makara in late 2010 to speed Red Hat's internal development of tools for moving and managing enterprise applications from the networks of corporate clients to hosted facilities enabling cloud computing.

EXECUTIVES

Chief Financial Officer; Executive Vice President, Charles E. (Charlie) Peters Jr., age 61, $425,000 total compensation
President - Products and Technologies, Paul J. Cormier, age 56, $425,000 total compensation
VP Open Source Affairs, Michael (Mike) Tiemann, age 48
VP Management Solutions Business Unit, Katrinka B. McCallum, age 38
VP Middleware Business Unit, Craig Muzilla
Chairman, Gen. Henry H. (Hugh) Shelton, age 71
President; Chief Executive Officer; Director, James M. (Jim) Whitehurst, age 46, $700,000 total compensation
VP Worldwide Engineering and CTO, Brian Stevens
Executive Vice President; General Counsel, Michael R. Cunningham, age 52, $375,000 total compensation
CIO, Lee Congdon
Executive Vice President; Chief People Officer, DeLisa Alexander
Vice President Global Alliances and Channels, Mark Enzweiler
Vice President General Counsel, Rob Tiller
VP and General Manager Government Sales Operations, Paul Smith
VP Global Support Services, Marco Bill-Peter
Executive Vice President - Global Sales and Services, Arun Oberoi
Vice President Storage Business Unit, Sarangan Rangachari
Vice President Platform Business Unit, Jim Totton
Executive Vice President Strategy and Corporate Marketing, Jackie Yeaney
Director, Sohaib Abbasi, age 56
Director, Narendra K. (Naren) Gupta, age 64
Director, Micheline (Mich) Chau, age 60
Director, Jeffrey J. (Jeff) Clarke, age 51
Director, William S. (Bill) Kaiser, age 57
Director, Marye Anne Fox, age 65
President CEO and Director, James M. (Jim) Whitehurst, age 45
Auditors: PricewaterhouseCoopersLLP

LOCATIONS

HQ: Red Hat Inc.
1801 Varsity Dr., Raleigh NC 27606
Phone: 919-754-3700   **Fax:** 919-754-3701
Web: www.redhat.com

2012 Sales

	% of total
US	55
Other	45
Total	**100**

PRODUCTS/OPERATIONS

2012 Sales

	$ mil.	% of total
Subscriptions	965	85
Training & services	167	15
Total	**1,133**	**100**

Selected Mergers and Acquisitions

2012
FuseSource Corp. (undisclosed price; Bedford MA; provider of open-source integration and messaging products and services)

2011
Gluster ($136 million; Sunnyvale CA; provider of open-source storage systems for big data)

COMPETITORS

Apple Inc.	Microsoft
BMC Software	Novell
CA Inc.	Oracle
Hewlett-Packard	Unisys
IBM	Xandros
Mandriva	

HISTORICAL FINANCIALS

Company Type: Public

Income Statement

FYE: February 28

	REVENUE ($ mil.)	NET INCOME ($ mil.)	NET PROFIT MARGIN	EMPLOYEES
02/13	1,328.8	150.2	11.3%	5,600
02/12	1,133.1	146.6	12.9%	4,500
02/11	909.2	107.2	11.8%	3,700
02/10	748.2	87.2	11.7%	3,200
02/09	652.5	78.7	12.1%	2,800
Annual Growth	19.5%	17.5%	—	18.9%

2013 Year-End Financials

Debt ratio: —
Return on equity: 10.2%
Cash ($ mil.): 487
Current ratio: 1.39
Long-term debt ($ mil.): —

No. of shares (mil.): 193
Dividends
Yield: —
Payout: —
Market value ($ mil.): 9,807

	STOCK PRICE ($) FY Close	P/E High/Low	PER SHARE ($) Earnings	Dividends	Book Value
02/13	50.81	79 61	0.77	0.00	7.88
02/12	49.46	69 42	0.75	0.00	7.26
02/11	41.28	87 49	0.55	0.00	6.69
02/10	28.05	68 29	0.45	0.00	5.93
02/09	13.69	59 19	0.39	0.00	5.82
Annual Growth	38.8%	— —	18.5%	—	7.8%

Regeneron Pharmaceuticals, Inc.

Regeneron is fighting some serious enemies. Regeneron Pharmaceuticals develops protein-based drugs used to battle a variety of diseases and conditions including cancer inflammatory ailments and eye diseases. The biotechnology company's first commercialized product is ARCALYST a treatment for rare inflammatory diseases including Muckle-Wells Syndrome. Regeneron collaborates

with Sanofi to develop candidate aflibercept (VEGF Trap) as a possible treatment for cancerous tumors. It is also developing aflibercept with Bayer HealthCare to treat eye diseases using intraocular delivery with EYLEA approved in the US (2011) and Australia (2012) as a treatment of neovascular age-related macular degeneration (wet AMD).

In 2012 the company entered into a non-exclusive license to certain patents relating to VEGF receptor proteins and a partial settlement agreement with Roche member company Genentech related to ophthalmic sales of EYLEA (aflibercept) Injection in the US. Under the agreement Regeneron will make payments to Genentech based on sales of EYLEA in the US through May 2016. It will pay Genentech $60 million when US sales of EYLEA reach $400 million and royalties of 4.75% on cumulative US sales of EYLEA between $400 million and $3 billion and 5.5% on those that exceed $3 billion.

Also that year Regeneron and Bayer HealthCare converted their 50/50 global profit share agreement for marketing EYLEA (aflibercept) Injection as a treatment for wet AMD outside the US into a royalty arrangement in Japan where approval for the treatment is pending authorization. Applications for marketing EYLEA have been submitted by Bayer HealthCare in other countries and in Europe. The treatment is also in Phase 3 clinical studies for other indications including diabetic macular edema myopic choroidal neovascularization and branch retinal vein occlusion.

ARCALYST (rilonacept) was approved by the FDA in 2008 and subsequently became the company's first market-stage product. Regeneron has built up a small marketing force to promote the product in the US; ARCALYST is manufactured at the company's plant in New York and is distributed through third parties. ARCALYST targets Cryopyrin-Associated Periodic Syndromes (CAPS) a series of diseases caused by genetic mutations including Muckle-Wells Syndrome and Familial Cold Auto-inflammatory Syndrome. The drug is also being tested for the treatment of gout.

The company expanded the applications of its protein-based technology to include the creation of human monoclonal antibodies (laboratory produced cloned proteins). Outside of their partnership on aflibercept Regeneron has an antibody development agreement with Sanofi that includes $475 in potential milestone payments and covers potential treatments for ailments including cancer rheumatoid arthritis pain cholesterol and allergic conditions.

As its largest partner Sanofi (which also owns a 19% stake in Regeneron) accounts for about 65% of sales. The company's other collaborations account for more than 15% of sales; firms are working together to treat ophthalmic diseases including diabetic macular edema and wet age-related macular degeneration.

The company also licenses its human antibody technology out to drug developers which then use Regeneron's technology in researching their own antibody drugs. Licensing partners include AstraZeneca and Astellas Pharma. Astellas extended its agreement in 2010 licensing the technology for a longer period of time in a deal worth up to $295 million.

EXECUTIVES

SVP General Counsel and Secretary, Joseph J. (Joe) LaRosa, age 54

VP Controller and Assistant Treasurer, Douglas S. McCorkle, age 56

VP Regulatory Development and Medical Safety, William G. Roberts, age 55

Chairman, P. Roy Vagelos, age 83

VP Functional Genomics and Chief of VelociGene Operations, David M. Valenzuela

SVP Research and Development Sciences, Neil Stahl, age 56, $390,400 total compensation

Chief Scientific Officer and Director; President Regeneron Research Laboratories, George D. Yancopoulos, age 53, $609,900 total compensation

SVP Finance and Administration CFO Assistant Secretary and Treasurer, Murray A. Goldberg, age 68, $419,300 total compensation

President CEO and Director, Leonard S. Schleifer, age 60, $734,400 total compensation

SVP Commercial, Robert J. Terifay, age 53, $337,300 total compensation

VP Information Systems and Technologies, Jeffrey Skulsky

SVP Clincal Development, Peter Powchik, age 56

SVP Finance and CFO, Robert E. Landry Jr.

SVP and General Manager Industrial Operations and Product Supply, Daniel P. Van Plew, age 40, $337,700 total compensation

VP Corporate Communications, Peter G. Dworkin, age 60

Vice President - Strategy and Investor Relations, Michael Aberman, age 42

Senior Vice President; General Manager - Industrial Operations and Product Supply, Daniel Plew

VP Protein Expression Sciences, Jim Fandl

Chief Scientific Officer and Director; President Regeneron Research Laboratories, George D. Yancopoulos, age 53

President CEO and Director, Leonard S. Schleifer, age 60

Director, Charles A. Baker, age 80

Director, Arthur F. (Art) Ryan, age 70

Director, Michael S. Brown, age 72

Director, Alfred G. Gilman, age 71

Director, Joseph L. Goldstein, age 72

Director, Eric M. Shooter, age 88

Director, George L. Sing, age 63

Director, Christine A. (Chris) Poon, age 60

Auditors: PricewaterhouseCoopersLLP

LOCATIONS

HQ: Regeneron Pharmaceuticals Inc.
777 Old Saw Mill River Rd., Tarrytown NY 10591-6707
Phone: 914-345-7400 **Fax:** 914-347-2113
Web: www.regeneron.com

PRODUCTS/OPERATIONS

2010 Sales

	$ mil.	% of total
Sanofi collaboration	311	67
Other collaboration	76	17
Technology licensing	40	9
Net product sales	25	5
Contract research and other	6	2
Total	**459**	**100**

COMPETITORS

Abbott Labs	Merck
Amgen	Novartis
AstraZeneca	Onyx Pharmaceuticals
Bayer AG	Pfizer
Bristol-Myers Squibb	Roche Holding
Eli Lilly	Sanofi
GlaxoSmithKline	XOMA
Johnson & Johnson	

Company Type: Public

Income Statement
FYE: December 31

	REVENUE ($ mil.)	NET INCOME ($ mil.)	NET PROFIT MARGIN	EMPLOYEES
12/13	2,104.7	424.3	20.2%	2,340
12/12	1,378.4	750.2	54.4%	1,950
12/11	445.8	(221.7)	—	1,704
12/10	459.0	(104.4)	—	1,395
12/09	379.2	(67.8)	—	1,029
Annual Growth	53.5%	—	—	22.8%

2013 Year-End Financials

Debt ratio: 17.1%	No. of shares (mil.): 99
Return on equity: 26.5%	Dividends
Cash ($ mil.): 535	Yield: —
Current ratio: 6.01	Payout: —
Long-term debt ($ mil.): 504	Market value ($ mil.): 27,438

	STOCK PRICE ($) FY Close	P/E High/Low	PER SHARE ($) Earnings	Dividends	Book Value
12/13	275.24	73 37	3.81	0.00	19.58
12/12	171.07	24 7	6.75	0.00	12.80
12/11	55.43	— —	(2.45)	0.00	5.23
12/10	32.83	— —	(1.26)	0.00	5.90
12/09	24.18	— —	(0.85)	0.00	4.89
Annual Growth	83.7%	— —	—	—	41.4%

Repligen Corp.

Repligen replies to the needs of the pharmaceutical industry by supplying bioengineered drug ingredients. Repligen's bioprocessing business develops and commercializes proteins and other agents used in the production of biopharmaceuticals. The firm also conducts drug research activities include development of a pancreatic imaging agent and potential therapies for bipolar disorder Friedreich's ataxia (a debilitating early adulthood disease) and spinal muscular atrophy. While all of Repligen's own drugs are in the clinical development stage it does receive royalty payments from Bristol-Myers Squibb (BMS) on sales of BMS' Orencia rheumatoid arthritis drug as well as by licensing out its technologies.

Repligen receives the majority of its revenues from its bioprocessing business which primarily sells Protein A a recombinant protein used in the production of monoclonal antibodies and other biopharmaceutical manufacturing applications. Its primary customer in this area is GE Healthcare which accounts for about 40% of Repligen's income and with which it has a multi-year supply agreement.

Repligen in 2010 expanded its drug ingredients business through the acquisition of BioFlash Partners for some $1.8 million. The purchase added a technology platform and other assets related to the production of chromatography columns which are used in the making of monoclonal antibodies vaccines and recombinant proteins.

The company made an even bolder move to grow the bioprocessing business in late 2011 by acquiring Novozymes Biopharma Sweden from Danish chemicals firm Novozymes for some E17 million ($23 million) plus potential milestone payments. The Novozymes Biopharma division pro-

duces proteins and cell culture media used in the development of pharmaceuticals. By expanding its product offerings and doubling its manufacturing capacity Repligen believes the purchase will generate roughly $50 million in sales and contribute to profit growth in 2012.

As for its internal R&D programs Repligen focuses on developing its products through early stages and then licensing the late-stage development and commercialization rights to larger pharmaceutical partners. However the company suffered a setback with one of its lead candidates in 2011 when RG2417 a potential treatment for bipolar depression did not produce acceptable results in a late-stage trial. Though Repligen does not plan to drop the candidate from its pipeline it placed the drug's development on hold to focus on getting another late-stage candidate pancreatic imaging agent RG1068 to market.

As a development stage company commercializing its products is vital for Repligen and a setback like the one it experienced with RG2417 can spell trouble for a company depending upon just a few products for its income. To help combat possible problems with its pipeline Repligen has worked hard to diversify its offerings (with its royalty income and bioprocessing business) in order to ensure at least some income while it is developing its drug candidates. Royalty revenue from BMS represents about 40% of Repligen's income. Following the setback in its development pipeline in 2011 the company announced plans to focus on its commercial bioprocessing operation; the announcement was followed by the agreement to acquire Novozymes Biopharma later that year.

Prior to 2009 the company received significant revenues from commercial sales of SecreFlo a pancreatic imaging agent similar to its RG1068 candidate. However Repligen discontinued distribution of SecreFlo after its marketing agreement with ChiRhoClin for the drug expired.

EXECUTIVES

Chief Accounting Officer, William J. Kelly, age 42, $190,000 total compensation

Senior Vice President - Global Operations, Daniel P. Witt, age 66, $205,000 total compensation

SVP Research and Development, James R. Rusche, age 59, $246,000 total compensation

President; Chief Executive Officer; Director, Walter C. Herlihy, age 61, $365,000 total compensation

Chairman, Alexander Rich, age 88

Vice President Bioprocessing Sales and Marketing, Stephen Tingley

Senior Vice President - Sales and Marketing; Chief Commercial Officer, Robert Spurr

Vice President Business Development, Howard Benjamin

Chief Financial Officer; Treasurer; Principal Financial Officer, Jonathan Lieber

Chief Medical Officer and Senior Vice President - Clinical and Regulatory Affairs, Michael Hall

President CEO and Director, Walter C. Herlihy, age 61

Director, Glenn L. Cooper, age 61

Director, Alfred L. Goldberg, age 70

Director, Karen A. Dawes, age 61

Director, Thomas F. Ryan Jr., age 72

Director, Earl Webb Henry, age 66

Independent Director, Michael Griffith

Auditors: Ernst&YoungLLP

LOCATIONS

HQ: Repligen Corporation
41 Seyon St. Bldg. 1 Ste. 100, Waltham MA 02453
Phone: 781-250-0111 **Fax:** 781-250-0115
Web: www.repligen.com

2011 Sales

	% of total
US	50
Other countries	8

PRODUCTS/OPERATIONS

2011 Sales

	$ mil.	% of total
Bioprocessing	15	55
Total	**27**	**100**

Selected Pipeline Products
RG1068 (Phase III clinical trials to help with pancreatic imaging)
RG2417 (Phase II clinical trials for treatment of bipolar disorder)
RG2833 (Preclinical trials for treatment of Friedreich's Ataxia)
RG3039 (Preclinical trials for treatment of spinal muscular atrophy)
Commercial Assets
Bioprocessing Business (biologics purification)
Orencia royalties (rheumatoid arthritis)

COMPETITORS

Abbott Labs	Life Technologies
Bio-Rad Labs	Corporation
Cangene	NeuroNova
Human Genome Sciences	PDL BioPharma
Incyte	

HISTORICAL FINANCIALS
Company Type: Public

Income Statement
FYE: December 31

	REVENUE ($ mil.)	NET INCOME ($ mil.)	NET PROFIT MARGIN	EMPLOYEES
12/12	62.2	14.1	22.7%	120
12/11*	23.4	(1.6)	—	137
03/11	27.2	(0.0)	—	66
03/10	20.9	(4.0)	—	68
03/09	29.3	5.7	19.6%	69
Annual Growth	20.7%	25.3%	—	14.8%

*Fiscal year change

2012 Year-End Financials

Debt ratio: —	No. of shares (mil.): 31
Return on equity: 18.8%	Dividends
Cash ($ mil.): 29	Yield: —
Current ratio: 6.16	Payout: —
Long-term debt ($ mil.): —	Market value ($ mil.): 196

	STOCK PRICE ($) FY Close	P/E High/Low	PER SHARE ($) Earnings	Dividends	Book Value
12/12	6.28	16 7	0.45	0.00	2.70
12/11*	3.47	— —	(0.05)	0.00	2.15
03/11	3.74	— —	(0.00)	0.00	2.18
03/10	4.06	— —	(0.13)	0.00	2.15
03/09	4.79	33 17	0.18	0.00	2.25
Annual Growth	7.0%	— —	25.7%	—	4.6%

*Fiscal year change

Republic Bancorp, Inc. (KY)

The second-largest bank holding company based in Kentucky Republic Bancorp is the parent of Republic Bank & Trust which has about 40 branches in central Kentucky and southern Indiana. It also owns Republic Bank a thrift with a handful of branches in metropolitan Tampa and a single location in the Cincinnati area. In 2012 Republic Bancorp entered the Nashville and Minneapolis market through the FDIC-assisted acquisitions of the failed Tennessee Commerce Bank and First Commercial Bank respectively. The company's banks offer deposit accounts loans and mortgages credit cards private banking and trust services.

Republic Bancorp's lending activities mainly consist of residential mortgages and commercial real estate loans which together account for some three-fourths of the company's loan book. The company also offered loans secured by income tax refunds throughout the US. The segment provided refund anticipation loans to more than 3 million customers in 2010 but came under fire from regulators. That year the Internal Revenue Service announced it would stop supplying Debt Indicator information (used to determine whether a taxpayer is creditworthy) to institutions that issue such loans. As a result the FDIC in 2011 announced that Republic Bank & Trust's origination of refund anticipation loans without Debt Indication information was unsafe and issued a cease-and-desist order; the tax season of 2012 was the final season the company offered the loans.

Income tax refund loans are typically offered to unbanked and underbanked customers. Republic Bancorp hopes to otherwise tap into that market which includes some 30 million US households by offering nontraditional banking products. To that end the company is also offering prepaid cards. In addition Republic also offers electronic refund checks and deposits which carry no risk to the company.

In 2011 the company entered the warehouse lending business through which it offers short-term credit facilities secured by single-family residences to mortgage bankers nationwide. The move follows somewhat of a trend of community banks adding to their commercial loan operations by offering warehouse lending. Within a year Republic had committed lines of credit totaling some $108 million.

Republic Bancorp's revenues grew 12% in 2011 from $281 million in 2010 to $314 million. Profits grew even more from $65 million in 2010 to $94 million in 2011 (an increase of 45%). The growth was largely driven by an increase in net interest and noninterest income in the company's tax refund solutions segment. Republic also decreased its provision for loan losses in 2011. To offset declines in net interest income from its traditional banking segment the company has tweaked its investment strategy as well as boosted its loan portfolio through acquisitions. Republic has also cut its operating expenses.

The Trager family including the estate of founder Bernard his son Steven (chairman and CEO) and nephew Scott (president) controls a majority of Republic Bancorp.

EXECUTIVES

Vice Chairman; President Republic Bank & Trust, A. Scott Trager, age 60, $325,000 total compensation
President and CEO; CEO Republic Bank & Trust, Steven E. (Steve) Trager, age 52, $330,000 total compensation
Chairman, Bernard M. Trager, age 84, $587,000 total compensation
EVP CFO and Chief Accounting Officer Republic Bancorp and Republic Bank & Trust, Kevin Sipes, age 41, $260,000 total compensation
VP and Banking Center Manager Georgetown Kentucky Republic Bank & Trust, Susan Smith
VP and Business Banking Officer Crestwood Kentucky Republic Bank & Trust, Melissa Lyons
President Northern Kentucky Market Republic Bank & Trust, Steve Brunson
Executive Vice President of Republic Bank & Trust Company and Republic Bank, Steven E. (Steve) DeWeese, age 44
SVP Treasury Management Republic Bank & Trust, Jeff Nelson
SVP and COO Commercial Lending and Head Treasury Management Group Republic Bank & Trust; Executive Director Republic Bank, Robert J. Arnold, age 54
VP Trust Republic Bank & Trust, Joe Sutter
Managing Partner, Jeff Hallows
Owner President, Linden Long
Director, R. Wayne Stratton, age 65
Director, Sandra Metts Snowden, age 66
Director, Susan Stout Tamme, age 61
Director, Michael T. Rust, age 61
Director, Craig A. Greenberg, age 39
Independent Director, Sandra Snowden
Auditors: CroweHorwathLLP

LOCATIONS

HQ: Republic Bancorp, Inc. (KY)
  601 West Market Street, Louisville, KY 40202
Phone: 502 584-3600
Web: www.republicbank.com

PRODUCTS/OPERATIONS

2011 Sales

	$ mil.	% of total
Interest		
Loans including fees	177	56
Taxable investment securities	15	5
Other	2	1
Noninterest		
Electronic refund check fees	88	28
Service charges on deposit accounts	14	4
Debit card interchange fees	5	2
Mortgage banking	3	1
Gain on sale of banking center & other	7	3
Adjustments	(0.3)	-
Total	**314**	**100**

COMPETITORS

BB&T	Home Federal
Bank of America	KeyCorp
Citizens First	PNC Financial
Community Trust	S.Y. Bancorp
Farmers Capital Bank	U.S. Bancorp
Fifth Third	

HISTORICAL FINANCIALS

Company Type: Public

Income Statement

FYE: December 31

	ASSETS ($ mil.)	NET INCOME ($ mil.)	INCOME AS % OF ASSETS	EMPLOYEES
12/12	3,394.4	119.3	3.5%	820
12/11	3,419.9	94.1	2.8%	728
12/10	3,622.7	64.7	1.8%	766
12/09	3,918.7	42.1	1.1%	747
12/08	3,939.3	33.6	0.9%	756
Annual Growth	(3.7%)	37.2%	—	2.1%

2012 Year-End Financials

Return on assets: 3.4%	Dividends
Return on equity: 24.0%	Yield: 8.2%
Long-term debt ($ mil.): —	Payout: 30.7%
No. of shares (mil.): 20	Market value ($ mil.): 443
Sales ($ mil): 348	

	STOCK PRICE ($) FY Close	P/E High/Low		PER SHARE ($) Earnings	Dividends	Book Value
12/12	21.13	5	3	5.69	1.75	25.60
12/11	22.90	5	4	4.49	0.61	21.59
12/10	23.75	8	5	3.10	0.56	17.74
12/09	20.60	13	7	2.02	0.52	15.19
12/08	27.20	21	9	1.62	0.47	13.38
Annual Growth	(6.1%)	—	—	36.9%	38.7%	17.6%

ResMed Inc.

Breathe easy because you won't lose any sleep while using ResMed's products. ResMed develops makes and distributes medical equipment used to diagnose and treat respiratory disorders that occur during sleep such as sleep apnea. Most of its products treat obstructive sleep apnea (OSA) a condition in which a patient's air flow is periodically obstructed causing multiple disruptions during sleep that can lead to daytime sleepiness and other conditions such as high blood pressure. Its products include air-flow generators face masks diagnostic products and accessories. ResMed sells directly and through distributors worldwide to home health equipment dealers sleep clinics and hospitals.

Geographic Reach

ResMed manufactures its products primarily at its Australian facility though it has additional production plants in China France and the US. Its systems are sold in about 70 countries. The US accounts for about 55% of annual revenues with Germany making up the second-largest market (about 15%).

Operations

The company's main products are continuous positive airway pressure (CPAP) systems that deliver pressurized air from an airflow generator through a nasal mask or pillow keeping the upper airway open during sleep. It also makes variable positive airway pressure (VPAP) systems which operate on the same principle but deliver different air pressures for inhalation and exhalation.

Sales and Marketing

ResMed's products are sold through its own subsidiaries (mainly in the US Europe and Australia) and through independent distributors and representatives. Marketing efforts target consumers and health care professionals.

Financial Analysis

ResMed reported a 10% increase in revenues in 2012 to nearly $1.4 billion attributed to increased sales of flow generators masks and accessories. Growth in product sales also increased net income by more than 12% that year to some $255 million. The year's results follow a steady pattern of growth over the last decade.

Strategy

The company has been focused on expanding its geographic reach through the acquisition of a number of medical equipment makers distributors and technology service providers in Europe and elsewhere. It is also increasing product marketing efforts and launching consumer education programs to widen its footprint in core regions. In addition ResMed conducts extensive product development programs to create devices that are not only more effective but also more comfortable and convenient.

For instance in 2012 it introduced the Quattro FX for Her mask to cater to the female audience as well as the Narval CC mandibular repositioning device for patients that need an alternative to PAP therapy. ResMed is also expanding its research activities in new clinical areas building on research that shows links between sleep-disordered breathing and such conditions as hypertension stroke heart disease and even diabetes. It is also working to increase in-home diagnosis of sleep-disorders through new technologies such as the ApneaLink home testing device introduced in 2010.

Mergers and Acquisitions

In 2012 ResMed acquired Nova Scotia-based data services firm Umbian which makes the U-Sleep patient compliance management solution which helps care providers monitor patients' home CPAP usage. In 2011 ResMed acquired Irish start-up group BiancaMed developer of a touch-free apnea monitoring device and Gruendler a German maker of medical humidifier devices.

HISTORY

ResMed was founded as ResCare in 1989 after Peter Farrell led a management buyout of Baxter Healthcare's respiratory technology unit. ResCare initially developed the SULLIVAN nasal CPAP systems (named after inventor Colin Sullivan) in Australia. In 1991 it introduced the Bubble Mask and the APD2 portable CPAP device. Three years later ResCare began marketing its first VPAP which applied different air pressures for inhalation and exhalation in the US.

In 1995 the company went public changing its name to ResMed (its former name was already taken by another medical company). Over the next two years ResMed expended a lot of oxygen in court suing rival Respironics for patent infringements; judgments in 1997 and 1998 found in favor of Respironics but ResMed made plans to appeal. In 1998 the firm received FDA approval to market its VPAP device as a critical-care treatment for lung diseases.

The firm's listing was switched from Nasdaq to the NYSE in 1999 to stabilize stock prices after court losses against Respironics; it also listed on the Australian Stock Exchange. The introduction of two new products the AutoSet CPAP unit and the Mirage face mask boosted sales that year. In 2001 ResMed bought MAP Medizin-Technologie a German manufacturer of sleep-disordered breathing treatment devices. The acquisition enhanced ResMed's position in Germany which is the company's second-biggest market for its products.

In 2004 ResMed bought its Dutch distributor Resprecare and snapped up Scandinavian German

and Austrian distributors the following year. Also in 2005 it bought Saime a French maker of home ventilation products.

The company voluntarily recalled some 300000 units of a major line of flow generators in 2007 after determining that there was a slight risk of short circuiting in the products. The action hurt profits that year but the company largely recovered by the following year buoyed by strong sales of its newer products.

Also in 2007 ResMed's R&D efforts paid off when it won FDA approval for a device called Adapt SV used to treat central sleep apnea a form of the disorder in which the brain temporarily fails to tell the appropriate muscles to breathe. Besides creating devices that are more effective the company also works to make devices more comfortable and convenient. In 2008 for example the company introduced the Swift LT nasal mask which includes a pillow system for support and stability and in 2009 it launched the Mirage SoftGel nasal mask with interchangeable gel cushions.

ResMed added to its OSA product line with the 2009 buy of Laboratories Narval a French maker of a mandibular repositioning device (MRD) designed to help patients who snore or have mild OSA problems by repositioning the joint that connects the lower jaw (mandible) to the skull thereby relieving some of the pressure in that area.

EXECUTIVES

Founder and Executive Chairman, Peter C. Farrell, age 71, $466,875 total compensation

Chief Administrative Officer and Global General Counsel, David Pendarvis, age 53, $405,144 total compensation

Chief Executive Officer; Director, Michael J. Farrell, age 41

Chief Financial Officer, Brett Sandercock, age 46, $378,025 total compensation

President and Chief Operating Officer, Robert (Rob) Douglas, age 54, $347,524 total compensation

President; Europe, Anne Reiser

President SDB Strategic Business Unit, Don Darkin, age 60

President Americas, Jim Hollingshead

President Respiratory Care Strategic Business Unit, Geoff Neilson

President Asia-Pacific, Karen Borg

Chief Information Officer, Frank Lacagnina

Director, John P. (Jack) Wareham, age 71

Director, Richard (Rich) Sulpizio, age 63

Director, Christopher G. Roberts, age 59

Director, Gary W. Pace, age 65

Director, Michael A. Quinn, age 65

Director, Ronald (Ron) Taylor, age 65

Auditors: KPMGLLP

LOCATIONS

HQ: ResMed Inc.
9001 Spectrum Center Blvd., San Diego CA 92123
Phone: 858-836-5000   **Fax:** 858-836-5501
Web: www.resmed.com

2012 Sales

US	749	55
France	139	10
Other countries	263	19

PRODUCTS/OPERATIONS

Selected Acquisitions

2012
  Umbian Inc. (Nova Scotia; data services U-Sleep patient compliance management device)
2011

BiancaMed Ltd. (Ireland; developer of touch-free sleep and breath measuring device to reduce apnea-related deaths)
Gruendler GmbH (Germany; developer and manufacturer of medical humidification products)

Selected Products

Automatic PAP devices (automatically adjust positive airway pressure)
  S8 Autoset II
  S9 AutoSet
CPAP (continuous positive airway pressure) devices
  C-Series Tango
  ResMed S8 Series II
  S8 Elite II
  S8 Escape II
  S9 Elite
  S9 Escape
Diagnostic products
  ApneaLink + Oximetry (sleep apnea screening device)
  ApneaLink Plus
Mask systems
  Activa LT
  Hospital NV full face mask
  Meridian nasal Mask
  Mirage masks
  Papillon mask
  Pixi pediatric mask
  Quatro masks
  Swift FX
  Swift LT
Patient Management/Data Products
  EasyCare
  ResScan
  ResTraxx
  S9 Embletta adapter
Ventilators
  Elisee 150
  Stellar 100
  Stellar 150
  VS III
VPAP (variable positive airway pressure) devices
  Adapt SV (for central sleep apnea)
  Auto
  Auto 25
  Comfort
  Malibu
  VPAP III STA
  VPAP IV

COMPETITORS

Allied Healthcare Products	Philips Healthcare
Cephalon	SleepMed
Cleveland Medical	Sunrise Medical
Covidien	Vanda
Dehaier	Vapotherm
Lincare Holdings	Vital Signs

HISTORICAL FINANCIALS

Company Type: Public

Income Statement

FYE: June 30

	REVENUE ($ mil.)	NET INCOME ($ mil.)	NET PROFIT MARGIN	EMPLOYEES
06/13	1,514.4	307.1	20.3%	3,900
06/12	1,368.5	254.8	18.6%	3,700
06/11	1,243.1	226.9	18.3%	3,450
06/10	1,092.3	190.0	17.4%	3,200
06/09	920.7	146.4	15.9%	2,900
Annual Growth	13.2%	20.3%	—	7.7%

2013 Year-End Financials

Debt ratio: 13.6%	No. of shares (mil.): 142
Return on equity: 19.0%	Dividends
Cash ($ mil.): 876	Yield: 0.0%
Current ratio: 2.52	Payout: 32.3%
Long-term debt ($ mil.): 0	Market value ($ mil.): 6,409

	STOCK PRICE ($) FY Close	P/E High/Low	PER SHARE ($) Earnings	PER SHARE ($) Dividends	PER SHARE ($) Book Value
06/13	45.13	24 14	2.10	0.68	11.34
06/12	31.20	20 13	1.71	0.00	11.32
06/11	30.95	46 20	1.44	0.00	11.41
06/10	60.81	55 31	1.23	0.00	8.51
06/09	40.73	49 31	0.95	0.00	7.41
Annual Growth	2.6%	— —	21.9%	—	11.2%

Rex Energy Corp

Though it isn't exactly the T. Rex of the oil and gas industry Rex Energy is taking a bite out of available hydrocarbon assets. The oil and gas exploration and production company has estimated proved reserves of 11 million barrels of oil equivalent primarily from three regions: the Illinois Basin (in Illinois and Indiana) and the Appalachian Basin (Pennsylvania and West Virginia). The company's Lawrence Field ASP (alkaline-surfactant-polymer) Flood Project utilizes ASP technology which washes residual oil from reservoir rock thereby improving the existing waterflow's ability to sweep the residual oil and increasing ultimate oil recoveries. Lawrence Field is in Illinois.

Growing by acquisitions Rex has completed more than a dozen purchases —including acquisitions of acreage in the Illinois Basin and of producing properties (which added 13.1 million barrels of oil equivalent to its portfolio) —since 2004.

However in 2009 Rex Energy sold its assets in the southwestern US New Mexico and Texas to Adventure Exploration Partners for about $17 million. Prompting the sale was that the state of the economy and current commodity prices which made it financially wiser for the company to focus on its core assets in the Appalachian and Illinois Basins.

Growing its midstream business to support its core downstream operations that year Rex Energy formed a joint venture with Stonehenge Energy Resources to build a high pressure gathering system and cryogenic gas processing plant in Butler County Pennsylvania. In 2010 it raised $99.5 million to pay down debt by selling Marcellus shale assets to a joint venture with Sumitomo. In 2012 the company decided to sell its Butler County assets to pay down debt.

In 2010 the company appointed chairman Lance Shaner as interim president and CEO replacing Benjamin Hulburt who left Rex Energy to pursue other opportunities. Industry veteran Daniel Churay was then brought in as president and CEO. Shaner retained the chairman position. In 2011 Shaner took up the interim president and CEO position following the departure of Churay.

EXECUTIVES

Chairman and Interim President and CEO, Lance T. Shaner, age 59
EVP and CFO, Thomas C. Stabley, age 42, $210,000 total compensation
VP and Exploration Manager, David E. Pratt, age 61
VP and Appalachian Drilling Manager, James F. Watson, age 47, $107,960 total compensation
SVP and Illinois Regional Manager, Bryan J. Clayton, age 54, $169,491 total compensation

President; Chief Operating Officer, Patrick M. McKinney, age 54
Manager Investor Relations, Julia Williams
VP General Counsel and Secretary, Jennifer L. McDonough
Senior Vice President - Human Resources and Administration, Christina Marshall
Chief Accounting Officer, Curtis Walker
Chief Financial Officer, Michael Hodges
Senior Vice President - Land, Scott Hodges
Director, John A. Lombardi, age 47
Director, Eric L. Mattson, age 61
Director, John W. Higbee, age 70
Director, John J. Zak

LOCATIONS

HQ: Rex Energy Corp
366 Walker Drive, State College, PA 16801
Phone: 814 278-7267
Web: www.rexenergy.com

PRODUCTS/OPERATIONS

2012 Sales

	$ mil.	% of total
Exploration and production	134	91
Field services	13	9
Total	**148**	**100**

2012 Sales

	$ mil.	% of total
Oil	66	45
Natural gas	53	36
NGL	15	10
Field services	13	9
other services	0	-
Total	**148**	**100**

COMPETITORS

Cabot Oil & Gas
EQT Corporation
Penn Virginia

HISTORICAL FINANCIALS

Company Type: Public

Income Statement
FYE: December 31

	REVENUE ($ mil.)	NET INCOME ($ mil.)	NET PROFIT MARGIN	EMPLOYEES
12/12	148.1	45.4	30.7%	230
12/11	114.6	(15.3)	—	204
12/10	68.7	6.0	8.8%	191
12/09	48.6	(16.2)	—	163
12/08	67.9	(48.6)	—	147
Annual Growth	**21.5%**	**—**		**11.8%**

2012 Year-End Financials

Debt ratio: 32.2%
Return on equity: 12.8%
Cash ($ mil.): 43
Current ratio: 1.64
Long-term debt ($ mil.): 249
No. of shares (mil.): 53
Dividends
  Yield: —
  Payout: —
Market value ($ mil.): 693

	STOCK PRICE ($) FY Close	P/E High/Low	PER SHARE ($) Earnings	PER SHARE ($) Dividends	PER SHARE ($) Book Value
12/12	13.02	17 10	0.87	0.00	7.73
12/11	14.76	— —	(0.35)	0.00	6.51
12/10	13.65	105 63	0.14	0.00	6.87
12/09	12.00	— —	(0.44)	0.00	5.89
12/08	2.94	— —	(1.40)	0.00	6.34
Annual Growth	**45.1%**	**— —**			**5.1%**

Rick's Cabaret International Inc.

Far from Casablanca these night clubs offer topless entertainment as part of the floor show. Rick's Cabaret International operates more than 30 adult night clubs in Arizona Florida Minnesota New York North Carolina and Texas. Most of the gentlemen's clubs are run under the Rick's Cabaret name while others operate under such banners as Club Onyx and XTC. Rick's caters to highbrow patrons with dough to blow: It offers VIP memberships for individual and corporate clients that can cost hundreds of dollars annually. In addition to its night clubs Rick's operates adult websites and an auction site for adult entertainment products.

Rick's is focused on expanding its nightclub estate gradually by adding new locations organically and through acquisitions. In 2012 the company purchased 11 clubs in Texas and Arizona along with associated real estate through its acquisition of Jaguars Acquisitions. It made the deal —which included clubs in Phoenix Lubbock El Paso and Beaumont —for some $26 million.

Before the Jaguar deal a proposed deal to purchase rival strip club operator VCG Holding in 2010 fell through. The VCG deal valued at about $45 million in cash and stock would have expanded Rick's holdings to about 40 locations in about a dozen states.

Previous to its failed buyout of VCG Rick's added Dallas to its sphere of operations with the purchase of The Executive Club for $9.5 million in 2008. The company added another Dallas club with the purchase of Platinum Club II. Also in 2008 Rick's launched itself into print and online media when it acquired trade publisher ED Publications for a little more than $1 million. The deal included such adult industry titles as Adult Store Buyer and Exotic Dancer as well as trade shows and websites.

CEO Eric Langan owns about 14% of the company.

HISTORY

Dallas Fontenot and Salah Izzedin founded Trumps in 1982. The following year they bought a disco and turned it into a swank topless bar called Rick's Cabaret (the name came from an encounter with a drunk in a taxi who was looking for "Rick's"). Izzedin's attorney Robert Watters bought a 10% interest in Trumps in 1987 the same year that the company opened the first members-only VIP room in Houston. The partnership of Fontenot Izzedin and Watters soured in 1989 with allegations that Izzedin pocketed unreported money supplied narcotics to waitresses and dancers and forced some of them to have sex with him.

Watters took over as CEO in 1991 and became sole owner in 1993. He converted Trumps into Rick's Cabaret International the next year and made Rick's the first topless bar to go public in 1995. The company expanded to New Orleans the following year opening a club on Bourbon Street. Rick's opened a new club in Minneapolis in 1998 and bought a 93% stake in Taurus Entertainment. Watters resigned in 1999 sold his stock in the company to new CEO Eric Langan and his investment partner Ralph McElroy and acquired the firm's New Orleans location which operated as a Rick's Cabaret under a licensing agreement. (The company sold it the same year.) Later in 1999 Rick's launched its adult Web sites.

In 2000 the company bought a third topless bar in Houston as well as another adult Web site xxxPasswords.com. It also began selling pre-paid debit cards that allow customers to anonymously buy access to adult entertainment Web sites. Rick's purchased the Chesapeake Bay Cabaret an upscale club in Houston in November. Later that year the company inked a deal with adult Web site operator Entertainment Network to offer its content through CandidCam.com.

Rick's launched NaughtyBids.com an auction site for adult products in 2001. It also began buying a number of porn auction sites including Pornauction.com and XXXbids.com in an effort to enhance the products available on NaughtyBids.com. Late that year it opened Encounters an upscale club for swinging couples in Houston.

During 2003 Rick's acquired a 51% stake in Houston's Wild Horse Cabaret and opened a sports bar called Hummers (later renamed under the Club Onyx brand). It also acquired the XTC clubs outright from Taurus Entertainment and reorganized some of its other holdings leaving it with a 51% stake in Encounters (sold 2004).

The company in 2004 converted its original Rick's Cabaret nightclub in Houston into Club Onyx an upscale venue that caters to urban professionals businessmen and professional athletes. It also bought a new location in Manhattan near Madison Square Garden. The following year the company closed on its acquisition of a three-in-one complex in North Carolina that included a men's club a male revue for women and a traditional night club. Also in 2005 it bought swingers-oriented dating Web site CouplesClick.net.

During 2006 Rick's purchased four new nightclubs in Texas. The following year it inked a licensing deal with a subsidiary of Argentina-based Latin Entertainment to open adult clubs in Buenos Aires and other Latin American cities under the Rick's Cabaret name.

EXECUTIVES

Chairman of the Board; President; Chief Executive Officer, Eric S. Langan, age 45, $623,077 total compensation
Executive Vice President; Director, Travis Reese, age 44, $194,204 total compensation
Chief Financial Officer, Phillip K. (Phil) Marshall, age 64, $189,423 total compensation
VP Director Technology and Director, Travis Reese, age 42
Director, Robert L. Watters, age 62
Director, Steven L. Jenkins, age 56
Director, Luke Lirot, age 56
Independent Director, Nour Anakar
Auditors: WhitleyPenn

LOCATIONS

HQ: Rick's Cabaret International Inc.
10959 Cutten Rd., Houston TX 77066
Phone: 281-397-6730   **Fax:** 718-758-3803
Web: www.mathmadeeasy.com

PRODUCTS/OPERATIONS

2011 Sales

	$ mil.	% of total
Nightclubs		
Alcohol	32	39
Media	1	2
Other	3	4

Selected Operations

Nightclubs
 Club Onyx (adult entertainment for urban professionals and professional athletes)
 Rick's Cabaret
 Rick's Sports Cabaret
 Tootsie's Cabaret
 XTC
Media
 Club Bulletin (trade magazine for adult clubs)
 Storerotica (trade magazine for adult stores and products)
 VIP Guide (directory of clubs industry vendors entertainers)
Internet
 CouplesClick.net (85% adult content and online dating)
 CouplesTouch.com (85% adult content and online dating)
 NaughtyBids.com (adult auction Web site)
 xxxPassword.com (adult content)

Selected Subsidiaries

Adult Store Buyer Magazine LLC
Bobby's Novelty Inc.
Broadstreets Cabaret Inc.
ED Publications Inc.
Miami Gardens Square One Inc.
Playmates Gentlemen's Club LLC
RCI Dating Services Inc.
RCI Entertainment (Austin) Inc.
RCI Entertainment (Fort Worth) Inc.
RCI Entertainment (Las Vegas) Inc.
RCI Entertainment (Media Holdings) Inc.
RCI Entertainment (Minnesota) Inc.
RCI Entertainment (New York) Inc.
RCI Entertainment (North Carolina) Inc.
RCI Entertainment (Northwest Highway) Inc.
RCI Entertainment (Philadelphia) Inc.
RCI Entertainment (San Antonio) Inc.
RCI Entertainment (Texas) Inc.
Tantra Dance Inc.
Teeze International Inc.
TEZ Real Estate LP Philadelphia
Top Shelf Entertainment LLC
XTC Cabaret Inc.

COMPETITORS

FriendFinder Networks	Playboy.com
Galardi South	Private Media Group
LFP	Scores Holding
Million Dollar Saloon	Vivid Entertainment
New Frontier Media	

HISTORICAL FINANCIALS

Company Type: Public

Income Statement

FYE: September 30

	REVENUE ($ mil.)	NET INCOME ($ mil.)	NET PROFIT MARGIN	EMPLOYEES
09/13	112.2	9.1	8.2%	1,750
09/12	95.2	7.5	8.0%	1,400
09/11	83.4	7.8	9.4%	1,200
09/10	82.9	(7.9)	—	1,200
09/09	75.1	5.2	6.9%	1,000
Annual Growth	10.5%	15.3%	—	15.0%

2013 Year-End Financials

Debt ratio: 35.2%	No. of shares (mil.): 9
Return on equity: 10.3%	Dividends
Cash ($ mil.): 10	Yield: —
Current ratio: 0.71	Payout: —
Long-term debt ($ mil.): 69	Market value ($ mil.): 112

	STOCK PRICE ($) FY Close	P/E High/Low		PER SHARE ($) Earnings	Dividends	Book Value
09/13	11.79	13	8	0.96	0.00	9.87
09/12	8.28	13	8	0.78	0.00	8.82
09/11	6.65	14	8	0.79	0.00	8.17
09/10	7.28	—	—	(0.82)	0.00	7.61
09/09	8.60	18	4	0.55	0.00	8.67
Annual Growth	8.2%	—	—	14.9%	—	3.3%

RigNet Inc

Because no one wants to be stranded on a desert island much less an offshore oil rig there's RigNet. A telecommunications company that caters mainly to the oil and gas drilling industry it provides Cisco-powered Internet protocol-based voice fax video and high-speed Internet to remote offshore and land-based locations. It serves drilling rigs and production platforms in the Gulf of Mexico South America West Africa the Middle East the North Sea and Asia. RigNet's 400 customers such as Noble Corporation (12% of sales) span 1000 remote sites in more than 30 countries. Customers outside the US make up the majority of sales.

Operations

RigNet estimates that it has about a third of the market share of the types of rigs it services (jackups semi-submersibles and drillships) and about a 17% market share in its onshore sites in the Continental US.

The company does not own any of the offsite infrastructure or equipment such as satellites opting instead to buy bandwidth from satellite operators such as Intelsat and other telecommunications providers. It focuses on providing the equipment and infrastructure deployed on the sites themselves. This strategy enables better quality control while keeping capital investments at a minimum. RigNet is one of a scant 1% of Cisco service providers in the world to hold the Cisco Powered Network designation which is granted based on meeting specific quality-of-service performance metrics.

It also provides a range of ancillary services in support of its core communications service. It manages equipment installation software configuration systems testing video conferencing Wi-Fi hotspots and Web access.

Geographic Reach

RigNet operates in the US from two offices in Houston and Lafayette Louisiana both hubs for the Gulf Coast offshore oil industry. Customers outside the US make up about 75% of sales. It has international offices in Australia Brazil Nigeria Norway Qatar Scotland and Singapore.

Financial Performance

Overall revenues rose almost 50% in 2012 to $162 million due to increased sales to new and existing customers with upgrades and value-added services. RigNet has been profitable since 2011.

Strategy

RigNet's strategy ticks all the boxes one might expect: it seeks to expand its take of offshore and onshore drilling rig clients cross-sell to similar customers on existing sites grow its products and services and explore related markets in the energy sector for its remote communications offerings using organic and inorganic growth.

Mergers and Acquisitions

In 2012 RigNet acquired Nessco a provider of telecommunications systems integration services for the oil and gas industry based in Scotland. The $46.4 million cash deal gives RigNet a broader range of communications offerings across the entire spectrum of oil and gas operations. Nessco's technologies include closed-circuit TV digital radio fiber-optic marine satellite and voice and data communications networks.

Ownership

Norwegian investment firm Cubera Private Equity owns almost 30% of RigNet's stock. Denver-based VC firm Altira Group owns anouth 15% and T. Rowe Price has a 12% stake.

EXECUTIVES

Chief Financial Officer, Martin L. (Marty) Jimmerson Jr., age 49, $218,784 total compensation
Vice President; General Counsel; Company Secretary, William D. (Bill) Sutton, age 58, $172,784 total compensation
President and CEO, Mark B. Slaughter, age 54, $262,784 total compensation
Vice President; General Manager - Eastern Hemisphere, Hector Maytorena, age 51, $140,838 total compensation
VP and General Manager Europe Middle East Africa, Lars Eliassen, age 40, $165,734 total compensation
Vice President Global Engineering and Operations, Morten Hagland Hansen
Vice President Ta, Tonya McDermott
Chairman, James H. Browning, age 63
Manager Planning and Marketing, Boyd Skelton
Vice President Energy Maritime Services, Joe Conboy
Director Global Human Resources, Barise Hatfield
Director of Product Management, Molly McGuirk
VP Chief Accounting Officer and Controller, Todd Moser
Non-Executive Chairman of the Board, James Browning
Vice President and General Manager Western Hemisphere, James Crenshaw
Vice President Sales and Business Development, Chad Winkle
Vice President Chief Accounting Officer, Pam Thompson
Vice President Corporate Development, Brad Alexander
Vice President Business Services, Morten Hansen
Director, Kevin A. Neveu, age 51
Director, Charles L. (Chip) Davis, age 47
Independent Director, Brent Whittington
Independent Director, Ditlef Vibe
Independent Director, Keith Olsen
Independent Director, Kevin Mulloy
Independent Director, Kevin OHara
Auditors: Deloitte&ToucheLLP

LOCATIONS

HQ: RigNet Inc.
1880 S. Dairy Ashford Ste. 300, Houston TX 77077-4760
Phone: 281-674-0100 **Fax:** 281-674-0101
Web: www.rignet.com

2012 Sales

	$ mil.	% of total
US	37	23
Other countries	124	77
Total	**161**	**100**

PRODUCTS/OPERATIONS

2012 Sales

	$ mil.	% of total
Europe/Africa	65	40
Americas	49	31
Middle East/Asia Pacific	46	29
Total	**161**	**100**

COMPETITORS

Blast Energy Services	NesscoInvsat
Harris CapRock	Schlumberger
Inmarsat	Stratos Global

HISTORICAL FINANCIALS

Company Type: Public

Income Statement

FYE: December 31

	REVENUE ($ mil.)	NET INCOME ($ mil.)	NET PROFIT MARGIN	EMPLOYEES
12/12	161.6	11.8	7.3%	375
12/11	109.3	9.5	8.7%	243
12/10	92.9	(15.5)	—	204
12/09	80.9	(19.9)	—	197
12/08	89.9	8.4	9.3%	0
Annual Growth	**15.8%**	**9.0%**	**—**	**—**

2012 Year-End Financials

Debt ratio: 28.3%
Return on equity: 12.8%
Cash ($ mil.): 59
Current ratio: 2.54
Long-term debt ($ mil.): 51
No. of shares (mil.): 15
Dividends
  Yield: —
  Payout: —
Market value ($ mil.): 321

	STOCK PRICE ($) FY Close	P/E High/Low		PER SHARE ($) Earnings	Dividends	Book Value
12/12	20.43	27	20	0.70	0.00	6.49
12/11	16.74	32	21	0.57	0.00	5.39
12/10	13.63	—	—	(3.38)	0.00	4.59
Annual Growth	**22.4%**	**—**	**—**	**—**	**—**	**18.9%**

Riverbed Technology Inc

Riverbed Technology keeps data flowing. The company develops hardware and software that improves the performance of software shared over wide area networks (WANs) and reduce network traffic. Its Steelhead network appliances and software tools are designed for small businesses and global enterprises. Riverbed's other products enable mobile access to business software and data facilitate online data storage (Whitewater) and manage network performance (Cascade). Customers have included Carhartt OMV and Tatts Group. The company makes most of its sales through resellers distributors and systems integrators. Riverbed sells worldwide but it does more than half of its business in the US.

Geographic Reach

The US accounts for 55% of the company's total sales and the UK is its second-largest country market representing 15% of sales. Riverbed has primary support centers in Amsterdam London New York San Francisco Singapore Sydney and Tokyo.

Financial Performance

Riverbed has enjoyed exceptional revenue growth over the last four years. Revenues rose 15% from $726 million in 2011 to $837 million in 2012 a historic milestone for the company. Profits however dipped 14% from $64 million in 2011 to $55 million in 2012.

The growth in 2012 was driven by a 28% surge in support and services revenue. It was also helped by a 9% jump in product revenue due to an increase in unit volume from more sales from existing customers and the addition of new customers.

The erosion of profits for 2012 was the result of increased operational expenses particularly a spike in personnel facilities and information technology costs. Riverbed also experienced higher research and development expenses for 2012.

Sales and Marketing

Riverbed sells its products through 2000 channel partners and a sales force responsible for managing all direct and indirect sales within their regional territories. Major distributors include Arrow Electronics and Avnet which accounted for 17% and 11% of its consolidated revenue in 2012.

The company spent $3.6 million on advertising in 2012.

Mergers and Acquisitions

The company uses periodic acquisitions to augment its internal product development and to enter new markets. In late 2012 Riverbed acquired OPNET Technologies for about $1 billion; OPNET's application performance management tools complement Riverbed's network performance management products to create an integrated solution for customers.

Also that year the company bought the intellectual property of Expand Networks from its liquidator in 2012 to expand its customer base. It purchased UK-based Zeus Technology and New Zealand-based Aptimize the previous year to add network resource management technology. Zeus specialized in software used to balance data traffic in virtual and cloud computing systems while Aptimize offered tools for optimizing Web content that complemented Riverbed's Steelhead product family.

EXECUTIVES

EVP and CFO, Ernest E. (Ernie) Maddock, age 55
Chairman and CEO, Jerry M. Kennelly, age 62, $435,000 total compensation
General Manager Cloud Storage Acceleration, Ray Villeneuve
President Products Group, Eric Wolford, age 46, $328,889 total compensation
Senior Vice President and General Manager Riverbed Performance Management, Paul Brady
SVP and CIO, Ginna Raahauge
Senior Vice President Engineering, Gordon Chaffee, age 43
VP Worldwide Channel Sales, Randy Schirman, age 51
SVP Employee Services, Mike Guerchon
Chief Scientist, Mark S. Day
SVP Tech Operations, Stephen R. Smoot, age 45
Chief Technology Officer, David Wu
SVP and General Counsel, Brett A. Nissenberg, age 39
Chief Marketing Officer, Kate Hutchison
VP Sales Europe Middle East and Africa, Marcus Chambers
VP Product Management, John Martin
SVP Corporate Development & Strategy, Paul O'Farrell

VP Alliances, Venugopal Pai
President Worldwide Field Operations, David M.
  (Dave) Peranich, age 51, $300,000 total compensation
VP Cloud Storage Acceleration Products, Edward
  J. (Ed) Chapman
SVP Manufacturing and Operations, Dave Olson
VP Worldwide Marketing, Carolyn Crandall
Chief Marketing Officer, David Greene
Vice President, Glenn Brewer
Vice President of Research, Jim Frey
Auditors: Ernst&YoungLLP

LOCATIONS

HQ: Riverbed Technology Inc.
  199 Fremont St., San Francisco CA 94105
Phone: 415-247-8800   **Fax:** 415-247-8801
Web: www.riverbed.com

2012 Sales

Americas		
UK	124	15
Other EMEA	101	12
Asia Pacific	116	14

PRODUCTS/OPERATIONS

2012 Sales

Product	548	65
Total	**836**	**100**

Selected Products and Brands
Application Delivery (Stingray)
Cloud Storage (Whitewater)
Network Planning and Simulation (OPNET)
Performance Management (Cascade and OPNET)
Storage Delivery (Granite)
WAN Optimization (Steelhead)

COMPETITORS

Arbor Networks	Internap Network
Blue Coat	Services
Certeon	Juniper Networks
Cisco Systems	Lancope
Citrix Systems	NetScout Systems
F5 Networks	OPNET
Fluke Networks	Radware

HISTORICAL FINANCIALS

Company Type: Public

Income Statement   FYE: December 31

	REVENUE ($ mil.)	NET INCOME ($ mil.)	NET PROFIT MARGIN	EMPLOYEES
12/12	836.8	54.6	6.5%	2,566
12/11	726.4	63.8	8.8%	1,610
12/10	551.8	34.1	6.2%	1,244
12/09	394.1	7.0	1.8%	1,013
12/08	333.3	10.6	3.2%	857
Annual Growth	**25.9%**	**50.6%**	**—**	**31.5%**

2012 Year-End Financials

Debt ratio: 28.2%	No. of shares (mil.): 163
Return on equity: 6.7%	Dividends
Cash ($ mil.): 280	Yield: —
Current ratio: 1.91	Payout: —
Long-term debt ($ mil.): 566	Market value ($ mil.): 3,221

	STOCK PRICE ($) FY Close	P/E High/Low	PER SHARE ($) Earnings	Dividends	Book Value
12/12	19.72	85 39	0.33	0.00	5.47
12/11	23.50	108 48	0.38	0.00	4.52
12/10	35.17	247 93	0.22	0.00	3.56
12/09	22.97	509180	0.05	0.00	2.51
12/08	11.39	373 99	0.07	0.00	2.12
Annual Growth	14.7%	— —	47.4%	—	26.7%

Roadrunner Transportation Systems Inc

Running your cargo down the road is Roadrunner Transportation Systems (RRTS) business. The company offers less-than-truckload (LTL) freight transportation which combines freight from multiple shippers into a single truckload. In addition it arranges the transportation of truckload freight as well as provides logistics services. RRTS caters to small and mid-size shippers and some large national accounts throughout the US via a network of 15-plus service centers. Rather than owning trucks and trailers the company relies on a network of independent contractors and on purchased transportation capacity. Investment firm Thayer | Hidden Creek owns a majority of RRTS.

IPO

In 2010 RRTS concluded a $148 million IPO. The proceeds were used to retire $15.9 million in debt. It was the company's second attempt to go public. The first in 2008 stalled in the face of soaring fuel prices coupled with a sharp drop in demand and the onset of the global economic recession.

Operations

RRTS operates through three chief segments: Less-than-Truckload Truckload and Logistics and Transportation Management Solutions. The less-than-truckload (LTL) business manages the pickup consolidation linehaul deconsolidation and delivery of LTL shipments throughout the US and into Mexico Puerto Rico and Canada. Within the truckload and logistics (TL) business it arranges for the pickup delivery and inventory management of TL freight through its network of 24 TL service centers four consolidation/warehousing facilities almost 10 company dispatch offices and roughly 75 independent brokerage agents. Transportation management solutions offers access to the most cost-effective and time-sensitive modes of transportation within the company's broad network.

Financial Analysis

With the recession in its rear-view window RRTS has been enjoying steady growth over the years. From 2010 to 2011 its revenues increased by 33% reaching $843 million its highest total in at least 10 years. RRTS saw its profits skyrocket from nearly $4 million to almost $26 million from 2010 to 2011.

The sizable growth was attributed to its TL revenues surging by 90% in 2011. Growth within this segment was due to previous acquisitions an uptick in the number of loads a year-over-year increase in revenue per load and the ongoing expansion of its TL agent network.

Strategy

RRTS' recent growth has largely been attributed to strategic acquisitions. In 2012 it obtained A&A Express a refrigerated truckload services provider in South Dakota for $24 million. Months later the company scooped up R&M Transportation and Sortino Transportation truckload services providers based in Nebraska for $24 million. Also in 2012 RRTS picked up Minnesota-based D&E Transport a flatbed carrier with expertise in transporting agriculture products and New Hampshire-based Capital Transportation Logistics for $6.25 million.

In early 2011 RRTS purchased Morgan Southern a provider of intermodal transportation and related services for about $20 million. Headquartered in Georgia Morgan Southern's 19 terminals serve key markets in the US where shipments are transported by more than one mode (such as rail and truck). That acquisition was followed by RRTS' purchase of Prime Logistics for approximately $97.5 million mostly in cash. Prime is a provider of logistics and freight consolidation services primarily to food producers that ship to retailers distributors and warehouses. Also in 2011 RRTS picked up Bruenger Trucking Company a truckload services provider in Kansas for $10.6 million.

Looking ahead RRTS intends to maintain its asset-free approach to the transportation business. Under this strategy the company uses contractors and buys capacity from other carriers when needed as opposed to owning its own fleet thereby more efficiently deploying resources to meet demand and generating better returns.

Ownership

While Thayer | Hidden Creek holds more than 50% of the company Scott Rued RRT's chairman is managing partner of Thayer | Hidden Creek. Rued has voting power over all the shares held by that entity.

Company Background

RRTS took its current shape in 2005 when investors led by Thayer | Hidden Creek bought Dawes Transport and Roadrunner Freight Systems and combined them to form Roadrunner Dawes Freight Systems. The Roadrunner Transportation Systems name was adopted in mid-2008 as part of a comprehensive rebranding campaign.

EXECUTIVES

VP CFO Secretary and Treasurer, Peter R.
  Armbruster, $175,100 total compensation
President and CEO, Mark A. DiBlasi, $275,000 total
  compensation
President Less-than-Truckload, Scott L. Dobak,
  $230,769 total compensation
President Truckload, Brian J. van Helden, $124,231
  total compensation
Chairman, Scott D. Rued
Auditors: Deloitte&ToucheLLP

LOCATIONS

HQ: Roadrunner Transportation Systems Inc.
  4900 S. Pennsylvania Ave., Cudahy WI 53110-8903
Phone: 414-615-1500   **Fax:** 414-615-1513
Web: www.rrts.com

Selected Locations
Atlanta
Baltimore
Boston
Charlotte NC

Chicago
Cincinnati
Cleveland
Dallas
Detroit
Houston
Indianapolis
Los Angeles
Memphis
Milwaukee
Minneapolis/St. Paul
Nashville TN
Philadelphia
Pittsburgh
Portland OR
San Francisco
Seattle
St. Louis

PRODUCTS/OPERATIONS

2011 Sales

	$ mil.	% of total
Less-than-truckload (LTL)	466	55
Transportation Management Solutions (TMS)	79	9
Total	**843**	**100**

Selected Mergers and Acquisitions

FY2012
  A&A Express ($24 million; Brandon South Dakota;
    refrigerated truckload services)
  Central Cal Transportation ($4 million; California;
    transports primarily nuts wine and retail import
    products)
  R&M Transportation and Sortino Transportation
    ($24.4 million; Omaha Nebraska; refrigerated
    truckload services)
  D&E Transport ($11.2 million; Clearwater Minnesota;
    asset-light flatbed carrier focused primarily on food
    and agricultural products)
  Capital Transportation Logics ($6.25 million; Nashua
    New Hampshire; transportation management
    solutions)
FY2011
  Bruenger Trucking Company ($10.6 million; Wichita
    Kansas; truckload services)

COMPETITORS

Arkansas Best	FedEx
C.H. Robinson	Landstar System
Worldwide	Menlo Worldwide
CRST International	Saia
Central Freight Lines	Schneider Logistics
Con-way Freight	Total Quality
Covenant	Logistics
Transportation	Transplace
Echo Global	UPS
Estes Express	YRC Worldwide

HISTORICAL FINANCIALS

Company Type: Public

Income Statement

FYE: December 31

	REVENUE ($ mil.)	NET INCOME ($ mil.)	NET PROFIT MARGIN	EMPLOYEES
12/12	1,073.3	37.5	3.5%	2,395
12/11	843.6	25.8	3.1%	1,848
12/10	632.0	3.5	0.6%	1,054
12/09	450.3	0.1	0.0%	925
12/08	537.3	(3.8)	—	0
Annual Growth	**18.9%**	—	—	—

2012 Year-End Financials

Debt ratio: 23.0%
Return on equity: 10.8%
Cash ($ mil.): 11
Current ratio: 1.63
Long-term debt ($ mil.): 144

No. of shares (mil.): 34
Dividends
  Yield: —
  Payout: —
Market value ($ mil.): 623

	STOCK PRICE ($) FY Close	P/E High/Low	PER SHARE ($) Earnings	Dividends	Book Value
12/12	18.14	16 12	1.16	0.00	11.41
12/11	14.13	20 15	0.82	0.00	9.64
12/10	14.46	135 95	0.11	0.00	8.81
Annual Growth	**12.0%**	—	**—224.7%**	—	**13.8%**

Rockville Financial, Inc.

Rockville Financial likes it when customers roll
right into Rockville Bank. The holding company
owns the regional thrift which serves Connecticut's Hartford New London and Tolland counties
from 20 branch locations. Rockville Bank offers
traditional deposit products and services including
checking savings and NOW accounts. One-to-four
family residential mortgages account for more than
60% of the bank's lending portfolio which also includes commercial real estate business construction and consumer loans. Several of the bank's
branches are located in supermarkets and operate
seven days a week. Mutual holding company
Rockville Financial MHC owns 55% of Rockville Financial.

Rockville Financial plans to grow the company
by opening new Rockville Bank branches and by
acquiring existing branches of other financial institutions.

EXECUTIVES

Secretary Rockville Financial and Rockville Bank,
  Judy L. Keppner, age 54
SVP Human Resources and Organizational
  Development Rockville Bank, Richard J.
  Trachimowicz, age 58, $138,531 total compensation
SVP and CFO Rockville Financial SVP and CFO
  Rockville Bank, John T. Lund, age 42
President and CEO; President and CEO Rockville
  Bank, William H. W. Crawford IV
Senior Vice President Investor Relations, Marliese
  Shaw
Director, William J. (Bill) McGurk, age 71
Director, Michael A. Bars, age 57
Director, C. Perry Chilberg, age 64
Director, David A. Engelson, age 69
Director, Raymond H. Lefurge Jr., age 63
Director, Stuart E. Magdefrau, age 58
Director, Rosemarie Novello Papa, age 68
Director, Richard M. Tkacz, age 60
Auditors: Wolf&CompanyP.C.

LOCATIONS

HQ: Rockville Financial Inc.
  25 Park St., Rockville CT 06066
Phone: 860-291-3600   **Fax:** 860-291-3666
Web: www.rockvillefinancialinc.com

PRODUCTS/OPERATIONS

2007 Sales

	$ mil.	% of total
Interest		
Loans	66	85
Securities — interest	5	7
Securities — dividends	1	2
Interest-bearing deposits	0	-
Noninterest		

		5	6
Service charges & fees		5	6
Net gain from sale of securities		0	
Total		**79**	**100**

COMPETITORS

Bank of America	RBS Citizens Financial
Citibank	Group
Liberty Bank	SI Financial
Naugatuck Valley	Sovereign Bank
Financial	TD Bank USA
New England Bancshares	United Financial
PSB Holdings Inc.	Bancorp
People' s United	Webster Financial
Financial	Westfield Financial

HISTORICAL FINANCIALS

Company Type: Public

Income Statement

FYE: December 31

	REVENUE ($ mil.)	NET INCOME ($ mil.)	NET PROFIT MARGIN	EMPLOYEES
12/12	92.6	15.8	17.0%	331
12/11	90.3	7.0	7.9%	281
12/10	85.1	12.2	14.4%	236
12/09	83.0	9.7	11.7%	235
12/08	68.5	(1.5)	—	0
Annual Growth	**7.8%**	—	—	—

2012 Year-End Financials

Debt ratio: 7.5%
Return on equity: 4.8%
Cash ($ mil.): 35
Current ratio: 0.20
Long-term debt ($ mil.): 149

No. of shares (mil.): 28
Dividends
  Yield: 4.0%
  Payout: 94.5%
Market value ($ mil.): 363

	STOCK PRICE ($) FY Close	P/E High/Low	PER SHARE ($) Earnings	Dividends	Book Value
12/12	12.90	24 18	0.56	0.52	11.39
12/11	10.36	43 36	0.25	0.21	11.30
Annual Growth	**24.5%**	—	**—124.0%**	**153.7%**	**0.8%**

Rofin Sinar Technologies Inc.

Any way you slice it ROFIN-SINAR Technologies is one of the world's leading makers of industrial lasers. The company designs manufactures
and markets lasers primarily used for cutting welding and marking a wide range of materials. Its
macro (cutting and welding) line is targeted at the
machine tool and automotive markets while its
laser marking and micro (fine cutting and welding)
product lines are principally geared toward the
semiconductor electronics and photovoltaic markets. ROFIN sells directly to OEMs systems integrators and industrial end users that integrate its
lasers into their own systems. Europe (mainly Germany) is its largest market followed by Asia and
North America.

In addition to its portfolio of laser products
ROFIN offers laser components (including power
supplies fiber optic beam splitters and high-brightness modules for semiconductors) replacement
parts and aftersales service in approximately 70
countries through a global manufacturing distribu-

tion and service network. The company has a direct sales force that works in some 24 countries. It also has independent representatives marketing its products around the world. A smaller portion of revenue is derived from ROFIN providing applications development for customers seeking alternatives to conventional manufacturing techniques.

ROFIN's product lineup is designed to meet a broad range of customers' material processing requirements. Lasers for cutting applications are marketed and sold primarily to OEMs in the machine tool industry that incorporate ROFIN's products into their own laser cutting machines. They are also sold to automotive OEMs for the cutting and welding of metals. Lasers for welding applications are marketed and sold to systems integrators and end users. Laser marking products are sold largely to semiconductor and electronics OEMs and end users for the marking of integrated circuits wafers solar cells electronic components and smart cards. Its laser micro products serve OEMs and end users in the medical device photovoltaic semiconductor and electronics dental and jewelry markets with spot welding fine cutting and micro structuring. Laser micro products also perforate cigarette paper and plastic foils for the consumer packaging and paper industries.

Unlike some competitors that may only specialize in one or two of the principal laser technologies ROFIN offers all three principal types used in material processing: CO2 lasers use carbon dioxide as the medium for cutting and welding metal and for marking and engraving non-metal materials; solid-state lasers (including fiber lasers) use solid-state crystal in rod or disc form as the medium; and diode lasers generate laser light and are used for surface treatment soldering and plastic welding.

Although ROFIN's fiscal results in 2010 reflect an overall improvement in the global economic environment the company is still struggling to boost sales numbers back up to pre-recession levels. It is trying to focus growth efforts in the Asia/Pacific region where recovery is occurring at a faster rate and where it anticipates that demand will increase substantially over the next five years. In particular it's banking on China and India due to the rapid expansion of their economies and production in their domestic machine tool automotive electronics and photovoltaic industries.

Over the past several years ROFIN has broadened its geographic footprint and product portfolio in China and elsewhere through both acquisitions and the formation of new subsidiaries and business entities. In 2009 it took control of Chinese laser manufacturer Nanjing Eastern Laser Company (NELC) through two separate cash transactions. The following year ROFIN acquired LASAG a Swiss specialist for laser micro material processing from The Swatch Group for an undisclosed amount. As LASAG is fully integrated into the ROFIN group it is expected to strengthen the company's laser micro and marking segment.

EXECUTIVES

Chairman, Peter Wirth, age 67, $203,915 total compensation

President; Chief Executive Officer; Director, Gunther Braun, age 56, $368,407 total compensation

IR Contact Officer, Katharina Manok

EVP Finance and Administration CFO and Treasurer, Ingrid Mittelstaedt, age 48, $221,588 total compensation

COO ROFIN Laser Micro and ROFIN Laser Marking; Managing Director Carl Baasel Lasertechnik GmbH, Thomas Merk, age 51, $224,997 total compensation

COO Rofin Laser Macro; President ROFIN-SINAR Inc. and ROFIN-BAASEL Inc. and ROFIN-BAASEL Canada, Louis (Lou) Molnar, age 60, $245,000 total compensation

CTO, Uli Hefter, age 61, $231,104 total compensation

Director, Gary K. Willis, age 67

President CEO and Director, Gunther Braun, age 55

Director, Stephen D. Fantone, age 60

Director, Ralph E. Reins, age 73

Director, Carl F. Baasel, age 71

Director, Gary K. Willis, age 68

Director, Daniel J. Smoke, age 64

Auditors: Deloitte&ToucheLLP

LOCATIONS

HQ: ROFIN-SINAR Technologies Inc.
40984 Concept Dr., Plymouth MI 48170
Phone: 734-455-5400   **Fax:** 734-455-2741
Web: www.rofin-sinar.com

2010 Sales

	$ mil.	% of total
Germany	306	53
North America	113	20
Other	158	27
Adjustments	(155.2)	-
Total	**423**	**100**

PRODUCTS/OPERATIONS

2010 Sales

	$ mil.	% of total
Laser marking & micro products	206	49
Laser macro products	172	41
Components	44	10
Total	**423**	**100**

2010 Sales by Market

	% of total
Machine	39
Semiconductor electronics &	26
Automotive &	5
Other	30
Total	**100**

Selected Products

Components
  Active and passive fibers and amplifiers
  Fiber couplings
  Fiber optic beam deliveries
  Optical engines
  Power supplies
  Semiconductor components (laser diodes and modules)
Laser macro
  CO2 lasers
    DC Slab series (cutting and welding)
    FH series (cutting and welding)
    SC series (cutting and structuring)
    SM series (cutting and welding)
    STS series (cutting and welding)
    XL Series (cutting and welding)
  Solid-state and fiber lasers
    DS series (cutting and welding)
    DQ series (surface treatment)
    FL series (cutting and welding)
  Diode lasers (plastic welding soldering and surface treatment)
Laser marking
  CombiLine series (general marking of metals and plastics)
  EasyJewel (marking of metal jewelry)
  EasyMark (marking of medical component and tool metals and plastics)
  LabelMarker series (marking of automotive labels)
  MultiScan (marking of consumer goods)

PowerLine/StarMark series (marking of integrated circuits metals organic materials plastics and smart cards)
Laser micro
  DS Disc series (cutting and structuring)
  PerfoLas systems (paper perforating)
  StarCut series (fine cutting)
  StarFiber (fine cutting)
  StarPulse (spot and seam welding)
  StarShape (cutting drilling structuring)
  StarWeld series (spot and steam welding)
  X-Lase (micro structuring)

COMPETITORS

Coherent Inc.	Jenoptik
FANUC	Quantel
GSI Group	Spectra-Physics
IPG Photonics	TRUMPF
JDS Uniphase	Virtek Vision
JMAR Technologies	

HISTORICAL FINANCIALS

Company Type: Public

Income Statement

FYE: September 30

	REVENUE ($ mil.)	NET INCOME ($ mil.)	NET PROFIT MARGIN	EMPLOYEES
09/13	560.0	34.7	6.2%	2,265
09/12	540.1	34.5	6.4%	2,213
09/11	597.7	60.0	10.0%	2,108
09/10	423.5	29.8	7.0%	1,822
09/09	349.5	9.1	2.6%	1,726
Annual Growth	**12.5%**	**39.6%**	**—**	**7.0%**

2013 Year-End Financials

Debt ratio: 2.6%	No. of shares (mil.): 28
Return on equity: 6.7%	Dividends
Cash ($ mil.): 133	Yield: —
Current ratio: 4.44	Payout: —
Long-term debt ($ mil.): 14	Market value ($ mil.): 681

	STOCK PRICE ($) FY Close	P/E High/Low		Earnings	PER SHARE ($) Dividends	Book Value
09/13	24.21	23	15	1.22	0.00	19.19
09/12	19.73	24	14	1.20	0.00	17.40
09/11	19.20	21	9	2.06	0.00	16.64
09/10	25.38	26	19	1.02	0.00	14.64
09/09	22.96	96	39	0.31	0.00	14.47
Annual Growth	**1.3%**	**—**	**—**	**40.8%**	**—**	**7.3%**

Rogers Corp.

Rogers lives in a material world and it is a materials company. The company's specialty materials are used in a variety of electronic and consumer products. Its products include printed circuit board laminates and polyester-based industrial laminates which are used in wireless communications systems including hand-held devices GPS and direct broadcast TV. Rogers' high-performance foams include urethane and silicone foams used for making vehicle gaskets and seals communication devices computers and footwear insoles. It also makes high-performance elastomer components sold to OEMs in various markets including ground transportation office equipment and consumer industries.

Geographic Reach

A global player Rogers has operations in the US (Arizona Connecticut and Illinois) Europe (Belgium and Germany) and Asia (China Japan Singapore South Korea and Taiwan).

Operations

The company operates in three segments: High Performance Foams (polyurethane and silicone foam products sold to fabricators and OEMs);Printed Circuit Materials (circuit board laminate products for high frequency high performance applications to meet the demands of increasing speed complexity and power in analog digital and microwave equipment); and Power Electronics Solutions (Curamik Electronics Solutions and Power Distribution Systems). Curamik Electronics Solutions makes direct copper bonded ceramic substrate products used in the design of intelligent power management devices such as insulated gate bipolar transistor modules. Power Distribution Systems makes busbar power distribution products for manufacturers of high power electrical inverter and converter systems for use in mass transit and clean technology applications (such as electric vehicles solar farms and wind turbines).

Sales and Marketing

Rogers sells though direct channels. It sold its products to 3000 customers worldwide in 2012. The company's largest customer accounted for 4% of sales.

Financial Performance

Revenues decreased by 9% in 2012 due to 31% drop in Curamik Electronics Solutions sales due to the continued lower demand in renewable energy and industrial motor drive applications. Power Distribution Systems' revenues decreased by 11% reflecting a slowdown in spending on infrastructure projects in the mass transit and renewable energy (wind and solar) markets especially in Europe and China. These declines were offset by a slight rise in sales in the High Performance Foams segment.However net income increased by 85% in 2012 primarily due to an increase in the fair value of investments decreased selling and lower administrative expenses due to weaker sales volumes and a drop in research and development expenses.

Strategy

The company focuses on offering advanced high-tech products at competitive prices in markets around the globe. It also seeks to be close to its customers marketing its products through direct sales channels in concentrated areas within its three major geographic regions. Rogers pursues growth organically by expanding its product line and market share as well as growth through acquisitions.

Its current strategy for growth focuses on developing high-tech products for industries involved in the Internet mass transit and clean technology. The growth of mobile devices for example has driven sales of one of the company's latest product brand lines its PORON molded components. In addition to being used in mobile devices such as iPADs and iPhones the shock-absorbing material is also used in sports apparel to protect athletes from crashes. The company's busbar products are used primarily in power distribution systems for mass transit and clean technology. It manufactures these components under the RO-LINX brand name.

In Asia it formed a strategic alliance with Hitachi Chemical in 2011 to provide high-speed digital printed circuit materials. The materials produced help meet the growing demand for increased speed in Internet data and video transmission.

In late 2011 Rogers ceased operations at its underperforming Thermal Management Solutions segment after failing to gain traction in the market and having problems with the manufacturing process. With the acquisition of Curamik Electron-

ics in 2011 Rogers restructured its business segments to add Power Electronics Solutions as one of its three core strategic units along with High Performance Foams and Printed Circuit Materials. Curamik Electronic Solutions and Power Distribution Systems comprise the Power Electronics Solutions business segment.

Mergers and Acquisitions

In 2011 Rogers acquired Curamik Electronics a manufacturer of power electronic substrate products in Eschenbach Germany for $153 million. Curamik Electronics is a global leader for the development of direct copper bonded ceramic substrate products which are used in industrial motor drives wind and solar energy converters and hybrid electric vehicle drive systems. The acquisition enhanced Rogers' existing power electronic products portfolio.

EXECUTIVES

VP and Secretary, Robert M. Soffer, age 65, $179,970 total compensation

VP Corporate Compliance and Controls, Debra J. Granger, age 53

Director Finance Treasury Operations New Business Development and Corporate Treasurer, Paul B. Middleton, age 45, $184,116 total compensation

SVP and CTO, Robert C. (Bob) Daigle, age 50, $254,410 total compensation

VP Logistics, Michael L. Cooper, age 60, $21,702 total compensation

President; Chief Executive Officer; Director, Bruce D. Hoechner, age 52

VP Finance and CFO, Dennis M. Loughran, age 55, $283,920 total compensation

VP Europe, Luc Van Eenaeme, age 54

Manager Investor and Public Relations, William J. (Bill) Tryon

VP Advanced Circuit Materials Division, Jeffrey M. Grudzien, age 50

Corporate Controller and Principal Accounting Officer, Ronald J. Pelletier, age 39

VP and General Counsel, Terrence W. Mahoney, age 65

VP Rogers Asia, Michael N. Sehnert, age 49

Director, Robert G. Paul, age 71

Director, Michael F. Barry, age 55

Director, Eileen S. Kraus, age 74

Director, Charles M. Brennan III, age 71

Director, Peter C. Wallace, age 59

President CEO and Director, Bruce D. Hoechner, age 51

Director, J. Carl Hsu, age 71

Director, Carol R. Jensen, age 60

Auditors: Ernst&YoungLLP

LOCATIONS

HQ: Rogers Corporation
1 Technology Dr., Rogers CT 06263
Phone: 860-774-9605   **Fax:** 860-779-5509
Web: www.rogerscorp.com

2012 Sales

Asia	250	50
US	115	23
Total	**498**	**100**

PRODUCTS/OPERATIONS

2012 Sales

High Performance Foams	179	36
Power Electronic Solutions		
Curamik Electronics Solutions	92	19
Power Distribution Systems	41	8
Total	**498**	**100**

Selected Products and Brands

High Performance Foams
   Plate backing and mounts for printing plates (R/bak)
   Silicon foams and sponges (BISCO)
   Urethane and silicon foams for high-impact cushioning gaskets and seals portable communications devices computers (PORON)
Printed Circuit Materials
   Flexible circuit materials (R/flex)
   Printed circuit board materials (DUROID ULTRALAM)
Power Electronics Solutions
   Curamik Electronics Solutions
      Direct copper bonded (DCB) ceramic substrate products
   Power distribution systems
      Busbar products used in mass transit and clean technology (RO-LINX)
Other Polymer Products
   Elastomer rollers and belts (ENDUR)
   Floats for fuel-level sensors (NITROPHYL)

Selected Mergers and Acquisitions

2011
Curamik Electronics GmbH ($153 million; Eschenbach Germany; power electronic substrate products manufacturer)

COMPETITORS

Hexcel	Kingboard
Honeywell Electronic	Park Electrochemical
Materials	Plexus
Insulectro	Vesuvius

HISTORICAL FINANCIALS

Company Type: Public

Income Statement

FYE: December 31

	REVENUE ($ mil.)	NET INCOME ($ mil.)	NET PROFIT MARGIN	EMPLOYEES
12/12	498.7	68.6	13.8%	2,400
12/11	553.1	37.0	6.7%	2,600
12/10	379.1	34.5	9.1%	1,940
12/09	291.8	(62.8)	—	1,735
12/08	365.3	26.5	7.3%	1,960
Annual Growth	**8.1%**	**26.9%**	**—**	**5.2%**

2012 Year-End Financials

Debt ratio: 14.0%	No. of shares (mil.): 16	
Return on equity: 17.7%	Dividends	
Cash ($ mil.): 114	Yield: —	
Current ratio: 3.63	Payout: —	
Long-term debt ($ mil.): 84	Market value ($ mil.): 839	

	STOCK PRICE ($) FY Close	P/E High/Low		PER SHARE ($) Earnings	Dividends	Book Value
12/12	49.66	12	8	4.04	0.00	25.68
12/11	36.86	22	16	2.21	0.00	20.85
12/10	38.25	17	11	2.16	0.00	20.87
12/09	30.31	—	—	(4.01)	0.00	18.61
12/08	27.77	26	14	1.67	0.00	21.47
Annual Growth	**15.6%**	**—**	**—**	**24.7%**	**—**	**4.6%**

Rose Rock Midstream L P

A rose by any other name would smell as sweet or so says Rose Rock Midstream the new name for SemCrude L.P. Rose Rock Midstream was established in 2011 to take over the assets of Sem-Crude the storage and pipeline division of Sem-Group. Rose Rock Midstream's new assets include SemCrude's crude oil storage terminal in Cushing Oklahoma; its gathering and transportation system in Kansas and Oklahoma; its Bakken Shale operations and its Platteville Colorado crude oil unloading facility. The only midstream operation Rose Rock won't handle is the White Cliffs Pipeline which will continue to be 51%-owned by Sem-Crude Pipeline L.L.C. Rose Rock Midstream went public in 2011 with a $181 million IPO.

Rose Rock Midstream used the net proceeds from its initial public offering to pay back Sem-Group for the partnership interests in SemCrude L.P. SemGroup also used the proceeds to pay down two loans totaling $275 million.

SemGroup filed for bankruptcy in 2008 and has been selling off and spinning off noncore assets beginning with SemGroup Energy Partners which was renamed Blueknight Energy Partners in 2009. Rose Rock Midstream was formed as a master limited partnership (MLP) a publicly traded legal entity exempt from paying corporate income taxes. MLPs are specific to the energy industry and enjoy tax-exempt status provided they pay taxable quarterly distributions to shareholders. As an MLP Rose Rock Midstream and its operating subsidiary Rose Rock Midstream Operating LLC don't have any employees and are managed by a general partner SemGroup.

The company's crude oil terminal in Cushing Oklahoma has a storage capacity of 5 million barrels and is undergoing expansion to hold an additional 1.95 million barrels by 2013. About 95% of its storage is under long-term contracts with third parties none of which expire before 2015. It also owns a 640-mile crude oil gathering and transportation pipeline system across Kansas and Oklahoma that connects to the Cushing terminal and other third-party pipelines and refineries; a crude oil gathering storage transportation and marketing business in the Bakken Shale in North Dakota and Montana that handles about 5800 barrels of crude oil per day; and a 10-lane crude oil truck unloading facility in Platteville Colorado that connects to SemCrude Pipeline's White Cliffs Pipeline. The Platteville facility has a storage capacity of 120000 barrels and is also undergoing expansion to store an additional 100000 barrels and add six more truck unloading lanes by 2013. The whole company's operations depend on a small number of customers; three companies accounted for 69% of sales in 2010.

EXECUTIVES

President CEO and Director, Norman J. (Norm) Szydlowski, age 62
COO and Director, Peter L. Schwiering, age 69
Auditors: BDOUSALLP

LOCATIONS

HQ: Rose Rock Midstream L P
Two Warren Place, 6120 South Yale Avenue, Suite 700, Tulsa, OK 74136-4216
Phone: 918 524-7700
Web: www.rrmidstream.com

PRODUCTS/OPERATIONS

2010 Sales

	$ mil.	% of total
$ mil % of total		
Products	158	76
Services	49	34
Other .4 -		
Total	**208**	**100**

COMPETITORS

ConocoPhillips	NuStar Energy
Enbridge Energy	Plains All American
Enterprise Products	Pipeline
Magellan Midstream	Sunoco Logistics
National Cooperative	Tesoro Logistics
Refinery Association	

HISTORICAL FINANCIALS
Company Type: Public

Income Statement

FYE: December 31

	REVENUE ($ mil.)	NET INCOME ($ mil.)	NET PROFIT MARGIN	EMPLOYEES
12/12	620.4	23.9	3.9%	80
12/11	431.3	23.2	5.4%	80
12/10	208.0	23.4	11.3%	0
12/09	10.6	1.2	12.1%	0
Annual Growth	288.1%	165.2%	—	—

2012 Year-End Financials

Debt ratio: 0.8%	No. of shares (mil.): 16
Return on equity: 7.7%	Dividends
Cash ($ mil.): 0	Yield: 3.8%
Current ratio: 1.08	Payout: 86.7%
Long-term debt ($ mil.): 4	Market value ($ mil.): 528

	STOCK PRICE ($) FY Close	P/E High/Low	PER SHARE ($) Earnings	Dividends	Book Value
12/12	31.47	24 14	1.40	1.21	18.37
12/11	20.58	343319	0.06	0.00	17.80
12/10	0.00	— —	(0.00)	0.00	(0.00)
Annual Growth	—		—	—	—

Royal Gold, Inc.

Royal Gold deals only with royalty. Rather than operating gold mines the company buys the right to collect royalties from mine operators. This strategy allows Royal Gold to minimize its exposure to the costs of mineral exploration and development. More than one-third of the company's revenue comes from its royalty interests related to the Cortez Pipeline Mining Complex a project in Nevada operated by Barrick; the Robinson mine operated by Quadra accounts for 24%. Royal Gold holds royalty stakes in other producing properties elsewhere in the Americas as well as in Africa. The company also owns interests in exploration- and development-stage projects in the US and in Argentina Finland and Russia.

Royal Gold revenues increased 85% in 2010 due to the rising market price of gold copper and other metals. Despite the increase in royalty payments net income was down for the year by 44% due to increased operating costs and expenses related to severance payments and acquisitions.

The company is expanding its portfolio. It has invested $35 million in the construction and development of High River Gold Mines' Taparko open pit gold project in Burkina Faso in West Africa. Royal Gold has acquired royalty stakes in projects operated by Kennecott Minerals (in projects in Nevada and Mexico) Nevada Star Resource Corp. (a smelter return royalty) Minefinders (a smelter return royalty interest on a Mexican property) Kennecott Exploration (Mexico) and Barrick.

In 2010 Royal Gold acquired the rights to 25% of the payable gold produced from the Mt. Milligan copper-gold project in British Columbia from Thompson Creek Metals Company. Royal Gold paid some $311 million for the rights.

It added another acquisition in 2009 when it paid Teck $100 million for a percentage of a Chilean gold mine's output. Early the next year it bought International Royalty for about $700 million. International Royalty owns percentage stakes in mines in Australia Canada and Chile.

EXECUTIVES

Vice President; Corporate Secretary, Karen P. Gross, age 59, $182,000 total compensation
Chairman, Stanley Dempsey, age 74, $138,500 total compensation
President CEO and Director, Tony Jensen, age 51, $375,500 total compensation
CFO and Treasurer, Stefan L. Wenger, age 40, $182,000 total compensation
VP Operations, William M. Zisch, age 55
Vice President; General Counsel, Bruce C. Kirchhoff, age 54, $237,000 total compensation
Vice President - Corporate Development, William Heissenbuttel, age 48, $182,000 total compensation
Director, William M. (Bill) Hayes, age 67
Director, M. Craig Haase, age 69
Director, James W. Stuckert, age 74
Director, S. Oden Howell Jr., age 72
Director, Donald J. Worth, age 80
President CEO and Director, Tony Jensen, age 50
Independent Director, Gordon Bogden
Auditors: Ernst&YoungLLP

LOCATIONS

HQ: Royal Gold Inc.
1660 Wynkoop St. Ste. 1000, Denver CO 80202-1132
Phone: 303-573-1660 **Fax:** 303-595-9385
Web: www.royalgold.com

2011 Royalty Revenue

	% of total
US	24
Chile	21
Canada	19
Mexico	18
Africa	9
Other	9
Total	**100**

COMPETITORS

Anglo American	Franco-Nevada
BHP Billiton	Rio Tinto Limited

HISTORICAL FINANCIALS
Company Type: Public

Income Statement

FYE: June 30

	REVENUE ($ mil.)	NET INCOME ($ mil.)	NET PROFIT MARGIN	EMPLOYEES
06/13	289.2	73.4	25.4%	21
06/12	263.0	98.3	37.4%	19
06/11	216.4	77.3	35.7%	21
06/10	136.5	21.4	15.7%	20
06/09	73.7	38.3	52.0%	17
Annual Growth	40.7%	17.6%	—	5.4%

2013 Year-End Financials

Debt ratio: 10.4%	No. of shares (mil.): 64
Return on equity: 3.5%	Dividends
Cash ($ mil.): 664	Yield: 0.0%
Current ratio: 21.22	Payout: 64.2%
Long-term debt ($ mil.): 302	Market value ($ mil.): 2,729

STOCK PRICE ($)	P/E	PER SHARE ($)		
FY Close	High/Low	Earnings	Dividends	Book Value
06/13	42.08	92 36	1.09	0.70	36.22
06/12	78.40	51 36	1.61	0.41	30.94
06/11	58.57	48 33	1.29	0.42	26.48
06/10	48.00	114 79	0.49	0.35	26.32
06/09	41.69	45 21	1.07	0.31	18.51
Annual Growth	0.2%	— —	0.5%	22.6%	18.3%

RPC, Inc.

RPC helps to grease the wheels of oil and gas production through a number of business units. Through its Cudd Energy Services division the company provides oil industry consulting and technical services including snubbing coiled tubing nitrogen services and well control. Another unit Patterson Services rents specialized tools and equipment such as drill pipe tubing and blowout preventers. RPC also provides maintenance emergency services and storage and inspection services for offshore and inland vessels. The company operates in most of the world's major oil producing regions.

Geographic Reach

The company has administrative offices in Texas and Louisiana. The headquarters location in Houston Texas also houses engineering and sales and marketing departments. The US market accounts for most of revenues though the company has limited international operations primarily in Africa Canada China Latin America the Middle East and New Zealand. In the US the company's operations are focused on gas producing regions such as the southwestern and midwestern regions the Gulf of Mexico the Rocky Mountains and the Appalachian Mountains.

Operations

RPC's operations are divided into two segments: Technical services (about 90% of revenues) and support services. Technical services include pressure pumping services snubbing services coiled tubing services nitrogen service firefighting and well control. Pressure pumping services account for more than half of the company's annual revenues and include the provision of fracturing and acidizing equipment and materials that stimulate the production of oil and gas. Meanwhile support services include the rental of drill pipe and other specialized oilfield equipment downhole tool rentals pipe inspection and storage services and oilfield training services.

Sales and Marketing

RPC serves major oilfield companies –including multi-national national and independent firms — that are involved in oil and gas exploration production and development activities.

Financial Performance

Higher oil prices and increased customer activity (mostly in the US) have lifted the company's revenues each year since 2009. In 2012 revenues increased 7% due to an 8% rise in technical service revenues attributed to growth in customer demand and fleet expansion efforts. The support services segment also increased sales by 3% on customer activity growth. Net income fell 7% in 2012 however due to increased employment and

capital spending (equipment) costs associated with its expansion efforts.

Strategy

The company has built its portfolio of technical and support services through a series of acquisitions and strategic partnerships. It has also increased its service capacity in recent years by widening its equipment fleets in both the technical services and support services segments. RPC is looking to a rebounding world economy with its increased demand for oil and gas operations to open up further opportunities for acquisitions geographic expansion and market share growth.

Ownership

Chairman R. Randall Rollins and his brother Vice Chairman Gary Rollins (CEO of Rollins Inc.) own about two-thirds of RPC.

EXECUTIVES

VP Secretary and Director, Linda H. Graham, age 76, $147,469 total compensation
President CEO and Director, Richard A. Hubbell, age 69, $625,624 total compensation
VP CFO and Treasurer, Ben M. Palmer, age 53, $223,437 total compensation
Chairman, R. Randall Rollins, age 81, $536,250 total compensation
VP Corporate Finance, James C. (Jim) Landers
VP and General Manager Patterson Services, Jim Daniel
VP and General Manager Patterson Services, Len Denson
Manager Investor Relations and Corporate Communications, Sharon A. Lennon
Director, Larry L. Prince, age 74
Director, Henry B. Tippie, age 86
VP Secretary and Director, Linda H. Graham, age 76
President CEO and Director, Richard A. Hubbell, age 69
Director, Gary W. Rollins, age 68
Director, James B. Williams, age 80
Director, Wilton Looney, age 93
Director, James A. Lane Jr., age 71
Director, Bill J. Dismuke, age 77
Auditors: GrantThorntonLLP

LOCATIONS

HQ: RPC Inc.
2170 Piedmont Rd. NE, Atlanta GA 30324
Phone: 404-321-2140   **Fax:** 404-321-5483
Web: www.rpc.net

2012 Sales

	$ mil.	% of total
US	1,870	96
Other countries	74	4
Total	**1,945**	**100**

PRODUCTS/OPERATIONS

2012 Sales

	$ mil.	% of total
Technical services	1,794	92
Support services	151	8
Total	**1,945**	**100**

Selected Services

Technical Services
  Coiled Tubing
  Nitrogen Units
  Pressure Pumping
  Snubbing
  Thru Tubing Solution
  Well Control
  Wireline
Support Services
  Energy Personnel International

Patterson Rental Tools
Patterson Tubular Services
Well Control School

COMPETITORS

Baker Hughes	Schlumberger
Ensign Energy Services	Transocean
Exterran	Weatherford
Halliburton	International
Precision Drilling	

HISTORICAL FINANCIALS

Company Type: Public

Income Statement

FYE: December 31

	REVENUE ($ mil.)	NET INCOME ($ mil.)	NET PROFIT MARGIN	EMPLOYEES
12/12	1,945.0	274.4	14.1%	3,600
12/11	1,809.8	296.3	16.4%	3,400
12/10	1,096.3	146.7	13.4%	2,500
12/09	587.8	(22.7)	—	1,980
12/08	876.9	83.4	9.5%	2,532
Annual Growth	22.0%	34.7%	—	9.2%

2012 Year-End Financials

Debt ratio: 7.8%
Return on equity: 32.9%
Cash ($ mil.): 14
Current ratio: 3.45
Long-term debt ($ mil.): 107

No. of shares (mil.): 220
Dividends
  Yield: 4.2%
  Payout: 38.8%
Market value ($ mil.): 2,695

	STOCK PRICE ($)	P/E	PER SHARE ($)		
	FY Close	High/Low	Earnings	Dividends	Book Value
12/12	12.24	16 7	1.27	0.52	4.08
12/11	18.25	20 11	1.35	0.21	3.45
12/10	18.12	48 15	0.67	0.09	2.42
12/09	10.40	— —	(0.11)	0.10	1.85
12/08	9.76	49 16	0.38	0.11	2.04
Annual Growth	5.8%	— —	35.4%	48.6%	18.9%

RPX Corp

In our litigious society RPX Corporation helps keep technology companies out of the courtroom. RPX owns a portfolio of more than 1500 intellectual property patents that it licenses to customers in order to prevent patent infringement lawsuits. (So one company can't sue another over a patent since it's RPX that owns the patent). Its patent portfolio spans six industries –consumer electronics software media content mobile communications and devices networking and semiconductors. RPX counts more than 70 customers including Cisco Google Nokia Sharp Sony and Verizon and earns one-third of its revenues from Asian firms. Founded in 2008 RPX launched an IPO in 2011.

Patent litigation is an emerging multi-billion dollar industry that even has its own insults - companies that make big business of suing others over alleged patent infringement are called non-practicing entities (NPEs) but are known derogatively as patent trolls or patent pirates. Tech companies of all sizes have had their business operations disrupted by major verdicts and high settlement costs. Many patents can overlap; for example there are more than 6200 patents for the semiconductor technology known as DRAM (dynamic random access memory). Potential infringement can happen for any company that makes uses or sells a device with DRAM technology.

RPX operates as a legal middleman; so far it has spent about $250 million acquiring patents to help customers mitigate litigation risks. Its customers pay between $40000 to more than $5 million a year to license its intellectual property. RPX's separates itself from competitors (such as Acacia) by charging its subscription fees based on a company's revenues not the perceived value of the patent.

RPX is experiencing significant growth as its revenues doubled from 2009 its first full year of operations to the first nine months of 2010. Continuing this impressive trajectory the company saw its revenues increase from $32 million in 2009 to almost $95 million in 2010 —a staggering increase of 189%. In May 2011 the company raised almost $160 million by going public. It wants to use the proceeds to acquire additional patents in 2011 as well as hire more personnel for client relations patent research and analysis and to develop reporting systems. PRX also plans to offer complementary services such as facilitating joint defense agreements and cross-licensing arrangements for its clients. Finally it aims to recruit more clients that are consistently faced with IP-related lawsuits.

Several investment vehicles own major stakes in the company. Index Ventures Growth; Charles River Partnership; and Kleiner Perkins Caufield & Byers each own about 18%. They are represented on the company's board by Giuseppe Zocco Izhar Armony and Randy Komisar respectively.

EXECUTIVES

SVP Memberships, Paul Reidy, age 50
CEO and Director, John A. Amster, age 42
VP Marketing, Lily Loh
COO and Director, Geoffrey T. Barker, age 49
President and Director, Eran Zur, age 42
SVP Finance CFO and Treasurer, Adam C. Spiegel, age 47
EVP, Mallun Yen
SVP Memberships and General Manager, Henri Linde, age 52
VP and Head of Acquisitions, Kevin Barhydt
Director Acquisitions, Reza Mashouf
VP Client Relations, Steve Swank
Senior Director Client Relations, Shoichi Endo
Director Client Relations, Francois Thuiliere
VP Corporate Development, David Ruder
Director Corporate Development, David Anderson
VP and Corporate Controller, Paul Chopra
General Counsel, Marty Roberts
Chief Intellectual Property Officer, Paul M. Saraceni
VP Memberships and Legal, Eric Olsen
Vice President Memberships and General Manager, David Potts
VP Memberships, Anderson R. Scott
VP Memberships, France Szeto
VP RPX Corp and President RPX Asia Corp, Hisao Yamasaki
VP Structured Acquisitions, Thomas Westerlund
Chief Knowledge Officer, Mike MacKay
CTO, Steve Waterhouse
Managing Partner of Technology Opportunity Partners, Steven L. Fingerhood
Investor Relations Officer, Cynthia Hiponia
Senior Vice President Corporate Development, Robert Heath
Vice President Finance, Shig Hamamatsu
Director, Thomas O. (Tom) Ryder, age 66
Director, Randy Komisar, age 56
Director, Giuseppe P. Zocco, age 45

CEO and Director, John A. Amster, age 42
Director, Izhar Armony, age 47
President and Director, Eran Zur, age 42
Auditors: PricewaterhouseCoopersLLP

LOCATIONS

HQ: RPX Corporation
1 Market Plaza Ste. 700, San Francisco CA 94105
Phone: 866-779-7641   **Fax:** -8861
Web: cleantechsolutionsinternational.com/

2010 Sales

Americas	53	56
Europe	10	11

COMPETITORS

Acacia Research	Jones Day
Alston & Bird	Kirkland & Ellis
Baker & McKenzie	Walker Digital
Convex Group	White & Case
Duane Morris	

HISTORICAL FINANCIALS
Company Type: Public

Income Statement
FYE: December 31

	REVENUE ($ mil.)	NET INCOME ($ mil.)	NET PROFIT MARGIN	EMPLOYEES
12/12	197.6	38.9	19.7%	125
12/11	154.0	29.1	18.9%	110
12/10	94.8	13.8	14.6%	76
12/09	32.8	1.9	5.9%	0
12/08	0.7	(5.1)	—	0
Annual Growth	297.5%	—	—	—

2012 Year-End Financials

Debt ratio: —	No. of shares (mil.): 51
Return on equity: 11.7%	Dividends
Cash ($ mil.): 73	Yield: —
Current ratio: 2.44	Payout: —
Long-term debt ($ mil.): —	Market value ($ mil.): 462

	STOCK PRICE ($) FY Close	P/E High/Low		PER SHARE ($) Earnings	Dividends	Book Value
12/12	9.04	26	11	0.74	0.00	7.05
12/11	12.65	51	20	0.57	0.00	6.09
Annual Growth	(28.5%)	—	—	29.8%	—	15.9%

Rudolph Technologies, Inc.

Rudolph Technologies' inspection and metrology systems lead the way to better yields for chip makers. To create semiconductors manufacturers deposit precise layers of conducting and insulating materials on silicon wafers. Rudolph makes process control metrology equipment that monitors these layers to ensure that the material doesn't get too thick or too thin. Its inspection equipment (around half of sales) looks for defects not obvious to the human eye such as tiny scratches or gouges in the surface of a silicon wafer. The company also makes a range of data analysis and process control software. Rudolph gets nearly

three-quarters of sales from customers located outside the US primarily in Asia.

The company sells its products to more than 90 semiconductor makers in 20 countries. Significant customers include Infineon Technologies and Samsung Semiconductor which account for about 13% and 12% respectively. Other customers have included Intel Avago Technologies and Taiwan Semiconductor Manufacturing. The company operates in a highly competitive market with Camtek and KLA-Tencor as its principal rivals. While Camtek is roughly the size of Rudolph KLA-Tencor dwarfs both companies in terms of annual sales employees and financial resources.

After rebounding from the 2008-2009 global economic downturn with a 148% increase in sales and return to profitability in 2010 revenues in 2011 were down 4% due to sluggish system sales in the latter half of the year. Revenues related to data analysis and review software parts and service all rose for the year. Rudolph remained profitable though net income fell slightly.

Rudolph has expanded into new markets and applications through internal growth and through acquisitions that add complementary products. In 2012 It bought assets of Germany-based NanoPhotonics to expand its intellectual property holdings related to unpatterned wafer and mask blank inspection. The previous year the company boosted its presence in the LED device manufacturing sector which uses technologies that are similar to chip manufacturing. It has also expanded its product offerings with data analysis process control and factory automation software for semiconductor solar and LED applications.

Two acquisitions significantly expanded its software offerings. In 2010 Rudolph bought the Yield Dynamics software business of MKS Instruments expanding its process control software portfolio. In 2009 the company acquired Plano Texas-based Adventa Control Technologies. Adventa develops advanced process control technologies to semiconductor manufacturers especially for tool automation and fault detection.

Rudolph's manufacturing consists of assembly test and calibration which is performed at its facility in Minnesota. The company maintains application sales and service offices throughout Asia and Europe.

EXECUTIVES

SVP Finance and Administration CFO and Secretary, Steven R. Roth, age 52, $268,065 total compensation
Chairman and CEO, Paul F. McLaughlin, age 67, $555,864 total compensation
SVP Worldwide Sales and Field Operations, D. Mayson Brooks, age 54, $328,727 total compensation
Vice President - Global Customer Support, Robert DiCrosta, age 65
EVP; General Manager Inspection Business Unit, Nathan H. Little, age 61, $232,786 total compensation
Vice President - Manufacturing, Jeffrey T. (Jeff) Nelson, age 57
Vice President; General Counsel, Robert A. Koch, age 51
VP Corporate Marketing, Ardelle R. Johnson, age 57
VP; General Manager Data Analysis and Review, Michael P. Plisinski, age 43, $242,413 total compensation
Vice President - Engineering, Scott R. Danciak, age 43
VP Business Development and Director Back-end Product Management, Rajiv Roy, age 54
General Manager Europe, Martin Molan

VP; General Manager Metrology, Avishai Kepten, age 57
Vice President; General Manager - Inspection Business Unit, Michael Jost
Senior Vice President - Worldwide Sales & Field Operations, Mayson Brooks
Director, John R. Whitten, age 66
Director, Daniel H. Berry, age 67
Director, Leo Berlinghieri, age 59
Chairman Emeritus, Richard F. Spanier, age 73
Director, Thomas G. (Tom) Greig, age 65
Director, Aubrey C. (Bill) Tobey, age 87
Auditors: Ernst&YoungLLP

LOCATIONS

HQ: Rudolph Technologies Inc.
  1 Rudolph Rd., Flanders NJ 07836
Phone: 973-691-1300   **Fax:** 973-691-4863
Web: www.rudolphtech.com

2011 Sales

	$ mil.	% of total
US	52	28
Taiwan	26	14
South Korea	26	14
Singapore	16	9
Japan	14	8
China	11	6
Europe		
Austria	16	9
Germany	14	8
Other countries	7	4
Total	**187**	**100**

PRODUCTS/OPERATIONS

2011 Sales

	$ mil.	% of total
Systems		
Inspection	91	49
Metrology	38	21
Data analysis & review	23	12
Parts	21	12
Services	11	6
Total	**187**	**100**

Selected Products

Data Analysis and Review Software
  ARTIST Software (real-time monitoring software)
  AutoShell Software (equipment automation software)
  ControlWORKS Software (process control software)
  Discover Software (yield enhancement and process management software)
  GateWay Software(diagnostic and communications software)
  Genesis Software (data acquisition and integration data mining parametric analysis)
  HarmonyASR (off-line defect review and classification)
  Process Sentinel Software (spatial process control system)
  ProcessWORKS (process control software)
  RecipeWORKS (recipe management software)
  TrackWORKS (preventive maintenance management software)
  TrueADC Software (automatic defect classification)
  Yield Optimizer (yield management and predictive modeling software)
Inspection and Test Systems
  AXi Series (defect inspection for various process steps)
  B30 Inspection Module (2D defect detection on wafer's backside)
  E30 Inspection Module (2D defect detection of wafer's edge)
  Explorer Inspection Cluster (multi-surface inspection tools)
  F30 Inspection Module (multiple resolution defect inspection)
  NSX Series (macro-defect inspection)
  PrecisionWoRx System (probe card test and analysis)
  ProbeWoRx System (probe card production metrology)

Wafer Scanner Inspection System (2-D/3-D bump dimensional inspection 2-D bump and surface defect inspection)
  WaferWoRx System (probing process and tip analysis)
Metrology Systems
  MetaPULSE Systems (optical acoustic-based systems for opaque thin-film layers)
  S3000 System (transparent thin-film measurement systems)

COMPETITORS

Applied Materials	KLA-Tencor
Camtek	Metara
Carl Zeiss	Nanometrics
Dainippon Screen	Nikon
FEI	Nova Measuring
Hexagon AB	PANalytical
Hitachi	PDF Solutions
High-Technologies	Qcept Technologies

HISTORICAL FINANCIALS

Company Type: Public

Income Statement

FYE: December 31

	REVENUE ($ mil.)	NET INCOME ($ mil.)	NET PROFIT MARGIN	EMPLOYEES
12/12	218.4	43.8	20.1%	651
12/11	187.2	25.2	13.5%	564
12/10	195.3	27.0	13.8%	550
12/09	78.6	(29.6)	—	497
12/08	131.0	(249.6)	—	536
Annual Growth	13.6%	—	—	5.0%

2012 Year-End Financials

Debt ratio: 13.3%
Return on equity: 17.7%
Cash ($ mil.): 104
Current ratio: 7.94
Long-term debt ($ mil.): 49
No. of shares (mil.): 32
Dividends
  Yield: —
  Payout: —
Market value ($ mil.): 435

	STOCK PRICE ($) FY Close	P/E High	P/E Low	Earnings	Dividends	Book Value
12/12	13.44	10	6	1.34	0.00	8.36
12/11	9.26	16	8	0.78	0.00	6.96
12/10	8.23	13	7	0.86	0.00	5.89
12/09	6.72	—	—	(0.96)	0.00	4.88
12/08	3.53	—	—	(8.16)	0.00	5.74
Annual Growth	39.7%	—	—	—	—	9.9%

Salix Pharmaceuticals Ltd

Salix Pharmaceuticals is a finishing school for drugs. With a focus on treating gastrointestinal ailments the company prefers to acquire drug candidates nearing commercial viability. It then takes them through the final development stages and brings them to market. The company's marketed products include Xifaxan (an antibiotic for gastrointestinal troubles) Pepcid (gastric ulcers and acid reflux) and Apriso and Colazal (for ulcerative colitis). Other products include colonoscopy preparatory bowel purgatives MoviPrep OsmoPrep and Visicol. Its late-stage candidates include both new drugs and new uses for existing drugs.

Geographic Reach

Salix primarily conducts sales in the US market though it has limited commercial drug operations in Europe and about 20 countries in other global regions.

Operations

The company's biggest seller is Xifaxan (rifaximin) an antibiotic that has the ability to get into the gut but not into the bloodstream. The drug is approved as a treatment for travelers' diarrhea and other disorders and Salix is looking to expand its indications. Other medicines include fecal incontinence medication Solesta and Deflux a treatment for vesicoureteral reflux (a malformation of the bladder in children). The company launched a new proprietary product in 2012 after receiving FDA approval for Fulyzaq which treats diarrhea in HIV/AIDS patients.

Salix's Colazal Anusol Pepcid and Proctocort brands are mature with no patent protection but enjoy name brand recognition.

In the drug development realm Salix avoids the riskier capital intensive process of early-stage research by sticking strictly to late stage trials and commercialization activities. It holds the development and marketing rights to many of its products through long-standing licensing agreements with other drug companies. It also sidesteps the expense of maintaining manufacturing facilities by relying on third-party manufacturers to produce its materials.

Sales and Marketing

Salix's direct sales and marketing teams primarily targets US gastroenterologists as well as colorectal surgeons hepatologists and other medical professionals. The company has a small direct sales force in Europe and it uses independent distributors in Europe and other regions. Advertising expenses totaled about $21 million in 2012 up from $11 million the previous year.

Financial Performance

Salix has truly enjoyed the payoff of drug development and other growth efforts in recent years. Revenues increased 36% to $735 million in 2012 due to higher sales of Xifaxan Apriso Deflux and Relistor. Revenues jumped 60% in 2011 due in part to expanded indications for Xifaxan strong sales of purgatives and new products from acquisitions.

The revenue jump in 2011 also helped to give the company its first positive net income report since 2007; another profit of $36 million was reported in 2012 down 26% from the prior year due to increased expenses from sales force expansion and acquisition efforts.

Strategy

Salix is investing heavily in developing the Xifaxan antibiotic for additional uses including irritable bowel syndrome and Crohn's disease. It also aims to license or develop new late-stage pharmaceuticals and bring development-stage candidates to market.

Mergers and Acquisitions

To keep its operations nimble in the face of future additional patent expirations Salix depends on regular shopping trips to keep its pipeline well stocked. Sometimes it buys the rights to develop a candidate and sometimes it buys whole portfolios that include approved and marketed drugs.

In 2012 it paid $10 million for the licensing rights to an extended-release version of rifaximin with plans to use it as a treatment for Crohn's disease. Its 2011 purchase of US drugmaker Oceana Therapeutics added gastroenterology and urology therapeutics including Solesta and Deflux; the buy also added international operations as both drugs are sold overseas. The company also licensed rights to another drug Relistor which was launched in the US later that year.

Ownership

Wellington Management owns some 13% of the company.

EXECUTIVES

President CEO and Director, Carolyn J. Logan, age 64, $741,500 total compensation

EVP Finance and Administration and CFO, Adam C. Derbyshire, age 47, $410,000 total compensation

Chairman, Thomas W. (Tom) D'Alonzo, age 69

Associate VP Investor Relations and Corporate Communications, G. Michael Freeman

EVP Research and Development and Chief Development Officer, William P. (Bill) Forbes, age 51, $360,000 total compensation

EVP Business Development, Rick D. Scruggs

President CEO and Director, Carolyn J. Logan, age 64

Director, John F. Chappell, age 76

Director, William P. Keane, age 58

Director, Mark A. Sirgo, age 59

Auditors: PricewaterhouseCoopersLLP

LOCATIONS

HQ: Salix Pharmaceuticals Ltd.
8510 Colonnade Center Dr., Raleigh NC 27615
Phone: 919-862-1000   **Fax:** 919-862-1095
Web: www.salix.com

PRODUCTS/OPERATIONS

2012 Sales

Xifaxan	514	70
Purgatives (OsmoPrep/MoviPrep)	64	10
Total	**735**	**100**

Selected Products

Marketed
Anusol (hydrocortisone suppositories)
Apriso (ulcerative colitis)
Azasan (rheumatoid arthritix kidney transplantation)
Colazal (ulcerative colitis)
Deflux (vesicoureteral reflux)
Diuril (hypertension edema)
Giazo (inflammatory bowel disease)
Metozolv (gastroesophageal reflux)
MoviPrep (purgative)
OsmoPrep (purgative)
Pepcid (ulcers)
Proctocort (hydrocortisone suppositories)
Relistor (treatment for opiod-induced constipation)
Solesta (fecal incontinence)
Visicol (purgative)
Xifaxan (gastrointestinal antibiotic)

Selected Licensing Agreements

2012
Extended-release rifaximin (Crohn' s disease)
2011
Relistor ($60 million upfront from Progenics Pharmaceuticals opiod-induced constipation)
2010
Lumacan ($4 million from Photocure ASA colonoscopy fluorescent agent)

Selected Acquisitions

2011
Oceana Therapeutics ($300 million gastroenterology & urology drugs)

COMPETITORS

Abbott Labs	Prometheus Labs
Aptalis Pharma	Ranbaxy
Bayer AG	Pharmaceuticals
Cubist Pharmaceuticals	Shire
Ferndale Pharma Group	Takeda Pharmaceutical

GlaxoSmithKline   Warner Chilcott
Pfizer

HISTORICAL FINANCIALS

Company Type: Public

Income Statement

FYE: December 31

	REVENUE ($ mil.)	NET INCOME ($ mil.)	NET PROFIT MARGIN	EMPLOYEES
12/12	735.4	64.2	8.7%	525
12/11	540.4	87.4	16.2%	490
12/10	336.9	(27.0)	—	390
12/09	232.8	(43.6)	—	395
12/08	178.7	(47.0)	—	280
Annual Growth	**42.4%**	**—**	**—**	**17.0%**

2012 Year-End Financials

Debt ratio: 46.1%
Return on equity: 11.5%
Cash ($ mil.): 751
Current ratio: 4.56
Long-term debt ($ mil.): 864

No. of shares (mil.): 60
Dividends
  Yield: —
  Payout: —
Market value ($ mil.): 2,465

	STOCK PRICE ($) FY Close	P/E High/Low		PER SHARE ($) Earnings	Dividends	Book Value
12/12	40.47	51	35	1.01	0.00	9.20
12/11	47.85	32	18	1.44	0.00	9.28
12/10	46.96	—	—	(0.47)	0.00	6.91
12/09	25.39	—	—	(0.88)	0.00	6.58
12/08	8.83	—	—	(0.98)	0.00	5.22
Annual Growth	**46.3%**	**—**	**—**	**—**	**—**	**15.2%**

Sanfilippo (John B.) & Son, Inc.

John B. Sanfilippo & Son (JBSS) has built an empire out of working for peanuts. One of the largest processors of peanuts almonds pecans walnuts cashews and other nuts in the US JBSS markets the nuts as a snack and a baking ingredient under a number of private labels as well as its own name brands including Fisher Orchard Valley Harvest and Sunshine Country. It also produces and distributes other foods and snacks such as peanut butter dried fruit and trail mixes corn snacks sesame sticks and candy. Its products are sold worldwide to consumers (via retailers) and less so commercial ingredient channels (food service and industrial markets) contract packagers and export distributors.

Geographic Reach

Most of JBSS's sales are in the US. Exports represented 5% of the company's sales. The company has processing packaging warehousing distribution operations and a warehouse in Elgin Illinois and owns production facilities in Bainbridge Georgia; Garysburg North Carolina; Selma Texas; and Gustine California. It runs an outlet store at its production facility in Elgin and a retail store in the Chicago area.

Sales and Marketing

Consumer demand drives about 60% of JBSS's sales. Big customers include Wal-Mart Stores Target and PepsiCo which accounted for 22%. 15% and 11% of sales in fiscal 2013 (ended June). Other

food retailers include Kroger Publix Hannaford Jewel-Osco and Giant Eagle.

JBSS markets its nuts through its own sales department and a network of some 90 independent brokers and various independent distributors and suppliers. Marketing and advertising expenses were about $11000 $8950 and $7865 in fiscal 2013 2012 and 2011 respectively.

Financial Performance

The nut company's sales increased 5% in fiscal 2013 (ended June) versus the prior year to $734 million. Net income rose 27% over the same period to $21.7 million. Sales volume (measured as pounds sold to customers) increased 4% due primarily to higher sales of Fisher snack and recipe nuts and private brand snack nuts to new and existing customers. Lower prices also helped spur consumer demand for nuts during the second half of fiscal 2013.

Over the past four years JBSS's sales have risen about a third which the company attributes to its five-year strategic plan (launched in fiscal 2009).

Strategy

JBSS's five-year plan for growth (adopted in fiscal 2009) includes acquisitions promotion of its branded products international expansion and other related strategies for increasing private brand product sales.

Mergers and Acquisitions

As part of its strategy to expand its market presence through an enhanced portfolio in fiscal 2010 JBSS acquired Modesto California-based Orchard Valley Harvest for approximately $32.9 million. The purchase gave JBSS an established manufacturer of branded and private-label nut and dried fruit products sold in the prized produce department of food stores. Produce is cited by JBSS as a fast growing sector in food retailing with consumers spending more time and more money in such "perimeter of the store" areas. This trend is fueled by the continued popularity of convenience foods paired with consumer demand for healthier-eating alternatives. To cut costs JBSS relocated Orchard Valley Harvest's operation in Modesto to facilities in Gustine California and Elgin Illinois.

Ownership

The Sanfilippo family owns about 51% of the company; the Valentine Group (headed by board member and former president Mathias Valentine) owns about 24%.

EXECUTIVES

President COO Assistant Secretary and Director, Jasper B. Sanfilippo Jr., age 46, $306,619 total compensation

Group President CFO Secretary and Director, Michael J. Valentine, age 55, $306,619 total compensation

Chairman and CEO, Jeffrey T. Sanfilippo, age 51, $306,619 total compensation

CIO, James A. Valentine, age 49, $298,157 total compensation

Vice President - Risk Management and Investor Relations; Treasurer, William R. Pokrajac, age 59

SVP Industrial Sales, Walter R. (Bobby) Tankersley Jr., age 61, $246,826 total compensation

SVP Pecan Operations and Procurement, Everado Soria, age 56

Director Financial Reporting and Taxation, Herbert J. Marros, age 55

VP Global Marketing and Innovation, Howard Brandeisky

SVP Corporate Operations, Michael G. Cannon, age 60, $227,074 total compensation

VP Finance and Corporate Controller, Frank S. Pellegrino, age 39

Senior Vice President - Consumer Sales; Strategy and Business Development, Robert J. Sarlls

Senior Vice President - Human Resources, Thomas J. (Tom) Fordonski, age 60

Director Corporate Marketing, Julie Nargang

VP Consumer Sales, Christopher Gardier

VP International Sales, Jose Cabanin, age 56

Vice President - Commercial Ingredient Sales, John Garoni

President COO Assistant Secretary and Director, Jasper B. Sanfilippo Jr., age 46

Group President CFO Secretary and Director, Michael J. Valentine, age 55

Director, Mathias A. Valentine, age 80

Director, Timothy R. (Tim) Donovan, age 57

VP Risk Management and Investor Relations and Director, William R. Pokrajac, age 58

Director, James R. (Jim) Edgar, age 67

Director, Daniel M. Wright, age 75

Director, Ellen Connelly Taaffe

Independent Director, Ellen Taaffe

Auditors: PricewaterhouseCoopersLLP

LOCATIONS

HQ: John B. Sanfilippo & Son Inc.
1703 N. Randall Rd., Elgin IL 60123-7820
Phone: 847-289-1800   Fax: 847-289-1843
Web: www.jbssinc.com

PRODUCTS/OPERATIONS

2013 Sales

	% of total
Cashews & mixed	19
Peanuts	18
Almonds	17
Pecans	16
Walnuts	12
Other	18
Total	**100**

2013 Sales

	$ mil.	% of total
Consumer	436	59
Commercial ingredients	177	24
Contract packaging	85	12
Export	34	5
Total	**734**	**100**

Selected Products

Nuts
  Almonds
  Cashews
  Pecans
  Peanuts
  Walnuts
Good and snack products
  Almond butter
  Candy and confections
  Corn snacks
  Dried fruit
  Natural snacks and trail mixes
  Peanut butter
  Sesame sticks
  Sunflower seeds

COMPETITORS

Arcade Industries	Kraft Foods Group Inc.
Beer Nuts	ML Macadamia Orchards
Betsy Ann Candies	Meridian Nut Growers
Blue Diamond Growers	Mondelez International
Diamond Foods	Paramount Farms
Frito-Lay	Poindexter Nut
Golden Peanut	Ralcorp
Golden West Nuts	Snyder' s-Lance
Kettle Foods	Texoma Peanut
King Nut Companies	The Peanut Roaster

HISTORICAL FINANCIALS

Company Type: Public

Income Statement

FYE: June 27

	REVENUE ($ mil.)	NET INCOME ($ mil.)	NET PROFIT MARGIN	EMPLOYEES
06/13	734.3	21.7	3.0%	1,300
06/12	700.5	17.1	2.4%	1,300
06/11	674.2	2.8	0.4%	1,400
06/10	561.6	14.4	2.6%	1,350
06/09	553.8	6.9	1.2%	1,350
Annual Growth	**7.3%**	**33.2%**	**—**	**(0.9%)**

2013 Year-End Financials

Debt ratio: 19.8%
Return on equity: 10.4%
Cash ($ mil.): 0
Current ratio: 2.06
Long-term debt ($ mil.): 33

No. of shares (mil.): 10
Dividends
  Yield: 5.0%
  Payout: 54.6%
Market value ($ mil.): 217

	STOCK PRICE ($) FY Close	P/E High/Low		PER SHARE ($) Earnings	Dividends	Book Value
06/13	19.86	11	6	1.98	1.00	19.72
06/12	16.87	10	4	1.58	0.00	18.68
06/11	8.46	60	29	0.26	0.00	17.23
06/10	15.15	13	5	1.34	0.00	16.90
06/09	7.37	15	7	0.65	0.00	15.58
Annual Growth	**28.1%**	**—**	**—**	**32.1%**	**—**	**6.1%**

Sapient Corp.

Sapient is no sap when it comes to helping businesses make the jump to the digital age. The company offers consulting software development digital marketing and other services that help clients transform their businesses to compete for a global digital audience. Its customers have included AT&T Mobility Unilever and the US government. Sapient has expertise in providing services for financial and commodity markets though it also targets global blue-chip customers in the consumer travel and automotive industries among others. It has more than 30 offices worldwide; about half of those are in North America.

Geographic Reach

Boston-based Sapient Corp. rings up more than 60% of its sales in the US. The company has offices in Canada Europe India Asia and Australia.

Operations

SapientNitro is the company's largest business segment accounting for two-thirds of its sales. SapientNitro provides branding and marketing services along with Web design and development media planning and buying marketing analytics and traditional advertising.

Its Sapient Global Markets division (representing about 25% of annual sales) primarily provides integrated advisory program management analytics technology development and operations services to clients who operate in the global financial and commodity sectors. The group has development and outsourcing centers in India.

Sapient Government Services (SGS) offers a range of services such as consulting technology development and marketing to federal government clients in the US and other governmental entities in Canada and Europe. The company's federal clients have included The Library of Congress the

US Department of Homeland Security the FBI and the National Institutes of Health. In fall 2013 SGS was awarded a five-year contract by the US General Services Administration valued at $300 million to support the government's ability to deliver strategic sourcing continuous improvement and performance management.

Sales and Marketing

Sapient targets clients in several industry sectors. The Consumer Travel & Automotive industry sector contributed about 43% of sales in 2012 followed by Financial Services which represented about 30%. Government Health & Education contributed about 10% of sales followed by Energy Service and Technology & Communications. The company's five largest clients accounted for about 20% of its sales in 2012.

Financial Performance

Sapient's sales increased 9% in 2012 versus 2011 to nearly $1.2 billion. It was the third consecutive year of increasing sales for the company following a decline in 2009 during the global financial crisis. Sapient credited the increase in service revenue to growing client demand for its SapientNitro and Sapient Global Markets products and the full-year impact of a pair of acquisitions completed in late 2011. Service revenue rose 10% in the US and 9% internationally in 2012 versus 2011. Despite the uptick in sales net income fell 11% in 2012 compared with 2011 to $65.2 million on lower interest and other income and higher provisions for income taxes.

Strategy

Sapient works with partners —including Microsoft Google IBM and Oracle —to support its IT development efforts and identify markets that offer long-term growth prospects. The company also works with other IT services and consulting firms as well as software and equipment providers to complete client projects. It outsources much of its software and technology development to its Indian operations which along with its cost reduction efforts and a benefit on its US tax valuation

With the business climate improving Sapient Corp. acquired five businesses at home and abroad between 2011 and 2013 to enhance SapientNitro's service offering.

Mergers and Acquisitions

In January 2013 the firm acquired an 81% stake in iThink a digital marketing agency based in Sao Paulo Brazil to better serve clients in Latin America. In December 2012 Sapient purchased (m)Phasize LLC a marketing analytics company in Connecticut to bolster its analytics services and marketing mix modeling capabilities. (The business was rebranded as Sapient (m)Phasize.) In November of the same year it bought Second Story Inc. an interactive studio in Portland Oregon. The Second Story purchase was made to strengthen SapientNitro's ability to craft immersive experiences that blend physical and digital environments from Web and movile to in-store and in-venue.

In September 2011 Sapient acquired D&D Holdings Ltd. a London-based advertising agency adding about 200 employees to its SapientNitro segment and extending its marketing campaign production and direct response measurement expertise. Also that year the company acquired Cologne Germany-based CLANMO a specialist in mobile strategy communications design and technological implementation. The deal added 50 people to SapientNitro and extended Sapient's access to the mobile market in Europe.

HISTORY

In 1991 information technology systems salesman Jerry Greenberg and software developer Stuart Moore saw a market for providing businesses with fixed-price software systems by a guaranteed delivery date. Greenberg and Moore charged more than $100000 on their credit cards and used $60000 of their personal savings to form Sapient.

As the company took off Moore managed internal operations such as creating software and Greenberg handled sales and finance. The two worked closely together and helped establish teamwork as Sapient's most prized trait (as co-CEOs they shared an office with only inches separating their desks and they required the same of all senior managers).

Sapient began specializing in distinct areas such as telecommunications manufacturing and energy and it found a third of its early clients in financial services. Specialization enabled the company to reuse software; coupling that with Sapient's proprietary team-based development process resulted in lower costs and shorter development times.

The company went public in 1996 and started expanding through acquisitions buying systems integrators and Internet consultants. It opened offices in London in 1998 and in Italy and Australia the next year. Also in 1999 Sapient increased its staff by more than 40% and expanded its consulting services with the purchase of customer behavior specialist E.Lab.

In 2000 Sapient opened an office in India and acquired Human Code a privately held developer of education e-commerce and entertainment software for about $104 million. The next year looking to cut costs the company closed its Australian office cut its workforce by about 35% and exited the gaming business. It also began to shift more of its project workload to its office in India in order to take advantage of lower operating costs.

Citing decreased demand for its services in the troubled economic climate Sapient posted a loss of nearly $190 million for 2001 followed by a loss of nearly $230 million for 2002. The company continued to reduce its workforce in 2002 cutting about 600 more jobs. The following year Sapient began to see its service revenues pick up and its workforce size stabilized.

In mid-2005 the company acquired Miami-based Business Information Solutions a provider of consulting services for companies using enterprise planning software developed by SAP.

Sapient purchased Planning Group International in 2006. Later that year the company sold its stake in its HWT subsidiary for about $5.4 million.

In 2008 Sapient acquired Derivatives Consulting Group (DCG) adding expertise in derivatives processing to its Global Markets practice. The following year looking to bolster its interactive advertising practice Sapient bought Nitro Group which provides traditional advertising services for $50 million. The deal expanded Sapient's digital marketing presence and client roster.

The company cut about 14% of its workforce that year in response to a dip in revenues.

EXECUTIVES

Co-Chairman of the Board; President; Chief Executive Officer, Alan J. Herrick, age 47, $550,000 total compensation
SVP General Counsel and Secretary, Joseph A. (Joe) LaSala Jr., age 59
VP Corporate Development, Preston B. Bradford, age 57, $225,000 total compensation

Director, Jerry A. Greenberg, age 47, $50,000 total compensation
Director Investor Relations, Dean Ridlon
Senior Vice President General Counsel Secretary, Jane E. Owens, age 59, $290,000 total compensation
Worldwide Head Commerce and Innovation, Christopher R. (Chris) Davey
Director Corporate Communications, David LaBar
SVP Global CFO and Managing Director, Joseph S. (Joe) Tibbetts Jr., age 60, $350,000 total compensation
Executive Vice President ? Managing Director North America & Europe, Alan M. Wexler, age 49, $350,000 total compensation
SVP; Managing Director New York, Hank G. Summy
Senior Vice President Managing Director Asia-Pacific, Christian Oversohl, age 45, $334,711 total compensation
Chief Marketing Officer, William (Bill) Kanarick
Managing Director Southeast Region, Chris Hall
VP Operations, Laurie MacLaren
VP-General Mgmt, Eric Healy
Executive Director and Worldwide Chief Creative Officer SapientNitro, Gaston Legorburu
SVP; Managing Director Global Markets, H. B. (Chip) Register, age 46
Managing Director India, Karandeep Singh
VP People Success, Frank Schettino
Senior Vice President European Managing Director, Nigel Vaz
Managing Director Sapient India and Global Delivery Lead SapientNitro, Rajdeep Endow
Creative Director, Scott Linnen
VP; Managing Director Sapient Government Services, Teresa Bozzelli
Co-Executive Director and Worldwide Chief Creative Officer SapientNitro, Chris Clarke
Head Creative European Union, Malcolm Poynton
VP Global Technology Global Markets, Simon Greig
Vice President - Finance; Chief Accounting Officer; Controller, Karl Stubelis
Senior Vice President & Managing Director Sapient Global Markets, Harry Register
Senior VP Global CFO; Managing Director, Joe Tibbetts
Senior Vice President & Managing Director Sapient Global Markets, Harry (Chip) Register
Co-Chairman of the Board; President; Chief Executive Officer, Alan J. Herrick, age 47
Director, James M. (Jim) Benson, age 66
Director, Ashok Shah, age 61
Director, Vijay Singal, age 58
Director, Robert Rosen, age 66
Auditors: PricewaterhouseCoopersLLP

LOCATIONS

HQ: Sapient Corporation
131 Dartmouth St. 3rd Fl., Boston MA 02116
Phone: 617-621-0200   **Fax:** 617-621-1300
Web: www.sapient.com

2012 Sales

	% of total
US	62
International	38
Total	**100**

PRODUCTS/OPERATIONS

2012 Sales

	$ mil.	% of total
SapientNitro	771	66
Sapient Global Markets	298	26
Sapient Government Services	51	4
Other	40	4
Total	**1,161**	**100**

Selected Services

Audits and process reviews
Business and operational consulting
Creative design
Custom software development
Interactive marketing
Internet consulting
Internet design
Operations outsourcing
Organizational design and change management
Process engineering
Software implementation
Strategy alignment
Supply chain consulting
Systems design and integration
Technology development
Trade and portfolio valuations
Training
User experience research

COMPETITORS

Accenture	HP Enterprise Services
Booz Allen	IBM
Boston Consulting	NTT Data
CIBER	Sapiens
Capgemini	Unisys
Computer Sciences Corp.	

HISTORICAL FINANCIALS

Company Type: Public

Income Statement

FYE: December 31

	REVENUE ($ mil.)	NET INCOME ($ mil.)	NET PROFIT MARGIN	EMPLOYEES
12/12	1,161.5	65.2	5.6%	10,700
12/11	1,062.2	73.6	6.9%	9,950
12/10	863.5	43.8	5.1%	9,015
12/09	666.6	88.1	13.2%	7,052
12/08	687.4	62.4	9.1%	6,360
Annual Growth	**14.0%**	**1.1%**	**—**	**13.9%**

2012 Year-End Financials

Debt ratio: —	No. of shares (mil.): 138
Return on equity: 13.0%	Dividends
Cash ($ mil.): 234	Yield: —
Current ratio: 2.87	Payout: —
Long-term debt ($ mil.): —	Market value ($ mil.): 1,457

	STOCK PRICE ($)	P/E		PER SHARE ($)		
	FY Close	High/Low	Earnings	Dividends	Book Value
12/12	10.56	29 20	0.46	0.00	3.77
12/11	12.60	30 18	0.52	0.35	3.42
12/10	12.10	40 23	0.32	0.35	3.23
12/09	8.27	13 5	0.66	0.00	3.21
12/08	4.44	19 7	0.48	0.00	2.39
Annual Growth	**24.2%**	**— —**	**(1.1%)**	**—**	**12.1%**

Schulman (A.), Inc.

A. Schulman might consider itself the master of all masterbatches. The company is a global leader in masterbatches color and additive concentrates that are combined with polymer resins by its customers to provide color to plastic products or enhance their performance in some way. A. Schulman also produces engineered plastics (compounded products used in making durable goods appliances and toys) and specialty powders (compounded resin powders used in rotationally molded products ranging from kayaks to gas tanks). It also serves as a distributor for polymer producers worldwide. Its high-performance plastic compounds and resins are used in packaging consumer products and automotive and industrial products.

The company now organizes its core businesses —masterbatch engineered plastics specialty powders and distribution services —into four main region-based segments: Europe Middle East and Africa (EMEA) the Americas and Asia/Pacific (APAC).

Its masterbatches are used as the key ingredient in a customer's product formula. A. Schulman's recent acquisitions expanded the company's masterbatch offerings as well as its geographic presence. Its additive compounds are used to provide a range of colors or to enhance performance properties including antibacterial heat-sensitive fluorescent and processing attributes.

A. Schulman's engineered plastics also impart certain performance characteristics by combining high-performance polymer resins with various modifiers reinforcements additives or pigments to form a compound to meet its customer's specifications. A. Schulman has been formulating compounds since the early 1950s to meet the needs of the plastics industry. Its blends include polyolefins nylons polyesters elastomers and PVC (polyvinyl chloride).

Specialty powders are used in applications such as powder coating cosmetics and the manufacture of additives. The rotational molding process is used to make plastic products including gas and water tanks and playground slides. The company provides other services such as grinding or size reduction of specialty powders for its customers.

A. Schulman also serves as a distributor of other global polymer producers to assist in markets which are not easily accessible to them or do not fit into their core supply chain or customer segment.

The company operates 36 manufacturing facilities: 21 in the EMEA and APAC regions and 15 in the Americas.

A. Schulman reported net sales of about $2.2 billion in fiscal 2011 a 38% hike over the previous year. The rise in sales resulted primarily from its integration of ICO acquired in 2010. Other drivers included increases in average selling prices volume and demand. Net sales increased in each of the company's reportable segments. Net income was $41 million down about 6% from the fiscal 2010 earnings of $44 million due to special charges related to a dispute settlement and the methodology used to calculate inventory reserves.

Acquisitions are a key part of the company's strategy for growth as it continually seeks to expand its global footprint to maximize opportunities. It targets strategic acquisitions that will speed its entry into underserved markets. A. Schulman also looks to new product development to drive growth and is focusing on higher margin applications. In its engineered plastics business it seeks to reduce its North American auto capacity and focus on its most profitable lines of business. It also wants to continue development of sustainable "green" products. To counteract the global economic slump the company has been cutting back on capacity and using the assets of its global operations effectively.

The company completed its acquisition of Brazilian plastics maker Mash Compostos Plasticos in 2011. Mash Compostos is a S?o Paulo-based producer of additives and engineered plastics compounds. That year it extended its presence in South America by agreeing to acquire a 51% interest in

a joint venture with Argentina-based Surplast. Surplast makes rotational molding products.

To broaden its stance as a global manfacturer of engineered plastics in niche markets the company agreed in 2012 to form a joint venture with Saudi Arabia-based National Petrochemical Industrial Company a subsidiary of Alujain Corp. The 50-50 joint venture is expected to be called NAT-PET-Schulman Engineering Plastic Compounds and will produce and market polypropylene compounds. The venture expects to begin production by the end of 2014.

HISTORY

Alex Schulman founded A. Schulman in 1928 as a rubber brokerage. In 1937 he hired William Zekan as an office boy after meeting the 18-year-old caddie on a golf course. With rubber in short supply during WWII A. Schulman began using scrap plastic. Zekan was appointed head of the firm's New York sales office in 1947 and became #2 in the company in 1953.

A. Schulman abandoned the scrap market in the 1950s to focus on plastic compounds. Schulman died in 1962 and Zekan headed the company taking it public in 1972. A. Schulman set up a joint venture in 1988 with Mitsubishi to supply plastic compounds to Honda Nissan and Toyota.

Zekan died in 1991 and was replaced by company veteran Terry Haines. He expanded A. Schulman through acquisitions that included Diffusion Plastique from Atochem (subsidiary of Elf Aquitaine now called TOTAL) in 1991 and Exxon's ComAlloy International in 1994. The next year the company bought a polymer unit from J. M. Huber and polypropylene interests from Eastman Chemical.

A. Schulman opened its first plant in Asia in 1997. The next year it cut production to compensate for an industry slowdown. The company also bought an Italy-based distributor and agreed to supply all of the color concentrate for Procter & Gamble's molded white containers. In 1999 A. Schulman spent $35 million to renovate manufacturing facilities. It joined DuPont that year to make bumper fascias and other moldings for cars such as the Dodge Neon.

As pricing pressures continued in 2000 A. Schulman moved to cut its costs by closing a number of sales offices and its plant in Akron Ohio. The company's 2001 sales were hurt by the weakening economy especially in the US where capacity utilization was down by 5%. Although A. Schulman's sales remained flat in 2002 the company managed to boost profits mostly through a workforce reduction and the closing of more costly facilities.

Haines and other members of management came under fire with investors' criticism that began in 2007 and Haines stepped down early in 2008. He was replaced by director Joseph Gingo a former Goodyear executive. Barington Capital Group had demanded the right to name a director in 2007. Its success spurred another investor group Ramius Capital to offer up its own set of directors for A. Schulman's early-2008 elections. Ramius like Barington was eager to get Schulman to consider a sale or merger of the company or at the very least a change in company strategy that had led to continually disappointing results. Ultimately Ramius won the right to nominate candidates for the board.

Encouraged by the investors and their representative board members the company idled one manufacturing facility and sold another in 2008; it also brought in UBS to explore possibilities of selling

part or all of the company. (An offer from an unidentified buyer was turned down in mid-2008.)

After failing to find a manufacturing partner for its Invision line of plastic sheet products it discontinued the line and shut down the operation in 2009. The next year it moved several of its operations from its Crumlin South Wales operation to larger facilities and eliminated 30 jobs in a move to improve efficiency.

In 2010 the company acquired McCann Color an Ohio-based producer of color concentrates. The deal for about $10 million in cash bolstered A. Schulman's existing master batch manufacturing and product development facilities in Akron Ohio and San Luis Potosi Mexico.

That year the company also acquired Houston-based ICO in a deal that valued the plastics maker at $190 million. The deal expanded A. Schulman's global presence and its masterbatch and molding businesses.

EXECUTIVES

VP Global Supply Chain and Chief Procurement Officer, Gary A. Miller, age 66
Chairman President and CEO, Joseph M. (Joe) Gingo, age 68, $768,600 total compensation
VP and CFO, Joseph J. (Joe) Levanduski, age 50
Director Corporate Communications and Investor Relations, Jennifer K. Beeman
General Manager ICO Australasia, Derek R. Bristow, age 53
General Manager and COO Americas, Gustavo Perez
EVP and COO, Bernard Rzepka, age 53, $452,857 total compensation
VP Chief Legal Officer and Secretary, David C. Minc, age 63
VP Global Human Resources, Kim L. Whiteman, age 55
Director Internal Audit, Stacy R. Walter
VP and CIO, John B. Broerman
Manager Corporate Marketing and Business Development, Sanja Valentic
VP and CIO, Donald B. (Mickey) McMillan
VP and Chief Marketing Officer, Patricia M. Mishic
Director, Howard R. Curd, age 73
Director, Michael A. McManus Jr., age 69
Director, John B. Yasinsky, age 72
Director, Irvin D. (Irv) Reid, age 71
Director, David G. Birney, age 69
Director, James A. Mitarotonda, age 58
Director, Ernest J. Novak Jr., age 67
Director, Lee D. Meyer, age 63
Auditors: PricewaterhouseCoopersLLP

LOCATIONS

HQ: Schulman (A.), Inc.
3637 Ridgewood Road, Fairlawn, OH 44333
Phone: 330 666-3751   **Fax:** 330 668-7204
Web: www.aschulman.com

2011 Sales

	$ mil.	% of total
Germany	617	28
US	337	15
Total	**2,193**	**100**

PRODUCTS/OPERATIONS

2011 Sales by Segment

	$ mil.	% of total
Europe Middle East & Africa (EMEA)	1,534	70
Asia/Pacific (APAC)	142	6
Total	**2,193**	**100**

2011 Sales by Product

Plastics Products		
Masterbatch	880	40
Specialty Powders	372	17
Distribution Services	393	18
Total	**2,193**	**100**

Selected Brands

Masterbatch Products
Polybatch (additive compounds)
Polyblak (carbon black concentrates)
Polywhite (white concentrates)
Polypearl (additive compounds)
Polystat (antistatic Concentrates)
Papermatch (masterbatch for synthetic paper)
Engineered Plastics
Clarix (thermoplastic iconomer resins)
Invision (thermoplastic elastomers and vulcanizates)
Schuladur (PBT compounds)
Schulamid (nylon compounds)
Schulablend M/MK (nylon/ABS alloys)
Polyflam (flame-retandant thermoplastics)
Polyfort (polypropylene polyethylene EVA compounds)
Polyvin (flexible thermoplastic PVC compounds)
Specialty Powders
Ecorene (renewably sourced thermoplastic powders)
ICO-Fine (ultra-fine thermoplastic powders)
Icorene (compound powders for custom colors)
Polyaxis (compounds for rotational molding)
Schulink (cross-linkable resin used in rotational molding)
Superlinear (material offers high heat-distortion temperatures)

COMPETITORS

Albemarle	DuPont
Ampacet	Ferro
Axiall	Momentive
BASF SE	PolyOne
Clariant	RTP Company
Dow Chemical	Spartech

HISTORICAL FINANCIALS

Company Type: Public

Income Statement

FYE: August 31

	REVENUE ($ mil.)	NET INCOME ($ mil.)	NET PROFIT MARGIN	EMPLOYEES
08/13	2,133.4	26.1	1.2%	3,200
08/12	2,106.7	50.8	2.4%	3,100
08/11	2,192.9	41.0	1.9%	3,000
08/10	1,590.4	43.9	2.8%	2,900
08/09	1,279.2	(2.7)	—	2,000
Annual Growth	**13.6%**			**12.5%**

2013 Year-End Financials

Debt ratio: 17.4%
Return on equity: 5.1%
Cash ($ mil.): 134
Current ratio: 2.01
Long-term debt ($ mil.): 207
No. of shares (mil.): 29
Dividends
  Yield: 0.0%
  Payout: 100.0%
Market value ($ mil.): 786

	STOCK PRICE ($) FY Close	P/E High/Low	PER SHARE ($) Earnings	Dividends	Book Value
08/13	26.96	37 26	0.78	0.78	17.40
08/12	24.29	16 10	1.72	0.72	17.11
08/11	18.24	20 13	1.32	0.62	17.92
08/10	18.17	17 10	1.57	0.60	15.50
08/09	20.09	— —	(0.11)	0.60	14.03
Annual Growth	**7.6%**	— —	—	**6.8%**	**5.5%**

SciClone Pharmaceuticals, Inc.

SciClone is hoping that as China grows so will the sales for its drugs. The drug firm's flagship product Zadaxin is approved for use in some 30 countries including China its primary market. Zadaxin is approved for use in treating hepatitis B as a vaccine adjuvant (to boost a vaccine's effectiveness) and to treat certain cancers. The company also partners with other drug makers to market their drugs in China. Such partnerships include Sanofi Aventis' anti-seizure drug Depakine and Stilnox (marketed as Ambien in the US). SciClone also maintains a pipeline of products that it is shepherding through the approval process in China.

SciClone's own sales force markets the drug to doctors and hospitals in China; distributors handle sales and marketing of the drug in other countries. SciClone relies upon third parties in Europe and the US to manufacture Zadaxin. However the drug has yet to receive the regulatory green light in the world's two largest drug markets —the US and the European Union (EU). SciClone is working with development partner Sigma-Tau to gain marketing approval in the US and EU. In the meantime the company figures that China will be the second largest market in the world soon enough so it is focusing more of its efforts on development there.

SciClone's revenues have reflected the increase in sales of Zadaxin. In 2011 those sales rose 33% to $113 million. Following its 2011 acquisition of NovaMed the company created a new segment promotion services which includes the distribution of products for other drug makers. That new segment added $20.6 million to the company's coffers in 2011 bringing its total revenues to $133.6 million. Its net income has kept up with revenue growth and rose to $28 million in 2011 up from $21 million in 2010.

SciClone's acquisition of China-based NovaMed Pharmaceuticals also added a handful of products in development including cancer neurology and pain medicines and broadened SciClone's existing sales force in the country. While SciClone's Zadaxin commands higher prices due to its reputation and branding lower-priced generics from local manufacturers are a constant threat to its market share.

As a research and development company SciClone has already gone through a couple of candidates that turned out to be duds. While such disappointments are expensive they are the nature of drug discovery and development.

EXECUTIVES

President and Managing Director SciClone Pharmaceuticals International, Hans P. Schmid, age 61, $318,000 total compensation
SVP Scientific Affairs and Chief Scientific Officer, Cynthia W. Tuthill
Chairman, Jon S. Saxe
Chief Financial Officer; Senior Vice President - Finance, Gary S. Titus, age 53, $17,925 total compensation
President and CEO, Friedhelm Blobel, $442,000 total compensation
SVP Finance and CFO, Wilson W. Cheung
VP Business Development, Jeffery Lange

Vice President Product Development and Manufacturing, Robert King
Chief Operating Officer of China Operations, Jackie Guan
Chief Executive Officer - China Operations; Director, Mark Lotter
Chief Financial Officer of China and VP of Fin, Lan Xie
Vice President - Compliance and Internal Audit, Min Yin
Vice President Controller, Raymond A. Low
CEO China, Hong Zhao
Director, Richard J. (Rick) Hawkins, age 64
Director, Dean S. Woodman, age 83
President; Chief Executive Officer; Acting Chief Financial Officer; Director, Friedhelm Blobel, age 64
Director, Ira D. Lawrence, age 59
Director, Gregg A. Lapointe, age 54
Director, Roberto Camerini, age 48
Director, Trevor M. Jones, age 70
Independent Director, Peter Barrett
Auditors: Ernst&YoungLLP

LOCATIONS

HQ: SciClone Pharmaceuticals Inc.
  950 Tower Lane Ste. 900, Foster City CA 94404-2125
Phone: 650-358-3456   **Fax:** 650-358-3469
Web: www.sciclone.com

2011 Revenues

	$ mil.	% of total
China	130	97
Rest of world	3	3
Total	**133**	**100**

PRODUCTS/OPERATIONS

2011 Revenues

	$ mil.	% of total
Product sales	113	85
Promotion sales	20	15
Total	**133**	**100**

Selected Acquisitions

NovaMed Pharmaceuticals (2011 $62 million)

COMPETITORS

Amgen	Hemispherx BioPharma
Biostar Pharmaceuticals	Idenix Pharmaceuticals
	Immtech
Bristol-Myers Squibb	Intarcia Therapeutics
Enzon	Merck
Gilead Sciences	Roche Holding
GlaxoSmithKline	Sanofi

HISTORICAL FINANCIALS

Company Type: Public

Income Statement

FYE: December 31

	REVENUE ($ mil.)	NET INCOME ($ mil.)	NET PROFIT MARGIN	EMPLOYEES
12/12	156.2	9.6	6.2%	870
12/11	133.6	28.4	21.3%	875
12/10	85.1	21.0	24.8%	261
12/09	72.4	11.9	16.5%	223
12/08	54.1	(8.3)	—	227
Annual Growth	**30.4%**	—	—	**39.9%**

2012 Year-End Financials

Debt ratio: 0.8%
Return on equity: 6.5%
Cash ($ mil.): 84
Current ratio: 4.46
Long-term debt ($ mil.): —
No. of shares (mil.): 54
Dividends
  Yield: —
  Payout: —
Market value ($ mil.): 235

	STOCK PRICE ($) FY Close	P/E High/Low		PER SHARE ($) Earnings	Dividends	Book Value
12/12	4.31	44	25	0.16	0.00	2.63
12/11	4.29	13	7	0.50	0.00	2.60
12/10	4.18	10	5	0.43	0.00	1.71
12/09	2.33	19	3	0.25	0.00	1.22
12/08	0.74	—	—	(0.18)	0.00	0.88
Annual Growth 55.3%				—		— 31.2%

SearchCore Inc

EXECUTIVES

Ceo, Mr Jim Pakulis

LOCATIONS

HQ: SearchCore Inc
26497 Rancho Parkway South, Lake Forest, CA 92630
Phone: 855 266-4663
Web: www.searchcore.com

PRODUCTS/OPERATIONS

HISTORICAL FINANCIALS

Company Type: Public

Income Statement
FYE: December 31

	REVENUE ($ mil.)	NET INCOME ($ mil.)	NET PROFIT MARGIN	EMPLOYEES
12/12	16.4	15.2	92.9%	20
12/11	11.9	(3.2)	—	0
12/08	0.6	(1.2)	—	0
12/07	0.5	(1.4)	—	0
12/06	0.2	(1.0)	—	0
Annual Growth 186.2%		—	—	—

2012 Year-End Financials

Debt ratio: —
Return on equity: ***,***.*%
Cash ($ mil.): 0
Current ratio: 0.72
Long-term debt ($ mil.): —

No. of shares (mil.): 37
Dividends
  Yield: —
  Payout: —
Market value ($ mil.): 15

	STOCK PRICE ($) FY Close	P/E High/Low		PER SHARE ($) Earnings	Dividends	Book Value
12/12	0.40	9	2	0.18	0.00	0.04
12/11	1.52	—	—	(0.04)	0.00	(0.23)
12/08	0.45	—	—	(0.17)	0.00	(0.17)
12/07	0.03	—	—	(0.60)	0.00	(1.67)
12/06	0.32	—	—	(0.40)	0.00	(1.00)
Annual Growth 5.7%		—	—	—	—	—

Select Comfort Corp.

Select Comfort has got your number. The firm's line of Sleep Number beds which can carry hefty price tags use air-chamber technology to allow sleepers to adjust the firmness on each side of the mattress providing better sleep quality and addressing sleep-related problems such as lower back pain. Select Comfort also offers foundations frames pillows and a sofa bed. A leading bedding retailer in the US Select Comfort operates more than 425 company-owned stores. The air-bed maker also sells through a company-operated call center its own website and on the QVC shopping channel. Select Comfort was founded in 1987 has grown to become one of the nation's leading bed makers and retailers.

Geographic Reach

Minneapolis-based Select Comfort operates company-owned retail stores in 45 US states. Its two largest markets are California and Texas which combined account for 20% of its store base. The mattress giant distributes its products in the US and Canada and in Alaska Hawaii and Australia through retail partners.

Operations

The firm operates two manufacturing plants (South Carolina and Utah) which supply beds on a just-in-time basis to its retail stores.

Sales and Marketing

Select Comfort spent about $398 million on sales and marketing efforts in 2012 compared with $317.5 million in 2011 and about $270 million in 2010. The year-over-year increase was primarily due to a 39% increase in media spending. The company advertises on television radio and in print and is increasing its use of digital advertising.

Financial Performance

After a rough patch during the deep recession and housing crisis which decreased the demand for beds (especially expensive ones) Select Comfort's sales and profits have rebounded sharply posting record highs in 2012. Indeed the company's sales jumped 26% in 2012 compared with 2011 to $935 million after posting a 22% increase in the previous annual comparison. Driving sales was the addition of about 30 new retail stores as well as increasing direct online and wholesale sales. Net income increased 29% over the same period to $78.1 million.

Strategy

While Select Comfort began as a direct marketer of its unique air-filled mattresses over the years it has evolved into a multichannel retailer with company-owned stores in about 45 states. Retail store sales have grown to account for nearly 90% of Select Comfort's total sales.

With its mattresses starting at about $700 and approaching $4000 for its premium product it's not surprising the recession and housing crisis took the air out of the air-bed maker's sales. The steep sales decline put a halt to Select Comfort's aggressive expansion plans. While the company had hoped to grow to more than 600 company-owned stores throughout the US in coming years it is instead looking to end 2013 with between 435 and 445 company-owned locations having shuttered about 100 stores since 2007.

After entering the Canadian market in 2005 Select Comfort in 2007 partnered with two Australian companies to make and distribute Sleep Number beds and accessories in Australia and New Zealand. Additionally the company's air mattresses are found in luxury motor homes and in nearly all of Radisson's hotel rooms in the US Canada and the Caribbean.

Mergers and Acquisitions

In January 2013 Select Comfort acquired Greenville South Carolina-based Comfortaire Corp. a maker of adjustable air-supported sleep systems for $15.5 million.

EXECUTIVES

Senior Vice President; Chief Administrative Officer; General Counsel; Secretary, Mark A. Kimball, age 54, $280,288 total compensation
Chairman, Jean-Michel Valette, age 52
Chief Financial Officer; Executive Vice President, Wendy L. Schoppert, age 46, $262,596 total compensation
EVP and Chief Services and Fulfillment Officer, Kathryn V. Roedel, age 52, $303,077 total compensation
President; Chief Executive Officer; Director, Shelly R. Ibach, age 53
SVP and Chief Human Capital Officer, Karen R. Richard
Independent Director, Michael A. (Mike) Peel, age 64
Independent Director, Stephen L. Gulis Jr., age 56
Director, David T. Kollat, age 74
Director, Brenda J. Lauderback, age 64
Director, Ervin R. Shames, age 72
Director, Kathy Nedorostek
President CEO and Director, Shelly R. Ibach, age 52
Independent Director, Michael Harrison
Auditors: Deloitte&ToucheLLP

LOCATIONS

HQ: Select Comfort Corporation
9800 59th Ave. North, Minneapolis MN 55442
Phone: 763-551-7000   **Fax:** 763-694-3300
Web: www.sleepnumber.com

2012 Company-Owned Stores

	No.
Alabama	4
Arizona	8
Arkansas	3
California	50
Colorado	11
Connecticut	6
Delaware	2
Florida	25
Georgia	13
Idaho	2
Illinois	19
Indiana	12
Iowa	6
Kansas	3
Kentucky	5
Louisiana	6
Maine	2
Maryland	11
Massachusetts	4
Michigan	12
Minnesota	13
Mississippi	3
Missouri	12
Montana	2
Nebraska	4
Nevada	4
New	5
New	12
New	3
New	9
North	13
North	2
Ohio	17
Oklahoma	4
Oregon	4
Pennsylvania	17
South	4
South	1
Tennessee	8
Texas	33
Utah	3
Vermont	1
Virginia	11
Washington	10
Wisconsin	11
Total	**410**

PRODUCTS/OPERATIONS

2012 Sales

	% of total
Retail	88
Direct & Wholesale	9
Wholesale	3
Total	**100**

Selected Products

Bed frames
Foundations
Mattress pads
Mattresses
Pillows
Pillowtops
Sleep Number SofaBed

COMPETITORS

1800Mattress.com	Simmons
Mattress Firm	Spring Air
Sealy	Tempur Sealy
Serta	

HISTORICAL FINANCIALS

Company Type: Public

Income Statement

FYE: December 29

	REVENUE ($ mil.)	NET INCOME ($ mil.)	NET PROFIT MARGIN	EMPLOYEES
12/12	934.9	78.0	8.4%	2,791
12/11*	743.2	60.4	8.1%	2,328
01/11	605.6	31.5	5.2%	2,165
01/10	544.2	35.5	6.5%	2,172
01/09	608.5	(70.1)	—	2,571
Annual Growth	**11.3%**	**—**	**—**	**2.1%**

*Fiscal year change

2012 Year-End Financials

Debt ratio: —
Return on equity: 48.4%
Cash ($ mil.): 87
Current ratio: 1.58
Long-term debt ($ mil.): —

No. of shares (mil.): 55
Dividends
  Yield: —
  Payout: —
Market value ($ mil.): 1,370

	STOCK PRICE ($) FY Close	P/E High/Low		PER SHARE ($) Earnings	Dividends	Book Value
12/12	24.51	25	14	1.37	0.00	3.46
12/11*	21.69	20	8	1.07	0.00	2.29
01/11	9.13	20	9	0.57	0.00	1.05
01/10	6.52	9	0	0.77	0.00	0.41
01/09	0.26	—	—	(1.59)	0.00	(0.93)
Annual Growth	**212.2%**	**—**	**—**	**—**	**—**	**—**

*Fiscal year change

Select Income Real Estate Investment Trust

It's common knowledge that you make bread out of dough; it's CommonWealth knowledge that real estate can bring in the dough. The real estate investment trust invests in office and industrial properties primarily in the US mainly located in suburbs of major metropolitan markets. Its portfolio includes about 265 properties about two-thirds of which are offices comprising some 51 million sq. ft. of leasable space. CommonWealth wasone of the largest industrial private land owners in Oahu until it spun off those assets in 2012; other markets include Boston Philadelphia Southern California the District of Columbia and Australia. GlaxoSmithKline and Office Depot are among the REIT's largest tenants.

Although the REIT is focused on office and industrial property investment especially assets located within central business districts it still has its fingers in a variety of property types. In 2010 CommonWealth transferred 15 government-leased properties to its 21%-owned Government Properties Income Trust. In a separate transaction the REIT sold 27 health care properties to affiliate Senior Housing Properties Trust (SHPT). Both buyers were formerly wholly owned subsidiaries of CommonWealth. In 2011 CommonWealth sold another 13 medical properties to SHPT further shedding noncore properties. The REIT also spun off most of its single-tenant holdings in Hawaii to Select Income REIT which went public in 2012. CommonWealth still holds a stake in Select Income REIT. In the meantime the company has been boosting its commercial property holdings buying more than 20 properties since early 2011.

In a move that took the REIT international CommonWealth bought Australian property trust MacarthurCook Industrial Property Fund in 2010. The deal added about 10 industrial properties (containing some 1.8 million sq. ft.) throughout the country and Australia is now the REIT's sixth-largest individual market. The Macarthur properties continue to be managed by MacarthurCook's former parent AIMS Financial Group.

CommonWealth's day-to-day activities are conducted by external manager Reit Management & Research (RMR) which is owned by the REIT's managing trustees Barry and Adam Portnoy.

In 2011 rental income rose in all of the REIT's markets other than metropolitan Washington DC where many of the formerly owned government-occupied properties were located. Although the rental income growth led to a 15% increase in revenues (up to $912 million) the REIT reported a 19% decline in profits that year. Like other commercial property owners CommonWealth has had to contend with the economic downturn which has caused occupancy rates to decline and net income to follow suit.

EXECUTIVES

Senior Vice President Chief Operating Officer, David M. Lepore, age 52, $51,640 total compensation
Treasurer Chief Financial Officer, John C. Popeo, age 53, $51,640 total compensation
Secretary, Jennifer B. Clark, age 52, $51,640 total compensation
Founder of CWH and has served as one of our Managing Trustees, Barry M. Portnoy, age 68
President, Adam D. Portnoy, age 43, $51,640 total compensation
VP Investor Relaions, Timothy A. (Tim) Bonang
President Pacific Region, Jan S. Yokota
Independent Trustee, Joseph Morea
Vice President Investor Relations, Tim Bonang
Managing Trustee, Barry M. Portnoy, age 66
President and Managing Trustee, Adam D. Portnoy, age 42
Senior Vice President Chief Operating Officer, David M. Lepore, age 52, $51,640 total compensation

Treasurer Chief Financial Officer, John C. Popeo, age 53, $51,640 total compensation
Secretary, Jennifer B. Clark, age 52, $51,640 total compensation
Founder of CWH and has served as one of our Managing Trustees, Barry M. Portnoy, age 68
President, Adam D. Portnoy, age 43, $51,640 total compensation
VP Investor Relaions, Timothy A. (Tim) Bonang
President Pacific Region, Jan S. Yokota
Independent Trustee, Joseph Morea
Vice President Investor Relations, Tim Bonang
Managing Trustee, Barry M. Portnoy, age 66
President and Managing Trustee, Adam D. Portnoy, age 42
Auditors: Deloitte&ToucheLLP

LOCATIONS

HQ: CommonWealth REIT
  400 Centre St., Newton MA 02458-2076
Phone: 617-332-3990   **Fax:** 617-332-2261
Web: www.cwhreit.com

2011 Sales

	$ mil.	% of total
Metro Philadelphia	119	13
Oahu	73	8
Metro Chicago	66	7
Metro Denver	44	5
Metro Washington DC	41	5
Australia	33	4
Other	532	58
Total	**911**	**100**

PRODUCTS/OPERATIONS

2011 Sales

	$ mil.	% of total
Central Business District offices	390	43
Suburban offices	358	39
Industrial & other	162	18
Total	**911**	**100**

COMPETITORS

Boston Properties	Liberty Property Trust
Boston Properties	Liberty Property Trust
Brandywine Realty	MPG Office Trust
Brandywine Realty	MPG Office Trust
Corporate Office Properties Trust	Mack-Cali
Corporate Office Properties Trust	Mack-Cali
Crescent Real Estate	Mission West Properties
Crescent Real Estate	Mission West Properties
Equity Office	Vornado Realty
Equity Office	Vornado Realty

HISTORICAL FINANCIALS

Company Type: Public

Income Statement

FYE: December 31

	REVENUE ($ mil.)	NET INCOME ($ mil.)	NET PROFIT MARGIN	EMPLOYEES
12/12	122.7	65.8	53.6%	0
12/11	108.6	68.9	63.5%	0
12/11	0.0	0.0	—	0
12/10	95.9	60.5	63.1%	0
Annual Growth	**8.6%**	**2.8%**	**—**	**—**

2012 Year-End Financials

Debt ratio: 33.0%
Return on equity: 7.2%
Cash ($ mil.): 20
Current ratio: —
Long-term debt ($ mil.): 472

No. of shares (mil.): 39
Dividends
  Yield: 3.6%
  Payout: 37.4%
Market value ($ mil.): 973

SemGroup Corp

Midstream energy player SemGroup moves oil and gas from the wellhead to the marketplace. Through its Crude unit it owns 58% of Rose Rock Midstream which has a 5 million-barrel storage terminal in Cushing Oklahoma and operates 640 miles of crude oil pipeline in Oklahoma and Kansas. Rose Rock Midstream owns 17% of the 530-mile White Cliffs Pipeline which links Midcontinent oil producers to the Cushing terminal. SemGas operates 1600 miles of natural gas and NGL transportation gathering and distribution pipelines. SemMexico makes asphalt products. The company also operates SemCAMS (Canadian natural gas) and SemLogistics (UK oil terminal).

Geographic Reach

The company has operations in Oklahoma City Oklahoma (US); Calgary Alberta (Canada); Puebla (Mexico); and Milford Haven (Wales).

Operations

the company's assets include1600 miles of natural gas and NGL transportation gathering and distribution pipelines in Kansas Oklahoma and Texas and Alberta Canada; 8.7 million barrels of storage capacity in the U.K.; 12 liquid asphalt cement terminals and two emulsion distribution terminals in Mexico; a controlling stake in four natural gas processing plants located in Alberta Canada with a combined capacity of 694 million cubic feet per day; three US-based natural gas processing plants (98 million cubic feet per day capacity).

Financial Performance

Revenues decreased by 16% primarily due to lower revenues from the SemLogistics segment as a result of a lower volume of storage leased and a drop in storage rates as well as a decline in SemStream results (it sold its last residential propane supply business in September 2012).

Net income increased by a whopping 830% in 2012 mainly due to the gain on disposal or impairment of long-lived assets (including the sale of a SemStream unit.

Strategy

In 2012 the company joined Gavilon Midstream Energy a subsidiary of The Gavilon Group and an affiliate of Chesapeake Energy Corporation to form a joint venture to build a 210-mile pipeline in Oklahoma to deliver crude oil to a 1 million barrel storage facility in Cushing Oklahoma. The pipeline and storage facility will serve the growing drilling industry in western Oklahoma including the Mississippi Lime play.

However despite expansion plans the company has been struggling to improve its financial position for several years. In 2013 it sold a 33% stake in SemCrude Pipeline L.L.C to Rose Rock Midstream for $274 million.

To raise further cash in 2011 the company sold most of its SemStream unit (which delivers natural gas liquids propane and feedstock supplies to customers in more than 40 US states) to NGL Energy Partners for about $282 million. It retained SemStream's residential Arizona propane business but sold that unit in 2012.

In 2011 Plains All-American Pipeline made an unsolicited $1.2 bid to acquire SemGroup which the SemGroup board rejected as substantially undervaluing the company. (The unsolicited bidder officially withdrew in 2012.)

Company Background

Facing a liquidity crisis (overextended by 64 acquisitions for $1.1 billion between 2000 and 2008) in 2008 SemGroup filed for bankruptcy protection from which it emerged in November 2009. Since then the company has been selling assets to pay down debt.

To raise cash as part of its reorganization in 2009 the company sold noncore assets. It sold its SemFuel refined petroleum terminals to Noble Americas (a subsidiary of a Chinese commodities conglomerate) for $65 million. It also sold its stake in SemGroup Energy Partners (now Blueknight Energy Partners) which provides gathering transporting terminalling and storage of crude oil in Oklahoma Kansas and Texas to Netherlands-based natural resources group Vitol for $614 million. In addition the company exited its US asphalt business (SemMaterials). It also sold SemCrude Canada (its Canadian crude oil operations) in 2010.

In 2010 the company realigned its SemGas and SemStream business under a common leadership team in a move to improve their operational efficiency.

EXECUTIVES

Chairman, John F. Chlebowski, age 67
VP Chief Accounting Officer and Controller, Paul F. Largess, age 62
VP and President SemCrude, Peter L. Schwiering, age 68
President of SemStream?, Kevin Clement
Vice President, Wayne Ziegler
VP Corporate Planning and Strategic Initiatives; Interim Business Unit SemCAMS, Timothy R. (Tim) O'Sullivan
VP Customer Services and Business Development SemCAMS, Dayle Chadbourne
President CEO and Director, Norman J. (Norm) Szydlowski, age 62
Managing Director SemLogistics, Nigel R. Passmore
SVP and CFO, Robert N. (Bob) Fitzgerald, age 54
Controller SemGas, Alice Helmke
General Counsel and Secretary, Candice L. Cheeseman, age 57
Vice President General Manager, David Williams
Vice President - Corporate Planning and Strategic Initiatives, Timothy OSullivan
Vice President Operations, David Gosse
Vice President Business Development, Nancy Anderson
Director, Thomas R. (Tom) McDaniel, age 63
Director, Sarah M. Barpoulis, age 48
Director, Karl F. Kurz, age 51
President CEO and Director, Norman J. (Norm) Szydlowski, age 62
Director, Ronald A. Ballschmiede, age 58
Independent Director, James Lytal
Auditors: BDOUSALLP

LOCATIONS

HQ: SemGroup Corporation
2 Warren Place 6120 S. Yale Ave. Ste. 700, Tulsa OK 74136-4216
Phone: 918-388-8100   **Fax:** 918-524-8290
Web: www.semgroupcorp.com

PRODUCTS/OPERATIONS

2012 Sales

	$ mil.	% of total
Crude	51	
SemCAMS	18	
SemGas	9	
Corporate & other	-	

COMPETITORS

Duke Energy	ONEOK
Dynegy	ProLiance Energy
Enbridge	Spectra Energy
Enogex	Williams Companies
Enterprise Products	

HISTORICAL FINANCIALS

Company Type: Public

Income Statement

FYE: December 31

	REVENUE ($ mil.)	NET INCOME ($ mil.)	NET PROFIT MARGIN	EMPLOYEES
12/12	1,237.5	22.1	1.8%	690
12/11	1,479.5	2.3	0.2%	710
12/10	1,630.3	(132.3)	—	800
12/09*	157.3	(37.8)	—	0
11/09	901.2	3,394.5	376.7%	0
Annual Growth	8.2%	(71.6%)	—	—

*Fiscal year change

2012 Year-End Financials

Debt ratio: 11.7%
Return on equity: 2.5%
Cash ($ mil.): 80
Current ratio: 1.39
Long-term debt ($ mil.): 206

No. of shares (mil.): 42
Dividends
 Yield: —
 Payout: —
Market value ($ mil.): 1,641

	STOCK PRICE ($) FY Close	P/E High/Low	PER SHARE ($) Earnings	Dividends	Book Value
12/12	39.08	75 50	0.52	0.00	21.25
12/11	26.06	562300	(0.60)	0.00	20.35
12/10	27.17	— —	(3.20)	0.00	20.61
Annual Growth	19.9%	— —	—	—	1.5%

Semtech Corp.

If Semtech's products seem highly technical it's because they are. Not to be confused with semiconductor research consortium SEMATECH Semtech makes analog and mixed-signal semiconductors used by manufacturers of computer communications consumer and industrial electronics. The company's chips are used for power management circuit protection transmission and other functions in a variety of devices including cellular phones and base stations notebook and desktop PCs network transmission equipment and automated test equipment. It counts Samsung Electronics (nearly 15% of sales) Frontek Technology (10%) and Huawei among its customers. Semtech generates more than 60% of its sales in Asia/Pacific.

Semtech's products fall into four product lines: voltage and electrostatic discharge protection high-speed network communications power management and rectifiers (AC/DC conversion) and wireless and sensing. Its products are used in settings such as automated meter reading cellular base stations aerospace and defense medical satellite communications TVs gaming systems and many other telecommunications and industrial environments.

With its fabless model the company doesn't make its own chips. Semtech relies on third-party manufacturers in China (a foundry there producing about 60% by cost of the company's silicon requirements) and the US with assembly and test activities going through subcontractors in China Malaysia the Philippines and Thailand.

The semiconductor industry is highly cyclical partly due to its dependence on the consumer electronics industry. Most of Semtech's sales go into big end-use markets: cell phones desktop computers and notebook computers. The company has suffered less than others though with only a 3% dip in revenues in fiscal 2010 after the global recession hit and still edging out a profit. That was followed by a nearly 60% rebounding of sales in fiscal 2011 and net income reaching a 10-year high.

Revenue growth for fiscal 2012 (closed at the end of January) benefitted from stronger communications and consumer end markets though the still-tentative global economic recovery kept component product orders on the decline. Its communications segment grew to the company's largest (40% of sales) as customers clamored for more speed with 40Gbps (Gigabit per second) and 100Gbps deployments.

Semtech seeks to identify and target fast-growing end-markets that need high-performance cutting edge equipment. Such markets include high-end consumer equipment communications infrastructure and select broad-based industrial destinations. Within those markets it seeks to capitalize on its analog design expertise focusing on the increasing demand in key areas: higher speeds for data voice and video delivery; more-portable integrated and feature-capable devices; and greater energy management capabilities in residential and commercial settings. Geographically it looks to grow and diversify its client pool by concentrating on Asia and Europe.

In 2012 Semtech acquired France-based Cycleo a developer of intellectual property (IP) for long-range wireless semiconductors for $5 million with an additional $16 million possible based on performance targets. Cycleo's wireless technology used primarily in smart metering and other automation and control applications expanded Semtech's extended-range radio-frequency (RF) products.

Also that year Semtech moved to broaden its high-speed communications infrastructure portfolio when it paid CDN$500 million (about $500 million) for Gennum a provider of high speed analog and mixed-signal semiconductors used in broadcasting networking storage telecom and consumer connectivity.

HISTORY

Founded in 1960 Semtech was the second semiconductor startup in as many years for Gustav Franzen and Harvey Stump. It went public in 1967. Catering to military customers enabled Semtech to reach $15 million in sales by the end of its second decade. When the price of silver one of Semtech's raw materials rose tenfold in 1979 and 1980 the panicked company switched to copper which didn't work as well. Facing mounting troubles in 1985 Semtech tapped former Silicon General executive John Poe as CEO (replacing Franzen who was on vacation at the time).

Poe cut costs raised capital and brought in new management; by the early 1990s he had moved Semtech into commercial markets. The acquisitions of Lambda Semiconductors in 1990 and Modupower in 1992 boosted the company's power regulation business.

Diversified industrial firm Allegheny Teledyne which had once owned nearly a fourth of Semtech sold most of its stake in 1997 (Allegheny Teledyne's operations were sold off separately in

1999). That year Semtech began providing chips to the fast-growing automated test equipment market when it bought Edge Semiconductor.

Semtech made two acquisitions in 1999: Practical Sciences a designer of high-speed communications components and analog integrated circuits (ICs) and USAR Systems a maker of input device and systems management ICs for PCs and portable electronics. In 2002 Semtech announced plans to close its last wafer fabrication plant as part of its strategy to outsource all wafer manufacturing operations.

COO Jason Carlson succeeded Poe as CEO in 2003. Poe remained chairman. In 2004 the company named Tony Giraudo as COO; Giraudo joined Semtech from TelASIC Communications where he was CEO and previously worked at Atmel Honeywell IBM and NCR.

In 2005 the company acquired XEMICS a Swiss developer of ultralow-power analog radio-frequency and digital ICs for $43 million in cash plus future earnout payments. XEMICS became Semtech's Wireless and Sensing Products business unit.

After two years Carlson left the board and the company. Poe stepped in as interim CEO. Mohan Maheswaran formerly an EVP/GM at Intersil was named president and CEO in 2006. Later that year Poe was succeeded as chairman by Rockell Hankin who previously served as Semtech's vice chairman for eight years and was on the board since 1988.

John Poe stated his intention to resign from the board in 2006 effective once Semtech completed its restatement of historical financial results. The company was reviewing its past practices in granting stock options partly during a period when Poe served as CEO. He previously took a leave of absence from the board to avoid the appearance of a conflict in interests while the board investigated option granting practices. Poe's resignation finally took effect in 2007.

In 2010 the company agreed to pay $20 million to settle a class-action lawsuit over allegations of backdating securities options. The settlement would resolve claims against the company and its current and former officers and directors. No parties conceded any wrongdoing as part of the proposed settlement.

EXECUTIVES

EVP and General Manager Protection Power and Hi-Reliability Product Group, Jeffrey T. (Jeff) Pohlman, $226,094 total compensation
Chairman, Rockell N. Hankin
Senior Vice President; General Counsel; Secretary, Randall H. Holliday, age 63
EVP General Counsel and Secretary, Charles B. Ammann
Vice Chairman, James P. Burra
VP Human Resources, Kenneth J. Barry, age 65
SVP Quality and Reliability, J. Michael (Mike) Wilson, age 57, $215,990 total compensation
SVP and General Manager Signal Integrity Product Group, Gary M. Beauchamp
VP and General Manager Power Management Product Group, Simon Prutton, age 48
VP Quality Reliability and Technology, Kevin P. Caffey, age 53
Marketing Communications Manager, Terry Sears
President and CEO, Mohan R. Maheswaran, $409,231 total compensation
SVP and General Manager Wireless Sensing and Timing Product Group, Alain Dantec, $287,789 total compensation

SVP and CFO, Emeka Chukwu, $241,787 total compensation
SVP Worldwide Sales and Marketing, James J. Kim, $239,232 total compensation
VP Worldwide Operations, Clemente (Clay) Beltran, age 42
Marketing Director Protection Products, Rick Hansen
Senior Vice President and General Manager - Advanced Communications Product Group, Sameer Vuyyuru
Investor Relations, Chris Rogers
VP Information Technology and CIO, Jonathan Hahn
CTO, Jean-Paul Bardyn
Controller, Buck-Boost Current-Mode
Controller with, Current-Sharing Circuitry
Senior Vice President; General Manager - Power Management and High Reliability Group, David Schie
Controller, Linear Regulator
SVP Operations, Asaf Silberstein
Senior Vice President - Strategy and Systems Innovation Group, Charles Harper
Executive Vice President Quality & Reliability, Mike Wilson
EVP Quality and Reliability, Michael (Mike) Wilson
Vice President - Investor Relations, Sharon Faltemier
Director, Glen M. Antle, age 74
Director, Bruce C. Edwards, age 60
Director, James P. Burra, age 70
Director, James T. Lindstrom, age 67
Director, John L. Piotrowski, age 79
President CEO and Director, Mohan R. Maheswaran, age 49
Director, Wilford Dean Baker, age 70
Auditors: Ernst&YoungLLP

LOCATIONS

HQ: Semtech Corporation
200 Flynn Rd., Camarillo CA 93012-8790
Phone: 805-498-2111   **Fax:** 805-498-3804
Web: www.semtech.com

2012 Sales

	$ mil.	% of total
Asia/Pacific	298	62
North America	114	24
Europe	67	14
Total	**480**	**100**

PRODUCTS/OPERATIONS

2012 Sales

	$ mil.	% of total
Communications	186	39
High-end consumer	168	35
Industrial & other	83	17
Computing	41	9
Total	**480**	**100**

Selected Products

Power management
　Battery chargers
　Charge pump regulators
　Inductive boost LED drivers
　Switching regulators
Circuit protection
　Electrostatic discharge-electromagnetic interference filter devices
　High-current lightning protection
High-reliability discrete semiconductors
　Half wave rectifier
　High voltage capacitor
　Single phase full wave bridge assemblies
Telecom & data telecom serializers/deserializers
　40/100Gbps mux & demux
　Clock & data recover

Timing & synchronization
  Jitter attenuation multiplying phased locket loop
  Timing over packet networks

Selected Customers

Apple
Dragon Technology
Frontek Technology
HP
Huawei Technologies
Intel
LG Electronics
Samsung
Sony

COMPETITORS

Advanced Analogic Technologies	Linear Technology
Analog Devices	Littelfuse
Broadcom	Maxim Integrated Products
Dialog Semiconductor	Micrel
Exar	Microsemi
Fairchild Semiconductor	Monolithic Power Systems
Hittite Microwave	NXP Semiconductors
IXYS	O2Micro
Infineon Technologies	ON Semiconductor
Inphi	Oki Semiconductor
Integrated Device Technology	Power Integrations
International Rectifier	STMicroelectronics
Intersil	Silicon Labs
L-3 Communications	Siliconix
	Texas Instruments
	Volterra Semiconductor

HISTORICAL FINANCIALS

Company Type: Public

Income Statement

FYE: January 27

	REVENUE ($ mil.)	NET INCOME ($ mil.)	NET PROFIT MARGIN	EMPLOYEES
01/13	578.8	41.9	7.2%	1,433
01/12	480.6	89.0	18.5%	929
01/11	454.5	72.5	16.0%	982
01/10	286.5	0.9	0.3%	915
01/09	294.8	37.5	12.7%	827
Annual Growth	18.4%	2.8%	—	14.7%

2013 Year-End Financials

Debt ratio: 28.2%
Return on equity: 6.3%
Cash ($ mil.): 223
Current ratio: 2.57
Long-term debt ($ mil.): 282

No. of shares (mil.): 66
Dividends
  Yield: —
  Payout: —
Market value ($ mil.): 1,988

	STOCK PRICE ($) FY Close	P/E High/Low	PER SHARE ($) Earnings	Dividends	Book Value
01/13	29.84	47 35	0.62	0.00	10.43
01/12	28.97	21 14	1.32	0.00	9.70
01/11	21.74	21 13	1.12	0.00	8.27
01/10	14.98	951542	0.02	0.00	6.62
01/09	11.51	30 14	0.61	0.00	6.27
Annual Growth	26.9%	— —	0.4%	—	13.6%

Senior Housing Properties Trust

Senior Housing Properties Trust (SHPT) offers those in their golden years a place to rest their weary heads. The real estate investment trust (REIT) owns some 300 health care-related properties in more than 30 states and Washington DC. Its portfolio includes senior apartments independent and assisted living facilities nursing homes medical office buildings biotechnology laboratories rehabilitation hospitals and gymnasiums. Tenants such as Sunrise Senior Living and Brookdale Senior Living sign triple-net leases which require them not only to pay rent but to also pay operating expenses remove hazardous waste and carry insurance on their properties.

SHPT was spun off from HRPT Properties Trust in 1999 when that REIT sold off its health facilities in order to focus on office and industrial properties. SHPT's business strategy is primarily focused on acquiring upscale senior living properties where the majority of residents pay rent through their own resources rather than through government programs. In 2008 and 2009 the company diversified its properties by purchasing nearly 50 medical office clinic and biotech laboratory buildings in a dozen states from HRPT for some $565 million. In 2011 SHPT arranged to buy 20 senior living facilities in the Southeast for more than $300 million. In another deal announced later in the year the company agreed to buy 13 medical office properties from Commonwealth REIT for $167 million. The properties are scattered throughout AZ CA IL MN NY OH PA and SC.

SHPT created Five Star Quality Care in 2000 to operate properties that it repossessed from other tenants. The management company was spun off the following year but remains SHPT's largest tenant and accounts for more than half of the REIT's annual rent. Reit Management Research a limited liability company owned by Barry Portnoy and his son Adam (who are also managing trustees of SHPT) manages the day-to-day activities of SHPT HRPT Five Star Quality Care and two other publicly traded REITs Hospitality Properties Trust and Government Properties Income Trust.

Institutional investors including Vanguard Deutsche Bank BlackRock and Morgan Stanley own more than 40% of SHPT's stock.

EXECUTIVES

Secretary, Jennifer B. Clark, age 52
President; Chief Operating Officer, David J. Hegarty, age 57, $141,811 total compensation
VP Investor Relations, Timothy A. (Tim) Bonang
Chief Financial Officer; Treasurer, Richard A. (Rick) Doyle Jr., age 45, $47,962 total compensation
Auditors: Ernst&YoungLLP

LOCATIONS

HQ: Senior Housing Properties Trust
  400 Centre St., Newton MA 02458-2076
Phone: 617-796-8350   **Fax:** 617-796-8349
Web: www.snhreit.com

2009 Properties

	No.
Wisconsin	21
Massachusetts	20
California	19
Florida	17
Georgia	17
Nebraska	17
Pennsylvania	17
Texas	15
Virginia	15
Maryland	13
South	13
Indiana	11
Tennessee	10
Kentucky	9
Arizona	8
Colorado	8
Delaware	6
Iowa	6
North	6
Alabama	5
Michigan	5
Kansas	4
New	4
New	4
New	4
Oklahoma	4
Illinois	3
Minnesota	3
South	3
Mississippi	2
Ohio	2
Washington	2
Wyoming	2
Missouri	1
Rhode	1
Washington	1
Total	**298**

PRODUCTS/OPERATIONS

2009 Sales

	$ mil.	% of total
Residential care facilities	227	76
Medical office buildings	53	18
Other	16	6
Total	**297**	**100**

2009 Properties

	No.
Senior living	230
Medical office	56
Wellness	10
Rehabilitation	2
Total	**298**

COMPETITORS

Chartwell Seniors Housing	LTC Properties
Extendicare	Legacy Healthcare
G & K Industries	National Health Investors
HCP	Omega Healthcare Investors
Health Care REIT	Sabra Health Care
Healthcare Realty Trust	Ventas

HISTORICAL FINANCIALS

Company Type: Public

Income Statement

FYE: December 31

	REVENUE ($ mil.)	NET INCOME ($ mil.)	NET PROFIT MARGIN	EMPLOYEES
12/12	644.8	135.8	21.1%	0
12/11	450.0	151.4	33.6%	0
12/10	339.0	116.4	34.4%	0
12/09	297.7	109.7	36.8%	0
12/08	235.5	106.5	45.2%	0
Annual Growth	28.6%	6.3%	—	—

2012 Year-End Financials

Debt ratio: 42.2%
Return on equity: 5.2%
Cash ($ mil.): 42
Current ratio: 1.90
Long-term debt ($ mil.): 2,006

No. of shares (mil.): 176
Dividends
  Yield: 6.4%
  Payout: 193.6%
Market value ($ mil.): 4,174

STOCK PRICE ($) FY Close	P/E High/Low		PER SHARE ($) Earnings	Dividends	Book Value
12/12	23.64	30 25	0.80	1.53	14.99
12/11	22.44	24 19	1.01	1.49	15.20
12/10	21.94	28 21	0.91	1.45	15.00
12/09	21.87	25 13	0.90	1.42	14.92
12/08	17.92	25 10	1.01	1.40	15.12
Annual Growth	7.2%	— —	(5.7%)	2.2%	(0.2%)

Shenandoah Telecommunications Co.

If Virginia is for lovers Shenandoah Telecommunications must carry some interesting conversations. Through a dozen subsidiaries the company (which also does business as Shentel) provides telecom services in the Shenandoah Valley and beyond. Shenandoah Telephone has more than 24000 access lines in service; (the population of Shenandoah County is 41000). The firm's wireless subsidiaries offer mobile phone paging and tower services; as a Sprint Nextel affiliate subsidiary Shenandoah Personal Communications offers wireless services to more than 270000 customers. The company's cable TV unit serves about 75000 customers while about 14000 households subscribe to its dial-up and broadband Internet access.

Recognizing that the market for wireline service is shrinking from the rise of mobile phones as a primary phone and VoIP technology Shentel is focused on growing its cable holdings. It paid $148 million for the cable business of JetBroadband in 2010 as part of an effort to expand its cable network. The deal added more than 60000 customers in southern Virginia and West Virginia. ShenTel plans spend about $33 million over the next two years to upgrade the Jet Broadband network to enable high definition broadcasting digital video recording faster Internet connections and digital telephone services. Later that year it bought cable assets in Salem West Virginia and Oakland Maryland from Cequel Communications (which does business as Suddenlink) adding about 7000 residential subscribers.

With revenues for resold Sprint wireless service accounting for a majority of the company's sales Shentel received a boost in 2010 by adding prepaid wireless service from Sprint subsidiaries Virgin Mobile and Boost. The OK from Sprint to enter the prepaid phone market in its service area from Harrisonburg to Altoona PA added an immediate 50000 customers to subsidiary Shenandoah Personal Communications Company.

Previous acquisitions include the assets of Mount Solon Virginia-based North River Telephone Cooperative for $600000 in 2009 which expanded Shentel's wireline footprint by about 1000 lines in rural areas of the state.

Other subsidiaries include Harrisonburg Virginia-based NTC which provides integrated telecommunications services to student apartment complexes and college dorms in the southeastern US. Its information services subsidiary ShenTel Service Company offers dial-up and digital subscriber line services to about 14000 households. Shenandoah Mobile Company owns and leases tower space within its 140-tower PCS service territory and offers paging services to customers in Maryland Pennsylvania Virginia and West Virginia. Shenandoah Long Distance Company resells long-distance service to almost 11000 customers.

EXECUTIVES

Vice President - Wireless, William L. (Willy) Pirtle, age 54, $203,018 total compensation
VP Customer Service, David E. Ferguson, age 67, $189,000 total compensation
Chairman President and CEO, Christopher E. (Chris) French, age 55, $367,822 total compensation
Executive Vice President and Chief Operating Officer, Earle A. MacKenzie, age 61, $309,982 total compensation
Vice Chairman, Douglas C. Arthur, age 70
Vice President of Finance Chief Financial Officer and Treasurer, Adele M. Skolits, age 54, $209,455 total compensation
VP Legal Secretary and General Counsel, Ann E. Flowers, age 56
Vice President of Information Technology, Richard A. Baughman
VP Sales and Marketing Cable, Christopher Kyle
Vice President of Wireline & Engineering, Edward McKay
Vice President - Cable, Thomas (Tom) Whitaker
Vice President - Legal; General Counsel, Raymond Ostroski
Director, Dale S. Lam, age 50
Director, Jonelle St. John, age 59
Director, James E. Zerkel II, age 68
Director, Ken L. Burch, age 68
Vice Chairman, Douglas C. Arthur, age 70
Director, Tracy Fitzsimmons, age 46
Director, Richard L. Koontz Jr., age 55
Director, John W. Flora, age 58
Independent Director, Jonelle John
Auditors: KPMGLLP

LOCATIONS

HQ: Shenandoah Telecommunications Company
500 Shentel Way, Edinburg VA 22824
Phone: 540-984-4141   **Fax:** 540-984-8192
Web: www.shentel.com

Selected Network Facilities (Points of Presence)
Maryland
  Hagerstown
Virginia
  Ashburn
  Berryville
  Edinburg
  Front Royal
  Harrisonburg
  Herndon
  Leesburg
  Stephen City
  Warrenton
  Winchester
West Virginia
  Martinsburg

PRODUCTS/OPERATIONS

2009 Sales

	$ mil.	% of total
Wireless	115	62
Wireline	45	28
Cable TV	15	10
Adjustments	(15.7)	-
Total	160	100

Selected Services
Business telephone products
Cable TV
Cellular products and services
Centrex
Fiber-optic capacity
Internet access
ISDN
Local telephone access
Long-distance
Paging
Security systems

COMPETITORS

AT&T	NTELOS
Aquis Communications Group	Suddenlink Communications
Cellco	T-Mobile USA
Comcast	Time Warner Cable
Cricket Communications	U.S. Cellular
DISH Network	Verizon
EarthLink	tw telecom
Lumos	

HISTORICAL FINANCIALS
Company Type: Public

Income Statement
FYE: December 31

	REVENUE ($ mil.)	NET INCOME ($ mil.)	NET PROFIT MARGIN	EMPLOYEES
12/12	288.0	16.3	5.7%	693
12/11	251.1	12.9	5.2%	669
12/10	194.8	18.0	9.3%	636
12/09	160.6	15.0	9.4%	461
12/08	144.4	24.4	16.9%	451
Annual Growth	18.8%	(9.6%)	—	11.3%

2012 Year-End Financials
Debt ratio: 40.6%
Return on equity: 8.0%
Cash ($ mil.): 71
Current ratio: 2.00
Long-term debt ($ mil.): 230
No. of shares (mil.): 23
Dividends
  Yield: 2.1%
  Payout: 48.5%
Market value ($ mil.): 367

	STOCK PRICE ($) FY Close	P/E High/Low	Earnings	PER SHARE ($) Dividends	Book Value
12/12	15.31	28 14	0.68	0.33	8.67
12/11	10.48	35 17	0.55	0.33	8.29
12/10	18.73	28 21	0.76	0.33	8.01
12/09	20.35	44 25	0.64	0.32	7.42
12/08	28.05	27 12	1.04	0.30	7.10
Annual Growth	(14.0%)	— —	(10.1%)	2.4%	5.1%

Shiloh Industries, Inc.

When Shiloh Industries draws a blank it's a good thing. The company produces stampings modular assemblies and steel and welded blanks for the automotive heating and air-conditioning and lawn and garden equipment industries. It also makes tools and assembly equipment for its own use and to sell to OEMs and other suppliers. Shiloh's largest customer is General Motors accounting for about 34% of sales. Other customers include Ford Chrysler and Toyota as well as home appliance manufacturers construction companies and steel producers. Its nine manufacturing plants are located in Georgia Michigan Ohio and Tennessee as well as Mexico. The company was founded in 1950 as Shiloh Tool & Die Manufacturing.

In the stamping process steel is formed into three-dimensional parts as it passes through dies (patterns) in a stamping press. For the automotive and light and heavy truck markets the stampings made by Shiloh Industries are used in heat shields mufflers seat frames structural rails and other structural body components. Shiloh also makes engineered welded blanks (two or more steel sheets welded together) and steel blanks (flat steel cut into two-dimensional shapes). The blanks are used primarily for exterior steel panels such as doors frames and hoods.

The success of Shiloh Industries is linked to the success of North American auto manufacturers who realized an overall industry production increase of 44% in 2010 over 2009. The company's net income went from a loss of almost $18 million in 2009 to a positive total of almost $4 million the next year. Shiloh's revenues followed suit and shot up more than 40% in 2010 compared to a year earlier. It announced in late 2010 its plans to invest about $10 million to build a new manufacturing facility in Kentucky which will produce first operation precision blanks and other related products. The facility is scheduled to open mid-2011.

Prior to this recovery however Shiloh was in the headlights of the global economic crisis along with its customers in the automotive industry. For 2009 the company saw its revenues decrease by 47% year-over-year. It responded by adjusting costs and production to match demand reducing headcount (through four rounds of layoffs) freezing wages and implementing 10% pay reductions for salaried personnel. It also closed its Liverpool plant in Ohio and consolidated other manufacturing operations. Despite the economic downturn the company invested almost $2 million on BMW and GM truck platforms as well as other new business development projects.

Through MTD Holdings (owner of outdoor power equipment maker MTD Products) Shiloh chairman Curtis Moll controls more than half of the company.

HISTORY

Dominick Fanello founded the company in 1950 as Shiloh Tool & Die Manufacturing; in 1954 Fanello became chairman and CEO. In the early 1960s the business expanded into blanking and stamping operations. Shiloh formed a joint venture in 1977 with MTD Products (power equipment) to develop additional steel-processing capabilities.

Shiloh went public in 1993. Seeking to expand beyond northeastern Ohio it formed a joint venture with Shiloh of Michigan and Rouge Steel in 1995 to produce engineered steel blanks in Romulus Michigan. That year 32-year Shiloh veteran Robert Grissinger replaced Fanello as CEO.

In 1996 Shiloh expanded into the automotive tool and stamping business buying Michigan-based Greenfield Die & Manufacturing. Automakers began to outsource more products and in 1997 Shiloh earmarked $60 million for improvements that included adding new equipment and expanding its welding capacity and warehouse space. It then formed a joint venture with Bing Steel to make steel blanks for cars. Also that year Shiloh bought Michigan steel processor C&H Design.

Fiscal 1998 brought a 23% dip in Shiloh's income in part from the GM strike increased tool and die competition falling prices for engineered scrap steel and the company's difficulty in assimilating

acquisitions. Shiloh became more vertically integrated by buying the automotive unit of its majority stockholder MTD Products (later MTD Holdings) in 1999. The company also built a plant in Mexico to serve GM operations there. That year former GM executive John Falcon became CEO.

Shiloh sold its Canton Tool & Die Valley City Steel and Utica Tool & Die subsidiaries in 2000 to concentrate on its automotive operations. The next year the company penned a joint product development agreement with Pullman Industries to offer larger and stronger assemblies.

In early 2002 Theodore Zampetis replaced Jack Falcon as CEO. That year Valley City Steel LLC which was 49%-owned by Shiloh filed Chapter 11 bankruptcy protection through its controlling owner Viking Steel LLC. The following year Shiloh returned to profitability despite lower production in the North American automobile and light truck sectors.

The company was later charged with "constructive fraudulent conveyance" by the bankrupt estate of Valley City Steel which was subsequently awarded almost $5 million in damages. The case which was tried by the US District Court was based on Valley City Steel's claim that Shiloh's part of the transaction —to receive over $12 million plus 49% of Valley City Steel LLC —had not left Valley City Steel enough capital to continue operations. The verdict does not mean that Shiloh intended to defraud rather that the circumstances of the transaction were not fair. Shiloh appealed the verdict in 2007.

In late 2012 Ramzi Y. Hermiz was introduced as the company's newest CEO.

EXECUTIVES

President CEO and Director, Theodore K. Zampetis, age 66, $212,885 total compensation
Chairman, Curtis E. Moll, age 73
Secretary and Director, David J. Hessler, age 68
VP Sales and Business Development, Craig S. Parsons, age 41
VP and CTO, Anthony M (Tony) Parente, age 50, $160,000 total compensation
Corporate Controller, Michael P. Randall
VP Finance and Treasurer, Thomas M. Dugan, age 47
VP Manufacturing Operations, Paul Harland, age 53
Vice President - Quality Assurance and Program Management, Elie Azzi
Vice President - Sales and Business Development, Tres K
President; Chief Executive Officer; Director, Ramzi Hermiz
Vice President - Sales and Business Development, Tres Kline
Vice President - Purchasing, Kimberly Buhl
Director, Robert J. (Bob) King Jr., age 56
President CEO and Director, Theodore K. Zampetis, age 66
Director, Dieter Kaesgen, age 75
Director, Cloyd J. Abruzzo, age 61
Secretary and Director, David J. Hessler, age 68
Director, John J. (Jack) Tanis, age 85
Director, Gary A. Oatey, age 63
Director, George G. Goodrich, age 71
Auditors: GrantThorntonLLP

LOCATIONS

HQ: Shiloh Industries Inc.
880 Steel Dr., Valley City OH 44280
Phone: 330-558-2600   **Fax:** 330-558-2666
Web: www.shiloh.com

PRODUCTS/OPERATIONS

2010 Sales

	$ mil.	% of total
Engineered welded blanks	218	48
Complex stampings & modular assemblies	133	29
Blanking	69	15
Tools dies steel processing scrap & other	35	8
Total	**457**	**100**

Selected Products and Services

Body structures
Chassis systems
Cleaning and coating
Cut-to-length
Deep draw engine applications
Edge trimming
Engineered welded blanks
Exhaust & heat management
First operation blanking
Heavy gauge blanking and forming
Hot- and cold-rolled steel
Inspection
Interior metallics
Laminated products
Pickling
Slitting
Stamped components
Steel processing
Tool building
Warehousing

COMPETITORS

Cosma International	Olympic Steel
Flex-N-Gate	Rose City
Gibbs Die Casting	Manufacturing
Midway Products Group	Tower International
Ogihara America	

HISTORICAL FINANCIALS

Company Type: Public

Income Statement

	REVENUE ($ mil.)	NET INCOME ($ mil.)	NET PROFIT MARGIN	EMPLOYEES		FYE: October 31
10/13	700.1	21.5	3.1%	1,824		
10/12	586.0	13.5	2.3%	1,430		
10/11	517.7	7.8	1.5%	1,270		
10/10	457.2	3.8	0.8%	1,250		
10/09	269.3	(17.7)	—	955		
Annual Growth	27.0%	—	—	17.6%		

2013 Year-End Financials

Debt ratio: 30.6%
Return on equity: 18.0%
Cash ($ mil.): 0
Current ratio: 1.43
Long-term debt ($ mil.): 119

No. of shares (mil.): 17
Dividends
  Yield: 4.5%
  Payout: 68.1%
Market value ($ mil.): 280

	STOCK PRICE ($) FY Close	P/E High/Low		PER SHARE ($) Earnings	Dividends	Book Value
10/13	16.42	12	7	1.27	0.75	7.70
10/12	11.38	14	10	0.80	0.50	6.35
10/11	7.90	29	18	0.47	0.12	6.42
10/10	10.08	45	17	0.23	0.00	6.17
10/09	4.50	—	—	(1.09)	0.00	5.79
Annual Growth	38.2%	—	—	—	—	7.4%

Shoe Carnival, Inc.

Shoe Carnival works hard to make shoe shopping a toe-tappin' good time. The company operates more than 350 family footwear stores across 30-plus US states including Puerto Rico that feature bright lights and neon signs. It also sells shoes online. In line with its name in-store "barkers" bellow out specials and organize games soliciting customer participation to promote the "carnival-like" atmosphere the retailer hopes will edge out rivals. Shoe Carnival sells brand-name and private-label men's and children's footwear as well as its primary women's and athletic shoes which together generate 64% of sales. The family of Chairman J. Wayne Weaver owns 25% of Shoe Carnival's shares.

Geographic Reach

Based in Indiana Shoe Carnival operates more than 350 stores in 30-plus US states and Puerto Rico. It also operates an e-commerce site at www.shoecarnival.com.

Strategy

After slowing its expansion in recent years the shoe seller is back in growth mode. Shoe Carnival in fiscal 2013 (ends January) added more than 30 new locations most of which are located in two new major markets for the chain: Puerto Rico and the Dallas/Fort Worth Metroplex. Previously it added a dozen stores in 2012. In 2014 the company anticipates opening up to 35 new stores while shuttering up to seven stores. It's looking to serve new under-penetrated markets that can accommodate one or two of its stores.

Along with its brick-and-mortar network of stores Shoe Carnival added an e-commerce site in 2012 and expanded with a mobile version during the third quarter of fiscal 2013. Traffic from mobile devices as a result has grown to more than 30% of the company's overall e-commerce site traffic. To this end Shoe Carnival is banking on its e-commerce site as a growth vehicle.

Financial Performance

In fiscal 2013 (ends January) the retailer's sales grew by about 12% vs. 2012. Same-store sales increased by 5% in 2013. The company attributes the rise to a higher average unit selling price for its footwear despite selling fewer footwear units. Shoe Carnival logged an 11% increase in profits during the same reporting period thanks to rising revenue.

Operations

Shoe Carnival's large stores (on average 10900 sq. ft.) stock about 28200 pairs of shoes with an emphasis on national and regional brands. Its current store prototype spans between 8000 and 12000 sq. ft. Stores are usually located in open-air shopping centers.

The company sources its merchandise from more than 170 footwear vendors.

Sales and Marketing

The chain's two biggest suppliers are NIKE and Sketchers U.S.A. whose brands combined accounted for more than 37% of Shoe Carnival's net sales in fiscal 2013 up two percentage points from 2012.

Shoe Carnival is relying on social media to get its brand name in front of new customers and markets. It also uses print television radio outdoor and digital media. Advertising expenses in 2013 were $37.4 million up from $33.5 million in 2012 and $31.1 million in 2011.

Company Ownership

The family of Chairman J. Wayne Weaver owns 25% of Shoe Carnival's shares. Royce & Associates owns about 15% of the company's shares making it Shoe Carnival's second-largest shareholder behind the Weaver family.

EXECUTIVES

President; Chief Executive Officer; Chief Merchandising Officer; Director, Clifton E. (Cliff) Sifford, age 60, $425,000 total compensation
Executive Vice President - Store Operations, Timothy T. (Tim) Baker, age 57, $425,000 total compensation
EVP CFO and Treasurer, W. Kerry Jackson, age 52, $400,000 total compensation
Chairman, J. Wayne Weaver, age 79, $300,000 total compensation
VP Human Resources and and In-House Counsel, Sean M. Georges
President CEO and Director, Mark L. Lemond, age 58, $703,500 total compensation
SVP Planning Allocation and Secretary, David A. Kapp
SVP and Divisional Merchandise Manager Athletics and Children's, Mitchell A. Chandler
SVP and CIO, Terry L. Clements
VP-Admin & Bus Dev, David M. Groff
Assistant VP and Buyer Men's Athletics, Tucker R. Robinson Sr.
SVP Store Operations, Steven D. (Steve) Meyer
Senior Vice President; Chief Accounting Officer; Controller, Kathy A. Yearwood, age 46
Assistant VP and Buyer Women's Sport and Casual, Thomas G. (Tom) Vernarsky
SVP Marketing, Todd A. Beurman
VP Distribution, W. Dwight Burton Jr.
VP and Divisional Merchandise Manager Women's Non-Athletics and Accessories, Lisa A. Rosenbaum
VP Real Estate, Michael C. Smith
Assistant Vice President Marketing, Samantha K. Payton
Executive Vice President; General Merchandise Manager, Carl Scibetta
VP-Distr, Dwight Burton
President CEO and Director, Mark L. Lemond, age 58
Director, William E. Bindley, age 71
Director, Kent A. Kleeberger, age 61
Independent Director, James A. Aschleman, age 68
Director, Gerald W. Schoor, age 78
Auditors: Deloitte&ToucheLLP

LOCATIONS

HQ: Shoe Carnival, Inc.
7500 East Columbia Street, Evansville, IN 47715
Phone: 812 867-6471
Web: www.shoecarnival.com

2013 Stores

	No.
Texas	46
Illinois	26
Indiana	22
Florida	23
Missouri	21
Ohio	19
North	18
Tennessee	18
Georgia	15
Kentucky	12
Louisiana	12
Alabama	11
South	12
Arkansas	9
Virginia	9
Iowa	7
Mississippi	7
Oklahoma	7
Pennsylvania	9
Utah	9
Idaho	5
Michigan	5
West	5
Colorado	3
Kansas	3
Arizona	4
Puerto	4
North	2
South	2
Wisconsin	2
Montana	2
Nebraska	1
Wyoming	1
Total	**351**

PRODUCTS/OPERATIONS

2013 Sales

	% of total
Athletics	38
Women's	26
Children's	17
Men's	15
Accessories & miscellaneous	4
Total	**100**

COMPETITORS

Bakers Footwear	Macy's
Brown Shoe	Nine West
Collective Brands	Payless ShoeSource
DSW	Rack Room Shoes
Dick's Sporting Goods	Sears
Dillard's	Sports Authority
Finish Line	Target Corporation
Foot Locker	Wal-Mart
J. C. Penney	shoebuy.com
Kohl's	

HISTORICAL FINANCIALS

Company Type: Public

Income Statement

FYE: February 2

	REVENUE ($ mil.)	NET INCOME ($ mil.)	NET PROFIT MARGIN	EMPLOYEES
02/13*	855.0	29.3	3.4%	5,000
01/12	762.5	26.3	3.5%	4,500
01/11	739.1	26.8	3.6%	4,300
01/10	682.4	15.1	2.2%	4,300
01/09	647.5	5.3	0.8%	4,200
Annual Growth	7.2%	53.2%	—	4.5%

*Fiscal year change

2013 Year-End Financials

Debt ratio: —
Return on equity: 10.0%
Cash ($ mil.): 45
Current ratio: 4.00
Long-term debt ($ mil.): —

No. of shares (mil.): 20
Dividends
  Yield: 0.0%
  Payout: 80.4%
Market value ($ mil.): 417

	STOCK PRICE ($) FY Close	P/E High/Low	PER SHARE ($) Earnings	Dividends	Book Value
02/13*	20.50	23 13	1.43	1.15	14.37
01/12	25.76	26 16	1.31	0.00	14.12
01/11	24.60	21 12	1.37	0.00	12.85
01/10	18.27	26 8	0.80	0.00	11.35
01/09	7.85	63 26	0.29	0.00	10.56
Annual Growth	27.1%	— —	49.4%	—	8.0%

*Fiscal year change

Shutterfly Inc

Whether or not you are the consummate shutterbug you can rely on Shutterfly for digital prints. An e-commerce company specializing in digital photo products and services for the consumer and professional photography markets the company offers customers the ability to upload share store and edit digital photos through its website. In addition to traditional 4-inch by 6-inch prints Shutterfly provides prints ranging from wallet-sized to jumbo enlargements. The company also offers personalized items including mugs photo books and calendars through its personalized products and services business segment. In 2012 Shutterfly acquired Kodak Imaging Network (doing business as KODAK Gallery).

The company purchased the online photo service of bankrupt photography company Eastman Kodak for nearly $24 million. Shutterfly made the deal to acquire Kodak's 75 million customers in the US and Canada. The purchase is helping it gain an even larger share of the online photo market which it shares with rivals such as Hewlett Packard's Snapfish and American Greetings' Photoworks and Webshots brands.

The deal comes after Shutterfly reported positive earnings in 2011. It earned revenue of $473.3 million and income of $35.4 million. These results were due to an increase in customers and orders combined with strong financial discipline. Customers for the year totaled more than 4.8 million (up from about 4 million in 2010) while orders equaled about 11.2 million (up from about 9.2 million in 2010). The average order in 2011 remained flat at about $33. The company also owes its success to investing in its personalized product line. In 2011 it reported an increase in sales of photo books and greeting and stationery cards.

The KODAK Gallery deal represents Shutterfly's efforts to grow all areas of the business through a steady stream of targeted acquisitions. It also acquired Penguin Digital in 2012. Penguin Digital is a mobile application developer that provides consumers with a way to create share and purchase photo merchandise directly from a mobile device.

In 2011 the company acquired personalized card and stationery seller Tiny Prints for $146.5 million in cash and about 4 million shares of common stock. Shutterfly made the deal to enhance efficiencies in product innovation merchandising manufacturing customer service and marketing. And in late 2010 Shutterfly enhanced its commercial printing services through the purchase of WSMG a digital direct marketing agency based in Dallas. Shutterfly is integrating WSMG's data management and marketing analytics capabilities with its own manufacturing and printing operations.

Shutterfly makes more than half its revenues during the fourth quarter of the year due to holiday sales. Sales of 4x6 prints account for about 7% of revenues. The company makes additional money through advertising —clients such as Sony ABC AT&T Universal Music and Proctor & Gamble have advertised on its website. Revenues from ads and sponsorship are included in the company's personalized products and services segment. Shutterfly also provides commercial printing services primarily to the direct marketing industry though that business accounts for only 3% of sales.

The company was founded in 1999 and was funded in part by Silicon Valley icon Jim Clark a co-founder of Netscape Communications. The company went public in a 2006 IPO.

EXECUTIVES

Chairman, Philip A. (Phil) Marineau, age 66
SVP Business and Corporate Development, Douglas J. (Doug) Galen, age 51, $258,667 total compensation
President CEO and Director, Jeffrey T. (Jeff) Housenbold, age 43, $485,000 total compensation
SVP and Chief Marketing Officer, Peter C. Elarde, age 48, $240,675 total compensation
VP Marketing Strategy, Sean Foley
SVP Products and Services, Daniel C. (Dan) McCormick, age 47
SVP Operations, Dwayne A. Black, age 45, $225,500 total compensation
VP Investor Relations and Treasurer, Michael Look
SVP Human Resources, Peter A. Navin, age 44
Senior Manager Corporate Communications, Gretchen Sloan
President Manufacturing, Eric Kok
VP-Brand Mktg, Brian Osborn
VP and Chief Accounting Officer, Brian R. Manca, age 38
Chief Marketing Officer, John Boris
Chairman, Philip MarineauBoard
Vice President Chief Financial Officer, Brian Regan
Director, Nancy J. Schoendorf, age 58
Director, Stephen J. Killeen, age 50
Director, Eric J. Keller, age 60
Director, James N. (Jim) White, age 51
President CEO and Director, Jeffrey T. (Jeff) Housenbold, age 43
Director, Brian T. Swette, age 59
Chairman, Philip MarineauBoard
Auditors: PricewaterhouseCoopersLLP

LOCATIONS

HQ: Shutterfly Inc.
2800 Bridge Pkwy. Ste. 101, Redwood City CA 94065
Phone: 650-610-5200 **Fax**: 650-654-1299
Web: www.shutterfly.com

PRODUCTS/OPERATIONS

2011 Sales

	$ mil.	% of total
Personalized products & services	374	79
Print	85	18
Commercial print	13	3
Total	**473**	**100**

Selected Products and Services

Online Services
 Edit and enhance
 Organize
 Print
 Share
 Upload
Photo-Based Products
 Greeting cards
 Personalized calendars
 Photo books
 Stationery

COMPETITORS

123Greetings	LifePics
AG Interactive	Rite Aid
Adobe Systems	Ritz Camera
CVS Caremark	Snapfish
Costco Wholesale	Vistaprint
Facebook	Wal-Mart
Google	Walgreen
Kodak Imaging Network	Yahoo!

HISTORICAL FINANCIALS

Company Type: Public

Income Statement

FYE: December 31

	REVENUE ($ mil.)	NET INCOME ($ mil.)	NET PROFIT MARGIN	EMPLOYEES
12/12	640.6	23.0	3.6%	1,107
12/11	473.2	14.0	3.0%	956
12/10	307.7	17.1	5.6%	611
12/09	246.4	5.8	2.4%	519
12/08	213.4	4.5	2.1%	514
Annual Growth	**31.6%**	**49.9%**	**—**	**21.1%**

2012 Year-End Financials

Debt ratio: —	No. of shares (mil.): 36
Return on equity: 3.5%	Dividends
Cash ($ mil.): 245	Yield: —
Current ratio: 2.08	Payout: —
Long-term debt ($ mil.): —	Market value ($ mil.): 1,086

	STOCK PRICE ($) FY Close	P/E High/Low		PER SHARE ($) Earnings	Dividends	Book Value
12/12	29.87	53	35	0.61	0.00	19.01
12/11	22.76	148	52	0.40	0.00	17.48
12/10	34.89	57	25	0.59	0.00	9.64
12/09	17.81	81	26	0.22	0.00	8.30
12/08	6.99	143	33	0.18	0.00	7.41
Annual Growth	**43.8%**	**—**	**—**	**35.7%**	**—**	**26.6%**

Signature Bank (New York, NY)

Signature Bank marks the spot where some professional New Yorkers bank. The institution provides customized banking and financial services to smaller private businesses their owners and their top executives through about two dozen locations throughout the metropolitan area including all five boroughs Long Island and affluent Westchester County. It attracts deposits by offering personal and business checking and money market accounts. The bank's lending activities mainly entail real estate and business loans. Subsidiary Signature Securities offers wealth management financial planning brokerage services and life and disability insurance.

Mortgage loans including commercial real estate loans multifamily residential mortgages home loans and lines of credit and construction and land loans comprise the bulk of Signature Bank's loan portfolio (and much of its asset base as well). The bank branched out into specialty lending in 2012 forming subsidiary Signature Financial to offer equipment finance and leasing transportation financing and funding for taxi medallions.

Founded in 2001 as an alternative to megabanks Signature Bank has grown into an institution with nearly $15 billion in assets a figure that has more than doubled since the bank was spun off from Bank Hapoalim in 2004. It plans to continue to fill a service void created by industry consolidation. The bank targets businesses that have fewer than 1000 employees and revenues of less than $50 million. Representative clients include real estate companies law firms entertainment agencies and foundations. Signature Bank has also been building its private client business by adding banking teams and opening offices throughout the New York metro area.

The bank's emphasis on personal service helped it to grow its deposit base and loan portfolio in 2011. During a time when many other banks struggled under the weight of bad loans in a bad economy Signature Bank achieved record earnings for the fourth consecutive year. Its 2011 revenue exceeded $622 million and its net income approached $150 million.

EXECUTIVES

President CEO and Director, Joseph J. DePaolo, $328,750 total compensation
EVP and COO, Mark T. Sigona
EVP and Chief Credit Officer, Michael J. Merlo, $223,269 total compensation
Senior Vice President; Chief Technology Officer, Michael Sharkey
EVP and CFO, Eric R. Howell
Executive Vice President; Treasurer, Peter S. Quinlan
Senior Vice President Chief Financial Officer, Vito Susca
President CEO and Director, Joseph J. DePaolo
Director, Alfred B. DelBello
Director, Yacov Levy
Director, Jeffrey W. (Jeff) Meshel
Independent Director, Alfonse Amato
Auditors: KPMGLLP

LOCATIONS

HQ: Signature Bank
565 5th Ave., New York NY 10017
Phone: 646-822-1500   **Fax:** 817-465-5065
Web: www.lelandscott.com

PRODUCTS/OPERATIONS

2011 Sales

	$ mil.	% of total
Interest		
Loans net	333	54
Securities available for sale	223	36
Securities held to maturity	18	3
Other	5	1
Noninterest		
Fees & service charges	15	2
Net gains on sales of securities	14	2
Commissions	9	1
Other	3	1
Total	**622**	**100**

COMPETITORS

Apple Bank for Savings	Herald National Bank
Astoria Financial	JPMorgan Chase
Bank Leumi USA	New York Community
Capital One	Bancorp
Citigroup	Safra Bank
HSBC USA	TD Bank USA

HISTORICAL FINANCIALS
Company Type: Public

Income Statement
FYE: December 31

	ASSETS ($ mil.)	NET INCOME ($ mil.)	INCOME AS % OF ASSETS	EMPLOYEES
12/12	17,456.0	185.4	1.1%	844
12/11	14,666.1	149.5	1.0%	720
12/10	11,673.0	102.0	0.9%	660
12/09	9,146.1	62.7	0.7%	614
12/08	7,192.2	43.3	0.6%	553
Annual Growth	24.8%	43.8%	—	11.1%

2012 Year-End Financials

Return on assets: 1.1%
Return on equity: 12.1%
Long-term debt ($ mil.): —
No. of shares (mil.): 47
Sales ($ mil): 696

Dividends
Yield: —
Payout: —
Market value ($ mil.): 3,369

	STOCK PRICE ($) FY Close	P/E High/Low	PER SHARE ($) Earnings	Dividends	Book Value
12/12	71.34	18 14	3.91	0.00	34.94
12/11	59.99	18 13	3.37	0.00	30.49
12/10	50.06	21 13	2.46	0.00	22.84
12/09	31.90	25 15	1.30	0.00	19.79
12/08	28.69	27 17	1.35	0.00	19.81
Annual Growth	25.6%	— —	30.5%	—	15.2%

Silicon Laboratories Inc

Silicon Laboratories keeps cooking up new chips in its labs. The company develops mixed-signal integrated circuits (ICs) which translate real-world analog signals (such as sound) into digital signals that can be processed by electronic products. Silicon Labs provides ICs used in set-top boxes game consoles portable electronics industrial monitoring and control devices and wireless handsets. Products include microcontrollers clocks and oscillators sensors and broadcast communications chips. Top customers include Cisco Huawei LG Electronics Pace Panasonic Samsung Technicolor Varian Medical Systems and ZTE. Almost 90% of the company's sales come from customers outside the US.

Geographic Reach

China and Taiwan are Texas-based Silicon Laboratories largest markets together representing 50% of its annual sales. The US and South Korea each represent about 10%. The company has operations in the US China France Germany Hungary India ireland Japan South Korea Singapore Taiwan and the UK.

Sales and Marketing

The company markets its products through a direct sales force and network of independent sales representatives and distributors. Silicon Lab's two largest customers are Edom Technology (22% of sales) and Avnet (11%). In 2012 the firm reported advertising costs of 1.7 million compared with $1.6 million and $1.4 million in 2011 and 2010 respectively.

Financial Performance

Silicon Labs reported 2012 revenue of $563.3 million a 15% increase versus 2011. Net income rose 79% over the same period. The increase was driven by market share gains and additional prod-

uct revenue from the midyear acquisition of Ember Corp. Unit volumes of products increased 18% while average selling prices declined by 3% compared with 2011. On a geographic basis China outperformed all of the company's other markets with annual sales there up 44% in 2012. The US South Korea and Japan all posted annual declines.

The overall double-digit increase in sales and profits in 2012 reversed declines in each in 2011 versus 2010. Still the company's sales have been trending upwards increasing by 67% since 2007.

Strategy

Silicon Labs attributes the stability in sales and profits to improvements in global demand for consumer products and in the global economy overall. Chip makers tend to experience regular declines in average selling prices and try to offset that trend by regularly introducing new higher-margin products that help the company gain market share as well as constantly reducing manufacturing and logistics costs. Silicon Labs typically spends around a quarter of its annual sales on research and development as the company looks to introduce new highly integrated products (such as an industry first single-chip hybrid TV receiver released in 2011) and simplify integration of its chips into customers' products. The fabless semiconductor company primarily relies on Taiwan Semiconductor Manufacturing to produce its ICs.

The company also makes regular acquisitions to diversify its product line and add new technologies and functionality.

Mergers and Acquisitions

In July 2013 the company acquired Oslo Norway-based Energy Micro AS whose portfolio boasts the industry's most energy-efficient range of 32-bit microcontrollers. Silicon Labs paid $115 million up front for Energy Micro plus an additional $55 million later as deferred and "earn-out" consideration is the business grows as planned.

In July 2012 Silicon Labs bought privately held Ember Corporation for about $72 million. Ember makes low-power wireless networking chips used in connected home lighting security smart energy and other monitoring and control applications. Ember's ZigBee products complement Silicon Labs' technology and software expertise in the low-power mesh sensor networks used in a wide range of residential industrial and commercial applications. Ember became part of the company's wireless product portfolio.

In 2011 Silicon Labs bought SpectraLinear for about $40 million to boost its presence in the consumer electronics market. The deal added a line of programmable clock devices used in such products as MP3 players and digital cameras that complement the company's existing timing product line.

In 2010 Silicon Labs bought Silicon Clocks a developer of microelectromechanical systems (MEMS) devices fabricated with a standard CMOS production process for $22 million. The acquired product portfolio which includes MEMS resonators and other sensors used in consumer electronics and other high-volume applications bolsters Silicon Labs' CMOS-based timing devices. Silicon Labs also bought Ireland-based sensor specialist ChipSensors Limited that year to expand its line of temperature humidity and gas detection sensors.

Ownership

Investment firms FMR LLC and T. Rowe Price Associates own about 13% and 14% of Silicon Lab's shares respectively.

EXECUTIVES

Senior Vice President of Broad-based Products, Mark A. Downing, age 52

Chairman, Navdeep S. (Nav) Sooch, age 51, $288,462 total compensation

VP and Director, David R. Welland, age 57, $175,000 total compensation

SVP Worldwide Operations, Jonathan D. (Jon) Ivester, age 57, $268,846 total compensation

President, William G. (Bill) Bock, age 62, $310,615 total compensation

CIO, Everett G. Plante Jr.

SVP and Chief Product Officer, David (Dave) Bresemann, $160,000 total compensation

CFO, John Hollister

Vice President of wireline products at Silicon Laboratories, Carlos Garcia

CEO, G. Tyson Tuttle, age 45

SVP and CFO, Paul V. Walsh Jr., age 48, $200,962 total compensation

SVP Worldwide Sales, Kurt W. Hoff, age 55, $255,385 total compensation

VP General Manager Access Power and Sensors, Mark Thompson

VP Human Resources, Diane Williams

VP and General Manager Broadcast Audio Products, James Stansberry

Manager Global Public Relations, Dale Weisman

SVP; General Manager Microcontroller Products, Geir F?rre

Director, Kristen Onken, age 63

Director, Nelson C. Chan, age 50

VP and Director, David R. Welland, age 57

Director, Laurence G. (Larry) Walker, age 64

Director, William P. Wood, age 57

Director, Harvey B. (Berry) Cash, age 75

Director, Robert (Ted) Enloe III, age 74

President CEO and Director, Necip Sayiner, age 46

CEO, G. Tyson Tuttle, age 45

Auditors: Ernst&YoungLLP

LOCATIONS

HQ: Silicon Laboratories Inc
400 West Cesar Chavez, Austin, TX 78701
Phone: 512 416-8500
Web: www.silabs.com

2012 Sales

	$ mil.	% of total
China	219	39
US	64	12
Taiwan	64	11
South Korea	57	10
Japan	31	6
Other countries	125	22
Total	**563**	**100**

PRODUCTS/OPERATIONS

Selected Products

Access products
  ISOmodem embedded modems
  Power over Ethernet (PoE) power source equipment and powered device ICs
  ProSLIC analog subscriber line interface (short-haul for customer premise and long-haul for central office)
Broad-based products
  Digital isolators
  EZRadio short-range wireless transceivers
  Human interface sensors (capacitive touch sensors infrared sensors)
  Microcontrollers
  Precision clocks and oscillators
  Wireless receivers
Broadcast products
  Radio receivers and transmitters
  Video tuners and demodulators

COMPETITORS

Analog Devices
Atmel
Maxim Integrated Products
Broadcom
Conexant Systems
Cypress Semiconductor
Dialog Semiconductor
Dover Corp.
Epson
Freescale Semiconductor
IXYS
Infineon Technologies
Integrated Device Technology
MaxLinear
Microchip Technology
Microsemi
NXP Semiconductors
RF Micro Devices
Renesas Electronics
ST-Ericsson
STMicroelectronics
Semtech
Skyworks
Sony
Texas Instruments
TriQuint
Vitesse Semiconductor

HISTORICAL FINANCIALS

Company Type: Public

Income Statement

FYE: December 28

	REVENUE ($ mil.)	NET INCOME ($ mil.)	NET PROFIT MARGIN	EMPLOYEES
12/13	580.0	49.8	8.6%	1,060
12/12	563.2	63.5	11.3%	997
12/11*	491.6	35.4	7.2%	908
01/11	493.3	73.2	14.8%	845
01/10	441.0	73.0	16.6%	736
Annual Growth	**7.1%**	**(9.1%)**	**—**	**9.5%**

*Fiscal year change

2013 Year-End Financials

Debt ratio: 9.5%
Return on equity: 7.2%
Cash ($ mil.): 95
Current ratio: 4.21
Long-term debt ($ mil.): 87

No. of shares (mil.): 42
Dividends
  Yield: —
  Payout: —
Market value ($ mil.): 1,812

	STOCK PRICE ($) FY Close	P/E High/Low	Earnings	Dividends	Book Value
12/13	42.35	39 32	1.14	0.00	17.26
12/12	41.49	31 22	1.47	0.00	15.52
12/11*	43.42	61 38	0.79	0.00	14.24
01/11	46.02	32 21	1.57	0.00	14.24
01/10	48.38	30 13	1.57	0.00	13.76
Annual Growth	**(3.3%)**	**— —**	**(7.7%)**	**—**	**5.8%**

*Fiscal year change

Sinclair Broadcast Group, Inc.

To find out what's happening at Sinclair Broadcast Group (SBG) you could consult the TV Guide. The company is a leading television operator with more than 70 stations serving 45 midsized markets. Its portfolio reaches 26% of US households and includes affiliates of all four major broadcast networks as well as several affiliates of The CW Network and MyNetworkTV. (Most of the stations are affiliated with FOX.) More than 45 of SBG's stations are owned and operated while the rest are operated under local market agreements; the company has duopolies (more than one station) in about 20 of markets. The family of founder Julian Sinclair Smith led by CEO David Smith controls the company.

Geographic Reach

SBG serves midsized markets all around the US.

Sales and Marketing

The company spent about $12.2 million on advertising and marketing promotions in fiscal 2012.

Financial Performance

Revenue increased 39% net income decreased 91% in fiscal 2012 compared with 2011 while the company's net cash inflow increased by $189 million in 2012 compared with the prior year.

The increase in revenues was attributed to stations acquired during fiscal 2012 and revenues earned from a LMA with the Freedom stations. In addition revenues increased increase in local broadcast revenues and an increase in advertising spending particularly in the automotive and direct response sectors.

Strategy

Like most other commercial television broadcasters SBG relies on advertising for the bulk of its revenue with most of that coming from local advertisers. The company focuses on providing its stations with the best possible programming through both network affiliation agreements and syndication deals in order to attract and retain audiences. Within each market its stations compete for audiences against stations owned by other big broadcasting groups including Hearst Television Local TV and Media General.

Mergers and Acquisitions

In 2013 SBG acquired Fisher Communications for approximately $373.3 million. In early 2012 SBG widened its broadcast reach when it bought Four Points Media and its seven TV stations for $200 million. The purchase helped the company to diversify its broadcast network with more non-FOX affiliates and added stations in four markets including Austin Texas; Providence Rhode Island; Salt Lake City; and West Palm Beach Florida. In addition to that deal SBG has an agreement in place to acquire eight TV stations owned by Freedom Communications for $385 million. Those stations reach 2.6% of US households across seven markets. In 2013 SBG agreed to acquire four TV stations from COX Media Group for some $95 million. Following the purchase the company's TV group will reach more than 27% of US households.

HISTORY

Julian Sinclair Smith founded the company in 1971 with TV station WBFF (one of the first UHF channels in the country) in Baltimore. Several years later came WPTT another UHF channel in Pittsburgh. A movement among the board's directors in 1985 to oust Smith (who controlled 40% of the company) was foiled when Smith and his son David allied with a director who held a 10.2% stake. Shortly after the family bought the dissidents out and hard-knuckled boss David took over management of the company renamed Sinclair Broadcasting Group (SBG) in 1986.

The company bought Pittsburgh station WPGH in 1991 selling its WPTT station the same day. It expanded again with its 1994 purchase of four stations from ABRY Partners. SBG went public in 1995 using the $75 million raised to trim its debt. It also used the funds to back its growing appetite for acquisitions buying five stations in 1995 and buying River City Broadcasting in 1996.

SBG came under fire in 1996 for pushing an FCC law barring duopolies (ownership of more than one UHF channel in a market) when a rival challenged its dealings with Glencairn a broadcasting company owned in part by Smith's mother Carolyn. The company's bad luck continued that year when David Smith was arrested (the charges were later dropped) after getting caught with a prostitute. Continuing Smith's philosophy to "get as many TV stations as we can" the company bought 14 TV stations from Sullivan Broadcast Holdings for $1 billion and seven TV stations from Guy Gannett Communications for $310 million in 1998. As its debt grew the company promised to sell some $500 million in noncore assets.

SBG followed through on that claim in 1999 and 2000 by exiting the radio market when it sold its radio holdings to Entercom Communications for about $920 million. Amid a decline in ad sales the company cut nearly 200 jobs in 2001. SBG created News Central in 2002 which centralizes all of the company's news operations so that it can more easily add coverage to all of its stations.

EXECUTIVES

VP Human Resources, Donald H. Thompson, age 46

VP Programming and Promotions, M. William (Bill) Butler, age 60

Chief Financial Officer; Executive Vice President, David B. Amy, age 60, $646,000 total compensation

VP Engineering and Operations, Delbert R. Parks III, age 60

Chief Operating Officer; Vice President, Steven M. Marks, age 56, $725,000 total compensation

VP Secretary and Director, J. Duncan Smith, age 59, $190,000 total compensation

VP and Director, Frederick G. Smith, age 63, $190,000 total compensation

Chairman of the Board; President; Chief Executive Officer, David D. Smith, age 62, $1,000,000 total compensation

Vice President; Chief Accounting Officer, David R. Bochenek, age 50

Executive Vice President; General Counsel, Barry M. Faber, age 51, $625,000 total compensation

Vice President - Corporate Finance; Treasurer, Lucy A. Rutishauser, age 48, $286,000 total compensation

VP National Sales, Gregg L. Siegel, age 52

VP New Business Sales, Darren J. Shapiro, age 52

VP Purchasing, Thomas I. (Tom) Waters III, age 44

President of Keyser Capital, W. Gary Dorsch, age 61

VP Finance Television, Robert Malandra, age 50

VP New Media, Rob Weisbord

VP Sales, Dave Schwartz, age 59

VP Advanced Technology Sinclair Television, Mark Aitken

VP Secretary and Director, J. Duncan Smith, age 59

VP and Director, Frederick G. Smith, age 63

Director, Robert E. Smith, age 49

Director, Lawrence E. McCanna, age 69

Director, Basil A. Thomas, age 97

Director, Daniel C. Keith, age 58

Director, Martin R. Leader, age 72

Auditors: Ernst&YoungLLP

LOCATIONS

HQ: Sinclair Broadcast Group Inc.
10706 Beaver Dam Rd., Hunt Valley MD 21030
Phone: 410-568-1500   **Fax:** 410-568-1533
Web: www.sbgi.net

Selected Television Markets

Asheville NC
Austin TX
Baltimore
Birmingham AL
Buffalo NY
Cape Girardeau MS
Cedar Rapids IA
Charleston SC
Charleston-Huntington WV
Cincinnati
Columbus OH
Dayton OH
Des Moines IA
Flint MI
Greensboro/Winston-Salem NC
Las Vegas
Lexington KY
Madison WI
Milwaukee
Minneapolis
Mobile AL
Nashville TN
Norfolk VA
Oklahoma City
Peoria-Bloomington IL
Pittsburgh
Portland ME
Providence RI
Raleigh-Durham NC
Richmond VA
Rochester NY
Salt Lake City
St. Louis
San Antonio
Springfield-Champaign IL
Syracuse NY
Tallahassee FL
Tampa
West Palm Beach FL

PRODUCTS/OPERATIONS

2012 Sales

	$ mil.	% of total
Broadcasting	1,007	95
Other operating divisions	54	5

COMPETITORS

Belo Corp.	LIN TV
CBS	Local TV
E. W. Scripps	Media General
FOX Broadcasting	Meredith Corporation
Gannett	Newport Television
Granite Broadcasting	Nexstar Broadcasting
Gray Television	Raycom Media
Hearst Television	
Journal Broadcast Group	

HISTORICAL FINANCIALS

Company Type: Public

Income Statement

FYE: December 31

	REVENUE ($ mil.)	NET INCOME ($ mil.)	NET PROFIT MARGIN	EMPLOYEES
12/12	1,061.6	144.6	13.6%	4,000
12/11	765.2	75.8	9.9%	3,130
12/10	767.1	76.1	9.9%	2,350
12/09	656.4	(135.6)	—	2,400
12/08	754.4	(241.4)	—	2,500
Annual Growth	8.9%	—	—	12.5%

2012 Year-End Financials

Debt ratio: 83.2%
Return on equity: ***,***.*%
Cash ($ mil.): 22
Current ratio: 0.99
Long-term debt ($ mil.): 2,224

No. of shares (mil.): 81
Dividends
 Yield: 4.2%
 Payout: 86.5%
Market value ($ mil.): 1,026

	STOCK PRICE ($) FY Close	P/E High/Low		PER SHARE ($) Earnings	Dividends	Book Value
12/12	12.62	7	4	1.78	1.54	(1.44)
12/11	11.33	14	7	0.94	0.48	(1.50)
12/10	8.18	9	4	0.94	0.43	(2.06)
12/09	4.03	—	—	(1.70)	0.60	(2.66)
12/08	3.10	—	—	(2.82)	0.80	(1.03)
Annual Growth	42.0%	—	—	—	17.8%	—

Sirona Dental Systems Inc

Factoid for the day: The first electric dental drill was invented in 1882 and the company that made it is now known as Sirona Dental Systems. The company still makes handheld dental instruments as well as imaging systems dental CAD/CAM systems used in restorations and a full line of other products used by dentists and dental laboratories worldwide. Its CEREC system is a 3-D computer-aided contraption for making ceramic restorations (such as crowns and bridges) in the dentist's office rather than a lab. The firm's imaging systems include traditional X-ray equipment and digital radiography systems. Other products include dental chairs (known as "treatment centers") and instrument cleaning systems.

Geographic Reach

The company operates globally with the US and Germany as its largest markets. Its top distributors are Patterson and Henry Schein and it uses Patterson exclusively to distribute its CEREC products in North America. Sirona has production facilities in China Denmark Germany Italy and the US; it also outsources the manufacturing of some components.

Operations

Sirona operates through four main segments: Imaging systems dental CAD/CAM systems treatment centers and instruments. Imaging systems contributed to 35% of the company's revenue in 2012 and produces diagnostic imaging equipment. Dental CAD/CAM systems products comprise CAD/CAM in-office systems for dentists and laboratories and a central manufacturing service for copings and bridge-frameworks. The dental CAD/CAM systems segment contributed 34% to Sirona's revenue.

Sirona's treatment centers (20% of revenue) make dentist chairs and centers with integrated diagnostic hygiene and ergonomic functionalities. Its instruments segment (around 11% of revenue) makes and supplies a range of handpiece products including handheld and power-operated devices used for cavity preparation endodontics period ontology and prophylaxis.

Financial Analysis

Sirona has enjoyed a steady rise in revenue profits and cash flow over the years. From 2011 to 2012 its revenue increased by 7% and its profits spiked by 7% to the highest amounts of total sales (almost $980 million) and net income ($135 million) in the company's history. The company is experiencing higher demand for its products on a global scales across all its segments. It also in 2012 benefited from a decrease in research and development expenses attributed to foreign currency exchange fluctuations.

Strategy

During the weakened global economy of the past few years dentists shied away from making non-crucial big-ticket equipment purchases which prompted the Sirona to restructure and reduce operating costs. However Sirona knows its customers still want cutting-edge technology and enjoy trading in their older Sirona systems for upgrades.

Growth has come from efforts to expand its distribution network both in the US and in international markets adding a number of sales and service centers in new regions of Asia/Pacific and

Europe. The company also prides itself on a history of innovation and invests in research and development of new products —its area of fastest growth. Sirona keeps tabs on trends and has introduced more digital products as the industry has trended away from older non-digital equipment.

EXECUTIVES

President and CEO, Jeffrey T. Slovin, age 49, $442,900 total compensation
General Counsel; Secretary, Jonathan I Friedman, age 43, $275,000 total compensation
Chief Executive Officer of Sirona, Jost Fischer, age 59, $768,008 total compensation
EVP CFO and Director, Simone Blank, age 50, $465,130 total compensation
VP Investor Relations, John Sweeney
EVP Sales, Walter Petersohn
VP-Sls & Mktg, Michael Williamson
President Sales and Marketing USA, Michael Augins
VP Treatment Centers, Michael Geil
VP Dental CAD/CAM Systems, Joachim Pfeiffer
VP Corporate Marketing, Jurgen Serafin
Vice President Instruments, Jan Siefert
Chairman, Thomas Jetter
Vice President Imaging Systems, Stefan Hehn
VP Dental CAD/CAM Systems, Bart Doedens
Territory Manager Arizona New Mexico, Bob Gess
Sales Manager Imaging Systems, Antonio Criado
Sales Manager CAD, Csilla Banyai
VP Intraoral Imaging, Kevin McNulty
National Accounts Manager, Steven Pryce
Vice President CAD CAM Systems, Roddy MacLeod
Territory Manager Delaware, Rick McLane
Sales Manager, Steen Yde
Finance Manager, Stephane Pirola
Territory Manager S. Florida, Stephen Ramsey
Territory Manager Iowa Minnesota, Tom Thuente
Territory Manager Illinois Michigan Superior Region, Vito DiPerte
Territory Manager N. and Central Alabama, Whit Wylie
Sales Director Sirona Italia, Roberto Canton
Territory Manager N. and Central Georgia, Lamar Lutz
Territory Manager Kansas Missouri, Clark Colwell
Territory Manager West Central and South Texas, Don Harvey
Territory Manager Southern California, Gary Fitzpatrick
Sales Manager Treatment Centers & Instruments Specialist, Javier Rodrigo
Territory Manager Maryland Washington DC, Jay Schroeder
Territory Manager Colorado Montana, John Sellyei
Sales Manager CAD, Juan Mu+?oz
Sales Manager CAD, Karl-Heinz Zunko
Head of CEREC and inLab Sales, Marcus Hoffmann
VP Sales, Maria Daglinger
Territory Manager Metro New York, Mark Hahn
Territory Manager Northern California, Mark Ilagan
Territory Manager Connecticut, Matt Schoeller
Vice President of Corporate Human Resources, Michael Elling
Territory Manager Central California, Mohamad Hamdan
Territory Manager Western New York, Pat Hess
Sales Manager Specialty Accounts Hospitals, Patricia Czaplinsky
Territory Manager New Hampshire, Peter Gavin
Territory Manager Indiana Michigan all but Superior Region, Kent Albrecht
Sales Manager, Bjorn Royr
Territory Manager N. Florida, Andrew Bretko
Sales Manager CAD, Andy Vetterli

Territory Manager Arkansas Oklahoma, Ross Webb
Executive Vice President, Rainer Berthan
Vice President Investor Relations, Joshua Zable
Director, Harry M. J. Kraemer Jr., age 59
President and Director, Jeffrey T. Slovin, age 48
Director, Nicholas W. Alexos, age 48
Director, Timothy P. Sullivan, age 56
Director, Timothy D. Sheehan, age 40
Director, David K. (Dave) Beecken, age 67
Director, William K. Hood, age 90
Director, Arthur D. Kowaloff, age 66
EVP CFO and Director, Simone Blank, age 50
Chairman, Thomas Jetter
Auditors: KPMGAGWirtschaftsprufungsgesellschaft

LOCATIONS

HQ: Sirona Dental Systems Inc.
30-00 47th Ave., Long Island City NY 11101
Phone: 718-937-5765   **Fax:** 718-937-5962
Web: www.sirona.com

2012 Sales

US	285	29
Other countries	535	55

PRODUCTS/OPERATIONS

2012 Sales

	$ mil.	% of total
Imaging systems	343	35
Dental CAD/CAM systems	334	34
Treatment centers	197	20
Other	1	.

Selected Products

Imaging systems
  Computed digital radiography system (intra-oral digital imaging system)
  Galileos Compact
  Orthophos XG (digital panoramic X-ray system)
  Sidexis XG (imaging software)
Dental CAD/CAM systems
  CEREC (in-office dental restoration system)
  infiniDent (central production service)
  inLab (laboratory dental restoration system)
Treatment centers
  Basic dentists chairs
  Integrated treatment centers
  TENEO treatment center
  Kappler Dental Cabinetry
Instruments
  SIROair (airscaler)
  SIROEndo (root canal preparation unit)
  SIROLaser (diode laser used in endodontics period ontology and oral surgery)

COMPETITORS

American Medical Systems	Kinetic Concepts
American Medical Technologies	Midmark Corporation
Astra Tech (Sweden)	National Dentex
CONMED Corporation	Nobel Biocare
Carestream Health	NuVasive
Cooper Companies	Orthofix
DENTSPLY	Patterson Companies
Glidewell Laboratories	Philips Electronics
Henry Schein	ResMed
Hu-Friedy	STERIS
IDEXX Labs	Siemens Healthcare
ImageWorks	Straumann
Integra LifeSciences	Sybron Dental
	Thoratec Corp
	Young Innovations

HISTORICAL FINANCIALS

Company Type: Public

Income Statement

FYE: September 30

	REVENUE ($ mil.)	NET INCOME ($ mil.)	NET PROFIT MARGIN	EMPLOYEES
09/13	1,101.4	146.7	13.3%	3,216
09/12	979.3	133.8	13.7%	2,979
09/11	913.8	121.7	13.3%	2,705
09/10	770.2	89.9	11.7%	2,345
09/09	713.2	53.3	7.5%	2,298
Annual Growth	11.5%	28.8%	—	8.8%

2013 Year-End Financials

Debt ratio: 4.3%	No. of shares (mil.): 55
Return on equity: 13.6%	Dividends
Cash ($ mil.): 241	Yield: —
Current ratio: 2.29	Payout: —
Long-term debt ($ mil.): 75	Market value ($ mil.): 3,681

	STOCK PRICE ($) FY Close	P/E High/Low		PER SHARE ($) Earnings	Dividends	Book Value
09/13	66.93	28	21	2.61	0.00	21.01
09/12	56.96	24	16	2.36	0.00	17.97
09/11	42.41	26	16	2.13	0.00	16.70
09/10	36.04	26	16	1.59	0.00	14.56
09/09	29.75	31	10	0.96	0.00	13.55
Annual Growth	22.5%		—	— 28.4%	—	— 11.6%

Skullcandy Inc

If your head craves sweet tunes Skullcandy has a treat for you. The youth-oriented firm designs and sells edgy stylish headphones ear buds docking station speakers and other audio goodies as well as apparel and accessories. Featuring an aesthetic design that appeals to its target audience of action sports enthusiasts the gear was originally sold at specialty shops but also can be found nationwide at Target and Best Buy through the company's website and in more than 70 countries where youth culture thrives. Skullcandy retains its street cred by sinking many marketing dollars into sponsoring boarders surfers and BMX bikers. Founded in 2003 Skullcandy went public in 2011.

The headphone maker whose shares priced at $20 apiece raised about $188 million in its July IPO. Strong demand for the deal led the shares to price above their expected range. Skullcandy will use the proceeds to pay off a debt load of $45 million provide working capital for general corporate purposes and to acquire other businesses products or technologies. (Indeed in August it acquired the distribution rights to its products in Europe for about $18.6 million.)

Skullcandy executives and directors collectively own 75% of the company. Of the 75% chairman Jeff Kearl (a manager at investment vehicle Ptarmigan and a trustee to The Alden Irrevocable Trust) holds 35%; CEO Jeremy Andrus directly holds 10% and another 8% jointly with his father Brent Andrus through the firm JA Cropston; and company directors Joe Ferreira Jr. and David Oddi (associated with Goode Skullcandy Holdings) each have a 17% share. Separately Ptarmigan owns 34% of Skullcandy and Goode Skullcandy Holdings holds a 17% stake.

A month after the January IPO filing Skullcandy founder and CEO Alden resigned which is unusual for a company in registration for an IPO. (Alden was named Entrepreneur of the Year in 2009 by Entrepreneur magazine.) He was replaced by Jeremy Andrus who joined the company in 2005 and had served as president and COO since 2008. Andrus joined Skullcandy from Kimpton Hotel & Restaurant Group Marriott and Monitor Company. Alden's resignation came shortly before the company revealed soaring costs —and a one-time charge for management incentive bonuses of $17.5 million —that led to a net loss of $9.7 million in 2010.

While the company generates some 90% of its sales from headphones and boasts 1200 products it's working to expand its product portfolio and extend its reach in the US and abroad where Skullcandy picks up about 30% of its revenue. Following the debut of its upscale Aviator and Mix Master headphones which sell for $150 and $250 respectively the audio equipment supplier made plans to pump out more premium products to cater to customers with higher discretionary incomes. Known to market headphones as a lifestyle product much like Oakley does with its eyeglasses Skullcandy has been expanding its product categories by introducing protective cases for smartphones and speakers for docking stations. It is also boosting its offerings in the video game space. To that end Skullcandy acquired the assets of gaming headset manufacturer Astro Gaming for $10 million in early 2011.

Besides the usual headphones ear buds and other audiophile gear the company serves its youthful target market by working with other manufacturers to include Skullcandy-branded audio technology into helmets hats jackets and bags. It also serves up the hip brand and skull logo through partnerships with rapper Jay-Z's Roc Nation entertainment company the NBA the NCAA and Hard Rock Hotel Holdings' Las Vegas hotel and casino.

Another goal for the company is to get more of its products on retailers' shelves and in in-store displays. It's doing so by strengthening its relationships with existing clients such as Dick's Sporting Goods and AT&T Wireless and increasing its visibility with new mass merchants and specialty shops particularly those who sell electronics sporting goods and mobile phones. Skullcandy also is investing in the interactive platforms on its website to drive sales by providing customers with ways to customize their shopping experience and by launching international websites with local content. Online sales account for about 4% of the firm's revenue.

Skullcandy which relies on about 20 Chinese manufacturers to make its products gets its namesake items in the hands of consumers overseas in more than 70 countries through agreements with third-party distributors. To accelerate its growth internationally the headphones maker plans to duplicate its marketing successes in the US by sponsoring international athletes musicians and artists. In mid-2012 it hired a new product development executive with experience at Burton Snowboards to boost the brand.

EXECUTIVES

Chief Financial Officer; Senior Vice President, Kyle B. Wescoat

President CEO and Director, Jeremy Andrus, age 41

Global VP Business Development and Marketing, Clarke Miyasaki

Manager Operations, Brad Smith

Executive VP Chief Marketing Officer Director of Industrial Design, Dan Levine, age 43

VP International Sales, Aaron Behle, age 41

VP North America Sales, Richard Sargente, age 45

Chairman, Jeff Kearl, age 40

Vice President - Global Business Development, Brent Wilkins

Chairman, Douglas Collier

Vice President - Global Marketing and Creative, Nate Morley

Vice President - Finance; Principal Accounting Officer, Ron Ross

Chief Commercial Officer, Sam Paschel

President and CEO, Hobi Darling

Head of Domestic Sales, Denny Bruce

Vice President Strategic Initiatives and Corporate Affairs, Patrick Grosso

Director, Rick Alden, age 48

President CEO and Director, Jeremy Andrus, age 41

Director, Greg Warnock, age 52

Independent Director, Douglas Collier

Independent Director, Scott Olivet

Auditors: Ernst&YoungLLP

LOCATIONS

HQ: Skullcandy Inc.
1441 W. Ute Blvd. Ste 250, Park City UT 84098
Phone: 435-940-1545   **Fax:** 714-619-9750
Web: www.universalpro.com

PRODUCTS/OPERATIONS

Selected Products

Accessories
  Bags
  Beanies
  Belts
  iPod docking stations
  Socks
  Wallets
Apparel
  Hoodies
  T-shirts
Headphones
  DJ
  Gaming
  In ear
  On ear
  Over ear
  Sports
  Wireless

COMPETITORS

Billabong	Pioneer Corporation
Bose	Plantronics
Harman International	Quiksilver
Koss	Sennheiser
NIKE	Sony USA
Oakley	VOXX International
Philips Consumer	adidas
Lifestyle	

HISTORICAL FINANCIALS

Company Type: Public

Income Statement

FYE: December 31

	REVENUE ($ mil.)	NET INCOME ($ mil.)	NET PROFIT MARGIN	EMPLOYEES
12/12	297.6	25.8	8.7%	335
12/11	232.4	18.6	8.0%	290
12/10	160.5	(9.6)	—	200
12/09	118.3	12.3	10.4%	0
12/08	80.3	13.0	16.2%	0
Annual Growth	38.7%	18.7%	—	—

2012 Year-End Financials

Debt ratio: —	No. of shares (mil.): 27
Return on equity: 20.7%	Dividends
Cash ($ mil.): 19	Yield: —
Current ratio: 3.32	Payout: —
Long-term debt ($ mil.): —	Market value ($ mil.): 216

	STOCK PRICE ($) FY Close	P/E High/Low		PER SHARE ($) Earnings	Dividends	Book Value
12/12	7.79	18	8	0.92	0.00	5.11
12/11	12.52	22	13	0.79	0.00	3.90
Annual Growth	(37.8%)	—	—	16.5%	—	31.2%

Skyworks Solutions, Inc.

The sky's the limit for Skyworks Solutions. The company makes integrated circuits (ICs) for wireless and other applications. Its flagship handset products include power amplifiers and front-end modules used by OEMs like Samsung Electronics Ericsson LG and Nokia in their mobile phones and communications infrastructure gear. Other analog devices include attenuators diodes couplers phase shifters receivers and switches used in a broad array of industries. Skyworks uses gallium arsenide (GaAs) a material that is faster and uses less energy than industry-standard silicon in many of its devices. The company gets more than 90% of its sales from customers in the Asia and Asia/Pacific regions.

Operations In addition to its handset business Skyworks sells its analog and mixed-signal (combines analog and digital circuits on a single chip) ICs to customers in the automotive energy management infrastructure medical and military markets. The company sells its portfolio of more than 2500 analog components to more than 2000 customers worldwide. It also licenses its intellectual property (IP) to encourage customers to incorporate its ICs into their products during the design phase.

Geographic Reach China leads the company's geographic segments accounting for more than half of sales; other Asian countries bring in an additional 33%. The Americas and the EMEA region contribute 6% or 2% of sales respectively. Skyworks saw year-over-year declines across nearly all regions (including China and South Korea) but that was offset by triple-digit growth in Taiwan and other countries in the Asia-Pacific region. Sales and Marketing Although Skyworks partners with some electronic components distributors it markets its products to OEMs primarily through its own global sales force. The company's largest customers include Foxconn and Samsung Electronics which each accounted for more than 10% of sales in 2012. Financial Analysis Revenue rose 11% in fiscal 2012 (ended September 30) to $1.6 billion as Skyworks brought new products to its customers through acquisitions. It also benefited from the ongoing wireless network upgrade to 3G and 4G as well as newly developed products for other markets. Acquisitions and high research and development costs led to an increase in expenses which contributed to an 11% drop in net income to $202 million.

Mergers and Acquisitions In 2012 Skyworks bought power management chip maker Advanced Analogic Technologies in a cash transaction valued at about $257 million. The deal added battery chargers DC/DC converters voltage regulators LED drivers and other devices for a wide range of electronic products and bolstered Skyworks' wireless communications portfolio by extending the company's reach into new vertical markets in the consumer and computing sectors. The analog power management market is expected to grow significantly over the next few years as manufacturers look to make their products more energy efficient and cost effective. In 2011 the company bought privately held wireless communications chip maker SiGe Semiconductor in a deal valued at around $275 million. Skyworks was looking to bolster its capabilities in wireless connectivity with a profitable and growing business. It was drawn to SiGe Semi which saw its business booming as its chips were increasingly included in home entertainment devices by Cisco Dell HP Microsoft Sony and other customers. SiGe filed an IPO in 2010 but never went public.

EXECUTIVES

President CEO and Director, David J. Aldrich, age 57, $583,404 total compensation
VP Human Resources, George M. LeVan, age 67, $197,885 total compensation
VP General Counsel and Secretary, Mark V. B. Tremallo, age 57
Vice President Quality, Kenneth J. Huening, age 48
SVP Worldwide Operations, Bruce J. Freyman, age 53, $343,000 total compensation
Chairman, David J. McLachlan, age 75
EVP; General Manager Front End Solutions, Gregory L. (Greg) Waters, age 53, $370,635 total compensation
EVP; General Manager High Performance Analog, Liam K. Griffin, age 46, $344,000 total compensation
VP Quality, Nien-Tsu Shen, age 60
VP and CFO, Donald W. (Don) Palette, age 56, $305,769 total compensation
Media Relations, Pilar Barrigas
SVP Worldwide Sales, Bradley C. Byk
Director, Robert A. (Rob) Schriesheim, age 53
Director, Kevin L. Beebe, age 54
President CEO and Director, David J. Aldrich, age 57
Director, Thomas C. Leonard, age 79
Director, Moiz M. Beguwala, age 67
Director, Balakrishnan S. (Bala) Iyer, age 57
Director, Timothy R. (Tim) Furey, age 55
Director, David P. McGlade, age 53
Auditors: KPMGLLP

LOCATIONS

HQ: Skyworks Solutions Inc.
20 Sylvan Rd., Woburn MA 01801
Phone: 781-376-3000   **Fax:** 201-549-4428
Web: www.alpine-group.net

2012 Sales

	$ mil.	% of total
Asia/Pacific		
China	820	52
Taiwan	311	20
South Korea	103	7
Other Asia/Pacific	207	13
Americas		
US	70	5
Other Americas	18	1
Europe Middle East & Africa	37	2
Total	**1,568**	**100**

PRODUCTS/OPERATIONS

Selected Products

Discrete semiconductors
  Gallium arsenide (GaAs) field-effect transistors (FETs)
  Receiving diodes
  Schottky diodes
  Varactor diodes
GaAs radio-frequency (RF) integrated circuits (ICs)
  Amplifiers
  Attenuators
  Control FETs
  Switches
Magnetic and dielectric materials
Microwave semiconductors
  Attenuators
  Schottky diodes
  Silicon pin diodes
  Step recovery diodes
  Switches
  Varactor diodes
Millimeter-wave semiconductors
  Attenuators
  Converters
  Driver low-noise multifunction and power amplifiers
  Mixers
  Schottky barrier mixer diodes
  Switches
Multifunction and passive components
  Directional couplers
  Mixers
  Power dividers
  Sampling phase directors
  Voltage variable attenuators
Phase shifters
Radio-frequency (RF) subsystems
Resonators
  Coaxial
  Dielectric
Technical ceramics
  Ceramic and technical powders
  Ceramic filters
Wireless infrastructure components

COMPETITORS

ANADIGICS	Murata Manufacturing
Analog Devices	Nitronex
Avago Technologies	Peregrine
Conexant Systems	Semiconductor
DSP Group	RF Micro Devices
Fairchild	ST-Ericsson
Semiconductor	Silicon Labs
Filtronic	Sumitomo Electric
Hittite Microwave	Device Innovations
Linear Technology	TDK
Maxim Integrated	TriQuint
Products	Vitesse Semiconductor
Microsemi	

HISTORICAL FINANCIALS

Company Type: Public

Income Statement

FYE: September 27

	REVENUE ($ mil.)	NET INCOME ($ mil.)	NET PROFIT MARGIN	EMPLOYEES
09/13	1,792.0	278.1	15.5%	4,750
09/12	1,568.5	202.0	12.9%	4,700
09/11*	1,418.9	226.5	16.0%	4,400
10/10	1,071.8	137.2	12.8%	3,700
10/09	802.5	93.2	11.6%	3,300
Annual Growth	**22.2%**	**31.4%**	**—**	**9.5%**

*Fiscal year change

2013 Year-End Financials

Debt ratio: —	No. of shares (mil.): 187
Return on equity: 13.9%	Dividends
Cash ($ mil.): 511	Yield: —
Current ratio: 5.97	Payout: —
Long-term debt ($ mil.): —	Market value ($ mil.): 4,654

	STOCK PRICE ($) FY Close	P/E High/Low		PER SHARE ($) Earnings	Dividends	Book Value
09/13	24.77	18	13	1.45	0.00	11.18
09/12	23.56	29	13	1.05	0.00	9.91
09/11*	17.96	30	15	1.19	0.00	8.63
10/10	20.65	27	13	0.75	0.00	7.30
10/09	11.90	26	7	0.55	0.00	6.39
Annual Growth	**20.1%**	—	—	**27.4%**	—	**15.0%**

*Fiscal year change

Smith & Wesson Holding Corp

Smith & Wesson has built a successful business shooting for the stars. Operating through subsidiary Smith & Wesson Corp. Smith & Wesson Holding Corporation makes and markets pistols revolvers tactical rifles and police accessories as well as gun-safety devices under the M&P Series name. The company founded in 1852 also sells handcuffs and hunting rifles and car boat and home alarm system packages. Smith & Wesson is the exclusive importer of Walther pistols with US production rights for the Walther PPK model. To diversify and add breadth to its brand the company licenses its name to makers of apparel watches sunglasses gift sets and more.

Geographic Reach

Smith & Wesson sells its products globally. Besides the US the company serves Europe Asia and Latin America. It maintains production facilities for its firearms in Springfield Massachusetts and in Houlton Maine.

Strategy

Smith & Wesson aims to diversify its products portfolio as the company evolves from being a gun maker to a top supplier of a variety of arms. As a result the company has traded sales of revolvers in favor of pistols. Smith & Wesson is also working to expand its products in the areas of tactical and long-gun lines as well as non-firearm products.

The company supports its firearms business through deals with other companies to make Smith & Wesson-branded products. A licensing agreement with BBC Imagewear inked in 2009 provides Smith & Wesson with branded T-shirts jackets and shirts. A similar deal with Kudzu/The Game offers branded hats and caps and hats T-shirts jackets gun pads license plates decals pins patches key chains glassware and mugs with the Thompson/Center Arms logo. Its licensing agreement with TruckVault calls for Smith & Wesson-brand lockable steel handgun safes for homes vehicles and public safety agencies including police government agencies fire departments and the military.

Financial Performance

Smith & Wesson has seen its net sales rise in recent years particularly following the November 2008 US presidential election as consumers began to stockpile arms for fear of losing some rights under new leadership. In 2011 however Smith & Wesson logged slightly fewer orders across the company's firearms businesses –returning to more normal levels temporarily as compared to the strong consumer demand it has experienced for years.

In fiscal 2012 net sales increased 20% and net income rose 119% as compared to 2011. Net cash outflow during the same reporting period was $1 million vs. $20 million in 2011. Net sales increases can be attributed to a 25% rise in handgun product sales and a 94% increase in sales of modern sporting rifles thanks to the late fiscal 2011 introduction of a new sport model that was competitively priced. International sales meanwhile accounted for 4% of Smith & Wesson's sales. The company's net income boost came from rising operating income due to increased sales volumes. Its net cash outflow in 2012 was primarily related to cash used in financing activities such as repurchasing Convertible Notes.

Sales and Marketing

Smith & Wesson taps several distribution channels to get its products in the hands of customers. Customers include distributors government and military agencies businesses retailers and consumers as well as federal state and municipal law enforcement agencies and officers. The company which spent $14.7 million on advertising and promotion expenses in 2012 leverages its websites to market products and services.

The company has increased its sales in recent years by forming and maintaining its own sales force instead of relying on the representatives of independent manufacturers to sell its products including its line of polymer pistols.

Company Background

Amid a shift in government spending the company exited the perimeter security systems business in 2011. It moved to divest its perimeter security division —Tennessee-based Universal Safety Response (later renamed Smith & Wesson Security Solutions) to Detroit Michigan-based FutureNet Group in mid-2012. Smith & Wesson Security Solutions has provided barriers and installation and other services used in approximately 110 military installations and more than a dozen federal agencies and commercial facilities. The operations generated about $130 million during the past three years accounting for some 10% of Smith & Wesson's sales.

EXECUTIVES

EVP CFO and Treasurer, Jeffrey D. Buchanan, age 58

Chairman, Barry M. Monheit, age 66

Vice Chairman, Robert L. (Bob) Scott, age 67, $240,032 total compensation

President CEO and Director, P. James Debney, age 46

SVP Marketing and International Sales, Mario Pasantes

VP Information Technology, Marc St. George

Director, Robert H. (Bob) Brust, age 70

Director, Mitchell A. Saltz, age 60

Vice Chairman, Robert L. (Bob) Scott, age 67

Director, John B. Furman, age 69

Director, I. Marie Wadecki, age 64

Director, Michael F. Golden, age 59

Director, David M. Stone, age 59

President CEO and Director, P. James Debney, age 46

Auditors: BDOUSALLP

LOCATIONS

HQ: Smith & Wesson Holding Corp
 2100 Roosevelt Avenue, Springfield, MA 01104
Phone: 800 331-0852
Web: www.smith-wesson.com

PRODUCTS/OPERATIONS

2012 Sales

	$ mil.	% of total
Handguns	238	58
Modern sporting rifles	75	18
Walther	32	8
Hunting firearms	27	7
Parts & accessories	20	5
Non-firearms	18	4
Total	**412**	**100**

Selected Products

Accessories
 Cases
 Fiber optic sights
 Gloves
 Grips
 Holsters
 Locks
 Magazins
Apparel
Firearms
 Pistols
 Revolvers
 Rifles
Knives
Handcuffs and restraints
Personal security
 Racks
 Safes
 Vaults

COMPETITORS

American Derringer	Marlin Firearms
Browning Arms	Mossberg
Bushmaster Firearms	Para USA
Colt Defense	Remington Arms
Colt' s	Ruger
Fabbrica D' Armi Pietro	Savage Arms
Beretta	Springfield Armory
Freedom Group	Taurus International
Glock	Tyco Fire &
Heckler & Koch	Security

HISTORICAL FINANCIALS

Company Type: Public

Income Statement

FYE: April 30

	REVENUE ($ mil.)	NET INCOME ($ mil.)	NET PROFIT MARGIN	EMPLOYEES
04/13	587.5	78.7	13.4%	1,475
04/12	412.0	16.1	3.9%	1,346
04/11	392.3	(82.7)	—	1,520
04/10	406.1	32.5	8.0%	1,563
04/09	334.9	(64.2)	—	1,362
Annual Growth	**15.1%**	**—**	**—**	**2.0%**

2013 Year-End Financials

Debt ratio: 13.3%
Return on equity: 53.5%
Cash ($ mil.): 100
Current ratio: 2.78
Long-term debt ($ mil.): 43

No. of shares (mil.): 64
Dividends
 Yield: —
 Payout: —
Market value ($ mil.): 565

	STOCK PRICE ($) FY Close	P/E High/Low		PER SHARE ($) Earnings	Dividends	Book Value
04/13	8.78	9	5	1.18	0.00	2.82
04/12	8.25	34	9	0.25	0.00	1.73
04/11	3.60	—	—	(1.37)	0.00	1.47
04/10	4.47	13	7	0.53	0.00	2.68
04/09	7.17	—	—	(1.37)	0.00	1.06
Annual Growth	**5.2%**			**—**	**—**	**27.7%**

Snyder's-Lance Inc.

If you're familiar with the munchies named Toastchee Nipchee and Captain's Wafers Snyder's-Lance (formerly Lance) has undoubtedly helped you satisfy a snack attack. The company produces single-serve multi-pack and family-sized packages of bakery products and sweet and savory snack foods including cookies crackers nuts potato chips and pretzels. Its snacks are sold under the Lance Cape Cod Tom's Archway and Snyder's brands at food retailers mass merchants and convenience and club stores in the US. The company also makes private-label and branded snacks for food makers. The company changed its name to Snyder's-Lance in late 2010 after buying pretzel maker Snyder's of Hanover.

Geographic Reach

Based in North Carolina Snyder's-Lance operates manufacturing facilities in the US in North Carolina Pennsylvania Iowa Indiana Georgia Arizona Massachusetts Florida and Ohio as well as in Ontario Canada.

Sales and Marketing

Snyder's-Lance logged $23.1 million in advertising expenses in fiscal 2012. The snack food giant sells its products to mass merchandisers club stores discount stores convenience stores foodservice operators and other retailers the likes of drug stores the military schools and government facilities. Wal-Mart its largest customer represented about 18% of the company's revenues in both 2012 and 2011.

The company distributes snack food products nationwide using a large direct-store-delivery (DSD) network consisting of some 3000 distribution routes served mostly by Independent Business Owners (IBOs) and others that are company-owned.

Operations

Blending the Snyder's and Lance businesses has made Snyder's-Lance the No. 2 salty snack maker in the US. Snyder's-Lance boasts about a dozen owned brands as well as a vast collection of popular licensed names such as Bugles. Snyder's and Lance retained their corporate offices in North Carolina and Pennsylvania and knit together their executive suites to form a snack food powerhouse.

Financial Performance

During the past five years Snyder's-Lance logged its highest revenue in 2011 (the first full year it reported combined sales) thanks to the positive impact of the merger due to its incremental branded and non-branded revenue. The combined company's net sales decreased 1% in fiscal 2012 as compared to 2011 driven primarily by lower revenue per unit sold as a result of the IBO conversion and planned private brand volume declines. The company's net income saw a 54% boost during the same reporting period due in part to increased activity associated with the IBO conversion in 2012 as compared to 2011.

Strategy

As part of the company's effort to merge the two businesses Snyder's-Lance is paying particular attention to what it has deemed its core brands — Snyder's of Hanover pretzels Lance sandwich crackers and Cape Cod potato chips. It's fueling growth among these brands by developing them and expanding their distribution. Within Snyder's-Lance's allied brands defined as branded products that are outside its core brands the company's exploring pricing strategies product packaging and product configuration to improve profit margins. The snack foods maker also is looking for add-on acquisitions to boost its core products portfolio. It added the popular Pretzel Crisps brand to its pretzel portfolio and entered the deli-bakery section of grocery stores —a retail area for snacks that's growing —through its $340-million purchase of Snack Factory in October 2012.

Following the merger Snyder's-Lance in early 2011 began to convert some 1300 company-owned direct-store-delivery (DSD) routes to independent operators to improve its distribution network's ability to serve customers. (At the time of the merger announcement Lance's DSD network was presented as a primary reason for Snyder's of Hanover's interest.) Snyder's-Lance is expanding its DSD network in the Southwestern US. Indeed it entered into a distribution agreement with Inventure Foods in fall 2012 to expand its route distribution system in Arizona.

Mergers and Acquisitions

The Snyder's deal attested to Lance's long-standing business strategy of growth through acquisitions. The company made it first purchase as a joint entity in mid-2012. Snyder's-Lance acquired O'Byrne Distributing a snack food distributor that serves the Augusta Georgia area. The deal marks the snack food company's continued push to expand and strengthen its national distribution network.

Previously Lance's takeovers included the Stella D'Oro brand of packaged cookies biscotti and breadsticks for which Lance paid $24 million. In 2008 Lance acquired the private-label gourmet cookie maker Brent & Sam's for $23 million as well as name brand cookie maker Archway for $31 million.

Snack food is a highly competitive sector in food manufacturing; there are many players from giants such as Frito-Lay (Lay's Potato Chips Doritos Cheetos Cracker Jack) to little guys like pork rinds maker Rudolph Foods that carve out a spot in either a regional or product niche. Whether large or small most snack food companies are bowing to customer demand to produce healthier products. The company has introduced 100-calorie snack packs and whole-grain snack crackers. (It had previously removed lard trans-fats and high-fructose corn syrup from its products.)

Company Ownership

Chairman Michael Warehime and his wife —director Patricia Warehime —own about 16% of the company's shares.

HISTORY

A business deal gone awry stuck coffee dealer Philip Lance with 500 pounds of peanuts in 1913. Selling nickel bags of roasted peanuts and then peanut butter Lance began packaging peanut-butter-and-cracker sandwiches. His son-in-law Salem Van Every joined him two years later to form Lance Packing. Lance introduced Toastchee in 1938 and by 1939 the year the firm became Lance sales reached $2 million. The company began serving the institutional market in 1953 and began selling through vending machines the next year. Lance went public in 1961.

The family continued to run the company until 1973 when Van Every's grandson retired as CEO. After decades of serving mom-and-pop retailers Lance found the snack market changing. Individual stores gave way to chains; Frito-Lay gobbled up grocery shelf space; and regional rival Austin Quality Foods nabbed sales in the new warehouse/club store market. Eventually the conservative company responded with an influx of new management restructuring and the advent of marketing.

Lance purchased Tamming Foods (sugar wafers) and Cape Cod Potato Chips (salty snacks) in 1999. Lance then signed an agreement with China Peregrine (now China Premium Food Corp) to export private-label snack foods to China. (Lance has since ceased distribution in China.)

In 2005 Lance's board of directors elected Bill Prezzano as chairman. David Singer formerly EVP and CFO of Coca-Cola Bottling Co. Consolidated was named president and CEO of the company. And in 2005 Lance purchased a Canadian sugar-wafer manufacturing plant from A&M Cookie Company Canada.

The $40 million acquisition of Tom's Foods in 2005 added four new bakery and potato chip manufacturing plants to the company's operations. Lance manufactures about 90% of its products; the remainder is purchased for resale.

While Frito-Lay dominates the snack-aisle grocery shelves Lance's stronghold has been its company-owned vending machines placed in 15000 locations such as break rooms and cafeterias. In order to concentrate on more profitable operations in 2006 Lance began phasing out its vending-machine sales and ceased vending operations altogether in 2007. In addition the company joined the ranks of munchies makers that offer healthier products in 2007 with the $2 million purchase of a minority interest in Late July Products a Massachusetts-based organic snack food maker (crackers and sandwich crackers and cookies).

In 2008 Lance acquired the private-label gourmet cookie maker Brent & Sam's for $23 million and name-brand cookie maker Archway for $31 million.

In 2009 Lance purchased the Stella D'Oro brand of packaged cookies biscotti and breadsticks for $24 million.

The company merged with pretzel maker Snyder's of Hanover in December 2010. As a result Snyder's became a wholly owned subsidiary of Lance and Lance changed its name to Snyder's-Lance.

In October 2012 Snyder's-Lance completed its acquisition of Snack Factory LLC from VMG Partners adding the Pretzel Crisps brand to its menu of snacks.

EXECUTIVES

CEO and Director, David V. Singer, age 58, $660,000 total compensation
VP Corporate Controller Principal Accounting Officer and Assistant Secretary, Margaret E. Wicklund, age 52
SVP, Charles E. (Ed) Good
EVP CFO and Secretary, Richard D. (Rick) Puckett, age 59, $401,310 total compensation
SVP and Chief Human Resources Officer, Kevin A. Henry, age 45
President and CEO, Carl E. Lee Jr.
Chairman, Patricia A. Warehime
Director, William R. Holland, age 73
CEO and Director, David V. Singer, age 58
Director, James W. Johnston, age 66
Director, Isaiah Tidwell, age 68
Director, Wilbur J. (Bill) Prezzano Jr., age 73
Director, Dan C. Swander, age 69
Director, Jeffrey A. (Jeff) Atkins, age 64
President and CEO, Carl E. Lee Jr.
Director, Patricia A. Warehime
Director, C. Peter Carlucci Jr.
Director, Sally W. Yelland
Director, Peter P. Brubaker
Director, John E. Denton
Auditors: KPMGLLP

LOCATIONS

HQ: Snyder' s-Lance Inc.
13024 Ballantyne Corporate Place Ste. 900, Charlotte NC 28277
Phone: 704-554-1421 **Fax:** 704-554-5562
Web: www.snyderslance.com

2012 Revenue

	$ mil.	% of total
US	1,564	97
Canada	54	3
Total	**1,618**	**100**

PRODUCTS/OPERATIONS

2012 Revenue

	% of total
Branded	59
Partner	17
Private	18
Other	5
Total	**100**

Selected Brands

Archway
Brent
Bugles
Cape Cod Potato Chips
Captain' s Wafers
Choc-o-Lunch
Delicious
Don Pablo' s
EatSmart
Grande
Jays
Krunchers!
Lance
Nekot
Nipchee
Pretzel Crisps
Sam' s
Salerno
Snyder' s of Hanover
Stella D' oro
Texas Pete
Thunder
Toastchee
Toasty
Tom' s
Van-o-Lunch
Vista

COMPETITORS

American Pop Corn	Kellogg U.S. Snacks
Beer Nuts	Kettle Foods
Bridgford Foods	King Nut Companies
Campbell Soup	Legacy Bakehouse
Chattanooga Bakery	McKee Foods
ConAgra	Mondelez International
Diamond Foods	Old Dutch Foods
Evans Food Products	Otis Spunkmeyer
Flowers Foods	Pepperidge Farm
Frito-Lay	Poindexter Nut
General Mills	Pretzels Inc.
Golden Enterprises	Procter & Gamble
Hostess Brands	Ralcorp
Inventure foods	Snappy Popcorn
John Sanfilippo & Son	Weaver Popcorn Company

HISTORICAL FINANCIALS
Company Type: Public

Income Statement
FYE: December 29

	REVENUE ($ mil.)	NET INCOME ($ mil.)	NET PROFIT MARGIN	EMPLOYEES
12/12	1,618.6	59.0	3.7%	5,900
12/11*	1,635.0	38.2	2.3%	6,100
01/11	979.8	2.5	0.3%	7,000
12/09	918.1	35.7	3.9%	4,800
12/08	852.4	17.7	2.1%	4,800
Annual Growth	17.4%	35.2%	—	5.3%

*Fiscal year change

2012 Year-End Financials
Debt ratio: 30.6%	No. of shares (mil.): 68
Return on equity: 6.9%	Dividends
Cash ($ mil.): 9	Yield: 0.0%
Current ratio: 2.07	Payout: 75.2%
Long-term debt ($ mil.): 514	Market value ($ mil.): 1,631

	STOCK PRICE ($) FY Close	P/E High/Low	PER SHARE ($) Earnings	Dividends	Book Value
12/12	23.68	31 25	0.85	0.64	12.63
12/11*	22.50	42 30	0.56	0.64	12.33
01/11	23.44	385229	0.07	4.39	12.55
12/09	26.42	24 17	1.11	0.64	8.56
12/08	22.02	43 29	0.56	0.64	7.47
Annual Growth	1.8%	— —	11.0%	(0.0%)	14.0%

*Fiscal year change

Sohu.com Inc

If you're hunting for something in China maybe a "search fox" can help. Sohu.com (Sohu means "search fox") operates China's leading Web portal and offers communication tools such as e-mail and instant messaging and more than 30 content channels covering news sports business and other topics. Sohu also operates Web sites devoted to alumni communities gaming and real estate. In addition the company provides Internet access through its Sohu Entertainment ISP and search services through Sogou ("search dog"). Chairman and CEO Charles Zhang founded Sohu in 1996 as Internet Technologies China. It launched Sohu.com in 1998 and changed its name the next year. Zhang owns more than 20% of the company.

Other Sohu offerings include Go2Map (a mapping service provider); ChinaRen (an online youth community); 17174.com (games information portal); GoodFeel.com.cn (wireless value-added services); and Focus.cn (real estate services).

In 2008 the company spun off its online games unit Changyou.com in an IPO allowing Sohu to focus on its core online media search and mobile services; Sohu remains Changyou's majority shareholder.

EXECUTIVES
Chairman and CEO, Charles Zhang, age 49, $280,000 total compensation
Co-President and COO, Xin Belinda Wang, age 41, $170,000 total compensation
COO, Yu Gong, age 45, $170,000 total compensation
Co-President and CFO, Carol Yu, age 51, $250,000 total compensation
VP, Luming Chen
CTO, Xiaochuan Wang, age 35
Secretary, Timothy B. Bancroft
VP Products, Gang Fang
VP Online Games Business, Tao Wang, age 37
Director Investor Relations and Corporate Communications, Helen Zhang
Vice President of Brand Advertising Sales, Lili Shi
Vice President of Technology, Lin Zhou
Director, Edward B. (Ed) Roberts, age 78
Director, Charles Huang, age 43
Director, Dave Qi, age 49
Director, Shi Wang, age 62
Director, John Z. H. Deng, age 45
Auditors: PricewaterhouseCoopersZhongTianCPAsLimitedCompany

LOCATIONS
HQ: Sohu.com Inc.
1 Zhongguancun East Road Haidian District, Beijing 100084 China
Phone: -12862   **Fax:** -2444
Web: www.ifcosystems.de

PRODUCTS/OPERATIONS

2007 Sales
	$ mil.	% of total
Advertising	119	63
Non-advertising	69	37
Total	**188**	**100**

Selected Operations
17173.com (games portal)
ChinaRen.com (online alumni club)
Focus.cn (real estate Web site)
Goodfeel.com (wireless services)
Sogou.com (search site)
Sohu.com (Web portal)

Selected Sohu.com Content Channels
Automobile
Business and finance
Career
Comics
Dating
Entertainment
Games
Going abroad
Health
Information technology
Learning
Lifestyle
Music
News
Real estate
Sports
Travel
Women

Selected Sohu.com Features and Offerings
Address book
Calendar
Chat rooms
Dating and friends matching
Directory
E-Commerce services
E-Mail
Greeting Cards
Internet access services
Instant messaging
Message boards
Online polling
Photo album
Search engine
Wireless services

COMPETITORS
AOL	SCMP
Baidu	SINA
CRIC	SOFTBANK
China.com	Shanda Games
Google	Shanda Interactive
KongZhong	Entertainment
Lenovo	SouFun
Linktone	TOM Group
Microsoft	The9
Mtone Wireless	Yahoo!
NetEase	

HISTORICAL FINANCIALS
Company Type: Public

Income Statement
FYE: December 31

	REVENUE ($ mil.)	NET INCOME ($ mil.)	NET PROFIT MARGIN	EMPLOYEES
12/12	1,067.2	87.1	8.2%	9,681
12/11	852.0	162.7	19.1%	8,035
12/10	612.7	148.6	24.3%	5,167
12/09	515.2	147.8	28.7%	3,997
12/08	429.0	158.6	37.0%	3,197
Annual Growth	25.6%	(13.9%)		31.9%

2012 Year-End Financials
Debt ratio: 11.5%	No. of shares (mil.): 38
Return on equity: 7.8%	Dividends
Cash ($ mil.): 833	Yield: —
Current ratio: 2.23	Payout: —
Long-term debt ($ mil.): 126	Market value ($ mil.): 1,803

	STOCK PRICE ($) FY Close	P/E High/Low	PER SHARE ($) Earnings	Dividends	Book Value
12/12	47.34	28 15	2.03	0.00	30.09
12/11	50.00	25 11	3.93	0.00	27.98
12/10	63.49	20 10	3.92	0.00	20.94
12/09	57.28	18 10	3.57	0.00	16.15
12/08	47.34	22 8	4.06	0.00	10.13
Annual Growth	(0.0%)	— —	(15.9%)	—	31.3%

SolarWinds Inc

SolarWinds helps IT professionals improve IT infrastructure management without burning holes in their wallets. The company provides fault and performance management configuration management and compliance and troubleshooting applications. Designed to work on single devices or networks with as many as 100000 machines its downloadable software can be installed and configured without professional implementation services. The company's customers range from small businesses to large enterprises and government agencies. Its clients have included Booz Allen Hamilton FedEx Lockheed Martin Microsoft Chevron and NASA. SolarWinds gets 70% of sales from customers in the US.

Geographic Reach

While the company generates most of its revenues in North America its expansion plans include increasing its presence globally. In addition to its Austin-Texas headquarters the company has offices in Salt Lake City and abroad in Australia the Czech Republic Ireland India Brazil and Singapore.

Sales and Marketing

While the company markets its products in all the typical ways it relies on word-of-mouth and free trials to really boost sales. Because its direct sales force (the biggest revenue generator) doesn't have to convince potential customers of the value of SolarWinds' products the sales cycle is shorter. The company also uses distributors to reach government agencies and enterprise customers who have deals with certain resellers.

Financial Performance

All lines continued to go up for SolarWinds. In 2012 sales were up 36% to $268 million. The record revenue was due to increased sales of new software licenses and new and renewal maintenance agreements related to an expanded customer base. Maintenance agreements continue to account for a little more than half of revenues. Net income increased 30% on higher sales and in spite of increased sales and administration expenses. Cash flow increased by $76 million due to the revenue growth and a lack of acquisitions.

Strategy

SolarWinds with a strategic focus on underselling its rivals with products that cost less to configure and maintain has experienced rapid revenue growth in recent years. It has a user base of more than 150000 customers that includes nearly all of the Fortune 500.

SolarWinds uses internal development and acquisitions to add new products (more than 80 in 2012) extend its reach into new markets and expand geographically. New products released during the year included localized products for Japan and Germany web-based help desks for IT pros to deploy within their networks and vendor firewall management software.

Mergers and Acquisitions

SolarWinds has also expanded through acquisitions. In 2013 it acquired for some $120 million privately held N-able Technologies which provides IT management and automation products for managed service providers. The deal expands SolarWinds' offerings to that customer segment as well as its cloud-based services. It also purchased database performance management software firm Confio for $103 million. The prior year it picked up companies that make web help desk firewall patch file transfer and mobile IT management software.

EXECUTIVES

President CEO and Director, Kevin B. Thompson, age 48, $300,000 total compensation
Senior Vice President General Counsel and Secretary, Bryan A. Sims, age 44
Executive Vice President and Chief Financial Officer, Michael J. (Mike) Berry, age 49
VP Public Sector Sales, David Kimball
EVP Strategic Operations, Douglas G. (Doug) Hibberd, age 48, $250,000 total compensation
SVP Finance and Chief Accountant, J. Barton (Bart) Kalsu, age 45
VP Finance and Operations EMEA, David Owens, age 41
EVP Worldwide Sales, Paul Strelzick, age 49
VP Human Resources and Corporate Infrastructure, Garry D. Strop, age 66
Director Corporate Marketing, Tiffany Nels
EVP and CFO, Jason Ream
VP Product Management and Product Marketing, Sanjay Castelino
SVP Marketing, Geeta Sachdev
EVP Chief Marketing Officer and Chief Customer Officer, John F. Rizzo, age 56
CIO, Jon Drake
EVP and Chief Accounting Officer, J. Barton Kalsu
Director, Lloyd G. (Buzz) Waterhouse, age 62
Director, Steven M. (Steve) Cakebread, age 62
Director, J. Benjamin H. (Ben) Nye, age 47

President CEO and Director, Kevin B. Thompson, age 48
Director, Ellen F. Siminoff, age 45
Director, Roger J. Sippl, age 58
Auditors: PricewaterhouseCoopersLLP

LOCATIONS

HQ: SolarWinds Inc.
3711 S. MoPac Expwy. Bldg. 2, Austin TX 78746
Phone: 512-682-9300   **Fax:** 512-682-9301
Web: www.solarwinds.com

2012 Sales

	$ mil.	% of total
US	188	70
Other countries	81	30
Total	**269**	**100**

PRODUCTS/OPERATIONS

2012 Sales

	$ mil.	% of total
License	124	46
Maintenance & other	145	54
Total	**269**	**100**

COMPETITORS

BMC Software	IBM
CA Inc.	Infoblox
Cisco Systems	NetApp
Dell Software	NetScout Systems
EMC	Tripwire
Hewlett-Packard	

HISTORICAL FINANCIALS

Company Type: Public

Income Statement

FYE: December 31

	REVENUE ($ mil.)	NET INCOME ($ mil.)	NET PROFIT MARGIN	EMPLOYEES
12/12	268.9	81.3	30.2%	865
12/11	198.3	62.4	31.5%	628
12/10	152.3	44.7	29.4%	458
12/09	116.4	29.5	25.3%	354
12/08	93.1	22.3	23.9%	268
Annual Growth	**30.4%**	**38.2%**	**—**	**34.0%**

2012 Year-End Financials

Debt ratio: —   No. of shares (mil.): 74
Return on equity: 25.0%   Dividends
Cash ($ mil.): 179   Yield: —
Current ratio: 2.22   Payout: —
Long-term debt ($ mil.): —   Market value ($ mil.): 3,915

	STOCK PRICE ($) FY Close	P/E High/Low	PER SHARE ($) Earnings	Dividends	Book Value
12/12	52.45	54 25	1.07	0.00	5.13
12/11	27.95	39 22	0.84	0.00	3.61
12/10	19.25	38 19	0.61	0.00	2.45
12/09	23.01	41 23	0.52	0.00	1.34
Annual Growth	**31.6%**	**— —**	**27.2%**	**—**	**56.5%**

Solera Holdings Inc

The next time you report a fender bender your adjuster might be using technology from Solera to process the claim. Solera Holdings develops software for the auto insurance industry. Its Audatex software automates such processes as auditing claims management and damage estimation. Solera serves insurance companies worldwide; other customers include auto repair shops and independent assessors. Its Hollander subsidiary provides the Hollander Interchange parts catalog in print or electronic form to auto recyclers as an inventory management supplement. In Brazil and Mexico it operates an online marketplace for salvage vehicle sales. Solera gets almost 60% of its sales in the Europe/Middle East/Africa region.

The company has only seen its revenue and profits grow since it became a public company in 2007. Overall revenue grew 8% in fiscal 2011 and profit grew by 79%. Its goal is to reach revenue of $1 billion by 2014.

Solera has grown by expanding its presence through acquisitions. The company expanded its US operations in early 2013 with the acquisition of Illinois-based HyperQuest and also increased its position in Australia with the purchase of Eziworks. In 2012 the company bought assets from Inventory Technology Systems (ITS) through subsidiary Hollander. The deal added logistics software used to control track and account for recycled parts inventory at salvage yards. Also that year it bought Actual Systems a global provider of operations management systems for parts recycling yard operators. The purchase strengthened Solera's parts-related strategy in North America and overseas as Actual Systems had a presence in Australia the UK the Netherlands Ireland and Spain. It also acquired License Monitor a developer of driver violation monitoring software designed to help operators of government and commercial vehicle fleets to quickly track driver violation activity and license status changes. Additionally Solera bought substantially all the assets of US-based PS Holdings which provides a cloud-based service for locating postconsumer original equipment parts for the vehicle repair market. PS Holdings' clients consist mainly of US insurance carriers.

In 2011 it bought a majority stake in Sinexia Corporacion Tecnologica a Spanish firm that makes software for processing property and casualty insurance claims and K&S Beheer B.V. a Netherlands-based company that makes collision repair shop management software.

Also that year Solera made some US-based acquisitions first buying Utah-based body shop management system software maker New Era Software. In mid-2011 it paid Altegrity about $520 million for Explore Information Services to boost its profile as a seller of re-underwriting and analytics data products for property and casualty insurers. In September it bought Michigan-based See Progress which makes software that keeps insurers and customers informed on vehicle repairs through text and photos.

In 2010 Solera announced a plan to invest $150 million into expanding its products and services in the US Canada and The Netherlands. It earmarked $40 million for new acquisitions for Hollander Interchange and $10 million for new technology. As part of the initiative the company acquired Netherlands-based Market Scan Holding a provider of data analytics and software to the Dutch insurance industry. It also made a minority investment in Digidentity another Dutch company which provides cloud-based certificates for authenticating online identities. The certification process is an important part of the back-office operations of ABZ Solera's operating subsidiary in The Netherlands. The investment strengthened ABZ' core offerings by adding increased security to the claims process.

HISTORY

Solera Holdings was founded in 2005 by CEO Tony Aquila and affiliates of private equity firm GTCR Golder Rauner. The next year it acquired ADP's Claims Services Group which comprises the bulk of Solera's current operations for about $1 billion. In 2007 it went public raising $350 million in its initial public offering.

The next year it bought three companies —UC Universal Consulting Software a software developer serving collision repair shops in Germany for $4 million; Inpart Servicos Ltda. an electronic exchange for the purchase and sale of vehicle replacement parts in Brazil; and UK-based HPI Ltd. from Aviva. The purchase of HPI which provides used vehicle validation services cost Solera about $117 million.

In 2009 it made two acquisitions in Europe. It bought GTLDATA an Austrian firm that provided software to insurance assessors to assess organize and communicate automobile claims data; and it paid about $87 million for 85% of AUTOonline GmbH Informationssyteme which operated AUTOonline.com an online marketplace for buyers and sellers of salvage and fleet remarketing vehicles in Europe and Mexico.

EXECUTIVES

Director Investor Relations, Kamal Hamid, age 52
Chairman President and CEO, Tony Aquila, age 48, $696,538 total compensation
Chief Marketing Officer, Atul Vohra
SVP General Counsel and Secretary, Jason Brady, age 44, $250,000 total compensation
CFO, Renato Giger, $270,833 total compensation
Senior Vice President Global Human Resources, Abilio Gonzalez
Marketing Coordinator, Lisa Collins
Vice President Human Resources, Joanne Woolfall
President Chief Operating Officer, Jack Sanders
Director, Arthur F. Kingsbury, age 64
Director, Stuart J. Yarbrough, age 61
Director, Kenneth A. Viellieu, age 55
Independent Director, Thomas Wajnert
Auditors: Deloitte&ToucheLLP

LOCATIONS

HQ: Solera Holdings Inc
7 Village Circle, Suite 100, Westlake, TX 76262
Phone: 817 961-2100
Web: www.solerainc.com

2010 Sales

	$ mil.	% of total
EMEA	390	57
Americas	294	43
Total	**684**	**100**

PRODUCTS/OPERATIONS

2011 Sales

	$ mil.	% of total
Insurance companies	275	40
Collision repair facilities	243	36
Independent assessors	71	10
Automotive recyclers and others	95	14
Total	**684**	**100**

Selected Acquisitions

2012
CarweB Limited (UK; vehicle history and technical data software)

COMPETITORS

Applied Systems   Crawford & Company

CCC Information   Experian
Cover-All   Mitchell International

HISTORICAL FINANCIALS
Company Type: Public

Income Statement
FYE: June 30

	REVENUE ($ mil.)	NET INCOME ($ mil.)	NET PROFIT MARGIN	EMPLOYEES
06/13	838.1	93.8	11.2%	2,767
06/12	790.2	106.9	13.5%	2,483
06/11	684.7	157.3	23.0%	2,247
06/10	631.3	84.4	13.4%	2,202
06/09	557.6	57.8	10.4%	2,176
Annual Growth	**10.7%**	**12.9%**	**—**	**6.2%**

2013 Year-End Financials

Debt ratio: 50.8%
Return on equity: 13.2%
Cash ($ mil.): 464
Current ratio: 3.04
Long-term debt ($ mil.): 1,144

No. of shares (mil.): 68
Dividends
　Yield: 0.0%
　Payout: 37.0%
Market value ($ mil.): 3,827

	STOCK PRICE ($) FY Close	P/E High/Low	PER SHARE ($) Earnings	Dividends	Book Value
06/13	55.65	43 27	1.35	0.50	10.71
06/12	41.79	41 27	1.51	0.40	9.83
06/11	59.16	26 16	2.22	0.30	10.95
06/10	36.20	33 20	1.20	0.25	7.24
06/09	25.40	36 18	0.85	0.00	8.04
Annual Growth	**21.7%**	**— —**	**12.3%**	**—**	**7.4%**

Southern Missouri Bancorp, Inc.

Southern Missouri Bancorp is the holding company for Southern Bank (formerly Southern Missouri Bank and Trust) which serves local residents and businesses in southeastern Missouri and northeastern Arkansas through more than 10 branches. Residential mortgages account for the largest percentage of the bank's loan portfolio followed by commercial mortgages and business loans. Construction and consumer loans round out its lending activities. Deposit products include checking savings and money market accounts CDs and IRAs. The bank also offers financial planning and investment services. Originally chartered in 1887 Southern Bank acquired Arkansas-based Southern Bank of Commerce in 2009.

Jeffrey Gendell of Tontine Financial Partners owns more than 9% of Southern Missouri Bancorp; independent investor Donald Crandell owns more than 8%; employees own around 6%; and president CEO and director Greg Steffens more than 5%.

EXECUTIVES

President and CEO, Greg A. Steffens, age 46, $190,292 total compensation
Chairman, Samuel H. Smith, age 75
Secretary and Director, Ronnie D. Black, age 65
Vice Chairman, L. Douglas Bagby, age 63

Regional Community President Jonesboro, Lindley Smith, age 60
COO and Treasurer, Kimberly A. Capps
Chief Lending Officer, William D. (Bill) Hribovsek, $143,278 total compensation
CFO, Matt Funke
Executive Secretary and Human Resources Officer, Lorna Brannum
Chief Credit Administration, Lora Daves
Independent Director, Dennis C. Robison
Secretary and Director, Ronnie D. Black, age 65
Vice Chairman, L. Douglas Bagby, age 63
Independent Director, Dennis C. Robison
Auditors: BKDLLP

LOCATIONS

HQ: Southern Missouri Bancorp Inc.
531 Vine St., Poplar Bluff MO 63901
Phone: 573-778-1800　　**Fax:** 573-686-2920
Web: www.smbtonline.com

COMPETITORS

Bank of America   Regions Financial
Commerce Bancshares   U.S. Bancorp
IBERIABANK   UMB Financial

HISTORICAL FINANCIALS
Company Type: Public

Income Statement
FYE: June 30

	ASSETS ($ mil.)	NET INCOME ($ mil.)	INCOME AS % OF ASSETS	EMPLOYEES
06/13	796.3	10.0	1.3%	181
06/12	739.1	10.1	1.4%	179
06/11	688.2	11.4	1.7%	174
06/10	552.0	4.6	0.8%	144
06/09	465.9	3.8	0.8%	119
Annual Growth	**14.3%**	**27.3%**	**—**	**11.1%**

2013 Year-End Financials

Return on assets: 1.3%
Return on equity: 10.2%
Long-term debt ($ mil.): —
No. of shares (mil.): 3
Sales ($ mil): 40

Dividends
　Yield: 0.0%
　Payout: 20.8%
Market value ($ mil.): 85

	STOCK PRICE ($) FY Close	P/E High/Low	PER SHARE ($) Earnings	Dividends	Book Value
06/13	25.67	9 7	2.88	0.60	30.91
06/12	21.50	8 6	3.32	0.48	29.14
06/11	20.78	5 3	5.12	0.48	26.55
06/10	15.01	8 5	1.98	0.48	21.86
06/09	9.95	9 5	1.67	0.48	20.12
Annual Growth	**26.7%**	**— —**	**14.6%**	**5.7%**	**11.3%**

Southern National Bancorp of Virginia Inc

Southern National Bancorp of Virginia is the holding company for Sonabank which has some 20 locations in central and northern Virginia and southern Maryland. Founded in 2005 the bank serves small and midsized businesses their owners and retail consumers. It offers standard deposit products including checking savings and money market accounts and CDs. The bank's lending is focused on commercial real estate single-family residential construction and single-family homes as well as other types of consumer and commercial loans. In 2009 Southern National Bancorp acquired the failed Greater Atlantic Bank in an FDIC-assisted transaction; in 2012 it acquired the loans and deposits of HarVest Bank of Maryland.

In 2006 Southern National Bancorp of Virginia acquired 1st Service Bank which operated three branches in Fairfax County Virginia.

The bank holding company intends to use IPO proceeds to support the asset growth expected to result from the acquired branches.

EXECUTIVES

SVP and CFO SNBV and Sonabank, William H. Lagos, age 62, $122,092 total compensation
Chairman and CEO SNBV and Sonabank, Georgia S. Derrico, age 68, $224,917 total compensation
Executive Vice President Credit, William H. Stevens, age 68, $178,883 total compensation
Vice Chairman and President and COO SNBV and Sonabank, R. Roderick Porter, age 67, $175,167 total compensation
Chief Credit Officer Sonabank, Tom Baker
Director, Fred L. Bollerer, age 70
Director, Neil J. Call, age 79
Vice Chairman and President and COO SNBV and Sonabank, R. Roderick Porter, age 67
Director, Charles A. Kabbash, age 75
Director, Robin R. Shield, age 50
Director, John J. Forch, age 63
Auditors: BDOSeidmanLLP

LOCATIONS

HQ: Southern National Bancorp of Virginia Inc.
6830 Old Dominion Dr., McLean VA 22101
Phone: 703-893-7400   **Fax:** 703-893-7489
Web: www.sonabank.com

COMPETITORS

BB&T	PNC Financial
Bank of America	SunTrust
Burke & Herbert Bank	Virginia Commerce Bancorp
Capital One	Wells Fargo

HISTORICAL FINANCIALS

Company Type: Public

Income Statement

FYE: December 31

	ASSETS ($ mil.)	NET INCOME ($ mil.)	INCOME AS % OF ASSETS	EMPLOYEES
12/12	723.8	6.5	0.9%	134
12/11	611.3	4.4	0.7%	112
12/10	590.8	1.8	0.3%	107
12/09	610.6	2.3	0.4%	103
12/08	431.9	1.2	0.3%	65
Annual Growth	13.8%	52.7%	—	19.8%

2012 Year-End Financials

Return on assets: 0.9%
Return on equity: 6.4%
Long-term debt ($ mil.): —
No. of shares (mil.): 11
Sales ($ mil): 40

Dividends
Yield: 3.0%
Payout: 42.9%
Market value ($ mil.): 94

	STOCK PRICE ($) FY Close	P/E High/Low	PER SHARE ($) Earnings	Dividends	Book Value
12/12	8.14	14 11	0.57	0.25	8.90
12/11	6.10	21 15	0.38	0.00	8.55
12/10	7.60	53 43	0.16	0.00	8.55
12/09	7.20	28 10	0.31	0.00	8.38
12/08	5.94	60 31	0.18	0.00	10.12
Annual Growth	8.2%	— —	33.4%	—	(3.1%)

Spectra Energy Partners LP

When you take one company's energy holdings and splinter them you get Spectra Energy Partners. Formed by Spectra Energy out of the former natural gas holdings of Duke Energy the company is a natural gas pipeline and storage facility operator. Its assets include a liquefied natural gas storage location in Tennessee 50% of Market Hub (two natural gas storage facilities in Texas and Louisiana) and 49% of Gulfstream Natural Gas System. All told Spectra Energy Partners has 3200 miles of natural gas transmission and gathering pipelines capable of moving about 3.6 billion cu. ft. per day. It also has 57 billion cu. ft. of gas storage capacity.

The company's core customers include distribution companies and utilities natural gas producers in Appalachia the Gulf Coast and the Mid-Continent power plants and major industrial companies. Major customers include EQT and the Tennessee Valley Authority.

Spectra Energy Partners' growth plans include expanding its pipeline and storage facilities (both by acquisitions and organic growth) to meet increased demand. In this regard in 2009 the company acquired Ozark Gas Transmission and Ozark Gas Gathering Systems from Atlas Pipeline Partners for $300 million.

In 2010 it acquired an additional 24.5% of a 745-mile interstate natural gas transportation system (Gulfstream Natural Gas System) from Spectra Energy for $330 million. The deal boosted Spectra Energy Partners' holdings to 49%.

Further expanding its Appalachian pipeline assets in 2011 the company bought a 70-mile natural gas pipeline (Big Sandy Pipeline) in eastern Kentucky from EQT Corp. for $390 million. That year the company also completed organinc expansion projects on the Gulfstream pipeline and at the Market Hub salt cavern storage complex.

The Big Sandy acquisition increased production and lifted the company's revenues and net income in 2011 offsetting decreased contract revenue (due to lower wholesale prices) from its Ozark Gas Transmission segment.

Expanding its Northeast pipeline operations in 2012 the company agreed to buy 39% of Maritimes & Northeast Pipeline L.L.C. from Spectra Energy for $319 million in cash and $56 million in newly issued partnership units.

EXECUTIVES

Chairman, Fred J. Fowler, age 67
President and CEO, Julie A. Dill

Chief Financial Officer; Vice President of Spectra Energy Partners GP; LLC, Laura Sayavedra
Chief Financial Officer of Spectra Energy Partners GP; LLC, John Reddy
Board Member, Steven D. Arnold
Board Member, Stewart A. Bliss, age 79
Board Member, Theopolis Holeman
Board Member, J.D. Woodward III
Board Member, Nora Mead Brownell, age 64
Board Member, Patrick J. (Pat) Hester, age 62
Auditors: Deloitte&ToucheLLP

LOCATIONS

HQ: Spectra Energy Partners LP
5400 Westheimer Ct., Houston TX 77056-5310
Phone: 713-627-5400   **Fax:** -10589
Web: www.merrionpharma.com

PRODUCTS/OPERATIONS

2011 Sales

	$ mil.	% of total
Transportation of natural gas	182	89
Storage of natural gas & other	22	11
Total	**205**	**100**

COMPETITORS

AGL Resources	Florida Gas
CenterPoint Energy	Transmission
Crestwood Midstream Partners LP	Occidental Petroleum
DCP Midstream Partners	Texas Gas Transmission
Enterprise Products	Transcontinental Gas
Exxon Mobil	Pipe Line
	Williams Companies

HISTORICAL FINANCIALS

Company Type: Public

Income Statement

FYE: December 31

	REVENUE ($ mil.)	NET INCOME ($ mil.)	NET PROFIT MARGIN	EMPLOYEES
12/12	236.8	193.5	81.7%	0
12/11	205.0	172.0	83.9%	0
12/10	197.7	147.9	74.8%	0
12/09	178.9	135.9	76.0%	0
12/08	124.9	101.3	81.1%	0
Annual Growth	17.3%	17.6%	—	—

2012 Year-End Financials

Debt ratio: 36.9%
Return on equity: —
Cash ($ mil.): 20
Current ratio: 0.14
Long-term debt ($ mil.): 699

No. of shares (mil.): 105
Dividends
Yield: 6.1%
Payout: 114.2%
Market value ($ mil.): 3,301

	STOCK PRICE ($) FY Close	P/E High/Low	PER SHARE ($) Earnings	Dividends	Book Value
12/12	31.23	20 16	1.69	1.93	16.14
12/11	31.96	21 16	1.63	1.85	17.27
12/10	32.85	21 16	1.70	1.70	16.42
12/09	29.57	17 11	1.71	1.51	16.47
12/08	19.78	18 11	1.40	1.34	15.55
Annual Growth	12.1%	— —	4.8%	9.6%	0.9%

Spectrum Pharmaceuticals Inc

Spectrum Pharmaceuticals sees a rainbow of opportunities in its drug development pipeline. The drug firm which focuses on anti-cancer therapies markets injectable Fusilev (levoleucovorin) for use by osteosarcoma (a type of bone cancer) and colorectal cancer patients; the drug reduces the toxic effects of a certain type of chemotherapy. Spectrum also sells Zevalin (ibritumomab) a treatment for non-Hodgkin's lymphoma; Marqibo for leukemia; and Folotyn for peripheral T-cell lymphoma. In addition the company has other oncology and urology therapeutic drug candidates in research and development stages partially through licensing agreements or collaborative partnerships with other drugmakers.

Operations

Spectrum does not have its own manufacturing facilities; its production operations are outsourced to third-party contract manufacturers. Spectrum also uses a third-party logistics provider to distribute its products to customers.

Geographic Reach

The company is headquartered in Henderson Nevada. It has R&D locations in the US Canada and India.

Sales and Marketing

The company has been expanding its sales force as it has added products.

Key customers include Oncology Supply (38% of sales) McKesson (26%) and ICS (19%).

Financial Performance

As more of the Spectrum's pipeline has been approved for sale it has seen an uptick in revenue net income and cash flow. In 2012 revenue increased nearly 40% due to the approval of Fusilev. Net income nearly doubled as positive income tax changes piggy backed on the improved revenue. With recent acquisitions filling the R&D pipeline Spectrum expects continued growth.

Strategy

As it has done with some degree of success Spectrum intends to continuing purchasing companies with late-stage development drugs as well as feeding its own R&D pipeline. It also pursues approval for other uses of its key products.

Mergers and Acquisitions

In 2012 Spectrum added its third commercial product when it acquired Allos Therapeutics for approximately $314 million. The purchase added Allos' marketed drug Folotyn (pralatrexate injection) which is used to treat patients with relapsed or refractory peripheral T-cell lymphoma (PTCL) to the company's hematology franchise.

In 2013 it purchased California-based biopharmaceutical company Talon Therapeutics for about $11 million. Talon came with approved leukemia drug Marqibo and Phase 2 skin treatment Menadione Topical Lotion.

EXECUTIVES

Chairman President and CEO, Rajesh C. Shrotriya, age 70, $600,000 total compensation

EVP and CFO, Kurt A. Gustafson, age 45

SVP Commercial, Rick Gonzalez

Senior Vice President - Finance, Brett L. Scott, age 62

EVP and COO, Ken Keller

SVP and Chief Medical Officer, Lee F. Allen, age 61

VP-Mktg & Sls, George C. Uy

SVP and Chief Commercial Officer, James E. (Jim) Shields

VP Clinical Development, Steven M. Fruchtman

VP Strategic Planning and Investor Relations, Shiv Kapoor

Vice President of Operations, Avi N. Oler

Vice President Corporate and Business Development, Bimal R. Shah

VP Pharmaceutical Operations, Pramod K. Gupta

SVP and Chief Commercial Officer, Joseph Turgeon

Director, Luigi (Gino) Lenaz, age 72

Director, Dilip J. Mehta, age 80

Director, Anton G. Gueth, age 56

Director, Anthony E. Maida III, age 61

Director, Stuart M. Krassner, age 78

Director, Krishan K. Arora, age 72

Director, Giles Gagnon

Auditors: Kelly&Company

LOCATIONS

HQ: Spectrum Pharmaceuticals Inc.
157 Technology Dr., Irvine CA 92618
Phone: 949-788-6700　　　**Fax:** 949-788-6706
Web: www.spectrumpharm.com

COMPETITORS

APP Pharmaceuticals	GlaxoSmithKline
Abbott Labs	Johnson & Johnson
AstraZeneca	Merck
Pharmaceuticals	Novartis
Bayer AG	Pharmaceuticals
Ben Venue	OSI Pharmaceuticals
Biogen Idec	Pfizer
Bristol-Myers Squibb	Poniard
Celgene	Pharmaceuticals
Cephalon	Roche Holding
Eli Lilly	Sanofi
Endo	Seattle Genetics
Genentech	Shire
Genta	Teva
Genzyme	

HISTORICAL FINANCIALS

Company Type: Public

Income Statement

FYE: December 31

	REVENUE ($ mil.)	NET INCOME ($ mil.)	NET PROFIT MARGIN	EMPLOYEES
12/12	267.7	94.5	35.3%	193
12/11	192.9	48.5	25.1%	176
12/10	74.1	(48.8)	—	139
12/09	38.0	(19.0)	—	158
12/08	28.7	(15.4)	—	84
Annual Growth 74.7%		—	—	23.1%

2012 Year-End Financials

Debt ratio: 14.8%
Return on equity: 39.8%
Cash ($ mil.): 139
Current ratio: 2.06
Long-term debt ($ mil.): 75

No. of shares (mil.): 60
Dividends
　Yield: 1.3%
　Payout: 10.2%
Market value ($ mil.): 671

	STOCK PRICE ($) FY Close	P/E High/Low		PER SHARE ($) Earnings	Dividends	Book Value
12/12	11.19	11	6	1.46	0.15	4.75
12/11	14.63	16	7	0.84	0.00	3.19
12/10	6.87	—	—	(0.99)	0.00	1.45
12/09	4.44	—	—	(0.48)	0.00	2.21
12/08	1.49	—	—	(0.49)	0.00	1.23
Annual Growth 65.5%		—	—	—	—	40.1%

Spirit Airlines Inc

Spirit Airlines can lift the spirits of people seeking sunshine. The ultra low-cost carrier (ULCC) makes connections between major US cities and popular vacation spots in South Florida the Caribbean and Latin America serving nearly 50 destinations. It operates an all Airbus fleet of nearly 40 single-aisle aircraft including A319s A320s and A321s. Spirit capitalizes on an ancillary service model charging separately for baggage advance seat selection and other travel-related upgrades. In addition to scheduled service the company partners with third-party vendors to offer a slate of vacation packages via its website. In 2011 Spirit Airlines sought public investors planning to land up to $300 million.

IPO The company's stock opened lower than its initial offering price selling fewer shares than expected. All told the offering raised $187 million. Spirit earmarked half of the proceeds for general corporate purposes (working capital sales and marketing expenses and capital expenditures including an order of new A320s to expand its fleet by 2015). Some of the money will be used to terminate a services agreement with aviation industry investment firm Indigo Partners and to pay down debt owed to Indigo and Spirit's other significant shareholder Oaktree Capital Management.

Sales and Marketing Spirit Airlines sells through its website an outsourced call center and third-party travel agents. Its spirit.com site accounts for about two-thirds of sales.

Strategy Despite the shaky economy and volatile fuel prices that have rocked airline industry giants Spirit has sustained a largely positive trajectory. It attributes its momentum to its ULCC business model coupled with concentrating its resources on the growing Caribbean and Latin American markets. Spirit's top issue is controlling costs in order sustain a profit from its low fares. To this end the company has moved to an aggressive unbundling strategy to stimulate passenger demand and revenues. Unbundling allows passengers to pay separately for products and services that they want to use. Charging for such extras as onboard beverages and snacks enables Spirit to offset its low ticket prices as well as maintain its competitive market presence. Spirit continuing its ULCC mantra aims to expand its network. It has targeted domestic vacation spots outside Florida (Atlantic City Los Angeles Las Vegas Phoenix).

Financial Analysis Spirit surpassed $1 billion in revenue in 2011 up more than 35% from 2010. It saw strong increases in both ticket and non-ticket sales as the company increased its fleet size. With the exception of 2009 when sales fell 11% Spirit has seen consistent growth over the past decade. Net income rose 5% to $76 million as sales growth was enough to overcome a more than 55% jump in fuel costs and a more than 15% rise in labor expenses associated with the fleet expansion.

Ownership Investment funds affiliated with Oaktree Capital Management and Indigo Partners own 18% and 17% of the company respectively.

EXECUTIVES

President Chief Executive Officer, B. Ben Baldanza, age 50, $457,200 total compensation

EVP and Chief Marketing Officer, Barry L. Biffle, age 40, $310,000 total compensation

Senior Vice President Chief Operating Officer, Tony Lefebvre, age 43, $240,000 total compensation

Vice President Pricing & Revenue Management, Graham Parker, age 48
Senior Vice President; General Counsel; Secretary, Thomas C. Canfield, age 56, $290,000 total compensation
VP and Treasurer, David Bradford, age 44
Corporate Communications, Misty Pinson
Chairman, Bill Franke, age 75
VP and Chief Information Officer, Craig Maccubbin, age 45
VP-Fin Plng & Analysis, Charlie Rue, age 41
Chief Financial Officer; Senior Vice President, Edward Christie
Senior Vice President - Human Resources, James Lynde
Vice President Flight Operations, Jyri Strandman
Vice President Consumer Marketing, Bobby Schroeter
Vice President Airport Services, Jake Filene
Vice President Controller, Edmundo Miranda
Vice President Financial Planning & Analysis, Scott Haralson
Director, Stuart I. Oran, age 62
Director, David G. Elkins, age 71
President CEO and Director, B. Ben Baldanza, age 50
Director, Barclay G. Jones III, age 51
Director, John R. Wilson, age 48
Director, H. McIntyre (Mac) Gardner, age 51
Director, Robert D. (Bob) Johnson, age 65
Director, Jordon Kruse, age 41
Director, Horacio Scapparone, age 60
Auditors: Ernst&YoungLLP

LOCATIONS

HQ: Spirit Airlines Inc
  2800 Executive Way, Miramar, FL 33025
Phone: 954 447-7920
Web: www.spirit.com

2011 Sales

	$ mil.	% of total
Domestic	900	84
Latin America	171	16
Total	**1,071**	**100**

PRODUCTS/OPERATIONS

2011 Sales

	$ mil.	% of total
Passenger	689	64
Non-ticket	381	36
Total	**1,071**	**100**

COMPETITORS

AMR Corp.	Southwest Airlines
AirTran Airways	US Airways
Allegiant Travel	United Continental
Delta Air Lines	Virgin America
JetBlue	

HISTORICAL FINANCIALS

Company Type: Public

Income Statement

FYE: December 31

	REVENUE ($ mil.)	NET INCOME ($ mil.)	NET PROFIT MARGIN	EMPLOYEES
12/12	1,318.3	108.4	8.2%	3,033
12/11	1,071.1	76.4	7.1%	2,580
12/10	781.2	72.4	9.3%	2,385
12/09	700.0	83.6	12.0%	0
12/08	787.2	33.2	4.2%	0
Annual Growth	**13.8%**	**34.4%**	**—**	**—**

SS&C Technologies Holdings, Inc.

SS&C Technologies helps its clients buy low and sell high. The company develops software for managing financial portfolios loans real estate equity back-office processing and securities trading and it provides consulting and outsourcing services. Its applications automate investment portfolio management asset and liability management for actuaries property and casualty insurance risk management trade ordering and financial modeling. SS&C serves asset managers insurance companies banks corporate treasuries hedge funds and government agencies among others. Clients have included Middlebury College and Monro Muffler Brake. It has offices in North America Europe Asia Pacific and Australia.

SS&C Technologies went public in 2010 in a $160 million IPO; proceeds from the public offering were used to pay down debt make acquisitions and to develop new products and services. Between going private in 2005 and its 2010 IPO SS&C Technologies had amassed about $400 million in debt and borrowed another $75 million from a revolving credit line.

Acquisitions play a key role in the company's strategy resulting in more than 30 purchases since 1995. SS&C typically pursues companies that either expand its product and service offerings into new markets or increase its client base within the financial services industry.

In 2012 the company acquired Thomson Reuters' PORTIA business a developer of middle-to-back office investment operations software for $170 million. PORTIA specialized in tools used by investment managers to track and manage the day-to-day investments; these applications complemented SS&C's existing product line and added operations in Boston London Dubai and several key Asian cities. That year the company also bought GlobeOp a provider of middle and back-office services and integrated risk reporting to hedge fund and account managers.

SS&C acquired Connecticut-based benefits administration software developer BenefitsXML in 2011 to expand its line of products for enterprise human resources management. Also that year the company expanded its global fund administration business with the acquisition of BDO Simpson Xavier Fund Administration Services the Dublin-based division of BDO.

2012 Year-End Financials

Debt ratio: —	No. of shares (mil.): 72
Return on equity: 20.6%	Dividends
Cash ($ mil.): 416	Yield: —
Current ratio: 1.98	Payout: —
Long-term debt ($ mil.): —	Market value ($ mil.): 1,285

	STOCK PRICE ($) FY Close	P/E High/Low		PER SHARE ($) Earnings	Dividends	Book Value
12/12	17.73	16	9	1.49	0.00	8.04
12/11	15.60	12	7	1.43	0.00	6.44
Annual Growth	**13.7%**	**—**	**—**	**4.2%**	**—**	**24.9%**

The Carlyle Group is the majority shareholder of SS&C Technologies; chairman and CEO William C. Stone owns another 22% of the company.

HISTORY

Former KPMG Peat Marwick (now KPMG International) executive William Stone founded Securities Software & Consulting in 1986. The company produced its first product in 1989 —a DOS-based portfolio management program geared toward large and medium-sized institutional investors —and called it CAMRA (complete asset management reporting and accounting).

SS&C introduced a Windows-based version of CAMRA in 1993. That year the company also introduced its first loan portfolio management product. SS&C acquired Chalke Inc. in 1995 and with it Chalke's PTS (profit testing system) economic modeling software for insurance companies.

The company went public as SS&C Technologies in 1996. The next year groups from New York and Connecticut filed a class-action suit claiming the company made misrepresentations in its prospectus (the case was dismissed in 1999). Also in 1997 SS&C acquired Dutch financial software company Mabel Systems and Shepro Braun Systems.

1998 purchases included software firms Quantra and Savid International. SS&C continued the trend in 1999 with the purchase of hedge fund software specialist HedgeWare. But the acquisition-fueled growth and a drop in software sales helped cause losses for 1999. In 2000 the company made its applications available for outsourcing on the Internet. The next year moving away from development and toward marketing of new projects SS&C cut 6% of its workforce.

In 2002 the company acquired finance applications service provider Real-Time USA and later that year it bought Thomson subsidiary DBC a provider of financial software for fixed-income analysis. In 2004 SS&C bought Automatic Data Processing subsidiary OMR Systems a provider of treasury processing software and the following year it acquired Eisnerfast a provider of services for hedge funds.

SS&C was acquired by Sunshine Acquisition Corporation an affiliate of private equity firm The Carlyle Group in 2005.

In 2006 and 2007 the company continued its acquisitive ways purchasing Cogent Management Zoologic and Northport. In 2008 it bought the assets of Micro Design Services a developer of investment and financial management software in a bid to increase its presence in the securities industry and to boost its mobile capabilities.

In 2009 SS&C purchased Unisys' MAXIMIS business line which provided institutional asset management applications and services. It also bought Evare a managed utility service provider for financial data acquisition enrichment transformation and delivery and TheNextRound a provider of software for the alternative investment and private equity sectors. Also that year the company bought Tradeware Global a provider of financial information exchange services to brokers and financial institutions for around $21.5 million.

SS&C went public again in 2010 raising nearly $161 million in the offering.

The company's acquisitions that year included the purchase of Geller Investment Partnership Services a provider of accounting reporting tax and investor services to private equity funds and hedge funds among others. It also bought TD AMERITRADE's thinklink business to expand its front office software and services and building its list of sell-side institutional clients. thinklink specialized in Web-based software used to enable trade order management among other functions. SS&C also bought Utah-based TimeShareWare a provider of software to shared-ownership properties such as condominium hotels timeshare vacation resorts and others.

EXECUTIVES

Managing Director SS&C Asia Pacific, Thanendra (Tee) Arasoo

President and COO, Normand A. (Norm) Boulanger, age 51, $450,000 total compensation

Chairman and CEO, William C. (Bill) Stone, age 58, $750,000 total compensation

SVP Secretary and General Counsel, Stephen V. R. (Steve) Whitman, age 66, $225,000 total compensation

SVP and CFO, Patrick J. Pedonti, age 62, $260,000 total compensation

SVP and Chief Development Officer, Steve H. Kremidas

SVP and General Manager DBC, Richard Shalowitz

SVP and General Manager Treasury Banks and Credit Unions Business, Colleen Nelsen

SVP and General Manager, Thomas (Tom) McMackin

VP-Strategic Accounts, Doug Benedetto

SVP and Managing Director International, David N. (Dave) Reid

SVP and Managing Director Alternative Assets, Rahul Kanwar

Managing Director SS&C Fund Services, Henry Toy

Managing Director SS&C Technologies Australia, Phil Banas

SVP Enterprise Risk, James (Jim) Ramenda

SVP and General Manager Financial Markets Division, Bob Moitoso

SVP and General Manager SS&C PORTIA, Christy Bremner

SVP and General Manager Asset Management Division, Alex Marasco

Senior Vice President; General Counsel; Secretary, Paul Igoe

SVP Institutional Outsourcing, Tim Reilly

Director, Jonathan E. Michael, age 59

President; Chief Operating Officer; Director, Normand A. (Norm) Boulanger, age 50

Director, Allan M. Holt, age 60

Director, Claudius E. (Bud) Watts IV, age 51

Director, William A. (Bill) Etherington, age 68

Director, Campbel R. (Cam) Dyer, age 38

Director, David Varsano

Auditors: PricewaterhouseCoopersLLP

LOCATIONS

HQ: SS&C Technologies Holdings, Inc.
80 Lamberton Road, Windsor, CT 06095
Phone: 860 298-4500
Web: www.ssctech.com

2012 Sales

	$ mil.	% of total
Americas		
US	360	65
Canada	59	11
Other countries	12	2
Europe	104	19
Asia/Pacific & Japan	15	3
Total	**551**	**100**

PRODUCTS/OPERATIONS

2012 Sales by Product Group

	$ mil.	% of total
Portfolio management/accounting	476	86
Trading/treasury operations	36	7
Property management	14	3
Financial modeling	8	2
Loan management/accounting	7	1
Money market processing	6	1
Training	2	-
Total	**551**	**100**

2012 Sales

	$ mil.	% of total
Software-enabled services	406	74
Maintenance	93	17
Professional services	29	5
Software licenses	22	4
Total	**551**	**100**

Selected Services

Application outsourcing and hosting
Consulting
Data conversion
Installation
Maintenance
Technical support
Training

Selected Software

AdvisorWare (portfolio management and investment accounting)
Altair (asset management for hedge funds and family offices)
AnalyticsExpress (financial modeling)
Antares (trade order management)
The BANC Mall (Internet-based lending and leasing tool)
CAMRA (asset management reporting and accounting)
DBC (financial modeling)
Debt & Derivatives (comprehensive derivative and debt portfolio analysis)
Finesse (dynamic financial analysis and simulation)
Lightning (office processing management and automation)
LMS (loan management)
PALMS (alternative investment managers)
PortPro (balance sheet and investment portfolio analysis and management)
PTS (life insurance modeling and decision support)
SamTrak (property management for real estate leasing agents and property managers)
SKYLINE II (property management accounting and reporting)
SS&C Wealth Management (wealth management)
TradeDesk (fixed-income transaction processing automation)
TradeThru (trading and treasury operations)

COMPETITORS

ADP	Intuit
Advent Software	Liquid Holdings
Algorithmics	McCracken Financial
Bank of New York	Solutions
Mellon	Misys
Bloomberg L.P.	Neovest
Charles River Systems	PNC Financial
Citigroup	StatPro Group
DST Systems	State Street
Eze Castle	SunGard
Fidessa	TradeStation
Frontline Technologies	Triple Point
HP Enterprise Services	Yardi Systems

HISTORICAL FINANCIALS

Company Type: Public

Income Statement

FYE: December 31

	REVENUE ($ mil.)	NET INCOME ($ mil.)	NET PROFIT MARGIN	EMPLOYEES
12/12	551.8	45.8	8.3%	4,086
12/11	370.8	51.0	13.8%	1,484
12/10	328.9	32.4	9.9%	1,399
12/09	270.9	19.0	7.0%	1,253
12/08	280.0	18.8	6.7%	0
Annual Growth	**18.5%**	**24.9%**	**—**	**—**

2012 Year-End Financials

Debt ratio: 42.8%
Return on equity: 4.4%
Cash ($ mil.): 86
Current ratio: 1.29
Long-term debt ($ mil.): 989

No. of shares (mil.): 79
Dividends
   Yield: —
   Payout: —
Market value ($ mil.): 1,826

	STOCK PRICE ($) FY Close	P/E High/Low		PER SHARE ($) Earnings	Dividends	Book Value
12/12	23.09	45	30	0.55	0.00	13.60
12/11	18.06	32	20	0.63	0.00	12.62
12/10	20.51	45	29	0.44	0.00	11.78
Annual Growth	**6.1%**	**—**	**—**	**11.8%**	**—**	**7.5%**

Stamps.com Inc.

Stamps.com hopes its customers keep putting letters in the mail. Its PC Postage Service lets registered users who have downloaded Stamps.com software buy stamps online and print the postage directly onto envelopes and labels. Customers can order US Postal Service options such as registered mail certified mail and delivery confirmation as well as print custom stamps using virtually any image through its PhotoStamps.com website. Stamps.com charges a monthly fee for its service which is aimed at consumers home offices and small businesses. In addition customers can buy mailing labels scales and dedicated postage printers from Stamps.com. Postage fees are sent directly to the US Postal Service.

The deep recession in the US and the rise in popularity of email vs. traditional mail have constrained Stamp.com's revenue and profit growth in recent years. In 2010 revenue increased by 4% while net income fell by more than 10% vs. the previous year. During the prior three years revenue has been flat or down as net income and cash flow have declined steeply.

The slump in its business has Stamps.com looking for new revenue streams. In July 2010 the company formed a partnership with online retail giant Amazon.com that makes its domestic and international shipping labels available to Amazon.com Marketplace users. More recently the Internet postage firm in early 2011 won a contract from the USPS to provide electronic postage for shipping transactions generated by the postal service's Click-N-Ship web-based service.

The Internet postage firm's PhotoStamps service is a form of postage that allows users to turn digital photos designs or other images into valid US postage. The product generated about 8% of 2010 revenue down from 10% in 2009. Photo-

Stamps is available under authorization of the US Postal Service. Rival Envelope Manager Software (aka Endicia.com) also operates a custom postage service called "PictureItPostage."

As the company rides out the recession Stamps.com is looking to lay a strong foundation for future sales increases. It's modestly boosting its spending on marketing to small business customers rather than risking losing this target niche and the company plans to increase its sales team ranks by about 25% during 2010 to cater to its enterprise customers. After having made enhancements to its high-volume shipping service in 2009 Stamps.com continues to invest in shipping technology and associated sales and marketing. It's also revamped its website in 2010 to improve its customers' experience.

Stamps.com was founded as as StampMaster in 1996. The company changed its name to Stamps.com in late-1998 and went public the following year. Director Lloyd Miller is Stamps.com's largest shareholder with about a 10% stake in the company.

EXECUTIVES

CEO and Director, Kenneth (Ken) McBride, age 43, $388,000 total compensation
CFO, Kyle Huebner, age 40, $260,000 total compensation
SVP Corporate and Business Development, James M. Bortnak, age 42, $240,000 total compensation
Chief Legal Officer and Secretary, Seth Weisberg, age 42, $252,000 total compensation
VP Postal Technology and Affairs, J.P. Leon, $185,691 total compensation
VP Product Strategy and New Product Development, John Clem, age 39, $201,667 total compensation
VP Development, Michael Biswas, age 34, $212,385 total compensation
Chief Marketing Officer, Sebastian Buerba
Director, G. Bradford (Brad) Jones, age 56
CEO and Director, Kenneth (Ken) McBride, age 43
Director, Mohan P. Ananda, age 65
Director, Lloyd I. Miller III, age 57
Auditors: Ernst&YoungLLP

LOCATIONS

HQ: Stamps.com Inc.
12959 Coral Tree Place, Los Angeles CA 90066
Phone: 310-482-5800   **Fax:** 310-482-5900
Web: www.stamps.com

PRODUCTS/OPERATIONS

2010 Sales

	$ mil.	% of total
Service	64	76
Product	11	14
PhotoStamps	7	8
Insurance	2	2
Total	**85**	**100**

COMPETITORS

Endicia	Pitney Bowes
FedEx	UPS
Neopost USA	US Postal Service
Newell Rubbermaid	eBay

HISTORICAL FINANCIALS
Company Type: Public

Income Statement
FYE: December 31

	REVENUE ($ mil.)	NET INCOME ($ mil.)	NET PROFIT MARGIN	EMPLOYEES
12/12	115.6	38.5	33.3%	233
12/11	101.5	26.2	25.9%	226
12/10	85.5	5.5	6.5%	220
12/09	82.1	6.1	7.5%	210
12/08	84.9	10.1	12.0%	190
Annual Growth	**8.0%**	**39.6%**	**—**	**5.2%**

2012 Year-End Financials

Debt ratio: —	No. of shares (mil.): 15
Return on equity: 37.1%	Dividends
Cash ($ mil.): 29	Yield: —
Current ratio: 3.13	Payout: —
Long-term debt ($ mil.): —	Market value ($ mil.): 386

	STOCK PRICE ($) FY Close	P/E High/Low		PER SHARE ($) Earnings	Dividends	Book Value
12/12	25.20	14	8	2.30	0.00	7.37
12/11	26.13	18	6	1.73	0.00	5.82
12/10	13.25	42	23	0.38	2.00	3.05
12/09	9.00	27	21	0.38	0.00	4.82
12/08	9.83	30	14	0.53	0.00	4.54
Annual Growth	**26.5%**	**—**	**—**	**44.3%**	**—**	**12.9%**

Star Gas Partners L.P.

Those who wish for heat and power can wish upon a star —Star Gas Partners. The company is the nation's largest retail distributor of home heating oil. Its Petro Holdings subsidiary provides heating oil and propane to 416000 customers in the US Northeast and Mid-Atlantic. The company sells home heating oil gasoline and diesel fuel to 48000 customers on a delivery only basis and provides HVAC and ancillary home services including home security and plumbing to 11500 customers. Investment firm Kestrel Energy Partners controls the general partner of Star Gas Partners.

Geographic Reach
The company has operations in Connecticut Maine Maryland Massachusetts New Hampshire New Jersey New York North Carolina Rhode Island Pennsylvania South Carolina Vermont Virginia and Washington DC.

Operations
Star Gas Partners' primary business is to provide services to residential and commercial customers to heat homes and buildings. Its operations are conducted through Petro Holdings. Other activities include the installation maintenance and repair of heating and air conditioning equipment and ancillary home services (home security and plumbing).

Star Gas Finance Company serves as the co-issuer jointly and severally with Star Gas Partners of the company's $125.0 million 8.875% Senior Notes (excluding discounts) which are due in December 2017.

Financial Performance
Revenues decreased by 6% in fiscal year 2012 due to a 7% drop in product sales as the decline in total volumes of 17.1% exceeded the lift of higher product selling prices. Selling prices in-

creased in response to higher wholesale product costs of $0.4465 per gallon. This was offset by 1.9% increase in installation and service sales because of the additional revenues from acquisitions of $9.3 million.

The slump of revenues is attributable to the decrease in home heating oil volume and a decline in sales of other petroleum products and the residual conditions of high unemployment reduced home equity loans and consumer credit and reduced consumer confidence which helped to cause a decline in the demand for new heating systems.

Star Gas Partners' net income increased by 7% in fiscal year 2012 due to a decrease in interest expense largely because of lower bank fees of $1 million resulting from lower rates on letters of credit and lower unused commitment fees a decrease in pretax income of $4.5 million (which was less than the decrease in income tax expense of $6.1 million) and a decrease in Amortization of Debt Issuance Costs due to an increase in the number of years over which such costs are amortized due to the extension in June 2011 of the Partnership's revolving credit facility termination date from July 2012 to June 2016.

Strategy
The company seeks to grow its business by making selected acquisitions to increase its presence in some of its existing geographic markets and selectively expanding into new markets and broadenening its products and services by marketing related and complementary products and services.

During fiscal 2012 Star Gas Partners completed seven acquisitions and added 41000 home heating oil and propane accounts (for $39.2 million reduced by working capital credits of $1.2 million). In fiscal 2011 it acquired four retail heating oil dealers with 8800 home heating oil and propane accounts for $9.7 million including working capital of $1.9 million.

Ownership
Kestrel Energy Partners owns about 23% of the company.

EXECUTIVES

Chairman, Paul A. Vermylen Jr., age 67
EVP CFO Secretary and Treasurer, Richard F. Ambury, age 57, $302,500 total compensation
President CEO and Director, Daniel P. Donovan, age 68, $388,333 total compensation
Vice President; Controller of Kestrel Heat; LLC, Richard G. Oakley, age 54, $199,600 total compensation
EVP and COO, Steven J. Goldman, age 54, $285,000 total compensation
General Partner of the company, Kestrel Heat
Director, Sheldon B. Lubar, age 84
Director, William P. Nicoletti, age 69
Director, Bryan H. Lawrence, age 71
President CEO and Director, Daniel P. Donovan, age 68
Director, Henry D. Babcock, age 74
Director, C. Scott Baxter, age 53
Auditors: KPMGLLP

LOCATIONS

HQ: Star Gas Partners L.P.
2187 Atlantic St., Stamford CT 06902
Phone: 203-328-7310   **Fax:** 203-328-7422
Web: www.star-gas.com

PRODUCTS/OPERATIONS

2012 Sales

	$ mil.	% of total
Product	1,295	86
Installations & service	202	14
Total	**1,497**	**100**

COMPETITORS

AmeriGas Partners	Global Partners
Benit Fuel	Inergy
Castle Oil	Meenan Oil
Connecticut Light and Power	NOCO
Energy Transfer Equity	Rice Cos.
Ferrellgas Partners	Superior Plus
Getty Petroleum Marketing	Woodfin Oil
	richland partners

HISTORICAL FINANCIALS

Company Type: Public

Income Statement
FYE: September 30

	REVENUE ($ mil.)	NET INCOME ($ mil.)	NET PROFIT MARGIN	EMPLOYEES
09/13	1,741.8	29.9	1.7%	2,577
09/12	1,497.5	25.9	1.7%	2,582
09/11	1,591.3	24.3	1.5%	2,677
09/10	1,212.7	28.3	2.3%	2,729
09/09	1,206.8	131.0	10.9%	2,655
Annual Growth	**9.6%**	**(30.9%)**	**—**	**(0.7%)**

2013 Year-End Financials

Debt ratio: 19.6%
Return on equity: —
Cash ($ mil.): 85
Current ratio: 1.39
Long-term debt ($ mil.): 124

No. of shares (mil.): 57
Dividends
  Yield: 6.5%
  Payout: 59.2%
Market value ($ mil.): 284

	STOCK PRICE ($) FY Close	P/E High/Low		Earnings	PER SHARE ($) Dividends	Book Value
09/13	4.92	11	8	0.47	0.32	4.49
09/12	4.32	13	9	0.40	0.31	4.26
09/11	4.90	17	13	0.35	0.31	4.20
09/10	4.74	12	9	0.38	0.29	4.17
09/09	3.63	3	1	1.43	0.20	4.08
Annual Growth	**7.9%**	**—**	**—**	**(24.3%)**	**12.1%**	**2.5%**

Starwood Property Trust Inc.

Starwood Property Trust hopes to shine brightly in the world of mortgages. A real estate investment trust (REIT) the company originates finances and manages US commercial and residential mortgage loans commercial mortgage-backed securities and other commercial real estate debt investments. It acquires discounted loans from failed banks and financial institutions some through the FDIC which typically auctions off large pools of loan portfolios. Starwood Property Trust is externally managed by SPT Management LLC an affiliate of Starwood Capital Group. As a REIT the trust is exempt from paying federal income tax so long as it distributes quarterly dividends to shareholders.

Financial Performance

Overall revenues grew 63% in 2012 to $327 million up from $201 million in 2011. The trust primarily earns money on interest income from mortgage-backed securities and loans.

Mergers and Acquisitions

In 2013 Starwood Property Trust bought LNR Property LLC a real estate investment finance management and development firm. The trust paid $862 million for LNR's US special servicer the US investment securities portfolio Archetype Mortgage Capital (now Starwood Mortgage Capital) Archetype Financial Institution Services LNR Europe and 50% of LNR's interest in Auction.com.

Later that year it moved to spin off its single-family residential business as a new REIT named Starwood Waypoint Residential Trust. The trust which will be affiliated with Waypoint Homes will invest own and operate single-family rental homes and non-performing residential mortgage loans in the US.

EXECUTIVES

Chairman and CEO, Barry S. Sternlicht, age 53
EVP and Interim Principal Financial Officer, Jerome C. (Jerry) Silvey, age 55
COO and General Counsel, Andrew J. Sossen, age 36
President and Managing Director, Boyd W. Fellows
CFO, Stew Ward
Chief Credit Officer and Managing Director, Chris Tokarski
Lead Independent Director, Richard Bronson
Chief Originations Officer and Managing Director, Warren de Haan
Independent Director, Camille J. Douglas
Independent Director, Jeffrey DiModica
Independent Director, Strauss Zelnick
Auditors: Deloitte&ToucheLLP

LOCATIONS

HQ: Starwood Property Trust Inc.
591 W. Putnam Ave., Greenwich CT 06830
Phone: 203-422-8100 **Fax:** 203-422-7784
Web: www.starwoodpropertytrust.com

2012 Sales

	% of total
Western	24
Northeastern	23
Southeastern	16
Mid-Atlantic	13
Midwest	9
International	9
Southwestern	6
Total	**100**

PRODUCTS/OPERATIONS

2012 Sales by Collateral Property Type

	% of total
Hospitality	45
Office	17
Retail	15
Residential	9
Mixed-Use	4
Industrial	3
Multifamily	2
Other	5
Total	**100**

COMPETITORS

American Capital Agency Corp.	Newcastle Investment
Annaly Capital Management	NorthStar Realty
	PennyMac Mortgage
	Petra Real Estate

Arbor Realty Trust	RAIT Financial Trust
CYS Investments	Realty Finance
Hatteras Financial	Corporation
Invesco Mortgage Capital	Redwood Trust
JER Investors Trust	Two Harbors
MFA Financial	iStar Financial Inc

HISTORICAL FINANCIALS

Company Type: Public

Income Statement
FYE: December 31

	REVENUE ($ mil.)	NET INCOME ($ mil.)	NET PROFIT MARGIN	EMPLOYEES
12/12	306.9	201.2	65.5%	0
12/11	204.9	119.3	58.2%	0
12/10	93.5	57.0	61.0%	0
12/09	6.9	(3.0)	—	0
Annual Growth	**253.9%**	**—**	**—**	**—**

2012 Year-End Financials

Debt ratio: 32.2%
Return on equity: 8.9%
Cash ($ mil.): 177
Current ratio: 1.91
Long-term debt ($ mil.): 1,393

No. of shares (mil.): 135
Dividends
  Yield: 7.6%
  Payout: 105.6%
Market value ($ mil.): 3,111

	STOCK PRICE ($) FY Close	P/E High/Low		Earnings	PER SHARE ($) Dividends	Book Value
12/12	22.96	14	11	1.76	1.86	20.07
12/11	18.51	17	12	1.38	1.74	18.88
12/10	21.48	19	14	1.14	1.20	18.69
12/09	18.89	—	—	(0.06)	0.11	18.66
/0.00	—	—	(0.00)	0.00	(0.00)	
Annual Growth	**—**	**—**	**—**	**—**	**—**	

State Bank Financial Corp

State Bank Financial Corp. aspires to one day live in the center of central Georgia's banking world. A holding company State Bank Financial operates through subsidiary State Bank and Trust Company a state-chartered commercial bank that serves individuals and businesses throughout central Georgia and in the Atlanta metropolitan area. Through some two dozen branches the bank offers traditional checking and savings accounts as well as commercial and residential real estate mortgages construction and commercial loans and consumer loans. Formed in 2010 State Bank Financial holds more than $2.8 billion in assets.

The holding company was formed to acquire the assets of distressed banks many of which fell victim to the 2008 credit crisis and ensuing recession. With the assistance of the FDIC and proceeds raised in a private offering of common stock State Bank Financial acquired seven community banks between 2009 and 2011 and re-branded them as State Bank and Trust Co. The acquisitions expanded the bank's presence in its core central Georgia and metro Atlanta markets. State Bank Financial intends to continue leveraging such acquisitions to strengthen its presence in these markets.

LOCATIONS

HQ: State Bank Financial Corporation
415 E. Paces Ferry Rd. NE Ste. 250, Atlanta GA 30305
Phone: 404-475-6599   **Fax:** 720-437-6501
Web: ampiopharma.com

PRODUCTS/OPERATIONS

2010 Sales

	$ mil.	% of total
Interest and dividend income		
Loans receivable	159	79
Investment securities	8	4
Deposits in other banks and other	0	
Noninterest income		
Accretion of FDIC receivable for loss sharing agreements	15	8
Service charges on deposit accounts	6	4
Gain on acquisitions	3	2
6.0	3	
Total	**200**	**100**

COMPETITORS

BB&T	SunTrust
Bank of America	Synovus
Citizens Bancshares	Wells Fargo
Regions Financial	

HISTORICAL FINANCIALS

Company Type: Public

Income Statement

FYE: December 31

	REVENUE ($ mil.)	NET INCOME ($ mil.)	NET PROFIT MARGIN	EMPLOYEES
12/12	149.2	22.7	15.2%	605
12/11	208.3	43.0	20.6%	605
12/10	200.3	45.5	22.7%	495
12/09*	68.1	18.0	26.5%	0
07/09	1.2	(0.2)	—	0
Annual Growth	**231.7%**	**—**	**—**	**—**

*Fiscal year change

2012 Year-End Financials

Debt ratio: 0.0%	No. of shares (mil.): 31
Return on equity: 5.4%	Dividends
Cash ($ mil.): 445	Yield: 0.3%
Current ratio: 0.21	Payout: 6.8%
Long-term debt ($ mil.): 2	Market value ($ mil.): 507

	STOCK PRICE ($) FY Close	P/E High/Low		PER SHARE ($) Earnings	Dividends	Book Value
12/12	15.88	25	20	0.69	0.06	13.48
12/11	15.11	13	9	1.32	0.00	12.52
12/10	14.50	11	10	1.40	0.00	11.37
12/09*	14.00	24	24	0.58	0.00	9.85
Annual Growth	**4.3%**	**—**	**—**	**6.0%**	**—**	**11.0%**

*Fiscal year change

Stericycle Inc.

Bubble bubble toil and trouble Stericycle treats medical rubble. A leading medical and pharmaceutical waste management company Stericycle serves some 541000 clients worldwide: 16500 large waste generators (pharmaceutical manufacturers hospitals and blood banks) and 524500 small waste generators (dental and medical offices veterinary offices pharmacies and municipalities).

Services include disposing of used needles and expired drugs. Through 153 processing and collection sites and 154 transfer sites and 64 recall and returns or communication services facilities Stericycle treats waste through incineration autoclaving (using high temperature and pressure to kill pathogens) and electro-thermal-deactivation (using low-frequency radio waves to kill pathogens).

Geographic Reach

The company operates regulated waste management networks in Argentina Brazil Canada Chile Ireland Japan Mexico Portugal Romania Spain the UK and the US.

Operations

Stericycle's operating segments are International Waste Management Services and Domestic Regulated Waste Management Services/Domestic Regulated Recall and Returns Management Services (which operate together as the US reporting segment).

Sales and Marketing

EXECUTIVES

EVP and COO, Richard T. Kogler, $229,473 total compensation
Chairman, Mark C. Miller, $305,964 total compensation
EVP and President Recall and Return Management Services, Michael J. Collins, $226,600 total compensation
President and CEO, Charles A. (Charlie) Alutto
EVP CFO and Chief Administrative Officer, Frank J. M. ten Brink
Director, John Patience, age 65
Director, Jack W. Schuler, age 72
Director, James W. P. (Jim) Reid-Anderson, age 53
Director, William K. Hall, age 69
Director, Jonathan T. (Jack) Lord, age 58
Director, Rod F. Dammeyer, age 72
Director, Ronald G. Spaeth, age 68
Director, Thomas D. Brown, age 65
Independent Director, James Anderson
Auditors: Ernst&YoungLLP

LOCATIONS

HQ: Stericycle Inc.
28161 N. Keith Dr., Lake Forest IL 60045
Phone: 847-367-5910   **Fax:** 847-367-9493
Web: www.stericycle.com

2012 Sales

	$ mil.	% of total
US	1,370	72
Europe	301	15
Other regions	240	13
Total	**1,913**	**100**

PRODUCTS/OPERATIONS

Selected Subsidiaries

Ambiface & Buffer SGPS Lda (Portugal)
BFI Medical Waste Inc.
Consenur SA (Spain)
Healthcare Waste Solutions Inc.
MedServe Inc.
MedSolutions Inc.
Notify MD Inc.
SRCL Ireland Limited
SRCL Limited (Ireland)
Stericare Romania
Stericycle Brazil Ltd.
Stericycle Chile S.A.
Stericycle Co. Ltd. (Japan)
Stericycle Espana Srl (Spain)
Stericycle Europe Limited (UK)
Stericycle International Ltd (UK)
Stericycle Mexico

Stericycle Operations Srl (Spain)
Stericycle UK Limited
Stericylce ULC CANADA
White Rose Environmental (UK)
ZooMed - Gestao Lda (Portugal)

COMPETITORS

Ascent Healthcare Solutions	Republic Services
BioMedical Technology Solutions	Shanks
	US Ecology
Ecolab UK	Waste Connections
Mercury Waste Solutions	Waste Industries USA
	Waste Management

HISTORICAL FINANCIALS

Company Type: Public

Income Statement

FYE: December 31

	REVENUE ($ mil.)	NET INCOME ($ mil.)	NET PROFIT MARGIN	EMPLOYEES
12/12	1,913.1	268.0	14.0%	13,245
12/11	1,676.0	234.7	14.0%	11,122
12/10	1,439.3	207.8	14.4%	9,715
12/09	1,177.7	175.6	14.9%	8,199
12/08	1,083.6	148.7	13.7%	6,883
Annual Growth	**15.3%**	**15.9%**	**—**	**17.8%**

2012 Year-End Financials

Debt ratio: 38.2%	No. of shares (mil.): 85
Return on equity: 19.5%	Dividends
Cash ($ mil.): 31	Yield: —
Current ratio: 1.33	Payout: —
Long-term debt ($ mil.): 1,268	Market value ($ mil.): 8,021

	STOCK PRICE ($) FY Close	P/E High/Low		PER SHARE ($) Earnings	Dividends	Book Value
12/12	93.28	30	24	3.08	0.00	17.93
12/11	77.92	34	27	2.69	0.00	14.15
12/10	80.92	34	21	2.39	0.00	12.30
12/09	55.17	28	22	2.03	0.00	9.98
12/08	52.08	37	28	1.68	0.00	7.86
Annual Growth	**15.7%**	**—**	**—**	**16.4%**	**—**	**22.9%**

Stifel Financial Corp.

Stifel Financial doesn't repress investors. The company serves individual corporate municipal and institutional clients through nearly 300 offices in the US with a concentration in the Midwest and mid-Atlantic regions. It also has locations in Canada and Europe. Through subsidiaries Stifel Nicolaus (founded 1890) Thomas Weisel (acquired in 2010) Century Securities Associates Stifel Bank & Trust and others the company provides asset management financial advice and banking services for private clients. Stifel also offers brokerage and mergers and acquisitions advisory services for corporate clients underwrites debt and equity and provides research on more than 1000 US and European equities.

Hoping to take advantage of the demise of bulge-bracket investment banks such as Bear Stearns and Lehman Brothers and turmoil in the industry in general Stifel Financial has been growing via acquisitions —nearly ten of them since 2005.

In mid-2013 Stifel Financial acquired Knight Capital Group's US institutional fixed income sales and trading business. Altogether Stifel Financial's and Knight Capital Group's combined teams boast some 90 sales and trading professionals across the US and Europe. The team covers high-yield and investment-grade corporate bonds asset-backed and mortgage-based securities loan trading and fixed income research in certain sectors and companies.

In 2011 the company bought Stone & Youngberg which specializes in municipal bonds and fixed income securities.

The 2010 Thomas Weisel deal worth more than $300 million and one of Stifel Financial's largest to date boosted the company's investment banking capabilities in the technology health care and energy sectors. Thomas Weisel's Canadian operations took on the Stifel Nicolaus name.

Stifel Financial has also built up its asset management and brokerage operations through acquisition. In 2010 the company bought investment advisor Missouri Valley Partners from First Banks; the year before it acquired more than 50 wealth management branches in the US from UBS Financial Services.

The additions along with improved market conditions helped Stifel Financial achieve record revenues in 2011 the 16th consecutive year that the figure increased. Net income was up too rebounding from nearly $2 million in 2010 to more than $84 million thanks in part to increased commissions and fees related to brokerage and asset management services and a decline in compensation costs.

In addition to acquisitions Stifel Financial also has strategies to grow organically. These include establishing trust services at Stifel Bank & Trust and utilizing the bank to cross-sell mortgages and securities-based loans to wealth management clients. Stifel Financial also wants to extend the reach of its private client business in the US and its institutional equity operations globally.

EXECUTIVES

Vice Chairman, Richard J. Himelfarb, age 72, $250,000 total compensation

Co-Chairman President and CEO, Ronald J. (Ron) Kruszewski, age 54, $200,000 total compensation

SVP CFO and Director, James M. Zemlyak, age 53, $175,000 total compensation

Vice Chairman, Ben A. Plotkin, age 57, $250,000 total compensation

Co-Chairman, Thomas W. (Thom) Weisel, age 72

EVP and Director Capital Markets Stifel Nicolaus, Thomas P. Mulroy, age 51, $250,000 total compensation

SVP and Director Equity Research Stifel Nicolaus, Hugo J. (Hugh) Warns III

Senior Vice President, David D. Sliney, age 43, $150,000 total compensation

Senior Vice President Director Denver Municipal Trading, Michael F. Imhoff

SVP and Director Denver Public Finance Stifel Nicolaus, Stephen H. Bell

SVP and Director Syndicate Stifel Nicolaus, Thomas R. Kendrick IV

SVP and General Counsel, David M. Minnick, age 56, $125,000 total compensation

Senior Vice President Director Private Markets, J. Joseph Schlafly III

Senior Vice President Co-Director Institutional Group Director, Victor J. Nesi, age 53

Senior Vice President; Treasurer; Controller, Bernard Burkemper

Senior Vice President, Chad Estep

Vice Chairman, Richard J. Himelfarb, age 72

Co-Chairman President and CEO, Ronald J. (Ron) Kruszewski, age 54

SVP CFO and Director, James M. Zemlyak, age 53

Vice Chairman, Ben A. Plotkin, age 57

Director, John P. Dubinsky, age 69

Co-Chairman, Thomas W. (Thom) Weisel, age 72

Director, Robert E. (Bob) Grady, age 55

Director, Charles A. Dill, age 73

Director, Richard F. (Dick) Ford, age 76

Director, Robert E. Lefton, age 81

Director, James M. Oates, age 66

Director, Bruce A. Beda, age 72

Director, Kelvin R. Westbrook, age 56

Director, Michael W. (Mike) Brown, age 67

Director, Alton F. Irby III, age 72

EVP and Director Capital Markets Stifel Nicolaus, Thomas P. Mulroy, age 51

Director, Frederick O. (Fred) Hanser, age 71

Senior Vice President Co-Director Institutional Group Director, Victor J. Nesi, age 53

Auditors: Ernst&YoungLLP

LOCATIONS

HQ: Stifel Financial Corp.
1 Financial Plaza 501 N. Broadway, St. Louis MO 63102-2102
Phone: 314-342-2000   **Fax:** 818-553-2388
Web: www.publicstorage.com

PRODUCTS/OPERATIONS

2011 Sales

	$ mil.	% of total
Commissions	561	40
Principal transactions	343	24
Asset management & service fees	228	16
Investment banking	199	14
Interest	89	6
Total	**1,422**	**100**

Selected Subsidiaries

Broadway Air Corp.
Butler Wick & Co. Inc.
Century Securities Associates Inc.
    CSA Insurance Agency Incorporated
Choice Financial Partners Inc.
First Service Financial Company
    Stifel Bank & Trust
Hanifen Imhoff Inc.
Missouri Valley Partners
Stifel Asset Management Corp.
Stifel Nicolaus Limited (UK)
Stifel Nicolaus & Company Incorporated
    Ryan Beck Holdings LLC
    Stifel Nicolaus Insurance Agency Incorporated
Stifel Nicholas Limited (UK)
Thomas Weisel Partners Group Inc.

COMPETITORS

Bank of America	Oppenheimer Holdings
Cowen Group	Piper Jaffray
Edward Jones	Raymond James
Goldman Sachs	Financial
JMP Group	Robert W. Baird &
Jefferies Group	Co.
Lazard	SWS Group
Morgan Stanley	Wells Fargo Advisors

HISTORICAL FINANCIALS

Company Type: Public

Income Statement

FYE: December 31

	ASSETS ($ mil.)	NET INCOME ($ mil.)	INCOME AS % OF ASSETS	EMPLOYEES
12/12	6,966.1	138.5	2.0%	5,343
12/11	4,951.9	84.1	1.7%	5,097
12/10	4,213.1	1.9	0.0%	4,906
12/09	3,167.3	75.8	2.4%	4,434
12/08	1,558.1	55.5	3.6%	3,371
Annual Growth	45.4%	25.7%	—	12.2%

2012 Year-End Financials

Return on assets: 2.3%
Return on equity: 9.8%
Long-term debt ($ mil.): —
No. of shares (mil.): 54
Sales ($ mil): 1,646
Dividends
Yield: —
Payout: —
Market value ($ mil.): 1,755

	STOCK PRICE ($) FY Close	P/E High/Low		PER SHARE ($) Earnings	Dividends	Book Value
12/12	31.97	15	11	2.20	0.00	27.23
12/11	32.05	46	15	1.33	0.00	25.15
12/10	62.04	157	11080	0.03	0.00	24.79
12/09	59.24	33	17	1.57	0.00	19.16
12/08	45.85	37	20	1.32	0.00	15.04
Annual Growth	(8.6%)	—	—	13.6%	—	16.0%

Strattec Security Corp.

STRATTEC SECURITY has your car under lock and key. The company designs and manufactures mechanical security locks electro-mechanical locks and keys and ignition lock housings primarily for global automakers. It also makes access control products including door handles latches power sliding doors and power lift gates. Chrysler Ford and General Motors account for the majority of STRATTEC's annual sales. In addition to cars and light trucks its products are used in the heavy truck and recreational vehicle markets as well as in precision die castings. With facilities in the US and Mexico STRATTEC delivers products mainly in North America but also abroad in Asia Europe and South America.

STRATTEC along with fellow automotive product suppliers WIITE Automotive and ADAC Automotive is a member of the Vehicle Access Systems Technology (VAST) Alliance. This alliance allows members to act as each others' sales marketing manufacturing and support representatives in North America and Europe. Members also own a joint venture Vehicle Access Systems Technology LLC which operates manufacturing facilities in China and Brazil and supports sales in the Asia/Pacific and Latin America regions.

Through a joint venture with ADAC Automotive called ADAC-STRATTEC LLC STRATTEC also supplies door handle components and related vehicle access hardware. In 2009 STRATTEC formed a new subsidiary with WIITE Automotive called STRATTEC Power Access LLC (SPA) to acquire the North American business of Delphi's Power Products group. SPA produces power access systems for sliding doors lift gates and trunk lids. Current customers for this set of products are Chrysler Ford GM and Taiwan-based Yulon.

As STRATTEC tries to grow its footprint geographically through these ventures it's also moving beyond its traditional lock and key products and diversifying with a more sophisticated set of power access control products. Purely mechanical devices are on the out and out. The company views electro-mechanical devices for vehicles –mechanical locks keys housings and latches that are enhanced by built-in electronics –as the future. These include devices that incorporate user bio-identification systems keys with remote entry capabilities and ignition interfaces with passive start capabilities among other technologies.

Following the global economic crisis STRATTEC faced a dismal performance in fiscal 2009 as two of its largest customers (Chrysler and GM) faced bankruptcy and the US auto industry was near collapse. Economic forecasts for auto production were very low compared to pre-2009 levels and industry analysts generally agreed that any recovery would be long and slow. But despite these negative conditions STRATTEC weathered the storm and managed to turn a small profit in fiscal 2010 an achievement compared to the losses of 2009. With vehicle production rates recovering faster than forecasted the company's sales are likewise showing improvement especially in terms of access control products.

EXECUTIVES

Chairman, Harold M. Stratton II, age 65, $373,814 total compensation

Senior Vice President - Chief Financial Officer Treasurer and Secretary, Patrick J. Hansen, age 54, $217,134 total compensation

President and Chief Executive Officer, Frank J. Krejci, age 63

Vice President of Milwaukee Operations, Kathryn E. Scherbarth, age 57, $155,223 total compensation

Vice President - Marketing and Sales, Dennis A. Kazmierski, age 62, $195,798 total compensation

Vice President of Mexican Operations, Rolando J. Guillot, age 45, $176,843 total compensation

Vice President - Security Products, Brian J. Reetz, age 55

Vice President - Access Control Products, Richard P. Messina, age 47

Board Member, Michael J. Koss, age 59

Board Member, Robert Feitler, age 82

President COO and Board Member, Frank J. Krejci, age 63

Board Member, David R. Zimmer, age 67

Auditors: GrantThorntonLLP

LOCATIONS

HQ: STRATTEC SECURITY CORPORATION
3333 W. Good Hope Rd., Milwaukee WI 53209
Phone: 414-247-3333   **Fax:** 414-247-3329
Web: www.strattec.com

PRODUCTS/OPERATIONS

2010 Sales by Customer

	$ mil.	% of total
Chrysler	68	33
General Motors	51	25
Ford Motor	18	9
Other customers	69	33
Total	**208**	**100**

COMPETITORS

AISIN World Corp.	Tokai Rika
Huf North America	Valeo
Automotive	Visteon
Magna International	

HISTORICAL FINANCIALS

Company Type: Public

Income Statement

FYE: June 30

	REVENUE ($ mil.)	NET INCOME ($ mil.)	NET PROFIT MARGIN	EMPLOYEES
06/13*	298.1	9.3	3.1%	2,670
07/12	279.2	8.7	3.1%	2,507
07/11	260.9	5.4	2.1%	2,556
06/10	207.9	3.4	1.6%	2,280
06/09	126.1	(6.1)	—	1,655
Annual Growth	**24.0%**	**—**	**—**	**12.7%**

*Fiscal year change

2013 Year-End Financials

Debt ratio: 1.3%	No. of shares (mil.): 3
Return on equity: 10.1%	Dividends
Cash ($ mil.): 20	Yield: 0.0%
Current ratio: 2.10	Payout: 14.7%
Long-term debt ($ mil.): —	Market value ($ mil.): 126

	STOCK PRICE ($) FY Close	P/E High/Low		PER SHARE ($) Earnings	Dividends	Book Value
06/13*	37.36	15	7	2.72	0.40	30.91
07/12	21.04	10	7	2.64	0.40	24.38
07/11	21.13	23	12	1.63	1.20	26.21
06/10	22.01	26	13	1.04	0.00	22.63
06/09	13.90	—	—	(1.87)	0.30	21.89
Annual Growth	**28.0%**	—	—	—	**7.5%**	**9.0%**

*Fiscal year change

Strayer Education, Inc.

Students who wander from traditional learning paths can turn to Strayer Education. The company's Strayer University offers more than 100 different degree diploma and certificate programs from more than 90 campuses in 22 states and Washington DC. The university which was founded in 1892 serves some 54000 students most of whom are working adults seeking degrees in such fields as business administration computer networking and information systems. Strayer Education offers internet-based classes in synchronous (real-time) and asynchronous formats through Strayer University Online. Strayer Education acquired the Jack Welsh Management Institute an online business education program in 2011.

Strayer University distinguishes itself from traditional universities through the online options that it offers on a global basis. In 2011 more than 32000 or 60% of its students who enrolled for the fall term took all of their classes online. Strayer supports its online initiatives through two Global Online Operations Centers in Chantilly Virginia and Salt Lake City Utah.

Strayer's main strategy for growth involves investing in new campuses where demand for adult education is high and investing in information technology infrastructure to support its online programs. Typically the company opens campuses in geographic locations where it already has a nearby presence mainly in growing metropolitan areas in mid-Atlantic and southern states. The rationale being that academic deans and administrators can focus on increasing academic quality rather than having to travel great distances to keep tabs on educational activities. In 2009 and 2010 Strayer

opened two dozen new campuses in 2011 eight were opened and another eight are planned for 2012.

Employing these strategies Strayer has seen its revenues grow more than 20% on a compounded annual basis between 2000 and 2011 increasing from $78 million in 2000 to almost $630 million in 2011. In 2011 however the company's revenue dropped from its 2010 level by 1% due to a 4% decline in its average enrollment. Its income from operations also fell 17% from the previous year and net income decreased 19%. Since 98% of the company's revenue comes from tuition its 2012 enrollment will be negatively impacted since fewer students enrolled in 2011 translates into lower associated continuing education revenue for the company. Suspect in the drop in enrollment is higher unemployment and lowered confidence in job prospects.

To hedge such times Strayer also develops and pursues growth opportunities by forming alliances with institutions and corporations to provide training and educational opportunities through its flexible evening weekend and online classes. The company relies on such alliances for enrolling new students and creating ongoing opportunities. In this way Strayer has established alliances with the FBI Northrop Grumman Verizon FedEx Capital One and more.

Physical growth can only be a component of an educational institution's expansion strategy. It also has to grow to meet its students educational needs. In order to do that Strayer introduces new courses and programs as demand warrants. For example it launched the Writing Across the Curriculum program to help Strayer students improve their writing skills across all disciplines including business computer science and the arts. It also started offering a bachelor's degree in criminal justice.

Strayer Education moved to add "name brand" education to its offerings through its 2011 acquisition of the Jack Welsh Management Institute. Its online executive MBA program and certification programs are based on the management lessons of the former General Electric chairman and CEO and are geared for both individual students and corporations seeking continuing education for their executives.

Various investment groups own more than half of the company. These include Macquarie Group Limited (almost 12%) Baron Capital Group (about 11%) Royce & Associates (about 10%) Generation Investment Management (co-founded by former US Vice President Al Gore; 7%) and others.

EXECUTIVES

Chairman and CEO, Robert S. Silberman, age 55, $665,000 total compensation

Chief Financial Officer; Executive Vice President, Mark C. Brown, age 53, $265,000 total compensation

Senior Vice President - Corporate Communications, Sonya G. Udler, age 45

President; Chief Executive Officer; Chief Operating Officer; Director, Karl McDonnell, age 46, $330,000 total compensation

Dean Schools of Business and Information Systems Strayer University, Deborah Snyder

General Counsel and Secretary, Viet D. Dinh, age 45

Senior Vice Provost Academic Administration, Randi Reich Cosentino, age 39

Executive Vice President; Chief Administrative Officer, Kelly J. Bozarth, age 45

President of Strayer University, Michael Plater, age 56

Provost and Chief Academic Officer, Randi
Cosentino
Director, Robert L. (Bob) Johnson, age 68
Director, Todd A. Milano, age 61
Director, David A. (Dave) Coulter, age 66
Director, J. David Wargo, age 59
Director, G. Thomas Waite III, age 62
Director, Charlotte F. Beason, age 66
Director, William E. (Bill) Brock, age 82
Director, Robert R. Grusky, age 56
Independent Director, John Casteen
Auditors: PricewaterhouseCoopersLLP

LOCATIONS

HQ: Strayer Education Inc.
2303 Dulles Station Blvd., Herndon VA 20171
Phone: 703-561-1600   **Fax:** 818-748-4600
Web: www.filmroman.com

Selected Campus Locations
Alabama
Arkansas
Delaware
Florida
Georgia
Illinois
Indiana
Kentucky
Louisiana
Maryland
Mississippi
New Jersey
North Carolina
Ohio
Pennsylvania
South Carolina
Tennessee
Texas
Utah
Virginia
Washington DC
West Virginia
Wisconsin

PRODUCTS/OPERATIONS

2011 Students by Program Level

	% of total
Bachelor's	56
Master's	30
Associate	12
Non-degree	2
Total	**100**

Selected Degrees and Programs
Master of Business Administration (M.B.A.) Degree
Master of Education (M.Ed.) Degree
Master of Health Services Administration (M.H.S.A.)
 Degree
Master of Public Administration (M.P.A.) Degree
Master of Science (M.S.) Degree
 Information Systems (with multiple concentrations)
 Professional Accounting
Executive Graduate Certificate Programs
 Business Administration
 Information Systems
 Professional Accounting
Bachelor of Science (B.S.) Degree
 Accounting
 Information Systems
 Economics
 International Business
 Criminal Justice
Bachelor of Business Administration (B.B.A.) Degree
Associate in Arts (A.A.) Degree
 Accounting
 Acquisition and Contract Management
 Business Administration
 Criminal Justice
 Information Systems
 Economics
 General Studies
 Marketing

Diploma Programs
 Accounting
 Acquisition and Contract Management
 Information Systems
Undergraduate Certificate Programs
 Accounting
 Business Administration
 Information Systems

COMPETITORS

Apollo Education	DeVry Education Group
Argosy Education	Education Management
Bridgepoint Education	ITT Educational
Cardean Learning Group	Kaplan
Career Education	Lincoln Educational
Corinthian Colleges	Services

HISTORICAL FINANCIALS
Company Type: Public

Income Statement
FYE: December 31

	REVENUE ($ mil.)	NET INCOME ($ mil.)	NET PROFIT MARGIN	EMPLOYEES
12/12	561.9	65.9	11.7%	2,152
12/11	627.4	106.0	16.9%	2,282
12/10	636.7	131.2	20.6%	2,291
12/09	511.9	105.0	20.5%	1,970
12/08	396.2	80.8	20.4%	3,863
Annual Growth	9.1%	(5.0%)	—	(13.6%)

2012 Year-End Financials

Debt ratio: 54.8%
Return on equity: 157.9%
Cash ($ mil.): 47
Current ratio: 2.08
Long-term debt ($ mil.): 121

No. of shares (mil.): 11
Dividends
 Yield: 7.1%
 Payout: 69.4%
Market value ($ mil.): 640

	STOCK PRICE ($) FY Close	P/E High/Low		PER SHARE ($) Earnings	Dividends	Book Value
12/12	56.17	20	8	5.76	4.00	3.60
12/11	97.19	17	8	8.88	4.00	3.59
12/10	152.22	26	13	9.70	3.25	13.22
12/09	212.52	30	20	7.60	2.25	13.60
12/08	214.41	42	25	5.67	3.63	12.50
Annual Growth	(28.5%) (26.7%)	—	—	0.4%	2.5%	

Sturm, Ruger & Co., Inc.

Whether you like to shoot birdies or bogeys Sturm Ruger & Company can accommodate you. The company also called Ruger is one of the nation's biggest gun makers and produces all four categories of firearms: pistols revolvers rifles and shotguns. Models include hunting and target rifles single- and double-action revolvers muzzleloading guns and double-barreled shotguns. Its guns are sold by independent wholesale distributors to independent firearms retailers and chains including Academy Sports and Cabelas. Ruger also makes metal products –known as castings –for the commercial and military markets. Sturm Ruger & Company was founded in 1949 by William Ruger and Alexander Sturm.

Geographic Reach

Connecticut-based Sturm Ruger & Company makes all of its products in the US and sells most of them here as well. Foreign sales primarily to law enforcement and government agencies accounted for only 3% of 2012 sales.

Sales and Marketing

Four top customers account for more than half of Ruger's sales. They are Davidson's (17%) Jerry's/Ellett Brothers (15%) Lipsey's (13%) and Sports South (12%).

Operations

Ruger manufactures all of its rifles and revolvers in Newport New Hampshire. All pistols (except for one model) are produced in Prescott Arizona.

Investment castings accounted for 1% of the firearms maker's 2012 sales. Ruger's Pine Tree Castings (PTC) division makes and sells castings made from steel alloys for both its own use and for use outside customers. PTC supplies the architectural hardware sporting goods marine hardware firearms precision machinery pneumatic and hand tools industries among others. The company stopped manufacturing titanium castings in 2007 and consolidated its Arizona casting operations into its New Hampshire facilities. Following the move Ruger produces only castings made from steel alloys.

Financial Performance

The company's firearm sales increased nearly 50% in 2012 vs. 2011 closing in on the $500 million mark. Net income rose 76% over the same period. Sales are soaring driven by extraordinary retail demand for its firearms beginning in late 2008. (Units ordered increased by 107% in 2012 vs. 2011 while the number of units on backorder more than tripled.) Ruger attributes the high demand to politics and the economy. Also sales of handguns –purchased for self defense –have been particularly strong. To keep pace Ruger has increased production and even temporarily stopped taking orders for several months in 2012.

Profits are on the rise as well peaking steadily since 2008. The company's shares soared in 2012 and Ruger declared a special dividend of $4.50 per share in late 2012. While the renewed debate over gun control in the US following the tragedy in Newtown Connecticut could cast a shadow over the outlook for firearms sales in the short-term it has spurred sales.

Strategy

In 2011 Ruger became the first commercial firearms company to produce a million firearms in a single year. By August of 2012 it easily surpassed that milestone. While struggling to meet demand for its guns the company is also chasing after one of the faster-growing segments of the hunting market and working to expand its products portfolio. To that end in mid-2012 Ruger acquired a minority stake in crossbow manufacturer Kodabow. The company hopes the crossbow manufacturer based in West Chester Pennsylvania will boost sales and broaden its customer base. Ruger plans to continue to look for acquisition opportunities and work to expand manufacturing capacity in 2013.

HISTORY

Sturm Ruger & Company was founded in 1949 by William Ruger who designed a notable machine gun used by the military during WWII and Alexander Sturm who backed the production of a new Ruger design by investing $50000. Sturm died of hepatitis in 1951 at age 28 and after a battle with Sturm's family Ruger took control of the company.

The gun maker's growth during the 1960s and 1970s was driven by demand for single-action revolvers and .22-caliber autoloading pistols produced at its original plant in Southport Connecticut. Ruger went public in 1969 still the only American gun company to do so.

In 1986 the company forced its distributors to choose between it and archrival Smith & Wesson; about half chose to stay with Ruger. By streamlining its distribution channels the manufacturer made its products more difficult to find thus increasing their prestige.

Decreasing firearms sales prompted the company to expand its castings operations. Ruger bought Callaway Golf's share in their joint foundry to become its sole owner in 1997. In 1998 Ruger unveiled its first muzzleloader the Ruger 77/50 to capitalize on the growing popularity of muzzle-loading rifles. Later that year New Orleans became the first municipality to sue gun makers including Ruger in an effort to recover the cost of gun violence. Other local governments followed suit.

In 2000 the company sent letters to gun distributors asking that its guns be sold at regular places of business not trade shows. In 2001 the Louisiana Supreme Court threw out New Orleans' suit but remained a defendant in some 37 lawsuits at the end of 2001.

Co-founder William Ruger died in July 2002. In early 2003 after 2 years of pretrial discovery the consolidated California cities suit against almost all firearms manufacturers (including Ruger) was dismissed.

EXECUTIVES

Corporate Secretary, Leslie M. Gasper, age 59, $121,000 total compensation
President CEO and Director, Michael O. Fifer, age 55, $400,000 total compensation
VP Prescott Firearms, Mark T. Lang, age 56, $196,154 total compensation
VP CFO and Treasurer, Thomas A. Dineen, age 44, $225,000 total compensation
VP Sales and Marketing, Christopher J. Killoy, age 54, $235,000 total compensation
VP Newport Operations, Thomas P. (Tom) Sullivan, age 52, $235,000 total compensation
VP and General Counsel, Kevin B. Reid Sr.
VP Lean Business Development, Steven M. (Steve) Maynard, $218,775 total compensation
Chairman, James Ser
Vice President - Lean Business Development, Stephen Maynard
President CEO and Director, Michael O. Fifer, age 55
Director, Amir P. Rosenthal, age 52
Director, Ronald C. (Ron) Whitaker, age 66
Chairman Emeritus, Vice Adm. James E. Service, age 81
Director, Phillip C. Widman, age 58
Director, John A. Cosentino Jr., age 63
Auditors: McGladreyLLP

LOCATIONS

HQ: Sturm Ruger & Company Inc.
Lacey Place, Southport CT 06890
Phone: 203-259-7843   **Fax:** 203-256-3367
Web: www.ruger-firearms.com

PRODUCTS/OPERATIONS

2012 Sales

	$ mil.	% of total
Firearms	484	99
Castings	6	1
Total	**491**	**100**

Selected Products
Firearms

Pistols
  P-Series (centerfire)
  Ruger 22/45 (rimfire)
  Ruger Mark II (rimfire)
Revolvers
  Single-actionBirds Head VaqueroBisley HunterNew
    BearcatNew Model BlackhawkNew Model Single
    SixNew Model .32 Magnum Super Single-SixNew
    Model Super BlackhawkOld Army Cap & BallRuger
    BisleySingle-SixSuper BlackhawkVaquero
  Double-actionGP100SP101RedhawkSuper Redhawk
Rifles
  10/22
  77/17
  77/22
  77/44
  77/50 Muzzle Loader
  96/17
  96/22
  96/44
  Deerfield Carbine
  M-77 Mark II
  M-77 Mark II Magnum
  Mini-14
  Mini Thirty
  Model 96 Rimfire
  No.1 Single Shot
  Ruger Carbine
Shotguns
  Gold Label (side-by-side 12 gauge)
  Red Label (12 20 28 gauge)
  Woodside (12 gauge)
Castings
  Aluminum
  Chrome-molybdenum
  Cobalt
  Nickel
  Stainless steel

COMPETITORS

A. Finkl & Sons
Beretta USA
Browning Arms
Colt Defense
Colt's
Fabbrica D' Armi Pietro
  Beretta
Freedom Group
GKN Sinter Metals
Gibbs Die Casting

Glock
Marlin Firearms
Mossberg
Remington Arms
SIG SAUER
Savage Arms
Smith & Wesson
  Holding
Springfield Armory

HISTORICAL FINANCIALS

Company Type: Public

Income Statement
FYE: December 31

	REVENUE ($ mil.)	NET INCOME ($ mil.)	NET PROFIT MARGIN	EMPLOYEES
12/12	491.8	70.6	14.4%	2,040
12/11	328.8	40.0	12.2%	1,540
12/10	255.2	28.2	11.1%	1,160
12/09	270.9	27.5	10.1%	1,150
12/08	181.4	8.6	4.8%	1,150
Annual Growth	**28.3%**	**69.0%**	—	**15.4%**

2012 Year-End Financials

Debt ratio: —
Return on equity: 60.6%
Cash ($ mil.): 30
Current ratio: 1.63
Long-term debt ($ mil.): —

No. of shares (mil.): 19
Dividends
  Yield: 12.7%
  Payout: 206.9%
Market value ($ mil.): 875

STOCK PRICE ($) FY Close	P/E High/Low		PER SHARE ($) Earnings	Dividends	Book Value
12/12	45.40	16	9	3.60	5.80	4.93
12/11	33.46	17	7	2.09	0.43	7.20
12/10	15.29	12	7	1.46	0.33	6.08
12/09	9.70	10	4	1.42	0.31	5.01
12/08	5.97	21	11	0.43	0.00	3.44
Annual Growth	**66.1%**	—	—	**70.1%**	—	**9.4%**

Suburban Propane Partners L.P.

Ranch-style homes are heated and backyard barbecues fueled by Suburban Propane Partners a leading US retail propane marketer which competes with Energy Transfer Partners AmeriGas Ferrellgas and other propane providers. With more than 300 service centers in 30 states Suburban Propane serves some 608000 retail customers. It annually sells about 300 million gallons of propane and more than 37 million gallons of fuel oil and refined petroleum products to wholesale and large end-users. It also sells natural gas and electricity and installs HVAC systems. In a major expansion in 2012 the company acquired Inergy's propane assets for $1.8 billion.

Before the acquisition Inergy Propane operated in 33 states from 338 customer service centers. Inergy's propane assets added 600000 propane customers and 325 million retail propane gallons to Suburban Propane's total assets.

Suburban Propane's business segments include propane; fuel oil and residual fuels; natural gas and electricity; and services). Through its fuel oil and refined fuels segment Suburban Propane distributes fuel oil diesel kerosene and gasoline to about 48000 residential and commercial customers in the northeast of the US.

Through its natural gas and electricity segment (Agway Energy Services) Suburban Propane offers gas and electric utility services to almost 87000 residential and commercial customers in New York and Pennsylvania.

In addition to the sale and installation of heating and air conditioning units the company also provides air cleaners humidifiers de-humidifiers as well as air duct cleaning and energy audit services.

Suburban Propane's growth strategy includes complementary acquisitions customer maintenance and growth and the selective selling of non-core assets.

Fiscal 2010 saw the company posting weaker revenues and income as the recession dragged down demand. However with the economy pulling out of the recession during the fiscal year Suburban Propane resumed its acquisitive ways buying four mid-sized propane operations that complement its existing businesses including Lyles's Propane of Nevada.

In 2011 the company reported an almost 5% jump in revenues primarily due to higher prices offsetting lower volumes sold. Net income was essentially flat. Suburban Propane made one acquisition that year buying a medium-sized propane business in a market where it already had a major presence.

Vice President; General Counsel; Secretary, Paul E. Abel, age 61

Chairman, Harold R. Logan Jr., age 69

President CEO and Supervisor, Michael J. (Mike) Dunn Jr., age 64, $475,000 total compensation

Senior Vice President - Administration, Michael M. Keating, age 60, $260,000 total compensation

VP Business Development, Mark Anton II, age 56

CFO, Michael A. Stivala, age 44, $275,000 total compensation

VP and Treasurer, A. Davin D'Ambrosio, age 49

VP Product Supply, Douglas T. Brinkworth, age 53, $245,000 total compensation

VP Operational Support and Analysis, Mark Wienberg, age 51

Vice President; Chief Accounting Officer, Michael A. Kuglin, age 43

VP Field Operations, Steven C. Boyd, age 49, $270,000 total compensation

VP Information Services, Neil Scanlon, age 48

Vice President; Treasurer, Davin Ambrosio

Vice President Treasurer, Davin DAmbrosio

Independent Member of the Supervisory Board, Lawrence Caldwell

Independent Member of the Supervisory Board, Matthew Chanin

Vice President; Treasurer, Davin D'Ambrosio

Supervisor, John H. Stookey, age 83

President CEO and Supervisor, Michael J. (Mike) Dunn Jr., age 64

Supervisor, Dudley C. Mecum II, age 78

Supervisor, Jane Swift, age 48

Supervisor, John D. Collins, age 75

Auditors: PricewaterhouseCoopersLLP

LOCATIONS

HQ: Suburban Propane Partners L.P.
1 Suburban Plaza 240 Rt. 10 W., Whippany NJ 07981
Phone: 973-887-5300   **Fax:** 610-359-6908
Web: www.allianceanytime.com

PRODUCTS/OPERATIONS

2010 Sales

	$ mil.	% of total
Propane	929	78
Fuel oil & refined fuels	139	12
Natural gas & electricity	84	7
Other	36	3
Total	**1,190**	**100**

COMPETITORS

AmeriGas Partners	Piedmont Natural Gas
Energy Transfer	Southern States
Ferrellgas Partners	Star Gas Partners

HISTORICAL FINANCIALS

Company Type: Public

Income Statement

FYE: September 28

	REVENUE ($ mil.)	NET INCOME ($ mil.)	NET PROFIT MARGIN	EMPLOYEES
09/13	1,703.6	78.8	4.6%	3,933
09/12	1,063.4	1.8	0.2%	4,144
09/11	1,190.5	114.9	9.7%	2,385
09/10	1,136.6	115.3	10.1%	2,598
09/09	1,143.1	165.2	14.5%	2,783
Annual Growth	**10.5%**	**(16.9%)**	**—**	**9.0%**

2013 Year-End Financials

Debt ratio: 45.6%	No. of shares (mil.): 60
Return on equity: —	Dividends
Cash ($ mil.): 107	Yield: 0.0%
Current ratio: 1.25	Payout: 259.5%
Long-term debt ($ mil.): 1,245	Market value ($ mil.): 2,791

	STOCK PRICE ($) FY Close	P/E High/Low		PER SHARE ($) Earnings	Dividends	Book Value
09/13	46.33	37	28	1.34	3.48	18.75
09/12	41.36	968696		0.05	3.41	19.15
09/11	46.41	18	13	3.22	3.41	10.11
09/10	53.70	17	13	3.24	3.35	10.33
09/09	41.17	9	5	4.96	3.26	10.21
Annual Growth	**3.0%**	**—**	**—**	**(27.9%)**	**1.7%**	**16.4%**

Sun Communities, Inc.

Sun Communities helps residents in the Sunshine State and around the US. The self-managed real estate investment trust (REIT) owns develops and operates manufactured housing communities (trailer and recreation vehicle parks) in 25 states. Its portfolio in May 2013 included about 185 properties with 67700 developed manufactured home and RV sites. Its Sun Home Services unit sells new and used homes for placement on its properties the majority of which are in Michigan Florida Indiana Texas and Ohio. Sun Communities also acquires at a discount and resells mobile homes that have been repossessed by lenders in its communities.

Geographic Reach

Sun Communities has properties in Arizona Colorado Connecticut Delaware Florida Georgia Illinois Indiana Iowa Kansas Maine Massachusetts Michigan Missouri Nevada New Jersey New York North Carolina Ohio Oregon Pennsylvania Tennessee Texas Virginia and Wisconsin.

Operations

Sun Communities operates two lines of business: Real property and homes sales and rentals.

The company's properties have trained on-site property managers and maintenance personnel as well as such amenities as clubhouses laundry facilities and swimming pools. At the end of 2012 the company owned and operated 182 properties in 19 states including 149 manufactured housing communities 13 RV communities and 11 properties containing both manufactured housing and RV sites. That year the average renewal rate for residents in Sun Communities' rental program was about 61%.

Financial Performance

The company's revenues grew by 17% in 2012 thanks to a 40% increase in revenues from home sales and a 14% increase in income from real property partially offset by decline in ancillary revenues. Sun Communities' manufactured home and RV portfolio increased by $9.5 million due to average rental rate increases of 2.8% and the growth in occupied home sites offset by rent concessions offered to residents who convert from home renters to home owners. The growth in home sales revenues was due to a hike in the sales volume of new home and pre-owned homes.The higher revenues allowed Sun Communities to post a net income of $5 million in 2012 as compared to a net loss in 2011 despite an increase in expenses. The company has seen an increase in revenues between

2010 and 2012 due to organic growth. Burdened by heavy debt from the collapse of the housing market and its equity investments in that market the company has steadily chipped away at its debt. Sun Communities saw a continuous decline in net loss from 2001 to 2011 and finally posted a net income figure in 2012.

Strategy

Sun Communities' solid performance is in part due to increased demand from retiring adults a growing demographic. The company also points to its rental program as key to its success during the recession. Home rentals have become a popular and affordable alternative to customers. The company is focusing on its growth strategy through acquisitions and expansion of its properties.

Mergers and Acquisitions

Expanding its geographic coverage in early 2013 the company acquired ten RV communities (Gwynns Island RV Resort LLC Indian Creek RV Resort LLC Lake Laurie RV Resort LLC Newpoint RV Resort LLC Peters Pond RV Resort Inc. Seaport LLC Virginia Tent LLC Wagon Wheel Maine LLC Westward Ho RV Resort LLC and Wild Acres LLC) with 3700 sites in Connecticut Maine Massachusetts New Jersey Ohio Virginia and Wisconsin for $112.8 million.In 2012 Sun Communities made seven acquisitions (which included 14 properties in total seven manufactured housing communities five RV communities and two communities containing both manufactured housing and RV communities. The acquisitions included Three Lakes RV Resort Blueberry Hill RV Resort and Grand Lake Estates located in Florida; Blazing Star RV Resort (260 sites located in San Antonio Texas); Northville Crossing Manufactured Home Community (756 sites in Northville Michigan); Rainbow RV Resort (500 sites in Frostproof Florida); four manufactured home communities (the Rudgate Acquisition Properties) in southeast Michigan and Palm Creek Golf & RV Resort (283 manufactured home sites 1580 RV sites and the expansion potential of 550 manufactured housing or 990 RV sites) in Casa Grande Arizona.

In 2011 Sun Communities grew its portfolio when it acquired 17 manufactured housing communities and one RV community in western Michigan from Kentland Corporation. That year Sun Communities also bought a RV resort in Florida for more than $6 million.

Ownership

FMR LLC and Edward C. Johnson III (the chairman of FMR LLC) own more than 12% of Sun Communities.

EXECUTIVES

EVP, Jonathan M. Colman, age 57, $172,450 total compensation

Chairman President and CEO, Gary A. Shiffman, age 59, $574,550 total compensation

EVP and COO, John B. McLaren

EVP CFO Treasurer and Secretary, Karen J. Dearing

Director, Stephanie W. Bergeron, age 59

Director, Ronald L. Piasecki, age 74

Director, Paul D. Lapides, age 59

Director, Clunet R. Lewis, age 66

Director, Ted J. Simon, age 81

Director, Arthur A. Weiss, age 64

Director, Robert H. Naftaly, age 75

Auditors: GrantThorntonLLP

LOCATIONS

HQ: Sun Communities Inc.
27777 Franklin Rd. Ste. 200, Southfield MI 48034
Phone: 248-208-2500   **Fax:** 248-208-2642
Web: www.suncommunities.com

2012 Properties

	% of total
Michigan	72
Florida	32
Texas	21
Indiana	18
Ohio	11
Other	28
Total	**182**

PRODUCTS/OPERATIONS

2012 Sales

	$ mil.	% of total
Real property income	255	75
Home sales	45.1	13
Home rentals	26	8
Interest and other	12	4
Total	**339**	**100**

Selected Mergers and Acquisitions

2013
Gwynns Island RV Resort LLC Indian Creek RV Resort LLC Lake Laurie RV Resort LLC Newpoint RV Resort LLC Peters Pond RV Resort Inc. Seaport LLC Virginia Tent LLC Wagon Wheel Maine LLC Westward Ho RV Resort LLC and Wild Acres LLC (Connecticut Maine Massach
2012
Three Lakes RV Resort Blueberry Hill RV Resort and Grand Lake Estates; Florida
Blazing Star RV Resort; San Antonio Texas
Northville Crossing Manufactured Home Community; Michigan

COMPETITORS

American Land Lease	Nobility Homes
Equity Lifestyle Properties	Outdoor Resorts
Hometown America	UMH Properties

HISTORICAL FINANCIALS

Company Type: Public

Income Statement

FYE: December 31

	REVENUE ($ mil.)	NET INCOME ($ mil.)	NET PROFIT MARGIN	EMPLOYEES
12/12	339.6	8.0	2.4%	915
12/11	289.1	(0.5)	—	775
12/10	263.1	(3.5)	—	747
12/09	256.6	(7.3)	—	664
12/08	255.0	(34.4)	—	644
Annual Growth	**7.4%**	**—**	**—**	**9.2%**

2012 Year-End Financials

Debt ratio: 82.8%
Return on equity: 24.1%
Cash ($ mil.): 29
Current ratio: 0.99
Long-term debt ($ mil.): 1,423

No. of shares (mil.): 29
Dividends
  Yield: 6.3%
  Payout: 1,680.0%
Market value ($ mil.): 1,187

	STOCK PRICE ($) FY Close	P/E High/Low	PER SHARE ($) Earnings	Dividends	Book Value
12/12	39.89	26 3201	0.18	2.52	6.47
12/11	36.53	— —	(0.05)	3.15	(5.81)
12/10	33.31	— —	(0.15)	2.52	(6.02)
12/09	19.75	— —	(0.34)	2.52	(5.57)
12/08	14.00	— —	(1.90)	2.52	(3.23)
Annual Growth	**29.9%**	**— —**	**—**	**(0.0%)**	

SunCoke Energy Inc

If you're looking for a new soda product look elsewhere; if you're looking to produce steel SunCoke Energy's products may be right up your alley. One of North America's largest coke producers SunCoke produces metallurgical coke (a coal-derived fuel used in steel production) for steel companies. Its five owned and operated plants –located in Virginia Indiana Ohio Illinois and Vitoria Brazil (operated only) —can produce an aggregate 5.9 million tons of coke per year. To support its coke production the company also has coal mining operations in Virginia and West Virginia. Major customers include ArcelorMittal US Steel and AK Steel.

IPO
SunCoke a spinoff from Sunoco went public in 2011.
SunCoke raised some $186 million in its IPO. The proceeds were issued to initial debt exchange parties which also received the option to purchase shares of company's common stock. In connection to the IPO SunCoke was spun off as an independent company and is no longer a Sunoco subsidiary. Sunoco sold SunCoke to focus on its other businesses and growth opportunities and to reduce its debt.
To raise cash in 2013 the company issued an IPO of a master limited partnership SunCoke Energy Partners L.P. selling 13.5 million common units of limited partner interests in SunCoke Energy Partners L.P. for $233.1 million of net proceeds. As a result SunCoke owns 2% of SunCoke Energy Partners GP LLC the general partner of SunCoke Energy Partners and about 56% of the master limited partnership.

Geographic Reach
The company has operations in the US (Illinois Indiana Ohio and Virginia) and Brazil. In Virginia and West Virginia known as Central Appalachian region it has more than 110 million tons of proven and probable reserves to support the coal mining operation. SunCoke also operates in India through a joint venture with VISA Steel.

Operations
SunCoke has four operating segments: Jewel Coke Other Domestic Coke International Coke and Coal Mining.
Jewell Coke manages the company's Virginia-based cokemaking operations.
Other Domestic Coke includes East Chicago Indiana Franklin Furnace Ohio coke making and Illinois based heat recovery operations.
Based in Brazil International Coke makes approximately 1.7 million tons of coke a year for a Brazilian subsidiary of ArcelorMittal.
Coal Mining consists of metallurgical and thermal coal mining activities in Appalachia (thirteen active underground mines two active surface mines and one active highwall mine as well as three preparation plants and four load-out facilities). In 2012 Coal Mining sold 1.3 million tons of metallurgical coal and 0.2 million tons of thermal coal.
SunCoke uses its coal for its own operations but it does generate some revenue through the sale of coal to outside parties. Aside from its core metallurgical coke sales other sources of revenue for the company include sales of steam and electricity to Sunoco and other parties as well as fees related to operating the Brazilian plant.
SunCoke also earns revenue through licensing fees for its proprietary coal-producing technologies which includes coke ovens (used to produce its

coke) that differ from more traditional by-product coke ovens. Unlike by-product ovens which recover production-related waste used to make by-products like oil and coal tar SunCoke's production process uses waste generated during coke production to produce steam and electricity.

Sales and Marketing
In 2012 AcelorMittal accounted for 54% of SunCoke's revenues; AK Steel 28%; and US Steel 16%.

Strategy
Going forward SunCoke intends to increase its metallurgical coke production capabilities bolster its presence in North America and Brazil and expand into key international markets like China Eastern Europe and India.
Expanding into India in 2013 SunCoke Energy and VISA Steel launched a joint venture named VISA SunCoke Limited (49% owned by SunCoke) in return for a $67 million investment.
In 2011 the company opened a new coke-producing facility in Middletown Ohio that increased its overall production capacity to nearly 6 million tons per year. The facility is expected to eventually produce 550000 tons of coal per year.

Mergers and Acquisitions
To support the increase in production SunCoke will also ramp up production in its coal mines and expand its mining operations through acquisitions.
To improve its coal logistics infrastructure in 2013 a SunCoke Energy Partners unit agreed to buy West Virginia based Kanawha River Terminals LLC from Traxys North America LLC for $86 million.
In early 2011 SunCoke acquired HKCC Companies and its related mining assets in Virginia. The purchase added 21 million tons of proved and probable coal reserves and brought the company's overall reserves to 106 million tons.

Company Background
SunCoke traces its roots back to the 1960s.

EXECUTIVES

President and COO, Michael J. (Mike) Thomson, age 54
Chairman and CEO, Frederick A. (Fritz) Henderson, age 54
SVP Sales and Commercial Operations, Michael Hardesty, age 51
Vice President; Controller, Fay West, age 44
SVP Operations, Michael White
SVP and CFO, Mark E. Newman, age 50
Vice President Asset Management, David Horowitz
Senior Vice President General Counsel Corporate Secretary, Denise R. Cade
Vice President of Human Resources, Gary Yeaw
Senior Vice President Sales and Commercial Operations, Michael Hardesty
Chief Financial Officer; Senior Vice President, Mark Newman
Lead Independent Director, Robert Darnall
Independent Director, Alvin Bledsoe
Independent Director, James Sweetnam
Independent Director, John Rowe
Independent Director, Karen Peetz
Independent Director, Peter Hamilton
Auditors: Ernst&YoungLLP

LOCATIONS

HQ: SunCoke Energy Inc.
1011 Warrenville Rd. 6th Fl., Lisle IL 60532
Phone: 630-824-1000   **Fax:** 865-288-5280
Web: www.suncoke.com

PRODUCTS/OPERATIONS

2012 Sales

Other Domestic Coke	1,530	79
Coal Mining	48	3
Total	**1,914**	**100**

COMPETITORS

Alliance Resource	Oxbow Carbon
Alpha Natural Resources	Severstal North America
CONSOL Energy	Vale
China Minmetals	Walter Coke
Drummond Company	

HISTORICAL FINANCIALS

Company Type: Public

Income Statement

FYE: December 31

	REVENUE ($ mil.)	NET INCOME ($ mil.)	NET PROFIT MARGIN	EMPLOYEES
12/12	1,914.1	98.8	5.2%	1,214
12/11	1,538.9	60.6	3.9%	1,160
12/10	1,326.5	139.2	10.5%	0
12/09	1,145.0	189.6	16.6%	0
Annual Growth	18.7%	(19.5%)	—	—

2012 Year-End Financials

Debt ratio: 35.9%
Return on equity: 18.5%
Cash ($ mil.): 239
Current ratio: 1.91
Long-term debt ($ mil.): 720

No. of shares (mil.): 69
Dividends
  Yield: —
  Payout: —
Market value ($ mil.): 1,091

	STOCK PRICE ($) FY Close	P/E High/Low		PER SHARE ($) Earnings	Dividends	Book Value
12/12	15.59	12	8	1.40	0.00	7.70
12/11	11.20	20	11	0.87	0.00	7.51
12/10	0.00	—	—	1.99	0.00	(0.00)
Annual Growth	—	—	—	(16.1%)	—	—

Super Micro Computer Inc

Super Micro Computer manufactures high-performance server products based on open standard components (including Intel AMD and NVIDIA processors). Its nearly 7000 offerings include motherboards and serverboards blade servers rackmounts GPU systems chassis and Ethernet switches and network adaptors. The company also sells a host of subsystems and accessories. Super Micro markets its products –primarily through distributors and resellers such as Ingram Micro and Arrow Electronics –to customers in some 90 countries; nearly half its sales are generated outside the US.

Geographic Reach The company generates nearly 60% of its sales from the US with Europe and Asia contributing 22% and 17% respectively. All of these regions saw solid year-over-year growth in fiscal 2012. Super Micro has operations in The Netherlands and Taiwan that support its international customers.

Sales and Marketing The company sells primarily through distributors resellers and systems integrators (about 55% of sales) but it also markets to OEMs and directly to end users. Leading distributors and resellers include Ingram Micro Avnet MA Labs Tech Data and ASI.

Financial Performance Super Micro has seen strong revenue growth over the past decade with the exception of 2009 when the recession led to a small decline. In fiscal 2012 (ended June) it reported sales of $1 billion up 8% from 2011. The growth in 2012 was primarily the result of increased server system sales and a jump of nearly 20% in the average selling price for server systems. Net income in fiscal 2012 fell about a quarter to nearly $30 million as expenses rose by double digits driven by personnel growth.

Strategy Key to Super Micro's strategy is the expansion of its product portfolio as technology evolves. The company works closely with AMD Intel and others to make sure its offerings are compatible with the standards. In addition it puts a special focus on energy efficient products such as its SuperBlade line of blade server products. The company also wants to further expand into Asia and Europe. In 2012 it opened the Science and Technology Park in Taiwan to increase capacity and better serves its customers in the Asia-Pacific region.

Ownership CEO Charles Liang and his wife VP Sara Liang together own about 22% of Super Micro Computer.

EXECUTIVES

VP Operations Treasurer and Director, Chiu-Chu Liu (Sara) Liang, age 51, $167,333 total compensation
Chairman President and CEO, Charles Liang, age 55, $285,460 total compensation
CFO, Howard Hideshima, age 54, $251,205 total compensation
VP International Sales Secretary and Director, Yih-Shyan (Wally) Liaw, age 58, $168,800 total compensation
VP Worldwide Sales, Phidias Chou, age 55, $199,981 total compensation
SVP Investor Relations, Perry Hayes
Co-Founder Vice President Treasurer Director, Sara Liu
Vice President - Worldwide Sales, Cheng-Hsien Chou
Co-Founder Vice President of International Sales, Wally Liaw
Director, Edward J. (Ned) Hayes Jr., age 58
Director, Gregory K. (Greg) Hinckley, age 64
VP Operations Treasurer and Director, Chiu-Chu Liu (Sara) Liang, age 51
Director, Sherman Tuan, age 60
VP International Sales Secretary and Director, Yih-Shyan (Wally) Liaw, age 58
Independent Director, Laura Black
Auditors: Deloitte&ToucheLLP

LOCATIONS

HQ: Super Micro Computer Inc.
  980 Rock Ave., San Jose CA 95131
Phone: 408-503-8000   **Fax:** 408-503-8008
Web: www.supermicro.com

2012 Sales

	$ mil.	% of total
US	589	58
Europe	221	22
Asia	176	17
Other regions	26	3
Total	**1,013**	**100**

PRODUCTS/OPERATIONS

2012 Sales

	$ mil.	% of total
Server systems	447	44
Subsystems & accessories	566	56
Total	**1,013**	**100**

Selected Products

Chassis enclosures (pedestal rack-mount tower)
Motherboards (desktop server workstation)
Power supplies
Serverboards
Servers (rack-mount tower)

COMPETITORS

Celestica	IBM
Cisco Systems	Intel
Dell	Quanta Computer
Flextronics	Silicon Graphics International
Hewlett-Packard	
Hon Hai	Wistron

HISTORICAL FINANCIALS

Company Type: Public

Income Statement

FYE: June 30

	REVENUE ($ mil.)	NET INCOME ($ mil.)	NET PROFIT MARGIN	EMPLOYEES
06/13	1,162.5	21.2	1.8%	1,595
06/12	1,013.8	29.8	2.9%	1,503
06/11	942.5	40.2	4.3%	499
06/10	721.4	26.9	3.7%	1,012
06/09	505.6	16.1	3.2%	843
Annual Growth	23.1%	7.2%	—	17.3%

2013 Year-End Financials

Debt ratio: 5.5%
Return on equity: 5.9%
Cash ($ mil.): 93
Current ratio: 2.16
Long-term debt ($ mil.): 6

No. of shares (mil.): 42
Dividends
  Yield: —
  Payout: —
Market value ($ mil.): 450

	STOCK PRICE ($) FY Close	P/E High/Low		PER SHARE ($) Earnings	Dividends	Book Value
06/13	10.64	33	16	0.48	0.00	8.83
06/12	15.86	25	16	0.67	0.00	8.14
06/11	16.09	18	8	0.93	0.00	7.13
06/10	13.50	26	10	0.65	0.00	6.07
06/09	7.66	23	8	0.41	0.00	5.07
Annual Growth	8.6%	—	—	4.0%	—	14.9%

SVB Financial Group

SVB Financial Group is the holding company for Silicon Valley Bank which serves emerging and established companies involved in technology life sciences and private equity and provides customized financing to entrepreneurs executives and investors in such industries. It also offers deposit accounts loans and international banking and plays matchmaker for young firms and private investors. SVB Financial also provides investment advisory brokerage and asset management services; and provides credit and banking services to wealthy individuals.

Geographic Reach

SVB Financial has 28 offices in the US as well as seven branches in China India Israel and the UK.

Operations

The company operates in three segments: Global Commercial Bank SVB Private Bank and SVB Capital.

Global Commercial Bank segment is comprised of Commercial Bank SVB Specialty Lending SVB Analytics and Debt Fund Investments. Commercial Bank serves commercial clients in the technology venture capital/private equity life science and cleantech industries. SVB Analytics provides equity valuation services to private companies and venture capital/private equity firms while Debt Fund Investments has investments in debt funds.

SVB Private Bank provides personal financial solutions for consumers.

SVB Capital SVB Financial's capital arm focuses primarily on funds management.

Sales and Marketing

SVB Financial's clients are primarily venture capital and private equity professionals. Its customers include Active Power Coskata EnerNOC Joule and Solexant.

Financial Performance

The company's revenues grew by 4% in 2012 due to a rise in total interest income (stemming from an increase in loans and an increase in taxable available-for-sale securities) partially offset by decline in total non-interest income. SVB Financial's net income increased by 2% as the result of a decrease in interest expenses attributed to decline in deposits and borrowings expenses partially offset by higher non-interest income costs.

Strategy

Looking to grow via international expansion in 2012 the company opened a banking branch in the UK as well as a joint venture bank in China.

Greg Becker who joined SVB Financial in 1993 was named the company's CEO in 2011. He succeeded Ken Wilcox who became chairman and is focused on the company's efforts to expand in China including a joint venture with Shanghai Pudong Development Bank.

As part of its lending activities Silicon Valley Bank sometimes pursues warrants to purchase equity stakes in its clients. About 80% of the bank's loan portfolio is dedicated to business loans. Traditionally focused on up-and-coming firms the bank has implemented a strategy of courting larger later-stage clients.

Company Background

The company was established in 1983.

HISTORY

Silicon Valley Bank was founded in 1983 by Roger Smith to provide banking services to tech startups in San Jose. The bank boomed along with tech companies during the 1980s lending to the likes of Cisco Systems.

In 1990 the bank spread east to Boston's burgeoning technology alley. It also expanded into residential and commercial real estate lending. The recession of 1989 to 1991 found Silicon Valley Bancshares with an overextended loan portfolio and in 1992 the bank booked a loss due to non-performing loans; the next year it was put under federal supervision.

To rally stockholder confidence the company brought in new management and demoted Smith from chairman to vice chairman; he left the in 1995. The bank reduced its real estate lending and diversified into factoring foreign exchange and executive banking for venture capitalists and clients' upper management.

The 1995 IPO frenzy aided the company's turnaround. Silicon Valley cashed in on warrants it had taken as collateral from young companies. Regulatory supervision was lifted in 1996 and the bank soon opened offices in the Atlanta; Austin Texas; Boulder Colorado; Phoenix; and Seattle areas.

In 1999 Silicon Valley Bancshares created a website targeted at technology firms in need of financing employees office space and equipment. However nonperforming loans began to dog the bank once again affecting profits and bringing a regulatory request to boost reserves.

In 2000 despite being hammered by the high-tech stock selloff the company continued to expand opening offices in West Palm Beach Florida and North Carolina's Research Triangle and successfully capitalizing its first venture fund. The following year it bought tech-focused investment bank Alliant Partners (later renamed SVB Alliant) to broaden its service offerings.

Still licking its wounds from the tech bust the company ceased lending to the entertainment industry and to churches in 2002. Silicon Valley Bancshares changed its name to SVB Financial Services in 2005.

SVB Alliant struggled with losses for years and SVB Financial explored its options including spinning the unit off to management. It ultimately decided to shut down the division which ceased operations in 2008.

EXECUTIVES

Chief Strategy Officer and Risk Officer, Marc J. Verissimo, age 58, $310,679 total compensation

Chairman Silicon Valley Bank, Kenneth P. (Ken) Wilcox, age 65, $790,223 total compensation

Head Relationship Management; Vice Chairman Silicon Valley Bank, Harry W. Kellogg Jr., age 70, $311,262 total compensation

General Counsel, Mary Dent, age 52

President; Chief Executive Officer; Director the Company and the Bank, Greg Becker, age 45

Independent Chairman of the Board, Roger F. Dunbar, age 48

Managing Director SVB India Advisors, Suresh Shanmugham

Director Investor Relations, Meghan O'Leary

Chief Operating Officer, Bruce Wallace

President Silicon Valley Bank, Gregory W. (Greg) Becker, age 46, $499,154 total compensation

Head Corporate Finance, Mark A. MacLennan, age 60, $338,013 total compensation

President India and China SVB Financial Group, Ash Lilani

Head - U.S. Banking, Joan Parsons

Chief Marketing Officer, Brian K. Dennehy

SVP and Senior Relationship Manager Mid-Atlantic Office Silicon Valley Bank, Sean Stone

Managing Director SVB Capital, Jonathan (Jon) Norris

Chief Financial Officer, Michael (Mike) Descheneaux, age 46, $408,548 total compensation

Director Public Relations, Carrie Merritt

Head Human Resources, Christopher (Chris) Edmonds-Waters, age 51

Head Relationship Management Dallas, Brian Brown

Managing Director SVB Capital, Doug Hamilton

Regional Manager Boston and New York SVB Silicon Valley Bank, James (Jim) Maynard

Head Relationship Management Venture Capital and Private Equity Division, John D. China

Managing Director Private Equity Group SVB Capital, Bill Howell

Managing Director SVB India Finance, Ajay Hattangdi

SVP SVB Global Asia, Daniel R. Quon

SVP SVB Financial Group UK, Andy Tsao

Managing Partner SVB Capital Funds, Aaron Gershenberg

General Counsel SVB Capital, Jason Doren

SVP SVB Global China, Mike Yahng

Marketing Director SVB Analytics, Christina Chiaramonte

Head UK Europe and Israel, Phil Cox

Chief Credit Officer, Dave A. Jones, age 56, $302,319 total compensation

Head Cleantech Practice, Matt Maloney

Head Life Sciences Eastern Division, Michael Hanewich

Director SVB Accelerator, Lafe Vittitoe

Senior Relationship Manager, Albert Martinez

Senior Relationship Manager, Oscar Jazdowski

Senior Relationship Manager, Andy Pelletier

Senior Relationship Manager, Dale Kirkland

Senior Relationship Manager, Jim Parsons

Manager Northwest Market, Bruce Helberg

Market Manager Rocky Mountain Region, Mike Devery

Head SVB Capital, Sven Weber

Founder, Harry Peterson-Nedry

Board Member, Eric A. Benhamou, age 58

Board Member, Lata Krishnan, age 53

Board Member, G. Felda Hardymon, age 65

Board Member, C. Richard (Dick) Kramlich, age 78

Board Member, Michaela K. Rodeno, age 66

Board Member, Joel P. Friedman, age 65

Board Member, Roger F. Dunbar, age 47

Board Member, Kyung H. Yoon, age 59

Board Member, Kate Mitchell, age 55

Board Member, David M. Clapper, age 61

Independent Director, Garen Staglin

Independent Director, John Robinson

Auditors: KPMGLLP

LOCATIONS

HQ: SVB Financial Group
3003 Tasman Dr., Santa Clara CA 95054-1191
Phone: 408-654-7400   **Fax:** 408-496-2405
Web: www.svb.com

Selected Offices
US
    Atlanta
    Austin TX
    Broomfield CO
    Chicago
    Dallas
    Irvine CA
    Menlo Park CA
    Minnetonka MN
    New York
    Newton MA
    Palo Alto CA
    Philadelphia
    Phoenix
    Pleasanton CA
    Portland OR
    Raleigh NC
    Salt Lake City
    San Diego
    San Francisco
    Santa Rosa CA
    Seattle
    St. Helena CA
    Tysons Corner VA
International
    Bangalore India
    Beijing
    Herzliya Pituach Israel
    London
    Mumbai India
    Shanghai

PRODUCTS/OPERATIONS

2012 Sales

Interest		
Taxable securities	171	18
Noninterest		
Foreign exchange fees	49	5
Credit card fees	24	3
Letters of credit	15	2
Other	54	6

Selected Subsidiaries and Affiliates

Silicon Valley Bank
SVB Analytics Inc.
SVB Asset Management
SVB Business Partners (Beijing) Co. Ltd.
SVB Business Partners (Shanghai) Co. Ltd.
SVB Global Financial Inc.
SVB Global Investors LLC
SVB Growth Investors LLC
SVB India Advisors Pvt. Ltd.
SVB Israel Advisors Ltd.
SVB Qualified Investors Fund LLC
SVB Real Estate Investment Trust
SVB Securities
SVB Strategic Investors LLC
SVB Strategic Investors Fund L.P.
Venture Investment Managers L.P.

COMPETITORS

BancWest	City National
Bank of America	Comerica
Bridge Capital	Heritage Commerce
Holdings	U.S. Bancorp
Citigroup	UnionBanCal

HISTORICAL FINANCIALS

Company Type: Public

Income Statement

FYE: December 31

	ASSETS ($ mil.)	NET INCOME ($ mil.)	INCOME AS % OF ASSETS	EMPLOYEES
12/12	22,766.1	175.1	0.8%	1,615
12/11	19,968.8	171.9	0.9%	1,526
12/10	17,527.7	94.9	0.5%	1,357
12/09	12,841.4	48.0	0.4%	1,258
12/08	10,020.8	78.6	0.8%	1,244
Annual Growth	22.8%	22.2%	—	6.7%

2012 Year-End Financials

Return on assets: 0.8%	Dividends
Return on equity: 10.2%	Yield: —
Long-term debt ($ mil.): —	Payout: —
No. of shares (mil.): 44	Market value ($ mil.): 2,498
Sales ($ mil): 984	

	STOCK PRICE ($) FY Close	P/E High/Low	PER SHARE ($) Earnings	Dividends	Book Value
12/12	55.97	17 12	3.91	0.00	41.02
12/11	47.69	16 9	3.94	0.00	36.07
12/10	53.05	24 16	2.24	0.00	30.15
12/09	41.66	68 18	0.66	0.00	27.30
12/08	26.23	28 10	2.29	0.00	30.04
Annual Growth	20.9%	— —	14.3%	—	8.1%

Sykes Enterprises, Inc.

When that software won't install Sykes can take your call. Sykes Enterprises operates more than 80 technical help and customer support centers in 24 countries across Africa the Americas Asia and Europe that use phone e-mail and chat to serve those in need of help. Sykes specializes in customer serv- ice and inbound technical support and also pro- vides large corporations with technical staffing and consulting relating to customer relationship man- agement. Sykes predominantly serves the commu- nications consumer financial services and technol- ogy industries.

Geographic Reach

Sykes is very international in its scope. The com- pany operates in 24 countries around the world with facilities in North America South America Africa Asia Australia and Europe. The Americas segment contributed 84% of total revenue while the EMEA segment contributed 16% of total rev- enue in 2012.

Operations

The company has operations in two reportable segments. The Americas segment includes the US Canada Latin America India and the Asia Pacific Rim. The company's EMEA segment includes Eu- rope the Middle East and Africa.

Sales from the communications industry ac- count for 31% of revenue while financial services generates 30%. Other markets include technology and consumer (16%) transportation and leisure (9%) health care (8%) retail (2%) and others (4%).

Sales and Marketing

Sykes' experience and depth in international op- erations serves the company well as customers worldwide continue to shift outsourced CRM tele- services overseas to markets with cheaper labor pools. AT&T accounted for $133.1 million or 12% of its consolidated revenue for 2012.

Financial Performance

After experiencing an upward trend in revenue the year before Sykes saw its revenues fall by 4% from $1.17 billion in 2011 to $1.13 billion in 2012. Its profits also declined by 41% from $48.3 million in 2011 to $28.4 million in 2012.

The company was stung by a 12% drop in sales from its EMEA segment and a 2% decline in sales from the Americas during 2012. This was due to the ending of client contracts and lower volumes of existing contracts. The profit erosion was attrib- uted to a loss from discontinued operations and a loss on the disposal of property and equipment.

Strategy

Like most companies in the industry Sykes' ef- forts to cut costs have included layoffs and call cen- ter closures. In 2012 it sold its Spanish operations to Iberphone S.A.U. (It suffered a loss on the sale of nearly $11 million.)

However the company's overall growth strategy includes adding to its call center seat capacity and expanding the number of service lines and markets it serves internationally. Sykes recently entered the market in Brazil Romania Egypt and El Salvador.

The company hopes to nurture long-term client relationships as it expands both organically and through acquisitions. Sykes has also been seeking to establish strategic technology partnerships with other organizations.Mergers and Acquisitions

The company completed its $150 million acqui- sition of Alpine Access in August 2012. The deal fit in with company's strategy of staying focused within the core customer contact management in- dustry. The acquisition bolstered the company's service portfolio and go-to-market offering.

Company Background

Former chairman and CEO John Sykes founded the company in 1977. His son Charles Sykes now leads the company as president and CEO.

HISTORY

Originally based in North Carolina Sykes Enter- prises was founded in 1977 to provide design and engineering services; it often acted as a temp agency for technical professionals. In 1992 Sykes' merger with programming firm Forrest Ford Con- sultants boosted the company's software services division. The big shift came in 1993 when Sykes moved its headquarters to Florida and refocused its operations on information technology outsourc- ing services. The company opened two call centers in 1994 and added two more the following year. It went public in 1996.

Targeting Europe as a market for growth Sykes acquired Scotland's McQueen International Lim- ited Germany's Telcare and TAS —all technical support companies —in 1997. In 1998 the com- pany started its employee benefits administration joint venture with HealthPlan Services and soon bought out its partner's interest (it sold all but 7% in 2000 to investment firm Welsh Carson Ander- son & Stowe).

In early 2000 the company restated 1999 sec- ond and third quarter earnings due to irregulari- ties related to delays in the recognition of software revenues. A class-action shareholder lawsuit fol- lowed the announcement. In 2001 Iain Macdonald resigned from the board of directors. Founder chairman and CEO John Sykes retired from the company in 2004; his son Charles Sykes was ap- pointed president and CEO.

Sykes acquired an Argentina-based operator of call centers Centro de Interaccion Multimedia SA (known as Apex) for $27 million in 2006. It also sold its SHPS subsidiary which provided employee benefits administration services to health care in- dustry investment firm Welsh Carson Anderson & Stowe.

After years of focusing on its core business and reducing costs the company acquired rival ICT Group in early 2010.

EXECUTIVES

EVP General Counsel and Corporate Secretary, James T. Holder, age 54, $219,673 total compensation

Executive Vice President - Global Human Resources, Jenna R. Nelson, age 49

EVP and CFO, W. Michael Kipphut, age 59, $374,558 total compensation

President CEO and Director, Charles E. (Chuck) Sykes, age 50, $500,000 total compensation

Global Vice President; Corporate Controller, William N. Rocktoff, age 50, $175,007 total compensation

EVP Global Operations, James C. Hobby, age 62, $310,866 total compensation

Executive Vice President - Global Strategy, Daniel L. Hernandez, age 46

Chairman, Paul L. Whiting, age 69

Chief Information Officer; Executive Vice President, David L. Pearson, age 54, $234,765 total compensation

IR Contact, Subhaash Kumar

EVP Global Sales and Client Management, Lawrence R. (Lance) Zingale, age 57, $316,769 total compensation

Executive Vice President - Global Delivery, Christopher Carrington

Director, Mark C. Bozek, age 51

Director, James S. MacLeod, age 65

Director, James K. (Jack) Murray Jr., age 77

President CEO and Director, Charles E. (Chuck) Sykes, age 50

Director, Iain A. Macdonald, age 68

Director, H. Parks Helms, age 77

Director, Linda F. McClintock-Greco, age 58

Director, William J. Meurer, age 69

Director, Furman P. Bodenheimer Jr., age 82

Director, Michael P. (Mike) DeLong, age 67

LOCATIONS

HQ: Sykes Enterprises Incorporated
400 N. Ashley Dr. Ste. 2800, Tampa FL 33602
Phone: 813-274-1000   **Fax:** 773-864-4601
Web: www.americanimaging.net

PRODUCTS/OPERATIONS

2012 Sales

Americas	947	84
Total	**1,127**	**100**

Selected Mergers and Acquisitions

FY2012
  Alpine Access ($150 million; Denver CO; call center
  service)
FY2010
  ICT Group ($263 million; Newtown PA; call centers)

COMPETITORS

24/7 Customer	HP Enterprise Services
APAC Customer Services	IBM
Accenture	Infosys
Aegis Communications	Keane
Amdocs	SFN Group
Arise Virtual	Satyam
Solutions	Sitel Worldwide
Atento Brasil	StarTek
Atos	Stream Global Services
Computer Generated	Sutherland Global
Solutions	Services
Computer Sciences	TRG Customer Solutions
Corp.	TechTeam
Concentrix	TeleTech
Convergys	Teleperformance
DecisionOne	West Corporation
Expert Global	Wipro Infotech
Solutions	vCustomer

HISTORICAL FINANCIALS

Company Type: Public

Income Statement

FYE: December 31

	REVENUE ($ mil.)	NET INCOME ($ mil.)	NET PROFIT MARGIN	EMPLOYEES
12/12	1,127.7	28.4	2.5%	46,200
12/11	1,169.2	48.3	4.1%	41,000
12/10	1,158.7	(10.2)	—	43,400
12/09	846.0	43.2	5.1%	49,200
12/08	819.1	60.5	7.4%	32,940
Annual Growth	8.3%	(17.2%)	—	8.8%

2012 Year-End Financials

Debt ratio: 10.0%	No. of shares (mil.): 43
Return on equity: 4.8%	Dividends
Cash ($ mil.): 187	Yield: —
Current ratio: 2.84	Payout: —
Long-term debt ($ mil.): 91	Market value ($ mil.): 665

	STOCK PRICE ($) FY Close	P/E High/Low		PER SHARE ($) Earnings	Dividends	Book Value
12/12	15.22	28	20	0.66	0.00	13.88
12/11	15.66	21	11	1.06	0.00	13.03
12/10	20.26	—	—	(0.22)	0.00	12.41
12/09	25.47	25	13	1.05	0.00	10.86
12/08	19.12	15	9	1.48	0.00	9.33
Annual Growth	(5.5%)	—	— (18.3%)	—	10.4%

Symetra Financial Corp

Symetra Financial seeks a symmetrical balance of work retirement and life insurance products. The holding company's subsidiaries offer life insurance annuities retirement plans health insurance and employee benefit plans to some 1.7 million customers throughout the US. Its workplace products include such goodies as medical stop-loss insurance disability insurance and group annuities. These products are distributed by brokers independent agents consultants financial institutions and third-party administrators. For individual consumers Symetra offers annuities individual retirement accounts and life insurance sold through banks.

Geographic Reach

From its headquarters in Bellevue Washington Symetra distributes products in all 50 US states plus Washington DC.

Operations

While selling and underwriting life health and accident policies and issuing annuity accounts are its main business activities the company earns more from investment income (about 60% of revenue) than from insurance premiums which leaves it somewhat vulnerable to market fluctuation.

Symetra's largest operating segment is its retirement division which conducts operations within two of the company's business segments: Deferred annuities (which accounts for more than 25% of annual sales) and income annuities (20% of sales). The benefits division accounts for about 30% of revenue and offers medical coverage (stop-loss and limited benefit plans) and group life and disability products. The individual life division (20% of revenue) provides term and universal life policies for independent consumers.

Sales and Marketing

Symetra distributes its products across the US through a network of more than 21000 brokers and agents as well as some 25 key institutional partners. The company launched its first broadcast television advertisement in 2013.

Financial Performance

After taking a hit financially in 2008 due to the economic downturn Symetra returned to revenue growth in 2009 and continued on an upward trajectory through 2012. Sales increased by more than 5% in 2012 to some $2.1 billion primarily due to higher premium revenue. The firm also reported profit growth in 2009 and 2010. The company reported a slight decline (less than 1%) in net income in 2011 on lower investment gains but then increased profits 3% to $205 million in 2012.

Strategy

Symetra's top strategy for growth is selling "simple to understand" products —which strongly appeal to consumers who are increasingly anxious about their retirement investments. This method is increasingly important as the firm seeks to capitalize on the aging of the "baby boomer" generation which is creating a larger market need for retirement products. And Symetra's conservative investment philosophy stands in contrast to some of its competitors whose bottom lines and reputations have been tarnished by complex and risky investment practices.

At the same time the firm balances out its risks by maintaining operations in a diverse range of businesses. It has expanded its stop-loss medical operations through acquisitions and customer growth and retention efforts. In addition to better reach mid-sized business customers Symetra

launched a new claims management unit in 2012 to help employers monitor short-term disability policies.

Internal product expansion efforts have included launches of the Symetra Classic universal life policy in 2011 and the True VA variable annuity in 2012. The company has also expanded by establishing more distribution relationships with new banks and brokers.

The company sold its Symetra Investment Services unit to John Hancock in 2013. The division provided broker dealer and investment advisory services. To further streamline operations in 2012 the company discontinued sales of structured settlement annuities though it continues to service existing structured accounts.

Ownership

Investor group Berkshire Hathaway and property/casualty insurance firm White Mountains Insurance each own 21% of Symetra. The two companies together owned a majority of Symetra's stock prior to its 2010 IPO.

Company Background

Founded in 1957 Symetra completed an IPO in early 2010. The company which earned proceeds of some $283 million from the IPO intended to use the proceeds for general purposes including bolstering its subsidiaries. Its primary investors Berkshire Hathaway and White Mountains Insurance Group earned proceeds of another $115 million from the IPO.

HISTORY

The oldest of Symetra's subsidiaries was established in 1957; all spent their formative years as part of regional insurance powerhouse Safeco.

When Safeco decided to focus on property/casualty insurance in 2004 it moved its life and investments operations into a new company named Symetra. Safeco then sold the new Symetra entity to an investor group led by Berkshire Hathaway and White Mountains Insurance Group for some $1.4 billion.

The company filed to go public in 2007 but postponed the launch due to unfavorable market conditions. In 2008 amid the global economic downturn the company posted a $158 million loss on investments compared to a $17 million gain the previous year. The losses moderated in 2009 and the company showed modest growth in overall revenue.

Not one to let the economy bring things down Symetra capitalized on opportunities created through the credit market decline by expanding its product lines and developing new distribution relationships. It also saw increased numbers of customers looking for investment products that produced fixed returns such as its SPIA (single premium immediate annuities) and fixed deferred annuity products.

Once market conditions improved Symetra successfully conducted an IPO in 2010. Both Berkshire Hathaway and White Mountains Insurance hung on to part of their holdings during Symetra's IPO each owning about 21% of the company.

In 2011 it strengthened its medical insurance operations by acquiring the renewal rights on stop-loss policies issued by American United Life (AUL a unit of OneAmerica) for some $26 million.

EXECUTIVES

Chairman, Lowndes A. (Lon) Smith, age 73
SVP and Chief Strategy Officer, Craig R. Raymond
President CEO and Director, Thomas M. (Tom)
Marra, age 55

Media Contact, Diana McSweeney
EVP Benefits Division, Michael W. Fry, age 52
Investor Relations, Jim Pirak
SVP and General Counsel, David S. Goldstein
EVP and CFO, Margaret A. Meister, age 48, $300,000 total compensation
SVP and Chief Actuary, Tommie D. Brooks, age 43
EVP Retirement Sales, Richard G. LaVoice
VP Symetra Group Distribution, Rick Lyons
Manager Community Relations, Jennifer Whitman
SVP and CIO, George McKinnon
EVP Retirement Division, Daniel R. Guilbert
SVP Human Resources and Administration, Christine A. Katzmar Holmes
Director, David T. Foy, age 46
Director, Robert R. Lusardi, age 56
Director, Lois W. Grady, age 68
President CEO and Director, Thomas M. (Tom) Marra, age 55
Director, Sander M. Levy, age 51
Director, Peter S. Burgess, age 71
Auditors: Ernst&YoungLLP

LOCATIONS

HQ: Symetra Financial Corporation
777 108th Ave. NE Ste. 1200, Bellevue WA 98004-5135
Phone: 425-256-8000   Fax: 425-256-5737
Web: www.symetra.com

PRODUCTS/OPERATIONS

2012 Revenues

Net investment income	1,275	61
Net realized investment gains	31	1
Total	2,101	100

2012 Revenues by Segment

Benefits	601	29
Individual life	444	21
Income annuities	426	20
Total	2,101	100

Selected Products

Benefits (employer groups of 50 to 5000 individuals)
  Accidental death and dismemberment insurance
  Disability income insurance
  Group life insurance
  Managing general underwriting (MGU) services
  Medical stop-loss insurance (for employers with self-funded health plans)
  Limited benefit medical plans
Retirement
  Deferred annuities
    Fixed deferred annuities
    Indexed annuities
    Individual retirement accounts (IRA)
    Variable deferred annuities
  Funding services (for existing structured settlement clients)
  Income annuities
    Single premium immediate annuities (SPIA reliable source of retirement income)
    Structured settlement annuities (fund third party personal injury settlements)
Life (individual)
  Bank-owned life insurance (BOLI)
  Single premium life insurance
  Term and universal life insurance

COMPETITORS

AEGON USA	Nationwide
Aetna	New York Life
Farmers Life	Northwestern Mutual
Guardian Life	SunAmerica Financial
HCC Insurance	Group
MassMutual	The Hartford
MetLife	Western National
Mutual of Omaha	Zurich Insurance Group

HISTORICAL FINANCIALS

Company Type: Public

Income Statement

FYE: December 31

	REVENUE ($ mil.)	NET INCOME ($ mil.)	NET PROFIT MARGIN	EMPLOYEES
12/12	2,101.2	205.4	9.8%	1,250
12/11	1,999.1	199.6	10.0%	1,100
12/10	1,878.5	200.9	10.7%	1,100
12/09	1,714.3	128.3	7.5%	1,100
12/08	1,451.1	22.1	1.5%	1,100
Annual Growth	9.7%	74.6%	—	3.2%

2012 Year-End Financials

Debt ratio: 1.5%
Return on equity: 6.0%
Cash ($ mil.): 130
Current ratio: 0.05
Long-term debt ($ mil.): 449
No. of shares (mil.): 119
Dividends
Yield: 2.1%
Payout: 15.4%
Market value ($ mil.): 1,546

	STOCK PRICE ($) FY Close	P/E High/Low		PER SHARE ($) Earnings	Dividends	Book Value
12/12	12.98	9	6	1.49	0.28	30.48
12/11	9.07	10	5	1.45	0.23	26.42
12/10	13.70	10	7	1.48	0.15	20.14
Annual Growth	(2.7%)	—	—	0.3%	36.6%	23.0%

Synaptics Inc

Synaptics keeps you in touch with your electronics. The company's human interface products are sold to contract manufacturers for use in mobile phones (more than half of sales) notebook and handheld computers and other mobile electronic devices. Its TouchPad product can be used in peripherals such as monitors and remote controls; ClickPad replaces a mouse for notebook PCs and netbooks; and ClearPad provides touchscreen control for various mobile devices. Synaptics also relies on contract manufacturers to make its products. Most sales go to manufacturers in Asia more than two thirds in China. US customers provide just 1% of sales.

Despite a notable hiccup in 2006 Synaptics has been profitable and has grown revenue and net income for most of the past 10 years. The company achieved record sales and profits for a third consecutive year in 2011 and closed the fiscal year with nearly $250 million in cash. Driving that growth was a more than 70% leap in sales for its mobile phone products. Its largest customers have receded into the background and now any single client accounts for less than 10% of sales.

As consumers shift to mobile computing products used in PCs have been edged out as Synaptics' largest source of revenues. End users of its products include OEM customers such as Dell Hewlett-Packard Lenovo and Toshiba. Some of its contract manufacturing customers include Compal Electronics Flextronics and Wistron.

Synaptics is expanding by adding applications such as home appliances for its touchpads as well as developing interface technologies such as proximity sensing which uses sensors to detect the presence of a user and activate certain functions.

The company is a founding member of the Open Handset Alliance an industry group utilizing the Android mobile device operating system software created by Google. The Nexus One smartphone unveiled by Google in 2010 used a ClearPad 2000 capacitive touchscreen sensor supplied by Synaptics.

EXECUTIVES

SVP CFO Secretary and Treasurer, Kathleen A. Bayless, age 56
Chairman, Francis F. Lee, age 61, $425,000 total compensation
VP and CTO, Shawn P. Day, age 46, $210,000 total compensation
Senior Vice President and General Manager Smart Display Division (SDD), Kevin D. Barber, age 52
Senior Vice President of Advanced Development and CTO, Stanley (Stan) Swearingen, age 53
Senior Vice President of Global Human Resources, James B. Harrington, $210,000 total compensation
VP Product Development, Kin Cheung
Senior Vice President of Worldwide Operations, Alex H.C. Wong, age 57, $190,000 total compensation
Senior Vice President of Worldwide Sales, Scott Deutsch
SVP Worldwide Sales, David B. Long, age 52, $230,410 total compensation
President CEO and Director, Richard A. (Rick) Bergman, age 49
SVP and General Manager PC Division, Mark N. Vena, age 50
Senior Vice President of Global Human Resources, Karen Gaydon
Senior Vice President - Corporate Development, Bret Sewell
Senior Vice President of Silicon Engineering, David Wang
Investor Relations Officer, Jennifer Jarman
VP-Sls, Dave Long
Director, Jeffrey D. Buchanan, age 57
Director, Nelson C. Chan, age 51
Director, Keith B. Geeslin, age 60
Director, James L. Whims, age 58
Director, Richard L. (Dick) Sanquini, age 78
President CEO and Director, Rick Bergman, age 49
Auditors: KPMGLLP

LOCATIONS

HQ: Synaptics Incorporated
3120 Scott Blvd. Ste. 130, Santa Clara CA 95054
Phone: 408-454-5100   Fax: 408-454-5200
Web: www.synaptics.com

2011 Sales

	$ mil.	% of total
China	399	67
Taiwan	76	13
Japan	65	11
South Korea	24	4
US	6	1
Other	25	4
Total	598	100

PRODUCTS/OPERATIONS

2011 Sales

	$ mil.	% of total
Digital lifestyle product applicatio		
Mobile phones	304	51
Other	4	1
PC applications	289	48
Total	598	100

Selected Products

ClearButtons (Sensor for scrolling and buttons)
ClearPad (Touch sensor for displays)

ClickPad (Click-enabled notebook computer cursor
control pad)
Dual Pointing (Notebook computer cursor control stick
and pad)
FlexPad (TouchPad functionality for conventional
keyboards)
NavPoint (TouchPad functionality for handheld form
factors)
OneTouch (Enablement of technology at customer level)
TouchPad (Notebook computer cursor control pad)
TouchStyk (Notebook computer cursor control stick)
TouchButtons (Capacitive alternative to mechanical
button and scrolling controls)

COMPETITORS

Alps Electric	Interlink Electronics
Atmel	Key Tronic
CTS Corp.	Logitech
Communication	Microsoft
Intelligence Corp.	Panasonic Corp
Cypress Semiconductor	Wacom
Elo Touch Solutions	

HISTORICAL FINANCIALS

Company Type: Public

Income Statement
FYE: June 29

	REVENUE ($ mil.)	NET INCOME ($ mil.)	NET PROFIT MARGIN	EMPLOYEES
06/13	663.5	98.9	14.9%	852
06/12	548.2	54.1	9.9%	697
06/11	598.5	63.8	10.7%	676
06/10	514.8	52.9	10.3%	586
06/09	473.3	54.3	11.5%	524
Annual Growth	8.8%	16.2%	—	12.9%

2013 Year-End Financials

Debt ratio: 0.3%
Return on equity: 21.6%
Cash ($ mil.): 355
Current ratio: 3.75
Long-term debt ($ mil.): 2

No. of shares (mil.): 33
Dividends
  Yield: —
  Payout: —
Market value ($ mil.): 1,284

	STOCK PRICE ($) FY Close	P/E High/Low		Earnings	PER SHARE ($) Dividends	Book Value
06/13	38.56	15	7	2.89	0.00	15.68
06/12	28.63	24	14	1.57	0.00	12.06
06/11	25.02	18	13	1.80	0.00	10.16
06/10	28.28	25	13	1.50	0.00	8.42
06/09	38.65	34	9	1.53	0.00	6.38
Annual Growth	(0.1%)	—	—	17.2%	—	25.2%

Synchronoss Technologies Inc

Synchronoss Technologies helps telephone companies synch up a variety of customer service efforts. The company provides hosted software and services that communications service providers use to manage tasks such as phone service activation account changes and customer transactions including credit card billing inventory management and trouble ticketing. Customers include service providers such as AT&T Mobility Level 3 Time Warner Cable Verizon and Vodafone as well as equipment manufacturers such as Apple Dell and Sony. Synchronoss was founded in 2001.

Geographic Reach

The company is headquartered in Bridgewater New Jersey and operates research and development facilities in Bethlehem Pennsylvania and Galway Ireland. It also has regional US offices in Chicago Denver Tucson Arizona; Fairpoint New York; Bellevue and Seattle Washington; and San Jose California as well as international offices in Germany the UK India and Australia.

Sales and Marketing

Synchronoss is heavily dependent on its largest customer AT&T which accounted for 46% of the company's sales in 2012. The company's five largest customers (AT&T Level 3 Time Warner Cable Verizon and Vodafone) combined accounted for about 76% of its total revenues the same year. Reliance on a relatively small number of customers for a majority of sales can be risky for companies such as Synchronoss as the loss of a single customer can dramatically impact sales. To that end Synchronoss has in recent years been working to diversify its customer base which has grown past its core base of telecom service providers to include mobile device makers like Apple and Nokia.

Financial Performance

The company's revenue was up 19% in 2012 driven by the expansion of its professional services to existing customers and an increase in licensing revenue for the company's cloud-based services. Higher revenues that year also helped drive Synchronoss' net income up 79%.

Strategy

While the majority of its sales come from North America Synchronoss has announced strategic plans to expand its international sales with a focus on Europe Latin America and Asia-Pacific. In early 2012 the company paid more than $45 million for France-based Miyowa which provides social network and messaging software for mobile devices. Miyowa's customers include Orange and ZTE. The company also made a handful of other acquisitions in 2012 —including SpeechCycle Spatial Systems Nominees PTY Ltd. and Newbay Software —that bolstered its operations in Europe and the Asia-Pacific region.

Mergers and Acquisitions

In 2012 Synchronoss acquired France-based Miyowa a provider of social network and messaging software for mobile devices for $45 million. The same year Synchronoss acquired SpeechCycle Spatial Systems Nominees PTY Ltd. and Newbay Software which together bolstered the company's presence in Europe and the Asia-Pacific region.

EXECUTIVES

EVP & President Broadband Solutions, Mark A. Mendes, age 50
Founder Chairman Chief Executive Officer, Stephen G. Waldis, age 44, $475,000 total compensation
Chief Financial Officer Executive Vice President & Treasurer, Lawrence R. Irving, age 56, $280,000 total compensation
Executive Vice President; Chief Innovation Officer, David E. Berry, age 44
President Chief Operating Officer, Robert E. (Bob) Garcia, age 44, $300,000 total compensation
EVp and Chief Sales Officer, Christopher S. (Chris) Putnam, age 44, $180,000 total compensation
Executive Vice President General Counsel, Ronald J. Prague, age 49
Executive Vice President Business Development, Daniel Rizer, age 49
Media Relations, Stacie Hiras

Executive Vice President Chief Technology Officer CIO, Patrick J. (Pat) Doran, age 38
Executive Vice President & Chief Corporate Strategy Officer, Biju Nair
Executive Vice President - Human Resources, Paula Hilbert
Senior Vice President; Chief Accounting Officer; Controller, Karen Rosenberger
Executive Vice President President North America, Nick Lazzaro
Executive Vice President Chief Innovation Officer, Dave Berry
Director, Donnie M. Moore, age 64
Director, Charles E. (Charlie) Hoffman, age 64
Director, William J. (Bill) Cadogan, age 64
Director, Thomas J. Hopkins, age 56
Director, James M. McCormick, age 53
Auditors: Ernst&YoungLLP

LOCATIONS

HQ: Synchronoss Technologies Inc.
750 Rte. 202 South Ste. 600, Bridgewater NJ 08807
Phone: 866-620-3940   **Fax:** -476
Web: www.hokkokubank.co.jp

COMPETITORS

Amdocs	Motive Inc.
CSG Systems	NeuStar
International	Syniverse
Comptel	Telcordia
Evolving Systems	VeriSign
Intec Telecom	

HISTORICAL FINANCIALS

Company Type: Public

Income Statement
FYE: December 31

	REVENUE ($ mil.)	NET INCOME ($ mil.)	NET PROFIT MARGIN	EMPLOYEES
12/12	273.6	27.0	9.9%	1,340
12/11	229.0	15.1	6.6%	970
12/10	165.9	3.8	2.3%	758
12/09	128.8	12.3	9.5%	511
12/08	110.9	11.8	10.7%	443
Annual Growth	25.3%	22.9%	—	31.9%

2012 Year-End Financials

Debt ratio: 2.1%
Return on equity: 7.6%
Cash ($ mil.): 36
Current ratio: 2.59
Long-term debt ($ mil.): 9

No. of shares (mil.): 38
Dividends
  Yield: —
  Payout: —
Market value ($ mil.): 816

	STOCK PRICE ($) FY Close	P/E High/Low		Earnings	PER SHARE ($) Dividends	Book Value
12/12	21.09	50	24	0.69	0.00	9.69
12/11	30.21	80	52	0.43	0.00	8.71
12/10	26.71	246	125	0.12	0.00	7.81
12/09	15.81	40	21	0.39	0.00	4.71
12/08	10.66	96	15	0.37	0.00	4.03
Annual Growth	18.6%	—	—	16.9%	—	24.5%

Synergy Resources Corp

Synergy Resources is on a quest to "synergize" the natural resources found in the Denver-Julesburg Basin (D-J Basin) which spans Colorado Kansas Nebraska and Wyoming. The company is exploring the Wattenberg Field a 50-mile area north of Denver rich with oil and gas deposits. Synergy Resources reports proved reserves of 42 billion cu. ft. of natural gas and 6.6 million barrels of oil and condensate. It has about 190000 net acres under lease with 220 producing wells. The company was founded in 2005 and began operations three years later.

Geographic Reach

All of the company's developed acreage is located in Colorado but it has substantial undeveloped acreage in Nebraska and a smaller holding in Wyoming.

Financial Performance

Revenue more than doubled in fiscal 2012 (ended August) hitting nearly $25 million (up from $10 million in 2011). Net income also showed significant improvement jumping from a loss of $11.6 million to a gain of about $12 million. The positive results are a result of the company's successful drilling strategy that saw 52 new wells move into production during the fiscal year. Synergy Resources saw an increase in production in 2012 of more than 150%; revenue from oil nearly tripled (and accounted for more than 80% of overall sales) while revenue from natural gas nearly doubled.

Strategy

Synergy Resources plans to continue its focus on the D-J Basin. All its current wells are in the Basin and its undeveloped holdings are either in or adjacent to the Basin. The company has identified more than 400 development and extension drilling locations. In 2013 it announced it was acquiring 38 wells concentrated in the Wattenberg Field.

EXECUTIVES

CFO, Frank L. Jennings
President and Co-CEO, Edward Holloway
Co-CEO and Treasurer, William E. Scaff Jr.
COO, Craig D. Rasmuson
Vice President Capital Markets & Investor Relations, Jon Kruljac
VP Land and Business Development, Ronald K. Morgenstern
Director, George L. Seward, age 63
Director, Rick A. Wilber, age 65
Director, Bill M. Conrad, age 57
President CEO and Director, Edward (Ed) Holloway, age 60
VP Secretary Treasurer and Director, William E. Scaff Jr., age 55
Director, R.W. (Bud) Noffsinger III, age 39
Auditors: EhrhardtKeefeSteiner&HottmanPC

LOCATIONS

HQ: Synergy Resources Corporation
20203 Hwy. 60, Platteville CO 80651
Phone: 970-737-1073   **Fax:** 970-737-1045
Web: www.syrginfo.com

PRODUCTS/OPERATIONS

2012 Sales

	$ mil.	% of total
Oil	20	82
Gas	4	18
Total	**25**	**100**

COMPETITORS

Bill Barrett	Gasco Energy
Brigham Exploration	PDC Energy
Cimarex	Par Petroleum
Double Eagle Petroleum	Resolute Energy
Earthstone Energy	Whiting Petroleum

HISTORICAL FINANCIALS

Company Type: Public

Income Statement

FYE: August 31

	REVENUE ($ mil.)	NET INCOME ($ mil.)	NET PROFIT MARGIN	EMPLOYEES
08/13	46.2	9.5	20.7%	16
08/12	24.9	12.1	48.6%	11
08/11	10.0	(11.6)	—	11
08/10	2.1	(10.7)	—	7
08/09	0.0	(12.3)	—	3
Annual Growth	**370.8%**	**—**	**—**	**52.0%**

2013 Year-End Financials

Debt ratio: 12.7%
Return on equity: 6.3%
Cash ($ mil.): 19
Current ratio: 2.22
Long-term debt ($ mil.): 37

No. of shares (mil.): 70
Dividends
  Yield: —
  Payout: —
Market value ($ mil.): 661

	STOCK PRICE ($) FY Close	P/E High/Low		PER SHARE ($) Earnings	Dividends	Book Value
08/13	9.36	55	16	0.16	0.00	2.88
08/12	2.80	14	9	0.25	0.00	1.97
08/11	3.11	—	—	(0.45)	0.00	1.36
08/10	2.25	—	—	(0.88)	0.00	(0.08)
08/09	1.14	—	—	(1.14)	0.00	0.25
Annual Growth	**69.3%**	**—**	**—**	**—**	**—**	**84.4%**

Synopsys Inc

To sum up Synopsys is a leading provider of electronic design automation (EDA) software and services. Its products are used by designers of integrated circuits (ICs) to develop simulate and test the physical design of ICs before production and then to test finished products. The company also provides semiconductor intellectual property (SIP) pre-designed circuits used as part of larger chips. Customers come from a variety of markets but particularly the semiconductor and electronics manufacturing industries. Synopsys offers time-based software licenses where customers make yearly payments for use and support. It generates about half its sales outside the US.

Geographic Reach The company has offices across the Americas Asia Australia and Europe. The US represents Synopsys' largest market accounting for nearly half of sales. Japan and Europe contributed 16% and 13% respectively. All regions reported year-over-year growth.

Sales and Marketing Synopsys markets its products primarily through direct sales efforts in the US and in select international markets.

Financial Analysis The company's revenue rose 14% in fiscal 2012 (ended October) to $1.8 billion. Synopsys saw growth in all areas of its business but results were driven primarily by time-based license revenue which jumped 15% year-over-year due to acquisitions and an extra week in the 2012 fiscal year. Net income that year was down 18% to $182 million as expenses outpaced sales due to acquisition-related personnel costs.

Mergers and Acquisitions Synopsys has used acquisitions to expand its product lines. It bought ExpertIO in 2012 to strengthen the delivery of its line of verification IP with a new collection of storage protocols. Also that year it acquired RSoft Design a provider of software used for design optimization and simulation in telecommunications components systems and networks. The purchase strengthened its position in the optical and photonics sectors as well as complementing its products that perform functions such as optical waveguide modeling. It followed that purchase with the acquisition of Ciranova adding EDA technology used to cut the time required to design transistor-level layouts for nanometer-scale and other advanced nodes. Additionally Synopsys paid $406 million to buy Taiwan-based SpringSoft a developer of IC design software to extend the functionality of its products particularly in the areas of verification and custom implementation. In 2011 Synopsys bought nSys Design Systems as part of an effort to address the system-on-a-chip (SoCs) verification market. Also that year the company acquired Extreme DA a maker of software used to improve circuit design performance power consumption and manufacturing output. It also agreed to buy Magma Design Automation completing the deal the following year for more than $520 million. That purchase helps Synopsys meet increasing electronic design automation demands in the marketplace.

Ownership Mutual fund manager Dodge & Cox owns nearly 15% of the company.

HISTORY

Aart de Geus founded Optimal Solutions in 1986 with funding from General Electric where he had been a manager in the company's Advanced Computer-Aided Engineering Group. The group built the prototype of a product that saved chip designers time by automating much of the design work.

In 1987 the company changed its name to Synopsys (an abbreviation of "synthesis and optimization systems") and moved to California. It went public in 1992 and two years later it introduced software that engineers used to design chips by function rather than structure.

As chips grew more complicated Synopsys bolstered its product development efforts through acquisitions. In 1995 the company purchased hardware emulation developer Silicon Architects. Synopsys bought transistor-level tool specialist EPIC Design Technology in 1997 to improve its submicron-level design capabilities. It acquired Viewlogic Systems to increase its design automation prowess. (Synopsys later sold Viewlogic's printed circuit board design software segment.)

Synopsys' acquisitions continued in 1998 with the purchase of Radiant Design Tools a supplier of technology for designing simulation performance and Everest Design Automation which specialized in system-on-a-chip devices. In 1999 Synopsys bought Stanza Systems which developed physical layout products; Smartech a developer of wireless market design products; and several others. It also introduced several products including one that combined design and physical layout of system-on-a-chip devices in one package.

In 2001 the company sold its Silicon Library Business. Synopsys' attempt to acquire IKOS Systems in 2002 was stymied by Mentor Graphics. However Synopsys did acquire troubled software developer Avant! for nearly $730 million and purchased inSilicon for $64 million.

In 2003 Synopsys acquired Numerical Technologies whose software helped prepare chip designs for manufacturing for about $250 million. Looking to beef up its design capabilities for analog and mixed-signal chips Synopsys in 2004 purchased the assets of Analog Design Automation (ADA) a company founded in 1999. Also in 2004 Synopsys bought Accelerant Networks Inc. of Beaverton Oregon a fabless semiconductor company. The purchase price was $22.5 million in cash. Later that year Synopsys acquired Integrated Systems Engineering AG (ISE) of Zurich Switzerland for about $95 million in cash plus another $20 million in future earnout payments. At the same time Synopsys acquired the assets of Monterey Design Systems and hired most of the engineers working in Armenia for Monterey. Synopsys did not acquire Monterey's software products. Synopsys added even more Armenian engineers with its 2004 asset acquisition of LEDA Design which had more than 80 people working in Yerevan Armenia.

Synopsys agreed to acquire Monolithic System Technology (now MoSys) for about $432 million in cash but called off the deal in 2004. MoSys sued; the companies settled the case after the trial began a few months later. Synopsys also agreed in 2004 to acquire rival Nassda for around $192 million in cash. The acquisition was completed in 2005.

In 2008 the company purchased Synplicity a provider of field programmable gate array (FPGA) IC design and verification software. Later that year the company also bought the CHIPit business unit of ProDesign. The move boosted Synopsys' aim to provide end-to-end products for the design and verification markets enhancing its system validation and embedded software development capabilities.

In 2010 the company made several acquisitions. It extended its virtual prototyping portfolio into automotive and consumer applications through the acquisition of VaST Systems Technology a developer of models and tools for designing embedded electronics. It acquired CoWare a provider of software and services for electronic systems design. Synopsys expanded its portfolio of high-level synthesis tools through the purchase of Synfora. In September 2010 Synopsys expanded its SIP portfolio with the acquisition Virage Logic.

EXECUTIVES

SVP; General Manager Implementation, Antun Domic, age 62, $390,000 total compensation
VP Investor Relations, Lisa L. Ewbank
President and Co-CEO, Chi-Foon Chan, age 64, $450,000 total compensation
European Public Relations EML, David Marsden
CFO, Brian M. Beattie, age 60, $400,000 total compensation
SVP Global Technical Services, Deirdre Hanford, age 51, $300,000 total compensation
SVP; General Manager Analog/Mixed Signal Group, Sheng-Chun (Paul) Lo

SVP Marketing and Strategic Development, John Chilton, age 55, $320,000 total compensation
SVP; General Manager Verification Group, Manoj Gandhi, age 53
SVP; General Manager Silicon Engineering Group, Howard Ko, age 57
VP Solutions Marketing, George Zafiropoulos
SVP; General Manager Solutions Group, Joachim Kunkel
VP Corporate Marketing and Strategic Alliances, Rich Goldman
VP Marketing Solutions Group, John Koeter
Senior Director Marketing Verification Group, Swami Venkat
VP Product Marketing Design and Manufacturing Products, Bijan Kiani
Director Worldwide Public Relations and Corporate Affairs, Yvette Huygen
Japan Public Relations, Hiromitsu Fujii
General Counsel and Corporate Secretary; Chief Ethics and Compliance Officer, Brian E. Cabrera, age 48, $325,000 total compensation
SVP Human Resources and Facilities, Janet S. (Jan) Collinson, age 52
Corporate Vice President of Synopsys Inc, Pradip K. Dutta
Senior Director Marketing Physical Design and DFM, Saleem Haider
Manager Worldwide Public Relations, Sheryl M. Gulizia
SVP Worldwide Sales and Corporate Marketing, Joseph W. (Joe) Logan, age 54, $357,200 total compensation
Investor Relations Specialist, Roberta Reid
European Public Relations, Emma Gardiner
Taiwan Public Relations, Jesse Ho
China Public Relations, Connie Bao
Manager Business Development Solutions Marketing, Doug Amos
Senior Manager Investor Relations, Nick Taber
Vice President Engineering Solutions Group, Andrew Dauman
Chairman and Co-CEO, Aart de Geus
Senior Vice President General Manager Analog Mixed Signal Group, Paul Lo
Director, Bruce R. Chizen, age 57
Director, Roy A. Vallee, age 60
Director, Steven C. (Steve) Walske, age 60
President COO and Director, Chi-Foon Chan, age 63
Director, Deborah A. (Debi) Coleman, age 60
Director, Alfred J. (Al) Castino, age 60
Director, John G. Schwarz, age 61
Director, Chrysostomos L. (Max) Nikias, age 60
Auditors: KPMG LLP

LOCATIONS

HQ: Synopsys Inc.
700 E. Middlefield Rd., Mountain View CA 94043-4024
Phone: 650-584-5000   **Fax:** 650-584-4249
Web: www.synopsys.com

2012 Sales

	$ mil.	% of total
US	834	48
Japan	289	16
Europe	226	13
Asia-Pacific and other	407	23
Total	**1,756**	**100**

PRODUCTS/OPERATIONS

2012 Sales

	$ mil.	% of total
Time-based license	1,449	83
Maintenance & service	202	11
Upfront license	105	6
Total	**1,756**	**100**

Selected Products

Astro (place and route)
Chip Architect (planning and analysis of various design phases)
coreBuilder (reusable design data)
CoCentric System Studio (system-level design and verification)
Design Compiler (logic synthesis)
Design Vision (design management and analysis)
DesignWare (implementation and verification design library)
Hercules (physical verification)
Module Compiler (synthesis of data paths)
NanoSim (memory and mixed-signal verification)
PathMill (static timing analysis)
Physical Compiler (physical synthesis)
PowerMill (circuit simulation and design)
Scirocco (VHDL-based simulation)
VCS (Verilog language-based simulation)

Selected Services

Tool & Methodology Consulting
Design Flow Deployment
IP Integration & SoC Verification
Core Optimization
Physical Design Assistance
FPGA-based Prototyping

Selected Acquisitions

2012
EVE (emulation software)
Ciranova (EDA software for transistor-level design of nanometer-scale nodes)
RSoft Design (software used in telecom product and network design and simulation)
ExpertIO (intellectual property for storage protocol verification)
Magma Design Automation (chip design software)
2011
Extreme DA (software used to improve chip performance power consumption and manufacturing output)
nSys Design Systems (system-on-chip verification software)
2010
VaST Systems Technology (models and tools used to design embedded electronics)

COMPETITORS

Agilent EEsof	Mentor Graphics
Altium	MoSys
Ansoft	PDF Solutions
CEVA	Rambus
Cadence Design	Silvaco
Intrinsix	SynTest
Magma Design	

HISTORICAL FINANCIALS

Company Type: Public

Income Statement

FYE: October 31

	REVENUE ($ mil.)	NET INCOME ($ mil.)	NET PROFIT MARGIN	EMPLOYEES
10/13	1,962.2	247.8	12.6%	8,573
10/12	1,756.0	182.4	10.4%	8,138
10/11	1,535.6	221.3	14.4%	6,803
10/10	1,380.6	237.0	17.2%	6,707
10/09	1,360.0	167.6	12.3%	5,928
Annual Growth	**9.6%**	**10.3%**	**—**	**9.7%**

2013 Year-End Financials

Debt ratio: 2.4%
Return on equity: 9.3%
Cash ($ mil.): 1,022
Current ratio: 1.18
Long-term debt ($ mil.): 75
No. of shares (mil.): 154
Dividends
Yield: —
Payout: —
Market value ($ mil.): 5,615

	STOCK PRICE ($) FY Close	P/E High/Low	PER SHARE ($) Earnings	Dividends	Book Value
10/13	36.42	24 19	1.58	0.00	18.09
10/12	32.20	28 21	1.21	0.00	16.58
10/11	26.81	19 14	1.47	0.00	14.66
10/10	25.58	16 13	1.56	0.00	14.14
10/09	22.02	20 12	1.15	0.00	12.55
Annual Growth	13.4%	— —	8.3%	—	9.6%

Syntel Inc.

Syntel is in the know about information technology. The IT services provider offers outsourced applications development knowledge process outsourcing (KPO) and IT consulting and staffing for global corporate client list. Its largest segment applications outsourcing focuses on the development management and maintenance of business software. Syntel offers KPO services for middle and back-office functions such as transaction processing and loan servicing to financial services health care and insurance companies. Its top clients include American Express and State Street. Co-founding spouses Bharat Desai and Neerja Sethi are the company's biggest shareholders.

Operations

Syntel is focused on its growing applications outsourcing business which accounted for three-quarters of sales in 2012 and KPO operations which accounted for 15%. Its traditional strengths include serving clients in banking financial services insurance and health care where outsourcing of business functions like claims processing commonly occurs. Other key markets include telecommunications automotive logistics and travel.

The company has all but transitioned away from its IT staffing roots. Overseen by its TeamSourcing division that business has accounted for only 2% of revenue in recent years. Syntel's e-Business division which specializes in Web applications and data warehousing accounted for 8% of revenue.

Geographic Reach

The company's application development centers and other facilities are located in India. The company also has about 20 sales offices worldwide. Although headquartered in the US 80% of the company's employees were based in India in 2012.

Sales and Marketing

Syntel markets and sells its services through sales teams operating throughout the US Canada Europe and Australia. Its two top clients American Express and State Street together accounted for just under half of the company's total revenue in 2012. American Express accounted for 27% while State Street accounted for 17%. The company served about 135 customers in 2012 most of which were in the US.

Financial Performance

With more than $720 million in revenues Syntel makes nowhere near the multibillion-dollar sales of its top Indian outsourcing rivals Infosys Tata Consultancy and Wipro. The company's sales continue to grow however and its average annual profit margin for the past five years is about 40%. Revenues grew by about 13% in 2012 driven by strong global demand for the offshore IT services. As in previous years Syntel also attributed the jump in sales for the year to the expansion of its workforce which enabled the company to scale up capacity. The company's cost of sales rose slightly for the year.

Ownership

Founder Bharat Desai holds a 38% stake in the company while co-founder Neerja Sethi holds 29%. Besides Desai and Sethi Syntel has a third major stakeholder Rakesh Vij who owns a household products trading company RK International Inc. in Houston. Vij controls 23% of the company.

Company Background

Desai and Sethi founded the company in 1980 while Desai was earning his Master's degree from the University of Michigan. The couple moved to the US in 1976 when Desai took a job with Tata Consultancy one of the top India-based IT outsourcing companies.

EXECUTIVES

Chief Administrative Officer Secretary and General Counsel, Daniel M. Moore, age 58, $255,185 total compensation

VP Corporate Affairs and Director, Neerja Sethi, age 58

Chairman, Bharat Desai, age 60, $256,602 total compensation

President CEO and Director, Prashant Ranade, age 61

CFO and Chief Information Security Officer, Arvind S. Godbole, age 55, $72,596 total compensation

COO, Rakesh Khanna, age 50, $165,241 total compensation

SVP; Head of Insurance Business Unit, Anil Jain, age 54

President - Americas; Business Development and Nearshoring Center, Nitin Rakesh, age 41

SVP; Head of Operations Healthcare and Life Sciences Business Unit, Murlidhar Reddy, age 43

VP and CEO State Street Syntel Services Private Limited, V. S. Raj, age 49

SVP Retail Logistics and Telecom Business Unit, Raja Ray, age 50

SVP and Head Europe, Amit Chatterjee, age 46

Global Head Human Resources, Rajesh Save, age 47

Director, George R. Mrkonic Jr., age 61

VP Corporate Affairs and Director, Neerja Sethi, age 58

Lead Director, Paritosh K. Choksi, age 60

President CEO and Director, Prashant Ranade, age 61

Auditors: CroweHorwathLLP

LOCATIONS

HQ: Syntel Inc.
525 E. Big Beaver Rd. Ste. 300, Troy MI 48083
Phone: 248-619-2800   **Fax:** 248-619-2888
Web: www.syntelinc.com

2011 Sales

	$ mil.	% of total
North America	594	92
Europe	43	7
Other countries	4	1
Total	**642**	**100**

PRODUCTS/OPERATIONS

2012 Sales

	$ mil.	% of total
Applications outsourcing	544	75
Knowledge process outsourcing	110	15
e-Business	54	8
TeamSourcing	14	2
Total	**723**	**100**

Selected Services

Applications outsourcing
  Applications development
  Applications maintenance
  Applications management
  Platforms conversion
Knowledge process outsourcing
e-Business
  Customer relationship management services
  Data warehousing and business intelligence
  E-business design development implementation and maintenance
  Enterprise applications outsourcing
  Web architecture
  Web-enablement of legacy applications
  Web portal design
TeamSourcing
  Design
  Development
  Implementation
  Information technology staffing
  Maintenance
  Systems specification
  Technical services

COMPETITORS

Accenture	HP Enterprise Services
Capgemini	IBM Global Services
Cognizant Tech Solutions	Infosys
Computer Sciences Corp.	NTT Data
	Patni Computer Systems
Datacraft Asia	PricewaterhouseCoopers
Deloitte	Satyam
First Data	TCS America
Getronics	Unisys
HCL Technologies	WNS (Holdings)
	Wipro

HISTORICAL FINANCIALS

Company Type: Public

Income Statement

FYE: December 31

	REVENUE ($ mil.)	NET INCOME ($ mil.)	NET PROFIT MARGIN	EMPLOYEES
12/12	723.9	185.5	25.6%	21,407
12/11	642.4	122.8	19.1%	19,484
12/10	532.1	113.5	21.3%	17,383
12/09	419.0	118.5	28.3%	12,567
12/08	410.4	86.6	21.1%	12,363
Annual Growth	**15.2%**	**21.0%**	**—**	**14.7%**

2012 Year-End Financials

Debt ratio: 6.8%	No. of shares (mil.): 41
Return on equity: 34.9%	Dividends
Cash ($ mil.): 94	Yield: 0.4%
Current ratio: 3.85	Payout: 56.0%
Long-term debt ($ mil.): —	Market value ($ mil.): 2,234

	STOCK PRICE ($) FY Close	P/E High/Low	PER SHARE ($) Earnings	Dividends	Book Value
12/12	53.63	15 10	4.44	2.49	13.58
12/11	46.77	21 13	2.94	0.24	11.86
12/10	47.80	19 12	2.73	0.74	10.88
12/09	38.03	17 6	2.86	0.24	8.46
12/08	23.12	18 9	2.10	0.74	5.50
Annual Growth	**23.4%**	**— —**	**20.6%**	**35.4%**	**25.4%**

Tal International Group Inc

If your freight is going by truck train or ship tall odds are it might be going in a container owned by TAL International Group. The company is a leading lessor of intermodal freight containers — steel boxes that come in standard sizes and can be used to move goods over the road over the rails or over the water. Marine shipping lines are among the company's top customers. TAL maintains a fleet of more than 1250000 containers or about 2.1 million 20-foot equivalent units (TEUs) of capacity. Besides its leasing operations TAL International sells used containers. Investment firm Jordan Company through its Resolute Fund affiliate and other entities controls about a 40% stake in TAL.

Geographic Reach

The company operates through nearly 20 leasing offices in over 10 countries. It has a geographically diverse revenue base with more than 200 container depot facilities in some 40 countries worldwide.

Operations

Through its equipment trading segment the company buys containers from its shipping line customers and resells the containers to traders. TAL handles about 40000 TEUs per year for resale.

Financial Performance

The company's revenue increased by 14% in fiscal 2012 compared to fiscal 2011 mainly due to an increase in its leasing revenues.

Its net income increased by 19% in fiscal 2012 compared to the previous fiscal year primarily due to the decrease of write-off of deferred financing costs and net loss on interest rate swaps. TAL's cash flow decreased by $153 million in fiscal 2012 compared to fiscal 2011 primarily due to a decrease in net borrowings.

Strategy

TAL constantly invests in maintaining its equipment and expanding its fleet to keep up with demand and customer expectations.

EXECUTIVES

Chairman of the Board; President; Chief Executive Officer, Brian M. Sondey, age 44, $525,000 total compensation
Chief Financial Officer; Senior Vice President, John Burns, age 51, $230,000 total compensation
Vice President; General Counsel; Secretary, Marc Pearlin, age 55
Senior Vice President; Asia Pacific, Adrian Dunner, age 47, $256,000 total compensation
Vice President, Aaron Cox
Director of Marketing, Alasdair Voisey
Vice President, Mike Broadhurst
Senior Vice President - Trader and Global Operations, Kevin Valentine
Director, Claude Germain
Director, Frederic H. Lindeberg, age 72
President CEO and Director, Brian M. Sondey, age 44
Director, Malcolm P. Baker, age 42
Auditors: Ernst&YoungLLP

LOCATIONS

HQ: TAL International Group Inc.
100 Manhattanville Rd., Purchase NY 10577-2135
Phone: 914-251-9000   **Fax:** 914-697-2886
Web: www.talinternational.com

2012 Sales

Europe	260	44
US	43	7
Total	**589**	**100**

PRODUCTS/OPERATIONS

2012 Sales

Leasing revenues	525	89
Management fee income	3	1
Total	**589**	**100**

Selected Products

Chassis
Flat racks
Generator sets
High cube dry containers
Open tops
Refrigerated containers
Standard dry containers
Tank containers

Selected Services

Chassis (leasing)
Container (leasing)
Container sales (trader)
GreySlot (logistic services)
SpaceWise (UK container rentals)
Tank container (leasing)

COMPETITORS

CAI International	SeaCube Container
COSCO Pacific	Seacastle
Chicago Freight Car Leasing	Seaco
	Union Tank Car
GATX	XTRA Corp.

HISTORICAL FINANCIALS

Company Type: Public

Income Statement

FYE: December 31

	REVENUE ($ mil.)	NET INCOME ($ mil.)	NET PROFIT MARGIN	EMPLOYEES
12/12	589.1	130.1	22.1%	173
12/11	516.6	109.7	21.2%	174
12/10	366.8	57.7	15.7%	172
12/09	352.5	71.5	20.3%	184
12/08	419.9	35.8	8.5%	200
Annual Growth	**8.8%**	**38.1%**	**—**	**(3.6%)**

2012 Year-End Financials

Debt ratio: 70.3%
Return on equity: 22.0%
Cash ($ mil.): 101
Current ratio: 0.36
Long-term debt ($ mil.): 2,604

No. of shares (mil.): 33
Dividends
  Yield: 6.4%
  Payout: 61.0%
Market value ($ mil.): 1,225

	STOCK PRICE ($) FY Close	P/E High/Low		PER SHARE ($) Earnings	Dividends	Book Value
12/12	36.38	11	8	3.87	2.35	18.29
12/11	28.79	11	7	3.34	1.99	16.85
12/10	30.87	17	7	1.88	1.30	13.95
12/09	13.23	6	2	2.30	0.04	13.69
12/08	14.10	25	8	1.09	1.61	11.24
Annual Growth	**26.7%**		**—**	**37.3%**	**9.9%**	**12.9%**

Tanger Factory Outlet Centers, Inc.

Brand name bargains are on shoppers' lists when they visit Tanger Factory Outlet Centers. One of the top outlet mall developers (along with retail giant Simon Property and its Chelsea Property Group subsidiary) Tanger is a real estate investment trust (REIT) that develops owns and manages about 45 retail outlet centers in 25 states and Canada. A typical center has 75 stores and totals at least 300000 sq. ft. housing shops from more than 400 brand name companies including The Gap Ralph Lauren Ann Taylor Phillips-Van Heusen and Nike. Tanger's outlet centers which maintain about 99% occupancy are built away from malls and shopping districts so tenants don't compete with their full-price stores.

Operations

Outlet mall stores share the same name as their brand name retail counterparts but sell merchandise at significant discounts due to overstock or off-season availability. Other retailers specifically earmark discounted merchandise to be sold at outlet stores. Outlet stores are also able to charge customers lower prices by eliminating the third-party retailer.

As a self-administered and self-managed REIT Tanger Factory Outlet Center focuses exclusively on developing acquiring owning operating and managing outlet shopping centers. REITs are exempt from paying federal income taxes as long as they distribute quarterly dividends to shareholders.

Geographic Reach

Tanger's outlet malls are mostly concentrated along the East Coast. It also owns interests in three outlet malls in Canada - two in Quebec and one in Ontario. Its Canadian malls were built in 2011 in partnership with RioCan Real Estate Investment Trust.

Financial Performance

Overall sales increased by 13% in 2012 to $357 million and profits shot up 20% to $53 million. The trust makes money on rent; as long as it has high occupancy rates and continues to open new malls it is profitable. In fact the outlet industry thrives during tough economic times as shoppers search for good deals.

Strategy

Tanger Factory Outlet Centers has been aggressively marketing to higher volume tenants replacing low-profile stores with the flash and appeal of trendier name brands. Attracting stronger more popular apparel footwear and housewares brands allows Tanger to renew leases at higher base rents.

The REIT also continues to seek opportunities for new development or acquisition of shopping centers. In particular the company targets markets that have at least 1 million residents and are located near high-traffic interstate highways.

Mergers and Acquisitions

To that end in 2013 the company began building two new outlet malls to add to its property portfolio. One near the Foxwoods Resort Casino in Mashantucket Connecticut is being developed with Gordon Group Holdings LLC. The 300000 sq.-ft. mall will sit between two casino hotels for added foot traffic.

The other is being developed with rival Simon Property Group as a 50/50 joint venture. The 400000 sq.-ft. Charlotte Premium Outlets in Charlotte North Carolina will have about 90 stores.

Tanger will provide site development and construction supervision while Simon will provide management services and marketing. The first phase is expected to open in 2014.

HISTORY

In 1948 Stanley Tanger became head of a shirt manufacturer his father had started in 1920. That company Tanger/Creighton eventually opened five successful outlet stores.

He sold the company to its employees in 1979 and came up with the idea of putting several factory-direct and off-price retailers together in a single mall. In 1981 he opened his first outlet center in North Carolina. His son Steven joined him in 1986. By 1992 the company had 17 centers but was heavily leveraged.

Tanger became the first publicly traded factory outlet center company when it completed its initial public offering in 1993. It used proceeds from its IPO to retire all debt and continue expansion.

Steven Tanger became president in 1995 the year the centers began putting in police substations to increase security. More new features cropped up in 1996 —cinemas restaurants and a 30-day cash-back guarantee on items purchased at Tanger centers. Although growth continued in 1997 a drop in REIT stocks the next year led the company to halt construction on two new centers.

Warren Buffett bought a 5% stake in the company in 1999 spurring other investors to return to REIT stocks. That year it took over its property management duties to cut costs. Also that year the company's outlet mall in Stroud Oklahoma was destroyed by a tornado.

In 2000 the firm sold two underperforming properties one in Kansas and the other in Oregon. In 2001 the company began work on a site in Myrtle Beach South Carolina.

In 2003 the company acquired in a joint venture with Blackstone Real Estate Advisors a portfolio of nine outlet malls located near upscale resort communites from Charter Oak Partners. In 2005 Tanger agreed to buy out Blackstone Real Estate Advisors' share in the Charter Oak portfolio for about $283 million. The deal closed near the end of that year.

Founder and chairman Stanley Tanger stepped down as CEO at the end of 2008; he was succeeded by son Steven Tanger. The economy also took its toll on the company that year as 14 stores with 500000 sq. ft. of space closed their doors due to the economy.

EXECUTIVES

VP Human Resources, Mary Anne Williams
Senior Vice President; Chief Marketing Officer, Carrie A. Geldner, age 50
VP Treasurer and Assistant Secretary, Virginia R. Summerell, age 54
Chief Financial Officer; Executive Vice President, Frank C. Marchisello Jr., age 54, $364,100 total compensation
President; Chief Executive Officer; Director, Steven B. Tanger, age 64, $538,900 total compensation
Interim Chairman, Jack Africk, age 84
Senior Vice President - Leasing, Lisa J. Morrison, age 53, $231,500 total compensation
VP Information Technology, Rick L. Farrar
VP Marketing, Laura M. Atwell
VP Operations, Elizabeth J. Coleman
Senior Vice President; Chief Accounting Officer; Controller, James F. Williams, age 48

Chief Operating Officer; Executive Vice President, Thomas E. (Tom) McDonough, age 55
Executive Vice President; General Counsel, Chad Perry
Senior Vice President - Human Resources, Manuel Jessup
Director, Allan L. Schuman, age 78
President CEO and Director, Steven B. Tanger, age 64
Director, Donald G. Drapkin, age 66
Director, William G. (Bill) Benton, age 67
Director, Thomas J. (Tom) Reddin, age 52
Director, Thomas E. (Tom) Robinson, age 65
Director, Bridget R. Berman, age 52
Auditors: PricewaterhouseCoopersLLP

LOCATIONS

HQ: Tanger Factory Outlet Centers, Inc.
3200 Northline Avenue, Suite 360, Greensboro, NC 27408
Phone: 336 292-3010   **Fax:** 336 297-0931
Web: www.tangeroutlet.com

2012 Locations

No. of centers	
South Carolina	5
Pennsylvania	3
North Carolina	3
Georgia	2
Maine	2
New Jersey	2
Texas	2
Michigan	2
Alabama	1
California	1
Connecticut	1
Delaware	1
Florida	1
Ohio	1
Illinois	1
Iowa	1
Louisiana	1
Maryland	1
Missouri	1
New Hampshire	1
New York	1
Oregon	1
Tennessee	1
Utah	1
Total	**0**	**36**

PRODUCTS/OPERATIONS

2012 Sales

	$ mil.	% of total
Base rents	235	66
Expense reimbursements	100	28
Percentage rentals	11	3
Other	10	3
Total	**357**	**100**
Ten Largest Tenants	2,012	

The Gap
Phillips-Van Heusen
Dress Barn
Nike
Adidas
VF Outlet Inc.
Ann Inc.
Polo Ralph Lauren
Carter's
Hanesbrands Direct

COMPETITORS

Belz	Macerich
CBL & Associates Properties	Ramco-Gershenson
Chelsea Property	Simon Property Group
General Growth Properties	Taubman Centers
Horizon Group Properties	Vornado Realty

HISTORICAL FINANCIALS
Company Type: Public

Income Statement
FYE: December 31

	REVENUE ($ mil.)	NET INCOME ($ mil.)	NET PROFIT MARGIN	EMPLOYEES
12/12	357.0	53.2	14.9%	542
12/11	315.2	44.6	14.2%	476
12/10	276.3	34.2	12.4%	432
12/09	271.6	58.0	21.4%	407
12/08	245.3	28.0	11.4%	440
Annual Growth	**9.8%**	**17.4%**	**—**	**5.4%**

2012 Year-End Financials

Debt ratio: 65.3%
Return on equity: 11.2%
Cash ($ mil.): 10
Current ratio: 0.21
Long-term debt ($ mil.): 1,093
No. of shares (mil.): 94
Dividends
Yield: 2.4%
Payout: 145.6%
Market value ($ mil.): 3,217

	STOCK PRICE ($) FY Close	P/E High/Low	PER SHARE ($)		
			Earnings	Dividends	Book Value
12/12	34.20	60 49	0.57	0.83	5.13
12/11	29.32	98 42	0.52	0.79	5.31
12/10	51.19	162 117	0.32	0.77	4.53
12/09	38.99	57 36	0.72	0.76	5.74
12/08	37.62	124 73	0.36	0.75	3.60
Annual Growth	**(2.4%)**	**— —**	**12.6%**	**2.6%**	**9.3%**

Taylor Capital Group, Inc

This company is tailor-made for small and mid-sized business owners. Taylor Capital Group is the holding company for Cole Taylor Bank which specializes in commercial banking real estate lending and wealth management services aimed primarily at closely-held and family-run businesses in the construction manufacturing distribution transportation and professional services industries. Business loans including working capital owner-occupied real estate financing and letters and lines of credit account for approximately 90% of the bank's loan portfolio. With about 10 branches in the Chicago metropolitan area the bank also offers traditional banking services to consumers.

Geographic Reach

Outside the Chicago area Taylor Capital Group has opened lending offices in about 10 other states including California Texas Washington and Wisconsin.

Financial Analysis

The bank's revenue fell more than 15% in 2011 vs. 2010 on declines in both interest and non-interest income down 10% and 32% respectively. A drop in interest and fees on loans and interest and dividends on securities depressed interest income. Despite falling revenue the bank returned to profitability in 2011 for the first year since 2006.

Chicago was one of the hardest hit areas during the recession and not coincidentally Taylor Capital Group reported losses each year between 2007 and 2010 as real estate prices plummeted. The company which increased its provisions for loan losses in 2010 is focusing on improving its asset quality. It has reduced its exposure to residential construction and land loans and ramped up its asset-based lending and residential mortgage operations.

Cole Taylor Bank sold its corporate trust business to Amalgamated Bank of Chicago in 2010 a move that allows it to focus on its core commercial banking business. The company supports organic growth by cross-selling financial products and services to middle-market businesses and their owners and executives.

Strategy

Taylor Capital Group is sticking to its "fix and grow" strategy in place since early 2008. The strategy focuses on remediating the asset quality issues caused by the downturn in the Chicago area real estate market in recent years while at the same time growing the diversifying its earnings. The bank has worked to reposition itself as a commercial and industrial lender to closely-held businesses in the Chicago area while reducing its exposure to risky residential real estate construction and land loans.

Ownership

Members of the Taylor family including brothers Bruce and Jeffrey Taylor (chairman and vice chairman of the company respectively) control nearly 19% of Taylor Capital's voting power. The bank was founded in 1929 by forefathers of the Taylor family.

EXECUTIVES

Vice Chairman, Jeffrey W. (Jeff) Taylor, age 60, $483,077 total compensation

Chairman, Bruce W. Taylor, age 57, $525,200 total compensation

EVP Cole Taylor Business Capital, Michael D. (Mike) Sharkey

President CEO and Director Taylor Capital Group and Cole Taylor Bank, Mark A. Hoppe, age 59, $475,962 total compensation

CFO and COO; EVP and COO Cole Taylor Bank, Randall T. (Randy) Conte, age 53

Head Cole Taylor Mortgage, William A. (Willie) Newman

EVP and Chief Lending Officer, Lawrence G. (Larry) Ryan, age 54, $245,423 total compensation

Executive Vice President; Chief Credit Officer, Michael J. Morton, age 50

Vice Chairman Cole Taylor Bank, John Lynch Jr.

IR Contact Officer, Ilene Stevens

Director, M. Hill Hammock, age 66

Vice Chairman, Jeffrey W. (Jeff) Taylor, age 60

Director, Ronald D. Emanuel, age 66

Director, Melvin E. Pearl, age 77

Director, Richard W. Tinberg, age 62

President CEO and Director Taylor Capital Group and Cole Taylor Bank, Mark A. Hoppe, age 59

Director, Shepherd G. (Shep) Pryor IV, age 66

Director, Michael H. Moskow, age 76

Director, Louise O'Sullivan, age 66

Director, Ronald L. (Ron) Bliwas, age 70

Director, Harrison I. Steans, age 77

Director, Jennifer W. Steans, age 49

Director, C. Bryan Daniels, age 53

Director, Elzie L. Higginbottom, age 71

Independent Director, Bryan Daniels

Independent Director, Hill Hammock

Independent Director, Louise OSullivan

Auditors: KPMGLLP

LOCATIONS

HQ: Taylor Capital Group, Inc
9550 West Higgins Road, Rosemont, IL 60018
Phone: 847 653-7978
Web: www.coletaylor.com

PRODUCTS/OPERATIONS

2011 Sales

	$ mil.	% of total
Interest		
Loans including fees	140	59
Taxable & tax-exempt investment securities	47	20
Other	0	-
Noninterest		
Mortgage origination revenue	20	9
Service charges	11	5
Gains on investment securities	5	2
Derivative & other	12	5
Total	**237**	**100**

COMPETITORS

Bank of America	MB Financial
Citigroup	Old Second Bancorp
Fifth Third	Park Bancorp
Harris	U.S. Bancorp
JPMorgan Chase	

HISTORICAL FINANCIALS

Company Type: Public

Income Statement

FYE: December 31

	ASSETS ($ mil.)	NET INCOME ($ mil.)	INCOME AS % OF ASSETS	EMPLOYEES
12/12	5,802.4	61.9	1.1%	938
12/11	4,685.8	91.1	1.9%	638
12/10	4,483.8	(53.8)	—	591
12/09	4,403.5	(31.5)	—	434
12/08	4,388.8	(124.5)	—	451
Annual Growth	**7.2%**	**—**	**—**	**20.1%**

2012 Year-End Financials

Return on assets: 1.1%	Dividends
Return on equity: 12.7%	Yield: —
Long-term debt ($ mil.): —	Payout: —
No. of shares (mil.): 28	Market value ($ mil.): 520
Sales ($ mil): 341	

	STOCK PRICE ($) FY Close	P/E High/Low		Earnings	Dividends	Book Value
12/12	18.05	10	5	1.79	0.00	19.44
12/11	9.72	4	2	3.45	2.00	14.44
12/10	13.15	—	—	(5.27)	2.22	11.68
12/09	11.39	—	—	(4.10)	2.00	23.36
12/08	5.85	—	—	(13.72)	0.20	27.63
Annual Growth	**32.5%**	—	—	—	—	**(8.4%)**

Team Health Holdings Inc

Team Health keeps its cool in an emergency room and it runs a smooth back office. The company is a leading provider of clinical outsourcing services across the US. It provides physician staffing and administrative services to hospital emergency rooms and handles everything from doctor recruitment to billing payroll and claims management. The company provides similar services for anesthesiology inpatient care (hospitalist) and pediatric programs. Team Health contracts with civilian and military hospitals clinics and physician groups across the US.

Geographic Reach

Team Health operates through a regional structure with about 20 management sites across the country that deliver services locally but are supported by integrated information systems and procedures. Its 9500 health care professionals serve hospitals and clinics in about 47 states. Florida and Tennessee are its largest markets accounting for about 15% and 13% of sales respectively.

Operations

More than 70% of Team Health's revenues are earned on a fee-for-service basis where it receives payments for services provided at hospitals from private insurers Medicare and Medicaid individuals and other health payers. The rest of its sales come through flat-rate or hourly contracts with government agencies for the management of health care facilities as well as certain hospitals.

Its largest service category is health care staffing which accounts for more than 80% of revenue. The staffing segment includes emergency anesthesia surgery and temporary worker placement and comprehensive health care services.

The remainder of revenue comes from hospital medicine clinical services government staffing call center operations after-hours pediatric clinics and billing services. Temporary staffing placement of doctors (locum tenens) is provided through subsidiary Daniel & Yeager while military facility staffing and management services are offered through its Spectrum Healthcare Resources unit.

Financial Performance

Keeping its pace on a steady growth trend over the past five years Team Health reported a 19% jump in revenue to nearly $2.1 billion in 2012 primarily due to increased fee-for-service revenue from gross fee schedule increases and higher patient and procedure volumes. Contract and other revenue also increased slightly offset by increased provisions for uncollected medical bills.

Profits have fluctuated in recent years however and Team Health reported a 3% decline in net income to $63.8 million in 2012 on higher professional service expenses related to acquisitions new contract growth and professional wage increases.

Sales and Marketing

The company serves about 850 community and military hospitals across the US. Reimbursements from Medicare and Medicaid plans accounted for about 36% of sales in 2012 while revenue from commercial plans accounted for 38%.

Team Health uses an inside sales force to promote its offerings. Marketing efforts include online publication and trade show advertisements; direct mail campaigns; and lead referral programs.

Strategy

The company sees growth opportunities in the pressures that hospitals are currently facing to control costs (while keeping service quality high). It intends to capitalize on those pressures by adding new outsourcing clients and providing new services to existing customers. It is also using its established market position in emergency room management to grow its business in other clinical areas such as anesthesia and pediatrics.

Additionally the company looks to increase market share by continuing to acquire (or form partnerships with) complementary businesses in the fragmented clinical outsourcing industry. At the same time Team Health controls risks by occasionally exiting noncore operations; for instance it stopped providing radiology staffing services in 2010.

Mergers and Acquisitions

Acquisitions of smaller regional groups have helped Team Health bulk up its roster of emergency physicians over the years. For instance the 2012 purchase of the operations of the physician-led diversified healthcare management organization The Exigence Group and its related entities expanded the company's presence in New York Ohio Pennsylvania and Texas. It also added ER groups in Alabama Arizona California Michigan New Jersey and Wisconsin that year. In addition Team Health strengthened its anesthesia and hospitalist divisions through 2012 acquisitions.

Ownership

Investment firms Lord Abbett & Co. and FMR each own about 10% of Team Health.

Company Background

The company was founded in 1979. Investment firm Blackstone Group owned nearly all of Team Health Holdings prior to the company's 2009 IPO. Blackstone's stake was reduced from 90% to about 68% through the IPO and Blackstone gradually sold off the rest of its shares through 2013. Proceeds from the public offering went toward Team Health's corporate expenses and debt repayment efforts.

EXECUTIVES

Chairman, H. Lynn Massingale, age 60, $532,693 total compensation

EVP and CFO, David P. Jones, age 45, $216,700 total compensation

CEO, Gregory S. (Greg) Roth, age 56

Chief Medical Officer; Executive Director TeamHealth Patient Safety Organization, Gar LaSalle

President Physician Recruitment and Retention, John R. Staley Jr.

President East Division TeamHealth Emergency Medicine, James George

President Midwest Division TeamHealth Emergency Services, James J. Rybak

President, Michael D. (Mike) Snow, age 58

SVP Operations, Kent Bristow

Chief Administrative Officer, Joseph B. (Joe) Carman

President Practice Development, Randal L. Dabbs

President of Health, David T. Grinbergs

COO Hospital Based Services, Barbara Blevins

President Northeast Group, Stephen G. Holtzclaw

President Hospital Based Services, Oliver Rogers

SVP and General Counsel, Heidi S. Allen, age 59

SVP Business Development and Marketing, Dan Wilbanks

VP Mergers and Acquisitions, Ernie Varvoutis

President Northwest Division TeamHealth Emergency Medicine, Mark W. Harris

Director Medical Operations After Hours Practice, Charles A. Welborn

President Smoky Mountain Division, Roger Brooksbank

Chief Compliance Officer, Paul Gleis

Chief Medical Officer; President Hospital Medicine, Jasen Gundersen

President Midsouth, John Proctor

President Urgent Care and Occupational Medicine, Gregory F. Daniel

President Great Lakes, Saif Nazir

President Southeast Group, Steve Schwartz

President West Group Emergency Services, Robert R. Frantz

President Anesthesia East Division, Jeffrey A. Weiss

President Anesthesia West Division, Elliott (Skip) Wohlner

Director, James L. (Jim) Bierman, age 60

Director, Glenn A. Davenport, age 59

Director, Neil P. Simpkins, age 46

Director, Earl P. Holland, age 67

President CEO and Director, Greg Roth, age 55

Director, Michael A. Dal Bello, age 41

Independent Director, Steven Epstein

Auditors: Ernst&YoungLLP

LOCATIONS

HQ: Team Health Holdings Inc.
265 Brookview Centre Way Ste. 400, Knoxville TN 37919

Phone: 865-693-1000   **Fax:** 865-539-3073
Web: www.teamhealth.com

PRODUCTS/OPERATIONS

2012 Sales

Healthcare staffing	1,708	83
Total	**2,069**	**100**

2012 Sales

Fee-for-service	1,490	72
Total	**2,069**	**100**

Selected Services
Coding and billing services
Collections
Continuing medical education
Contract management
Credentials
Employee benefits
Information systems
Locum tenens (temporary physician placement)
Medical call center services
Military treatment facilities management
Operations consulting
Patient safety
Payroll administration
Program management services
  Anesthesiologists
  Emergency medicine
  Hospitalists (coordination of care for hospitalized patients)
  Pediatrics
Recruitment
Risk management
Scheduling
Staffing

COMPETITORS

AMN Healthcare	Maxim Healthcare
CHG Healthcare	Services Inc.
Cogent HMG	McKesson
EmCare	Onward Healthcare
Envision Healthcare	Orion HealthCorp
Hospital Physician	STGi
Partners	Schumacher Group
IPC The Hospitalist	Sheridan Healthcare
Company	UCI
MEDNAX	

HISTORICAL FINANCIALS

Company Type: Public

Income Statement   FYE: December 31

	REVENUE ($ mil.)	NET INCOME ($ mil.)	NET PROFIT MARGIN	EMPLOYEES
12/12	2,069.0	63.7	3.1%	8,500
12/11	1,745.3	65.5	3.8%	6,800
12/10	1,519.2	13.3	0.9%	5,700
12/09	1,423.4	40.7	2.9%	5,900
12/08	1,331.3	44.6	3.4%	6,000
Annual Growth	**11.7%**	**9.3%**	**—**	**9.1%**

2012 Year-End Financials

Debt ratio: 43.1%	No. of shares (mil.): 67
Return on equity: 94.6%	Dividends
Cash ($ mil.): 41	Yield: —
Current ratio: 1.20	Payout: —
Long-term debt ($ mil.): 501	Market value ($ mil.): 1,950

	STOCK PRICE ($) FY Close	P/E High/Low		PER SHARE ($) Earnings	Dividends	Book Value
12/12	28.77	31	21	0.93	0.00	1.73
12/11	22.07	24	15	0.98	0.00	0.27
12/10	15.54	86	56	0.21	0.00	(0.80)
12/09	14.02	—	—	(0.00)	0.00	(1.48)
Annual Growth	**27.1%**	—	—	—	—	—

Team, Inc.

Consider it the A-Team for high-pressure situations. Team provides specialized maintenance services for piping systems including repairing leaks hot tapping (adding new connections to pressurized pipelines) and detecting escaping emissions. It also offers field heat treatment and testing and inspection services. The firm makes custom equipment clamps and enclosures to augment its standard materials and sealant products. Through two divisions TMS and TCM the company serves heavy industries including the chemical and petrochemical pulp and paper defense manufacturing and steel industries. Team operates from more than 125 locations worldwide but its largest markets are the US and Canada.

The company's TCM division provides inspections assessments and field heating treating. It accounts for nearly 60% of the group's revenues. Team's TMS division handles leak repair emissions control and other repair services. In addition to its traditional customer base Team serves clients in the aerospace and automotive sectors.

Sales and profits both grew by more than 20% in fiscal 2012 as both the TCM and TMS divisions increased earnings. Team's overall revenues grew 23% from the previous year to $623.7 million; the growth was solid across its customer and geographic bases. A joint venture to perform testing and inspection services in Alaska also saw growth that year. And although selling and administrative expenses rose (and the company paid a $0.8 million legal settlement related to a personal injury case) profits still grew 24% to $32.9 million.

Team has grown rapidly in the past decade increasing its revenues by more than sevenfold since 2000. It has acquired several competitors and expanded its presence internationally. In 2013 Team acquired industrial rope access service provider Global Ascent. In 2010 it bought Quest Integrity Group which performs inspection and engineering assessment services in markets around the globe. The acquired firm became part of Team's TCM division. In fiscal 2012 the company made two minor acquisitions further growing its operations.

EXECUTIVES

Senior Vice President - Operations Support and Technology Development, John P. Kearns, age 56, $222,686 total compensation

Chairman of the Board; Chief Executive Officer, Philip J. (Phil) Hawk, age 59, $528,846 total compensation
Chief Financial Officer; Executive Vice President; Treasurer, Ted W. Owen, age 61, $300,000 total compensation
Senior Vice President General Counsel Secretary, Andre C. (Butch) Bouchard, age 47
President Quest Integrity Group, Jeff Ott
Senior Vice President - TMS Division, David C. Palmore, age 57, $270,000 total compensation
Senior Vice President - TCM Division, Arthur F. (Art) Victorson, age 52, $270,000 total compensation
President Mechanical Services, Peter W. Wallace, age 50, $245,000 total compensation
Senior Vice President General Counsel Secretary, Butch Bouchard
VP-Equipment Center, Leo Kovel
Director, Louis A. (Lou) Waters Sr., age 75
Director, Vincent D. Foster, age 55
Director, Jack M. Johnson Jr., age 73
Director, Sidney B. Williams, age 77
Director, Robert A. Peiser, age 64
Director, Emmett J. Lescroart, age 61
Auditors: KPMGLLP

LOCATIONS

HQ: Team Inc.
200 Hermann Dr., Alvin TX 77511
Phone: 281-331-6154   **Fax:** 281-331-4107
Web: www.teamindustrialservices.com

2011 Sales

	$ mil.	% of total
US	438	70
Canada	121	20
Europe	36	6
Other	27	4
Total	**623**	**100**

PRODUCTS/OPERATIONS

2011 Sales

	$ mil.	% of total
TCM	354	57
TMS	268	43
Total	**623**	**100**

Selected Industrial Services

TCM
  Field heat treating
  Non-descriptive testing
TMS
  Field machining
  Fugitive emissions control
  Field valve repair
  Hot tapping
  Leak repair
  Technical bolting

COMPETITORS

APi Group
Flowserve
Furmanite
Halliburton
Halma
ITT Corp.

Mistras Group
Quality Inspection
  Services
Schlumberger
T. D. Williamson

HISTORICAL FINANCIALS

Company Type: Public

Income Statement
FYE: May 31

	REVENUE ($ mil.)	NET INCOME ($ mil.)	NET PROFIT MARGIN	EMPLOYEES
05/13	714.3	32.4	4.5%	4,200
05/12	623.7	32.9	5.3%	3,800
05/11	508.0	26.5	5.2%	3,500
05/10	453.8	12.2	2.7%	3,100
05/09	497.5	22.9	4.6%	3,400
Annual Growth	**9.5%**	**9.1%**	**—**	**5.4%**

2013 Year-End Financials

Debt ratio: 15.8%
Return on equity: 12.3%
Cash ($ mil.): 34
Current ratio: 3.39
Long-term debt ($ mil.): 72

No. of shares (mil.): 20
Dividends
Yield: —
Payout: —
Market value ($ mil.): 739

	STOCK PRICE ($) FY Close	P/E High/Low	Earnings	PER SHARE ($) Dividends	Book Value
05/13	36.07	29 16	1.53	0.00	13.99
05/12	26.68	20 12	1.59	0.00	12.08
05/11	23.00	21 9	1.32	0.00	10.50
05/10	15.04	32 21	0.63	0.00	8.70
05/09	14.15	33 8	1.16	0.00	7.78
Annual Growth	**26.4%**	**— —**	**7.2%**	**—**	**15.8%**

Telenav, Inc.

TeleNav offers a platform and suite of applications that provide mobile navigation and location-based services (LBS) to nearly 34 million users primarily in the US. Flagship product TeleNav GPS Navigator transmits voice and onscreen driving directions to mobile phones and smartphones and is marketed to end users by leading wireless carriers such as Sprint AT&T T-Mobile and U.S. Cellular. The company also offers automotive navigation services to automobile and auto parts manufacturers including Ford and Delphi Automotive Systems. In addition it is expanding into mobile advertising services through its Scout Advertising platform.

Geographic Reach Although the US accounts for 94% of sales the company provides its services across North and South America Asia and Europe. International sales as a percent of total have doubled in the last two years.

Sales and Marketing The company's sales and marketing expenses rose 27% in fiscal 2012 as it increased headcount in that area to strengthen and diversify its product suite. The primary sales and marketing activities for TeleNav products are handled by wireless carriers such as Sprint (37% of sales) and AT&T (36%) with the company supporting those efforts via marketing and promotional materials and sales tools. It also sells its products through Apple and Google app stores. In addition to the wireless carriers the company counts Ford (12% of sales) as one of its largest customers.

Financial Analysis TeleNav continued to see revenue growth in fiscal 2012 (ended June) with sales up 4% to about $219 million. The rise is attributable to an increase in sales to Ford growth in subscription fees from U.S. Cellular customers

and the conversion of some mobile applications from free to paid. The company's 2012 net income fell nearly a quarter to $32 million as expenses such as research and development sales and marketing and general and administrative far outpaced revenue growth primarily because of increased headcount. Strategy Although mobile navigation services represent nearly 80% of sales TeleNav is focused on opportunities in the growing automobile navigation and mobile advertising markets. The company's relationship with Ford continues to expand as its products are integrated into new Ford and Lincoln models. Also in 2012 TeleNav launched a new mobile local advertising platform Scout Advertising. Mergers and Acquisitions TeleNav acquired Boston-based local Web search service and mobile location-based software developer Goby Technologies in 2011 to supplement its own navigation products and services. In 2012 it purchased ThinkNear a hyper-local mobile advertising firm for $22.5 million; ThinkNear became part of the foundation for TeleNav's new Scout Advertising platform. Ownership Directors Samuel Chen (through Digital Mobile Venture) and Shawn Carolan (through Menlo Ventures) control about 28% and 15% of the company respectively.

EXECUTIVES

General Counsel and Secretary, Loren E. Hillberg, age 54
CFO, Douglas S. (Doug) Miller, age 55
Vice President of Enterprise Solutions, Thomas (Tom) Erdman
VP Enterprise Solutions, Tom Erdman
Chairman of the Board; President; Chief Executive Officer, H. P. Jin, age 48
CTO, Robert (Bob) Rennard, age 68
VP Research and Development, Y. C. Chao, age 48
Vice President - Growth Strategy and Partnerships, Salman (Sal) Dhanani, age 39
Vice President - Business Development and Carrier Sales, Hassan Wahla, age 40
Media Contact, Mary Beth Lowell
General Manager, Longxue Li
VP Marketing, Dariusz Paczuski, age 47
Chief Financial Officer, Michael Strambi
Vice President of Corporate Development and Strategy, Peter Bershatsky
Senior Vice President of Engineering, Marc Aronson
VP of Corporate Development and Strategy, Evan Berg
Vice President of Human Resources, Peg Wynn
Director, Joseph M. Zaelit, age 68
Director, Shawn T. Carolan, age 38
Director, Samuel Chen, age 62
Independent Director, Jane Chiu
Independent Director, Ken Xie
Auditors: Ernst&YoungLLP

LOCATIONS

HQ: TeleNav Inc.
1130 Kifer Rd., Sunnyvale CA 94086
Phone: 408-245-3800   **Fax:** 408-245-0238
Web: www.telenav.com

2012 Sales

	$ mil.	% of total
US	206	94
Other countries	12	6
Total	**218**	**100**

PRODUCTS/OPERATIONS

Selected Services
End-user billing and support
Location-based mobile advertising
Mobile resource management
Personalized navigation

COMPETITORS

ATX Group	Robert Bosch
Garmin	TeleCommunication
Google	Systems
Hemisphere GPS	TomTom
Ituran	Trimble Navigation
MapQuest	Vodafone
Microsoft	Webraska
Nokia	WirelessCar
Parrot S.A.	Yahoo!

HISTORICAL FINANCIALS
Company Type: Public

Income Statement
FYE: June 30

	REVENUE ($ mil.)	NET INCOME ($ mil.)	NET PROFIT MARGIN	EMPLOYEES
06/13	191.8	13.0	6.8%	682
06/12	218.5	32.4	14.8%	901
06/11	210.4	42.5	20.2%	1,039
06/10	171.1	41.4	24.2%	942
06/09	110.8	29.6	26.7%	878
Annual Growth 14.7%		(18.5%)	—	(6.1%)

2013 Year-End Financials

Debt ratio: —
Return on equity: 6.0%
Cash ($ mil.): 25
Current ratio: 5.31
Long-term debt ($ mil.): —

No. of shares (mil.): 39
Dividends
  Yield: —
  Payout: —
Market value ($ mil.): 206

	STOCK PRICE ($) FY Close	P/E High/Low		PER SHARE ($) Earnings	Dividends	Book Value
06/13	5.23	26	16	0.31	0.00	5.45
06/12	6.13	28	7	0.74	0.00	5.24
06/11	17.73	18	5	0.94	0.00	4.51
06/10	8.39	6	5	0.83	0.00	3.54
Annual Growth(14.6%)		—	—	(28.0%)	—	15.5%

Tempur Sealy International, Inc.

Tempur Sealy International's mattresses are made from material that is out of this world. Formerly Tempur-Pedic the company manufactures premium pressure-relieving temperature-sensitive mattresses pillows and other sleep products made from viscoelastic foam technology developed by NASA during the 1970s to help cushion astronauts during liftoff. Its TEMPUR Sealy and Tempur-Pedic brands are sold in more than 80 countries through four distribution channels: retail (furniture and department stores) direct (online and company-owned stores) health care (hospitals and medical retailers) and third-party distributors. Amid declining sales Tempur-Pedic acquired Sealy in 2013 in a deal valued at $1.3 billion.

Mergers and Acquisitions
Together Tempur-Pedic and former-rival Sealy create a $2.7 billion bedding company and give their iconic brands more traction globally. Following the deal which closed in March 2013 the company changed its name to Tempur Sealy International.

Operations
Tempur Sealy operates through two primary segments: domestic and international. The company's domestic segment comprises its US manufacturing facilities in Virginia and New Mexico which cater to its US distribution unit and certain third-party distributors in the Americas. Its domestic business accounts for about 70% of sales. Tempur Sealy's international segment which generates the remainder of sales boasts a manufacturing plant in Denmark that serves all of the company's distribution subsidiaries and third-party distributors outside North America. In 2010 Tempur Sealy bought out its Canadian distributor and made it a wholly owned subsidiary as the mattress maker works to gain market share in the country. It has inked similar deals during the past few years in Austria Australia China and New Zealand.

Financial Performance
Before hopping into bed with Sealy Tempur-Pedic International in 2012 rang up sales of $1.4 billion a 1% decline versus 2011. Net income of $106.8 million represented a 51% decline versus the prior year.

Strategy
Mattresses are the company's flagship product representing two-thirds of Tempur Sealy's total sales. The mattress maker isn't one to rest though. The company regularly rolls out new models of mattresses launches new products or updates existing mattresses globally. In summer 2012 it debuted two new mattresses featuring its new TEMPUR-Breeze technology designed to produce a cooling effect. On the retail front the company in 2012 opened its first flagship retail store in Natick Massachusetts near Boston. The 3500-square-foot store carries the company's full product line. Given its relatively small share of the mattress market Tempur Sealy believes it has plenty of room to steal market share away from spring mattress makers. In recent years Tempur Sealy has been mining the healthcare niche selling its products to hospitals nursing homes and healthcare professionals. The firm also partners with healthcare products makers to integrate its TEMPUR material into their products. Still the healthcare segment is a tiny part of the company's business accounting for just about 2% of 2011 sales. The company is also looking to increase its presence in furniture and bedding stores throughout North America and in international markets and increasing global awareness of its premium brand.

EXECUTIVES

EVP; President North America, Richard W. (Rick) Anderson, age 52, $328,000 total compensation
President CEO and Director, Mark A. Sarvary, age 53, $750,000 total compensation
Chairman, P. Andrews McLane, age 66
COO, W. Timothy (Tim) Yaggi
EVP and Chief Human Resources Officer, Brad Patrick, age 48
Vice Chairman, Robert B. (Bob) Trussell Jr., age 62, $566,800 total compensation
EVP and CFO, Dale E. Williams, age 50, $340,000 total compensation
EVP; President International Operations, David Montgomery, age 52, $375,865 total compensation
EVP Global Operations, Matthew D. (Matt) Clift, age 53, $360,000 total compensation
SVP Finance and Chief Accounting Officer, Bhaskar Rao, age 47
EVP General Counsel and Secretary, Lou H. Jones, age 62
President CEO and Director, Mark A. Sarvary, age 53
Director, Francis A. (Frank) Doyle III, age 65
Director, Evelyn S. Dilsaver, age 58
Director, Peter K. Hoffman, age 65
Director, John A. Heil, age 61
Vice Chairman, Robert B. (Bob) Trussell Jr., age 62
Director, Christopher A. Masto, age 46
Director, Nancy F. Koehn, age 54
Director, Sir Paul Judge, age 63
Auditors: Ernst&YoungLLP

LOCATIONS

HQ: Tempur Sealy International Inc.
  1713 Jaggie Fox Way, Lexington KY 40511
Phone: 859-259-0754   **Fax:** -2802
Web: www.redhallgroup.co.uk

2012 Sales

	$ mil.	% of total
North American	964	69
International	438	31
Total	**1,402**	**100**

PRODUCTS/OPERATIONS

2012 Sales

	$ mil.	% of total
Retail	1,228	88
Direct	113	8
Healthcare	31	2
Third party	30	2
Total	**1,402**	**100**

2012 Sales

	$ mil.	% of total
Mattresses	934	67
Pillows	158	11
Other	310	22
Total	**1,402**	**100**

COMPETITORS

Mattress Firm	Serta
Sealy	Simmons
Select Comfort	Spring Air

HISTORICAL FINANCIALS
Company Type: Public

Income Statement
FYE: December 31

	REVENUE ($ mil.)	NET INCOME ($ mil.)	NET PROFIT MARGIN	EMPLOYEES
12/12	1,402.9	106.8	7.6%	1,950
12/11	1,417.9	219.6	15.5%	1,800
12/10	1,105.4	157.1	14.2%	1,500
12/09	831.1	84.9	10.2%	1,150
12/08	927.8	58.8	6.3%	1,200
Annual Growth 10.9%		16.1%	—	12.9%

2012 Year-End Financials

Debt ratio: 78.0%
Return on equity: 401.2%
Cash ($ mil.): 179
Current ratio: 3.87
Long-term debt ($ mil.): 1,025

No. of shares (mil.): 59
Dividends
  Yield: —
  Payout: —
Market value ($ mil.): 1,880

	STOCK PRICE ($)	P/E		PER SHARE ($)		
	FY Close	High/Low	Earnings	Dividends	Book Value
12/12	31.49	50 12	1.70	0.00	0.37
12/11	52.53	22 12	3.18	0.00	0.48
12/10	40.06	18 11	2.16	0.00	1.84
12/09	23.63	21 3	1.12	0.00	2.29
12/08	7.09	33 7	0.79	0.24	0.97
Annual Growth (21.2%)	45.2%	— —		21.1%	—

Teradyne, Inc.

Teradyne has the anodyne for electronics makers concerned about quality and consistency. The company is a leading supplier of automated test equipment and a maker of systems for testing semiconductors. Teradyne caters to electronics manufacturing services suppliers as well as OEMs who use its test systems to analyze complex electronics used in the computing consumer electronics military/aerospace and telecommunications industries. Customers include Apple government contractors and the US government. Teradyne has operations in Asia Europe and the Americas; but it generates the majority of sales from customers in Asia.

HISTORY

College pals Nicholas DeWolf and Alexander d'Arbeloff (who met in an alphabetical ROTC lineup at MIT) founded Teradyne in 1960 to develop industrial-grade electronic test equipment. The name combines "tera" (10 to the 12th power) and "dyne" (a unit of force); to the founding duo it meant "rolling a 15000-ton boulder uphill." The company's first headquarters was a loft over Joe & Nemo's hot dog stand in downtown Boston. In 1961 the company sold its first product –an automatic tester for semiconductor diodes called a go/no-go diode tester –to Raytheon for $5000.

Teradyne grew rapidly during the 1960s as it introduced new products including testers for integrated circuits resistors transistors and diodes. In the latter part of the decade the company began using computers to speed up the testing process helping create the automatic test equipment (ATE) industry. It formed Teradyne Components (later Teradyne Connection Systems) in 1968 to produce electronics connection assemblies.

Teradyne went public in 1970. That year with the first slump in the semiconductor industry the company laid off 15% of its workforce and began diversifying its customer base. DeWolf departed Teradyne in 1971 leaving d'Arbeloff to run operations. The market quickly recovered and the company grew and prospered again. In 1972 it began working on a telephone system testing device the 4Tel. However the market slumped again and in 1975 Teradyne cut its staff by 15% a second time.

When trouble hit again in the mid-1980s Teradyne suffered back-to-back annual losses. Meanwhile Japanese companies overtook US semiconductor makers leaving Teradyne short of customers for its testers. Teradyne fought back in the late 1980s by lowering prices to undercut the competition and by pushing into the Japanese market. In addition the company formed a computer-aided engineering group by purchasing and combining Aida Corporation and Case Technologies.

The cycle continued in the early 1990s as military spending fell leading to further staff cuts salary freezes and even a temporary suspension of production. Through the mid-1990s a $63 million contract from the German national telephone system an upgrade in Teradyne's ATE line and a release of the TestMaster software development tool had Teradyne growing again.

High demand for PCs elevated sales of the company's semiconductor testing equipment helping it top $1 billion in sales for the first time in 1995. However the next year another semiconductor industry downturn caused a drop in profits and Teradyne laid off about 300 workers. In 1997 president George Chamillard succeeded d'Arbeloff as CEO. (D'Arbeloff remained chairman until 2000 when Chamillard succeeded him in that post as well.)

Teradyne turned a profit for 1998 despite one of the chip industry's worst-ever downturns. As chip sales and Asian economies rebounded Teradyne booked more than $2 billion in sales in 1999. Riding the crest of a chip industry boom Teradyne in 2000 posted record sales and its highest revenue growth in more than 25 years.

In the closing days of 2000 Teradyne sold its software testing division to a group of private investors led by Matrix Partners; that business became Empirix.

In 2001 Teradyne acquired GenRad for about $260 million in stock and debt assumption. GenRad was later renamed Teradyne Diagnostic Solutions. Also that year it laid off about 1000 employees (about 11% of its workforce) and reduced managerial salaries in response to a sharp downturn in the worldwide chip industry.

In 2004 George Chamillard stepped down as CEO (he remained chairman); president Michael Bradley took on the additional title of CEO.

To focus on its test systems business the company sold its Connection Systems division to Amphenol for about $390 million in 2005; Connection Systems accounted for about 20% of its revenue in 2004.

In 2006 the company moved out of its high-rise headquarters in downtown Boston relocating operations to its campus in suburban North Reading. Teradyne sold the HQ building to Nordic Properties for nearly $35 million. It sold another Boston building in 2006 to Millennium Partners.

Co-founder Nick DeWolf died in 2006 at the age of 77. At the end of 2006 George Chamillard retired from the board of directors after working at Teradyne for more than 35 years. Patricia Wolpert a director since 1996 and a retired IBM executive was named to succeed him as chairman.

In 2007 Teradyne acquired memory test assets from MOSAID Technologies a memory device testing technology developer for $17 million in cash. That same year it also sold its broadband test product line and related assets to competitor Tollgrade Communications for about $12 million.

Co-founder Alex d'Arbeloff died in 2008 at the age of 80.

Complementing its strength in SoC test the company moved into flash memory testing with the 2008 acquisition of Nextest Systems which got more than 80% of its sales from flash memory testers. Teradyne spent about $325 million to buy Nextest which became a business unit of the Semiconductor Test division. Also that year Teradyne purchased another competitor Eagle Test Systems which specialized in testing analog and power management chips. It became a business unit of the Semiconductor Test division. Teradyne spent about $250 million to acquire Eagle Test. Both deals were expected to help Teradyne compete against the combination of two leading test vendors Credence Systems and LTX which merged in 2008 to form LTX-Credence Corporation.

EXECUTIVES

President CEO and Director, Michael A. Bradley, age 64, $609,375 total compensation
VP CFO and Treasurer, Gregory R. (Greg) Beecher, age 55, $355,500 total compensation
Chairman, Albert Carnesale, age 76
President Semiconductor Test Division, Mark E. Jagiela, age 52, $344,214 total compensation
President Systems Test Group, Jeffrey R. (Jeff) Hotchkiss, age 64, $296,250 total compensation
Vice President - Corporate Relations, Andrew Blanchard
VP General Counsel and Secretary, Charles R. Gray, age 51
Regional Sales Manager, Ken Messerschmidt
General Manager - Asia, Yap Seng
Account Manager, Ken Kuai
Business Development Manager Teradyne Diagnostic Solutions Ltd, Dave Diffell
President Systems Test Group, Walter Vahey, age 48
President LitePoint, Benny Madsen
Director, James W. (Jim) Bagley, age 74
Director, Roy A. Vallee, age 60
President CEO and Director, Michael A. Bradley, age 64
Director, Paul J. Tufano, age 59
Director, Edwin J. (Ed) Gillis, age 64
Director, Timothy E. (Tim) Guertin, age 63
Director, Lt. Gen. Daniel W. Christman, age 69
Auditors: PricewaterhouseCoopersLLP

LOCATIONS

HQ: Teradyne Inc.
600 Riverpark Dr., North Reading MA 01864
Phone: 978-370-2700   **Fax:** 978-370-1440
Web: www.teradyne.com

2012 Sales

	$ mil.	% of total
China	354	21
Taiwan	303	18
US	233	14
Korea	225	14
Philippines	106	6
Japan	106	6
Europe	84	5
Singapore	80	5
Thailand	76	5
Malaysia	71	4
Rest of world	15	1
Total	**1,656**	**100**

PRODUCTS/OPERATIONS

2012 Sales

	$ mil.	% of total
Semiconductor test	1,127	68
Wireless test	286	17
Systems test	242	15
Total	**1,656**	**100**

2012 Sales

	$ mil.	% of total
Product	1,383	84
Service	273	16
Total	**1,656**	**100**

Selected Products

Semiconductor test systems
  Memory test
  Microcontroller test

Mixed-signal test (A5 line)
System-on-a-chip test
Very large scale integration (VLSI) chip test
Circuit board test and inspection systems
Automated optical inspection
In-circuit and functional board test
Software
Military and aerospace
Spectrum CTS (avionics systems)
VICTORY (boundary scan and fault diagnostic software)
Wireless test
IQfact (chipset)
IQflex (WLAN)
IQxstream (multi-device tester for devices)

COMPETITORS

Advantest	KLA-Tencor
Aeroflex	LTX-Credence
Agilent Technologies	Mitsui
Anritsu	National Instruments
Camtek	Orbotech
Cascade Microtech	Rohde & Schwarz
FormFactor	Tektronix
Hitachi	Xyratex
High-Technologies	Yokogawa Electric

HISTORICAL FINANCIALS

Company Type: Public

Income Statement

FYE: December 31

	REVENUE ($ mil.)	NET INCOME ($ mil.)	NET PROFIT MARGIN	EMPLOYEES
12/12	1,656.7	217.0	13.1%	3,600
12/11	1,429.0	373.8	26.2%	3,200
12/10	1,608.6	379.7	23.6%	3,000
12/09	819.4	(133.8)	—	2,900
12/08	1,107.0	(397.8)	—	3,800
Annual Growth	10.6%	—	—	(1.3%)

2012 Year-End Financials

Debt ratio: 7.1%
Return on equity: 13.1%
Cash ($ mil.): 338
Current ratio: 4.15
Long-term debt ($ mil.): 171

No. of shares (mil.): 187
Dividends
  Yield: —
  Payout: —
Market value ($ mil.): 3,174

	STOCK PRICE ($) FY Close	P/E High/Low		PER SHARE ($) Earnings	Dividends	Book Value
12/12	16.89	15	11	0.94	0.00	9.46
12/11	13.63	9	5	1.65	0.00	8.20
12/10	14.04	7	4	1.73	0.00	6.16
12/09	10.73	—	—	(0.77)	0.00	3.80
12/08	4.22	—	—	(2.33)	0.00	4.16
Annual Growth	41.4%			—	—	22.8%

Tesoro Logistics LP

Tesoro Logistics was created to serve its parent. The company a spinoff of oil refiner Tesoro Corporation owns and operates crude oil gathering transportation and storage facilities in the US. Its trucks and 700 miles of Montana and North Dakota pipeline serve Tesoro's Mandan refinery while eight refined product terminals hold petroleum in California Utah Washington Alaska and North Dakota. Tesoro Logistics' primary storage facility in Salt Lake City holds nearly 880000 barrels of crude and refined petroleum. Most of the

company's revenue comes from Tesoro and is evenly split between the gathering segment and the transporting and storing segment. It went public in 2011.

Though all of Tesoro Logistics' assets are on its parent company's land it plans to pursue business with and acquisitions from third-parties. The company used its $230 million in IPO proceeds for working capital and to pay down debt to Tesoro Corporation.

In 2013 the company acquired Chevron Pipe Line Company's Northwest Products System for $355 million and the first portion of integrated Carson logistics assets from Tesoro Corporation for $640 million.

Tesoro Logistics works within the volatile petroleum industry but because its business is fee-based and it doesn't actually own the petroleum it believes it is protected from the variations in the market.

EXECUTIVES

VP CFO and Director, G. Scott Spendlove, age 50
Chairman and CEO, Gregory J. Goff, age 57
VP General Counsel Secretary and Director, Charles S. (Chuck) Parrish, age 55
President and Director, Phillip M. (Phil) Anderson, age 48
VP Operations, Ralph J. Grimmer, age 62
Chief Operating Officer; Vice President; Director of the General Partner, Daniel Romasko
Independent Director of General Partner, James Lamanna
Lead Independent Director of General Partner, Raymond Bromark
Independent Director of General Partner, Thomas OConnor
VP CFO and Director, G. Scott Spendlove, age 50
VP General Counsel Secretary and Director, Charles S. (Chuck) Parrish, age 55
President and Director, Phillip M. (Phil) Anderson, age 48
Auditors: Ernst&YoungLLP

LOCATIONS

HQ: Tesoro Logistics LP
19100 Ridgewood Parkway, San Antonio, TX 78259-1828
Phone: 210 626-6000
Web: www.tesorologistics.com

PRODUCTS/OPERATIONS

2009 Sales

	$ mil.	% of total
Gathering		
Affiliate	19	86
Third party .1 -		
Terminalling transportation & storage		
Third party	3	14
Total	**22**	**100**

COMPETITORS

EOG	Plains All American
Enbridge	Pipeline
Encana	TransCanada

HISTORICAL FINANCIALS

Company Type: Public

Income Statement

FYE: December 31

	REVENUE ($ mil.)	NET INCOME ($ mil.)	NET PROFIT MARGIN	EMPLOYEES
12/12	156.8	55.5	35.4%	160
12/11	80.9	27.9	34.5%	114
12/10	23.3	(20.8)	—	0
12/09	22.6	(21.8)	—	0
Annual Growth	90.6%	—	—	—

2012 Year-End Financials

Debt ratio: 97.4%
Return on equity: 95.2%
Cash ($ mil.): 19
Current ratio: 1.41
Long-term debt ($ mil.): 353

No. of shares (mil.): 36
Dividends
  Yield: 3.6%
  Payout: 84.9%
Market value ($ mil.): 1,598

	STOCK PRICE ($) FY Close	P/E High/Low		PER SHARE ($) Earnings	Dividends	Book Value
12/12	43.80	25	16	1.89	1.61	(0.50)
12/11	32.90	30	19	1.11	0.59	3.50
12/10	0.00	—	—	(0.00)	0.00	(0.00)
Annual Growth						

Tessco Technologies, Inc.

TESSCO Technologies doesn't supply distributor caps but it does wear one. The company distributes communications products from about 380 manufacturers. TESSCO sells network systems products (broadband radios bi-directional amplifiers); base station infrastructure equipment (towers and site hardware antennas); installation test and maintenance equipment (tools device repair parts); and mobile devices and accessories. The company also offers training services. TESSCO sells to wireless carriers as well as wireless product resellers and installers manufacturers retailers government agencies and others. While 97% of its sales are in the US the remaining 3% are made in more than 100 countries.

Revenue rose about 16% in 2011. The commercial segment accounting for 97% of sales was up 16% thanks mainly to strong sales of commercial lines of network infrastructure and mobile devices and accessories. The consumer segment decreased 6%. The company has recorded a net income from 2007 to 2011.

Breaking down sales within the commercial segment network infrastructure sales rose 26% behind demand for radio frequency propagation site support and broadband products. Network infrastructure products are used for constructing and repairing wireless telecommunications computer and Internet networks.

Mobile devices and accessories (cell phone and data device accessories that include replacement batteries cases and hand-free kits) went up 14% mainly as a result of strong sales to smaller resellers. Sales to TESSCO's largest customer AT&T Mobility which accounts for about 26% of its revenue were flat in 2011. Most of the products bought from Otter Products which accounted for 13% of sales were sold to AT&T Mobility. That company also accounts for about 47% of sales of mobile devices and accessories.

Installation test and maintenance revenue fell 11% because of lower sales from Nokia which ended its agreement for repair and replacement parts in 2010. This category's products are used for the operations of wireless communications equipment.

Private-label products –which can compete with other branded products sold by TESSCO –account for about 10% of sales. A large share of these products are made in China.

TESSCO was founded in 1952 as an electronics distributor by the father of CEO Barney Barnhill. Barnhill owns about a quarter of TESSCO.

HISTORY

Towson Engineering Sales and Service Co. a small firm representing electronics manufacturers was founded in 1952 by Robert Barnhill Sr. In 1975 his son Robert Jr. (who goes by Barney) became the company's president and CEO; he eventually bought it from his father. In 1982 Barney renamed the company TESSCO and repositioned it as a distributor for the wireless communications market. The following year the Cellular One network was started in the Baltimore/Washington DC area with TESSCO as its original supplier.

The company spent the early 1990s fine-tuning operations developing a central system to integrate cataloging fulfillment financial control sales and other internal processes. TESSCO went public in 1994.

It became the exclusive sales agent for the SKY-CELL service unit of American Mobile Satellite (now TerreStar) in 1995. That year the company opened an office in Amsterdam to serve the global market. In 1996 Andrew Corporation which at one point accounted for a third of TESSCO's sales ended its 15-year distribution agreement with the company. (The two companies resumed their relationship in 2001.)

TESSCO filled the gap the following year by acquiring longtime competitor Cartwright Communications. Provisions for lost business and a slowing wireless market cut into the company's 1998 sales. In 1999 Ericsson chose TESSCO to handle its North American cellular phone accessory sales and fulfillment. In 2000 TESSCO partnered with Cisco Systems to provide support and technical services to the networking products giant's customers.

In 2001 the struggling telecom market caused a drop in sales of the company's traditional wireless infrastructure products; sales of its testing and maintenance equipment increased. Also that year TESSCO began offering gear for building wireless broadband data networks.

In 2006 the company expanded its offerings when it acquired two affiliated businesses –Terrawave Solutions and GigaWave Technologies –involved in manufacturing and distributing wireless LAN equipment and providing related training services.

In 2007 TESSCO acquired NetForce Solutions a provider of technical and sales training for wireless telecom and networking companies. TESSCO bought NetForce which boasted a catalog of 50 courses and also provided customized services to expand its training offerings.

EXECUTIVES

SVP Performance Systems and Operations, Douglas A. Rein, age 53, $250,000 total compensation

Chairman President and CEO, Robert B. (Barney) Barnhill Jr., age 69, $600,000 total compensation

SVP Solutions Development and Product Management, Gerald T. Garland, age 62, $300,000 total compensation

SVP CFO and Corporate Secretary, David M. Young, age 42, $250,000 total compensation

Principal Accounting Officer; Corporate Secretary, Aric M. Spitulnik

SVP Manufacturing Supply Chain, Saeed Tofighi, age 58, $250,000 total compensation

IR Contact Officer, Harriet Fried

Senior Vice President - Retail Segment and Global Manufacturer Supply Chain, Said Tofighi

Director, John D. Beletic, age 61

Director, Dennis J. Shaughnessy, age 66

Director, Benn R. Konsynski, age 62

Director, Morton F. Zifferer Jr., age 65

Director, Jay G. Baitler, age 66

Director, Daniel Okrent, age 65

Auditors: Ernst&YoungLLP

LOCATIONS

HQ: TESSCO Technologies Incorporated
11126 McCormick Rd., Hunt Valley MD 21031-1494
Phone: 410-229-1000 **Fax:** 410-527-0005
Web: www.tessco.com

2011 Sales

	% of total
US	97
Other	3
Total	**100**

PRODUCTS/OPERATIONS

2011 Sales

	$ mil.	% of total
Commercial		
Resellers	395	65
Self-maintained users & governments	109	18
Public carriers & network operators	86	15
Consumer	13	2
Total	**605**	**100**

2011 Sales

	$ mil.	% of total
Commercial		
Mobile devices & accessories	316	53
Network infrastructure	227	37
Installation test & maintenance	47	8
Consumer	13	2
Total	**605**	**100**

Selected Products and Services

Mobile Device Accessories
  Batteries
  Car antennas
  Cases
  Headsets
  Microphones
  Mobile amplifiers
  Mounts
  Power supplies
  Speakers
  Wireless data devices
Network Infrastructure Products
  Base station antennas
  Cable and transmission lines
  Connectors
  Filtering systems
  Lightning protection devices
  Towers
Network Infrastructure Services
  Connector installation
  Custom jumper assembly

Filter product tuning
Logistics integration
Site kitting
Test and Maintenance Products
  Analysis equipment
  Frequency voltage and power measuring devices
  Service tools supplies and replacement parts

COMPETITORS

America II Electronics	SED International
Anixter International	Talley
BearCom	Tech Data
Brightpoint	Westcon
Ingram Micro	Wincomm
KGP Logistics	

HISTORICAL FINANCIALS

Company Type: Public

Income Statement

FYE: March 31

	REVENUE ($ mil.)	NET INCOME ($ mil.)	NET PROFIT MARGIN	EMPLOYEES
03/13*	752.5	17.7	2.4%	838
04/12	733.3	16.4	2.2%	843
03/11	605.2	10.0	1.7%	874
03/10	522.0	9.1	1.8%	918
03/09	483.0	6.3	1.3%	894
Annual Growth	**11.7%**	**29.5%**	**—**	**(1.6%)**

*Fiscal year change

2013 Year-End Financials

Debt ratio: 1.3%	No. of shares (mil.): 7
Return on equity: 18.1%	Dividends
Cash ($ mil.): 4	Yield: 0.0%
Current ratio: 1.95	Payout: 68.3%
Long-term debt ($ mil.): 2	Market value ($ mil.): 173

	STOCK PRICE ($) FY Close	P/E High/Low		PER SHARE ($) Earnings	Dividends	Book Value
03/13*	21.64	12	8	2.15	1.47	12.87
04/12	25.47	12	5	2.03	0.55	12.09
03/11	11.74	21	8	1.27	0.45	10.57
03/10	23.46	20	6	1.19	0.20	9.63
03/09	7.92	18	6	0.84	0.00	8.49
Annual Growth	**28.6%**	**—**	**—**	**26.5%**	**—**	**11.0%**

*Fiscal year change

Texas Capital Bancshares Inc

Texas Capital Bancshares is the parent company of Texas Capital Bank with more than 10 branches in Austin Dallas Fort Worth Houston and San Antonio. The bank targets high-net-worth individuals and Texas-based businesses with more than $5 million in annual revenue with a focus on the real estate financial services transportation communications petrochemicals and mining sectors. Striving for personalized services for its clients the bank offers deposit accounts Visa credit cards commercial loans and mortgages equipment leasing wealth management and trust services. Its BankDirect division provides online banking services. Founded in 1998 Texas Capital Bancshares has about $11.7 billion in assets.

Financial Performance

The bank reported $488.6 million in revenue in 2013 an nearly 11% increase versus 2012. Net income was flat at about $121 million after posting three consecutive years of gains. Cash flow from operations continued its steep three year decline. The bank's total assets increased 11% from about $10.5 billion in 2012 to $11.7 billion in 2013. Total deposits increased 24% year over year to about $9.3 billion.

Strategy

Headquartered in Dallas Texas Capital Bank (TCB) believes that its Texas roots give it a competitive advantage over larger competitors that are headquartered out of state. Indeed TCB is gaining market share and is expanding by hiring experienced bankers and support staff. The bank is looking to grow within its main metropolitan markets but has also branched out beyond the borders of its home state. The bank has an Cayman Islands branch to offer offshore cash management and deposit products to it core clientele.

EXECUTIVES

CEO; Vice Chairman Texas Capital Bank, George F. Jones Jr., age 69, $484,167 total compensation

Chairman Emeritus, Joseph M. (Jody) Grant, age 74, $377,500 total compensation

President and CEO Texas Capital Bancshares Inc. President and CEO Texas Capital Bank, C. Keith Cargill, age 60, $300,000 total compensation

EVP Texas Capital Bank, David L. Cargill

President Texas; Chief Lending Officer Texas Capital Bank, Vince A. Ackerson, $265,000 total compensation

Chairman Texas Capital Bank San Antonio, Mark M. Johnson

Chairman, James R. (Jim) Holland Jr., age 69

Chairman, Larry L. Helm, age 65

President Austin, Kerry L. Hall

Regional President Texas Capital Bank Plano, Michael (Mike) Robnett

Investor Relations Contact, Myrna Vance

President Dallas Region, Russell Hartsfield

COO Texas Capital Bank, Jim White

Chief Financial Officer; Director, Peter B. Bartholow, age 64, $325,000 total compensation

Chief Credit Officer and Chief Risk Officer of the Bank, John D. Hudgens, $260,000 total compensation

President Houston, Bill Wilson

EVP and Controller, Julie Anderson

Executive Vice President Chief Operations Officer, James C. (Jim) White

Regional President Texas Capital Bank Fort Worth, Jeff Moten

Regional President Texas Capital Bank San Antonio, Clay Jett

Vice President, Jeff Kocher

Vice President JMEG LP, John Wall

Director, Robert W. Stallings, age 63

Director, Frederick B. (Fred) Hegi Jr., age 69

Director, Elysia Holt Ragusa, age 62

President CEO and Director; CEO Texas Capital Bank, George F. Jones Jr., age 69

Chairman Emeritus, Joseph M. (Jody) Grant, age 74

Director, Steven P. (Steve) Rosenberg, age 54

Chairman, James R. (Jim) Holland Jr., age 69

Chairman, Larry L. Helm, age 65

Director, Ian J. Turpin, age 68

CFO and Director; CFO Texas Capital Bank, Peter B. Bartholow, age 64

Director, Lee Roy Mitchell, age 75

Director, James H. Browning, age 63

Independent Director, Dale Tremblay

Auditors: Ernst&YoungLLP

LOCATIONS

HQ: Texas Capital Bancshares Inc.
2100 McKinney Ave. Ste. 700, Dallas TX 75201
Phone: 214-932-6600　　**Fax:** 214-932-6604
Web: www.texascapitalbank.com

COMPETITORS

Amegy	Cullen/Frost Bankers
BOK Financial	JPMorgan Chase
Bank of America	Prosperity Bancshares
Comerica	Wells Fargo
Compass Bancshares	

HISTORICAL FINANCIALS

Company Type: Public

Income Statement

FYE: December 31

	ASSETS ($ mil.)	NET INCOME ($ mil.)	INCOME AS % OF ASSETS	EMPLOYEES
12/12	10,540.8	120.6	1.1%	881
12/11	8,137.6	75.9	0.9%	786
12/10	6,446.1	37.1	0.6%	699
12/09	5,698.9	24.1	0.4%	631
12/08	5,140.2	24.2	0.5%	547
Annual Growth	19.7%	49.3%	—	12.7%

2012 Year-End Financials

Return on assets: 1.2%	Dividends
Return on equity: 16.5%	Yield: —
Long-term debt (mil.): —	Payout: —
No. of shares (mil.): 40	Market value ($ mil.): 1,825
Sales ($ mil): 441	

	STOCK PRICE ($) FY Close	P/E High/Low	PER SHARE ($) Earnings	Dividends	Book Value
12/12	44.82	17　10	3.01	0.00	20.53
12/11	30.61	15　10	1.98	0.00	16.36
12/10	21.34	22　13	1.00	0.00	14.30
12/09	13.96	33　12	0.55	0.00	13.40
12/08	13.36	25　15	0.87	0.00	12.53
Annual Growth	35.3%	—　—	36.4%	—	13.1%

Texas Pacific Land Trust

Texas Pacific Land Trust was created to sell the Texas & Pacific Railway's land after its 1888 bankruptcy and yup they're still workin' on it. The trust began with the railroad's 3.5 million acres; today it is one of the largest private landowners in Texas with around 960000 acres in 20 counties. Texas Pacific Land Trust's sales come from oil and gas royalties (70% of sales) grazing leases easements and land sales. It has a perpetual oil and gas royalty interest under some 470000 acres in West Texas. About 8% of the trust's oil and gas royalties are from leases operated by Chevron U.S.A. Texas Pacific Land Trust uses the revenues from sales and royalties to buy and retire its own shares.

The trust sold about 2200 acres of land in 2008 compared to some 1500 acres in 2007. While Texas Pacific Land Trust sold more acreage in 2008 the price per acre was less than a third of the price in 2007.

Grazing leases are in effect on 99% of the trust's land.

EXECUTIVES

CEO Secretary and General Agent, Roy Thomas, age 67, $187,917 total compensation

CFO and Assistant General Agent, David M. Peterson, age 48, $127,833 total compensation

Chairman, Maurice Meyer III, age 78

Auditors: LaneGormanTrubittL.L.P.

LOCATIONS

HQ: Texas Pacific Land Trust
1700 Pacific Ave. Ste. 2770, Dallas TX 75201
Phone: 214-969-5530　　**Fax:** 214-871-7139
Web: www.TPLTrust.com

PRODUCTS/OPERATIONS

2008 Sales

	$ mil.	% of total
Oil & gas royalties	13	71
Interest	1	7
Land sales　　0.8　　4		
Grazing leases	0	3
Easements & other	2	15
Total	19	100

COMPETITORS

American Realty Investors	Koch Industries Inc.
	Permian Basin

HISTORICAL FINANCIALS

Company Type: Public

Income Statement

FYE: December 31

	REVENUE ($ mil.)	NET INCOME ($ mil.)	NET PROFIT MARGIN	EMPLOYEES
12/12	32.5	19.6	60.3%	9
12/11	34.3	20.5	60.0%	9
12/10	20.0	11.3	56.4%	8
12/09	13.0	6.9	52.8%	8
12/08	19.3	10.9	56.7%	8
Annual Growth	14.0%	15.8%	—	3.0%

2012 Year-End Financials

Debt ratio: —	No. of shares (mil.): 8
Return on equity: 108.4%	Dividends
Cash ($ mil.): 8	Yield: 0.9%
Current ratio: 8.15	Payout: 19.6%
Long-term debt ($ mil.): —	Market value ($ mil.): 470

	STOCK PRICE ($) FY Close	P/E High/Low	PER SHARE ($) Earnings	Dividends	Book Value
12/12	53.43	28　18	2.20	0.48	1.77
12/11	40.69	22　16	2.21	0.21	2.24
12/10	36.48	37　22	1.17	0.20	1.92
12/09	30.05	54　24	0.69	0.19	1.99
12/08	23.10	52　18	1.06	0.18	2.30
Annual Growth	23.3%	—　—	20.0%	27.8%	(6.3%)

Texas Roadhouse Inc

If people are getting rowdy at this roadhouse it must be because of the steaks ribs or the famous sweet yeast rolls. Texas Roadhouse operates a leading full-service restaurant chain with more than 400 company-owned and franchised locations in 48 states. The Southwest-themed eateries serve a variety of hand-cut steaks ribs chicken pork chops and seafood entrees along with sandwiches chili starters and a variety of side dishes. The company also operates a small number of restaurants under the name Aspen Creek that specialize in hamburgers pasta entrees and pizza.

Geographic Reach

Although the chain is essentially nationwide now the bulk of Texas Roadhouse restaurants are located in the Midwest and Southeast. More than 50 of the company's restaurants are located in Texas and many units are located near interstate highways.

Operations

About 320 Texas Roadhouse locations are company-owned while the rest are franchised. The company gets nearly all of its revenue (about 99% in fiscal 2011 and 2012) from company-owned and operated units.

Sales and Marketing

Targeting the casual dining sector the Texas Roadhouse concept focuses on offering mid-priced menu items and a family-friendly dining atmosphere. The chain is primarily interested in serving the dinner segment offering its lunch menu only during the weekends. Its over-the-top Texas decor including such down home touches as jukeboxes and complimentary in-the-shell peanuts helps the chain distinguish itself in a crowded field of competitors that includes Logan's Roadhouse (owned by LRI Holdings) and Lone Star Steakhouse. Texas Roadhouse also faces stiff competition from industry heavyweights Chili's (Brinker International) and Outback Steakhouse (OSI Restaurant Partners).

Country singer Willie Nelson who is a partner in two restaurants located in Austin Texas serves as a celebrity spokesperson for Texas Roadhouse. The chain sponsors the popular artist's concert tours and each restaurant features "Willie's Corner" decorated with memorabilia.

Financial Performance

The company's revenue increased by 14% to $1.26 billion in fiscal 2012 compared to the $1.1 billion it reported bringing in during fiscal 2011 while its profit increased by 11% in fiscal 2012 compared to the previous year. The 2012 revenue spike was powered by double digit growth in both restaurant sales and franchise royalties and fees.

Restaurant sales increased by 14% due to the opening of new restaurants and an increase in average unit volumes from hikes in menu prices along with higher guest traffic counts. Franchise royalties and fees increased by 13% primarily due to an increase in average unit volumes increasing royalty rates and the opening of new franchise restaurants.

Strategy

The company is focused on ensuring quality and boosting traffic at its existing restaurants. The chain relies on specially-priced value menu items and targeted its marketing message toward cost-conscious families looking for affordable dining options.

Texas Roadhouse has taken steps to rein in development costs for new restaurants as it continues to expand. Its growth strategy includes expanding its restaurant base. In 2012 the chain opened 25 company-owned restaurants. The company plans to open about 28 company restaurants in 2013 all of which will be Texas Roadhouse restaurants. In addition it anticipates during 2013 its existing franchise partners will open as many as five Texas Roadhouse restaurants primarily in international markets.

Over the past several years the company has invested in improvements to its information systems real estate holdings human resources legal and marketing operations.

Company Background

Founder and chairman Kent Taylor opened the first Texas Roadhouse in 1993. A veteran of the restaurant business he previously served with such chains as Bennigan's (formerly owned by Metromedia Company) Hooters and KFC.

EXECUTIVES

President, Scott M. Colosi, age 48, $300,000 total compensation

Chairman, W. Kent Taylor, age 57, $300,000 total compensation

Chief Operating Officer, Steven L. Ortiz, age 55, $460,000 total compensation

General Counsel and Corporate Secretary, Sheila C. Brown, age 60, $225,000 total compensation

General Counsel, Jill Marchant

Chief Financial Officer, Price Cooper

Director, James F. (Jim) Parker, age 66

Director, James R. Zarley, age 68

Director, Martin T. Hart, age 77

Director, James R. Ramsey, age 64

Director, Gregory N. (Greg) Moore, age 63

Auditors: KPMGLLP

LOCATIONS

HQ: Texas Roadhouse Inc.
6040 Dutchmans Ln. Ste. 200, Louisville KY 40205
Phone: 502-426-9984   **Fax:** 502-426-3274
Web: www.texasroadhouse.com

PRODUCTS/OPERATIONS

2012 Sales

Restaurants	1,252	99
Total	**1,263**	**100**

2012 Locations

Company-owned	320	
Total	**0**	**392**

COMPETITORS

Applebee's International	LRI Holdings
Brinker	Landry's
Buffets Inc	Lone Star Steakhouse
Carlson Restaurants	O'Charley's
Cracker Barrel	OSI Restaurant Partners
Darden	P.F. Chang's
Golden Corral	Ruby Tuesday
Hooters	
Ignite Restaurant Group	

HISTORICAL FINANCIALS

Company Type: Public

Income Statement

FYE: December 25

	REVENUE ($ mil.)	NET INCOME ($ mil.)	NET PROFIT MARGIN	EMPLOYEES
12/12	1,263.3	71.1	5.6%	40,000
12/11	1,109.2	63.9	5.8%	33,000
12/10	1,004.9	58.2	5.8%	32,000
12/09	942.3	47.4	5.0%	31,000
12/08	880.4	38.1	4.3%	28,000
Annual Growth	**9.4%**	**16.9%**	**—**	**9.3%**

2012 Year-End Financials

Debt ratio: 6.5%	No. of shares (mil.): 68
Return on equity: 14.0%	Dividends
Cash ($ mil.): 81	Yield: 0.0%
Current ratio: 0.77	Payout: 46.0%
Long-term debt ($ mil.): 51	Market value ($ mil.): 1,160

	STOCK PRICE ($) FY Close	P/E High/Low		PER SHARE ($) Earnings	Dividends	Book Value
12/12	16.82	18	14	1.00	0.46	7.61
12/11	15.13	21	14	0.88	0.32	7.11
12/10	17.31	22	13	0.80	0.00	6.88
12/09	11.58	18	10	0.67	0.00	5.97
12/08	7.30	23	8	0.52	0.00	5.19
Annual Growth	**23.2%**	**—**	**—**	**17.8%**	**—**	**10.0%**

TGC Industries, Inc.

3-D technology has made TGC Industries one of the movers and shakers in the North American oil patch. From its inception TGC Industries has conducted seismic surveys for oil exploration companies. The company principally employs land surveys using Geospace Technologies and ARAM ARIES seismic systems which obtain 3-D seismic data related to subsurface geological features. Employing radio-frequency telemetry and multichannel recorders the system enables the exploration of rivers swamps and inaccessible terrain. TGC Industries also sells gravity information from its data bank to oil and gas exploration companies.

Geographic Reach

TGC Industries has operations across the continental US and Canada. It has offices in Houston Midland Oklahoma City and Calgary.

Operations

The company operates through three subsidiaries: Tidelands Geophysical (which conducts seismic gravity and magnetic surveys); Eagle Canada (which has expertise in conducting services in difficult-to-access and environmentally-sensitive areas); and Exploration Surveys (which has an extensive North American digital database).

TGC Industries owns enough equipment to serve 14 land-based seismic acquisition crews. In 2012 it has nine crews in the US and five in Canada.

Financial Performance

The company's revenues grew by 2012 thanks to increased market demand for land seismic acquisition activities and increased efficiencies of new wireless recording technology. It operated eight seismic crews in the US during the first and second quarters and added a ninth crew in the third quarter. The company had five crews operating in Canada during the fourth quarter of 2012 compared to four crews during the fourth quarter of 2011. TGC Industries' net income increased by 45% in 2012 thanks to higher revenues and lower selling general and administrative expenses.

Strategy

Expanding its technical resources in 2012 the company purchased 8000 stations of 3-channel GSX wireless recording equipment along with all peripheral equipment from Geospace Technologies. Following this delivery TGC Industries owns 70000 wireless channels the largest fleet of Geospace wireless data acquisition units in North America.

Company Background

A bid by Dawson Geophysical to acquire TGC Industries failed in 2011.

The deal which failed to get the requisite shareholder vote was expected to help Dawson Geophysical expand its seismic and geophysical services and client base. Following the transaction TGC Industries shareholders would have held 32% of Dawson Geophysical. However the volume weighted average price of Dawson common stock did not meet expectations of the required 80% of TGC Industries shareholders needed to agree to the acquisition.

Taking advantage of an opportunity to expand into Canada in late 2009 it bought bankrupt seismic data and surveying services provider Eagle Canada for $10.3 million. The purchase added two seismic crews and equipment and gave TGC Industries access to new industry segments (Canadian oil sands and potash mining).

The company was founded in 1980.

EXECUTIVES

President; Chief Executive Officer; Director, Wayne A. Whitener, age 61, $250,000 total compensation

Executive Vice President, Daniel G. (Danny) Winn, age 62, $142,593 total compensation

Chief Financial Officer; Vice President; Treasurer; Secretary, James K. Brata, age 57, $125,000 total compensation

IR Contact Officer, Jack Lascar

Director, William J. Barrett, age 73

Director, Herbert M. (Herb) Gardner, age 73

President CEO and Director, Wayne A. Whitener, age 61

Director, Allen T. McInnes, age 75

Director, Edward L. Flynn, age 78

Director, Stephanie P. Hurtt, age 68

Auditors: LaneGormanTrubittL.L.P.

LOCATIONS

HQ: TGC Industries Inc.
101 E. Park Blvd. Ste. 955, Plano TX 75074
Phone: 972-881-1099   **Fax:** 972-424-3943
Web: www.tgcseismic.com

COMPETITORS

CGG	Petroleum Geo-Services
Dawson Geophysical	Seitel
Geokinetics	TGS-NOPEC
ION Geophysical	WesternGeco
Landmark Graphics	

HISTORICAL FINANCIALS

Company Type: Public

Income Statement

FYE: December 31

	REVENUE ($ mil.)	NET INCOME ($ mil.)	NET PROFIT MARGIN	EMPLOYEES
12/12	196.3	15.6	8.0%	1,052
12/11	151.0	10.8	7.2%	935
12/10	108.3	(1.2)	—	804
12/09	90.4	1.8	2.1%	574
12/08	86.7	6.9	8.0%	651
Annual Growth	22.6%	22.8%	—	12.7%

2012 Year-End Financials

Debt ratio: 20.3%
Return on equity: 22.0%
Cash ($ mil.): 8
Current ratio: 1.30
Long-term debt ($ mil.): 16

No. of shares (mil.): 21
Dividends
 Yield: 1.9%
 Payout: 21.0%
Market value ($ mil.): 178

	STOCK PRICE ($) FY Close	P/E High/Low		PER SHARE ($) Earnings	Dividends	Book Value
12/12	8.19	16	8	0.71	0.15	3.60
12/11	7.14	17	7	0.50	0.00	2.99
12/10	3.80	—	—	(0.05)	0.00	2.50
12/09	3.91	63	20	0.09	0.00	2.49
12/08	2.03	31	4	0.33	0.00	2.38
Annual Growth	41.7%	—	—	21.4%	—	10.8%

The Bancorp, Inc.

The Bancorp is —what else? —the holding company for The Bancorp Bank which provides financial services in the virtual world. On its home turf of the Philadelphia and Wilmington Delaware metropolitan areas The Bancorp Bank offers deposit lending and related services targeting wealthy individuals and small to midsized businesses it believes are underserved by larger banks in the market. Nationally The Bancorp provides private-label online banking services for some 300 affinity groups issues prepaid debit cards processes merchant credit card transactions and acts as a custodian for health savings accounts (HSAs).

As an online bank the company has no branches; however it does operate three loan production offices in the Philadelphia area. The company also operates vehicle fleet leasing businesses Jefferson Leasing and Mears Motor Leasing which are active in about 40 states. Commercial and constructin loans and commercial mortgages dominate The Bancorp's loan portfolio.

The company's strategies for growth include generating deposits through its prepaid card community banking merchant processing and wealth management operations the funds of which it will expand its lending operations. It also hopes to market its offerings to customers of its affinity groups and generally drive up business in its home region. The Bancorp has also explored the possibility of establishing a new savings bank in southern New Jersey adjacent to its primary market area; the move would add a thrift charter to help accelerate the bank's nationwide expansion.

The Bancorp's earnings have been growing since the company lost money in 2008. Revenues in 2011 grew 15% to $119 million while profits grew 70% to $8.9 million. The increases were buoyed by higher prepaid card fees resulting from higher transaction volumes. Additionally prepaid card wealth management health care and merchant processing deposits all grew that year. However the company increased its provision for loan losses in both 2010 and 2011 allowing for challenges in the economic climate.

EXECUTIVES

Executive Vice President Chief Financial Officer Secretary, Paul Frenkiel, age 61

President, Frank M. Mastrangelo, age 45, $270,096 total compensation

Executive Vice President Chief Credit Officer, Donald F. (Don) McGraw Jr., age 56

Senior Vice President Chief Accounting Officer, Martin F. (Marty) Egan, age 45, $168,723 total compensation

Executive Vice President of Consumer Lending and Leasing, Scott R. Megargee, age 61, $202,541 total compensation

Executive Vice President of Commercial Lending, Arthur M. Birenbaum, age 56, $152,884 total compensation

Executive Vice President Chief Information Officer, Peter (Pete) Chiccino

Senior Vice President of, Jill E. Kelly

Senior Vice President of Loan Operations, Sandra C. Reel

SVP Merchant Acquiring, Terrence Crowley

Senior Vice President of Construction Lending, Mark A. Conners

Senior Vice President Chief Risk Officer, James D. Hilty

Senior Vice President Government Guaranteed Lending, Diane Gallion

Senior Vice President of Wealth Management, Ellen Rosen

Senior Vice President Payment Solutions Group Minneapolis, John Barbella

Senior Vice President The Bancorp Bank Wilmington, Michele Klesius

Senior Vice President Card Operations, Paul Landry

Senior Vice President of Business Development, Ryan Harris

Vice President Payment Solutions Group Chicago, Steve Turza

Senior Vice President Commercial Lending, Donald Tyson

Senior Vice President Managing Director of Payment Solutions Group, Jeremy Kuiper

Executive Vice President of Real Estate, Dan Sacho

Vice President Financial Operations, Dianne Bjork

Chief Executive Officer; Director; Chief Executive Officer; Chairman of the Bank, Betsy Cohen

Chairman of the Board, Daniel Cohen

General Counsel, Thomas Pareigat

Senior Vice President General Counsel, Thomas G. Pareigat

Director, William H. Lamb, age 73

Director, Michael J. Bradley, age 69

Director, Matthew Cohn, age 43

President COO and Director The Bancorp Inc. and The Bancorp Bank, Frank M. Mastrangelo, age 45

Director, Walter T. Beach, age 47

Director, Linda Schaeffer, age 49

Auditors: GrantThorntonLLP

LOCATIONS

HQ: The Bancorp, Inc.
409 Silverside Road, Wilmington, DE 19809
Phone: 302 385-5000
Web: www.thebancorp.com

PRODUCTS/OPERATIONS

2011 Sales

	$ mil.	% of total
Interest		
Loans including fees	74	63
Securities	12	10
Other	1	1
Noninterest		
Prepaid fees	18	16
Service fees on deposit accounts	2	2
Other	9	8
Adjustments	(0.1)	-
Total	**119**	**100**

COMPETITORS

E*TRADE Bank	Republic First Bank

ING DIRECT USA
M&T Bank
PNC Financial
RBS Citizens Financial
  Group

Royal Bancshares
Sovereign Bank
Sun Bancorp (NJ)
TD Bank USA
WSFS Financial

HISTORICAL FINANCIALS

Company Type: Public

Income Statement

FYE: December 31

	ASSETS ($ mil.)	NET INCOME ($ mil.)	INCOME AS % OF ASSETS	EMPLOYEES
12/12	3,699.6	16.6	0.4%	532
12/11	3,010.6	8.9	0.3%	428
12/10	2,395.7	5.2	0.2%	373
12/09	2,043.5	4.1	0.2%	367
12/08	1,792.3	(42.3)	—	306
Annual Growth	19.9%	—	—	14.8%

2012 Year-End Financials

Return on assets: 0.4%
Return on equity: 5.4%
Long-term debt ($ mil.): —
No. of shares (mil.): 37
Sales ($ mil): 146

Dividends
  Yield: —
  Payout: —
Market value ($ mil.): 408

	STOCK PRICE ($) FY Close	P/E High/Low	PER SHARE ($) Earnings	Dividends	Book Value
12/12	10.97	25 15	0.50	0.00	9.06
12/11	7.23	38 23	0.28	0.00	8.20
12/10	10.17	— —	(0.04)	0.00	7.60
12/09	6.86	397 129	0.02	0.00	9.37
12/08	3.75	— —	(2.93)	0.00	12.39
Annual Growth	30.8%	— —	—	—	(7.5%)

Thermon Group Holdings Inc

Thermon Group's heating products are not merely pipe dreams. Through its subsidiaries Thermon provides specialized cables tubes and control systems used in electric and steam "heat tracing" which involves externally applying heat to industrial-grade pipes tanks and instrumentation. Its core customers include energy chemical and power generation companies that use Thermon's products to maintain temperatures of materials transported or stored in pipes and vessels as well as for freeze protection in harsh environments. The company's customers have included dozens of multinational giants like Exxon Dow ConocoPhillips Procter and Gamble and Kellogg.

IPO

Founded in 1954 Thermon went public in 2011 and used the proceeds to repay debt and for general corporate purposes.

Geographic Reach

Thermon operates through a global network of some 30 sales engineering and other offices in cities across North America Europe Asia and Australia. It also operates four manufacturing facilities located in San Marcos Texas; Calgary Canada; Pijnacker the Netherlands; and Koregon Bhima India.

Canada generates 35% of its sales while the US accounts for nearly 30%. Europe and Asia bring in nearly 20% and 15% respectively.

Sales and Marketing

The company markets its products to customers around the world that are constructing brand new facilities as well as those performing maintenance on updating or expanding existing facilities. It has a team of nearly 100 direct sales agents and a network of over 100 independent sales agents and distributors in 30 countries.

Financial Performance

Thermon has successfully bounced back after suffering a net loss in 2011. Revenues were up nearly 5% from $271 million in 2012 to $284 million in 2013. Profits also more than doubled from $12 million in 2012 to $27 million in 2013 due to the higher revenues and the absence of loss on debt.

The company was helped by a 42% increase in sales from the important market of Asia and a 20% spike in sales from Canada during 2013. Its growth stemmed from an increased number of sales for the construction of new facilities as well as strong demand from maintenance and repair operations.

Strategy

As part of its growth strategy Thermon intends to expand its sales and marketing efforts into international growth markets like Russia China and India where the energy chemical and power generation sectors are expanding with economic and consumer demand. It will also use acquisitions and investments to complement its existing business lines.

In addition to geographic expansion other growth efforts include broadening its product and service lines to serve alternative energy companies that work in solar carbon capture and other areas.

Ownership

Eagle Asset Management owns about 10% of the company.

EXECUTIVES

Chief Financial Officer Vice President Secretary, Jay C. Peterson, age 55
President Chief Executive Officer Director, Rodney Bingham, age 61
Executive Vice President Global Sales, George P. Alexander, age 62
Regional Sales Manager, Luciano Rodriguez
Director, Richard E. Goodrich, age 69
Director, Marcus J. George, age 43
Director, Charles A. Sorrentino, age 66
Director, James A. Cooper, age 57
SVP Eastern Hemisphere and Director, George P. Alexander, age 62
Auditors: Ernst&YoungLLP

LOCATIONS

HQ: Thermon Group Holdings Inc.
  100 Thermon Dr., San Marcos TX 78666
Phone: 512-396-5801　　**Fax:** 512-396-3627
Web: www.thermon.com

2013 Sales

	$ mil.	% of total
Canada	99	35
US	83	29
Europe	59	21
Asia	41	15
Total	**284**	**100**

COMPETITORS

Hammond Manufacturing
Honeywell ACS

Schneider Electric
Siemens Water

Interpump
Pentair

Technologies
Tyco Thermal Controls

HISTORICAL FINANCIALS

Company Type: Public

Income Statement

FYE: March 31

	REVENUE ($ mil.)	NET INCOME ($ mil.)	NET PROFIT MARGIN	EMPLOYEES
03/13	284.0	26.9	9.5%	821
03/12	270.5	12.0	4.4%	755
03/11*	225.7	(14.9)	—	658
12/10	165.9	(10.9)	—	640
04/10	13.0	(0.2)	—	0
Annual Growth	115.9%	—	—	—

*Fiscal year change

2013 Year-End Financials

Debt ratio: 27.8%
Return on equity: 12.8%
Cash ($ mil.): 43
Current ratio: 3.32
Long-term debt ($ mil.): 118

No. of shares (mil.): 31
Dividends
  Yield: —
  Payout: —
Market value ($ mil.): 695

	STOCK PRICE ($) FY Close	P/E High/Low	PER SHARE ($) Earnings	Dividends	Book Value
03/13	22.21	30 22	0.85	0.00	7.22
03/12	20.45	52 28	0.40	0.00	6.37
Annual Growth	8.6%	—	—112.5%	—	13.3%

Thoratec Corp.

Suffering from a broken heart? Thoratec's there for the rebound. The company a world leader in mechanical circulatory support makes ventricular assist devices (VAD) for patients suffering late-stage heart failure including those awaiting a heart transplant. Thoratec offers external and implantable products that provide circulatory support for both acute and long-term needs. Its products are sold under the HeartMate CentriMag and Thoratec brands. The company works closely with hospitals and cardiac surgery centers primarily in the US and Europe.

Geographic Reach

Thoratec operates worldwide and has facilities in California and Massachusetts as well as in Switzerland and the UK. The company has more than 300 global centers (located within hospitals and surgery centers) for administration of its HeartMate II devices.

Operations

Treatments for late-stage heart failure are limited with a heart transplant typically serving as the only long-term option. While the Thoratec VAD products help many patients manage their heart disease while awaiting a transplant (known as bridge-to-transplantation or BTT) its HeartMate LVAS (left ventricular assist system) products –including the XVE and the II –are the only VAD devices with FDA approval as a permanent treatment (other than medication) for patients who do not qualify for transplantation. Such patients – known as destination therapy patients –account for half of US transplant volumes.

The company's devices have been implanted in more than 20000 patients worldwide. To meet the full range of heart failure patients' needs Thoratec also makes and distributes the CentriMag and Pedi-iMag/PediVAS product lines for temporary acute circulatory support in hospitalized patients. In addition it provides support services to clinicians and patients including software programs that provide device monitoring and assistance capabilities.

Sales and Marketing

Thoratec's products are sold to hospitals and other care centers through a direct sales force as well as through its clinical specialists and market development managers. The company also uses distribution partners in select international markets.

Advertising expenses in 2012 were $5.9 million up from $4.3 million the previous year. Promotional efforts include direct marketing medical journal advertising and educational seminar participation.

Financial Performance

Continuing with its multi-year growth trend the company reported a revenue increase of 16% to $492 million in 2012 primarily due to increased sales of its HeartMate and CentriMag products; the increases were attributed to higher volumes of HeartMate transplants for destination therapy patients and incremental CentriMag revenue increases generated by the Levitronix acquisition. Overall revenue growth was partially offset by a decline in sales of the Thoratec product line due to cannibalization by the HeartMate product line.

After several years of profit growth Thoratec's net income dropped by 22% to $56 million in 2012 due to higher sales general administrative and R&D expenses.

Strategy

Thoratec engages in a number of research and development efforts to stay on the cutting edge of medical technologies and keep ahead of the competition. The company's programs focus on developing new products and upgraded versions of existing products as well as on gaining new indication approvals for existing product versions. Thoratec is designing a next-generation HeartMate III device as well as a miniaturized version (the HeartMate X) and a percutaneous heart pump (PHP) for unstable heart failure patients. Its product enhancement activities include efforts to improve the cost effectiveness of its therapies.

In addition Thoratec pursues growth through the formation of strategic ventures and alliances as well as occasional acquisitions. It also works to expand its network of heart center partners (which conduct the implant procedures) —including facilities in new geographic territories —and to increase clinician and patient education programs.

Mergers and Acquisitions

In late 2012 Thoratec ensured the continued supply of replacement accessories and driveline dressing supplies for customers using its Heartmate II system by acquiring certain assets of CFK Cardiac Technologies for some $3 million.

In 2011 the company acquired Levitronix Medical the medical business of Levitronix LLC for about $150 million. The deal added the CentriMag product lines and solidified Thoratec's position as the leading full-line provider of mechanical circulatory support products for both acute and chronic needs.

EXECUTIVES

Chairman, Neil F. Dimick, age 63
SVP General Counsel and Secretary, David A. Lehman, age 52, $277,522 total compensation
VP Research and Development, Laxmi N. Peri

President CEO and Director, Gerhard F. (Gary) Burbach, age 50, $468,404 total compensation
VP-Ops, Patrick Schmitz
VP Fiance, Roxanne Oulman
VP and CFO, Taylor C. Harris
Director, Paul A. LaViolette, age 56
Director, Daniel M. Mulvena, age 64
Director, D. Keith Grossman, age 53
Director, Elisha W. Finney
Director, J. Daniel Cole, age 67
Director, Steven H. Collis, age 52
President CEO and Director, Gerhard F. (Gary) Burbach, age 50
Independent Director, William Hawkins
Auditors: Deloitte&ToucheLLP

LOCATIONS

HQ: Thoratec Corporation
6035 Stoneridge Dr., Pleasanton CA 94588
Phone: 925-847-8600   **Fax:** 925-847-8571
Web: www.thoratec.com

2012 Sales

US	400	81
Total	**491**	**100**

PRODUCTS/OPERATIONS

2012 Sales

	$ mil.	% of total
HeartMate	434	88
CentriMag	35	7
Thoratec	19	4
Other	2	1
Total	**491**	**100**

Selected Products

CentriMag Blood Pump System
HeartMate Left Ventricular Assist System (Heartmate XVE)
HeartMate II Left Ventricular Assist System (Heartmate II)
PediMag Blood Pump System
Thoratec Implantable Ventricular Assist Device (IVAD) System
Thoratec Paracorporeal Ventricular Assist Device (PVAD)
Thoratec Ventricular Assist Device (VAD) System
Vectra Vascular Access Graft (VAG)

COMPETITORS

ABIOMED	Medtronic
Abbott Labs	Merck KGaA
AdvanSource	Novartis
Bard	NuVasive
Becton Dickinson	Roche Diagnostics
Boston Scientific	St. Jude Medical
GlaxoSmithKline	Takeda Pharmaceutical
HeartWare	Terumo
Instrumentation	W.L. Gore
Laboratory Company	World Heart
Integra LifeSciences	

HISTORICAL FINANCIALS

Company Type: Public

Income Statement

FYE: December 29

	REVENUE ($ mil.)	NET INCOME ($ mil.)	NET PROFIT MARGIN	EMPLOYEES
12/12	491.6	56.1	11.4%	934
12/11*	422.7	71.5	16.9%	822
01/11	382.9	53.1	13.9%	714
01/10	373.9	28.5	7.6%	1,258
01/09	313.5	22.5	7.2%	1,209
Annual Growth	**11.9%**	**25.7%**	**—**	**(6.2%)**

*Fiscal year change

2012 Year-End Financials

Debt ratio: —	No. of shares (mil.): 57
Return on equity: 9.5%	Dividends
Cash ($ mil.): 101	Yield: —
Current ratio: 5.78	Payout: —
Long-term debt ($ mil.): —	Market value ($ mil.): 2,136

	STOCK PRICE ($) FY Close	P/E High/Low	PER SHARE ($) Earnings	Dividends	Book Value
12/12	37.09	41 30	0.94	0.00	10.36
12/11*	33.56	31 19	1.19	0.00	10.01
01/11	28.32	51 27	0.89	0.00	10.61
01/10	26.92	64 41	0.49	0.00	9.21
01/09	32.02	79 32	0.39	0.00	8.06
Annual Growth	**3.7%**	**— —**	**24.6%**	**—**	**6.5%**

*Fiscal year change

TIBCO Software, Inc.

TIBCO Software develops software that enables customers to integrate manage and monitor enterprise applications and information delivery. The company's software includes tools for coordinating business processes and workflows securely exchanging information with trading partners and managing distributed systems. Its core product line comprises applications for adopting service-oriented architecture (SOA) environments where reusable services are assembled to tackle common tasks such as business process management and application integration. TIBCO's other primary segments center on business optimization and process automation.

Sales and Marketing

TIBCO's clients come from a diverse mix of industries including financial services life sciences health care telecom and energy as well as from the public sector. The company tends to serve large global companies with diverse operations and substantial technology infrastructure; customers have included Home Depot Barclays and Grupo Santander.

Financial Performance

Despite higher operating expenses TIBCO's profits rose more than 40% in 2011 over 2010 on healthy revenue growth of 22%. Sales of software licenses and related maintenance services were both higher for the year. The company's SOA segment is still its largest money-maker but its business optimization unit is steadily growing. With the exception of 2009 when revenues dipped the company's total sales have steadily increased toward the $1 billion mark over the past decade.

Mergers and Acquisitions

TIBCO uses acquisitions to expand its product lines and to enter new vertical markets. In 2013 it bought private cloud-based location and geospatial data provider Maporama. The prior year it acquired LogLogic a developer of log and security management software for businesses.

In 2010 TIBCO purchased UK-based business process discover and analysis software developer Nimbus Partners to expand its selection of business process applications as well as Proginet a maker of file transfer and identity management software. The latter acquisition complemented TIBCO's core software and service offerings and expanded its global reach in managed file transfer technology. Also that year the company bought

San Francisco-based marketing software maker Loyalty Lab for $23 million to boost its presence in the travel hospitality and consumer products markets. Loyalty Lab offered its software as a service for clients to automate and manage such promotional efforts as frequent flyer mileage programs.

Previous purchases included the acquisitions of business intelligence software developers Spotfire and Insightful as well as of DataSynapse (which provided application virtualization software) and Foresight (transaction automation applications). The technology and products of Spotfire and Insightful were incorporated into TIBCO's Spotfire S+ product line while the DataSynapse deal expanded the company's reach into the financial services sector.

EXECUTIVES

Chairman and CEO, Vivek Y. Ranadive, age 55, $488,750 total compensation

EVP Products and Technology, Thomas J. (Tom) Laffey, age 57, $316,160 total compensation

EVP Analytics and Customer Loyalty, Peter Lee

EVP and CFO, Sydney L. Carey, age 48, $298,579 total compensation

EVP and COO, Murray D. Rode, age 49, $345,800 total compensation

EVP Global Field Operations, Murat Sonmez, age 49, $355,416 total compensation

EVP General Counsel and Secretary, William R. (Bill) Hughes, age 53, $279,583 total compensation

EVP and President Social Computing, Ram Menon, age 47

Vice President; Corporate Controller, Brent Hogenson

Chairman of the Board; Chief Executive Officer, Vivek Ranadive

CFO, Matt Langdon

Chief Marketing Officer, Lori Wright

Director, Eric Dunn

Director, Narendra K. (Naren) Gupta, age 64

Director, Sir Peter J. D. Job, age 71

Director, Nanci E. Caldwell, age 55

Director, Philip K. Wood, age 56

Auditors: PricewaterhouseCoopersLLP

LOCATIONS

HQ: TIBCO Software Inc.
3303 Hillview Ave., Palo Alto CA 94304
Phone: 650-846-1000   **Fax:** 650-846-1005
Web: www.tibco.com

2011 Sales

	$ mil.	% of total
Americas		
US	456	
Other countries	47	
Europe Middle East & Europe		
UK	80	
Other countries	245	
Asia Pacific	89	
Total	**920**	**100**

PRODUCTS/OPERATIONS

2011 Sales

	% of total
SOA & core	56
Business	33
Process automation &	11
Total	**100**

COMPETITORS

IBM	Progress Software
Microsoft	SAP
Oracle	Software AG
Pegasystems	Vitria Technology

HISTORICAL FINANCIALS

Company Type: Public

Income Statement

FYE: November 30

	REVENUE ($ mil.)	NET INCOME ($ mil.)	NET PROFIT MARGIN	EMPLOYEES
11/13	1,069.9	84.0	7.9%	3,856
11/12	1,024.6	122.0	11.9%	3,646
11/11	920.2	112.4	12.2%	2,965
11/10	754.0	78.0	10.4%	2,540
11/09	621.3	62.3	10.0%	2,097
Annual Growth	**14.6%**	**7.8%**	**—**	**16.4%**

2013 Year-End Financials

Debt ratio: 26.9%	No. of shares (mil.): 163
Return on equity: 9.0%	Dividends
Cash ($ mil.): 662	Yield: —
Current ratio: 2.46	Payout: —
Long-term debt ($ mil.): 540	Market value ($ mil.): 3,944

	STOCK PRICE ($) FY Close	P/E High/Low	PER SHARE ($) Earnings	Dividends	Book Value
11/13	24.17	52 35	0.50	0.00	5.84
11/12	25.05	45 29	0.72	0.00	5.53
11/11	27.40	45 26	0.65	0.00	5.10
11/10	19.64	41 17	0.46	0.00	4.91
11/09	8.60	27 12	0.36	0.00	4.75
Annual Growth	**29.5%**	**— —**	**8.6%**	**—**	**5.3%**

Titan International, Inc. (IL)

A colossus of off-roads Titan International makes off-highway steel wheels and tires for the agricultural construction mining and consumer markets. It assembles wheel-tire systems for original equipment manufacturers and aftermarket distributors of tractors cranes combines scrapers all-terrain vehicles golf carts and utility trailers. Other operations include the manufacture and distribution of wheels rims and tires to the military for trucks tanks and personnel carriers as well as boat and trailer wheels for the consumer. Titan sells its products directly to manufactures and through dealers distributors and at its own distribution centers.

Operations

Titan's agricultural wheels and rims range in diameter from 1 to 7 ft. the latter being the largest agricultural wheel manufactured in North America. Agricultural accounts for nearly 60% of sales. Its earthmoving/construction (also known as OTR or off-the-road) rims wheels and tires range in outside diameter from 3 to 13 ft. and can weigh as much as 12500 lbs.

For its consumer segment Titan made the decision to exit the OEM business for lawn and garden equipment and all terrain vehicles (ATVs) and instead focus on aftermarket products for the consumer market including ATV golf cart and trailer applications. The company also provides wheels and tires as well as assembles brakes actuators and components for the domestic boat recreational and utility trailer markets.

Sales and Marketing

Deere & Company Titan's largest customer accounts for nearly 20% of sales; CNH Global N.V. (another maker of agricultural equipment) represents about 10% of Titan's sales. Other customers have included Caterpillar Kubota Corporation and AGCO Corporation. It primarily targets the agriculture construction consumer forestry and mining sectors.

Financial Performance

Titan has experienced phenomenal growth over the last three years. Revenues jumped 22% from $1.5 billion in 2011 to reach $1.8 billion in 2012 a historic milestone for the company. Profits also surged 64% from $58 million in 2011 to a record high $96 million in 2012.

The growth for 2012 was attributed to a 63% rise in sales from its earthmoving/construction segment due to acquisitions pricing and product mix improvements and higher demand for products in the mining industry. Titan was also helped by a 12% spike from its agricultural segment and a 9% increase from consumer.

The rise in profits was due to the revenue spike coupled with about $16 million in gains it made from Titan Europe.

Strategy

With the mining industry showing promise the company has formed Titan Mining Services to build its presence in this sector around the globe. In 2012 it acquired a 56% interest in Planet Corporation an OTR tire and wheel specialist catering to mining agriculture and earthmoving companies based in Australia. Titan in late 2012 also acquired a 97% interest in Titan Europe which was founded by Titan in 1994 and spun off in 2004.

Titan purchased Goodyear's Latin American and European farm tire business in early 2011. The $130 million deal included a plant equipment and inventory in San Paulo Brazil and Goodyear Dunlop Tires' plant in Amiens France.

EXECUTIVES

Vice President; General Counsel, Cheri T. Holley, age 65, $275,000 total compensation

Director; CEO Titan Europe, J. Michael A. Akers, age 69, $237,000 total compensation

Vice Chairman, Erwin H. (Bill) Billig, age 87

EVP Corporate Development, Kent W. Hackamack, age 54, $275,000 total compensation

Chairman and CEO, Maurice M. (Morry) Taylor Jr., age 68, $750,000 total compensation

CFO, Paul G. Reitz, age 40

Vice President - Sales and Marketing, Richard Rose

VP-Quality, Tom DeNoi

President Titan Tire, Steve Briggs

President Titan Wheel, Dave Salen

EVP; Chairman Titan Tire, William Campbell

Director; CEO Titan Europe, J. Michael A. Akers, age 69

Vice Chairman, Erwin H. (Bill) Billig, age 86

Director, Richard M. (Dick) Cashin Jr., age 59

Director, Albert J. Febbo, age 73

Director, Mitchell I. (Mitch) Quain, age 61

Director, Anthony L. Soave, age 73

Auditors: PricewaterhouseCoopersLLP

LOCATIONS

HQ: Titan International Inc.
2701 Spruce St., Quincy IL 62301
Phone: 217-228-6011   **Fax:** 217-228-9831
Web: www.titan-intl.com

PRODUCTS/OPERATIONS

2012 Sales

Agricultural	1,080	59
Consumer	238	13

Selected Products

Tires
Trailer components
  Brakes and actuators
Wheels

COMPETITORS

Bridgestone	Meritor
Carlisle Tire &	Michelin
Wheel	Nokian Tyres
Falken Tire	Topy
GKN	Trelleborg
Hayes Lemmerz	

HISTORICAL FINANCIALS
Company Type: Public

Income Statement

FYE: December 31

	REVENUE ($ mil.)	NET INCOME ($ mil.)	NET PROFIT MARGIN	EMPLOYEES
12/12	1,820.6	95.5	5.2%	6,300
12/11	1,487.0	58.1	3.9%	3,600
12/10	881.5	0.3	0.0%	2,400
12/09	727.6	(24.6)	—	2,400
12/08	1,036.7	13.3	1.3%	2,900
Annual Growth	15.1%	63.6%	—	21.4%

2012 Year-End Financials

Debt ratio: 34.6%	No. of shares (mil.): 48
Return on equity: 19.2%	Dividends
Cash ($ mil.): 189	Yield: 0.0%
Current ratio: 2.12	Payout: 0.9%
Long-term debt ($ mil.): 441	Market value ($ mil.): 1,055

	STOCK PRICE ($) FY Close	P/E High/Low		PER SHARE ($) Earnings	Dividends	Book Value
12/12	21.72	13	8	1.83	0.02	12.24
12/11	19.46	22	10	1.18	0.02	9.36
12/10	19.54	1976	738	0.01	0.02	7.87
12/09	8.11	—	—	(0.71)	0.02	7.43
12/08	8.25	118	15	0.38	0.02	7.97
Annual Growth	27.4%	—	—	48.1%	2.7%	11.3%

Titan Machinery, Inc.

For getting the job done Titan Machinery is one titanic dealer. Titan owns one of North America's largest full-service networks that supply construction and agricultural equipment. Its more than 100 dealerships sell and rent new and used machinery and attachments parts as well as service equipment. It represents equipment by CNH's Case IH New Holland Agriculture Case Construction and New Holland Construction. Titan offers excavators seeders tillers and tractors to customers from large-scale farmers to home gardeners. Other products include earthmoving equipment and cranes used for heavy construction and light industrial jobs in commercial or residential building roadwork forestry and mining.

Geographic Reach

Based in North Dakota Titan operates a contiguous network of 105 North American dealerships in 11 states throughout the US including two outlet stores and 14 agriculture stores in Europe —located in Bulgaria Romania Serbia and Ukraine.

Sales and Marketing

Titan continues to expand its network of independent stores supported by a centralized administrative finance and marketing management. In tandem the company's full-service multi-point dealership approach is designed to leverage cross-selling equipment opportunities to a diverse group of customers.

Sales from the agriculture industry account for 83% of its total revenue; construction 17%.

Financial Performance

Titan has enjoyed unprecedented growth over the last four years. Revenues grew 33% from $1.7 billion in 2012 to reach $2.2 billion in 2013 a historic milestone for the company. Profits dipped 4% from $44 million to roughly $42 million due to higher costs associated with acquisitions.

The growth for 2013 was driven by a nearly 30% increase in same-store sales growth. Sales in the agriculture sector grew 32% due to acquisitions and Titan saw revenue growth across all its product lines: equipment (35%) parts (20%) and service (23%).

Strategy

One component for Titan's blueprint for growth involves acquisitions. In early 2012 Titan acquired Adobe Truck & Equipment which operates three Case Construction dealerships in Colorado. Outside the US Titan also acquired a majority stake in Rimex which operates seven agriculture equipment dealerships in Bulgaria during that same time period.

In 2011 Titan pursued several strategic acquisitions in its agricultural segment and its construction segment. The company purchased St. Joseph Equipment's construction business. The deal comprising four locations represented Titan's first construction equipment dealership in Wisconsin. Hard on its heels Titan took over ABC Rental a Montana-based independent construction rental yard with a large customer base that spans Montana North Dakota South Dakota and Wyoming.

Ownership

Founder David Meyer owns 14% of the company.

Company Background

David Meyer founded Titan in 1980.

EXECUTIVES

Chairman and CEO, David J. Meyer, age 60, $250,000 total compensation
President and COO, Peter Christianson, age 56, $250,000 total compensation
CFO, Mark Kalvoda
Director, Stan K. Dardis, age 61
Director, Theodore M. Wright, age 50
Director, John S. Bode, age 65
President and COO, Peter Christianson, age 56
Director, James Irwin, age 70
Director, James Williams, age 73
Auditors: EideBaillyLLP

LOCATIONS

HQ: Titan Machinery, Inc.
  644 East Beaton Drive, West Fargo, ND 58078-2648
Phone: 701 356-0130
Web: www.titanmachinery.com

PRODUCTS/OPERATIONS

2013 Sales

Agriculture	1,899	83
Construction	380	17
Total	**2,198**	**100**

2013 Sales

Equipment	1,763	80
Service	127	6
Total	**2,198**	**100**

Selected Products

Agricultural
  Application equipment
  Attachments
  Combines
  Forage equipment
  Hay equipment
  Planting equipment
  Precision farming technology
  Seeding
  Sprayers
  Tillage equipment
  Tractors
Construction
  Articulated trucks
  Compact track loaders
  Compaction equipment
  Cranes
  Crawler dozers
  Excavators
  Forklifts
  Loader/backhoes
  Loader/tool carriers
  Motor graders
  Skid steer loaders
  Telehandlers
  Wheel loaders

COMPETITORS

AGCO	Mustang CAT
Briggs Equipment	RDO Equipment
Caterpillar	Scott Equipment
Deere	Ziegler inc

HISTORICAL FINANCIALS
Company Type: Public

Income Statement

FYE: January 31

	REVENUE ($ mil.)	NET INCOME ($ mil.)	NET PROFIT MARGIN	EMPLOYEES
01/13	2,198.4	42.4	1.9%	2,813
01/12	1,658.9	44.1	2.7%	2,396
01/11	1,094.4	22.3	2.0%	1,874
01/10	838.7	15.7	1.9%	1,491
01/09	690.4	18.0	2.6%	1,288
Annual Growth	33.6%	23.8%	—	21.6%

2013 Year-End Financials

Debt ratio: 61.0%	No. of shares (mil.): 21
Return on equity: 11.5%	Dividends
Cash ($ mil.): 124	Yield: —
Current ratio: 1.48	Payout: —
Long-term debt ($ mil.): 182	Market value ($ mil.): 610

	STOCK PRICE ($) FY Close	P/E High/Low		PER SHARE ($) Earnings	Dividends	Book Value
01/13	28.91	18	10	2.00	0.00	18.80
01/12	24.74	14	7	2.18	0.00	16.08
01/11	24.23	19	9	1.23	0.00	11.98
01/10	11.02	18	9	0.88	0.00	10.72
01/09	10.15	30	8	1.08	0.00	9.84
Annual Growth	29.9%	—	—	16.7%	—	17.6%

Toro Co. (The)

Need to repair the 13th green after wild rampaging bulls charge through? Call The Toro Company. Toro makes lawn mowers and other tools for professional and residential use. Its professional lineup includes irrigation equipment mowers for commercial projects riding and walk-behind power mowers for fairways and greens trimmers lighting and utility vehicles. Some professional brands are Toro Rain Master Exmark Odyssey and Irritrol. Its residential lines sold to distributors home centers and mass merchants include walk-behind and riding mowers lawn tractors electrical trimmers lighting and snow blowers. Brand names in this segment include Toro Rain Master Irritrol Lawn Genie and Lawn-Boy.

Geographic Reach

The Toro Company rings up 70% of its sales in the US. The remainder comes from sone 90 other countries including Australia Canada and parts of Europe. Toro manufactures its products in the US Mexico Australia the UK Italy and Romania.

Operations

The company has two primary business segments. Toro's Professional business representing more than two-thirds of sales designs turf landscape construction and agricultural products and markets them worldwide. Its Residential arm (about 30% of sales) markets walking and riding mowers snow removal equipment and outdoor power equipment such as hedge trimmers blowers among other handy gadgets.

Sales and Marketing

Toro markets most of its products through approximately 40 domestic and 120 international distributors as well as a large number of outdoor power equipment dealers hardware stores home centers and mass merchants in more than 90 countries. The company's residential business is reliant upon Home Depot which represented about 11% of net sales in fiscal 2012 (ends October) and fiscal 2011. The company has sales offices in about a dozen countries including China Japan Korea the UK and the US.

Financial Performance

Toro approached $2 billion in sales in fiscal 2012 (ends October) representing a 4% increase over the prior year. Net income increased 10% over the same period. Fiscal 2012 marked the third consecutive year of rising sales and profits for the company. The increase was driven by new and improved products and acquisitions. Sales of the company's professional products (up 7% year over year) outperformed residential ones (down more than 2%) due to decreased demand for snow throwing products. Sales in the US Toro's largest market increased 7% while the sluggish economy in Europe contributed to a 2% decline in international sales.

Strategy

The company intends to fuel growth through business acquisitions that aide in staying on top of the latest technologies expanding into new and developing global markets as well as fending off competition. (Competitor Deere & Company has passed Toro in the micro-irrigation products market through such acquisitions as T-Systems International and Israel-based Plasto Irrigation.)

In early 2012 Toro committed to the underground and utilities marketplace by purchasing some of the assets of Astec Underground (part of Astec Industries). The deal gave Toro a hefty line of vibratory plows trenchers and horizontal directional drills used in installing repairing and replacing utilities yet designed to limit damage to neighboring landscapes and structures.

To give its core market distributors and irrigation contractors another reason to do business with Toro the company entered the outdoor professional lighting market in 2011. It did so by purchasing Unique Lighting a nationwide provider of professionally installed low-voltage outdoor lighting systems. The acquired landscape lighting brands include Odyssey Signature Series and Brass and Copper Knights.

Toro has also furthered its foothold in the sports field and golf course markets through a stream of deals. During the last several years it purchased certain assets from TY-Crop Manufacturing Ltd. which makes equipment to maintain golf courses and sports fields; Southern Green a top maker of deep-tine aeration equipment under the Soil Reliever name; Rain Master Irrigation Systems a leader for some 25 years in helping customers monitor their turf; and the Turf Guard wireless monitoring technology from JLH Labs.

Mergers and Acquisitions

In April 2012 Toro acquired light construction and hardscape products assets of Stone Construction Equipment a manufacturer of concrete and hardscape equipment for rental and construction companies. The purchase bolstered Toro's position in the growing rental market with a line of branded products.

HISTORY

Toro —Spanish for "bull" —was founded in 1914 as The Toro Motor Company to make engines for The Bull Tractor Company. In 1921 Toro provided a tractor fitted with 30-inch lawn mower blades to replace a horse-drawn grass-cutting machine at a Minneapolis country club and the modern power mower industry was born. By 1925 Toro turf maintenance machines were used on many of the US's major golf courses and parks and by 1928 its products were used in Europe.

The company went public in 1935. Toro introduced its first walk-behind power mower for consumers four years later. In 1948 the company entered the rotary mower market when it bought Whirlwind. Toro started making snow removal equipment in 1951. With its 1962 purchase of Moist O' Matic the company's offerings included automatic irrigation for golf courses.

It was renamed The Toro Company in 1971. Consumer sales of snow removal equipment began to pile up but those sales melted away when little snow fell during the winters of 1980 and 1981 and Toro suffered immense losses.

Kendrick Melrose a 13-year Toro veteran became CEO in 1983. He cut staff closed plants and revamped the company's inventory system. During the 1980s Toro diversified acquiring two lighting manufacturers including Lunalite (1984). The company also established an outdoor electrical appliance division.

In 1986 Toro purchased lawn tractor manufacturer Wheel Horse and it entered the mid-priced market with the acquisition of rival Lawn-Boy three years later. Toro kept the Lawn-Boy brand trying to capitalize on its name recognition in mass-merchandise retail channels.

Sales fell during the recession of the early 1990s causing another round of plant closures and layoffs. The company introduced its "environmentally friendly" bagless Toro Recycler mower (1990) entered the fertilizer market with its Toro BioPro line (1992) and formed a Recycling Equipment division (1994). Toro found success with such new products as cordless electric mowers in 1995.

Trying to insulate itself against weather-related downturns the company bought a unit (now called Irritrol) from irrigation products maker James Hardie Industries (1996); professional landscaping equipment maker Exmark (1997); and Motorola's OSMAC irrigation unit (1997). Toro's other late-1990s acquisitions included the US rights of Dingo Digging Systems and micro-irrigation products maker Drip In (1998).

Despite the company's growing sales of commercial products earnings plunged in 1998 in part because of declining consumer products sales (particularly snow blowers thanks to uncooperative weather patterns) troubled sales in Asia and restructuring costs.

Breaking with its policy to sell mainly through independent dealers Toro opted to distribute its Toro-brand lawn mowers to selected home centers adding nearly 1500 distribution outlets in 1998. To mow down costs in 1998 and 1999 it sold its Recycling Equipment business and fertilizer products business. Also in 1999 the company bought Multi-Core Aerators a European distributor of large turf aeration equipment and stopped making outdoor lighting products (but licensed the Toro name to Electa Industrial Company).

In 2000 the company acquired Sitework Systems (US sales representative of the Dingo compact utility loader) and completed the purchase of two distributors of turf maintenance and creation products. The next year Toro acquired Electronic Industrial Controls which provides computer control systems for irrigation products.

Toro formed a financing unit with GE Capital in 2002 to help cities and golf courses buy irrigation systems and grounds maintenance equipment. Additionally that year Toro expanded facilities in Nebraska and Juarez Mexico where it also opened a plant for the production of walk-behind lawn mowers. During the same year Toro closed facilities in Evansville Indiana and Riverside California.

Toro acquired R & D Engineering which markets wireless rain and freeze switches for residential irrigation systems in 2003.

EXECUTIVES

VP Irrigation and Lighting Business, Philip A. Burkart, age 51

Chairman and CEO, Michael J. (Mike) Hoffman, age 58, $766,665 total compensation

Vice President Global Micro Irrigation Business, Michael D. Drazan, age 56

Vice President Human Resources and Business Development, Peter M. (Pete) Ramstad, age 55, $304,553 total compensation

VP Commercial and Irrigation Businesses, William E. (Bill) Brown Jr., age 52, $252,573 total compensation

Vice President Secretary and General Counsel, Timothy P. (Tim) Dordell, age 50, $288,157 total compensation

VP Global Operations, Blake M. Grams, age 46

VP Residential and Landscape Contractor Businesses, Michael J. Happe, age 42

VP Commercial Business, Darren Redetzke, age 49

VP and Treasurer, Thomas J. Larson, age 55

VP Exmark, Judy L. Altmaier, age 52

VP Information Services, Kurt D. Svendsen

Vice President Finance and CFO, Renee J. Peterson, age 52

VP International Business, Richard M. Olson

Director, Gregg W. Steinhafel, age 58

Director, Robert C. Buhrmaster, age 65

Director, Jeffrey M. Ettinger, age 54

Director, Christopher A. Twomey, age 65
Director, Katherine J. (Kathy) Harless, age 62
Director, Janet K. Cooper, age 59
Director, Robert H. Nassau, age 71
Director, Inge G. Thulin, age 59
Director, Gary L. Ellis, age 56
Director, James O'Rourke
Auditors: KPMGLLP

LOCATIONS

HQ: Toro Co. (The)
8111 Lyndale Avenue South, Bloomington, MN 55420-1196
Phone: 952 888-8801
Web: www.thetorocompany.com

2012 Sales

	$ mil.	% of total
US	1,364	70
Other countries	594	30
Total	**1,958**	**100**

PRODUCTS/OPERATIONS

2012 Sales

	$ mil.	% of total
Equipment	1,568	81
Irrigation & lighting	371	19
Total	**1,958**	**100**

2012 Sales

	$ mil.	% of total
Professional	1,329	68
Residential	607	31
Other	21	1
Total	**1,958**	**100**

Selected Products

Professional
  Agricultural irrigation
    Aqua-TraXX irrigation tape
    Blue Stripe polyethylene tubing
    Drip In drip line
  Golf course
    Bunker maintenance equipment
    Turf aerators
    Walking and riding mowers
  Landscape contractor
    Backhoes
    Compact utility loaders
    Heavy-duty walk-behind mowers
    Lighting
    Trenchers
    Zero-turning-radius riding mowers
  Sports fields and grounds
    Blowers
    Multipurpose vehicles
    Sweepers
    Vacuums
Residential
  Home solutions
    Electric blower-vacuums
    Grass trimmers
    Lighting
  Riding products
    Garden tractor models
    Lawn tractor models
    Zero-turning-radius mowers
  Snow removal
    Single-stage snow throwers
    Two-stage snow throwers
  Walk power mowers
    Bagging mowers
    Mulching mowers
    Side discharging mowers

COMPETITORS

Alamo Group	Kubota
Deere	MTD Products
Emak Group	Tecumseh Products
Honda	Textron

HISTORICAL FINANCIALS

Company Type: Public

Income Statement

FYE: October 31

	REVENUE ($ mil.)	NET INCOME ($ mil.)	NET PROFIT MARGIN	EMPLOYEES
10/13	2,041.4	154.8	7.6%	5,057
10/12	1,958.6	129.5	6.6%	5,055
10/11	1,883.9	117.6	6.2%	4,618
10/10	1,690.3	93.2	5.5%	4,609
10/09	1,523.4	62.8	4.1%	4,414
Annual Growth	**7.6%**	**25.3%**	**—**	**3.5%**

2013 Year-End Financials

Debt ratio: 22.2%
Return on equity: 46.1%
Cash ($ mil.): 182
Current ratio: 1.68
Long-term debt ($ mil.): 223

No. of shares (mil.): 56
Dividends
  Yield: 0.9%
  Payout: 22.0%
Market value ($ mil.): 3,347

	STOCK PRICE ($) FY Close	P/E High/Low	PER SHARE ($) Earnings	Dividends	Book Value
10/13	58.94	22 15	2.62	0.56	6.32
10/12	42.22	35 17	2.14	0.44	5.36
10/11	54.04	36 24	1.85	0.40	4.51
10/10	56.76	41 26	1.40	0.36	4.39
10/09	37.02	47 23	0.87	0.30	4.72
Annual Growth	**12.3%**	**— —**	**31.9%**	**16.9%**	**7.5%**

Transdigm Group Inc

TransDigm's aviation components transcend any single airframe. Operating through subsidiaries TransDigm Group makes and distributes a wide range of components for commercial and military aircraft. Subsidiaries include AeroControlex (mechanical controls pumps valves) Adams Rite Aerospace (cockpit security products electromechanical controls interior latches and locks) Marathon Norco Aerospace (batteries connectors) and Champion Aerospace (ignition systems and components). 56% of TransDigm's sales come from aftermarket products mostly for commercial and military aircraft from manufacturers such as Boeing Bombardier and Cessna.

Other subsidiaries include ADS/Transcoil (LCDs clocks transducers brushless motors) Adel Wiggins (clamps connectors heaters refueling systems) and Avionic Instruments (power conversion equipment). Additional subsidiaries include Avtech which makes flight deck PA systems and cabin lighting and power products; Bruce Aerospace which offers aircraft interior exterior and emergency lighting; CDA InterCorp a maker of actuators motors and gears; and Skurka Aerospace which provides electric motors generators speed transducers and tachometers.

Strategically TransDigm focuses on specialized products rather than commodities. Most of the company's sales come from proprietary products for which TransDigm owns the design and/or is the sole-source provider for a particular aircraft. And although the company grows organically through contracts for work on next-generation aircraft such as the Airbus A380 and the Boeing 787 the company's acquisitions have fueled its significant growth.

TransDigm acquires companies that offer niche products that fit well with other subsidiary operations or have significant aftermarket sales. In 2012 the company acquired aviation passenger seatbelt and airbag maker AmSafe Global Holdings for $750 million in cash. The previous year it completed a deal to acquire the actuation business of Teleflex's Telair International for a reported $94 million. The California-based operations make electromechanical products and landing gear for both commercial and military aircraft. Other acquisitions include Schneller LLC maker of engineered laminates and Harco Laboratories a manufacturer of engine components.

The company also made some key acquisitions in 2010 including its purchase of McKechnie Aerospace an aircraft parts supplier for a reported cash price of more than $1.2 billion. The McKechnie deal gave TransDigm additional contracts with Boeing and Airbus two existing customers. Also included in the acquisition was McKechnie's aerospace fastener business which TransDigm subsequently sold to aluminum producer Alcoa for a reported $240 million in 2011.

The company's strategy is well proven given the recent economic downturn and its effect on the aviation market. While other aviation manufacturers have seen drops in revenue or lackluster growth TransDigm has put together solid growth in both revenue (+46%) and net income (+5%).

EXECUTIVES

Executive Vice President, Robert S. Henderson, age 57, $261,250 total compensation
President; Chief Operating Officer of the Company and TransDigm Inc., Raymond F. Laubenthal, age 52, $343,125 total compensation
Executive Vice President, John F. Leary, age 66, $172,125 total compensation
Chief Financial Officer; Executive Vice President; Secretary, Gregory Rufus, age 57, $279,750 total compensation
General Manager CDA Intercorp, Joseph (Joe) Grote
President ADS Transicoil, Jack Planchak
President AeroControlex Group, Roger V. Jones, age 54
EVP Mergers and Acquisitions, Albert J. Rodriguez, age 53, $215,375 total compensation
Executive Vice President, Peter Palmer
President MarathonNorco Aerospace, Jack Stiffler
Executive Vice President, James Skulina
Chief Executive Officer of Satair A, John Staer
Director, Michael S. Graff, age 61
Director, David A. Barr, age 50
Director, Sean P. Hennessy, age 56
Director, Robert J. (Rob) Small, age 47
Auditors: Ernst&YoungLLP

LOCATIONS

HQ: Transdigm Group Inc
1301 East 9th Street, Suite 3000, Cleveland, OH 44114
Phone: 216 706-2960
Web: www.transdigm.com

2010 Sales

	$ mil.	% of total
US	657	79
Other countries	170	21
Total	**827**	**100**

PRODUCTS/OPERATIONS

	% of total
Aftermarket	56
OEM	44
Total	**100**

2011 Sales

	$ mil.	% of total
Mechanical/electromechanical actuators & controls	168	15
Ignition systems & components	153	14
Engineered latching and locking devices	150	12
Specialized valves	102	8
Rods adn locking devices	99	7
AC/DC electric motors & generators	84	7
Specialized pumps	72	6
Power conditioning devices	58	5
Engineered connectors	57	5
NiCad batteries/chargers	57	4
Power lighting and control	55	4
Audio systems	44	4
Lavatory hardware	38	3
Specialized cockpit displays	27	3
Elastomers	24	
Other	10	3
Total	**1,206**	**100**

Primary Operating Units
Acme Aerospace Inc.
Adams Rite Aerospace
Adel Wiggins Group
ADS/Transicoil
AeroControlex Group
Avionic Instruments Inc.
Avtech Corporatio
Bruce Aerospace
CDA InterCorp
CEF Industries
Champion Aerospace
Marathon Norco
Skurka Aerospace Inc.

Selected Customers

Airbus S.A.S.
The Boeing Company
Bombardier Inc.
Cessna Aircraft Company
Embresa Brasileira de Aeronautica S.A. (Embraer)
Gulfstream Aerospace Corporation
Honeywell International Inc.
Lockheed Martin Corporation
Northrop Grumman Corporation
Raytheon Company

COMPETITORS

BAE Systems Inc.	Honeywell
Boeing	International
GE Aviation	Lockheed Martin
Goodrich Corp.	United Technologies

HISTORICAL FINANCIALS

Company Type: Public

Income Statement

FYE: September 30

	REVENUE ($ mil.)	NET INCOME ($ mil.)	NET PROFIT MARGIN	EMPLOYEES
09/13	1,924.4	302.7	15.7%	6,100
09/12	1,700.2	324.9	19.1%	5,400
09/11	1,206.0	172.1	14.3%	3,800
09/10	827.6	163.4	19.7%	2,400
09/09	761.5	162.9	21.4%	2,000
Annual Growth	**26.1%**	**16.8%**	**—**	**32.2%**

2013 Year-End Financials

Debt ratio: 93.2%
Return on equity: 68.6%
Cash ($ mil.): 564
Current ratio: 4.09
Long-term debt ($ mil.): 5,700

No. of shares (mil.): 52
Dividends
  Yield: 25.1%
  Payout: 820.0%
Market value ($ mil.): 7,305

	STOCK PRICE ($) FY Close	P/E High/Low	PER SHARE ($) Earnings	Dividends	Book Value
09/13	138.70	68 53	2.39	34.85	(6.39)
09/12	141.87	24 13	5.97	0.00	23.60
09/11	81.67	30 19	3.17	0.00	16.11
09/10	62.05	25 16	2.52	7.65	12.00
09/09	49.81	14 7	3.23	0.00	16.73
Annual Growth	**29.2%**	**— —**	**(7.3%)**		

TravelZoo Inc

Travelzoo keeps the search for travel deals tame. On its websites users find discount offers promotions and related information provided by more than 2000 travel companies. Airlines car rental companies cruise lines hotels and travel agencies pay Travelzoo to publicize fares and promotions on its eponymous website through its Travelzoo Top 20 newsletter and across its Newsflash e-mail alert service. Travelzoo also operates SuperSearch a pay-per-click search engine specializing in travel content and Fly.com a search engine that compares flight information. The company has operations in North America and Europe. Travelzoo founder Ralph Bartel owns about 66% of the company's shares.

Travelzoo reaches more than 22 million subscribers worldwide and is committed to growing its subscriber base by increasing the number of people who are signed up for its newsletter. The company counts companies such as JetBlue Airways Avis Rent A Car Fairmont Hotels and Resorts and Travelocity among its roster of clients.

In 2010 Travelzoo saw its revenues and income increase as the travel and leisure markets continued to recover. Its revenue grew primarily as a result of receiving more revenue from publications including the Travelzoo website the Travelzoo Top 20 e-mail newsletter the Newsflash e-mail alert service and the Local Deals e-mail alert service as well as an increase in revenues from its Super-Search and Fly.com search products.

Joining the red-hot local services bandwagon in 2010 the company launched Local Deals a service that sends discounts from local businesses to existing subscribers of Travelzoo's e-mail newsletter. With Local Deals the company has branched out from travel-related offerings to include spas and restaurants and competes with the likes of Groupon and Hungry Machine's LivingSocial. The company publishes Local Deals in 30 cities across the US UK and Spain.

All total the company has European operations in four countries: France Germany Spain and the UK. Much of Travelzoo's growth comes from Europe which accounted for more than 20% of revenues in 2010 (up from 15% in 2009) as consumers there have more vacation time than consumers in North America.

Travelzoo had previously expanded with additional international operations in Australia China Hong Kong Japan and Taiwan. However after experiencing losses associated with starting up its Asia/Pacific operations the company in 2009 sold the division to majority shareholder Bartel. It did so in order to focus its efforts on Europe and North America while also enhancing its Fly.com operations. (The company had purchased the Fly.com domain earlier in 2009 for $1.8 million.)

EXECUTIVES

Chairman, Holger Bartel, age 45, $400,000 total compensation
President North America, Shirley Tafoya, age 47, $518,010 total compensation
CEO, Christopher (Chris) Loughlin, age 38, $324,418 total compensation
CFO and Secretary, Wayne Lee, age 40, $240,000 total compensation
CEO Asia Pacific, Jason Yap, age 42
Director Human Resources, Kaity Benedicto
Head Human Resources Europe, Ulrike Geissler
VP Network Entertainment and Destinations for Travelzoo, Melanie Bower
President China, Vivian Hong
Owner, Doug Katz
Associate Director of Marketing, Iain Newbigin
Director of Marketing, Ken Gruber
VP Marketing & Communications, Scott Higley
Chief Financial Officer, Glen Ceremony
President - Products & Emerging Businesses, Simon Talling-Smith
Director, Donovan Neale-May, age 59
Director, Ralph Bartel, age 46
Director, David J. Ehrlich, age 49
Director, Kelly M. Urso, age 46
Independent Director, Donovan May
Auditors: KPMGLLP

LOCATIONS

HQ: Travelzoo Inc.
  590 Madison Ave. 37th Fl., New York NY 10022
Phone: 212-484-4900   **Fax:** 212-484-4944
Web: www.travelzoo.com

2010 Sales

	$ mil.	% of total
North America	87	78
Europe	25	22
Total	**112**	**100**

PRODUCTS/OPERATIONS

Selected Products & Services

Publications
  Travelzoo website
  Travelzoo Top 20 e-mail newsletter
  Newsflash e-mail alert service
  Local Deals e-mail alert service
Search
  SuperSearch
  Fly.com

Selected Clients

ATA
Avis Rent A Car
British Airways
Budget Rent A Car
Caesars Entertainment
Expedia
Fairmont Hotels and Resorts
Interstate Hotels & Resorts
JetBlue Airways
Kimpton Hotels
Liberty Travel
Lufthansa
Marriott Hotels
Royal Caribbean
Spirit Airlines
Starwood Hotels & Resorts Worldwide
Vanguard Rent-A-Car

COMPETITORS

AOL	LivingSocial
Expedia	MSN
Google	Orbitz Worldwide
Groupon	Travelocity
Hotels.com	TripAdvisor

Hotwire Inc.
Kayak Software

Yahoo!
priceline.com

HISTORICAL FINANCIALS

Company Type: Public

Income Statement

FYE: December 31

	REVENUE ($ mil.)	NET INCOME ($ mil.)	NET PROFIT MARGIN	EMPLOYEES
12/12	151.1	18.2	12.0%	417
12/11	148.3	3.3	2.2%	350
12/10	112.7	13.1	11.7%	255
12/09	93.9	5.1	5.5%	193
12/08	81.4	(4.1)	—	214
Annual Growth	16.7%	—	—	18.1%

2012 Year-End Financials

Debt ratio: —
Return on equity: 46.4%
Cash ($ mil.): 61
Current ratio: 1.98
Long-term debt ($ mil.): —

No. of shares (mil.): 15
Dividends
Yield: —
Payout: —
Market value ($ mil.): 292

	STOCK PRICE ($) FY Close	P/E High/Low	PER SHARE ($) Earnings	Dividends	Book Value
12/12	18.99	27 15	1.14	0.00	2.82
12/11	24.58	505 105	0.20	0.00	2.18
12/10	41.38	56 13	0.80	0.00	2.79
12/09	12.29	48 12	0.32	0.00	1.87
12/08	5.56	— —	(0.29)	0.00	1.45
Annual Growth	35.9%	— —	—	—	18.0%

TreeHouse Foods Inc

This TreeHouse is stocked. A manufacturer TreeHouse Foods is the nation's #1 producer of non-dairy powdered creamer sold under the Cremora brand and pickles (Farman's Nalley's Peter Piper and Steinfeld). The company also makes and private-label soups salad dressings and Mexican sauces drink mixes hot cereals macaroni and cheese skillet dinners and jams. TreeHouse makes private label products for food service distributors and restaurant chains and retailers such as supermarkets and mass merchandisers —the company's largest market that also buys its own brands. TreeHouse has some co-pack business and industrial customers. Founded in 2005 TreeHouse Foods has branched out through acquisitions.

Geographic Reach

TreeHouse Foods rings up more than 85% of its sales in the US and Canada. Exports account for the rest.

Operations

TreeHouse Foods' wholly-owned subsidiary Bay Valley Foods LLC is a leading supplier of private-label foods to grocery stores and food service operators. In turn Bay Valley operates several of its own subsidiaries: ST Specialty Foods (acquired in 2010) a maker of rice and pasta dishes as well as add-meat skillet dinners and potato side dishes; Sturm Foods (also acquired in 2010) a manufacturer of hot cereals and powdered drink mixes; and jam-and-spread-maker E.D. Smith.

Sales and Marketing

Retail-giant Wal-Mart Stores in TreeHouse Foods' largest customer accounting for more than 20% of its annual sales in 2012.

Financial Performance

TreeHouse Foods' sales climbed more than 6% in 2012 vs. the prior year while net income fell by 6% over the same period. 2012 marked the fourth consecutive year of rising sales for the company. However profits have been harder to come since 2009. The uptick in sales in 2012 was driven by the acquisition of Naturally Fresh in April and price increases (to offset higher costs). Net income came under pressure from higher operating and input costs accelerated depreciation associated with restructurings and a shift in the mix of products sold.

Strategy

With its profits under pressure the company is restructuring to reduce manufacturing costs. In 2012 TreeHouse Foods announced plans to close in soup plant in Illinois and transfer production to another plant in Pennsylvania. The company also closed a salad dressing plant in Ontario Canada and transferred production to facilities with lower production costs. TreeHouse is also looking to higher margin businesses. To that end in fall 2012 it launched a single-serve roast coffee product line and is working to increase its distribution points and product offerings. The rollout of the single-serve hot beverage line is expected to increase throughout 2013.

TreeHouse has grown by strengthening ties with retail grocers who are demanding private label food products as cash-strapped consumers seek goods with equivalent quality at a lower price. Well-positioned the company's largest customer is Wal-Mart. To maintain momentum the food maker focuses on the most-purchased categories of private label products typically canned soup salad dressings powdered creamer and pickles. Acquisitions have enabled TreeHouse to expand its production capacity and breadth of food products capturing an ever greater amount of retail shelf space.

Mergers and Acquisitions

In April 2012 the company acquired Naturally Fresh a privately owned maker of refrigerated dressings sauces dips and marinades. The $25 million deal is poised to take TreeHouse from the shelf-stable grocery aisle to the refrigerated produce section providing a premium presence. Later in the year TreeHouse acquired the Aseptic Cheese and Pudding business of the Minnesota-based diary cooperative Associated Milk Producers Inc. thereby strengthening Bay Valley's market-leading position in the two product categories.

The 2012 purchases follow two significant deals completed in 2010. TreeHouse acquired Sturm Foods a maker of private-label hot cereal and powdered soft drink mixes from HM Capital Partners for $660 million. The move strengthened TreeHouse's private-label operations as well as its packaging mixing and flavoring capabilities. Extending its reach in shelf-stable foods TreeHouse bought out S.T. Specialty Foods from Windjammer Capital Investors in an all-cash deal valued at about $180 million. S.T. Specialty Foods primarily makes private-label macaroni and cheese and skillet dinners mainstream staples of the dine-at-home consumer.

Ownership

T. Rowe Price Associates owns more than 13% of TreeHouse Foods' shares.

HISTORY

Dean Foods combined the businesses of its specialty foods group and its foodservice salad-dress-

ing business in 2005 in order to create publicly traded TreeHouse Foods.

In 2006 the company it purchased pickle-maker Oxford Foods. It paid $275 million for the private-label soup and baby food (Nature's Goodness) businesses of Del Monte Foods. The following year it acquired San Antonio Farms a private-label Mexican sauce maker for about $89 million in cash. That year it also purchased DeGraffenreid a processor and distributor of pickles and related products for the foodservice industry from Bell-Carter Foods for $10.8 million. Strengthening its Canadian footprint in 2007 the company acquired Ontario-based E.D. Smith & Sons a manufacturer of branded sauces jellies jams and pie fillings for $220 million in cash plus the assumption of $100 million in debt.

In November 2012 TreeHouse Foods acquired the assets of the Aseptic Cheese and Pudding business from Associated Milk Producers Inc. The business sells products to foodservice and retail customers and strengthens the TreeHouse's existing Bay Valley Foods aseptic operation.

EXECUTIVES

Chairman President and CEO, Sam K. Reed, age 66, $856,167 total compensation
SVP Human Resources; Chief Administrative Officer Bay Valley Foods, Alan T. Gambrel, age 59
EVP and CFO, Dennis F. Riordan, age 55, $571,667 total compensation
EVP General Counsel and Chief Administrative Officer, Thomas E. O'Neill, age 58, $400,583 compensation
EVP Acquisitions Integration, Harry J. Walsh, age 57, $400,583 total compensation
SVP Supply Chain, Danny J. (Joe) Coning, age 64
SVP Corporate Development, Erik T. Kahler, age 48
SVP Strategy, Sharon M. Flanagan, age 48
EVP; President Bay Valley Foods, Christopher D. Sliva, age 51
CIO, Robert Hanlon
Director, Diana S. Ferguson, age 49
Director, Frank J. O'Connell, age 69
Director, Terdema L. Ussery II, age 54
Director, George V. Bayly, age 70
Director, Gary D. Smith, age 70
Director, Ann M. Sardini, age 62
Director, Dennis F. O'Brien, age 56
Director, David B. Vermylen, age 62
Auditors: Deloitte&ToucheLLP

LOCATIONS

HQ: TreeHouse Foods Inc.
2021 Spring Rd. Ste. 600, Oak Brook IL 60523
Phone: 708-483-1300   **Fax:** 708-409-1062
Web: www.treehousefoods.com

2012 Sales

	% of total
North	87
Outside North	13
Total	**100**

PRODUCTS/OPERATIONS

2012 Sales

	$ mil.	% of total
North American Retail Grocery	1,568	72
Food Away From Home	338	15
Industrial & Export	275	13
Total	**2,182**	**100**

2012 Sales

	$ mil.	% of total
Non-dairy powdered creamer	362	16

Pickles	308	14
Salad dressings	284	13
Soup & infant feeding	281	13
Powdered drinks	234	11
Mexican and other sauces	232	11
Hot cereals	163	7
Dry dinners	126	6
Aseptic products	91	4
Jams	61	3
Other products	36	2
Total	**2,182**	**100**

Selected Products and Brands

Food Away From Home (foodservice)
 Saucemaker
 Schwartz
Jams and jellies
 E.D. Smith
 Habitant
Liquid egg substitute
 Second Nature
Non-dairy creamer
 Cremora
Pickles
 Farman' s
 Nalley' s
 Peter Piper
 Steinfeld
Refrigerated
 Mocha Mix
Salad dressings sauces and marinades
 Private label
Sauces and syrups
 Bennett' s
 Hoffman House
 Roddenberry' s Northwoods
 San Antonio Farms
Soups broths and gravies
 Private label

COMPETITORS

Annie' s Inc.	Lancaster Colony
B&G Foods	Marzetti
Baldwin Richardson Foods	McCormick & Company
Beech-Nut	Mondelez International
Campbell Soup	Monterey Gourmet Foods
ConAgra	Nestle USA
Del Monte Foods	Newman' s Own
Gerber Products	Pinnacle Foods
Goya	Ralcorp
Hain Celestial	Reser' s Fine Foods
Heinz	Rich Products
Kraft Foods Group Inc.	Smucker

HISTORICAL FINANCIALS

Company Type: Public

Income Statement

FYE: December 31

	REVENUE ($ mil.)	NET INCOME ($ mil.)	NET PROFIT MARGIN	EMPLOYEES
12/12	2,182.1	88.3	4.0%	4,300
12/11	2,049.9	94.4	4.6%	3,900
12/10	1,817.0	90.9	5.0%	4,000
12/09	1,511.6	81.3	5.4%	3,100
12/08	1,500.6	28.2	1.9%	3,300
Annual Growth	**9.8%**	**33.0%**	**—**	**6.8%**

2012 Year-End Financials

Debt ratio: 35.6%	No. of shares (mil.): 36
Return on equity: 7.8%	Dividends
Cash ($ mil.): 94	Yield: —
Current ratio: 3.15	Payout: —
Long-term debt ($ mil.): 898	Market value ($ mil.): 1,887

	STOCK PRICE ($) FY Close	P/E High/Low		PER SHARE ($) Earnings	Dividends	Book Value
12/12	52.13	27	20	2.38	0.00	32.58
12/11	65.38	25	18	2.56	0.00	29.89
12/10	51.09	20	14	2.51	0.00	27.60
12/09	38.86	16	10	2.48	0.00	23.63
12/08	27.24	35	22	0.90	0.00	19.66
Annual Growth	**17.6%**	**—**	**—**	**27.5%**	**—**	**13.5%**

Triangle Capital Corp

Triangle Capital lends to companies but they must be of a certain shape and size. An internally managed business-development company Triangle provides loans to and invests in lower-middle-market US companies with annual revenues of $20 million-$100 million. The company which likes to partner with its portfolio companies' management prefers to invest in established businesses with stable financial histories. Triangle most often invests in senior and subordinated debt securities and usually takes a equity interest; it contributes between $5 million and $15 million per transaction. The company's portfolio includes some 50 manufacturers business services food services and other types of enterprises.

Its portfolio comprises a diverse spread of businesses ranging from Ann's House of Nuts to Great Expressions Dental Center. Many of its investments are in companies that manufacture food products or equipment chemicals industrial goods or textiles.

The company targets lower-midsized companies because it believes such businesses are underserved by the business lending industry (which generally tends to lend capital to larger commercial enterprises). Formed in 2006 Triangle Capital has grown over the years by serving smaller midsized enterprises.

Triangle Capital's investment activity reached record levels in 2010. The company funded more than $170 million in investments that year (compared to about $49 million the year before). Its number of portfolio companies also increased by about 30% in 2010. As the economy slowly recovers Triangle is looking to make more investments in new and existing portfolio companies.

EXECUTIVES

CFO Secretary Treasurer and Director, Steven C. Lilly, age 42
Chairman President and CEO, Garland S. Tucker III, age 64
Chief Investment Officer and Director, Brent P.W. Burgess, age 46
VP and Principal Accounting Officer, C. Robert Knox Jr.
VP, James J. Burke
VP Investor Relations, Sheri B. Colquitt
VP, Matthew A Young
Director, Simon B. Rich, age 68
CFO Secretary Treasurer and Director, Steven C. Lilly, age 42
Director, W. McComb Dunwoody, age 67
Director, Mark M. Gambill, age 62
Director, Sherwood H. Smith Jr., age 77

Chief Investment Officer and Director, Brent P.W. Burgess, age 46
Director, Benjamin S. Goldstein, age 56
Auditors: Ernst&YoungLLP

LOCATIONS

HQ: Triangle Capital Corp
 3700 Glenwood Avenue, Suite 530, Raleigh, NC 27612
Phone: 919 719-4770
Web: www.tcap.com

PRODUCTS/OPERATIONS

2010 Sales

	$ mil.	% of total
$ in mil. % of total		
Loan interest fee & dividend income	29	83
Total	**6**	**17**
Interest income from cash & cash equivalent investments	0	-
Total	**36**	**100**

Selected Portfolio Companies

Ambient Air Corporation
American De-Rosa Lamparts & Hallmark Lighting LLC
Ann's House of Nuts Inc
AP Services
Art Headquarters Inc.
Botanical Laboratories
Brantley Transportation
Carolina Beer and Beverage
CRS Reprocessing Services
CV Holdings LLC
Cyrus Networks LLC
Dyson Corporation
Emerald Waste Services
Energy Solutions
Equisales LLC
ESP
Fire Sprinkler Systems
Fischbein LLC
Flint Acquisition
Garden Fresh Restaurant Corp.
Genapure (QC Labs)
Gerli & Company
Great Expressions Dental Center
Hatch
An Industrial Distributor
Inland Pipe Rehabilitation
Jenkins Restorations
Library Systems & Services
Media Temple
Minco Technology Labs
Syrgis Holdings Inc.
TrustHouse Services Group
Tulsa Inspection Resources
Twin Star International
Wholesale Floors Inc.
Yellowstone Landscape Group
Zoom Systems

COMPETITORS

American Capital	Gladstone Capital
Ares Management	MCG Capital
Fifth Street Finance	MVC Capital
Full Circle Capital	Solar Capital

HISTORICAL FINANCIALS

Company Type: Public

Income Statement

FYE: December 31

	ASSETS ($ mil.)	NET INCOME ($ mil.)	INCOME AS % OF ASSETS	EMPLOYEES
12/12	794.5	57.6	7.3%	22
12/11	583.1	40.3	6.9%	19
12/10	388.0	20.1	5.2%	17
12/09	261.0	14.0	5.4%	14
12/08	213.6	10.6	5.0%	14
Annual Growth	**38.9%**	**52.6%**	**—**	**12.0%**

STOCK PRICE ($)	P/E		PER SHARE ($)		
FY Close	High/Low		Earnings	Dividends	Book Value
12/12 25.49	12	9	2.16	2.02	15.30
12/11 19.12	10	7	2.06	1.77	14.68
12/10 19.00	13	7	1.58	1.65	12.09
12/09 12.09	8	3	1.63	1.67	11.03
12/08 10.20	9	6	1.54	1.44	13.22
Annual Growth 25.7%	—	—	8.8%	8.8%	3.7%

Trimble Navigation Ltd.

Those who fear not knowing their place in the world should Trimble. Trimble Navigation makes systems and software that combines global positioning technology with wireless communications to provide location and position data and make it actionable. Using GPS laser optical and other technologies the company's products target areas such as surveying construction site project management mapping mobile personnel management and mobile and fixed asset management. They are offered to end users such as government entities farmers engineering firms and public safety workers as well as equipment manufacturers (OEMs). More than half of sales are made outside the US.

HISTORY

Charles Trimble founded Trimble Navigation in 1978 to design navigation products for recreational boating. In 1982 the company began developing devices using the Global Positioning System (GPS) satellite network; in 1984 Trimble introduced its first GPS product. The company went public in 1990 10 days before Saddam Hussein invaded Kuwait. Trimble gained worldwide recognition when allied troops used its GPS devices during the Persian Gulf War.

The war left Trimble expanding too quickly and overproducing. In 1992 Trimble rebounded after reorganizing to focus on nonmilitary products. Two years later it introduced a low-cost handheld unit that helped with utilities fieldwork. In 1998 Trimble ceased manufacturing products for general aviation and allied with Siemens to develop GPS products. That year Charles Trimble was named vice chairman after he stepped down as the company's CEO. The company in 1998 also launched a cost reduction plan that cut its workforce by 8%.

The next year Trimble sold its Sunnyvale California manufacturing operations to contract manufacturer Solectron which agreed to make Trimble's GPS and radio-frequency products for three years. Also in 1999 Steven Berglund a former president of a Spectra-Physics subsidiary was named CEO of Trimble.

In 2000 Trimble acquired the Spectra Precision businesses of Thermo Electron (which later became Thermo Fisher Scientific) for about $294 million. That year the US government stopped scrambling GPS signals opening the door for more precise devices. In 2001 the company formed a subsidiary Trimble Information Services to expand the company's wireless location-based services including fleet management.

The next year Trimble and Caterpillar formed a joint venture Caterpillar Trimble Control Technolo-

gies to develop advanced electronic guidance and control technologies for earth-moving construction and mining machines.

The company acquired Eleven Technology a mobile application software developer focused on the consumer packaged goods market in 2006. The company also expanded its laser scanning business by acquiring the assets —including software for engineering and construction plant design —of BitWyse Solutions. Later in 2006 it purchased Visual Statement a developer of crime and collision incident investigation software and XYZ Solutions a 3-D intelligence software provider. It also acquired Meridian Systems a provider of enterprise project management and lifecycle software. Still later in 2006 Trimble bought Spacient Technologies a privately held provider of field service management and mobile mapping software used by municipalities and utilities.

Trimble's buying spree continued in 2007 when it purchased @Road a developer of mobile resource management systems for about $493 million.

The company expanded its ability to serve the farming industry when it acquired NTech Industries in 2009. NTech developed optical crop-sensing technology that helps farmers reduce costs by managing the application of nitrogen herbicides and other crop inputs. Also that year Trimble purchased Accutest Engineering Solutions a UK-based maker of mobile resource management applications for trucking fleets.

In 2010 Trimble acquired Punch Telematix from majority shareholder Punch International for nearly ?14 million ($18 million) in cash and rebranded it as Trimble Transport and Logistics. Punch Telematix made onboard computers for trucks. That year the company also bought Thing-Magic a developer of radio frequency identification (RFID) products and RFID integration services for commercial clients in the construction and transportation industries and Cengea a provider of operations and supply chain management software for the forestry agriculture and natural resource industries.

Additionally Trimble bought Mumbai-based Tata AutoComp Mobility Telematics (TMT) in a move to expand its mobile resource management services business in India. TMT provided vehicle tracking and other telematics services to such customers as Bharat Petroleum and Tata Motors. Also that year expanding its engineering and construction portfolio for electrical and mechanical contractors Trimble bought the assets of Accubid a provider of estimating project management and service management software.

Trimble bought 3D modeling software maker Tekla in 2011 in a deal valued at nearly ?340 million ($485 million) to better equip building contractors and engineers to manage construction projects. The follow-up investment came in 2012 when Trimble completed the acquisition of the StruCad and StruEngineer business from AceCad Software. StruCad offers 3D structural detailing while StruEngineer provides engineering companies with 3D steelwork modeling and construction management.

The company acquired a line of software products in 2011 from Norway-based Mesta Entrepren?r a subsidiary of road and highway construction contractor Mesta Konsern. The deal added office and field data collection applications and improved the company's ability to provide customized systems to construction clients particularly in the area of managing local application requirements compliance. Also in 2011 Trimble strengthened its portfolio and Asia presence with the pur-

chase of China-based Yamei Electronics a manufacturer of electronic automotive products including anti-theft GPS monitoring and tracking systems RFID smart keys and diagnostics systems.

Also that year Trimble acquired the OmniSTAR satellite system assets of Dutch geological engineering company Fugro. The company was interested in OmniSTAR's GPS signal correction technology (used to improve the accuracy of satellite navigation devices) which it is using to expand the functionality of its mapping systems for agricultural and construction purposes among others. It also acquired France-based Ashtech to expand Garmin's selection of survey products including the flagship application Spectra Precision for construction clients. Ashtech became part of Trimble's engineering and construction division.

EXECUTIVES

VP Strategic Policy, Ann Ciganer
Vice President Executive Committee Member, Dennis L. Workman, age 68, $232,885 total compensation
Vice Chairman, Nickolas W. Vande Steeg, age 70
President CEO and Director, Steven W. Berglund, age 61, $618,000 total compensation
VP Advanced Technology and Systems, Bruce E. Peetz, age 60
Chairman, Ulf J. Johansson, age 68
VP Heavy Civil Construction Division, Joseph S. Denniston Jr., age 51, $229,932 total compensation
CFO, Francois Delepine, age 51
VP Heavy and Highway Construction Division, Bryn A. Fosburgh, age 51, $256,529 total compensation
VP and General Counsel, James A. Kirkland, age 53
VP Agriculture Forestry Water and Energy Utilities and Public Safety, Mark A. Harrington, age 58, $297,400 total compensation
CFO, Rajat Bahri, age 48, $297,400 total compensation
VP Strategy and Business Development, Jurgen Kliem, age 55
VP Finance and Principal Accounting Officer, Julie Shepard, age 55
VP Mobile Solutions Data Services and Hosting Global Services, James M. Veneziano
VP Transportation & Logistics Division, Ron Konezny
VP Human Resources, Mary Kay Strangis
VP Survey Geospatial Geographic Information System (GIS) Infrastructure Rail Land Administration and Environmental Solutions, Christopher W. Gibson, age 52
VP OEM Solutions & Mining, Christopher J. Shephard
Vice President Technology Innovation, Doug Brent
VP Operations and CIO, Leah K. Lambertson
Vice President Software Architecture and Strategy, Prakash Iyer
Vice President, Roz D. Buick
VP Geospatial Division, Erik J. Arvesen
Independent Vice Chairman of the Board, Nickolas Steeg
Vice Chairman, Nickolas W. Vande Steeg, age 70
President CEO and Director, Steven W. Berglund, age 61
Director, Bradford W. Parkinson, age 78
Director, John B. Goodrich, age 71
Director, William Hart, age 72
Director, Mark S. Peek, age 55
Director, Merit E. Janow, age 54
Director, Ron Nersesian, age 53
Director, Mark S. Peek, age 54
Independent Director, Ronald Nersesian
Auditors: Ernst&YoungLLP

LOCATIONS

HQ: Trimble Navigation Ltd.
935 Stewart Drive, Sunnyvale, CA 94085
Phone: 408 481-8000   **Fax:** 408 481-2218
Web: www.trimble.com

2012 Sales

	$ mil.	% of total
US	962	47
Europe	456	22
Asia/Pacific	320	16
Other	300	15
Total	**2,040**	**100**

PRODUCTS/OPERATIONS

2012 Sales

	$ mil.	% of total
Engineering & construction	1,089	53
Field solutions	482	24
Mobile solutions	348	17
Advanced devices	120	6
Total	**2,040**	**100**

Selected Products

Engineering and Construction
Global positioning system (GPS) data collection
systems (GPS Total Station)
Grade control systems (SiteVision)
Laser transmitters (Spectra)
Optical surveying equipment
Field Solutions
Agricultural information systems
Automatic tractor steering systems (AgGPS Autopilot)
Farm equipment guidance systems
Laser-based water management systems
Mapping equipment (AgGPS 132)
Geographical information systems
GPS data collection and maintenance systems
(GeoExplorer)
Mobile Solutions
Fleet management system hardware software and
service (Telvisant)
GPS vehicle module (CrossCheck)
Advanced Devices
GPS chipsets for mobile communication and
computing (FirstGPS)
GPS clocks (Thunderbolt)
GPS receiver cards/modules for military applications
(Force 5)
GPS receivers for battery powered applications (Lassen
LP)
Handheld GPS survey data collectors (Tripod Data
Systems Ranger)

COMPETITORS

AirIQ	Navico
Deere	NovAtel
Garmin	Novariant
Hemisphere GPS	QUALCOMM
Hexagon AB	Raven Industries
L-3 Communications	Raytheon
Leica Geosystems	Rockwell Collins
MacDonald Dettwiler	TOPCON
MiTAC	Thales
Minorplanet	TomTom
Motorola Solutions	XRS

HISTORICAL FINANCIALS

Company Type: Public

Income Statement

FYE: December 28

	REVENUE ($ mil.)	NET INCOME ($ mil.)	NET PROFIT MARGIN	EMPLOYEES
12/12	2,040.1	191.0	9.4%	6,561
12/11	1,644.0	150.7	9.2%	5,301
12/10*	1,293.9	103.6	8.0%	4,166
01/10	1,126.2	63.4	5.6%	3,794
01/09	1,329.2	141.4	10.6%	3,940
Annual Growth	**11.3%**	**7.8%**	**—**	**13.6%**

*Fiscal year change

2012 Year-End Financials

Debt ratio: 26.2%
Return on equity: 11.0%
Cash ($ mil.): 157
Current ratio: 1.74
Long-term debt ($ mil.): 873

No. of shares (mil.): 254
Dividends
  Yield: —
  Payout: —
Market value ($ mil.): 14,913

	STOCK PRICE ($) FY Close	P/E High/Low	Earnings	Dividends	Book Value
12/12	58.60	79 53	0.75	0.00	7.46
12/11	43.40	84 53	0.60	0.00	6.35
12/10*	39.93	97 53	0.42	0.00	5.65
01/10	25.20	98 46	0.26	0.00	5.23
01/09	22.30	69 27	0.57	0.00	4.79
Annual Growth	**27.3%**	**— —**	**6.9%**	**—**	**11.7%**

*Fiscal year change

Two Harbors Investment Corp

Two Harbors Investment Corp. is ready to double its money. The real estate investment trust (REIT) is managed and advised by (and was founded by) PRCM Advisers a subsidiary of Pine River Capital Management. The trust primarily invests in agency residential mortgage-backed securities (RMBS) with fixed or adjustable interest rates that are backed by government-supported enterprises Fannie Mae Freddie Mac or Ginnie Mae. About a quarter of its mortgage portfolio is made up of non-agency RMBS such as subprime mortgages which carry more risk than federally-backed securities but offer higher yields. Chairman (and Pine River CEO) Brian Taylor controls almost 20% of the trust's stock.

Pine River Capital Management set up Two Harbors in 2009 through a reverse merger with a blank-check company named Capitol Acquisition Corp. Since then the company has completed three follow-on public offerings that netted more than $520 million which it has used to invest in agency and non-agency RMBS and other financial assets. Two Harbors plans to continue to maintain its portfolio of agency RMBS sprinkled with riskier investments to boost yield.

EXECUTIVES

Vice Chairman, Mark D. Ein, age 48
Chairman, Brian C. Taylor, age 49
Chief Financial Officer Treasurer, Steven (Steve) Kuhn, age 44
Co-Chief Investment Officer, William (Bill) Roth, age 56
General Counsel and Secretary, Timothy (Tim) O?Brien, age 54
Controller, Brad Farrell
VP Business Development, Andrew Garcia
Investor Relations, Anh Huynh
Managing Director, Paul Richardson
General Counsel; Secretary, Timothy OBrien
Director, Stephen G. Kasnet, age 67
Director, Peter S. Niculescu, age 54
Vice Chairman, Mark D. Ein, age 48
Director, W. Reid Sanders, age 64
Director, William W. Johnson, age 51
Auditors: Ernst&YoungLLP

LOCATIONS

HQ: Two Harbors Investment Corp.
601 Carlson Pkwy. Ste. 330, Minnetonka MN 55305
Phone: 612-238-3300   **Fax:** 612-238-3301
Web: www.twoharborsinvestment.com

COMPETITORS

American Capital Agency Corp.	MFA Financial
Annaly Capital Management	New York Mortgage Trust
Capstead Mortgage	Newcastle Investment
Chimera	Putnam Mortgage
Gramercy	Redwood Trust
Invesco Mortgage Capital	iStar Financial Inc

HISTORICAL FINANCIALS

Company Type: Public

Income Statement

FYE: December 31

	REVENUE ($ mil.)	NET INCOME ($ mil.)	NET PROFIT MARGIN	EMPLOYEES
12/12	296.0	291.9	98.6%	0
12/11	150.3	127.4	84.8%	0
12/10	42.6	35.7	83.9%	0
12/09	3.4	(8.7)	—	0
12/08	4.4	2.2	51.7%	0
Annual Growth	**185.7%**	**235.8%**	**—**	**—**

2012 Year-End Financials

Debt ratio: —
Return on equity: 12.3%
Cash ($ mil.): 1,123
Current ratio: 0.21
Long-term debt ($ mil.): —

No. of shares (mil.): 298
Dividends
  Yield: 16.5%
  Payout: 153.0%
Market value ($ mil.): 3,311

	STOCK PRICE ($) FY Close	P/E High/Low	Earnings	Dividends	Book Value
12/12	11.08	10 7	1.20	1.71	11.55
12/11	9.24	9 6	1.29	1.60	9.03
12/10	9.79	6 5	1.60	1.48	9.44
12/09	9.80	— —	(0.39)	0.26	9.10
12/08	9.10	118 108	0.08	0.00	7.98
Annual Growth	**5.0%**	**— —**	**96.8%**	**—**	**9.7%**

Tyler Technologies, Inc.

Tyler Technologies doesn't want local governments tied up in red tape. The company provides software and services intended to help state and local government offices operate more efficiently. Specializing in applications for local governments and public schools Tyler's products include software for accounting and financial management filing court documents electronically tracking and managing court cases and automating appraisals and assessments. Other products include applications that allow citizens to access utility accounts or pay traffic fines online. Tyler complements its software with hosting support and maintenance services. It has customers in all 50 states Canada the Caribbean and the UK.

Operations

The company divides its operations into two segments —enterprise software and appraisal and tax software. Enterprise software which accounts for 87% of sales provides local governments and schools with software and services for back-office functions such as financial management and courts and justice processes. Appraisal and tax software which makes up the other 13% of sales is used by local governments and taxing authorities to automate property appraisal and assessment including physical inspection data collection property valuation preparing tax rolls and arbitration.

Geographic Reach

Tyler Technologies operates from about two dozen offices in the US and one in Canada.

Sales and Marketing

The company uses a direct sales force. It's also active in government associations and participates in annual meetings trade shows and educational events to attract new customers.

Financial Performance

In recent years the company has increasingly relied on long-term service contracts with customers for revenue. These recurring revenues —primarily related to maintenance and support and subscription-based services —account for 70% of total sales and have very low customer turnover.

Subscription revenues increased 43% in 2012 over 2011 and were the biggest driver behind Tyler's 17% sales growth with revenues of $363 million. That year it added 76 new customers and 68 existing customers transitioned to a hosted product. The company continued to report solid profits on the higher sales even as expenses continue to rise.

Strategy

In addition to acquisitions the company expands its software product line with new offerings and product upgrades including the Odyssey judicial case management system and public-use Internet portals that enable users to pay property taxes utility bills and complete other transactions electronically. The company is also looking to grow by selling new products and services to its existing customer base expanding its market focus to include larger customers and entering new geographic regions.

Mergers and Acquisitions

Having seen its revenue increase in recent years the company continues to invest in acquisitions and research and development efforts. Acquisitions in particular add new customers across product lines as the company rebrands and integrates acquired product offerings fairly quickly under the Tyler name.

In 2012 the company made four acquisitions beginning with Toronto-based partner Akanda Innovation a specialist in geographic information system (GIS) applications. The two companies began working together in 1997 when Tyler tapped Akanda to develop complementary applications for its iasWorld tax and appraisal software product. Next it bought UniFund for $4.6 million to enhance its Infinite Visions school enterprise product. Then it paid $9.4 million for Computer Software Associates a financial management systems provider that resells Tyler's Infinite Visions software to schools. Finally it bought EnerGov Solutions for $10.5 million. EnerGov provides land management software to government agencies.

Company Background

Formerly an auto parts and supplies company established in 1966 Tyler sold its chain of auto parts stores in 1999 and used acquisitions to transform itself into a provider of software for the local government and education markets.

EXECUTIVES

EVP CFO and Treasurer, Brian K. Miller, age 54, $257,500 total compensation
Chairman, John M. Yeaman, age 72, $312,500 total compensation
VP and CTO, Rick L. Hoff
President CEO and Director, John S. Marr Jr., age 54, $407,000 total compensation
EVP General Counsel and Secretary, H. Lynn Moore Jr., age 45, $257,500 total compensation
Controller, Terri L. Alford
EVP, Dustin R. Womble, age 54, $343,000 total compensation
President EDEN Systems, Jeff Green
President ERP and School Division, Richard E. Peterson Jr., age 63
President Local Government Division, Brett Cate
VP Finance and Chief Accounting Officer, W. Michael Smith
VP and CIO, Matthew (Matt) Bieri
VP and Chief Marketing Officer, Samantha Crosby
VP Human Resources, Robert Sansone
President Courts and Justice Division, Bruce Graham
President Appraisal and Tax Division, Andrew D. Teed
President CLT Appraisal Services, David J. Johnson
President School Division, Christopher P. (Chris) Hepburn
operations Manager that the perfect job for me, Genie Flynn
Director, G. Stuart Reeves, age 73
President CEO and Director, John S. Marr Jr., age 53
Director, Michael D. Richards, age 62
EVP and Director; CEO Courts and Justice and INCODE Divisions, Dustin R. Womble, age 53
Director, Donald R. Brattain, age 72
Director, J. Luther King Jr., age 73
Auditors: Ernst&YoungLLP

LOCATIONS

HQ: Tyler Technologies Inc.
5949 Sherry Ln. Ste. 1400, Dallas TX 75225
Phone: 972-713-3700   **Fax:** 972-713-3741
Web: www.tylertech.com
Mergers and Acquisitio
FY2012
Akanda Innovation (geographic information system software)
Computer Software Associates (financial management systems)
EnerGov Solutions (land management software)
UniFund (enterprise resource planning)
FY2011
Windsor Management Group (education software)
Yotta MVS (field property data verification and collection software)
FY2010
Cole-Layer-Trumble (government appraisal software)
Wiznet (electronic document filing software)
FY2009
PulseMark (data warehousing software)

PRODUCTS/OPERATIONS

2012 Sales

	% of total
Enterprise	87
Appraisal & tax	13
Total	**100**

2012 Sales

	% of total
Maintenance	47
Software	23
Subscriptions	12
Software	9
Appraisal	6
Hardware &	3
Total	**100**

Selected Products

Appraisal and assessment software (property appraisal and assessment)
Criminal justice software (court case tracking and management)
Document management and recording software (image storage and retrieval)
Education software
Finance and accounting software
Law enforcement and corrections software (police dispatch records and jail management)
Municipal court software (case management)
Odyssey (case and court management)
Public Records and content management
Tax collections software (tax collections office operations)
Utility billing software (billing and collections)

Selected Services

Information technology and professional services
Maintenance
Outsourced property appraisals for tax jurisdictions

COMPETITORS

Affiliated Computer Services	Manatron
CACI International	Official Payments Holdings
Constellation Software	Oracle
DynTek	SAP
HP Enterprise Services	SunGard
IBM	USTI
Lawson Software	Xerox
MAXIMUS	

HISTORICAL FINANCIALS

Company Type: Public

Income Statement

FYE: December 31

	REVENUE ($ mil.)	NET INCOME ($ mil.)	NET PROFIT MARGIN	EMPLOYEES
12/12	363.3	32.9	9.1%	2,388
12/11	309.3	27.5	8.9%	2,091
12/10	288.6	25.0	8.7%	2,054
12/09	290.2	27.0	9.3%	2,018
12/08	265.1	14.8	5.6%	1,940
Annual Growth	**8.2%**	**22.1%**	**—**	**5.3%**

2012 Year-End Financials

Debt ratio: 5.3%
Return on equity: —
Cash ($ mil.): 6
Current ratio: 0.72
Long-term debt ($ mil.): 18

No. of shares (mil.): 31
Dividends
  Yield: —
  Payout: —
Market value ($ mil.): 1,518

	STOCK PRICE ($) FY Close	P/E High/Low	Earnings	PER SHARE ($) Dividends	Book Value
12/12	48.44	45 28	1.00	0.00	4.64
12/11	30.11	37 23	0.83	0.00	2.61
12/10	20.76	30 20	0.71	0.00	3.31
12/09	19.91	27 15	0.74	0.00	3.83
12/08	11.98	44 28	0.38	0.00	3.19
Annual Growth	**41.8%**	**— —**	**27.4%**	**—**	**9.8%**

U.S. Physical Therapy, Inc.

U.S. Physical Therapy (USPh) through its subsidiaries lends a hand to injured workers athletes and others in need of some TLC. With almost 420 outpatient clinics in more than 40 states USPh provides physical therapy services for work-related and sports injuries trauma orthopedic conditions osteoarthritis treatment and post-surgical rehabilitation. The clinics operate under a number of local or regional brands including Red River Valley Physical Therapy Pioneer Physical Therapy Bluegrass Physical Therapy and Apex Rehabilitation Center.

Geographic Reach

States where USPh has a significant presence include Arizona Florida Georgia Indiana Maryland Michigan New Jersey Oklahoma Tennessee Texas Virginia Washington and Wisconsin.

Operations

Most of USPh's clinics are joint ventures in which the company owns a majority stake and the licensed therapists/clinic managers own a minority stake. Other facilities are wholly owned by the company but are operated through profit-sharing agreements with physical therapists. The company also manages a handful of physician-owned and hospital-owned clinics on a contract basis.

USPh relies on its therapist-managers to maintain relationships with local physicians who refer patients to the clinics. Services are paid for by commercial health insurance managed care programs Medicare workers' compensation insurance or proceeds from personal injury cases.

Financial Analysis

Revenues for USPh have continued to increase over the years as the company has expanded its network of clinics. In 2011 revenues increased 12% to some $237 million due to increased patient visits (2.2 million up from 1.9 million in 2010) at both new and mature clinics. As a result of increased sales as well as gains on acquisitions/divestitures net income also rose by 34% in 2011 to some $21 million.

Strategy

USPh grows by developing and acquiring new clinics throughout the US. Of the 21 clinics it opened in 2011 six were new clinic partnerships and 15 were satellite clinics of existing partnerships. That year the company also acquired another 20 clinics and closed 17 underperforming clinics.

Along with developing new partnerships and opening new clinics USPh seeks to increase its market share by upping its patient volume through marketing campaigns and by adding new services. It also works to recruit and retain physical therapists that have strong relationships with referring physicians by offering competitive salaries and opportunities to own a stake in or share profits in the clinics where they work.

Mergers and Acquisitions

In mid-2011 USPh paid $8.4 million in 2011 for a 51% stake in a 20-clinic multi-partner practice group. The company carried on with its acquisition activities in 2012 including the purchase of a 70% stake in a group that operates seven clinics for about $6.3 million.

EXECUTIVES

Vice Chairman, Daniel C. Arnold, age 83
Chairman, Jerald L. Pullins, age 71
Chief Financial Officer, Lawrance W. (Larry) McAfee, age 58, $366,923 total compensation
Chief Executive Officer, Christopher J. (Chris) Reading, age 49, $382,212 total compensation
Chief Operating Officer, Glenn D. McDowell, age 56, $229,423 total compensation
Director; Managing Director STAR Physical Therapy, Regg E. Swanson, age 59
Director, Bernard A. Harris Jr., age 56
Director, Mark J. Brookner, age 68
Vice Chairman, Daniel C. Arnold, age 83
Director, Bruce D. Broussard, age 49
Director, Marlin W. Johnston, age 81
EVP CFO and Director, Lawrance W. (Larry) McAfee, age 58
President CEO and Director, Christopher J. (Chris) Reading, age 49
Director, Clayton K. Trier, age 61
Director; Managing Director STAR Physical Therapy, Regg E. Swanson, age 59
Director, Harry S. Chapman, age 68
Auditors: GrantThorntonLLP

LOCATIONS

HQ: U.S. Physical Therapy Inc.
1300 W. Sam Houston Pkwy. South Ste. 300, Houston TX 77042
Phone: 713-297-7000   **Fax:** 713-297-7090
Web: corporate.usph.com

PRODUCTS/OPERATIONS

2011 Sales

	$ mil.	% of total
Patient revenue		
Managed care	66	28
Medicare/Medicaid	56	24
Commercial insurance	52	22
Wokers' compensation	39	17
Other patient revenue	12	5
Other	10	4
Total	**237**	**100**

COMPETITORS

Concentra
Five Star Quality Care
Physiotherapy Associates
RehabCare
Select Medical
Spaulding Rehabilitation Hospital
U.S. HealthWorks

HISTORICAL FINANCIALS

Company Type: Public

Income Statement

FYE: December 31

	REVENUE ($ mil.)	NET INCOME ($ mil.)	NET PROFIT MARGIN	EMPLOYEES
12/12	252.0	17.9	7.1%	2,677
12/11	237.0	20.9	8.8%	2,522
12/10	211.2	15.6	7.4%	2,338
12/09	201.4	11.7	5.8%	2,132
12/08	187.6	10.0	5.3%	2,049
Annual Growth	**7.7%**	**15.7%**	**—**	**6.9%**

2012 Year-End Financials

Debt ratio: 10.5%
Return on equity: 15.9%
Cash ($ mil.): 11
Current ratio: 2.78
Long-term debt ($ mil.): 17
No. of shares (mil.): 11
Dividends
  Yield: 2.7%
  Payout: 41.7%
Market value ($ mil.): 328

	STOCK PRICE ($) FY Close	P/E High/Low		PER SHARE ($) Earnings	Dividends	Book Value
12/12	27.54	18	12	1.51	0.76	9.85
12/11	19.68	15	9	1.75	0.32	9.15
12/10	19.82	15	11	1.32	0.00	8.90
12/09	16.93	17	7	1.00	0.00	7.52
12/08	13.33	24	12	0.83	0.00	6.78
Annual Growth	**19.9%**	**—**	**—**	**16.1%**	**—**	**9.8%**

UIL Holding Corp

UIL Holdings parent of electric utility The United Illuminating Company (UI) hopes its well-regulated business will result in regular revenue growth. The public utility distributes electricity to 321000 customers in southwestern Connecticut. Its service area largely urban and suburban includes the principal cities of Bridgeport (population 146000) and New Haven (population 130000) and their surrounding areas. UIL Holdings has teamed up with NRG Energy to operate GenConn Energy LLC a joint venture that focuses on developing new power generation facilities in Connecticut. The company has also diversified through the acquisition of three gas utilities in New England from IBERDROLA USA for $1.3 billion.

Operations

The 2010 acquisition of Southern Connecticut Gas Connecticut Natural Gas and Berkshire Gas diversified the company's portfolio to include natural gas distribution operations in its core geographic area and boosted UIL Holdings' customer base (706000 in 2012).

UIL Holdings operates Electric Distribution and Transmission and Gas Distribution segments. UI is a regulated operating electric public utility engaged in the purchase transmission distribution and sale of electricity for residential commercial and industrial purposes in a service area in the southwestern part of Connecticut.

The holding company's gas companies engage in natural gas transportation distribution and sales operations in Connecticut and western Massachusetts.

Financial Performance

UIL Holding's revenues decreased by 5% in 2012 primarily due to 2% lower revenues from the electric distribution and transmission segment because of decreased retail revenues and distribution sales volumes resulting from warmer-than-normal winter temperatures in 2012. Gas distribution segment revenues decreased by 9% due to increased lower sales volume as a result of warmer weather.

The company's net income increased by 4% in 2012 due to lower purchases of natural gas and decreased operation and maintenance expense of electric distribution and transmission segment due to a drop in outside services expenses offset by increased operating and maintenance expenses of the gas distribution segment due to shared services costs and increased uncollectible expenses.

Strategy

In 2012 the company adopted a new comprehensive energy strategy focused on promoting energy efficiency and expanding the use of natural gas in order to make Connecticut more competitive as it the state seeks to attract and retain business and industry.

In 2011 GenConn Energy brought its 200 MW peaking power plant at NRG Energy's Middletown Station online to serve the ISO New England markets. The new unit will provide power to Connecticut homes and businesses during periods of peak demand such as severe weather conditions.

Company Background

UIL Holdings' non-regulated units (once a more significant part of its operations before it refocused on its regulated business in the mid-2000s) consist of an operating lease and passive minority ownership interests in two investment funds (collectively held by United Capital Investments Inc.) a heating and cooling facility and a unit that manages claims for Xcelecom a mechanical contracting business it divested in 2006.

UI was established as a regulated electric public utility in 1899.

EXECUTIVES

EVP and COO; President and COO United Illuminating, Anthony J. Vallillo, age 64, $390,000 total compensation

VP Corporate Affairs; VP Corporate Affairs United Illuminating, Dennis E. Hrabchak

VP Investor Relations and Treasurer; VP Investor Relations and Treasurer United Illuminating, Susan E. (Sue) Allen, age 54, $190,800 total compensation

VP Engineering and Project Excellence United Illuminating, Richard J. Reed, age 61, $228,000 total compensation

VP Technical Services, John J. Prete, age 54

Chief Financial Officer; Executive Vice President, Richard J. Nicholas, age 58, $300,000 total compensation

President; Chief Executive Officer; Director, James P. Torgerson, age 61, $625,000 total compensation

VP Client Fulfillment United Illuminating, Joseph D. Thomas

Associate VP Strategic Business Services United Illuminating, Edward (Ed) Drew

VP Business Services, Anthony Marone III, age 50

Manager Investor Relations United Illuminating, Michelle Hanson

VP and Controller UIL Holdings and UI, Steven P. (Steve) Favuzza, age 60

VP Audit Services and Chief Compliance Officer; VP Audit Services and Chief Compliance Officer United Illuminating, Deborah C. Hoffman, age 57

SVP General Counsel and Corporate Secretary UIL Holdings and UI, Linda L. Randell, age 63, $290,000 total compensation

Senior Communications Specialist United Illuminating, Anita Steeves

VP Human Resources, Diane Pivirotto, age 62

Director Corporate Communications United Illuminating, Steve Bravar

Director Communications United Illuminating, Michael A. West

Chief Information Officer; Vice President - Information Technology, Joseph Santamaria

Senior Vice President - Government Relations, Alex Deboissiere

Vice President - Connecticut Gas Operations, Robert Allessio

Director, Thelma R. (Rosie) Albright, age 67

Director, Betsy Henley-Cohn, age 61

Director, William F. (Bill) Murdy, age 72

Director, Marc C. Breslawsky, age 69

Director, Arnold L. Chase, age 62

Director, Daniel J. Miglio, age 73

Director, John L. Lahey, age 67

Director, James A. (Jim) Thomas, age 73

President; Chief Executive Officer; Director, James P. Torgerson, age 60

Director, Donald R. (Don) Shassian, age 58

Independent Director, Suedeen Kelly

Independent Director, Betsy Cohn

Auditors: PricewaterhouseCoopersLLP

LOCATIONS

HQ: UIL Holdings Corporation
157 Church St., New Haven CT 06506
Phone: 203-499-2000   **Fax:** 203-499-2414
Web: www.uil.com

PRODUCTS/OPERATIONS

2012 Sales

	$ mil.	% of total
Utility		
Electric		
Distribution	561	38
Transmission	222	15
Gas		
Distribution	703	47
Total	**1,486**	**100**

COMPETITORS

Central Vermont Public Service	National Grid USA
Columbia Gas of Massachusetts	Northeast Utilities
Con Edison	PPL Corporation
Connecticut Light and Power	PPL Generation
Green Mountain Energy	Unitil
Green Mountain Power	Wayne J. Griffin Electric
Iberdrola USA	Western Massachusetts Electric
NSTAR Electric	Yankee Gas

HISTORICAL FINANCIALS

Company Type: Public

Income Statement

FYE: December 31

	REVENUE ($ mil.)	NET INCOME ($ mil.)	NET PROFIT MARGIN	EMPLOYEES
12/12	1,486.5	103.7	7.0%	1,865
12/11	1,570.4	99.7	6.3%	1,868
12/10	997.6	54.8	5.5%	1,824
12/09	896.5	54.3	6.1%	1,066
12/08	948.7	48.1	5.1%	1,039
Annual Growth	11.9%	21.1%	—	15.7%

2012 Year-End Financials

Debt ratio: 37.0%
Return on equity: 9.3%
Cash ($ mil.): 17
Current ratio: 1.00
Long-term debt ($ mil.): 1,600

No. of shares (mil.): 50
Dividends
  Yield: 4.8%
  Payout: 92.4%
Market value ($ mil.): 1,822

	STOCK PRICE ($) FY Close	P/E High/Low		PER SHARE ($) Earnings	Dividends	Book Value
12/12	35.81	18	16	2.02	1.73	21.95
12/11	35.37	18	15	1.95	1.73	21.62
12/10	29.96	20	16	1.52	1.73	21.32
12/09	28.08	16	9	1.93	1.73	19.15
12/08	30.03	19	14	1.89	1.73	18.85
Annual Growth	4.5%	—	—	1.7%	(0.0%)	3.9%

Ulta Salon Cosmetics & Fragrance Inc.

Ulta Salon Cosmetics & Fragrance wants to be every woman's ultimate beauty stop. The company operates some 575 stores in 46 states. About a third of its locations are in Illinois Texas Florida and California. Ulta stocks more than 20000 prestige and mass-market products including cosmetics fragrances skin and hair care products salon styling tools and accessories. Stores offer hair salon services as well as manicures pedicures massages waxing and other beauty treatments. In addition to its brick-and-mortar presence the company markets more than 11000 products and more than 500 brand names through its e-commerce site. Ulta was founded in 1990 by Terry Hanson and Dick George.

Geographic Reach

Ulta operates about 575 stores across 46 states. Illinois Texas Florida and California make up more than a third of its stores network.

Operations

The retailer operates its business through one reportable segment. Ulta combined its three operating segments –retail stores salon services and e-commerce –into one reportable segment because it determined that each previous segment boasts a similar consumer economic characteristics nature of products and distribution methods.

Ulta's operations are supported by three distribution facilities located in Illinois Arizona and Pennsylvania. The retailer carries more than 20000 products and replenishes its stores with less-than-case quantities to allow it to ship less than an entire case when only one or two of a particular product is required. Its distribution facilities use warehouse management and warehouse control software systems which has been upgraded or installed during the past three years.

Strategy

Ulta's ultimate goal is to grow its US stores network to 1200. It aims to continue opening stores in markets where it currently operates and in new markets as it tracks its long-term target of 15% to 20% new store growth rates. It has found success opening new locations in diverse markets nationwide. To this end the retailer opened 102 new stores in fiscal 2013 marking a 23% increase in square footage growth and a 67% rise in the number of new stores opened as compared to 61 new stores in fiscal 2012. Meanwhile in fiscal 2013 Ulta remodeled 21 stores and relocated 3 others. During the past two years the company has focused on opening new stores in existing centers. It anticipates following this store growth strategy for several more years.

Ulta's strategy is to benefit from a change in where women –especially younger generations – purchase their beauty products. As department store operators have consolidated and slumped in recent years specialty stores (such as rival Sephora) have been looking to capture a bigger share of the market for prestige beauty products. To that end Ulta is focused on expanding its range of higher-priced "prestige" products such as Estee Lauder fragrances Frederic Fekkai hair care products and Smashbox cosmetics. The prestige category is the beauty industry's highest growth category. As part of this push Ulta added popular fragrance brands Coach Dolce and Gabbana Cartier Fendi Chloe Marc Jacobs Oscar de la Renta and Thierry Mugler. New cosmetics brands include Dermalogica Philosophy Dr. Brandt Juice Beauty Vichy and La Roche-Posay Benefit Butter London CK One and Laura Geller. It hair care additions include DermOrganic Living Proof Ouidad and Carol's Daughter.

It is also working to drive more customers to its revenue-generating salon areas for hair nail and facial treatments. A cornerstone of the Ulta business is its work to build customer loyalty. The beauty retailer maintains an ULTAmate Rewards program (for purchase-based points) and a nationwide program that offers certificates for free beauty products.

Financial Performance

The beauty products chain has been logging positive growth in both its revenue and profits since fiscal 2008 despite the challenging economy. Indeed its revenue doubled in fiscal 2012 as compared to fiscal 2008.

Ulta's sales increased 25% –to $2.2 billion in fiscal 2013 from $1.8 billion in fiscal 2012 –while its profits rose 43% during the same reporting period. The company attributes the revenue boost to several successes including a salon service sales increase of 23% opening 101 new stores in fiscal 2013 and a 9% increase in comparable store sales primarily due to a 7% increase in store traffic. Non-comparable stores which include stores opened in fiscal 2013 as well as stores opened in fiscal 2012 that have not yet turned comparable contributed $291 million of the sales increase; comparable stores contributed $153.1 million of the total sales increase. Ulta attributes the increase in comparable store sales to its successful marketing and merchandise strategies.The company logged net income increases as well due to a $166.9 million jump in gross profit offset in part by a $78.2 million increase in SG&A expenses and a $31.9 million increase in income tax expenses.

IPO

Since its IPO in 2007 which raised more than $150 million Ulta has aggressively expanded its retail footprint opening hundreds of stores. With a goal of growing its stores network to 1000 locations Ulta's expanding its distribution capacity. The company operates two distribution facilities —located in Illinois and Arizona —that support both its retail and e-commerce businesses. To keep pace with its expansion plans Ulta's building a third 370000-sq.-ft. distribution facility in Pennsylvania in 2012.

Sales and Marketing

Ulta's advertising expenses consist of paper print and distribution costs related to its advertising circulars. Total advertising costs excluding incentives from vendors and start-up advertising expenses came to $118365 $99446 and $84796 in fiscal 2012 2011 and 2010 respectively.

Through a multi-faceted marketing strategy Ulta looks to increase brand awareness drive traffic to its stores and e-commerce website acquire new customers improve customer retention and increase the frequency of shopping. It communicates with customers and prospective customers through direct mail catalogs and free-standing newspaper inserts which aim to highlight the breadth of its selection of prestige mass and salon beauty products new products and services and special offers.Its online marketing strategy includes search engine optimization (SEO) paid search mobile advertising affiliate relationships social media display advertising and other digital marketing channels. Ulta's email marketing programs are effective in communicating with and driving sales from online and retail store customers.

Ulta offers private label products in key categories such as cosmetics skin care and bath. Because its products portfolio includes items targeted to the prestige mass and salon markets Ulta appeals to a wide range of customers including women of all ages demographics and lifestyles.

The retailer fills its stores with help from some 300 product vendors which altogether offer more than 500 brands. Its top 10 vendors include the likes of Bare Escentuals Farouk Systems Procter & Gamble Coty and L'Oreal. The group represents about 53% of Ulta's total annual sales.

Company Ownership

Investment firm Netherlands-based Doublemousse B.V. (led by director Charles Heilbronn) owns about 18% of the company's shares.

EXECUTIVES

SVP General Counsel and Secretary, Robert S. Guttman, age 59, $290,285 total compensation
CEO and Director, Mary N. Dillon, age 52
Senior Vice President Marketing, Jeffrey Severts
CFO and Assistant Secretary, Scott Settersten
SVP Store Operations, Cynthia Payne
SVP Merchandising, Janet Taake
Director, Robert F. DiRomualdo, age 68
Director, Charles J. Philippin, age 61
Director, Charles Heilbronn, age 58
Director, Lorna E. Nagler, age 55
President CEO and Director, Carl (Chuck) Rubin, age 52
Independent Director, Catherine Halligan
Independent Director, Kenneth Stevens
Independent Director, Michael MacDonald
Auditors: Ernst&YoungLLP

LOCATIONS

HQ: Ulta Salon Cosmetics & Fragrance Inc.
1000 Remington Blvd. Ste. 120, Bolingbrook IL 60440
Phone: 630-410-4800   **Fax:** 630-766-6395
Web: www.phoenixintl.com

2013 Stores

	No.
Alabama	10
Arizona	23
Arkansas	4
California	55
Colorado	12
Connecticut	5
Delaware	1
Florida	39
Georgia	21
Idaho	3
Illinois	38
Indiana	10
Iowa	6
Kansas	3
Kentucky	6
Louisiana	9
Maine	3
Maryland	9
Massachusetts	7
Michigan	23
Minnesota	11
Mississippi	4
Missouri	9
Montana	1
Nebraska	3
Nevada	6
New	2
New	14
New	1
New	19
North	17
North	1
Ohio	18
Oklahoma	8
Oregon	6
Pennsylvania	20
Rhode	1
South	10
Tennessee	8
Texas	67
Utah	6
Virginia	14
Washington	9
West	1
Wisconsin	7
Total	**550**

PRODUCTS/OPERATIONS

Selected Products

Accessories
  Brush sets
  Eyelash curlers
  Hair accessories
  Manicure sets
  Yoga accessories
Appliances
  Curling irons
  Flat irons
  Hair dryers
  Microdermabrasion systems
  Shavers
Bath and body
  Aromatherapy
  Body butter
  Body souffle
  Deodorants
  Exfoliators
  Scrubs
  Soaps
Cosmetics
  Blush
  Concealer
  Eye liner
  Eye shadow
  Lipstick
Fragrance
  Candles
  Cologne
  Perfume
  Potpourri
Hair care
  Coloring
  Conditioner
  Masks
  Shampoo
  Styling creams
Skin care
  Cellulite cream
  Anti-aging cream
  Face wash
  Gloves
  Lotions
  Nail strengthening cream
  Sunscreens

COMPETITORS

Bath & Body Works	Nordstrom
Bed Bath & Beyond	Premier Salons
Body Shop	Regis Corporation
CVS Caremark	Sally Beauty
Dillard' s	Sephora USA
J. C. Penney	Supercuts
L' Oreal USA	Target Corporation
Lush Ltd.	Wal-Mart
Macy' s	Walgreen
Merle Norman	

HISTORICAL FINANCIALS

Company Type: Public

Income Statement

FYE: February 2

	REVENUE ($ mil.)	NET INCOME ($ mil.)	NET PROFIT MARGIN	EMPLOYEES
02/13*	2,220.2	172.5	7.8%	16,100
01/12	1,776.1	120.2	6.8%	14,000
01/11	1,454.8	71.0	4.9%	11,700
01/10	1,222.7	39.3	3.2%	10,300
01/09	1,084.6	25.2	2.3%	9,800
Annual Growth	19.6%	61.7%	—	13.2%

*Fiscal year change

2013 Year-End Financials

Debt ratio: —	No. of shares (mil.): 64
Return on equity: 24.7%	Dividends
Cash ($ mil.): 320	Yield: 0.0%
Current ratio: 3.57	Payout: 37.3%
Long-term debt ($ mil.): —	Market value ($ mil.): 6,243

	STOCK PRICE ($) FY Close	P/E High/Low	PER SHARE ($) Earnings	Dividends	Book Value
02/13*	97.54	37 28	2.68	1.00	12.29
01/12	77.31	40 19	1.90	0.00	9.40
01/11	36.73	32 14	1.16	0.00	6.69
01/10	19.40	32 6	0.66	0.00	5.03
01/09	5.83	36 13	0.43	0.00	4.24
Annual Growth	102.2%	— —	58.0%	—	30.5%

*Fiscal year change

Ultimate Software Group, Inc.

The Ultimate Software Group isn't timid about the benefits of its workforce management products. Businesses use its cloud-based UltiPro software suite to manage hiring human resources compliance benefits enrollment payroll appraisals and time and attendance. Primarily serving clients in the US the company offers UltiPro Enterprise for businesses with more than 1000 employees and UltiPro Workplace for those with fewer than 1000 employees. It targets the communications finance health care retail technology and transportation industries among others.

Sales and Marketing The company markets its software through direct sales teams organized by geographic region. It boasts more than 2300 customers including Adobe Systems Major League Baseball and The Container Store.

Financial Performance Ultimate Software has enjoyed a decade of consistent growth. In 2011 it reported revenue of $269 million up nearly 20% from 2010. Net income was also up doubling to more than $4 million. A 25% rise in recurring sales (primarily the cloud-based offering) was more than enough to overcome a slight decrease in services revenue.

Strategy

In the highly competitive market for human capital management software Ultimate Software focuses on product enhancements (including add-ons) and customer satisfaction. The company spent more than $50 million on research and development in 2011 up more than 20% from the prior year. It also opened a new office in Santa Ana California to better serve its West Coast clients. Ultimate Software reports an annual customer retention rate of about 96%.

EXECUTIVES

SVP and General Manager Enterprise Services, Jon Harris, age 48
SVP Chief People Officer and Secretary, Vivian Maza, age 51
EVP CFO and Treasurer, Mitchell K. (Mitch) Dauerman, age 55, $475,000 total compensation
Chairman President and CEO, Scott Scherr, age 60, $700,000 total compensation
SVP and General Counsel, Robert Manne, age 59
SVP and Chief Enterprise Sales Officer, Greg Swick, age 49
Vice Chairman and COO, Marc D. Scherr, age 55, $625,000 total compensation
Chief Technology Officer & Senior Vice President of Product Development, Adam Rogers, age 38
SVP and CIO, William (Bill) Hicks, age 47
Director Public Relations, Darlene Marcroft
VP Technology Strategy, Ted Malley
SVP and Chief Workplace Sales Officer, Chris Phenicie, age 41
VP Market Strategy, Andrew McCarthy
Vice President of strategic HCM, Cecile Alper-Leroux
Director Global Talent Management, Lisa Sterling
Assistant Director of Human Resources, Lisa Shea
Vice President of Human Resources, Thomas Mazzocco
Chief Information Officer and VP of Shared Services, Bill Hicks
Director, James A. FitzPatrick Jr., age 63
Director, Robert A. Yanover, age 76
Vice Chairman and COO, Marc D. Scherr, age 55
Director, LeRoy A. Vander Putten, age 78
Director, Rick A. Wilber, age 64
Director, Alois T. (Al) Leiter, age 47
Independent Director, LeRoy Putten
Auditors: KPMGLLP

LOCATIONS

HQ: The Ultimate Software Group Inc.
2000 Ultimate Way, Weston FL 33326
Phone: 954-331-7000 **Fax:** 202-346-6370
Web: www.costar.com

PRODUCTS/OPERATIONS

2011 Sales

	$ mil.	% of total
Recurring	213	79
Services	53	20
Licenses	2	1
Total	269	100

COMPETITORS

ADP	Peopleclick Authoria
Ceridian	SAP
Kronos	Sage Software
Lawson Software	Synygy
Oracle	Workscape
Paychex	

HISTORICAL FINANCIALS

Company Type: Public

Income Statement

FYE: December 31

	REVENUE ($ mil.)	NET INCOME ($ mil.)	NET PROFIT MARGIN	EMPLOYEES
12/12	332.2	14.6	4.4%	1,614
12/11	269.2	4.2	1.6%	1,328
12/10	227.8	2.1	0.9%	1,134
12/09	196.5	(1.1)	—	989
12/08	178.5	(2.9)	—	933
Annual Growth	16.8%	—	—	14.7%

2012 Year-End Financials

Debt ratio: 1.9%	No. of shares (mil.): 27
Return on equity: 14.5%	Dividends
Cash ($ mil.): 58	Yield: —
Current ratio: 1.12	Payout: —
Long-term debt ($ mil.): 5	Market value ($ mil.): 2,581

	STOCK PRICE ($) FY Close	P/E High/Low	PER SHARE ($) Earnings	Dividends	Book Value
12/12	94.41	191 117	0.52	0.00	4.19
12/11	65.12	413 267	0.15	0.00	3.26
12/10	48.63	550 308	0.08	0.00	2.87
12/09	29.37	— —	(0.05)	0.00	2.35
12/08	14.60	— —	(0.12)	0.00	2.10
Annual Growth	59.5%	— —	—	—	18.8%

Ultratech Inc

Ultratech's machines take the ultimate in high-tech baby steps. The company makes step-and-repeat photolithography systems —called steppers — that help manufacturers produce semiconductors thin-film heads for disk drives and micromachined components. Chip makers use the steppers in photolithography a process during which device features are imprinted on semiconductor wafer surfaces through repeated exposures to patterns of light. The company's steppers expose a small section of the wafer then "step" to an adjacent site to repeat the process. Customers outside the US generate about 60% of sales.

More than half of its international customers are located in the Asia/Pacific region. In order to better serve those clients Ultratech established a manufacturing facility in Singapore though the company continues to produce most of its products in San Jose California. It also maintains sales and support offices in China Germany Japan the Philippines Singapore South Korea Taiwan Thailand and the US.

Semiconductor makers (including companies involved in chip packaging) continue to dominate Ultratech's customer ranks while a small portion of sales goes to firms in nanotechnology which includes manufacturers of optical networking gear thin-film head magnetic recording devices laser diodes and high-brightness light-emitting diodes (HBLEDs). Intel (24% of sales) Samsung (18%) and Taiwan Semiconductor Manufacturing Corporation (12%) are among its top customers.

Overall sales for 2011 rose 51% to $212 million on top of a 61% year-over-year increase in 2010 on continued strong demand for its products. Ultratech remained profitable reporting net income that more than doubled for the year to $39 million on the higher sales and in spite of higher operating expenses.

Systems Ultratech's largest segment at more than 80% of revenues reported sales were up 55% on a 90% increase in the number of units sold. Ultratech also gets a small amount of sales from services (9%) and spare parts (8%); both product lines saw double-digit growth for the year on higher demand and an expanded customer base.

Ultratech partners with potential customers to develop new process technologies which helps the company sell equipment based on the technology to its partner. Once a customer makes a capital equipment purchasing decision that company will generally rely on the equipment for a specific application and until it needs next-generation technology making it difficult to sell a similar product to a manufacturer once the purchasing decision has been made.

Ultratech sells a niche product rather than a broad line of semiconductor manufacturing equipment. The company has diversified into a few key markets including 3-D packaging and high-brightness LEDs to reduce its overall exposure to downturns in the chip industry and extend its market share once next-generation technologies go into production.

EXECUTIVES

SVP Worldwide Service Operations, S. David (Dave) Holmes
Chief Financial Officer; Senior Vice President - Finance; Secretary, Bruce R. Wright, age 64, $320,385 total compensation
Chairman of the Board; President; Chief Executive Officer, Arthur W. (Art) Zafiropoulo, age 74, $555,000 total compensation
CTO, Andrew M. (Andy) Hawryluk
VP Corporate Services and Human Resources, David (Dave) Ghosh
Director, Joel F. Gemunder, age 73
Director, Dennis R. Raney, age 70
Director, Nicholas (Nick) Konidaris, age 68
Director, Rick Timmins, age 61
Director, Henri Richard
Director, Bin-ming Benjamin (Ben) Tsai, age 54
Independent Director, Michael Child
Auditors: Ernst&YoungLLP

LOCATIONS

HQ: Ultratech Inc
3050 Zanker Road, San Jose, CA 95134
Phone: 408 321-8835
Web: www.ultratech.com

2011 Sales

	$ mil.	% of total
US	84	40
Taiwan	51	24
Europe	20	10
South Korea	13	6
Japan	8	4
Singapore	3	2
Other regions	30	14
Total	**212**	**100**

PRODUCTS/OPERATIONS

2011 Sales

	$ mil.	% of total
Products	191	90
Services	19	9
Licenses	1	1
Total	**212**	**100**

Selected Products

Advanced packaging lithography steppers

Laser thermal annealing systems
Refurbished systems
Semiconductor lithography systems
Thin-film head (rowbar) lithography steppers

COMPETITORS

ASML	FSI International
Amtech Systems	JMAR Technologies
Applied Materials	Mattson Technology
Axcelis Technologies	Nikon
Canon	Suss MicroTec
Dainippon Screen	USHIO

HISTORICAL FINANCIALS

Company Type: Public

Income Statement

FYE: December 31

	REVENUE ($ mil.)	NET INCOME ($ mil.)	NET PROFIT MARGIN	EMPLOYEES
12/12	234.8	47.1	20.1%	353
12/11	212.3	39.2	18.5%	322
12/10	140.6	16.7	11.9%	295
12/09	95.8	2.1	2.2%	253
12/08	131.7	11.7	8.9%	270
Annual Growth	**15.5%**	**41.5%**	**—**	**6.9%**

2012 Year-End Financials

Debt ratio: 0.0%	No. of shares (mil.): 27
Return on equity: 14.0%	Dividends
Cash ($ mil.): 96	Yield: —
Current ratio: 7.91	Payout: —
Long-term debt ($ mil.): —	Market value ($ mil.): 1,011

	STOCK PRICE ($) FY Close	P/E High/Low	PER SHARE ($) Earnings	Dividends	Book Value
12/12	37.30	20 14	1.70	0.00	13.85
12/11	24.57	22 11	1.47	0.00	11.46
12/10	19.88	31 18	0.67	0.00	9.34
12/09	14.84	175 108	0.09	0.00	8.39
12/08	11.96	34 17	0.50	0.00	8.23
Annual Growth	**32.9%**	**— —**	**35.8%**	**—**	**13.9%**

Under Armour Inc

Under Armour is proving its mettle as an apparel warrior. Since its foray into the sports apparel market the maker of performance athletic undies and clothing has risen to the top of the industry pack boasting a big portion of the compression garment market. It is gaining a foothold in footwear too. Under Armour is the official footwear supplier of the NFL and MLB and partners with the NBA. Specializing in sport-specific garments it dresses its consumers from head (COLDGEAR) to toe. Products are made from its moisture-wicking and heat-dispersing fabrics able to keep athletes dry during workouts. Under Armour sells its wares online by catalog through its own factory house stores and in more than 25000 retail stores worldwide.

Geographic Reach

Headquartered in Baltimore Under Armour operates its business globally. It has European and Asian subsidiaries and sources from suppliers worldwide. Besides North America where it generates about 95% of sales Under Armour's products are sold primarily in Austria France Germany Ire-

land and the UK. It sells its wares in Japan as well through a minority-owned licensee.

Sales and Marketing

Under Armour generates about 70% of its sales through its wholesale business. Its customers include the likes of Cabela's and the Army and Air Force Exchange as well as Dick's Sporting Goods and The Sports Authority which as a pair accounted for 22% of Under Armour's 2012 revenue. The company's direct-to-consumer business is growing rapidly. In 2012 it logged an increase of about 34% vs. 2011 with the help of more than 20 stores added during the year. Under Armour operates about 100 of its own factory house and specialty stores.

Financial Performance

Under Armour has shown strong growth in both revenue and net income over the past decade with 2012 sales of $1.8 billion 25% higher than the prior year. The company saw about 25%-30% growth in all categories (apparel footwear accessories) as well as in licensing. The results were powered by an increase in direct to consumer sales (Under Armour opened 22 new factory house stores in 2012) new product offerings and higher average selling prices. Net income that year rose a third to about $129 million on the strength of revenue.

Strategy

To compete against its larger rivals Under Armour spends heavily to promote its products forming endorsement deals with athletes across multiple sports. Its strategy is to identify the next generation of stars such as skier Lindsey Vonn and Milwaukee Bucks point guard Brandon Jennings and sign them to multiyear endorsement deals. The company also spends about 11% of its net income each year on marketing. It spends its money on commercials and print ads as well as sponsorships for leagues teams players and events. To date Under Armour's primary consumer segment has been men but it is actively working to expand its apparel offerings for women and children. Product lines are sold to almost 400 women's sports teams at NCAA Division I-A colleges. The sports apparel maker is looking to expand into wearable technology.

Mergers and Acquisitions

To this end in late 2013 Under Armour acquired fitness-tracking firm MapMyFitness for $150 million as it seeks to expand into the growing fitness technology market. It was the company's first acquisition.

EXECUTIVES

VP Retail, Daniel J. Sawall, age 58
SVP Talent, Melissa A. Wallace, age 54, $269,712 total compensation
Chairman President and CEO, Kevin A. Plank, age 40, $26,000 total compensation
EVP Business Development, J. Scott Plank, age 47, $183,327 total compensation
SVP Brand, Stephen J. (Steve) Battista, age 39
EVP Global Brand & Sports Marketing, Matthew C. Mirchin, age 53, $260,000 total compensation
COO, Kip J. Fulks, age 40
President and Managing Director Under Armour Europe, Peter Mahrer, age 53, $404,619 total compensation
Chief Supply Chain Officer, James H. (Jim) Hardy Jr., age 54
President North America, Henry B. Stafford, age 38
Chief Performance Officer, Byron K. Adams Jr., age 58
SVP Consumer Insights, Kevin M. Haley, age 44

CFO, Brad Dickerson, age 48, $260,000 total compensation
SVP US Sales, Adam Peake, age 44
SVP Footwear, Eugene R. (Gene) McCarthy, age 56, $153,846 total compensation
VP and General Manager E-commerce, John S. Rogers, age 50
Senior Vice President - Human Resources, Fred Knowles
President International, Karl-Heinz (Charlie) Maurath
Director, Douglas E. (Doug) Coltharp, age 51
Director, Anthony W. (Tony) Deering, age 68
Director, Harvey L. Sanders, age 63
Director, William R. (Bill) McDermott, age 51
Director, A. B. Krongard, age 76
Chief Performance Officer and Director, Byron K. Adams Jr., age 58
Director, Thomas J. Sippel, age 66
Auditors: PricewaterhouseCoopersLLP

LOCATIONS

HQ: Under Armour Inc.
1020 Hull St. 3rd Fl., Baltimore MD 21230-2080
Phone: 410-454-6428   **Fax:** 410-468-2516
Web: www.underarmour.com

2012 Sales

	$ mil.	% of total
North America	1,726	94
Other countries	108	6
Total	**1,834**	**100**

PRODUCTS/OPERATIONS

2012 Sales

	$ mil.	% of total
Apparel	1,385	76
Footwear	239	13
Accessories	165	9
Licensing	44	2
Total	**1,834**	**100**

COMPETITORS

Calvin Klein	North Face
Columbia Sportswear	Patagonia Inc.
Fruit of the Loom	Victoria' s Secret
Hanesbrands	Stores
Jockey International	Warnaco Swimwear
L.L. Bean	adidas
NIKE	

HISTORICAL FINANCIALS

Company Type: Public

Income Statement

FYE: December 31

	REVENUE ($ mil.)	NET INCOME ($ mil.)	NET PROFIT MARGIN	EMPLOYEES
12/12	1,834.9	128.7	7.0%	5,900
12/11	1,472.6	96.9	6.6%	5,400
12/10	1,063.9	68.4	6.4%	3,900
12/09	856.4	46.7	5.5%	3,000
12/08	725.2	38.2	5.3%	2,200
Annual Growth	26.1%	35.5%	—	28.0%

2012 Year-End Financials

Debt ratio: 5.3%
Return on equity: 17.6%
Cash ($ mil.): 341
Current ratio: 3.58
Long-term debt ($ mil.): 52
No. of shares (mil.): 104
Dividends
 Yield: —
 Payout: —
Market value ($ mil.): 5,084

	STOCK PRICE ($) FY Close	P/E High/Low	PER SHARE ($) Earnings	Dividends	Book Value
12/12	48.53	87 37	1.21	0.00	7.80
12/11	71.79	91 56	0.93	0.00	6.15
12/10	54.84	89 35	0.67	0.00	4.86
12/09	27.27	70 26	0.46	0.00	3.98
12/08	23.84	116 44	0.39	0.00	3.36
Annual Growth	19.4%	— —	33.1%	—	23.5%

Unifirst Corp.

Think removing lipstick from your collar is tough? Try decontaminating radioactive clothing; in addition UniFirst designs makes sells or rents launders and delivers work uniforms and protective clothing (shirts pants coveralls coats smocks and aprons) as well as non-garment items (floor mats and mops). Another business segment provides first-aid cabinet services and supplies. UniFirst produces about 65% of the garments it supplies enabling customization through 200-plus facilities in North America and Europe. Customers include auto service centers restaurants transportation companies and utilities operating nuclear reactors; about 90% of sales are generated through its core laundry operations.

The deep recession in the US and Canada drove many businesses with employees dressed in uniform to either lay off workers or shut down. UniFirst's Specialty Garments business which includes its nuclear and cleanroom operations buoyed sales in fiscal 2010. (Results that year also benefited from re-use of garments returned by customers due to workforce cuts.) In 2011 all business segments posted roughly double-digit sales increases driven by new business accounts and increased use of protective garments. Nonetheless UniFirst's earnings remained flat for a third-consecutive year. The company cited the impact of rising prices for cotton and oil-based fabrics along with the higher cost of fuel and energy needed to operate vehicles and equipment.

Although UniFirst aims to fuel growth through acquisitions and geographic expansion it faces stiff competition from Aramark Cintas and G&K Services. Rivals have also cut prices in recent years as companies fie for every customer. UniFirst's response has been to persuade customers of the effectiveness of raising brand awareness through branded employee uniforms versus other methods of advertising. Among its competitors the company is believed to have the largest in-house digital image processing capability.

UniFirst's future is ultimately guided by members of the founding Croatti family. The family controls more than 60% of the business.

HISTORY

Chairman Aldo Croatti founded the National Overall Drycleaning Co. in 1936 cleaning the overalls of Boston factory workers from his garage. His nephew Robert joined the company in 1959 and his son Ronald joined in 1965. Although the company was located primarily in New England during the 1950s and 1960s it established its first nuclear decontamination facility in Santa Fe New

Mexico in 1961. The company also opened its first manufacturing plant in Puerto Rico in 1967.

Aldo's daughter Cynthia joined up in 1980. The company went public in 1983 as Interstate Uniform Services and was renamed UniFirst in 1984. The next year UniFirst paid $1 million as settlement in a lawsuit brought against it and other companies for allegedly polluting wells in Woburn Massachusetts in the 1970s (plaintiffs alleged that the pollution led to a high incidence of leukemia in the town). The case was the inspiration for the book and film "A Civil Action."

UniFirst continued to expand in the 1990s buying other uniform businesses and opening new service centers including a new decontamination facility in the Netherlands in 1996 its first European operation. In 1997 it opened a central distribution facility in Owensboro Kentucky which helped boost profits the following year. UniFirst continued to expand over the next two years opening new service centers across the US. The company branched into e-commerce in 1999 allowing customers to rent and buy garments over the Internet. In 2000 Unifirst closed its 33-year-old manufacturing plant in Puerto Rico moving its operations to Ebano Mexico. Aldo Croatti died in 2001 and was replaced as chairman by his son Ronald.

In 2003 Unifirst purchased uniform provider Textilease Corporation for $178 million. The company expanded in Europe and Canada and constructed a new radiological laundering plant in the UK in 2009.

EXECUTIVES

Secretary, Raymond C. Zemlin
EVP Treasurer and Director, Cynthia Croatti, age 58, $332,013 total compensation
SVP Operations, Bruce P. Boynton, age 65, $263,412 total compensation
Assistant Secretary and Assistant Treasurer, John B. Bartlett, age 71, $343,761 total compensation
Chairman President and CEO, Ronald D. Croatti, age 69, $499,765 total compensation
VP UniTech Services Group, George J. Bakevich
SVP Operations, David A. DiFillippo, age 56, $253,024 total compensation
VP Manufacturing, Stephen A. Gaykan
VP First Aid Group, Todd T. Lewis
VP Southwest Rental Group, Robert E. Middleton
VP Texas Rental Group, Gary L. Rogers
VP Canadian Rental Group, Michael J. Szymanski
VP Southern Rental Group, Robert A. Kuhn
VP Distribution and Engineering, John R. Badey
VP Northeast Regional Group, William M. Ross
VP Central Rental Group, Michael A. Croatti
VP-Mid-Atlantic Rental Grp, Reis V. LaMontagne
VP National Accounts, Michael E. Ruttner
VP Western Rental Group, Benjamin F. Childers
VP and CFO, Steven S. Sintros, age 39, $239,610 total compensation
VP Sales and Marketing, David Katz, age 49, $276,482 total compensation
Controller, Shane F. O'Connor
EVP Treasurer and Director, Cynthia Croatti, age 58
Director, Michael J. Iandoli, age 68
Director, Phillip L. Cohen, age 82
Director, Donald J. Evans, age 87
Director, Anthony F. DiFilippo, age 85
Director, Robert F. Collings, age 74
Director, Thomas S. Postek, age 71
Auditors: Ernst&YoungLLP

LOCATIONS

HQ: UniFirst Corporation
68 Jonspin Rd., Wilmington MA 01887-1086
Phone: 978-658-8888   **Fax:** 978-657-5821
Web: www.unifirst.com

2011 Sales

	$ mil.	% of total
US	1,029	91
Total	**1,025**	**100**

PRODUCTS/OPERATIONS

2011 Sales

	$ mil.	% of total
Core laundry operations	997	88
First aid	33	3

Selected Products and Services

Products
 Corporate casual attire
 Custom image programs
 Protective clothing
  Flame resistant clothing
  High visibility clothing
 Standard workwear
Facility services
 Floorcare and dust control services
 Restroom services
First aid cabinet services
Garment services
 Full-service rental programs
 Lease programs
 Purchase programs
Industry specific programs
 Food distributors
 Food processors
 Healthcare professionals
 HVAC/plumbing
 Industrial wholesalers
 Protective garment programs
 Specialty retailers
 Supermarkets
 Transportation and warehousing
Non-garment items
 Dry and wet mops
 Floor mats
 Industrial wiping products
 Restroom supplies

COMPETITORS

ARAMARK	Cintas
Alsco	G&K Services
Angelica Corporation	Superior Uniform Group

HISTORICAL FINANCIALS

Company Type: Public

Income Statement
FYE: August 31

	REVENUE ($ mil.)	NET INCOME ($ mil.)	NET PROFIT MARGIN	EMPLOYEES
08/13	1,355.5	116.6	8.6%	11,500
08/12	1,256.2	94.9	7.6%	11,000
08/11	1,134.1	76.4	6.7%	11,000
08/10	1,025.9	76.4	7.4%	10,000
08/09	1,013.4	75.8	7.5%	9,700
Annual Growth	**7.5%**	**11.4%**	**—**	**4.3%**

2013 Year-End Financials

Debt ratio: 8.1%	No. of shares (mil.): 20
Return on equity: 12.0%	Dividends
Cash ($ mil.): 197	Yield: 0.0%
Current ratio: 2.17	Payout: 2.5%
Long-term debt ($ mil.): 0	Market value ($ mil.): 1,918

	STOCK PRICE ($) FY Close	P/E High/Low		PER SHARE ($) Earnings	Dividends	Book Value
08/13	95.88	17	10	5.81	0.15	50.66
08/12	65.20	14	9	4.76	0.15	44.96
08/11	49.02	15	10	3.85	0.15	40.15
08/10	40.47	14	9	3.90	0.15	35.71
08/09	41.54	11	5	3.92	0.15	32.37
Annual Growth	**23.3%**	**—**	**—**	**10.3%**	**(0.0%)**	**11.8%**

Union First Market Bankshares Corp.

Union First Market Bankshares is the holding company for Union Bank & Trust which operates approximately 100 branches in central northern and coastal portions of Virginia. The bank offers standard services such as checking and savings accounts credit cards and certificates of deposit. Union Bank & Trust maintains a loan portfolio heavily weighted towards real estate: Commercial real estate loans make up more than 30% while one- to four-family residential mortgages and construction loans account for approximately 15% and 20% respectively. The bank also originates personal and business loans.

Other financial services are provided through subsidiaries Union Investment Services (brokerage and investment advisory services through an arrangement with Raymond James Financial) Union Insurance Group (long-term care and business owner coverage) and Union Mortgage Group which provides mortgage brokerage services from about 15 offices.

Union First Market Bankshares primarily operates in Virginia. Its Union Mortgage Group provides mortgage brokerage services from offices in Virginia Maryland and the Carolinas. Union Mortgage is additionally licensed to operate in states in the Mid-Atlantic the Southeast and in Washington DC.

The company's profits have risen dramatically due to the 2010 acquisition of First Market Bank. In 2010 profits nearly tripled (to $22.9 million from the 2009 earnings of $8.4 million) while in 2011 they rose a further 33% to $30.5 million. The acquisition led to an increase in net interest income a primary contributor to the company's growth. Also in 2011 Union First lowered it provision for loan losses as its loan portfolio continued to improve post-recession. Expenses that year were lower than in 2010 when the acquisition closed. Slightly offsetting the improvements mortgage earnings fell by nearly half in 2011 due to the stagnant residential mortgage market.Although profits have risen revenues have remained relatively flat falling 2% in 2011 to $232.9 million.

Union First Market Bankshares' strategy for growth includes buying other banks as well as opening new branches of its own. Then named Union Bank and Trust the company acquired First Market Bank in 2010 to nearly double its branch total. (The holding company then also added "First Market" to its name and moved its headquarters to Richmond.) The company has also grown through "de novo" branching and through purchases of branches and related companies. It ac-

quired an existing branch in Harrisonburg plus some $74 million in loan assets from NewBridge Bank in 2011.

Also that year the bank opened up seven new locations inside Martin's grocery stores where it already had more than 20 in-store branches. In the past couple of years the company has consolidated its bank subsidiaries creating operating efficiencies as well as a stronger unified brand.

Virginia-based specialty insurer Markel Corporation owns 14% of Union First Market Bankshares.

EXECUTIVES

Chairman, Ronald L. Hicks, age 66
CEO and Director; CEO Union First Market Bank, G. William Beale, age 63, $354,200 total compensation
President of Union First Market Bank, John C. Neal, age 63, $246,400 total compensation
Vice Chairman, W. Tayloe Murphy Jr., age 80
Regional President Rappahannock Region, Michael T. Leake
Executive Vice President; Director - Retail Banking, Elizabeth M. Bentley, age 52, $139,575 total compensation
EVP and Director Information Technology and Operations, Rex A. Hockemeyer, age 59, $102,708 total compensation
President and Director, David J. Fairchild
Regional President Northern Neck Region, Russell G. Brown
SVP and Chief Marketing Officer, W. Olen Thomas
EVP and Senior Credit Officer, Douglas F. Wooley III
Executive Vice President Chief Financial Officer, Robert Gorman
Executive Vice President Chief Banking Officer, D. Anthony Peay
President Trust Department, Stuart W. Blain
Regional President Hampton Roads Region, Frank W. Haislip
Regional President Richmond Region, Harry A. Turton Jr.
Regional President Fredericksburg Region, Jon D. Wallace
Regional President Charlottesville Region, John J. Young
Executive Vice President and Chief Credit Officer, William H. Hutton
Director, Patrick J. McCann, age 55
Director, Steven A. Markel, age 63
CEO and Director; CEO Union First Market Bank, G. William Beale, age 63
Director, James E. (Jim) Ukrop, age 74
Director, Douglas E. Caton, age 69
Vice Chairman, W. Tayloe Murphy Jr., age 80
Director, Ronald L. (Ron) Tillett, age 56
President and Director, David J. Fairchild
Director, R. Hunter Morin, age 68
Director, Hullihen W. Moore, age 69
Director, L. Bradford (Brad) Armstrong
Director, Daniel I. Hansen, age 55
Auditors: YountHyde&BarbourP.C.

LOCATIONS

HQ: Union First Market Bankshares Corporation
111 Virginia St. Ste. 200, Richmond VA 23219
Phone: 804-633-5031   **Fax:** 408-546-4300
Web: www.jdsu.com

PRODUCTS/OPERATIONS

2011 Sales

	$ mil.	% of total
Interest		
Loans including fees	168	72
Securities including dividends	20	9
Other	0	.
Noninterest		
Gains on sales of loans	19	8
Service charges on deposit accounts	8	4
Other service charges commissions & fees	12	5
Other	4	2
Adjustments	(2.5)	
Total	**232**	**100**

Selected Mergers and Acquisitions

2011
    NewBridge Bank branch (Harrisonburg VA)
2010
    First Market Bank ($105 million; Richmond VA;
        federal savings bank)

Selected Subsidiaries

Union First Market Bank
Union Insurance Group LLC
Union Investment Services Inc.
Union Mortgage Group Inc.

COMPETITORS

BB&T	PNC Financial
Bank of America	Regions Financial
C&F Financial	SunTrust
Eastern Virginia Bankshares	TowneBank
JPMorgan Chase	Wells Fargo

HISTORICAL FINANCIALS

Company Type: Public

Income Statement
FYE: December 31

	ASSETS ($ mil.)	NET INCOME ($ mil.)	INCOME AS % OF ASSETS	EMPLOYEES
12/12	4,095.8	35.4	0.9%	1,044
12/11	3,907.0	30.4	0.8%	1,045
12/10	3,837.2	22.9	0.6%	1,005
12/09	2,587.2	8.3	0.3%	662
12/08	2,551.9	14.5	0.6%	670
Annual Growth	**12.6%**	**25.0%**	**—**	**11.7%**

2012 Year-End Financials

Return on assets: 0.8%
Return on equity: 8.2%
Long-term debt ($ mil.): —
No. of shares (mil.): 25
Sales ($ mil): 222

Dividends
    Yield: 2.3%
    Payout: 27.0%
Market value ($ mil.): 399

	STOCK PRICE ($) FY Close	P/E High/Low		PER SHARE ($) Earnings	Dividends	Book Value
12/12	15.77	12	10	1.37	0.37	17.25
12/11	13.29	14	9	1.07	0.28	16.13
12/10	14.78	22	14	0.83	0.25	16.46
12/09	12.39	131	47	0.19	0.30	15.31
12/08	24.80	27	13	1.07	0.74	20.18
Annual Growth	**(10.7%)**	**—**	**—**	**6.4%**	**(15.9%)**	**(3.8%)**

United Capital Corp.

Making a profit is a capital idea that unites United Capital. The company invests in and manages real estate properties as well as manufactures and sells engineered products using knitted wire. United Capital owns and oversees about 150 retail office hotel and day care properties across the US. Subsidiary Metal Textiles makes knitted wire products and parts for a range of sealing and filtering applications. Under the AFP Transformers brand the company makes transformers for switchgear to motor starters and inverters. The lines are sold to commercial and industrial customers in the automotive electronic aerospace and process and chemical market. CEO Attilio Petrocelli and his wife own 70% of the company.

EXECUTIVES

VP CFO Secretary and Director, Anthony J. Miceli, age 50, $275,000 total compensation
Chairman President and CEO, Attilio F. Petrocelli, age 69, $800,000 total compensation
VP Real Estate Operations and Director, Michael T. Lamoretti, age 46, $250,000 total compensation
VP Real Estate Operations and Director, Michael J. Weinbaum, age 46, $250,000 total compensation
Vice President Operations, Stephen Kronick
VP CFO Secretary and Director, Anthony J. Miceli, age 50
Director, Howard M. Lorber, age 64
Director, Arnold S. Penner, age 76
Director, Robert M. Mann, age 72
VP Real Estate Operations and Director, Michael T. Lamoretti, age 46
VP Real Estate Operations and Director, Michael J. Weinbaum, age 46
Auditors: HoltzRubensteinReminickLLP

LOCATIONS

HQ: United Capital Corp.
    9 Park Place, Great Neck, NY 11021
Phone: 516 466-6464   **Fax:** 516 829-4301
Web: www.unitedcapitalcorp.net

PRODUCTS/OPERATIONS

2010 Sales

	$ mil.	% of total
Engineered products	31	40
Hotel operations	27	34
Real estate investment & management	20	26
Total	**60**	**100**

Selected Subsidiaries

AFP Hospitality Corp.
AFP Management Corp.
AFP Realty Corp.
AFP Transformers Corporation
Metal Textiles Corporation
Metex Mfg. Corporation

COMPETITORS

ACS Industries	Keystone Consolidated
Dana Holding	LeFrak Organization
Duke Realty	Siemens AG
G. Bopp USA	Tishman Construction
Helmsley Enterprises	

HISTORICAL FINANCIALS

Company Type: Public

Income Statement
FYE: December 31

	REVENUE ($ mil.)	NET INCOME ($ mil.)	NET PROFIT MARGIN	EMPLOYEES
12/12	115.7	16.6	14.4%	630
12/11	90.1	17.4	19.4%	460
12/10	80.6	12.7	15.8%	470
12/09	60.1	5.6	9.5%	390
12/08	72.9	1.6	2.2%	370
Annual Growth	**12.3%**	**79.2%**	**—**	**14.2%**

2012 Year-End Financials

Debt ratio: 22.7%
Return on equity: 11.6%
Cash ($ mil.): 10
Current ratio: 0.92
Long-term debt ($ mil.): 27

No. of shares (mil.): 5
Dividends
    Yield: —
    Payout: —
Market value ($ mil.): 161

	STOCK PRICE ($) FY Close	P/E High/Low		PER SHARE ($) Earnings	Dividends	Book Value
12/12	27.50	13	9	2.37	0.00	21.87
12/11	21.50	16	9	2.03	0.00	21.06
12/10	32.50	23	15	1.31	0.00	24.01
12/09	23.82	39	22	0.58	0.00	23.12
12/08	18.14	143	88	0.19	0.00	22.39
Annual Growth	**11.0%**	**—**	**—**	**87.9%**	**—**	**(0.6%)**

United Fire Group, Inc.

The United Fire Group companies join together to offer a unified range of property/casualty and life insurance products. The group operates through its United Fire & Casualty subsidiary which in turn holds entities that carry a variety of property/casualty offerings including fidelity and surety bonds and fire auto employee liability homeowners and workers' compensation lines. More than 1300 independent agencies in some 45 states sell its property/casualty products to businesses and individuals. The United Life division of United Fire & Casualty sells life annuity and credit life products to individuals and groups through some 950 independent agents in more than 30 states.

The company completed a corporate reorganization in 2012 through which United Fire Group became the ultimate parent of the United Fire & Casualty group of companies. The conversion to a holding company structure gave the group a more flexible operating platform to conduct future growth measures. Through the restructuring United Fire Group took on the publicly traded status of United Fire & Casualty while United Fire & Casualty became an intermediate holding entity for the group's operating subsidiaries including property/casualty providers Addison Insurance Lafayette Insurance United Fire Lloyd's Mercer Insurance Franklin Insurance and Financial Pacific Insurance as well as United Life.

United Fire's property/casualty insurance offerings account for more than 90% of its annual insurance premiums with a majority of those policies being written to commercial group customers. The company also offers certain personal policies to individual customers. It markets its products from its headquarters in Iowa and from four regional offices in California Colorado New Jersey and Texas and it operates primarily in adjacent areas of the midwestern southern and western US. About two-thirds of United Fire's 2011 property/casualty business was written in Texas Iowa California Missouri Louisiana New Jersey Illinois and Colorado. In the life insurance realm Iowa is the largest operating territory acounting for about 30% of premiums; other key states include Minnesota Illinois Nebraska and Wisconsin.

In order to increase policy placement in its existing markets United Fire offers profit-sharing and commission programs to its independent agents. It also seeks to provide modern technological tools to best serve both its agents and its policyholders. At the same time United Fire looks to expand into new markets to reduce the risk potential in its concentrated areas of operation.

Towards that end United Fire entered the Mid-Atlantic and West Coast markets in 2011 when it acquired Mercer Insurance (and its Franklin Insurance and Financial Pacific Insurance subsidiaries) in a cash-and-debt deal worth some $192 million. The purchase strengthened United Fire's property/casualty offerings adding some 200 agents in states where United Fire lacked an existing presence; it also diversified United Fire's commercial customer base as Mercer largely serves small to midsized businesses (along with some large businesses and individual customers).

However the company has occasionally had to reduce operations in some less-profitable territories. Its Lafayette Insurance Company subsidiary ceased writing new property/casualty policies in Louisiana in 2010 due to instability in that regional market. United Fire experienced a high volume of claims in the state following the disastrous 2005 Hurricane Katrina and had trouble recovering from the catastrophe losses.

Natural catastrophes took a heavy toll on United Fire's profits in 2011 a year of record losses for the property/casualty industry. The company's net income levels declined from $47 million to a meager $11000 that year. Conversely revenues increased some 19% to $705 million due to increased premium rates across all of its product lines; the company had experienced reduced revenues in 2009 and 2010 due to a decline in commercial premium levels from the economic recession and competitive conditions in the insurance marketplace. Such ups and downs are typical for property/casualty insurers' financial results which are highly cyclical in nature.

United Fire was founded by Scott McIntyre in 1946; descendants of the founder own a 14% stake in the company.

EXECUTIVES

VP General Counsel and Secretary, Neal R. Scharmer, age 55
Vice Chairman, John A. Rife, age 69, $250,000 total compensation
VP and CFO, Dianne M. Lyons, age 48, $225,000 total compensation
EVP Corporate Administration, Michael T. Wilkins, age 48, $240,000 total compensation
Chairman, Jack B. Evans, age 63
VP and Chief Investment Officer, Barrie W. Ernst, age 57, $230,000 total compensation
Resident VP Denver Regional Office, David L. Hellen, age 59
Corporate Secretary and Fidelity and Surety Claims Manager, David A. Lange, age 54
President and CEO, Randy A. Ramlo, age 50, $350,000 total compensation
Treasurer, Galen E. Underwood, age 71

VP and Chief Claims Officer, David E. Conner, age 53
VP Human Resources, Timothy G. Spain, age 60
VP Fidelity and Surety, Dennis J. Richmann, age 47
Branch Manager Gulf Coast Regional Office, Joseph B. Johnson, age 59
VP and General Manager United Life Insurance Company, Kent J. Hutchins, age 53
VP Great Lakes Regional Office, Brian S. Berta, age 47
Controller, Kevin Helbing
VP Information Services, Scott A. Minkel, age 50
VP Midwest Regional Office, Douglas A. Penn, age 63
VP Corporate Underwriting, Allen R. Sorensen, age 54
VP E-Solutions, Colleen R. Sova, age 58
Vice President and Chief Operating Officer of United Life Insurance Company, Michael Sheeley
Vice Chairman, John A. Rife, age 69
Director, Douglas M. (Doug) Hultquist, age 56
Director, Mary K. Quass, age 61
Director, James W. (Jim) Noyce, age 56
Director, Christopher R. Drahozal, age 50
Director, Kyle D. Skogman, age 61
Director, Casey D. Mahon, age 60
Director, George D. Milligan, age 55
Director, Frank S. Wilkinson Jr., age 72
Director, Thomas W. Hanley, age 59
Auditors: Ernst&YoungLLP

LOCATIONS

HQ: United Fire Group Inc.
118 2nd Ave. SE, Cedar Rapids IA 52401
Phone: 319-399-5700   **Fax:** 319-399-5499
Web: www.unitedfiregroup.com

PRODUCTS/OPERATIONS

2011 Premiums

	% of total
Property/casualty	
General liability (including	27
Fire & allied	26
Automobile	23
Workers'	9
Fidelity &	3
Reinsurance & other	3
Life	9
Total	**100**

Selected Subsidiaries

United Fire & Casualty Company
  Addison Insurance Company
  American Indemnity Financial Corporation
    Texas General Indemnity Company
  Lafayette Insurance Company
  Mercer Insurance Group Inc.
    Financial Pacific Insurance Company
    Mercer Insurance CompanyFranklin Insurance
      CompanyMercer Insurance Company of New Jersey
      Inc.
  United Fire & Indemnity Company
  United Fire Lloyds
United Life Insurance Company

COMPETITORS

ACE Limited	GEICO
AIG	Hanover Insurance
Allstate	John Hancock Financial
American Family	Services
Insurance	Liberty Mutual
American Financial	MassMutual
Group	Progressive
Arrowpoint Capital	Corporation
Corp.	Prudential
CNA Surety	State Farm
Chubb Corp	The Hartford

Erie Indemnity
Farmers Group
Fireman's Fund Insurance
Travelers Companies
White Mountains Insurance Group

HISTORICAL FINANCIALS

Company Type: Public

Income Statement

FYE: December 31

	ASSETS ($ mil.)	NET INCOME ($ mil.)	INCOME AS % OF ASSETS	EMPLOYEES
12/12	3,694.6	40.2	1.1%	909
12/11	3,618.9	0.0	0.0%	894
12/10	3,007.4	47.5	1.6%	654
12/09	2,902.5	(10.4)	—	673
12/08	2,687.1	(13.0)	—	674
Annual Growth	**8.3%**	**—**	**—**	**7.8%**

2012 Year-End Financials

Return on assets: 1.1%
Return on equity: 5.6%
Long-term debt ($ mil.): —
No. of shares (mil.): 25
Sales ($ mil): 813
Dividends
  Yield: 2.7%
  Payout: 37.9%
Market value ($ mil.): 551

	STOCK PRICE ($) FY Close	P/E High/Low		PER SHARE ($) Earnings	Dividends	Book Value
12/12	21.84	17	10	1.58	0.60	28.90
12/11	20.18	—	—	(0.00)	0.60	27.29
12/10	22.32	13	9	1.80	0.60	27.35
12/09	18.23	—	—	(0.39)	0.60	25.35
12/08	31.07	—	—	(0.48)	0.60	24.10
Annual Growth	**(8.4%)**	**—**	**—**	**—**	**(0.0%)**	**4.6%**

United Therapeutics Corp

United Therapeutics hopes its products will be in vein. Its injectable drug Remodulin treats pulmonary hypertension which affects the blood vessels between the heart and lungs. The product is marketed directly and through distributors in North America Europe and other regions. Other hypertension treatments include Adcirca and Tyvaso. The company's development pipeline includes additional treatments for cardiovascular disease as well as various cancers respiratory conditions and infectious diseases. United Therapeutics has divested its cardiac monitoring division.

Operations

Remodulin accounted for about half of United Therapeutics' 2012 sales.

The company's development pipeline includes an investigational cancer drug licensed from the Memorial Sloan-Kettering Cancer Center. The antibody candidates aim to treat metastatic brain cancer. A second candidate (for neuroblastoma) was returned to Memorial Sloan-Kettering when United Therapeutics partnered on a different neuroblastoma candidate with the National Cancer Institute. United Therapeutics also has antiviral agents under development for treatment of ailments including hepatitis C. The company has additional early stage research programs and it regularly evaluates opportunities to license additional compounds for development.

In 2012 United Therapeutics entered into a license agreement with Ascendis Pharma to develop a self-injectable therapeutic alternative for PAH patients by applying Ascendis Pharma's TransCon technology platform to its treprostinil molecule. The agreement also gives United Therapeutics exclusive rights to develop prostacyclin prostacyclin analog and prostacyclin-related products for treating PAH using the TransCon technology as well as rights to commercialize any products developed from the collaboration on a global basis.

Geographic Reach

Remodulin is approved for sale throughout North America and Europe as well as in nine other countries. Tyvaso and Adcirca are only approved in the US. The company's home country accounts for 90% of revenues.

Sales and Marketing

The company uses a direct sales force in the US and distributors abroad for Remodulin. It sells Tyvaso through pharma distributors and Adcira to pharma wholesalers.

Financial Performance

United Therapeutics' revenue increased 23% in 2012 due to higher prices improved sales and development contract payments. Net income jumped 40% on the increased revenue and $31 million in insurance proceeds. Cash flow followed the others and improved substantially.

Strategy

The company pursues growth by developing new drugs either through R&D or in partnership with other firms.

EXECUTIVES

Chairman and CEO, Martine A. Rothblatt, age 58, $798,203 total compensation
EVP General Counsel and Corporate Secretary, Paul A. Mahon, age 49, $615,000 total compensation
President COO and Director, Roger Jeffs, age 51, $710,000 total compensation
CFO and Treasurer, John M. Ferrari, age 58, $407,692 total compensation
CIO, Shola Oyewole
Vice Chairman, Christopher Patusky, age 49
SVP Human Resources, Alyssa Friedrich
EVP Pharmaceutical Development and Chief Manufacturing Officer, David Zaccardelli
Director, Tommy G. Thompson
Director, Raymond C. (Ray) Kurzweil, age 65
Director, Louis W. Sullivan, age 78
Director, Prof Raymond A. Dwek, age 71
President COO and Director, Roger Jeffs, age 51
Director, Christopher Causey, age 50
Vice Chairman, Christopher Patusky, age 49
Director, R. Paul Gray, age 49
Director, Richard Giltner, age 49
Auditors: Ernst&YoungLLP

LOCATIONS

HQ: United Therapeutics Corporation
1040 Spring St., Silver Spring MD 20910
Phone: 301-608-9292   **Fax:** 301-608-9291
Web: www.unither.com

2012 Sales

	$ mil.	% of total
US	846	92
Other countries	69	8
Total	**916**	**100**

PRODUCTS/OPERATIONS

2012 Sales

	$ mil.	% of total
Cardiovascular products		
Remodulin	458	50
Tyvasco	325	36
Adcirca	122	13
Other	10	1
Total	**916**	**100**

Selected Products

Marketed
Remodulin (pulmonary arterial hypertension)
Tyvaso (pulmonary arterial hypertension)
Adcirca (pulmonary arterial hypertension)
In Development
8H9 MAb (metastatic brain cancer)
Beraprost (cardiovascular disease)
Ch14.18 (neuroblastoma)
Miglustat and other Glycobiology Antiviral Agents (hepatitis C and other infectious diseases)
IW001 (pulmonary disease)
Treprostinil (oral form for pulmonary arterial hypertension and peripheral vascular disease)

Selected Subsidiaries

Lung Biotechnology Hong Kong Limited
Lung Biotechnology (Nanjing) Co. Ltd.
Lung LLC
Lung RX Ltd. (UK)
Revivicor Inc.
United Therapeutics Europe Ltd. (UK)
Unither Biotech Inc. (Canada)
Unither Pharma LLC
Unither Pharmaceuticals Inc.

COMPETITORS

Abbott Labs	Gilead Sciences
Actelion	GlaxoSmithKline
American HealthChoice	NIPPON SHINYAKU
Anadys Pharmaceuticals	CO.LTD.
Ark Therapeutics Group	Novartis
AstraZeneca	Pfizer
Bayer HealthCare	Sandoz
Pharmaceuticals	Teva
Eli Lilly	

HISTORICAL FINANCIALS

Company Type: Public

Income Statement

FYE: December 31

	REVENUE ($ mil.)	NET INCOME ($ mil.)	NET PROFIT MARGIN	EMPLOYEES
12/12	916.0	304.4	33.2%	623
12/11	743.1	217.8	29.3%	543
12/10	603.8	105.9	17.5%	520
12/09	369.8	19.4	5.3%	410
12/08	281.5	(42.7)	—	360
Annual Growth	34.3%	—	—	14.7%

2012 Year-End Financials

Debt ratio: 16.9%	No. of shares (mil.): 50
Return on equity: 29.5%	Dividends
Cash ($ mil.): 154	Yield: —
Current ratio: 3.78	Payout: —
Long-term debt ($ mil.): 275	Market value ($ mil.): 2,680

	STOCK PRICE ($) FY Close	P/E High/Low		PER SHARE ($) Earnings	Dividends	Book Value
12/12	53.42	10	7	5.71	0.00	21.82
12/11	47.25	19	10	3.67	0.00	17.90
12/10	63.22	34	24	1.78	0.00	15.55
12/09	52.65	272	110	0.35	0.00	12.24
12/08	62.55	—	—	(0.94)	0.00	9.81
Annual Growth	(3.9%)	—	—	—	—	22.1%

Universal Display Corp

Universal Display is putting organic technology on display. The company through sponsored research agreements with Princeton University the University of Southern California and the University of Michigan is developing organic light-emitting diodes (OLEDs) for flat-panel displays solid-state lighting and other applications. Its OLED technologies use organic semiconductor materials to overcome limitations in LCDs such as poor image and color quality. Universal Display is licensing its technology to makers of televisions computer screens and consumer electronics devices. The company gets the majority of its revenues outside North America.

Universal Display is expanding through development and licensing agreements with partners such as Samsung Mobile Display and LG Display (together the two customers made up nearly 60% of sales). Other companies with licensing agreements include AU Optronics Moser Baer Seiko Epson Sony and the US government. The company is researching applications for the US Army that include head-mounted displays displays on durable metal foil and pen-like communication devices with roll-up displays. Universal Display owns exclusively licenses or has the sole right to sublicense more than 1000 issued and pending patents.

The company has expanded its portfolio with the acquisition of patents covering a wide array of OLED device designs architectures materials and processing technologies from Motorola Solutions. The purchase included applications ranging from stacked and flexible OLED technologies to phosphorescent transparent white and patterned technologies and materials.

Universal Display is also expanding its research efforts into related OLED display technologies such as phosphorescent OLEDs (PHOLEDs) printable PHOLEDs flexible OLEDs (FOLEDs) and transparent OLEDs (TOLEDs) as well as organic vapor phase deposition tools for manufacturing the displays. Universal Display is providing red PHOLED chemicals to Tohoku Pioneer a subsidiary of Pioneer Corp. for use in passive-matrix OLED cell phone displays.

Many applications for the company's products involve consumer electronics sales of which were severely depressed during the global recession. In addition the markets for flat-panel displays and lighting products are highly competitive. In 2010 sales were up more than 45% over 2009 primarily reflecting increased chemical sales and development revenues that doubled for the year. Universal Display continued to be unprofitable however in spite of increased sales

EXECUTIVES

Chief Technical Officer; Senior Vice President, Julia J. Brown, age 52, $356,125 total compensation
President; Chief Executive Officer; Director, Steven V. Abramson, age 61, $506,552 total compensation
EVP CFO Secretary Treasurer and Director, Sidney D. Rosenblatt, age 65, $506,552 total compensation
Chairman, Sherwin I. Seligsohn, age 77, $306,464 total compensation
Vice President - Technology Commercialization; General Manager - PHOLED Material Sales Business, Janice K. Mahon, age 55, $249,367 total compensation

VP Strategic Product Development and General Manager OLED Lighting and Custom Displays, Michael G. Hack, age 56

President CEO and Director, Steven V. Abramson, age 61

EVP CFO Secretary Treasurer and Director, Sidney D. Rosenblatt, age 65

Director, Lawrence (Larry) Lacerte, age 60

Director, Elizabeth H. Gemmill, age 67

Director, Leonard Becker, age 89

Director, C. Keith Hartley, age 70

Auditors: KPMGLLP

LOCATIONS

HQ: Universal Display Corporation
375 Phillips Blvd., Ewing NJ 08618
Phone: 609-671-0980   **Fax:** 609-671-0995
Web: www.universaldisplay.com

2010 Sales

	% of total
North	18
Other	82
Total	**100**

PRODUCTS/OPERATIONS

2010 Sales

	$ mil.	% of total
Development revenue	19	64
Commercial revenue	11	36
Total	**30**	**100**

COMPETITORS

AU Optronics	Merck KGaA
BASF SE	Microvision
Dow Chemical	Pioneer Corporation
DuPont	Samsung Electronics
Eastman Kodak	Sony
Epson	Sumitomo Chemical
Fujitsu	Texas Instruments
Idemitsu Kosan	Toshiba
LG Display	eMagin

HISTORICAL FINANCIALS

Company Type: Public

Income Statement

FYE: December 31

	REVENUE ($ mil.)	NET INCOME ($ mil.)	NET PROFIT MARGIN	EMPLOYEES
12/12	83.2	9.6	11.6%	117
12/11	61.2	3.1	5.1%	93
12/10	30.5	(19.9)	—	86
12/09	15.7	(20.5)	—	84
12/08	11.0	(19.1)	—	80
Annual Growth	65.6%	—	—	10.0%

2012 Year-End Financials

Debt ratio: —	No. of shares (mil.): 46
Return on equity: 2.7%	Dividends
Cash ($ mil.): 85	Yield: —
Current ratio: 12.00	Payout: —
Long-term debt ($ mil.): —	Market value ($ mil.): 1,188

	STOCK PRICE ($) FY Close	P/E High/Low		PER SHARE ($) Earnings	Dividends	Book Value
12/12	25.62	228	107	0.21	0.00	7.56
12/11	36.69	858	326	0.07	0.00	7.42
12/10	30.65	—	—	(0.53)	0.00	1.47
12/09	12.36	—	—	(0.56)	0.00	1.62
12/08	9.45	—	—	(0.53)	0.00	2.12
Annual Growth	28.3%	—	—	—	—	37.3%

Universal Electronics Inc.

Universal Electronics can help couch potatoes and TV junkies end multiple remote madness. The company makes One For All-branded universal remote controls with preprogrammed infrared codes allowing them to operate virtually any remote-capable device including TVs DVD players digital video recorders and set-top boxes. Its One For All remotes are sold by retailers worldwide. Universal Electronics also markets audiovisual accessories under the One For All name outside North America and it develops Nevo-branded wireless networking products. The company sells and licenses its technologies to consumer electronics and computer manufacturers and cable companies including DIRECTV its largest customer.

Geographic Reach

Universal Electronics rings up almost two-thirds of its sales overseas. China is its largest foreign market accounting for about a quarter of the company's international sales. Europe contributes about 13% of sales with the remainder originating in Asia and Latin America.

Operations

Universal Electronics operates about two dozen subsidiaries located in Argentina Cayman Islands France Germany Hong Kong (6) India Italy the Netherlands Singapore Spain Brazil British Virgin Islands (3) China (4) and the UK.

Sales and Marketing

DIRECTV is Universal Electronics' largest customer representing 17% of its 2012 sales up from 12% in 2011.

Financial Performance

The company's sales declined by about 1% in 2012 versus the prior year while net income fell 17% over the same period. Net sales of the company's Business lines (subscription broadcasting OEM and computing companies) declined 2% in 2012 compared with 2011 while its smaller Consumer business posted more than a 10% increase in sales. The company blamed the prolonged sluggish global economy for depressing television sales which affects its sales to consumer electronics companies.

Strategy

Demand for Universal Electronics' products has increased even as tough economic conditions lingered worldwide. Indeed sales have grown steadily albeit gradually (with the exception of the big jump in 2011) throughout the global financial crisis. The firm attributes the growth (and banks its future advances) on the steady adoption of high-definition TV and digital video recording devices which have become less expensive and more widely available as well as by increased subscription broadcasting rates.

Universal Electronics is pursuing further penetration of the more traditional OEM consumer electronics markets while also looking to expand its sales and marketing efforts with subscription broadcasters and OEMs in Asia Latin America and Europe. Its purchase of Enson in late 2010 enhanced its ability to compete in the OEM and subscription broadcasting markets particularly in Asia. In 2010 it launched a new subsidiary in Brazil which has fostered business growth in Latin America.

Mergers and Acquisitions

In November 2010 subsidiary UEI Hong Kong Private Ltd. acquired Enson Assets Ltd. for about $126 million. Hong Kong-based Enson was a leading manufacturer of remote controls and was a big supplier to the company prior to its acquisition. Enson operated two factories in China. The deal fortified Universal's relationships with such key electronics firms as Sony Panasonic and Toshiba

Ownership

Eagle Asset Management owns more than 17% of Universal Electronics' shares.

EXECUTIVES

SVP General Counsel and Secretary, Richard A. Firehammer Jr., age 55, $250,000 total compensation

Chairman and CEO, Paul D. Arling, age 50, $765 total compensation

EVP and Managing Director Europe, Paul J. M. Bennett, age 57, $348,500 total compensation

SVP, Graham S. Williams

SVP and CFO, Bryan M. Hackworth, age 43, $250,000 total compensation

EVP and General Manager US, Mark S. Kopaskie, age 55, $310,000 total compensation

SVP Subscription Broadcast, Olav B.M. Pouw

SVP Global Product Planning and Strategy, Ramzi S. Ammari

VP Cable Sales Americas, Stephen L. Gutman

VP-Retail Sls-EMEA/Intl, Menno V. Koopmans

VP Subscription Broadcast OEM Americas, Hrag G. Ohannessian

VP Global OEM Sales, Kenneth G. Sweeney

IR Contact Officer, Becky Herrick

Director, Gregory P. Stapleton, age 63

Director, Carl E. Vogel, age 56

Director, William C. Mulligan, age 60

Director, J. C. Sparkman, age 80

Director, Satjiv S. Chahil, age 62

Director, Edward K. (Ed) Zinser, age 56

Auditors: GrantThorntonLLP

LOCATIONS

HQ: Universal Electronics Inc.
6101 Gateway Dr., Cypress CA 90630-4841
Phone: 714-820-1000   **Fax:** 714-918-4100
Web: www.uei.com

2012 Sales

	$ mil.	% of total
US	165	36
International		
China	76	17
Rest of Asia	109	24
Europe	61	13
Latin America	28	6
Other countries	21	4
Total	**463**	**100**

PRODUCTS/OPERATIONS

2012 Sales

	$ mil.	% of total
Business	410	89
Consumer	52	11
Total	**463**	**100**

COMPETITORS

AMX Corp.	Philips Electronics
Crestron Electronics	SMK
Interlink Electronics	Sony Electronics
Logitech	Technicolor
Motorola Solutions	
Philips Consumer	
Lifestyle	

HISTORICAL FINANCIALS

Company Type: Public

Income Statement

FYE: December 31

	REVENUE ($ mil.)	NET INCOME ($ mil.)	NET PROFIT MARGIN	EMPLOYEES
12/12	463.0	16.5	3.6%	1,807
12/11	468.6	19.9	4.3%	9,803
12/10	331.7	15.0	4.5%	1,843
12/09	317.5	14.6	4.6%	565
12/08	287.1	15.8	5.5%	433
Annual Growth	12.7%	1.2%	—	42.9%

2012 Year-End Financials

Debt ratio: —
Return on equity: 6.8%
Cash ($ mil.): 44
Current ratio: 1.98
Long-term debt ($ mil.): —

No. of shares (mil.): 14
Dividends
Yield: —
Payout: —
Market value ($ mil.): 290

	STOCK PRICE ($) FY Close	P/E High/Low	PER SHARE ($) Earnings	Dividends	Book Value
12/12	19.35	19 10	1.10	0.00	16.74
12/11	16.87	22 11	1.31	0.00	15.55
12/10	28.37	27 15	1.07	0.00	14.13
12/09	23.22	22 10	1.05	0.00	12.40
12/08	16.22	30 11	1.09	0.00	11.24
Annual Growth	4.5%	— —	0.2%	—	10.5%

Universal Health Realty Income Trust

Universal Health Realty Income Trust (UHT) is a real estate investment trust (REIT) that primarily invests in health care related facilities. The REIT owns more than 45 facilities in 14 states including acute care rehabilitation medical office childcare centers and psychiatric hospitals. McAllen Medical Center in Texas is UHT's largest facility. Many properties are owned through limited liability companies in which the trust holds an equity interest. UHT's six hospital facilities hold about 1000 beds total. Subsidiaries of Universal Health Services (founded by UHT CEO Alan Miller) lease most of the trust's hospitals and generally provide their own maintenance and renovation services for those properties.

Universal Health Services owns about 7% of Universal Health Realty Income Trust; institutional investors own another 12%.

EXECUTIVES

VP Acquisition and Development, Timothy J. Fowler, age 57
Chief Financial Officer; Vice President, Charles F. Boyle, age 53
Chairman President and CEO, Alan B. Miller, age 74
VP Secretary and Treasurer, Cheryl K. Ramagano, age 50
Controller, Genevieve P. Owsiany
Auditors: KPMGLLP

LOCATIONS

HQ: Universal Health Realty Income Trust
367 S. Gulph Rd., King of Prussia PA 19406-0958
Phone: 610-265-0688 **Fax:** 610-768-3336
Web: www.uhrit.com

PRODUCTS/OPERATIONS

2007 Sales

	$ mil.	% of total
Base rentalUHS facilities	12	44
Base rentalNon-related parties	9	34
Bonus rentalUHS facilities	4	14
Tenant reimbursements and otherNon-related parties	2	8
Tenant reimbursements and otherUHS facilities	0	-
Total	**28**	**100**

2007 Properties

	No.
Medical office	36
Hospitals	
Acute	3
Behavioral	1
Rehabilitation	1
Sub-acute	1
Preschools	4
Total	**46**

COMPETITORS

G&L Realty Properties
HCP
Healthcare Realty Trust
Lend Lease (US)
Medical Properties Trust
Ventas

HISTORICAL FINANCIALS

Company Type: Public

Income Statement

FYE: December 31

	REVENUE ($ mil.)	NET INCOME ($ mil.)	NET PROFIT MARGIN	EMPLOYEES
12/12	53.9	19.4	36.1%	0
12/11	29.4	73.7	250.2%	0
12/10	28.8	16.3	56.5%	0
12/09	31.9	18.5	58.2%	0
12/08	29.1	11.6	39.9%	0
Annual Growth	16.6%	13.7%	—	—

2012 Year-End Financials

Debt ratio: 51.6%
Return on equity: 10.6%
Cash ($ mil.): 3
Current ratio: 14.60
Long-term debt ($ mil.): 197

No. of shares (mil.): 12
Dividends
Yield: 4.8%
Payout: 40.1%
Market value ($ mil.): 642

	STOCK PRICE ($) FY Close	P/E High/Low	PER SHARE ($) Earnings	Dividends	Book Value
12/12	50.61	32 25	1.54	2.46	14.00
12/11	39.00	7 6	5.83	2.43	14.91
12/10	36.53	29 23	1.33	2.42	11.49
12/09	32.03	23 16	1.56	2.38	11.66
12/08	32.91	40 24	0.98	2.34	12.21
Annual Growth	11.4%	— —	12.0%	1.3%	3.5%

Universal Insurance Holdings Inc

While some companies shy away from insuring homes in hurricane-prone Florida Universal Insurance Holdings is right at home there. Operating through its Universal Property & Casualty Insurance Company and American Platinum Property and Casualty Insurance Company subsidiaries the company underwrites distributes and administers homeowners property and personal liability insurance. Additional subsidiaries process claims perform claims adjustments and property inspections provide administrative duties and negotiate reinsurance. The company distributes its products through a network of independent agents.

Universal Property & Casualty Insurance (UPCIC) is taking its expertise in flood and wind coverage to other markets. While Florida remains its largest market it also operates in Georgia Hawaii and the Carolinas. Although it doesn't currently operate in Maryland and Massachusetts the company is licensed in those states as well.

American Platinum Property and Casualty Insurance (APPCIC) operates only in Florida. APPCIC began writing homeowners' multi-peril and inland marine insurance on homes worth more than $1 million in 2011 expanding the limits and coverages unavailable through UPCIC.

Chairman and CEO Bradley Meier and his parents control the company which he founded.

EXECUTIVES

Chairman President and Chief Executive Officer, Sean P. Downes, age 43, $820,800 total compensation
CFO, George R. De Heer, age 52
Chief Administration Officer, Stephen J. Donaghy
COO, Jon Springer
President CEO and Director; President Universal Property and Casualty Insurance, Bradley I. Meier, age 44
Secretary and Director, Norman M. Meier, age 73
Director, Reed J. Slogoff, age 43
Director, Michael A. (Mike) Pietrangelo, age 69
SVP COO and Director; COO and Director Universal Property and Casualty Insurance, Sean P. Downes, age 42
Director, Ozzie A. Schindler, age 43
Auditors: BlackmanKallickBartelsteinLLP

LOCATIONS

HQ: Universal Insurance Holdings Inc.
1110 W. Commerical Blvd. Ste. 300, Fort Lauderdale FL 33309
Phone: 954-958-1200 **Fax:** 954-958-1201
Web: www.universalinsuranceholdings.com

PRODUCTS/OPERATIONS

2011 Revenues

	$ mil.	% of total
Net premiums earned	198	88
Commissions	19	8
Realized gains on investments	2	1
Other revenue	6	3
Total	**225**	**100**

Selected Products and Services

Condominium policy
Dwelling coverage
Dwelling fire policy

Homeowners policy
Other structures coverage
Personal liability coverage
Personal property coverage
Renter's policy

COMPETITORS

Allstate	Liberty Mutual
Bouchard Insurance	State Farm
Citizens Property	Travelers Companies
Insurance	USAA
Federated National	United Insurance
Holding	Holdings
HCI Group	

HISTORICAL FINANCIALS

Company Type: Public

Income Statement
FYE: December 31

	REVENUE ($ mil.)	NET INCOME ($ mil.)	NET PROFIT MARGIN	EMPLOYEES
12/12	269.9	30.3	11.2%	279
12/11	225.8	20.1	8.9%	271
12/10	239.9	36.9	15.4%	252
12/09	210.6	28.7	13.7%	217
12/08	182.6	40.0	21.9%	182
Annual Growth	10.3%	(6.7%)	—	11.3%

2012 Year-End Financials

Debt ratio: 2.1%	No. of shares (mil.): 40
Return on equity: 19.2%	Dividends
Cash ($ mil.): 347	Yield: 8.6%
Current ratio: 5.40	Payout: 61.3%
Long-term debt ($ mil.): 20	Market value ($ mil.): 179

	STOCK PRICE ($) FY Close	P/E High/Low		PER SHARE ($) Earnings	Dividends	Book Value
12/12	4.38	6	4	0.75	0.46	4.00
12/11	3.58	12	7	0.50	0.32	3.74
12/10	4.87	7	4	0.92	0.52	3.55
12/09	5.87	8	3	0.71	0.54	3.00
12/08	2.43	7	2	0.99	0.49	2.71
Annual Growth	15.9%	—	—	(6.7%)	(1.6%)	10.3%

Universal Truckload Services Inc

Universal Truckload Services (UTSI) hasn't hauled freight beyond its own galaxy but the company does cover the US and parts of Canada (Ontario and Quebec) and Mexico. As an "asset-light" provider of truckload freight transportation the company operates through a network of truck owner-operators rather than employing drivers and investing heavily in equipment. It can call upon a fleet of some 2800 tractors and 4750 trailers including standard dry vans and flatbeds; the majority of its tractors and trailers are owned by others. Its flagship transportation segment transports general commodities such as automotive parts building materials paper food consumer goods furniture steel and other metals.

Geographic Reach

UTSI operates 90 terminals with key locations in Dearborn Michigan; Columbus Reading Latty and Cleveland Ohio; Gary Indiana; Dallas; South Kearney New Jersey; Garden City Georgia; Millwood West Virginia; Monroeville Pennsylvania; Memphis; Tampa; and Houston. The US accounts for around 95% of its total revenue.

Operations

Besides its transportation business which generates more than 70% of company revenues UTSI also serves customers through its intermodal and value-added services segments. Value-added services accounts for about 15% of the company's sales and matches customers' freight with carriers' capacity.

Intermodal support services (15%) involve picking up shipping containers at ports and railheads and delivering them by truck to customers. The company's intermodal support services is a key source of growth and is expanding its agent network as well as encouraging agents to promote the intermodal business line.

Financial Performance

Mostly as a result of a recent acquisition UTSI has enjoyed unprecedented growth over the years. Revenues jumped 48% from nearly $700 million to reach the $1 billion mark in 2012 for the first time in the company's history. Its profits more than tripled from $16 million in 2011 to reach a record high of $48 million in 2012. (Note: the company restated its 2011 numbers due to its 2012 acquisition of LINC Logistics.)

UTSI has benefited from the additional revenues stream from LINC and increased demand for its value-added services from both new and existing customers. The company was also helped by higher intermodal sales due to increased domestic container freight transportation as a whole.

Strategy

The trucking industry has entered a phase of consolidation. Based on rising insurance costs scarcity of capital fuel prices and expensive regulatory environmental equipment smaller trucking firms are combining through merger or acquisition. However UTSI's size and its continuing organic and acquisitive growth gives it a competitive edge over smaller more vulnerable trucking companies.

To establish one of the largest full-service asset light logistics services in North America UTSI in late 2012 purchased LINC Logistics a third-party logistics company for about $350 million including the assumption of debt. Prior to striking the LINC deal UTSI acquired more than 20 companies between 2000 and 2010. Acquired businesses typically retain their names so Universal Truckload Services operates under several brands including Great American Lines Louisiana Transportation Mason & Dixon Lines Universal Am-Can and Universal Logistics among others.

Now that the industry has made a comeback since the recession UTSI is once again targeting the automotive sector as it is one of the largest users of global outsourced logistics services. In 2012 it generated 31% of the company's revenues.

Ownership

Trucking magnates Matthew Moroun and his father Manuel Moroun control Universal Truckload Services (UTSI). Along with UTSI the Morouns control diversified transportation company CenTra and Matthew Moroun owns a significant stake in truckload carrier P.A.M. Transportation Services.

EXECUTIVES

Chairman, Matthew T. Moroun, age 40
CFO and Treasurer, David A. Crittenden, age 51
Vice Chairman and President, Donald B. Cochran, age 62, $352,036 total compensation
Executive Vice President and Secretary, Robert E. (Bob) Sigler, age 68, $305,036 total compensation
CEO, H. E. (Scott) Wolfe, age 67
Director, Manuel J. (Matty) Moroun, age 85
Director, Daniel C. Sullivan, age 72
Director, Frederick P. Calderone, age 62
Director, Ted B. Wahby, age 82
President and Vice-chairman of the Board of Directors, Donald B. Cochran, age 62
Director, Joseph J. Casaroll, age 76
Director, Richard P. Urban, age 71
Director, Daniel J. Deane
Auditors: KPMGLLP

LOCATIONS

HQ: Universal Truckload Services Inc.
12755 E. Nine Mile Rd., Warren MI 48089
Phone: 586-920-0100   **Fax:** 586-920-0258
Web: www.goutsi.com

2012 Sales

	$ mil.	% of total
US	999	96
Mexico	20	2
Canada	13	1
Europe	2	1
Other	1	-
Total	**1,037**	**100**

PRODUCTS/OPERATIONS

2012 Sales

Transportation services	741	71
Intermodal services	120	12

Selected Subsidiaries

Cavalry Logistics
Great American Lines Inc.
LINC
Louisiana Transportation Inc.
Mason & Dixon Lines Inc.
Mason Dixon Intermodal Inc.
NYP of Michigan Inc.
Universal Am-Can Ltd.
Universal Logistics Inc.

COMPETITORS

C.H. Robinson	Schneider National
Worldwide	Swift Transportation
Crete Carrier	U.S. Xpress
Hub Group	USA Truck
J.B. Hunt	Werner Enterprises
Landstar System	

HISTORICAL FINANCIALS

Company Type: Public

Income Statement
FYE: December 31

	REVENUE ($ mil.)	NET INCOME ($ mil.)	NET PROFIT MARGIN	EMPLOYEES
12/12	1,037.0	47.6	4.6%	2,519
12/11	699.7	15.8	2.3%	675
12/10	605.9	12.7	2.1%	714
12/09	503.2	4.9	1.0%	630
12/08	759.5	14.8	2.0%	649
Annual Growth	8.1%	33.8%	—	40.4%

2012 Year-End Financials

Debt ratio: 44.6%	No. of shares (mil.): 30
Return on equity: 43.3%	Dividends
Cash ($ mil.): 2	Yield: 10.9%
Current ratio: 1.63	Payout: 125.7%
Long-term debt ($ mil.): 146	Market value ($ mil.): 548

STOCK PRICE ($)		P/E		PER SHARE ($)		
	FY Close	High/Low		Earnings	Dividends	Book Value
12/12	18.25	12	8	1.59	2.00	1.91
12/11	18.15	18	12	1.01	1.00	10.42
12/10	15.92	24	17	0.80	1.00	10.48
12/09	18.10	61	34	0.31	1.00	9.66
12/08	14.16	30	13	0.93	0.00	10.28
Annual Growth (34.3%)	6.5%	—	—	14.3%	—	

US Silica Holdings, Inc.

Life's a beach for the sand-sellers at U.S. Silica. The industrial mineral company provides silica and aplite for the glass foundry chemical and construction industries; and fine ground silica and kaolin clay used to make paint plastics and ceramics. Its "frac sand" product —currently its fastest-growing offering –is used by natural gas and oil producers in hydraulic fracturing a process to boost oil and gas production. The company supplies customers in the US and Canada. In addition to its main facility in West Virginia U S. Silica also has a dozen plants in the East. A portfolio holding of private equity firm Golden Gate Capital U.S. Silica went public in 2012.

The move to go public coincides with an increasing demand for frac sand as advances in hydraulic fracturing methods allow for more effective and inexpensive production of oil and natural gas. Another area of promise for U.S. Silica is resin-coated sand which is also used in hydraulic fracturing. In fact the company predicts a 15% increase in demand annually for its frac sands and resin-coated sands. The company will use proceeds from it initial public offering (IPO) to invest in in those operations by upgrading its current plants and building a new resin-coated sand facility in Illinois. Upon completion of the public offering sister firm GGC RCS will be merged into U.S. Silica. However there are still some concerns around the safety of hydraulic fracturing which could potentially impact the demand of the company's products.

U.S. Silica fought against thousands of lawsuits that had been filed against the company since the early 2000s. Many of the suits claim that the company's silica causes people to fall ill from a rare lung disease called silicosis. However the company has diligently fought off the claims and even managed to expose a massive scam in which lawyers and doctors had fabricated diagnoses.

U.S. Silica was formed by the merger of Pennsylvania Glass and Ottawa Silica in 1987.

EXECUTIVES

CFO, Donald A. Merril, age 48
VP and General Manager Oil & Gas, Don D. Weinheimer
President and CEO, Bryan A. Shinn, age 52
VP Strategic Planning, Bradford B. (Brad) Casper, age 37
VP Operations, Michael L. (Mike) Winkler
General Counsel, James I. Manion, age 61
Director Mine Planning and Development, Jeff Jahn
Treasurer, Michael (Mike) Thompson
VP Supply Chain, Jason Tedrow

VP and General Manager Industrial and Specialties, John P. Blanchard
Vice President and Chief Administrative Officerhttp, Adam Yoxtheimer
Vice President of Strategic Planning, Brad Casper
VP and COO, Mike Winkler
Director, Charles W. (Charlie) Shaver, age 53
Director, Prescott H. Ashe, age 45
Director, Rajeev Amara, age 36
Auditors: GrantThorntonLLP

LOCATIONS

HQ: U.S. Silica Holdings Inc.
8490 Progress Dr. Ste. 300, Frederick MD 21701
Phone: 301-682-0600   **Fax:** 301-682-0691
Web: www.ussilica.com

PRODUCTS/OPERATIONS

2010 Sales

	$ mil.	% of total
Industrial & specialty products	175	72
Oil & gas proppants	69	28
Total	**245**	**100**

COMPETITORS

Carmeuse Lime & Stone Inc.	Martin Marietta Materials
Emerge Energy	Reserve Industries
Fairmount Minerals	Unimin
Hi-Crush	Vulcan Materials
Martin Marietta Aggregates	

HISTORICAL FINANCIALS
Company Type: Public

Income Statement
FYE: December 31

	REVENUE ($ mil.)	NET INCOME ($ mil.)	NET PROFIT MARGIN	EMPLOYEES
12/12	441.9	79.1	17.9%	785
12/11	295.6	30.2	10.2%	701
12/10	244.9	11.3	4.7%	685
12/09	191.6	5.5	2.9%	0
12/08	17.2	(1.8)	—	0
Annual Growth	125.2%	—	—	—

2012 Year-End Financials

Debt ratio: 37.1%
Return on equity: 44.6%
Cash ($ mil.): 61
Current ratio: 2.21
Long-term debt ($ mil.): 252

No. of shares (mil.): 52
Dividends
　Yield: 2.9%
　Payout: 33.3%
Market value ($ mil.): 885

	STOCK PRICE ($)	P/E		PER SHARE ($)		
	FY Close	High/Low		Earnings	Dividends	Book Value
12/12	16.73	15	6	1.50	0.50	4.38
Annual Growth	—	—	—	—	—	—

USANA Health Sciences Inc

Health is a matter of science at USANA Health Sciences. The company makes nutritional personal care and weight management products selling them through a direct-sales network marketing system of more than 250000 independent distributors (or associates). USANA Health Sciences also sells directly to 64000 customers deemed preferred. USANA's associates operate throughout North America as well as the Asia/Pacific region. The company's products portfolio includes nutritional supplements (76% of sales) and foods (12%) sold under the USANA brand and a line of skin and hair care products (9%) marketed under the Sense label. Chairman Myron Wentz owns more than 50% of the company he founded.

Operations

USANA operates its business through one reportable business segment. The direct seller which has operations in 20 markets worldwide makes the majority of its products at its facilities in Utah. It manufactures all of its tablet products and its beauty products in-house. It also develops capsules drink mixes nutrition bars and personal care items. Previously USANA served as a third-party manufacturer for a limited number of body care companies. At the time contract manufacturing accounted for a larger share of the company's sales. However once the Sense line took off USANA sold its third-party manufacturing business and devoted its manufacturing capacity to its own products. In keeping with its emphasis on developing science-based products the company has a collaboration with the Linus Pauling Institute at Oregon State University to research the role of vitamins and minerals in human health.

Geographic Reach

The company divides its operations into two regions: North America/Europe and Asia/Pacific. Together they cover about 15 countries. The latter accounts for more than 60% of revenue.

Sales and Marketing

USANA intends to fight sagging sales by increasing brand awareness and acquiring more associates and preferred customers in North America. Along with direct selling USANA sells its products in natural health food retailers via mail order and the Internet and in drug stores and supermarkets.

Financial Analysis

Sales growth in most countries where it operates helped USANA log an 11% increase in revenue in 2012. The results represented strong growth in the Phillipines China Mexico France and Belgium.The higher sales led to a 30% increase in net income; cash flow dipped slightly as the company bought back some of its stock.

Strategy

USANA looks to grow its business through efforts overseas. In 2012 it entered the Thailand market with a dozen products consisting of four key nutritional supplements and eight skin-care products. The company also expanded its operations into France and Belgium as well.

The company builds sales by getting its associates to manage their own business groups by recruiting and training others to sell the company's products. Sales associates are paid on sales generated by those groups. They might also receive compensation by purchasing products at wholesale prices and reselling them at retail prices. USANA attempts to recruit sales people who are looking for a second income and want to start a home-based business.

EXECUTIVES

Chief Financial Officer, Paul Jones
CEO, David A. (Dave) Wentz, age 42, $553,846 total compensation
Chairman, Myron W. Wentz, age 72
Executive Vice President of North America, Mark H. Wilson, age 48, $502,462 total compensation
EVP Research and Development, Timothy E. (Tim) Wood, age 64, $228,077 total compensation
Executive Director Product Development, John Cuomo
Senior Scientist, John McDonald
Chief Information Officer, Rick Stambaugh
President Chief Operating Officer, Fred W. Cooper, age 50, $559,846 total compensation
VP Special Projects, Bryan Wentz
President of the Americas Europe and South Pacific, Kevin G. Guest, age 50, $422,846 total compensation
President Asia Pacific, Deborah Woo, age 59, $397,056 total compensation
Vice President of Customer Service, Alan Bergstrom
Chief Legal Officer, James H. (Jim) Bramble, age 43
Chief Production Officer, Jim Brown
VP-Media & Events, Shawn McLelland
Vice President of Finance, Riley Timmer
Chief Communications Officer, Dan Macuga
Vice President of Human Resources, Marilyn Hardy
Director Marketing Public Relations and Social Media, Ashley Collins
Vice President of Research and Development, Carsten Smidt
Chief Marketing Officer, Doug Braun
Vice President of Financial Strategy, Doug Hekking
Executive Vice President of Research and Development, Tim Wood
Vice President of Project Management, Diane LeRoy
Director, Gilbert A. (Gil) Fuller, age 71
Director, Ronald S. Poelman, age 58
Director, Robert Anciaux, age 66
Director, Jerry G. McClain, age 71
Auditors: PricewaterhouseCoopersLLP

LOCATIONS

HQ: USANA Health Sciences Inc.
3838 W. Parkway Blvd., Salt Lake City UT 84120
Phone: 801-954-7100   **Fax:** -2258
Web: www.coop.co.il/en/index.asp

2013 Sales

	$ mil.	% of total
North America/Europe	244	38
Asia/Pacific		
Greater China	235	36
Southeast Asia	139	22
North Asia	29	4
Total	**648**	**100**

COMPETITORS

AIM International	NAI
AMS Health Sciences	NBTY
Amazon Herb	Nature' s Sunshine
Amway	Nu Skin
Avon	Perrigo
GNC	Reliv' International
Hain Celestial	Schiff Nutrition
Herbalife Ltd.	International
Lifeway Foods	Shaklee
Mannatech	Sunrider
Market America	ViSalus
Mary Kay	

HISTORICAL FINANCIALS

Company Type: Public

Income Statement

FYE: December 29

	REVENUE ($ mil.)	NET INCOME ($ mil.)	NET PROFIT MARGIN	EMPLOYEES
12/12	648.7	66.4	10.2%	1,330
12/11*	581.9	50.7	8.7%	1,290
01/11	517.6	45.6	8.8%	1,240
01/10	436.9	33.5	7.7%	930
01/09	429.0	29.9	7.0%	948
Annual Growth	10.9%	22.0%	—	8.8%

*Fiscal year change

2012 Year-End Financials

Debt ratio: —	No. of shares (mil.): 13
Return on equity: 37.0%	Dividends
Cash ($ mil.): 70	Yield: —
Current ratio: 1.87	Payout: —
Long-term debt ($ mil.): —	Market value ($ mil.): 437

	STOCK PRICE ($) FY Close	P/E High/Low		PER SHARE ($) Earnings	Dividends	Book Value
12/12	31.60	11	7	4.45	0.00	13.43
12/11*	30.37	13	7	3.26	0.00	11.64
01/11	43.45	15	8	2.86	0.00	9.08
01/10	31.90	17	8	2.17	0.00	4.86
01/09	33.36	26	10	1.85	0.00	2.07
Annual Growth	(1.3%)	—	—	24.5%	—	59.5%

*Fiscal year change

Utah Medical Products, Inc.

Utah Medical Products focuses on expectant moms new moms and newborns. The company designs and makes a variety of medical products used in labor and delivery and neonatal intensive care as well as products for other gynecological and female urinary problems. Products include disposable pressure transducers to monitor blood pressure intrauterine catheters used to monitor pressure in the womb during high-risk births and a device that clamps and cuts the umbilical cord and collects a blood sample from the cord. Utah Medical which has manufacturing facilities in the US and Ireland sells its products around the world through a domestic sales force and more than 100 international distributors.

More than two-thirds of the company's annual sales come from hospitals outpatient clinics and physicians' offices in the US. UM's neonatal intensive care products include oxygen hoods aspirators feeding tubes and chest-drainage tubes as well as peritoneal dialysis products for babies and children.

The company also makes products for assessment and treatment of cervical and uterine diseases and incontinence in women. For example UM's ENDOCURETTE allows tissue sampling in a doctor's office that can rule out precancerous or cancerous conditions while its LIBERTY System is a battery-operated system that women can use at home to treat and control urinary incontinence. In addition UM makes electrosurgical generators accessories and instruments such as speculas forceps and hands-free lights.

The firm expanded its women's health offerings through the acquisition of Femcare in 2011. The purchase added a tubal ligation product the Filshie Clip System.

HISTORY

Medical equipment maker Utah Medical (UM) was formed in 1978. In 1982 it went public and the next year bought Medicor (vital sign monitors). Medicor co-founder William Wallace —who was involved in developing many of of the company's patents —became president in 1987.

In 1992 Wallace was charged with breaking income tax and insider trading laws as a result of his 1987 purchase of UM shares acquired through a third party during negotiations for a supply contract with Baxter Healthcare. Despite his exoneration at trial Wallace was fired. He struck back with a wrongful termination suit and UM bought out his interest in 1993.

UM was disappointed by its 1995 launch of Cordguard which harvests umbilical cord cells for later therapeutic use. The next year UM lost its Baxter contract (and about half of its sales). In response UM opened facilities in Ireland and built its product line with the purchases of Columbia Medical (vacuum-assisted obstetrical delivery systems 1997) and C. R. Bard affiliate Gesco International (neonatal intensive care products 1998).

The company's R&D efforts were disappointing. Its Fowler EndoCurette endometrial tissue sampling device (developed with the Mayo Clinic) did not make it to market in 1999 and the company abandoned development of a fetal pH monitor.

In 1999 the company agreed to supply intrauterine pressure catheters to Novation LLC a purchaser serving 25% of US hospitals. But to escape from the pricing pressures of such contract sales the company revitalized its internal sales force to sell its products on the basis of quality. Continuing to enhance sales UM launched an online sales system in 2000. UM acquired Abcorp in 2004; the maker of fetal monitoring belts was a UM supplier prior to the acquisition.

EXECUTIVES

Chief Administrative Officer Treasurer Assistant Secretary and Director, Paul O. Richins, age 51, $97,724 total compensation
Chairman President CEO and Secretary, Kevin L. Cornwell, age 65, $256,100 total compensation
VP Product Development and Quality Assurance, Ben D. Shirley
VP Corporate Sales, Marcena H. Clawson
VP Manufacturing, Jean P. Teasdale
Chief Administrative Officer Treasurer Assistant Secretary and Director, Paul O. Richins, age 51
Director, Ernst G. Hoyer, age 74
Director, Barbara A. Payne, age 65
Director, James H. Beeson, age 70
Auditors: JonesSimkinsPC

LOCATIONS

HQ: Utah Medical Products Inc.
7043 S. 300 W., Midvale UT 84047-1048
Phone: 801-566-1200   **Fax:** 801-566-7305
Web: www.utahmed.com

2008 Sales

	$ mil.	% of total
US	19	69
Europe	4	17
Other	3	14
Total	**27**	**100**

PRODUCTS/OPERATIONS

2008 Sales

	$ mil.	% of total
Neonatal	7	27
Blood pressure monitoring & accessories	7	26
Obstetrics	7	25
Gynecology electrosurgery & urology	6	22
Total	**27**	**100**

Selected Products

Cordguard (umbilical cord management tool)
Deltran (needleless blood pressure monitoring system)
Disposa-Hood (infant oxygen hood)
Epitome (electrosurgical scalpel)
Finesse (electrosurgical generators)
FILTRESSE (surgical smoke filtration system)
Hemo-Nate (blood filtration system)
Intran Plus (transducer-tipped catheter)
LETZ (electrosurgical system)
Liberty (electrical stimulation device for urinary incontinence)
Nutri-Cath (enteral feeding tubes)

COMPETITORS

Becton Dickinson	Ethicon
Boston Scientific	Kimberly-Clark Health
CONMED Corporation	Rochester Medical
Cook Incorporated	Teleflex
Covidien	

HISTORICAL FINANCIALS

Company Type: Public

Income Statement

FYE: December 31

	REVENUE ($ mil.)	NET INCOME ($ mil.)	NET PROFIT MARGIN	EMPLOYEES
12/12	41.5	10.1	24.5%	189
12/11	37.8	7.4	19.6%	187
12/10	25.1	6.0	23.9%	172
12/09	25.9	6.2	24.1%	165
12/08	27.7	7.2	25.9%	186
Annual Growth	**10.6%**	**9.0%**	**—**	**0.4%**

2012 Year-End Financials

Debt ratio: 16.9%
Return on equity: 22.1%
Cash ($ mil.): 8
Current ratio: 2.37
Long-term debt ($ mil.): 9

No. of shares (mil.): 3
Dividends
  Yield: 2.6%
  Payout: 36.5%
Market value ($ mil.): 133

	STOCK PRICE ($) FY Close	P/E High/Low	PER SHARE ($) Earnings	Dividends	Book Value
12/12	36.05	13 10	2.74	0.97	13.77
12/11	27.00	14 12	2.03	0.95	11.20
12/10	26.88	18 15	1.65	1.67	10.44
12/09	29.32	17 12	1.72	0.93	10.52
12/08	21.95	17 11	1.86	0.91	9.66
Annual Growth	**13.2%**	**— —**	**10.2%**	**1.6%**	**9.3%**

Valhi, Inc.

Valhi keeps it interesting by pursuing a variety of things. The company's NL Industries unit operating through subsidiary Kronos is a leading maker of titanium dioxide pigment which is used to whiten and add opacity to fibers paper paint and plastic. Other subsidiaries include CompX (ergonomic computer support systems and office security products) Tremont (titanium metal products for the aerospace and other markets through its stake in Titanium Metals) and Waste Control Specialists (operator of hazardous-waste treatment facilities in Texas).

Geographic Reach

Valhi operates worldwide through its 17 fully owned and six majority owned subsidiaries. Its global operations span several geographical segments including North America Europe and Asia. Europe accounted for 47% of the company's revenues in 2012.

Operations

The company operates in three segments: Chemicals (titanium dioxide); Component Products (computer and office equipment); and Waste Management. Valhi subsidiary Kronos is among the world's largest makers of titanium dioxide behind DuPont Tronox and Huntsman. Other companies making up Harold Simmons' portfolio include wire-maker Keystone Consolidated Industries.

Financial Performance

Valhi's revenues increased by 1% in 2012 thanks to higher Waste Management revenues as the result of the inclusion of new low-level radioactive waste (LLRW) sites. The company's net income dropped by 27% in 2012 due to a loss on prepayment of debt and goodwill impairment charges.

Strategy

Bringing new waste sites online in 2012 the company commenced full scale operations at the Compact LLRW disposal facility and the Federal LLRW disposal location both in Texas.

To raise cash that year Valhi's CompX unit sold its furniture components business for $58 million.

Ownership

Chairman Harold Simmons and his family control about 93% of Valhi and thus control all of the company's subsidiaries.

EXECUTIVES

President CEO and Director, Steven L. (Steve) Watson, age 62, $1,773,200 total compensation
Vice Chairman, Glenn R. Simmons, age 85
Chairman, Harold C. Simmons, age 81, $4,044,000 total compensation
VP and Controller, Gregory M. (Greg) Swalwell, age 56, $942,300 total compensation
VP and Tax Director, Kelly D. Luttmer, age 49
SVP, William J. Lindquist, age 55, $1,037,000 total compensation
VP General Counsel and Assistant Secretary, J. Mark Hollingsworth, age 60
Secretary and Associate General Counsel, A. Andrew R. Louis, age 51
Personnel Manager, Kathy Brownlee
VP and CFO, Bobby D. O'Brien, age 55, $950,200 total compensation
VP and Assistant Secretary, Robert D. Graham, age 57, $1,197,800 total compensation
VP and Treasurer, John A. St. Wrba, age 56
President CEO and Director, Steven L. (Steve) Watson, age 62

Director, J. Walter Tucker Jr., age 87
Vice Chairman, Glenn R. Simmons, age 85
Director, Thomas E. Barry, age 70
Director, Norman S. Edelcup, age 77
Director, W. Hayden McIlroy, age 73
Auditors: PricewaterhouseCoopersLLP

LOCATIONS

HQ: Valhi Inc.
  5430 LBJ Fwy. Ste. 1700, Dallas TX 75240-2697
Phone: 972-233-1700   **Fax:** 972-448-1445
Web: www.valhi.net

2012 Sales

Europe	1,011	47
Asia	315	15
Total	**2,157**	**100**

PRODUCTS/OPERATIONS

2012 Sales

Chemicals	1,976	92
Waste Management	27	1
Total	**2,157**	**100**

COMPETITORS

Allegheny Technologies	Safety-Kleen
DuPont	Tronox
EnergySolutions	Tronox Limited
Huntsman Corp	US Ecology
Kemira	Waste Management
Perma-Fix	
Environmental	

HISTORICAL FINANCIALS

Company Type: Public

Income Statement

FYE: December 31

	REVENUE ($ mil.)	NET INCOME ($ mil.)	NET PROFIT MARGIN	EMPLOYEES
12/12	2,157.9	159.8	7.4%	2,555
12/11	2,141.0	217.5	10.2%	2,470
12/10	1,651.2	50.3	3.0%	3,412
12/09	1,341.8	(34.2)	—	3,402
12/08	1,578.0	(0.8)	—	3,547
Annual Growth	**8.1%**	**—**	**—**	**(7.9%)**

2012 Year-End Financials

Debt ratio: 28.7%
Return on equity: 22.9%
Cash ($ mil.): 366
Current ratio: 3.42
Long-term debt ($ mil.): 880

No. of shares (mil.): 342
Dividends
  Yield: 1.5%
  Payout: 40.7%
Market value ($ mil.): 4,275

	STOCK PRICE ($) FY Close	P/E High/Low	PER SHARE ($) Earnings	Dividends	Book Value
12/12	12.50	132 23	0.47	0.19	2.15
12/11	60.47	99 31	0.64	0.16	1.92
12/10	22.11	230 82	0.14	0.13	1.58
12/09	13.97	— —	(0.10)	0.13	1.25
12/08	10.70	— —	(0.00)	0.13	1.37
Annual Growth	**4.0%**	**— —**	**—**	**9.5%**	**11.9%**

Vascular Solutions Inc

Vascular Solutions helps interventional cardiologists intervene into veins. The company develops manufactures and markets catheters used during treatment of vascular conditions. Its product line includes the Pronto extraction catheter which removes arterial clots and other tools used to get under the skin and into blood vessels. Its hemostat products include the D-Stat a thrombin-infused bandage used to control bleeding following catheterization. It also makes the Vari-Lase a laser system for treating varicose veins. Vascular Solutions markets the devices to interventional cardiologists and radiologists through its own sales team in the US; it uses independent distributors overseas.

The company manufactures its products at its main facility in Minnesota. It maintains manufacturing and supply agreement with King Pharmaceuticalsgiving King marketing rights to the company's ThrombiGel hemostat products in non-interventional cardiology markets. In exchange King supplies Vascular Solutions with thrombin (a coagulation protein) for use in devices that aren't in competition with King's products. The company also purchases thrombin from Sigma-Aldrich Fine Chemicals for its international products.

Vascular Solutions' growth strategy is a mix of new product development and acquisitions to extend its product line. It develops new products and next-generation versions of its existing medical devices through its own research and development efforts and by partnering with other medical device makers through marketing and licensing deals.

Historically the company maintained a fairly selective pace with its acquisitions. However in 2010 it first paid almost $6 million to acquire two guided-needle access products from Escalon Medical then later in the year spent another $6.5 million to acquire a line of snare and retrieval products. The deal brought in the EXPRO Elite and MICRO Elite snares and the Oracle retrieval system which it had been distributing for Radius Medical Technologies. Vascular Solutions then took over manufacturing the products at its own facilities.

In 2011 the company made a similar move and acquired the assets of Zerusa Ltd consisting of a hemostatic valve used during catheterization which it had been distributing in the US. In 2012 it paid $1.5 million for Accumed Systems' radial artery access wrist-positioning splint product assets and another $3 million for the Venture line of guidewire control catheters from St. Jude Medical. In late 2010 the company struck an agreement with Shepherd Scientific to distribute that company's docking station and device organizer which are used to keep guidewires and catheters neat and available during medical procedures. Internationally the company shuttered its German distribution subsidiary in 2008 but established a subsidiary in Ireland in 2011 to run its newly acquired Zerusa hemostasis valve production.

Sales of its catheter products have grown in recent years while its hemostat and vein products have remained steady or flat. Damages awarded in a legal settlement helped to nudge up the company's 2008 and 2010 net income.

EXECUTIVES

SVP Operations, Charmaine Sutton

CEO, Howard C. Root, $330,000 total compensation
Chairman, John Erb
SVP Finance CFO and Corporate Secretary, James Hennen, $200,000 total compensation
VP Quality, Brett Demchuk, age 49, $163,000 total compensation
SVP Worldwide Sales, William (Bill) Rutstein
VP Sales Operations, Susan Christian, age 44
Vice President - Corporate Development, Phillip Nalbone
Vice President; General Counsel; Corporate Secretary, Michael Blum
VP Manufacturing Engineering, Jonathan (Jon) Hammond
VP Marketing, Carrie Powers
Director, Richard J. (Dick) Nigon, age 65
CEO and Director, Howard C. Root, age 52
Director, John Erb, age 64
Director, Martin J. Emerson, age 49
Director, Michael Kopp, age 56
Director, Jorge Saucedo, age 49
Independent Director, Paul Connell
Independent Director, Paul OConnell
Auditors: BakerTillyVirchowKrauseLLP

LOCATIONS

HQ: Vascular Solutions Inc.
6464 Sycamore Ct., Minneapolis MN 55369
Phone: 763-656-4300 **Fax:** 763-656-4251
Web: www.vascularsolutions.com

PRODUCTS/OPERATIONS

2011 Sales

	$ mil.	% of total
Products		
Hemostat products	23	25
License & collaboration	3	4

Selected Products

Catheter products
  Elite Snares
  Gopher Cold catheter
  GuideLiner
  Guardian II hemostasis valve
  Langston catheter
  Minnie support catheter
  Pronto Extraction catheters
  SmartNeedle Vascular Access System
  SuperCross microcatheter
  VSI guidewires micro-HV introducer kit
Hemostat products
  D-Stat Dry hemostat bandage
  D-Stat Flowable topical hemostat
  D-Stat Rad Band
Vein products
  Auto-Fill anesthetic syringe
  Klein infiltration pump
  Vari-Lase procedure kit
Other products
  Acolysis ultrasound thrombolysis system

COMPETITORS

Abbott Labs	Johnson & Johnson
AngioDynamics	Kensey Nash
Bard	MEDRAD
Boston Scientific	Medtronic
Cook Incorporated	Merit Medical Systems
Covidien	Spectranetics
HemCon Medical Technologies	St. Jude Medical
	Terumo

HISTORICAL FINANCIALS

Company Type: Public

Income Statement

FYE: December 31

	REVENUE ($ mil.)	NET INCOME ($ mil.)	NET PROFIT MARGIN	EMPLOYEES
12/13	110.5	11.1	10.1%	406
12/12	98.3	9.9	10.1%	377
12/11	89.9	9.7	10.8%	355
12/10	78.4	21.3	27.3%	296
12/09	68.4	5.3	7.9%	266
Annual Growth	12.7%	20.0%	—	11.2%

2013 Year-End Financials

Debt ratio: —
Return on equity: 12.8%
Cash ($ mil.): 30
Current ratio: 5.95
Long-term debt ($ mil.): —

No. of shares (mil.): 16
Dividends
  Yield: —
  Payout: —
Market value ($ mil.): 393

	STOCK PRICE ($) FY Close	P/E High/Low	PER SHARE ($) Earnings	Dividends	Book Value
12/13	23.15	34 21	0.65	0.00	5.68
12/12	15.80	25 16	0.60	0.00	4.69
12/11	11.13	23 17	0.57	0.00	4.07
12/10	11.72	10 6	1.26	0.00	3.80
12/09	8.39	28 15	0.33	0.00	2.44
Annual Growth	28.9%	— —	18.5%	—	23.5%

VCA Antech Inc

When VCA Antech says health care has gone to the dogs it means it. VCA operates the nation's largest chain of animal hospitals –more than 600 in some 40 states and Canada. Its hospitals offer basic wellness checkups dental care neutering and spaying vaccinations and specialty surgeries. With about 55 diagnostic laboratories nationwide VCA also interacts with the animal kingdom by testing blood tissue and urine samples for more than 16000 animal hospitals and practices universities and government agencies. Founded in 1986 as Veterinary Centers of America the company has grown over the years through acquisitions of other animal hospitals and veterinary product suppliers.

Geographic Reach

The US accounts for about 95% of VCA Antech's revenue. The company expanded into Canada in 2012 where it operates more than 45 animal hospitals and four laboratories in three provinces.

Operations

VCA's fast-growing chain of animal hospitals accounts for three-quarters of its sales. About 7.4 million animals visited its hospitals in 2012 compared with 6.8 million in 2010. VCA's 50-plus diagnostic laboratories account for almost 20% of sales. In addition to providing animal care and testing VCA Antech sells diagnostic equipment and other medical technology products and related services to the veterinary market.

Sales and Marketing

VCA takes a multifaceted approach to growing its business seeking to increase the number of visits by existing clients and attracting new customers through online and offline initiatives. The company's HealthyPet Magazine focuses and pet care and wellness. VCA Antech also reaches pet owners via direct mail and collateral material available at its animal hospitals. It also enters into referral arrangements with local pet shops and humane societies. Marketing and advertising expenses amounted to $7.6 million in 2012 versus $3.2 million and $2.8 million in 2011 and 2010 respectively.

Financial Performance

The company reported $1.7 billion in revenue in 2012 a 14% increase compared with 2011. Net income fell 52% over the same period to about $45.5 million. The double-digit increase in revenue was primarily due to acquisitions of animal hospitals in the US and Canada although sales at existing facilities increased as well. Indeed 2012 capped a decade growth for the company during which revenue has more than tripled. However profits have been trending downward in recent years due to the slow economic recovery increased expenses and other factors.

Strategy

VCA's aggressive expansion strategy has driven steady revenue growth over the years despite the deep recession and weak recovery taking a toll on consumer confidence. Nevertheless the company continues to pursue acquisitions. With its business picking up in the US in 2011 the company entered the Canadian market in 2012 with its purchase of the remaining shares of Calgary-based Associate Veterinary Clinics (AVC) the operator of 44 hospitals in Alberta British Columbia and Ontario. (VCA which first invested in AVC in 2008 spent $77 million to acquire the company outright.) AVC is Canada's largest pet health care service company.

VCA is also extending its reach into new areas of pet healthcare business. In 2011 it purchased MediMedia Animal Health (better known as Vetstreet) from parent MediMedia for $146 million. Vetstreet is a provider of Web and educational content and marketing services geared to veterinarians and pet owners. With the addition of Vetstreet's online communications expertise VCA hopes to spur pet owner visits to its clinics and drive business for its more than 16000 clients involved in animal health. It will also attract veterinarians with Vetstreet's continuing education programs.

Ownership

Veritas Asset Management (UK) Ltd./The Real Return Group Ltd. owns about 10% of the company's shares.

EXECUTIVES

VP Principal Accounting Officer and Controller, Dawn R. Olsen, age 54, $219,615 total compensation
Senior Vice President - Development, Neil Tauber, age 62, $383,968 total compensation
Co-Founder Chief Operating Officer Vice President Secretary Director, Arthur J. Antin, age 66, $567,840 total compensation
Chief Financial Officer Vice President, Tomas W. (Tom) Fuller, age 55, $383,968 total compensation
Chairman of the Board; President; Chief Executive Officer, Robert L. (Bob) Antin, age 63, $892,320 total compensation
President - Laboratory Division; Antech Diagnostic, Josh Drake, age 45, $325,000 total compensation
Vice President Controller, Jeff M. Framer
Director, John M. Baumer, age 45
Director, Frank Reddick, age 60
Director, John A. Heil, age 61
Director, John B. Chickering Jr., age 64
Auditors: KPMGLLP

LOCATIONS

HQ: VCA Antech Inc.
12401 W. Olympic Blvd., Los Angeles CA 90064-1022
Phone: 310-571-6500 **Fax:** 310-571-6700
Web: www.vcaantech.com

2012 Hospitals

California	110
Washington	33
New York	30
Massachusetts	27
Illinois	19
Virginia	19
Colorado	18
Georgia	18
Connecticut	16
Arizona	14
New Jersey	13
Indiana	12
Maryland	12
Ohio	12
Oregon	12
North Carolina	8
Nevada	7
Hawaii	6
Minnesota	6
New Mexico	6
Alaska	5
New Hampshire	4
Wisconsin	4
Missouri	3
Nebraska	3
Rhode Island	3
Louisiana	2
Tennessee	2
Vermont	2
Alabama	1
Kentucky	1
Utah	1
West Virginia	1
Canada	26

PRODUCTS/OPERATIONS

2012 Sales

		% of total
Animal hospitals	1,331	75
Other	112	7
Total	**1,699**	**100**

Selected Mergers and Acquisitions

2012
Associate Veterinary Clinics Ltd. ($77 million; Calgary Canada; animal healthcare)
2011
MediMedia USA Inc. ($146 million; Yardley Pennsylvania; online communications)
BrightHeart Veterinary Centers ($50 million; Charlotte North Carolina; animal hospital)

COMPETITORS

IDEXX Labs	PetMed
Medical Management	PetSmart
International	

HISTORICAL FINANCIALS

Company Type: Public

Income Statement

FYE: December 31

	REVENUE ($ mil.)	NET INCOME ($ mil.)	NET PROFIT MARGIN	EMPLOYEES
12/12	1,699.6	45.5	2.7%	10,500
12/11	1,485.3	95.4	6.4%	9,900
12/10	1,381.4	110.2	8.0%	9,400
12/09	1,314.5	131.4	10.0%	8,500
12/08	1,277.4	132.9	10.4%	9,000
Annual Growth	**7.4%**	**(23.5%)**	**—**	**3.9%**

2012 Year-End Financials

Debt ratio: 30.1%	No. of shares (mil.): 88
Return on equity: 3.9%	Dividends
Cash ($ mil.): 68	Yield: —
Current ratio: 1.31	Payout: —
Long-term debt ($ mil.): 591	Market value ($ mil.): 1,860

	STOCK PRICE ($) FY Close	P/E High/Low	PER SHARE ($) Earnings	Dividends	Book Value
12/12	21.05	46 35	0.51	0.00	13.39
12/11	19.75	24 14	1.09	0.00	12.76
12/10	23.29	23 15	1.27	0.00	11.59
12/09	24.92	18 12	1.53	0.00	10.22
12/08	19.88	28 9	1.55	0.00	8.40
Annual Growth	**1.4%**	**—**	**(24.3%)**	**—**	**12.4%**

Vector Group Ltd

Vector Group is small potatoes next to Big Tobacco running a distant fourth in the US market. The holding company's Liggett and Vector Tobacco subsidiaries manufacture discount cigarettes under brands including Liggett Select Grand Prix Pyramid and Eve and several private-label brands of cigarettes for other companies including the USA brand. The company manufactures cigarettes in North Carolina and distributes them throughout the US. Vector Group's real estate unit New Valley owns about 70% stake in the New York City broker Douglas Elliman Realty. It's looking to acquire other properties. All of Vector Group's revenue is derived from the sale of discount cigarettes.

HISTORY

Former computer analyst Bennett LeBow founded Brooke Partners in 1980 (renamed Brooke Group in 1990) to acquire troubled companies and turn them around. Many of LeBow's early investments were in the computer industry. He eventually expanded into other areas including tobacco (with the purchase of Liggett in 1986).

Founded in 1822 by the Liggett family as a snuff maker and joined by George Myers in 1873 Liggett & Myers produced several popular cigarette brands including L&M and Chesterfield. Liggett slipped during the 1950s and 1960s by failing to exploit the market for filtered and low-tar cigarettes. Although Liggett launched a successful discount brand under LeBow (Pyramid) its US market share continued to dwindle.

Like Liggett many of LeBow's other businesses were slipping. In 1993 Western Union (bought in 1987 and renamed New Valley) and computer maker MAI Systems (bought in 1985) entered Chapter 11 bankruptcy. That year LeBow paid about $20 million to Brooke Group shareholders who sued a group of company officers who they believed were stripping assets and using the company for personal loans.

Frustrated in the US Brooke Group turned to developing new markets. In 1993 the company began a joint venture with Russian cigarette maker Ducat. In 1995 New Valley emerged from bankruptcy.

In 1997 the company made deals with 41 states regarding tobacco-related Medicaid payments. But most of Liggett's state deals were negated when in late 1998 it joined a $206 billion settlement hammered out with 46 states by its much larger rivals. As part of the deal Liggett did not have to chip in as long as its market share stayed below its 1997 level of 1.67%.

To cut debt Liggett sold its L&M Chesterfield and Lark brands to Philip Morris for $300 million in 1999. (The deal also kept Liggett's market share well below 1.67%.) Also in 1999 an Alabama court rejected an agreement that would have allowed Liggett to settle tobacco-related lawsuits in a limited fund. That year the US government filed a massive lawsuit against the Big Tobacco companies to recover health care costs and profits allegedly derived from fraud.

In 2000 the firm changed its name to Vector Group to remove the old name's stigma of sick-smoker lawsuits. The company said it would appeal a Florida's $790 million verdict against it. Later Vector Group sold its Liggett-Ducat subsidiary (Russia) to cigarette manufacturer Gallaher for $400 million. A Florida judge upheld the July 2000 verdict; meanwhile Vector angled for a global settlement of all punitive cases payable to a public health trust fund over a 30-year period.

The company along with Brown & Williamson Lorillard (Carolina Group) Philip Morris and R.J. Reynolds faced paying Florida smokers $145 billion after losing a lengthy court battle in 2000. Three years later a state appeals court threw out the case saying that the thousands of Florida smokers named in the case could not lump their complaints in a single lawsuit. That decision is now under review by the Florida Supreme Court.

In late 2001 Vector launched OMNI a reduced-carcinogen cigarette which received a lukewarm acceptance and hit a slow burn in sales. OMNI generated a disappointing $5.1 million in revenue for 70.7 million units. (Vector gave up on the product several years later.)

The next year the company created Liggett Vector Brands a new unit that combines the sales and marketing functions of its Liggett Group and Vector Tobacco subsidiaries. Vector also bought The Medallion Company a discount cigarette manufacturer (USA and Marlin brands) for $110 million.

Vector closed its Timberlake North Carolina production plant and laid off 150 workers in 2003. The company moved operations to a nearby cigarette plant in Mebane North Carolina.

Vector announced in August 2004 that it would sell its reduced-nicotine cigarette brand QUEST on the Internet beginning in 2005 and is seeking FDA approval to sell QUEST as a device for quitting smoking. (In 2009 the company decided against seeking FDA approval of Quest as a smoking cessation aide citing the significant time and expense involved in seeking it.) However it switched gears in November 2004 by putting an indefinite hold on a national rollout of QUEST. The company said a review of marketing data made such a move necessary. Vector laid off approximately 330 full-time and 135 part-time positions that December.

In March 2005 the company began supplying Montego deep-discount brand cigarettes exclusively to more than 2200 Circle K and Mac's convenience stores in the US. In November it entered into a similar deal with Sunoco which operates 800-plus Sonoco APlus convenience stores to make and supply Silver Eagle brand cigarettes to its stores.

Howard Lorber succeeded LeBow as CEO in 2006. Later that year Vector entered into a settlement with the Internal Revenue Service that called for the company to pay about $42 million related to a gain stemming from a 1998 and 1999 deal with Philip Morris.

To tap the popular and more politically correct smokeless tobacco market Vector launched Grand Prix-branded snus in May 2008. The pouched tobacco product is made in Sweden and rolls out in a trio of varieties.

EXECUTIVES

Vice President General Counsel Secretary, Marc N. Bell, age 53, $400,000 total compensation
Vice President Chief Financial Officer Treasurer, J. Bryant Kirkland III, age 47, $375,000 total compensation
Executive Vice President, Richard J. (Dick) Lampen, age 60, $800,000 total compensation
President Chief Executive Officer, Howard M. Lorber, age 64, $2,807,729 total compensation
Chairman, Bennett S. LeBow, age 75, $3,950,000 total compensation
President and CEO Liggett Group and Liggett Vector Brands and Director, Ronald J. Bernstein, age 59, $829,959 total compensation
Investor Relations, Carrie Bloom
IR Contact Officer, Jonathan Doorley
President CEO and Director, Howard M. Lorber, age 64
President and CEO Liggett Group and Liggett Vector Brands and Director, Ronald J. Bernstein, age 59
Director, Robert J. Eide, age 60
Director, Jeffrey S. Podell, age 72
Director, Jean E. Sharpe, age 67
Director, Henry C. Beinstein, age 70
Independent Director, Stanley Arkin
Auditors: PricewaterhouseCoopersLLP

LOCATIONS

HQ: Vector Group Ltd.
100 SE 2nd St., Miami FL 33131
Phone: 305-579-8000   **Fax:** 305-579-8001
Web: www.vectorgroupltd.com

PRODUCTS/OPERATIONS

2012 Sales

	$ mil.	% of total
Tobacco	1,084	100
Real estate - -		
Total	**1,084**	**100**

Selected Cigarette Brands

Eve
Grand Prix
Jade (licensed)
Liggett Select
Pyramid
USA

Selected Subsidiaries

Liggett Group LLC
Liggett Vector Brands LLC
New Valley LLC
Vector Tobacco Inc.
VGR Holing LLC

COMPETITORS

800-JR Cigar	RE/MAX
Century 21 Real Estate	Reynolds American
Commonwealth Brands	Smokin Joes
Lorillard	Sotheby's
Philip Morris USA	International Realty

HISTORICAL FINANCIALS

Company Type: Public

Income Statement

FYE: December 31

	REVENUE ($ mil.)	NET INCOME ($ mil.)	NET PROFIT MARGIN	EMPLOYEES
12/12	1,084.5	30.6	2.8%	587
12/11	1,133.3	75.0	6.6%	559
12/10	1,063.2	54.0	5.1%	512
12/09	801.4	24.8	3.1%	435
12/08	565.1	60.5	10.7%	430
Annual Growth	17.7%	(15.7%)	—	8.1%

2012 Year-End Financials

Debt ratio: 57.3%
Return on equity: ***,***.*%
Cash ($ mil.): 405
Current ratio: 3.27
Long-term debt ($ mil.): 586

No. of shares (mil.): 94
Dividends
  Yield: 10.8%
  Payout: 463.3%
Market value ($ mil.): 1,404

	STOCK PRICE ($) FY Close	P/E High/Low	PER SHARE ($) Earnings	Dividends	Book Value
12/12	14.87	56 44	0.33	1.54	(0.84)
12/11	17.76	23 19	0.84	1.40	(1.02)
12/10	17.32	34 22	0.61	1.40	(0.53)
12/09	14.00	60 40	0.28	1.33	(0.05)
12/08	13.62	28 19	0.63	1.27	0.40
Annual Growth	2.2%	— —(14.6%)		5.0%	

Ventas, Inc.

Ventas puts a roof over many a gray or aching head. A real estate investment trust (REIT) Ventas owns more than 1400 health care properties including senior housing communities skilled nursing facilities hospitals and medical office buildings. The REITs properties are located throughout the US and Canada. Ventas leases more than a third of its properties to long-term care providers Sunrise Senior Living Brookdale Senior Living and Kindred Healthcare. The company also is a major player in medical office buildings owning or managing nearly 21 million square feet of space. Already the largest owner of senior housing facilities in the US Ventas has been busily building its portfolio through acquisitions.

Geographic Reach

Chicago-based Ventas has properties in 46 US states and the District of Columbia. California is the REIT's largest market accounting for 14% of 2012 revenue. New York contributes about 10%. Overall the US accounts for 96% of Ventas' revenue. Two Canadian provinces account for the rest.

Operations

The health care REIT's Liilbridge Healthcare Services (acquired in 2010)subsidiary and its ownership interest in PMB Real Estate Services provide medical office building management leasing marketing and facility development and advisory services to hospitals and health care systems throughout the US.

Financial Analysis

Acquisitive Ventas has seen its revenue more than double since 2010 to about $2.5 billion in 2012. The health care REIT's 2012 sales increased by 41% vs. 2011 while net income declined by less than 1% over the same period. Medical office buildings account for a growing portion of Ventas' sales after a boost from the 2011 acquisition of Nationwide Health Properties. Cash flow from operations is also surging approaching $1 billion in 2012 (up from about $447 in 2010).

Mergers and Acquisitions

The REIT has been investing more in medical office buildings of late. It created a network of medical office building partnerships with other firms and has several multi-tenant projects under development. Ventas's biggest transaction to date came in 2011 when the REIT bought rival Nationwide Health Properties for some $7.6 billion. The deal nearly doubled the size of Ventas' portfolio. Earlier that year the company bought the real estate assets of Atria Senior Living Group one of the country's largest facilities operators. It paid $1.3 billion in stock in the deal which included nearly 120 senior housing communities located in wealthy metro areas around New York New England and Canada.

Other recent buys include the 2010 acquisition of Lillibridge Health Services which added more than 150 medical office buildings and ambulatory care centers to its holdings and the purchase of minority interests in nearly 60 communities from Sunrise Senior Living (bringing its Sunrise-managed portfolio to almost 80 properties). In 2012 Ventas added to its Lillibridge arm with the acquisition of Cogdell Spencer. The deal which includes more than 70 medical office properties expanded Ventas' holdings to about 21 million sq. ft. of owned and managed properties.

EXECUTIVES

EVP Chief Administrative Officer and General Counsel, T. Richard Riney, $336,000 total compensation
Chairman and CEO, Debra A. Cafaro, $630,000 total compensation
EVP and CFO, Richard A. Schweinhart, $362,250 total compensation
President, Raymond J. Lewis, $380,000 total compensation
SVP and Chief Portfolio Officer, Timothy A. Doman
SVP Tax, Brian K. Wood, age 51
Chief Accounting Officer and Controller, Robert J. Brehl, age 51
Senior Vice President Medical Property Operations, Vincent M. Cozzi, age 47
EVP; President and CEO Lillibridge Healthcare Services, Todd W. Lillibridge
EVP and Chief Investment Officer, John D. Cobb
SVP and CIO, John K. Hart
Director, Jay M. Gellert, age 59
Director, Ronald G. Geary, age 65
Director, Douglas Crocker II, age 73
Director, Robert D. (Bob) Reed, age 60
Director, Sheli Z. Rosenberg, age 71
Director, Glenn J. Rufrano, age 63
Director, Thomas C. Theobald, age 75
Director, James D. (Denny) Shelton, age 59
Independent Director, Richard Gilchrist
Auditors: Ernst&YoungLLP

LOCATIONS

HQ: Ventas Inc.
  111 S. Wacker Dr. Ste. 4800, Chicago IL 60606
Phone: 312-660-3800   **Fax:** 312-660-3850
Web: www.ventasreit.com

2012 Sales

	$ mil.	% of total
US	2,389	96
Canada	96	4
Total	**2,485**	**100**

PRODUCTS/OPERATIONS

2012 Properties

	No.
Seniors housing	679
Skilled nursing & other	395
Medical office	321
Hospitals	47
Total	**1,442**

2012 Sales

	$ mil.	% of total
Resident fees & services	1,229	49
Triple-net leased	831	33
Medical office buildings	362	15
Loans & investments	39	2
Medical office building & other services	20	1
Interest & other	1	-
Total	**2,485**	**100**

COMPETITORS

HCP
HCR ManorCare
Health Care REIT
Healthcare Realty Trust
LTC Properties
Medical Properties Trust
National Health Investors
Omega Healthcare Investors
Sabra Health Care
Senior Housing Properties
Sun Healthcare
Universal Health Realty

HISTORICAL FINANCIALS

Company Type: Public

Income Statement

FYE: December 31

	REVENUE ($ mil.)	NET INCOME ($ mil.)	NET PROFIT MARGIN	EMPLOYEES
12/12	2,485.3	361.7	14.6%	439
12/11	1,764.9	363.2	20.6%	328
12/10	1,016.8	249.7	24.6%	263
12/09	936.0	269.3	28.8%	61
12/08	929.7	226.2	24.3%	63
Annual Growth	**27.9%**	**12.4%**	—	**62.5%**

2012 Year-End Financials

Debt ratio: 44.3%	No. of shares (mil.): 291
Return on equity: 3.8%	Dividends
Cash ($ mil.): 67	Yield: 3.8%
Current ratio: 0.05	Payout: 201.6%
Long-term debt ($ mil.): 8,413	Market value ($ mil.): 18,890

	STOCK PRICE ($) FY Close	P/E High/Low		PER SHARE ($) Earnings	Dividends	Book Value
12/12	64.72	54	43	1.23	2.48	31.50
12/11	55.13	36	27	1.58	2.30	32.47
12/10	52.48	35	26	1.56	2.14	15.18
12/09	43.74	26	12	1.74	2.05	15.74
12/08	33.57	32	11	1.62	2.05	14.99
Annual Growth	**17.8%**	—	—	**(6.7%)**	**4.9%**	**20.4%**

Verisk Analytics Inc

Insurance is a risky business and Verisk Analytics is in the business of helping to manage that risk. The company compiles data designed to detect fraud and predict loss for customers in the US property and casualty insurance health care and mortgage industries. Its Decision Analytics unit provides health care claim payers and mortgage lenders with predictive models loss estimation tools and fraud ID applications. Its Risk Assessment unit runs databases that hold billions of records containing statistical and underwriting data used to price insurance policies and write policy language. Verisk was created by subsidiary Insurance Services Office (ISO) as a means of going public; Verisk completed its IPO in 2009.

Geographic Reach

Verisk has offices in more than 20 US states as well as international locations in countries including Canada China Denmark Germany India Israel Japan Nepal Singapore and the UK.

Operations

The company is experiencing steady revenue growth in both of its main business segments –Decision Analytics and Risk Assessment —as businesses pay ever-increasing attention to risk management and loss control. The Decision Analytics division (which accounts for more than 60% of revenues) is seeing growth in its main insurance division as well as from customers in finance and other industries. The division's health care business is booming growing more than 100% in 2012 as medical firms adjust to changing industry laws. Within the Risk Assessment segment the primary industry-standard insurance program business continues to grow; however the smaller property rating business saw some decline in 2012.

The company aggregates data about premiums and losses throughout the US and internationally to help firms standardize coverage assess future potential risks and losses and comply with insurance regulators. Verisk's databases hold more than 500 terabytes of data on property/casualty insurance including catastrophe models for more than 50 countries fire-suppression capabilities for 47000 US communities 700 million claims records and more than 60 million residential and commercial properties.

Sales and Marketing

A majority of Verisk's revenue is generated through annual subscriptions and long-term agreements within the US property/casualty insurance industry. Major customers in this category include AIG Allstate Hartford and Liberty Mutual. It sells its products and services through a direct sales force. Customers in the health care mortgage lending and government categories include numerous Blue Cross and Blue Shield plans Wells Fargo and FEMA. Verisk also serves select clients in the supply chain human resources and risk management industries.

Advertising costs from branding and promotional activities totaled some $7455 in 2012 up from $7065 in 2011.

Financial Performance

In fiscal 2012 Verisk achieved revenues of more than $1.5 billion a 15% increase over 2011 results. Through organic revenue growth new product development and selected acquisitions the company has been able to grow its revenues at a steady rate over the past five years. Net income also increased 16% to some $ in 2012 following profit growth in both 2010 and 2011.

Strategy

Verisk's strategy for further growth includes increasing sales to insurance customers developing proprietary data sets and predictive analytics continuing to acquire complementary businesses and leveraging its intellectual property into new markets.

Verisk is working to widen its offerings for players in the insurance market as catastrophic events and other market developments increase the demand for the company's services. In 2010 the firm launched its QuickFill analytics solution which provides auto and property databases to insurers at their point-of-service. The company has also integrated weather and climate risks into its predictive models. Verisk Analytics is also expanding rapidly in the health care and financial services segments and it is working to enter new markets and additional customer sectors through both acquisitive and organic growth strategies.

On the organic growth side Verisk Analytics conducts internal programs to create new and enhanced products. Its product development process incorporates market research internal software development and alliances with other information providers and technology companies. For instance the company formed a partnership with loan registry provider MERSCORP (2009) to develop a fraud-prevention database for the US mortgage lending industry.

Mergers and Acquisitions

To expand in the insurance market in 2012 the company acquired Minneapolis-based Aspect Loss Prevention a leading provider of loss prevention software for $8 million to gain its analytic solutions to the retail entertainment and food industries. Verisk Analytics further enhanced its health care solution set by paying about $349 million for MediConnect Global a large cloud-based health information exchange with proprietary systems and services to help aggregate and analyze medical records. The company then positioned MediConnect Global under its Verisk Health umbrella.

On the financial services side the company paid $425 million to acquire New York-based Argus Information & Advisory Services LLC in 2012. The purchase bolstered Verisk Analytics' service capabilities to the financial services industry by adding Argus' information analytics benchmarking scoring and customized services in the Americas and Europe.

Ownership

GreatBanc Trust which serves as trustee of the ISO employee stock ownership trust owns more than 10% of Verisk.

Company Background

The company traces its roots back to 1971 when ISO was created by an association of insurance companies. Verisk went public in 2009 in one of the largest offerings of the year raising almost $2 billion.

EXECUTIVES

Chairman and CEO, Frank J. Coyne, age 64, $1,036,154 total compensation
President ? ISO Insurance Programs and Analytic Services, Kevin B. Thompson, age 61, $246,538 total compensation
Senior Vice President Chief Information Officer, Perry F. Rotella, age 49
President and COO, Scott G. Stephenson, age 55, $451,539 total compensation
EVP General Counsel and Corporate Secretary, Kenneth E. Thompson, age 53, $385,385 total compensation
EVP and CFO, Mark V. Anquillare, age 47, $303,462 total compensation
Senior Vice President President Xactware Solutions, Jim Loveland
President ? Verisk Insurance Solutions ? Claims and Crime Analytics, Vincent Cialdella, age 62
VP Marketing and Corporate Communications, Christopher H. Perini
President ISO Innovative Analytics, Marty Ellingsworth

President ? Verisk Insurance Solutions ? Commercial Property, William M. Raichle
President ? Verisk Insurance Solutions ? Underwriting, Neil Spector
President - Interthin, Kevin Coop
President AIR Worldwide, S. Ming Lee
SVP Corporate Development and Strategy, Vincent P. McCarthy
Head Investor Relations, Eva Huston
CIO, Perry Blogs
Vice President in AIR s Business Development Group, John Elbl
Vice President of product for origination solutions, Jim Portner
EVP Client Development MediConnect Global, Kim Bresnan
Senior Vice President - Corporate Development and Strategy, Vincent de McCarthy
President Interthin, Jeff Moyer
senior Vice President of, Jim Bogdan
President Verisk, Joel Portice
President Atmospheric and Environmental Research, Ron Isaacs
President Argus Information & Advisory Services, Michael Heller
President 3E Company, Robert S. Christie
Senior Vice President Corporate Development and Strategy, Vince McCarthy
President Verisk Climate, Kyle Beatty
President Verisk Insurance Solutions Claims and Crime Analytics, Richard Rocca
Director, Constantine P. (Dinos) Iordanou, age 63
Director, Thomas F. (Tom) Motamed, age 64
Director, John F. Lehman Jr., age 70
Director, J. Hyatt Brown, age 75
Director, David B. (Dave) Wright, age 64
Director, Andrew G. Mills, age 60
Director, Samuel G. Liss, age 56
Director, Glen A. Dell, age 77
Director, Christopher M. Foskett, age 55
Director, Arthur J. Rothkopf
Auditors: Deloitte&ToucheLLP

LOCATIONS

HQ: Verisk Analytics Inc.
545 Washington Blvd., Jersey City NJ 07310-1686
Phone: 201-469-2000   **Fax:** 201-748-1472
Web: www.verisk.com

PRODUCTS/OPERATIONS

2012 Revenues

	$ mil.	% of total
Decision Analytics		
Insurance	493	32
Healthcare	222	15
Financial Services	153	10
Specialized markets	85	6
Risk Assessment		
Industry-standard insurance programs	450	29
Property-specific rating & underwriting info	128	8
Total	**1,534**	**100**

Selected Acquisitions

2012
Insurance Risk Management Solutions (IRMS property risk assessment technology)
MediConnect Global (about $349 million; cloud-based health information exchange; Sandy Utah)
2011
3E Co. ($110 million; environmental health and safety compliance management)
Bloodhound Technologies (ConVergence Point claims editing software used by commercial health plans state Medicaid agencies and others to detect and control health insurance fraud)
Health Risk Partners ($60 million; database of Medicare and Medicaid participants)
2010

Crowe Paradis Services (claims analysis and Medicare compliance solutions)
Strategic Analytics (credit risk management services for consumer and mortgage lenders)
2009
D2 Hawkeye (health care data management and analysis)
Enabl-u Technologies (loss-prevention service provider for banks and other retail clients)
TierMed Systems (health care data management and analysis)

COMPETITORS

Computer Sciences Corp.	LexisNexis
CoreLogic	MSCI
DMG Information	McKesson
Deloitte Consulting	OptumnInsight
FNC	Thomson Reuters
Fair Isaac	Towers Watson

HISTORICAL FINANCIALS

Company Type: Public

Income Statement

FYE: December 31

	REVENUE ($ mil.)	NET INCOME ($ mil.)	NET PROFIT MARGIN	EMPLOYEES
12/12	1,534.3	329.1	21.5%	6,495
12/11	1,331.8	282.7	21.2%	5,401
12/10	1,138.3	242.5	21.3%	4,890
12/09	1,027.1	126.6	12.3%	4,253
12/08	893.5	158.2	17.7%	0
Annual Growth	14.5%	20.1%	—	—

2012 Year-End Financials

Debt ratio: 61.9%	No. of shares (mil.): 167
Return on equity: 417.8%	Dividends
Cash ($ mil.): 89	Yield: —
Current ratio: 0.67	Payout: —
Long-term debt ($ mil.): 1,266	Market value ($ mil.): 8,549

	STOCK PRICE ($) FY Close	P/E High/Low	PER SHARE ($) Earnings	Dividends	Book Value
12/12	50.97	26 20	1.92	0.00	1.52
12/11	40.13	24 18	1.63	0.00	(0.60)
12/10	34.08	25 20	1.30	0.00	(0.67)
12/09	30.28	43 36	0.70	0.00	(0.19)
Annual Growth	19.0%	— —	40.0%	—	—

Viewpoint Financial Group Inc, MD

With its eye on the Lone Star State ViewPoint Financial provides retail and commercial banking through its ViewPoint Bank subsidiary. The thrift operates about 30 branches located mostly in the Dallas/Fort Worth area. ViewPoint offers standard deposit products such as checking and savings accounts and CDs and uses deposit funds to originate primarily real estate loans: Residential mortages commercial mortgages and home equity loans account for about 90% of its lending portfolio. ViewPoint Mortgage a subsidiary of ViewPoint Bank operates a dozen loan production offices in Texas and Oklahoma. ViewPoint Financial converted from a mutual holding company to a stock holding company in 2010.

Formerly a credit union the company became a bank in 2006 and has been transitioning itself into a diversified community-based institution. ViewPoint is increasingly writing commercial and industrial loans which are often more lucrative than consumer loans while keeping conservative underwriting practices. The company also provides warehouse purchase services to third-party mortgage banks bringing it millions in added fee and interest revenues.

Meanwhile the bank has also been expanding its mortgage operations geographically. In 2008 it took over the loan production offices of CTX Mortgage the financing division of homebuilder Centex allowing it to into new markets including Houston and San Antonio.

ViewPoint closed 10 limited-service banking locations in 2009 as part of its efforts to concentrate on full-service branches. Located in grocery stores such as Kroger and Albertsons most of its limited-services branches were shut down when Albertsons shuttered several of its Texas stores that year. Since then the bank has been phasing out its grocery store locations. The company has also been opening new full-service branches in its market. In 2012 it expanded in North Texas through the acquisition of Highlands Bank which operated six branches in the Dallas area.

EXECUTIVES

EVP CFO and Treasurer, Pathie E. (Patti) McKee, age 48, $208,000 total compensation
EVP COO and Chief Information Officer, James C. Parks, age 60, $218,400 total compensation
Chairman, James B. McCarley, age 68
Vice Chairman, Gary D. Basham, age 69
Executive Vice President and Chief Credit Officer of ViewPoint Bank, Mark Williamson
President; Chief Executive Officer; Director of the Company and the Bank, Kevin Hanigan
Director, Anthony J. LeVecchio, age 66
Director, Jack D. Ersman, age 70
Director, V. Keith Sockwell, age 70
Vice Chairman, Gary D. Basham, age 69
Director, Brian McCall
Auditors: Ernst&YoungLLP

LOCATIONS

HQ: Viewpoint Financial Group Inc, MD
1309 W. 15th Street, Plano, TX 75075
Phone: 972 578-5000
Web: www.viewpointfinancialgroup.com

PRODUCTS/OPERATIONS

2010 Sales

	$ mil.	% of total
Interest		
Loans including fees	88	59
Securities	26	18
Other	0	-
Noninterest		
Service charges & fees	18	12
Net gain on sale of loans	13	9
Other	2	2
Adjustments	(0.4)	
Total	**148**	**100**

COMPETITORS

Amegy	PlainsCapital
Bank of America	SP Bancorp
Compass Bancshares	Texas Capital
Cullen/Frost Bankers	Bancshares

North Dallas Bank   Wells Fargo
OmniAmerican

HISTORICAL FINANCIALS
Company Type: Public

Income Statement
FYE: December 31

	REVENUE ($ mil.)	NET INCOME ($ mil.)	NET PROFIT MARGIN	EMPLOYEES
12/12	167.5	35.2	21.0%	572
12/11	150.7	26.3	17.5%	598
12/10	148.8	17.8	12.0%	613
12/09	135.5	2.6	2.0%	0
12/08	116.1	(3.3)	—	0
Annual Growth	**9.6%**	**—**	**—**	**—**

2012 Year-End Financials

Debt ratio: 24.3%
Return on equity: 7.5%
Cash ($ mil.): 68
Current ratio: 0.06
Long-term debt ($ mil.): 892

No. of shares (mil.): 39
Dividends
Yield: 1.9%
Payout: 40.8%
Market value ($ mil.): 829

	STOCK PRICE ($) FY Close	P/E High/Low		Earnings	PER SHARE ($) Dividends	Book Value
12/12	20.94	22	13	0.98	0.40	13.15
12/11	13.01	17	13	0.81	0.20	12.06
12/10	11.69	30	15	0.59	0.08	11.38
12/09	14.41	146	96	0.11	0.23	8.25
12/08	16.05	—	—	(0.14)	0.29	7.79
Annual Growth	**6.9%**		**—**	**—**	**8.4%**	**14.0%**

Virtus Investment Partners, Inc

Virtus Investment Partners provides investment management services to wealthy individuals corporations pension funds endowments and foundations and insurance companies. With more than $50 billion of assets under management it operates through affiliated advisors including Duff & Phelps Kayne Anderson Rudnick and Newfleet Asset Management as well as outside subadvisors. Virtus markets diverse investment products such as wrap fee programs open- and closed-end funds and managed account services to high-net-worth individuals. It also manages institutional accounts for corporations and other investors. The firm was formed in 1995 through a reverse merger with Duff & Phelps.

Geographic Reach

Hartford Connecticut-based Virtus has offices in California Illinois Massachusetts and New York.

Operations

The asset manager operates through its growing group of boutique investment firms including: Zweig/Euclid Advisors Newfound Investments (established in 2012) and recently-acquired Rampart Investment Management among other affiliated firms. Virtus offers investors a menu of investment products and services through its affiliates.

Financial Performance

The investment firm's revenue topped $280 million in 2012 an increase of 37% versus 2011. Net income fell 78% in 2012 to $37.7 million. Virtus's revenue has more more than doubled since 2009 as the firm's assets under management has grown and management fees and fee rates increased. Also driving revenue is market appreciation and the acquisition of Rampart Investment Management in 2012. The decline in net income was due primarily to income tax expenses in 2012 compared with benefits in 2011.

Strategy

Virtus has grown in scope and assets through the addition of investment partners. To strengthen its presence in the US Virtus in 2013 partnered with Kleinwort Benson Investors a provider of specialized equity strategies. The alliance is focused on developing business interests in the US retail marketplace.

Mergers and Acquisitions

Virtus in October 2012 acquired the business and assets of Boston-based Rampart Investment Management Co. a registered investment adviser specializing in customized options strategies for institutional and high-net-worth individuals for $700000 in cash. The Rampart purchase added $1.3 billion in assets under management and added another investment partner to Virtus' group of boutique investment managers.

Company Ownership

Bank of Montreal subsidiary BMO Bankcorp owns about 22% of Virtus.

EXECUTIVES

Executive Vice President Product Management, Francis G. (Frank) Waltman, age 48, $250,000 total compensation
Executive Vice President General Counsel Chief Compliance Officer, Mark S. Flynn, age 58
President CIO, Nathan I. Partain, age 57
President Chief Executive Officer, George R. Aylward, age 49, $425,000 total compensation
Executive Vice President Chief Financial Officer, Michael A. (Mike) Angerthal, age 46, $350,000 total compensation
SVP Fund Services, W. Patrick Bradley
Executive Vice President Retail Distribution, Jeffrey T. Cerutti
Chairman, Mark C. Treanor, age 64
Senior Vice President Human Resources, Mardelle W. Pe?a
Chief Investment Officer Manager, Robert L. Bishop
Senior Vice President - Human Resources, Mardelle Pena
Senior Vice President Fund Services, Patrick Bradley
Executive Vice President Chief Investment Officer, Cecilia L. Gondor
Chief Investment Officer Manager, Corey Hoffstein
President CEO and Director, George R. Aylward, age 49
Director, James R. Baio, age 59
Director, Susan Fleming Cabrera, age 42
Director, Hugh M. S. McKee, age 46
Director, Diane M. Coffey, age 71
Director, Timothy A. Holt, age 60
Director, Ross F. Kappele, age 48
Director, Edward M. Swan, age 71
Auditors: PricewaterhouseCoopersLLP

LOCATIONS

HQ: Virtus Investment Partners Inc.
100 Pearl St. 9th Fl., Hartford CT 06103
Phone: 860-248-7971   **Fax:** 860-241-1113
Web: www.virtus.com

PRODUCTS/OPERATIONS

2012 Sales

	$ mil.	% of total
Investment management fees	187	67
Distribution & service fees	56	20
Administration & transfer agent fees	33	12
Other	1	1
Total	**280**	**100**

Selected Subsidiaries & Affiliates

Duff & Phelps Investment Management (Chicago)
Kayne Anderson Rudnick Investment Management (Los Angeles)
Newfleet Asset Management (Hartford Connecticut)
Rampart Investment Management Company LLC (Boston)
Virtus Investment Advisers Inc. (Massachusetts)
Zweig/Euclid Advisors LLC (New York)

COMPETITORS

Affiliated Managers Group	GAMCO Investors
BlackRock	Invesco
Citigroup Global Markets	Janus Capital
	Legg Mason
Cohen & Steers	Neuberger Berman
Conning	Putnam
Diamond Hill Investment	T. Rowe Price
	TCW
Eaton Vance	The Hartford
Epoch	The Vanguard Group
FMR	US Global Investors
Federated Investors	Waddell & Reed
Franklin Templeton	Westwood Holdings

HISTORICAL FINANCIALS

Company Type: Public

Income Statement
FYE: December 31

	REVENUE ($ mil.)	NET INCOME ($ mil.)	NET PROFIT MARGIN	EMPLOYEES
12/12	280.0	37.7	13.5%	336
12/11	204.6	145.4	71.1%	299
12/10	144.5	9.6	6.7%	273
12/09	117.1	(6.4)	—	278
12/08	178.2	(529.0)	—	0
Annual Growth	**12.0%**	**—**	**—**	**—**

2012 Year-End Financials

Debt ratio: 4.5%
Return on equity: 16.2%
Cash ($ mil.): 63
Current ratio: 2.64
Long-term debt ($ mil.): 15
No. of shares (mil.): 7
Dividends
  Yield: —
  Payout: —
Market value ($ mil.): 947

	STOCK PRICE ($) FY Close	P/E High/Low	Earnings	PER SHARE ($) Dividends	Book Value
12/12	120.94	25 14	4.66	0.00	31.24
12/11	76.01	4 2	16.34	0.00	35.29
12/10	45.37	58 18	0.81	0.00	13.47
12/09	15.90	— —	(1.76)	0.00	12.99
Annual Growth	**96.7%**			**—**	**34.0%**

Virtusa Corp

Virtusa believes that virtually any business can improve its technology. Founded in 1996 the company provides a variety of software development and information technology services including software engineering application development application outsourcing maintenance systems integration and legacy system conversion. Virtusa's customers come from industries such as financial services insurance telecommunications and media and healthcare. Its top two customers JPMorgan Chase and insurance giant AIG together account for about 30% of sales.

Geographic Reach

Virtusa generates 75% of sales in North America and 20% of sales from customers located in Europe.

It has offices in Austria Germany Singapore The Netherlands the UK and the US. Its IT staff is located in Hungary India and Sri Lanka.

Sales and Marketing

The company's sales strategy involves developing long-term relationships with IT and business executives not just landing a short-term contract with no opportunity for recurring revenue.

Financial Performance

Overall sales grew 20% in fiscal 2013 (year-end March) to $333 million. That year Virtusa counted 92 active clients up from 89 in 2011. The company has also been profitable for years; in 2012 profits increased 42% to a record $28 million.

Strategy

The company's strategy for growth includes focusing on services for healthcare and developing more business for its customer relationship management and business process management services. Performing more than 80% of billable hours at offshore sites the company is making significant investments in its Indian and Sri Lankan facilities.

EXECUTIVES

Chairman and CEO, Kris A. Canekeratne, age 47, $301,154 total compensation
Executive Vice President Chief Strategy Officer, Thomas R. (Tom) Holler, age 50, $210,809 total compensation
Executive Vice President Chief Operating Officer, Roger K. (Keith) Modder, age 49, $146,563 total compensation
Executive Vice President - Client Services and Business Development, John Gillis
President Business Development and Client Services, Raj Rajgopal, age 53
SVP Business Development and Head Banking Financial Services and Insurance Business Unit, Jim Francis
Executive Vice President Chief Financial Officer, Ranjan Kalia, age 53, $180,769 total compensation
Managing Director Europe, Clayton Locke
SVP Marketing, Doug Mow
Senior Vice President General Counsel Secretary, Paul D. Tutun
EVP Chief Delivery Officer and Head of India Operations, Samir Dhir
Director, William K. (Bill) O'Brien, age 68
Director, Rowland T. (Row) Moriarty, age 66
Director, Robert E. (Bob) Davoli, age 64
Director, Martin Trust, age 78
Director, Al-Noor Ramji, age 58
Director, Ronald T. Maheu, age 71
Director, Izhar Armony, age 49
Independent Director, William OBrien
Auditors: KPMGLLP

LOCATIONS

HQ: Virtusa Corporation
2000 West Park Dr., Westborough MA 01581
Phone: 508-389-7300   **Fax:** 508-366-9901
Web: www.virtusa.com

2013 Sales

	% of total
North	75
Europe	20
Other	5
Total	**100**

COMPETITORS

Accenture	IBM Global Services
Capgemini	Infosys
Cognizant Tech Solutions	Patni Computer Systems
	Sapient
Computer Sciences Corp.	Satyam
	Tata Consultancy
Deloitte Consulting	Tech Mahindra
HCL Technologies	Wipro
HP Enterprise Services	

HISTORICAL FINANCIALS

Company Type: Public

Income Statement
FYE: March 31

	REVENUE ($ mil.)	NET INCOME ($ mil.)	NET PROFIT MARGIN	EMPLOYEES
03/13	333.1	28.4	8.5%	6,911
03/12	277.7	20.0	7.2%	5,672
03/11	217.9	16.2	7.4%	3,056
03/10	164.3	12.1	7.4%	4,038
03/09	172.9	12.0	7.0%	3,764
Annual Growth	**17.8%**	**23.9%**		**16.4%**

2013 Year-End Financials

Debt ratio: 0.0%
Return on equity: 12.0%
Cash ($ mil.): 57
Current ratio: 3.96
Long-term debt ($ mil.): —
No. of shares (mil.): 25
Dividends
  Yield: —
  Payout: —
Market value ($ mil.): 598

	STOCK PRICE ($) FY Close	P/E High/Low	Earnings	PER SHARE ($) Dividends	Book Value
03/13	23.76	21 10	1.11	0.00	10.02
03/12	17.27	26 15	0.79	0.00	8.80
03/11	18.73	27 12	0.66	0.00	8.52
03/10	10.31	20 12	0.50	0.00	7.76
03/09	6.20	23 8	0.50	0.00	6.73
Annual Growth	**39.9%**	**— —**	**22.1%**	**—**	**10.4%**

Vitamin Shoppe Inc

Vitamin Shoppe helps vitamin-takers meet their recommended daily requirements. The fast-growing company sells vitamins supplements and minerals as well as herbal homeopathic and sports nutrition and wellness products at more than 600 company-operated The Vitamin Shoppe stores located in some 45 US states the District of Columbia Puerto Rico and Canada. It also sells directly via catalog and the websites VitaminShoppe.com and BodyTech.com. Stores offer about 17500 items including food and beverages and pet products under more than 400 national and private-label brands. Founded in 1977 Vitamin Shoppe entered the Canadian market in 2012.

Geographic Reach

The New Jersey-based company's largest markets are California New York and Florida home to about a third of its stores. Vitamin Shoppe opened its first two stores in Canada in late 2012 and has plans to expand internationally through franchise and wholesale opportunities.

Operations

The company operates retail stores under the Vitamin Shoppe and Super Supplements banners. The retail segment accounted for 89% of sales in 2012 with the rest coming from the Internet and catalogs.

Sales and Marketing

Vitamin Shoppe relies on location location location! as a prime marketing tool adhering to the belief that situating its stores on prime real estate draws customers. It advertises in magazines and relies on radio and television ads to promote certain new stores. Direct mail is another avenue for promotion. The company reported $14.7 million in advertising and promotion costs in 2012 up 16% from 2011.

Financial Performance

The Vitamin Shoppe is full of vim and vigor having more than doubled its net sales from 2005 to 2012 and posting positive same-store sales for 19 consecutive years. Its sales increased 11% in 2012 versus 2011 to $951 million. Net income rose 36% to nearly $61 million over the same period. Driving the double-digit sales gain was the addition of about 50 new stores an 8% increase in same-store sales and rising direct sales partially offset by a $3 million reduction in sales as a result of Super Storm Sandy in October 2012. Specialty supplements sports nutrition products and vitamins minerals and herbs were all strong performers. Sports nutrition and weight management categories are among the chain's fastest-growing categories.

Strategy

Vitamin Shoppe is extending its retail reach through organic growth and acquisitions. After adding 50 stores in 2013 the chain looks to open another 60 in 2014. Its long-term goal is to operate more than 900 US stores. The retailer prefers to locate shops in freestanding buildings or corner locations in strip malls rather than traditional shopping malls. To supply its growing store base the company opened a distribution center in Ashland Virginia in 2013. The new 311740-square-foot facility began receiving inbound inventory in June 2013 and began outbound shipments to store in September.

Besides adding stores Vitamin Shoppe is experimenting with new store formats and products. Eco Shoppe —launched in Austin Texas in 2009 — as its name suggests sells green-living products including apparel home garden and gift items; office and pet supplies; baby and kids products; and yoga gear. Previously the company launched an e-commerce site called BodyTech.com devoted to products for bodybuilders and other athletes.

Mergers and Acquisitions

In February 2013 the company acquired the assets of Super Supplements Inc. (SSI) a specialty retailer of vitamins minerals and supplements for about $50 million. SSI operates about 30 stores in Washington Oregon and Idaho and extends Vitamin Shoppe's retail presence in the Pacific Northwest.

Ownership

Wells Fargo & Co. owns 12% of Vitamin Shoppe's shares. Eagle Asset Management owns about 10%.

IPO

Vitamin Shoppe raised about $155 million in its October 2009 initial public offering. Concurrent with its IPO the company changed its name from VS Holdings to the more familiar Vitamin Shoppe

moniker. Proceeds from the offering went to the selling shareholders and not to the company.

EXECUTIVES

VP Real Estate, Brian R. Bootay, age 57
CEO and Director, Anthony N. (Tony) Truesdale, age 51, $498,710 total compensation
EVP and CFO, Brenda M. Galgano, age 44
SVP and Chief Marketing Officer, Louis H. Weiss, age 44, $377,885 total compensation
Chairman, Richard L. Markee, age 60, $192,588 total compensation
VP Corporate Brands, Joseph J. Weiss, age 46
SVP Merchandising, Doug Jones
VP Scientific and Regulatory Affairs, David Morrison
SVP Supply Chain Management, Richard Tannenbaum
SVP Retail, Douglas Henson
SVP Human Resources, Teresa Orth
VP e-Commerce, Stephen Bontempo
VP and CIO, John Kirk
VP Inventory and Transportation, Jason Scheffer
Director, John H. Edmondson, age 68
Director, Beth M. Pritchard, age 65
CEO and Director, Anthony N. (Tony) Truesdale, age 49
Director, Catherine E (Kate) Buggeln, age 51
Director, Katherine J. (Kathy) Savitt-Lennon, age 48
Director, David H. Edwab, age 57
Director, Douglas R. Korn, age 49
Director, Richard L. Perkal, age 58
Director, B. Michael Becker, age 66
Auditors: Deloitte&ToucheLLP

LOCATIONS

HQ: Vitamin Shoppe Inc.
2101 91st St., North Bergen NJ 07047
Phone: 201-868-5959   **Fax:** 800-852-7153
Web: www.vitaminshoppe.com

2012 Locations

	No.
California	71
New	64
Florida	63
Texas	45
Illinois	33
New	27
Virginia	22
Ohio	19
Maryland	18
Pennsylvania	18
North	17
Georgia	16
Massachusetts	15
Michigan	12
Arizona	10
Washington	10
Connecticut	9
Indiana	9
Tennessee	9
Colorado	8
South	8
Minnesota	7
Hawaii	6
Oregon	6
Wisconsin	6
Kentucky	5
Missouri	5
Alabama	4
Louisiana	4
New	4
Delaware	3
Iowa	3
Kansas	3
Nevada	3
New	3
Nebraska	2
Puerto	2
Utah	2
District of	1
Idaho	1
Maine	1
Oklahoma	1
Rhode	1
Vermont	1
Canada	2
Total	**579**

PRODUCTS/OPERATIONS

2012 Sales

	$ mil.	% of total
Stores	849	89
Direct (catalog & Internet)	101	11
Total	**950**	**100**

2012 Sales

	$ mil.	% of total
Specialty supplements & sports nutrition	500	53
Vitamins minerals & herbs	366	39
Delivery revenue	2	
Other	81	8
Total	**950**	**100**

Selected Products

Herbal products
Homeopathic products
Personal care products
   Foot care
   Hair care
   Mouth care
   Pet care
   Skin care
   Women' s products
Supplements
Vitamins

COMPETITORS

CVS Caremark	Nature' s Sunshine
Costco Wholesale	PureTek
Forever Living	Rite Aid
GNC	Safeway
Gaiam	Target Corporation
Herbalife Ltd.	Vitacost
Kmart	Vitamin World
Kroger	Wal-Mart
MotherNature.com	Walgreen
NBTY	Whole Foods

HISTORICAL FINANCIALS

Company Type: Public

Income Statement

FYE: December 29

	REVENUE ($ mil.)	NET INCOME ($ mil.)	NET PROFIT MARGIN	EMPLOYEES
12/12	950.9	60.8	6.4%	4,247
12/11	856.5	44.8	5.2%	3,907
12/10	751.4	29.2	3.9%	3,581
12/09	674.5	12.6	1.9%	3,358
12/08	601.5	8.2	1.4%	3,114
Annual Growth	**12.1%**	**65.0%**	**—**	**8.1%**

2012 Year-End Financials

Debt ratio: 0.0%
Return on equity: 15.1%
Cash ($ mil.): 81
Current ratio: 2.75
Long-term debt ($ mil.): 0
No. of shares (mil.): 30
Dividends
   Yield: —
   Payout: —
Market value ($ mil.): 1,689

	STOCK PRICE ($)	P/E	PER SHARE ($)		
	FY Close	High/Low	Earnings	Dividends	Book Value
12/12	55.98	30 19	2.02	0.00	14.83
12/11	39.88	31 20	1.52	0.00	12.18
12/10	33.74	32 18	1.03	0.00	10.40
12/09	22.63	73 57	0.28	0.00	8.76
Annual Growth	35.2%	— —	93.2%	—	19.2%

Volcano Corporation

Volcano creates its own sound and light show to get your heart's blood flowing. The company develops manufactures and sells medical imaging devices for cardiovascular care and other specialties. Its products include intravascular ultrasound (IVUS) and fractional flow reserve (FFR) consoles and imaging catheters that provide information about the condition of arteries as well as plaque and lesions. Its functional management (FM) consoles and single-use pressure and flow guidewires measure characteristics of blood around plaque in arteries. Volcano sells its products to physicians hospitals and other health care providers worldwide through a direct sales force and distributors.

Volcano also operates an industrial segment through its Axsun Technologies subsidiary. The unit which makes up only about 3% of sales makes lasers and optical engines used in OCT imaging systems and is responsible for Volcano's activities in the telecommunications market where Axsun sells spectrometers and optical channel monitors to telecom firms.

The US accounts for about half of the company's sales and Japan brings in about 30%; other markets include Europe and South Africa where Volcano employs direct sales employees. The company uses independent distributors to sell its products in the Middle East the rest of Asia and other regions. With more than 6800 consoles installed at facilities worldwide Volcano is working to expand its distribution network in emerging markets. In recent years sales in Japan have seen significant growth thanks in part to its contractual relationship with Johnson & Johnson which distributes Volcano's IVUS products there. Volcano gets more than 80% of its medical segment revenues from sales of its single-use disposable catheters and guidewires used with its IVUS and FM systems.

The company makes continuous improvements on its products (especially its top-selling IVUS systems) hoping to improve the diagnosis of heart conditions and take advantage of the growing trend of using minimally invasive surgical treatment procedures. As part of a development program that aimed to allow the company's products to network with interventional devices made by other manufacturers Volcano has developed an IVUS console (s5i) customized for use in cardiac catheterization laboratories in hospital surgery suites.

Along with in-house research and development Volcano grows through acquisitions such as the 2010 purchase of Fluid Medical a company that develops imaging technology for use in various structural heart applications including mitral valve repair. Fluid Medical's technology is being used to develop a Forward-Looking Intra-Cardiac Echo or FLICE catheter to expand Volcano's minimally invasive structural heart applications. The $4 million purchase also enhances the company's suite of visualization products.

To further grow its interventional cardiology development pipeline the company purchased IVUS technology firm Novelis for $12 million in 2008. Novelis' development-stage FLIVUS technology widened Volcano's product applications in minimally invasive heart procedures.

By acquiring marketing rights to the Xtract line of thrombus aspiration catheters from private medical device firm Lumen Biomedical in 2010 the company expanded into the clot removal market. Through similar acquisitions and development efforts Volcano aims to offer diagnostic and treatment options for a wide range of vascular conditions.

Volcano's strategy includes building its sales and marketing infrastructure to market to physicians and PCI (percutaneous interventional) procedure technicians in hospitals as well as to personnel who make purchases for hospitals.

Over the past three years Volcano's revenues have increased year-over-year from about $228 million in 2009 to $343.5 million in 2011. This was mainly driven by increased product sales most notably a 44% increase in its FFR single-procedure disposables and a 34% jump in sales to Japan. The company's operating income exceeded $25 million for fiscal 2011 continuing its run of profitability for the second consecutive year.

EXECUTIVES

President Clinical and Scientific Affairs, Michel E. Lussier, age 56, $389,171 total compensation
Executive Vice President Global Operations and Japan, David M. Sheehan, age 49
President Axsun Division, Dale C. Flanders, age 61
Chief Financial Officer, John T. Dahldorf, age 56, $273,000 total compensation
President US & APLAC Commercial Sales, George Quinoy
VP-Global HR, Connie L. Garrett
President Managing Director, Junichi Osawa
Executive Vice President Strategy Business Development, John Onopchenko, age 54
President CEO and Director, R. Scott Huennekens, age 48, $412,000 total compensation
President U.S. & APLAC CommercialSales, Jorge J. (George) Quinoy, age 58, $300,000 total compensation
Vice President and General Manager Axsun Structural Heart and Impact Medical Business Unit, Jonathan T. Hartmann, age 42
EVP Marketing and General Manager Functional Measurement and IGT, Joseph M. (Joe) Burnett, age 36
President EMEAI, Michele Perrino, age 42
Executive Vice President General Counsel Secretary and Chief Compliance Officer, Darin M. Lippoldt, age 46
Associate Director External Affairs and Education, Edrienne Brandon
SVP Regulatory Affairs Quality & Systems Test Engineering, Nancy Lelicoff
Vice President of Global Corporate Marketing and Imaging, Donna Collins
Executive Vice President Human Resources, Heather Ace
IR Contact, Neal Rosen
Vice President General Manager Peripheral Vascular Business Unit, Neil Hattangadi
President Chief Executive Officer, Scott Huennekens
Director, Michael J. Coyle, age 50

Director, Ronald A. (Ron) Matricaria, age 70
Independent Director, Eric J. Topol
Director, Lesley H. (Les) Howe, age 68
Director, Alexis V. Lukianov, age 57
President CEO and Director, R. Scott Huennekens, age 48
Director, Kieran T. Gallahue, age 49
Director, Roy A. Tanaka, age 65
Independent Director, Leslie Norwalk
Auditors: Ernst&YoungLLP

LOCATIONS

HQ: Volcano Corporation
  3661 Valley Centre Dr. Ste. 200, San Diego CA 92130
Phone: 916-638-8008   **Fax:** 858-720-0325
Web: www.volcanocorp.com

2011 Sales
US	157	46
Japan	105	31
Total	**343**	**100**

Selected Locations
Alpharetta Georgia (sales)
Billerica Massachusetts (Axsun operations and R&D)
Cleveland (R&D)
Costa Rica (manufacturing)
Forsyth County Georgia (R&D)
Rancho Cordova California (manufacturing and R&D)
San Diego (headquarters and R&D)
Tokyo (sales and third-party distribution)
Woodmead South Africa (sales and distribution)
Zaventem Belgium (sales and distribution)

PRODUCTS/OPERATIONS

2011 Sales
Medical segment		
Single-procedure disposable		
FFR	67	20
Consoles	40	12
Other	23	7
Total	**343**	**100**

2011 Medical Segment Sales
	% of total
Single-procedure	81
Consoles	12
Other	7
Total	**100**

Selected Subsidiaries
Axsun Technologies Inc.
CardioSpectra Inc.
Volcano Europe B.V.B.A. (Belgium)
Volcano Japan Co. Ltd.
Volcano Netherlands Holdings B.V.
Volcarica Socieded de Responsabilidad Limitada (Costa Rica)
Fluid Medical Inc.

COMPETITORS

Abbott Labs	Cordis
Aegis Corp.	Covidien
Bard	Edwards Lifesciences
Becton Dickinson	Medtronic
Boston Scientific	CardioVascular
CONMED Corporation	St. Jude Medical
Cook Group	Terumo

HISTORICAL FINANCIALS

Company Type: Public

Income Statement

FYE: December 31

	REVENUE ($ mil.)	NET INCOME ($ mil.)	NET PROFIT MARGIN	EMPLOYEES
12/12	381.8	8.0	2.1%	1,565
12/11	343.5	38.0	11.1%	1,289
12/10	294.1	5.2	1.8%	1,144
12/09	227.8	(28.9)	—	969
12/08	171.5	(13.7)	—	883
Annual Growth	22.2%	—	—	15.4%

2012 Year-End Financials

Debt ratio: 42.5%
Return on equity: 2.1%
Cash ($ mil.): 330
Current ratio: 8.22
Long-term debt ($ mil.): 383

No. of shares (mil.): 53
Dividends
Yield: —
Payout: —
Market value ($ mil.): 1,274

	STOCK PRICE ($) FY Close	P/E High/Low	PER SHARE ($) Earnings	Dividends	Book Value
12/12	23.61	203151	0.15	0.00	7.57
12/11	23.79	46 30	0.70	0.00	6.44
12/10	27.31	287174	0.10	0.00	5.34
12/09	17.38	— —	(0.60)	0.00	4.40
12/08	15.00	— —	(0.29)	0.00	4.80
Annual Growth	12.0%	— —	—	—	12.1%

Voxx International Corp

VOXX International Corporation (formerly Audiovox) works to be the one-stop-shop for electronics. It sells consumer electronics for communications mobile and home use and acts as an original equipment manufacturer (OEM) for car makers. Its products include automotive security devices digital picture frames HD TV antennae stereo and speaker systems portable DVD players two-way radios and universal remotes. They are marketed under such names as Acoustic Research Advent Audiovox Code-Alarm Energizer Invision Jensen Mac Audio Schwaiger and Terk. VOXX's distribution network comprises retailers distributors car dealers and other OEMs. Founded by John Shalam in 1960 VOXX went public in 1987.

Strategy

As an electronics maker and OEM VOXX relies on consumer spending and vehicle sales. The US which comprises its largest market has struggled through the down economy with stalled car sales and concerned consumers. While revenues have improved slightly VOXX's top line took a hit in recent years spurring the company to exit the unprofitable and competitive LCD flat-panel TV and portable GPS markets.

The company uses contract manufacturers in Asia which enables VOXX to respond quickly to changes in technology and tastes as well as keep costs low.

Mergers and Acquisitions

Aiming to rev up its revenue VOXX has focused on expanding its products portfolio. To that end it acquired Germany's Car Communication Holding a maker and supplier of Hirschmann-brand in-car communications and entertainment systems for ?85 million ($112 million) in 2012. Its customers include Audi BMW and Volkswagen among oth-

ers. Hirschmann became a wholly-owned subsidiary of VOXX. Previously VOXX bought high-end audio gear maker Klipsch Group for $166 million in 2011. Klipsch is renowned for its branded speakers sound systems headphones and other audio equipment. Klipsch is now a subsidiary of VOXX and operates as a stand-alone entity headquartered in Indiana.

Financial Performance

Buying Klipsch helped VOXX boost its 2011 net sales some 26% as compared to 2010. Revenue rose across all business segments but particularly in electronics sales (which include mobile and consumer electronics) with its 79% contribution to overall net sales that year. Launching new programs and logging sales spikes in domestic automotive sales helped to offset declines among its accessories business for products such as rechargeable batteries and surge protectors as well as other chargers VOXX had decided to phase out. Thanks to Klipsch net income increased 11% during the same reporting period.

Sales and Marketing

VOXX markets its products to a variety of customers including regional chain stores mass merchants power retailers specialty and Internet retailers new car dealers distributors the US military cinema operators and vehicle equipment manufacturers. VOXX's five largest customers generated some 30% of its 2011 sales and 36% in 2010. Its OEM customers which include Ford Motor Company General Motors Kia Porsche Subaru and Toyota bring in about 10% of sales.

Ownership

John J. Shalam owns about 18% of VOXX's shares; Kahn Brothers LLC holds another 10% stake.

HISTORY

Egyptian-born John Shalam founded Custom Imports in 1960 to import Japanese goods into the US. After quickly selling out of car radios in 1965 Shalam refocused and renamed the company Audiovox. Depending solely on car stereos caused a loss in 1982 so Audiovox diversified into auto alarm systems rust-proofing chemicals radar detectors cruise controls and car phones. Between 1983 and 1987 (the year Audiovox went public) cellular phones rose to 43% of the company's sales.

In 1995 Audiovox closed two-thirds of its retail outlets in response to competitive pressure. The next year the company established a new subsidiary Audiovox Communications to deal exclusively with cellular phones and accessories. In 1997 Audiovox formed a joint venture with ASA Electronics to market audio security and video systems to the automotive and aviation industries.

Instability in Asia led the company to withdraw from a planned distribution joint venture with Namsung (Korea) in 1998. Late that year it struck a deal with Nissan to provide entertainment systems (including TV VCR and video game jacks) for Quest minivans.

Audiovox introduced its first Internet-related products in 1999: MP3 players and recorders and a Web-browsing phone. The next year it marketed different cellular handsets for all three wireless technologies (TDMA GSM and CDMA) leading North America in CDMA sales. In 2001 Audiovox and Toshiba began developing a personal digital assistant (PDA) combined with a cell phone for cellular carriers Verizon Wireless and Sprint PCS.

In July 2003 Audiovox acquired the audio operations of Recoton including its Jensen Advent and Acoustic Research brands as well as Recoton German Holdings GmbH for about $40 million.

Audiovox sold a controlling interest in its wireless subsidiary Audiovox Communications to Curitel Communications in late 2004. Later that year the company decided that it could not compete with larger cell phone manufacturers and exited the handset business entirely when it sold its wireless business to handset maker UTStarcom.

In July 2005 Audiovox appointed Patrick Lavelle as president and CEO of the company; Shalam remained as chairman of the board.

In March 2007 the company's German subsidiary Audiovox German Holdings acquired OEHLBACH Kabel for about $6.6 million. OEHLBACH makes accessories primarily cables for the consumer electronics industry. Later that year Audiovox bought certain assets of UK-based Incaar which produces rear seat entertainment systems for the likes of BMW and Toyota to strengthen its European operations. It also acquired Technuity for its expertise in battery and power products. The deal made Audiovox the exclusive licensee of the Energizer brand in North America —for rechargeable batteries and battery packs to be used with camcorders digital cameras DVD players cordless phones and other power supply devices.

In March 2011 Audiovox acquired high-end audio gear maker Klipsch Group for $166 million. Klipsch is best known for its branded speakers sound systems headphones and other audio equipment.

Because the company is known for more than just its Audiovox brand the company changed its name to VOXX International Corporation in late 2011.

EXECUTIVES

President and CEO, Patrick M. (Pat) Lavelle, $812,602 total compensation
SVP and CFO, Charles M. Stoehr, $360,000 total compensation
Chairman, John J. Shalam, $149,224 total compensation
President Audiovox Electronics Corporation, Thomas C. Malone, $191,250 total compensation
CEO Klipsch Group Inc., T. Paul Jacobs
SVP Accounting and Credit, Loriann Shelton, $270,000 total compensation
President VOXX Accessories Corporation, C. David Geise, $191,250 total compensation
CEO and Managing Director Audiovox German Holdings, Mark Finger
President CEO and Director, Patrick M. (Pat) Lavelle, age 61
SVP CFO and Director, Charles M. Stoehr, age 66
Director; President and CEO UTStarcom Personal Communications, Philip Christopher, age 63
Director, Dennis F. McManus, age 62
Director, Peter A. Lesser, age 78
Auditors: GrantThorntonLLP

LOCATIONS

HQ: VOXX International Corporation
180 Marcus Blvd., Hauppauge NY 11788
Phone: 631-231-7750   **Fax:** 631-434-3995
Web: www.voxxintl.com

PRODUCTS/OPERATIONS

2011 Sales

	$ mil.	% of total
Electronics	561	79
Accessories	146	21
Total	**707**	**100**

Selected Mergers and Acqusitions

FY2012
  Car Communication Holding (Germany E85 million/$112 million)
FY2011
  Klipsch Group (Indiana $166 million)
FY2010
  INViSiON Industries ($15 million)
FY2009
  Schwaiger (Germany $4 million)
FY2007
  Incaar (UK)

Selected Products

Automotive sound equipment
Camcorders
Clock-radios
Digital picture frames
DVD players
Home and portable stereos
Mobile video equipment
MP3 players and recorders
Power inverters
Remote start systems
Vehicle security systems
Vehicle tracking systems

COMPETITORS

Alpine Electronics of America	Intrinsic Audio Solutions
Bang & Olufsen	JVC KENWOOD
Belkin	LG Electronics
Bose	Meyer Sound
Clarion	Monster Cable
Community Professional Loudspeakers	Panasonic Electronic Devices America
D&M	Philips North America
DEI Holdings	Pioneer Corporation
Daimler	Samson Technologies
Delphi Automotive Systems	Samsung Electronics
Eminence Speaker	Sennheiser
Ford Motor	Sony
General Motors	SpeakerCraft
Harman International	Yorkville Sound

HISTORICAL FINANCIALS

Company Type: Public

Income Statement

FYE: February 28

	REVENUE ($ mil.)	NET INCOME ($ mil.)	NET PROFIT MARGIN	EMPLOYEES
02/13	835.5	22.4	2.7%	2,100
02/12	707.0	25.6	3.6%	1,238
02/11	561.6	23.0	4.1%	1,020
02/10	550.7	22.4	4.1%	970
02/09	603.1	(71.0)	—	800
Annual Growth	8.5%	—		27.3%

2013 Year-End Financials

Debt ratio: 21.8%
Return on equity: 5.1%
Cash ($ mil.): 19
Current ratio: 2.28
Long-term debt ($ mil.): 154

No. of shares (mil.): 23
Dividends
  Yield: —
  Payout: —
Market value ($ mil.): 234

	STOCK PRICE ($) FY Close	P/E High/Low		PER SHARE ($) Earnings	Dividends	Book Value
02/13	9.95	15	6	0.95	0.00	18.87
02/12	12.79	13	4	1.10	0.00	18.23
02/11	8.28	10	6	1.00	0.00	17.03
02/10	7.22	8	2	0.98	0.00	15.92
02/09	2.80	—	—	(3.11)	0.00	14.89
Annual Growth	37.3%	—	—	—	—	6.1%

W.P. Carey Inc

Need help managing your property portfolio? Keep calm and Carey on. W. P. Carey invests in and manages commercial real estate including office distribution retail and industrial facilities. The company owns some 955 properties mainly in the US and Europe and manages properties for several non-traded real estate investment trusts (REITs). Its management portfolio totals some $12 billion. W. P. Carey typically acquires properties and then leases them back to the sellers/occupants on a long-term basis. It also provides build-to-suit financing for investors worldwide. W. P. Carey is converting to a REIT a corporate structure that comes with tax benefits and more flexibilty in investing in real estate.

The company in 2010 invested more than $1 billion on behalf of its REITs and its own portfolio. More than 40% of its transactions were international investments. W.P. Carey expanded its presence to China in 2010 and made its first transaction there the following year.

W.P. Carey looks to diversify its managed funds and make investments in properties that provide consistent long-term sources of income. Property diversity helps shield W.P. from being reliant on any single industry. A few of its recent investments include storage facilities industrial facilities and retailers.

In addition to making property investments the company is focused on diversifying its asset management capabilities. W.P. Carey has launched a lodging-focused fund (Carey Watermark Investors). The new investment program is dedicated to investing in the lodging sector and made its first investments in 2011.

The W. P. Carey Foundation established by late founder and chairman William Carey owns about 30% of the company.

EXECUTIVES

EVP Managing Director and Chief Administrative Officer, Claude Fernandez
Chief Ethics Officer and Director, Francis J. (Frank) Carey, age 87, $250,000 total compensation
Chairman, William Polk (Bill) Carey, age 82, $300,000 total compensation
Chief Operating Officer; Managing Director, Thomas E. Zacharias, age 59, $350,000 total compensation
Managing Director Chief Marketing Officer Corporate Secretary, Susan C. Hyde
Managing Director and Co-Head of Domestic Investments, Gino Sabatini
Chief Financial Officer; Chief Administrative Officer; Managing Director; Director, Mark J. DeCesaris, age 54, $250,000 total compensation
Managing Director; President Carey Financial, Mark M. Goldberg
Chief Investment Officer, John D. Miller, age 68, $250,000 total compensation
President, Jason E. Fox
President; Chief Executive Officer; Director, Trevor P. Bond, age 51
Executive Director Chief Risk Officer, Thomas Ridings, age 45
VP, Zachary J. Pack
VP, W. Fort Parker II
Public Relations, Kristina McMenamin
Chief Accounting Officer, Hisham Kader
Executive Director Vice President Carey Financial, Jay Steigerwald
Chief Financial Officer, Catherine Rice

Executive Director Chief Legal Officer, Paul Marcotrigiano
Vice President, Guillermo Silberman
Director Emeritus, Charles C. Townsend Jr., age 85
Director, Lawrence R. Klein, age 92
Chief Ethics Officer and Director, Francis J. (Frank) Carey, age 87
Director, Eberhard Faber IV, age 76
Director, Reginald Winssinger, age 70
Director, Benjamin H. (Ben) Griswold IV, age 73
Director, Robert E. Mittelstaedt Jr., age 69
Director, Nathaniel S. Coolidge, age 74
Director, Karsten von Koller, age 72
Director, Charles E. Parente, age 72
President CEO and Director, Trevor P. Bond, age 50
Auditors: PricewaterhouseCoopersLLP

LOCATIONS

HQ: W. P. Carey & Co. LLC
  50 Rockefeller Plaza 2nd Fl., New York NY 10020
Phone: 212-492-1100   **Fax:** 212-492-8922
Web: www.wpcarey.com

PRODUCTS/OPERATIONS

2010 Sales

	$ mil.	% of total
Asset management revenue	76	28
Lease revenue	63	23
Reimbursed costs from affiliates	60	22
Structuring revenue	44	16
Wholesaling revenue	11	4
Other real estate income	18	7
Total	**273**	**100**

COMPETITORS

Brandywine Realty	Inland Group
CNL Financial	Jones Lang LaSalle
Crescent Real Estate	Lexington Realty Trust
Equity Office	Vornado Realty
First Industrial Realty	

HISTORICAL FINANCIALS

Company Type: Public

Income Statement

FYE: December 31

	REVENUE ($ mil.)	NET INCOME ($ mil.)	NET PROFIT MARGIN	EMPLOYEES
12/12	374.0	62.1	16.6%	216
12/11	336.4	139.0	41.3%	212
12/10	273.9	73.9	27.0%	170
12/09	235.8	69.0	29.3%	156
12/08	243.8	78.0	32.0%	154
Annual Growth	11.3%	(5.5%)	—	8.8%

2012 Year-End Financials

Debt ratio: 42.7%
Return on equity: 4.5%
Cash ($ mil.): 123
Current ratio: 0.48
Long-term debt ($ mil.): 1,968

No. of shares (mil.): 68
Dividends
  Yield: 1.2%
  Payout: 48.5%
Market value ($ mil.): 3,572

	STOCK PRICE ($) FY Close	P/E High/Low		PER SHARE ($) Earnings	Dividends	Book Value
12/12	52.15	42	32	1.28	0.66	29.60
12/11	40.94	13	9	3.42	2.19	17.18
12/10	31.29	17	13	1.86	2.03	15.84
12/09	27.68	17	10	1.74	2.00	15.96
12/08	23.43	17	9	1.96	1.96	16.37
Annual Growth	22.1% 16.0%	—	—	(10.1%)	(23.8%)	—

Wabash National Corp.

The teaser trailer for trailer industry giant Great Dane is Wabash National. Wabash is one of North America's top manufacturers of dry freight and refrigerated vans flatbed and drop deck trailers and intermodal equipment. The trailers are marketed under such brands as DuraPlate ArcticLite and RoadRailer via a network of factory-direct sales representatives independent dealers and factory-owned retail outlets. Customers have included Averitt Express FedEx Knight SAIA and Swift. The company operates two subsidiaries Transcraft Corporation (flatbed and drop deck trailers) and Wabash National Trailer Centers (retail distributor of trailers and aftermarket parts). Wabash makes most of its sales in the US.

Amid declines in US new home construction and the automotive market trailer industry shipments plummeted in 2009 by almost 50% from 2008 more than 60% from 2007. Wabash revenues earnings and liquidity fell to historic lows. In mid-2009 Lincolnshire Management-affiliate Trailer Investments made a $35 million purchase of Wabash stock giving the company a much needed cash infusion but taking about a 44% stake. The following year Trailer Investment sold its entire stake in a public offering.

Trailer Investment exited just as Wabash sales reflected a glimmer of the economic recovery; higher new trailer volumes drove roughly a 90% increase in sales in 2010 over 2009's dismal results. But the company's bottom line declined further into the red despite a number of belt-tightening measures. In 2010 it consolidated its platform and dump manufacturing facilities into one site. Wabash has also reduced about one-third of its workforce cut employee salaries and idled plants. The company's restructuring coupled with another public offering in mid-2010 buoyed business in the face of continuing to consume more cash than it generates.

Wabash has traditionally sold to the largest operators of trailer fleets. Although it preserves its core customer base the company is striving to diversify its offerings and win business from the next tier of trucking companies —carriers with fleets of between 250 and 7500 trailers. Mid-market customers of Wabash include CR England Celadon Group and Xtra Lease.

HISTORY

Donald Ehrlich was president of trailer maker Monon when its parent company was purchased in 1983. Disillusioned by the new management Ehrlich took several key employees with him to create Wabash in 1985. The business got a jumpstart when Ehrlich's Sears contacts ordered 10 trailers. In 1991 Wabash bought the rights to RoadRailer (bimodal railcar construction technology developed in 1956) and went public.

Business boomed in 1993 and Wabash expanded facilities the next year. In 1995 it started shipping RoadRailer units to Germany and received its first order from the French National Railways. Wabash upped its annual production capacity to 70000 units that year.

In 1996 Wabash's sales dipped as many of its customers delayed advanced ordering of its innovative composite-plate trailers. Aggravating this problem was a nationwide slump in the trailer industry: Two of the top 10 trailer makers filed for bankruptcy.

Wabash bounced back in 1997 and acquired bankrupt Fruehauf. It also bought 25% of ETZ-Europaische Trailerzug Beteiligungsgesellschaft (RoadRailer service) of Germany —its first non-US purchase. In 1998 Wabash set up a joint venture to market RoadRailer bimodal technology in South America.

Wabash merged Wabash National Finance Corp into Apex Trailer Leasing and Rentals in 2000 to consolidate its rental leasing and finance activities. The next year Wabash continued restructuring in the face of poor market conditions. The company ceased exporting manufactured products outside North America and announced plans to cut its workforce by 18%. It closed two assembly plants and a distribution center.

Early in 2002 Wabash announced that it was laying off 480 workers. The job cuts reduced the company's workforce to about two-thirds of the size it was at the beginning of 2001. Wabash announced the sale of its financial operations to Milestone Capital Corporation and Cypress Leasing Corporation in early 2004.

In 2006 Wabash acquired Transcraft a maker of flatbed and drop deck trailers that posted sales of about $120 million in 2006 from private equity firm Lincolnshire Management.

In mid-2008 Wabash bought certain operating assets of Benson International a manufacturer of aluminum flatbeds dump trailers and other truck bodies for approximately $5 million.

In 2009 facing liquidity problems in the credit crunch and global economic downturn Wabash sold preferred and common shares of its stock to Trailer Investment (a Lincolnshire Investment affiliate) for $35 million giving Trailer Investment ownership of about 44% of the company. With the capital infusion Wabash was able to amend its existing credit agreement.

EXECUTIVES

Senior Vice President; Chief Technology Officer, Rodney P. (Rod) Ehrlich, age 66, $253,984 total compensation
Chairman, Martin C. Jischke, age 71
President; Chief Executive Officer; Director, Richard J. Giromini, age 59, $533,796 total compensation
SVP Human Resources, Timothy J. Monahan, age 60, $217,823 total compensation
Senior Vice President - Sales and Marketing, Bruce N. Ewald, age 61, $253,984 total compensation
VP; Group President Commercial Trailer Products, Brent Yeagy
SVP; Group President Diversified Products Group, Mark J. Weber, age 40, $184,301 total compensation
Senior Vice President; General Counsel; Secretary, Erin J. Roth, age 36
VP Acting CFO and Treasurer, Jeffery L. Taylor
Director, Scott K. Sorensen, age 51
Director, James D. (Jim) Kelly, age 60
Director, John E. Kunz
President CEO and Director, Richard J. Giromini, age 59
Director, Larry J. Magee, age 58
Auditors: Ernst&YoungLLP

LOCATIONS

HQ: Wabash National Corporation
1000 Sagamore Pkwy. South, Lafayette IN 47905
Phone: 765-771-5300   **Fax:** 765-771-5474
Web: www.wabashnational.com

PRODUCTS/OPERATIONS

2010 Sales

	$ mil.	% of total
Manufacturing	542	85
Retail & distribution	98	15
Total	**640**	**100**

2010 Sales by Category

	$ mil.	% of total
New trailers	550	86
Used trailers	22	4
Parts service & other	67	10
Total	**640**	**100**

2010 Sales by Product Line

	% of total
Dry freight	77
Refrigerated	15
Platform	6
Specialty	2
Total	**100**

Selected Products

ArcticLite refrigerated vans
Dump trailers
DuraPlate vans
DuraPlate HD vans
DuraPlate Pups
Intermodal
Platform trailers
Sheet and post vans

COMPETITORS

Featherlite
Fontaine Trailer
Great Dane
Hyundai Translead
Trinity Industries
Utility Trailer
Wells Cargo

HISTORICAL FINANCIALS

Company Type: Public

Income Statement

FYE: December 31

	REVENUE ($ mil.)	NET INCOME ($ mil.)	NET PROFIT MARGIN	EMPLOYEES
12/12	1,461.8	105.6	7.2%	4,400
12/11	1,187.2	15.0	1.3%	2,600
12/10	640.3	(141.7)	—	1,800
12/09	337.8	(101.7)	—	1,600
12/08	836.2	(125.8)	—	2,800
Annual Growth	**15.0%**	**—**	**—**	**12.0%**

2012 Year-End Financials

Debt ratio: 47.1%
Return on equity: 50.7%
Cash ($ mil.): 81
Current ratio: 2.13
Long-term debt ($ mil.): 420

No. of shares (mil.): 68
Dividends
  Yield: —
  Payout: —
Market value ($ mil.): 613

	STOCK PRICE ($) FY Close	P/E High/Low		PER SHARE ($) Earnings	Dividends	Book Value
12/12	8.97	7	4	1.53	0.00	3.93
12/11	7.84	57	20	0.22	0.00	2.15
12/10	11.85	—	—	(3.36)	0.00	1.90
12/09	1.89	—	—	(3.48)	0.00	2.50
12/08	4.50	—	—	(4.20)	0.18	5.41
Annual Growth	**18.8%**	**—**	**—**	**—**	**—**	**(7.7%)**

Walker & Dunlop Inc

When it comes to its commercial real estate loans Walker & Dunlop has the government on its side. The company provides commercial real estate financial services —mainly multifamily loans for apartments health care properties and student housing —to real estate owners and developers across the US. It originates and sells its products (e.g. mortgages supplemental financing construction loans and mezzanine loans) primarily through government-sponsored enterprises (GSEs) like Fannie Mae and Freddie Mac as well as through HUD. To a lesser extent the company originates loans for insurance companies banks and institutional investors.

IPO

Walker & Dunlop went public via a 2010 IPO and raised some $100 million from the offering. It used the proceeds for general corporate purposes and for acquisitions of complementary businesses and products.

Geographic Reach

Walker & Dunlop operates through 20 offices across the country with locations residing in Atlanta; Chicago; Dallas; Ft. Lauderdale Florida; Irvine California; Nashville Tennessee; New Orleans; New York; Seattle; San Francisco; Needham Massachusetts; and Walnut Creek California.

Operations

The company generates its revenue from five main revenue streams: mortgage banking (73% of total revenue) servicing fees (20%) warehouse interest (2%) escrow earnings (1%) and other (4%).

Sales and Marketing

Walker & Dunlop originates and sells loans through the programs of the Federal National Mortgage Association the Federal Home Loan Mortgage Corporation the Government National Mortgage Association and the Federal Housing Administration a division of the US Department of Housing and Urban Development.

Financial Performance

As the mortgage banking industry recovers from the devastating effects of the recession Walker & Dunlop has enjoyed record-setting revenue growth over the last few years. Revenues skyrocketed by nearly 70% from $152 million in 2011 to $257 million in 2012. Its profits also reached historic heights in 2011 and 2012 hovering around the $30 to $35 million mark.

The company has achieved exceptional growth from all its channels of revenue. Mortgage banking revenue rose 82% from 2011 to 2012 while revenues stemming from service fees jumped by 55%. Walker & Dunlop attributes the growth largely to an increase in the volume of loans in addition to a previous acquisition it made.

Strategy

Walker & Dunlop has shaped its growth strategy (and timed its IPO) around certain opportunities in the commercial real estate market on which it believes it can capitalize. It intends to invest in origination activities and products to meet the expected increase in demand for real estate financing. In addition Walker & Dunlop's focus on growing its services to health care facilities is centered on an expected rise in the demand for health care real estate loans. It hopes to serve an expected increased demand for such facilities as baby boomers reach retirement age. The company is also motivated by the fact that many commercial health care loans are sought after through GSE and HUD programs.

In 2012 the company bought rival lender CW-Capital from CW Financial Services in a $220 million cash-and-stock transaction. The deal gave Walker & Dunlop a combined portfolio of $7.7 billion of commercial real estate loan originations and an aggregate servicing portfolio of more than $35 billion. Funded through IPO funds the transaction should allow the company to further grow its lending operations.

Ownership

Fortress Investment Group owns about 43% of Walker & Dunlop.

Company Background

Walker & Dunlop's relationship with government-related housing finance companies began in the late 1980s after it started originating underwriting and selling loans through Fannie Mae. In 2008 it began working with Freddie Mac and HUD after acquiring a loan servicing portfolio worth $5 billion from Column Guaranteed LLC. The acquisition served to widen Walker & Dunlop's revenue base and increase its sales volume.

EXECUTIVES

Chairman President and CEO, William M. (Willy) Walker, age 47, $300,000 total compensation
General Counsel Secretary Vice President, Richard M. (Rich) Lucas, age 48
EVP and COO, Howard W. Smith III, age 54, $250,000 total compensation
SVP CFO Secretary and Treasurer, Deborah A. Wilson, age 57, $250,000 total compensation
EVP and Chief Credit Officer, Richard C. Warner, age 58, $205,000 total compensation
EVP and CFO, Stephen P. Theobald
Vice President - Investor Relations, Claire Harvey
EVP and Chief Production Officer, Donald P. King
EVP Proprietary Capital, Jeffrey M. (Jeff) Goodman
Director Information Technology, Bill Granger
Director Marketing, Susan Weber
Director, Richard M. (Rich) Lucas, age 48
EVP COO and Director, Howard W. Smith III, age 54
Director, Mitchell M. Gaynor, age 54
Director, John Rice, age 46
Director, Edmund F. Taylor, age 53
Director, Robert A. Wrzosek, age 41
Independent Director, Alan Bowers
Independent Director, Cynthia Hallenbeck
Independent Director, Dana Schmaltz
Auditors: KPMGLLP

LOCATIONS

HQ: Walker & Dunlop Inc.
7501 Wisconsin Ave. Ste. 1200, Bethesda MD 20814
Phone: 301-215-5500   **Fax:** 301-634-2151
Web: web.walkerdunlop.com

PRODUCTS/OPERATIONS

2012 Sales

	% mil.	% of total
Gains from mortgage banking activities	186	73
Servicing fees	52	20
Net warehouse interest income	4	2
Escrow earnings & other interest income	3	1
Other	10	4
Total	**256**	**100**

Selected Products and Services

Capital Markets and Investment Services
Construction loans
Equity investments
FHA Finance
First mortgage loans
Healthcare Finance
Mezzanine loans
Multifamily Finance
Second trust loans
Supplemental financings
Underwriting

COMPETITORS

American Capital
Arbor Commercial
CapitalSource
Centerline Holding Co.
Deutsche Bank
Deutsche Bank
  Berkshire Mortgage
Encore Capital Group
HFF
Kennedy-Wilson
MetLife
NewStar Financial
Ocwen Financial
Pzena Investment
  Management
Redwood Trust
Walter Investment
  Management
Wells Fargo

HISTORICAL FINANCIALS

Company Type: Public

Income Statement

FYE: December 31

	REVENUE ($ mil.)	NET INCOME ($ mil.)	NET PROFIT MARGIN	EMPLOYEES
12/12	256.7	33.7	13.2%	420
12/11	152.3	34.8	22.9%	189
12/10	121.8	8.2	6.8%	157
12/09	88.7	24.7	27.9%	150
12/08	49.1	14.0	28.5%	0
Annual Growth	**51.2%**	**24.6%**		

2012 Year-End Financials

Debt ratio: 69.0%	No. of shares (mil.): 33
Return on equity: 13.0%	Dividends
Cash ($ mil.): 65	Yield: —
Current ratio: 0.95	Payout: —
Long-term debt ($ mil.): 1,165	Market value ($ mil.): 559

	STOCK PRICE ($) FY Close	P/E High/Low		PER SHARE ($) Earnings	Dividends	Book Value
12/12	16.66	13	8	1.31	0.00	10.52
12/11	12.56	9	6	1.60	0.00	7.52
12/10	10.09	18	18	0.55	0.00	5.82
Annual Growth	**28.5%**	—	—	**54.3%**	—	**34.4%**

Washington Banking Co. (Oak Harbor, WA)

Washington Banking is the holding company for Whidbey Island Bank which serves individuals and businesses through some 30 branches in northwestern Washington. The bank offers standard deposit services such as checking and savings accounts CDs and IRAs. It primarily originates commercial mortgages and consumer and construction loans. To a lesser extent the bank offers one- to four-family residential mortgages and business loans. Whidbey Island Bank sells investment and insurance products through agreements with third-party providers. The bank added about a dozen branches in 2010 from the acquisitions of failed financial institutions City Bank and North County Bank in separate FDIC-assisted transactions.

After calling off the $191 million deal Washington Banking sited Frontier's inability to obtain regulatory approval in a timely manner and in doing so Frontier breached the merger agreement.

Frontier disagreed and blamed Washington Banking for backing out of the deal which they believe is a breach of the merger agreement.

Each company is seeking a $5 million termination fee from the other for failing to meet the approval deadline.

About a month after terminating the merger deal Washington Banking's CEO and president Michal Cann announced his retirement.

EXECUTIVES

Chairman Washington Banking Company and Whidbey Island Bank, Anthony B. (Tony) Pickering, age 65, $40,700 total compensation

President and CEO; President and CEO Whidbey Island Bank, John L. (Jack) Wagner, age 69, $266,000 total compensation

EVP and CFO; EVP and CFO Whidbey Island Bank, Richard A (Rick) Shields, age 53, $176,400 total compensation

President and Chief Executive Officer of the Bank, Bryan McDonald

Executive Vice President; Chief Credit Officer of the Bank, Daniel Kuenzi

Executive Vice President; Chief Administrative Officer of the Bank, Edward Eng

Executive Vice President; Chief Banking Officer of the Bank, George Bowen

Auditors: MossAdamsLLP

LOCATIONS

HQ: Washington Banking Company
450 SW Bayshore Dr., Oak Harbor WA 98277
Phone: 360-679-3121   **Fax:** 360-675-7282
Web: www.wibank.com

PRODUCTS/OPERATIONS

2007 Sales

	$ mil.	% of total
Interest		
Loans including fees	61	88
Investment securities & other	1	2
Noninterest		
Service charges & fees	3	4
Electronic banking	1	2
Other	3	4
Total	**69**	**100**

COMPETITORS

Bank of America
Banner Corp
KeyCorp

U.S. Bancorp
Washington Federal

HISTORICAL FINANCIALS

Company Type: Public

Income Statement

FYE: December 31

	ASSETS ($ mil.)	NET INCOME ($ mil.)	INCOME AS % OF ASSETS	EMPLOYEES
12/12	1,687.6	16.8	1.0%	467
12/11	1,670.6	15.9	1.0%	450
12/10	1,704.4	25.5	1.5%	448
12/09	1,045.8	6.2	0.6%	281
12/08	899.6	8.3	0.9%	258
Annual Growth	**17.0%**	**19.2%**	**—**	**16.0%**

2012 Year-End Financials

Return on assets: 1.0%
Return on equity: 9.5%
Long-term debt ($ mil.): —
No. of shares (mil.): 15
Sales ($ mil.): 97

Dividends
Yield: 3.6%
Payout: 45.8%
Market value ($ mil.): 211

	STOCK PRICE ($) FY Close	P/E High/Low	PER SHARE ($) Earnings	Dividends	Book Value
12/12	13.62	14 11	1.09	0.50	11.79
12/11	11.91	15 10	0.97	0.20	11.09
12/10	13.71	10 7	1.55	0.14	11.86
12/09	11.94	27 13	0.46	0.18	10.43
12/08	8.70	20 8	0.88	0.26	8.47
Annual Growth	**11.9%**	**— —**	**5.5%**	**18.3%**	**8.6%**

Waste Connections, Inc.

Waste Connections does the dirty work so you don't have to. The company provides solid waste collection transfer disposal and recycling services to more than 2 million commercial industrial and residential customers in 31 states. The integrated solid waste services company does business mainly in smaller markets. Waste Connections owns or operates about 151 solid waste collection operations 53 transfer stations 43 landfills and 38 recycling facilities. It also operates 20 liquid exploration and production waste injection wells and offers other cleanup services to oil and gas companies. In addition Waste Connections offers intermodal logistics services in the Pacific Northwest.

Geographic Reach

Through three geographic segments (Eastern Western and Central) Waste Connections serves commercial industrial and residential solid waste customers in 31 states. Its exploration and production segment serves oil and gas customers from locations in Louisiana New Mexico North Dakota Oklahoma Texas and Wyoming. Waste Connections' intermodal operations take place in the Pacific Northwest.

Operations

In addition to providing solid waste collection transfer disposal and recycling services the company is a leading provider of non-hazardous exploration and production waste treatment recovery and disposal services in oil and gas patches across the US through R360 Environmental Solutions which operates 26 facilities in six states. Waste Connections also provides intermodal services for the rail transportation of cargo and solid waste containers through a network of intermodal facilities.

Financial Performance

Waste Connections reported a 10% growth in revenues in 2012 due to a strong performance from all its segments revenue thanks to acquisitions and other revenue growth.The company posted net income of $159.1 million in 2012 (4% down on 2011) due to increased operating expenses primarily the result of higher depreciation expenses (due to the purchase of equipment to support existing operation) and increased amortization of intangibles costs.

Strategy

By focusing on acquiring mom-and-pop operations in secondary markets rather than large urban areas the company has been able to continue riding the crest of a consolidation trend in the waste management industry that began in the 1990s. While other large waste management companies –including major players Waste Management and Republic Services –have slowed or halted their buying sprees Waste Connections has continued to acquire although selectively.

It targets markets where it can provide waste collection under franchises or exclusive contracts or where it can hold a leading market position and provide integrated collection and disposal services. More than half of its revenues come from market areas where it has franchise or exclusive arrangements.

In a major strategic shift in 2012 the company also expanded its business offerings by moving to the arena of oil field clean up services.

Mergers and Acquisitions

In 2012 Waste Connections bought R360 Environmental Solutions which treats recovers and disposes of nonhazardous wastes in oilfields for $1.3 billion.

Expanding its geographic coverage for solid waste services in 2012 the company bought Alaska Pacific Environmental Services Anchorage and Alaska Green Waste Solutions. It also purchased SKB Environmental a provider of solid waste transfer and disposal services in Minnesota.

Ownership

T. Rowe Price Associates owns about 12% of the company.

HISTORY

When United Waste Systems and USA Waste Services merged in 1997 Ron Mittelstaedt who was managing United's western operations at the time saw an opening for mid-market waste haulers created by that consolidation and others. Mittelstaedt put together a group of investors that acquired the Washington operations of Browning-Ferris Industries (BFI) in 1997 and named the firm Waste Connections of Washington. Mittelstaedt Bradford Bishop and James Cutler then formed Waste Connections of Idaho and bought BFI operations in eastern Idaho.

In early 1998 Waste Connections of Washington acquired Waste Connections of Idaho. The company expanded into California that year when it purchased Madera Disposal Systems and added Hunter Enterprises a solid-waste hauler in eastern Idaho. Waste Connections also purchased firms in such midwestern and western states as Kansas Montana Nebraska Oklahoma Oregon South Dakota Texas and Wyoming.

Waste Connections went public in 1998 and used the money raised to buy more than 75 waste management facilities and service companies. In 1999 it added the Denver area to its territory after the US Justice Department required merger partners Allied Waste Industries and BFI to sell off operations there. Waste Connections also moved into New Mexico by purchasing landfill and collection company International Environmental Industries — one of more than 35 acquisitions in 1999.

Waste Connections in 2000 swapped some holdings with Allied Waste. Waste Connections sold its Idaho operations to Allied which in turn sold its operations in Iowa Montana and Wyoming to Waste Connections. Later that year Waste Connections purchased some of Allied's Kansas operations.

Consolidation in the waste industry hadn't stopped by 2002. That year Waste Connections made various tuck-in acquisitions in Washington Oregon Texas Tennessee Oklahoma and Colorado. One of its largest deals that year was the acquisition of San Luis Garbage Co. of San Luis Obispo California.

In 2003 Waste Connections bought two companies in California that together annually generated about $29 million. Other purchases that year included two collection and landfill operating companies in Mississippi and tuck-in acquisitions in Iowa Nebraska and South Dakota. The company acquired nine nonhazardous solid waste collection and disposal businesses in 2004.

Also in 2004 Waste Connections and Waste Industries USA traded some assets in the southern US. Waste Connections bought Waste Industries' hauling and landfill operations in the greater Memphis market and its hauling and transfer station operation (including an early stage municipal solid waste landfill development project) in Crossville Tennessee and the company sold to Waste Industries its hauling transfer station and construction and demolition landfill operations in Atlanta's north and northwestern suburbs.

Waste Connections stepped outside the solid waste business for the first time in 2004 when it bought Northwest Container Services a provider of intermodal logistics services in Washington and Oregon. Intermodal logistics involves arranging freight transportation by multiple methods such as truck and train. The synergy between solid waste and intermodal logistics might not be obvious but Waste Connections uses its presence in both markets to gain a share of the market for transporting solid waste by rail from the Seattle area to landfills in eastern Washington and eastern Oregon.

In 2007 Waste Connections acquired 15 nonhazardous solid waste collection transfer disposal and recycling businesses. The following year it made one large acquisition of Harold LeMay Enterprises in Washington for more than $200 million and 14 other smaller deals.

The company acquired a number of operations in 2009 from Republic Services (which that company was required to sell to meet the regulatory requirements of its acquisition of Allied Waste Industries) for $377 million. Waste Connections also made six smaller acquisitions that year and only a couple of small acquisitions in 2010.

EXECUTIVES

SVP People Safety and Development, Eric M. Merrill, age 61, $270,000 total compensation
Senior Vice President Sales and Marketing of Waste Connections, David M. Hall, age 56
VP Employee Relations, Jerri L. Hunt, age 62
EVP and COO, Darrell W. Chambliss, age 49, $346,725 total compensation
President, Steven F. (Steve) Bouck, age 56, $398,475 total compensation
Chairman and CEO, Ronald J. (Ron) Mittelstaedt, age 50, $538,200 total compensation
SVP Engineering and Disposal, James M. (Jim) Little, age 52
VP Disposal Operations, Scott I. Schreiber, age 56
VP and CIO, Eric O. Hansen, age 48
EVP and CFO, Worthing F. Jackman, age 49, $320,850 total compensation
Senior Vice President Chief Accounting Officer of Waste Connections, David G. Eddie, age 44
VP General Counsel and Secretary, Patrick J. Shea, age 42
VP Business Development, Richard K. Wojahn, age 55
Business Development Manager, Ed Quinnan
Business Development Manager, Greg Popovich
Business Development Manager, Jeff Meredith
Vice President - Maintenance and Fleet Management, Gregory Thibodeaux

Vice President - Finance of Waste Connections, Mary Whitney
Vice President Chief Tax Officer of Waste Connections, Matthew S. Black
Vice President People Training and Development, Susan R. Netherton
Director, Edward E. (Ned) Guillet, age 61
Director, Robert H. (Bob) Davis, age 71
Director, Michael W. Harlan, age 52
Director, William J. Razzouk, age 66
Auditors: PricewaterhouseCoopersLLP

LOCATIONS

HQ: Waste Connections Inc.
Waterway Plaza 2 10001 Woodloch Forest Dr. Ste. 400, The Woodlands TX 77380
Phone: 832-442-2200   **Fax:** 832-442-2290
Web: www.wasteconnections.com

2012 Sales

Western	782	48
Eastern	366	22
E&P	40	2

PRODUCTS/OPERATIONS

2012 Sales

Solid waste collection	1,176	62
Solid wast recycling	81	4
E&P waste treatment disposal & recovery	61	3
Intermodal & other	50	3
Total	**1,661**	**100**

COMPETITORS

Casella Waste Systems	Recology
Clean Harbors	Republic Services
Hub Group	Veolia ES Solid Waste
Newpark Resources	Waste Industries USA
Pacer International	Waste Management
Progressive Waste	

HISTORICAL FINANCIALS

Company Type: Public

Income Statement

FYE: December 31

	REVENUE ($ mil.)	NET INCOME ($ mil.)	NET PROFIT MARGIN	EMPLOYEES
12/13	1,928.8	195.6	10.1%	6,633
12/12	1,661.6	159.0	9.6%	6,606
12/11	1,505.3	165.2	11.0%	5,909
12/10	1,319.7	135.1	10.2%	5,510
12/09	1,191.3	109.8	9.2%	5,409
Annual Growth	**12.8%**	**15.5%**	**—**	**5.2%**

2013 Year-End Financials

Debt ratio: 40.9%	No. of shares (mil.): 123
Return on equity: 9.9%	Dividends
Cash ($ mil.): 13	Yield: 0.9%
Current ratio: 0.95	Payout: 28.2%
Long-term debt ($ mil.): 2,067	Market value ($ mil.): 5,391

	STOCK PRICE ($) FY Close	P/E High/Low	PER SHARE ($) Earnings	Dividends	Book Value
12/13	43.63	29 21	1.58	0.42	16.53
12/12	33.79	26 22	1.31	0.37	15.27
12/11	33.14	24 18	1.45	0.32	12.58
12/10	27.53	35 22	1.16	0.08	11.99
12/09	33.34	37 23	0.91	0.00	11.48
Annual Growth	**7.0%**	**— —**	**14.7%**	**—**	**9.5%**

Wesco Aircraft Holdings Inc.

Planes may fly around the world but they can't leave the ground without Wesco Aircraft Holdings. One of the largest logistics and supply chain companies serving the aerospace industry it provides distribution vendor relationship management just-in-time (JIT) delivery quality assurance and kitting. Operating through Wesco Aircraft Hardware and other subsidiaries the company stocks about 450000 different pieces of hardware bearings tools electronic components and machined parts from more than 1100 suppliers. Its 7200 customers can choose from JIT or long-term contracts or ad hoc sales. Formed in 1953 by the father of chairman president and CEO Randy Snyder the company filed to go public in 2011.

The IPO is initially valued at $300 million though Wesco Aircraft Holdings says it won't see any of the proceeds. Selling shareholders include parent Carlyle Group (holding 83% pre-IPO through Falcon Aerospace) and Snyder (16%). The company plans to grow by increasing business with existing customers adding new customers and expanding internationally. It recently began operations in China India and Saudi Arabia with Mexico on the radar.

To create a new MRO (maintenance repair overhaul) operation expand its global footprint and provide more service for several strategic customers Wesco Aircraft Holdings acquired Canada-based Interfast in 2012 for about CDN$134 million (about $130.9 million). Interfast distributes specialty fasteners fastening systems and production installation tooling for the aerospace electronics and general industrial sectors.

Wesco Aircraft Holdings counts major airplane OEMs among its customers; Boeing accounts for about 15% of sales. Despite a global recession that hit some of its customers hard the company managed to continue growing sales and improving the bottom line on the strength of improved cost control and reduced expenses.

EXECUTIVES

EVP, Tommy Lee, age 64
Chairman President and CEO, Randy J. Snyder, age 62
EVP Sales and Marketing, Hal Weinstein, age 58
Director of Outside Sales Americas, Brad Strella
EVP and CFO, Gregory A. (Greg) Hann, age 57
VP Global Operations, Alex Murray, age 42
Global Controller, J. Shawn Trogdon
Director of Outside Sales Europe, Mark Johnson
Director, David L. Squier, age 66
Director, Paul E. Fulchino, age 65
Director, Peter J. Clare, age 47
Director, Gen. John P. Jumper, age 66
Director, Robert D. Paulson, age 66
Director, Adam J. Palmer, age 39
Director, Dayne A. Baird, age 35
Auditors: PricewaterhouseCoopersLLP

LOCATIONS

HQ: Wesco Aircraft Holdings Inc.
27727 Avenue Scott, Valencia, CA 91355
Phone: 661 775-7200
Web: www.wescoair.com

2010 Sales

	$ mil.	% of total
North America	603	92
Rest of the world	95	15
Adjustments	(43.11)	-
Total	**656**	**100**

PRODUCTS/OPERATIONS

2010 Sales

	$ mil.	% of total
Hardware	527	80
Electronic components	70	11
Bearings	42	7
Machined parts & other	17	2
Total	**656**	**100**

COMPETITORS

AAR Corp.	First Aviation
Align Aerospace	GECAS Asset Management
Aviall Services	Services
BE Aerospace	Kellstrom Aerospace
Banner Aerospace	

HISTORICAL FINANCIALS

Company Type: Public

Income Statement

FYE: September 30

	REVENUE ($ mil.)	NET INCOME ($ mil.)	NET PROFIT MARGIN	EMPLOYEES
09/13	901.6	104.8	11.6%	1,354
09/12	776.2	92.1	11.9%	1,218
09/11	710.8	75.6	10.6%	1,014
09/10	656.0	73.6	11.2%	1,021
09/09	612.6	58.4	9.5%	0
Annual Growth	**10.1%**	**15.7%**	—	—

2013 Year-End Financials

Debt ratio: 34.9%	No. of shares (mil.): 94
Return on equity: 12.9%	Dividends
Cash ($ mil.): 78	Yield: —
Current ratio: 7.52	Payout: —
Long-term debt ($ mil.): 569	Market value ($ mil.): 1,984

	STOCK PRICE ($) FY Close	P/E High/Low		PER SHARE ($) Earnings	Dividends	Book Value
09/13	20.93	19	11	1.09	0.00	9.13
09/12	13.66	17	9	0.96	0.00	8.09
09/11	10.93	18	13	0.81	0.00	7.33
Annual Growth	**38.4%**	—	—	**16.0%**	—	**11.6%**

Western Alliance Bancorporation

The allies behind holding company Western Alliance Bancorporation are Western Alliance Bank (which operates as Alliance Bank of Arizona and First Independent Bank of Nevada) Las Vegas-based Bank of Nevada and Torrey Pines Bank which is active throughout California. Together the banks operate about 40 branches. Serving local businesses real estate developers and investors not-for-profit organizations and consumers the banks provide standard deposit products such as checking savings and money market accounts and CDs. Loans to businesses including real estate mortgages commercial and industrial loans and construction and land development loans dominate the banks' lending activities.

Other subsidiaries of Western Alliance Bancorporation include Shine Investment Advisory Services (80% owned) and Western Alliance Equipment Leasing. To build up its operations in Las Vegas in 2012 the company agreed to buy Western Liberty Bancorp holding company of the three-branch Service1st Bank of Nevada.

After three consecutive years of losses Western Alliance Bancorporation recorded positive net income in 2011 as all three of its subsidiary banks were profitable for the first time since 2007. The company's results were bolstered by loan growth improved interest rate margins and spreads and a decrease in loan loss provisions. The economic turmoil that had gripped its key markets of California Phoenix and Las Vegas during the depths of the recession also abated.

The company exited or divested some non-core businesses during its years in the red. In 2009 it sold a majority of investment advisor Miller/Russell & Associates to that firm's management and sold wealth manager Premier Trust to Ladenburg Thalmann the following year. Also in 2010 Western Alliance ceased operations related to PartnersFirst its affinity credit card platform.

The company did not totally retrench however. Its Bank of Nevada subsidiary was approved by the FDIC in 2009 to acquire deposits and assets of the failed Security Savings Bank in a transaction that included loss-sharing agreements with the regulator. Western Alliance Bancorporation also opened three new bank branches in 2010.

Western Alliance's chairman president and CEO Robert Sarver is also majority owner of the Phoenix Suns NBA franchise.

EXECUTIVES

Executive Vice President; Chief Credit Officer, Robert R. (Bob) McAuslan, age 60
Chairman of the Board; Chief Executive Officer, Robert G. Sarver, age 52, $597,141 total compensation
Chief Financial Officer; Executive Vice President, Dale M. Gibbons, age 52, $311,539 total compensation
Executive Vice President; Chief Administrative Officer, Merrill S. Wall, age 65, $290,096 total compensation
President COO and Director, Kenneth A. (Ken) Vecchione, age 58
Executive Vice President; California Administration, Gerald (Gary) Cady, age 58, $283,942 total compensation
Executive Vice President - Credit Administration, Duane Froeschle, age 60, $222,307 total compensation
Executive Vice President - Arizona Administration, James H. (Jim) Lundy, age 63, $231,246 total compensation
Executive Vice President; Southern Nevada Administration, Bruce Hendricks, age 63, $275,192 total compensation
President and CEO Western Alliance Leasing, Michael (Mike) Brown
Executive Vice President - Technology and Operations, Dennis Rygwalski
Executive Vice President; Chief Risk Officer, Patricia Taylor
Director, Steven J. (Steve) Hilton, age 52
Director, Donald D. (Don) Snyder, age 65
Director, William S. (Bill) Boyd, age 81
Director, James E. Nave, age 68
Director, Cary P. Mack, age 53
President COO and Director, Kenneth A. (Ken) Vecchione, age 58
Director, Sung Won Sohn, age 68
Director, Marianne B. Johnson, age 54
Director, Todd Marshall, age 56
Director, M. Nafees Nagy, age 69
Director, Bruce Beach, age 63
Director, John P. Sande III, age 63
Auditors: McGladreyLLP

LOCATIONS

HQ: Western Alliance Bancorporation
1 E. Washington St. Ste. 1400, Phoenix AZ 85004
Phone: 602-389-3500 **Fax:** 604-684-8092
Web: www.northerndynastyminerals.com

PRODUCTS/OPERATIONS

2011 Sales

	$ mil.	% of total
Interest		
Loans including fees	261	79
Taxable securities	28	8
Other	6	2
Noninterest		
Service charges & fees	9	3
Mark to market gains net	5	2
Bank-owned life insurance	5	2
Net gain on sales of securities	4	1
Trust & investment advisory fees	2	1
Other fee revenue	3	1
Other	3	1
Total	**331**	**100**

COMPETITORS

BancWest	U.S. Bancorp
Bank of America	UnionBanCal
Bank of the West	Wells Fargo
Desert Schools FCU	Westamerica
First Banks	Zions Bancorporation
PacWest Bancorp	

HISTORICAL FINANCIALS

Company Type: Public

Income Statement

FYE: December 31

	ASSETS ($ mil.)	NET INCOME ($ mil.)	INCOME AS % OF ASSETS	EMPLOYEES
12/12	7,622.6	72.8	1.0%	982
12/11	6,844.5	31.4	0.5%	942
12/10	6,193.8	(7.2)	—	908
12/09	5,753.2	(151.4)	—	930
12/08	5,242.7	(236.4)	—	1,020
Annual Growth	**9.8%**	—	—	**(0.9%)**

2012 Year-End Financials

Return on assets: 1.0%	Dividends
Return on equity: 10.4%	Yield: —
Long-term debt ($ mil.): —	Payout: —
No. of shares (mil.): 86	Market value ($ mil.): 910
Sales ($ mil): 363	

	STOCK PRICE ($) FY Close	P/E High/Low		PER SHARE ($) Earnings	Dividends	Book Value
12/12	10.53	13	8	0.83	0.00	8.79
12/11	6.23	44	25	0.19	0.00	7.73
12/10	7.36	—	—	(0.23)	0.00	7.37
12/09	3.78	—	—	(2.74)	0.00	7.94
12/08	10.09	—	—	(7.27)	0.00	12.84
Annual Growth	**1.1%**	—	—	—	—	**(9.0%)**

Western Gas Partners LP

Western Gas Partners' style is to gather and go. The company gathers and transports natural gas for its largest customer and parent Anadarko Petroleum and delivers natural gas and natural gas liquids (NGLs) to end-users. It handles gathering processing and throughput of about 2.2 billion cu. ft. of gas a day through eleven natural gas gathering systems seven treating facilities one natural gas liquids pipeline and one interstate pipeline (totaling more than 8820 miles across Wyoming Utah Texas Oklahoma and Kansas). Operating principally under long-term contracts the company gathers natural gas from individual wells after which it is compressed treated and delivered to customers.

Western Gas Partners was formed to handle certain petroleum processing storage and transport operations for Anadarko and to make complementary acquisitions. Its partnership business structure allows it seek to increase its cash distribution per unit over time.

In 2009 the company made its first acquisition when it bought $210 million of midstream assets located in the Powder River Basin from its parent. It later acquired assets in the Uintah Basin in northeastern Utah for $107 million. In 2010 it acquired properties in southwest Wyoming from Anadarko for $254 million. That year Western Gas Partners also bought natural gas assets in northeastern Colorado from its parent for about $498 million. Making a complementary acquisition in 2011 it acquired a natural gas processing plant and other assets in Colorado from Encana Oil and Gas (USA) for $303 million.

That year Western Gas Partners also acquired the Bison gas treating facility and related assets in the Powder River Basin from Anadarko Petroleum for $130 million.

System capacity expansion increased throughput and higher NGL prices lifted Western Gas Partners' revenues and net income in 2011.

In 2012 the company bought midstream assets from Anadarko Petroleum for $483 million (Mountain Gas Resources which owns the Red Desert Complex a 22% stake in gas processor Rendezvous Gas Services). It also went public that year Anadarko Petroleum spun off Western Gas Partners in 2008. In 2012 held a 44% stake in the company.

EXECUTIVES

Senior Vice President Chief Financial Officer, Benjamin M. (Ben) Fink, age 43
Chairman, Robert G. Gwin, age 50, $107,392 total compensation
Chief Operating Officer; Senior Vice President of Western Gas Holdings; LLC, Danny J. Rea, $65,699 total compensation
VP General Counsel and Corporate Secretary, Amanda M. McMillian, $48,011 total compensation
Investor Relations, Chris Campbell
President Chief Executive Officer, Donald R. Sinclair
Vice President; General Counsel; Corporate Secretary of Western Gas Holdings; LLC, Philip Peacock
Director, Robert K. (Bobby) Reeves Sr., age 54
Director, James R. (Jim) Crane, age 58
Director, Anthony R. (Tony) Chase, age 58
Director, Milton Carroll, age 62
Director, R. A. (Al) Walker, age 56
Director, David J. Tudor, age 53
Director, Charles A. (Chuck) Meloy Sr., age 53
SVP and COO, Danny J. Rea
President CEO and Director, Donald R. Sinclair
Auditors: KPMGLLP

LOCATIONS

HQ: Western Gas Partners LP
1201 Lake Robbins Dr., The Woodlands TX 77380-1046
Phone: 832-636-6000   **Fax:** 832-636-6001
Web: www.westerngas.com

PRODUCTS/OPERATIONS

2011 Sales

	$ mil.	% of total
Natural gas natural gas liquids and condensate sales	361	55
Gathering processing & transportation of natural gas & NGLs	287	43
Equity income & other	15	2
Total	**664**	**100**

COMPETITORS

DCP Midstream Partners
Enbridge Energy
Kinder Morgan Energy Partners
ONEOK Partners
Questar
Tallgrass Energy Partners
XTO Energy

HISTORICAL FINANCIALS

Company Type: Public

Income Statement

FYE: December 31

	REVENUE ($ mil.)	NET INCOME ($ mil.)	NET PROFIT MARGIN	EMPLOYEES
12/12	849.4	106.9	12.6%	0
12/11	664.0	142.9	21.5%	0
12/10	503.3	126.0	25.0%	0
12/09	245.1	77.3	31.6%	0
12/08	311.6	65.2	20.9%	167
Annual Growth	**28.5%**	**13.1%**	**—**	**—**

2012 Year-End Financials

Debt ratio: 33.6%
Return on equity: —
Cash ($ mil.): 419
Current ratio: 2.96
Long-term debt ($ mil.): 1,168

No. of shares (mil.): 106
Dividends
Yield: 3.9%
Payout: 128.7%
Market value ($ mil.): 5,087

	STOCK PRICE ($) FY Close	P/E High/Low		PER SHARE ($) Earnings	Dividends	Book Value
12/12	47.63	63	47	0.84	1.88	18.82
12/11	41.27	25	18	1.64	1.60	16.60
12/10	30.30	19	12	1.64	1.39	14.08
12/09	19.49	16	10	1.24	1.23	12.27
12/08	12.83	22	14	0.77	0.46	11.54
Annual Growth	**38.8%**	**—**	**—**	**2.2%**	**42.3%**	**13.0%**

Westwood Holdings Group, Inc.

Westwood Ho! Westwood Holdings Group is an asset manager that provides investment management services to institutions mutual funds and high-net-worth clients. The company operates through its subsidiaries. Westwood Trust handles trust custody and account management for companies institutions and high-net-worth individuals. Westwood Management is the group's institutional investment management unit overseeing accounts for corporations municipalities and charitable organizations with at least $10 million in investable assets. The firm is also the administrator of the Westwood family of mutual funds WHG Funds. Westwood Holdings Group has about $10 billion in assets under management.

Assets under management grew by more than 40% from 2008 to 2009. The firm attributes the growth to market appreciation of assets under management and a robust inflow of assets from new clients. Revenues didn't exactly reflect the growth in 2009 as the company earned no performance-based fees that year.

Westwood was founded in 1983 by chairman and CEO Susan Byrne. The company was spun off from investment bank and brokerage SWS Group in 2002. Over the years Westwood has grown from a small company to a firm that offers diverse products to a variety of clients. The company continuously looks for opportunities to grow in the institutional private wealth and mutual fund markets.

In 2009 Westwood expanded its mutual fund business with the acquisition of $52 million in mutual fund assets from the Philadelphia Fund. The deal helped increase WHG Funds' revenue and asset level in order to attract new clients.

The following year Westwood grew its business in additional markets with the acquisition of Omaha-based investment advisory McCarthy Group. The deal added more than $1.1 billion in private wealth and institutional client assets under management.

Byrne owns about 12% of the company. GAMCO Investors owns some 13%; Westwood in turn owns about 20% of GAMCO Investors' Gabelli Advisers (which distributes the Westwood mutual funds).

EXECUTIVES

Chairman and Co-Chief Investment Officer, Susan M. Byrne, age 66, $750,000 total compensation
Chief Financial Officer, Mark A. Wallace, age 55
President CEO Secretary and Director, Brian O. Casey, age 49, $450,000 total compensation
EVP and Co-Chief Investment Officer, Mark Freeman, age 46
SVP Private Wealth Management Team Westwood Holdings Group, Gregg Ballew
Director, Richard M. Frank, age 65
Director, Tom C. Davis, age 65
Director, Frederick R. Meyer, age 84
Director, Jon L. Mosle Jr., age 82
President CEO Secretary and Director, Brian O. Casey, age 49
Director, Robert D. (Bob) McTeer Jr., age 70
Director, Geoffrey R. Norman, age 69
Auditors: GrantThorntonLLP

LOCATIONS

HQ: Westwood Holdings Group Inc.
200 Crescent Ct. Ste. 1200, Dallas TX 75201
Phone: 214-756-6900   **Fax:** 214-756-6979
Web: www.westwoodgroup.com

PRODUCTS/OPERATIONS

2009 Sales

$ in mil. % of total	$ mil.	% of total
Advisory fees	31	75
Trust fees	10	24
Other	0	1
Total	**42**	**100**

2009 Assets under Management

	% of total
Separate	48
Subadvisory	19
Commingled	15
WHG	6
Managed	4
Westwood	3
Other	5
Total	**100**

COMPETITORS

American Century	NFJ Investment
Atalanta Sosnoff	Neuberger Berman
Duncan-Hurst	Nuveen
Eaton Vance	Oak Associates
FMR	Putnam
Franklin Templeton	T. Rowe Price
Janus Capital	US Global Investors
Martin Capital	W.P. Stewart

HISTORICAL FINANCIALS

Company Type: Public

Income Statement

FYE: December 31

	REVENUE ($ mil.)	NET INCOME ($ mil.)	NET PROFIT MARGIN	EMPLOYEES
12/12	77.5	12.0	15.6%	96
12/11	68.9	14.6	21.3%	80
12/10	55.3	11.2	20.4%	77
12/09	42.5	7.9	18.6%	64
12/08	46.4	10.5	22.7%	63
Annual Growth	**13.6%**	**3.5%**	**—**	**11.1%**

2012 Year-End Financials

Debt ratio: —
Return on equity: 16.3%
Cash ($ mil.): 3
Current ratio: 4.11
Long-term debt ($ mil.): —

No. of shares (mil.): 8
Dividends
Yield: 3.6%
Payout: 87.2%
Market value ($ mil.): 328

	STOCK PRICE ($) FY Close	P/E High/Low	PER SHARE ($) Earnings	Dividends	Book Value
12/12	40.90	24 20	1.65	1.51	9.53
12/11	36.55	19 15	2.04	1.42	9.18
12/10	39.96	25 18	1.58	1.65	7.94
12/09	36.34	35 20	1.18	1.23	6.60
12/08	28.41	30 14	1.63	1.20	5.58
Annual Growth	**9.5%**	**— —**	**0.3%**	**5.9%**	**14.3%**

Wex Inc

WEX (formerly Wright Express) provides payment processing and information management services to commercial and government vehicle fleets through a network that tracks purchases made on fleet charge cards at more than 190000 fuel and vehicle maintenance facilities throughout the US Canada Australia New Zealand and Europe. The company provides clients with transaction data analysis tools and purchase control capabilities for every vehicle in their fleets. Data collected at the point of sale include expenditures lists of items purchased odometer readings and driver vehicle and vendor identification. WEX serves some 350000 fleets that collectively have a total of approximately 6.6 million vehicles.

The company's subsidiaries include TelaPoint which provides supply-chain software to bulk petroleum distributors and retailers; and Pacific Pride Services a fuel distributor network with more than 340 independent fuel franchisees. WEX also issues corporate MasterCard credit cards through its Wright Express Financial Services subsidiary an industrial bank that issues the company's fleet cards as well. In 2011 WEX added prepaid cards to its product menu when it acquired rapid! PayCard a provider of payroll debit cards and other prepaid products to small and medium businesses.

WEX's closed-loop card network allows it access to both sides of every card transaction which provides it with usage data for its cardholder customer base as well as revenues from merchant fees charged. Its cards are accepted at more than 90% of the country's service stations and the company enjoys a leading market share of nearly 10% of all the fleet vehicles in the US. What's more there is room for growth for the firm as WEX estimates that a majority of fleets don't use fleet cards to manage fuel costs.

The company's strategy for growth includes diversifying beyond its traditional domestic markets through acquisitions. It purchased the Australian fuel and prepaid card operations of Retail Decisions for $318 million in 2010 making it a major player in the fleet card sector there. In 2012 WEX acquired CorporatePay a provider of prepaid virtual cards to the corporate travel industry in the UK for $27.5 million. The company later entered Brazil by acquiring a 51% stake in payroll card provider UNIK for nearly $22 million. At home it purchased fuel card provider Fleet One in an all-cash deal that closed in late2012.

WEX derives a significant portion of its revenue from charging a fee each time each time a client's driver uses his or her fleet card; the company processes more than 250 million such transactions annually. Although the company's sales increased in 2010 thanks in part to an increase in fuel prices its net income declined as expenses were up as well mainly related to its international acquisition. In 2011 transaction processing transactions increased by about a third partly due to the company's operations in Australia and New Zealand. Fuel prices also rose benefitting WEX further. As a result net income and revenues rose that year the former by 52% to $133.6 million and the latter by 42% to $553.1 million.

EXECUTIVES

Vice Chairman, Rowland T. (Row) Moriarty, age 66
Chairman President and CEO, Michael E. Dubyak, age 62, $515,000 total compensation
President The Americas, Melissa D. Smith, age 44, $320,000 total compensation
President International, David D. Maxsimic, age 53, $300,000 total compensation
SVP General Counsel and Corporate Secretary, Hilary A. Rapkin, age 46, $230,000 total compensation
Manager Communications, Jessica Roy
Senior Vice President Client Service Operations, Jamie Morin, age 48
SVP and CFO, Steven A. Elder, age 44
SVP and CIO, George W. Hogan, age 52
Senior Vice President Corporate Payment Solutions, Richard K. Stecklair, age 64
SVP Corporate Development, Gregory S. Strzegowski
Senior Vice President of Small Business Solutions, Kenneth W. Janosick
General Manager EMEA, Ketil Thorsen

Business Development Director EMEA, Philippe Chautard
Managing Director, David Howell
Director, Shikhar Ghosh, age 55
Director, Kirk P. Pond, age 67
Vice Chairman, Rowland T. (Row) Moriarty, age 65
Director, Jack A. VanWoerkom, age 59
Director, Regina O. (Reggie) Sommer, age 55
Director, Ronald T. Maheu, age 70
Director, George L. (Larry) McTavish, age 71
Auditors: Deloitte&ToucheLLP

LOCATIONS

HQ: WEX Inc.
97 Darling Ave., South Portland ME 04106-2301
Phone: 207-773-8171 **Fax:** 207-828-5181
Web: www.wexinc.com

PRODUCTS/OPERATIONS

2011 Sales

	$ mil.	% of total
Fleet payment solutions	436	79
Other payment solutions	116	21
Total	**553**	**100**

COMPETITORS

Comdata	Retail Decisions
FleetCor	U.S. Bancorp
Multi Service	

HISTORICAL FINANCIALS

Company Type: Public

Income Statement

FYE: December 31

	REVENUE ($ mil.)	NET INCOME ($ mil.)	NET PROFIT MARGIN	EMPLOYEES
12/12	623.1	96.9	15.6%	1,302
12/11	553.0	133.6	24.2%	899
12/10	390.4	87.6	22.4%	881
12/09	318.2	139.6	43.9%	725
12/08	393.5	127.6	32.4%	703
Annual Growth	**12.2%**	**(6.7%)**	**—**	**16.7%**

2012 Year-End Financials

Debt ratio: 19.9%
Return on equity: 12.6%
Cash ($ mil.): 197
Current ratio: 1.14
Long-term debt ($ mil.): 621

No. of shares (mil.): 38
Dividends
Yield: —
Payout: —
Market value ($ mil.): 2,932

	STOCK PRICE ($) FY Close	P/E High/Low	PER SHARE ($) Earnings	Dividends	Book Value
12/12	75.37	30 21	2.48	0.00	21.02
12/11	54.28	17 11	3.43	0.00	18.30
12/10	46.00	20 12	2.25	0.00	14.54
12/09	31.86	9 3	3.55	0.00	11.55
12/08	12.60	11 3	3.22	0.00	7.70
Annual Growth	**56.4%**	**— —**	**(6.3%)**	**—**	**28.5%**

Weyco Group, Inc

Weyco Group has him –or at least his feet –covered. The company imports men's footwear including mid-priced leather dress and casual shoes sold under the Florsheim Nunn Bush and Stacy Adams brands. It also offers casual footwear for women and children under the BOGS Rafters and Umi labels. Weyco sells its shoes to more than

10000 shoe clothing and department stores. The company also operates about two dozen Florsheim retail stores in the US and markets shoes online. In addition it licenses the Stacy Adams name for men's clothing and accessories. Founded in 1906 as Weyenberg Shoe Manufacturing the company changed its name to Weyco Group in 1990 and stopped manufacturing shoes in 2003.

Geographic Reach

From its headquarters in Milwaukee Wisconsin Weyco imports all of its products from independent manufacturers primarily in China and India. The company's wholesale and retail businesses reach from Europe to Australia South Africa and Asia Pacific —comprising the Florsheim Australia operation. It supplies retailers with its products from its distribution center located in Glendale Wisconsin.

Operations

The footwear maker operates through two reportable segments: North American wholesale and North American retail.

Strategy

Weyco generates most of its revenue through its wholesale distribution segment which also includes licensing efforts. The segment contributed 74% of 2012 sales while the company's retail segment rang up about 8%. While the US accounts for 77% of its sales Weyco's international business (wholesale and retail) is growing.

Mergers and Acquisitions

Weyco's $10-million acquisition of Florsheim Australia (in 2009) bolstered both its wholesale and retail businesses with 24 Florsheim stores in Australia one Florsheim store in New Zealand and a single shop in Macau. Beyond North America Weyco has a presence in Australia South Africa Europe and the Asia Pacific region.

Along with its international expansion Weyco has been diversifying its assortment of casual footwear. The company acquired The Combs Company for about $30 million in 2011. Combs designs waterproof shoes and boots under the BOGS and Rafters brands —footwear suited for gardening hunting fishing and other outdoor activities. The deal expands Weyco's assortment of casual shoes especially in the outdoor recreation category. Previously Weyco paid nearly $2 million for the Umi brand of casual footwear for infants and children from footwear maker Umi to cater to a younger demographic.

Financial Performance

Net sales increased 8% in fiscal 2012 as compared to 2011 spurred by its North American wholesale unit which logged higher sales volumes across all of its wholesale brands including BOGS. Net income rose 24% for the same reporting period thanks to a boost in earnings from operations in the North American wholesale and retail segments. Earnings from operations in the North American wholesale increased mainly due to higher sales volumes across all wholesale brands as well as slightly higher gross margins partially offset by higher selling and administrative costs related to the Canadian distribution of Bogs as well as higher pension and advertising expenses in 2012. Selling and administrative expenses for the retail segment decreased in 2012 and were primarily related to rent and occupancy costs employee costs and depreciation.

Sales and Marketing

The company uses a decentralized sales force to sell products to retail outlets. J. C. Penney was Weyco's largest customer in 2010 with 12% of sales. Since then however no single customer has generated sales above 10%.

Company Ownership

The Florsheim family — descendants of the founder of rival Florsheim Group which Weyco acquired in 2002 —owns more than a third of the company's shares. CEO Thomas Florsheim Jr. and President and COO John Florsheim run the business.

EXECUTIVES

SVP; President Nunn Bush Brand and Retail Division, Peter S. Grossman, age 69, $320,000 total compensation

President; Chief Operating Officer; Assistant Secretary; Director, John W. Florsheim, age 49, $525,000 total compensation

Chief Financial Officer; Senior Vice President; Secretary, John F. Wittkowske, age 53, $324,000 total compensation

Chairman Emeritus, Thomas W. Florsheim Sr., age 82

VP and President Stacy Adams Division, Brian Flannery

VP Retail Division, Tim Then

VP-Sls-Nunn Bush Brand, Matthew J. (Matt) Engerman

VP Purchasing, Allison Woss

VP Information Technology, George Sotiros

VP Finance and Treasurer, Judy Anderson

VP-Design, Keven Ringgold

VP-Sls-Florsheim Brand, Beverly Goldberg

VP Distribution, James G. Kehoe

VP Customer Relations and Vendor Compliance, Al Jackson

Vice President President UMI, Mark Kohlenberg

Vice President Sales BOGS, William (Bill) Combs

VP Sales BOGS/Rafters, Riley Combs

Vice President and President of Nunn Bush Brand, Mike Bernsteen

Director, Frederick P. Stratton Jr., age 73

President COO Assistant Secretary and Director, John W. Florsheim, age 49

Chairman Emeritus, Thomas W. Florsheim Sr., age 81

Director, Robert Feitler, age 82

Director, Cory L. Nettles, age 43

Director, Tina M. Chang, age 41

Auditors: Deloitte&ToucheLLP

LOCATIONS

HQ: Weyco Group Inc.
333 W. Estabrook Blvd., Milwaukee WI 53201
Phone: 414-908-1600   **Fax:** 414-908-1601
Web: www.weycogroup.com

2012 Sales

	$ mil.	% of total
US	225	77
Australia	29	10
Canada	16	6
Asia	9	3
Europe	7	2
South Africa	5	2
Total	**293**	**100**

PRODUCTS/OPERATIONS

2012 Sales

	$ mil.	% of total
North American Wholesale	217	74
North American Retail	24	8
Other	51	17
Total	**293**	**100**

2012 North American Wholesale Sales

	$ mil.	% of total
Nunn Bush	64	30
Stacy Adams	59	28
Florsheim	50	23
BOGS/Rafters	36	17
Umi	4	2
Licensing	3	2
Total	**217**	**100**

Selected Brands

BOGS
Brass Boot
Florsheim
Florsheim by Duckie Brown
Nunn Bush
Rafters
Stacy Adams
Umi

COMPETITORS

Allen-Edmonds	Kenneth Cole
Bally	NIKE
Berkshire Hathaway	PVH
Brown Shoe	R. Griggs
Collective Brands	Wolverine World Wide
Genesco	adidas

HISTORICAL FINANCIALS

Company Type: Public

Income Statement

FYE: December 31

	REVENUE ($ mil.)	NET INCOME ($ mil.)	NET PROFIT MARGIN	EMPLOYEES
12/12	293.4	18.9	6.5%	633
12/11	271.1	15.2	5.6%	621
12/10	229.2	13.6	6.0%	562
12/09	225.3	12.8	5.7%	553
12/08	221.4	17.0	7.7%	418
Annual Growth	**7.3%**	**2.7%**	**—**	**10.9%**

2012 Year-End Financials

Debt ratio: 15.7%
Return on equity: 11.1%
Cash ($ mil.): 17
Current ratio: 2.09
Long-term debt ($ mil.): —

No. of shares (mil.): 10
Dividends
  Yield: 3.6%
  Payout: 48.5%
Market value ($ mil.): 253

	STOCK PRICE ($) FY Close	P/E High/Low	PER SHARE ($) Earnings	Dividends	Book Value
12/12	23.36	15 13	1.73	0.84	16.08
12/11	24.55	19 15	1.37	0.64	15.20
12/10	24.49	22 18	1.19	0.63	15.18
12/09	23.64	29 18	1.11	0.59	14.50
12/08	33.05	26 16	1.45	0.53	13.97
Annual Growth	**(8.3%)**	**— —**	**4.5%**	**12.2%**	**3.6%**

Whiting Petroleum Corp

Whiting Petroleum is a fair-sized fish in an ocean full of oil and gas explorers. The company engages in oil and natural gas exploration and production activities mainly in the Gulf Coast Michigan and the mid-continent Permian Basin and Rocky Mountains. In 2012 it reported estimated proved reserves of 378.8 million barrels of oil equivalent and produced 67890 barrels of oil equivalent per day. That year Whiting produced 82.5 million barrels of oil equivalent per day. It sells oil and gas production to end users marketers and other purchasers that have access to nearby pipeline facilities.

IPO

In March 2012 Whiting completed its initial public offering of 18400000 units of beneficial interest in Whiting USA Trust II at $20.00 per trust unit. The number of trust units included the sale of 2400000 trust units. As a result it received net proceeds of $341.6 million which used to repay debt.

Geographic Reach

Whiting explores for oil and gas in the Rocky Mountains Permian Basin Mid-Continent Michigan and Gulf Coast regions of the US.

The company's biggest projects are in the Williston Bakken and Three Forks plays (North Dakota).

Sales and Marketing

In 2012 it got 20% of its revenues from Plains Marketing LP 14% from Shell Trading US 11% each from Eighty Eight Oil Company and Bridger Trading LLC.

Financial Performance

Whiting's revenues grew by 14% in 2012. Oil sales volumes increased 26% primarily from drilling success at its Sanish field Lewis & Clark/Pronghorn prospects and its Hidden Bench/Tarpon prospects. NGL sales volumes went up by 33% (from the same production areas) However natural gas sales volumes decreased by 2% as the result of normal field production decline across several of its areas (including the Flat Rock and Canyon fields) as well as the IOP-related Trust II divestiture. Partially offsetting the crude oil and NGL production-related increases in net revenues were lower oil NGLs and natural gas prices. Despite the higher revenues the company's net income declined by 16% in 2012 due to higher expenses (including ease operating; production taxes; depreciation depletion and amortization; interest expense; exploration and impairment; general and administrative; and a change in production participation plan liability).

Strategy

The company has grown through the acquisition of new reserves (such as Bakken shale plays and new areas in the Rockies) and through the continued exploitation of its core assets (such as its Permian Basin and Piceance Basin properties). From 2004 to 2012 it has made 16 significant acquisitions of producing properties with estimated proved reserves of 231 million barrels of oil equivalent.

Its business strategy is to maintain a balanced portfolio of lower risk long-lived oil and gas properties that provide stable cash flows while seeking property acquisitions that complement its core assets. It plans to continue to acquire properties to generate good rates of return and provide stable cash flows for its business.

Growing its production assets in 2011 Whiting reported significant new production from six western Williston Basin areas within its Lewis and Clark prospect and three nearby prospects. By the end of 2012 it has assembled 1.1 million gross (703700 net) developed and undeveloped acres in the Williston Basin and was operating 20 drilling rigs there.

The company plans drill an additional 2400 gross wells across all of its operational areas by 2017.

To focus on its growth areas (like the Williston basin) and to pay down debt in 2013 it agreed to sell its Enhanced Oil Recovery (EOR) assets in Oklahoma to BreitBurn Energy Partners for about $860 million.

Mergers and Acquisitions

In 2011 the company acquired 23400 net acres and one well in the Missouri Breaks prospect in Richland County Montana for an unadjusted purchase price of $46.9 million.

That year it also formed Sustainable Water Resources LLC with a third party (spending $25 million for a 75% stake) to develop a water project in Colorado. It also completed the purchase of 6000 net undeveloped acres in the Pronghorn field in Billings and Stark Counties North Dakota for $40 million.

To raise cash to pay down debt Whiting petroleum sold its stakes in several non-core oil and gas producing properties in the Karnes Live Oak and DeWitt counties of Texas for $64.8 million.

Ownership

Investment firm BlackRock Inc held 10% of the company in 2012.

EXECUTIVES

VP Land, David M. Seery
VP General Counsel and Secretary, Bruce R. DeBoer, age 60
VP and CFO, Michael J. Stevens, $255,000 total compensation
Chairman and CEO, James J. Volker, $550,000 total compensation
President and COO, James T. Brown, $272,500 total compensation
SVP Exploration and Development, Mark R. Williams, $220,000 total compensation
VP Marketing, Charles (Chuck) LaCouture
VP Information Technology Whiting Oil and Gas, Gale N. Keithline
VP Human Resources, Heather M. Duncan, age 42
VP Reservoir Engineering and Acquisitions, J. Douglas Lang, age 63, $212,500 total compensation
Controller Treasurer and Chief Accounting Officer, Brent P. Jensen, age 42
VP National Drilling Manager, Douglas L. (Doug) Walton
VP Permian Exploration, John K. Southwell
VP Operations, Rick A. Ross
VP Permian Operations, Peter W. Hagist
VP Corporate and Government Relations, Jack R. Ekstrom
VP Acquisitions/Reservoir Engineering, Steven A Kranker
VP Information Technology, Mike Craig
VP Geosciences, Mark D. Sonnenfeld
Director, William N. (Bill) Hahne, age 61
Director, Thomas P. (Tom) Briggs, age 64
Director, Thomas L. (Tom) Aller, age 63
Director, D. Sherwin Artus, age 75
Director, Philip E. Doty, age 69
Director, Allan R. Larson, age 73
Auditors: Deloitte&ToucheLLP

LOCATIONS

HQ: Whiting Petroleum Corporation
1700 Broadway Ste. 2300, Denver CO 80290-2300
Phone: 303-837-1661　　**Fax:** 303-861-4023
Web: www.whiting.com

PRODUCTS/OPERATIONS

2012 Sales

	$ mil.	% of total
Oil	1,940	90
NGLs	108	5
Natural gas	88	4
Amortization of deferred gain on sale	29	1
Gain on sale of properties	3	-
Gain on hedging activities	2	-
Interest income	0	-
Total	**2,173**	**100**

COMPETITORS

Anadarko Petroleum	EOG
Black Hills	Forest Oil
CREDO Petroleum	Key Energy
Cabot Oil & Gas	Newfield Exploration
Chesapeake Energy	Pioneer Natural
Cimarex	Resources
Comstock Resources	Range Resources
Denbury Resources	SM Energy
Devon Energy	Stone Energy

HISTORICAL FINANCIALS

Company Type: Public

Income Statement

FYE: December 31

	REVENUE ($ mil.)	NET INCOME ($ mil.)	NET PROFIT MARGIN	EMPLOYEES
12/12	2,173.4	414.1	19.1%	829
12/11	1,899.6	491.6	25.9%	692
12/10	1,516.1	336.6	22.2%	561
12/09	979.3	(106.8)	—	481
12/08	1,222.1	252.1	20.6%	470
Annual Growth	**15.5%**	**13.2%**	**—**	**15.2%**

2012 Year-End Financials

Debt ratio: 24.7%	No. of shares (mil.): 117
Return on equity: 12.7%	Dividends
Cash ($ mil.): 44	Yield: —
Current ratio: 0.60	Payout: —
Long-term debt ($ mil.): 1,800	Market value ($ mil.): 5,102

	STOCK PRICE ($) FY Close	P/E High/Low		PER SHARE ($) Earnings	Dividends	Book Value
12/12	43.37	18	10	3.48	0.00	29.29
12/11	46.69	30	7	4.14	0.00	25.74
12/10	117.19	46	25	2.55	0.00	21.62
12/09	71.45	—	—	(1.18)	0.00	22.32
12/08	33.46	37	9	2.97	0.00	21.24
Annual Growth	**6.7%**	**—**	**—**	**4.0%**	**—**	**8.4%**

Winmark Corp

Winmark Corporation loves recycling but it's not collecting cans and paper. Winmark franchises retail chains that buy sell and consign used goods (and some new items) at more than 965 stores. The chains sell sporting goods (Play It Again Sports) children's items (Once Upon A Child) teen apparel (Plato's Closet) women's apparel and accessories (Style Encore) and musical instruments and electronics (Music Go Round). Most operations are in the US but it does have about 70 stores in Canada. In addition the company leases IT equipment to midsized and large businesses through its Winmark Capital unit and it offers financing services to small businesses through its Wirth Business Credit subsidiary.

Geographic Reach

Winmark's retail franchises number about 900 stores across the US and nearly 70 locations in Canada.

Operations

Winmark operates two primary businesses. The franchising of its value-oriented retail stores accounts for about three-quarters of its total sales while equipment leasing through Winmark Capital Corp. (WCC) makes up the rest. WCC targets businesses with annual sales between $30 million and several billion dollars. It provides high-tech and business equipment including computers telecommunications equipment point-of-sales systems and more. Also the firm operates a small-ticket (typically $5000 to $100000) financing business through subsidiary Wirth Business Credit.

Financial Performance

Winmark reported about $52 million in revenue in 2012 an increase of just 1% versus 2011. Net income fell 8% over the same period. The slight uptick in revenue was due to an increase in royalties franchise fees and merchandise sales offset by a drop off in leasing income. The expansion of its Plato's Closet and Once Upon a Child franchises and accompanying increase in merchandise sales boosted revenue in 2012. Franchise fees increased 19% as a result of the addition of 11 more franchises in 2012 compared with 2011. The company blamed the decline in profits on increased cost of merchandise sold provisions for credit losses among other rising costs.

Strategy

One of the keys to Winmark's revenue growth has been retail network expansion. In 2012 the company signed 65 retail franchise agreements for stores expected to open in 2013. Also in 2013 the company added a new women's apparel and accessories resale concept called Style Encore a reseller of women's apparel shoes and accessories.

The company markets franchises to individuals with sufficient net worth prior retail management and operations experience and intentions of being involved in running the business. To ensure success Winmark provides a mandatory training program for franchisees and field support to assist with operational issues. Franchisees also have the option to transfer their franchise agreements to new owners or close their stores altogether.

Ownership

Chairman and CEO John Morgan owns more than a third of Winmark's shares. Bares Capital Management holds about 17% of the stock while Ronald Olson the company's founder and former CEO holds about 12%.

HISTORY

Jeffrey Dahlberg (son of the founder of Dahlberg maker of Miracle Ear hearing aids) and Ron Olson started a consulting firm in 1986. Martha Morris their third client and the founder of Play It Again Sports showed them how profitable used goods could be. In 1989 the pair bought out Morris and Olson was named CEO; by 1992 they had built the concept into a chain of 281 stores. The company started franchising stores internationally in 1991.

The firm expanded by acquiring Once Upon a Child (1992); Hi Tech Consignments which became Music Go Round (1993); and Computer Renaissance (1993). Named Grow Biz International the company went public in 1993. The following year it acquired CDX Audio changing the name to Disc Go Round. By the end of 1994 Grow Biz had 765 stores.

By capitalizing on consumers' desire for value and on the growing market trend for recycled goods the company built its sales from $2.3 million in 1991 to over $100 million in 1995 making it #1 on both the "FORTUNE" and "Inc." lists of fastest-growing US companies.

Grow Biz opened its 1000th store in 1996. The next year it bought 40 Video Game Exchange stores which became the nucleus of what was then its sixth franchise It's About Games.

In 1998 Grow Biz sold the Disc Go Round franchise and purchased Tool Traders (renaming it

ReTool) and the franchise rights to Plato's Closet sellers of new and used clothing for teens. In late 1998 Dahlberg and Olson offered to take the company private by purchasing the 33% of its stock they didn't already own for about $24 million. They shelved their offer in 1999 after shareholder protests and soon thereafter Dahlberg took the CEO reigns from Olson. Also in 1999 the company closed It's About Games chain resulting in a loss for the year.

Dahlberg and Olson left the company in May 2000 retaining 50%. John Morgan who sold his successful equipment leasing firm to retire took over as chairman president and CEO and soon inducted a new board and shuffled management vowing to focus the company on stabilizing cash flow. In August 2000 the company sold its Computer Renaissance franchise to Hollis Technologies for $3 million.

In November 2001 the company changed its name to Winmark Corporation. It also ceased franchising its ReTool brand and subsequently terminated relationships with ReTool franchisees.

In late 2002 Winmark formed Winmark Business Solutions to provide more in-depth support to its franchisees. Services include detailed information services training and other products and services that are not typically part of a franchise agreement. The company also offers these services to other small businesses.

On December 2 2003 the company's stock moved from the Nasdaq small cap market to the Nasdaq national market.

Winmark launched its business equipment (computers POS systems telecom) leasing services in 2004 and business financing services in 2005.

The company's retail footprint has steadily grown over the years even amid the deep recession in the US. Its network included about 800 stores in 2005 and by the end of 2009 that figure grew to nearly 880.

EXECUTIVES

President, Brett D. Heffes, age 45, $242,500 total compensation
Vice President - Human Resources, Leah A. Goff, age 51
President Franchising, Steven A. (Steve) Murphy, age 47, $242,500 total compensation
Chief Financial Officer Treasurer, Anthony D. (Tony) Ishaug, age 41, $154,200 total compensation
VP Marketing, Merry Beth Hovey, age 49
President Winmark Capital Corporation, Steven C. Zola, age 51, $242,500 total compensation
Chief Executive Officer, Lawrence A. Barbetta
Director, Paul C. Reyelts, age 66
Director, Jenele C. Grassle, age 53
Director, Mark L. Wilson, age 64
Director; President Winmark Capital Corporation, Steven C. Zola, age 50
Director, Dean B. Phillips, age 44
Auditors: GrantThorntonLLP

LOCATIONS

HQ: Winmark Corporation
605 Highway 169 N Ste. 400, Minneapolis MN 55441
Phone: 763-520-8500   **Fax:** 763-520-8410
Web: www.winmarkcorporation.com

2010 Franchised Stores

	No.
Play It Again	328
Plato's	301
Once Upon A	241
Music Go	33
Total	**903**

PRODUCTS/OPERATIONS

2012 Sales

	$ mil.	% of total
Royalties	33	65
Leasing	13	25
Merchandise	2	5
Franchise fees	1	3
Other	0	2
Total	**51**	**100**

2012 Stores

	No.
Play It Again	325
Plato's	324
Once Upon A	247
Music Go	24
Total	**930**

Selected Franchise Brands

Music Go Round (used and new musical instruments speakers amplifiers music-related electronics and related accessories)
Once Upon a Child (used and new clothing toys furniture and accessories for infants and children up to 10 years of age)
Plato's Closet (used and new clothing and accessories for teenagers)
Play It Again Sports (used and new sporting goods equipment and accessories)
Style Encore (used women's apparel and accessories)

COMPETITORS

Abercrombie & Fitch	Gymboree
Academy Sports	Hibbett Sports
Amazon.com	Kmart
American Express	Salvation Army
Babies "R" Us	Sam Ash Music
Cash America	Sears
Comerica	Sports Authority
Costco Wholesale	T. Rowe Price
Dick's Sporting Goods	Target Corporation
EZCORP	The Gap
Forever 21	Wal-Mart
Goodwill Industries	craigslist
Guitar Center	eBay

HISTORICAL FINANCIALS

Company Type: Public

Income Statement

	REVENUE ($ mil.)	NET INCOME ($ mil.)	NET PROFIT MARGIN	EMPLOYEES	FYE: December 29
12/12	51.9	12.9	24.9%	103	
12/11	51.3	14.1	27.5%	103	
12/10	41.2	10.3	25.1%	100	
12/09	37.3	5.8	15.7%	106	
12/08	35.4	1.1	3.2%	106	
Annual Growth	**10.0%**	**83.6%**	**—**	**(0.7%)**	

2012 Year-End Financials

Debt ratio: 24.8%	No. of shares (mil.): 5
Return on equity: 48.9%	Dividends
Cash ($ mil.): 2	Yield: 0.0%
Current ratio: 0.92	Payout: 208.5%
Long-term debt ($ mil.): —	Market value ($ mil.): 288

	STOCK PRICE ($) FY Close	P/E High/Low		PER SHARE ($) Earnings	Dividends	Book Value
12/12	57.55	28	19	2.47	5.15	3.59
12/11	57.37	21	11	2.69	0.11	7.04
12/10	32.15	17	10	1.98	0.06	4.58
12/09	21.91	21	8	1.10	0.00	2.99
12/08	11.50	105	53	0.21	0.00	2.56
Annual Growth	**49.6%**		**— —**	**85.2%**	**—**	**8.8%**

Winnebago Industries, Inc.

A pioneer in the world of recreational vehicles Winnebago Industries makes products intended to encourage exploration and outdoor escape. Almost all of the company's sales come from its motor homes and towables which are sold via independent dealers throughout the US and Canada under the Winnebago Itasca SunnyBrook and ERA brands. Winnebago Industries also sells RV parts and provides related services; in addition the company produces OEM parts such as extruded aluminum components for other RV manufacturers and for use in commercial vehicles. In mid-2012 Winnebago Industries received a $322 million bid to be bought by private equity firm North Street Capital but deemed the offer untenable.

Strategy

North Street placed its bid for Winnebago in May 2012 but Winnebago has stated further negotiations need to take place before any serious consideration for the proposal can be made.

HISTORY

During a mid-1950s economic downturn furniture store owner John Hanson convinced Forest City officials to welcome a local subsidiary of California trailer maker Modernistic Industries. The company's first trailer rolled off the line in 1958. Hanson later bought the plant and in 1960 named the business Winnebago Industries after Forest City's home county. Winnebago Industries went public in 1966. Sales took off when the company offered less-expensive RVs than its competitors.

The 1970s energy crisis and increased competition eroded the company's sales prompting it to make lower-cost more fuel-efficient motor homes. Hanson retired in 1972; he returned in 1979 and in 1986 diversified Winnebago Industries by buying Cycle Video (renamed Cycle-Sat; operations discontinued beginning in 1996) for distributing TV and radio commercials via satellite.

Winnebago Industries' sales suffered again during the early 1990s when recession hit and gas prices increased in response to the Gulf War. Sales rebounded in 1992 but remained stagnant for several years. Hanson died in 1996. That year and the next the company divested non-RV assets and sold its European operations.

During an industry-wide slump Winnebago Industries and other RV makers formed the Go RVing Coalition (1997) targeting baby boomers with a $15 million ad campaign. Lower gas prices and interest rates fed RV demand in 1998 and 1999. In 2000 the company spent $14.5 million on upgrading its equipment and expanding its manufacturing facilities.

In 2003 Winnebago ceased manufacturing its EuroVan RV. Also that year the company sold its dealer financing business to GE Commercial Distribution Finance. A new shipping facility located at its Charles City Iowa Class C motor home manufacturing plant was opened in 2004.

Winnebago weathered the economic crisis in 2008 and 2009 and managed to get on a positive trajectory in 2010 as demand for big-ticket items slowly returned.

EXECUTIVES

Vice President - Administration, Robert L. Gossett, age 62, $192,154 total compensation
Controller, Brian J. Hrubes, age 61
Chairman, Robert J. (Bob) Olson, age 62, $371,200 total compensation
VP General Counsel and Secretary, Raymond M. Beebe, age 70, $232,924 total compensation
Vice President - Product Development, William J. O'Leary, age 64, $222,160 total compensation
VP Sales and Marketing, Roger W. Martin, age 52, $223,330 total compensation
Manager Public Relations and Investor Relations, Sheila Davis
Chief Financial Officer; Vice President, Sarah N. Nielsen, age 40, $221,364 total compensation
Chairman of the Board; President; Chief Executive Officer, Randy J. Potts, age 54
Treasurer, Donald L. Heidemann, age 41
Vice President - Manufacturing, Daryl W. Krieger, age 50
Vice President - Product Development, William Leary
Vice President - Sales And Product Management, Scott Degnan
Vice President; General Counsel; Secretary, Scott Folkers
Vice President - Product Development, William OLeary
President Towables, Johnny Hernandez, age 57
Director, Joseph W. England, age 72
Director, Robert M. (Bob) Chiusano, age 62
Director, Lawrence A. (Larry) Erickson, age 64
Director, Jerry N. Currie, age 68
Director, John V. Hanson, age 71
Director, Gerald C. Kitch, age 75
Director, Irvin E. Aal, age 74
Independent Director, Mark Schroepfer
Auditors: Deloitte&ToucheLLP

LOCATIONS

HQ: Winnebago Industries Inc.
  605 W. Crystal Lake Rd., Forest City IA 50436
Phone: 641-585-3535   **Fax:** 641-585-6966
Web: www.winnebagoind.com

PRODUCTS/OPERATIONS

Selected Products
ERA
  ERA
Itasca
  Cambria
  Ellipse
  Impulse
  Impulse Silver
  Meridian
  Meridian V Class
  Navion
  Navion IQ
  Reyo
  Suncruiser
  Sunova
  Sunstar
Winnebago
  Access
  Access Premier
  Adventurer
  Aspect
  Journey
  Journey Express
  Sightseer
  Tour
  Via
  View
  View Profile
  Vista

COMPETITORS

Airstream	Newmar Corporation
Elixir Industries	Patrick Industries
Featherlite	Prevost Car
Forest River	Rexhall Industries
Gulf Stream Coach	Skyline
Jayco Inc.	Supreme Industries
Keystone RV	TRIGANO
Motor Coach Industries	Thor Industries
Navistar RV	Tiffin Motorhomes

HISTORICAL FINANCIALS

Company Type: Public

Income Statement

FYE: August 31

	REVENUE ($ mil.)	NET INCOME ($ mil.)	NET PROFIT MARGIN	EMPLOYEES
08/13	803.1	31.9	4.0%	2,680
08/12	581.6	44.9	7.7%	2,380
08/11	496.4	11.8	2.4%	2,130
08/10	449.4	10.2	2.3%	1,950
08/09	211.5	(78.7)	—	1,630
Annual Growth 39.6%		—	—	13.2%

2013 Year-End Financials

Debt ratio: —
Return on equity: 19.9%
Cash ($ mil.): 64
Current ratio: 3.18
Long-term debt ($ mil.): —

No. of shares (mil.): 27
Dividends
  Yield: —
  Payout: —
Market value ($ mil.): 620

	STOCK PRICE ($) FY Close	P/E High/Low		PER SHARE ($) Earnings	Dividends	Book Value
08/13	22.27	23	10	1.13	0.00	6.13
08/12	11.01	7	4	1.54	0.00	5.05
08/11	7.14	40	16	0.41	0.00	3.73
08/10	9.05	49	24	0.35	0.00	3.35
08/09	11.62	—	—	(2.71)	0.12	3.17
Annual Growth 17.7%		—	—	—	—	17.9%

Winthrop Realty Trust

Winthrop Realty Trust thinks real estate loans can be just as profitable as the real thing. The externally managed real estate investment trust (REIT) invests in property real estate-related collateralized debt and other REITs. Its property portfolio consists of more than a dozen office buildings a handful of retail properties and seven apartment buildings across 15 states totaling 3.5 million square feet. Top commercial tenants include Spectra Energy's Houston headquarters grocer Kroger and e-tailer Football Fanatics' 500000-sq.-ft. distribution center. As a REIT the trust is exempt from paying federal income tax so long as it makes quarterly dividends to shareholders.

Operations

The trust's bread and butter come from rental payments on its real estate which account for 70% of revenues. Interest and dividends from its loans account for the other 30%.

Strategy

The trust's loan investment strategy focuses on acquiring loans at a discount or with the expectation of a borrower default or recapitalization that will lead to an equity ownership interest. For example it bought the first mortgage loan on an office building in downtown Philadelphia that was in maturity default. After restructuring the loan and paying $10000 for an indirect 49% interest Winthrop became the general partner of the property owner.

As for tangible property the trust periodically acquires new buildings to add to its portfolio. In 2013 it bought four apartment buildings in four different states for a combined $246 million. Three of the buildings are mixed use with retail space on the ground floor and luxury apartments on the upper floors. The year before it paid $21 million for a foreclosure apartment complex in suburban Memphis.

Also in 2013 the trust sold a medical office building in Arizona for a $10 million profit. The trust originally bought the building for $10.6 million in 2010 and sold it for $20.5 million.

EXECUTIVES

Chairman and CEO, Michael L. Ashner, age 61
Vice Chairman, Peter Braverman, age 62
CFO, Thomas Staples, age 56
President; Trustee, Carolyn Tiffany, age 47
Chief Investment Officer and Secretary, John Alba, age 43
Chief Financial Officer, John Garilli
Vice Chairman, Peter Braverman, age 62
President and Trustee, Carolyn Tiffany, age 46
Auditors: PricewaterhouseCoopersLLP

LOCATIONS

HQ: Winthrop Realty Trust
7 Bulfinch Place Ste. 500, Boston MA 02114
Phone: 617-570-4614   **Fax:** 617-570-4746
Web: www.winthropreit.com

PRODUCTS/OPERATIONS

2012 Sales

	$ mil.	% of total
Rents & reimbursements	51	71
Interest & dividends	21	29
Total	**72**	**100**

COMPETITORS

Acadia Realty Trust	Highwoods Properties
Boston Properties	Kimco Realty
Brandywine Realty	Liberty Property Trust
CommonWealth REIT	Mack-Cali
Cousins Properties	Pennsylvania Real
Douglas Emmett	Estate
Duke Realty	Piedmont Office Realty
Equity Office	Trust
Franklin Street	Regency Centers
Properties	SL Green Realty
Glimcher Realty	

HISTORICAL FINANCIALS

Company Type: Public

Income Statement

FYE: December 31

	REVENUE ($ mil.)	NET INCOME ($ mil.)	NET PROFIT MARGIN	EMPLOYEES
12/12	72.5	24.6	34.0%	0
12/11	70.0	10.9	15.6%	0
12/10	55.3	16.4	29.8%	0
12/09	47.9	(84.3)	—	0
12/08	45.7	(68.1)	—	0
Annual Growth	**12.2%**	**—**	**—**	**—**

2012 Year-End Financials

Debt ratio: 45.6%	No. of shares (mil.): 33
Return on equity: 5.8%	Dividends
Cash ($ mil.): 110	Yield: 5.8%
Current ratio: 4.54	Payout: 250.0%
Long-term debt ($ mil.): 421	Market value ($ mil.): 365

	STOCK PRICE ($) FY Close	P/E High/Low	PER SHARE ($) Earnings	Dividends	Book Value
12/12	11.05	27 22	0.46	0.65	13.77
12/11	10.17	41 26	0.32	0.65	11.74
12/10	12.79	20 15	0.72	0.65	10.94
12/09	10.86	— —	(5.19)	0.91	10.65
12/08	10.84	— —	(4.59)	0.38	15.76
Annual Growth	**0.5%**	**— —**	**—**	**14.7%**	**(3.3%)**

Wintrust Financial Corp. (IL)

Wintrust Financial is a holding company engaged in personal and commercial banking wealth management and specialty lending services primarily in the metropolitan Chicago and Milwaukee areas. With assets of more than $17 billion it operates about 15 subsidiary banks (most bear the name of the community they serve) with more than 100 branches in all. The banks offer traditional deposit services and emphasize business and commercial real estate lending which accounts for about half of the company's loan portfolio. Specifically Wintrust's banks target small business customers. Some of Wintrust's banks also provide niche lending for homeowners associations medical practices franchisees and municipalities.

Wintrust's nonbank subsidiaries include First Insurance Funding which provides financing for commercial insurance and life insurance premiums. In 2012 Wintrust expanded its premium funding business into Canada with the acquisition of Macquarie Premium Funding Inc which was a subsidiary of Macquarie Group. The deal marked Wintrust's first international venture.

Other Wintrust subsidiaries include Tricom Funding which offers financing and administrative services to the temporary staffing industry in the US and Wintrust Mortgage Corporation (formerly known as WestAmerica Mortgage Company) which deals in the origination and purchase of residential loans for sale. In 2011 Wintrust bought certain mortgage banking assets of Minnesota-based River City and Woodfield Planning Corporation in Chicago.

Wintrust's wealth management arm offers financial planning and brokerage services through a trio of companies bearing the Wayne Hummer name. The company built the business through the 2011 acquisition of institutional asset manager Great Lakes Advisors. The deal significantly increased Wintrust's assets under management to more than $13 billion.

On the banking side Wintrust has developed its community-based franchise through the formation of nine de novo (or new) banks new branch openings and acquisitions. Wintrust has also taken advantage of the rash of bank seizures in the Chicago area. Since 2010 the company has snapped up seven failed institutions in FDIC-assisted transac-

tions adding some 20 branches. Acquisitions in 2011 included Community First Bank (now Rogers Park Community Bank) Bank of Commerce (now Wood Dale Bank & Trust) and First Chicago Bank & Trust. Also in 2011 Wintrust bought Elgin State Bank in its first non-FDIC-assisted deal in several years. The purchase added three branches in Illinois. Also in a traditional transaction the company acquired HPK Financial the parent of Hyde Park Bank & Trust in late 2012. It will add two branches in the Hyde Park neighborhood of Chicago. And in 2013 Wintrust agreed to acquire First Lansing Bancorp the parent company of First National Bank of Illinois. The deal is expected to close during the second quarter of 2013.

But Wintrust has not been unscathed by the economic crisis either. It has significant exposure to commercial real estate in the hard-hit Chicago area and in 2008 formed a new division to resolve problem loans usually through liquidation. The company remained profitable though its net income was down in 2010 as it dealt with an uptick in nonperforming loans and increased its allowance for loan losses. Wintrust has also formed a division to manage problem loans acquired from the failed banks.

By 2011 the economy and Wintrust's results improved. The company reported a more than 22% increase in net income. Assets deposits and loan amounts all increased that year as well. Wintrust's calculated growth strategy has helped it expand by reaching new customers and further deepening its relationship with current ones by offering new services.

EXECUTIVES

EVP Technology; President Wintrust Information Technology Services, Lloyd M. Bowden, age 60, $167,333 total compensation
SEVP COO Secretary and Treasurer; Regional Market Head Crystal Lake Bank State Bank of the Lakes and Town Bank, David A. Dykstra, age 53, $675,000 total compensation
President CEO and Director, Edward J. Wehmer, age 58, $900,000 total compensation
EVP, Frank J. Burke
EVP and Chief Credit Officer; Regional Market Head Hinsdale Bank, Richard B. Murphy, age 54, $413,750 total compensation
Executive Vice President - Regional Market Head, James H. Bishop, age 70
Executive Vice President; Chief Administrative Officer, Leona A. Gleason
Chairman, Peter D. Crist, age 62
EVP and CFO, David L. Stoehr, age 54, $315,000 total compensation
Executive Vice President and Regional Market Head, Timothy S. (Tim) Crane, age 51
VP-Audit, Raj V. Nagarajan
SVP Marketing, Matthew E. Doubleday
Executive Vice President - Risk Management, John S. Fleshood, age 51, $292,750 total compensation
Executive Vice President; Market Head - Wealth Management Services, Thomas P. (Tom) Zidar
Executive Vice President, John A. Carstens, age 57
Executive Vice President, Michael (Mike) Johnstone
Executive Vice President; General Counsel and Corporate Secretary, Lisa J. Pattis
Executive Vice President and Regional Market Head, David Larson
President CEO and Director, Edward J. Wehmer, age 58
Director, Bruce K. Crowther, age 62
Director, Bert A. Getz Jr., age 46
Director, Christopher J. Perry, age 57
Director, Ingrid S. Stafford, age 60

Director, Thomas J. Neis, age 65
Director, Hollis W. Rademacher, age 77
Director, Scott K. Heitmann, age 65
Director, Joseph F. Damico, age 59
Director, Albin F. (Al) Moschner, age 60
Director, Charles H. (Chuck) James III, age 55
Director, H. Patrick Hackett Jr., age 61
Auditors: Ernst&YoungLLP

LOCATIONS

HQ: Wintrust Financial Corporation
  727 N. Bank Ln., Lake Forest IL 60045
Phone: 847-615-4096   **Fax:** 847-615-4091
Web: www.wintrust.com

PRODUCTS/OPERATIONS

2011 Sales

	$ mil.	% of total
Interest		
Loans including fees	552	70
Securities	46	6
Other	6	1
Noninterest		
Mortgage banking	56	7
Wealth management	44	6
Gain on bargain purchases	38	5
Service charges on deposit accounts	15	2
Other	35	3
Total	**795**	**100**

Selected Subsidiaries and Affiliates

Banking
  Barrington Bank & Trust Company N.A.
  Beverly Bank & Trust Company N.A.
  Crystal Lake Bank & Trust Company N.A.
  Hinsdale Bank & Trust Company
  Lake Forest Bank & Trust Company
  Libertyville Bank & Trust Company
  North Shore Community Bank & Trust Company
  Northbrook Bank & Trust Company
  Old Plank Trail Community Bank N.A.
  Schaumburg Bank & Trust Company N.A.
  St. Charles Bank & Trust
  State Bank of The Lakes
  Town Bank
  Village Bank & Trust
  Wheaton Bank and Trust Company
Non-banking
  Chicago Trust Company N.A.
  First Insurance Funding Corporation
  Great Lakes Advisors LLC
  Tricom Inc. of Milwaukee
  Wayne Hummer Asset Management Company
  Wayne Hummer Investments LLC
  Wayne Hummer Trust Company N.A.
  Wintrust Information Technology Services Company
  Wintrust Mortgage Corporation (formerly
    WestAmerica Mortgage Company)

COMPETITORS

Associated Banc-Corp	MB Financial
Bank of America	Northern Trust
Citigroup	PrivateBancorp
Fifth Third	RBS Citizens Financial
First Midwest Bancorp	Group
Harris	U.S. Bancorp
JPMorgan Chase	

HISTORICAL FINANCIALS

Company Type: Public

Income Statement

FYE: December 31

	ASSETS ($ mil.)	NET INCOME ($ mil.)	INCOME AS % OF ASSETS	EMPLOYEES
12/12	17,519.6	111.2	0.6%	3,269
12/11	15,893.8	77.5	0.5%	2,933
12/10	13,980.1	63.3	0.5%	2,588
12/09	12,215.6	73.0	0.6%	2,381
12/08	10,658.3	20.4	0.2%	2,326
Annual Growth	**13.2%**	**52.6%**	**—**	**8.9%**

2012 Year-End Financials

Return on assets: 0.6%	Dividends
Return on equity: 6.6%	Yield: 0.4%
Long-term debt ($ mil.): —	Payout: 7.7%
No. of shares (mil.): 36	Market value ($ mil.): 1,353
Sales ($ mil): 853	

	STOCK PRICE ($) FY Close	P/E High/Low	PER SHARE ($) Earnings	Dividends	Book Value
12/12	36.70	14 10	2.31	0.18	48.96
12/11	28.05	18 12	1.67	0.18	42.90
12/10	33.03	41 26	1.02	0.18	41.20
12/09	30.79	15 4	2.18	0.27	47.04
12/08	20.57	50 22	0.76	0.36	44.90
Annual Growth	**15.6%**	**— —**	**32.0%**	**(15.9%)**	**2.2%**

Wolverine World Wide, Inc.

Wolverine World Wide has the shoes to quiet your barking dogs. The company makes Hush Puppies casual shoes and slippers as well as boots sandals and related apparel and accessories. Its boot lines include Merrell (outdoor) Bates (military) HyTest and Wolverine (industrial); footwear is made under the Cushe brand and private labels. Wolverine also boasts several licenses from Caterpillar ("CAT") Harley-Davidson and Patagonia to make branded footwear. It sells worldwide through department and specialty stores independent distributors Internet retailers and more than 440 company-owned retail stores in North America and the UK. Wolverine also maintains more than 60 consumer-direct Internet sites.

Geographic Reach

Wolverine's footwear brands are sold in about 200 countries and territories. The US accounts for two-thirds of the company's sales followed by Europe (nearly 20% of sales) and Canada (7% of sales).

Operations

Wolverine designs manufactures sources markets licenses and distributes branded footwear apparel and accessories. The firm operates two primary business segments. The largest accounting for about 85% of sales is the Branded Wholesale Footwear Apparel and Licensing segment. Following the purchase of the Performance + Lifestyle Group in late 2012 Wolverine divides this segment into four parts: the Outdoor Group (Merrell Patagonia and Chaco brands); the Heritage Group (Wolverine Cats Bates Harley-Davidson and

HyTest); the Lifestyle Group (Hush Puppies Sebago Cushe Soft Style); and the PLG (Sperry Top-Sider Saucony Stride Rite and Keds). The company's consumer-direct segment which accounts for about 15% of Wolverine's annual sales includes the company's 440-plus retail stores in the US Canada and the Uk and the online businesses including the Wolverine Retail and PLG Retail groups.

Financial Performance

Acquisitions have fueled Wolverine's recent growth. Indeed in 2012 the footwear company's sales increased 16% versus 2011 to $1.64 billion. Net income declined 35% over the same period. The double-digit uptick in annual sales was helped by the purchase of the Performance + Lifestyle Group (PLG) from Collective Brands which contributed to a 28% gain in domestic sales for the year. Sales also got a boost from increases volume sales of existing brands. 2012 marked the third consecutive year of strong annual sales comparisons for the company following a decline in sales in 2009 due to the economic downturn.

The company attributed the 35% decline in net income to a non-recurring transactions and and integration costs related to the purchase of PLG.

Strategy

While Wolverine maintains a portfolio of more than 15 brands it regularly looks for add-on companies to extend its global reach and to expand into new niches. (The 2009 purchase of casual footwear maker Cushe gave Wolverine a UK presence among high-end retailers and boosted its Hush Puppies business in 20 other countries.)

Wolverine gives its brands –and its bottom line –a leg up worldwide through licensing and distribution agreements with third parties. Indeed most of its footwear is now made by third parties in the Asia-Pacific region Central and South America Europe and India. To this end the company partnered with Forus SA in 2012 to form joint venture Lifestyle Brands of Colombia aimed at marketing the Wolverine portfolio in Colombia. A similar joint venture agreement with Tata International gives Wolverine a foot in the door in India. The footwear firm also licenses the Hush Puppies and Wolverine brand names. Wolverine has expanded its sporty Merrell name to be included on backpacks handbags luggage and accessories. Its Bates Uniform Footwear Division contracts with the US Department of Defense and the militaries of several foreign countries to supply military footwear.

Mergers and Acquisitions

In a move that greatly expanded its collection of footwear brands and retail footprint Wolverine in October 2012 acquired the wholesale and retail operations of the Sperry Top-Sider Saucony Stride Rite and Keds brands by buying the Performance + Lifestyle Group (PLG) from Collective Brands for more than $1.2 billion. Collective Brands which also owned the Payless ShoeSource chain of stores was taken private and split up by Wolverine and a pair of private equity firms. With more than $1 billion in sales 345 retail stores and almost 40 million pairs shipped in its latest fiscal year PLG is now Wolverine's largest operating group. (As part of the agreement PLG retained its headquarters in Lexington Massachusetts.) In 2010 Wolverine purchased Colorado-based footwear firm Chaco and winter boot maker ULU folding both into its Outdoor Group.

Ownership

Janus Capital Management owns more than 10% of Wolverine's shares. Investment firm BlackRock owns nearly 10%.

HISTORY

Wolverine World Wide traces its origins back to 1883 when G. A. Krause and his uncle Fred Hirth founded Hirth-Krause Co. to make leather soles and other shoemaking goods. It added shoes in 1903 and in 1908 it started the Wolverine Tanning Co. to supply leather for its shoes.

During the early part of the century the Wolverine brand gained popularity with its heavy-duty boots made (via a proprietary tanning process) from "shell horsehide" straight from the animal's rear. The company became Wolverine Shoe and Tanning Corp. in 1921.

The company made pigskin gloves for the military during WWII. Victor Krause the founder's son became convinced that pigskin was superior to cowhide. He designed a pair of casual pigskin shoes named Hush Puppies (named after a treat Southerners gave dogs to keep them quiet). From their debut in 1958 Hush Puppies became a huge seller for the next decade. Wolverine World Wide went public in 1965.

By the early 1980s however cheap foreign competition had sent Hush Puppies back to the pound and uninspired management (Krause family leadership ended in 1972) dogged the company's efforts to regain sales. To get back on track in 1993 Wolverine closed about 100 retail stores converting the rest to outlet stores. Geoffrey Bloom became CEO that year. The company then revamped its production lines and its product image.

Bolstering its boot unit Wolverine acquired HYTEST (work boots) in 1996 and Merrell (outdoor footwear) in 1997. It also began making branded footwear for Caterpillar in 1997 and Harley-Davidson in 1998. Wolverine launched its first children's product line in 1999 and later closed its unprofitable Russian operations. In April 2000 president Timothy O'Donovan succeeded Bloom as CEO; Bloom remained on as chairman. In 2001 the company completed a restructuring plan which included closing five plants and cutting 25% of its workforce.

In 2003 Wolverine acquired Sebago including the recognizable Sebago and Dockside brands. In 2004 the company entered into a licensing agreement with Kid Brands for the production of plush stuffed Hush Puppies-branded basset hound toys.

In April 2005 O'Donovan succeeded Bloom as chairman of the board. Blake Krueger became president and CEO in April 2007 and chairman as well in January 2010.

The footwear maker sold off its NCAA College Clogs unit considered to be an ancillary business in 2007 to Dearfoams owner R.G. Barry Corporation. The sports clogs which featured embroidered logos and official college and university colors were sold through specialty and online retailers college bookstores and select department stores.

In October 2012 Wolverine acquired Collective Brand's Performance + Lifestyle Group for $1.24 billion. Acquired brands include Keds Saucony Sperry Top-Sider and Stride Rite.

EXECUTIVES

SVP; President Performance Group, James D. (Jim) Zwiers, age 46, $6,648 total compensation

Chairman President and CEO, Blake W. Krueger, age 59, $735,000 total compensation

SVP Global Human Resources, Pamela L. Linton, age 64, $292,000 total compensation

SVP CFO and Treasurer, Donald T. (Don) Grimes, age 50, $385,000 total compensation

President Global Operations Group, Michael Jeppesen

CIO, Dee Slater

President - Merrell Brand, Gene McCarthy

President - Consumer Direct, Jodi Watson

Director, Jeffrey M. (Jeff) Boromisa, age 58

Director, Timothy J. O'Donovan, age 67

Director, Michael A. Volkema, age 57

Director, William K. (Bill) Gerber, age 59

Director, David T. Kollat, age 74

Director, Brenda J. Lauderback, age 64

Director, Shirley D. Peterson, age 71

Director, David P. Mehney, age 72

Director, Alberto L. Grimoldi, age 72

Director, Joseph R. (Joe) Gromek, age 66

Director, Nicholas T. Long, age 54

Auditors: Ernst&YoungLLP

LOCATIONS

HQ: Wolverine World Wide, Inc.
9341 Courtland Drive N.E., Rockford, MI 49351
Phone: 616 866-5500
Web: www.wolverineworldwide.com

2012 Sales

	$ mil.	% of total
US	1,079	66
Europe	310	19
Canada	112	7
Other	138	8
Total	**1,640**	**100**

PRODUCTS/OPERATIONS

2012 Sales

	$ mil.	% of total
Branded wholesale footwearapparel & licensing		
Outdoor Group	545	33
Heritage Group	502	31
Lifestyle Group	203	12
Performance + Lifestyle Group	150	9
Other	17	1
Consumer direct	183	11
Other business units	37	3
Total	**1,640**	**100**

Selected Brands

Bates
Cat Footwear
Chaco
Cushe
Harley-Davidson Footwear
Hush Puppies
HyTest
Keds
Merrell
Patagonia
Saucony
Sebago
Sperry Top-Sider
Stride Rite
Wolverine

COMPETITORS

Allen-Edmonds	North Face
Bakers Footwear	R. Griggs
Deckers Outdoor	Red Wing Shoe
Genesco	Reebok
Jimlar	Skechers U.S.A.
Justin Brands	Stride Rite
Kenneth Cole	Timberland
L.L. Bean	Wellco Enterprises
LaCrosse Footwear	

HISTORICAL FINANCIALS

Company Type: Public

Income Statement

FYE: December 29

	REVENUE ($ mil.)	NET INCOME ($ mil.)	NET PROFIT MARGIN	EMPLOYEES
12/12	1,640.8	80.6	4.9%	8,299
12/11*	1,409.0	123.2	8.7%	4,435
01/11	1,248.5	104.4	8.4%	4,139
01/10	1,101.0	61.9	5.6%	4,018
01/09	1,220.5	95.8	7.9%	4,578
Annual Growth	**7.7%**	**(4.2%)**	**—**	**16.0%**

*Fiscal year change

2012 Year-End Financials

Debt ratio: 47.8%
Return on equity: 13.2%
Cash ($ mil.): 171
Current ratio: 3.37
Long-term debt ($ mil.): 1,219

No. of shares (mil.): 98
Dividends
  Yield: 0.0%
  Payout: 58.9%
Market value ($ mil.): 3,964

	STOCK PRICE ($) FY Close	P/E High/Low		PER SHARE ($) Earnings	Dividends	Book Value
12/12	40.18	57	41	0.82	0.48	6.51
12/11*	35.64	34	24	1.24	0.48	6.01
01/11	31.88	31	22	1.06	0.44	5.55
01/10	27.22	44	21	0.62	0.44	4.86
01/09	21.52	31	17	0.95	0.44	4.40
Annual Growth	**16.9%**	**—**	**—**	**(3.8%)**	**2.2%**	**10.3%**

*Fiscal year change

Woodward, Inc.

Woodward likes to remain in control. The company manufactures and services a slew of energy control and optimization systems used in aircraft and vehicles turbine and piston engines and electrical power equipment. Woodward serves OEMs and prime contractors worldwide in commercial and military aerospace power generation and distribution and transportation. These include such noteworthy names as GE Caterpillar Boeing and United Technologies. Woodward's products are primarily made in the US where the company garners more than half of its sales.

Geographic Reach

The company has its production and assembly facilities China Germany Poland and the US. It operates sales and service facilities in Brazil Bulgaria India Japan the Netherlands Peru the Republic of Korea Russia Switzerland and the UK.

The US accounts for 55% of total sales while Europe generates 25%. Asia follows with 15%.

Operations

To create a better fit with its markets Woodward restructured into two segments aerospace (55% of net sales) and energy (45%) which each unify several businesses while concentrating on specific technical applications. Aerospace includes aircraft turbine systems and airframe systems. Energy comprises industrial turbomachinery systems engine systems and electrical power systems.

Sales and Marketing

The company sells primarily to OEMs and equipment packagers. GE is the company's largest customer representing 15% of its total sales in 2013. Direct sales from the US government accounted for

6%. Other big customers include Boeing United Technologies and Weichai Westport.

Financial Performance

Woodward has enjoyed unprecedented growth over the last three years. Revenues jumped 4% from $1.87 billion in 2012 to $1.84 billion in 2013 a historic milestone for the company. Profits also increased 3% from $142 million in 2012 to a record-high $146 million in 2013.

The company attributes the growth in 2013 to a previous acquisition a spike in selling prices and increased volumes in its aerospace segment due to higher commercial OEM and defense aftermarket sales. This was partially offset by decreased volumes in its energy segment attributable to significantly lower wind turbine converter sales.

Strategy

Woodward uses acquisitions as a means for growth. In 2012 it acquired the assets of GE Aviation Systems' hydraulic thrust reverser actuation systems business located in Duarte California for $200 million in cash. The move enhanced the motion control technologies business within its aerospace segment and contributed additional revenue for 2013.

In 2011 Woodward acquired Integral Drive Systems (IDS) and the Switzerland-based company's European subsidiaries as well as the key assets for its China business for about $38 million in cash. Besides increasing its business in wind converters the acquisition of IDS brought Woodward into the solar market.

To support development projects that include next generation fuel systems for aircraft turbines Woodward has built a $21.2 million 48000 sq. ft. test facility in Illinois that features several environmental system test cells and a vibration lab. In 2011 the new facility helped Woodward win the largest contract in its history to provide the fuel system air management and actuation hardware for the GE Passport 20 engine and NG34 technology development program.

Company Background

As a nod toward the direction the company is going in 2011 Woodward dropped "Governor" from its name. Although the company's energy segment still makes governors (a device used to regulate a machine's speed) the new more general name better reflects the dramatic expansion of Woodward's product menu. Founder Amos Woodward developed a governor to control water wheels in 1870.

HISTORY

The company's airframe systems business was formed in late 2008 with the acquisition of MPC Products Corp. (Woodward's largest acquisition in its history) and Techni-Core. In 2009 Woodward boosted the airframe system's business further by purchasing the HR Textron (HRT) unit of Textron. HRT brought experience in aircraft combat vehicles turbine engines and weapons. Woodward subsequently sold the fuel and pneumatics product line acquired with HRT to TransDigm Group in 2009.

Plans for the electrical power systems grew in late 2010 when Woodward inked a deal with RE-power Systems to supply wind turbine power converters. The power converters were integral to the development of five projects under the Hydro-Quebec Distribution wind power project.

EXECUTIVES

Chairman President and CEO, Thomas A. Gendron, age 52, $698,077 total compensation

President Airframe Systems, Martin V. (Marty) Glass, age 56, $324,519 total compensation
President Electrical Power Systems, Gerhard Lauffer, age 51, $324,232 total compensation
President Engine Systems, Chad R. Preiss, age 48
Vice Chairman CFO and Treasurer, Robert F. (Bob) Weber Jr., age 59, $358,754 total compensation
President Aircraft Turbine Systems, Sagar A. Patel, age 47
Corporate VP Information Technology, Harlan G. Barkley
Corporate VP Human Resources, Steven J. Meyer
President Industrial Turbomachinery Systems, James D. Rudolph, age 52
Corporate VP Supply Chain, Matthew F. Taylor, age 50
Founder, Amos Woodward
Director, John D. Cohn, age 58
Director, Paul Donovan, age 65
Director, Michael H. Joyce, age 73
Director, John A. Halbrook, age 66
Director, James R. Rulseh, age 58
Director, Michael T. (Tim) Yonker, age 69
Director, Mary L. Petrovich, age 49
Director, Larry E. Rittenberg, age 66
Vice Chairman CFO and Treasurer, Robert F. (Bob) Weber Jr., age 58
Director, Ronald M. (Ron) Sega, age 59
Auditors: Deloitte&ToucheLLP

LOCATIONS

HQ: Woodward Inc.
1000 E. Drake Rd., Fort Collins CO 80525
Phone: 970-482-5811   **Fax:** 970-498-3050
Web: www.woodward.com

2013 Sales

	$ mil.	% of total
US	1,058	55
Europe	480	25
Asia	287	15
Rest of the world	108	5
Total	**1,936**	**100**

PRODUCTS/OPERATIONS

2013 Sales

	$ mil.	% of total
Aerospace	1,061	55
Energy	874	45
Total	**1,936**	**100**

Selected Products

Aerospace
  Actuators
  Cockpit controls
  Fuel nozzles
  Metering units
  Motors
  Pumps
  Sensors
  Valves
Energy
  Actuators
  Governors
  Ignition systems
  Injectors
  Power converters
  Pumps
  Solenoids
  Valves

COMPETITORS

AREVA	Hamilton Sundstrand
Argo-Tech	Honeywell
Cobham	International
Cummins	ITT Corp.
Dresser-Rand	Parker-Hannifin
Fisher Controls	Robert Bosch LLC
Goodrich Corp.	Warren CAT
Greenbrier Rail Services	Westinghouse Air Brake
	Westport Innovations

HISTORICAL FINANCIALS

Company Type: Public

Income Statement

FYE: September 30

	REVENUE ($ mil.)	NET INCOME ($ mil.)	NET PROFIT MARGIN	EMPLOYEES
09/13	1,935.9	145.9	7.5%	6,750
09/12	1,865.6	141.5	7.6%	6,600
09/11	1,711.7	132.2	7.7%	6,200
09/10	1,457.0	110.8	7.6%	5,452
09/09	1,430.1	94.3	6.6%	5,660
Annual Growth	7.9%	11.5%	—	4.5%

2013 Year-End Financials

Debt ratio: 24.9%	No. of shares (mil.): 68
Return on equity: 13.5%	Dividends
Cash ($ mil.): 48	Yield: 0.7%
Current ratio: 2.32	Payout: 16.0%
Long-term debt ($ mil.): 450	Market value ($ mil.): 2,780

	STOCK PRICE ($) FY Close	P/E High/Low	PER SHARE ($) Earnings	Dividends	Book Value
09/13	40.83	20 15	2.10	0.32	16.78
09/12	33.98	22 12	2.01	0.31	14.73
09/11	27.40	20 13	1.89	0.27	13.34
09/10	32.42	21 14	1.59	0.24	11.69
09/09	24.26	25 6	1.37	0.24	10.38
Annual Growth	13.9%	— —	11.3%	7.5%	12.8%

World Acceptance Corp.

Who in the world will accept your poor credit? World Acceptance Corp. just might. The consumer finance company offers short-term and medium-term loans and credit insurance to individuals with limited access to other credit sources. Borrowers use the loans of $300 to $4000 to meet temporary or unanticipated cash needs such as car repairs and medical bills filling a void left by banks and credit unions which typically don't make loans of less than $5000. Convenience comes at a price: World Acceptance often charges the maximum interest rates and related fees allowed by law. The fast-growing company has more than 1100 offices in a dozen states in the US South and Midwest as well as Mexico.

Geographic Reach

World Acceptance Corp's largest US markets are Texas Georgia Tennessee and South Carolina. Since entering Mexico in 2005 the firm has grown to more than 100 offices there.

Operations

In addition to loans World Acceptance also offers income tax preparation services refund anticipation loans and unemployment and credit-related insurance through third parties. Subsidiary ParaData Financial Systems markets data processing software and related services to other consumer finance companies. Via its World Class Buying Club World Acceptance markets and finances home electronics and appliances to its customers in Texas Georgia Tennessee New Mexico and Missouri where it is permitted by law.

Financial Performance

World Acceptance's fiscal 2012 (ends March) sales climbed 10% vs. the prior year while net income also increased 10% over the same period. The addition of 70 new offices in in 2012 vs. 2011 helped propel the revenue gain. Interest and fees on loans account for about 85% of the company's sales. Indeed sales and profits at the loan maker have been increasing steadily for nearly a decade as the company grows its network of offices.

Strategy

World Acceptance is following a path of organic growth. Indeed the firm has opened more than 660 new office locations since 2003 and plans to open or acquire at least 50 more in the US in fiscal 2013. In Mexico it plans to add about 15 new offices in the coming year. The company plans to continue its expansion in both countries including entering new markets as approvals and licenses are gained. It commenced operations in Wisconsin in 2010. World Acceptance also grows through acquisitions.

The company's physical growth has translated in more new customers and more loans and in turn higher revenues and income. It originated some $2.8 billion in loans in fiscal 2012 vs. $2.6 billion in the previous year. The economic downturn and weak recovery for its low-income customers has benefitted World Acceptance as consumers seek short-term funding to make ends meet. It is a double-edged sword for World Acceptance however as higher unemployment often leads to more delinquencies.

Ownership

A private investment limited partnership Prescott Associates owns about 22% of World Acceptance. Investment advisor Columbia Wanger Asset Management holds about 16%.

HISTORY

World Acceptance was founded in 1962 by Southern Bancorp. In 1989 president Charles Walters led a management buyout from First Union which had acquired Southern three years earlier. World Acceptance went public in 1991.

Moving further into its existing markets primarily in the South the company began expanding its services. It started marketing auto club memberships to clients in 1993. That year it bought data processing firm ParaData Financial Systems which in 1995 contracted to provide data processing for Mercury Finance. Also in 1995 World Acceptance began its World Class Buying Club program in Texas and expanded into other states in following years. In 1997 it acquired San Antonio-based Personal Credit Plan a local consumer lender.

Buoyed by shrinking default rates the company moved into larger lower-margin loans in 1998. That year it settled a class-action lawsuit regarding a type of insurance it had used to cover borrowers' collateral; the $5 million settlement hit the company's bottom line. In 1999 World Acceptance launched a pilot program to prepare tax returns and provide loans on anticipated refunds. It expanded the program through most of its network over the next two years.

EXECUTIVES

SVP Human Resources, Marilyn M. Messer, age 62
President ParaData Financial Systems, James J. Rosenauer
President; Chief Operating Officer, Mark C. Roland, age 56, $295,000 total compensation

Chairman and CEO, A. Alexander (Sandy) McLean III, age 62, $389,167 total compensation
SVP Secretary and General Counsel, Judson K. Chapin III, age 67
Chief Financial Officer; Senior Vice President, Kelly M. Malson, age 42, $171,667 total compensation
Senior Vice President Southern Division, James D. Walters, age 45, $128,520 total compensation
Senior Vice President Western Division, Jeff L. Tinney, age 51, $110,000 total compensation
Senior Vice President Central Division, D. Clinton Dyer, age 40, $94,950 total compensation
Senior Vice President; Mexico, Francisco J. (Javier) Sauza Del Pozo, age 60, $181,164 total compensation
VP Internal Audit, Robyn Yarborough
VP Lease Administration, Stacey Estes
VP and Director Marketing, Yvette Drake
VP Operations Illinois, Stephen A. Bifano
VP Operations Southwest Texas, Delia A. Brigman
VP Operations Missouri, Erik T. Brown
VP Operations West Texas, Rudolph R. Cruz
VP Operations New Mexico, Jeanne Davis
VP Operations East Texas, Rodney D. Ernest
VP Operations Tennessee, James W. Littlepage
VP Operations Georgia, Scot H. Mozingo
VP Operations Oklahoma, Rodney Owens
VP Operations South Carolina, D. Scott Phillips
VP Operations Mexico, Fidencio Reyna
VP Operations Louisiana, Anthony B. Seney
VP Operations Kentucky, Jackie C. Willyard
Vice President Tax and Assistant Secretary, Keith T. Littrell
Senior Vice President; Mexico, Francisco Pozo
Senior Vice President Central Division, Clinton Dyer
Vice President of Operations, Scott Phillips
Vice President Accounting US, Scott McIntyre
Vice President General Counsel Secretary, Tara E. Trantham
Jr. Vice President of Operations, Willard Pipkin
Vice President External Affairs and Government Relations, Willie A. Green
Director, William S. Hummers III, age 67
President COO and Director, Mark C. Roland, age 56
Director, Charles D. Way, age 60
Director, Ken R. Bramlett Jr., age 53
Director, James R. Gilreath, age 71
Director, Darrell E. Whitaker, age 55
Independent Director, Scott Vassalluzzo
Auditors: KPMGLLP

LOCATIONS

HQ: World Acceptance Corporation
108 Frederick St., Greenville SC 29607
Phone: 864-298-9800   **Fax:** 864-298-9810
Web: www.worldacceptance.com

2012 Locations

	No.
US	
Texas	262
Georgia	105
Tennessee	105
South	97
Oklahoma	82
Illinois	75
Missouri	72
Kentucky	70
Alabama	62
Lousiana	44
New	44
Wisconsin	14
Mexico	105
Total	**1,137**

2012 Loans Receivable

	% of total
US	

Texas	19
Tennessee	14
Georgia	13
South	11
Kentucky	9
Illinois	7
Missouri	6
Oklahoma	6
Alabama	4
Louisiana	2
New	2
Wisconsin	1
Mexico	6
Total	**100**

PRODUCTS/OPERATIONS

2012 Sales

	$ mil.	% of total
Interest & fees	466	86
Insurance commissions & other	73	14
Total	**540**	**100**

Selected Subsidiaries

Servicios World Acceptance Corporation de Mexico
WAC de Mexico
WAC Insurance Company Ltd. (Turks and Caicos Islands)
WFC Limited Partnership
WFC of South Carolina Inc.
WFC Services Inc.
World Acceptance Corporation of Alabama
World Acceptance Corporation of Missouri
World Acceptance Corporation of Oklahoma Inc.
World Finance Corporation of Colorado
World Finance Corporation of Georgia
World Finance Corporation of Illinois
World Finance Corporation of Kentucky
World Finance Corporation of Louisiana
World Finance Corporation of New Mexico
World Finance Corporation of South Carolina
World Finance Corporation of Tennessee
World Finance Corporation of Texas

COMPETITORS

ACE Cash Express	DFC Global
Advance America	EZCORP
Capital One	First Cash Financial
Cash America	Services
Check ' n Go	GM Financial
Check Into Cash	HSBC Finance
Citigroup	Springleaf
Community Choice	
Financial	

HISTORICAL FINANCIALS
Company Type: Public

Income Statement
FYE: March 31

	REVENUE ($ mil.)	NET INCOME ($ mil.)	NET PROFIT MARGIN	EMPLOYEES
03/12	540.1	100.6	18.6%	3,435
03/11	491.4	91.2	18.6%	3,292
03/10	440.6	73.6	16.7%	3,631
03/09	393.7	60.7	15.4%	2,969
03/08	346.0	53.0	15.3%	3,017
Annual Growth	**11.8%**	**17.4%**	**—**	**3.3%**

2012 Year-End Financials

Debt ratio: 37.9%	No. of shares (mil.): 13
Return on equity: 23.3%	Dividends
Cash ($ mil.): 10	Yield: —
Current ratio: 0.29	Payout: —
Long-term debt ($ mil.): 279	Market value ($ mil.): 851

STOCK PRICE ($)		P/E		PER SHARE ($)		
	FY Close	High/Low		Earnings	Dividends	Book Value
03/12	61.25	11	8	6.59	0.00	30.14
03/11	65.20	11	6	5.63	0.00	28.17
03/10	36.08	10	4	4.45	0.00	23.18
03/09	17.10	12	3	3.69	0.00	17.91
03/08	31.85	14	7	3.05	0.00	14.39
Annual Growth	17.8%	—	—	21.2%	—	20.3%

WORLD OF JEANS & TOPS

Tilly's likely has an Ollie or a Hang Ten up its stores' sleeves. Through its World of Jeans & Tops subsidiary the company operates a chain of specialty retail stores and website that sell surf and skateboard apparel footwear skateboards and accessories. Its stores offer Hurley Levi's LRG Neff and other brands as well as its own brands (RSQ Full Tilt Blue Crown and Infamous). The fast-growing retail chain operates about 140 stores in more than a dozen states under the Tilly's banner; most are in California Arizona and Florida. The company traces its roots back to 1982 when founders Hezy Shaked and Tilly Levine opened their first store in Orange Country California. Tilly's went public in 2012.

The apparel retailer raised about $124 million with its May IPO. Tilly's will use a portion of the proceeds to fund a distribution to pre-IPO company shareholders. The distribution is related to a change in World of Jeans & Tops' company type from an "S" to a "C" corporation a designation that affects the way the company is taxed. Tilly's may also use some of the proceeds for general corporate purposes and to acquire other businesses. Prior to its filing Tilly's was majority-owned by Levine (29%) and Shaked (48%) through two separate trusts. Post IPO the Shaked and Levine families control about 96% of the company's voting power.

The IPO capitalized on the company's strong sales growth and operating results. In fiscal 2012 (ends January) net sales increased 20% vs. the prior year with operating income up 40% over the same period. Same-store sales (generally considered the best indicator of a retailer's overall health) at Tilly's stores increased more than 10% in fiscal 2012.

Since its founding the company has been growing rapidly especially in recent years during which the number of its store locations have gone from 32 in 2004 to 140 2012. Tilly's future ambitions include opening new stores in an effort to establish a national presence. The company believes it can expand its store base to more than 500 locations by 2022.

EXECUTIVES

VP Marketing, Cheryl A. Rudich, age 51
President CEO and Director, Daniel (Dan) Griesemer, age 52
VP Real Estate, John Burgess, age 59
Chairman and Chief Strategy Officer, Hezy Shaked, age 57

SVP and CFO, William (Bill) Langsdorf, age 55
VP COO and Chief Information Officer, Craig DeMerit, age 42
VP and General Merchandising Manager, Debbie Anker-Boetes, age 53
VP General Counsel and Secretary, Patrick Grosso, age 39
VP Stores, Shelly Johnson, age 42
VP Vendor Relations, Tilly Levine, age 56
VP Merchandise Planning and Allocation, Carolyn S. McNamara, age 47
VP Finance and Controller, Rochelle Myers, age 45
Founder, Chet Thomas
Director, Seth R. Johnson, age 58
Director, Bernard Zeichner, age 68
President CEO and Director, Daniel (Dan) Griesemer, age 52
Director, Jerold H. Rubinstein, age 73
Director, Janet E. Kerr, age 57
Auditors: Deloitte&ToucheLLP

LOCATIONS

HQ: WORLD OF JEANS & TOPS
10 WHATNEY, IRVINE, CA 92618-2807
Phone: 949-609-5599
Web: WWW.TILLYS.COM

2012 Stores

	No.
Arizona	18
California	78
Colorado	3
Delaware	1
Florida	16
Maryland	2
Nevada	6
New	7
New	2
Pennsylvania	1
Utah	1
Virginia	3
Washington	1
Wisconsin	1
Total	**140**

COMPETITORS

Abercrombie & Fitch	Hot Topic
Aeropostale	Pacific Sunwear
American Eagle Outfitters	The Buckle
	Urban Outfitters
Forever 21	Wet Seal
	Zumiez

HISTORICAL FINANCIALS

Company Type: Public

Income Statement

FYE: January 28

	REVENUE ($ mil.)	NET INCOME ($ mil.)	NET PROFIT MARGIN	EMPLOYEES
01/12	400.6	34.3	8.6%	4,000
01/11	332.6	24.4	7.3%	0
01/10	282.7	20.6	7.3%	0
01/09	254.9	23.6	9.3%	0
Annual Growth	16.3%	13.3%	—	—

2012 Year-End Financials

Debt ratio: —
Return on equity: 8.6%
Cash ($ mil.): 25
Current ratio: 0.50
Long-term debt ($ mil.): —

Xenith Bankshares Inc

Xenith Bankshares formerly First Bankshares is the holding company of SuffolkFirst Bank a community bank with a handful of offices in southeastern Virginia. The bank targets commercial customers wealthy individuals and investors. It offers traditional products and services including checking and savings accounts CDs debit cards and merchant card processing. Its lending portfolio is primarily made up of real estate loans namely residential and commercial mortgages. Xenith Bankshares was created in late 2009 through the merger of the six-year-old First Bankshares and Xenith Corporation which had originally been established to open a new banking institution.

EXECUTIVES

SVP Commercial Banking Xenith Bank, Eddie Phillips
EVP and Chief Lending Officer; EVP and Chief Lending Officer Xenith Bank, Ronald E. Davis
Independent Chairman of the Board, Malcolm S. McDonald
EVP CFO and Chief Administrative Officer; EVP CFO and Chief Administrative Officer Xenith Bank, Thomas W. Osgood
EVP and Chief Credit Officer; EVP and Chief Credit Officer Xenith Bank, Wellington W. (Chris) Cottrell III
Principal Accounting Officer; SVP and Controller Xenith Bank, Judy C. Gavant, age 53
Executive Vice President President, Michael E. Keck
Executive Vice President of Banking, Jefferson OFlaherty
Auditors: PKFWittMaresPLC

LOCATIONS

HQ: Xenith Bankshares Inc
One James Center, 901 E. Cary Street, Suite 1700, Richmond, VA 23219
Phone: 804 433-2200
Web: www.xenithbank.com

COMPETITORS

BB&T	Sistersville Bancorp
Bank of America	SunTrust
Hampton Roads Bankshares	

HISTORICAL FINANCIALS

Company Type: Public

Income Statement

FYE: December 31

	ASSETS ($ mil.)	NET INCOME ($ mil.)	INCOME AS % OF ASSETS	EMPLOYEES
12/12	563.2	7.3	1.3%	104
12/11	477.4	4.4	0.9%	105
12/10	251.2	(5.9)	—	78
12/09	201.5	(6.2)	—	63
12/09	0.0	(4.3)	—	0
Annual Growth	—	—	—	—

2012 Year-End Financials

Return on assets: 1.4%
Return on equity: 8.7%
Long-term debt ($ mil.): —
No. of shares (mil.): 10
Sales ($ mil): 26
Dividends
Yield: —
Payout: —
Market value ($ mil.): 49

STOCK PRICE ($) FY Close	P/E High/Low		PER SHARE ($) Earnings	Dividends	Book Value
12/12 4.63	8	5	0.70	0.00	8.35
12/11 3.73	12	6	0.48	0.00	7.69
12/10 5.50	—	—	(1.01)	0.00	8.34
12/09 7.00	—	—	(2.76)	0.00	9.25
12/09 4.01	—	—	(1.90)	0.00	(0.00)
Annual Growth 3.7%	—	—	—	—	—

Zagg Inc

ZAGG hopes to stand in the way when a little zig threatens to scratch your iPhone or iPad. Short for "Zealous About Great Gadgets" ZAGG designs makes and sells protective coverings and other products for electronic devices. Its flagship product invisibleSHIELD is a thin scratch-resistant polyurethane film covering that's custom cut to fit invisibly on the screens and displays of Apple iPhones and other smartphones tablets laptops GPS devices and watch faces. ZAGG also offers additional accessories including keyboards headphones for iPods and MP3 players and decorative cases for phones. It sells its products through retailers the likes of Best Buy and Wal-Mart mall kiosks and its own website.

Geographic Reach

The US is ZAGG's largest market. accounting for about 85% of its sales. Europe contributes about 5% of sales with other countries representing the rest. The company's international arm is based in Shannon Ireland.

Operations

The company's operations are divided into three segments. The largest accounting for about three-quarters of total sales is ZAGG which designs makes and distributes products including protective coverings keyboards keyboard cases earbuds mobile power devices and cleaning accessories for mobiles devices under the ZAGG brand. iFrogz accounts for about 25% of sales. It makes cases Near-Field Audio amplifying speakers earbuds and regular and gaming headphones for mobile devices. The company's HzO segment is engaged in the development of water blocking coating technologies for consumer and industrial applications. It had no revenue in 2012.

Sales and Marketing

ZAGG's biggest customer is consumer electronics chain Best Buy which accounts for about a third of its total sales. Next is retail-giant Wal-Mart Stores which accounts for about 10%. Historically the company has focused on distributing through sales channels like kiosk vendors and through its e-commerce site; however more recently it has brought in more and more income through retailers (including Target RadioShack and Staples) and wireless carriers (AT&T Sprint Verizon). Ultimately demand for its products has been driven by the growing popularity of iPads iPhones and other smartphones. (iPhone accessories are its biggest sellers.) The company sells throughout Europe and other global regions through international distributors.

Financial Performance

In 2012 ZAGG's sales exceeded $264 million a 48% jump versus 2011. Driving the heady increase was the 2011 purchase of iFrogz which con-

tributed about $68 million in sales in 2012. Strong demand from wholesale customers the addition of new distribution partners and continued growth of invisibleSHIELD products coupled with increased sales of ZAGG's keyboards audio and case product lines also pumped up sales. 2012 marked the fourth year of accelerating sales for the company. Indeed over the past four years sales have increased by more than a factor of 10: from nearly $20 million in 2008 to $264 million in 2012.

After four years of steep increases net income fell 21% in 2012 compared with 2011. ZAGG attributed the decline to higher operating expenses. Also marketing advertising and promotion expenses rose as the company invested heavily for key product launches including the invisibleSHIELD HD invisibleSHIELD EXTREME and ZAGGkeys PRO among other new products.

Strategy

Going forward ZAGG hopes to keep its growth momentum swinging in an upward direction by expanding its sales channels to include more telecom companies like U.S. Cellular and retailers like Amazon.com. It has also been broadening its range of accessories for the mobile phone market by adding car chargers and power supplies to its product offerings. Other growth strategies include focusing its sales and marketing efforts on cross-selling accessories to customers that purchase its invisibleSHIELD products.

Mergers and Acquisitions

In a move that simultaneously broadened its brand and product portfolio and increases its retail reach ZAGG in mid-2011 acquired iFrogz a maker and distributor of protective cases headphones and earbuds and other accessories for smartphones tablets and other mobile devices under the iFrogz and EarPollution brands. ZAGG paid $50 million in cash acquired 4.4 million restricted shares of ZAGG common stock and assumed about $5 million in debt. Utah-based iFrogz which counts Wal-Mart Stores among its customers became a wholly-owned subsidiary of ZAGG.

EXECUTIVES

EVP Sales, Derek M. Smith
Media Contact, Nathan Nelson
President and CEO, Randall Hales
EVP Marketing, Kent Wuthrich
Chairman, Cheryl A. Larabee
Financial Controller, Geraldine Stanley
CFO, Brandon T. OBrien
COO, Jason Schwartz
EVP Product Development, Ben Godfrey
Director, Edward D. (Ed) Ekstrom, age 56
Interim CEO and Director, Randall (Randy) Hales
Independent Director, Bradley Holiday
Independent Director, Daniel Maurer
Independent Director, Todd Heiner
Auditors: KPMGLLP

LOCATIONS

HQ: ZAGG Inc.
3855 S. 500 West Ste. J, Salt Lake City UT 84115-4279
Phone: 801-263-0699 **Fax:** 410-712-4760
Web: www.conmedinc.com

2012 Sales

	% of total
US	87
Europe	6
Other	7
Total	**100**

PRODUCTS/OPERATIONS

2012 Sales

	$ mil.	% of total
ZAGG	196	74
iFrogz	68	26
HzO - -		
Total	**264**	**100**

Selected Brands

EarPollution
iFrogz
invisibleSHIELD (film coatings)
ZAGGbuds (audio headphones)
ZAGGskins (cell phone cases and covers)
ZAGGsmartbuds (audio headphones)

COMPETITORS

Apple Inc.	Kyocera Communications
Bose	Motorola Mobility
Dooney & Bourke	Otterbox
Forward Industries	Plantronics

HISTORICAL FINANCIALS

Company Type: Public

Income Statement
FYE: December 31

	REVENUE ($ mil.)	NET INCOME ($ mil.)	NET PROFIT MARGIN	EMPLOYEES
12/12	264.4	14.5	5.5%	273
12/11	179.1	18.2	10.2%	261
12/10	76.1	9.9	13.1%	183
12/09	38.3	3.3	8.8%	122
12/08	19.7	2.1	10.6%	74
Annual Growth	91.2%	62.1%	—	38.6%

2012 Year-End Financials

Debt ratio: 22.4%	No. of shares (mil.): 31
Return on equity: 12.7%	Dividends
Cash ($ mil.): 20	Yield: —
Current ratio: 3.14	Payout: —
Long-term debt ($ mil.): 40	Market value ($ mil.): 230

STOCK PRICE ($) FY Close	P/E High/Low		PER SHARE ($) Earnings	Dividends	Book Value
12/12	7.36	27 14	0.46	0.00	3.98
12/11	7.07	25 9	0.63	0.00	3.45
12/10	7.62	20 5	0.41	0.00	1.26
12/09	3.92	47 6	0.15	0.00	0.64
12/08	0.93	11 5	0.11	0.00	0.30
Annual Growth	67.7%	— —	43.0%	—	90.2%

Zep Inc

Zep hates a mess. A manufacturer of commercial industrial institutional and consumer chemical products it makes such brand lines as Enforcer (fertilizer pest control and drain cleaners) Selig (environmentally friendly hand cleaners and degreasers and equipment used to clean aerospace and automotive parts) and Zep (automotive and janitorial supplies such as hand cleaners degreasers and floor polish). Through its Niagara National unit it provides truck and fleet washing systems and products. The company operates eight manufacturing sites in Europe and North America. It generates more than 80% of sales from the US.

Zep began trading publicly in 2007 after a spinoff from former parent Acuity Brands.

After three major acquisitions in 2010 that gave it access to new customers brands and distribution channels Zep began building up its products and distribution systems. The company wants to strengthen its position as a leading provider of cleaning and maintenance products for commercial and industrial markets. It seeks to expand its "pro" customers by expanding its distribution and retail channels. To do this it plans to build on its existing European operations and grow internationally. Expanding through selected acquisitions mostly privately held targets is also a part of the company's strategy.

Following its spinoff the company began slimming its operations cutting its product offerings in half consolidating its North American distribution network from 42 to 17 locations and cutting non-sales staff by 28%. The changes freed up cash for Zep to make the three significant acquisitions: Amrep which manufactures specialty chemicals for the automotive aftermarket and janitorial market; the North American operations of Waterbury Companies which provide air-care products; and Niagara National which provides truck wash equipment and cleaning chemicals. The company completed integrating its three acquisitions in 2011. That year it also centralized its supply chain operations so that its manufacturing sites could produce for multiple sales channels.

The strategy resulted in strong financial results in 2011 with revenues of $646 million a 14% increase over 2010 and net income of $17.4 million a 29% jump over 2010. Revenue and net income were boosted mainly on the strength of Zep's 2010 acquisitions higher selling prices for many of its products and favorable currency exchange rates. The increases help offet declines in sales volume across several end markets. Zep intends to sell more though distributors and retailers to improve its sales margins. Its net income hike benefitted from an extension of the domestic research and development credit that gave it a favorable tax rate and a gain on the sale of a facility in Boston.

The company also holds a license to manufacture a line of car wash products with the Armor All brand name that it markets to car wash sales professionals. After completing its Atlanta-based Niagara National unit Zep added the Niagara brand to its transportation products that included the Armor All Professional Zep and EnviroEdge brands.

Zep tries to get its products out in a variety of ways. Its distributor sales organization markets products to large national and regional distributors that target the industrial maintenance janitorial/sanitation and automotive markets. Distributors include W.W. Grainger Bunzle and Interline Brands. Its retail sales group markets products to contractors small business owners and homeowners through retailers such as home-improvement stores (Lowe's Home Depot) discount stores (Wal-Mart) and autoparts stores (Advance Auto Parts). Its direct sales group markets cleaning and maintenance products to commercial industrial institutional and governmental customers ranging in size from small businesses to federal government agencies.

In early 2012 the company acquired the UK-based Hale Group for an undisclosed price. Hale Group's two subsidiaries Forward Chemicals and Rexodan International manufacture and supply liquid powder and aerosol chemicals for industrial and commercial laundries. It soon followed that acquisition by having another UK-based Mykal Industries which makes a range of branded and private-

label cleaning and degreasing products for the European retail DIY and professional distribution markets. The acquisitions continue Zep's strategy of expanding its market access in Europe as well as broadening its product offering and distribution channels.

That year the company also expanded its relationship with Lowe's where 50 Zep Commercial products are now offered in 1360 Lowe's stores across the US and on its website. Products in the Zep Commercial line include All Purpose Cleaner-Degreaser Oxy Carpet and Upholstery Cleaner and Hardwood-Floor Cleaner.

EXECUTIVES

EVP and CFO, Mark R. Bachmann, age 55, $296,434 total compensation
VP and Chief Administrative Officer, Robert P. Collins, age 60, $229,577 total compensation
Chairman President and CEO, John K. Morgan, age 59, $541,500 total compensation
VP General Counsel and Secretary, Philip A. (Phil) Theodore, age 60, $21,635 total compensation
Chief Operating Officer, Ronald D. Brown, age 60
VP and Chief Supply Chain Officer, Jeffrey L. Fleck
Executive Vice President of Manufacturing and Engineering, Carol Williams
Director, O. B. Grayson Hall Jr.
Director, Timothy M. (Tim) Manganello, age 63
Director, Timothy T. (Tim) Tevens, age 57
Director, Joseph Squicciarino, age 57
Director, Sidney J. (Sid) Nurkin, age 72
Director, Ronald D. Brown, age 60
Auditors: Ernst&YoungLLP

LOCATIONS

HQ: Zep Inc.
1310 Seaboard Industrial Blvd., Atlanta GA 30318
Phone: 404-352-1680   **Fax:** 404-603-7958
Web: www.zepinc.com

2011 Sales

	$ mil.	% of total
$ mil % of total		
US	529	82
International	116	18
Total	**645**	**100**

COMPETITORS

Arch Chemicals	Georgia-Pacific
Bayer AG	Chemicals
Cantol	NCH
Church & Dwight	Procter & Gamble
Clorox	RPM International
Diversey	S.C. Johnson
Ecolab	WD-40

HISTORICAL FINANCIALS

Company Type: Public

Income Statement

FYE: August 31

	REVENUE ($ mil.)	NET INCOME ($ mil.)	NET PROFIT MARGIN	EMPLOYEES
08/13	689.5	15.1	2.2%	2,400
08/12	653.5	21.9	3.4%	2,400
08/11	645.9	17.4	2.7%	2,300
08/10	568.5	13.5	2.4%	2,350
08/09	501.0	9.2	1.8%	2,200
Annual Growth	**8.3%**	**13.2%**	**—**	**2.2%**

2013 Year-End Financials

Debt ratio: 38.3%
Return on equity: 8.6%
Cash ($ mil.): 2
Current ratio: 1.33
Long-term debt ($ mil.): 184

No. of shares (mil.): 22
Dividends
  Yield: 0.0%
  Payout: 23.5%
Market value ($ mil.): 311

	STOCK PRICE ($) FY Close	P/E High/Low		PER SHARE ($) Earnings	Dividends	Book Value
08/13	14.08	24	18	0.68	0.16	8.34
08/12	14.47	18	12	0.98	0.16	7.69
08/11	17.63	26	19	0.78	0.16	6.89
08/10	17.31	39	24	0.61	0.16	5.73
08/09	15.98	48	16	0.43	0.16	5.16
Annual Growth	**(3.1%)**	**—**	**—**	**12.1%**	**(0.0%)**	**12.7%**

Zillow Inc

Wonder how much your home is really worth? Zillow has the answer. Its website for homeowners and buyers provides a free estimated market value using its proprietary formula ("Zestimate") for more than 110 million homes in America. Users enter an address into a search field and Zillow computes the Zestimate and overlays it on a satellite map. The firm also provides home listings neighborhood information photos purchase and sale data and rental price estimates; offers mobile real estate apps; and sells subscription services that help find real estate agents and mortgage rates. Zillow was established in 2004 by Expedia founder Rich Barton and former Expedia exec Lloyd Frink. It went public in 2011.

Geographic Reach

The company is headquartered in Seattle Washington. It also has offices in California Illinois Nebraska and New York.

Sales and Marketing

Zillow's Seattle-based sales team sells "Premier Agent" subscriptions to real estate agents. Its Lincoln Nebraska and San Francisco California sales teams handle the company's mortgage and rental marketplaces. The company maintains a field sales team to target larger advertising customers. Zillow itself spent more than $11 million on advertising during fiscal 2012.

Financial Performance

The company's revenue has been surging year-over-year since 2008. In fiscal 2012 the company's profits increased by 439% compared to fiscal 2011 due to its revenue nearly doubling. Zillow's revenue increased by 77% in fiscal 2012 compared to fiscal 2011 as the company focused on growing its marketplace revenue which accounted for the majority of its revenue growth over that period. Zillow claimed $116.8 million in revenue for fiscal 2012 after bringing in about $66.1 million in fiscal 2011 and $30.5 million in fiscal 2010.

Strategy

The company has been extending its reach across the Web through strategic partnerships signing several agreements with third-party media firms. Through a deal with Yahoo! it places home listings and ads from local real estate brokers on Yahoo!. It also launched an advertising relationship with Century 21 Real Estate for listings to appear on the Yahoo!/Zillow Real Estate Network. It also signed a pact with real estate website Curbed that allows Curbed.com visitors to search for local listings nationwide and another with AOL that brings Zillow Mortgage Marketplace to the AOL Real Estate and DailyFinance websites.

Mergers and Acquisitions

Zillow has been using acquisitions to grow funded in part through its IPO that raised some $69 million. In 2012 it acquired four companies including Rent Juice a maker of software that landlords use to manage their properties for $40 million. It did did so in order to boost its new push into the rental marketplace.

In 2011 it purchased the assets of Postlet a real estate agent and rental property manager marketing service. Postlet created a platform that makes it easier for agents property managers and landlords to distribute listings on real estate and social media sites across the Web. Also that year it acquired Diverse Solutions a company that helps real estate agents market their businesses and improve their personal websites.

Company Background

The name "Zillow" combines the words pillow (where you lay your head at night) and zillions (the number of data points the firm desires to provide).

EXECUTIVES

Chairman, Richard N. (Rich) Barton, age 46
VP IT and Operations, Chris Staats
Vice Chairman and President, Lloyd D. Frink, age 48
General Counsel; Secretary, Kathleen Philips, age 46
Chief Marketing Officer, Amy Bohutinsky, age 38
CTO, David A. Beitel, age 44
VP Product Teams, Kristin Acker
Chief Revenue Officer, Greg M. Schwartz, age 40
Chief Economist, Stan Humphries
VP Product Teams, Christopher Roberts
Chief Financial Officer, Chad M. Cohen, age 38
VP Product Management and Strategy, Chloe Harford
VP Local Advertising Sales, Doug Slotkin
VP Product Teams, Garrett McAuliffe
VP Sales Strategy and Operations, Tony Small
Owner, Leslie Ln
Owner, Debra Ct
Director, Erik C. Blachford, age 46
Director, Jay C. Hoag, age 54
Director, Gregory B. (Greg) Maffei, age 52
Vice Chairman and President, Lloyd D. Frink, age 48
Director, J. William (Bill) Gurley, age 46
Director, Gordon Stephenson, age 47
Auditors: Ernst&YoungLLP

LOCATIONS

HQ: Zillow Inc.
999 3rd Ave. Ste. 4600, Seattle WA 98104
Phone: 206-470-7000   **Fax:** 650-253-0001
Web: www.youtube.com

PRODUCTS/OPERATIONS

2012 Sales

Marketplace	86	74
Total	**116**	**100**

Selected Products & Operations

Website and Mobile Offerings
  Local information (neighborhoods schools demographics)
  Sale and rental listings
  Zestimate values (determines a home' s worth)
  Zillow Mobile (real estate app for smart phones)
Marketplace Offerings
  Mortgage Marketplace (instant loan quotes)
  Premier Agent (real estate agent listing)

COMPETITORS

Classified Ventures	PropertyInfo
Google	RE/MAX
HomeGain.com	Trulia
Market Leader	Zaio
Move Inc.	craigslist

HISTORICAL FINANCIALS

Company Type: Public

Income Statement

FYE: December 31

	REVENUE ($ mil.)	NET INCOME ($ mil.)	NET PROFIT MARGIN	EMPLOYEES
12/12	116.8	5.9	5.1%	560
12/11	66.0	1.1	1.7%	329
12/10	30.4	(6.7)	—	275
12/09	17.4	(12.8)	—	0
12/08	10.5	(21.2)	—	0
Annual Growth 82.2%		—	—	—

2012 Year-End Financials

Debt ratio: —	No. of shares (mil.): 33
Return on equity: 3.1%	Dividends
Cash ($ mil.): 150	Yield: —
Current ratio: 10.05	Payout: —
Long-term debt ($ mil.): —	Market value ($ mil.): 940

	STOCK PRICE ($) FY Close	P/E High/Low	PER SHARE ($) Earnings	Dividends	Book Value
12/12	27.75	231115	0.18	0.00	8.27
12/11	22.48	— —	(0.00)	0.00	3.60
Annual Growth 23.4% 129.8%	— —	— —	—	—

Zix Corp

Zix wants to nix the idea of unsavory characters reading your e-mail. The company offers secure e-mail encryption data loss prevention and transmission services. Its technology enables users to transmit encrypted e-mail and documents to any address in the world; recipients who are not service subscribers can access the messages through the company's Web-based portal. Zix targets customers in the health care financial services insurance and government sectors and it has an e-mail encryption community with tens of millions of members growing by 100000 members per week. Trademarks and brand names for its products include ZixCorp. ZixGateway ZixDirectory ZixIT ZixPort and PocketScript.

Operations

ZixCorp. Email Encryption is a Software-as-a-Service (SaaS) offering that allows customers to pay an annual subscription fee to have access to ZixDirectory the company's e-mail encryption community. Within the community the company offers ZixGateway a gateway that decrypts messages. In early 2013 Zix launched ZixDLPTM (DLP) a data loss prevention product catering to enterprise customers. DLP is available as a bundle to ZixCorp. Email Encryption for new customers and is also available as a standalone offering.

Geographic Reach

Zix operates through leased properties in Austin Texas; Dallas; Burlington Massachusetts; Ottawa

Canada; and the UK. Almost all of its total sales derive from US customers.

Sales and Marketing

Zix sells its Email Encryption SaaS through a direct sales for that zeroes in on larger business while a telesales force caters to small and midsized accounts. It also uses a network of 170 value-added resellers and other distribution partners including service clients needing encryption offerings. Google is its largest third party reseller and represented 22% of its first year orders in 2012.

As the company pursues multi-year subscription contracts a high percentage of customers subscribe to its Email Encryption SaaS for a three-year term versus a one-year term.

Financial Performance

Zix has enjoyed steady revenue growth over the last three years; however its profits have nosedived over the last two years. Revenues were up by 14% from $38 million in 2011 to $43 million in 2012. Profits were down by 51% from nearly $23 million in 2011 to $11 million in 2012.

Zix attributes the revenue growth to higher demand for its subscriptions coupled with a high rate of renewing existing customers. It experienced growth in its three main verticals: health care finance and government. New orders from its value-added reseller OEM and third party distribution channels for 2012 was 63% of its total new orders compared to 52% in 2011.

Its erosion of profits from 2011 to 2012 was mainly due to a $2 million income tax benefit it received in 2012 compared to $12 million in 2012. It also paid higher research development selling general and administrative expenses for 2012. (This was due to a higher headcount related to new product development.)

Strategy

Zix plans to focus on core vertical markets: health care finance and government. It is looking to add new customers through an enlarged distribution network value-added retailers and a existing base of customers who continue to renew their subscriptions.

The company is also looking to offer new tools and service upgrades to its existing customer base. Along these lines Zix launched ZixDLPTM (DLP) a data loss prevention product catering to enterprise customers in early 2013. DLP is available as a bundle to ZixCorp. Email Encryption for new customers and is also sold as a standalone offering.

HISTORY

Zix Corporation traces its circuitous history back to five scientists from Los Alamos National Laboratory who in 1983 took possession of the patents on a system used by the Department of Agriculture to track livestock. Working to develop commercial applications for the technology their enterprise called Amtech gained the attention of David Cook the co-founder of Blockbuster Entertainment as well as Ross Perot.

Work progressed slowly and Cook brought in Dallas attorney Russell Mortenson to lead the company. In 1988 Amtech struck a deal to develop a toll collection system for the Lincoln Tunnel in New York. Its system proved successful and was chosen for the Dallas North Tollway the next year. The company reported its first profit in 1992. The Union Internationale des Chemins de fer adopted Amtech's toll system technology in 1993 as the standard for European railroads.

Diminishing sales to the rail industry spurred the firm to expand its market base. Amtech acquired Swedish firm Cardkey Systems (electronic access systems) in 1995 and later became involved in radio-frequency (RF) security systems and wireless LAN equipment (WaveNet). Its acquisitions could not help stabilize Amtech's roller coaster financial position however and in 1997 the company agreed to shed its WaveNet unit. That year the company won a $39 million contract to create a statewide electronic road toll system for Florida. Cost overruns led to a loss on the project further straining an already divided board and in 1998 Cook returned as CEO.

With interest in the Internet heating up Amtech sold its Transportation Systems Group for $31 million and announced it would shift its business to digital content distribution. Changing its name to CustomTracks and selling Cardkey Systems to Johnson Controls for $41 million the company began developing a secure system for downloading encrypted digital music files called ZixMail. CustomTracks also developed a system for collecting money for the music called ZixCharge.

While the music industry failed to adopt CustomTrack's technology customers in need of secure e-mail applications such as law firms did. In 1999 the company changed its name to ZixIt to focus on encrypted messaging. The next year the company received some real tech cache when former Lotus CEO Jeff Papows joined as chairman.

Developing and marketing its new product proved costly and ZixIt ran deep into the red. Its business was further hurt in 2001 when a security breach at its Anacom credit card processing subsidiary allowed credit card accounts to be illegally accessed. (Anacom was subsequently shut down.) Later that year Cook and Papows stepped aside as former Entrust CEO John Ryan took over as chairman and CEO.

In 2002 the company changed its name to Zix Corporation.

Zix acquired electronic prescription company PocketScript for $1.5 million in July 2003. PocketScript allows for doctors to file prescriptions using a BlackBerry PDA or regular computer connected to the Internet and is affiliated with various pharmaceutical benefit management firms.

Also in 2003 Zix acquired Elron Software a maker of spam email and online filtering software for $7 million.

Early in 2005 Ryan resigned as CEO remaining chairman; president and COO Rick Spurr stepped in as CEO.

EXECUTIVES

Chairman CEO and COO, Richard D. (Rick) Spurr, age 59, $300,000 total compensation
VP General Counsel and Corporate Secretary, James F. Brashear
VP Engineering, David J. Robertson, age 54, $200,000 total compensation
VP Client Services, Russell J. Morgan, age 53, $207,702 total compensation
VP Business Development and Product Management, Nigel P. Johnson
VP Business Operations, William J. Kadonsky
VP Sales amd Marketing, James J. (Jim) Lesniak
VP Corporate Marketing, Geoffrey R. (Geoff) Bibby
CFO, Michael W. English, age 57
VP Corporate Sales Channels and Marketing, Steven D. Irons
Vice President, Eric Ouellet
Vice President Technology Vanguard, Harold Bandy
Director, Robert C. (Bob) Hausmann, age 50
Director, James S. Marston, age 79
Director, Antonio R. Sanchez III, age 39
Director, Paul E. Schlosberg, age 61
Director, Maribess L. Miller

Independent Director, Taher Elgamal
Auditors: WhitleyPenn

LOCATIONS

HQ: Zix Corporation
2711 N. Haskell Ave. Ste. 2200 LB 36, Dallas TX 75204-2960
Phone: 214-370-2000   **Fax:** 214-370-2070
Web: www.zixcorp.com

PRODUCTS/OPERATIONS

Selected Products and Services
Receivers
  Secure Compose
  ZixDirect
  ZixMobility
  ZixPort
Senders
  Cloud Hosted Email
  Reporting
  Superior TLS
  Transparency
  ZixGateway
  ZixMail
Other Services
  ZixAuditor
  ZixConnect
  ZixEnable
  ZixGateway Inbound

COMPETITORS

Barracuda Networks	Sophos
Cisco Systems	Symantec
EMC	Trend Micro
McAfee	Voltage Security
Proofpoint	

HISTORICAL FINANCIALS

Company Type: Public

Income Statement

FYE: December 31

	REVENUE ($ mil.)	NET INCOME ($ mil.)	NET PROFIT MARGIN	EMPLOYEES
12/12	43.3	11.0	25.4%	144
12/11	38.1	22.5	59.1%	127
12/10	33.0	41.2	124.6%	123
12/09	30.6	(4.4)	—	136
12/08	28.0	(5.4)	—	165
Annual Growth	**11.5%**	—	—	**(3.3%)**

2012 Year-End Financials

Debt ratio: —	No. of shares (mil.): 61
Return on equity: 18.4%	Dividends
Cash ($ mil.): 22	Yield: —
Current ratio: 1.32	Payout: —
Long-term debt ($ mil.): —	Market value ($ mil.): 171

	STOCK PRICE ($) FY Close	P/E High/Low		PER SHARE ($) Earnings	Dividends	Book Value
12/12	2.79	19	13	0.17	0.00	1.00
12/11	2.82	14	6	0.34	0.00	0.91
12/10	4.27	7	3	0.62	0.00	0.70
12/09	1.71	—	—	(0.07)	0.00	(0.03)
12/08	1.19	—	—	(0.09)	0.00	(0.02)
Annual Growth	**23.7%**	—	—	—	—	—

Zumiez Inc

Zumiez's young customers like to zoom. The fast-growing retailer outfits action sports enthusiasts offering apparel footwear accessories and sports equipment for 12- to 24-year-olds who enjoy board sports BMX biking and surfing. It stocks such brands as Billabong Burton Quiksilver Vans and Spy Optic as well as private-label goods. Zumiez operates about 500 mall-based stores across North America and in Europe as well as an online store. Aside from the usual action sports merchandise (hoodies and puffy skater shoes) stores also feature couches video games and sales clerks who really use the gear –all designed to encourage shoppers to chill. Zumiez was founded in 1978 by chairman Thomas Campion.

Geographic Reach
Zumiez operates about 475 stores in some 40 US states and another 20 stores in Canada (seven in Ontario three in British Columbia). California Texas and New York are the retailer's largest market accounting for about a third of its stores. In Europe a new market for the retailer the company operates stores under the name Blue Tomato.

Operations
In addition to its fast-growing retail store chain Zumiez sells merchandise online and provides content and community for its young customers. E-commerce sales accounted for more than 7% of the company's sales in fiscal 2012 (ends January).

Sales and Marketing
To increase brand awareness and strengthen its connection to its customers Zumiez participates in various music and local sporting events that embody the action sports lifestyle. The Zumiez Couch Tour is a series of entertainment events that includes skateboarding demonstrations from top professionals autograph sessions competitions and live music. In fiscal 2012 (ends January) the Couch Tour completed a 12-city tour of the US. Zumiez also advertises in magazines popular with its target market and sponsors interactive contests and maintains a presence on various social network channels such as Facebook and Twitter.

Financial Performance
Zumiez's fiscal 2012 (ends January) sales increased 16% vs. the prior year while net income grew by 54% over the same period. The double-digit uptick in sales and profits was driven by the addition of more than 40 new stores including the retailer's first in Canada and a 9% rise in sales at stores open more than one year. Footwear men's apparel accessories and junior's apparel posted increases in same-store sales while hardgoods and boy's apparel declined.

Indeed thanks to its rapidly-expanding retail store network Zumiez's sales have quintupled over the past decade and the chain is consistently profitable.

Strategy
Growth is the mantra at Zumiez. The company has made great strides in extending its retail network adding about 250 stores since the end of fiscal 2005 (ends January). In fiscal 2012 the chain entered the Canadian market and has since made an acquisition in Europe. Going forward the chain plans to open about 50 new stores including 10 more in Canada in fiscal 2013 and grow its online sales. In the US the chain is adding stores in existing and new markets.

To that end in mid-2012 the company acquired Blue Tomato a multi-channel action sports retailer based in Austria for E59.5 million ($78 million).

Blue Tomato operates five stores in Austria as well as an e-commerce site serving the broader European market.

Ownership

Founder Campion owns about a 16% stake in Zumiez while CEO Richard Brooks holds 12% of the shares. The investment firm T. Rowe Price Associates owns about 16% while Waddell & Reed Financial Services owns 8% of the company.

EXECUTIVES

Chairman, Thomas D. Campion, $262,500 total compensation
CEO, Richard M. Brooks, $262,500 total compensation
President and General Merchandising Manager, Lynn K. Kilbourne, $350,000 total compensation
EVP Stores, Ford K. Wright, $225,000 total compensation
Director Finance and Investor Relations, Brian Leith
CFO, Christopher C. Work
EVP E-commerce and Omni-channel, Troy R. Brown
Director, James M. (Jim) Weber, age 53
Director, William M. Barnum Jr., age 59
Director, Gerald F. Ryles, age 76
Director, Sarah (Sally) McCoy, age 52
Director, Matthew L. Hyde, age 50
Independent Director, Ernest Johnson
Independent Director, Travis Smith
Auditors: MossAdamsLLP

LOCATIONS

HQ: Zumiez Inc.
6300 Merrill Creek Pkwy. Ste. B, Everett WA 98203
Phone: 425-551-1500   **Fax:** 425-551-1555
Web: www.zumiez.com

2012 Stores

	No.
California	77
Texas	45
New	30
Washington	24
Colorado	18
Florida	18
New	18
Pennsylvania	18
Illinois	16
Arizona	13
Wisconsin	13
Oregon	12
Utah	12
Minnesota	11
Maryland	9
Nevada	9
Connecticut	8
Indiana	8
Massachusetts	8
Virginia	7
Idaho	6
Michigan	6
Oklahoma	6
New	5
Montana	4
New	4
North	4
Alaska	3
Delaware	3
Georgia	3
Kansas	3
Hawaii	2
Iowa	2
Maine	2
Missouri	2
South	2
Wyoming	2
Rhode	1
Canada	10
Total	**444**

PRODUCTS/OPERATIONS

2012 Sales

	% of total
Men's	33
Footwear	24
Accessories	20
Hardgoods	11
Junior's	10
Other	2
Total	**100**

COMPETITORS

Abercrombie & Fitch	Hot Topic
Aeropostale	Old Navy
American Apparel	Pacific Sunwear
American Eagle Outfitters	Sport Chalet
Big 5	Sports Authority
Dick's Sporting Goods	The Buckle
Forever 21	Urban Outfitters
	Wet Seal

HISTORICAL FINANCIALS

Company Type: Public

Income Statement

FYE: February 2

	REVENUE ($ mil.)	NET INCOME ($ mil.)	NET PROFIT MARGIN	EMPLOYEES
02/13*	669.3	42.1	6.3%	5,300
01/12	555.8	37.3	6.7%	4,680
01/11	478.8	24.2	5.1%	4,840
01/10	407.6	9.1	2.2%	4,330
01/09	408.6	17.2	4.2%	3,650
Annual Growth	13.1%	25.1%	—	9.8%

*Fiscal year change

2013 Year-End Financials

Debt ratio: —
Return on equity: 14.4%
Cash ($ mil.): 17
Current ratio: 3.55
Long-term debt ($ mil.): —
No. of shares (mil.): 30
Dividends
　Yield: —
　Payout: —
Market value ($ mil.): 636

	STOCK PRICE ($) FY Close	P/E High/Low	PER SHARE ($) Earnings	Dividends	Book Value
02/13*	21.11	30 14	1.35	0.00	10.08
01/12	28.33	26 14	1.20	0.00	8.74
01/11	22.31	39 16	0.79	0.00	7.35
01/10	12.73	55 21	0.30	0.00	6.37
01/09	7.15	39 10	0.58	0.00	6.03
Annual Growth	31.1%	— —	23.5%	—	13.7%

*Fiscal year change

Hoover's Handbook of

Emerging Companies

Master Index for all
2014 Hoover's Handbooks

Index by Headquarters

ARE

Abu Dhabi
National Bank of Abu Dhabi W302

AUS

Melbourne
BHP Billiton Ltd. W86

Perth
Wesfarmers Ltd. W480

Sydney
Woolworths Ltd. W487

Melbourne
Rio Tinto Ltd W358
National Australia Bank Ltd. W300

Sydney
Commonwealth Bank of Australia
W129

Melbourne
Australia and New Zealand Banking
Group Ltd W45

Sydney
Westpac Banking Corp W483

Melbourne
Telstra Corp., Ltd. W437

Sydney
AMP Ltd. W32
QBE Insurance Group Ltd. W349

Brisbane
Suncorp Group Ltd. W423

Sydney
Macquarie Group Ltd W272

AUT

Vienna
OMV AG (Austria) W331
Erste Group Bank AG W166

BEL

Leuven
Anheuser-Busch Inbev SA W36

Brussels
Etablissements Delhaize Freres et Cie
Le Lion S.A. (Belgium) W168
KBC Group NV W247
Umicore S.A. W462
Solvay S.A. W406
Banque Nationale de Belgique
(National Bank of Belgium) W71

BMU

Hamilton
Jardine Matheson Holdings Ltd. W242
Jardine Strategic Holdings Ltd
(Bermuda) W242

BRA

Rio de Janeiro
Petroleo Brasileiro S.A. W339

Sao Paulo
Itau Unibanco Holding S.A. W237

Osasco
Banco Bradesco S.A. W56

Rio de Janeiro
Vale S. A. W467

Sao Paulo
JBS S.A. W242
Banco Santander Brasil SA W59

CAN

Calgary
Suncor Energy Inc. W422

Toronto
Royal Bank of Canada W365

Laval
Alimentation-Couche Tard, Inc. W26

Montreal
Power Corp. of Canada W345

Toronto
Weston (George) Limited W482

Montreal
Power Financial Corp W346

Toronto
Toronto Dominion Bank W449

Brampton
Loblaw Cos. Ltd. W270

Calgary
Imperial Oil Ltd. W225

Aurora
Magna International Inc. W273

Winnipeg
Great-West Lifeco Inc. W193

Toronto
Bank of Nova Scotia Halifax W68
Manulife Financial Corp. W277

Verdun
BCE Inc. W81

Montreal
Bank of Montreal W67

Toronto
Sun Life Financial Inc W421

Montreal
Bombardier Inc. W90

Calgary
Agrium, Inc. W17

Toronto
Canadian Imperial Bank of Commerce
W103

Montreal
National Bank of Canada W302

Vancouver
HSBC Bank Canada W215

CHE

Baar
Glencore Xstrata PLC W192

Vevey
Nestle S.A. W307

Zurich
Zurich Insurance Group Ltd W490

Basel
Novartis AG Basel W322
Roche Holding Ltd. W361

Zurich
ABB Asea Brown Boveri Ltd.
(Switzerland) W4
ABB Ltd W4
UBS AG (Switzerland) W460
Swiss Re Ltd. W426

Glattbrugg
Adecco S.A. (Switzerland) W11

Zurich
Migros-Genossenschafts-Bund
(Switzerland) W287
Credit Suisse Group W138

Jona
Holcim Ltd W211

Schindellegi
Kuehne & Nagel International AG
W259

Zurich
ACE, Ltd. W8

Basel
Baloise Holding AG W53

CHN

Beijing
China Petroleum & Chemical Corp.
Inc W120
PetroChina Co Ltd W339
China International United Petroleum
& Chemicals Co Ltd W118
Industrial and Commercial Bank of
China Ltd W229
China Construction Bank Corp W118
Agricultural Bank of China W17
Bank of China Ltd., Beijing W63
China Railway Construction Corp Ltd
W121

Shanghai
SAIC Motor Corp Ltd W376

Beijing
China Railway Group Ltd W121
China Life Insurance Co Ltd W118

Shenzhen
Ping An Insurance (Group) Co of
China Ltd. W343

Beijing
China Communications Construction
Company Ltd W117
China Telecom Corp Ltd W121

Shanghai
Bank of Communications Co., Ltd.
W64
China United Network
Communications Ltd W123

Beijing
China Shenhua Energy Co., Ltd.
W121
Metallurgical Corp China Ltd W285

Shanghai
Baoshan Iron & Steel Co Ltd W71

Beijing
China Minsheng Banking Corp Ltd
W119

Shenzhen
China Merchants Bank Co Ltd W118

Beijing
PICC Property and Casualty Co Ltd
W342

Fuzhou
Industrial Bank Co., Ltd. W229

Shenzhen
Shenzhen Development Bank Co., Ltd.
W391

A = AMERICAN BUSINESS
E = EMERGING COMPANIES
P = PRIVATE COMPANIES
W = WORLD BUSINESS

COL

Bogota
Ecopetrol SA W159

DEU

Wolfsburg
Volkswagen A.G. (Germany, Fed. Rep.)
W476

Duesseldorf
E.ON SE W158

Stuttgart
Daimler AG W142

Munich
Allianz SE W27

Ludwigshafen
BASF SE W74

Munich
Siemens AG (Germany) W394
Bayerische Motoren Werke AG W79

Duesseldorf
Metro AG W285

Munich
Muenchener Rueckversicherungs-
Gesellschaft AG (Germany) W299

Bonn
Deutsche Telekom AG W153
Deutsche Post RG W152
Deutsche Post AG W151

Essen
RWE AG W370

Frankfurt am Main
Deutsche Bank AG W149

Ingolstadt
AUDI AG Vormals Audi-NSU Auto
Union AG W45

Stuttgart
Landesbank Baden-Wurttemberg
W262

Leverkusen
Bayer AG W76

Essen
ThyssenKrupp AG W444

Hanover
Continental AG (Germany, Fed. Rep.)
W134

Frankfurt
Deutsche Lufthansa AG (Germany,
Fed. Rep.) W150

Hannover
Talanx AG W429

Duesseldorf
Ergo Versicherungsgruppe AG W164

Frankfurt am Main
DZ Bank AG Deutsche Zentral-
Genossenschaftsbank W157

Essen
Hochtief AG W209

Stuttgart
Celesio AG W112

Hanau
Heraeus Holding GmbH (Germany
Fed. Rep.) W204

Frankfurt am Main
Commerzbank AG (Germany, Fed.
Rep.) W128

Bad Homburg
Fresenius SE & Co KGaA W178

Hanover
TUI AG W456

Friedrichshafen
ZF Friedrichshafen AG (Germany)
W489

Duesseldorf
Henkel AG & Co KGAA W201

Guetersloh
Bertelsmann AG (Germany, Fed. Rep.)
W83

Walldorf
SAP AG W383

Munich
Man SE W276
Linde AG (Germany, Fed. Rep.) W268

Herzogenaurach
Adidas AG W12

Heidelberg
HeidelbergCement AG W196

Hannover
Hannover Rueckversicherung SE
W195

Hamburg
Otto Versand (GmbH & Co.)
(Germany, Fed. Rep.) W334

Munich
Bayerische Landesbank (Germany)
W78

Frankfurt am Main
Deutsche Bundesbank (Germany, Fed.
Rep.) W149

Bonn
Deutsche Postbank AG W153

Frankfurt am Main
Landesbank Hessen-Thueringen
Girozentrale (Helaba) (Germany,
Fed. Rep.) W264

Frankfurt
Dekabank Deutsche Girozentrale
W148

Berlin
Landesbank Berlin Holding AG
(Berlin) W263
Landesbank Berlin - Gironzentrale
(Germany, Fed. Rep.) W262

Frankfurt am Main
Landwirtschaftliche Rentenbank
(Germany, Fed. Rep.) W264

Duesseldorf
WestLB AG W481
Westdeutsche Genossenschafts-
Zentralbank EG (Germany, Fed.
Rep.) W481

Hamburg
Deutsche Genossenschafts-
Hypothekenbank (Germany, Fed.
Rep.) W

DNK

Copenhagen K
AP Moller AS W37
A.P. Moller - Maersk A/S W1
Danske Bank AS (Denmark) W146

Copenhagen C
Nordea Bank Denmark A/S W321

Bagsvaerd
Novo-Nordisk A/S W324

ESP

Madrid
Banco Santander SA W59
Telefonica, S.A. W433
Repsol S.A. W355

Bilbao
Banco Bilbao Vizcaya Argentaria SA
(BBVA) W55

Madrid
ACS Actividades de Construccion y
Servicios, S.A. W9
Iberdrola SA W222
Endesa S.A. W162

Barcelona
Gas Natural SDG, S.A. W185

Madrid
Mapfre SA W278

La Coruna
Industria De Diseno Textil (Inditex) SA
W227

Madrid
Fomento de Construcciones y
Contratas, S.A. W176

Barcelona
Banco De Sabadell SA W57

Madrid
Banco Popular Espanol, S.A. W58
Bankinter, S.A. W70

FIN

Espoo
Nokia Corp. W317

FRA

Courbevoie
Total S.A. W452

Paris
AXA S.A. W48
BNP Paribas (France) W89

Courbevoie
GDF SUEZ W188

Paris
Societe Generale W401

Boulogne-Billancourt
Carrefour S.A. W108

Paris
Peugeot S.A. (France) W341
CNP Assurances S.A. W125
Orange W332

Courbevoie
Compagnie de Saint-Gobain W130

Paris
Rallye S.A. W351

Saint-Etienne
Casino Guichard Perrachon S.A.
W110

Boulogne-Billancourt
Renault S.A. (France) W354

Rueil-Malmaison
Vinci SA W471

Paris
Sanofi W381
Schlumberger Ltd. W386
Bouygues S.A. W92
Christian Dior SA W123
Veolia Environnement W470
Vivendi W473
LVMH Moet Hennessy Louis Vuitton
W270
Air France-KLM W18

Rueil-Malmaison
Schneider Electric S.A. W386

Clermont-Ferrand
Compagnie Generale des
Etablissements Michelin (France)
W132

Paris
Danone W144

Levallois-Perret
Alstom W30

Issy-les-Moulineaux
Sodexo W402

Paris
L'Air Liquide S.A. (France) W
Safran S.A. W374
Alcatel-Lucent W24

Neuilly-sur-Seine
THALES W442

Boulogne-Billancourt
Colas SA Boulogne W126

Paris
Valeo S.A. (France) W468

GBR

London
BP p.l.c. W94
EDF Trading Ltd W160
HSBC Holdings Plc W216

Cheshunt
Tesco PLC (United Kingdom) W438

London
Internetq Plc, London W233
Prudential Plc W347
Lloyds Banking Group Plc W269
Aviva Plc (United Kingdom) W46
Unilever Plc (United Kingdom) W465

Newbury
Vodafone Group Plc W474

Victoria
BHP Billiton Plc W88

London
Legal & General Group PLC (United
Kingdom) W264
Barclays PLC W73
Barclays Bank Plc W72
Rio Tinto Plc W360

Bristol
Imperial Tobacco Group Plc W226

Perth
SSE PLC W409

Universal Electronics Inc. E511
Collectors Universe Inc E113

SANTA CLARA
Intel Corp A444
Applied Materials, Inc. A68
Agilent Technologies, Inc. A20
Svb Financial Group A761
Robinson Oil Corporation P438
President And Board Of Trustees Of
   Santa Clara College P414
Omnivision Technologies Inc E379
Svb Financial Group A761 E468
Coherent, Inc. E111

SANTA CLARITA
Henry Mayo Newhall Memorial
   Hospital P239

SANTA MONICA
Activision Blizzard, Inc. A8
Anworth Mortgage Asset Corp. A64
Demand Media Inc E142
Colony Financial Inc. E113

SANTA PAULA
Calavo Growers, Inc. E84

SANTA ROSA
Santa Rosa Memorial Hospital
   Inc P455

SHERMAN OAKS
Fruit Growers Supply Company
   Inc P208

SOUTH SAN FRANCISCO
Core Mark Holding Co Inc A221

STANFORD
Stanford University A741 P505

STOCKTON
Coastal Pacific Food Distributors
   Inc. P127
University Of The Pacific P610

SUNNYVALE
Netapp, Inc. A575
Advanced Micro Devices, Inc. A11
Yahoo! Inc. A882
Juniper Networks Inc A472
R.s. Hughes Company Inc. P425
Actiontec Electronics Inc. P4
Intuitive Surgical Inc E278
Trimble Navigation Ltd. E498
Fortinet Inc E200
Telenav, Inc. E481
Financial Engines Inc E193

TEMECULA
Genica Corporation P213

THOUSAND OAKS
Amgen Inc A57

TORRANCE
Toyota Motor Credit Corp. A799
Torrance Memorial Medical
   Center P575
Ocean Duke Corporation P380

TURLOCK
Yosemite Farm Credit Aca P657

UNION CITY
Abaxis, Inc. E6

VALENCIA
Wesco Aircraft Holdings Inc. E531

VAN NUYS
Valley Presbyterian Hospital P618
Electro Rent Corp. E168

WALNUT CREEK
Csaa Insurance Group P150

WEST COVINA
Citrus Valley Medical Center
   Inc. P122

WEST HOLLYWOOD
Cedars-sinai Medical Center P102

WEST SACRAMENTO
Raley's P426
River City Petroleum Inc. P436

WESTLAKE VILLAGE
Ltc Properties, Inc. E307

WHITTIER
Presbyterian Intercommunity Hospital
   Inc. P414
The Oltmans Construction Co P557

WOODLAND
St John's Retirement Village P493

WOODLAND HILLS
Health Net, Inc. A408

YUBA CITY
Sunsweet Growers Inc. P518

COLORADO

AURORA
Graebel Companies Inc. P219
Aurora Public Schools P38

BOULDER
University Corporation For
   Atmospheric Research P598

BROOMFIELD
Ball Corp A91
Level 3 Communications, Inc. A502
Mwh Global Inc. P351

CENTENNIAL
Western States Fire Protection
   Company Inc P639

COLORADO SPRINGS
Compassion International Inc P135
Young Life P657
Intelligent Software Solutions
   Inc. P260

DENVER
Davita Healthcare Partners Inc A240
Cobiz Financial Inc A195
Pcl Construction Enterprises
   Inc P397
Exempla Inc. P186
Colorado Seminary P130
Alta Colleges Inc. P16
Whiting Petroleum Corp E535
Dcp Midstream Partners Lp E138
M.d.c. Holdings, Inc. E312
Intrepid Potash Inc E277
Royal Gold, Inc. E426
Hallador Energy Co E231

DURANGO
Saddle Butte Pipeline Llc P447

ENGLEWOOD
Arrow Electronics, Inc. A73
Dish Network Corp A256
Liberty Interactive Corp A505
Western Union Co. A865
Ihs Inc E263
Air Methods Corp. E20
Csg Systems International Inc. E130

EVERGREEN
Catamount Constructors Inc. P99

FORT COLLINS
Colorado State University P131
Otter Products Llc P388

Woodward, Inc. E541
Advanced Energy Industries Inc. E14

GOLDEN
Alliance For Sustainable Energy
   Llc P14

GRAND JUNCTION
St. Mary's Hospital & Medical Center
   Inc P503
Fci Constructors Inc. P193

GREELEY
Pilgrims Pride Corp. A642
Hensel Phelps Construction Co P240

GREENWOOD VILLAGE
Newmont Mining Corp. (holding
   Co.) A580
Great-west Life & Annuity Insurance
   Co. A387
Xanterra Holding Corp P654
Parks Xanterra & Resorts Inc P395
Xanterra Inc. P654

LAKEWOOD
Mesa Laboratories, Inc. E335

LONGMONT
Digitalglobe Inc E147

NIWOT
Crocs Inc E128

PLATTEVILLE
Synergy Resources Corp E474

CONNECTICUT

BLOOMFIELD
Cigna Corp A178
Metlife Insurance Company Of
   Connecticut A546

BRIDGEPORT
People's United Financial, Inc. A632
Bridgeport Hospital P79
Bridgeport Hospital & Healthcare
   Services Inc P79

CHESHIRE
The Lane Construction
   Corporation P548
Lane Industries Incorporated P294
Alexion Pharmaceuticals Inc. E23

CLINTON
Connecticut Water Service, Inc. E117

DANBURY
Praxair, Inc. A653
Hospital The Danbury Inc P251
Danbury Hospital Development Fund
   Inc P154

DARIEN
Genesee & Wyoming Inc. E213

FAIRFIELD
General Electric Co A366
Fairfield University P187

GREENWICH
Berkley (w. R.) Corp. A113
Tudor Investment Corporation P587
Greenwich Hospital Association
   Inc P222
Starwood Property Trust Inc. E460

HAMDEN
Quinnipiac University P424

HARTFORD
United Technologies Corp. A829
Aetna Inc. A16
Hartford Financial Services Group
   Inc. A403

Hartford Hospital P231
Saint Francis Hospital And Medical
   Center P449
Connecticut State University
   System P136
Connecticut Children's Medical
   Center P136
Virtus Investment Partners, Inc E522

MIDDLETOWN
Wesleyan University P636

MILFORD
Doctor's Associates Inc. P163
Ebp Supply Solutions P172

NEW BRITAIN
Stanley Black & Decker, Inc. A741
Hospital Of Central Connecticut P250
James M D Hoffman P268

NEW CANAAN
Csc Sugar Llc P150

NEW HAVEN
Knights Of Columbus P288
Uil Holding Corp E501
Higher One Holdings Inc. E248

NEW LONDON
Lawrence & Memorial Hospital
   Inc. P294

NORWALK
Xerox Corp A880
Emcor Group, Inc. A285
Priceline.com, Inc. A656
Norwalk Health Services
   Corporation P374
The Norwalk Hospital
   Association P557
Factset Research Systems Inc. E188

OLD GREENWICH
Ellington Financial Llc E170

RIDGEFIELD
Northern Tier Energy Lp A593

ROCKVILLE
Rockville Financial, Inc. E423

ROGERS
Rogers Corp. E424

SHELTON
Prudential Annuities Life Assurance
   Corp A668

SIMSBURY
Hartford Life Insurance Co A404

SOUTHPORT
Sturm, Ruger & Co., Inc. E464

STAMFORD
Charter Communications Inc A170
Starwood Hotels & Resorts Worldwide
   Inc A745
Frontier Communications Corp A358
United Rentals, Inc. A824
Pitney Bowes Inc A644
Navigators Group, Inc. (the) A571
Lexa International Corporation P298
Americares Foundation Inc. P23
Star Gas Partners L.p. E459
Hexcel Corp. E243

WATERBURY
Webster Financial Corp (waterbury,
   Conn) A855
The Waterbury Hospital P570

WEST HARTFORD
The University Of Hartford P567

WESTPORT
Terex Corp. A781

NEVADA

CARSON CITY
Carson Tahoe Regional
Healthcare P97

HENDERSON
Global Pacific Produce Inc. P217
Spectrum Pharmaceuticals Inc E456

LAS VEGAS
Las Vegas Sands Corp A496
Mgm Resorts International A549
Caesars Entertainment Corp A141
Wynn Resorts Ltd A878
Cannery Casino Resorts Llc P90
M & H Enterprises Inc. P306
Allegiant Travel Company E25
Full House Resorts, Inc. E206

RENO
Employers Holdings Inc A288

NEW HAMPSHIRE

CONCORD
Concord Hospital Inc. P135

LEBANON
Dartmouth-hitchcock Medical
Center P155

LEE
University System Of New
Hampshire P614

MANCHESTER
Elliot Hospital Of The City Of
Manchester P178
Catholic Medical Center P101

NASHUA
Southern New Hampshire Medical
Center P485

PEMBROKE
Associated Grocers Of New England
Inc. P33

NEW JERSEY

BEDMINSTER
Peapack-gladstone Financial
Corp. E391

BLOOMFIELD
World Finer Foods Inc P650

BRANCHVILLE
Selective Insurance Group Inc A718

BRIDGEWATER
Somerset Tire Service Inc. P481
Synchronoss Technologies Inc E473

CAMDEN
Campbell Soup Co. A146
Our Lady Of Lourdes Medical Center
Inc P389

CRANFORD
Mack-cali Realty L. P. A518 P307

DENVILLE
Saint Clare's Hospital Inc. P448

EDISON
Jfk Health System Inc. P272
The Community Hospital Group
Inc P538
Conti Enterprises Inc. P140

ELIZABETH
Atalanta Corporation P35

ELMWOOD PARK
Sealed Air Corp. A716
Bio-reference Laboratories, Inc. E60

EWING
Universal Display Corp E510

FAIRFIELD
Kearny Financial Corp A475
Kmm Telecommunications P288

FLANDERS
Rudolph Technologies, Inc. E428

FORT LEE
Wicked Fashions Inc. P642

FRANKLIN LAKES
Becton, Dickinson And Co. A109

FREEHOLD
Centrastate Healthcare System
Inc P107
Monmouth Real Estate Investment
Corp E346

HACKENSACK
Hackensack University Medical
Center P228

HOBOKEN
Stevens Institute Of Technology
(inc) P508

JERSEY CITY
Provident Financial Services Inc A667
Jersey City Medical Center Inc P271
Verisk Analytics Inc E520

KEASBEY
Wakefern Food Corp. A847 P627

LINDEN
Turtle & Hughes Inc P587

LITTLE FALLS
Cantel Medical Corp E87

LIVINGSTON
St Barnabas Medical Center Inc P492

LONG BRANCH
Monmouth Medical Center Inc. P343

LONG VALLEY
Frazier Industrial Company P205

MADISON
Quest Diagnostics, Inc. A678
Realogy Holdings Corp A686
Realogy Group Llc A686
Zoetis Inc A888

MARLTON
Holtec International
Corporation P248

MATAWAN
Creative Management Inc P146

MILLBURN
Hatch Mott Macdonald Group
Inc. P231

MONTCLAIR
Montclair State University P345

MONTVALE
Aep Industries Inc E18

MORRIS TOWNSHIP
Honeywell International, Inc. A420

MORRISTOWN
Covanta Holding Corp A226
Atlantic Health System Inc. P36
Ahs Hospital Corp. P8

MOUNT HOLLY
Memorial Hospital Of Burlington
County (inc) P327

NEW BRUNSWICK
Johnson & Johnson A465
Johnson & Johnson Patient Assistance
Foundation Inc P275
St Peter's University Hospital P495

NEWARK
Prudential Financial, Inc. A668
Public Service Enterprise Group
Inc. A670
Pseg Power Llc A669
Newark Beth Israel Medical Center
Inc. P364
New Jersey Institute Of
Technology P359

NORTH BERGEN
Vitamin Shoppe Inc E523

OAK RIDGE
Lakeland Bancorp, Inc. A494

OCEANPORT
Commvault Systems Inc E115

PARAMUS
Hudson City Bancorp Inc A428

PARK RIDGE
Hertz Global Holdings Inc A412

PARSIPPANY
Avis Budget Group Inc A86
Wyndham Worldwide Corp A877
Medicines Co (the) E327

PATERSON
St. Joseph's Hospital And Medical
Center P499

PENNSAUKEN
J&j Snack Foods Corp. E285

PERTH AMBOY
Raritan Bay Medical Center. P428

POINT PLEASANT BEACH
Norkus Enterprises Inc. P366

POINT PLEASANT BORO
Claremont Health System Inc P124

POMONA
Atlanticare Regional Medical
Center P37

PRINCETON
Nrg Energy Inc A598
Educational Testing Service Inc P174
Princeton Healthcare System A New
Jersey Nonprofit Corporation P417

PRINCETON JUNCTION
Mistras Group, Inc. E343

RIDGEWOOD
The Valley Hospital Inc P567

ROCHELLE PARK
Orbcomm Inc E382

ROSELAND
Automatic Data Processing Inc. A80

SHORT HILLS
Investors Bancorp Inc A458
Roseland Partners L.l.c. P443
Investors Bancorp Inc A458 E279

SOMERS POINT
Shore Memorial Hospital P475

SOMERSET
Shi International Corp. A722 P475

SOMERVILLE
Somerset Medical Center P480

SOUTH ORANGE
Seton Hall University P468

SUMMIT
Celgene Corp. A162

SWEDESBORO
Global Trading Enterprises Llc P217

TEANECK
Cognizant Technology Solutions
Corp. A199
Fairleigh Dickinson University P187

TOWNSHIP OF WASHINGTON
Oritani Financial Corp (de) E383

UNION
Bed, Bath & Beyond, Inc. A110

VINELAND
Sun Bancorp Inc. (nj) A754
Riggins Inc. P435

VOORHEES
Kennedy Memorial Hospital University
Medical Center Inc P283
Kennedy Health System Inc. P282

WARREN
Chubb Corp. A176

WAYNE
Valley National Bancorp A838
The William Paterson University Of
New Jersey P572

WEST ORANGE
Green Hill Inc P221

WESTVILLE
Brown's Super Stores Inc. P83

WHIPPANY
Stephen Gould Corporation P507
Suburban Propane Partners L.p. E465

WHITEHOUSE STATION
Merck & Co., Inc A541

NEW MEXICO

ALBUQUERQUE
Summit Electric Supply Co. Inc P516
Applied Research Associates Inc. P28

ESPANOLA
Akal Security Inc. P8

SANTA FE
St. Vincent Hospital P504

NEW YORK

ALBANY
The Research Foundation Of State
University Of New York P558
Capital District Physicians' Health
Plan Inc. P91
State University Construction
Fund P506
Albany Medical Center Hospital P11
St Peter's Health Care Services P495

AMITYVILLE
Hi-tech Pharmacal Co., Inc. E246

ANNANDALE ON HUDSON
Bard College P46

ARDSLEY
Acorda Therapeutics Inc E12

PURCHASE

Pepsico Inc. A634
Mastercard Inc A528
Tal International Group Inc E477

REGO PARK

New York State Catholic Health Plan
Inc P363

RENSSELAER

The New York Independent System
Operator Inc P555

ROCHESTER

Closing Usa Llc A190 P126
Rochester City School District P439
Rochester General Hospital Inc P439
Rochester Institute Of Technology
(inc) P439
Monro Muffler Brake, Inc. E348

ROCKVILLE CENTRE

Mercy Medical Center P331

ROSLYN

St Francis Hospital P492

RYE

Jarden Corp. A462
Gamco Investors Inc E210

SCHENECTADY

The Golub Corporation P543
Ellis Hospital P179
Trustees Of Union College In The
Town Of Schenectady In The
Stat P586

SHIRLEY

Clare Rose Inc. P124

SLEEPY HOLLOW

Phelps Memorial Hospital
Association P402

STATEN ISLAND

Key Food Stores Co-operative
Inc. P284

SUFFERN

Ascena Retail Group Inc A74

SYRACUSE

Syracuse University P523
Src Tec Inc. P491
St. Joseph's Hospital Health
Center P500
O'brien & Gere Limited P377

TARRYTOWN

Regeneron Pharmaceuticals,
Inc. E415
Prestige Brands Holdings Inc E401

UNIONDALE

Open Link Financial Inc. P383

VALHALLA

New York Medical College P361

VALLEY STREAM

Franklin Hospital P204

WARSAW

Financial Institutions Inc. A326

WEST NYACK

The Salvation Army P560

WESTBURY

New York Community Bancorp
Inc. A578

WESTFIELD

National Grape Co-operative
Association Inc. P353

WHITE PLAINS

Bunge Ltd. A101

New York Power Authority P362
March Of Dimes Foundation P312
Drew Industries, Inc. E151
Fifth Street Finance Corp E192

YONKERS

Hudson Valley Holding Corp. A429
Consumers Union Of United States
Inc P139

NORTH CAROLINA

BOONE

Samaritan's Purse P453

BURLINGTON

Laboratory Corp. Of America
Holdings A493
Burlington Health Care Center (66)
Inc. P85
Alamance Regional Medical Center
Inc. P9

CANTON

Silver Bluff Llc P477

CARY

Pantry Inc. (the) A625
Cary Oil Co. Inc. P98
Coc Properties Inc. P128
Wake County Public School
System P627

CHAPEL HILL

University Of North Carolina
Hospitals P604
Investors Title Co. E280

CHARLOTTE

Bank Of America Corp. A95
Duke Energy Corp A273
Nucor Corp. A599
Sonic Automotive, Inc. A728
Spx Corp. A737
Charlotte Health Care Center (68)
Inc P111
Premier Healthcare Solutions
Inc. P412
Presbyterian Hospital P413
Premier Purchasing Partners
L.p. P413
Crowder Construction Company
Inc P149

CHERRYVILLE

Carolina Care Center Of Cherryville
Inc. P96

CLINTON

Sampson-bladen Oil Company
Incorporated P454

DURHAM

Quintiles Transnational Holdings
Inc A680
The North Carolina Mutual Wholesale
Drug Company P556
Research Triangle Institute Inc P433
M. M. Fowler Inc. P307
Durham Public Schools P168
Family Health International Inc P190
American Institute Of Certified Public
Accountants P20
Cree, Inc. E126

FAYETTEVILLE

Carolina Healthcare Center Of
Cumberland Lp P96
Cumberland County Hospital System
Inc. P151
Cumberland County Schools P151

GASTONIA

Belaire Health Care Center Inc. P57
Caromont Health Inc. P96

Gaston Memorial Hospital Inc P211

GOLDSBORO

Southco Distributing Company P483

GREENSBORO

Vf Corp. A841
Lorillard, Inc. A514
The Moses H Cone Memorial
Hospital P554
Guilford County School System P224
Market America Inc. P314
Fresh Market, Inc. E205
Tanger Factory Outlet Centers,
Inc. E477
Carolina Bank Holdings Inc E91

GREENVILLE

University Health Systems Of Eastern
Carolina Inc. P599
Pitt County Memorial Hospital
Incorporated P406

HIGH POINT

Bnc Bancorp A123
High Point Regional Health
System P242
Culp Inc. E133
Bnc Bancorp A123 E67

JACKSON

Hampton Woods Health &
Rehabilitation Center P230

KINSTON

Hillco Ltd. P244

MATTHEWS

Family Dollar Stores, Inc. A310

MOORESVILLE

Lowe's Companies Inc A515

MORGANTON

Grace Heights Health And
Rehabilitation Centre P219

MOUNT AIRY

Central Continuing Care Inc. P104
Pike Corp P395
Insteel Industries, Inc. E271

MOUNT GILEAD

Mcrae Industries, Inc. E324

PINEHURST

Firsthealth Of The Carolinas
Inc. P196
Moore Regional Hospital P346

PLEASANT GARDEN

Clapp S Nursing Center Inc. P123

RALEIGH

First Citizens Bancshares, Inc.
(nc) A331
North Carolina Electric Membership
Corporation P366
Wakemed P628
Rex Healthcare Inc. P433
Rex Hospital Inc. P434
Bjt Inc. P65
Coastal Federal Credit Union P127
Red Hat Inc E414
Salix Pharmaceuticals Ltd E429
Triangle Capital Corp E497

ROCKY MOUNT

Boddie-noell Enterprises Inc. P74

SANFORD

Static Control Components Inc. P506

SOUTHERN PINES

First Bancorp (nc) A328
St Joseph Of The Pines Inc P494

STATESVILLE

Energyunited Electric Membership
Corporation P183
Carolina Farm Credit Aca P96

THOMASVILLE

Old Dominion Freight Line,
Inc. E377

WILMINGTON

New Hanover Regional Medical
Center P359

WILSON

Wilmed Nursing Care Center P645

WINSTON SALEM

Wake Forest Baptist Medical
Center P627
Quality Oil Company Llc P423
Winston-salem/forsyth County
Schools P647
Hatteras Financial Corp E233

WINSTON-SALEM

Bb&t Corp. A106
Reynolds American Inc A695
Hanesbrands Inc A396

NORTH DAKOTA

BISMARCK

Bank Of North Dakota (bismarck,
N.d.) A99
North Dakota University System P367
St. Alexius Medical Center P496

FARGO

Rdo Equipment Co P429
Sanford North P455
Sanford Clinic North P454
Dakota Supply Group Inc. P153
Eide Bailly Llp P175

GRAND FORKS

University Of North Dakota P604
North Dakota Mill & Elevator
Association Inc P367

MINOT

Spf Energy Inc. P491
Farstad Oil Inc. P192

WEST FARGO

Titan Machinery, Inc. E492

WILLISTON

Horizon Resources P250

OHIO

AKRON

Goodyear Tire & Rubber Co. A381
Firstenergy Corp. A340
Firstmerit Corp A342
Childrens Hospital Medical Center Of
Akron P117
Summa Health System P515

BATAVIA

Multi-color Corp. E354

BLUE ASH

Belcan Corporation P57
Belcan Engineering Group Inc. P57

CANTON

Timken Co. (the) A794
Fresh Mark Inc. P207

CHARDON

Fml Holdings Inc P200

CHILLICOTHE

Adena Health System P4

Index of Executives

A

A-nanthothai, Thongchai W61
A.V.K., Mohan E184
Aa, Terry L. Van Der P566
Aa, Richard Olav W435
Aagaard-Svendsen, Birgit W147
Aagard, Tammy P614
Aaholm, Sherry A. A232
Aaholm, Sherry A. A321
Aaker, Tom W411
Aakre, D. Scott A423
Aal, Irvin E. E538
Aanensen, Theodore J. A475
Aanestad, Ola M. W414
Aardsma, David A. (Dave) A854
Aardsma, Wayne P477
Aaron, Barth F. E206
Aaron, Sammy E209
Aaron, Carol P398
Aaron, Clay M. P509
Aaron, Todd S. P509
Aaron, Steven L. P509
Aaron, Todd S. P509
Aaser, Svein W435
Aasheim, Kristine M. P609
Aasnaes, Hans W415
Aasved, Craig P495
Abad, Gary E188
Abad, Alfredo Saenz W60
Abad, Roberto Lopez W457
Abadessa, Virginia P384
Abadie, Laurent W338
Abadin, Antonio Abril W228
Abadir, Nabil P228
Aballo, Paul G. P162
Abanumay, Mohammed S. W385
Abate, Thomas M. E166
Abate, Rene W110
Abatti, Mike P255
Abbasi, Sohaib E270
Abbasi, Sohaib E414
Abbasi, Osama W139
Abbate, Mark L. E333
Abbatecola, Vincent P. E254
Abbeele, Annick D. Van den P154
Abbey, Douglas E45
Abbey, Richard E. A768
Abbey, Ellen P572
Abbot, Edward A. P163
Abbott, James A. A548
Abbott, Mark A684
Abbott, Dean A689
Abbott, Frederick C. (Fred) A819
Abbott, James R. A888
Abbott, Jon P420
Abbott, Cal P529
Abbott, John W370
Abboud, Ali El A749
Abdalla, Zein A635
Abdalla, Zein A796
Abdelnour, Gaby A. A471
Abdo, Hatem P205
Abdoo, Richard A. (Dick) A27
Abdoo, Elizabeth A. A426

Abdoo, Richard A. A587
Abdul-Latif, Saad A635
Abdullah, Jon Eddy W435
Abdun-Nabi, Daniel J. E171
Abe, Ken W295
Abe, Ken W296
Abe, Yasushi W307
Abe, Yasuyuki W417
Abe, Yasuyuki W418
Abe, Ken W468
Abel, Leonard L. E160
Abel, Paul E. E466
Abel, Gregory E. (Greg) A115
Abel, Leonard L. A276
Abel, Virginia K. A617
Abel, Gregory E. (Greg) A623
Abel, James E. A652
Abel, Dawn P632
Abele, John E. A132
Abelenda, Gustavo H. A559
Abell, Elaine D. E256
Abell, Elaine D. A436
Abella, Roland W156
Abelli, Donna L. A440
Abello, Vincent W109
Abelson, Sigmund H. P611
Abely, Susan Cerrone P441
Abendschein, Robert D. A61
Aber, John D. P614
Aber, Suzanne (Sue) P620
Aberdeen, Jeffery D. A206
Aberle, Derek K. A676
Aberle, Jim P655
Aberman, Michael E415
Abernathy, Kathleen Q. A358
Abernathy, Robert E. A482
Abernethy, Hugh E139
Abernethy, Janet D. A329
Abersoch, Lord E. Mervyn Davies of W156
Abi-Karam, Leslie R. A645
Abitabilo, Louis J. E371
Abji, Minaz B. A426
Able, Michael W300
Ables, Dorothy M. A735
Abney, David P. A468
Abney, David P. A824
Abney, Donna A. P334
Abogado, Scott E91
Abood, Steve A689
Aboodi, Henry J. P78
Aboud, Mark W384
Aboulafia, Itzhak W63
Abouljoud, Marwan S. P239
Aboumrad, Daniel Hajj W32
Abounader, Charlie P590
Abraham, Cecelia M. E172
Abraham, Allison H. E386
Abraham, Chad R. E397
Abraham, Cecelia M. A289
Abraham, Spencer A604
Abraham, Karen P71
Abraham, Leopold W332
Abrahamowicz, Dan P652
Abrahams, Samuel W235
Abrahamsson, Jonas W159

Abramcheck, Frank J. E257
Abramowicz, Daniel A. A228
Abramowitsch, Peter E329
Abramowitz, Kenneth S. (Ken) E22
Abrams, David C. E129
Abrams, Leigh J. E152
Abrams, Robin E189
Abrams, Bruce R. A53
Abrams, David C. A161
Abrams, George S. A842
Abrams, Jon F. P267
Abrams, Jim P267
Abrams, David P368
Abramson, Steven V. E510
Abramson, Steven V. E511
Abramson, Joel A15
Abramson, Andrew B. A838
Abramson, Richard P491
Abramson, Morrie K. P550
Abravanel, Isaac (Ika) W441
Abravanel, Roger W441
Abreu, Steven M. (Steve) A39
Abreu, Domingos W57
Abreu, Antonio W161
Abrial, Francois W261
Abriola, Linda M. P586
Abrouk, Nacer E. Dean E156
Abruzzese, Joseph (Joe) A255
Abruzzo, Cloyd J. E441
Abston, Larry J. A61
Abts, Douglas C. E73
Abu-Hadba, Walid E44
Abu-Nasrah, Khaled A475
Aburatani, Yoshihiro Yoshihiro Aburatani W452
Abzug, Barry M. A703
Accomando, Marianna P615
Accum, Claude A. W422
Ace, Heather E525
Ace, Brian R. A209
Acevedo, Jorge A. A301
Aceves, Salvador P607
Ach, J. Wickliffe E196
Ach, J. Wickliffe A333
Achary, Michael M. E231
Achary, Michael M. A395
Achatz, Reinhold W396
ACHE, Jennifer Weiss Wilkerson P544
Achleitner, Paul W78
Achleitner, Paul W144
Achleitner, Paul W371
Achten, Dominik von W197
Achurra, Emiliano W185
Ackart, Jennifer C. A684
Acker, Kristin E547
Acker, Laurens G. van den W355
Ackerley, Margaret L. P651
Ackerman, Jeffrey (Jeff) E206
Ackerman, F. Duane A38
Ackerman, Paul R. A315
Ackerman, F. Duane A419
Ackerman, Joel A485
Ackerman, F. Duane A824
Ackerman, Jeff P4
Ackerman, Denise P46
Ackermann, Josef W370

Ackermann, Josef W395
Ackermann, Josef W396
Ackermann, Josef W491
Ackermann, Josef W492
Ackerson, Vince A. E486
Ackerson, Vince A. A784
Ackley, Sheri P613
Ackman, William A. A631
Acosta, Fernando J. A90
Acosta, Arcilia C. A292
Acosta, Lydia M. P375
Acranis, Tina W278
Acuff, A. Marshall A618
Adachi, Yoroku (Joe) W105
Adachi, Yoroku (Joe) W106
Adachi, Michio W149
Adachi, Toshio W390
Adachi, Naoki W448
Adachi, Takemi Takemi Adachi W452
Adachi, Seiichiro W456
Adair, A. Jayson E121
Adair, James R. A546
Adair, Charles E. (Eddie) A775
Adair, Charles E. (Eddie) A798
Adair, Don P522
Adair-Potts, Janna A771
Adali, Erhan W459
Adam, Don E301
Adam, Deborah J. A853
Adam, Annette W335
Adam, Herve W472
Adamany, Linda W305
Adamczyk, Marilyn P187
Adami, Norman J. W373
Adamo, Nicholas A. (Nick) A181
Adamo, Victor T. A660
Adamo, Emma Emma Adamo W42
Adams, Timothy M. (Tim) E49
Adams, Adrian E51
Adams, Fred R. E83
Adams, Mark E178
Adams, Joseph P. E202
Adams, Kenneth R (Ken) E206
Adams, Lynn E213
Adams, Robbin B. E219
Adams, Matthew E277
Adams, Robert C. E339
Adams, W. Andrew (Andy) E360
Adams, Mark L. E375
Adams, Alan S. (Al) E405
Adams, Byron K. E505
Adams, Byron K. E506
Adams, Kelly A23
Adams, Rex D. A32
Adams, Diana A45
Adams, Robert D. A101
Adams, Richard C. A104
Adams, Robin J. A130
Adams, John A143
Adams, Kent M. A155
Adams, Kevin D. A170
Adams, Tom A171
Adams, Thomas E. A171
Adams, Harold L. A208
Adams, John L. A269
Adams, Richard L. A290

Blanchard, James H. (Jim) A79
Blanchard, Robert W. A569
Blanchard, William R. (Billy) A767
Blanchard, James H. (Jim) A767
Blanchard, Eric A. A829
Blanchard, Cheryl R. A887
Blanchet, Paul J. E252
Blanchet, Michael C. (Mike) P134
Blanchfield, Molly P191
Blanck, Susan R. A18
Blanck, Ronald R. P365
Blanco, Santiago A197
Blanco, Alex A282
Blanco, Rafael Bermejo W56
Blanco, Alejandro Alvarez W352
Blanco, Paulina Beato W356
Bland, Christopher P188
Bland, Donald P637
Blandford, Rob P606
Blanford, Lawrence J. (Larry) A389
Blangiardi, Richard J. A166
Blank, Matthew C. (Matt) E212
Blank, Simone E447
Blank, Matthew C. (Matt) A160
Blank, Stephen R. A547
Blank, Steven A. (Steve) A601
Blank, Arthur M. A744
Blank, Kenneth (Ken) P526
Blank, Rebecca M. P613
Blank, Ingrid Jonasson W436
Blankemeyer, Bob A540
Blankenhorn, David P163
Blankenship, Charles P. (Chip) A368
Blankenship, Walter (Smokey) P404
Blankfein, Lloyd C. A380
Blankfield, Bryan J. A617
Blankshain, Mona P144
Blas, Jessica A368
Blaschke, Terrence F. E156
Blase, William A. (Bill) A79
Blaser, Brian J. A4
Blasi, Simone W234
Blasing, Karen E227
Blasingame, David T. P569
Blastland, Dermot W458
Blatt, Louis E392
Blau, Bennett A265
Blau, Peter W159
Blaylock, Ronald E. (Ron) A114
Blaylock, Ronald E. (Ron) A153
Blazer, Randolph C. (Rand) E381
Blazheev, Victor W329
Blazier, Rick P487
Blazquez, Nicholas B. (Nick) W155
Blazquez, Pedro Azagra W223
Blazye, Andrew E198
Bleasel, Len W350
Bledsoe, Alvin E467
Bledsoe, W. Earl P550
Bleeker, Gary L. P226
Bleicken, Linda M. P214
Blend, Michael L. E142
Bleser, Philip F. A471
Bleser, Philip F. P391
Bleske, Mitchell A805
Blessing, William R. (Bill) A474
Blessing, Martin W128
Blevins, Barbara E480
Blevins, Rody P623
Bley, Daniel H. A855
Bleyleben, Peter R. E337
Blickle, John C. A342
Bliesmer, Allan J. P240
Bligh, Margaret M. P430
Blight, Andrew R. E13
Blincow, Andrew W410
Blinder, David P562
Blinn, Mark A. A346
Bliss, Stewart A. E455

Bliss, Tyrone J. A101
Bliwas, Ronald L. (Ron) E479
Bliwas, Ronald L. (Ron) A772
Blixt, Dianne Neal A515
Blobel, Friedhelm E434
Bloch, Simon E332
Bloch, Richard L. A187
Bloch, Thomas M. P348
Block, Andrew E80
Block, Peter E307
Block, Arthur R. A203
Block, Keith G. A615
Block, Susan D. P154
Block, Ellen P566
Block, Vicki P628
Blocker, Adrian M. A867
Blodgett, Lynn R. A881
Blodgett, Tom A881
Blodnick, Michael J. (Mick) A378
Bloem, James H. (Jim) A430
Bloemker, Sylvia A92
Blogs, Perry E521
Blok, Eelco W256
Blom, David P. P382
Blomquist, Brian A433
Blomquist, Steven R. (Steve) A459
Blomquist, Per-Arne W436
Blomqvist, Anders W401
Blood, Larry E272
Bloodworth, Lucian F. A660
Bloom, Bill E184
Bloom, Carrie E519
Bloom, Mike A235
Bloom, Michael K. A311
Bloom, Douglas P. A735
Bloom, Ellen P139
Bloom, Margaret L. P315
Bloom, Joel S. A360
Bloom, Jordan P394
Bloom, Floyd E. P562
Bloom, Floyd E. P570
Bloomberg, Lawrence S. W302
Bloomfield, Douglas (Doug) E373
Bloomfield, Doug E373
Bloomquist, Steve J. A758
Bloss, Bradley A495
Blosser, Courtney E391
Blouin, Scott E. P28
Blouin, Ann Scott P277
Blount, W. Frank A156
Blount, Michael A212
Blount, W. Frank A295
Blount, Daniel J. A384
Blount, Susan L. A669
Blount, W. Frank W25
Blowers, David C. (Dave) A594
Blowers, Julie P439
Blubaugh, Sharon E. A626
Blucas, Ted P444
Blue, John E109
Blue, Robert M. (Bob) A262
Blue, Daniel T. A329
Blue, Frank W. A565
Bluestone, Marisa A740
Bluford, John W. P584
Bluhm, Nancy A. P69
Bluhm, Neil P399
Blum, Peter H. E344
Blum, Donald W. E406
Blum, Michael E517
Blum, Richard C. A158
Blum, Jonathan D. A485
Blum, Kristen E. A631
Blum, Donald W. A664
Blum, Donald W. A667
Blum, Jonathan D. A885
Blum, Blair P455
Blum, Jonathan P563
Blum, Clemens W387
Blumberg, David E259
Blumer, David A122
Blumofe, Robert E21
Blunck, Thomas W300
Blunt, Matt E121
Blunt, Mary L. P467

Bluntzer, Rick E187
Bluntzer, James R. (Rick) A602
Blust, Roby P315
Bluth, Thomas J. (Tom) A155
Bluth, Mark J. A576
Blutt, Mitchell J. E410
Bly, Mark W95
Blyth, Lord James A63
Blythe, James C. A627
Bo, Qiliang W339
Bo+?l, Nicolas W407
Boake, Douglas E382
Boal, Greg W47
Boals, Richard L. (Rich) P71
Boas, Marie A. A626
Boast, Jerrel P270
Boat, Thomas F. P114
Bob, Robert E373
Bob, Bruce A. P244
Bobak, Thomas R. A774
Bobay, Nicholas E. A300
Bobins, Norman R. (Norm) E3
Bobins, Norman R. (Norm) E405
Bobins, Norman R. (Norm) A659
Bobko, Gary E18
Bobo, Donald E. E166
Bobo, Lawrence D. P21
Bobrinskoy, Charles K. (Charlie) E271
Bocardo, Carlo P88
Boccard, Georges-Antoine W54
Boccassino, Piero W234
Boccolini, Giovanni W234
Bochenek, David R. A446
Bochniarz, Henryka W463
Bocian, Peter J. (Pete) A471
Bocian, Peter J. (Pete) A708
Bock, Thomas E23
Bock, Lawrence A. (Larry) E190
Bock, David R. E369
Bock, William G. (Bill) E445
Bock, Laszlo A383
Bock, Greg P379
Bock, Kurt W. W76
Bockel, David R. E191
Bockel, David R. A324
Bockhorst, Daniel E97
Bockhorst, Thomas A. P353
Boddapati, Sam E22
Bodde, David L. E224
Boddie, William L. (Bill) P74
Boddie, Mike P74
Boddie, Nick B. P74
Bode, John S. E492
Bode, Susan D. A774
Bode, Hank P39
Bode, Jorg W477
Bodecker, Sandy A586
Bodell, Bradley (Brad) A193
Bodenbender, Jim A536
Bodenheimer, Furman P. E470
Bodenheimer, George W. A258
Bodenheimer, Henry C. P62
Bodlovic, Kirk P495
Bodman, Samuel W. A414
Bodwell, Mark A244
Body, Serge W127
Boebinger, Michael A359
Boecke, William W. E250
Boecking, Tom A334
Boeckmann, Alan L. A720
Boeckmann, Alan L. W87
Boeckmann, Alan L. W88
Boehm, William E366
Boehm, Don P68
Boehm-Bezing, Carl-Ludwig W371
Boehm-Bezing, Carl Ludwig von W371
Boehm-Bezing, Carl-Ludwig W371
Boehms, Dennis P178
Boehne, Edward G. A113
Boekhoff, Hannes W135
Boel, Nicolas W407
Boenning, Dickson G. A853
Boer, Ralf R. E398
Boer, Adrian P373
Boer, A. Dick W255

Boerke, David C. A95
Boerm, Chris A72
Boersig, Clemens Clemens
  Boersig W144
Boersma, Rochelle J. A826
Boesch, Marc A796
Boesch, Dina Dina Boesch W300
Boese, Christine P432
Boesenberg, Charles M. (Chuck) E70
Boethius, Ulrika W425
Boettcher, Rene A99
Boeuf, Daniel W454
Bogan, Thomas E409
Bogan, Marc J. A56
Bogan, Willie C. A536
Bogard, Richard L. (Dick) P113
Bogard, Tom P385
Bogart, Karen E347
Bogart, Karen A555
Bogart, Thomas A. W421
Bogarty, W. J. W448
Bogdan, Jim E521
Bogdan, Thomas J. P598
Bogden, Gordon E426
Bogert, L. Michael E110
Boggan, Daniel A189
Boggs, Thomas Hale P396
Boggs, Douglas C. (Doug) P396
Bogner, Glen A556
Boguski, Michael E159
Bohan, David J. P468
Bohannon, Lon M. E366
Bohanon, David P423
Bohart, Stuart H. (Stu) E202
Bohbrink, Marshall A392
Bohbrink, Marshall P223
Bohen, Frederick M. (Fred) A66
Bohigian, Catherine A171
Bohlen, Patricia P36
Bohlooli, Keyvan A706
Bohlsen, John E56
Bohman, Diane R. E249
Bohmer, Sascha A709
Bohmer, Gregor W263
Bohn, Christopher D. (Chris) A169
Bohn, Robert G. (Bob) A629
Bohne, Meg P139
Bohnett, David C. P89
Bohr, Mark T. A446
Bohuny, Bruce D. A495
Bohutinsky, Amy E547
Boice, Bonny G. P558
Boien, Chuck E407
Boigegrain, Barbara A. A339
Boilini, Enrique H. W102
Boillat, Pascal A312
Boily, Cindy A. P628
Boire, Ronald D. (Ron) A718
Boireau, Christian W19
Bois, Michel W126
Boise, Cordelia E316
Boise, April M. P600
Boisier, Pierre A109
Boissard, Gael de W139
Boisseau, Philippe W453
Boisselle, Andrew P653
Boisvert, Gerald J. P136
Boitmann, Paul G. A579
Boivin, Alain A694
Boix, Javier A4
Bojalad, Ronald (Ron) A239
Bojdak, Robert J. A518
Bok, Arthur de A382
Bokan, Michael W. A551
Bokhorst, Willem van E209
Bokhorst, Willem E209
Bokor, Samuel R. A305
Boland, James C. (Jim) A382
Boland, James C. (Jim) A722
Boland, C. Richard P52
Boland, Mary P443
Boland, Susan E. P641
Bolander, Sherry P384
Bold, William (Bill) A676
Bolding, Barry C. E125

Boldrini, Giosue W54
Bole, Mark F. A39
Bole, Colin A453
Bolen, Michael D. (Mike) P321
Boles, Donna M. A109
Boles, Steven Lee P486
Bolesta, Dave E260
Boley, Warren M. A830
Bolg, Julee P536
Bolger, David P. A532
Bolger, Brian P470
Bolin, Tom A251
Bolinder, William H. A375
Boling, Paul F. E94
Bolinger, Robert S. E149
Bolinger, John P591
Bolis, Alex Alex Bolis W432
Boll, Yin A641
Bolla, Robert (Bob) P78
Bolland, Marc J. (M. J.) A520
Bolland, Marc J. (M. J.) W280
Bollenbach, Stephen F. A793
Bollerer, Fred L. E455
Bolles, Albert D. (Al) A217
Bolliger, Herbert W287
Bolling, Tim P623
Bollinger, Kathy A101
Bollinger, Lee C. A319
Bollinger, Kathy P42
Bollone, Ann P497
Bollore, Vincent W40
Bollore, Vincent W41
Bollore, Vincent W284
Bollore, Thierry W355
Bollwage, Mary P480
Bolotin, Irving A500
Bolourchi, Habib P56
Bols, Ivo A24
Bolt, William J. E7
Bolte, Tony A251
Bolte, David A. A457
Bolton, H. Eric E341
Bolton, William J. A112
Bolton, C. Anderson A228
Bolton, M. Stuart A262
Bolton, Tony A416
Bolton, Linda Burnes P99
Bolton, Linda Burnes P102
Bolton, Teresa M. P449
Bolton, Hugh J. W450
Bolus, Mark A209
Bolwell, Andrew A415
Bolyai, Stephen P572
Bolyard, Joe P314
Bolze, Steve A367
Bolzenius, Beda-Helmut A468
Boman, Par W425
Bomar, Anne E. A262
Bomba, Jane Okun E264
Bombara, Beth A. A404
Bombardier, J.R. Andre W91
Bombardier, Janine W92
Bombassei, James A842
Bombino, Paige A711
Bomesberger, Blake P482
Bomgardner, Kim P118
Bomhard, Nikolaus von W128
Bomhard, Nikolaus von W164
Bomhard, Nikolaus Nikolaus von
    Bomhard W300
Bommensath, Eric W72
Bommensath, Eric W74
Bomzer, David E216
Bona, Fabrizio W432
Bonacci, Elizabeth E413
Bonaccorsi, Joseph P. E22
Bonaccorso, Matthew J. E54
Bonach, Edward J. (Ed) A193
Bonacum, Bryan P507
Bonamy, Jean-Michel W474
Bonang, Timothy A. (Tim) E222
Bonang, Timothy A. (Tim) E436
Bonang, Tim E436
Bonang, Tim E436
Bonang, Timothy A. (Tim) E439

Bonanni, Fabrizio A58
Bonanno, John P. E62
Bonanno, Phyllis O. A130
Bonanno, Phyllis O. A555
Bonanotte, Gino A. A563
Bonard, Nicolas A256
Bonarti, Michael A. A81
Bond, Trevor P. E527
Bond, Timothy G. (Tim) A85
Bond, John M. A359
Bond, Robert W. (Bob) A628
Bond, Ron A678
Bond, David F. A708
Bond, Carey E. A830
Bond, Howard P268
Bond, Jeffrey C. (Jeff) P298
Bond, Randy P623
Bond, Amelia P634
Bond, Sir John R. H. W2
Bondar, Lori J. A85
Bonderman, David E123
Bonderman, David A292
Bonderman, David A372
Bondroff, Barry B. E330
Bonds, Gary C. A94
Bonds, Michael P. (Mike) A819
Bondy, Rupert W95
Bone, Harold G. A644
Bone, Gordon P553
Boneparth, Peter A464
Boneparth, Peter A487
Boner, Rex R. P539
Bones, Amy S. P148
Bonesteele, Jeannine N. E235
Bonetti, Elizabeth P82
Bonfield, Sir Peter L. E332
Bonfield, Sir Peter L. W166
Bonfield, Andrew R. J. W250
Bonfield, Andrew R. J. W304
Bonfield, Sir Peter L. W409
Bonfield, Sir Peter L. W429
Bonfig, Jason A118
Bonforte, Jeff A883
Bong, Francis S. Y. A13
Bongiorno, Joseph N. (Joe) A351
Bongiovanni, Lisa Marie A531
Bongiovanni, Joe P355
Bonhomme, Thierry W333
Boni, Eric N. A75
Boni, Aurelio Conrado W56
Bonick, Marty A210
Bonilla, Jennifer A645
Bonilla, Ivanette A661
Bonilla, Erick P400
Bonina, Grace P200
Bonini, Mark L. E54
Bonitati, Michael P441
Bonitatibus, Amy A312
Bonk, John M. E392
Bonke, Neil R. A711
Bonn, Nicholas T. (Nick) A749
Bonnafe, Jean-Laurent W89
Bonnafe, Jean-Laurent W90
Bonnafe, Jean-Laurent W110
Bonneau, Walt E132
Bonnell, Bruno W145
Bonnell, William W302
Bonner, Robert E. A404
Bonner, E. V. (Chip) A760
Bonner, Brian A786
Bonner, Tom W. P30
Bonner, Carol P110
Bonner, Karen P118
Bonner, Olin P480
Bonner, Joseph P559
Bonnesen, Christian A71
Bonnesen, Birgitte W426
Bonnet, Jo E180
Bonneu, Theo A779
Bonney, Michael W. (Mike) E133
Bonney, Paul R. A301
Bonning, Kenneth (Ken) A487
Bonnot, Alain W472
Bonocore, Joseph J. P607
Bonomo, Charles E351

Bonovitz, Sheldon M. A204
Bonsall, Mark B. P403
Bonta, Diana M. E38
Bonta, Diana E38
Bontempo, Stephen E524
Bontempo, C. Angela A518
Bontrager, D. Brett A742
Bonvin, Bertrand A641
Bonynge, Kathy P650
Bonzani, Andrew A452
Bonzani, Andrew A456
Boocock, Richard A24
Boogaard, Harry van den A368
Book, Robert M. E366
Booker, John P. E377
Booker, Toni L. P280
Booker, Robert W85
Booker, Niall S. K. W217
Bookhammer, Eugene D. P56
Bookout, John F. P550
Bookout, James M. P582
Boom, Marc L. P550
Boomer, Walter E. A106
Boon, Ron P191
Boone, Danny E300
Boone, Steve A346
Boone, Charles S. A609
Boone, Frank D. P128
Boone, Cecilia Guthrie P409
Boone, Richard P498
Boone, Kenneth H. P574
Boone, Haynes W429
Boor, Anthony W. (Tony) E63
Boor, William C. (Bill) A188
Boor, David A. A230
Boorman, Chris E270
Boos, Frederick J. E233
Boos, Brad P27
Boot, Arnoud W. A. A689
Bootay, Brian R. E524
Booth, Kenneth S. E126
Booth, Cynthia E196
Booth, Daniel J. E378
Booth, Stuart W. A222
Booth, Cynthia A333
Booth, Richard H. A593
Booth, George H. A691
Booth, Joseph W. P56
Booth, Kathryn Ryan P256
Booth, Scott P314
Booth, Otis P537
Booth, Clement B. W28
Booth, David W72
Booth, David W74
Booth, Richard W422
BoothFormer, Lewis E216
Bootsma, Pieter W19
Boran, Pat P368
Boratto, Eva C. A235
Borba, George A. A233
Borba, John A. A233
Borcherding, Tricia L. A193
Borchers, Susan C. A690
Borchers, Patrick J. P148
Bordas, Stephen P201
Bordeaux, Darren J. E235
Bordelon, John W. E252
Borden, Paul J. E253
Bordenave, Philippe W89
Borders, Carolynne A713
Borders, Denise Glyn P492
Bordes, Michael P. (Mike) A286
Bordes, Constance A452
Bordet, A. W245
Bordner, Dave E213
Bordoni, Mirco E260
Borel, James C. A272
Borel, Daniel V. W309
Boren, Robin B. A23
Boren, Caroline A29
Boren, David L. A786
Boren, David L. A798
Boren, Kevin P331
Borer, Mark A. E138
Boretz, J. Craig A215

Borg, Karen E418
Borgen, Thomas F. W146
Borghgraef, Paul W248
Borghi, Gilberto W54
Borgklint, Per G. W166
Borgman, Robert M. A624
Borgmann, Kevin A149
Borgstrom, Robert C. A773
Borich, Joseph J. E299
Borick, Steven J. E312
Borig, Klaus G. W157
Boris, John E443
Borja, Paul D. E197
Borja, Paul D. A344
Borjesson, Rolf A85
Borkar, Rani N. A447
Borkar, Shekhar Y. A447
Borkovich, Kris D. A81
Borkowski, Jim E338
Borkowski, Maureen A. A46
Borkowski, Ellen P587
Borland, Mark A. E388
Borland, Alisa P539
Borman, J. Richard A373
Bormuth, John P68
Born, John R. P105
Born, Jorge W102
Born, Ulrika W426
Borneman, J. Ralph A299
Bornia, Antonio W56
Bornia, Antonio W57
Bornmann, David E. A672
Bornstein, Jeffrey S. (Jeff) A367
Borodovsky, Yan A. A446
Boroff, Karen P468
Borofsky, Gary M. A251
Borok, Gil A158
Boromisa, Jeffrey M. (Jeff) E541
Boroughs, Rev Philip L. P130
Boroughs, Rev Philip L. P607
Boroughs, Timothy A. W9
Borowicz, Klaus W173
Borowsky, Kurt T. P468
Boroyevich, Dushan P545
Borr, Craig A. P649
Borra, Pier C. E236
Borras, Maria Claudia A91
Borras, Michelle P288
Borrelli, Jerry G. A32
Borries, Daniel von W164
Borrini, Amerigo W41
Borrows, Brian E292
Borsig, Clemens A. H. A288
Borsig, Clemens A. H. W78
Borsig, Clemens A. H. W144
Borsig, Clemens A. H. W268
Borst, Walter G. A573
Borst, George E. A799
Bortnak, James M. E459
Bortner, Andrea R. A402
Borton, Craig S. P649
Boruch, Robert F. P21
Boruch, James P545
Borus, David M. P620
Borwankar, Satish B. W430
Bos, Hans P21
Boscan, Mauricio A201
Bosch, John L. E32
Bosch, Joseph A. (Joe) A253
Bosch, Jose W57
Bosch, Dina W300
Boschelli, John M. A479
Boschetto, Laurence J. A456
Boschini, Victor J. P529
Boschulte, Alfred F. (Al) P556
Boscia, Jon A. A731
Boscia, Jon A. P526
Boscia, Jon A. W422
Bosco, S. Y. A288
Bosco, John P204
Bosco, Pat P281
Bosco, John P370
Bose, Michael A66
Bose, Supratim A132
Bose, Henry P607

A = AMERICAN BUSINESS
E = EMERGING COMPANIES
P = PRIVATE COMPANIES
W = WORLD BUSINESS

Camperlengo, John N. E217
Campi, John P. P99
Campion, Thomas D. E549
Campion, Andy A586
Campisi, David J. (Dave) A120
Campling, Andrew W100
Campo, Eli E307
Campo, Mary Beth P280
Campopiano, David G. A381
Campos, Tim A309
Campos, Louis J. A773
Campos, Roberto H. A869
Campos, Becky P110
Campos, Joselito D. W379
Campot, Peter P514
Camus, Philippe E182
Camus, Philippe W25
Camus, Daniel W474
Canada, Judy P169
Canaday, Charles T. E36
Canale, Stephen R. A819
Canales, Debra A. (Deb) P580
Canan, John A543
Canario, Mike E244
Canarios, Michael (Mike) P501
Canavan, Alex E274
Cancelmi, Daniel J. (Dan) A778
Cancilla, Russell J. (Russ) A91
Candel, Filomeno Mira W279
Candia, Gary R. P2
Candio, Christine P13
Candris, Aristides A587
Candullo, Carl P349
Canekeratne, Kris A. E523
Canepa, Steven L. (Steve) A452
Canessa, Mark P306
Canestrari, Ken A796
Canetta, Renzo A134
Canevari, Roberto W109
Canfield, Thomas C. E457
Canfield, Mike P195
Canfield, Brian T. P196
Cangemi, Thomas R. (Tom) A578
Cangeri, Antonio W41
Cangialosi, Loretta V. A638
Cangilla, Dan P168
Canida, Maria Teresa A. E269
Canik, Robert E362
Canizares, Claude R. A493
Cankat, Burc A201
Canlas, Christopher E383
Cann-Taylor, Julie P654
Cannan, Chad E89
Cannatelli, Len P571
Cannell, Will P522
Canner, Debra E21
Canney, Jane P609
Canning, John A. A301
Canning, Kim Paper A391
Canning, Tim A610
Cannon, Stephen J. E75
Cannon, W. Stephen E129
Cannon, Michael G. E430
Cannon, Marc A82
Cannon, Alexander A675
Cannon, James A742
Cannon, John A858
Cannon, Cynthia J. P250
Cannon, Jerry P483
Cannon, Michael R. P569
Cannon, Tyrone H. P607
Cannon, Dick P614
Cano, Nestor A775
Cano, Andre W57
Canon, Joseph E. A334
Canosa, Albert P424
Cantafio, Siomara Marquez de A784
Cantara, Daniel E. E196
Cantara, Daniel E. A339

Canter, Richard J. P641
Cantera, Jose Garcia W60
Canterna, Don L. A738
Cantet, Michel W472
Cantie, Joseph S. A806
Canton, Roberto E447
Cantor, Ilya E174
Cantor, Nancy E. P21
Cantor, Nancy E. P523
Cantor-Grable, Marcia W348
Cantow, Don E332
Cantrell, Brian L. E26
Cantrell, Brian L. E27
Cantrell, Dean A232
Cantrell, Gary L. A460
Cantrell, Kevin L. A647
Cantrell, Gary A787
Cantrell, Rhonda P572
Cantu, Joseph J. A54
Cantu, Alfredo Livas W177
Cantu, Alessandra W432
Cantwell, Christopher D. (Chris) A183
Cantwell, Paul M. A209
Canty, Tara D. P388
Cao, Ken J. A237
Cao, Xinghe W125
Cao, Shifan W343
Cao, Stefano W432
Caouette, David A543
Capanna, Fred P444
Caparella, John P. A496
Caparros, Ann M. A422
Caparros, Ann A422
Caparroso, Ricardo A. Chavez W212
Capasso, John P100
Capek, John M. A4
Capel, Mary Clara A329
Capel, William R. (Bill) P596
Capell, Peter J. A370
Capellas, Michael D. A181
Capello, Jeffrey D. (Jeff) A132
Caperton, W. Gaston A669
Caperton, W. Gaston A817
Caperton, W. Gaston P129
Capezza, Joseph C. A409
Capezzuti, Nancy E311
Capistran, Rene P489
Capito, Jost A353
Caplan, David L. A19
Caplan, Deborah H. A583
Caplan, Marcie S. P271
Caplan, Michael S. P372
Caplan, Russell R. W370
Caple, Roy W218
Caplin, Mortimer M. A238
Caplin, Stacie P204
Capo, Thomas P. (Tom) A497
Capodici, Lisa A368
Capone, Mark C. A359
Capone, Jeff E367
Capone, Michael L. A81
Caponi, Julie A. A30
Caponi, Julie A. A332
Capossela, Chris A553
Capossela, Nicole P354
Capozzi, Barbara P362
Capozzoli, Matt A824
Cappa, John P402
Cappi, Luiz W57
Cappiello, John P79
Capps, Robert P. (Rob) E344
Capps, Robert P. (Rob) E345
Capps, Kimberly A. E454
Capps, John R. A207
Capps, John E. A463
Capps, Allen A735
Capps, Travis A837
Capps, Kenneth P317
Capps, John R. P634
Cappuccio, Paul T. A793
Capraro, James (Jim) A201
Caprio, Anthony (Tony) A151
Capron, Philippe G. H. A9
Capron, Philippe G. H. W474

Capuano, Linda A. A521
Capuano, Anthony G. (Tony) A525
Capuano, Christopher A. P188
Caputo, Lisa M. A118
Caputo, Lisa M. A803
Caputo, James J. P167
Caputo, Michael P. (Mike) P570
Capuzzi, Mike A664
Caraballo, Julieta P468
Caraballo, Octavio W102
Caracciolo, Kathleen M. (Kathy) E206
Carapella, Victor P. A339
Carapezzi, Bob E115
Carapezzi, Ronald F. (Ron) A367
Carapiet, Michael W273
Caras, Jim P495
Caravati, Charles M. P114
Carbajal, Jose A. Fernandez W114
Carbajal, Jose Antonio
  Fernandez W177
Carbajal, Francisco Javier
  Fernandez W177
Carbajal, Jose Antonio
  Fernandez W199
Carbo, Angelique A8
Carbon, Davide M. A778
Carbone, Egidio E85
Carbone, Richard A. A109
Carbone, Richard J. A669
Carbone, Anthony J. A703
Carbone, Valerie P424
Carboni, Rita W432
Carbonnel, Francois de A58
Carbonnel, Francois A58
Carcaci, Kathy P439
Carchedi, Francis E123
Carcich, Matthew E383
Card, Andrew H. (Andy) A515
Card, Andrew H. (Andy) A817
Cardell, Brad P290
Cardell, Anna W47
Cardello, John J. A546
Cardenas, Jorge E34
Cardenas, Jorge L. A671
Cardenas, Teri P118
Cardenas, Mitzi P584
Cardenas, Mauricio W160
Cardenuto, Rodolpho W384
Cardillo, Rosaleen P620
Cardinal, Stephen P. A422
Cardinal, Donald N. P110
Cardinale, Gerald P. (Jerry) A697
Cardis, John T. E166
Cardis, John T. A85
Cardon, Wilford A. A102
Cardon, Wilford A. P43
Cardona, Maria W161
Cardone, Rev Thomas A. P566
Cardoso, Carlos M. A742
Cardoso, Aldo W189
Cardoza, Darryl P244
Cardwell, E. Wayne A93
Caret, Leanne P642
Carey, Thomas M. (Tom) E100
Carey, Matthew E212
Carey, Sydney L. E491
Carey, Francis J. (Frank) E527
Carey, William Polk (Bill) E527
Carey, Francis J. (Frank) E527
Carey, Jaime A103
Carey, James S. A114
Carey, Christopher J. (Chris) A186
Carey, Matthew A. (Matt) A419
Carey, Albert P. (Al) A419
Carey, Albert P. (Al) A635
Carey, Anthony A749
Carey, Chase A807
Carey, Michael P75
Carey, Judith A. P101
Carey, John P238
Carey, Karen P653
Carey, Michael P370
Carfagna, Angelo P187
Carfang, Anthony J. P168
Carfora, Jeffrey J. E391

Carges, Mark T. A279
Cargile, Richard A293
Cargill, C. Keith E486
Cargill, David L. E486
Cargill, C. Keith A784
Cargill, David L. A784
Cargill, Jan W368
Cargo, Rick A684
Cargo, Tracy P132
Cariker, J. Chris P32
Carilli, Vincent P608
Carino, James L. A706
Carioba, Andre M. A20
Carius, J. R. A288
Carl, Casey A771
Carl, Curtis (Curt) P338
Carl, Traci P533
Carl, Christian W491
Carlander, Magnus W479
Carlberg, Robert M. (Bob) E79
Carlberg, Inga-Lill W321
Carlborg, W. Eric E67
Carleton, Mark D. E20
Carleton, Mark D. A103
Carleton, Mark D. A511
Carleton, David P618
Carleton, Sean R. W225
Carley, Thomas J. E57
Carley, Vera A77
Carli, Maurizio A846
Carlier, Didier W111
Carlile, Jane A448
Carlile, Jane A449
Carlile, Jane P262
Carlin, Michele (Shelly) Aguilar A563
Carlin, Greg P399
Carlini, Barbara D. A242
Carlini, Barbara D. A389
Carlino, Donald S. A25
Carlisi, John A315
Carlisle, Gordon A210
Carlisle, Paul W. (Chip) A859
Carlo, Waldemar A. E331
Carlo, Massimo Di W284
Carlock, Craig E206
Carlon, Todd P148
Carlos, Mark F. E344
Carls, Rod P479
Carlson, Debra C. E36
Carlson, F. Paul E95
Carlson, Randy E106
Carlson, Norman A. E218
Carlson, Thomas J. E225
Carlson, Derek P. E337
Carlson, Jan A130
Carlson, Dennis A176
Carlson, W. Erik A257
Carlson, Thomas J. A387
Carlson, Tim A439
Carlson, Craig A. A624
Carlson, J. D. A632
Carlson, Valerie C. A633
Carlson, LeRoy T. (Ted) A776
Carlson, Walter C. D. A776
Carlson, LeRoy T. (Ted) A776
Carlson, Letitia G. A776
Carlson, Prudence E. A776
Carlson, Jennie P. A810
Carlson, LeRoy T. (Ted) A826
Carlson, Walter C. D. A826
Carlson, Wendie P52
Carlson, Pamela J. P404
Carlson, Richard V. P446
Carlson, Curtis R. P491
Carlson, Curtis R. P492
Carlson, John A. P495
Carlson, Brian P502
Carlson, Chris P571
Carlson, Gary P621
Carlsson, Magnus W399
Carlsson, Srefan W436
Carlstedt, Moira P121
Carlton, Charles D. E98
Carlton, Donald M. E362
Carlton, William F. A54

Carlton, Larry M. A210
Carlton, Frank P326
Carlucci, Leonard E383
Carlucci, C. Peter E451
Carlucci, David R. (Dave) A529
Carmac, Phillip B. E92
Carmack, Steve P52
Carman, Trent J. E20
Carman, Joseph B. (Joe) E480
Carmean, Jeffrey B. (Jeff) A600
Carmichael, Clare M. E23
Carmichael, Dan R. A32
Carmichael, Matt A61
Carmichael, Greg D. A325
Carmichael, Lawson P20
Carmichael, William P. P256
Carmichael, Gene P623
Carmichael, Brian W278
Carmody, Cora L. A462
Carmody, Edward P547
Carmona, Richard H. A189
Carmony, David A66
Carnal, Landers A207
Carne, John D. A145
Carnes, Paul E399
Carnesale, Albert E483
Carney, Mark A. A407
Carney, Thomas D. (Tom) A625
Carney, David C. A681
Carney, Craig A804
Carney, Bruce P34
Carney, Lt. Gen. Thomas P. (Tom) P88
Carniciu, Sanda P402
Carnwath, Alison J. A622
Carnwath, Alison J. W72
Carnwath, Alison J. W74
Caro, Antonio A201
Caro, Robert V. P304
Caro, Alvaro Castaneda W160
Carola, Christopher E383
Carolan, Brian E115
Carolan, Shawn T. E481
Caroll, Austen D. A56
Carollo, Ann P455
Carolus, Cheryl W235
Caron, Daniel N. (Dan) E23
Caron, David J. E147
Caron, John A239
Caron, Richard A784
Caron, Joseph P. W278
Carone, Christa B. A881
Carothers, Robert L. P606
Carovillano, Brian P533
Carp, Daniel A. (Dan) A246
Carp, Daniel A. (Dan) A591
Carp, Jeffrey N. A749
Carp, Daniel A. (Dan) A786
Carpenter, Douglas T. E87
Carpenter, Kyle M. E88
Carpenter, Michele E251
Carpenter, Patty E272
Carpenter, Patrick S. E319
Carpenter, Michael A. (Mike) A39
Carpenter, Edmund M. A147
Carpenter, Kenneth V. A378
Carpenter, James J. A578
Carpenter, Randy A610
Carpenter, Harold R. A644
Carpenter, Walton T. A695
Carpenter, Lonny J. A753
Carpenter, Peter P132
Carpenter, Wade P169
Carpenter, Darlene H. P428
Carpenter, Rick P595
Carpenter, Alan W480
Carpentier, Elisabeth W403
Carper, William G. (Bill) A591
Carper, Howell P. (Hal) A809
Carpino, Lorraine P402
Carpowich, Steve P462
Carr, Michael K. E3
Carr, George E. E92
Carr, Lauren A. E337
Carr, Alison A15
Carr, John A32

Carr, Muneera S. A205
Carr, Tom A255
Carr, Jeffrey W. A350
Carr, James A474
Carr, Gwenn L. A545
Carr, James A. A627
Carr, Chris A745
Carr, James P44
Carr, Robert W. P167
Carr, Joanne P269
Carr, Stephen J. P365
Carr, Justine M. P510
Carr, Keith W31
Carr, Sir Roger M. W116
Carr, Jeff W255
Carr, David W412
Carrabba, Joseph A. (Joe) A188
Carrabba, Joseph A. A480
Carrabba, Joseph A. A581
Carrabes, Brian R. A305
Carrato, Thomas F. (Tom) A409
Carrazana, Enrique J E13
Carrazana, Carlos P457
Carreiro, Manuel P424
Carreiro, Maj. Paul W384
Carrera, Luis F. Verela de la P217
Carrick, Linda A. P283
Carrico, Stephen J. (Steve) P240
Carrier, Patrick B. P118
Carrier, Jeffrey P206
Carrig, John A. E203
Carrig, Kenneth J. (Ken) A756
Carrigg, John P594
Carrillo, Jesse P244
Carrington, Christopher E470
Carrington, John E. P362
Carrion, Richard L. A319
Carrion, Richard L. A650
Carrion, Richard L. A840
Carro, Jose P619
Carro, Fernando W84
Carroll, Ed E30
Carroll, John R. E198
Carroll, John R. E200
Carroll, John E230
Carroll, Kevin E232
Carroll, Barry E256
Carroll, John A. E333
Carroll, Milton E533
Carroll, Frederick A148
Carroll, Milton A165
Carroll, Chuck A233
Carroll, Mary Beth A341
Carroll, Kevin A392
Carroll, Milton A394
Carroll, Barry A436
Carroll, Christopher F. A456
Carroll, Loren K. A475
Carroll, Teresa S. A478
Carroll, John M. A543
Carroll, Dan A673
Carroll, J. Randall (Randy) A766
Carroll, David M. A859
Carroll, Allen P93
Carroll, Kevin P130
Carroll, David (Dave) P159
Carroll, Frank J. P187
Carroll, Terry P189
Carroll, Donna M. P201
Carroll, Kevin P223
Carroll, Patrick P290
Carroll, L. James P295
Carroll, Al P321
Carroll, Dale P440
Carroll, John F. P480
Carroll, Rev Michael J. P493
Carroll, Kathleen P533
Carroll, Alan P538
Carroll, William Y. P610
Carroll, Richard W. P651
Carroll, Cynthia B. W35
Carroll, Cynthia B. W95
Carroll-Solomon, Pamela (Pam) P100
Carron, Jennifer P52
Carron, Rene W172

Carron, Rene W189
Carruth, Nancy A487
Carruth, Richard A. W393
Carruthers, Garrey A556
Carryl, Stephen P82
Carscaddon, Michael (Mike) P228
Carsky, Jack A844
Carson, Randolph W. (Randy) E373
Carson, Karen A263
Carson, Brian M. A555
Carson, John C. A684
Carson, John C. A688
Carson, Sandra G. A768
Carson, Phil P355
Carson, Russell L. P559
Carson, John J. P567
Carson, Daniel P645
Carson, Neil A. P. W245
Carstanjen, William C. (Bill) E104
Carstens, Charles E69
Carstens, John A. E539
Carstens, John A. A874
Carter, Trey E9
Carter, Nicholas N. E46
Carter, Thomas L. E94
Carter, John C. E106
Carter, Walter N. (Walt) E197
Carter, George J. E205
Carter, Scott H. E205
Carter, Jeffrey B. E205
Carter, John E215
Carter, Gerald F. (Jerry) E261
Carter, Thomas E. (Tom) E371
Carter, David E377
Carter, Bill A10
Carter, William H. A11
Carter, Donald F. (Don) A22
Carter, Scott A22
Carter, Jim A48
Carter, Mollie H. A72
Carter, James P. A94
Carter, Zachary W. A141
Carter, James S. A144
Carter, Wayne A201
Carter, Nick A212
Carter, Pamela L. (Pam) A230
Carter, Pamela L. (Pam) A232
Carter, Brett C. A274
Carter, Michael A292
Carter, Robert B. (Rob) A321
Carter, Mike A334
Carter, Robert B. (Rob) A337
Carter, Walter N. (Walt) A344
Carter, Richard P. (Ric) A348
Carter, Cary V. A373
Carter, Larry N. A448
Carter, Susan K. (Sue) A475
Carter, Zachary W. A526
Carter, Patrick A536
Carter, William H. (Bill) A557
Carter, George P. A632
Carter, Ron A714
Carter, Pamela L. (Pam) A735
Carter, William P33
Carter, Roland W. P88
Carter, Warrick L. P132
Carter, Larry W. P262
Carter, Chip P329
Carter, Chip P413
Carter, William S. P414
Carter, Elyse P468
Carter, Montez P503
Carter, Mike P521
Carter, Steven (Steve) P556
Carter, Joyce M. P566
Carter, Benjamin R. (Ben) P580
Carter, Robert C. (Bob) P647
Carter, Stephen A. W25
Carter, Colin B. W480
Carter-Miller, Jocelyn E. E367
Carter-Miller, Jocelyn E. A456
Carter-Miller, Jocelyn E. A658
Cartier, Karen P152
Cartledge, R. Eugene E65
Cartner, C. Edgar P183

Cartt, Stephen L. (Steve) E410
Cartwright, Carol A. A341
Cartwright, Carol A. A480
Cartwright, James A685
Cartwright, Stacey W192
Carty, Donald J. (Don) E234
Carty, Douglas A. A884
Carty, Brian P509
Caruana, Ken A704
Caruana, Maureen A280
Carucci, Richard T. (Rick) A841
Carucci, Richard T. (Rick) A885
Caruso, Joe A140
Caruso, Dominic J. A466
Caruso, Thomas P72
Carusso, Alessandro A709
Carvalho, Orlando D. A512
Carvalho, Michel de W199
Carvana, John P611
Carver, Howard L. A77
Carver, Bruce C. A232
Carver, Deborah P657
Carver, Deb P657
Carwein, Vicki P279
Carwell, Keith P630
Cary, William H. (Bill) A367
Casablanca, Anthony S. E249
Casady, Paul A543
Casagrande, Shelley E312
Casagrande, Daniel J. P365
Casale, Carl M. A176
Casale, Jeff A846
Casaletto, Daniel J. A446
Casar, Bernhard W54
Casares, Jeanne P439
Casaroll, Joseph J. E513
Casas, Isidro Faine W65
Casas, Isidro W356
Casas, Isidro Faine W434
CasaSanta, Daniel J. (Dan) A130
Casati, Gianfranco W7
Casazza, William J. A16
Casbon, John N. E256
Casbon, John N. A436
Case, Thurman E106
Case, Karen B. E405
Case, Richard J. A155
Case, Gregory C. (Greg) A254
Case, Karen B. A659
Case, Rick P375
Case, William H. P599
Casella, Michael J. A177
Casella, Annette P566
Casellas, Gilbert F. (Gil) A669
Casellas, Ignacio W57
Casellas, Carlos Colomer W434
Caselli, Ettore W54
Caselli, G. W376
Caselton, Ervin P185
Caserta, Jennifer E30
Casey, Michael D. (Mike) E6
Casey, Michael D. (Mike) E95
Casey, Michael D. (Mike) E156
Casey, Diane E237
Casey, Michael E308
Casey, Elizabeth E382
Casey, Theresa M. E413
Casey, Brian O. E533
Casey, Don B. A48
Casey, Donald M. (Don) A151
Casey, Thomas W. (Tom) A161
Casey, Michael D. (Mike) A163
Casey, Larry J. A297
Casey, John P. A365
Casey, Donald J. (Don) A687
Casey, William J. A804
Casey, Patrick H. P30
Casey, Donald P36
Casey, Keith P90
Casey, Juliana P101
Casey, Donald E. P156
Casey, Brian W. P159
Casey, E. Paul P239
Casey, George (Skip) P305
Casey, Rose P385

A = AMERICAN BUSINESS
E = EMERGING COMPANIES
P = PRIVATE COMPANIES
W = WORLD BUSINESS

Dean, Greg P64
Dean, JoAnn P143
Dean, Douglas (Doug) P178
Dean, Douglas (Doug) P179
Dean, Morre P216
Dean, Corey M. W104
Deane, Daniel J. E513
Deane, John M. A6
Deane, Jonathan W33
Deane, Roderick S. W488
DeAngelis, Kenneth P. (Ken) E253
DeAngelis, Yamynn A233
DeAngelis, Mike A235
DeAngelis, Robert A. A480
DeAngelis, Peter L. (Pete) P100
DeAngelis, Christine P299
Deans, Bob E6
Deans, Darren J. P493
deAraujo, Maria P. P361
Dearborn, Jennifer M. P135
Deardorff, Kevin L. A495
Dearing, Karen J. E466
Dearman, Timothy E. A260
Dearman, Richard M. P389
Dearth, Randall S. (Randy) E86
Dease, Father Dennis P609
Dease, Father Dennis P610
Deason, David S. A103
Deaton, Chadwick C. (Chad) A24
Deaton, Chadwick C. (Chad) A91
Deaton, John A419
Deavenport, Earnest W. (Earnie) A688
Deaver, W. Scott A87
Debaillie, Luc W248
DeBarros, Janice S. E32
Debbink, Dirk J. A179
DeBeer, Anne M. A318
Debel, Marlene A545
Debelak, Doug A170
Debelak, Doug P109
DeBell, Mike E129
DeBenedictis, Nicholas A301
DeBenedittis, Frank E11
DeBeradine, Lisa A543
DeBernardi, Michael A. E383
DeBerry, Blake E153
Deberry, Herb P178
Debertin, Jay D. A176
Deblaere, Johan G. (Jo) W7
DeBlois, Robert E. P93
DeBlois, Arthur J. P549
Debman, Henry A403
Debney, P. James E450
DeBoer, Bruce R. E536
DeBoer, Tammy L. A311
DeBoer, Scott J. A551
Deboissiere, Alex E502
deBoom, Fred A. E8
Deborah, DiSanzo W258
DeBord, Thomas P515
DeBose, Angela P608
DeBriyn, Paul A. E190
DeBriyn, Paul A. A314
Debrosse, Didier W199
Debrowski, Thomas A. A530
DeBrunner, David J. (Dave) A39
DeBrusk, Ryan W91
DeBuck, Donald G. A213
DeCabia, Phil A140
DeCampli, David G. A652
DeCaprio, Vincent P360
DeCardy, Chris P541
DeCarlo, Donald T. E41
DeCarlo, Donald T. A59
DeCarlo, Don D. A248
DeCarlo, Annamarie P26
Decarnin, Philippe W127
DeCesaris, Mark J. E527
Dechant, Timothy L. P625
DeChellis, Anthony A227
Decherd, Robert A414
Decherd, Robert W. A482
Decio, Alessandro W463
Deckard, Steven R. A260
Deckard, Steve P257

Deckelman, William L. (Bill) A213
Decker, Craig E76
Decker, Emily C. E80
Decker, Michael B. (Mike) E143
Decker, Daniel E236
Decker, Thomas A. (Tad) E258
Decker, Scott E409
Decker, Susan L. A116
Decker, Susan L. A225
Decker, Susan L. A447
Decker, Susan L. P457
Decker, Chris P525
Decker, Janet P544
DeCoeur, Daniel H. (Dan) P649
DeCola, Michael A. (Mike) A296
Deconinck, Patrick A2
DeCoudreaux, Alecia A. A507
DeCoudreaux, Alecia A. P256
DeCourcy, Patrick J. A34
DeCourcy, Debra A325
DeCross, Derek A48
Dedi, Wang W342
Dedicoat, Chris A181
Dedinsky, John G. A628
Dedman, David A. A512
Dedo, Jacqueline A. A237
Dedrick, Tracey A429
Dee, Ronald F. E72
Dee, Karen L. A325
dEeckenbrugge, Herve W407
Deegan, Gail E283
Deegan, Gail A285
Deegan, Donald J. (Don) P583
Deegan, Don P583
Deek, Fadi P360
Deek, Amnon W62
Deeks, Terence N. A571
Deely, Brendan E152
Deenihan, Ed A576
Deepak, Anurag W85
Deer, Jill V. A691
Deere, John P183
Deering, Anthony W. (Tony) E506
Dees, Charles R. P360
Deese, Willie A. A542
Deess, Eugene P. P360
Deessen, Ulrich von W76
Defa, Dennis P345
DeFalco, Ciro M. A571
DeFazio, Gary M. A109
DeFelice, Eugene V. (Gene) A103
DeFelice, Gene A103
DeFeo, Ronald M. A782
DeFerrari, H. Andrew (Drew) E158
Deffebach, Harry L. P247
Deffenbaugh, Danny M. P488
Defieuw, Luc W25
DeFillippo, Robert (Bob) A669
DeFontes, Kenneth W. (Ken) A301
DeFord, R. Sam A125
DeFord, Drexel P510
DeFosset, Donald (Don) E364
DeFosset, Donald (Don) E688
DeFosset, Donald (Don) A782
Defourny, Michel W407
DeFranco, James (Jim) A257
DeFreece, Michael T. P147
Degen, Alfred P. P549
Degen, Urs W54
Degenhart, William J. P326
Degenhart, Elmar W135
DeGeorge, Peter R. P424
Deggendorf, Michael L. E224
deGhetaldi, Larry D. P393
DeGioia, John J. P324
DeGiorgio, Kenneth D. A327
Deglomine, Anthony A402
Degnan, Scott E538
Degoumois, Christophe W91
DeGraan, Edward F. A109
DeGraff, Doug E39
DeGrand, Robert P208
DeGraw, Kevin A46
DeGregorio, Ronald J. (Ron) A301
DeGregorio, Ron A302

DeGroot, Therese M. A330
DeGroot, Mary Kay P325
Deguchi, Toshihisa W416
DeHaan, Jan P224
Dehaene, Jean-Luc W37
Dehaene, Jean-Luc W462
Dehaini, Nader P213
DeHart, Brad G. P625
DeHaven, Michael A. (Mike) P634
Dehayes, Donald H. P606
Dehaze, Alain W11
Dehecq, Jean-Francois W471
Dehen, Wolfgang W395
Dehio, Peter A829
Dehn, Jeffrey R. (Jeff) A114
Dehne, Timothy R. E106
Dehne, Timothy R. (Tim) E310
Deich, Faye P447
Deidiker, Jim D. A143
Deighton, Tim A688
Deily, Linnet F. A175
Deily, Linnet F. A421
Deily, Karl R. A717
Deininger, Hermann W13
Deister, Michael W136
Deitch, Michael N. E407
Deitchle, Gerald W. (Jerry) E62
Deiters, David P556
Dejoux, Pierre W830
DeJulio, Thomas E. P201
Dekang, Chen W229
Dekant, Willy W489
Dekker, Tom E127
Dekker, Colleen Parr A508
Dekker, Angela Van P201
Dekkers, Marijn A368
Dekkers, Marijn E. W78
DeKrey, Susan P620
Delafield, John E96
Delagi, R. Gregory (Greg) A786
Delahunt, Susan B. A167
Delahunt, Tom P166
Delahunt, Thomas F. P166
Delamere, Sandra L. W422
Delaney, Katy A104
Delaney, Mike A125
Delaney, Eugene A. (Gene) A563
Delaney, Timothy E. (Tim) A574
Delaney, John J. A706
DeLaney, William J. (Bill) A768
Delaney, Katy P49
Delano, Jose G. Zozaya E292
Delano, Jose E292
Delasotta, Fernando P476
Delaune, Christophe E271
Delaup, Chris J. A665
DeLawder, C. Daniel (Dan) A626
DelBello, Alfred B. E444
DelBello, Alfred B. A723
DelBene, Robert A. A452
DelBene, Kurt A553
Delbridge, Kip A457
Delbridge, Richard W. W412
Delcourt, Gregg A684
DeLeeuw, Patricia P585
Delehant, Mike A734
Delen, Daniel M. (Daan) A695
Delen, Daniel M. (Daan) A696
deLeon, Dennis P216
DeLeon, Marcos P584
Delepine, Didier J. E383
Delepine, Francois E498
Deleplace, Christian W355
Delevacque, Guy W443
Delfino, Sharon A. A853
Delfino, John P537
Delforge, Dan P87
Delfrate, Marco W234
Delgadillo, Dan A774
Delgado, Joaquin A2
Delgado, Michael A711
Delgado, Sebastian P290
Delgado, Laurie S. P600
Delgado, Luisa Deplazes W384
DelGatto, Lawrence C. A681

Delgiorno, Rick P161
Delicourt, Patrick W402
Delie, Vincent J. (Vince) A308
Delinsky, Jeremy E49
Delity, Dan E164
Delk, Marcia P636
Delker, Wayne L. A189
Dell, Adam R. E382
Dell, Glen A. E521
Della-Rodolfa, Carolyn P165
Dellaquila, Frank J. A288
Delleani, Riccardo W432
Deller, Sandra P572
DelliBovi, Alfred A. A315
Dellinger, Eugene P183
Dellocono, John P108
Delly, Gayla J. A346
Dell'Osso, Domenic J. (Nick) A173
Delmonico, Domenic F. P93
Delnevo, Ronald (Ron) E91
DeLoach, Thomas C. A73
DeLoach, Harris E. A729
Delohery, Andrew P424
Deloney, Mike A403
DeLong, Michael P. (Mike) E470
DeLong, Russell P629
DeLongchamps, Peter C. A391
DeLorenzo, Marianne A201
Delorier, Rilla S. A756
Delorme, Philippe W387
Delpech, Philippe A830
Delpit, Bernard W355
Delson, Donald W. A877
DelToro, Gustavo P653
DeLuca, Richard R. A543
DeLuca, Frederick A. (Fred) P164
DeLuca, Vincent P302
DeLuca, Vince P302
DeLuca, Greg P525
DeLuca, Tony P538
DeLuke, Ray A300
DeLuzio, Mark C. E249
Delvecchio, Helena Irene
  Revoredo W59
DeManche, Joseph P. E32
Demaray, Rick P197
DeMarco, Victor P81
Demare, Michel W5
Demare, Michel W461
Demaree, Jack L. A338
DeMarines, Victor A. P554
DeMarinis, Don A338
DeMark, Eugene F. E56
DeMars, Regina A217
DeMartini, Jim A365
DeMatteo, Daniel A. A361
Dematteo, Anthony F. P162
Demchak, William S. (Bill) A123
Demchak, William S. (Bill) A649
Demchuk, Brett E517
Demeautis, Jean-Marie A717
Demel, Herbert W274
Dement, Dan P553
DeMerit, Craig E544
DeMerit, Craig P651
Demeritt, John G. E205
Demeritt, Stephen R. (Steve) A278
Demers, Sharon W. P614
Demesmaeker, Koen W462
Demeter, Lisa E180
Demetriades, James P430
Demetriou, Achilles A. P600
DEmic, Susana A359
DeMichele, Robert P587
Demiddeleer, Leopold W407
Deming, Ronald J. E169
Deming, Claiborne P. A564
Deming, Claiborne P. A565
DeMita, Michelle A368
Deml, Wolfgang A20
Demleitner, Nora V. P569
Demling, Dee P361
Demming, John A204
Demoliere, Serge W263

Dharia, Arvind E314
Dhawan, Atam P360
Dhawan, Neelam W258
Dhillon, Tara A576
Dhillon, Janet L. A630
Dhir, Samir E523
Dhoheyan, Mohammed Al W461
Diaconu, Lacramiorara W332
Diallo, Thierno A641
Diamond, Jeremy A64
Diamond, Robert E. (Bob) A123
Diamond, Harris A456
Diamond, Greg A533
Diamond, David A. A566
Diamond, A. Patrick (Pat) A647
Diamond, Jared M. P651
Diamond, Jared M. P652
Diamond, Vickie P654
Diamond, Robert E. (Bob) W72
Diamond, Howard W443
Diamond-Gelinas, Nicole W302
Diana, Denise A404
DiAngelo, Joseph A. P450
Dianwu, Lei W120
Dias, Fiona P. A11
Dias, Selwyn J. A607
Dias, Ricardo W57
Diaz, Jorge M. E91
Diaz, Edgar E292
Diaz, Abe E309
Diaz, Denys E345
Diaz, Anthony (Tony) A183
Diaz, Paul J. A241
Diaz, Romulo L. (Romy) A301
Diaz, Nelson A. A302
Diaz, Paul J. A485
Diaz, Rosie P89
Diaz, Jacob P464
Diaz, Nelson A. P526
Diaz, Alvaro W104
DiBattista, Andrew J. P375
DiBattiste, Carol E211
Dibble, David E. A883
DiBease, Michael L. E249
DiBenedetto, Tony E177
DiBenedetto, Joseph (Joe) A672
DiBerardino, Krista A580
DiBerardino, Jennifer A719
DiBlasi, Mark A. E422
DiBona, Anthony Paul (Tony) E408
DiCamillo, Gary T. A869
DiCarlo, David M. P531
Dicciani, Nance K. A654
Dicciani, Nance K. P622
Dice, Ken A586
DiCerbo, Nicholas A. A209
DiChiaro, Steve A798
DiChristina, Michael F. E189
DiCicco, Wendy F. E266
DiCiurcio, John A. W210
Dick, Timothy A. (Tim) E22
Dick, Herman F. E122
Dick, Michael P445
Dick, Barry L. P449
Dick, Russell A. P463
Dick, Brendan W100
Dickard, Paul A13
Dickel, Ronald D. A446
Dickel, Ronald D. A447
Dickenson, Lawrence B. P534
Dickerson, Brad E506
Dickerson, Gary E. A69
Dickerson, Jill A256
Dickerson, Ronald L. A600
Dickerson, Marshall H. A691
Dickerson, Mark S. P39
Dickey, Boh A. E108
Dickey, William P. E295
Dickey, Robert J. (Bob) A362
Dickey, Rose M. A773
Dickie, Robert A53
Dickinson, Hunter E110
Dickinson, Doug E304
Dickinson, Daniel M. E344
Dickinson, Daniel M. A156

Dickinson, William H. P44
Dickinson, Rick P185
Dickinson, Michele P279
Dickinson, Martin P462
Dickinson, Lawrence W74
Dickinson, Robert H. (Bob) W107
Dickseski, Jerri Fuller A434
Dickson, Richard L. E132
Dickson, Tom A101
Dickson, John D. A213
Dickson, Kristopher (Kris) A756
Dickson, Joe A870
Dickson, Tom P42
Dickson, Mark P93
Dickson, Gina P486
Dickson, Dick P558
DiCola, Adam P383
DiCrosta, Robert E428
Dicus-Johnson, Coreen P641
Didawick, Kathy P70
Didion, James J. P134
Die, Roy A698
Diebold, Raymond J. P152
Diebold, Ann E. P622
Dieck, Lonni L. A49
Diederich, Raymond A389
Diederich, Raymond P222
Diederich, Thomas J. (Tom) P404
Diederich, Prof Francois W76
Diederichs, Klaus A471
Diedrich, Robert P. A339
Diedrich, Christian W164
Diefenbach, Nina P552
Diefenderfer, William M. A726
Diefenderfer, Jeannie H. P586
Diefenthaler, Aaron P. A698
Diehl, Sandy A830
Diehl, Carmen P7
Diehl, Bonnie P188
Diehl, Thomas H. P212
Diehl, Bob P423
Diekmann, Michael W28
Diekmann, Michael W76
Diekmann, Michael W268
Diekmann, Michael W396
Diem, John S. A114
Dienhart, Mark P609
Diep, Winnie K. P318
Diepenbrock, Amy P47
Dierberg, James F. (Jim) A330
Diercksen, John W. A840
Diesbach, Patrice Lambert-de W109
Diess, Herbert W81
Diethelm, Markus U. W461
Dietrich, Martin A. A574
Dietrich, Peter T. A730
Dietrich, Michael P205
Dietrichs, Hans W202
Dietrick, William M. E406
Dietrick, Donavon P324
Dietterich, Linda P151
Dietz, W. Ronald A149
Dietz, Robert W. (Bob) A201
Dietz, Kit D. A515
Dietz, William H. A684
Dietz, Diane M. A708
Dietz, Tyane P325
Dietz, Mariah P496
Dietz, Francis R. P549
Dietze, Steven J. P643
Diewald, Wayne P212
Diez, Nicole P47
Diezi, Reto W54
DiFebo, Val A456
Diffell, Dave E483
DiFillippo, David A. E506
DiFillippo, Anthony F. E506
DiFranco, Vincent B. A102
DiFranco, Vincent B. P42
Diganci, Todd P195
DiGeronimo, Rich A171
Diggelmann, Roland W362
Digges, Kennerly H. P139
Diggs, James C. A34
Diggs, James C. P99

DiGirolamo, Robert P162
Diglio, Joseph P337
Dijk, Robert J. van W57
Diker, Charles M. E87
Diker, Mark N. E87
Diker, Charles M. A514
Dikken, Tineke W24
Dill, Julie A. E455
Dill, Charles A. E462
Dill, Robert C. A724
Dill, Charles A. A752
Dill, Michael A. A773
Dill, Claudia W491
Dilland, John P337
Dillane, Catherine A201
Dillard, James E. (Jim) A42
Dillard, Stephen G. (Steve) A76
Dillard, William (Bill) A103
Dillard, Mike A251
Dillard, Alex A251
Dillard, William (Bill) A251
Dillard, William T. A251
Dillard, Mike A251
Dillard, Alex A251
Dillard, Stephen G. (Steve) P34
Dillard, Jamie P121
Dillard, Tom P144
Dillard, Evan S. P202
Dillard, Enid P285
Dillard, Denise C. P551
Dillard, Gary K. P630
Diller, Barry A197
Diller, Barry A303
Dillingham, Donald (Don) E227
Dillingham, John P237
Dillis, Mike P267
Dillman, Linda M. A415
Dillon, Roderick H. (Ric) E145
Dillon, John C. E373
Dillon, Mary N. E503
Dillon, John T. A156
Dillon, David B. (Dave) A253
Dillon, Donald F. A343
Dillon, Ricky T. A469
Dillon, John T. A477
Dillon, David B. (Dave) A489
Dillon, Ben A588
Dillon, Mary N. A771
Dillon, Mary N. A776
Dillon, Mary N. A826
Dillon, Patricia M. A853
Dillon, Robyn P39
Dillon, Timothy P160
Dillon, Mary N. P372
Dillon, Thomas C. (Tom) P651
Dillon, Tom P652
DiLorenzo, Thomas P605
Dilsaver, Evelyn S. E482
Dilworth, Timothy E386
DiMarco, Stephanie G. E15
DiMarco, Bret M. E112
DiMaria, Edward J. (Ed) E55
DiMaria, Anna R. E333
DiMartino, Michele Bailey P276
DiMartino, Joseph S. P350
DiMelfi, Ronald P110
Dimeo, Bradford S. P162
DiMicco, Daniel R. (Dan) A274
DiMicco, Daniel R. (Dan) A600
Dimick, Neil F. E490
Dimick, Neil F. A568
Dimitriadis, Andre C. E307
Dimitrief, Alexander (Alex) A368
Dimitrov, Ivelin M. E192
Dimock, Rodney C. E58
Dimock, Rodney C. A117
DiModica, Jeffrey E460
Dimon, James (Jamie) A319
Dimon, James (Jamie) A471
Dimon, Jamie P396
Dimopoulos, Dimitrios G. W303
DiMuccio, Robert A. (Bob) A853
Dinaker, J. W86
Dinan, Curtis L. A613
Dinan, Curtis L. A614

DiNapoli, Mark L. P514
DiNapoli, Michael (Mike) P514
DiNardo, Sheila S. E44
DiNardo, David A99
Dinauer, Cathy P97
Dindo, Kathryn W. (Kitty) A727
Dine, Jim Van E140
Dine, Jim E140
Dineen, Thomas A. E465
Dineen, John M. A367
Dineen, Robert W. (Bob) A509
Dineen, Robert E. W278
Dinella, Donald E276
DiNello, Alessandro P. E197
DiNello, Alessandro P. A344
Dinerstein, Eric P651
Dingemans, Simon W191
Dingemans, Simon W192
Dinges, Dan O. A828
Dinges, Andreas W11
Dingle, David K. W107
Dingus, David H. E52
Dinh, Viet D. E463
Dinh, Viet D. A807
Diniz, Abilio dos Santos W111
Dinkel, Thomas T. A335
Dinon, Nancy P386
Dinsbeer, Daniel P423
Dinsmore, Brad R. A756
Dinterman, Terry A464
Dion, Jeffrey P. P510
Dionisio, John M. A13
Dionne, John E188
Dionne, Bruce P120
DIorio, Steven A349
DiOrio, Joseph P476
Diouane, Marc E408
DiPalma, Sheila E111
DiPaolo, Edward J. E183
DiPaolo, Nicholas (Nick) A351
DiPaolo, Judy P339
DiPasquale, Michael (Mike) E30
DiPerte, Vito E447
DiPetro, David P167
DiPiazza, Samuel A. (Sam) A253
DiPietro, Kenneth A. (Ken) A121
DiPietro, Joseph P93
DiPietro, Joseph A. P610
DiPietro, Kenneth A. (Ken) W266
Diradoorian, Raymond H. (Ray) A36
dIribarne, Benoit W131
DiRienzo, Tony P131
Dirisio, Derek A671
Dirks, Douglas D. E172
Dirks, Douglas D. A289
Dirks, Douglas P189
Dirks, Thorsten W256
Dirks, Detlef W277
DiRomualdo, Robert F. E503
Dirst, Eric E144
Dirvin, Gerald V. A180
DiSaia, Kenneth F. P276
DiSalle, Christopher E236
DiSalvio, Philip P468
DiSanto, Myrna A233
DiSanto, Kristen A853
DiSanzo, Deborah W257
Dishaw, Wayne P267
DiSibio, Ralph R. A678
DiSilvestro, Anthony P. A147
Diskul, Mom Rajawongse
  Disnadda W394
Dismuke, Keith E199
Dismuke, Bill J. E427
Disney, Anthea A428
Dispense, Russell J. (Russ) A489
Disseler, Jean A. P69
Dissette, Mark R. P248
Dissinger, Ronald L. (Ron) A477
DiStanislao, Mary P315
DiStasio, James S. A285
DiStasio, James A593
DiStaso, David A459
Distler, Stephen P570
Ditkoff, James H. A238

A = AMERICAN BUSINESS
E = EMERGING COMPANIES
P = PRIVATE COMPANIES
W = WORLD BUSINESS

Felsinger, Donald E. A72
Felsinger, Donald E. A597
Felten, Ronald P335
Feltes, Carol A. P559
Felton, Stephen P33
Felton, Tom P321
Feltrop, Cassandra P642
Fendley, Charles R. P215
Fendrich, Steven G. (Steve) E321
Fendrich, Stephen E321
Fenglan, Yin W119
Fenlason, Laurie P564
Fenn, Samuel P466
Fenn, Samuel P467
Fenne, Rob W352
Fennebresque, Kim S. A39
Fennell, David C. P422
Fennell, Charles J. P500
Fennell, Andy W156
Fenner, Mark A99
Fenner, Madeline P562
Fennessey, Mike A427
Fennessey, Mike P252
Fennessy, Gary A598
Fennessy, Gary P374
Fenno, J. Brooks E101
Fenstermaker, William H. E256
Fenstermaker, William H. A436
Fenton, Stuart A. A444
Fenton, Timothy J. (Tim) A534
Fenton, Jeffrey J. (Jeff) A825
Fenton, Dennis M. P562
Fenton, Dan P579
Fenwick, Charles C. P221
Fenwick, Sandra L. P536
Fenza, Dan P120
Feola, Dorothy P572
Feragen, Jody H. A423
Ferando, Jim A102
Ferando, Jim P42
Feray, John W. A260
Ferber, Norman A. A704
Ferber, Alan D. A826
Ferchland-Parella, Joanne P375
Fercho, Gerhard A213
Ferdinand, Norma J. P293
Ferdinandtsen, G. Richard A54
Ferebee, Spencer A260
Ferencz, Steven M. P103
Ferencz, Szabolcs I. W297
Fergestad, Ingvald W435
Fergus, Allison M. E213
Ferguson, Paul F. E138
Ferguson, Bradley A. (Brad) E161
Ferguson, Randall C. E224
Ferguson, David E. E440
Ferguson, Diana S. E496
Ferguson, J. Philip (Phil) A8
Ferguson, John D. A54
Ferguson, Donald A139
Ferguson, Curtis A. (Curt) A197
Ferguson, Thomas D. A292
Ferguson, Rhonda S. A341
Ferguson, Thomas E. (Tom) A346
Ferguson, Robert E. (Bob) A372
Ferguson, J. Brian A583
Ferguson, Sam A870
Ferguson, Stewart P10
Ferguson, Massey P183
Ferguson, Stephen L. (Steve) P256
Ferguson, Tom E. P295
Ferguson, Robert L. P298
Ferguson, Anthony (Tony) P381
Ferguson, Richard C. P424
Ferguson, Paul W. P602
Ferguson, Susan Portis P631
Ferguson, Iain W53
Ferguson, Alan W245
Ferguson, John T. W366
Ferguson, Karen W387
Ferguson, John T. W423
Ferguson-McHugh, Mary L. A661
Fergusson, Frances D. A531
Fergusson, Frances D. A638
Feringa, David E188

Ferlic, Randolph M. A66
Ferman, Carrie P314
Fernald, John G. A320
Fernandes, Valmir E105
Fernandes, Anthony G. (Tony) A8
Fernandes, Anthony G. (Tony) A91
Fernandes, Gary J. A139
Fernandes, Andre M. A853
Fernandes, Anthony G. (Tony) P67
Fernandes, Paul A. P511
Fernandes, Ana Maria M. W161
Fernandez, Jorge A. E91
Fernandez, Michael B. E331
Fernandez, Richard F. E333
Fernandez, Sebas E343
Fernandez, Henry A. E352
Fernandez, Emil E393
Fernandez, Claude E527
Fernandez, Lynn A96
Fernandez, Manuel A. (Manny) A742
Fernandez, Manuel A. (Manny) A768
Fernandez, Alfonso (Al) P267
Fernandez, Gerald A. P276
Fernandez, Keith P326
Fernandez, Gene P334
Fernandez, Luis G. P581
Fernandez, Jose Maria Aguirre W10
Fernandez, Angel W55
Fernandez, Enrique Medina W56
Fernandez, Enrique W56
Fernandez, Daniel W109
Fernandez, Ignacio W114
Fernandez, Felipe W161
Fernandez, Carlos W185
Fernandez, Ramon W189
Fernandez-Carbajal, Francisco J. A844
Fernandez-Farrand, Giselle P537
Fernandez-Moreno, Luis A75
Fernandi, Jack S. P488
Feroe, Louise H. P137
Feroni, Marco Cerrina W234
Ferragamo, Massimo A885
Ferraiolo, Jill E. P137
Ferran, Javier W42
Ferrando, Jonathan P. A82
Ferranti, Richard M. P435
Ferrara, Albert E. A27
Ferrara, Hania P187
Ferrara, Phylis P515
Ferrari, John M. E510
Ferrari, Ray A125
Ferrari, Christine A. A251
Ferrari, Alessandro A452
Ferrari, Elva B. P160
Ferrari, Dan P516
Ferrari, Mauro P550
Ferrari, Piero W54
Ferraris, Luigi W162
Ferraris, Laura W466
Ferraro, Francis S. E86
Ferraro, Kathleen E188
Ferraro, Karen M. E391
Ferraro, Madeline P36
Ferraro, John F. P314
Ferrarone, Sandro E110
Ferre, Maria Luisa A650
Ferre, Barbara K. P296
Ferre, Virleen P311
Ferre, Fernando P533
Ferree, Deborah L. E153
Ferree, Deborah L. E154
Ferree, John N. P461
Ferreira, Paulo W57
Ferreira, Miguel Ribeiro W161
Ferreira, Murilo Pinto de Oliveira W468
Ferreira, Monica W468
Ferrell, Kristin K. E413
Ferrell, James A647
Ferrell, Jim P268
Ferrell, Joyce P539
Ferrell, James M. P548
Ferren, Eric K. A428
Ferren, Alison L. P2
Ferrer, Antonio Garcia W10

Ferrera, Rocco P511
Ferrero, Lisa A223
Ferrero, Marcia P618
Ferrero, Gianluca W234
Ferrero, Pietro W284
Ferrero, Dominique W472
Ferrero-Waldner, Benita W300
Ferri, Stefano W41
Ferri, William J. (Bill) W461
Ferrie, John E280
Ferrie, Cheryl A. A299
Ferrillo, Patrick J. P611
Ferriola, John J. A600
Ferris, Peter T. E178
Ferris, Robert C. (Rob) A421
Ferris, Melinda J. (Mindy) A610
Ferris, Robert A. P201
Ferris, Colleen P422
Ferro, Dennis H. A658
Ferro, Claudio Braz W37
Ferro, Claudio W37
Ferrone, Linda P557
Ferrucci, Gabriel P424
Ferry, Michael J. E58
Ferry, Leslie E76
Ferry, Rachel E411
Ferry, Michael J. A116
Ferry, Thomas P. (Tom) P358
Ferry, Steve P518
Ferstl, James H. E289
Fesen, Michael R. (Mike) A591
Fesette, Neil A209
Fesik, Stephen W. E77
Fesler, Craig M. P11
Fessard, Jerome W131
Fessenden, Daniel A797
Fessenden, Elizabeth A. P377
Fessler, Paul A247
Fessler, Paul A271
Festa, Stephen V. E172
Festa, Stephen V. A289
Festa, Michael R. (Mike) A881
Fetch, Mary T. E354
Fetscher, Allen J. A378
Fetsko, Francis M. A797
Fett, Neil P446
Fetter, Trevor A404
Fetter, Trevor A778
Fetter, Lynda Boone P537
Fetter, Thompson P658
Fetterman, Jim E190
Fettig, Jeff M. A268
Fettig, Jeff M. A869
Fetzer, Oliver S. E51
Feuer, Bruce P558
Feuer, Zvi W396
Feuerberg, Stan C. P371
Feuerhake, Rainer W459
Feurle, Robert A. A551
Few, Warren P629
Fey, Joe A490
Feyten, Carine P336
Fezzey, Mike A433
Ffolkes, Marie A779
FFRDCs, DoD P553
Fhima, David E302
Fiala, Brian R. A697
Fiala, Robert A. A788
Fiala, Andrew C. P297
Fiatte, Traci W352
Fibig, Andreas W78
Ficalora, Joseph R. A578
Fick, David M. E364
Fick, Jeffrey D. A698
Fick, Brandt P477
Fickenscher, James E. (Jim) E51
Fickinger, Paul C. A725
Fico, Dayna P78
Fidalgo, Julio Sacristan W10
Fidanza, Virginio W466
Fidgeon, Michael E407
Fiebiger, James R. (Jim) E332
Fiedler, Hanno C. A92
Fiedler, John F. A555
Fiedorek, Eugene C. A66

Fiedorek, R. Mark A735
Fiege, Roland E340
Fiegel, Jacqueline E289
Fiegel, Jacque A665
Fiehler, Sharon D. A630
Field, James M. A244
Field, Burton J. A531
Field, Meredith Paige P84
Field, Marshall P652
Field, Richard W47
Field, Bernard W131
Fielder, John R. E38
Fielding, Ronald W. A423
Fielding, Ross W438
Fields, Glen E313
Fields, John M. E383
Fields, Heidi A21
Fields, Mark A353
Fields, Felicia J. A353
Fields, Robert D. A514
Fields, Janice L. (Jan) A534
Fields, Janice L. (Jan) A560
Fields, James P. (Jim) P407
Fieler, Steve A416
Fienberg, Andrew S. E50
Fienberg, Linda D. P195
Fiereck, Ken P137
Fierens, Louis J. (Lou) P580
Fierro, Barbara P492
Fife, Eugene A606
Fifer, Michael O. E465
Figlar, Marilyn A512
Figlioli, Keith J. P413
Figueredo, Grace A404
Figueredo, Jorge L. A536
Figuereo, Juan R. A579
Figuereo, Juan R. A584
Figuereo, Juan A675
Figueroa, John G. A610
Figueroa, John G. A690
Figueroa, Adam P653
Figura, James S. A201
Fike, Carin A490
Fike, Randy K. P657
Filby, John A343
Filcek, Rodney R. A236
File, William H. A185
Filene, Jake E457
Filer, Philip J. (Phil) A25
Filgueiras, Carlos E144
Filho, Eleazar de Carvalho A350
Filho, Eleazar A350
Filho, Armando Trivelato W56
Filho, Oscar Augusto de Camargo W468
Fili-Krushel, Patricia A260
Filiatrault, John E143
Filiberto, Ruth E. A349
Filipi, Bruno A197
Filipiak, Ellen A253
Filipov, Steve A782
Filippi, Daniel A265
Filippi, Charles-Henri W333
Filipps, Frank P. E200
Filizetti, Gary P160
Filkins, Scott P655
Filo, David A883
Filter, Phillip P519
Filton, Steve G. A833
Fimiano, Andrew A. P487
Finan, Irial A197
Finan, Richard H. P566
Finard, Jeri B. A90
Finard, Jeri B. A359
Finch, Whitney A852
Finch, Norman D. (Norm) A887
Finch, Mike P123
Finch, Yuki W412
Fincher, Ron E9
Fincher, C. Anderson A266
Finco, Tom P23
Findlay, W. B. (Willy) A145
Findlay, David M. A495
Findlay, D. Cameron A540

Flanigan, John W. A260
Flanigan, John P7
Flannery, Brian E535
Flannery, John L. A367
Flannery, Matthew J. A825
Flannery, Teresa (Terry) P23
Flannery, Francis X. P514
Flannigan, Michael J. A630
Flater, Marybeth A301
Flathman, Christian H. P214
Flatley, Jay T. E112
Flatley, Jay T. E267
Flatt, Dean M. E155
Flatt, L. W. A288
Flavin, Patrick B. E134
Flavin, Laura A201
Flavin, L. A. A288
Flaws, James B. A223
Flax, Samuel A. E35
Flax, Arlen A338
Flechler, Ken E395
Fleck, Jeffrey L. E546
Flecknoe, Ronald J. (Ron) A145
Fleekop, Kenneth P422
Fleet, Clifford B. A42
Flegel, Heinrich W144
Fleischman, Alan R. P312
Fleischmann, Kenneth P451
Fleisher, Gary R. P536
Fleishman, Joel L. A682
Fleming, Denis B. E28
Fleming, Nigel Ten E268
Fleming, Michael J. A319
Fleming, Jeff A337
Fleming, John A353
Fleming, Chris A399
Fleming, Gregory J. (Greg) A561
Fleming, Russ P31
Fleming, David W. P89
Fleming, Robert P181
Fleming, John H. P210
Fleming, Thomas O. P304
Fleming, Edwina W. P508
Fleming, William P510
Fleming, Lawrence P612
Fleming, Dan P638
Fleming, James W461
Flemming, James B. A766
Flemming, William (Bill) W400
Flencher, Ben P72
Fleshood, John S. E539
Fleshood, John S. A874
Fletcher, Karen A. A272
Fletcher, James C. A298
Fletcher, Jeremy A603
Fletcher, John P. A873
Fletcher, Dave C. P47
Fletcher, Arlen M. P130
Fletcher, Andrew P162
Fletcher, Frank P201
Fletcher, Michele A. P283
Fletcher, Bridget P451
Fletcher, Len F. P519
Fletcher, Maria P565
Fletcher, Eric K. P630
Fletcher, Rees W9
Fletcher, M. W298
Flett, Angus W100
Fleurant, Jacques W216
Fleury, Alison J. P472
Flick, Michael A. E75
Flick, Tim P110
Flick, James A. P275
Flickinger, Jennifer A814
Fliesler, Martin C. P509
Flietner, Rudie P612
Flink, Linda P404
Flinois, Xavier E390
Flint, Douglas J. W217
Flint, John W218
Flippin, J. Mark A54
Flipse, Mary S. E239
Fliss, Timothy S. A112
Floch, Dominique W443
Flocken, Jeffery (Jeff) A778

Flockhart, Alexander A. (Sandy) W194
Flockhart, Alexander A. (Sandy) W218
Floersch, Richard R. (Rich) A534
Floether, Karl-Heinz W7
Flood, David E262
Flood, Bryan W. E291
Flood, David L. A448
Flood, Gary J. A529
Flood, David P167
Flood, David L. P262
Flood, Rebecca P362
Flora, John W. E440
Flora, Jon C. A489
Flora, Roy E. A878
Florance, Andrew C. E123
Florance, Ken A577
Florence, Janine P391
Flores, Rodrigo E292
Flores, Debbie A102
Flores, Rafael A292
Flores, James C. (Jim) A357
Flores, I. D. A762
Flores, Gregorio R. (Greg) A796
Flores, Debbie P43
Flores, Jeanne P102
Flores, Silvia M. P375
Flores, Debra A. P467
Flores, Jose P558
Floriani, Lodovico W41
Florida, John P553
Florida, Dan P553
Florio, Carl A. E196
Florio, Carl A. A340
Floris, Jean-Pierre W131
Florsheim, John W. E535
Floum, Joshua R. (Josh) A844
Flowe, Aaron A419
Flower, Craig A415
Flowers, Debbie E225
Flowers, Ann E. E440
Flowers, Garry W. A348
Flowers, Debbie A387
Flowers, Robert E. A660
Flowers, Kimberly D. (Kim) A731
Flowers, George G. A766
Flowers, Stephen D. (Steven) A824
Flowers, Richard Bowen P144
Flowers, Woodie C. P376
Flowers, Lana P417
Flowers, Ray P483
Flowers, Mark P583
Flowers, J. Christopher W392
Floyd, Dennis A125
Floyd, Diane E. A627
Floyd, David K. A753
Floyd, Virginia Davis P312
Floyd, Allen P335
Floyd, Bryan P406
Fludder, Steven (Steve) A368
Flueckiger, Joe A187
Flug, Pat P189
Fluharty, Scot P. A678
Fluhler, Stephan H. A338
Fluor, Peter J. A61
Fluor, Peter J. A145
Fluor, Peter J. A348
Flur, Dorlisa K. A311
Flury, Elizabeth P116
Fluss, John A. E358
Fly, Robin B. A627
Flygt, Flora P23
Flynn, Chris E15
Flynn, Timothy P. E26
Flynn, Michael E50
Flynn, Michael T. (Mike) E159
Flynn, Michael C. E197
Flynn, Paul E215
Flynn, Edward L. E488
Flynn, Genie E500
Flynn, Mark S. E522
Flynn, Philip B. (Phil) A75
Flynn, Edward B. A81
Flynn, James M. A167
Flynn, Nadine A201
Flynn, John J. A252

Flynn, Michael T. (Mike) A276
Flynn, Paul G. A297
Flynn, Michael C. A344
Flynn, Michael C. (Mike) A358
Flynn, Larry R. A365
Flynn, Thomas L. A409
Flynn, Thomas L. A410
Flynn, Brian M. A495
Flynn, Thomas A. (Tom) A608
Flynn, Lucy A. A685
Flynn, William J. (Bill) A693
Flynn, Brian A698
Flynn, Timothy A850
Flynn, Kathleen P3
Flynn, John J. P19
Flynn, John P23
Flynn, Gregory G. (Greg) P28
Flynn, Patrick W. P264
Flynn, Joan P305
Flynn, Brendon P519
Flynn, Timothy P. P610
Flynn, Father Harry J. P610
Flynn, Lisa Delisle P634
Flynn, Lisa P634
Flynn, Patrick G. W231
Flynn, Catherine Catherine
  Flynn W488
Flyte, Jonathan P490
Foate, Dean A. E398
Foden, Hugh A232
Foe, Bryan D. A699
Foehl, Brooks P414
Foehr, Matthew J. (Matt) A174
Foellmer, Frank P522
Foerster, Christina W263
Fogarty, Jim A171
Fogarty, Stephen J. A201
Fogarty, Bernard A. A627
Fogarty, Rev John P168
Fogarty, Larry P334
Fogarty, Des W350
Fogel, Arthur A511
Fogel, Arthur J. A594
Fogel, Glenn D. A657
Fogel, Robert P40
Fogel, Leonard B. P402
Fogelberg, Anders W401
Fogelman, Gen. Ronald R. (Ron) E3
Fogelson, Georgia P132
Fogg, Jeremy E215
Fogg, David H. A365
Fogg, Richard E. A619
Fogle, M. Oswald A336
Fogle, Oswald A336
Fogleman, Gen. Ronald R. (Ron) P554
Foglesong, William G. (Greg) E95
Foglia, Robert P116
Fohl, Blake A. P583
Fohrer, Jon P134
Fois, Candido W463
Fok, Canning K. N. W219
Folan, McDara P. A695
Foland, Jeffrey T. (Jeff) A819
Folden, Rodney E. E120
Folena, Chris E44
Foley, Edward J. E213
Foley, Sean E443
Foley, John A103
Foley, J. Michael A114
Foley, Michael E. A275
Foley, William P. (Bill) A322
Foley, William P. (Bill) A323
Foley, Patrick A409
Foley, Donald E. A518
Foley, Margaret L. A626
Foley, Rita V. A637
Foley, Joseph R. (Joe) A834
Foley, Anne E. P132
Foley, Liz P139
Foley, W. F. P339
Foley, Daniel M. P445
Foley, James T. P476
Foley, James P. P603
Foley, Donough W258
Foley, John W348

Foley, Dan W352
Foley, Mike W491
Folino, Paul F. E339
Folk, Jim P582
Folkers, Scott E538
Folland, Nick W250
Folley, Gregory S. (Greg) A155
Folliard, Thomas J. (Tom) A152
Folliard, Thomas J. (Tom) A153
Folman, Robert P79
Folmar, William A. E149
Folonari, Alberto W466
Folsom, John P. E114
Folsom, John P. A202
Folsom, Grant A416
Folsom, Laurie P424
Folta, Carl D. A842
Folts, Jacque P35
Folz, Paul E. A100
Folz, Jean-Martin W31
Folz, Jean-Martin W49
Folz, Jean-Martin W131
Folz, Jean-Martin W402
Folz, Jean-Martin W407
Fong, William H. E162
Fong, Clayton E299
Fong, Ivan K. A2
Fong, Chester P.W. A201
Fong, William H. A277
Fong, David J. (Dave) A708
Fong, Nathan P302
Fong, Harry P414
Fonseca, Victor A301
Fonseca, Dhiren R. A303
Fonseca, Lidia L. A494
Font, Artur Carulla W356
Fontaine, Elizabeth E. E195
Fontaine, Elizabeth E. A333
Fontaine, R. Richard (Dick) A361
Fontaine, Anne Elizabeth P82
Fontaine, Anne Elizabeth P83
Fontaine, Jean-Louis W91
Fontana, Bernard W39
Fontana, Enio W466
Fontanesi, Donato W463
Fonteno, James W. (Jim) P410
Fontenot, Gregory P. A315
Fonville, Kerry P656
Foong, Seong Seong Yew Foong W275
Foos, John A32
Foote, Susan Bartlett E228
Foote, Susan E228
Foote, Robert H. (Bob) E377
Foote, Susan Bartlett A102
Foote, Christopher J. A193
Foote, William C. A318
Foote, Susan Bartlett P43
Footwear, Ahnu E140
Fopeano, Nicole P468
Foraker, John M. E44
Foraker, Randy P. A93
Foran, Margaret M. (Peggy) A604
Forbes, Darcey P180
Forbes, Christian E234
Forbes, Karrie D. E321
Forbes, John E391
Forbes, William P. (Bill) E430
Forbes, Mark J. A186
Forbes, Dee A256
Forbes, Jeff S. A295
Forbes, James D. A405
Forbes, Glenn A423
Forbes, Ricardo P44
Forbes, Kay P. P244
Forbes, Lois P269
Forbes, Mara P301
Forbes, Geri P524
Forbes, David P603
Forbes, Cindy W278
Forbis, Mark S. E289
Force, Paul P140
Forch, John J. E455
Ford, Amy E81
Ford, Lawrence G. (Russ) E256
Ford, Richard F. (Dick) E462

A = AMERICAN BUSINESS
E = EMERGING COMPANIES
P = PRIVATE COMPANIES
W = WORLD BUSINESS

Goldenstein, Ihno W113
Goldfarb, Morris E209
Goldfarb, Jeffrey E209
Goldfarb, Michael P343
Goldfarb, Shlomo W63
Goldfein, Jocelyn A309
Goldfield, H. P. P67
Goldie, Hal J. A145
Golding, Cornelius E. (Neal) A429
Goldklang, Kenneth P508
Goldman, Kenneth A. E201
Goldman, Robert N. (Bob) E409
Goldman, Steven J. E459
Goldman, Rich E475
Goldman, Carol E. A164
Goldman, Marshall I. A167
Goldman, Jay C. A185
Goldman, Nathan A230
Goldman, Robert W. (Bob) A784
Goldman, Kenneth (Ken) A883
Goldman, Ray P591
Goldman, Amy R. P610
Goldman, George P646
Goldman, Marc P656
Goldman, Yaacov W63
Goldsberry, John P. A711
Goldsberry, Ronald E. A834
Goldschmid, Steven P565
Goldschmidt, Pascal J. E331
Goldsmith, Harry L. A84
Goldsmith, Russell D. A186
Goldsmith, Bram A186
Goldsmith, Russell D. A187
Goldsmith, Russell D. A320
Goldsmith, Russell D. A879
Goldstein, Albert E97
Goldstein, Barry J. E212
Goldstein, Joseph L. E415
Goldstein, David S. E472
Goldstein, Benjamin S. E497
Goldstein, Rob L. A122
Goldstein, Donald B. (Don) A158
Goldstein, Kenneth T. A177
Goldstein, Gregg M. A204
Goldstein, Brooke A256
Goldstein, Robert B. A308
Goldstein, Adam A315
Goldstein, Richard A. A456
Goldstein, Robert G. (Rob) A496
Goldstein, Jeff A576
Goldstein, Daniel J. A645
Goldstein, Bruce A675
Goldstein, Steven A818
Goldstein, Steve A. N. P78
Goldstein, Paul P386
Goldstein, Cynthia Greer P391
Goldstein, Joseph L. P559
Goldstein, Rodney L. (Rod) P566
Goldstein, Stuart P572
Goldstein, Steven A. P586
Goldstein, Brian P. P604
Goldstone, Steven F. (Steve) A217
Goldstone, Steven F. (Steve) A543
Goldsworthy, Nigel W365
Goldwater, John K. A114
Goldwyn, Martin M. E246
Golemis, Stilianos D. W343
Goler, Lori A309
Goler, Michael R. P292
Golestani, Clark A543
Golisano, B. Thomas P439
Golizio, Lisa P508
Golko, Yaroslav Y. W188
Golla, Linae A779
Golladay, Catherine A714
Golliher, Kristin P389
Gollin, Kathleen M. (Kathy) P322
Gollust, Allison A368
Golm, Louis C. A678

Golsby, Stephen W. (Steve) A134
Golston, Allan C. A753
Golten, Robert P130
Goltz, Frederick M. A292
Golub, Bennett W. A122
Golub, Harvey P301
Golub, Neil M. P543
Golub, Jerel T. (Jerry) P543
Golub, Mona J. P543
Golub, David P543
Golub, Jane N. P543
Golubev, Valery W186
Golubev, Valery A. W187
Golubkov, Dmitry E22
Gomach, David G. E317
Gombos, Carrie P539
Gomersall, Sir Stephen W208
Gomes, Anita A677
Gomes, Sergio W5
Gomes, Antonio F. B. de Sousa W161
Gomes, Renato W468
Gomez, Henry E63
Gomez, Henry A415
Gomez, Dolores P339
Gomez, Albert P421
Gomez, Genoveva G. P421
Gomez, Sara P611
Gomez, Eugenio Llorente W10
Gomez, Jose Ramon Arce W70
Gomez, Christa W84
Gomez, Hernando J. W160
Gomez-Lavin, Javier Polanco W10
Gomi, Kazuhiro W314
Gomo, Steven J. (Steve) A709
Gomulka, Robert P594
Gomwe, Godfrey G. W35
Gonabe, Steven B. (Steve) E173
Gonabe, Steve E173
Goncalves, Armando F. A633
Goncalves, Vitor W161
Goncalves, Prof Vitor F. de
  Conceicao W161
Gonda, Leslie L. A453
Gonda, Louis L. P562
Gonda, Toshihiro W22
Gonda, Barbara Garza Laguera W177
Gonda, Eva Garza Laguera W177
Gonda, Mariana Garza Laguera W177
Gondor, Cecilia L. E522
Gonensin, Turgay W459
Gong, Yu E452
Gong, Kevin A. A315
Gong, Jin P611
Gong, Huazhang W121
Gonick, Lev S. P99
Gontarski, Gregory G. A627
Gontrum, John P205
Gonz?lez, JosT A315
Gonzales, Arthur J. E362
Gonzales, David A374
Gonzales, Jorge P316
Gonzales, Richard (Rick) P555
Gonzales, Miguel W169
Gonzales-Hurtado, Jose C. W109
Gonzalez, Abilio E454
Gonzalez, Rick E456
Gonzalez, Richard A. (Rick) A4
Gonzalez, Richard A. (Rick) A5
Gonzalez, Saul A215
Gonzalez, Jaime A225
Gonzalez, Rachel A. A242
Gonzalez, Carlos Fernandez A288
Gonzalez, Alexander A374
Gonzalez, Ileana A650
Gonzalez, Edward A. (Eddie) A716
Gonzalez, Aldo P140
Gonzalez, Alicia P216
Gonzalez, Francisco T. P566
Gonzalez, Jacqueline L. (Jackie) P619
Gonzalez, Juan Enrique Ruiz W10
Gonzalez, Jose Maria Aguirre W10
Gonzalez, Fernando A. W114
Gonzalez-Albo, Jose Romero de
  Avila W10
Gonzalez-Beltran, Ernesto A237

Gonzalez-Mendoza, Luis P619
Gonzalez-Vallina, Ruben P619
Gooch, Mark A. A212
Gooch, Cecily S. A292
Gooch, David J. A626
Gooch, Jay A662
Good, Steven C. (Steve) E384
Good, Charles E. (Ed) E451
Good, Lynn J. A274
Good, Michael R. A687
Good, Katlyn E. P305
Goodale, Greg E183
Goodall, David C. A18
Goodall, David G. A342
Goodbarn, Steven R. A257
Goode, Gary F. E215
Goode, Gene M. E292
Goode, David R. A156
Goode, David R. A247
Goode, James A416
Goode, Earl A. A726
Goode, David R. A786
Goode, Jeff P111
Goodell, Timothy B. A414
Goodell, Jeffrey (Jeff) A464
Gooden, Linda R. A81
Gooden, Clarence W. A230
Gooden, Linda R. A512
Gooden, Beverley P375
Goodenow, Stephen J. (Steve) A318
Gooderick, Nadine A689
Goodfellow, Thomas A. A626
Goodfliesh, Greg A689
Goodgion, Sean A170
Goodgion, Sean P109
Goodhart, Ross E175
Goodhue, John L. E159
Goodin, Debbie P394
Gooding, Marie C. A318
Gooding, Yvonne P270
Gooding, Valerie F. (Val) W240
Gooding, Valerie F. (Val) W412
Goodman, Roy E111
Goodman, Robert P. (Bob) E75
Goodman, Gail F. E118
Goodman, Harvey M. E160
Goodman, Barbara E301
Goodman, Jason E321
Goodman, Jeffrey M. (Jeff) E529
Goodman, Andrew (Andy) A139
Goodman, Shira D. A153
Goodman, Stacey A183
Goodman, Andrew A275
Goodman, Harvey M. A276
Goodman, Bruce J. A430
Goodman, Richard A. A468
Goodman, Patrick J. A623
Goodman, Cheryl A677
Goodman, Gregg M. A725
Goodman, Shira D. A744
Goodman, Richard A. A866
Goodman, Norman B. P80
Goodman, Lawrence (Larry) P177
Goodman, Nancy P209
Goodman, M. H. P531
Goodman, W. H. P531
Goodman, Wayne H. P531
Goodman, Alan P. P535
Goodman, Chip P646
Goodman, Julie L. P647
Goodmanson, Richard R. W360
Goodmanson, Richard R. W361
Goodner, Bob A334
Goodrich, Richard E. E100
Goodrich, George G. E441
Goodrich, Richard E. E489
Goodrich, John B. E498
Goodrich, Donna C. A108
Goodrich, Carol A466
Goodrich, T. Michael (Mike) A767
Goodrich, Zane P170
Goodrich, David W. P258
Goodrich, John P277
Goodrich, Rev Richard W. P550
Goodroe, Michael A. P458

Goodson, Robert H. (Bob) P366
Goodson, Charles T. P389
Goodson, Simon W364
Goodspeed, Linda A. A49
Goodwin, James E. E3
Goodwin, C. Kim E21
Goodwin, Lewis E226
Goodwin, Keith A181
Goodwin, Cynthia C. A318
Goodwin, William J. (Bill) A519
Goodwin, John P. A661
Goodwin, Michael P19
Goodwin, Keith D. P170
Goodwin, Terry W. P424
Goodwin, Neva R. P559
Goodwin, Michael W350
Goodwin-Adams, Valerie E6
Goodwyn, Bill A255
Goody, Cynthia M. A534
Goone, David S. E275
Goorevich, Charlie P469
Goot, Stephen B. P474
Gopal, Ajei E44
Gopal, Ajei S. A139
Gopalakrishnan, Ravi A103
Gopinath, S. A346
Goplen, Mitch P64
Gora, Jo Ann M. A338
Gora, Jo Ann M. P41
Gorbach, Pat A382
Gorder, Joseph W. (Joe) A837
Gorder, Chrisoph P24
Gorder, Christopher D. Van P462
Gordillo, Rodrigo Echenique W60
Gordo, Juan Ignacio Apoita W55
Gordo, Juan W55
Gordon, Crystal E20
Gordon, Dan E227
Gordon, Mikael E228
Gordon, Frank E238
Gordon, John J. E304
Gordon, Mark E371
Gordon, Mary A. A42
Gordon, William B. (Bing) A44
Gordon, John R. A61
Gordon, Andrew M. A98
Gordon, Bruce S. A160
Gordon, Mary Winn A260
Gordon, Christopher R. (Chris) A405
Gordon, Ilene S. A442
Gordon, Ilene A455
Gordon, Bruce S. A597
Gordon, Tim A657
Gordon, Robert A. A708
Gordon, Barry A818
Gordon, Scott R. P30
Gordon, Robert S. (Bob) P46
Gordon, Thomas D. P102
Gordon, Sydney Smith P132
Gordon, Jeffrey D. P296
Gordon, Mark P329
Gordon, Steven P536
Gordon, Helen W368
Gore, Doug A42
Gore, Albert A. (Al) A67
Gore, Judy P366
Gore, Millie P656
Gorel, Michelle A88
Gorelick, Jamie S. A830
Goren, David E339
Goren, Isabella D. (Bella) A48
Goren, Denise L. P41
Gorey, Christopher M. A495
Gorham, Roger B. A32
Gorham, Doug P545
Gorin, William S. A547
Gorjanc, Christine M. E367
Gorman, Robert E507
Gorman, Matt A227
Gorman, Stephen E. (Steve) A246
Gorman, Christopher M. (Chris) A480
Gorman, James S. A561
Gorman, James P. A562
Gorman, Mark J. A647
Gorman, Robert A815

Griffin, David F. A127
Griffin, Kenneth C. (Ken) A275
Griffin, Griffin L. A374
Griffin, Bobby J. A396
Griffin, Brian A532
Griffin, Monty J. A721
Griffin, Sean F. A822
Griffin, Bobby J. A825
Griffin, Thomas J. A826
Griffin, Mark E. P5
Griffin, Mark E. P6
Griffin, Michael J. P47
Griffin, James D. P154
Griffin, Barbara L.J. P252
Griffin, Maggi P273
Griffin, Randall M. P305
Griffin, Dawn P350
Griffin, Mark P436
Griffin, Dawn P503
Griffin, David W. P570
Griffin, Wayne J. P633
Griffin, Garth W71
Griffis, William I. P214
Griffith, Dennis M. E90
Griffith, Michael E416
Griffith, John B. A1
Griffith, Michael J. (Mike) A9
Griffith, Dennis M. A150
Griffith, Jennifer M. A338
Griffith, James A438
Griffith, Timothy A522
Griffith, Susan Patricia A663
Griffith, Tricia A664
Griffith, Derek A697
Griffith, Kelly A708
Griffith, John D. A770
Griffith, James W. A795
Griffith, Darrell P283
Griffith, J. Brian P335
Griffith, Janice C. P514
Griffith, Chris W35
Griffiths, Scott A. E176
Griffiths, Jeffrey W. (Jeff) E309
Griffiths, Francis E361
Griffiths, Peter J.L. A139
Griffiths, David J. A298
Griffiths, Guy W51
Griffiths, Gareth W159
Griger, Christine A. P394
Grigg, David G. A329
Grigg, William E. P332
Grigg, Paul W440
Griggs, Jonathan E135
Griggs, Kathleen M. (Kathy) E288
Griggs, Francis W. A600
Griggs, H. James P134
Griggs, Judith P167
Grigioni, Carlo W461
Grigsby, Jennifer M. A173
Grigsby, Phillip C. (Phil) A274
Grigsby, Lane P87
Grigsby, Todd P88
Grigson, David David Grigson W413
Grijalva, Ernesto E403
Grillea, Thomas A822
Grillo, Frank P. E278
Grimaldi, Paula A. A167
Grimaldi, Gerard J. P584
Grimeh, Mohammed W411
Grimes, F. Virginia E92
Grimes, Bill E260
Grimes, Thomas L. (Tom) E341
Grimes, Donald T. (Don) E541
Grimes, Kirk D. A348
Grimes, Bob A602
Grimes, Teri P474
Grimestad, Dwight E. A71
Grimm, Michael K. A294
Grimm, Robert D. P576
Grimmer, Ralph J. E484
Grimmer, Steven J. A305
Grimmett, Scott A708
Grimoldi, Alberto L. E541
Grimshaw, Eric A613
Grimshaw, Eric A614

Grimsrud, Knut S. A447
Grimstone, Gerry E. W413
Grinalds, John S. E341
Grinberg, Paul E70
Grinberg, Paul J. E173
Grinberg, Paul A126
Grinbergs, David T. E480
Grindel, Isabella W335
Grinnell, David A. E71
Grinsven, Mark J. Van A595
Grinsven, Gerard van P238
Grint, Paul C. E267
Grisard, Jean-Marie W111
Grise, Cheryl W. A546
Grise, Cheryl W. A673
Grisham, Arnold T. A320
Grismer, Patrick A885
Grison, Arnaud W472
Grissen, David J. A525
Grissom, Taylor B. E345
Grissom, J. David A885
Grissom, Rusty P638
Grist, Thomas M. P612
Griswold, Jim P575
Gritsch, Klaus W144
Grivetti, Bruce A793
Grix, Alain Le W39
Gro?, Thomas W482
Groark, Eunice S. A633
Grob, Matt A677
Grob, Bruno A830
Grobbel, Brian A536
Grobstein, Michael A134
Groch, James R. (Jim) A158
Grocholski, Greg A268
Grodman, Marc D. E61
Groeneveld, Oscar Y. L. W360
Groenwald, Susan L. E144
Groeschel, Craig E227
Groff, David M. E442
Groff, Michael R. A799
Groff, Christopher P188
Grogin, Scott A807
Groh, James A795
Groh, Diane P3
Grohowski, Leo P. A98
Grojean, Doug P207
Grolman, Christoph V. E264
Gromek, Joseph R. (Joe) E541
Gronda, Mark P146
Grondin, Rick A643
Grondin, Paul A694
Gronenthal, Harold E30
Groninger, James D. E412
Grono, Anthony P201
Gronwall, Katarina W401
Groom, Marshall H. A710
Groome, Brent P250
Grooms, Tom A359
Groos, Holyce Hess (Holly) A840
Gros, Thomas D. A599
Gros, David-Alexandre W383
Gros-Pietro, Gian Maria W172
Grosby, Karen P375
Grosdidier, Richard A599
Groseth, Rolf P345
Groseth, Jaynee P345
Grosfeld, James A123
Grosfeld, James P239
Gross, Neal R. E160
Gross, Stewart K. P. E248
Gross, Karen P. E426
Gross, Patrick W. (Pat) A149
Gross, Robert A222
Gross, Edmund S. A234
Gross, Neal R. A276
Gross, Michael S. A463
Gross, Marc A464
Gross, Bruce E. A500
Gross, Patrick W. (Pat) A855
Gross, Jorge A. P47
Gross, Ashley N. P130
Gross, Barry L. P436
Gross, Joseph W. P449
Gross, Daniel L. (Dan) P472

Gross, Marc W199
Grossenbacher, Vice Adm. John J. A104
Grossenbacher, Vice Adm. John J. P49
Grosser, Joy M. P597
Grossett, James M. (Jim) W18
Grossholz, Bill E100
Grossi, Rich P384
Grossman, Blake R. E193
Grossman, D. Keith E278
Grossman, Woodrin (Woody) E281
Grossman, Jay M. E371
Grossman, D. Keith E490
Grossman, Peter S. E535
Grossman, Eric F. A562
Grossman, Allen P329
Grossman, Robert P550
Grossman, Jeffrey P612
Grosso, Helen Del E86
Grosso, Helen E86
Grosso, Patrick E448
Grosso, Patrick E544
Grosso, Patrick P651
Grosu, Daniel E267
Grosveld, Gerard P501
Grote, Joseph (Joe) E494
Grote, Larry A867
Grote, Byron E. W95
Grote, Byron E. W464
Grote, Byron E. W465
Grothaus, Chuck A540
Grottes, Jacques Marraud des W453
Grounds, Matthew W461
Grove, Janet E. A708
Grove, Hannah A749
Grove, Todd W. P17
Grove, Walter R. P371
Grover, James N.D. (Jim) W155
Groves, Eric S. E118
Groves, Jason L. E330
Groves, Vaughn R. A41
Groves, Rick A694
Groves, Tina M. A724
Groves, Penni P341
Grow, Greg A71
Grow, Patricia A. P254
Grow, Timothy E. P353
Grow, Timothy E. P354
Growcock, Terry D. A403
Grua, Peter J. E16
Grua, Peter J. E236
Grubb, Edgar H. (Ed) A153
Grubb, Lois P180
Grubbs, Robert W. A63
Grubbs, Jimmy G. A329
Grube, Craig E399
Grube, F. William A144
Grube, Jeffrey D. A706
Grube, Bruce P214
Gruben, Steven E. Von A288
Gruber, Gary J. E362
Gruber, Ken E495
Gruber, Frank A325
Gruber, David P. A749
Gruber, Scott L. A797
Gruber, Seth P13
Grubka, Robert (Rob) A509
Grubman, Eric P. A588
Grucan, Sally P636
Gruchacz, Christopher J. P47
Grudzien, Jeffrey M. E425
Grue, Kim W321
Gruel, Frederick L. P573
Gruen, Karen A. A29
Gruen, David P614
Gruendl, Ronald R. (Ron) A99
Gruener, Jordan A536
Grunberg, Hubertus von W5
Grunberg, Hubertus von W154
Grund, Frank W54
Grund, Birgit W179
Grundfest, Joseph A. (Joe) E193
Grundhofer, John F. (Jack) E63
Grundhofer, Jerry A. A282
Grundman, Eric A. A613
Grundmann, Hans-Jorg W395

Grune, Thomas J. E336
Grunebach, Russell C. P168
Grunley, Martin P223
Grunley, Kenneth (Ken) P223
Grunwald, Pat P331
Grunzweig, Jeremy E338
Grupel, Ron W441
Grusky, Robert R. E464
Grusky, Robert R. A82
Grusky, Robert R. A84
Gruss, Peter W300
Gruss, Peter W396
Gruttner, Rick A694
Gryder, Rodney A. (Rod) A66
Grynberg, Marc W462
Grzebinski, David W. E296
Grzesiek, Artur W263
Gu, Jia-Yan W100
Gu, Liansong W139
Guadagnoli, Donald A. P90
Guajardo, Pablo Roberto Gonzalez W32
Guan, Jackie E434
Guanghua, Zhang W119
Guarasci, Robert P573
Guarguaglini, Pier Francesco W173
Guarino, John M. A197
Guarr, Tom E215
Guarracino, Joseph J. P82
Guarrera, David A545
Guay, Simon A641
Guay, Charles W413
Guber, Peter E142
Gubert, Walter A. A471
Guccione, Salvatore J. E11
Gudenas, Mark P522
Gudino, Nancy A840
Gue, W. Kenneth P544
Gueldner, Sara P594
Guelfand, Greg W300
Guelich, Karl D. E188
Guell, Miquel W57
Guell, Carmen Riu W457
Guena, Yves W375
Guenter-Schlesinger, Sue P640
Guenther, Paul B. A393
Guenther, Roger P410
Guenther, Paul B. P559
Guenthner, C. Steven (Steve) E28
Guenthner, Kevin J. A337
Guerchon, Mike E421
Guerci, Alan D. P331
Guerci, Alan D. P492
Guericke, Keith R. E180
Guerin, Vera P102
Guerlain, Eric W124
Gueron, Judith M. A31
Guerra, R. David A450
Guerra, David A450
Guerra, R. David A450
Guerra, Emilia P421
Guerrera, Linda N. E18
Guerreri, John E174
Guerreri, Bart G. P440
Guerrero, Jesus E343
Guerrero, Angel E400
Guerrero, Edda A134
Guerrero, Manuel A364
Guerrero, Juan A606
Guerrero, Juan O. A650
Guerrero, Pedro Guerrero W70
Guerrero, Jose-Luis W218
Guerrieri, Gary A308
Guers, Jacques A881
Guertin, Timothy E. (Tim) E483
Guertin, Shawn M. A17
Guertin, Alexandre J. W193
Guesnier, Dan P338
Guess, Charlie P384
Guest, Barry E187
Guest, Kevin G. E515
Guest, Robert E. A296
Guest, James A. (Jim) P139
Guest, Anne P495
Gueth, Anton G. E456
Guetta, Bentzi W218

A = AMERICAN BUSINESS
E = EMERGING COMPANIES
P = PRIVATE COMPANIES
W = WORLD BUSINESS

Hallin, Jeffrey J. (Jeff) A740
Halling, Marie W426
Hallingstad, Nicole D. P463
Hallman, Richard P. E172
Hallman, Richard P. A289
Hallman, Dwayne D. A422
Hallmark, John T. E296
Halloin, Jeff P446
Halloin, Jeff P447
Halloran, Patrick E137
Halloran, Jean M. A21
Halloran, Brian A208
Halloran, Jean P139
Halloran, Owen W. P286
Hallowell, Christian P135
Hallows, Jeff E417
Hallows, Jeff A692
Hallqvist, Louise Louise
    Hallqvist W401
Hallstrom, Craig A593
Hallum, Jack A737
Halmy, Christopher A39
Halnon, William G. (Bill) A693
Halonen, Robert P280
Halpern, Linda Cabe P269
Halpin, Edward D. A640
Halprin, Stephen E. E299
Halseth, Michael J. P617
Haltebourg, Patrice W127
Halter, Timothy P. E157
Halter, Michael P. A778
Halverson, Clint E185
Halverson, Gary M. A145
Halverson, Bradley M. A155
Halverson, Steven T. (Steve) A230
Halverson, Linda P609
Halverstadt, Donald B. A93
Halvin, Fred D. A423
Halvorsen, Tore H. A350
Halvorson, Eric H. E278
Halvorson, Bruce P197
Ham, Kerby S. A115
Hamaba, Masaaki W183
Hamad, Abdlatif A123
Hamada, Richard P. (Rick) A88
Hamada, Tatsuro W97
Hamada, Akio W214
Hamada, Toyosaku W417
Hamakawa, Ichiro W294
Hamamatsu, Shig E428
Hamamoto, Yasuo W312
Hamamoto, Misao W393
Hamano, Wayne Y. A97
Hamano, Toshishige W390
Hamasaki, Yuji W419
Hamatsuka, Junichi W405
Hamblen, Don A311
Hamblin, Connie E215
Hambrecht, Jurgen W144
Hambrecht, Jurgen W151
Hambrick, David W. A185
Hamburg, Marc D. A115
Hamburg, Edward L. P21
Hamburg, Margaret A. P559
Hamburger, Daniel M. E144
Hamburger, John E304
Hamby, Thomas L. (Tom) A666
Hamdan, Mohamad E447
Hamdani, Kausar A319
Hamelmann, Stefan W202
Hamer, Jack E. E292
Hamer, Nancy P614
Hamerslag, Steven J. E122
Hames, Scott A111
Hamid, Kamal E454
Hamill, Clare L. A585
Hamilton, Gail E. E285
Hamilton, Russ E371

Hamilton, Peter E467
Hamilton, Doug E469
Hamilton, Jonathon A4
Hamilton, Scott D. A161
Hamilton, Raymond K. A261
Hamilton, Judith H. A265
Hamilton, Thomas M. (Tom) A350
Hamilton, Robert A. A365
Hamilton, Tonya A368
Hamilton, Thomas M. (Tom) A407
Hamilton, Joanne G. A426
Hamilton, Peter B. A617
Hamilton, Peter B. A735
Hamilton, Arthur A736
Hamilton, Doug A761
Hamilton, Stephen G. (Steve) P151
Hamilton, Karin P188
Hamilton, Ann H. P214
Hamilton, Mike P231
Hamilton, Annette P246
Hamilton, William (Bill) P264
Hamilton, DeAnne P. A420
Hamilton, Heather P424
Hamilton, Dennie P466
Hamilton, John P568
Hamilton, Billie Jo P608
Hamilton, Mike P610
Hamilton, Mark P612
Hamilton, Judith H. P644
Hamilton, Stewart P657
Hamilton, Anthony J. W49
Hamli, Mohamed D. Al W137
Hamlin, Todd E157
Hamlin, John S. E393
Hamlin, Stephen E. A772
Hamlin, Scott J. P114
Hamlin, Stephen E. P524
Hamlin, Rick W26
Hamm, Richard F. A286
Hamm, David (Dave) P186
Hammad, Malak P160
Hammadi, Yousuf Ahmad Al W472
Hammarstrom, David A545
Hammel, Charles L. (Chuck) P407
Hammel, Victor P430
Hammer, N. Robert (Bob) E115
Hammer, Wolfgang A160
Hammer, David A433
Hammer, Douglas J. A449
Hammer, Douglas J. P262
Hammer, Lydia P309
Hammer, Hans Jorg W335
Hammergren, John H. A416
Hammergren, John H. A536
Hammes, Michael N. (Mike) A573
Hammett, Samuel J. (Jack) P317
Hammett, Seth P412
Hammill, Gregory P188
Hammock, M. Hill E479
Hammock, Hill E479
Hammock, Kelli M. A565
Hammock, M. Hill A772
Hammock, Hill A772
Hammock, Preston P9
Hammond, Owen E174
Hammond, Kirstin A. E197
Hammond, Thomas J. (Tom) E275
Hammond, Jonathan (Jon) E517
Hammond, Kirstin A. A344
Hammond, Elizabeth A449
Hammond, Thomas R. A461
Hammond, Patti P179
Hammond, Pamela P230
Hammond, Elizabeth P262
Hammond, Ulysses B. P294
Hammond, Al P354
Hammond, John C. P361
Hammond, Michael J. P389
Hammonds, Kim A125
Hammons, Kevin A210
Hammons, Brian P341
Hamner, R. Steven E327
Hamoui, Omar A383
Hampden, Bridget-Anne P391
Hampel, Ronald E212

Hampel, M.J. P277
Hampel, Daniel W128
Hampshire-Cowan, Artis G. P252
Hampton, Robert W. A607
Hampton, Bill P181
Hampton, Barbara P215
Hampton, Debra P404
Hampton, Mark P579
Hampton, Sir Philip W35
Hampton, Sir Philip W305
Hampton, Sir Philip W368
Hamre, John J. A300
Hamre, John J. P554
Hamrock, Joseph (Joe) A49
Hamrock, Joseph (Joe) A587
Hamson, Michael S. A581
Hamson, Ginny P259
Han, Kong Yeu E273
Han, Chang-Chaio (James) E273
Han, Kong Yeu E273
Han, Bernard L. (Bernie) A257
Han, Sam S. K. A349
Han, Edward S. A872
Han, Jianguo W121
Han, Dae-Soo W358
Han, Woosung W378
Han, Dong Woo W391
Han, Young-Suk W397
Han, In-Goo W397
Han, Seung-Soo W412
Hanada, Yoshihiko W183
Hanafin, Mark W116
Hanagarne, Frank E110
Hanai, Masayuki W405
Hanan, Shelley A562
Hanashima, Kyoichi W117
Hanatani, Shinji W408
Hanauer, Sue P273
Hanazawa, Hiroyuki W124
Hanbury, George L. P375
Hanby, Dorothy J. P631
Hance, Robert B. (Chip) A4
Hance, James H. (Jim) A274
Hance, James H. (Jim) A353
Hance, James H. (Jim) A562
Hance, James H. (Jim) P276
Hance, James H. (Jim) P570
Hanchera, Daniel R. A565
Hancock, H. Gary E39
Hancock, Thomas E. E236
Hancock, Ellen M. A17
Hancock, Peter D. A53
Hancock, Paul J. A114
Hancock, Ellen M. A201
Hancock, Lain A269
Hancock, Larry D. A448
Hancock, Ron A646
Hancock, Dain M. A787
Hancock, Ben E. P41
Hancock, Frank P41
Hancock, Michael (Mike) P74
Hancock, Larry D. P262
Hancock, Dean P369
Hancock, Myra P386
Hancock, Ron P408
Hancock, Stacey J. P486
Hancock, Kirk P556
Hand, Martin A819
Hand, Scott M. W278
Handel, Nancy H. A135
Handel, Michael J. Van A520
Handelman, Justine P70
Handelsbanken, Svenska W401
Handler, Richard B. A501
Handler, Richard B. A502
Handley, Thomas W. E207
Handley, Terry W. A154
Handley, Thomas W. A282
Handley, Alan P12
Handley, Allyson Hughes P602
Handlon, Carolyn B. A525
Handrick, Gabriele W195
Handwerk, Thomas P. P430
Handy, Wayne J. E92
Handy, Alice W. E352

Handy, F. Philip A63
Handy, John K. A207
Handy, Clay A448
Handy, Scott A452
Handy, Clay P262
Hanemann, Kim C. A671
Hanes, Angus P410
Hanewich, Michael E469
Hanewich, Michael A761
Haney, Byron J. E192
Haney, Megan A70
Haney, James R. A341
Haney, James E. A401
Haney, Harlow P281
Haney, Gregory K. (Greg) P451
Haney, Mark P636
Hanford, Deirdre E475
Hanford, Ann P648
Hanft, Noah J. A529
Hanggi, Rolf W309
Haniel, Franz M. W81
Haniel, Franz W286
Hanifin, Christopher J. P559
Hanigan, Kevin E522
Hankin, Rockell N. E438
Hankin, Robert P443
Hankins, Randal L. A251
Hankins, Anthony P. A435
Hankins, Joe A646
Hankins, Joe P408
Hankins, Angie M. P509
Hankins, Joseph A. P539
Hanks, John E361
Hanks, W. Bruce A168
Hanks, James C. P255
Hanley, Mary Ann E117
Hanley, Patrick D. E370
Hanley, Thomas W. E509
Hanley, Mark A60
Hanley, Joe A452
Hanley, Joseph R. A776
Hanley, Thomas W. A821
Hanley, Rev Francis P167
Hanley, Jane P315
Hanley, George P566
Hanlon, Brenton G. A. E6
Hanlon, Susan M. E228
Hanlon, Robert E496
Hanlon, John F. A285
Hanlon, Phil P315
Hanlon, Peter W484
Hann, Gregory A. (Greg) E531
Hann, Cecelia P239
Hanna, Steve E1

Hanna, Gary C. E176
Hanna, Virginia L. E226
Hanna, Randy W. E231
Hanna, Ben E306
Hanna, Randy W. A395
Hanna, Jeffery G. P569
Hanna, Ken G. W440
Hannabach, William D. E250
Hannafin, Robert P302
Hannah, D. Jay A93
Hannah, Deborah A482
Hannah, Kenneth H. (Ken) A630
Hannah, David H. A690
Hannah, Eddy L. (Ed) P74
Hannah, Glenn C. P551
Hannah, Ashley W100
Hannam, Wendy G. W69
Hannan, Stephen E182
Hannasch, Brian P. W26
Hanneffy, Kay W66
Hannen, Louis E. E272
Hanners, Rodney B. P537
Hannervall, Sverker W436
Hannigan, Amy J. A113
Hannigan, Matt P525
Hanning, Franz S. A878
Hannis, Mark P379
Hanno, Dennis P40
Hannon, Michael J. A648
Hannon, Bill A803

Jasinski, Steve A603
Jaska, James M. (Jim) A13
Jaskolski, Stanley V. P314
Jasper, William A. (Bill) E213
Jasper, Philip J. (Phil) A703
Jasper, Thomas F. (Tom) A773
Jasper, Thomas F. (Tom) A774
Jassy, Andrew R. A44
Jassy, Andy A320
Jastrow, Kenneth M. (Kenny) A548
Jastrzebski, Thaddeus J. (Ted) A411
Jaubert, Jean-Marc W453
Jaunich, Robert A215
Jaunich, Robert P394
Jauntig, Thomas F. A751
Javersack, Dawn P. P74
Javor, Dan P337
Jaworski, Peter W. A860
Jay, Colleen E. A662
Jay, Lady Sylvia W25
Jay, Lord Michael W42
Jay, Lady Sylvia W131
Jayakar, Prasanna P619
Jayaraman, N. Jay A201
Jayawickrema, Arosha P567
Jaye, James R. (Jim) E373
Jaynes, Steven P439
Jazdowski, Oscar E469
Jazdowski, Oscar A761
Jazwick, Andy E132
Jazwinski, Robert C. P471
Jean, Heidi St. A509
Jeanbart, Paul W403
Jeancourt-Galignani, Antoine W454
Jeanneret, Bran P240
Jeanniot, Lynn W302
Jeanson, Virginia W261
Jebson, Alan W. W476
Jeff, Jeffrey E391
Jeffcoat, Sally E. P448
Jeffe, Robert (Bob) A75
Jeffers, Rich A240
Jefferson, Michael A. A626
Jefferson, Frederick D. (Fred) A766
Jeffery, John J. E157
Jeffery, W. Jeremy (Jerry) A18
Jeffery, Scott W. A201
Jeffery, Barry A564
Jeffery, Reuben W72
Jeffery, Reuben W74
Jeffrey, David K. P269
Jeffrey, Don P582
Jeffries, Michael S. (Mike) A6
Jeffries, Jamie A586
Jeffs, Roger E510
Jegen, Tjeerd W488
Jeka, Mary R. P586
Jelenko, Jane A157
Jelinek, W. Craig A225
Jellison, Douglas J. A600
Jellison, William R. A753
Jemison, Mae C. A482
Jemmott, Nina P572
Jen, Enoch E215
Jendzejec, Mark A P511
Jenereaux, Joyce A362
Jeng, Joseph E379
Jenkin, Thomas M. (Tom) A142
Jenkins, Scott M. E78
Jenkins, David E83
Jenkins, Ab E132
Jenkins, Craig A. E218
Jenkins, Neil E. E355
Jenkins, John E393
Jenkins, Steven L. E420
Jenkins, Robert H. A27
Jenkins, James R. A244
Jenkins, Jeremy A265
Jenkins, William (B. J.) A285
Jenkins, Charles W A292
Jenkins, Roger W. A565
Jenkins, Ernest L. A633
Jenkins, Charles H. (Charlie) A672
Jenkins, Margaret L. A675
Jenkins, Derek L. A770

Jenkins, Dustee Tucker A770
Jenkins, Francis P. P40
Jenkins, Decosta E. P178
Jenkins, Roger L. P335
Jenkins, Charlie P410
Jenkins, Buddy P423
Jenkins, A. Dale P433
Jenkins, Kathy P536
Jenkins, Marten R. P539
Jenkins, Maurice E. P595
Jenkins, Rt. Hon. Martin J. P607
Jenkins, Antony W71
Jenkins, Antony W72
Jenkins, Antony W74
Jenkins, Chris W443
Jenkins-Scott, Jackie A167
Jenks, Maria E224
Jenks-Jay, Nan P415
Jenkyn, Oliver A844
Jenness, Calvin E. E64
Jenness, James M. (Jim) A476
Jenness, James M. (Jim) A482
Jennette, Mark E395
Jenney, Todd P316
Jenniches, F. Suzanne E338
Jennings, John E39
Jennings, James B. (Jim) E89
Jennings, Donna N. E144
Jennings, Richard B. E364
Jennings, Frank L. E474
Jennings, H. Keith A145
Jennings, William N. A210
Jennings, Karen E. A230
Jennings, Michael C. A417
Jennings, Toni A583
Jennings, Michael A670
Jennings, Scott S. A671
Jennings, James W. A681
Jennings, William M. (Bill) P79
Jennings, Stephen G. P289
Jennings, Mary P315
Jennings, A. Drue P348
Jennings, Toni P358
Jennings, Frank P553
Jennings, Reynold J. P636
Jennings, Austin W66
Jenny, Sacha E324
Jenny, Klaus W54
Jensen, Peder E13
Jensen, Rick W. E118
Jensen, Mac E176
Jensen, Traci L. E207
Jensen, Brett C. E292
Jensen, Keith A. E362
Jensen, Carol R. E425
Jensen, Tony E426
Jensen, Brent P. E536
Jensen, Keith A. A51
Jensen, Christopher W. A162
Jensen, Dan W. A251
Jensen, Richard C. A296
Jensen, Barry A440
Jensen, Bruce A449
Jensen, Julia A531
Jensen, Derrick A. A678
Jensen, Anita K. P100
Jensen, Gail M. P148
Jensen, Bruce P262
Jensen, Mark T. P324
Jensen, Karen P386
Jensen, Linda P546
Jensen, Mark T. P564
Jensen, Tommy W102
Jensen, Luke W240
Jensen, Anders W321
Jensen, Anders W435
Jenson, Warren C. E147
Jenson, Randall L. E234
Jenssen, Jens R. W414
Jentsch, Dieter W. W69
Jentzsch, Stefan W13
Jeon, Andrew E144
Jeon, Danny A872
Jeon, Lawrence A872
Jeppesen, Michael E541

Jeppesen, Jon A. A66
Jepsen, Edward G. E284
Jepson, Robert S. A262
Jepson, Robert P6
Jepson, Mark P477
Jeremiah, Barbara S. E196
Jeremiah, Barbara S. A34
Jeremiah, Dai W100
Jernigan, Nancy S. A56
Jernigan, Wyatt E. A234
Jernigan, Tania A439
Jerome, Chris J. A834
Jerschke, Tobias W260
Jerv?e, Johan A447
Jerves, Wayne E. P607
Jerzyk, Timothy P. (Tim) A885
Jesanis, Michael E32
Jesanis, Michael E. A587
Jesiolowski, Craig A. P510
Jesion, Paula J. A30
Jeske, Guy C. E109
Jesse, Sandra E228
Jesse, Jay P260
Jesse, David P518
Jessick, David R. (Dave) A697
Jessup, R. Judd E122
Jessup, Manuel E478
Jester, Lisa H. A661
Jesudas, Sajeev P590
Jesudason, Rob W130
Jesup, Barbara A73
Jesurasa, Jebashini P653
Jeter, Daniel B. A56
Jeter, Mark L. A773
Jeter, John H. A234
Jett, Clay E486
Jett, Clay A785
Jett, Paul P23
Jetter, Thomas E447
Jetton, Ann Marie E383
Jetzer-Chung, Alexandre F. W323
Jeunet, Philippe W189
Jewell, Greg A60
Jewell, William R. A865
Jewell, Tony W44
Jewett, Patrick (Pat) A88
Jewett, Joshua R. (Josh) A310
Jewett, Ellen A464
Jeworrek, Torsten W300
Jezek-Taussig, Jennifer P634
Jha, Prabir W430
Jhaveri, Vishu P71
Jiafu, Wei W118
Jiafu, Wei W119
Jian, Liu W125
Jian, Qiao W266
Jiang, Shibo P361
Jiang, Yansong W64
Jiang, Yongzhi W125
Jianguo, Han W121
Jianguo, Li W122
Jianhua, Zhang W120
Jianqing, Jiang W229
Jianzhou, Wang W119
Jichuan, Wu W122
Jick, Daniel J. P78
Jidong, Zhao W122
Jie, Yang W122
Jiemin, Jiang W339
Jigger, Anne Bachan P393
Jikumaru, Yusuke W34
Jilian, Xue W121
Jilu, Tong W122
Jimenez, Luis A. E50
Jimenez, Joseph (Joe) A201
Jimenez, Rey Y. A341
Jimenez, Linda A858
Jimenez, Steven A. P41
Jimenez, A. David P75
Jimenez, Pedro Lopez W10
Jimenez, Frank W102
Jimenez, Pedro Pedro Jose Lopez
  Jimenez W210
Jimenez, Joseph (Joe) W323

Jimenez, Menardo R. W379
Jimmerson, Martin L. (Marty) E421
Jimmie, Andrew (Andy) P10
Jin, H. P. E481
Jin, Jeoung (A. J.) A349
Jin, Shaoliang W343
Jindrich, Morgan P140
Jinglian, Wu W122
Jinks, Mary P610
Jinli, Wang W121
Jiping, Zhang W122
Jiping, Zhou W339
Jipping, Jon E. E284
Jischke, Martin C. E528
JNoderer, Nancee P297
Joas, Irmgard W300
Job, John E31
Job, Sir Peter J. D. E491
Job, Lyndsay P. A627
Job, Lisa H. P368
Jobe, Larry A. A762
Jobe, Warren Y. A858
Jobes, Elizabeth E51
Jobin, Luc A696
Jobkar, Kathi M. A34
Jodeit, Mel R. E296
Joe, David E183
Joei, Bernard W492
Joel, Richard M. P656
Joerres, Jeffrey A. A318
Joerres, Jeffrey A. A468
Joerres, Jeffrey A. A520
Joffe, Elya P545
Joggerst, Patrick E75
Joh, Bill A368
Johannesen, James (Jim) A534
Johanneson, Gerald B. A20
Johanneson, David A573
Johannessen, Morten S. W414
Johannessen, Tuve W399
Johannpeter, Jorge Gerdau W340
Johansen, Danny G. E108
Johansen, Michael Holm A197
Johansen, Trond-Erik A218
Johansen, Bob P39
Johansson, Ulf J. E498
Johansson, Thomas O. A511
Johansson, Nicole W804
Johansson, Hasse W3
Johansson, Leif W44
Johansson, Leif W166
Johansson, Ulf J. W166
Johansson, Ann-Sofie W203
Johansson, Martin W399
Johansson, Mats W400
Johansson, Inge W401
Johansson, Jan C. W425
Johansson, Christer W479
John, Jonelle St. E440
John, Jonelle E440
John, Robert (Bob) St. A742
John, Mike P316
John, Mark W. P401
John, Elaine P423
John, Barbara P614
John, Andrew W458
Johns, Frank G. E48
Johns, John D. A28
Johns, Derrick A. A282
Johns, Michael M. E. A374
Johns, John D. A374
Johns, Michael M. E. A466
Johns, Douglas A. (Doug) A557
Johns, David L. A620
Johns, Christopher P. (Chris) A640
Johns, John D. A666
Johns, John D. A667
Johns, John A688
Johns, Susan Carter P563
Johnsen, Andrew K. A138
Johnsen, Ken C. A469
Johnsen, Kjell-Morten W435
Johnson, Andrew E1
Johnson, James C. E5
Johnson, Ronald M. E22

Johnston, Camille W396
Johnston, Colleen M. W450
Johnstone, Michael (Mike) E539
Johnstone, William O. A93
Johnstone, Michael (Mike) A874
Johri, Rajive A217
Johs, Frederick C. P274
Joice, Judy E156
Joiner, Kathy P629
Joiner, Mark A. W301
Joint, David A357
Jollay, David L. P157
Jolley, Steve E262
Jolley, David A781
Jolley, Jay P182
Jolley, Clyde P623
Jolliffe, Lynn A441
Joly, Hubert A118
Joly, Hubert A682
Joly, Alain W261
Jonah, Samuel E. (Sam) W476
Jonas, Royal F. P375
Jonas, John F. P396
Jonas, Tina W. P531
Jonasson, Anders W203
Jones, Jennifer E34
Jones, Wayne L. E62
Jones, Sheri E73
Jones, John B. E125
Jones, Steven M. E126
Jones, Craig R. E169
Jones, Paul B. E176
Jones, Christopher L. (Chris) E193
Jones, William H. (Tony) E196
Jones, Charles E. (Charlie) E203
Jones, Marc E206
Jones, Robert L. E222
Jones, Rebecca A. (Becky) E247
Jones, Buck E292
Jones, Shane E309
Jones, Robbin W. E342
Jones, Douglas (Doug) E351
Jones, Brian E371
Jones, Jerry E371
Jones, Jeremy M. E381
Jones, Jeff C. E387
Jones, Richard H. (Rick) E392
Jones, Ginger M. E398
Jones, Trevor M. E434
Jones, Barclay G. E457
Jones, G. Bradford (Brad) E459
Jones, Dave A. E469
Jones, David P. E480
Jones, Lou H. E482
Jones, George F. E486
Jones, Roger V. E494
Jones, Paul E515
Jones, Doug E524
Jones, Wellington D. (Duke) A1
Jones, Tami A4
Jones, Darilyn A22
Jones, Stephen J. A24
Jones, Douglas L. (Doug) A25
Jones, Wendy F. A29
Jones, Trevor M. A36
Jones, John R. A39
Jones, Thomas W. (Tom) A42
Jones, Charles J. A54
Jones, John P. A81
Jones, W. O. A94
Jones, D. Paul A96
Jones, D. Michael A101
Jones, Christopher A109
Jones, Rendle A. A144
Jones, Hunter W. A145
Jones, Richard M. A160
Jones, John A168
Jones, Ingrid Saunders A197
Jones, Malcolm A201
Jones, Larry W. A212
Jones, Andrew A212
Jones, Tim A217
Jones, Mary K. W. A244
Jones, Clayton M. (Clay) A244
Jones, Adrian M. A260

Jones, Richard A. A318
Jones, William D. A320
Jones, Susie C. A329
Jones, Lucius S. A331
Jones, Mark L. A334
Jones, William H. (Tony) A340
Jones, Charles E. (Chuck) A341
Jones, Nicholas A351
Jones, Matt A362
Jones, Sidney G. (Sid) A373
Jones, Thomas A. A374
Jones, Douglas E. (Doug) A376
Jones, Travis A389
Jones, Paul J. A401
Jones, Michael A412
Jones, David A. A431
Jones, Kevin A433
Jones, Kevin J. A440
Jones, Robertson C. A444
Jones, Franklin B. A446
Jones, Barclay G. A459
Jones, Michelle A462
Jones, Sharon A475
Jones, Kevin A483
Jones, Dale E. A487
Jones, Michael A. A516
Jones, Rene F. A518
Jones, Charles L. A528
Jones, Chris A553
Jones, Leslie M. A563
Jones, Charles L. A579
Jones, Charles A580
Jones, Craig S. A584
Jones, Hannah A586
Jones, Dan A586
Jones, Christopher T. A596
Jones, Robert G. (Bob) A608
Jones, Wilson R. A617
Jones, David K. A632
Jones, Damon A661
Jones, Janice M. A673
Jones, Ellen A688
Jones, Mick A689
Jones, Clayton M. (Clay) A703
Jones, Karen M. A706
Jones, William C. (Bill) A706
Jones, Frank W. A706
Jones, William D. A720
Jones, Tim A742
Jones, Dave A. A761
Jones, Jeffrey L. A770
Jones, Keri A770
Jones, Michael S. A773
Jones, George F. A784
Jones, George F. A785
Jones, Michael (Mike) A807
Jones, Ernest E. A812
Jones, Mary S. A816
Jones, Ben A816
Jones, Chris A818
Jones, Tony A838
Jones, Graham O. A838
Jones, Walter H. A838
Jones, Jeffrey D. A845
Jones, Judy K. A874
Jones, Edson P37
Jones, Neal T. (Buddy) P52
Jones, Andy P68
Jones, Billy P79
Jones, Michael G. P90
Jones, Terry P96
Jones, Howard P108
Jones, Ellen P118
Jones, Gary S. P135
Jones, Sterling P. P144
Jones, Bernard Bryan P144
Jones, Tammy P145
Jones, Ed P163
Jones, D. B. P166
Jones, Marie M. P167
Jones, Marie M. P168
Jones, Tyler P171
Jones, Brad P178
Jones, Carolyn M. P179
Jones, Larry P193

Jones, Larri Sue P193
Jones, Frances P193
Jones, Larry P193
Jones, Travis P222
Jones, Michael (Mike) P258
Jones, Craig W. P277
Jones, Wayne P286
Jones, Jack M. P326
Jones, Barbara P335
Jones, Peter Lawson P336
Jones, Jackie P338
Jones, Mike P367
Jones, Gregory K. P372
Jones, Mark A. P375
Jones, Milton P375
Jones, Mark A. P386
Jones, Ronald P412
Jones, J. Thomas P413
Jones, Michael D. P420
Jones, Richard W. P430
Jones, Kendall C. P437
Jones, Jim P438
Jones, Lori P442
Jones, Chip P444
Jones, Patrice P471
Jones, Michael L. P474
Jones, Gerald P483
Jones, Jim P489
Jones, Douglas P513
Jones, Warren P524
Jones, Peter P526
Jones, Boisfeuillet (Bo) P533
Jones, Rhonda P538
Jones, Calvin P538
Jones, Ed P550
Jones, Tony P551
Jones, Chris P553
Jones, Tom P554
Jones, Dorothy P563
Jones, Mike P595
Jones, Michael (Mike) P596
Jones, M. Steven P600
Jones, Daniel W. P603
Jones, Clayton H. (Clay) P603
Jones, John P. P622
Jones, Terri P634
Jones, Charles J. (Charlie) P636
Jones, Tom P637
Jones, Mark W44
Jones, Graham W47
Jones, Den W85
Jones, Martyn W298
Jones, Sheldon W323
Jones, Philip W438
Jones, Richard W440
Jones, Andy W458
Jong, Ad de E39
Jong, Jan M. de W199
Jong, Peter W231
Jong, Ronald W258
Jong-Tae, Choi W345
Jongstra, Robert A661
Jono, Kazuya W420
Jonsson, Thomas W318
Jonsson, Jonas W330
Joo, In Ki W267
Joo, Jong Nam W267
Jooma, Imran A718
Joon-Ho, Han W345
Joos, David W. A190
Joos, David W. A221
Jooss, Gerhard W164
Joosten, Ruud W24
Jope, Alan W464
Jope, Alan Alan Jope W465
Jorda, Carlos E. A245
Jorda, Daniel W185
Jordahl, Mark S. P15
Jordan, Jamie E89
Jordan, William L. E153
Jordan, John E240
Jordan, Ray A58
Jordan, Vernon E. A73
Jordan, David A. A114
Jordan, Linda A134

Jordan, Deborah A. A144
Jordan, Sheila A181
Jordan, Glenn G. A199
Jordan, Ellen A296
Jordan, Myriah A309
Jordan, Courtney A334
Jordan, D. Bryan A336
Jordan, D. Bryan A337
Jordan, Raymond C. A466
Jordan, James E. A502
Jordan, Michael A536
Jordan, Jeffrey C. A626
Jordan, J. Craig A651
Jordan, Robert E. (Bob) A733
Jordan, Louis A745
Jordan, Henry K. A859
Jordan, Harold E. P32
Jordan, Darelene L. P201
Jordan, Joseph R. P239
Jordan, Betty F. P250
Jordan, Vernon E. P252
Jordan, Charles F. (Paco) P277
Jordan, Bradley R. P351
Jordan, Robert L. (Jay) P380
Jordan, Robert L. (Jay) P381
Jordan, Charles N. P391
Jordan, Randy P403
Jordan, Shawn P479
Jordan, Charles R. P540
Jordan, Will P553
Jorden, Yon Y. E324
Jordi, Markus W54
Jordi, Ignacio Ferrero W56
Jordis, Theresa W167
Jorgensen, Marlyn E136
Jorgensen, Mark E260
Jorgensen, Margaret E291
Jorgensen, Steven C. A435
Jorgenson, Mary Ann P99
Jornayvaz, Robert P. E277
Jose, Rodney San P78
Josefowicz, Gregory P. A636
Josefowicz, Gregory P. A637
Josefowicz, Gregory P. A826
Josefowicz, Gregory P. P583
Joseph, Tamara L. E133
Joseph, Gregory G. A51
Joseph, Pamela A. (Pam) A164
Joseph, Thomas A. A178
Joseph, Susan R. A205
Joseph, Tommy S. A455
Joseph, George A544
Joseph, Pamela A. (Pam) A810
Joseph, Lynne P232
Joseph, Ulrick P. P526
Joseph, Josh P656
Joseph, Rabbi P656
Josephs, Robin A459
Josephs, Robin A547
Josephson, Gordon W. P53
Josephson, Louis P135
Josey, Scott D. A66
Josey, Charles P292
Joshi, Satish E262
Joshi, Vyomesh (VJ) A415
Joshi, Prasoon A456
Joshi, Nina P652
Joshi, S.K. W85
Josi, Jean-Louis Laurent W49
Josiah, Timothy W. A685
Joskow, Paul L. A302
Joslin, James J. A378
Joslyn, Scott P302
Joslyn, Bari P449
Jospin, Deborah R. (Deb) P586
Joss, David P591
Joss, Michael E429
Joswiak, Greg A67
Joubert, Philippe W31
Joullie, Madeleine M. P18
Joulwan, Gen. George A. A365
Joung, Chansoo A66
Jourquin, Christian W406
Jourquin, Christian W407
Joussen, Friedrich P. (Fritz) W475

Kellner, Petr W41
Kellogg, Joseph K. (Keith) E131
Kellogg, Harry W. E469
Kellogg, William S. (Bill) A487
Kellogg, Peter N. A542
Kellogg, James A. (Jim) A609
Kellogg, Harry W. A761
Kellogg, Susan A841
Kellow, Glenn A630
Kellow, Glenn W88
Kelly, Patrick J. E3
Kelly, Edward E11
Kelly, Michael E55
Kelly, John P. E129
Kelly, Michael L. E132
Kelly, Thomas F. (Tom) E190
Kelly, Michael (Mike) E228
Kelly, John D. E237
Kelly, James T. E251
Kelly, John E328
Kelly, David M. E335
Kelly, Thomas J. E350
Kelly, Denis E351
Kelly, Thomas Patrick E388
Kelly, Peter E398
Kelly, David E411
Kelly, William J. E416
Kelly, Jill E. E488
Kelly, Suedeen E502
Kelly, James D. (Jim) E528
Kelly, Michael A. A2
Kelly, Brian G. A9
Kelly, Thomas B. (Tom) A14
Kelly, Thomas L. (Tom) A17
Kelly, Anne Gill A45
Kelly, Michael A. A58
Kelly, James P. (Jim) A79
Kelly, Edmund F. (Ted) A99
Kelly, Stephen E. A104
Kelly, Wally C. A159
Kelly, Kathleen A. A167
Kelly, Jackson A197
Kelly, Janet Langford A218
Kelly, Thomas A. A228
Kelly, Edward J. (Ned) A230
Kelly, Jim A232
Kelly, Michael A257
Kelly, Edmund F. (Ted) A285
Kelly, J.F. A288
Kelly, Scott M. A305
Kelly, Allan J. A307
Kelly, Theresa A349
Kelly, Thomas A361
Kelly, Jack W. A389
Kelly, John E. A452
Kelly, Tom A471
Kelly, Gary C. A509
Kelly, Alex A542
Kelly, Alfred F. (Al) A546
Kelly, Anastasia D. (Stasia) A621
Kelly, Michael A675
Kelly, David N. A697
Kelly, Gary C. A733
Kelly, Michael A735
Kelly, Steve A784
Kelly, Jill E. A789
Kelly, Thomas A827
Kelly, John P. P2
Kelly, David L. P2
Kelly, Thomas B. (Tom) P7
Kelly, Stephen E. P49
Kelly, William M. P72
Kelly, Kim P108
Kelly, Sam P128
Kelly, Mark P132
Kelly, Annice M. P132
Kelly, Michael E. P148
Kelly, Jack L. P187
Kelly, Paul P209
Kelly, Jack W. P222
Kelly, Tom P302
Kelly, Timothy E. (Tim) P312
Kelly, Terri L. P358
Kelly, Kathryn P360
Kelly, Michael J. (Mike) P420

Kelly, Lyn P439
Kelly, Alan B. P461
Kelly, John P465
Kelly, Sister Mary P580
Kelly, Tom W100
Kelly, Greg W316
Kelly, Gail P. W484
Kelly-Ennis, Debra J. A673
Kelly-Ennis, Debra W107
Kelman, Naomi W323
Kelmar, Steven B. A17
Kelp, Jamie P540
Kelsall, Bruce W413
Kelsey, Todd P. E398
Kelsey, Joel P139
Kelsheimer, Brad P159
Kelso, David B. E184
Kelso, J. Peter A18
Kelso, Harry B. A54
Kelso, David B. A77
Kelso, April D. A378
Kelso, Alan W. A768
Kelso, Stacey P410
Kelson, Richard B. (Rick) A208
Kelson, Richard B. (Rick) A539
Kelson, Richard B. (Rick) A649
Keltner, Robert P295
Kemball, Benjamin (Benj) W98
Kemmel, Gerard Van W383
Kemmochi, Masatoshi W334
Kemp, Derek E262
Kemp, Kruise E374
Kemp, Steve P394
Kemp, Adrian W44
Kemp, Jacques P.M. W247
Kempe, Rick P69
Kempen, Wouter van E138
Kempen, Wouter van A735
Kempen, Jake P32
Kemper, William B. E312
Kemper, Alexander C. (Sandy) E372
Kemper, Jonathan M. A206
Kemper, David W. A206
Kemper, Jonathan M. A207
Kemper, Alexander C. (Sandy) A813
Kemper, J. Mariner A813
Kemper, Alexander C. (Sandy) A813
Kemper, Jonathan M. P348
Kemper, Jeffrey H. (Jeff) P382
Kemper, David W. P569
Kemper, David W. P570
Kemper, Nikola W300
Kempf, Karl G. A447
Kempner, James C. E315
Kemppel, Denali P30
Kemps, Steven J. A242
Kempton, Will P384
Kenagy, John P296
Kenan, Wilfred M. (Mills) A223
Kenard, Deanna P333
Kenchel, Kurt T. P100
Kendall, Sara S. A867
Kendall, Randy P531
Kendall-Rijos, Pamela P132
Kendell, Ross E226
Kender, Joseph P297
Kendle, Candace A824
Kendra, Thomas W. (Tom) A139
Kendrella, Brian A736
Kendrick, Robin A130
Kendrick, Lynn A644
Kendrick, Don C. A859
Kendrick, Ken P404
Kendricks, Sam B. E231
Kendricks, Samuel E231
Kendricks, Sam B. A395
Kendricks, Samuel A395
Kengeter, Carsten W461
Kenison, Dani E115
Kenison, Tracy P207
KenKnight, Bruce H. E136
Kenley, William A. P334
Kenna, John A31
Kennan, Elizabeth T. A593
Kennard, Lydia H. A836

Kenne, Leslie F. A403
Kenne, Leslie F. A617
Kenne, Leslie F. P492
Kennedy, Kelly J. E44
Kennedy, Robert E. E46
Kennedy, Paul L. E92
Kennedy, Ken E130
Kennedy, Kieran M. E189
Kennedy, Jack E313
Kennedy, Len E368
Kennedy, Douglas L. E391
Kennedy, Brad E14
Kennedy, Nicole A70
Kennedy, John J. A177
Kennedy, W. Keith A215
Kennedy, Maria A256
Kennedy, Parker S. A327
Kennedy, Rick A368
Kennedy, Kevin W. A380
Kennedy, Laura A499
Kennedy, Wendy S. A662
Kennedy, Thomas A. (Tom) A685
Kennedy, Daniel O. A698
Kennedy, R. Michael A751
Kennedy, Scott A771
Kennedy, Barbara J. A829
Kennedy, Charles D. A858
Kennedy, Michael J. A859
Kennedy, Brad P7
Kennedy, Charles A P95
Kennedy, Robert T. (Bobby) P121
Kennedy, Ann P132
Kennedy, P. Todd P200
Kennedy, Leroy P254
Kennedy, Daniel E. P309
Kennedy, Terris P436
Kennedy, Terris P437
Kennedy, Bill P519
Kennedy, James M. (Jim) P533
Kennedy, Patrick T. W66
Kennedy, Jerome J. W66
Kennedy, John W156
Kennedy, Keith N. W330
Kennedy-Lahiff, Kristi P443
Kennelly, Jerry M. E421
Kennemur, Dan E84
Kenney, Jim E332
Kenney, Anthony R. (Tony) A522
Kenney, Thomas F. (Tom) A852
Kenney, Tom A852
Kenningham, Daryl A391
Kenny, Maria E155
Kenny, Steven E207
Kenny, Gregory B. A151
Kenny, Katharine A153
Kenny, Kate A156
Kenny, Gregory B. A364
Kenny, Gregory B. A442
Kenny, John J. A514
Kenny, Patrick J. A651
Kenny, Chris T. A819
Kenny, David W. A883
Kenny, Richard A197
Kenny, John R. P197
Kenny, Brian P540
Kenny, Shirley S. P559
Kent, E. Budge E36
Kent, Williams B. E93
Kent, William E277
Kent, Steven J. E390
Kent, Lena A138
Kent, Muhtar A197
Kent, Mark A431
Kent, Robert N. (Bob) A626
Kent, Philip I. (Phil) A793
Kent, Robert R. A853
Kent, Evelyn P29
Kent, William M. P114
Kent, Gregg P290
Kent, Robert P515
Kent, Thomas P533
Kent, Jerald L. (Jerry) P570
Kent, K. Craig P612
Keny-Guyer, Neal L. P328
Keny-Guyer, Neal L. P329

Kenyon, Chuck E104
Kenyon, Norman M. P44
Kenyon, John P120
Kenyon-Slaney, Harry W361
Keogan, Janet M. P493
Keogh, Brian D. E181
Keogh, Tracy A415
Keogh, John W. W9
Keohane, Ellen J. P130
Keon-Soo, Shin W249
Keough, Donald R. (Don) A116
Keough, Donald R. (Don) A197
Kephart, Bruce M. A342
Kephart, Bruce M. P292
Kephart, Kevin D. P481
Kepler, David E. (Dave) A268
Keppel, Karen E381
Keppner, Judy L. E423
Kepten, Avishai E429
Kerber, Lynn A172
Kerby, Brad A772
Kerby, Brad P524
Kerckhove, Ghislaine Van W248
Kerek, W. Damain P516
Kerger, Paula A. P420
Kerin, Matthew A. E197
Kerin, Matthew A. A344
Kerins, Ray A638
Kerkhof, Paul P. M. van de W352
Kerkhoff, Guido W445
Kerley, Jay A69
Kern, Paul J. E283
Kern, Paul J. A300
Kern, Peter M. A303
Kern, Ric L. A579
Kern, Dave A581
Kern, Howard P. P467
Kern, Mark P506
Kern, Andreas W197
Kern, Harald W396
Kernan, May P93
Kerner, John A. A305
Kerner, Douglas E. A530
Kerner, Jurgen W277
Kerner, Michael G. (Mike) W491
Kerns, Mike A883
Keroack, Mark A. P53
Keroack, Mark A. P54
Kerr, Keagan E110
Kerr, Mercedes E236
Kerr, Janet E. E544
Kerr, Derek J. A48
Kerr, William A. (Woody) A99
Kerr, William T. (Bill) A456
Kerr, Thomas R. A581
Kerr, Thomas P. (Tom) A651
Kerr, William T. (Bill) A869
Kerr, Mary E. P99
Kerr, Theresa P132
Kerr, Laurie P137
Kerr, Howard J. P138
Kerr, Donald M. P554
Kerr, Janet E. P651
Kerr, John C. W69
Kerr, Graham W87
Kerr, Graham W88
Kerr, John W361
Kerr, David W. W422
Kerrey, J. Robert (Bob) A778
Kerridge, Jeffrey S. (Jeff) E147
Kerrigan, Sylvia J. A521
Kerrigan, Sandra A846
Kerrigan, John P414
Kerrigan, Adrian P493
Kerris, Robert (Bob) E164
Kerris, Richard A415
Kerrmann, Dirk-Uwe W113
Kerschbaum, Manfred A69
Kershaw, James B. P72
Kershaw, Ed P578
Kerstetter, R.P. A288
Kerwin, Cornelius M. (Neil) P23
Keryer, Philippe W25
Kesavan, Sudhakar E257
Kesavan, Sudhakar A8

Koch, Olaf W286
Kocher, Jeff E486
Kocher, Jeff A785
Kocher, Edward P167
Kocher, Prof Renate W28
Kocher, Isabelle W49
Kocher, Prof Renate W81
Kocher, Isabelle W189
Kocher, Renate W277
Kochevar, Deborah T. P586
Kochhar, Rakesh W316
Kochubey, Viktor E22
Kochuparampil, Augustine W39
Kochvar, Mark A706
Kocis, Robert E408
Kock, Gerard de W352
Kockmann, Siegfried W335
Kocsondy, Lou P416
Kocur, John A. A66
Kodaira, Nobuyori W455
Koder, Matthew W461
Kodesh, Harel A284
Kodilla, Kenneth V. E366
Kodosky, Jeffrey L. E362
Kody, Thomas M. E10
Koecher, Renate W28
Koecher, Renate Renate Koecher W81
Koechlin, Michael J. E250
Koedijk, Dirk-Stephan W202
Koehl, Dennis L. A880
Koehler, Michael F. (Mike) A412
Koehler, William R. (Bill) A480
Koehler, Peter A586
Koehler, Suzanne P427
Koehn, Nancy F. E482
Koehnen, Michael W. A804
Koelbl, Tom A102
Koelbl, Tom P42
Koelbl, Konrad W179
Koele, Chad A14
Koele, Chad P7
Koelemay, Brenda T. A54
Koelkebeck, Debi P206
Koelker, June P529
Koellner, Laurette T. A53
Koellner, Laurette T. A453
Koelmel, John R. E196
Koelmel, John R. A340
Koelmel, John R. P280
Koenen, Patrick F. P245
Koenig, Karl J. A373
Koenigs, Todd P430
Koenigsberg, Steve P564
Koepfgen, Bruce L. A548
Koeppel, Holly K. A696
Koerber, Hans-Joachim A768
Koerner, John E256
Koerner, John A436
Koerner, Judith P315
Koerner, Cynthia P657
Koerner, Ulrich W461
Koerselman, Linda P175
Koertner, William A. (Bill) E358
Koessel, Kathryn C. A476
Koester, Jack A389
Koester, Jack P222
Koeter, John E475
Koets, Stephen P416
Koezuka, Masahiro W183
Koezuka, Masahiro W184
Koff, Howard M. P611
Koffel, Martin M. A836
Kofman, Clyde P590
Koga, Akira W283
Kogai, Masamichi W283
Kogan, Richard J. A99
Kogan, Richard J. A201
Kogler, Richard T. E461
Kogod, Dennis L. A241
Koguchi, Shigeo W452
Kogure, Makoto W408
Koh, Steven S. A872
Kohart-Kleine, Barbara L. P648
Kohl, Theresa W. E132
Kohl, Terry W. E132

Kohlberg, Prof Elon W441
Kohle, Tommy W479
Kohlenberg, Mark E535
Kohler, Mark L. E249
Kohler, Mark H. E261
Kohler, Pete B. A130
Kohler, Peter O. A741
Kohler, Roland W212
Kohler, Alexis W355
Kohlhepp, Robert J. (Bob) A180
Kohlhepp, Robert J. (Bob) A629
Kohlhepp, Robert J. (Bob) P655
Kohli, Raj A201
Kohlinger, Jorg W136
Kohlligian, Ann Marie A320
Kohlmann, Thomas P274
Kohlruss, Chuck P247
Kohn, Gary A. E277
Kohn, Robert A. A15
Kohn, Thomas W. A172
Kohn, Scott A255
Kohn, Pamela K. (Pam) A850
Kohnen, Scott E413
Kohnke, Matthew S. E150
Kohnke, Gilbert W336
Kohnstamm, Abby F. A645
Koide, Masatoshi A18
Koide, Thomas J. (Tom) A97
Koide, Sadayuki W194
Koike, Atsuyoshi A709
Koike, Tetsuya W117
Koike, Masato W140
Koike, Koh W327
Kois, John P58
Koizumi, Mitsuomi W241
Kojima, Keiji W208
Kojima, Yorihiko W289
Kojima, Nobuaki W289
Kojima, Kazuo W334
Kojima, Yorihiko W409
Kok, Eric E443
Kok, Wim W370
Kokensparger, Thomas L. A626
Kokubu, Fumiya W281
Kokubun, Ryosei W184
Kolady, Ashok E. E52
Kolakowska, Malgorzata W231
Kolarek, Angela E381
Kolarik, Tyler S. A399
Kolasa, Neta P47
Kolassa, Sean A640
Kolb, David L. E5
Kolb, David L. A555
Kolb, Jurgen A750
Kolb, Mark E. P480
Kolbe, Martin W260
Kolbeck, Steve A168
Kolberg, Robert (Bob) P519
Kolbl, Konrad W179
Kolcun, Liz P394
Kolding, Eivind W147
Kole, Bill P302
Kolesar, Robert J. E172
Kolesar, Robert J. A289
Kolff, Han W352
Kolison, Stephen P613
Kolkhorst, Mark L. A72
Koll, Norbert W202
Kollat, David T. E435
Kollat, David T. E541
Kollat, David T. A120
Kollatz-Ahnen, Matthias W170
Koller, Karsten von E527
Koller, Stephan A368
Koller, Dan W62
Kolligian, Lee Jay P448
Kolling, Johann F. (John) A651
Kolodgy, Robert J. (Bob) P70
Kolodzieski, Edward J. A849
Kolopajlo, Bruce D. A626
Kolstad, Gary A. E89
Kolumber, Dennis J. P446
Komai, Masayoshi W296
Komakhuk, Trudi P120
Komaki, Tatsuo W141

Komamura, Yoshinori W253
Komansky, David H. A123
Komar, Samuel E100
Komar, June P462
Komaroff, Stanley A713
Komatsu, Shunji W70
Komatsu, Hiroshi W180
Komejan, Donald (Don) P247
Komins, Jeffry P101
Komisar, Randy E428
Komiya, Shinichirou W253
Komiyama, Masahiro W405
Komola, Christine T. A744
Komori, Shigetaka W182
Komori, Mitsunobu W326
Komori, Mitsunobu W327
Kompkoff, Gabriel P120
Komsa, Kathryn A526
Komura, Yoshifumi W236
Konantz, James E291
Konar, Edward J. A479
Konczaty, Michel W89
Kondamudi, Vasantha P82
Kondo, Jun W180
Kondo, Hiroaki Hiroaki Kondo W183
Kondo, Yoshiki Yoshiki Kondo W184
Kondo, Koichi W214
Kondo, Kunio W307
Kondo, Shiro W358
Kondo, Yoshimasa W456
Kondrat, Michael E95
Konen, Mark E. A509
Konezny, Ron E498
Kong, David T. P61
Kong, Dong W121
Kong, Janis W250
Kong, Cheong Choong W336
Konidaris, Nicholas (Nick) E505
Konig, Andreas A576
Konijnenburg, Robin H. von W199
Konishi, Masahide W293
Konishi, Shunichi W455
Konkel, Kevin P426
Konkol, Ron P267
Konno, Hidehiro W290
Konno, Masaru W320
Konoda, Tetsuya W405
Konrad, Kristopher R. A64
Konstantakopoulos, Vassilios W303
Konsynski, Benn R. E485
Kontney, Christopher J. P576
Kontopanos, Kostas A201
Kontos, Mark W. P553
Konz, Jim P561
Koo, Jerry E343
Koo, George P. A496
Koo, Jeffrey L. S. W139
Koo, George C.G. W242
Koo, Bon Joon W267
Koo, Ja-Young W397
Koob, Beth P526
Koogler, David F. P427
Kooi, Joel A. Vander A477
Kookesh, Albert M. P463
Kool, Katie A662
Koon, James L. A773
Koonce, Paul D. A262
Koonce, Paul D. A843
Koondel, Scott A160
Koonin, Steven R. (Steve) A361
Koonin, Steven R. (Steve) A793
Koons, Frank A690
Koons, Anne E. A754
Koontz, Paul G. E193
Koontz, Richard L. A440
Koontz, Leah A734
Koontz, Timothy D. P69
Koontz, Gene C. P197
Koop, Peter W384
Kooperstein, Susan P3
Koopman, Nancy P185
Koopmann, Andreas N. W139
Koopmann, Andreas N. W309
Koopmans, Menno V. E511
Kooyker, Willem A359

Kooyman, John A201
Kopaskie, Mark S. E511
Kopel, Samuel P308
Kopell, Brian E368
Kopelson, Arnold A160
Kopetic, Thomas F. E364
Kopetic, Thomas F. A570
Kopf, Robert Y. A827
Kopf, MaryKay W3
Kopfman, Joe P22
Kopinski, Donna M. P149
Kopischke, Leanne A330
Koplovitz, Kay A139
Koplow, Meyer G. P78
Koplowitz, Esther W471
Kopnisky, Jack L. A751
Kopp, Michael E517
Kopp, Stephen J. P316
Kopp, Charles G. P574
Kopp, Cathy W387
Koppel, Michael G. A590
Koppelman, Catherine S. (Cathy) P600
Koppen, Roger P191
Koppy, Brian D. A77
Kopsa, Melroy P281
Koraleski, John J. (Jack) A816
Korbell, John C. P488
Korda, Peter P469
Korde, Gerald A838
Koremans, Robert W441
Koren, Moshe W62
Koren, Zvi W63
Koretz, David E161
Koreyva, Ken W9
Korfiatis, George P. P508
Korkuch, Marylu A177
Korlath, William J. A678
Korman, Bernard J. (Bernie) E378
Korman, Harry A. (Hal) A568
Kormeluk, Nicholas M. (Nick) A158
Kormos, Michael J. P408
Korn, Douglas R. E524
Korn, Allan M. P70
Kornachuk, Lisa M. E333
Kornberg, Mindy R. P611
Kornberg, Prof Roger D. W441
Korner, Lisa J. E315
Korner, Ulrich W461
Kornetzke, Mark A401
Kornicker, Peter W323
Kornowski-Bonnet, Sophie W362
Koro, Kimberly M. A676
Korologos, Ann McLaughlin A48
Korologos, Ann McLaughlin A426
Korologos, Ann McLaughlin A477
Korsgaard, Mark A177
Korstange, James E. (Jason) A773
Korte, Daniel G. (Dan) W364
Kortum, Joseph M. P398
Korzekwinski, Francis W. (Frank) A349
Korzen, Joyce P151
Korzen, Joyce P. P280
Kos, Heather A573
Kosakai, Yasuo W180
Kosasa, Paul J. A166
Kosch, Gregory L. (Greg) A325
Koschka, Ed P134
Kosecoff, Jacqueline B. (Jackie) A717
Koseki, Shuichi W238
Koser, Abram G. (Abe) A759
Koshida, Susumu W70
Koski, Kenneth L. (Ken) E109
Koski, Susan A767
Koski, John P27
Koski, Jim P506
Koskie, Doug A784
Koskinen, John A. A15
Koskull, Casper von W321
Kosmacher, Jeffrey B. P620
Koss, Michael J. E463
Koss, Richard P277
Koss, Richard P283
Kossover, Victoria A751
Kossubek, Peter W28
Kostelni, Jeffrey C. E326

A = AMERICAN BUSINESS
E = EMERGING COMPANIES
P = PRIVATE COMPANIES
W = WORLD BUSINESS

Koster, Karen A557
Koster, Barbara G. A669
Koster, Harry P653
Kostov, Todor W212
Kosturko, MaryEllen P79
Kosugi, Takeo W452
Kotagal, Uma P114
Kotagiri, Seetarama W274
Kotake, Nobukazu W253
Kotick, Robert A. (Bobby) A9
Kotkins, Henry L. (Skip) A8
Kotler, Christine P44
Kotler, Ofer W12
Kotsur, Robert P365
Kottler, Robert E256
Kottler, Robert A436
Kotula, Marty P199
Kotula, Leszek P361
Kotylo, Kenneth M. A776
Kotz, Hans-Helmut W149
Koudouris, Maria P122
Kouduki, Kazuo W446
Koumantzelis, Arthur G. A802
Koumettis, Nilolaos (Nikos) A197
Kouninis, Efstathios A. (Stathis) E392
Kourany, Ed P557
Kourgialis, Nicholas P237
Kourilsky, Philippe W471
Kourkoumelis, Dan P. A305
Kourtis, Spyro A456
Koury, Jeffrey (Jeff) A778
Koushik, Srinivas (Srini) A416
Kovac, Caroline P99
Kovacevich, Richard M. (Dick) A181
Kovach, Ronald E37
Kovach, Thomas J. E149
Kovach, Michael I. E307
Kovach, Andrew L. E36
Kovach, Keith P568
Kovacs, Michael A711
Kovalchick, Ann P166
Kovalchik, Michael T. E260
Kovar, Tom A174
Kovel, Leo E481
Koven, Andrew E51
Koverman, Robert P132
Kovzan, Stephen M. (Steve) E372
Kowalkowski, Michael A296
Kowaloff, Arthur D. E447
Kowaloff, Harvey P510
Kowalski, Michael J. A99
Kowalski, Michael A690
Kowalski, David A. A738
Kowalsky, Matthias P607
Kownacki, Hamila P521
Kozak, Sara A256
Kozak, Michael J. A339
Kozak, Conrad J. A471
Kozak, John W. A626
Kozak, Charlie P30
Kozal, Mike P416
Kozano, Yoshiaki W392
Kozberg, Joanne Corday P89
Kozek, William R. A622
Kozel, David A. A675
Kozero, Kathleen A49
Kozich, Gregory H. A649
Kozicz, Gregory J. (Greg) P11
Koziel, Mark P20
Kozik, Catherine E. P105
Kozikowski, Tami E302
Koziner, Pablo A156
Koziol, Ken A534
Kozlak, Jodeen A. A770
Kozlov, Alexander N. W187
Kozlov, Aleksandr W188
Kozoman, Robert L. (Bob) P156
Kozuka, Syuichiro W312
Kozy, Dave E179

Kozy, William A. A109
Kra, Douglas I. (Doug) E392
Kraal, Rob E260
Kraats, Robert-Jan van de W352
Krablin, Steven W. (Steve) E100
Kraemer, Harry M. J. E447
Kraft, Herbert A. E39
Kraft, Robert A. E132
Kraft, Robert (Rocky) A610
Kraft, Robert K. A842
Kraft, Arthur P110
Kraft, Walter P171
Kraft, Daniel A. (Dan) P586
Kraft, Sally P612
Kraich, Rick P623
Krajewski, David P299
Krajewski, David P478
Krakauer, Andrew A. E87
Krakauer, Mary A285
Krakaur, Kenneth M. (Ken) E467
Krakoff, Jeffrey A194
Krakower, Ira J. E244
Krakowsky, Philippe A456
Kralingen, Bridget A van A452
Kralingen, Bridget A452
Kralingen, Bridget van A366
Kralingen, Bridget W367
Kralingen, Tony van W373
Krall, Edward J. P465
Kramer, James S. (Jim) E48
Kramer, William J. E196
Kramer, Francis J. E266
Kramer, Jeffrey A24
Kramer, Andy A101
Kramer, Lawrence S. (Larry) A256
Kramer, William J. A333
Kramer, Larry A362
Kramer, Richard J. (Rich) A381
Kramer, Lewis A493
Kramer, Curt A. A573
Kramer, Michael W. A630
Kramer, Phillip D. (Phil) A647
Kramer, Jennifer (Jenn) A670
Kramer, Eli A754
Kramer, Andy P42
Kramer, Sean P47
Kramer, David A. P86
Kramer, Karen P298
Kramer, Jim P385
Kramer, Janie P472
Kramer, Peter W. P538
Kramer, Markus W76
Kramer, Marcus W79
Kramer, Terry D. W475
Kramlich, C. Richard (Dick) E469
Kramlich, C. Richard (Dick) A761
Kramp, Uwe W195
Kramvis, Andreas C. A421
Kran, Bob P337
Kranc, Lisa R. A84
Krane, Spencer D. A318
Krane, Hilary K. A586
Kranjc, James (Jim) P446
Kranker, Steven A E536
Krantz, Theodor E111
Krantz, Donald G. E406
Krantz, Jack F. P568
Kranz, James C. A428
Kranzler, Michael P656
Krapek, Karl J. A597
Krapek, Karl J. A669
Krapek, Karl J. A845
Kraras, Chris G. P430
Krasnoff, Jeffrey P. A500
Krasnoff, Eric P648
Krasnow, Lineene N. E329
Krasowski, Valerie A664
Krasowski, Janet D. A667
Krassner, Stuart M. E456
Kratz, Owen E239
Kratz, Carol A. A54
Kratz, Charles E. P608
Krauch, R.H. (Bobby) A695
Krauel, Jose W185

Kraus, Eileen S. E425
Kraus, Robert G. A319
Kraus, Eileen S. A742
Kraus, Carl P188
Kraus, Barbara P579
Kraus, Peter S. W49
Krause, L. William (Bill) E112
Krause, Douglas P. E162
Krause, Kendra E201
Krause, Lawrence B. E403
Krause, L. William (Bill) A222
Krause, Douglas P. A276
Krause, Daryl A733
Krause, Jean P224
Krause, Alan J. P351
Krause, Robert (Bob) P446
Krause, Rick P542
Krauss, George H. A547
Krausz, Steven M. E227
Krausz, George A563
Kraut, Jeffrey A. P370
Kraut, Hans G. W197
Krauter, Mark J. A548
Krauthamer, Ruth P653
Kravas, Constance H. (Connie) A101
Kravas, Gus K. J. P611
Kravchenko, Kirill W186
Kravcik, Keith A758
Kraversky, Gary A488
Kravis, Henry R. P559
Krawczyk, Joseph R. E337
Krayer, Georg F. W54
Kraynak, Lisa E142
Krc, Victor J. A54
Krebs, Mitchell J. E109
Krebs, Mitchell J. E110
Krebs, Karl E194
Krebs, David M. A233
Krebs, Bruce J. A305
Krebs, Karl A326
Krebs, Robert D. A372
Krebs, Donald E. A474
Krebs, Prof Rolf W261
Krebsbach, Dan P28
Krecek, John A. P148
Krecke, Jeannot W39
Kreckman, James A. E626
Kreczko, Alan J. A404
Kreeger, Craig S. A48
Kreeke, Jeffrey Van De P208
Kreger, Jeffrey M. E301
Kreh, Susan M. A468
Krehbiel, Bruce A457
Kreider, Torsten J. A228
Kreider, Robert Q. (Bob) P160
Kreidler, Robert C. (Chris) A768
Kreimeyer, Andreas W76
Kreisher, William F. (Bill) E50
Kreitzer, Gary A. E62
Kreitzer, Joseph L. P609
Krejci, Frank J. E463
Krell, Joanne K. P625
Kremer, Lawrence J. (Larry) P289
Kremidas, Steve H. A458
Kremin, Donald H. (Don) A423
Kremling, Ernest C. (Ernie) E297
Krempa, Jerry S. A112
Krenek, Alan E58
Krenek, Bryant H. P325
Krenicki, John A367
Krenke, Brian P290
Krenkel, David S. E149
Krentzman, Stewart P188
Krenz, Scott J. A73
Krenz, Douglas V. A290
Krenz, William C. (Willie) P531
Krepps, John P477
Kresa, Kent A348
Kress, Robert E. (Bob) W8
Kressel, Henry P492
Kretschmer, Eduardo W212
Kretzinger, Curt P236
Kretzmer, William B. (Brian) E288
Kretzschmar, Robert D. P355
Kreul, John A112

Kreutzer, Sharon P402
Kreutzer, Gerhard W277
Krick, Robert W. (Bob) A812
Krickbaum, Ravan P635
Kriebel, Bruce A457
Krieble, William R. A335
Krieg, John A595
Krieger, Daryl W. E538
Krieger, Sandra C. (Sandy) A319
Krieger, David L. A706
Krieger, James (Jim) P210
Krieger, Luke G. P446
Krieger, Susan P490
Krieger, Kenneth F. P547
Krieger, Alexandra W128
Kriegshauser, David (Dave) E39
Kriens, Scott G. E178
Kriens, Scott G. A472
Krift, Tom P457
Krikorian, Lazarus A57
Krill, Bill P522
Krimbill, H. Michael A584
Krimmel, Robert E242
Kring, Gail P422
Krinsky, Prof Itzhak W441
Krise, Thomas P611
Krishna, Arvind A452
Krishnakumar, Thirumalai A197
Krishnan, Lata E469
Krishnan, Lata A761
Krishnan, Ramayya P95
Kriss, V. John P201
Kristensen, Peter W325
Kritenbrink, Ron P456
Kritsanamara, Ayut W61
Kritzmacher, John A. E276
Krivanec, Ken A867
Krivoshik, William P. (Bill) A793
Kriz, Brian S. P246
Krmpotic, Deb A102
Krmpotic, Deb P42
Kroeger, Terry J. P148
Kroener, Ulrike Ulrike Kroener W210
Kroenke, Paul P78
Kroese, Hayko W257
Krogman, Martin J. A774
Kroh, William A. P221
Krohman, Barbara L. P449
Krohn, Scott D. A2
Krol, Wojciech A201
Krol, John A. (Jack) W9
Krolewicz, Randall A. A518
Kroll, Mark W. A228
Kroll, Edmund E. (Ed) A164
Kroll, Teresa M. A626
Kroll, Sue A793
Kroll, Fred L. P27
Kromer, Steve P21
Krominga, Lynn A87
Kron, Patrick W31
Kronau, Denice W396
Krone, Roger A. A125
Krone, Kevin M. A733
Kronemeyer, John P337
Kronen, Petra W78
Kroner, Ellen E30
Kroner, Kenneth F. (Ken) A122
Kroner, Ulrike W210
Krongard, A. B. E506
Kronick, Stephen E508
Kronseder, Volker P290
Kronsfoth, Ingo W457
Kroon, Hans van der W352
Kropelnicki, Martin A. (Marty) E86
Kropf, Susan J. A194
Kropf, Susan J. A490
Kropf, Susan J. A539
Kropf, Susan J. A622
Kropiunik, Frank C. P11
Kropp, Ronald D. (Ron) A438
Kropp, Richard P389
Kroshko, Igor A641
Krossa, Hubertus W53
Krotowski, Randy A156
Krouse, Michael P382

A = AMERICAN BUSINESS
E = EMERGING COMPANIES
P = PRIVATE COMPANIES
W = WORLD BUSINESS

Lash, James H. (Jim) A341
Lasher, Jeffrey (Jeff) E129
Lashlee, Turner O. A94
Lashley, Joseph A373
Laska, Christopher W435
Laskaris, George W304
Laskawy, Philip A. (Phil) A312
Laskawy, Philip A. (Phil) A372
Laskawy, Philip A. (Phil) A514
Laskawy, Philip A. (Phil) A713
Laskey, Sara P551
Laskowski, Igor P402
Lasky, Charles D. (Charlie) A341
Lasky, John P82
LaSorda, Thomas W. A20
Lass, John J. A358
Lass, Jan P87
Lassen, Lars Christian W325
Lasseter, Aline P359
Lassiter, E.G. A32
Lassiter, Susan S. P599
Last, Gabriel A245
Laster, Benjamin P508
Lastowski, Kevin E83
Lastra, Domingo A. A72
Lastra, Juan March de la W10
Laszkiewicz, Michael (Mike) A702
Lataif, Louis E. E7
Lataif, Louis E. A391
Lategan, Willie T. W71
Latella, Robert N. E194
Latella, Robert N. A326
Latham, Sara L. A54
Lathan, Kris A598
Lathan, Kris P374
Lathren, James E. (Jim) P393
Latimer, Greg A29
Latimer, Dale P. A332
Latimer, Dewitt P345
Latimer, Simon W51
Latimore, Autumn A75
Latino, Niki P130
Latka, John R. A671
Latno, Arthur C. A862
LaTorre, Craig M. A784
Latour, Richard F. E337
Latour, Deirdre A368
Latour, Richard A. A547
Latourette, Debra A765
Latta, Marcia S. P159
Lattin, William W. (Bill) E190
Latz, Jeanie A348
Lau, Jannie K. E276
Lau, Andrew E297
Lau, Angela E375
Lau, Vanessa A31
Lau, Timothy J. A75
Lau, Betty S. A319
Lau, James K. A576
Lau, Dennis P197
Lau, Mona P457
Lau, Leng W87
Lau, Lawrence J. W125
Lau, M. W130
Laubach, Harold E. P375
Laubenthal, Raymond F. E494
Lauberts, Peteris W479
Laubie, Christian W145
Lauble-Meffert, Inge W260
Lauckner, Jon J. A372
Laud, Katharine A668
Lauder, William P. A463
Lauder, Estee W280
Lauderback, Brenda J. E435
Lauderback, Brenda J. E541
Lauderback, Brenda J. A120
Lauderback, Brenda J. A563
Lauderdale, Katherine P420
Lauenroth-Mago, Jorg W113

Lauer, David P. E145
Lauer, Gary L. E167
Lauer, Trevor F. A247
Lauer, Trevor F. A271
Lauer, David P. A433
Lauer, J. Michael A548
Lauer, Len J. A864
Lauer, David P. P380
Lauer, David P. P381
Lauer, Michael P451
Lauer, Larry D. P529
Lauer, Andrew J. P656
Lauer, Stefan W151
Lauf, Michael K. (Mike) P90
Lauffer, Gerhard E542
Lauffer, Dave A708
Lauffer, Margaret M. (Marlee) P239
Laufgraben, Jodi Levine P526
Laughery, Debra Z. P628
Laughinghouse, Durwood S. A591
Laughlin, Terrence P. (Terry) A96
Laughlin, Vince A532
Laughlin, John P. A689
Laughlin, Patricia P254
Laughlin, Cheryl H. P609
Lauk, Kurt W274
Lauke, Harald W76
Laukien, Frank H. E77
Laukien, Joerg C. E77
Laukien, Dirk D. E77
Laukien, Joerg C. E77
Laukien, Dirk D. E77
Laukkanen, Lisa E170
Laun, Max W. A31
Launer, Lee A399
Launius, Steve P168
Lauraguais, Bernard de La Tour
  d'Auvergne W102
Lauraguais, Bernard W102
Laurance, Dale R. A441
Lauren, Ralph A682
Lauren, David A682
Laurence, Scott A464
Laurence, Travis P169
Laurence, Guy W475
Laurent, Jean Gaston Pierre Marie
  Victor W145
Laures, Steve P197
Lauri, Greg P641
Lauria, Dorothy M. P424
Lauritzen, Bruce R. P148
Lauroesch, Mark W. A223
Laursen, Chris A678
Laursen, Thomas E. (Thom) A888
Laury-Deroubaix, Veronique W250
Lautenbach, Marc B. A452
Lautenbach, Marc B. A645
Lautenbach, Ned C. P187
Lautenschlaeger-Peit, Sabine W150
Lauterbach, Ervin F. (Erv) A830
Lauth, Thomas P. P601
Lauvergeon, Anne W189
Lauvergeon, Anne W453
Lauvergeon, Anne W476
Lauwagie, Kevin P593
Lavan, Kevin C. E307
Lavan, Maryanne R. A512
LaVanture, Richard E. P249
LaVay, Matt E170
LaVecchia, Daniel M. E59
LaVecchia, Jean M. A593
Lavedrine, Christian W127
Lavelle, Patrick M. (Pat) E526
Lavelle, Larna P335
Lavender, Kevin P. E40
Lavender, Shelley K. A126
Lavender, Kevin P. A325
Lavengood, Carol A232
Laver, Joseph P501
Laverty, D. Scott (Scott) A630
Lavery, Roger P41
Lavery, Robert P179
Lavery, Dave P241
Lavery, William R. (Bill) P519
Lavespere, Mike P87

Lavey, Richard (Dick) A398
Lavigne, Jean E324
Lavigne, Louis J. A36
LaVigne, Mark S. A291
Lavigne, Patrick P355
Lavilla, Antonio Massanell W434
Lavimodiere, Keith A. A853
Lavin, George J. E330
Lavin, William K. A32
Lavin, Richard P. (Rich) A155
Lavin, Peggy P277
Lavinay, Gerard W109
LaViolette, Paul A. E490
Lavitt, Mel S. A460
Lavizzo-Mourey, Risa J. A414
LaVoice, Richard G. E472
Lavoie, Blair P351
Law, Gerard (Jerry) E286
Law, Christina A370
Law, Scott D. A409
Law, Robert W. A766
Law, Gerard A858
Law, John C. P102
Law, Linda P563
Law, Tom P575
Lawal, Kase L. P410
Lawhorn, Caron A. A613
Lawler, R. Douglas (Doug) A61
Lawler, Robert D. (Doug) A173
Lawler, John A353
Lawler, Julia M. A658
Lawler, Charles P329
Lawler, Stephen J. P406
Lawler, Stephen J. P599
Lawless, Stephen T. P358
Lawlor, Richard J. A414
Lawlor, Elizabeth A591
Lawlor, Kevin P187
Lawlor, Edward F. P570
Lawn, John P241
Lawonn, Ken P147
Lawrence, David E13
Lawrence, Bryan H. E46
Lawrence, Thomas R. E135
Lawrence, R. Bradley (Brad) E181
Lawrence, Bryan H. E231
Lawrence, Larry M. E292
Lawrence, James R. E300
Lawrence, G. Larry E300
Lawrence, William B. E319
Lawrence, Ira D. E434
Lawrence, Bryan H. E459
Lawrence, Gary A13
Lawrence, David M. A21
Lawrence, George D. A66
Lawrence, Jim A240
Lawrence, Wes A480
Lawrence, David M. A536
Lawrence, Taylor W. A685
Lawrence, James G. A838
Lawrence, Frederick M. P78
Lawrence, Stephen (Steve) P107
Lawrence, Ida P174
Lawrence, Sandra A. J. P328
Lawrence, William B. P484
Lawrence, Kenneth (Ken) P526
Lawrence, Paul J. A217
Lawrence, James A. (Jim) W233
Lawrence, Christian W300
Lawrence, Ken W370
Lawrence, Ben W480
Lawrence-Apfelbaum, Marc A792
Lawrie, J. Michael (Mike) A214
Lawrie, J. Michael A472
Lawson, Rodger A. A275
Lawson, Jimmie A334
Lawson, Peter (Pete) A353
Lawson, Larry A512
Lawson, Scott P. A581
Lawson, David T. A591
Lawson, Thomas J. A626
Lawson, Larry A737
Lawson, Rodger A. A832
Lawson, Ralph E. P44

Lawson, Ralf P45
Lawson, James W. (Jim) P48
Lawson, Doug P52
Lawson, Frank P188
Lawson, Matt P321
Lawson, Paul E. P399
Lawson, Jason P399
Lawson, Jennifer P420
Lawson, H. West P628
Lawson, John P640
Lawton, Leonard E11
Lawton, Alison E133
Lawton, Graham A66
Lawton, Gregory E. A364
Lawton, Hal A419
Lawton, Edgar H A729
Lawton, Father Robert B. P304
Lawton, Joseph P501
Lawton, Keith W100
Laxer, Richard A. (Rich) A367
Laxson, Dawn P508
Laxton, Stephen D. A600
Lay, Jack B. A688
Lay, Robert P585
Lay, Patrick Le W127
Laybourne, Geraldine B. (Gerry) A631
Laybourne, Geraldine B. (Gerry) A764
Layden, Steve E345
Layman, Harold E. E65
Layman, Harold E. E269
Layman, John R. A101
Laymon, Joe W. A174
Layton, Thomas H. E382
Layton, Donald H. (Don) A53
Layton, Wade A183
Layton, Donald H. (Don) A356
Layton, John A. P203
Lazar, Greg E21
Lazar, Gerry P144
Lazare, Aaron P376
Lazarus, Larry S. A102
Lazarus, Franz E. A225
Lazarus, Rochelle B. (Shelly) A368
Lazarus, Rochelle B. (Shelly) A543
Lazarus, Larry S. P43
Lazberger, Mark J. W130
Lazenby, Larry P43
Lazer, Stephen P174
Lazo, Nelson P44
Lazzaretti, V.A. A288
Lazzaro, Nick E473
Lazzarotti, Michelle P495
Le, Duy-Loan T. E362
Lea, Doretha F. (DeDe) A842
Lea, Jerrold P. P244
Lea-Maijala, Barb P144
Leach, Charles N. E58
Leach, Timothy A. E117
Leach, Charles N. A116
Leach, Brian A184
Leach, Ronald G. A729
Leach, A. John A873
Leach, Les P325
Leach, Scott A. P548
Leach, Karen P558
Leach, Craig P575
Leach, Lord C. G. Rodney W242
Leadbeater, Seth M. A206
Leadbeater, Seth M. A207
Leader, Jay E283
Leader, Martin R. E446
Leader-Smith, Elizabeth A870
Leahy, John J. E283
Leahy, Kevin P204
Leahy, Joyce A. P308
Leahy, Joseph P485
Leahy, Debra P540
Leahy, William P. P585
Leahy, Patrick P608
Leake, Michael T. E507
Leake, Michael T. A815
Leal, Carlos E. Ortega A584
Leaman, J. Richard P180
Leaman, J. Richard (Rick) W461
Leaming, Nancy L. A121

A = AMERICAN BUSINESS
E = EMERGING COMPANIES
P = PRIVATE COMPANIES
W = WORLD BUSINESS

A = AMERICAN BUSINESS
E = EMERGING COMPANIES
P = PRIVATE COMPANIES
W = WORLD BUSINESS

Lundgren, Charlene P164
Lundgren, Cully P329
Lundgren, Johan W458
Lundgren, Johan W459
Lundius, Annika W415
Lundquist, Andrew D. E110
Lundquist, Andrew D. A218
Lundquist, Jane L. A440
Lundquist, Keith P247
Lundquist, Bo W203
Lundsberg, Suann A138
Lundy, James H. (Jim) E532
Lundy, James H. (Jim) A863
Lundy, R. D. P466
Lundy, R. D. P467
Lundy, Larry P563
Lundy, Nicki W413
Lung, Cha (Laura) May W122
Lunn, Robert J. A61
Lunn, Steven (Steve) A806
Lunn, Catherine A. P620
Lunnen, Cheryl P564
Lunsen, Gil J. Van A614
Lunsford, Rich E166
Luo, Solomon C. P526
Luo, Lianfu W139
Luongo, Peter P566
Luongo, Manfredi W54
Luongo, Piero W234
Luparello, Stephen I. P195
Lupfer, Rev William P296
Lupica, John W9
Lupinacci, Giovanni W466
Lupinetti, Martin P557
Lupo, John S. W3
Lupo, L. Patrick W102
Lupone, E. Robert A787
Luppino, Frank J. E43
Lupton, Laurie W278
Luqman, Mo P240
Luque, Santiago A4
Lurie, Alexander J. (Zander) A160
Lurie, Robert F. P363
Lurker, Nancy E51
Lusak, Richard P274
Lusardi, Robert R. E472
Lusby, James P67
Luscan, Philippe W382
Lusch, Andreas W31
Lusco, C. Matthew A688
Lusignani, Giuseppe W54
Lusk, James S. A8
Lusk, Michael A71
Lusk, John M. A354
Luskin, Meyer E384
Luskin, Bernard J. P576
Lussier, Michel E. E525
Lustigman, Sara P361
Lutek, Ben W. A798
Luterman, Gerald (Gerry) A599
Luthar, Vikram A71
Luther, Siegfried W482
Luthringer, Liff P168
Lutkestratkotter, Herbert W197
Lutnick, Howard W. E59
Lutt, Kris A72
Luttecke, Kurt A822
Luttig, J. Michael (Mike) A125
Luttmer, Kelly D. E298
Luttmer, Kelly D. E516
Luttrell, Peter E142
Luttrell, Nancy P26
Luttrell, Claudia S. P562
Lutz, Lamar E447
Lutz, Robert S. A238
Lutz, Laurent C. A726
Lutz, Susan L. P130
Lutz, Frank H. W277
Lutz, Rolf W489
Lutz-Lento, Karen L. A120
Lutzke, Rhonda A358
Luu, Michael B E86
Luu, Hang W278
Lux, Robert A356
Lux, Robert H. P526

Luxembourg, Guillaume Guillaume de
   Luxembourg W39
Luxembourg, Prince Guillaume
   de W39
Ly, Debbie A175
Lyall, Thomas M. A626
Lyall, Jennifer P305
Lybarger, Stanley A. (Stan) A127
Lydecker, Kent P552
Lydon, Jean P180
Lyew, Peter G. E307
Lyght, Rose-Marie A64
Lyght, William L. (Bill) P326
Lykins, Gregory B. (Greg) A330
Lykins, Carey B. P121
Lyles, Patrick (Todd) E28
Lyles, Todd E28
Lyles, Gen. Lester L. A105
Lyles, Gen. Lester L. A365
Lyles, Gen. Lester L. A475
Lyles, Gen. Lester L. A655
Lyles, Gen. Lester L. P49
Lyles, LaJuan H. P595
Lyman, Kevin H. E29
Lyman, Robert D. P609
Lyman, Gregory A. (Greg) P625
Lynam, Terry P204
Lynam, Aidan W212
Lynas, Peter W51
Lynch, Dennis F. E91
Lynch, Brian J. E95
Lynch, Jason M. E250
Lynch, Robert M. E309
Lynch, Edward L. E333
Lynch, Kevin J. E383
Lynch, Thomas E. E388
Lynch, John E479
Lynch, Christopher S. A53
Lynch, Robert P. A56
Lynch, Gary G. A96
Lynch, William J. A103
Lynch, Michael A. (Mike) A151
Lynch, Jerome J. A193
Lynch, Matthew J. (Matt) A249
Lynch, Charles J. A305
Lynch, Donald M. A341
Lynch, Christopher S. A356
Lynch, John F. A367
Lynch, Mike A416
Lynch, Denise I. A479
Lynch, Edward A526
Lynch, Brian A684
Lynch, John A772
Lynch, Thomas J. (Tom) A791
Lynch, Richard A840
Lynch, Patrick D. A862
Lynch, Bob P23
Lynch, Lisa M. P78
Lynch, Mary P118
Lynch, Mel P120
Lynch, William F. P166
Lynch, Cecelia (CeCe) P179
Lynch, John J. (Jack) P270
Lynch, John J. (Jack) P309
Lynch, Jeremiah T. P446
Lynch, Ted P487
Lynch, Christopher W361
Lynchard, Ken E355
Lynd, Michael M. A210
Lynde, James E457
Lynds, Gregory S. (Greg) E62
Lyne, Sister Sheila P329
Lyness, James D. (Jim) A174
Lynn, Shaun D. E59
Lynn, Mitchell E403
Lynn, Denise A48
Lynn, Christine E. P74
Lynn, Steven W. P565
Lynton, Michael M. W408
Lyon, Anne E333
Lyon, Diana B. A378
Lyon, J. Larry P52
Lyon, Freda P524
Lyon, Lew P564
Lyons, William J. E86

Lyons, John J. E150
Lyons, Irving F. (Bud) E178
Lyons, William M. (Bill) E372
Lyons, Melissa E417
Lyons, Rick E472
Lyons, Dianne M. E509
Lyons, Martin J. A46
Lyons, Jeffrey A225
Lyons, Jim A232
Lyons, Robert C. A386
Lyons, Garry A529
Lyons, Matthew J. A600
Lyons, Michael P. A649
Lyons, Thomas M. A667
Lyons, Melissa A691
Lyons, Brenda A749
Lyons, Rick A778
Lyons, Warren R. A787
Lyons, Dianne M. A821
Lyons, Bethany A. A853
Lyons, Walter G. P41
Lyons, Peter A. P53
Lyons, Scott P166
Lyons, William J. P168
Lyons, B.W. P630
Lyons, Gerard W411
Lytal, James E437
Lytle, L. Ben E239
Lytle, Walter A. P264
Lytle, Cherie P615
Lyublinsky, Michael W368

M

M, Adrian A867
M.B.A, James E23
M?rch, Lars Stensgaard W146
Ma, Ken P375
Ma, Yuzhu W122
Ma, Peter M. Z. W343
Ma, Yun W404
Maag, Allen W. (Al) A88
Maag, Maureen A215
Maag-Spieler, Jacqueline W12
Maartensz, Jon A709
Maas, Werner E77
Maas, Brian J. E235
Maas, Pamela P224
Maass, Paul A217
Mabe, Katherine (Kathy) A38
Mabey, Rendell P188
Mable, Richard P430
Mabrey, Larry P634
Mabry, Steven A271
Mabry, Joseph M. (Mike) A516
Mabuchi, Akira W180
Macaione, Katheryn B. P424
Macak, Jeffrey W. A310
Macaluso, Charles E136
Macaluso, Charles A643
Macan, W. Andrew A177
Macan, Drew P415
Macarchuk, Nicole J. E296
Macarchuk, Nicole J. A486
Macaronis, Nicholas A. P514
MacArthur, Barbara P524
Macaskill, Blake A183
Macaskill, Bridget A. W348
Macau, Carlos E241
Macauda, Michele M. P187
Macaulay, Bruce A. A489
Macchia, Richard E198
Macchiarola, Doreen A. E391
Macchiaverna, Frank R. A591
MacConnell, Sally W. P275
MacCormack, George F. A633
MacCormick, Ron P462
Maccubbin, Craig E457
Maccubbin, Craig A734
MacDiarmid, Bruce P471
Macdonald, Jeff E13
MacDonald, Robert W. E80
MacDonald, Laura E111
MacDonald, Michael R. (Mike) E153

MacDonald, Michael R. (Mike) E154
MacDonald, Michael C. E330
Macdonald, Iain A. E470
MacDonald, Michael E503
MacDonald, Timothy A131
MacDonald, Donald A265
MacDonald, Donald J. (Don) A343
Macdonald, Thomas R. (Tom) A446
MacDonald, J. Randall (Randy) A452
Macdonald, Deborah A. (Deb) A483
Macdonald, Deborah A484
MacDonald, George P124
Macdonald, Deborah A. P148
MacDonald, Walt P174
MacDonald, Mott P232
MacDonald, Mariann T. P357
MacDonald, Kathleen V. P493
MacDonald, Shelley P549
MacDonald, Neil P564
Macdonald, John Paul W91
MacDonald-Sheetz, Margaret E330
MacDougall, Michael G. A292
MacDougall, Michael G. A385
MacDougall, Harriett P375
MacDougall, Dave P647
Mace, Alexander P484
Macedo, Jorge W161
Macek, Charles W480
Macey, Gerry E223
MacFarland, Lisa P614
Macfarlane, C.N. (Sandy) A174
Macfarlane, Ken A353
MacFarlane, Stuart W37
Macfarlane, Ian J. W46
Macfarlane, Ian J. W488
MacGibbon, Glen E326
MacGowan, William N. (Bill) A581
MacGowan, Bill A581
MacGregor, J. Scott A508
MacGregor, Alastair P334
Macgregor, Nancy P563
MacGuire, Mary P654
Machado, A. Ricardo A628
Machado, Luiz Pasteur
   Vasconcellos W56
Machado, Diogo C. B. de Lacerda W161
MacHale, Joseph P. (Joe) W368
Machell, Simon W47
Macher, Erin K. A414
Macheras, Kostas W169
Machetti, Claudio W162
Machida, Yukio W405
Machida, Kiyomi W417
Machon, Monika A53
Machones, Melinda P502
Macht, Michael W477
Machtolf, Paul A694
Machuca, Luis F. A814
Machuzick, John T. A370
Macias, Stephen A430
Macias, Edward S. P569
Maciel, Jason P623
Macina, Robert P. P293
Macina, Lucy O. P648
MacInnes, Glenn I. A855
MacInnis, Frank T. A286
MacInnis, David G. (Dave) A773
MacInnis, G. Brian A774
Macino, Jean H. E122
MacIntyre, Michael J. E244
MacIntyre, Sandy P533
MacIntyre, Gregg W330
Macip, Marcus E301
Mack, Timothy A. E24
Mack, Warren E. E80
Mack, Cary P. E532
Mack, Connie A240
Mack, Michael J. A244
Mack, Peter A325
Mack, Cary P. A863
Mack, Don P74
Mack, Timothy P. P214
Mackay, Martin E23
Mackay, Tara E61
MacKay, Mike E428

Maier, Stuart E227
Maier, Lothar E304
Maier, Henry J. A321
Maier, Joe P98
Maier, Peter K. P607
Maier, Gerhard W384
Mailloux, J. Wayne A242
Maiman, Dana A456
Maiman, Janice M. P20
Main, Timothy L. A460
Mainardi-Rosenthal, Helen W432
Maine, Douglas L. E76
Maines, Dean A. E19
Maingot, Rhonda P200
Mainous, Rosalie O'Dell P652
Mainwaring, Brenda A816
Maio, Keith D. A888
Mair, Jim P611
Maire, Kathleen P101
Maissel, Gerda P53
Maisto, Mark A583
Maitland, James A99
Maitland, Alister Alister Maitland W275
Maitlin, Larry A439
Maiz, Jose A. A447
Maizey, Silla W233
Majima, Nobuaki W358
Majni, Christopher P323
Major, Sandra E18
Major, John E. E383
Major, John E. A135
Major, Sean D. A469
Major, Philip L. P260
Major, William B. P617
Majoras, Deborah P. A661
Majoros, George L. P99
Majors, Charles H. (Charlie) E36
Majors, Mike A798
Mak, Patrick P531
Maki, Craig A. E12
Maki, Corinne A. E253
Maki, Mark A. A290
Maki, Shinsuke W34
Makino, Fujiatsu W291
Makino, Masashi W338
Makoul, Gregory P449
Makovsky, Evan A195
Makowka, Vicki L. A773
Makowski, Rogean B. A853
Makridis, Alexandros W303
Makris, George A. A724
Maksymow, Michael J. P56
Malach, Itzhak W63
Malandra, Robert E446
Malandro, Edward (Ed) A754
Malanga, J. D. W245
Malasto, Thomas A. P134
Malatesta, Matthew J. P586
Malave, Andres P375
Malavez, Patricia W468
Malchoff, Kevin R. P435
Malchuk, Daniel E64
Malchuk, Daniel W87
Malchuk, Daniel W88
MalchukBE, Daniel W88
Malcolm, Steven J. (Steve) A127
Malcolm, Robert M. (Rob) A411
Malcolm, Steven A613
Malcolm, Andrew L. (Andy) A768
Malden, Guy E344
Maldonado, Bill W218
Male, Jeremy J. A160
Malecky, Robert A. A137
Malehorn, Jeffrey (Jeff) A367
Malek, Frederic V. E156
Malek, Frederic V. A158
Malek, Kamran P27
Malek, Philip G. (Phil) W422
Malempati, Krishna M. A212
Malerba, James J. A749
Malerba, Marilynn R. (Lynn) P294
Malerba, Marilynn R. (Lynn) P295
Maleson, Diane P526
Maletira, Amar A416
Maletta, Matthew J. A36

Maley, Heather A180
Maley, Ernie A341
Maleyeva, Maria A244
Malfatti, Carole P658
Malgieri, James A99
Malhotra, Kanuj A103
Malik, Irfan A2
Malik, Ashraf K. A169
Malik, Rajiv A568
Malik, Shahid A671
Malik, Asif W24
Malik, Yogesh W435
Malin, Clint B. E307
Malin, John P191
Malina, John A232
Malina, Brian C. A840
Malino, Gary M. E413
Malinoski, Steven P303
Malinovitch, Aviv E98
Malinowski, Rafal A709
Malinskas, Linda P362
Maliszewski, Kenneth A751
Malkiel, Shahar W63
Malkiewicz, Steve A452
Malkiewicz, Janet P277
Malkin, Roy K. E87
Mallac, David W373
Malleau, Anne A870
Mallery, Edwina P292
Mallesch, Eileen A. A747
Mallet, Chuck E247
Mallett, Leonard W. A297
Mallett, Conrad L. A497
Mallett, Cynthia A545
Malley, Ted E504
Malliet, Dan W396
Mallinckrodt, Thomas von W429
Mallino, Sue A39
Mallon, Mark W44
Mallon, Gerry W147
Mallory, Robin D. A548
Mallory, Bradley L. (Brad) P41
Mallory, Kenny P246
Mallory, Susan H. P537
Mallory, Bruce L. P614
Mallott, Byron I. A29
Mallott, Philip E. A120
Mallott, Anthony P463
Mallott, Byron I. P463
Mallow, Amanda E201
Mallow, Matthew J. A122
Malloy, Jim A439
Malloy, William A. P187
Malloy, Tara P321
Malloy, Thomas E. P607
Malloy, Richard P608
Malloy, Rev Edward A. P610
Malloy, Dorothy A. P622
Malloy, Thomas K. P642
Malm, C. Michael E107
Malmborg, Joe A820
Malnight, Steven A640
Malone, Ronald A. (Ron) E217
Malone, Thomas C. E526
Malone, Mary Alice D. A147
Malone, Daniel J. (Dan) A221
Malone, John C. A256
Malone, John C. A303
Malone, Michael J. A305
Malone, David J. A308
Malone, Robert A. (Bob) A394
Malone, John C. A506
Malone, Evan D. A506
Malone, Robert A. (Bob) A630
Malone, James R. (Jim) A688
Malone, Judith P59
Malone, Michael P. P245
Malone, Thomas P515
Malone, Rev H.S. P551
Malone, Rev John M. P609
Malone, Rev John M. P610
Maloney, Mary D. E255
Maloney, Matt E469
Maloney, Don A102
Maloney, Drew A414

Maloney, Michael P. A429
Maloney, Sean M. A446
Maloney, Dan A610
Maloney, Matt A761
Maloney, Don P42
Maloney, Robin P559
Maloney, Bill W414
Maloof, Thomas A. E174
Mals, Deb P336
Malson, Kelly M. E543
Maltezos, Louis P. E32
Maltsbarger, Richard D. A516
Malungani, Mangalani W235
Malus, Alan J. A791
Malveaux, Floyd J. P148
Malveaux, Antoinette M. P607
Malz, Nick E6
Mamillapalle, Venkatram W430
Mammen, Timothy P. V. E282
Mamonov, Pavel A709
Manabe, Hiroshi W311
Manaf, Nora Nora Abd Manaf W275
Manager, Vada O. A75
Manahan, Vincent D. E280
Manahan, Vincent D. A458
Manas, Jean A711
Manber, Udi A383
Manca, Brian R. E443
Manca, Marcello P590
Mancheski, Frederick J. P424
Mancho, Javier de Paz W434
Manchot, Thomas W202
Manchur, Fred P284
Mancinelli, Louis A201
Mancini, Louis J. (Lou) A125
Mancini, Lisa A. A230
Mancini, Joseph H. (Joe) A881
Mancino, Carol P537
Mancino, Joseph P648
Mancuso, Salvatore A42
Mancuso, Michael J. A738
Mancuso, Martin P147
Mandarich, David D. E312
Mandato, Joseph M P99
Mandato, Joseph (Joe) P457
Mande, Sidharth A244
Mandekic, Anthony L. A550
Mandel, Mary M. A318
Mandel, Joseph G. A462
Mandel, Gail A878
Mandel, Barbara A. P78
Mandelbaum, Jay A471
Mandelbaum, Richard P468
Mandelid, Glenn W435
Mandell, James P536
Mandeng, Mathieu W412
Mander, Lynn S. E78
Manderino, Louis A. E383
Manders, Carrie P490
Mandersson, Magnus W166
Mandil, Claude W453
Mandino, Matthew W. (Matt) A673
Mandracchia, Stephen P. E254
Mandraccia, Crocifissa (Croci) A71
Manduca, Paul W348
Manes, Gianna M. A274
Maness, Terry S. P52
Manfredi, Christine S. E15
Manfredi, Steven P. P59
Mang, Thomas W263
Mangalaseril, Jasmine W278
Mangalindan, Mylene A416
Mangan, Jocelyn E382
Mangan, Daniel A. A690
Manganello, Timothy M. (Tim) E546
Manganello, Timothy M. (Tim) A112
Manganello, Ed P387
Mangel, Allen W. P433
Mangel, Barry P636
Manger, Mary L. E222
Manger, Chris P175
Manger, Richard W157
Mangiagalli, Marco W234
Mangiagalli, Marco W376
Mangino, Lou P58

Mangione, Robert A. P493
Manglik, Harsh W7
Mangold, Klaus J. W31
Mangold, Klaus W136
Mangold, Klaus J. W286
Mangone, Ken A631
Mangoni, Andrea W432
Mangum, David E. E220
Manheim, Paul E208
Manion, Kelly J. E235
Manion, James I. E514
Manion, Doug A134
Manion, Mark D. A591
Manire, Ross W. A62
Manis, G. Scott A778
Maniscalco, Giuseppe P558
Mankin, Eric P526
Manley, Ann E39
Manley, Frederick E. (Fred) A25
Manley, Rose Marie A34
Manley, Lisa A197
Manley, John L. A876
Manley, John P. W104
Manley, Patrick W492
Manly, Marc E. A274
Mann, James L. (Jim) E49
Mann, Bruce A. E98
Mann, Darren E178
Mann, Robert M. E508
Mann, Bill A139
Mann, Eric A576
Mann, Erica L. A638
Mann, Alejandro M. A643
Mann, Laurie A883
Mann, C. Randall P3
Mann, Dave P250
Mann, William N. P299
Mann, Lindsay W130
Mann, Trevor W316
Mann, Peter W330
Mann, Jim W458
Manna, Joe A511
Manne, Robert E504
Mannekens, Henk W100
Mannelly, Matthew M. (Matt) E402
Manning, David L. E40
Manning, Bradley W. A54
Manning, Stephanie A102
Manning, Anna A689
Manning, Kenneth P. A717
Manning, Robin E. (Rob) A781
Manning, Peter J. A791
Manning, Stephanie P43
Manning, Kim B. P148
Manning, Bradley L. P332
Manning, MaryKay P446
Manning, Danielle P514
Manning, Lynn D. P559
Manning, Ken P643
Manning, Sir David G. W85
Manning, Andre W257
Manning, Robert J. (Rob) W422
Mannis, Avi E234
Mannis, Raymond P83
Manno, John A. E296
Manno, Eralba E383
Manok, Katharina E424
Manoogian, Richard A. A353
Manoogian, Richard A. A528
Manos, Arlene E30
Manos, Kristen L. A480
Manos, Steven S. P78
Manos, Kristen P247
Manos, Alexandros S. W343
Manoushagian, Ralph P. E46
Manring, Lewis E. A272
Mansanti, John G. E277
Manseau, James E72
Mansell, Kevin B. A487
Manser, John W373
Mansfield, Robert (Bob) A67
Mansfield, John C. A386
Mansfield, Douglas A. P287
Mansfield, Stephen L. (Steve) P333
Mansh, Steven H. P160

A = AMERICAN BUSINESS
E = EMERGING COMPANIES
P = PRIVATE COMPANIES
W = WORLD BUSINESS

Mead, Gina R. A853
Mead, Andy W304
Meade, Lucian (Ricky) A212
Meade, Michael G. A548
Meade, Andrew F. P620
Meador, David E. A247
Meador, David E. A271
Meador, Mark A602
Meadow, Patricia T. A319
Meadows, A. Stephen (Steve) A700
Meadows, Steve A700
Meadows, Robert E. P346
Meadows, Elizabeth (Betty) P346
Meadows, Randall G. P479
Meadows, Rick W107
Meadows, Richard D. (Rick) W107
Meadows, Paul W480
Meagher, Laura C. A841
Meakins, Ian K. W116
Meakins, Ian K. W486
Meals, Christopher A773
Meaney, Daniel J. E117
Means, Samuel A622
Means, Barbara P491
Meanwell, Clive A. E328
Meara, Robert A339
Meares, Ron P17
Mears, Michael N. (Mike) E315
Mears, Richard W. (Rick) A618
Mearse, Mike A334
Measel, Kevin S. A516
Meason, John P401
Mecham, Rex P31
Meckeler, Amy P508
Mecklenburg, Gary A. A109
Mecum, Dudley C. E466
Medaglia, Anthony J. E111
Medd, Gary L. A244
Medda, Ettore W466
Meddings, Richard H. W411
Meddings, Richard H. W412
Medeiros, David J. (Dave) E410
Medel, Roger J. E331
Meden, Scott A. A590
Meder, Dietmar W144
Mederos, Ana A778
Medica, John K. E362
Medici, Frank T. A114
Medin, Milo S. A383
Medina, John V. A852
Medina, Dionisio Garza W114
Medina, Dionisio W114
Medina, Amilkar Acosta W160
Medina-Mora, Manuel A184
Medini, Paul B. W9
Meditz, John C. P187
Medley, Martha W. E36
Medley, David M. A210
Medley, Loren P280
Mednick, David P188
Medniuk, Tony W300
Medori, Rene W35
Medori, Rene W410
Medvec, Barbara (Barb) P379
Medvec, Barb P379
Medvedev, Alexander I. W187
Medvedev, Aleksandr W188
Medvin, Harvey N. A617
Medvin, Harvey N. P372
Mee, Thomas A. E160
Mee, Terence R. A188
Mee, Thomas A. A276
Mee, David G. A432
Mee, Michael F. A509
Mee, Todd P379
Meehan, David O. E218
Meehan, D. Nathan A91
Meehan, William F. (Bill) A472
Meehan, Steven W461
Meek, Oliver H. E310
Meek, Terry O. A207
Meek, Julie P279
Meek, Joan P386
Meek, Bob P626
Meeker, Anthony E57

Meeker, David P311
Meekin, Peter T. E283
Meeks, James E. E121
Meeks, Philip G. A792
Meelia, Richard J. (Rich) E228
Meers, Lisa A63
Meerts, John P636
Mees, Matthew J. A73
Mees, Bob P484
Meffert, Walt E232
Mega, John S. A493
Megargee, Scott R. E488
Megargee, Scott R. A789
Meggers, Kay A30
Meghdessian, Mira A268
Megian, Rose A409
Megli, Steven C. A447
Meguiar, Ramon V. P326
Mehboob-Kahn, Adil A661
Mehdi, Yusuf A553
Mehdorn, Hartmut W384
Meheut, Bertrand W474
Mehindru, Vinay P199
Mehlman, Guillaume W31
Mehnert, Dana A. A402
Mehney, David P. E541
Mehra, Ajay E384
Mehra, Asit A612
Mehra, R. K. W85
Mehrabian, Robert A651
Mehrberg, Randall E. (Randy) A671
Mehrer, Edward W. (Ed) A313
Mehrotra, Louise A466
Mehrotra, Sanjay A709
Mehta, Dilip J. E456
Mehta, Rajeev (Raj) A199
Mehta, Kavan J. A772
Mehta, Kavan J. P524
Mehta, Tarak W5
Mehta, Aman W231
Meibergen, J. L. (Lew) P276
Meibergen, J. L. (Butch) P276
Meibergen, Joey P276
Meier, Linda R. E86
Meier, James D. E206
Meier, Lisa G. E374
Meier, Bradley I. E512
Meier, Norman M. E512
Meier, Richard A. (Randy) A618
Meier, Steven A749
Meier, April A867
Meier, Anthony P. P394
Meier, Hans-bernd Hans-bernd
    Meier W384
Meier, Andre W491
Meiers, James R. (Jim) E230
Meignie, Yves W472
Meigs, Gen. Montgomery C. P554
Meijden, Erik van der W256
Meijer, Hendrik G. (Hank) A325
Meijer, Gert W464
Meiklejohn, Mark E76
Meiklejohn, Mark A136
Meiklejohn, David E. W46
Mein, David P190
Meincke, Christina P201
Meindel, Nympha P285
Meine, Hartmut W136
Meine, Hartmut W477
Meinecke, Ulrich W335
Meinerding, James A. A338
Meinitz, Sabine A786
Meins, Dan P434
Meintjes, Charles F. A630
Meints, Kristi L. E407
Meirvenne, Dirk Van W78
Meis, Tom P338
Meisenbach, John W. A225
Meisenbach, John W. A305
Meisenberg, Barry R. P26
Meisetschlaeger, Katherine S. A54
Meisler, Luiz A615
Meismer, Denise A325
Meisner, Nancy K. A784
Meissner, Doris P142

Meissner, Martin W489
Meister, Margaret A. E472
Meister, Kurt A305
Meister, Edgar W128
Meister, Hans-Ulrich W139
Meitz, Mary P80
Mejia, Maria Fernanda A201
Mejia, Carols E. A477
Mejia, Maria F. A477
Mekawi, Hesham W95
Melamed, A. Douglas (Doug) A447
Melamud, Marcelo E333
Melancon, Barry C. P20
Meland, Greg R. E137
Melaniuk, Michal W401
Melaragno, Tony P296
Melby, Randy R. E56
Melby, Michael P257
Melcher, David F. A300
Melching, Ed A573
Melchior, Thomas V. A378
Melchior, Eric L. P221
Meldrum, Peter D. E359
Meleis, Afaf I. P142
Melendez, Yvette P137
Melendez, Nestor P188
Melendez, Sara P624
Melendi, Robert J. A208
Meler, Suzanne P110
Melgaard, Dag W435
Melgar, Sergio P602
Meli, Salvatore W163
Melia, Kevin C. E42
Melin, Olga P47
Meline, David W. A2
Melinson, Gregg R. A415
Melius, Jason J. A167
Mellbye, Peter W414
Meller, Craig W33
Mellin, Mark P. E411
Mello, Flavio A. C. A232
Mello, Vasco M. G. Jose de W161
Mellody, Ellen A204
Mellody, James G. A341
Mellor, Robert E. (Rob) E109
Mellor, Robert E. (Rob) E110
Mellor, Robert E. (Rob) E349
Mellor, Amanda W280
Mellowes, John A. P112
Mellowes, John W. P112
Mellowes, Charles P112
Melmed, Shlomo P102
Melnick, Perri E281
Melnick, Jackie E341
Melnik, Marina E87
Melo, Cesar A201
Melo, Murilo B. A654
Melonas, Gus A138
Meloni, Vittorio W234
Meloy, Mattthew J. (Matt) A769
Meloy, Catherine P324
Melson, Donald B. (Don) E42
Melson, Benjamin (Ben) P528
Melton, Stephen A56
Melton, Darrell W. A627
Melton, Carol A. A793
Melton, William P562
Meltzer, Roger E230
Meltzer, Mark J. E278
Meltzer, Cliff A139
Meltzer, Carol A736
Meltzer, Neil M. P299
Meltzer, Neil M. P478
Melumad, Nahum E394
Melville, C. G. A168
Melvin, Mark C. E177
Melvin, Rosetta P653
Melzer, Robert M. E213
Melzi, Bruno A. A887
Memis, Adnan W459
Menanteau, Jean-Pierre W47
Menasce, Eduardo E249
Menasce, Eduardo R. A645
Mencarini, Steven J. (Steve) E177
Menchel, Marc P195

Mencoff, Samuel M. P372
Mendelowitz, Lawrence P402
Mendelsohn, Karen R. A528
Mendelsohn, Robert V. (Bob) A571
Mendelsohn, Howard P132
Mendelson, Johnathan E70
Mendelson, Victor H. E241
Mendelson, Eric A. E241
Mendelson, Laurans A. E241
Mendelson, Victor H. E241
Mendelson, Eric A. E241
Mendelson, Avner W63
Mendenhall, Paula E156
Mendenhall, Candice E257
Mendenhall, Kelley E. A341
Mendes, Mark A. E473
Mendez, Angel L. A181
Mendez, Roberto D. (Bobby) A282
Mendez, John M. A332
Mendez, John M. A333
Mendez, Lincoln P44
Mendez, Fernando W9
Mendicino, Frank J. A70
Mendick, Kay P605
Mendiola, Cristina Sanz W356
Mendiola, Cristina W356
Mendiratta, Sham P653
Mendis, Paul P357
Mendizabal, Lorenzo E175
Mendler, Frederick E411
Mendoza, Roberto G. A520
Mendoza, Eugenio A533
Mendoza, Thomas F. (Tom) A576
Mendoza, Roberto G. A866
Mendoza, Stella P255
Mendoza, Ted P516
Mendoza, Estelito P. W379
Menear, Craig A401
Menear, Craig A. A419
Menefee, Kim P636
Menendez, Manuel Menendez W161
Menendez-Cortada, Jose A328
Mener, Richard A201
Meneses, Alex P537
Menezes, Ivan M. A194
Menezes, Eduardo F. A654
Menezes, Alfredo A. Lima de W56
Menezes, Alfredo W57
Menezes, Ivan M. W155
Meng, Mark P493
Mengebier, David G. A190
Mengebier, David G. A221
Mengel, Tammi P242
Menges, Sascha A412
Menges, Kathrin W202
Menichini, Leslie P443
Menikoff, Peter W9
Menke, Sean E264
Menne, Michael L. A46
Mennel, Donald L. A62
Menning, J. Ron (Ron) A795
Meno, Philip F. A63
Menon, Ram E491
Menon, Raj A232
Mensah, Nana A696
Mensah, Michael O. P608
Mensch, Mariana B. P620
Mense, D. Craig A192
Menser, Michael K. A516
Menten, Eric de W453
Mentesana, Beth K. A24
Mentz, John W. P41
Mentzer, W. Eric A446
Menvielle, John P. P255
Menzel, David B. (Dave) E164
Menzel, Susan L. (Sue) A193
Menzer, John B. A288
Menzie, Anthony A251
Menzies, John K. P468
Meo, Francesco De W179
Meo, Francesco W179
Merav, Avraham P402
Merbach, Dick P189
Mercado, Luis A869
Mercer, James W. (Jim) E235

Midyett, Ronald (Ron) E299
Mieghem, Dennis P. Van A609
Mielcuszny, A. D. A288
Miele, Angelo P105
Miele, Markus W164
Mielke, William J. A95
Mielke, Wayne J. A205
Mielke, Neal R. A446
Mielke, Thomas J. (Tom) A482
Mielke, Lane P367
Mier, Joseph (Joe) E39
Mieres, Victor E361
Miers, Sheppard F. (Mike) A613
Miers, Sheppard A614
Miers, Mike A614
Mies, Adm. Richard W. A302
Mies, Adm. Richard W. A566
Migita, Ronald K. (Ron) A166
Migliardi, Antonio W432
Miglio, Daniel J. E502
Migliori, Richard A832
Migliori, Barbara P508
Migliorini, Peter E314
Migliozzi, John E333
Mignini, Luca A147
Mignogna, Mark A768
Mignonat, Eric W407
Mignone, Linda E73
Migoya, Carlos A. A82
Miguel, Barry A841
Miguel, Josu W356
Miguelsanz, Luis Nogueira W10
Mihaila, J. Ted A795
Mihalik, Trevor A720
Mihaly, John S. P620
Mihlmester, Philip E257
Miiller, Ron E115
Mijuskovic, Srdjan A90
Mikan, G. Mike A118
Mikells, Kathryn A. A404
Mikells, Kathryn A. A881
Mikeska, Robert P72
Mikhailov, Sergei W329
Mikhailova, Elena W188
Mikhaylova, Elena W188
Miki, Shigemitsu W291
Miki, Shohei W311
Mikkelsen, B?rd W159
Mikkilineni, Krishna A421
Mikl, Mark J. E180
Mikles, Lee E. E208
Mikolasy, Russ E84
Mikoshiba, Toshiaki W215
Mikoyan, Aleksandr A415
Miksztal, Andrew R. (Andy) E156
Mikuen, Scott T. A402
Mikulecky, Donna P118
Mikuska, Mike A647
Milan, Lawrence P136
Milando, Anthony W. (Tony) A742
Milano, Todd A. E464
Milano, James V. A706
Milano, Enrico W234
Milavetz, Barry P604
Milberg, Joachim A244
Milberg, Joachim W80
Milberg, Joachim W84
Milberg, Joachim W384
Milberg, Joachim W490
Milburn, Byron W. A351
Milburn, Nathaniel S. (Nat) A579
Milch, Randal S. (Randy) A840
Milde, Johannes W395
Mildenhall, Joseph E224
Milefchik, Edward F. A532
Milenkov, Aleksey E22
Miles, John B. E39
Miles, Carolyn S. E64
Miles, Michael A. A48
Miles, George L. A53
Miles, George L. A401
Miles, Mark D. A625
Miles, Aled A764
Miles, Michael A. A793
Miles, George L. A862

Miles, Michael A. (Mike) A866
Miles, David P188
Miles, John P192
Miles, Martin P230
Miles, Brett P338
Miles, Robert P386
Miles, Carolyn S. P457
Miles, Veryl V. P535
Mileti, Joe P446
Miletich, Joseph P. (Joe) A58
Milette, Nicolas W302
Milevoj, Andy A103
Miley, Greg A4
Miley, Richard L. A747
Miley, Cathy B. A747
Milhollon, David A334
Milhorn, David P610
Milina, Tracy L. A54
Miliote, Tony P472
Milis, Ilias D. W343
Milis, Ilias D. W344
Milito, Erik P21
Milkie, Brett P. E79
Millar, Doug A72
Millar, Andrew P240
Millar, James E. P246
Millard, Mark D. A115
Millard, Robert B. A493
Millard, Suzanne Turtle P587
Millard, Jayne P587
Millegan, Michael H. A840
Millen, Robert P. (Bob) P382
Miller, Simone E11
Miller, Cormac F. E16
Miller, Matt E16
Miller, Lowell D. E20
Miller, Cynthia E40
Miller, Jay J. E41
Miller, Richard C. (Rick) E48
Miller, Gary W. E54
Miller, James D. E57
Miller, Catherine B. E58
Miller, Kendra P. E63
Miller, Andrew E74
Miller, Don E75
Miller, Sherman E83
Miller, Jody G. E88
Miller, Austin E104
Miller, Jeffrey B. E111
Miller, William J. (Bill) E146
Miller, Jeffrey D. E149
Miller, Kenneth H. E157
Miller, William J. E182
Miller, Gary J. E183
Miller, David S. E185
Miller, James B. E191
Miller, Scott E204
Miller, Mark J. E206
Miller, Wayne S. E209
Miller, Michael O. E213
Miller, Jeffrey D. E233
Miller, Jeffrey H. (Jeff) E236
Miller, William F. E251
Miller, Lauren E. E255
Miller, Peter K. E258
Miller, Thomas B. (Tom) E285
Miller, Monte E296
Miller, Franklin J. E334
Miller, John R. E343
Miller, Kevin S. E346
Miller, Mike E368
Miller, Donald E373
Miller, Stephen S. E391
Miller, Tere H. E413
Miller, Gary A. E433
Miller, Lloyd I. E459
Miller, Mark C. E461
Miller, Douglas S. (Doug) E481
Miller, Brian K. E500
Miller, Alan B. E512
Miller, John D. E527
Miller, Maribess L. E548
Miller, Donald E. A1
Miller, Rosa M. A2
Miller, Brian A. A15

Miller, Mark A. A15
Miller, Ted B. A26
Miller, Robert S. (Steve) A53
Miller, Henry S. A53
Miller, Jay J. A59
Miller, Susan C. A85
Miller, MaryAnn G. A88
Miller, Irene R. A103
Miller, Melanie E. R. A112
Miller, Catherine B. A117
Miller, Greg A142
Miller, W. Thaddeus A143
Miller, Debbie A160
Miller, John R. A171
Miller, Stephen W. A173
Miller, Thomas R. (Thom) A186
Miller, Gwen T. A186
Miller, Irene R. A194
Miller, David L. A210
Miller, Thomas D. (Tom) A210
Miller, Christopher M. (Chris) A222
Miller, Stephen P. A223
Miller, Russell D. (Russ) A225
Miller, James H. (Jim) A228
Miller, William I. (Will) A232
Miller, Pepe A255
Miller, James L. A260
Miller, Eugene A. (Gene) A271
Miller, David B. A272
Miller, Rik L. A272
Miller, James A. A282
Miller, Susan E. A290

Miller, Jill A298
Miller, Steven (Steve) A306
Miller, Kenneth C. A315
Miller, James B. A324
Miller, Jordan A. A325
Miller, David W. A337
Miller, Karen A358
Miller, Jamie S. A368
Miller, Heidi G. A370
Miller, Joseph A. (Buzz) A376
Miller, Anthony E. (Tony) A382
Miller, John R. A384
Miller, John R. A385
Miller, Scot A. A387
Miller, Randy A392
Miller, Jeffrey A. (Jeff) A394
Miller, Gary A427
Miller, Suzan A. A446
Miller, Jim A456
Miller, Robert A. A457
Miller, Heidi G. A471
Miller, Daniel A472
Miller, Cecil R. A474
Miller, Michael A483
Miller, Michael A484
Miller, Gregory C. (Greg) A485
Miller, Brian F. A487
Miller, Stuart A. A500
Miller, Charles C. (Buddy) A503
Miller, Jonathan F. (Jon) A511
Miller, Ken A514
Miller, Merrill A. (Pete) A569
Miller, Robert G. (Bob) A590
Miller, Tomas A. A600
Miller, Mark A600
Miller, Lydia E. A626
Miller, Matthew R. A627
Miller, Dennis P. A630
Miller, Laurie Beja A631
Miller, Forrest E. A640
Miller, Kevin A643
Miller, Jocelyn A658
Miller, Brent A662
Miller, Heidi G. A664
Miller, Hans H. A666
Miller, Dan A697
Miller, John M. A702
Miller, James C. A706
Miller, Norman L. (Norm) A718
Miller, Kenneth A. A727
Miller, Guy W. A759
Miller, Robert S. (Steve) A764

Miller, W. Keith A768
Miller, Annette A771
Miller, Charles F. A778
Miller, Richard A. (Rick) A804
Miller, Jody G. A806
Miller, Heather K. A813
Miller, Diane D. A814
Miller, Zell B. A818
Miller, Alan B. A833
Miller, Marc D. A833
Miller, Kate A834
Miller, Richard S. A838
Miller, Carl A. A859
Miller, Rory L. A872
Miller, Robert J. A879
Miller, William K. P6
Miller, Karen P22
Miller, Michael M. (Mike) P32
Miller, Richard K. P40
Miller, Adam P56
Miller, Thomas H. P69
Miller, Jeff P80
Miller, Silvana P89
Miller, Mark P98
Miller, Robert P99
Miller, Kathleen J. (Kay) P100
Miller, Scott P123
Miller, Stan P131
Miller, John W. (Jack) P137
Miller, Richard P147
Miller, David P156
Miller, James P168
Miller, Kendall P185
Miller, Jane E. P210
Miller, Randy P223
Miller, Edwin (Glen) P240
Miller, Jeffrey S. (Jeff) P242
Miller, Gary P252
Miller, Don P257
Miller, Robert (Bob) P258
Miller, Jesse P260
Miller, Jennie P273
Miller, Edward D. P275
Miller, Kristine P277
Miller, Mike P277
Miller, P. Daniel (Dan) P289
Miller, Rudy P299
Miller, Roy P310
Miller, Mark P314
Miller, L. Christopher P315
Miller, Brigid O'Brien P315
Miller, Edward D. P324
Miller, Rick P332
Miller, Marc J. P349
Miller, Tony P353
Miller, H. Gilbert P365
Miller, Todd P393
Miller, Charles P. (Charlie) P396
Miller, Michael C. P402
Miller, Michael H. P402
Miller, Nic P430
Miller, Marlin P430
Miller, Ethan P431
Miller, Daryl P435
Miller, Henry S. P457
Miller, Peter C. P469
Miller, Greg P471
Miller, Leonard S. P471
Miller, Rudy P478
Miller, James P484
Miller, Mike P487
Miller, Gary P. P496
Miller, Steve P518
Miller, Allan P518
Miller, Dionne P521
Miller, Marty W. P537
Miller, Richard B. P566
Miller, Marc H. P578
Miller, Ben P590
Miller, Carol P594
Miller, Melissa P598
Miller, Janet L. P600
Miller, Pamela P607
Miller, Michelle P610
Miller, Diane D. P611

Morea, Joseph E436
Morea, Donna A756
Moreau, Maxine A168
Moreau, Claude P. A783
Moreau, Steven C. P499
Moreau, Nicolas W49
Morefield, Daniel J. E409
Morehead, Jere W. P601
Moreira, Julio Cesar E223
Moreira, Prof Vital M. W161
Morel, Hugo W462
Moreland, W. Benjamin (Ben) E129
Moreland, W. Benjamin (Ben) A143
Morelli, Marco W234
Morello, Michael A. A759
Morem, David N. E12
Moreno, Karen R. A362
Moreno, Rafael A365
Moreno, Albert F. A880
Moreno, Georgina A. P540
Moreno, Vicente W8
Moreno, Pablo W57
Moreno, Hector W57
Moreno, Joaquin W160
Moreno, Sergio W185
Moreno-Barreda, Jose Fernando de Almansa W434
Moret, Alan P. A40
Moret, Blake A702
Moreton, William W. (Bill) E388
Moretti, Marissa A368
Moretto, Riccardo W492
Morey, Charlotte P188
Morfas, Craig C. E54
Morfitt, Martha A. (Marti) E302
Morfitt, Martha A. (Marti) E308
Morford, Craig S. A151
Morgado, Robert J. A9
Morgan, Calvert A. (Cal) E103
Morgan, Dianna F. E103
Morgan, Jay E236
Morgan, James C. E257
Morgan, R. Kirk E258
Morgan, Harold E261
Morgan, John K. E546
Morgan, Russell J. E548
Morgan, James C. (Jim) A69
Morgan, Mary F. A137
Morgan, Sidney A181
Morgan, Harvey A311
Morgan, Thomas B. A448
Morgan, Thomas B. A449
Morgan, Michael C. (Mike) A484
Morgan, Rodney D. (Rod) A551
Morgan, Mary F. A602
Morgan, Michael P. (Mike) A685
Morgan, Thomas I. (Tom) A775
Morgan, Kimberly (Kim) A786
Morgan, Melanie A. A805
Morgan, Mitchell A818
Morgan, John K. A862
Morgan, Calvert A. (Cal) A877
Morgan, Geoffrey P5
Morgan, Todd M. P102
Morgan, Lance P246
Morgan, Randall C. P256
Morgan, Thomas B. P262
Morgan, Chuck P270
Morgan, Lori P295
Morgan, Lori P296
Morgan, David L. P320
Morgan, Dianna P386
Morgan, Richard P394
Morgan, Robert P410
Morgan, Damon P412
Morgan, James P501
Morgan, Mitchell L. P526
Morgan, Warren P578
Morgan, Marsha Lee P584
Morgan, Joe P609
Morgan, Michael P613
Morgan, Cindy P626
Morgan, Flemming W145
Morgan, Andrew W155
Morgan, Gwyn W218

Morgan, Peter W364
Morgan, Jennifer W384
Morgan-Olson, Cindy E175
Morge, Ken A247
Morgenroth, Matthew J. W485
Morgensen, Jerry L. P240
Morgenstern, Ronald K. E474
Morgenstern, Robert P471
Morgese, Vincent P423
Morhaime, Michael (Mike) A9
Mori, Frank R. A251
Mori, Yoshiki W15
Mori, Yoshiki W16
Mori, Shosuke W34
Mori, Shigeru W141
Mori, Ikuo W180
Mori, Takashi W183
Mori, Ryosuke W184
Mori, Kazuhiro W208
Mori, Kazuyuki W289
Mori, Takahiro W338
Mori, Yasutomo W358
Mori, Masayuki Masayuki Mori W390
Moriarty, John E23
Moriarty, Rowland T. (Row) E523
Moriarty, Rowland T. (Row) E534
Moriarty, Kevin A88
Moriarty, Thomas M. A163
Moriarty, Thomas M. A235
Moriarty, Rowland T. (Row) A744
Moriarty, Donna P362
Morikawa, Keizo W137
Morikawa, Toshio W307
Morikis, John G. A721
Morillo, Manuel W59
Morimoto, David A166
Morimoto, Mitsuo W34
Morimoto, Yoshiyuki W96
Morimoto, Masao W117
Morimoto, Hiroshi W390
Morimoto, Yoshihisa W447
Morin, Richard A. E111
Morin, R. Hunter E507
Morin, Jamie E534
Morin, Pierre A30
Morin, R. Hunter A815
Morin, Stephen P515
Morin, Buddy P516
Morin, Isabelle W345
Morin, Isabelle W346
Morin-Postel, Christine W98
Morin-Postel, Christine W370
Morino, Tetsuji W140
Morino, Tetsuji W141
Morioka, John A771
Morishita, Yoichi W455
Morison, Francis J. P201
Morita, Takashi W22
Morita, Takayuki W306
Morita, Toshio W320
Morita, Ken W338
Morita, Masao W408
Morita, Tomijirou W447
Moritani, Mamoru W419
Moritz, Michael J. (Mike) E226
Moritz, Michael J. (Mike) E305
Moritz, Stephanie A217
Moritz, Helen E. P414
Moritz, Claire L. P628
Moritz, Peter W396
Moriwaki, Lee Y. A97
Moriyama, Toru W289
Moriyama, Takahiro W417
Moriyasu, Masaharu W291
Moriyasu, Isao W327
Morland, Miles W373
Morley, Bradford C. (Brad) E44
Morley, Curtis J. E204
Morley, Nate E448
Morlion, Lode W248
Mormann, James J. P388
Morneau, Mark A362
Morner, Claudia P614
Mornhinweg, Volker W144
Moro, Masahiro W283

Morohoshi, Toshio A284
Moroney, Sister Kathleen P580
Morosoli, Dave P431
Moroun, Matthew T. E513
Moroun, Manuel J. (Matty) E513
Morray, Jeffrey P. P404
Morreale, Charles A. (Chuck) E125
Morreale, Chuck E125
Morrell, Elner L. P187
Morrical, Terri A. E366
Morrill, R. Layne P32
Morrill, Peter P420
Morrin, Noel W401
Morris, David F. E17
Morris, David E82
Morris, Kyle E83
Morris, William C. E89
Morris, Milton M. E136
Morris, Thomas C. E138
Morris, James J. E181
Morris, William M. E300
Morris, Hugh N. E377
Morris, Michael G. (Mike) A31
Morris, Jeff D. A40
Morris, Leigh A46
Morris, Michael G. (Mike) A49
Morris, Michael G. (Mike) A105
Morris, Michael J. A113
Morris, George C. A144
Morris, Douglas P. (Doug) A160
Morris, Herschel E. A169
Morris, Michael J. A215
Morris, Emily Kolinski A353
Morris, JoAnna H. A368
Morris, Grant L. A373
Morris, P. Harris A402
Morris, James D. (Jim) A402
Morris, Michael G. (Mike) A404
Morris, Bret A. A409
Morris, Robert L. A480
Morris, Sandra A. A543
Morris, Maria R. A545
Morris, James T. A608
Morris, David P. (Dave) A651
Morris, Jesse E. A768
Morris, Robert (Bob) A781
Morris, Edna K. A800
Morris, Wes A809
Morris, James D. A864
Morris, Scott A874
Morris, Michael A888
Morris, Michael G. (Mike) P49
Morris, Craig A. P87
Morris, Rebekah P170
Morris, Kevin H. P251
Morris, Ruth Ann P257
Morris, Jeffery (Bob) P281
Morris, Granville P294
Morris, Granville P295
Morris, Tony P299
Morris, Don P325
Morris, Olin F. P350
Morris, Jon P444
Morris, Doug P463
Morris, Gary R. P547
Morris, Michael P579
Morris, Jon P636
Morris, Clive W44
Morris, Peter W66
Morris, Mark W364
Morris, Doug W409
Morris, Simon W411
Morris, Jonathan W412
Morris, Doug W461
Morrisey, Locke J. P607
Morrison, Hugh M. E135
Morrison, Cynthia M. E172
Morrison, Robert W. E309
Morrison, William T. E345
Morrison, Lisa J. E478
Morrison, David E524
Morrison, Robert S. (Bob) A2
Morrison, Kelly A4
Morrison, Glen G. A30
Morrison, Scott C. A92

Morrison, J. Holmes A108
Morrison, Victoria A. (Vicki) A111
Morrison, David H. (Dave) A125
Morrison, Denise M. A147
Morrison, Patricia B. (Patty) A151
Morrison, Harold L. A177
Morrison, Cynthia M. A289
Morrison, Lucian L. A299
Morrison, Albert A360
Morrison, John L. (Jack) A423
Morrison, Robert S. A438
Morrison, Ronald M. (Ron) A439
Morrison, Craig O. A557
Morrison, William L. (Bill) A594
Morrison, Christine A. P15
Morrison, Thomas P41
Morrison, Deane P135
Morrison, Jim P245
Morrison, Samuel F. P375
Morrison, Karen Jefferson P382
Morrison, Deborah P419
Morrison, Evelyn P551
Morrison, John M. P610
Morrison, Briggs W44
Morriss, Stephen (Steve) A13
Morriss, Steve A13
Morrissey, Bob A147
Morrissey, John A440
Morrissey, Michael J. A719
Morrissey, Brian P91
Morrissey, John P143
Morrow, George J. E24
Morrow, Steve A125
Morrow, John C. A127
Morrow, William T. (Bill) A136
Morrow, Keith P28
Morrow, W. Robert P30
Morrow, Joseph T. P256
Morschel, John P. W46
Morse, Peter C. E55
Morse, John B. (Jay) A15
Morse, David L. A223
Morse, John B. (Jay) A426
Morse, Capt. Wendy J. A819
Morse, Laurence C. A855
Morse, Andy P135
Morse, Ted P346
Morse, William P605
Morsiani, Gian Guido Sacchi W234
Mortazavi, Kia P384
Mortensen, Eric J. A503
Mortensen, Pam A630
Mortensen, James R. (Jim) A641
Mortensen, Peggy P325
Mortenson, Bob A457
Mortimer, Mark E44
Mortimer, Renee J. P245
Mortman, Jacqueline A. A404
Morton, Gerry E94
Morton, Sarah E163
Morton, Drew E232
Morton, Andrew E233
Morton, James R. E280
Morton, Shirley E371
Morton, Michael J. E479
Morton, John B. A108
Morton, John A131
Morton, Rick A298
Morton, Randy A549
Morton, Michael J. A772
Morton, Max G. P403
Morton, Tony P422
Morton, Michael P629
Morton, Paul W74
Morttinen, Leena W321
Morvan, Yves Alain Marie W168
Morway, Joe P469
Mory, Miguel P88
Morzaria, Tushar W72
Morzaria, Tushar W74
Mosakowski, William S. E251
Mosanko, Harold F. A195
Mosbacher, Robert A. A143
Mosbacher, Robert A. A248
Mosby, Christel E224

A = AMERICAN BUSINESS
E = EMERGING COMPANIES
P = PRIVATE COMPANIES
W = WORLD BUSINESS

Myers, Rita A. A495
Myers, Daniel A559
Myers, Margaret A590
Myers, Richard B. (Dick) A597
Myers, Terry C. A626
Myers, Doug A633
Myers, Dale S. A672
Myers, Richard B. (Dick) A831
Myers, Robert W. A859
Myers, Mark L. A859
Myers, A. Ross P19
Myers, David P21
Myers, Donald L. (Don) P23
Myers, Lora P82
Myers, Richard David P84
Myers, Douglas T. (Doug) P116
Myers, Frank P128
Myers, Pamela (Pam) P190
Myers, James (Jim) P257
Myers, Mary P259
Myers, John P306
Myers, Dwayne P316
Myers, Adam L. P333
Myers, Diana K. P457
Myers, Rev John J. P468
Myers, Margaret P605
Myers, Regis P618
Myers, Rochelle P651
Myers, Douglas G. P658
Myerson, Terry A553
Myklebust, Egil W381
Mylander, Paul H. P56
Mylin, Scott L. E292
Mylonas, Paul W303
Mylonas, Theodoros P. W344
Mylrea, David R. P245
Mynsberge, Steven C. P321
Myochin, Toru W392
Myones, Seth A226
Myrben, Rob A733
Myrmel-Johansen, Elin M. W415
Myron, Thomas R. A120
Myung, Daniel C. P89
M'Guinness, Thomas A. (Tom) A844

N

Naatz, Michael J. (Mike) E292
Nabers, Drayton E269
Nabers, Drayton A660
Nabeshima, Hideyuki W289
Nabeshima, Hideyuki W290
Nabiullina, Elvira W188
Naccach-Hoff, Selma P179
Nace, David A536
Nachatilo, Craig P293
Nachbar, Mark L. P446
Nachbar, Moacir W57
Nachmias, Richard S. P177
Nachtsheim, Jami E191
Nachtsheim, Stephen P. P609
Nackel, John G. E174
Nackman, Neal S. E209
Nackstad, Caj W380
Naddaff, Alexander C. E227
Naddaff, Alex E227
Naddeo, Eric A812
Nadeau, Gerard F. A440
Nadeau, Bertin F. W422
Nadella, Satya A553
Nadenicek, Daniel J. P601
Nadkarni, Gurudatta D. A220
Nadler, Mitch A464
Nadler, David A. A526
Nadler, Lee M. P154
Nadolny, Mark E. P563
Naegle, Sue A793

Naert, Philippe W248
Naeve, Clayton P501
Naff, John E132
Naficy, Susan J. P422
Naftaly, Robert H. E325
Naftaly, Robert H. E466
Naftaly, Robert H. A537
Nafus, Edward C. (Ed) E130
Nagae, Shusaku W338
Nagahama, Morinobu W141
Nagai, Takashi W215
Nagai, Katsumasa W236
Nagai, Yasuo W289
Nagai, Yasuo W290
Nagai, Noriaki W320
Nagai, Koji W320
Nagamatsu, Shoichi W320
Nagamatsu, Soichi W320
Nagamatsu, Shoichi W358
Nagano, Yoshiaki W141
Nagano, Hisashi W180
Nagano, Tsuyoshi W446
Nagao, Kimitsugu W1
Nagarajan, Raj V. E539
Nagarajan, Sundaram (Naga) A438
Nagarajan, Raj V. A874
Nagarajan, Sridhar W412
Nagarkatti, Jai P. P570
Nagasawa, Kenichi W106
Nagase, Shin W34
Nagata, Ryoko W241
Nagata, Kiyohito W326
Nagata, Osamu W455
Nagato, Masatsugu W180
Nagayama, Yoshiaki W1
Nagayama, Atsushi W141
Nagayama, Osamu W362
Nagayasu, Yojiro W67
Nagayasu, Katsunori W294
Nagel, David C. (Dave) E24
Nagel, Andrew P108
Nagel, Alberto N. W41
Nagel, Thomas W151
Nagel, Wilfred F. W231
Nagel, Alberto N. W284
Nager, Lorenz W197
Naggan, Zvi W62
Nagle, Zachary A. (Zac) A109
Nagle, H. Troy P433
Nagle, Carl W9
Nagler, Lorna E. E503
Nagler, Harris M. P62
Nagowski, Michael P151
Nagrath, Moheet A661
Nagura, Toshikazu W22
Nagy, M. Nafees E532
Nagy, M. Nafees A863
Nahl, Michael C. E303
Nahmias, Jacques-Alexandre W145
Nahra, Lynda A624
Naidoo, Shirley P375
Naidoo, N. Alfie W71
Naidu, Taryn E142
Naik, Rajan A12
Naimoli, Vincent J. P188
Nair, Biju E473
Nair, Raj A353
Nair, Hari N. A779
Naito, Yoshihiro W447
Nakada, Stephen Y. P612
Nakae, Gosuke W289
Nakae, Yasuyuki W307
Nakae, Kiyohiko W416
Nakagaki, Keiichi W289
Nakagawa, Jon P301
Nakagawa, Hideki W289
Nakagawa, Junko W320
Nakagawa, Yutaka W408
Nakagome, Kenji W427
Nakahara, Hideto W289
Nakahara, Hideto W290
Nakai, Tsuyoshi Tsuyoshi Nakai W180
Nakajima, Shigehiro W182
Nakajima, Junzo W208
Nakajima, Shigeki W224

Nakajima, Hajime W252
Nakajima, Kazuhiko W405
Nakamae, Koji W357
Nakamine, Yuji W283
Nakamoto, Gary A710
Nakamura, Shunichi W22
Nakamura, Ryuji W22
Nakamura, Shunichi W22
Nakamura, Katsumi W34
Nakamura, Akihiko W34
Nakamura, Hisayoshi W67
Nakamura, Toyoaki W208
Nakamura, Ichiro W238
Nakamura, Tsuyoshi W291
Nakamura, Yoshikazu W293
Nakamura, Koji W295
Nakamura, Kimiyasu W316
Nakamura, Toshiyuki W316
Nakamura, Shiro W316
Nakamura, Katsuhiro W326
Nakamura, Katsuhiro W327
Nakamura, Yuji W328
Nakamura, Kunio W338
Nakamura, Katsumi W354
Nakamura, Masahiro W358
Nakamura, Takashi W358
Nakamura, Yukio W392
Nakamura, Akihiro W393
Nakamura, Moritaka W393
Nakamura, Akihiro W393
Nakamura, Makoto W417
Nakamura, Kuniharu W417
Nakamura, Masaru W417
Nakamura, Kuniharu W417
Nakanishi, Hiroshi W208
Nakanishi, Yasuyuki W291
Nakanishi, Akinori W292
Nakanishi, Katsunori W393
Nakanishi, Satoru W420
Nakanishi, Shinzo W424
Nakano, Mamoru E125
Nakano, Tom A597
Nakano, Tom P373
Nakano, Takashi W211
Nakano, Kazuhisa W224
Nakano, Masafumi W283
Nakano, Takahiro W419
Nakao, Ryugo W293
Nakaoka, Masaki W106
Nakas, Victor A. P535
Nakashima, Toshihiro W311
Nakasone, Robert C. (Bob) A423
Nakata, Yuji W320
Nakatani, Yoshiaki W291
Nakatsugawa, Masaki W455
Nakayama, Hiroshi W208
Nakayama, Haruhide W326
Nakayama, Fujikazu W390
Nakayama, Jun W456
Nakhata, Yaowadee W61
Nakura, Shuji W295
Nalamasu, Omkaram (Om) A69
Nalbandian, Gary L. A546
Nalbone, Phillip E517
Naldi, Robert P308
Nallen, John P. A807
Nam, Sung-Il W222
Nam, Dae-Woo W397
Nam-Hai, Chua W485
Naman, Ananth E81
Namaroff, Mark J. E42
Namba, Yoshimi A632
Namba, Hajime W141
Nambiar, Vinod A201
Namgoong, Hun Hun Namgoong W392
Namiki, Masao W452
Namm, Sheila J. P308
Nammack, Nancy P648
Nanaiah, K. M. A645
Nanavaty, Maulik A132
Nance, Carlyle A. E67
Nance, Carlyle A. A123
Nance, Penni P64
Nance, William A. (Bill) P531
Nandakumar, E. W85

Nandkishore, Nandu W309
Nandra, Navtej S. A275
Naney, Dave P446
Nanney, Nancy P268
Nantais, Thomas S. P238
Nanterme, Pierre W7
Nanterme, Pierre W8
Nanthawithaya, Arthid W394
Nanton, James (Jim) A396
Naouri, Jean-Charles W111
Napalan, Joel A233
Napier, A. Lanham E411
Napier, Laine P260
Napier, Katherine P. E617
Napier, Iain J. G. W227
Napierski, Ryan E375
Napoli, Andre (Andy) A404
Napoli, John P. P469
Napolitan, Raymond S. A600
Napolitano, James A. A201
Napolitano, Rich A285
Napolitano, Chris A736
Nappi, Ralph A. P370
Nappi, Mark P596
Napuda, Jim P444
Naqvi, Sy A649
Narang, Steve A102
Narang, Steve P43
Naratil, Thomas C. (Tom) W461
Narayanan, Sean S. E262
Narayanan, Lakshmi A199
Narayanan, Lakshmi A200
Narayanan, Sundaram P652
Narayanan, K. B. W86
Narayanaswamy, Ramprakash E2
Narcisse, Colbert A562
Narcisso, Deborah P34
Nard, Christopher S. A609
Nardello, Charles R. E234
Nardi, Yoav E63
Nardini, Erika E142
Nardone, Randal A. E202
Nardone, Mary Kaye A495
Narev, Ian W130
Nargang, Julie E431
Narla, Mohandas P361
Narlow, Greg P132
Narodick, Sally G. E125
Naruke, Yasuo Yasuo Naruke W452
Narvinger, Anders W436
Nasard, Alexis W199
Nascimento, Alvaro Jose Barrigas do W103
Nasella, Henry J. A675
Naselow, Craig S. E55
Nash, Sarah E. E64
Nash, Thomas F. E111
Nash, Chris E144
Nash, William D. (Bill) A153
Nash, Thomas M. (Tom) A310
Nash, Cheryl A343
Nash, David B. A431
Nash, Patrick L. A626
Nash, Ron A781
Nash, Cynthia B. (Cindy) A873
Nash, Bruce D. P91
Nash, Dick P238
Nash, James P410
Nash, Glenn W409
Nasir, Louis P. A768
Naslund, Charles D. A46
Naso, Thomas (Tom) E292
Nason, Robert A. W438
Naspinski, Ed A772
Naspinski, Ed P524
Nasr, Nabil P439
Nasrallah, Lynne G. P200
Nassar, Zeina T. A251
Nassau, Robert H. E494
Nasser, Jacques A. (Jac) W87
Nassetta, Christopher J. (Chris) E123
Nassner, Jeffrey P315
Nastase, Dave A596
Natale, J. Peter A109
Natale, Marina W463

A = AMERICAN BUSINESS
E = EMERGING COMPANIES
P = PRIVATE COMPANIES
W = WORLD BUSINESS

Ousley, James E. (Jim) A168
Outcalt, John R. A651
Outlaw, James M. A805
Ouziel, Sylvie W8
Ouzounian, Robert A457
Ovel, Jack P328
Ovenden, James A. E197
Ovenden, James A. A344
Overbeek, Edzard J.C. A181
Overbey, Cecel E. (Chip) E377
Overbey, William J. (Bill) P234
Overby, Jeannette P183
Overlan, Matthew C. A407
Overland, Keith P518
Overlock, Willard J. (Mike) A109
Overlock, Willard J. (Mike) P559
Oversohl, Christian E432
Overton, Camie P657
Overturf, James E185
Ovesen, Jesper W399
Ovitt, Kimberly P501
Ovrum, Margareth W414
Ovtchinnikov, Alexander (Alex) E282
Owad, Bill A151
Owades, Ruth M. E140
Owcar, Gary J. A192
Oweida, Steven W. P636
Owen, Claude B. E36
Owen, Marlene E89
Owen, Jeri E146
Owen, Randel G. (Randy) E195
Owen, Robert H. E337
Owen, Kenneth F. E376
Owen, Ted W. E481
Owen, Rt. Hon. David A. L. A4
Owen, John F. A89
Owen, Julie A118
Owen, Richard A176
Owen, Jeffery C. A260
Owen, David A471
Owen, Marc E. A536
Owen, John B. A688
Owen, Sharon K. A827
Owen, Kenneth A. (Ken) P159
Owen, Tamara (Tammy) P280
Owen, Patti P373
Owen, William P448
Owen, Laura P581
Owen-Jones, Lindsay W383
Owens, Tom E105
Owens, James J. (Jim) E207
Owens, Gary D. E219
Owens, Jane E. E432
Owens, David E453
Owens, Rodney E543
Owens, James W. (Jim) A31
Owens, B. Craig A147
Owens, William A. (Bill) A168
Owens, Ed A325
Owens, James W. (Jim) A452
Owens, James W. (Jim) A562
Owens, Duane A. A694
Owens, O'dell M. A811
Owens, Christine M. A824
Owens, James A. P3
Owens, Tom P245
Owens, Albert H. P275
Owens, Sister Helen P389
Owens, Tosha P426
Owens, Rita R. P585
Owens, Craig P636
Ownby, Dan A137
Ownjazayeri, Vahid A13
Owsiany, Genevieve P. E512
Oxford, Ed A102
Oxford, Ed P42
Oxley, Michael J. (Mike) A272
Oxley, Robert P181
Oyama, Nagahisa W16
Oyama, Tatsuhiro W214
Oyama, Tatsuhiro W215
Oyamada, Takashi W294
Oyewole, Shola E510
Oz, Ran W62
Ozaki, Teruo W252

Ozaki, Kiyoshi W283
Ozan, Kevin M. A534
Ozan, Terrence R. (Terry) A788
Ozark, Timothy K. A1
Ozawa, Hitoshi W61
Ozawa, Hideki W106
Ozawa, Motoyuki Motoyuki
    Ozawa W184
Ozawa, Satoshi W455
Ozen, Ergun W459
Ozer, Esra A31
O'Boyle, Ed P210
O'Bradovich, Derek A678
O'Brien, Robert P. (Bob) E85
O'Brien, Stuart E109
O'Brien, James P. E161
O'Brien, Jim E211
O'Brien, Gordon J. E343
O'Brien, Brien M. E397
O'Brien, Jenette E413
O'Brien, Dennis F. E496
O'Brien, Bobby D. E516
O'Brien, William K. (Bill) E523
O'Brien, Urban F. (Obie) A66
O'Brien, James J. (Jim) A74
O'Brien, Dermot J. A81
O'Brien, Mollie A118
O'Brien, Thomas H. A123
O'Brien, Tom A201
O'Brien, Ken A265
O'Brien, Lucy A288
O'Brien, John A292
O'Brien, Donna M. A349
O'Brien, Paul D. A389
O'Brien, James J. (Jim) A431
O'Brien, James J. A431
O'Brien, Daniel F. A440
O'Brien, Michael A471
O'Brien, Thomas M. A519
O'Brien, Richard T. A581
O'Brien, Michael J. A612
O'Brien, J. Brice A695
O'Brien, David M. A741
O'Brien, John F. A796
O'Brien, Thomas M. A801
O'Brien, Thomas M. A802
O'Brien, Rick A855
O'Brien, Anne T. P18
O'Brien, Carolyn P24
O'Brien, Theresa P137
O'Brien, John E. P181
O'Brien, Steve D. P210
O'Brien, Anne P315
O'Brien, James J. P361
O'Brien, Thomas P408
O'Brien, Brien M. P566
O'Brien, Barry P650
O'Brien, Fiona W266
O'Brien, Patrick D. W338
O'Brien, David P. W366
O'Brien, Michael W. (Mike) W423
O'Brien, Grant W488
O'Bryan, John A158
O'Bryan, Frank E. A327
O'Bryant, Allan E. A689
O'Bryant, G. Mark P524
O'Byrne, Kevin W250
O'Callaghan, Rev John J. P607
O'Callaghan, Jeremiah A. (Jerry) W243
O'Casek, Jim P37
O'Connell, Desmond H. E7
O'Connell, Frank J. E496
O'Connell, Robert T. A165
O'Connell, Alfred A315
O'Connell, Brendan A402
O'Connell, Brian A511
O'Connell, Christopher J. (Chris) A540
O'Connell, John A594
O'Connell, Terry A792
O'Connell, Brian A870
O'Connell, Gloria P15
O'Connell, Ralph A. P361
O'Connell, Kathleen P384
O'Connell, Mary Adams P537
O'Connell, B. M. W245

O'Connor, Michael J. E32
O'Connor, John P. E42
O'Connor, William F. E107
O'Connor, Sharon E122
O'Connor, Thomas C. (Tom) E138
O'Connor, William B. (Bill) E328
O'Connor, Daniel W. (Dan) E385
O'Connor, Shane F. E506
O'Connor, Kevin P. A204
O'Connor, Carey A. A346
O'Connor, Carey A346
O'Connor, Nigel A368
O'Connor, Sean M. A457
O'Connor, Marty L. A480
O'Connor, Joseph M. A502
O'Connor, Joseph E. A816
O'Connor, James J. A819
O'Connor, Tim A880
O'Connor, Thomas (TJ) A884
O'Connor, Thomas (Tom) P15
O'Connor, Timothy P. P89
O'Connor, David P96
O'Connor, Rev Roc P148
O'Connor, Susan P188
O'Connor, Jim P238
O'Connor, Dan P349
O'Connor, John T. P391
O'Connor, Edward R. P424
O'Connor, Patrick J. (Pat) P526
O'Connor, John J. P558
O'Connor, Lawrence R. P607
O'Connor, Richard W368
O'Connor, Michael J. W422
O'Day, Terence L. A411
O'Day, Jennifer P21
O'Day, Jodi R. P539
O'Day, Daniel W362
O'Dell, John A613
O'Dell, John D. A614
O'Dell, Mike P426
O'Dell, Allen P516
O'Donald, Lewis W320
O'Donell, William J. (Bill) P519
O'Donnell, Clem E31
O'Donnell, Terrence (Terry) E177
O'Donnell, Kelly S. E193
O'Donnell, Philip J. E236
O'Donnell, Michael J. E387
O'Donnell, John A. (Andy) A91
O'Donnell, Nancy A579
O'Donnell, Edward A668
O'Donnell, Peter G A834
O'Donnell, Debra P105
O'Donnell, William P172
O'Donnell, Simon P245
O'Donnell, Randall L. P328
O'Donnell, Laura E. P543
O'Donnell, James V. P570
O'Donnell, Hugh J. (James) W376
O'Donoghue, Dennis A125
O'Donoghue, Sister Hannah P118
O'Donoghue, Patricia P156
O'Donoghue, Leslie A. W18
O'Donovan, Terrence J. (Terry) E122
O'Donovan, Timothy J. E541
O'Donovan, James J. A578
O'Donovan, Sister Magdalen P389
O'Donovan, Rose W29
O'Donovan, Anne Marie W69
O'Donovan, Kathleen A. W348
O'Dowd, Joseph P. A495
O'Dwyer, Barry W348
O'Farrell, Paul E421
O'Farrell, Elizabeth G. A507
O'Farrell, Ray A846
O'Flynn, Thomas M. (Tom) A15
O'Grady, Shawn E137
O'Grady, Shawn P. A370
O'Grady, Rebecca L. (Becky) A370
O'Grady, Michael G. A595
O'Hagan, Sarah Robb E635
O'Halloran, J. Patrick E137
O'Halloran, James P. E392
O'Halloran, Frank W350
O'Hara, Kevin E238

O'Hara, C. Scott A282
O'Hara, J. Brooks A391
O'Hara, John A645
O'Hara, Curt P33
O'Hara, Jim W29
O'Hare, Elizabeth E166
O'Hare, Dean R. A23
O'Hare, John A223
O'Hare, Dean R. A348
O'Hare, Patrick P490
O'Haver, Cort A814
O'Herlihy, Christopher (Chris) A438
O'Kane, Katie A723
O'Kane, Katie P475
O'Keane, Brian J. E190
O'Keane, Brian J. A314
O'Keefe, Timothy M. A56
O'Keefe, Edward (Ed) A96
O'Keefe, Sean A105
O'Keefe, Mary A. A658
O'Keefe, Sean P49
O'Keefe, Peggy P112
O'Keefe, Richard P384
O'Keefe, Sharon P566
O'Keefe, Joseph M. P585
O'Keefe, Tim P605
O'Keefe, Sean C. W21
O'Keeffe, Patrick A48
O'Kelley, Ronald L. A719
O'Kelly, Stafford A4
O'Leary, George P. E96
O'Leary, Bernie E109
O'Leary, Hazel E284
O'Leary, Patrick E397
O'Leary, Meghan E469
O'Leary, William J. E538
O'Leary, Denise M. A143
O'Leary, Patrick A335
O'Leary, Denis J. A344
O'Leary, Christopher D. (Chris) A370
O'Leary, Denise M. A541
O'Leary, Joseph D. (Joe) A636
O'Leary, Joseph A637
O'Leary, Patrick J. A673
O'Leary, Patrick J. A738
O'Leary, Meghan A761
O'Leary, Christopher D. (Chris) A776
O'Leary, Christopher A776
O'Leary, Rev John P82
O'Leary, Thomas M. (Tom) P399
O'Leary, Rev Patrick B. P607
O'Leary, Tom W480
O'Looney, Michael W74
O'Loughlin, Dennis P143
O'Loughlin, Kathleen T. (Kathy) P586
O'Maley, David B. A810
O'Malley, Brian E72
O'Malley, Chris A139
O'Malley, Thomas A342
O'Malley, Patrick (Pat) A817
O'Malley, Carla P379
O'Mara, Frank A. E49
O'Mara, John M. E54
O'Mara, Paul E95
O'Meara, George A181
O'Meara, Robert P. (Bob) A339
O'Meara, Vicki A. A645
O'Meara, Vicki A645
O'Meara, Mary Jane P318
O'Meara, John-Paul W13
O'Neal, Bill E39
O'Neal, E. Stanley (Stan) A31
O'Neal, Rodney A382
O'Neal, Jim A590
O'Neal, Dennis L. P52
O'Neal, Frederick (Fred) P151
O'Neil, Mark F. E139
O'Neil, William C. E239
O'Neil, Thomas M. (Tom) A334
O'Neil, Frank B. A660
O'Neil, James F. A678
O'Neil, Mark T. A778
O'Neil, Michael O. P47
O'Neil, William E. P377
O'Neill, Michael E18

A = AMERICAN BUSINESS
E = EMERGING COMPANIES
P = PRIVATE COMPANIES
W = WORLD BUSINESS

O'Neill, Katie E70
O'Neill, Terrance P. E117
O'Neill, Timothy E410
O'Neill, Thomas E. E496
O'Neill, Thomas F. A72
O'Neill, Donald F. A113
O'Neill, James (Jim) A126
O'Neill, Paul H. A162
O'Neill, Michael E. A184
O'Neill, Michael E. A185
O'Neill, Eileen A255
O'Neill, Timothy J. A380
O'Neill, Chris A383
O'Neill, Myles A508
O'Neill, John J. A627
O'Neill, John P. A655
O'Neill, Peter A749
O'Neill, Paul H. A806
O'Neill, Paul A806
O'Neill, Daniel W. (Dan) P328
O'Neill, Daniel W. (Dan) P329
O'Neill, William J. P514
O'Neill, Connie P563
O'Neill, Thomas B. P565
O'Neill, Michael J. (Mike) P622
O'Neill, Thomas W12
O'Neill, Tim W66
O'Neill, Thomas C. (Tom) W69
O'Neill, Brian D. W167
O'Neill, Sean W199
O'Neill, Michael J. W266
O'Reagan, Richard A528
O'Reilly, Michael E317
O'Reilly, Lawrence P. (Larry) A603
O'Reilly, David E. A603
O'Reilly, Lawrence P. (Larry) A603
O'Reilly, Charles H. A603
O'Reilly, Tom A702
O'Reilly, Charles P227
O'Reilly, Michael P391
O'Reilly, Michael P510
O'Reilly, William R. (Bill) P586
O'Reilly-Wooten, Rosalie A603
O'Rourke, Tiarnan E182
O'Rourke, James E494
O'Rourke, William J. (Bill) A30
O'Rourke, Timothy C. P526
O'Rourke, P. Terrence (Terry) P580
O'Rourke, Ray W35
O'Shaughnessy, James (Jim) E228
O'Shaughnessy, Roger D. A112
O'Shaughnessy, Robert T. (Bob) A673
O'Shaughnessy, Brian P. P440
O'Shaughnessy, John F. P610
O'Shea, Robert J. P201
O'Shea, Denny P511
O'Shea-Owens, Maura P47
O'Steen, Gloria P553
O'Sullivan, Timothy R. (Tim) E437
O'Sullivan, Louise E479
O'Sullivan, Barry A181
O'Sullivan, Sharon A255
O'Sullivan, John A402
O'Sullivan, Michael A583
O'Sullivan, Michael B. A704
O'Sullivan, Louise A772
O'Sullivan, Richard A804
O'Sullivan, Paul P326
O'Sullivan, Angela P578
O'Sullivan, Patrick H. W66
O'Sullivan, Francis K. (Fran) W266
O'Sullivan, James J. (Jim) W283
O'Toole, James P. E237
O'Toole, Timothy T. (Tim) A230
O'Toole, Frank A363
O'Toole, Peter A368
O'Toole, Audry A772
O'Toole, Thomas F. (Tom) A819
O'Toole, Audry P524

O'Toole, Terence M. P622

P

P., John P. E42
Paanakker, Roland A586
Paasche, Sascha W143
Paasschen, Frits D. van A746
Pace, Gen. Peter E3
Pace, Daniel J. E216
Pace, John H. E231
Pace, Gen. Peter E395
Pace, Gary W. E418
Pace, John H. A395
Pace, Wayne H. A792
Pace, Fred E. A872
Pace, Thomas J. P550
Pacey, Amy P186
Pachauri, Rajendra W332
Pache, Kildine A641
Pacheco, Steve A321
Pacheco, Maximo A455
Pacheco, Jorge Luiz W468
Pachler, Johan W212
Pachta-Reyhofen, Georg W276
Pacilio, Michael J. A301
Pacilio, Mike A302
Pack, Zachary J. E527
Pack, Mike A10
Packard, Ronald J. (Ron) E291
Packard, Julie E. P541
Packer, Richard A. E77
Packer, Roger J. P116
Packer, Steven J. P134
Packer, Gayle P527
Packman, Robert C. A164
Paczkowski, John P. E257
Paczuski, Dariusz E481
Padalino, Michael L. A766
Padgett, Pamela (Pam) A402
Padierna, Pedro A635
Padilla, Jaime E84
Padilla, Buddy E241
Padilla, Jose D. P156
Padilla, Raul W102
Padmanabhan, Srikanth A232
Padmanabhan, Krishnan A576
Padmanabhan, P. W86
Pados, Frank J. P585
Padovani, Roberto A676
Padval, Umesh E347
Pae, Judy W267
Paefgen, Franz-Josef W489
Paesana, Bruno W234
Paesler, Klaus W195
Paetz, Michael C. A54
Paez, Pablo E. A218
Paganelli, Mark P610
Pagano, Robert P. E71
Pagano, John E383
Pagano, Christopher J. A77
Pagano, Michael A186
Pagano, Stephen P179
Page, Timothy E82
Page, Scott H. E163
Page, David K. E325
Page, James H. A144
Page, Scott A195
Page, Dan A358
Page, Larry E. A383
Page, Stephen F. (Steve) A516
Page, David K. A537
Page, Stephen F. (Steve) A622
Page, H. Lynn A767
Page, Richard W. A797
Page, Douglas F. (Doug) A813
Page, Michael J. P59
Page, Kerry P124
Page, Alexander (Bob) P205
Page, Glenda P250
Page, Malcolm V. P466
Page, Malcolm V. P467
Page, James P602
Page, Richard P612

Paglia, Fred A488
Paglia, Richard A735
Pagliarini, James R. P420
Pagliaro, Renato W432
Paglino, Joe A255
Pagliuca, Stephen G. (Steve) A405
Pagoaga, Carlos A197
Pagorek, Bob A573
Pahne, Erika W426
Pai, Venugopal E422
Paiement, Luc W302
Paige, Bill P657
Paik, Elaine C. A201
Paine, Andrew A480
Paine, Gail F. P355
Painter, Corning F. A24
Painter, Craig C. P286
Paisley, Christopher B. (Chris) E178
Paisley, Christopher B. (Chris) E201
Paisley, Andy A261
Paiva, Louise P549
Paiva, Bernardo Pinto W37
Pajonas, Thomas L. A346
Pak, Barb E180
Pak, Young Hi A872
Pakonen, Diane P579
Pakulis, Mr Jim E435
Palacio, Vivian Kobeh de W318
Palacios, Elizabeth D. P52
Paladino, Steven A713
Palagiano, Vincent F. A252
Palame, David E114
PalamT, David A. E114
Palande, Pandit W196
Palander, Katia E114
Palander, Katia A202
Palandjian, Tracy E19
Palazzolo, Vincent (Vince) E124
Palczynski, James E209
Palenbaum, Gary A765
Palensky, Frederick J. A2
Palenzona, Fabrizio W284
Palenzona, Fabrizio W463
Paleologos, David P514
Palermo, James P. (Jim) A98
Palermo, James P. (Jim) A99
Palestrant, David P102
Palette, Donald W. (Don) E449
Paley, Marc L. P297
Palfenier, David A. A217
Palia, S. M. (Sam) W430
Palin, Stephen C. P377
Palisch, Terry E89
Palkovic, Michael W. (Mike) A253
Palladino, Cynthia A315
Palladino, Camilla W163
Pallash, Robert C. A845
Paller, Mark P189
Palleschi, Ralph F. A78
Pallesen, Lars W2
Pallotta, Karen R. A312
Palluth, Ed E30
Palm, Joseph E46
Palm, James D. (Jim) E227
Palm, Gregory K. A380
Palm, Risa I. P559
Palma, Stephen De P360
Palmarini, Simone Piattelli A641
Palmberg, Kent P512
Palmer, Grant E132
Palmer, Ben M. E427
Palmer, Peter E494
Palmer, Adam J. E531
Palmer, Robert B. A12
Palmer, Richard W. A181
Palmer, Bart A255
Palmer, Thomas W. A299
Palmer, Vicki R. A337
Palmer, Anthony J. (Tony) A411
Palmer, Kay A432
Palmer, Carolyn A478
Palmer, Anthony J. (Tony) A482
Palmer, C. Michael A522
Palmer, Todd A576
Palmer, James F. (Jim) A596

Palmer, Duncan J. A617
Palmer, Fredrick D. (Fred) A630
Palmer, Mark A. A768
Palmer, Jodie L. A773
Palmer, Nicola A840
Palmer, R. Roy A880
Palmer, Cassandra P212
Palmer, Mark P379
Palmer, Kevin P379
Palmer, Richard M. P430
Palmer, Harvey P439
Palmer, Bradley C. P457
Palmer, Stephen R. (Steve) P511
Palmer, John W33
Palmer, Jeffrey O. W274
Palmer, John R. V. W278
Palmer, Andy W316
Palmieri, Daniela A509
Palmieri, Bonnie S. A840
Palmisano, Samuel J. (Sam) A308
Palmisano, Samuel J. (Sam) A452
Palmore, David C. E481
Palmore, Roderick A. (Rick) A370
Palmquist, Steven C. E236
Palmquist, Mark A176
Palms, John M. A77
Paloian, John R. A264
Palomo, Benjamin W356
Palsen, P. C. A288
Paltrinieri, Massimo W41
Palumbo, Andrew (Drew) P105
Palumbo, Drew P105
Palumbo, Angela P471
Pambianchi, Christine M. A223
Pamer-Wieser, Charlotte W323
Pan, Allen J. E70
Pan, Nicholas D. Le W104
Pan, Richard W345
Pan, Richard W346
Panagiotopoulos, Theofanis W303
Panagopoulos, Ioannis P. W303
Panasewicz, Stanley (Stan) A466
Panattoni, Lisa A504
Panayiotou, Drew A118
Panayotopoulos, E. Dimitri A661
Panayotopoulos, E. Dimitri A662
Pancaccini, Gianluca Gianluca
  Pancaccini W432
Pancha, Girish E270
Pancini, Josue A. W56
Panda, Brendan E182
Pande, Arvind W196
Pande, N. K. W328
Pandey, Sanjay E149
Pandiri, Samir A99
Pandit, Vikram S. A185
Pandora, Frank T. P382
Pane, Lisa Marie P533
Paneak, Raymond P30
Panem, Sandra E13
Panepento, Nancy P305
Panetta, Sarah P385
Pang, Paul E169
Pang, Thomas H. E407
Pang, Adrian A183
Pang, Sarah A192
Pang, Laurinda A503
Pang, David J. A844
Pang, Joseph Y. W. W65
Pangalos, Menelas W44
Pangburn, James W. A54
Pangelinan, Julie E211
Paniccia, Mario J. A447
Panichella, John E. A75
Panicker, Prasad K. W86
Panikar, John M. A654
Panizza, Florencia E59
Panizza, Florencia E316
Panizzo, Jose M. Carrera W356
Panizzo, Jose W356
Panke, Helmut A553
Panke, Helmut W78
Panke, Helmut W461
Pankow, David P439
Pann, Stuart C. A446

Pannell, Derek G. W18
Pannkuk, Stu P217
Pannone, Gary R. P441
Panos, David E. (Dave) E142
Panpiemras, Kosit W61
Panpiemrat, Kosit W61
Pansa, Alessandro W173
Pansegrau, Wolfgang W263
Pant, Pradeep A559
Pant, Micky A885
Pantages-Baker, Danielle E30
Pantaleoni, Anthony A833
Pantaleoni, Anthony (Tony) P597
Pantling, Shaun W. A881
Pantzar, Anna Tillberg W203
Pantzar, Anna Anna Pantzar W203
Panyarachun, Anand W394
Panzarella, Amy E37
Panzarino, James V. A254
Panzer, Mark C. A718
Pao-In, Bussakorn W61
Paoli, Mary W422
Paolini, Nonce W93
Paolucci, Jane A536
Papa, George A. E29
Papa, Rosemarie Novello E423
Papa, Mark G. A298
Papa, John A. A466
Papa, Mark G. A607
Papa, Mark Del P454
Papacostas, Arthur P526
Papadellis, Randy P634
Papadimitriou, Dimitri B. P46
Papadopoulos, Stelios A121
Papadopoulos, Robert P332
Papadopulos, John M. A859
Papagrigoris, Gregory W303
Papakipos, Matthew (Matt) A309
Papakonstantinou, Lambros W303
Papalexopoulou-Benop,
  Alexandra W303
Papar, Riyaz E254
Paparelli, Sandro A779
Paparone, Bruce J. P283
Papaspyrou, Spyros A. W343
Papaspyrou, Spyros A. W344
Papastavrou, Jason D. A825
Papay, Mike A597
Papazian, Steve A793
Pape, Robert J. E286
Pape, Craig A44
Pape, Sabrina P620
Pape, Jacques W19
Papermaster, Mark A12
Papermaster, Mark A181
Papernick, Alan A706
Papesh, G. Bruce E366
Papiasse, Alain W90
Papilsky, Gary E139
Papke, Paul P588
Papola, Maria P154
Pappacena, Bonnie M. E13
Pappas, Christopher E102
Pappas, John E102
Pappas, Arthur (Art) A48
Pappas, Cary C. A321
Pappas, Christopher D. A341
Pappathopoulos, Nick E91
Pappelendam, Marc Van A586
Pappert, P. David P167
Pappis, Charlie A69
Papworth, David B. A446
Paquette, Justin D. P26
Paquin, Daniel R. A856
Paquot, Guy W462
Paradie, Terrance M. A188
Paradies, Gregg P558
Paradies, James N. (Jim) P558
Paradies, Jill P558
Paradis, Paul P245
Paradis, Jim P309
Paradise, William (Will) A870
Paradise, Edward P126
Paranicas, Dean J. A109
Paranjpe, Nitin W465

Paras, Marios W352
Parasida, Anthony M. (Tony) A125
Paraskevopoulo, Nicholas g. A596
Parasuraman, Bala A265
Parayre, Jean-Paul W342
Parcells, Patrick R. (Pat) P436
Parcells, Patrick R. (Pat) P437
Parcot, Christophe A883
Parde, Erin P554
Pardee, Charles G. (Chip) A301
Pardee, Charles G. (Chip) A302
Pardee, Chip A781
Pardo, Jaime Chico A79
Pardo, Jaime Chico A421
Pardo, Virginia C. P375
Pardo, Jaime Chico W32
Pardun, Thomas E. E84
Pardun, Thomas E. A864
Pare, Raymond W27
Pare, Jean-Philippe W145
Pareigat, Thomas E488
Pareigat, Thomas A789
Parekh, David E. A830
Parent, June B. A144
Parent, Ghislain W302
Parent, Brigitte W422
Parent, Bruno W443
Parente, Anthony M (Tony) E441
Parente, Charles E. E527
Parente, John A209
Parente, Pedro Pullen W102
Parenti, Julie P274
Paresky, Susan S. P154
Parfet, Donald R. A478
Parfet, William U. A560
Parfet, Donald R. A702
Parfet, William U. A753
Pargament, Jeffrey J. P6
Parham, Joseph G. (Joe) A73
Parham, Tracy P604
Pariegat, Thomas G. E488
Pariegat, Thomas G. A789
Parikh, Ashish R. E243
Parikh, Purvish M. P24
Parikh, Bobby W196
Paris, Scott G. P174
Paris, Tom Van P250
Parish, Brady A66
Parish, Helen P492
Parisi, Erika S. A475
Parisot, Laurence W133
Parizeau, Robert W345
Park, Ed E49
Park, Arlington E104
Park, Jeana H. E235
Park, Jae H. E347
Park, Ernest (Ernie) A2
Park, John A. A99
Park, Ellen A201
Park, Chong S. A214
Park, Tae A237
Park, Anthony J. (Tony) A322
Park, Ernest (Ernie) A441
Park, Hyun A640
Park, Mike P397
Park, Gary L. P604
Park, Jin-won W220
Park, Young-june W220
Park, Jong-Seok W267
Park, Oh-Soo W378
Parke, James A. A375
Parke, Pat P338
Parker, F. Gardner E94
Parker, Prof George G. C. E114
Parker, Victor E. (Vic) E142
Parker, James R. E149
Parker, Gerhard H. (Gerry) E190
Parker, Jefferson G. (Jeff) E256
Parker, Christina E291
Parker, David E331
Parker, Prof George G. C. E367
Parker, Graham E457
Parker, James F. (Jim) E487
Parker, W. Fort E527
Parker, W. Douglas (Doug) A48

Parker, Gerhard H. (Gerry) A69
Parker, Donald T. (Don) A127
Parker, Stan A171
Parker, Scott T. A183
Parker, John R. A198
Parker, Jayne A258
Parker, John O. A306
Parker, James M. (Jay) A331
Parker, John A338
Parker, Charles A. A422
Parker, Jefferson G. (Jeff) A436
Parker, Jeffrey A. (Jeff) A490
Parker, Ialantha A539
Parker, Jackie A580
Parker, Mark G. A585
Parker, Mark G. A586
Parker, Deborah S. A587
Parker, Teresa A. A594
Parker, Krystal J. A613
Parker, Gary D. A613
Parker, Kenneth J. (Ken) A633
Parker, Sean T. A661
Parker, Beau A742
Parker, Sandra A. A797
Parker, P. William (Bill) A810
Parker, David A837
Parker, James A870
Parker, Bobby P78
Parker, Thomas A. (Tap) P144
Parker, Andy P161
Parker, Annette S. P161
Parker, Francine (Fran) P171
Parker, Connie P180
Parker, Tom P215
Parker, Jack C. P251
Parker, Frank P251
Parker, Jim P277
Parker, Liza P301
Parker, Robin Leigh P335
Parker, Ashley P417
Parker, Sandra A. P440
Parker, Craig W. P535
Parker, Elizabeth Rindskopf P611
Parker, Sir John W21
Parker, Sir John W35
Parker, Sue Graham W69
Parker, Sue W69
Parker, Andrew W100
Parker, Sir John W107
Parker, Josh W368
Parker, Christine W484
Parker-Selby, Esthelda R. P56
Parkes, David W51
Parkhill, Karen L. A205
Parkhurst, Kleyton L. (Kley) E177
Parkington, Richard J. P511
Parkinson, John F. A402
Parkinson, Bradford W. E498
Parkinson, Robert L. A106
Parkinson, Jerry P614
Parks, Fred B. E42
Parks, Ralph T. E247
Parks, Delbert R. A446
Parks, James C. E522
Parks, David A205
Parks, Michael K. A275
Parks, Lawrence H. A315
Parks, Julie A531
Parks, Charles A784
Parks, Kenneth S. A862
Parks, Crockett P110
Parks, Richard H. P145
Parks, Carol Sawyer P514
Parlapiano, Donna A82
Parlavecchio, Joe E193
Parlett, Kristopher A662
Parman, Travis M. A673
Parman, John P647
Parmelee, Ferole P292
Parmiter, Ian A255
Parnaby, Nathan W413
Parnell, Gordon W. E336
Parnell, Jack C. E366
Parnell, Tim P504
Parnell, Dennis P513

Parneros, Demos A744
Parod, Richard W. (Rick) E303
Paroski, Margaret P280
Parr, Kevin C. A825
Parr, Stephen E. P280
Parr, Nick W195
Parra, Rosendo G. (Ro) A584
Parra, Rosendo G. (Ro) A640
Parra, Alfred P400
Parreira, Rodrigo P302
Parrett, William G. (Bill) A791
Parrett, Chanda P499
Parrett, William G. (Bill) W461
Parrini, Dante E207
Parriott, Ann B. E207
Parris, Lydia P6
Parris, Jill P134
Parrish, Charles S. (Chuck) E484
Parrish, Marc A103
Parrish, M. Lynn A212
Parrish, Mark W. A568
Parrish, Julie A576
Parrish, Charles S. (Chuck) A783
Parrish, Benjamin F. A800
Parrish, Martin A838
Parrish, Deborah P21
Parrish, Thomas (Tom) P21
Parrish, Mike P368
Parrott, Sharon Thomas E144
Parrott, Cindy A210
Parrs, Marianne Miller A183
Parrs, Marianne Miller A742
Parry, David M. E107
Parry, Michael J. (Mike) A286
Parry, David C. A438
Parry, Robert T. A622
Parry, Susan P157
Parry, Lyle J. P311
Parsel, Lori P385
Parsley, E. William (Bill) A649
Parslow, Darren A844
Parsons, Craig S. E441
Parsons, Joan E469
Parsons, Jim E469
Parsons, Kelli A312
Parsons, Joseph E. (Joe) A367
Parsons, Eric E. A741
Parsons, Joan A761
Parsons, Jim A761
Parsons, Stephen P44
Parsons, Susan E. P215
Parsons, Susan E. P289
Parsons, William P323
Parsons, Gary P357
Parsons, Alex W227
ParT, David A265
Partain, Nathan I. E522
Partamian, Gregory P149
Partch, Judy Gerrard P162
Partee, W. Cal A94
Partee, Terrell A201
Parthasarathi, Arvind E125
Parthasarthy, Ashish W196
Parthemore, Eric A457
Partridge, Tom A325
Partridge, John M. A844
Partridge, Thomas L. P534
Parvarandeh, Pirooz E322
Parven, Alvin S. E24
Parvis, Sharon J. A804
Pasantes, Mario E450
Pascal, Amy W408
Pascale, John C P39
Pascavis, Roger E212
Pasch, Reinhard W164
Pasch, Reinhard W300
Paschalis, Konstantinos W343
Paschel, Sam E448
Pascoe, Kevin E360
Pascoe, Ricardo W302
Pascualy, Ralph P521
Pasek, Ronald J. (Ron) E29
Pasha, Ahmed A15
Pashamova, Bistra A65
Pasik, Alexander P545

Purcell, John R. (Jack) A612
Purcell, J. Neal A767
Purcell, Susan Kaufman A838
Purcell, Stacy P172
Purcell, Alfred L. P236
Purcell, James (Jim) P414
Purdom, E. Stephen A18
Purdue, Jeff P76
Purdy, William J. A804
Purfeerst, Laura P175
Puri, Ravi P557
Puri, Aditya W196
Puri, Navin W196
Puri, Aditya W196
Purinthawarakun, Amphorn W61
Puron, Jose M. Rincon Gallardo W114
Puron, Jose W114
Purpura, Nate E167
Purtilar, Mark W. A382
Purves, Stephen A. (Steve) P349
Purvis, Edgar M. (Ed) A288
Purvis, Robert P361
Purwin, Alan P537
Puryear, Alvin N. E35
Puryear, Kay A661
Pusch, Rick G. Von E139
Pusch, Rick E139
Pusey, Stephen C. (Steve) W475
Pusey, Stephen C. (Steve) W476
Pushis, Glenn A750
Pushor, Kathleen S. A444
Puskar, George R. A459
Put, Dirk A531
Putallaz, Ann F. A660
Puterbaugh, Harry L. P78
Putkiranta, Juha W318
Putnam, Dana E53
Putnam, Philip G. E343
Putnam, Christopher S. (Chris) E473
Putnam, Robert P372
Putnam, Skip P373
Putnam, Michael C. (Mike) W400
Puto, Christopher P609
Putten, LeRoy A. Vander E504
Putten, LeRoy E504
Putter, Joshua S. P509
Putter, Bernd W210
Putur, Christine (Chris) A194
Puxsupachat, Teera E400
Pyatt, Shawn P87
Pye, Ken N. E337
Pye, Hugh W218
Pyle, Michael R. (Mike) E392
Pyle, Bob A237
Pyle, Larry P156
Pylipow, David E. (Dave) A758
Pym, Richard A. W330
Pyne, Joseph H. (Joe) E296
Pynn, David P498
Pynnonen, Brett A316
PynnonenSr, Brett A317
Pyott, David E. I. E166
Pyott, David E. I. A36
Pyott, David E. I. A85
Python, Frantz P74

Q

Qi, Dave E452
Qi, Zhu W119
Qi, Lan W119
Qi, Gao W368
Qing, Huang W121
Qingshan, Wen W339
Qiu, Olivia W131
Qu, Zhang W229
Quackenbos, Jim P88
Quader, Khandker Nazrul A709
Quaid, John J. A827
Quain, Mitchell I. (Mitch) E241
Quain, Mitchell I. (Mitch) E491
Qualey, Allen R. A1
Qualls, R. L. A100
Qualters, Irene M. P168

Quan, Nancy W. A197
Quandt, James R. (Jim) E142
Quandt, Stefan W80
Quandt, Stefan W81
Quant, Shawn E397
Quaranta, Mary Ann P201
Quarles, David A. E304
Quartermain, Mark W370
Quass, Mary K. E509
Quass, Mary K. A821
Quast, Shelley P593
Quatrano, Ralph S. P570
Quattrochi, Dana E49
Quazzo, Stephen R. A746
Qubaisi, Khadem W332
Qubein, Nido R. A108
Quee, Michael Chin P200
Queenan, Daniel (Danny) A158
Queenan, Thomas P162
Queener, Hugh M. A644
Quehl, Dick A698
Querner, Immo W195
Querner, Immo W429
Querrey, Dale A678
Query, K. Rex A600
Quesenberry, Tammy E291
Quesnel, Gregory L. (Greg) A704
Quesnel, Gregory L. (Greg) A765
Quest, Donald O. A429
Questrom, Allen I. A351
Quezada, David M. E172
Quezada, David M. A289
Qui?ones, Eduardo E5
Quick, Chuck M. E256
Quick, J. Douglas A75
Quick, Chuck M. A436
Quick, Michael M. A759
Quick, Christopher C. P187
Quick, Paul M. P194
Quick, James E. P484
Quicksilver, Robert E. A171
Quigley, Brian W. A42
Quigley, William G. (Bill) A237
Quigley, Margaret A784
Quigley, Philip J. (Phil) A859
Quigley, Philip J. (Phil) P492
Quijano, Lorena Diaz E333
Quijano, Melisa T. E375
Quillen, Denise P566
Quincey, James R. A197
Quindlen, Thomas M. (Tom) A367
Quiniones, Gil C. P363
Quinlan, Kevin W. E43
Quinlan, Francis E173
Quinlan, Steven J. (Steve) E366
Quinlan, Peter S. E444
Quinlan, Mark D. A75
Quinlan, Raymond J. (Ray) A183
Quinlan, Michael T. A185
Quinlan, Thomas J. A264
Quinlan, Thomas J. (Tom) A265
Quinlan, Mark D. A342
Quinlan, Tim A573
Quinlan, William J. A593
Quinlan, Mark J. A613
Quinlan, Peter S. A723
Quinlan, Thomas W. A853
Quinlan, Thomas J. P391
Quinlan, Gerard P446
Quinlan, Joe P468
Quinn, Francis D. E52
Quinn, James E140
Quinn, Robert C. E163
Quinn, Michael A E380
Quinn, Michael A. E418
Quinn, J. F. (Jack) A57
Quinn, Stephen D. A391
Quinn, Andrew D. A440
Quinn, John A475
Quinn, R. Patrick A578
Quinn, T. Kyle A622
Quinn, Jean A668
Quinn, Kevin J. A671
Quinn, Barney A725
Quinn, John A778

Quinn, Stephen F. A849
Quinn, Stephen D. A888
Quinn, Judith C. P91
Quinn, Victoria P237
Quinn, Michael P. P276
Quinn, Brandi P314
Quinn, Andrew S. P382
Quinn, Father Kevin P. P414
Quinn, Erin P415
Quinn, Don P455
Quinn, Mary Anna P501
Quinn, Kevin C. P523
Quinn, Father Kevin P. P608
Quinn, Teresa P620
Quinn, Noel W218
Quinn-Quintin, Karen P553
Quinnan, Ed E531
Quinoy, George E525
Quinoy, Jorge J. (George) E525
Quint, C. Robert (Bob) A681
Quintavell, Roberta (Bobbi) P29
Quintavell, Roberta (Bobbi) P30
Quintella, Antonio W139
Quintella, Sergio F. W340
Quintero, Julio E292
Quintero-Johnson, Marie D. A197
Quintin, Brent P643
Quinto, Marcos de A197
Quinton, Jody P165
Quirk, Raymond R. (Randy) A322
Quirk, Kathleen L. A357
Quirk, Alison A. A749
Quirk, Robert F. A853
Quirke, Kelly W87
Quon, Daniel R. E469
Quon, Daniel R. A761
Quon, Cindy P385
Qureshi, Muhammad E343
Qureshi, Rima A529
Qureshi, Rima W166
Qureshy, Farhan A468
Qutub, Robert E352

R

R-CA, Mary P396
R., Claudia L. Castellanos W160
R?d, St?le W401
R?ed, Anders W415
Raab, Dennis A433
Raabe, James C. E303
Raad, Mark E317
Raad, M. P. M. (Theo) de W286
Raahauge, Ginna E421
Raasch, Jona S. E363
Raba, Todd A115
Rabb, Madeline Murphy P132
Rabb, Harriet P559
Rabbit, Daniel J. A92
Rabbitt, Linda D. A319
Rabbitt, Kara P572
Rabe, D. J. A288
Rabe, Thomas W83
Rabin, Edward W. (Ed) E405
Rabin, Edward W. (Ed) A659
Rabin, Anthony L. P. W53
Rabinovich, Daniel E333
Rabinovitch, Issie N. E180
Rabinowicz, Adrian L. E13
Rabinowitz, Mark A. A596
Rabinowitz, Jacqueline P326
Rable, George P58
Raborn, Francis A737
Raby, Paul W53
Racer, Janie P292
Racey, Barry A27
Rachou, Nathalie W402
Racioppi, Michael A713
Rada, Huberto E109
Radano, Robert M. E286
Radcliffe, Harry F. A308
Rade, Arnoud de E213
Radecki, Brian J. E123
Rademacher, Hollis W. E540

Rademacher, John A151
Rademacher, Hollis W. A874
Rademacher, Tom W210
Rademacher, Lilo W490
Rader, Judy A301
Rader, David J. A859
Rader, Lynn P185
Rader, Machelle P269
Rader, Rodney P360
Radford, Lawrence E240
Radikas, Ray A509
Radin, Amy P636
Radke, Roger W396
Radley, Diane W330
Radosevich, Teri A88
Radous, Barbara A49
Radovan, Patty E175
Radtke, Duane C. A248
Radue, Mark M. A617
Radue, Jane P613
Rady, Ernest S. P462
Radziwill, John A457
Rae, Duane A735
Rae, John A. A345
Raeck, Mathias A846
Raese, John P215
Rafaeli, Dolev E394
Rafalski, Ed P334
Raff, Beryl B. A391
Raffaelle, Ryne P439
Raffaelli, John D. P563
Raffelhuschen, Prof Bernd W164
Rafferty, James B. E18
Rafferty, Emily K. A319
Rafferty, Lawrence C. P187
Rafferty, Beth Ann P488
Rafferty, Gary J. P522
Rafferty, Emily K. P552
Raffin, Margaret I. P394
Raffin, Philippe W127
Raffone, Lawrence M. (Larry) E193
Rafky, Janet P205
Raftery, Ellyn A323
Ragan, John W. A599
Ragan, Albert J. P271
Ragan, Cynthia P271
Ragan, Michael E. P371
Ragauss, Peter A. A91
Ragen, York A. E212
Rager, Jon F. E285
Rager, R. Scott A609
Raggi, Robert P653
Raghuram, Raghu A846
Ragland, David E. A93
Ragone, Daniel J. P283
Ragsdale, Howard E20
Ragsdale, John P31
Ragsdale, Lyn P645
Ragusa, Elysia Holt E486
Ragusa, Elysia Holt A785
Ragusa, Frank P379
Raguz, Steven M. A188
Rahardja, Francisca A42
Rahe, Maribeth S. E196
Rahe, Maribeth S. A333
Rahilly, Thomas F. (Tom) W483
Rahim, Rami A472
Rahl, Leslie W104
Rahlf, Christine P189
Rahmberg, Lee A837
Rahn, Joel A172
Rahn, Daniel W. P30
Rai, Raj E22
Raia, Cathryn A594
Raich, Charles E360
Raichle, William M. E521
Raico, Nick D. P246
Raiden, Sally P647
Raiguel, Darren E177
Raikes, Jeffrey S. (Jeff) A225
Raim, Ellen E95
Raimonde, Michael A. A667
Raimondi, Christian W127
Raina, Robin E164
Rainbolt, H. E. (Gene) A93

A = AMERICAN BUSINESS
E = EMERGING COMPANIES
P = PRIVATE COMPANIES
W = WORLD BUSINESS

Rainbolt, David E. A93
Rainer, Sallie A295
Rainer, Thom S. P300
Rainer, Majda W280
Raines, John D. E190
Raines, J. Paul (Paul) A11
Raines, John D. A314
Raines, Ellen A341
Raines, J. Paul (Paul) A361
Raines, Marjorie D. A571
Rainey, Phyllis D. E92
Rainey, Joseph D. (Joe) A394
Rainey, John A819
Rainey, Craig A872
Rainey, James P83
Rainwater, Tom P169
Rainwater, Gary L. P570
Raisanen, Alan P439
Raisbeck, David W. A151
Raisbeck, David W. A278
Raisl, Gary F. P455
Raiss, Sarah E. A208
Raj, V. S. E476

Raj, Raman P303
Raj, Niraj P392
Raja, Prabu A69
Rajagopal, Sukumar A199
Rajala, Mike P137
Rajamanickam, Ramachandran A4
Rajamannar, Venkata A652
Rajapakse, Suresh Suresh
  Rajapakse W39
Rajasigamany, Stephen A641
Rajavashisth, Tripathi P102
Rajczak, Daniel S. A662
Rajgopal, Raj E523
Rajkowski, E. Mark A539
Rajparia, Anish D. A81
Rakatansky, Carol R. A726
Rake, Sir Michael D. V. (Mike) W72
Rake, Sir Michael D. V. (Mike) W74
Rake, Sir Michael D. V. (Mike) W100
Rakes, Thomas A. P610
Rakesh, Nitin E476
Rakic, Mark E112
Rakusin, Jeremy A684
Ralapanawa, Mahanama W212
Rales, Steven M. A238
Rales, Mitchell P. A238
Raley, Fred D. P489
Ralles, Mary A662
Ralli, Georges W471
Rallo, James M. (Jim) E306
Ralls, Matt A757
Ralph, K. Douglas (Doug) E93
Ralph, Sherrie E213
Ralph, Thomas A. A228
Ralph, Julie H. A627
Ralph, Steven A. P395
Ralph, James (Maggie) P415
Ralph, Jay W28
Ralston, Joseph W. A512
Ralston, Joseph W. A795
Ralston, Douglas A805
Ralston, Joseph W. A836
Ralston, Mark P503
Ramachandran, M. S. W224
Ramagano, Cheryl K. E512
Ramaker, David B. A172
Ramakrishnan, C. W430
Ramalho, Kimberly A512
Ramanathan, Guru E221
Ramaphosa, M. Cyril W373
Ramaprakash, Tarini E381
Ramas, Guillermo E340
Ramaswami, Rajiv A135
Ramberg, Agneta W203
Rambo, Amy A72

Rambo, Barbara L. A640
Ramchander, Pranill W35
Ramenda, James (Jim) E458
Ramesh, S. W85
Ramey, Diana M. P51
Ramirez, Michael E5
Ramirez, Ted E39
Ramirez, Warren E76
Ramirez, Warren A136
Ramirez, Francisco Munoz A201
Ramirez, John A315
Ramirez, Raul A584
Ramirez, Jaime A. A742
Ramirez, Edith P303
Ramirez, Maria Fiorini P391
Ramirez, Gilda P410
Ramji, Al-Noor E523
Ramkissoon, Rev Gregory P200
Ramkumar, Krishnaswamy W224
Ramlau-Hansen, Henrik W147
Ramlo, Randy A. E509
Ramlo, Randy A. A821
Rammohan, Ashok A641
Ramnath, Suja E313
Ramo, Joshua A321
Ramo, Joshua C. A745
Ramon, David E212
Ramonat, R. Whitfield A632
Ramoneda, Dede F. A331
Ramos, Marcos R. A30
Ramos, Ricardo (Ricky) A201
Ramos, William M. A290
Ramos, Anelsie A661
Ramos, Suzanne M. A859
Ramos, Rev Marcos A. P44
Ramos, Rick P313
Ramos, Jose Maldonado W55
Ramos, Maria W71
Ramos, Maria W72
Ramos, Maria W74
Ramos, Luis W91
Rampacek, Charles M. (Charlie) A346
Rampalli, Prasad L. A284
Ramphele, Mamphela W35
Rampinelli, Audrey A. A514
Rampl, Dieter W284
Rampl, Dieter W463
Rampley, R. M. (Mike) P250
Rampone, Thomas A. (Tom) A446
Rampone, Thomas A709
Rampone, Wayne P274
Ramraj, Sreeram (Sam) A836
Ramrath, Joseph R. A398
Ramsay, Paul D. A516
Ramsay, Brian G. P377
Ramsay, Duncan A350
Ramsburg, Lara A568
Ramsburg, Kevin S. A617
Ramsby, Ole W325
Ramsden, Jonathan E. A6
Ramsey, Roger A. E94
Ramsey, James E175
Ramsey, Craig E227
Ramsey, Patrick J. E355
Ramsey, Stephen E447
Ramsey, James R. E487
Ramsey, James R. A212
Ramsey, Jane L. A491
Ramsey, David L. P111
Ramsey, Betsy P535
Ramsey, Beryl P550
Ramsey, Paul G. P611
Ramsower, Reagan M. P51
Ramstad, Peter M. (Pete) E493
Ramstad, James A774
Ramundo, Katherine Hargrove A201
Rana, Basudev W85
Ranade, Prashant E476
Ranadive, Vivek Y. E491
Ranadive, Vivek E491
Ranaldi, Robert (Bob) E408
Ranalli, Marco E216
Ranck, Bruce E. A678
Rand, A. Barry A21
Rand, A. Barry A147

Rand, Edward L. (Ned) A660
Rand, A. Barry P252
Randall, Richard P. (Dick) E11
Randall, Lorin J. (Jeff) E13
Randall, Richard P. (Dick) E314
Randall, Michael P. E441
Randall, Carol A. A114
Randall, H. Douglas A853
Randall, Benny P483
Randall, Bryan J. P618
Randel, Don M. A192
Randel, Don M. P559
Randell, Linda L. E502
Randhawa, Sabah P385
Randich, Steven J. (Steve) P195
Randle, Paul R. W283
Randlett, Thomas E. (Tom) E180
Randolfi, Mike A247
Randolph, John M. E213
Randolph, Sabrina E324
Randolph, Michael P565
Randolph, Marcus P. W87
Randopoulos, Anthoula P162
Randt, Thomas P. A468
Randt, Clark T. (Sandy) A824
Rane, Keith P100
Raney, Dennis R. E505
Raney, Steven M. A684
Raney, W. Grant A873
Raney, Carolyn P397
Rangachari, Sarangan E414
Range, Jean E. P277
Rangen, Eric S. A832
Ranger, Michael W. A220
Rango, Robert A. (Bob) A135
Ranieri, John P. A272
Raniolo, Robert P402
Rankin, R. Alex E104
Rankin, Alfred M. E255
Rankin, Jean F. E276
Rankin, Norman J. (Norm) A120
Rankin, B. M. A357
Rankin, Kurt J. A649
Rankin, David A716
Rankin, Donald P219
Rankin, Stephen (Steve) P484
Rankin, Mary Ann P488
Rankin, David J. P548
Rankin, Alfred M. P600
Rankin, Fred M. P630
Ranney, George A. P539
Ranney, George A. P540
Ranninger, Rebecca A. A764
Rannou, Jean W375
Ranong, Chok W61
Ranque, Denis W131
Ransburg, David P. (Dave) P78
Ransier, Kathleen H. A433
Ransom, James W. (Jim) A112
Ransom, Curtis E. P230
Ranson, Brine A75
Ranspot, James A40
Rao, Alice E30
Rao, Meera A347
Rao, Bhaskar E482
Rao, Shailesh A383
Rao, Valluri A447
Rao, Anand S. A509
Rao, Addagada C. P653
Rao, I. Srinivas W86
Rapaczynski, Wanda W12
Rapanos, Prof Vassilios T. W303
Rapaport, Marc P102
Raper, Steve P268
Raphael, Joanne H. A652
Raphael, Carol P391
Raphaelson, Ira H. A496
Rapino, Michael (Mike) A511
Rapiya, Marshall W330
Rapken, Michael P211
Rapkin, Hilary A. E534
Rapley, David E. A506
Raposa, Sheila M. A853
Rapoza, Dean P136
Rapp, Matthew E6

Rapp, Edward J. (Ed) A5
Rapp, Edward J. (Ed) A155
Rapp, Peter F. P385
Rappaport, Felix A549
Rappaport, Steven N. (Steve) P570
Rappe, Kristine P315
Rappo, Bruno W54
Raps, Jurgen W151
Rasch, Carl P337
Rasche, Charlotte A665
Raschke, Klaus-Dieter W159
Rashid, Richard F. (Rick) A553
Rashkow, Ronald A603
Rasinger, Wilhelm G. W167
Raskas, Daniel A. A238
Raskin, Geoffroy W462
Raskind, Peter A149
Rasky, Lawrence P181
Rasmuson, Craig D. E474
Rasmuson, Michael (Mike) A91
Rasmussen, Hans E110
Rasmussen, James W. A756
Rasmussen, Steven A. P93
Rasmussen, Kimball P159
Rasmussen, Dennis F. P205
Rasmussen, Erik P349
Rasmussen, Steve P403
Rasmussen, Michael P. W2
Rasmussen, Michael W321
Rasmusson, Paul A530
Rassieur, Benjamin F. A207
Rastetter, William H. E267
Rasulo, James A. (Jay) A258
Ratcliff, Mary P417
Ratcliff, Margaret P624
Ratcliff, David P631
Ratcliffe, David M. A230
Ratcliffe, David M. A376
Ratcliffe, David A756
Ratcliffe, Peter G. W107
Rath, Connie P210
Rath, Tom P210
Rath, Connie P210
Rath, Cornelia W371
Rathbone, John P. A591
Rathbun, Dan A13
Rathbun, Robert A172
Rathbun, Elizabeth P468
Rathburn, Jim A689
Rathe, Bente W425
Rathgaber, Steven A. (Steve) E91
Rathgaber, Scott P225
Rathke, Frances G. (Fran) A389
Rathlev, Niels K. P53
Rathmann, Thomas W396
Ratinoff, Edward E70
Ratinoff, Edward A126
Ratley, Warren P141
Ratliff, Brent A294
Ratliff, Joe P270
Ratnathicam, Sanchayan (Chutta) A354
Ratner, Hank J. A140
Ratner, Hank J. A141
Ratner, Ronald A. P78
Ratner, Brian J. P99
Rattanacharoensiri, Chaiyong W61
Ratti, Michela A662
Rattner, Justin R. A446
Ratts, Gary P518
Rau, Guy J. A773
Rauch, Pamela M. A345
Rauch, Pamela M. A583
Rauchenberger, Louis A471
Raudys, Renata P277
Rauen, Aloysius A782
Rauenhorst, Mark H. P148
Rauenhorst, Gerald A. (Gerry) P610
Rauf, Zamir A143
Rauh, John M. E396
Rausch, Timothy S. (Tim) A652
Rauscher, Steven M. E13
Rauscher, Robert J. A206
Rautenberg, Yennie A677
Raven, David E. A574
Ravener, Robert D. (Bob) A260

A = AMERICAN BUSINESS
E = EMERGING COMPANIES
P = PRIVATE COMPANIES
W = WORLD BUSINESS

Robertson, Patricia P623
Robertson, Kai P652
Robertson, Ian W80
Robertson, Steve W100
Robertson, Brian W217
Robertson, Sir Simon W217
Robertson, Sir Simon W218
Robertson, Nigel W298
Robertson, Sir Simon W364
Robertson-Keck, Karen P205
Robeson, Rose M. E138
Robey, Donald E213
Robichaud, Chris A456
Robin, Vincent A651
Robinov, Jeff A793
Robins, Ronald A. A6
Robins, Scott P145
Robinson, Ray M. E5
Robinson, John H. E27
Robinson, David E. (Dave) E49
Robinson, Kirk E67
Robinson, John H. E110
Robinson, Scott D. E137
Robinson, James L. E194
Robinson, Peter B. E196
Robinson, Andy E257
Robinson, Ian E299
Robinson, Michael R. (Mike) E302
Robinson, Peter B. E309
Robinson, Michael K. E311
Robinson, Timothy E330
Robinson, William L. E373
Robinson, Tim E393
Robinson, Andy E399
Robinson, John E469
Robinson, Thomas E. (Tom) E478
Robinson, Ray M. A48
Robinson, Ray M. A88
Robinson, Ryan D. A118
Robinson, Linda Gosden A122
Robinson, Kirk A123
Robinson, James D. A197
Robinson, Jon R. A221
Robinson, Joseph R. A325
Robinson, James L. A326
Robinson, Peter B. A340
Robinson, Michael G. A342
Robinson, Brian J. A364
Robinson, Lonny A397
Robinson, Andrew S. A398
Robinson, Jamie A448
Robinson, William D. (Doug) A516
Robinson, John A556
Robinson, Adrien T. A571
Robinson, Bruce E. A673
Robinson, Malcolm A675
Robinson, Mike A698
Robinson, Sonal P. A727
Robinson, John A761
Robinson, Bert A781
Robinson, Jon M. A813
Robinson, Michelle A. A840
Robinson, David L. A862
Robinson, Eileen A869
Robinson, Nellie C. P116
Robinson, Lowry P144
Robinson, Wayne P179
Robinson, Jackie P198
Robinson, Dan P244
Robinson, Jamie P262
Robinson, David P264
Robinson, Lynn M. P276
Robinson, Sylvia E. P276
Robinson, Gary P292
Robinson, Phillip D. P309
Robinson, Jan P319
Robinson, Karen Donahue P329
Robinson, James L. (Jay) P334
Robinson, Kayne P354
Robinson, Rich P356
Robinson, Jo Nell P404
Robinson, Phil P448
Robinson, Ted P449
Robinson, Larry A. P468
Robinson, Newell P492

Robinson, Mixon P503
Robinson, Shawn P566
Robinson, Theotis P610
Robinson, Michelle M. P636
Robinson, Walter G. P636
Robinson, John G. P644
Robinson, David W9
Robinson, Sir Ian W134
Robinson, S. P. W245
Robinson, T. W298
Robinson, Thomas J. W422
Robison, Byron E225
Robison, William J. E357
Robison, Dennis C. E454
Robison, Ronald O. A5
Robison, M. La Voy A256
Robison, Byron A387
Robison, M. La Voy A506
Robison, Chris J. A581
Robison, Andrea Lee A588
Robison, John E. A698
Robison, Bruce P298
Robison, Deborah P455
Robison, Les P501
Robles, Mary Beth A201
Robles, Maj. Gen. Josue (Joe) A271
Robnett, Michael (Mike) E486
Robnett, Michael (Mike) A785
Robo, James L. (Jim) A432
Robo, James L. (Jim) A583
Robredo, Rafael Miranda W162
Robson, Craig E100
Robson, Glenn R. A13
Robson, K. Grant A114
Robusto, Dino E. A177
Roby, Lisa M. A251
Roby, Anne K. A654
Robyak, Richard A. P41
Robyck, Bret A. A373
Rocca, Richard E521
Rocca, Michael S. (Mike) Della A13
Rocca, Michael A. A740
Rocchio, Leland P277
Rocchio, Leland P522
Roces, Santiago A758
Roch, Eric E393
Rocha, Victor A540
Rocha, Robson W468
Roche, Collin E. E405
Roche, Michael J. A38
Roche, Joyce M. A79
Roche, Joyce A79
Roche, Joyce M. A269
Roche, Joyce A269
Roche, David A303
Roche, John C. (Jack) A398
Roche, Elaine A526
Roche, Collin E. A659
Roche, Jerome J. P186
Roche, Kathleen M. (Kate) P449
Rochelle, Tia A662
Rochon, Thomas R. A797
Rochow, Garrick J. A221
Rock, Amy Dix E135
Rock, Michael (Mike) A816
Rock, Ann P502
Rock, Milton L. P526
Rock, David P653
Rocke, Elisabeth W479
Rockefeller, Sharon Percy A635
Rockefeller, Sharon Percy P420
Rockefeller, David P559
Rocker, J. Thomas E98
Rockers, Thomas H. P497
Rockford, Marc A. A204
Rockoff, Karen A. E392
Rocks, M. Joseph P365
Rocktoff, William N. E470
Rockwood, Beth A255
Rockwood, Robin A. A320
Rockwood, John D. P324
Rocole, Therese M. (Terri) P641
Rocole, Terri P641
Roczniak, Benjamin J. E87
Roda, Craig A. A359

Rodato, Vadis A. E354
Roday, Leon E. A375
Roddenberry, Stephen K. A876
Roddy, Peter S. E387
Rode, Murray D. E491
Roden, John C. van E207
Roden, John E207
Roden, John C. van A26
Roden, John A26
Roden, George P344
Roden, Neil W368
Roden, Joerg W462
Rodeno, Michaela K. E469
Rodeno, Michaela K. A761
Roder, Steve W278
Roder, Peter W300
Rodero, Vicente Rodero W55
Rodgers, Ben E117
Rodgers, Abby A197
Rodgers, Johnathan A204
Rodgers, Johnathan A. A586
Rodgers, Michael (Mike) A630
Rodgers, Johnathan A. A662
Rodgers, Ralph E. A781
Rodgers, Theo C. P275
Rodgers, Paige A. P276
Rodgers, Lanny P355
Rodgers, Robert P362
Rodgers, Mary Anne P541
Rodin, Judith (Judy) A185
Rodin, Judith (Judy) A204
Rodino, Jeffrey E391
Rodkin, Gary M. A90
Rodkin, Gary M. A217
Rodler, Friedrich W167
Rodman, Donald H. E114
Rodman, Donald H. A202
Rodman, Leonard C. (Len) P67
Rodman, Steve P68
Rodocanachi, Pierre W474
Rodocker, Julee M. P538
Rodrigo, Javier E447
Rodrigues, Ron A174
Rodrigues, Stephen P575
Rodriguez, Rita E19
Rodriguez, Shari E73
Rodriguez, John E187
Rodriguez, David E395
Rodriguez, Luciano E489
Rodriguez, Albert J. E494
Rodriguez, Carlos A. A81
Rodriguez, Karyn E. A85
Rodriguez, Lawrence D. (Larry) A166
Rodriguez, Enrique A181
Rodriguez, Javier J. A241
Rodriguez, L. A. A288
Rodriguez, Sean A318
Rodriguez, Jose F. A328
Rodriguez, David A. A525
Rodriguez, Antonio A583
Rodriguez, Rita E. A612
Rodriguez, Eduardo A. (Eddie) A613
Rodriguez, Rita M. A675
Rodriguez, Ramon A. A693
Rodriguez, Armando G. A716
Rodriguez, Ben A. A778
Rodriguez, Richard P. P97
Rodriguez, Dora P188
Rodriguez, Jose P400
Rodriguez, Alex P449
Rodriguez, Holly P606
Rodriguez, Cecilia M. P611
Rodriguez, Ramon J. P653
Rodriguez, Florentino Perez W10
Rodriguez, Paul W26
Rodriguez, Jose W57
Rodriguez, Jose R. W59
Rodriguez, Julio W387
Rodriguez-Borjas, Carlos A690
Rodriquez, Rita M. E19
Rodstrom, Daniel (Dan) A286
Rodstrom, Claudette P657
Rodwell, Peter A534
Roe, Scott A841
Roedel, Richard W. (Rich) E264

Roedel, Kathryn V. E435
Roedel, Richard W. (Rich) A515
Roeder, Kris P543
Roeder, Peter Peter Roeder W300
Roeglin, Ginnie M. A225
Roegner, Eric V. A31
Roegner, Harry W268
Roehm, Arthur W. A446
Roehr, David A. (Dave) E20
Roekel, Dennis Van P352
Roelandts, Willem P. (Wim) A69
Roell, Stephen A. A468
Roellgen, Andreas A795
Roellke, Prof Christopher F. P620
Roelofs, Nicholas H. (Nick) A21
Roelofs, Nicolas H. A21
Roemer, Mickey D. (Mick) E355
Roemer, Mick E355
Roemer, S. C. A288
Roenigk, Mark E411
Roeschley, Steve P143
Roese, John A285
Roesel, Larry M. A84
Roeske, Richard A479
Roesler, Rick A676
Roessink, Henk E343
Roesslein, Charles J. E50
Roesslein, Charles J. E362
Roessner, Karl A. A275
Roeth, George C. A189
Roetzel, Frank M. P457
Roever, Carol P236
Rogala, Richard E. (Rick) E371
Rogan, Brian G. A98
Rogan, Thomas I. A830
Roge, Carrol P170
Rogel, Steven R. (Steve) A490
Rogel, Steven R. (Steve) A817
Roger, Robin A399
Rogers, Amy Tam E11
Rogers, Steven E11
Rogers, Michael W. E13
Rogers, Douglas B. (Doug) E58
Rogers, Rosalie F. (Rose) E155
Rogers, Donald R. E160
Rogers, Sandy E204
Rogers, Terry V. E240
Rogers, W. Allen E272
Rogers, Peter J. E338
Rogers, Paul G. (Guy) E344
Rogers, Ronald E359
Rogers, Tamesa E367
Rogers, James E. E370
Rogers, Robert M. E391
Rogers, Robert M. E392
Rogers, Chris E438
Rogers, Oliver E480
Rogers, Adam E504
Rogers, John S. E506
Rogers, Gary L. E506
Rogers, James E. (Jim) A69
Rogers, J. Michael A93
Rogers, Michael D. (Mike) A143
Rogers, Ross E. A205
Rogers, Kenneth C. A247
Rogers, Steven A. A262
Rogers, Ronald G. (Ron) A269
Rogers, James E. (Jim) A274
Rogers, Donald R. A276
Rogers, James P. (Jim) A278
Rogers, John W. A302
Rogers, Kevin G. A313
Rogers, Karen A321
Rogers, John F. W. A380
Rogers, R. Scott A382
Rogers, Melissa A389
Rogers, R. Wade A435
Rogers, Eddy J. A485
Rogers, John W. A534
Rogers, Ronald A543
Rogers, Patrick A576
Rogers, Gerry A586
Rogers, James E. A618
Rogers, Ellen Sheriff A633
Rogers, Cynthia M. (Cindy) A688

A = AMERICAN BUSINESS
E = EMERGING COMPANIES
P = PRIVATE COMPANIES
W = WORLD BUSINESS

Rogers, T. Gary A708
Rogers, Michael F. A749
Rogers, William H. (Bill) A756
Rogers, Prof Steven S. A758
Rogers, Boyd A841
Rogers, Emma A846
Rogers, Jeffrey A. (Jeff) A884
Rogers, Brian P89
Rogers, Sam P156
Rogers, Julie P199
Rogers, Mark P212
Rogers, Melissa P222
Rogers, Rob P260
Rogers, Cynthia P277
Rogers, Brian C. P305
Rogers, Malcolm P350
Rogers, Erin P385
Rogers, Timothy D. P466
Rogers, Russell P508
Rogers, Mike P611
Rogers, David W47
Rogers, Neil W100
Rogers, John W240
Rogers, Dene L. W480
Rogerson, Garry E14
Rogerson, Garry W. E112
Rogerson, Craig A. A652
Roggemann, Gerhard W179
Roggenbuck, Scott A389
Roggenbuck, Scott P222
Roggie, Brent J. P353
Roglieri, John E61
Rogoff, Joe A870
Rogowski, Michael W429
Rogstad, Gunnar W415
Rogus, Mark S. A223
Rohan, Karen S. A17
Rohatgi, Sanjay A764
Rohatyn, Nicolas S. E317
Rohatyn, Felix G. W271
Rohde, Michael E. A25
Rohde, David J. A626
Rohde, Mark W. A773
Rohde, Bruce C. P148
Roheim, John P356
Rohkamm, Prof Eckhard W429
Rohleder, Stephen J. (Steve) W7
Rohling, Jennifer K. A774
Rohlman, Katie P563
Rohman, John M. A144
Rohner, Randall W. E235
Rohner, William J. A155
Rohner, Urs W139
Rohosy, Anne A504
Rohr, James E. (Jim) A34
Rohr, Mark C. A75
Rohr, James E. (Jim) A123
Rohr, Mark C. A162
Rohr, James E. (Jim) A648
Rohr, James E. (Jim) P95
Rohr-Dralle, Rondi A701
Rohrbaugh, Philmer A359
Rohrbaugh, James P419
Rohrer, Hans E148
Rohret, M.G. A288
Rohrkaste, Michael K. A617
Rohrs, Thomas M. (Tom) E14
Roidt, Michael A773
Roig, Ismael A71
Roiko, John E361
Roitman, Jonathan (Jon) A819
Roiz, Araceli E262
Rojas, Jorge E174
Rojas, Carlos E292
Rojas, Elizabeth A. A773
Rojas, Jose P290
Rojas, Hector Manosalva W160
Rojas, Jose Fernando Calderon W177
Rojas, Julio W412

Rojo, Richard P611
Rokoff, Ken E76
Roland, Mark C. E543
Roland, David H. P430
Roland, John P430
Rolen, Heather P656
Roley, Robert E15
Rolfe, Cynthia P70
Rolfe, Lauren P317
Rolheiser, Eric J. A222
Rolin, Steve A800
Roll, Mike E132
Roll, Eberhard W482
Rolland, Ian M. A587
Rolland, Martial C. W309
Rollans, James O. A346
Roller, Wolfgang W151
Rolli, Nicholas A641
Rolli, Guy W131
Rollier, Philippe R. A729
Rollins, Thomas E. E133
Rollins, Ted W. E200
Rollins, R. Randall E427
Rollins, Gary W. E427
Rollins, James D. (Dan) A94
Rollins, Doug A197
Rollins, Gary W. A374
Rollins, Jonathan A409
Rollins, James D. (Dan) A665
Rollins, Barrett J. P154
Rollins, Anne-Herbert P205
Rollins, David P292
Rollins, Kent P565
Rollison, Marvin L. E224
Rollman, Barry P267
Roloff, ReBecca (Becky) Koenig A699
Roloff, ReBecca (Becky) Koenig P15
Roloff, Craig P345
Rolston, Richard P147
Roma, Elise E204
Roma, Francesco W234
Roma, Eugenio W234
Romaine, Christopher E200
Romaine, Mark A379
Romaine, Stephen S. A797
Roman, Thomas S. E81
Roman, Peter J. (Pete) E301
Roman, George C. A125
Roman, Brian A568
Roman, Rica A662
Roman, George C. P634
Roman, David A. W266
Roman, Francisco (Paco) W475
Romanelli, Jim A192
Romanelli, Joe A543
Romanescu, Roxana A641
Romano, Paul S. E200
Romano, Frank E333
Romano, Kelly A. A830
Romano, Albert V. P41
Romano, Nicholas A. P201
Romano, Judie P593
Romano, Massimo W40
Romano, Javier Marin W60
Romano-Connors, Debora P137
Romasko, Daniel E484
Romasko, Daniel R. (Dan) A784
Romberger, William A. A305
Rome, Aaron P338
Romenesko, Timothy J. E3
Romer, Bruce F. P637
Romero, Pedro A328
Romero, Jerry P3
Romero, Guillermo de la Dehesa W60
Romero, Juan W114
Romes, David F. A627
Rometty, Virginia M. (Ginni) A452
Romick, Steven P102
Romine, Darlene E410
Romine, James C. A272
Romine, Bill A697
Rominger, Eileen P187
Romito, Ed P212
Rommer, Hans W325
Romney, Ronna E. A556

Romo, Tammy A733
Romo, Ricardo P488
Romojaro, Jaime W57
Romrell, Larry E. A506
Romuld, Trine S?ther W157
Romy, Isabelle W461
Romyarup, Aphichat W61
Ronaghi, Mostafa E267
Ronan, Joseph E. (Joe) A143
Ronco, Garry E178
Roncoroni, Marie-Helene W342
Rond, Theo de W199
Rondeau, Isabelle W91
Rondolat, Eric W258
Rondolat, Eric W387
Rone, David A792
Roney, Scott A. A71
Roney, Jo L. A120
Roney, Linda M. P242
Roney, Michael J. (Mike) W245
Rongone, Chris A786
Ronner, Markus W461
Ronstrom, Stephen (Steve) P446
Ronstrom, Stephen (Steve) P447
Roof, Richard E170
Roof??s, Richard E170
Roohparvar, Frankie F. A551
Rooke, Andrew M. E316
Roolf, James P477
Roome, Hugh R. P586
Rooney, Philip A. (Phil) E258
Rooney, Arthur J. (Art) A308
Rooney, Jerome A690
Rooney, Kathleen M. A797
Rooney, George P485
Rooney, Davis P518
Rooney, Paul L. W278
Roos, Jeff A500
Roos, Linda P168
Roos, Bill W157
Roosevelt, Anna E. (Anne) A125
Root, Howard C. E517
Root, Ralph H. A626
Root, Linda P76
Root, Jim W126
Rooy, Yvonne W231
Roozen, Marnie P422
Ropell, Jason A577
Roper, Martin F. E71
Roper, Martin F. E309
Roper, John A218
Roper, William L. A241
Roper, Ruth A717
Roper, William L. P604
Roquemaurel, Gerald de W111
Roquemore, James W. A336
Rorick, Jeffrey A. P286
Rorison, James A. (Jim) A673
Rork, Christopher W. (Chris) E95
Rorsg?rd, Veronica W401
Rorsgard, Veronica Veronica
  Rorsgard W401
Rorsted, Kasper B. W84
Rorsted, Kasper B. W202
Ros, Francisco A677
Ros, Carl Wilhelm W399
Rosa, Thomas M. (Tom) E77
Rosa, David J. (Dave) E278
Rosa, Christopher J. P350
Rosa, Catherine K. (Cathy) De P380
Rosales, Sara A531
Rosamilia, Tom A452
Rosanvallon, Jean G. P181
Rosar, Alexander W78
Rosario, Christine del P508
Rosatella, Marco W432
Rosati, Mario M. A711
Roschelle, Jeremy P492
Roscitt, Richard R. (Rick) P509
Roscoe, Lizzie A534
Roscoe, Joan P617
Roscoe, Joan P646
Rose, Eric A. E7
Rose, Robert E76
Rose, Jerry R. E80

Rose, Richard D. E84
Rose, Richard D. (Rick) E86
Rose, Steven E115
Rose, Kyle E117
Rose, Edward W. (Rusty) E152
Rose, Crystal K. E234
Rose, Tyler H. E295
Rose, Richard E491
Rose, George L. A9
Rose, Matthew K. (Matt) A48
Rose, Matthew K. (Matt) A79
Rose, Robert A136
Rose, Matthew K. (Matt) A138
Rose, Crystal K. A166
Rose, Timothy L. A225
Rose, Marya M. A232
Rose, Michael D. A240
Rose, Peter J. A305
Rose, John W. A308
Rose, Dan A309
Rose, Michael D. A336
Rose, Clayton S. A356
Rose, Michael D. A370
Rose, Les A493
Rose, Edward A. A539
Rose, Amy A543
Rose, Ernie A586
Rose, Teryl C. A613
Rose, John W. A624
Rose, Tressie A662
Rose, Mary P40
Rose, Rob P60
Rose, Mark P72
Rose, Lisa P124
Rose, Sean P124
Rose, John P265
Rose, Linwood H. P269
Rose, Daniel P406
Rose, Curtis P410
Rose, Michael S. P485
Rose, Vera P504
Rose, Kathy Luppen P537
Rose, Clare P550
Rose, Nicholas C. (Nick) W51
Rose, Andy W53
Rose, Nicholas Nicholas Rose W101
Rose, Marlies W151
Rose, George W. W304
Roseberry, Robert W. E231
Roseberry, Robert W. A395
Roseberry, David P433
Roseborough, Teresa A401
Roseborough, Teresa W. A419
Roselle, David P. P381
Roselli, John P. E144
Rosello, Patricia M. P47
Rosen, David E11
Rosen, Sam E52
Rosen, Benedict P. (Dick) E373
Rosen, Robert E432
Rosen, Ellen E488
Rosen, Neal E525
Rosen, Elaine D. A77
Rosen, Michael A79
Rosen, Michael N. A361
Rosen, Ellen A789
Rosen, Mickie A883
Rosen, Seth P133
Rosen, Harris P443
Rosen, Sharon P478
Rosen, Raymond P656
Rosen, Michel de W5
Rosen, Andrea W278
Rosenauer, James J. E543
Rosenbach, Ed P353
Rosenbaum, Jerrold S. E69
Rosenbaum, Lisa A. E442
Rosenbaum, Mark A151
Rosenbaum, Thomas F. P566
Rosenberg, Steven P. (Steve) E105
Rosenberg, Steven E120
Rosenberg, Martin E133
Rosenberg, Seth E179
Rosenberg, Sheli Z. E179
Rosenberg, Richard M. E235

Rosenberg, Marvin B. E316
Rosenberg, Steven P. (Steve) E486
Rosenberg, Sheli Z. E520
Rosenberg, Joseph A192
Rosenberg, Joshua A319
Rosenberg, David J. A412
Rosenberg, Donald J. A676
Rosenberg, Steven P. (Steve) A785
Rosenberg, Alan P19
Rosenberg, Donald S. P47
Rosenberg, Nathan O. P77
Rosenberg, Liz P105
Rosenberg, Ken P172
Rosenberg, Gary P177
Rosenberg, Michael P228
Rosenberg, Eric P508
Rosenberg, Wade P550
Rosenberg, Philip W409
Rosenberg, Joachim W479
Rosenberger, Karen E473
Rosenblatt, Richard M. E142
Rosenblatt, Sidney D. E510
Rosenblatt, Sidney D. E511
Rosenblatt, Michael A542
Rosenblum, Bruce A187
Rosenblum, Bruce A793
Rosenblum, Mendel A846
Rosenblum, Don P375
Rosener, Sabra P597
Rosenfeld, Douglas B. (Doug) E42
Rosenfeld, Eric S. E124
Rosenfeld, Edward R. (Ed) E314
Rosenfeld, Eric S. E404
Rosenfeld, Gerald (Jerry) A183
Rosenfeld, Manny A208
Rosenfeld, Irene B. A559
Rosenfeld, Ronald A578
Rosenfeld, Stephen P13
Rosenfeld, Klaus W136
Rosengart, Jorg E178
Rosengarten, Jeffrey P656
Rosenstein, Greg A757
Rosenstein, Donald L. P604
Rosenstock, Carl J. A751
Rosenstock, Josh W364
Rosenthal, Arthur J. E136
Rosenthal, Bennett E233
Rosenthal, Jeffry O. E247
Rosenthal, Amir P. E465
Rosenthal, Alison H. A82
Rosenthal, David S. A307
Rosenthal, James A. (Jim) A561
Rosenthal, Gary L. A607
Rosenthal, Michael A731
Rosenthal, Susan A. P47
Rosenthal, Lesley F. P301
Rosenthal, Monica P537
Rosenthal, Sheldon P653
Rosenthal, Terese W300
Rosenthaler, Albert E. A506
Rosenwald, Patricia P. P559
Rosevear, Kenneth (Ken) A549
Rosher, Wendy P179
Rosholt, Robert A. A407
Rosinoer, Serge E274
Roskovich, Charles B. A672
Roslin, Matthew I. E197
Roslin, Matthew I. A344
Rosman, Andrew J. P303
Rosoff, Cary E281
Rospond, Raylene P166
Ross, Lloyd E. E38
Ross, Donaldson M. E55
Ross, Wilbur L. E56
Ross, Stephen E288
Ross, Ron E448
Ross, William M. E506
Ross, Rick A. E536
Ross, Christopher J. A27
Ross, Kimberly A. A90
Ross, Cynthia A93
Ross, Mark A100
Ross, David A. A145
Ross, Mark A160
Ross, Jackie A181

Ross, Richard A. A188
Ross, Andrew A217
Ross, Rich A258
Ross, Rex A297
Ross, Steven D. A495
Ross, Kelly C. A516
Ross, A.J. A579
Ross, Andrew D. A629
Ross, Frank K. A633
Ross, Michael D. A691
Ross, Dennis E. A749
Ross, Wilbur L. A754
Ross, James H. (Jim) A762
Ross, Kevin E. A820
Ross, Michael P. A844
Ross, Donna J. P53
Ross, Samuel L. P75
Ross, Matthew P105
Ross, George E. P107
Ross, Amena P230
Ross, Richard S. P275
Ross, Henry J. P360
Ross, Terryl P385
Ross, Jerrold P493
Ross, Barry P501
Ross, Charles E. P515
Ross, Scott P538
Ross, Thomas L. P549
Ross, Wilbur L. W39
Ross, Wayne W47
Ross, James H. W348
Ross-Dronzek, Nancy C. A63
Ross-Dulan, Brenda K. A859
Rosseau, Jon B. A485
Rosser, Harold O. E72
Rosser, Troy D. E116
Rosser, James M. A283
Rosser, James M. A730
Rosser, James M. P89
Rossetti, Carl U. J. A792
Rossetti, Eugenio W234
Rossetto, Ronald B. A722
Rossi, Dino A. E53
Rossi, Michael J. E86
Rossi, Mark E91
Rossi, Mark E324
Rossi, James P. Del E333
Rossi, Mark A. A97
Rossi, James L. A185
Rossi, Walter A249
Rossi, Hugo A716
Rossi, Jerome A796
Rossi, Nicola A878
Rossi, Rev Philip J. P148
Rossi, Deanna W54
Rossi, Marco W57
Rossi, Orazio W234
Rossi, Jean W472
Rossini, Lynn P449
Rossiter, Jay A883
Rossman, Bruce P490
Rossmann, Gregory J. E367
Rossmann, Barbara W. P238
Rossmann, Martin W332
Rosso, Paul D. A2
Rosso, Jean-Pierre A540
Rosso, Clar P20
Rosso, Jean-Pierre W91
Rosson, Mark W100
Rossotti, Charles O. A15
Rossotti, Charles O. A96
Rossotti, Charles O. A128
Rossum, Anton Anton van
    Rossum W139
Rossum, Anton van W139
Rossum, Anton van W300
Rossum, Anton Anton van
    Rossum W300
Rossum, Anton van W407
Rossum, Anton W407
Rost, Uwe W335
Rostan, Richard H. A305
Rostiac, Sheila A671
Rostom, Rania A368
Rosty, Nicolas von W396

Rosumek, Anke W300
Roswell, Clint A452
Roszczyk, Al E196
Roszczyk, Al A333
Roszkowski, Joanne E383
Rote, Simon E. E121
Rotella, Perry F. E521
Rotella, William (Bill) P604
Rotenberg, Lesli P420
Roth, Douglas E11
Roth, Theodore D. E62
Roth, John M. E245
Roth, Heidi R. E295
Roth, Mark A. E303
Roth, Steven R. E428
Roth, Gregory S. (Greg) E480
Roth, Greg E480
Roth, William (Bill) E499
Roth, Erin J. E528
Roth, Lance J. E. A23
Roth, Stanley O. A125
Roth, Michael I. A456
Roth, Jennifer A540
Roth, Tara A553
Roth, Donald C. A581
Roth, David E. A613
Roth, Steven A631
Roth, Michael I. A645
Roth, Renee S. A767
Roth, Peter A793
Roth, Frank A. P297
Roth, Ben P443
Roth, Adam P443
Roth, Brett P443
Roth, Shirley P543
Roth, Martin (Marty) P567
Roth, Michael S. P636
Roth, Martin W158
Roth, Klaus W164
Roth, Jean-Pierre W309
Rothamel, Paul E. E187
Rothberg, Jay P20
Rothberger, Richard K. P462
Rothblatt, Martine A. E510
Rothenberg, Mace L. A638
Rothenhaus, Todd E49
Rothermel, Elizabeth B. P430
Rothkopf, Arthur J. E521
Rothman, Noel N. A195
Rothman, Fred A500
Rothman, Prof Martin A540
Rothman, Paul B. P275
Rothmeier, Steven G. (Steve) A655
Rothschild, David de W111
Rothstein, Stuart A. E45
Rothstein, Sharon A745
Rothstein, Daniel G. A751
Rothstein, Robert P513
Rothstein, Fred C. P600
Rothweiler, Alan C. A626
Rothwell, Allan R. E380
Rothwell, Sharon J. A528
Rothwell, Dame Nancy W. W44
Rotner, Phil P536
Rotolo, Chris P511
Rottenberg, Erika E305
Rotter, Jerome P102
Rottier, Eric M. E100
Roty, Chris P45
Roualet, Mark C. A365
Roubin, Augustin de W261
Roubin, Augustin W261
Roubos, Gary L. A612
Roudebush, Jenni A75
Roueche, John E. (Jay) A346
Rouf, Shah W47
Rougas, Tye P528
Roughead, Gary A597
Roughton, Keith P214
Roulet, Marcel W333
Roulis, Eleni P610
Roumeliotis, Panagiotis W343
Round, Austin P17
Round, Garry P446
Rounds, Michael E284

Rountree, Gordon P292
Rouot, Mattieu W49
Rouquet, Jerome A316
Rouret, Hugues du A228
Roush, Robin S. A378
Roush, William R. P562
Roussat, Olivier W93
Rousseau, Michael S. (Mike) A694
Rousseau, Michael T. A740
Rousseau, Jeff P151
Rousseau, Henri-Paul W193
Rousseau, Henri-Paul W345
Rousseau, Henri-Paul W346
Rousseau, Luc W355
Roussel, Patrick W333
Roussel, Stephane W474
Roussinos, Don S. W365
Roussis, Theodoros W248
Rousso, Doug A160
Rout, Robert E. (Bob) A332
Routh, Benton C. E198
Routs, Rob J. A13
Routs, Rob J. W256
Rouvillois, Patrick W109
Roux, Bob A511
Roux, Roger G. P425
Roux, Didier W131
Rover, Michael (Mike) E39
Rovira, Alfredo L. E207
Rovit, Sam A488
Rovner, Robert A. P526
Rowan, Marc J. A142
Rowan, Jeffrey P86
Rowden, Diana P563
Rowe, Stanton J. E166
Rowe, Sylvia B. E330
Rowe, John E467
Rowe, John A38
Rowe, Zane C. A67
Rowe, R. Scott A145
Rowe, Robert C. A183
Rowe, Sharon H. A185
Rowe, John W. A301
Rowe, John W. A302
Rowe, John W. A595
Rowe, Michael A. A801
Rowe, Michael (Mike) P23
Rowe, Mike P23
Rowe, Rachel M. P135
Rowe, John W. P254
Rowe, Theresa M. (Terrie) P378
Rowe, Margie P479
Rowe, Patrick B. F. W8
Rowe, Jeremy W24
Rowe, Steve W280
Rowell, Christine A251
Rowerdink, Jeff S. E180
Rowinsky, Eric K. A121
Rowlan, Steven J. A600
Rowland, Tom A42
Rowland, G. Joyce A720
Rowland, Robert O. A787
Rowland, Amber A846
Rowland, David J. P469
Rowland, David P. W7
Rowlands, Sharon T. E118
Rowlands, Sharon T. A81
Rowles, Michael G. A511
Rowley, Stuart A353
Rowny, Michael J. E368
Roy, G. Gayce (Cayce) E306
Roy, Sumit E413
Roy, Rajiv E428
Roy, Jessica E534
Roy, Peter A. A822
Roy, Michael P415
Roy, Mark S. P469
Roy, Charles P557
Roy, Sumita Bose W85
Roy, Anami W196
Roy, Sylvie W302
Roy, Louise W346
Royal, Kevin S. E324
Royal, Frank S. A262
Royal, Frank S. A756

Ryan, James B. E109
Ryan, Kimberly K. E249
Ryan, James P. (Jim) E320
Ryan, John R. E356
Ryan, Arthur F. (Art) E415
Ryan, Thomas F. E416
Ryan, Lawrence G. (Larry) E479
Ryan, Elizabeth A29
Ryan, Ed A36
Ryan, Stephen J. A36
Ryan, Vice Adm. John R. A141
Ryan, J. Stuart A143
Ryan, Vice Adm. John R. A183
Ryan, Robert L. (Bob) A185
Ryan, JoAnn F. A220
Ryan, Jerry E. A286
Ryan, Robert L. (Bob) A370
Ryan, David C. A380
Ryan, Tom A455
Ryan, Sharon R. A455
Ryan, Kevin T. A480
Ryan, John M. A503
Ryan, Edward A. (Ed) A525
Ryan, D. Edward A600
Ryan, James C. A608
Ryan, Michael (Mike) A733
Ryan, Robert L. (Bob) A742
Ryan, Lawrence G. (Larry) A772
Ryan, Joseph A820
Ryan, William J. (Bill) A834
Ryan, Bob A837
Ryan, William J. (Bill) A858
Ryan, Robert A. A859
Ryan, Geof A870
Ryan, Thomas M. (Tom) A885
Ryan, Michael (Mike) P41
Ryan, David P90
Ryan, Dave P90
Ryan, David P91
Ryan, Constance M. P148
Ryan, Brendan P201
Ryan, Rev Patrick P201
Ryan, Michael P317
Ryan, Pat P339
Ryan, Prof Joseph F. P391
Ryan, Sister Mary Jean P413
Ryan, Kathy P419
Ryan, Barbara P426
Ryan, G. Brint P446
Ryan, Michael P481
Ryan, Paul P523
Ryan, Michael J. P549
Ryan, Thomas F. P556
Ryan, Sharon P573
Ryan, Lee P607
Ryan, J. Thomas (Tom) P630
Ryan, Fergus D. W130
Ryan, Philip K. W193
Ryan, T. Timothy W270
Ryan, Arthur F. (Art) W368
Ryan, Jim W409
Ryba, Tomi S. P15
Rybak, William R. E405
Rybak, James J. E480
Rybak, William R. A659
Ryburn, Harry L. A724
Ryckman, Gail A. P378
Ryczek, Edward J. A774
Rydberg, Dennis (Denny) P657
Rydberg-Dumont, Josephine W401
Ryder, Thomas O. (Tom) E428
Ryder, Paul A44
Ryder, Thomas O. (Tom) A44
Ryder, Thomas O. (Tom) A746
Ryder, Maritza P47
Ryder, Ellen P130
Rydin, Craig W. A657
Rydin, Craig W. A675
Rygwalski, Dennis E532
Rygwalski, Dennis A863
Ryker, Tarra A507
Rykert, Lauren P550
Rykhoek, Phil E143
Rykhus, Daniel A. (Dan) E412
Ryland, Jane N. P381

Ryles, Scott A. E296
Ryles, Gerald F. E549
Ryles, Scott A. A486
Ryman, David (Dave) P109
Rynearson, Danny P632
Ryopponen, Hannu W325
Rysdam, Rex E39
Ryser, Phillip P. P505
Rystedt, Joachim A709
Rystedt, Fredrik W321
Ryu, Marcus S. E227
Ryu, Yul W372
Ryu, Seung Seung Heon Ryu W391
Ryuto, Yasuo W96
Rzepka, Bernard E433
Rzonzef, Michel A382

S

S., Glenn G. Jordan A197
S.p.A, Generali W41
S?derberg, Jess A177
S?rensen, Lars R. W84
S?rensen, Lars Rebien W325
S?rensen, Lars W325
S?rensen, Lars Troen W414
Sa, Paulo de W464
Saabas, John A830
Saacke, Dave P569
Saarony, Gadi E390
Saathoff, Kent P178
Sabala, James A. (Jim) E240
Saban, Cheryl P537
Sabat, John R. E22
Sabatacakis, Petros K. W303
Sabath, John E196
Sabath, John A333
Sabatini, Gino E527
Sabatini, Joseph A. P99
Sabel, Ivan R. E232
Sabella, Lauren M. E13
Sabens, Steven P484
Saber, Rommel C. A305
Sabharwal, Rajiv W224
Sabi, Babak A446
Sabin, Julia L. A727
Sabino, Joao W57
Sabloff, Barry M. P132
Sabo, Richard A471
Sabo, Sue A528
Sabonnadiere, Emmanuel A364
Saborio, Bernal A201
Sabroe, Tania W325
Saccavino, Tierney E13
Sacco, Michael P19
Sacco, Daniel P74
Sacco, Michele M. P277
Sacerdote, Peter M. A355
Sach, Derek S. W368
Sachdev, Ravi E314
Sachdev, Geeta E453
Sachdev, Neil W240
Sachedina, Alaudin W35
Sacho, Dan E488
Sacho, Dan A789
Sachs, Fred P259
Sachse, Robert G. E26
Sachse, Robert G. E27
Sachtjen, Brendan A855
Sachtleben, Michael (Mike) P325
Sack, Brian P. A319
Sackett, John P5
Sackett, Neil C. P534
Sackrison, Jeffrey N. P599
Sacks, Kenneth D. E54
Sacks, Rodney C. E350
Sackson, Nancy P607
Sada, Armando Garza W177
Sadana, Sumit A709
Sadau, Ernie W. P118
Sadeghi, Mchael P338
Sadeler, Sophie W127
Sadid, Hossein P606
Sadigh, Mandana A531

Sadka, Prof Efraim W63
Sadler, A. Graham E59
Sadler, Robert E. (Bob) A518
Sadler, Michael W. A551
Sado, Masaaki W326
Sadove, Stephen I. (Steve) A201
Sadowski, Shauna E44
Sadowski, Raymond (Ray) A88
Sadowski, Peter T. A322
Sadowski, John D. A710
Sadvary, Thomas J. (Tom) P461
Saeger, Rebecca (Becky) A275
Saeki, Akira W241
Saelinger, Thomas R. E195
Saelinger, Thomas R. A333
Saenz, Mauricio A641
Saenz, Fernando P421
Saetre, Eldar W414
Saeys, David E169
Saez, Engle E. E66
Saez, Antonio Gomis W356
Saez, Antonio W356
Safaii, Matthew J. E258
Saffell, Kirk A838
Safian, Keith F. P402
Safran, Andrew P586
Saga, Koei W455
Sagan, Paul L. E21
Sagan, Paul L. E283
Sagan, Paul L. A285
Sagar, Madhu W86
Sagbakken, Per W157
Sage, Richard D. E187
Sage, John P6
Sage, Gordon H. W53
Sagebiel, Ed A507
Sagehorn, David M. A617
Sager, Thomas L. A272
Sager, Mikki P539
Sager, Oskar W287
Sagheer, Omer P561
Sagnak, Yagmar A717
Sahay, Anupam W47
Sahenk, Ferit Faik W459
Sahlman, Scott P565
Sahm, Amy A359
Sahney, Nitin A610
SahniMohanty, Purnima A368
Saia, Andrea A199
Saiga, Daisuke W295
Saiga, Daisuke W296
Saigal, Sunil P360
Saik, Clifton J. E231
Saik, Clifton J. A395
Saikawa, Hiroto W316
Saikawa, Hiroto W355
Saiki, Denise A. A512
Sailly, Michel W355
Saimpert, Philippe W189
Saines, Ian W129
Sainsbury, Jon E67
Saint-Affrique, Antoine W464
Saint-Affrique, Antoine Antoine de
 Saint-Affrique W
Saint-Aignan, Patrick de A749
Saint-Clair, Guillaume E11
Saint-Cyr, Louis D. E234
Saint-Geours, Frederic W111
Sait, Suaad H. E411
Saito, Kenneth O. E64
Saito, Masayasu W22
Saito, Takashi W140
Saito, Katsutoshi W141
Saito, Yutaka W208
Saito, Fumihiko W214
Saito, Hiroki W393
Saito, Tadashi (Tan) W408
Saito, Shigeo W419
Saito, Hiroshi W451
Saito, Shozo W451
Saivatz, Carol R. P78
Sajdak, Robert A205
Saji, Makoto A99
Saka, Yoshihiro W149
Sakai, Hitoshi W184

Sakai, Hiroyoshi W236
Sakai, Yoshikiyo W327
Sakamoto, Noriaki W296
Sakamoto, Hideyuki W316
Sakamoto, Toshihiro W338
Sakamoto, Yoshitsugu W416
Sakane, Masahiro W253
Sakane, Masahiro W320
Sakas, Chris E114
Sakas, Chris A202
Sakata, Ryo W236
Sakata, Shoichi W291
Sakata, Seiji W358
Sakellaris, George P. E32
Sakellaris, Ploutarchos K. W170
Sakhnini, Humam A9
Sakishima, Takafumi W281
Sakishima, Takafumi W282
Sakkab, Nabil Y. A42
Sako, Naohiro W320
Sako, Tatsunobu W405
Sakowicz, Adrian W. A266
Saks, David H. E41
Saks, David H. A59
Saksti, Hendri W485
Sakuma, Hidetoshi W117
Sakuma, Kaichiro W208
Sakunphram, Songkhram W61
Sakurai, Kenji W141
Sakurai, Akira W316
Sakurai, Masamitsu W358
Sakurai, Tohru W393
Sakuyama, Masaki W291
Sakys, John E335
Sala, Bernard W127
Saladrigas, Carlos A. A11
Salaerts, Jozef A228
Salame, Mansour E2
Salame, Pablo J. A380
Salamone, Denis J. A429
Salandra, Michael (Mike) A34
Salandra, Michael (Mike) P14
Salanger, Matthew J. P594
Salata, Robert A. P600
Salazar, Lisa M. A774
Salazar, Deanna P71
Salazar, Ben P586
Salazar-Simpson, Luis Alberto W60
Salchenberger, Linda M. P315
Saldinger, Pierre F. P361
Saldivar, Ricardo E. A419
Saldivar, Kathryn P332
Saleh, Paul N. A213
Saleh, Donald P523
Salehpour, Ali A69
Saleki-Gerhardt, Azita A5
Salem, Enrique T. A81
Salem, Enrique T. A764
Salen, Dave E491
Salenbauch, Hermann A353
Salerno, Frederic V. (Fred) E21
Salerno, Frederic V. (Fred) E275
Salerno, F. Robert (Bob) A86
Salerno, F. Robert (Bob) A87
Salerno, Frederic V. (Fred) A160
Salerno, Frederic V. (Fred) A842
Sales, William K. A690
Sales, Wayne C. A758
Sales, Angel R. (A. R.) P580
Salgado, Ricardo Espirito Santo
 Silva W57
Salgado, Ricardo Espirito Santo W58
Salganik, Laura P21
Salguero, Jeff A201
Salguero, Carlos W177
Salhus, Victoria D. A140
Saliba, Anis K. P56
Saliba, Joseph P566
Salice, Thomas P. P201
Saligman, Harvey P570
Salinas, Martin A293
Salinas, Martin A294
Salinas, Leonardo A450
Salinas, Anjy P457
Salisbury, Mark W. A490

Sheets, Jeffrey W. (Jeff) A218
Sheets, Cindy P347
Sheets, Wayne P354
Sheetz, Margaret E330
Sheetz, Guy E330
Sheetz, Stanton R. (Stan) A308
Sheetz-Zugmaier, Kim A359
Sheff, Paul E. P129
Sheffer, Gary A368
Sheffert, Mark W. P15
Sheffield, John E327
Sheffield, Martin P. A299
Sheffield, Peter A735
Sheffield, Angela P215
Sheffield, Vonne P540
Sheffy, F. K. W245
Sheftel, David P6
Sheid, Mary P341
Sheils, David P504
Shein, Jeffries A668
Sheinbaum, Marc A471
Sheinbaum, Gary A675
Sheiness, Alan A81
Sheinheit, Jaime E259
Sheldon, Scott E26
Sheldon, Craig A. E87
Sheldon, Brooks A56
Sheldon, Mike A456
Sheldon, Amanda A540
Sheldon, Greg A568
Sheldon, Todd N. A758
Sheldon, Jim P153
Sheline, Douglas A. A518
Shell, Frederick E. (Fred) A271
Shellenberger, Dee A. P615
Shelley, Bob E89
Shelley-Kessler, Pamela (Pam) E307
Shellman, Carolyn E. P122
Shelton, Charlita E73
Shelton, Gen. Henry H. (Hugh) E414
Shelton, James D. (Denny) E520
Shelton, Loriann E526
Shelton, Michael W. (Mike) A286
Shelton, Ralph K. A331
Shelton, Gen. Henry H. (Hugh) A493
Shelton, James D. (Denny) A610
Shelton, Todd A. A829
Shelton, Russell M. P149
Shelton, John A. P157
Shelton, Robert A. P221
Shelton, Scott P336
Shelton, Mark S. P464
Shelton, Jimmy P483
Shelton, Mark W461
Shelton-DeLapp, Marva P82
Shen, Nien-Tsu E449
Shen, Simon P245
Shendell-Falik, Nancy P53
Sheng, Rodney T. (Rocky) E73
Shengchen, Guo W342
Shenk, Robert G. E149
Shenk, Thomas E. (Tom) A543
Shennan, James G. (Jamie) A745
Shenoy, Navin A447
Shenoy, K. V. W86
Shepard, Alfred E196
Shepard, Bridget E213
Shepard, Julie E498
Shepard, Toya A66
Shepard, Donald J. A230
Shepard, Alfred A333
Shepard, Donald J. A649
Shepard, Donald J. A803
Shepard, Bruce P640
Shephard, Christopher J. E498
Shephard, John A300
Shepherd, W. Clyde E191
Shepherd, Carl G. E252
Shepherd, Carl G. E253
Shepherd, Marla K. E289
Shepherd, Ann E382
Shepherd, Brian E408
Shepherd, W. Clyde A324
Shepherd, Scott D. A613
Shepherd, Betty A698

Shepherd, Colin P245
Shepherd, Mary P373
Shepherd, James H. P474
Shepherd, Alana P474
Sheppard, Valarie L. A661
Sheppard, James J. A880
Sheppard, Eric P230
Sheppard, Mark P397
Sher, Susan S. P566
Sher, Harold W459
Sherbahn, R. Richard E150
Sherbell, Stanley P362
Sherburne, Jane C. A98
Shergold, Peter W33
Sheridan, Diane L. A24
Sheridan, Bert A389
Sheridan, Jean E. A594
Sheridan, Jerry E. A812
Sheridan, Chris P99
Sheridan, Bert P222
Sheridan, Richard R. P462
Sheridan, Dennis P648
Sheridan, Ronan W29
Sherif, Tarek E329
Sherin, Keith S. A367
Sherin, Keith S. A368
Sherin, Jonathan P624
Sherland, Barbara C. P422
Sherlock, Peter P553
Sherman, William D. E106
Sherman, John J. E224
Sherman, Richard H. E260
Sherman, George A11
Sherman, Scott D. A36
Sherman, Jeffrey S. A109
Sherman, George A118
Sherman, Patrick A. A338
Sherman, Belinda A433
Sherman, Malcolm L. P78
Sherman, Merrill W. P276
Sherman, Don P338
Sherman, Melanie P410
Sherman, Mark P466
Sherman, Jeremy P. P469
Sherman, Glen P572
Sherman, Bruce P597
Sherman, Frank W24
Shern, Stephanie M. A361
Shern, Stephanie M. W255
Sherr, Richard A796
Sherr, Charles P501
Sherrard, Roger S. A628
Sherrick, Bruce E190
Sherrick, Bruce A314
Sherriff, Jim A181
Sherrill, Gregg M. A779
Sherringham, Philip R. A633
Sherry, Peter J. A353
Sherry, Karl P549
Sherry, Ann C. W107
Sherwell, Keith A718
Sherwin, John E319
Sherwin, Stephen A. (Steve) A121
Sherwood, Charles H. E43
Sherwood, Julie A49
Sherwood, Scott A201
Sherwood, Robert J. A282
Sherwood, Michael S. A380
Sherwood, Bill P484
Sherwood, William B. P597
Shetler, Charles P257
Shetye, Rajesh (Raj) E301
Shevchik, Joan O. A178
Shevlin, Bianca W373
Shevrin, Phil W404
Shewmake, Charles W. A138
Shewmaker, Stephen O. (Steve) E132
Shewman, Teresa A508
Shi, Lili E452
Shi, Christiana A586
Shi, Zhenchun A630
Shibata, Takumi E202
Shibata, Tsukasa W34
Shibata, Takumi W320
Shibata, Masaharu W320

Shibata, Kenichi W328
Shickich, Mary Lynne P654
Shiel, James G. A114
Shield, Robin R. E455
Shields, Maria T. E44
Shields, Thomas J. (Tom) E107
Shields, William J. E272
Shields, Mike E295
Shields, Lori E329
Shields, James E. (Jim) E456
Shields, Richard A (Rick) E530
Shields, Joanna A309
Shields, Brian J. A551
Shields, Patrick P491
Shields, Kevin P571
Shields, Charlie P584
Shields, Dennis P613
Shiely, John S. A617
Shier, Richard A187
Shiff, Deena W438
Shiffler, Ronald E. P214
Shiffman, Gary A. E466
Shiffman, Steven B. A675
Shifman, Edward I. A716
Shiga, Toshiyuki W316
Shiga, Shigenori Shigenori
  Shiga W452
Shigemura, Dean Y. A97
Shigeta, Hiroaki E328
Shigeta, Osamu W291
Shih, Jessica A662
Shih, Willy C. W176
Shih, Ming-Hsiung W178
Shih, Edith W219
Shih, Lee Tih W336
Shih, Stan W429
Shih, Kathryn W461
Shikama, Chihiro W281
Shikamura, Akio (Alex) W149
Shikata, Susumu W291
Shiki, Takashi W34
Shikiar, Mindy Sloane P74
Shilen, Thomas S. (Tom) A160
Shill, Walt W7
Shillman, Robert J. (Bob) E111
Shilo, Gabriella W63
Shilston, Andrew B. W95
Shilston, Andrew B. W365
Shim, Gun A640
Shim, Dal Sup W398
Shima, Kiyoshi E111
Shimada, Takashi A540
Shimada, Kurt A784
Shimada, Hideo W420
Shimanouchi, Ken W452
Shimanuki, Shizuo W22
Shimao, Matt W318
Shimek, Andrew E175
Shimer, Julie A. E367
Shimizu, Minoru W97
Shimizu, Katsuichi W106
Shimizu, Takao W140
Shimizu, Takao W141
Shimizu, Masakazu W241
Shimizu, Minoru W278
Shimizu, Takaaki W307
Shimizu, Noritaka W388
Shimizu, Junzo W456
Shimkos, Dan P505
Shimo, Sister Mary P75
Shimojima, Bunmei W183
Shimokawa, Ryoichi W180
Shimokobe, Kazuhiko W447
Shimomitsu, Hidejiro W451
Shimomura, Setsuhiro W291
Shimoni, Micha W62
Shimotsuji, Shigeyoshi Shigeyoshi
  Shimotsuji W253
Shimoyama, Yoichi W289
Shimp, Robert G. A615
Shimura, Yasuhiro W452
Shin, Hyun Seop (Steve) E373
Shin, Hak Cheol (H. C.) A2
Shin, Hak Cheol (H. C.) A671
Shin, Il-Soon W258

Shin, Moon-Bum W267
Shindler, Steven M. (Steve) A584
Shindo, Kosei W312
Shindou, Tsutomu W326
Shine, Kenneth I. A832
Shiner, William S. (Bill) E282
Shingai, Yasushi W241
Shinichi, Iguchi P643
Shinkai, Hisayuki A18
Shinn, Bryan A. E514
Shinn, Stephanie A. A106
Shinobe, Osamu W34
Shinohara, Kenta P588
Shinohara, Hiromichi W314
Shinohara, Minoru W316
Shinohara, Minoru W320
Shinohara, Masashi W405
Shinozuka, Hisashi W253
Shintaku, Masaaki W327
Shiokawa, Yorihisa W338
Shiomi, Takao W238
Shipley, Susan B. (Susie) A433
Shipley, Marcus B. P580
Shipley, Richard L. P616
Shipman, Shane P27
Shipway, Jane W100
Shirai, Yoshio W206
Shirai, Yoshio W456
Shirai, Takumi W456
Shiraishi, Toru W328
Shiraji, Kozo W289
Shirakawa, Susumu W447
Shiraki, Seiji W289
Shirane, Takeshi W455
Shirasaki, Shinji W149
Shire, Willow B. A796
Shirk, John O. A359
Shirk, Brett A764
Shirk, Michael F. P242
Shirley, Ben D. E515
Shirley, Brian M. A551
Shirley, Edward D. (Ed) A661
Shirley, Edward D. (Ed) A792
Shirley, Doyle P52
Shirley, Mark P463
Shirota, Norihisa W408
Shirtliff, Bryan A697
Shiseki, Koji Koji Shiseki W184
Shitara, Hisataka E111
Shiung, Albert W139
Shive, Dunia A. P533
Shivers, William C. A433
Shivery, Charles W. (Chuck) A593
Shivery, Charles W. (Chuck) A855
Shizhong, Huang W64
Shizuta, Atsushi W316
Shlanta, Paul R. A23
Shlpman, Shane P27
Shmatko, Sergey I. W188
Shmerling, Michael D. E238
Shmerling, Michael D. A691
Shmidman, Yehuda E259
Shoaf, Thomas R. (Tom) A602
Shoaf, N. Mack P183
Shoaf, Victoria P494
Shobuda, Kiyotaka W283
Shockey, Vicki P419
Shockley, Jesse E345
Shockley, Joe T. A93
Shoemaker, Robert C. E10
Shoemaker, John C. E29
Shoemaker, Allen E115
Shoemaker, Rodney A. A63
Shoemaker, Alvin V. A435
Shoemaker, Alvin V. A879
Shoemate, Charles R. (Dick) A175
Shofe, Allen E171
Shoff, Larry A. A342
Shoff, Lonnie A713
Shokhin, Alexander W329
Sholders, James R. (Jim) E34
Shon, Larry De A87
Shonka, Michael J. E197
Shonka, Michael J. A344
Shoop, Randall A. (Randy) A593

A = AMERICAN BUSINESS
E = EMERGING COMPANIES
P = PRIVATE COMPANIES
W = WORLD BUSINESS

Sklarsky, Frank S. A651
Sklarsky, Frank S. P439
Skoch, Daniel A. E319
Skodol, Ted W465
Skoglund, Peter A227
Skogman, Kyle D. E509
Skogman, Kyle D. A821
Skokan, Marian P301
Skoko, Goran E189
Skolits, Adele M. E440
Skolnik, David A205
Skornicki, Eliezer A208
Skory, John E. A341
Skoufalos, Yannis A662
Skousen, K. Fred E186
Skove, David J. A664
Skovhus, Per Damborg W146
Skrebneski, Victor P132
Skrobialowski, Sophie E213
Skrzat, William A878
Skudutis, Tom W274
Skulina, James E494
Skulsky, Jeffrey E415
Skuteris, Lucille P277
Skuthan, Frank J. A429
Skwara, Steve A610
Skyler, Edward A184
Slaats, Paul E258
Slacik, Marek W435
Slack, Randy A503
Slade, Bert P161
Sladek, Michael E164
Sladich, Harry H. P540
Slager, Donald W. (Don) A693
Slagle, Dennis R. (Denny) W479
Slagter, Martin E252
Slaoui, Moncef W191
Slaoui, Moncef W192
Slap, Leonard E50
Slappey, Carol W. E242
Slark, Martin P. A595
Slater, Rodney E. E292
Slater, Anthony K. E395
Slater, Dee E541
Slater, James E.R. A98
Slater, Richard J. A475
Slater, Dudley A814
Slater, Rodney E. A840
Slater, Catherine I. A867
Slater, Austin J. P317
Slater, Mark P461
Slater, Gavin R. W301
Slatin, Mike A288
Slattery, William A749
Slattery, Anne M. A855
Slaughter, Mark B. E421
Slaughter, Owen P257
Slavin, Richard P393
Slavinsky, Eric A652
Slavitt, Andrew M. (Andy) E88
Slawin, Kevin R. A313
Slechter, Eric P205
Sledd, Robert C. A618
Sledge, Charles M. A145
Sleiman, Houssam H. (Sam) P318
Sleyster, Scott G. A669
Slifka, Alfred A. A379
Slifka, Eric A379
Slifka, Richard A379
Slifka, Andrew A379
Slifka, Eric A379
Slifka, Richard A379
Slifka, Andrew A379
Sliney, David D. E462
Sliney, David D. A752
Slingluff, Ed P346
Slipsager, Henrik C. A8
Sliter, Everit A. A378
Sliva, Christopher D. E496

Sload, Michael A201
Sloan, Thomas R. E67
Sloan, Jeffrey S. E220
Sloan, Gretchen E443
Sloan, Stuart M. A63
Sloan, Thomas R. A123
Sloan, Thomas G. A330
Sloan, Rodney L. A410
Sloan, Randy A734
Sloan, Gary A778
Sloan, Timothy J. (Tim) A859
Sloan, O. Temple P77
Sloan, Karen G. P249
Sloan, Hugh W. W278
Sloane, Barry R. E59
Sloane, Marshall M. A167
Sloane, Barry R. A167
Sloane, Jonathan G. A167
Sloane, Barry R. A167
Sloane, Jonathan G. A167
Sloane, Scott P135
Sloane, Peter P565
Slobodin, Mikhail W186
Slocum, Brian E284
Slocum, Michael C. A149
Slogoff, Reed J. E512
Slom, Julia Anne M. A853
Slom, Julia A853
Sloman, Aaron E393
Slominski, Donald D. (Don) P322
Sloneker, Karen L. A607
Slonim, Ory W441
Slonina, Kajetan W352
Sloppy, Richard L. (Rick) E109
Slotkin, Doug E547
Slotnik, Joseph J. E76
Slotnik, Joseph J. A136
Slotten, David P582
Slovensky, David E. A23
Sloves, Evan A181
Slovin, Bruce E87
Slovin, Jeffrey T. E447
Slowey, Patrick (Pat) E129
Sluitner, Zsolt W396
Sluka, Joseph P427
Slusher, John F. A586
Slusser, Eric R. E217
Sly, Patrick J. (Pat) A288
Slym, Karl W430
Sm, Steven P. E46
Sm, Justin W. E295
Smach, Thomas J. E129
Smale, Cindy P257
Small, Robert J. (Rob) E494
Small, Tony E547
Small, Lawrence M. A177
Small, Tim A293
Small, Michael J. A339
Small, Harold I. A414
Small, Lawrence M. A525
Small, Gary A706
Small, Richard G. P126
Small, Mark T. P126
Smalley, Gary G. A348
Smart, Steven P. E46
Smart, Justin W. E295
Smart, George M. A92
Smart, Steven R. A120
Smart, George M. A341
Smart, Clif P341
Smart, Kacey P513
Smart, Jill B. W7
Smart, Ken W233
Smart, Katherine W373
Smeaton, John W. P297
Smeby-Udesen, Lena W426
Smedman, Johan W426
Smegal, Thomas F. E86
Smejc, Jiri W344
Smeltser, Jeremy W. A738
Smetana, Mark A280
Smetana, Mark P173
Smette, Darryl E389
Smette, Darryl G. A248
Smialek, Robert L. A364

Smidt, Carsten E515
Smidt, Jonathan D. A292
Smigel, David E237
Smigel, Suzan P537
Smiles, P. W350
Smiley, Melody E97
Smirnov, Maxim A31
Smirnov, Stephanie A456
Smisek, Jeffery A. (Jeff) A569
Smisek, Jeffery A. (Jeff) A819
Smit, Neil A204
Smit, Peter F. A411
Smit, Stephen A749
Smit, Willie W39
Smith, Ian F. E13
Smith, Robert C. E33
Smith, Peter J. E44
Smith, John F. E44
Smith, Barry M. E50
Smith, Mark W. E50
Smith, Chris E61
Smith, Thomas R. E67
Smith, J. Duncan E78
Smith, Kari G. E79
Smith, Sally J. E80
Smith, Stephen R. (Steve) E81
Smith, Brent E86
Smith, David W. E88
Smith, Richard H. E94
Smith, Robert H. (Bob) E106
Smith, Peter F. E109
Smith, Terry E110
Smith, Gary B. E115
Smith, Robert D. E116
Smith, Thomas W. E121
Smith, Donald V. E130
Smith, Larry G. E132
Smith, Greg K. E138
Smith, Peter W. E146
Smith, Jim E147
Smith, Sheri O. E149
Smith, Christopher L. E152
Smith, Winthrop H. E163
Smith, Laci E166
Smith, William A. E168
Smith, Stephen M. (Steve) E178
Smith, Willard H. E180
Smith, Richard C. E183
Smith, Rankin M. E191
Smith, Derek E211
Smith, Stephen J. (Steve) E230
Smith, Darrin L. E235
Smith, O. Mitchell E242
Smith, Michael L. E245
Smith, Maggie E254
Smith, Roger E269
Smith, Lonnie M. E278
Smith, C. Thomas E281
Smith, Jim E285
Smith, Lansing G. E320
Smith, Steven (Steve) E326
Smith, Cameron O. E342
Smith, Karen A. E347
Smith, Jerome E355
Smith, Mike E371
Smith, Galen E385
Smith, Kent J. E387
Smith, Susan K. E392
Smith, Philip W. E392
Smith, Thomas G. (Tom) E397
Smith, Randy E411
Smith, Paul E414
Smith, Susan E417
Smith, Michael C. E442
Smith, J. Duncan E446
Smith, Frederick G. E446
Smith, David D. E446
Smith, J. Duncan E446
Smith, Frederick G. E446
Smith, Robert E. E446
Smith, Brad E448
Smith, Samuel H. E454
Smith, Lindley E454
Smith, Lowndes A. (Lon) E471
Smith, Gary D. E496

Smith, Sherwood H. E497
Smith, W. Michael E500
Smith, Howard W. E529
Smith, Melissa D. E534
Smith, Derek M. E545
Smith, Travis E549
Smith, Marschall I. A2
Smith, Lucinda B. A20
Smith, Rob A20
Smith, Dave A22
Smith, Lawrence S. A24
Smith, Zeke W. A27
Smith, Joshua I. A38
Smith, A. Wade A49
Smith, Wayne A. A54
Smith, J. Truitt A54
Smith, Shannon A. A54
Smith, Rodney A. A63
Smith, Dan A70
Smith, David J. A71
Smith, Gene F. A71
Smith, Donna N. A75
Smith, Edward J. (Ed) A88
Smith, James N. (Jim) A88
Smith, Ed A88
Smith, Andrea B. A96
Smith, Daniel J. A99
Smith, Kennith A100
Smith, Michael M. A101
Smith, Quentin P. A102
Smith, Michelle A103
Smith, Lisa A118
Smith, Sharon A. A120
Smith, Jeffrey A. A122
Smith, Thomas R. A123
Smith, Gregory D (Greg) A125
Smith, Clark C. A137
Smith, Tad A140
Smith, Jeffrey D. A144
Smith, William G. A148
Smith, Richard M. A153
Smith, Joshua I. A156
Smith, Clifford T. A188
Smith, Brian J. A197
Smith, Scott A201
Smith, Barbara R. A208
Smith, J. David A208
Smith, Wayne T. A210
Smith, Martin D. (Marty) A210
Smith, Jim A213
Smith, Harold C. (Hal) A213
Smith, Jean A226
Smith, Mike A230
Smith, Derrick A230
Smith, Mark A232
Smith, Terry A251
Smith, E. Follin A254
Smith, Mark A256
Smith, Orin C. A258
Smith, Wade L. A260
Smith, Don A292
Smith, Richard J. (Rick) A295
Smith, Michael C. A297
Smith, Edwin E. A297
Smith, Gary L. A298
Smith, Robert C. A298
Smith, Douglas E. A299
Smith, Kenneth T. (Ken) A310
Smith, Edward C. A319
Smith, Kathryn K. A319
Smith, Frederick W. (Fred) A321
Smith, Joshua I. A321
Smith, Rankin M. A324
Smith, Donald E. A335
Smith, Virginia L. A335
Smith, Trent A. A341
Smith, Brigid A358
Smith, Jennifer A359
Smith, R. Scott A359
Smith, Scott C. A373
Smith, Sarah E. A380
Smith, Gregory L. (Greg) A382
Smith, Megan J. A383
Smith, Patrick A401
Smith, Hugh C. A423

Smith, Gordon H. A426
Smith, LuJean A433
Smith, David B. A438
Smith, David A440
Smith, Michael T. (Mike) A441
Smith, Stephen L. A446
Smith, Stacy J. A446
Smith, Stacy J. A447
Smith, Jeff S. A452
Smith, Patrick A456
Smith, Gregory W. A456
Smith, Gordon A. A471
Smith, Charles D. A495
Smith, Gregory C. (Greg) A497
Smith, Jared A511
Smith, Paul A522
Smith, Zack A539
Smith, Bradford L. (Brad) A553
Smith, David J. H. A565
Smith, Michael A568
Smith, Orin C. A586
Smith, Stephen P. (Steve) A587
Smith, Tricia A590
Smith, Daniel D. (Danny) A591
Smith, David B. A595
Smith, Judith G. (Judy) A600
Smith, David R. A600
Smith, Roland C. A606
Smith, Gerald B. A613
Smith, Gerald B. A614
Smith, Craig R. A618
Smith, Judy R. A627
Smith, Phil A647
Smith, Wayne T. A654
Smith, J. Brian A671
Smith, Michael R. (Mike) A672
Smith, Harmon D. A673
Smith, Richard A. A686
Smith, Ronald G. (Ronnie) A688
Smith, Sally A689
Smith, Scott A. A690
Smith, William A. (Will) A690
Smith, Matthew L. (Matt) A690
Smith, Susan A691
Smith, Karen A697
Smith, Abbie J. A706
Smith, E. Follin A706
Smith, Anne S. A720
Smith, J. Albert A725
Smith, Daniel C. (Dan) A725
Smith, Michael S. A731
Smith, William G. A731
Smith, Preston A732
Smith, Alfred J. (Jack) A733
Smith, Elizabeth A. A744
Smith, Sherry M. A758
Smith, Mark A784
Smith, Douglas H. A795
Smith, Roger C. A798
Smith, Scott A798
Smith, Lamar C. A798
Smith, Kevin C. A803
Smith, Richard P. A804
Smith, Robert A806
Smith, Donnie A809
Smith, Lawrence G. A813
Smith, Craige A817
Smith, Craig H. A822
Smith, S. Dawn A846
Smith, Doug A846
Smith, Dawn A846
Smith, Steve A850
Smith, Cathy A850
Smith, Shannon E. A852
Smith, Barbara L. A852
Smith, Linda S. A853
Smith, James C. A855
Smith, James P. A859
Smith, Phil D. A859
Smith, Mark J. A865
Smith, Thomas M. A867
Smith, Claibourne D. A877
Smith, Brad D. A883
Smith, William H. P5
Smith, H. Sally P10

Smith, Elizabeth Truesdell P15
Smith, Richard A. P21
Smith, Peter P22
Smith, Joseph P28
Smith, William S. (Bill) P34
Smith, Chris P34
Smith, William S. (Bill) P34
Smith, Quentin P. P42
Smith, Tommy J. P45
Smith, Scott F. P47
Smith, Hal E. P67
Smith, Rick R. P78
Smith, Diane P78
Smith, Mel J. P78
Smith, Jean Bixby P89
Smith, Bethany R. P92
Smith, Carleen P. P93
Smith, Terrance B. (Terry) P97
Smith, Michael P134
Smith, Harry L. P156
Smith, Michael L. P159
Smith, Carol L. P159
Smith, Rick P159
Smith, John P166
Smith, Les P168
Smith, Greg P169
Smith, Glenn B. P183
Smith, Molly Easo P188
Smith, Timothy P214
Smith, Michael (Mike) P215
Smith, Matt P217
Smith, Douglas G. P221
Smith, Juel Shannon P228
Smith, Scott P229
Smith, Rodney D. P230
Smith, Martha P232
Smith, J. Steven P250
Smith, Wayman F. P252
Smith, James E. P256
Smith, Albert E. P283
Smith, Mark P284
Smith, Mike P293
Smith, Daniel E. (Dan) P297
Smith, Joshua P305
Smith, Thomas (Tom) P308
Smith, David R. P312
Smith, Steve P319
Smith, Wes P320
Smith, Doug P321
Smith, Ira P327
Smith, Louis W. P348
Smith, Gregory E. P365
Smith, Lawrence G. P370
Smith, Tom P372
Smith, Franklin L. P375
Smith, Kelly P379
Smith, Paula F. P379
Smith, J. Walter P391
Smith, Van P406
Smith, Gary L. P412
Smith, Robert H. P414
Smith, Cecilia M. P430
Smith, Sheri L. P441
Smith, Linda Payne P448
Smith, Kenneth P457
Smith, C. M. P466
Smith, C. M. P467
Smith, Tim P472
Smith, Craig P483
Smith, Gary P488
Smith, Douglas G. P500
Smith, Frank L. P500
Smith, Susan P501
Smith, Eric P505
Smith, Scott P508
Smith, Tim D. P519
Smith, Hans F. P519
Smith, Ken P519
Smith, Bernadette P521
Smith, Donna G. P529
Smith, Joanne P531
Smith, Jeffrey H. P531
Smith, Robert A. P536
Smith, Matthew P538
Smith, Richard P538

Smith, Evan P539
Smith, Pliny C. P550
Smith, Dan P553
Smith, Kevin P558
Smith, Jocelyn M. P564
Smith, Joseph B. P564
Smith, Jennifer R. P570
Smith, Richard J. P570
Smith, Lawrence P574
Smith, Mike P575
Smith, Randy P578
Smith, Michael P578
Smith, Norma P580
Smith, Vicki P584
Smith, Gerald P585
Smith, Jeffrey B. (Jeff) P590
Smith, Rhonda P591
Smith, Cheryl L. P595
Smith, Van P599
Smith, Charles H. P607
Smith, Dwayne P608
Smith, Linda P609
Smith, Jeff P610
Smith, Brent P613
Smith, Robert R. (Bob) P616
Smith, Aubie P624
Smith, Cindy W. P625
Smith, James E. P637
Smith, Ray P638
Smith, Gregory A. (Greg) P641
Smith, Herman D. P644
Smith, Tonya P646
Smith, Peter W42
Smith, David W44
Smith, Michael R. P. W46
Smith, Wayne T. W76
Smith, Dorothy W100
Smith, Guy L. W156
Smith, David W156
Smith, Maura Abeln W169
Smith, Roland C. W169
Smith, Jeremy W212
Smith, Simon M. W225
Smith, Gerry P. W266
Smith, Malcolm W348
Smith, Jenni W350
Smith, David W360
Smith, Colin P. W364
Smith, Colin P. W365
Smith, James W370
Smith, Andrew W370
Smith, Kate W370
Smith, Keith J. W385
Smith, Lord Robert W410
Smith, Jim W410
Smith, Kris W423
Smith, Brian W450
Smith, Kelly W461
Smith-Abbott, Katy P415
Smith-Acuna, Shelly P130
Smith-Bogart, Karen A. E347
Smith-Simmons, Margie P257
Smithburg, William D. (Bill) A4
Smithburg, William D. (Bill) A223
Smither, Nicholas J. (Nick) A353
Smithers, John A. P276
Smithmier, Matt P554
Smits, Peter W5
Smits, Ivar W24
Smits, Didier W169
Smoke, Daniel J. E424
Smoldt, Dave A457
Smolev, James K. P544
Smoley, David E. W176
Smolinski, Wally E31
Smoot, Stephen R. E421
Smoot, Dan A846
Smoot, JoAnn P305
Smoter, Jennifer A4
Smothers, Frederick W. A696
Smucker, Richard K. A722
Smucker, Richard K. A727
Smucker, Timothy P. (Tim) A727
Smucker, Mark T. A727
Smucker, Richard K. A727

Smucker, Mark T. A727
Smulevitz, Morry A508
Smullen, Richard (Dick) A427
Smullen, Richard (Dick) P252
Smyer, Michael A. (Mick) P84
Smyer, Michael A. P585
Smyley, Kevin P653
Smyth, Thomas M. A25
Smyth, Robert E. (Bob) P536
Smytka, Daniel (Dan) A382
Snabe, Jim Hagemann W384
Snake, Sarah P246
Snapper, Suzanne D. E174
Snarr, Trent A158
Snead, George A. E280
Snead, Robert K. A618
Snead, Ronald P23
Snee, James P. A423
Sneed, Paula A. A26
Sneed, Thomas K. A521
Sneed, Paula A. A714
Snekvik, Rick P162
Snell, Richard S. A297
Snell, Mark A. A720
Snelling, Heather R. E92
Snider, Alva V. E85
Sniderman, Howard D. P186
Snipes, Bobby P503
Snively, David F. (Dave) A560
Snodgrass, Steven T. A548
Snodgrass, John P110
Snook, Jonathan D. (Jon) A48
Snow, Lester A. E86
Snow, Michael D. (Mike) E480
Snow, Kristine A. (Kris) A181
Snow, John W. A522
Snow, John A522
Snow, David B. A645
Snow, John W. A840
Snow, Russell K. P537
Snow, Richard C. W475
Snowball, Patrick W423
Snowberger, Thomas D. A105
Snowberger, Tom A105
Snowberger, Thomas D. P49
Snowberger, Tom P49
Snowden, Sandra Metts E417
Snowden, Sandra E417
Snowden, Tamara A135
Snowden, Joseph I. A655
Snowden, Sandra Metts A692
Snowden, Sandra A692
Snowdon, Mark A595
Snyder, James E84
Snyder, David E. (Dave) E102
Snyder, Charles J. E189
Snyder, Matt E225
Snyder, Deborah E463
Snyder, Randy J. E531
Snyder, Donald D. (Don) E532
Snyder, Window A67
Snyder, Jim A218
Snyder, Shea A248
Snyder, Andrew A255
Snyder, James C. (Jim) A311
Snyder, Matt A387
Snyder, Burton H. (Burt) A411
Snyder, William F. A423
Snyder, Judy A478
Snyder, Barbara R. A480
Snyder, Cheryl L. A626
Snyder, David A. A626
Snyder, Mark J. A. A749
Snyder, Stuart C. A793
Snyder, Donald D. (Don) A863
Snyder, Barbara R. P99
Snyder, David H. P179
Snyder, John P188
Snyder, Donna L. P250
Snyder, Alan P297
Snyder, Timothy Law P305
Snyder, Stephen D. P335
Snyder, Mary Beth P378
Snyder, Stephen P. P433
Snyder, Michael P495

Sparks, Timothy J. A221
Sparks, Gregory A. (Greg) A260
Sparks, Gregory A. (Greg) A708
Sparks, Robbie P19
Sparks, David P116
Sparks, George E. P269
Sparks, Steven R. P358
Sparks, Larry D. P603
Sparrow, Randy P257
Spatz, Tim P50
Spaulding, Jean G. A151
Spaun, Karen M. E325
Spaun, Karen M. A537
Spayde, Tammi P380
Spear, Timothy J. E172
Spear, Timothy J. A289
Spear, James T. (Jim) P105
Spears, Ronald E. (Ron) A79
Spears, Christopher C. A155
Spears, Timothy P415
Spears, William G. P424
Spechler, Julie P375
Specker, Steven R. A731
Spector, Neil E521
Spector, Jon P312
Spedowski, Jeff P194
Speed, James H. E280
Speer, David B. A244
Speer, David B. A438
Speer, David B. A702
Speers, Laurie A. W193
Speert, Arnold P572
Speert, Arnold P573
Speiller, Michael J. E230
Speirn, Sterling K. A477
Speirn, Sterling K. P625
Speirs, Jim A870
Spek, Hanspeter W113
Spek, Hanspeter W382
Spell, Randy B. A515
Spellecy, Mike P313
Spellings, James M. A307
Spells, Doretha J. P230
Spelman, Mark W7
Spence, Andrew B. E32
Spence, Michael E333
Spence, Jean E. A488
Spence, Jean E. A559
Spence, William H. A652
Spence, Kenneth F. (Ken) A803
Spence, Carlton P335
Spencer, David B. E67
Spencer, Donald P. E174
Spencer, David B. A123
Spencer, Stuart A. A177
Spencer, Tim A263
Spencer, Gaylord M. A374
Spencer, Jan B. A482
Spencer, Terry K. A613
Spencer, Terry K. A614
Spencer, Jody D. A626
Spencer, Steven R. (Steve) A731
Spencer, Robert P17
Spencer, Dave P50
Spencer, Terry P85
Spencer, Raymond J. P132
Spencer, James P286
Spencer, Andrea M. (Penny) P391
Spencer, Bruce P614
Spencer, Ruth E. P620
Spencer, Robin W47
Spendlove, G. Scott E484
Spendlove, G. Scott A783
Spengeman, Craig C. E391
Spengeman, Craig C. E392
Spengler, Richard S. E280
Spengler, Richard S. A458
Spera, Mike A534
Sperber, Julie K. A548
Sperling, Anthony E15
Sperling, Scott M. A161
Sperling, Scott M. A791
Sperling, Katrine W325
Spero, Vincent A. E391
Spero, Joan E. A452

Spero, Joan E. A455
Sperry, Doug E31
Spertus, Wendy S. Jablow A169
Speth, Ralf W430
Speyer, Sharon S. A433
SPHR, Cheryl Flynn P333
Spiegel, Adam C. E428
Spiegel, Mark M. A320
Spiegel, Noel J. A681
Spiegel, John W. A700
Spiegel, Marilyn W. A879
Spiegel, Scott H. P20
Spiegel, Allen M. P656
Spiegel, Eric A. W396
Spiegelman, Rande A714
Spielberg, Steven P102
Spielman, Bryan E329
Spielman, Stephen P550
Spierkel, Gregory M. E. (Greg) A441
Spierkel, Gregory M. E. (Greg) A622
Spiers, William A368
Spiers-Lopez, Pernille P457
Spies, Jorg W144
Spiesshofer, Ulrich W5
Spigarelli, James L. P348
Spigelman, Melvin K. (Mel) E328
Spikes, Jesse J. A666
Spillane, Richard J. (Rick) E163
Spilling, Rolv-Erik W435
Spillmann, Antoine W39
Spilman, Robert H. (Rob) A262
Spina, Eric F. P523
Spina, Jessica W284
Spinale, Joseph W. P93
Spincer, Ben W438
Spinelli, Luis E112
Spinelli, Stephen P40
Spinelli, Patty P439
Spinetta, Jean-Cyril W19
Spinetta, Jean-Cyril W25
Spinetta, Jean-Cyril W131
Spinner, Steven L. (Steve) A822
Spira, Steven S. A793
Spires, Kenneth D. (Ken) E141
Spires, Roger P479
Spirito, Paula R. A853
Spiro, Richard G. A177
Spitalnick, David A. P476
Spitulnik, Aric M. E485
Spitulnik, Aric P300
Spitulnik, Aric P478
Spitz, Erich W469
Spitzer, Alan R. E331
Spitzer, Brent A255
Spitzer, Gary W. A272
Spitznogle, Gary A607
Spivack, Maureen E409
Spivak, Glen P604
Spivey, William R. E96
Spivey, William R. A685
Spivey, Donald H. P366
Spivey, David P580
Splain, Michael E. (Mike) A615
Splaine, Thomas F. E280
Splaine, Thomas F. A458
Splaine, Kevin P490
Splinter, Michael R. (Mike) A69
Splinter, James M. A423
Spoales, Gary E37
Spoelberch, Gregoire de W37
Spoelman, Roger W. P229
Spoelman, Roger W. P580
Spoerry, Robert F. W212
Spohr, Carsten W151
Spolver, Michelle E201
Spong, Doug A456
Spong, Bernadette P433
Sponholz, Joseph G. A429
Sponic, David W. E149
Spoo, Sibylle W154
Spoon, Alan G. A238
Spooner, Ed M. E395
Spooner, William A. P472
Sporing, Eileen P536
Spottiswood, Juli C. E91

Spotz, Jeff A240
Spradlin, Jim A392
Spradlin, Shane M. A632
Spradlin, Jim P223
Spragg, Anna M. P424
Sprague, Robert W. A2
Sprague, Joseph A. (Joe) A29
Sprague, Charles W. A343
Sprague, F. Remington P229
Sprague, William P310
Spratt, William C. A378
Spratt, Regina M. A526
Spratt, Randall N. (Randy) A536
Sprecher, Jeffrey C. (Jeff) E275
Sprecher, Steven W. E276
Spreng, Anne K. A627
Sprieser, Judith A. (Judy) E275
Sprieser, Judith A. (Judy) A38
Sprieser, Judith A. (Judy) W255
Spriestersbach, Ben E389
Sprigg, Robert G. W443
Spriggs, James E28
Spring, Mark E. E59
Spring, R. Christopher E325
Spring, R. Christopher A537
Spring, Rich A764
Spring, Dick W29
Spring, Annabel F. W130
Springer, Stephen R. E138
Springer, Christina M. E149
Springer, Jon E512
Springer, William F. (Bill) A155
Springer, Robert G. A626
Springer, Thomas M. (Tom) P625
Springer, Jenny P651
Springfield, Susan A337
Springhorn, Jeremy P. E23
Springmann, Tressa P221
Springmann, Tressa P299
Springmann, Tressa P478
Springs, Heber P43
Springs, Jimmy D. P355
Springsteel, Ronald D. P355
Sprinter, Dodge P453
Sproger, Philip C. (Phil) A24
Sprott, Colin D. A571
Sproule, Simon A553
Sprowl, Chris P398
Sprowls, Robert J. E38
Spruill, Yancey L. E147
Sprunk, Eric D. A585
Spry, Michael J. (Mike) P410
Spuehler, Donald R. A544
Spurgeon, William W. (Bill) A266
Spurgeon, Thomas E. P78
Spurlin, Michael A684
Spurlock, Michael E28
Spurr, Robert E416
Spurr, Richard D. (Rick) E548
Spurr, John H. A440
Spurrier, Lauren P652
Spychala, Michael R. A518
Spychala, Darlene A. A518
Spyriouni, Garyfallia W303
Spyrow, Florence (Flo) P212
Squeri, Stephen J. (Steve) A393
Squicciarino, Joseph E546
Squier, David L. E531
Squier-Dow, Mae S. E161
Squinto, Stephen P. E23
Squire, Geoffrey W. (Geoff) E270
Squires, Nelson J. A24
Squires, Burt A251
Squires, James A. (Jim) A591
Squires, Paula C. P53
Squires, Paula C. P54
Squyres, Tyri E26
Sr., R. Charles (Charlie) Loudermilk E5
Sr., David A. (Dave) Boggan E5
Sr., Danny Walker E5
Sr., Thomas M. Davidson E26
Sr., Harley A. Whitfield E36
Sr., Sam Singer E61
Sr., D. James Guzy E106
Sr., Thomas L. Matson E114

Sr., V. Gordon Clemons E122
Sr., Robert E. Staton E141
Sr., Mark C. Allen E143
Sr., Kevin M. Kraft E150
Sr., Robert G. (Bob) Kramer E171
Sr., Jerry D. Dumas E199
Sr., W. Keith McDonald E273
Sr., Patrick J. Balthrop E310
Sr., Patrick J. Balthrop E311
Sr., Marvin G. Kiser E324
Sr., Robert (Bob) Lentz E348
Sr., Michael J. (Mike) Maples E355
Sr., Robert L. Moody E364
Sr., Tucker R. Robinson E442
Sr., Kevin B. Reid E465
Sr., Louis A. (Lou) Waters E481
Sr., Robert K. (Bobby) Reeves E533
Sr., Charles A. (Chuck) Meloy E533
Sr., Thomas W. Florsheim E535
Sr., Earl G. Graves A17
Sr., David J. Cooper A28
Sr., Gary F. Kennedy A48
Sr., Robert L. Moody A54
Sr., Robert K. (Bobby) Reeves A60
Sr., Charles A. (Chuck) Meloy A60
Sr., Thomas J. Lopina A95
Sr., Frank P. Bramble A96
Sr., Glenn G. Jordan A197
Sr., Thomas L. Matson A202
Sr., William H. (Bill Sr.) Gates A225
Sr., Benjamin S. Carson A225
Sr., G. Alex Bernhardt A274
Sr., Gen. William Lyon A322
Sr., George L. Argyros A327
Sr., Richard E. Clayton A329
Sr., Frank B. Holding A331
Sr., John E. Roe A349
Sr., Gerard P. Tully A349
Sr., Jerome L. Davis A361
Sr., David E. Dudick A370
Sr., Benjamin S. Carson A477
Sr., Arthur (Art) Stawski A490
Sr., Stephen R. Tilton A495
Sr., Andrew J. (Andy) McKenna A534
Sr., Robert L. Moody A570
Sr., Randall T. Jones A672
Sr., Baron David J. Cooper A688
Sr., Joseph B. Wolf A690
Sr., Ronald J. Zaleski A719
Sr., Christopher W. (Chris) Nolan A736
Sr., Roger V. Wiest A759
Sr., Anthony J. Agnone A759
Sr., Drew P. Kahn A778
Sr., Robert M. (Bob) Deacy A781
Sr., Roger B. Vincent A812
Sr., LeRoy T. Carlson A826
Sr., Richard T. Burke A832
Sr., Anthony J. (Tony) Melone A840
Sr., Lincoln A. Bean P10
Sr., Lee R. Anderson P27
Sr., Rex A. Rock P29
Sr., Estefano E. Isaias P40
Sr., Mayo Boddie P74
Sr., Earl G. Graves P77
Sr., David J. Totemoff P120
Sr., Forrest E. (Eddie) Harrell P121
Sr., David G. Carter P137
Sr., Peter J. Sheldon P146
Sr., Robert A. Reed P148
Sr., James Holmes P149
Sr., Gregory B. Levett P157
Sr., Felix W. Cook P186
Sr., Richard W. Single P205
Sr., Steve E. Rawl P215
Sr., Earl G. Graves P252
Sr., Ed Getts P257
Sr., Brad Slawson P264
Sr., Joseph R. (Joe) Daniel P270
Sr., Stanley J.C. Giberson P283
Sr., Charles A. Collat P320
Sr., E. E. Witt P339
Sr., Percy L. Berger P372
Sr., William T. (Ted) Phillips P403
Sr., Harold L. Martin P433
Sr., Thomas H. Brouster P451

Steele, Erik P515
Steele, Catherine J. P531
Steele, S. K. P531
Steele, Mark T. P584
Steele, David F. P609
Steelhammer, Robert A665
Steen, Andrew A114
Steen, Ida Clement A230
Steen, Ida A230
Steen, Lias J. (Jeff) A607
Steen, Bernie P553
Steenland, Douglas M. (Doug) A53
Steenland, Douglas M. (Doug) A453
Steenman, Bernard F. A351
Steenman, Ton H. A447
Steenrod, Mitchell D. A153
Steer, Robert L. A716
Steers, Bill W39
Steeves, Anita E502
Steeves, Frank L. A288
Stefani, Mark A368
Stefanik, Paul W. A788
Stefanko, Robert A. (Bob) E380
Stefano, Julie de A662
Stefano, Christine M. De A671
Stefano, Ron A685
Stefano, Mariane P358
Stefano, George B. P559
Stefanski, Marc A. A788
Stefanski, Jodi P290
Steffen, Mark E84
Steffen, Carolyn P89
Steffens, John L. (Launny) E114
Steffens, Greg A. E454
Steffens, Ray A392
Steffens, Ray P223
Steffens, Earl P518
Steffensen, Dwight E379
Steffensen, Dwight A765
Steffes, James (Jim) A599
Steffes, Lorene K. A649
Steffl, Carol P593
Stegemann, Klaus P. W396
Stegmann, Stefan von A244
Stegner, Robert L. (Bob) A765
Stehn, Michael P. E22
Steiger, Nancy P398
Steigerwald, Jay E527
Steigerwald, Joseph M. (Joe) A447
Steil, Justin W. E182
Steimel, Ron P331
Steimer, Olivier W9
Steimle, Kimberly P514
Stein, Richard M. E77
Stein, Thomas (Tom) E106
Stein, Clint E. E114
Stein, Randy E143
Stein, A. William E147
Stein, David L. A75
Stein, Robert A77
Stein, Martin A. A97
Stein, Derek K. A123
Stein, Laura A189
Stein, Clint E. A202
Stein, William G. A222
Stein, Laura A355
Stein, Jonathan C. A414
Stein, Robin L. A627
Stein, Kevin M. A655
Stein, Michael S. A689
Stein, Theodore P102
Stein, John P362
Stein, Eric L. P446
Stein, Rainer A179
Stein, Darrell W280
Stein, Paul W364
Stein, Nigel M. W486
Steinback, Kenneth B. (Ken) P151
Steinbeck, Daryl P571
Steinbecker, Roger J. A422
Steinberg, Gary E87
Steinberg, Mitchell V. E87
Steinberg, David E123
Steinberg, Joseph S. E253
Steinberg, Gregory (Greg) A17

Steinberg, Sandra A251
Steinberg, Stanley (Mickey) A361
Steinberg, Matt A493
Steinberg, Joseph S. A501
Steinberg, Joseph S. A502
Steinberg, Paul A563
Steinberg, Burt A751
Steinberg, David J. P302
Steinberg, Scott A. W408
Steinberger, Georg A88
Steinborn, Birgit W396
Steinbrink, William H. A727
Steinbruck, Peer W445
Steinebach, Lothar W202
Steinel, Gail P. E353
Steiner, James R. A223
Steiner, David P. A321
Steiner, Judith A. (Judy) A342
Steiner, Gerald A. (Jerry) A560
Steiner, Arnold L. A609
Steiner, Melanie A675
Steiner, David P. A854
Steiner, David P. A855
Steiner, Thomas M. P56
Steiner, Lara P95
Steinert, Earl A. E225
Steinert, Earl A. A387
Steines, Brian P461
Steingraber, Fred G. P256
Steinhafel, Gregg W. E493
Steinhafel, Gregg W. A770
Steinhardt, John E317
Steinhart, Ronald G. (Ron) A632
Steinhart, Ronald G. (Ron) A760
Steinhorn, Jeff L. A414
Steinike, Edmund R. (Ed) A197
Steininger, Frank-Dirk W197
Steinke, Marcy E147
Steinke, Bruce A46
Steinke-Fike, Marcy E147
Steinkrauss, Robert A. P585
Steinle, Karl W195
Steinmann, Katrin W335
Steinmetz, Edward J. P608
Steinour, Stephen D. (Steve) A302
Steinour, Stephen D. (Steve) A433
Stella, Giovanni W432
Stellato, Louis E. A721
Stelling, Sandy A29
Stelling, James P. A54
Stelling, Kessel D. A766
Stelling, Kessel D. A767
Stelly, Donald D. (Don) E301
Stelly, Berch P389
Stelnik, Jeff P71
Stelzer, John P217
Stemberg, Thomas G. (Tom) E308
Stemberg, Thomas G. (Tom) A153
Stemberg, Thomas G. (Tom) A637
Stemmer, Ralf W153
Stenberg, Marie E30
Stenberg, Patrik W479
Stenbit, John P. P554
Stendardi, Deborah P439
Stende, David L. (Dave) P175
Stender, Arnold E410
Stengel, William P. E251
Stengel, Steve A583
Stennes, Vicky A464
Stenske, Douglas E. A703
Stenson, Tom D. E190
Stenson, Tom D. A314
Stensrud, William R. (Bill) A472
Stenstadvold, Halvor W415
Stenvinkel, Kristina W203
Stephan, Timothy A846
Stephen, Michael E236
Stephen, Clarencia J. P6
Stephens, Thomas E284
Stephens, John M. E312
Stephens, Martin R. (Marty) E334
Stephens, John J. A79
Stephens, Danny A88
Stephens, Douglas A91
Stephens, Richard D. (Rick) A125

Stephens, Warren A. A251
Stephens, Keith A348
Stephens, Melvin L. (Mel) A497
Stephens, Cindy L. A627
Stephens, Jay B. A685
Stephens, John D. A818
Stephens, Burton R. A818
Stephens, John D. A818
Stephens, Steven D. A888
Stephens, Gary A. P82
Stephens, Shane P144
Stephens, James R. (Jim) P316
Stephens, Linda P402
Stephens, George A. P466
Stephens, George A. P467
Stephens-Collins, Ruth P149
Stephenson, Robert O. E378
Stephenson, Scott G. E521
Stephenson, Gordon E547
Stephenson, Randall L. A79
Stephenson, Vivian M. A153
Stephenson, Robert R. A260
Stephenson, Randall L. A288
Stephenson, Carol M. A372
Stephenson, Jack M. A471
Stephenson, Matt P41
Stephenson, Randall P77
Stephenson, Roland G. (Rollie) P189
Stephenson, Gordon P397
Stephenson, I. F. W245
Stepic, Herbert W332
Stepp, E. Kay E204
Stepp, E. Kay A741
Stepp, Lisa M. P526
Sterin, Steven M. (Steve) A162
Sterling, John F. E136
Sterling, Lisa E504
Sterling, John L. A339
Sterling, Steven (Steve) A477
Sterling, Dan A873
Sterling, Stephanie W370
Sterling, Eric W396
Stern, Menachem E98
Stern, Rachel R. E189
Stern, Neal E399
Stern, Paula A90
Stern, Paul G. A268
Stern, Carl W. A343
Stern, Ronald A. A367
Stern, Rick A663
Stern, Marc I. A677
Stern, David R. A708
Stern, Peter C. A792
Stern, Paul G. A869
Stern, Holly P360
Stern, James A. (Jim) P586
Stern, Caryl M. P597
Stern, Prof Yedidia (Zvi) W63
Sternberg, Seymour (Sy) A183
Sternberg, Seymour (Sy) A306
Sterner, Jeffrey L. P242
Sterner, Jeffery L. P243
Sternlicht, Barry S. E460
Sternlicht, Leo P274
Sterrett, Stephen E. A725
Sterry, Barbara P375
Sterthous, Diane P365
Stesny, Anne P506
Stetzer, Ed P300
Steuert, Michael A348
Steuert, D. Michael A867
Steur, Christine van der W100
Steven, Wayne P197
Steven, Anna W100
Stevens, Bruce A. E113
Stevens, George E145
Stevens, Brian E414
Stevens, William H. E455
Stevens, Ilene E479
Stevens, Kenneth E503
Stevens, Michael J. E536
Stevens, Chip A18
Stevens, Michele P. A334
Stevens, William J. (Bill) A373
Stevens, Thomas C. (Tom) A480

Stevens, Robert J. (Bob) A512
Stevens, Anne L. A512
Stevens, Robert J. (Bob) A560
Stevens, Meredith A580
Stevens, Bert A586
Stevens, Todd A. A604
Stevens, Ilene A772
Stevens, Wayne A805
Stevens, Simon A832
Stevens, Lisa J. A859
Stevens, Jeff A. A865
Stevens, Chris P64
Stevens, George Q. P193
Stevens, Max P483
Stevens, Lori P579
Stevens, Ben W98
Stevens, Franzo Grande W172
Stevens, Jason W289
Stevenson, Colin E136
Stevenson, Kevin P. E399
Stevenson, Jennifer A4
Stevenson, Bruce A. A290
Stevenson, Kimberly S. (Kim) A446
Stevenson, Shannan A662
Stevenson, Lord Dennis A866
Stevenson, Tom A877
Stevenson, David A. P136
Stevenson, Jim P321
Stevenson, Leslie Williams P606
Stevenson, Sarah A. P609
Stevenson, Katharine B. (Kate) W104
Stevenson, Tim E. P. W245
Steverlynck, Juan A482
Steverson, Lewis A. A223
Steverson, Lewis A. A563
Stevick, Tom P171
Stew, Robert E8
Stew, Peter E291
Stew, Amy A315
Stew, Nicole P401
Steward, David L. A164
Steward, Larry E. A271
Steward, H. Leighton A298
Steward, David L. A330
Steward, Russ A781
Steward, David P634
Stewart, Robert B. (Rob) E8
Stewart, Lee C. E18
Stewart, Robert E80
Stewart, Brian T. E234
Stewart, Lee C. E284
Stewart, Gordon B. E284
Stewart, Peter G. E291
Stewart, Richard R. E296
Stewart, Michael R. E394
Stewart, Laurie K. A24
Stewart, David K. A55
Stewart, Julia A. A85
Stewart, J. W. A91
Stewart, Ian A99
Stewart, Beth A. A153
Stewart, Cecelia (Cece) A185
Stewart, David L. A260
Stewart, Shelley A272
Stewart, Tara A272
Stewart, Amy A315
Stewart, Michael J. (Mike) A338
Stewart, Gary A. A359
Stewart, James T. (Jim) A475
Stewart, Carol A477
Stewart, Ron A490
Stewart, Michael K. A521
Stewart, Derek M. A565
Stewart, Marta R. A591
Stewart, Scott D. A596
Stewart, John A689
Stewart, Jim A818
Stewart, Andrew P29
Stewart, Douglas S. P78
Stewart, Christopher P254
Stewart, David P255
Stewart, Milton R. (Milt) P256
Stewart, Concetta M. P328
Stewart, Nathaniel Johnson (John) P393

A = AMERICAN BUSINESS
E = EMERGING COMPANIES
P = PRIVATE COMPANIES
W = WORLD BUSINESS

Thomas, Roy E486
Thomas, Joseph D. E502
Thomas, James A. (Jim) E502
Thomas, W. Olen E507
Thomas, Chet E544
Thomas, John B. A4
Thomas, Lee M. A26
Thomas, Louis J. A34
Thomas, Laura J. A49
Thomas, Dan A100
Thomas, Ian A125
Thomas, Chris A130
Thomas, Mary H. A142
Thomas, Tuesday N. A167
Thomas, Peter M. A187
Thomas, Richard A233
Thomas, Kent B. A245
Thomas, Richard L. A263
Thomas, David J. A269
Thomas, Lee A272
Thomas, William R. A298
Thomas, Gary L. A298
Thomas, Vincent A300
Thomas, Robert W. A373
Thomas, Brad A393
Thomas, Suzanne A395
Thomas, J. Darrell A401
Thomas, David M. A456
Thomas, Bruce V. A539
Thomas, Kurt J. A548
Thomas, Owen D. A562
Thomas, Geevy S. K. A590
Thomas, Paige L. A590
Thomas, Dan A610
Thomas, James A. (Jim) A633
Thomas, Timothy G. A643
Thomas, Darryl K. A660
Thomas, Martin (Marty) A702
Thomas, Randy A711
Thomas, Earl A772
Thomas, John M. A781
Thomas, Matt A784
Thomas, W. Olen A815
Thomas, Cheryl A837
Thomas, Andrea A850
Thomas, Jesse L. A856
Thomas, Stephen F. St. A859
Thomas, Anthony W. (Tony) A873
Thomas, Arleen R. P20
Thomas, Brenda P90
Thomas, Darwin P124
Thomas, Kennon J. P135
Thomas, Stephen P157
Thomas, Mark F. P189
Thomas, Terry P197
Thomas, David B. P197
Thomas, Mark R. P221
Thomas, Ralph Albert P297
Thomas, Karen P298
Thomas, Karen P309
Thomas, J. Mikesell (Mike) P372
Thomas, Brian P389
Thomas, Dean P461
Thomas, Theodore P462
Thomas, Patric P462
Thomas, Edward K. P463
Thomas, William (Bill) P463
Thomas, Brad P479
Thomas, Brad P480
Thomas, Earl P524
Thomas, Cary E. P562
Thomas, Barbara Schaps P570
Thomas, Jack E. P570
Thomas, Lawrence E. P570
Thomas, Huw F. P586
Thomas, Ronald R. P605
Thomas, Linda L. P607
Thomas, Mike P643
Thomas, Patrick R. P644

Thomas, Edwin P645
Thomas, Chet P651
Thomas, Barbara S. W69
Thomas, Patrick W. W78
Thomas, Patrick W. W85
Thomas, Claire W191
Thomas, Peter W235
Thomas, Ralf P. W395
Thomas, Eira M. W423
Thomas, Geoff W488
Thomas-Graham, Pamela A. A189
Thomas-Graham, Pamela A. W139
Thomashauer, Robin P6
Thomason, Linton J. (Lin) E225
Thomason, Shannon E225
Thomason, Linton J. (Lin) A387
Thomason, Shannon A387
Thomason, Joe A778
Thomason, Joel D. P399
Thomasson, Virginia C. A329
Thomasson, Bob P638
Thome, Paul A726
Thoming, Christopher S. P296
Thomlinson, David C. W7
Thomopoulos, Anthimos C. W303
Thompsen, Kelvin P. P485
Thompson, Jeffery S. E43
Thompson, Diane L. E73
Thompson, Carleton K. (Tres) E91
Thompson, Mark W. E97
Thompson, Stephen C. (Steve) E102
Thompson, J. Kenneth E110
Thompson, Bruce E183
Thompson, Scott E188
Thompson, James R. E323
Thompson, Mitch E326
Thompson, Kenneth E. E326
Thompson, Harris E331
Thompson, Mary Patricia B. E356
Thompson, C. John E396
Thompson, Virgil D. E410
Thompson, Pam E421
Thompson, Mark E445
Thompson, Donald H. E446
Thompson, Kevin B. E453
Thompson, Tommy G. E510
Thompson, Michael (Mike) E514
Thompson, Kevin B. E521
Thompson, Kenneth E. E521
Thompson, Connie A2
Thompson, James F. A13
Thompson, David G. A18
Thompson, J. Samuel (Sam) A25
Thompson, J. Kenneth A29
Thompson, Bruce R. A96
Thompson, Shelley B. A97
Thompson, Theresa A103
Thompson, Thomas N. (Tommy) A108
Thompson, Bill A118
Thompson, Betty A128
Thompson, Mark D. A130
Thompson, Mark A139
Thompson, Dale A. A148
Thompson, Tommy G. A164
Thompson, Michael L. A180
Thompson, William S. (Bill) A185
Thompson, Delia H. (Bina) A201
Thompson, Neil A201
Thompson, Duanne A212
Thompson, Lori A232
Thompson, Bob A251
Thompson, Donald (Don) A302
Thompson, Cary H. A322
Thompson, D. Gary A376
Thompson, Laura K. A381
Thompson, G. Kennedy (Ken) A416
Thompson, William G. A418
Thompson, Craig S. A429
Thompson, Kirk A432
Thompson, Mark E. A433
Thompson, Christopher A462
Thompson, Donald (Don) A534
Thompson, Craig B. A543
Thompson, Steven M. A548
Thompson, John W. A553

Thompson, Simon R. A581
Thompson, Greg A586
Thompson, John R. A586
Thompson, Richard L. (Rich) A587
Thompson, Karen A602
Thompson, Michael L. A624
Thompson, H. Brian A632
Thompson, Larry D. A635
Thompson, Larry A635
Thompson, Jay A. A673
Thompson, James H. (Jim) A677
Thompson, Robert K. (Bob) A697
Thompson, Robert I. A697
Thompson, E. Earle A709
Thompson, Edward C. A721
Thompson, Marcy J. A729
Thompson, Larry D. A731
Thompson, W. Norman A762
Thompson, David A764
Thompson, John W. A824
Thompson, Geroge H. A828
Thompson, John D. (David) A866
Thompson, Joan P15
Thompson, Paul C. P19
Thompson, Delia H. (Bina) P40
Thompson, Rev Tom P44
Thompson, Dean P123
Thompson, Bill P124
Thompson, Barbara W. P203
Thompson, Kim P214
Thompson, Teresa E. P214
Thompson, Marion G. P221
Thompson, Jeffrey E. (Jeff) P224
Thompson, Greg P225
Thompson, Fred P269
Thompson, Steven P275
Thompson, Kirk P281
Thompson, Steve P282
Thompson, Elaine C. P309
Thompson, Harry P335
Thompson, Helen P357
Thompson, William T. (Tee) P358
Thompson, Joseph F. P360
Thompson, Keith P370
Thompson, Richard L. (Dick) P396
Thompson, Steve D. P403
Thompson, Gilbert P410
Thompson, Mark A. P424
Thompson, Debra (Deb) P440
Thompson, Richard H. P446
Thompson, Robert P457
Thompson, Penny P471
Thompson, Kevin P472
Thompson, James D. P474
Thompson, Dennis P479
Thompson, Andrew P514
Thompson, David P524
Thompson, Tracy P529
Thompson, Kara P529
Thompson, Sara P535
Thompson, Elizabeth (Liz) P563
Thompson, Ronald L. P570
Thompson, Ray P581
Thompson, Robert P597
Thompson, Richard P602
Thompson, Mark P605
Thompson, Christopher P610
Thompson, Larry P629
Thompson, Jan P637
Thompson, James R. P646
Thompson, Jack E. W35
Thompson, Dorothy W245
Thompson, John M. W257
Thompson, John M. W258
Thompson, Simon W298
Thompson, Simon R. W381
Thompson, Peter M. W403
Thompson, Egil W415
Thompson, Westley V. (Wes) W421
Thompson, Kevin W450
Thompson, John M. W450
Thompson-Van, Debra A645
Thomsen, Laurie J. A803
Thomsen, Mads K. W325
Thomsen-Bendixen, Carsten W159

Thomson, Mark E326
Thomson, Mark E395
Thomson, Michael J. (Mike) E467
Thomson, James A. A27
Thomson, Karma A784
Thomson, Andrew J. (Andy) A791
Thomson, Alan M. W31
Thomson, Philip (Phil) W191
Thomson, Phil W192
Thomson, Alan M. W245
Thomson, Warren A. W278
Thomure, Anne P418
Thonis, Peter W. A840
Thoralfsson, Barbara M. W3
Thoralfsson, Barbara M. W435
Thorburn, Andrew W301
Thoresen, Roar W415
Thorin, Suzanne P523
Thorington, Stephen A. (Steve) E297
Thorington, Trevor P137
Thorley, Giles W459
Thormann, Dominique W355
Thorn, Jackie E393
Thorn, Bruce K. A636
Thorn, John G. W301
Thornbrough, Matt A456
Thornburg, Eric W. E117
Thornburg, Kirk A733
Thornburg, Ann P536
Thornburgh, Ron E372
Thornburgh, Richard A696
Thornburgh, Richard E. W139
Thorne, Louis D. E202
Thorne, James W. (Jim) E289
Thorne, David F. A244
Thorne, Nathan C. (Nate) A405
Thorne, Michael G. A741
Thorne, James P135
Thorne, Grant W360
Thornhill, Larry P382
Thornhill, Hugh P382
Thornley, G. Thomas (Tom) A180
Thornock, Mindy Mills A483
Thornton, George (Ben) E387
Thornton, Randolph I. A222
Thornton, Mark A338
Thornton, John L. A353
Thornton, David H. (Dave) A357
Thornton, Felicia A590
Thornton, Daniel P. (Dan) A633
Thornton, John L. A807
Thornton, Elizabeth P40
Thornton, Sharon P398
Thornton, Gray N. P540
Thornton, Amanda L. P620
Thornton, Robert P622
Thornton, John L. W122
Thornton, John L. W218
Thorp, Kenneth E301
Thorp, H. Holden P570
Thorpe, Kenneth E301
Thorpe, Linda A102
Thorpe, James W. (Jim) A260
Thorpe, Debra A478
Thorpe, Roger G. A614
Thorpe, Linda P42
Thorpe, Annette W100
Thorsen, Ketil E534
Thorsen, Steven L (Steve) A551
Thorsgaard, Marybeth A540
Thorson, John A. (Robert) A862
Thouin, Stephane W109
Thrailkill, Sister Francis Marie P566
Thrane, Linda L. P645
Thrasher, Don A549
Thrasher, Bradley A. A817
Threadgill, W. James A94
Throgmartin, Gregg W. E245
Throneberry, Garen A210
Throneberry, Ken P553
Throsby, Tim A471
Thuente, Tom E447
Thuiliere, Francois E428
Thukral, Rohit E104
Thulin, Inge G. E494

Thulin, Inge G. A2
Thulin, Anders W166
Thulin, Berth W479
Thumann, Jurgen R. W445
Thun, David L. P430
Thun, Fredrick W18
Thune, Chris P525
Thunstrom, Jason E302
Thurber, Robert C. A809
Thureen, Sheri A214
Thurk, Michael C. E44
Thurm, Kevin L. A184
Thurman, Carole E332
Thurman, Mark A. E404
Thurston, Corydon L. E58
Thurston, Corydon L. A117
Thurston, Ken P169
Thurston, Paul A. W217
Thurston, Richard (Dick) W429
Thwaites, George W350
Thyen, Gary L. P609
Thygesen, Mikael A725
Tian, Edward S. A529
Tianpu, Wang W120
Tibbetts, Joseph S. (Joe) E432
Tibbetts, Joe E432
Tibbitts, Tom P597
Tibbs, Brian P351
Tiberi, Debbie E381
Tible, Phillippe W250
Tice, Phil P159
Tickles, Chuck E224
Ticknor, Carolyn M. A189
Tidmore, Lloyd Keith A251
Tidwell, James M. (Jim) E100
Tidwell, Isaiah E451
Tidwell, Isaiah A509
Tidwell, Jerry A708
Tidwell, Laura S. P178
Tidwell, Jerry P290
Tiede, Bryan E225
Tiede, Bryan A387
Tiede, Robert C. (Rob) A729
Tiedemann, Andrew P181
Tiefel, William R. A152
Tieken, Robert W. A384
Tiel, Jeroen W352
Tieman, Nancy P398
Tiemann, Michael (Mike) E414
Tiemeyer, Peter E. A265
Tien, Chao-Chi P362
Tieqi, Teng W65
Tierce, Stephane W333
Tiernan, Bernadette P572
Tierney, Yevette E59
Tierney, Michael J. E197
Tierney, Kathleen (Kathy) E245
Tierney, Patrick J. (Pat) E352
Tierney, Brian X. A49
Tierney, Kathleen M. A177
Tierney, Thomas J. (Tom) A279
Tierney, Michael J. A344
Tietbohl, Jeffrey R. (Jeff) E102
Tietjen, Jill P215
Tiffany, Carolyn E539
Tiffin, John A296
Tiffin, Tim P574
Tiffin, Van P574
Tiffin, Lex P574
Tigges, Uwe W371
Tighe, Mary Ann A158
Tighe, John J. A630
Tighe, Thomas P162
Tight, Steven M. A142
Tiitinen, Pekka W5
Tilden, Bradley D. (Brad) A29
Tilden, Cindy P337
Tilenius, Stephanie A383
Tiles, Lindsay A714
Tilger, Carsten W202
Tilghman, Shirley M. A383
Tilghman, Richard G. A768
Tilghman, Richard H. (Rich) P399
Till, Kimberly E148
Till, Brian P655

Tillema, Dowe S. A351
Tiller, Rob E414
Tillerson, Rex W. A307
Tillerson, Rex W. P77
Tillett, Ronald L. (Ron) E507
Tillett, Ronald L. (Ron) A815
Tillett, Bill R. P44
Tillett, Jamie P283
Tillman, Robert L. (Bob) E127
Tillman, Audrey Boone A18
Tillman, Lee M. A521
Tillotson, Sandra N. (Sandie) E375
Tillotson, Sandra N. (Sandie) E376
Tilltoson, Sandie E376
Tilton, Glenn F. A4
Tilton, Glenn F. A5
Tilton, Glenn F. A223
Tilton, Glenn F. A471
Tilton, Glenn F. A819
Tilton, Colette D. P485
Timanus, H.E. (Tim) A665
Timanus, H. E. (Tim) A665
Timberman, Terri L. A135
Timcho, Thomas P. (Tom) P271
Timian, David P28
Timken, Ward J. (Tim) A795
Timken, Ward J. A795
Timken, John M. A795
Timko, Joseph H. (Joe) A645
Timm, Christopher J. E325
Timm, Christopher J. A537
Timm, Stephen J. (Steve) A703
Timm, Bryan L. A814
Timmel, Timothy L. A178
Timmer, Riley E515
Timmerman, Doug A39
Timmermans, Ted A872
Timmermans, J. V. (Koos) W231
Timmins, Rick E505
Timmins, Scott P40
Timmons, James T. A500
Timms, Anna A468
Timpe, Chuck E281
Timpe, Ronald E. A741
Timpone, Leonard P204
Timuray, Serpil W475
Tin, Kng W336
Tinberg, Richard W. E479
Tinberg, Richard W. A772
Tindal, Ted P9
Tindell, William A. (Kip) A871
Tindle, Leah P281
Tiner, John W139
Ting, Sharon P440
Tingley, Stephen E416
Tinkler, Richard A676
Tinney, Jeff L. E543
Tinney, Steve P24
Tinsey, Frederick C. E321
Tintsman, Robert E404
Tipirneni, Praveen E133
Tippeconnic, David J. E320
Tippeconnic, David J. A613
Tippie, Henry B. E427
Tippl, Thomas A9
Tipton, Clarence E. A54
Tirado, Isabel P572
Tirador, Gabriel A544
Tirri, Henry W318
Tirva, Robert L. A135
Tisch, Andrew H. E68
Tisch, Andrew H. A192
Tisch, James S. A192
Tisch, James S. A319
Tisch, James S. A368
Tisch, Andrew H. A514
Tisch, Jonathan M. A514
Tisch, James S. A514
Tisch, Jonathan M. A514
Tisch, James S. A514
Tisch, Ann Rubenstein P570
Tisch, Jonathan M. (Jon) P586
Tisch, Andrew H. P644
Tischler, Howard L. E139
Tisdale, Donna P205

Tishkoff, Dennis B. A120
Tishman, Daniel R. (Dan) A13
Tishman, Daniel R. (Dan) P546
Tissot, Nicolas W31
Titi, Fani W235
Tito, Benjamin J. Del E51
Tito, Benjamin E51
Titterton, Charles F. A609
Titus, Gary S. E434
Titus-Johnson, Suzanne A315
Titzman, Donna M. A837
Tivy, James W. A457
Tizzio, Vincent C. A571
Tjosvold, Robert P462
Tkach, Douglas W193
Tkacz, Richard M. E423
Toal, Anne W193
Tobe, Michael (Mike) P68
Toben, Bradley J. B. P52
Tober, Stephen J. E316
Tobey, Aubrey C. (Bill) E429
Tobias, Joey P426
Tobin, Thomas J. (Tom) E72
Tobin, Robert E299
Tobin, Peter J. A183
Tobin, Bruce A725
Tobin, Lee A870
Tobin, Bill P159
Tobin, Greg P468
Tobin, John H. P570
Tobin, Graham P608
Toburen, Paul P430
Toby, Leo H. E205
Tocatly, Dan E98
Toczydlowski, Greg A803
Toda, Larry E332
Toda, Yuzo W182
Todd, Aaron D. E20
Todd, Charles T. E61
Todd, Glenn E178
Todd, Matthew E193
Todd, Stephen M. A266
Todd, Clarence B. (C. B.) A568
Todd, L. T. P466
Todd, L. T. P467
Todman, Michael A. A580
Todman, Michael A. A869
Todoroff, Christopher M. (Chris) A430
Todt, Blair W. A856
Toevs, Alden W130
Toffey, Bryan A14
Toffey, Bryan P7
Toffler, Van A842
Tofighi, Saeed E485
Tofighi, Said E485
Togashi, Kazuhisa W417
Togher, Renee A532
Togneri, Gabriel B. (Gabe) A640
Togni, Fabrizio W54
Togni, Alberto W64
Toikkanen, Timo W318
Toit, Philippus Philippus du Toit W39
Toit, Hendrik W235
Toizer, Eric L. A183
Tok, Dan W401
Tokarczyk, Peter P24
Tokarski, Chris E460
Tokarz, Michael T. E261
Tokarz, Michael T. A193
Tokarz, Michael T. A852
Token, Eric P442
Tokubutsu, Fumio W420
Tokuda, Hiromi W149
Tokuhiro, Kiyoshi W326
Tokumitsu, Shigenori Shigenori
   Tokumitsu W452
Tokunaga, Takenori W253
Tokunari, Muneaki W294
Tokura, Masakazu W416
Tolan, Julie P315
Tolbert, J. David A463
Tolda, Stelleo E333
Toledano, Sidney W124
Toledo, Laura P468
Toledo, Richard P611

Tolentino, Ryan P110
Toliver, Dennis P. A374
Tollison, D. Tip A374
Tolosky, Mark R. P53
Tolot, Jerome W189
Tolstedt, Carrie L. A859
Tom, Walker P223
Toma, Shigeki W392
Toman, Troy E411
Tomarchio, Joseph E349
Tomasek, Adam P652
Tomasino, Peter E11
Tomasky, Susan A49
Tomasky, Susan A784
Tomason, Bruce P468
Tomassini, Luca W432
Tomasuolo, Henry P536
Tomb, David R. A332
Tomb, Matthew A332
Tomb, David R. A332
Tomb, Greg W384
Tomczyk, James E. A172
Tome, Carol B. A419
Tome, Lores A476
Tome, Carol B. A824
Tome, Carol A824
Tomecka, Anna P78
Tomich, Rosemary A604
Tomita, Kimio W316
Tomka, Dave P50
Tomkalski, Mark J. P548
Tomkinson, Joseph R. A439
Tomlin, Darcy A256
Tomlinson, Lawrence J. (Larry) E112
Tomlinson, Tricia E214
Tomlinson, Joel E413
Tomlinson, Janice C. A571
Tomlinson, Philip W. (Phil) A766
Tomlinson, Philip W. (Phil) A767
Tomlinson, Tommy P124
Tomlinson, D. J. W245
Tomlinson, Geoffrey A. (Geoff) W301
Tommiska, Kati W321
Tomnitz, Donald J. (Don) A425
Tomono, Hiroshi W312
Tomozoe, Masanao W455
Tompkins, Nicholas (Nick) E299
Tompkins, Cathlyn L. (Cathy) A173
Tompkins, P. Kelly A188
Tompkins, Paul A223
Tompkins, James A271
Tomsicek, Michael E133
Tomson, Louis R. P559
Tonar, William (Bill) E215
Toner, Susan P53
Toney, Frederiek A353
Toney, Charles A544
Tong, Chris A769
Tong, William P68
Tong, Hon shing W65
Tong, Lim Khiang W336
Tonges, Mary P604
Tongson, Timothy J. (Tim) A193
Tonne, Hilde M. W435
Tonnison, John A775
Tonnu, DiemLan (Lannie) P537
Tonoike, Tohru A18
Tonomoto, Kiyoshi W34
Toohey, Robert A. A840
Toohey, Robert A. P36
Toohey, Garritt P443
Tooke, Nancy B. E163
Tooker, Gary L. A88
Tooker, Jean E. (Jeanie) P491
Tookes, Hansel E. A223
Tookes, Hansel E. A403
Tookes, Hansel E. A583
Tookes, Hansel E. A706
Toole, John H. E156
Toole, Laura L. P41
Toomajian, Marty A105
Toomajian, Marty P49
Toomajian, Charles R. P414
Toomey, Rebecca J. A626
Toomey, John M. A776

Trotter, Lloyd G. A635
Trotter, Lloyd G. A787
Trotter, Lloyd G. W144
Troubh, Raymond S. E217
Trout, Patricia A. E92
Trout, Gil L. A813
Troutman, Wilson E22
Trowbridge, Rick P457
Trowbridge, Kim J. W26
Troxel, Suzanne P607
Troy, George E140
Troy, Dan W191
Troy, Daniel W192
Trpik, Joseph R. (Joe) A301
Trubeck, William L. (Bill) A856
Trucano, David P. (Dave) A237
Truchard, James J. E361
Trucking, Oakley P83
Trudeau, Robert W. E317
Trudell, Cynthia M. A635
True, Bradford G. A600
Trueax, Paul A201
Trueblood, Jim A232
Trueblood, Nora P14
Trueheart, William E. P276
Trueheart, Harry P. P439
Truelove, Brian A414
Truesdale, Ken E288
Truesdale, Anthony N. (Tony) E524
Truesdale, Donald J. P440
Truesdell, John P442
Truex, Ron A495
Trujillo, Solomon D. (Sol) A771
Trujillo, Roy B. P578
Trumbo, Judith P440
Trumbull, R. Scott E236
Trumka, Richard L. P19
Trunfio, Joseph A. P36
Truong, Jack G. W3
Trupiano, Anthony P636
Truscott, William F. (Ted) A55
Truskowski, Brian J. A452
Trussell, Jason A. E262
Trussell, Robert B. (Bob) E482
Trust, Martin E523
Trust, Rockland A440
Trutzschler, Klaus W113
Truwit, Mitch E55
Truxal, Bill P549
Truzinski, Dave P. A584
Tryforos, Thomas E121
Tryforos, Thomas M. E126
Tryniski, Mark E. E209
Tryon, Stephen P. E386
Tryon, William J. (Bill) E425
Tryon, Geoff P477
Tsai, Michael K. C. E148
Tsai, Bin-ming Benjamin (Ben) E505
Tsai, John Chieh Jung A24
Tsai, Gerald C. A320
Tsai, Hong-Tu W112
Tsai, Cheng-Ta W112
Tsai, Cheng-Chiu W112
Tsai, Cheng-Ta W112
Tsai, Cheng-Chiu W112
Tsai, Chiu-Jung W427
Tsai, Rick W429
Tsai, N. S. W429
Tsai, Rick W429
Tsang, Chi-Hwa A447
Tsang, Katherine W411
Tsao, Tom E167
Tsao, Andy E469
Tsao, Andy A761
Tsaparis, Paul A415
Tschage, Uwe W128
Tschanen, Erin E. A627
Tschanz, Lee A702
Tschinkel, Victoria J. A218
Tse, Alan K. E104
Tse, Irene A471
Tse, Aloysius H. Y. W122
Tse, Aloysius H. Y. W125
Tse, Edward W320
Tse, Edmund S.W. W342

Tseng, Saria E347
Tseng, Eric A309
Tseng, Vivian S. Y. P353
Tseng, Vivian S. Y. P634
Tseng, F. C. W428
Tseng, F. C. W429
Tsiddon, Prof Daniel W63
Tsien, Robert Y. (Bob) A356
Tsien, Samuel N. (Sam) W336
Tsimbinos, John M. A578
Tso, Christina A545
Tso, Stephen T. (Steve) W429
Tsokova, Olga A186
Tsou, Rose A883
Tsoumas, Richard M. P625
Tsoumas, Athanasios W344
Tsounis, George E175
Tsourapas, Panagiotis A201
Tsuboi, Kenneth (Ken) P541
Tsuboi, Hiromichi W124
Tsubouchi, Kazuto W326
Tsubouchi, Kazuto W327
Tsuchida, Osamu W140
Tsuchida, Osamu W141
Tsuchiya, Jun-ichi W141
Tsuchiya, Sojiro W149
Tsuchiya, Munehiko W452
Tsuda, Toru W96
Tsuda, Toru W97
Tsuda, Shingo W282
Tsuda, Noboru W288
Tsue, Sik W125
Tsuga, Kazuhiro W338
Tsuha, Wallace K. E215
Tsuji, Haruyoshi W16
Tsuji, Masahito W97
Tsuji, Haruo W320
Tsuji, Kiyoshi W448
Tsujigami, Hiroshi W327
Tsujihara, Kevin A793
Tsujimura, Kenji W22
Tsujimura, Kiyoyuki W326
Tsujimura, Kiyoyuki W327
Tsujiyama, Eiko W334
Tsukada, Masaki W141
Tsukada, Tadao W141
Tsukamoto, Makoto W206
Tsukamoto, Shigeru W392
Tsukioka, Takashi W224
Tsukioka, Takashi W225
Tsukioka, Ryozo W236
Tsukuda, Scott P539
Tsukuda, Kazuo W290
Tsunekage, Hitoshi W421
Tsuritani, Naomasa W145
Tsuruta, Masaaki W408
Tsutsui, William M. P484
Tsutsui, Yoshinobu W311
Tsutsumi, Tomio W290
Tsutsumi, Kazuhiko W291
Tsuya, Masaaki W96
Tsuya, Masaaki W97
Tsuyuki, Shigeo W141
Tsuzumi, Norio W447
Tu, L.C. W429
Tuan, Sherman E468
Tubb, Allen R. A762
Tubb, Joe P408
Tubbs, Jeffrey A. P267
Tucci, Michael E206
Tucci, Michael (Mike) A194
Tucci, Joseph M. (Joe) A284
Tucci, Gary A. A678
Tucci, Angela A764
Tucci, Joseph M. (Joe) A846
Tucci, James M. P490
Tuchman, Bruce E30
Tuchman, Mendel P116
Tuck, Steven L. P6
Tucker, Ernest S. E6
Tucker, Thomas E. E404
Tucker, Garland S. E497
Tucker, J. Walter E516
Tucker, Sara Martinez A49
Tucker, Michael K. A87

Tucker, Patrick A137
Tucker, Lew A181
Tucker, Chris A300
Tucker, Laurie A. A321
Tucker, Gary A334
Tucker, Mark A380
Tucker, Mel A637
Tucker, Daniel S. A731
Tucker, Sara Martinez A881
Tucker, Dan P6
Tucker, Barrett P19
Tucker, Archie P107
Tucker, Ron P163
Tucker, Harold P221
Tucker, Richard G. P240
Tucker, Dennis P321
Tucker, Jeff P422
Tucker, Jacquelynn E. P625
Tucker, Greg W14
Tucker-Datrio, Nancy A670
Tuckson, Reed V. A832
Tudor, David J. E533
Tudor, Andy P229
Tuebner, Peter F. P89
Tufano, Paul J. E483
Tufano, Joseph J. P493
Tufano, Paul A. P622
Tufano, Paul J. W25
Tufariello, Anthony B. E202
Tuffin, Mark A490
Tuffy, Daniel P96
Tuffy, William W51
Tufly, Jerry E58
Tuggle, Clyde C. A197
Tuggle, Charles T. A336
Tuggle, Clyde C. A376
Tuggle, Rosalynn A416
Tuggle, Deloris P221
Tugnait, Sanjay E262
Tuite, James M. P114
Tukua, Darrell R. E88
Tulanan, Decha W61
Tulananda, Deja W61
Tulchinsky, Alex E368
Tulin, Stanley A689
Tullai-McGuinness, Susan P292
Tullman, Glen E27
Tulloch, Maurice W47
Tulloch, Angus W130
Tulloh, Brian A292
Tully, Chris E147
Tully, Timothy A99
Tully, Bruce C. P142
Tully, Herbert B. P643
Tumelty, John B. E406
Tummel, Lord Iain D. T. Vallance
 of W396
Tummel, Iain W396
Tumminello, Peter I. (Pete) A22
Tung, Savio W. A775
Tung, Chee-Chen W339
Tungesvik, Stale W414
Tunmore, Neil R. A447
Tunnacliffe, Paul D. W155
Tuntland, Trisha E81
Tuomanen, Elaine P501
Tupper, Janice L. E149
Tupper, Nicholas A368
Turben, John F. (Jack) E255
Turben, Daniel H. A627
Turbes, Darv P593
Turcke, Mary Ann W82
Turco, Christopher (Kip) A873
Turcotte, Denis A. A263
Turcotte, Brian A606
Turcotte, Martine W82
Turgeon, Joseph E456
Turgeon, Mary K. A853
Turiano, Vincent E109
Turicchi, R. Scott E288
Turilli, M. Louise (Lou) A213
Turina, Mary P385
Turk, Tim E106

Turkal, Nick W. P413
Turke, Thomas H. P466
Turkovich, Joe P519
Turley, James S. P77
Turmel, Jean W27
Turmo, Rafael Sanchez-Lozano W233
Turnas, Jeff A870
Turnbull, Thomas P624
Turnbull, Lord Andrew W348
Turner, Brent E9
Turner, Kathryn C. E93
Turner, Bert E147
Turner, Brent E187
Turner, Joseph W. (Joe) E225
Turner, William V. E225
Turner, Joseph W. (Joe) E225
Turner, Troy J. E249
Turner, Jason W. E320
Turner, James E395
Turner, John F. A49
Turner, William H. A55
Turner, John F. A75
Turner, Robb E. A137
Turner, John G. A193
Turner, Reginald M. (Reggie) A205
Turner, Nancy E. A218
Turner, Kathryn C. A218
Turner, Jim L. A228
Turner, Jim L. A242
Turner, Dan A272
Turner, K. Rick A293
Turner, K. Rick A294
Turner, Scott C. A320
Turner, Joseph W. (Joe) A387
Turner, William V. A387
Turner, Joseph W. (Joe) A387
Turner, Brad A402
Turner, Leslie M. A411
Turner, Michael R. A414
Turner, John G. A423
Turner, Simon A435
Turner, Fred L. A534
Turner, Mervyn (Merv) A543
Turner, B. Kevin A553
Turner, John C. A555
Turner, B. Kevin A590
Turner, Michael L. (Mike) A614
Turner, Paul E. A626
Turner, John F. A630
Turner, R. Gerald A631
Turner, M. Terry A644
Turner, John M. A688
Turner, David J. A688
Turner, George W. A700
Turner, Jeffrey L. (Jeff) A703
Turner, Robyn P. A719
Turner, Jeffrey L. (Jeff) A737
Turner, Simon M. A746
Turner, William B. (Brad) A767
Turner, Marlin E. A768
Turner, Robert W. A816
Turner, William R. (Rick) A816
Turner, Bobby A870
Turner, Mark A. A877
Turner, Robert E. P78
Turner, Allen M. P132
Turner, Deborah M. P205
Turner, Kelly P216
Turner, Chris P300
Turner, Lynn H. P315
Turner, Skip P347
Turner, Kay P360
Turner, Ben P403
Turner, Mark J. P418
Turner, Rick P448
Turner, R. Gerald P484
Turner, Michael (Mike) P572
Turner, Shannon R. P598
Turner, Howard P629
Turner, Cathy W72
Turner, Cathy W74
Turner, David J. W129
Turner, Nigel W151
Turney, Doug A456
Turney, Sharen J. A491

A = AMERICAN BUSINESS
E = EMERGING COMPANIES
P = PRIVATE COMPANIES
W = WORLD BUSINESS

Vaca, Nina G. A205
Vaca, Nina G. A487
Vaca-Wilkens, Mirtha P422
Vaccari, Richard A. A720
Vaccariello, Caroline S. E400
Vaccaro, San E. A233
Vacco, Dennis C. P354
Vacher, Guy W472
Vachher, Monica P142
Vachon, Mark L. A367
Vachon, Jacques P. A694
Vachon, Jennifer P70
Vachon, Louis W302
Vachris, Ronald M. (Ron) A225
Vacirca, Sal P188
Vadari, Mani A105
Vadari, Mani P49
Vadell, Pablo Vallbona W10
Vadera, Shriti W44
Vadera, Baroness Shriti W87
Vadera, Baroness Shriti W88
Vadlamannati, Ram A651
Vadon, Mark E66
Vaeth, Michelle A661
Vagelos, P. Roy E415
Vaghul, Narayanan W39
Vagt, Robert A484
Vahaviolos, Sotirios J. E344
Vahey, Walter E483
Vahidi, Virasb A48
Vahlbrock, Martin W371
Vaidya, Vinay P404
Vaillant, Gerard E311
Vaillaud, Pierre W454
Vaina, Alan A293
Vainboim, Israel W237
Vaishnav, Mike A765
Vaitkus, Joe P545
Vajda, David J. (Dave) A587
Vakharia, Harish P442
Valade, Peter E213
Valade, Charles R. A820
Valas, Paul E64
Valberg, H?kan E15
Valborgland, Kirsti W415
Valdemoro, Juan W356
Valdes, Max O. A327
Valdes, Luis A658
Valdes, Lou W27
Valdez, Lupe A816
Valdman, Bertrand A. (Bert) A283
Vale, Michael G. A2
Valenta, Tommy A. A417
Valenta, Katherina A694
Valenta, Mary Ann P257
Valente, Ralph A440
Valenti, Fortunato N. (Nick) E72
Valenti, Kathleen E. A548
Valenti, Susan M. A797
Valenti, Kellie P179
Valenti, Robert P187
Valentic, Sanja E433
Valentine, Michael E201
Valentine, Michael J. E430
Valentine, James A. E430
Valentine, Michael J. E431
Valentine, Mathias A. E431
Valentine, Kevin E477
Valentine, H. Brian A44
Valentine, David L. A768
Valentine, Mark H. A773
Valentine, Nancy P309
Valentine, Erin P321
Valentine, Mike P420
Valentine, Fred P578
Valentine, Debra A. W360
Valentine, Debra A. W361
Valentovic, Dennis J. A429
Valenzuela, David M. E415
Valenzuela, Troy E. A647
Valenzuela, Daniel J. (Dan) A708
Valera, Marc P201
Valerio, J. Scott Di E385
Valero, Karina W401
Valette, Jean-Michel E71

Valette, Jean-Michel E435
Valice, Brian E. P649
Valine, Roger J. A241
Valine, Yousef A. A336
Vall, Luis W57
Valladares, Gui P283
Vallance, Patrick W191
Vallance, Paul W364
Vallarino, Juan A405
Vallaude, Jean-Pierre W355
Valle, Thomas R. (Tom) Del A48
Valle, Debora Del P655
Valle, Diego Della W41
Valle, Dean Della W88
Valle, Margherita Della W116
Valle, Margherita Margherita Della Valle W116
Valle, Margherita Della W475
Vallee, Rodolphe M. E352
Vallee, Roy A. E475
Vallee, Roy A. E483
Vallee, Roy A. A88
Vallejo, Edmundo M. A367
Vallejo, Victor de Urrutia W223
Vallejo, Vincent W474
Valletta, Angelo J. A754
Valletta, John A878
Vallillo, Anthony J. E502
Vallo, Stephen W. A626
Vallone, James (Jim) A98
Vallone-Raffaele, Helene P597
Valls, Juan A438
Valls, Ramon W55
Vallverdu, Jaime W57
Valosky, Kenneth G. (Ken) P622
Valstorp, Per W325
Vamos, Steven W438
VanAmringe, Margaret A. P276
Vanaselja, Siim A. W82
Vanasse, Kelly A662
VanAusdle, Leonard P639
VanBrocklin, Laurie A365
Vance, Rick E31
Vance, Robert (Bob) E215
Vance, Myrna E486
Vance, Tyler A100
Vance, Charles R. A329
Vance, Myrna A785
Vance, Michael P3
Vance, Richard P159
Vance, Janet E. P209
Vance, Rick P245
Vandebroek, Sophie V. E42
Vandebroek, Sophie V. A881
Vandeman, Robert T. P6
Vandenberg, Marnie A597
Vandenberg, Veronika Kwan A793
Vandenberg, Marnie P373
Vandenbergh, Robert A. A495
Vandenberghe, James H. (Jim) W271
Vandenberghe, James H. (Jim) A317
Vandenhende, Christian W355
VandenHoven, Tom P635
Vanderhoff, Bruce P382
VanderLaan, Meg P351
Vanderlinde, Daisy L. A606
VanderLinden, Shauna P654
Vanderslice, Doug P536
VanderStaay, Steven P640
Vanderveen, Randall L. (Pete) A568
Vandervelden, Ludo W462
VanderWaal, Brent P265
Vanderwoude, J. Stephen (Steve) A339
VanderZanden, James L. (Jake) E64
VanderZee, John P257
Vandevelde, Luc W402
Vandevelde, Luc W476
Vandevere, Chip E444
Vandiver, Donna M. P634
VanDort, Patti P247
VanDyke, Michelle L. A325
Vanek, Yul E140
Vanek, Kim E321
Vanek, Kate W. A742
VanEpps, Ron P338

Vangsgard, Mark D. P609
VanGundy, Michael P392
Vanhevel, Jan W248
VanHoose, Mary E16
VanHuss, Susie H. A336
VanHyfte, Curtis H. A673
Vanier, Jacques J. A30
Vanlancker, Thierry F. J. A272
VanLandingham, Robert S. A56
VanLaningham, Nathan P449
Vann, Kyle D. E300
Vannan, E. Bradley (Brad) E275
VanNess, William C. (Bill) P134
Vanneste, Jeffrey H. A497
Vanneste, Luc A. W69
Vanni, Enrico W323
Vannuccini, Robert H. E121
vanOstenberg, Paul P277
Vanot, Jean-Philippe W333
Vanselow, Alex W88
Vansickle, Lisa K. A330
Vansteenkiste, Baron Luc W169
Vantieghem, Germain W248
VanWinkle, David P215
VanWoerkom, Jack A. E534
Vanzo, Kendra L. A608
VanZyl, Gail P460
Vara, Raymond P. P232
Vara, Fabiola Arredondo de W70
Varadarajan, S. W85
Varaldo, Riccardo W234
Varco, Tony P141
Varda, Rich A771
Vardaman, Lee P582
Vardas, Michael A. A595
Vardeman, Robert A61
Vardi, Judith W441
Vardinogiannis, Ioannis W343
Varela, Amelia Newton E314
Varela, Claudia A. A456
Varela, Joaquin Gonzalez A850
Varela, Luis P593
Varello, Joseph A140
Vareschi, William J. (Bill) A862
Varettoni, Robert (Bob) A840
Vargas, Mauricio A15
Vargas, Jennifer Dwyer A90
Vargas, Michele A455
Vargas, Gricelly A662
Vargas-Pharis, Alicia P110
Vargo, Mark E21
Vargo, Amy A649
Varin, Philippe W85
Varkey, Alex C. P550
Varley, John S. A123
Varley, Thomas P615
Varley, John S. W44
Varley, John S. W360
Varma, Girish K. A168
Varma, Vivek A745
Varnado, Darryl P116
Varner, Ruby E120
Varner, Ted A232
Varner, Deanne P529
Varner, Clark P557
Varon, Leslie F. A881
Varone, P. W376
Varoquiers, Carrie A536
Varsano, David E458
Vartanian, David P378
Varvel, Eric A227
Varvel, Eric W139
Varvoutis, Ernie E480
Varwijk, Erik W19
Vasantasingh, Chulasingh W349
Vasconcellos, Wallim A643
Vasella, Daniel L. A635
Vasella, Daniel L. W323
Vashishat, Ajay E384
Vasilakis, Eftychios W344
Vasileva, Elena W188
Vasilyeva, Elena A. W187
Vasino, Christian W11
Vaskevitch, David E307
Vasos, Todd J. A260

Vasquez, Jaime E93
Vasquez, Francisco M. P280
Vasquez, Sharon L. P567
Vassall, John H. P521
Vassallo, Susan A713
Vassalluzzo, Scott J. E126
Vassalluzzo, Joseph S. (Joe) E302
Vassalluzzo, Scott E543
Vasseur, Denis Le W345
Vasseur, Denis W345
Vasseur, Denis Le W346
Vasseur, Denis W346
Vassiliadis, Michael W76
Vassiliadis, Michael W202
Vastardis, William E207
Vastrup, Prof Claus W147
Vasudev, C.M. W196
Vasudeva, Nishi W205
Vaswani, Ashok W72
Vaswani, Ashok W74
Vatier, Bernard W375
Vats, Trib P326
Vaucleroy, Jacques de W49
Vaucleroy, Jacques de W169
Vaughan, Richard C. (Rich) A533
Vaughan, Curtis P488
Vaughan, Chris W53
Vaughn, Gregory R. (Greg) E57
Vaughn, Alex E97
Vaughn, Jim E214
Vaughn, C. Richard E272
Vaughn, Jerry E. E311
Vaughn, Mike E371
Vaughn, Anthony D. (Tony) A248
Vaughn, Tony D. A248
Vaughn, Joe A694
Vaughn, Donnie P110
Vaughn-Furlow, Rebecca N. A805
Vaule, Rosamond B. E76
Vaule, Rosamond B. A136
Vaux, Robert G. (Bob) W483
Vavalidis, Stefanos C. W303
Vawdrey, Rod W183
Vayda, Joseph M. A480
Vaz, Nigel E432
Vazquez, Mario E333
Vazquez, John M. A545
Vazquez, Carlos J. A650
Vazquez, Raul A850
Vazquez, Ronald O. P303
Veach, Shae C. P234
Veal, Jimmy D. A56
Veale, Dick P231
Veazey, Beth P48
Vecchio, Jules A. del A389
Vecchio, Jules A389
Vecchio, Robb P621
Vecchione, Kenneth A. (Ken) E532
Vecchione, Kenneth A. (Ken) A863
Vedak, Bharat S. A244
Vedrine, Hubert W271
Veer, Andre P.M. de E373
Veer, Ben van der W14
Veer, Jeroen W231
Veer, Jeroen W258
Veer, Jeroen van der W370
Veerasingham, Daisy P533
Vega, Ralph de la A79
Vega, Ralph A79
Vega, Teresita P89
Vega, Sonia Marie De Leon de P89
Vega, Guadalupe P355
Vegas, Pablo A. A49
Vegas, Pablo A. A607
Veghte, Bill A415
Vegliante, Paul C. E18
Vehrkens, Kenneth P188
Veillette, Robert E. E373
Veitia, Diego J. A457
Veksler, Angela D. A852
Vela, Manuel R. A778
Velarde, Jorge E267
Velarde, Georgia E. A852
Velarde, Randy E. P558
Velarde, Vicki P558

A = AMERICAN BUSINESS
E = EMERGING COMPANIES
P = PRIVATE COMPANIES
W = WORLD BUSINESS

Williams, Mark J. R. A480
Williams, R. Pete A489
Williams, Douglas L. A491
Williams, Robert Sanders (Sandy) A494
Williams, Clay C. A569
Williams, Dennis D. A573
Williams, Cindy A581
Williams, Frederica A593
Williams, Mike A603
Williams, Robert J. A604
Williams, Derek H. A615
Williams, Dennis K. A621
Williams, Thomas L. (Tom) A628
Williams, Geisha J. A640
Williams, Barry L. A640
Williams, Greg A684
Williams, William A691
Williams, Tim A708
Williams, Barry L. A726
Williams, Larry D. A747
Williams, Paul S. A747
Williams, Joel T. A762
Williams, Katrina A774
Williams, Glenn D. A798
Williams, Andrew M. A818
Williams, Steven W. A818
Williams, Michael S. A827
Williams, Ellen A838
Williams, Susan L. A841
Williams, Christopher J. (Chris) A850
Williams, James A. A860
Williams, Richard A866
Williams, Kim A867
Williams, Kim A880
Williams, Shelley Thomas A888
Williams, Brad P1
Williams, James A. P19
Williams, James B. P41
Williams, Mark E. P61
Williams, David P98
Williams, Char P110
Williams, Steve P126
Williams, James H. P130
Williams, Bob P139
Williams, Sandra P151
Williams, Lawrence W. P160
Williams, Brett P162
Williams, Theodore E. P214
Williams, Everett P215
Williams, Rodney P221
Williams, Jim P223
Williams, Kristy P255
Williams, Candy P271
Williams, Scott P277
Williams, Brian P298
Williams, Tom P321
Williams, Wayne P323
Williams, Darlene P325
Williams, Monique P326
Williams, Mark P369
Williams, Brad P375
Williams, Althea P398
Williams, Ingrid C. P414
Williams, Thomas K. P420
Williams, Aaron S. P433
Williams, Tom P433
Williams, Ed P434
Williams, Shauna P448
Williams, Pat P489
Williams, Stratton P517
Williams, Noman L. P518
Williams, Michael P. P527
Williams, Pat P538
Williams, Mark P541
Williams, Mike P563
Williams, James C. (Jim) P577
Williams, Keith E. P590
Williams, Robert A. P590
Williams, Phillip L. P601

Williams, Eliot P612
Williams, Kellie P616
Williams, Bobby P629
Williams, John P635
Williams, Scott P638
Williams, Pam P642
Williams, Christopher P652
Williams, Margaret P652
Williams, Nigel W46
Williams, Sheila W95
Williams, Sean M.G. W100
Williams, Suzi W100
Williams, Gareth W155
Williams, Keith W233
Williams, Damon W366
Williams, Mark W370
Williams, Steven W. (Steve) W423
Williams, Steve W465
Williamson, Mark D. E46
Williamson, Michael E447
Williamson, Mark E522
Williamson, Frank P. A54
Williamson, Keith H. A164
Williamson, Francis M. A201
Williamson, Billie I. A300
Williamson, Kenneth A. (Ken) A334
Williamson, John W. A336
Williamson, Charles R. (Chuck) A622
Williamson, Kemal A630
Williamson, Keith H. A652
Williamson, Scott H. A776
Williamson, Charles R. (Chuck) A867
Williamson, Deanna P278
Williamson, Sonya P421
Williamson, Alyce P537
Williamson, James R. (Jamie) P562
Williamson, Dave P649
Williamson, J. David W104
Williamson, Sir Brian W218
Williamson, Mark W227
Williamson, Sir Malcolm W301
Williamson, Mats W400
Williamson-Hughes, Andrea P457
Willie, James P225
Williford, D. Vann E67
Williford, V. Wayne A56
Williford, D. Vann A123
Williford, John H. A706
Williford, S. Hart P326
Willingham, Gary W. A588
Willis, Don E113
Willis, Mark A. E195
Willis, Gary K. E424
Willis, J. Kevin A75
Willis, Richard T. A210
Willis, John C. A329
Willis, Mark A. A333
Willis, Rhonda L. A627
Willis, Diane H. P114
Willis, John P144
Willis, Willie P422
Willis, David N. P565
Willis, Robert G. (Bob) P582
Willis, Russell H. P609
Willis, Margaret W216
Willison, Bruce G. A409
Willman, Ed P56
Willmer, Brian P39
Willmott, David A. E64
Willoughby, Dawn A189
Willoughby, Michele A249
Willoughby, Scott P. A597
Willox, Timothy P617
Willrich, Chris P521
Wills, Jason R. E34
Wills, Alan J. E51
Wills, Richard H. (Rick) E190
Wills, David A212
Wills, Lock P573
Willsey, Kevin D. A471
Willyard, Jackie C. E543
Wilmer, Gregory W. A120
Wilmerding, Harold P. P509
Wilmers, Robert G. (Bob) A518
Wilmers, Robert G. (Bob) W29

Wilmington, W. Philip P78
Wilmot, Jeremy E12
Wilmot, Kenneth S. P32
Wilsman, Stu P7
Wilson, Donn R. E2
Wilson, M. Faye E62
Wilson, Jimmy E65
Wilson, Michael A. R. E91
Wilson, Jill A. E95
Wilson, Richard O. (Dick) E199
Wilson, Elisa M. E210
Wilson, Kenneth W. E232
Wilson, P. Douglas (Doug) E249
Wilson, Frank E283
Wilson, Tom E289
Wilson, Dennis J. (Chip) E308
Wilson, Cheryl E345
Wilson, Linda S. E359
Wilson, Pete E372
Wilson, Robert E407
Wilson, J. Michael (Mike) E438
Wilson, Mike E438
Wilson, Michael (Mike) E438
Wilson, John R. E457
Wilson, Bill E486
Wilson, Mark H. E515
Wilson, Deborah A. E529
Wilson, Mark L. E537
Wilson, Dwight T. A25
Wilson, Thomas J. A38
Wilson, L. Michelle A44
Wilson, Stephen R. A47
Wilson, David A. A103
Wilson, Leon A107
Wilson, Ron A118
Wilson, Harold A. (Hal) A120
Wilson, Kendrick R. A122
Wilson, Kendrick R. A123
Wilson, Gary L. A158
Wilson, Raymond W. (Bill) A166
Wilson, Stephen R. A169
Wilson, Peter W. A192
Wilson, Jerry S. A197
Wilson, J. Michael A209
Wilson, James A. A209
Wilson, James D. A228
Wilson, Amy A268
Wilson, Phil A292
Wilson, Deanna L. A305
Wilson, Dwayne A. A348
Wilson, Cathy A351
Wilson, Michael S. A365
Wilson, A.D. (Sandy) A365
Wilson, Darryl L. A368
Wilson, Anthony L. A376
Wilson, Gayle E. A377
Wilson, Jay R. A414
Wilson, Robert N. A414
Wilson, Dwayne A. A442
Wilson, Debora J. A524
Wilson, Chuck A536
Wilson, Alan D. A539
Wilson, Michael M. A583
Wilson, Darrell A591
Wilson, Denise M. A599
Wilson, Dennis A610
Wilson, James Paul A613
Wilson, William R. A626
Wilson, Barbara A. A626
Wilson, Jeffrey A. A627
Wilson, Vanessa A666
Wilson, Susan B. A695
Wilson, Robert N. A714
Wilson, Tom A731
Wilson, David J. A738
Wilson, John A744
Wilson, Michael J. A749
Wilson, Charley A768
Wilson, Kevin A. A772
Wilson, Bill A785
Wilson, Steven E. A817
Wilson, Joe L. A817
Wilson, D. Ellen A832
Wilson, Harry J. A845
Wilson, Harry J. A883

Wilson, Harry J. A884
Wilson, Steven F. P41
Wilson, Jacquelyn O. P56
Wilson, Kristianne P64
Wilson, Roger G. P70
Wilson, Thomas P89
Wilson, Greg P103
Wilson, Helena Chapellin P132
Wilson, David P152
Wilson, Robert E. P157
Wilson, R. Lee P159
Wilson, Arthur H. P162
Wilson, Eleanor P165
Wilson, David E. P167
Wilson, Karla R. P175
Wilson, Carolyn S. P189
Wilson, Gary P196
Wilson, Terrance E. P204
Wilson, John P236
Wilson, Eric L. P240
Wilson, James C. P266
Wilson, Selma P300
Wilson, Brent P337
Wilson, John I. P352
Wilson, David P356
Wilson, Lizabeth A. (Betsy) P381
Wilson, Meredith P385
Wilson, John F. P420
Wilson, Charlton P487
Wilson, James (Jim) P490
Wilson, Kevin A. P524
Wilson, Cale P527
Wilson, Sam P529
Wilson, Nancy P529
Wilson, Welcome W. P529
Wilson, Amy P535
Wilson, Alan J. P537
Wilson, Scott O. P547
Wilson, Carolyn S. P566
Wilson, Nancy P586
Wilson, H. David P604
Wilson, Steve P621
Wilson, Patricia A. (Patti) P625
Wilson, Margaret Bush P634
Wilson, Hamlin P635
Wilson, Monte P636
Wilson, Barbara-Jan P636
Wilson, C. L. (Chuck) P645
Wilson, T. Guy P645
Wilson, Stephen W9
Wilson, Michael M. (Mike) W18
Wilson, Thomas C. W28
Wilson, Jimmy W88
Wilson, Lynton R. W144
Wilson, Sir Robert P. W192
Wilson, Nigel P265
Wilson, Julia W265
Wilson, Charles W286
Wilson, Helen W330
Wilson, Andrew W368
Wilson, James (Jamie) W373
Wilson, Geoffrey H. (Geoff) W483
Wilson, Peter W484
Wilson-Taylor, Sharon P132
Wilt, Robert G. (Bob) A31
Wilt, William M. A32
Wiltbank, J. Kelley P602
Wilten, Mark F. A652
Wiltgen, Russell J. (Russ) A313
Wiltse, Steven E90
Wiltse, Steven A150
Wilver, Peter M. A791
Wilwerding, Craig A305
Wimberly, Kenneth W. A48
Wimberly, Gary A306
Wimbleton, John W458
Wimbush, Jane Ann A362
Wimbush, F. Blair A591
Wimbush, Lawrence K. (Keith) A825
Wimmer, Peter D. A330
Wimsett, Thomas E289
Win, Teresa P. P607
Win, Thomas de W78
Winarsky, Norman D. P491
Winblad, Ann L. P610

A = AMERICAN BUSINESS
E = EMERGING COMPANIES
P = PRIVATE COMPANIES
W = WORLD BUSINESS

Wong, Vivian E170
Wong, Eugene (Gene) E255
Wong, Caroline E307
Wong, Alex H.C. E472
Wong, Raymond L.M. A32
Wong, Stephen A88
Wong, Irwin A157
Wong, Jocelyn A311
Wong, Stephen A402
Wong, Andrea L. A506
Wong, Clara A531
Wong, Mike A709
Wong, Gordon A783
Wong, Helen P82
Wong, Desmond C. P256
Wong, Caron P277
Wong, Irene P541
Wong, Lorna P566
Wong, James J. P586
Wong, Allan C. Y. W65
Wong, Chung-hin W65
Wong, David S. H. W90
Wong, Frank K. S. W119
Wong, Jeanette W147
Wong, Tung Shun (Peter) W194
Wong, Kin Tung (Marvin) W194
Wong, Peter T. S. W217
Wong, Helen W218
Wong, Wai Ming W266
Wong, Ai Fong W318
Wong, Peter T. S. W343
Wong, Jenny Mei Leng W467
Wong, Meng Meng W467
Wonka, Birgit E11
Woo, Deborah E515
Woo, Jennifer A24
Woo, Carolyn Y. A587
Woo, Kathy P607
Woo, Susan M. F. Chow W219
Woo, Mo W219
Woo, Susan M. F. Chow W219
Wood, Donald P. (Don) E6
Wood, Robert E21
Wood, Jon E39
Wood, Barbara S. E58
Wood, Karen J. E65
Wood, Richard F. E67
Wood, Michael B. E133
Wood, Larry L. E166
Wood, Michelle L. E235
Wood, Ritch N. E375
Wood, Michael A. (Mike) E377
Wood, Chris E382
Wood, Lt. Gen. John R. (Bob) E383
Wood, William P. E445
Wood, Philip K. E491
Wood, Timothy E. (Tim) E515
Wood, Tim E515
Wood, Brian K. E520
Wood, Mary E. A15
Wood, Frank J. A41
Wood, Ted G. A41
Wood, Richard F. A123
Wood, William C. (Cliff) A153
Wood, Phoebe A199
Wood, Roger J. A236
Wood, Roger J. A237
Wood, Fred G. A262
Wood, Robert L. A463
Wood, Mark E. A518
Wood, David M. A564
Wood, David M. A565
Wood, Steven P. A613
Wood, Robert L. A654
Wood, Patrick Henry (Pat) A678
Wood, Michael J. A685
Wood, Heidi A737
Wood, Chester A. (Buddy) A805
Wood, Thomas J. A813

Wood, Donald P. (Don) A860
Wood, Jan P26
Wood, Terry F. P127
Wood, Calvin P152
Wood, Ken P264
Wood, Davidson P279
Wood, Joseph W. (Joe) P312
Wood, Rev Philip Bertolo P332
Wood, Michael P339
Wood, Vickie P454
Wood, Tom P521
Wood, Cathy P535
Wood, Doug P538
Wood, Rosemary P549
Wood, Howard L. P570
Wood, Charles (Pete) P636
Wood, Steven Steven Wood W39
Wood, Karen J. W87
Wood, Ian W100
Wood, Greg W116
Wood, Alan W130
Wood, John W240
Wood, Alison W304
Wood, Tony W364
Wood, Douglas W393
Wood, Malcolm W413
Woodall, James W. (Woody) A323
Woodall, James O. P466
Woodall, Nancy P606
Woodard, Ronald B. E3
Woodard, Ross L. E73
Woodard, Ronald B. E385
Woodard, Jack D. A47
Woodard, Beth P412
Woodbridge, Christopher C. A717
Woodbury, J.J. A307
Woodbury, Cliff P185
Woodbury, Timothy S. P466
Wooden, Tom A735
Wooden, Maurice A879
Woodford, Brent A. A258
Woodhams, William H. A660
Woodhouse, Hope E397
Woodhouse, Tim A265
Woodland, Mark P110
Woodlief, H. Graham P533
Woodman, Dean S. E434
Woodman, Linda F. P527
Woodman, Paul W100
Woodrich, John T. P84
Woodring, A. Greig A688
Woodring, A. Greig A689
Woodroffe, Sean N. W422
Woodrow, Kenneth B. (Ken) A247
Woodruff, Anthony C. P40
Woodruff, Lawrence P152
Woodruff, David S. P658
Woods, Tracy E37
Woods, David A. E92
Woods, Jacqueline F. A62
Woods, Charles H. A126
Woods, E. Anthony (Tony) A179
Woods, J. Pat A298
Woods, D.W. A307
Woods, Jennifer J. A627
Woods, Mary A662
Woods, Jacqueline F. A795
Woods, Charles A805
Woods, Consuella K. P104
Woods, Eugene A. P118
Woods, Douglas E. (Doug) P165
Woods, Forrest P185
Woods, Ethel P315
Woods, Ruby P480
Woods, Christopher P514
Woods, Mike P553
Woods, Chris P571
Woods, Kristin P606
Woods, Dan P636
Woods, Ward W. P644
Woods, Catherine W29
Woods, Tom D. W104
Woodside, Jim P557
Woodson, Nathaniel D. (Nat) E196
Woodson, Gregory P. (Greg) A201

Woodson, Nathaniel D. (Nat) A340
Woodson, R. Peyton P190
Woodward, J.D. E455
Woodward, Amos E542
Woodward, Keith A. A370
Woodward, Joan Kois A803
Woodward, David P160
Woodward, James L. P331
Woodward, James L. P332
Woodward, Keith P424
Woodward, Charles P479
Woodworth, John K. A2
Woody, Ron E92
Woody, Craig W. P130
Woody, Darren G. P277
Woodyard, Elizabeth (Liz) A102
Woodyard, Elizabeth (Liz) P42
Wook, Sun W345
Woolbright, Kathy (Akua) A870
Wooldridge, Mark D. E388
Wooldridge, Kevin P169
Woolery, Jim A471
Woolever, Prof Kristin R. P614
Wooley, Bruce A. E273
Wooley, Douglas F. E507
Wooley, Jeffrey I. A73
Wooley, Douglas F. A815
Woolf, Brian P. E69
Woolf, Paul K. P361
Woolfall, Joanne E454
Woolford, Lauris A325
Woolley, Kenneth M. E185
Woolley, Kenneth M. E186
Woolsey, Suzanne H. (Sue) A348
Woolsey, Christine P186
Woolsey, Suzanne H. (Sue) P260
Woolway, Paul V. A714
Woonton, David B. A167
Woosnam, Richard E. P256
Wooten, Scott P147
Wooten, Sonny P483
Work, Christopher C. E549
Work, C. Thomas P430
Workman, Dennis L. E498
Workman, John L. A610
Workman, Gail A760
Works, David A874
Worl, Rosita F. P463
Worle, Erwin W136
Worley, Peter K. (Pete) E140
Worley, Robert B. E256
Worley, R. Jay A25
Worley, Robert B. A436
Worley, Marianne P325
Worley, Kristi P462
Worley, Phil W. P529
Wormer, Geoffrey G. (Geoff) P100
Wormington, Tony L. E289
Wormeester, Jerry L. A548
Worms, Nicholas C. W271
Worrall, James M. A368
Worrall, Lawrence D. W274
Worrell, Brian A368
Worrell, W. Alan A766
Worrell, Judy P61
Worrell, Larry P64
Worrell, C. P. (Pat) P267
Worrell, Doug P489
Worth, Donald J. E426
Worth, Robert D. (Bob) A859
Wortham, Tom P247
Worthe, Jeffrey P537
Worthington, John M. A487
Worthy, Bob P519
Wortman, Rand P279
Worzel, Kenneth J. (Ken) A590
Woseth, Rob A758
Woslager, Ron P50
Woss, Allison E535
Wotring, Randall A. (Randy) A836
Woudstra, F. Robert (Bob) P312
Woyczynski, Elizabeth P99
Woys, James E. (Jim) A409
Wozniak, John K. A563
Wozniak, Robert P462

Wraase, Dennis R. A593
Wrang, William E. A855
Wray, Grover N. E147
Wray, D. Michael E377
Wray, Monica P124
Wray, Christine P324
Wrba, John A. St. E516
Wrede, Bernd W260
Wren, Thomas D. E233
Wren, John D. A612
Wrench, Mike W100
Wrend, Mark J. A773
Wrenn, Donna C. P129
Wright, Frank E23
Wright, Emory M. E24
Wright, Lynn E37
Wright, Sheryl E73
Wright, E. Joseph E117
Wright, Doreen E129
Wright, Sheryl E173
Wright, David E175
Wright, David B. (Dave) E212
Wright, Lori A. E224
Wright, Anne-Marie E334
Wright, Joseph (Joe) E334
Wright, Daniel M. E431
Wright, Lori E491
Wright, Theodore M. E492
Wright, Bruce E. E505
Wright, David B. (Dave) E521
Wright, Ford K. E549
Wright, Elease E. A16
Wright, Robert L. A18
Wright, Carolyn E. (Carol) A48
Wright, Stuart A114
Wright, James E. (Jim) A145
Wright, Brian A209
Wright, John W. A218
Wright, Maj. Michael A. A226
Wright, Doreen A. A242
Wright, Megan A292
Wright, Robert R. A305
Wright, David M. A320
Wright, Charles R. A422
Wright, Randy A435
Wright, Christa D. A626
Wright, Mark A645
Wright, David E. A647
Wright, Scott A673
Wright, Robert C. (Bob) A682
Wright, Donald P. A708
Wright, Laura H. A733
Wright, Dornett A773
Wright, Murray A775
Wright, Deborah C. (Debbie) A793
Wright, James F. (Jim) A800
Wright, Nick B. A826
Wright, Richard M. (Rick) A877
Wright, Kathy Wills P52
Wright, Coleen P68
Wright, Joseph P116
Wright, Stephen P118
Wright, Jeanine P140
Wright, Vicky P268
Wright, Jean P326
Wright, Dan P328
Wright, James P338
Wright, Lloyd P420
Wright, Trevor P473
Wright, Sandra Gayle P550
Wright, Karina H. P553
Wright, Troy W69
Wright, Ian W156
Wright, A. W245
Wright, Craig W366
Wright, Jeremy W368
Wright, Sam W440
Wright, Peter J. W492
Wrighton, Mark S. A223
Wrighton, Mark S. P569
Wrigley, William (Bill) P372
Wrinkle, Scott E169
Wroblowski, Peter W202
Wroe, Thomas (Tom) E101
Wroe, Thomas P90

Wrzosek, Robert A. E529
Wtizig, Marshall P143
Wtulich, Peter C. P392
Wu, Jiang E167
Wu, Ting E170
Wu, Cooper E379
Wu, David E421
Wu, Peter A157
Wu, Kevin A162
Wu, Frank A181
Wu, Jesse A466
Wu, Chunping (Willie) A651
Wu, Helen A846
Wu, Andi W122
Wu, Guangqi W125
Wu, Zhenfang W125
Wu, Jong-Chang W137
Wu, Ching-Yang W137
Wu, Jung-Chung W137
Wu, Eric W139
Wu, Shengliang W161
Wu, Pe-Chu W427
Wubbenhorst, Klaus L. W164
Wucherer, Klaus W384
Wudrick, David K. A290
Wueerst, Alexander W482
Wuellner, James (Jim) P502
Wuerfl, Karen P266
Wuerl, Donald W. P535
Wuerth, James P. (Jim) A484
Wuerthele, Rich A580
Wuest, James R. P286
Wulf, Tom P384
Wulf, Alf H. W25
Wulff, John K. A162
Wulff, Barbel W263
Wulfsohn, William A. (Bill) E93
Wummer, Kathy Egan W166
Wunder, Christopher G. P565
Wunderle, Richard E132
Wunning, Steven H. A155
Wunning, Steven H. P67
Wunrow, Steven P439
Wuori, Stephen J. (Steve) A290
Wurl, Douglas N. (Doug) A120
Wurl, Douglas N. (Doug) A249
Wurtenberger, Joan P449
Wurth, Michel W39
Wurtz, Thomas A. (Tom) P334
Wurzbacher, Bonnie P. A196
Wussler, Deborah L. E337
Wuthrich, Kent E545
Wutke, Steve P360
Wyand, Anthony B. W402
Wyand, Anthony B. W463
Wyant, Jill A282
Wyat, C. Earnest P193
Wyatt, Joe M. E83
Wyatt, Andrew E125
Wyatt, Elizabeth H. S. E328
Wyatt, Natalie A153
Wyatt, Kenneth A168
Wyatt, Joe B. A441
Wyatt, Gary E. A516
Wyatt, Michael P. A673
Wyatt, John H. A. A742
Wyatt, Rufus P183
Wyatt, Bill P269
Wyatt, Carl Van P531
Wyatt, Van P531
Wyatt-Tilby, James W35
Wybrew-Bond, Ian W376
Wyckoff, James H. E194
Wyckoff, James H. A326
Wydock, Edward J. A759
Wyett, Roger A586
Wyk, Sharon van E37
Wyk, Steven C. (Steve) Van A649
Wyk, Steve Van W231
Wykpisz, Elizabeth P631
Wyks, Philip M. E383
Wylde, Kathryn S. A319
Wylie, Scott E29
Wylie, Thomas E. E121
Wylie, Whit E447

Wylie, Forrest E. A137
Wyllie, Melissa E239
Wyman, Jill L. E195
Wyman, William W. (Bill) E392
Wyman, Mary A70
Wyman, Jill L. A333
Wyman, Scott R A341
Wyman, Alan P419
Wyman, J. Vernon P606
Wyman, Malcolm W227
Wymeersch, Charles Van W248
Wymer, Norm P215
Wynaendts, Alexander R. (Alex) W14
Wynia, Marvin P191
Wynn, Peg E481
Wynn, Jean A99
Wynn, Phail A756
Wynn, Stephen A. A879
Wynn, Elaine P. A879
Wynn, Curtis P355
Wynn, Phail P433
Wynn, Joan D. P599
Wynne, Thomas M. E26
Wynne, Thomas M. E27
Wynne, Susan P293
Wynne, Linda P463
Wynne, Craig P479
Wynne, Kaye P562
Wynne, Joshua P604
Wyper, Jay P245
Wyrick, G. Georgeanne E92
Wyrick, Cynthia G. (Cindy) A97
Wyrick, Cindy A97
Wyrsch, Anne E164
Wyrsch, Martha B. A720
Wyrsch, Martha B. A738
Wyse, Beverly A125
Wyse, Kenneth L. (Ken) A675
Wyshner, David B. A86
Wysocki, Bob P463
Wysolmierski, Jill M. A88
Wyss, Andre (Andy) W323

X

Xenakis, Michael E382
Xia, Bailing E81
Xia, Howard E266
Xia, Liping W343
Xianfeng, Sun W339
Xiangdong, Lu W119
Xiao, Peng E340
Xiao, Deming E347
Xiao, Gang W64
Xiao, Qin W122
Xiaobing, Chang W122
Xiaochu, Wang W122
Xiaojin, Chen W120
Xiaopeng, Li W229
Xiaowei, Yang W122
Xiaoyuan, Hong W119
Xie, Ken E201
Xie, Michael E201
Xie, Ken E201
Xie, Zhi E299
Xie, Lan E434
Xie, Ken E481
Xie, Songlin W121
Xinhua, Wang W120
Xinhua, Li W339
Xiong, Bo P4
Xiqun, Yi W119
Xiwu, Zhang W121
Xiyou, Cai W120
Xu, Bin W229
Xue, Jilian W121
Xuewu, Zhang W343
Xuezheng, Ma W266
Xunsheng, Zuo W122

Y

Yaari, Aharon (Arik) W441
Yabe, Nobuhiro W282
Yablonski, Cathy P630
Yabuki, Jeffery W. A343
Yabuki, Jeffery W. (Jeff) A344
Yabunaka, Mitoji W291
Yachi, Shotaro W184
Yacovelli, Derrick P365
Yadav, Ranjit W430
Yaeger, Douglas H. A330
Yaffa, Glenn D. A42
Yaggi, W. Timothy (Tim) E482
Yaggi, W. Timothy (Tim) A528
Yagi, Shinsuke W22
Yagil, Oren P634
Yahagi, Mitsuaki W409
Yahng, Mike E469
Yahng, Mike A761
Yajima, Ryoji W141
Yajima, Tsutomu W244
Yajima, Hidetoshi W293
Yajnik, Sanjiv A149
Yakovlev, Gennady E87
Yakovlev, Vadim W186
Yakushev, Vladimir W457
Yalcintas, M. Guven P558
Yale, Phyllis R. A485
Yali, Yu W65
Yam, Zipora Gal W63
Yam, Joseph W461
Yamabayashi, Naoyuki W419
Yamada, Tadataka (Tachi) A21
Yamada, Masayuki W1
Yamada, Masanori W106
Yamada, Masayoshi W140
Yamada, Masayoshi W141
Yamada, Takuji W214
Yamada, Takuji W215
Yamada, Hiroyuki W215
Yamada, Tsutomu W236
Yamada, Noriaki W283
Yamada, Ryuji W314
Yamada, Ryuji W326
Yamada, Ryuji W327
Yamada, Yoshihiko (Yoshi) W338
Yamada, Kiyotaka W393
Yamagiwa, Kuniaki W456
Yamaguchi, Masato W141
Yamaguchi, Masanobu W307
Yamaguchi, Tsuyoshi W316
Yamaguchi, Yoji W420
Yamaguchi, Hiroshi W447
Yamakawa, Yoichiro W420
Yamakawa, Kiyoshi W456
Yamaki, Hiroshi P590
Yamaki, Masaharu W283
Yamamoto, Steve A439
Yamamoto, Steve A676
Yamamoto, Yoshinori W124
Yamamoto, Tatsusaburo W141
Yamamoto, Tadahito W182
Yamamoto, Masami W183
Yamamoto, Mikio W184
Yamamoto, Takahiko W206
Yamamoto, Akimasa W206
Yamamoto, Takashi W214
Yamamoto, Yoshiharu W215
Yamamoto, Hiroshi W283
Yamamoto, Masato W307
Yamamoto, Toshihiko W393
Yamamoto, Tetsuro W448
Yamamoto, Hisashi W456
Yamamura, Shinichiro W22
Yamanaka, Yasushi W149
Yamanaka, Akira W183
Yamane, Yoshi W215
Yamane, Kosuke W253
Yamane, Kenji W338
Yamanishi, Kenichiro W291
Yamanouchi, Takashi W283
Yamarone, Charles A. A819
Yamasaki, Hisao E428

Yamasato, Maurice H. A166
Yamase, Masanori W456
Yamashina, Tadashi W455
Yamashita, Hideo W206
Yamashita, Masaya W214
Yamashita, Masaya W215
Yamashita, Mitsuhiko (Mike) W316
Yamashita, Yoshinori W358
Yamashita, Masashi W392
Yamauchi, Hiroshi A18
Yamauchi, Yasuhito W22
Yamauchi, Takashi W295
Yamauchi, Yasuhiro W316
Yamauchi, Yoshiaki W409
Yamauchi, Yoshiaki W420
Yamaura, Yoshiyuki W194
Yamazaki, Kazuhiro A18
Yamazaki, Kunio W34
Yamazaki, Fujio W140
Yamazaki, Toshikuni W244
Yamazaki, hajime W244
Yamazaki, Toshikuni W244
Yamazaki, hajime W244
Yamazaki, Hiromasa W320
Yamazawa, Noboru Noboru
  Yamazawa W390
Yamazoe, Shigeru W281
Yan, Christine Yingli A742
Yan, Lu W266
Yan, Wu W342
Yanaga, Fumihiro W96
Yanagi, Jeff E392
Yanagihara, Tsunehiko W289
Yanaginuma, Nobuyuki W307
Yanagisawa, David A495
Yanai, Jun W289
Yanai, Shunji W291
Yanai, Tadashi W404
Yanakov, Konstantin W344
Yance, Gordon E. A626
Yancey, Carol B. A373
Yancey, James D. (Jimmy) A767
Yancey, Shaun P. P397
Yancopoulos, George D. E415
Yancy, Luke A337
Yancy, Clyde W. P52
Yandolino, Philip E72
Yanez, Maria P45
Yang, Helen E21
Yang, Andrew T. E44
Yang, Qingming E46
Yang, Wendy E110
Yang, Sue E162
Yang, Jingcai E299
Yang, William E337
Yang, Henry E379
Yang, Jerry A181
Yang, Sue A277
Yang, Geoffrey A355
Yang, Xu (Ian) A446
Yang, Chiang Yuan A447
Yang, Jennifer A571
Yang, Patrick Y. (Pat) A784
Yang, K. Lisa P160
Yang, Honggang P375
Yang, J. S. W137
Yang, Julie L. W139
Yang, Ya W161
Yang, Yuanqing W266
Yang, Marjorie M. T. W323
Yankowski, Daniel H. (Dan) A654
Yanney, Michael B. A503
Yano, James A. (Jay) A747
Yano, Masahide W290
Yano, Kaoru W306
Yano, Atsushi W419
Yanos, Neal A. A779
Yanover, Robert A. E504
Yao, Jun W343
Yaocang, Zhang W120
Yaofeng, Cao W120
Yaouanc, J-P.D. A288
Yap, Sin Min E408
Yap, Jason E495